Holt California Mathematics
COURSE 2: PRE-ALGEBRA

California Resources in the Student Edition and Teacher's Edition

Additional Resources to Support Mastering the California Standards

Focus on California Standards: Benchmark Tests includes pre-tests and post-tests for each of the standards with emphasis on the key standards. The **Standards Doctor** contains complete solutions and error analysis of incorrect answers.

Focus on California Standards: Intervention targets the key standards. It includes scaffolded intervention for skills and problem-solving, alternate teaching strategies, worksheets for skills and problem solving practice, key vocabulary words, and standards review. Also available as a consumable workbook.

California Countdown to Mastery Transparencies provide twenty-four weeks of daily warm-up problems addressing the California Mathematics Content Standards.

California On-Course Mapping: A Teacher's Guide for Planning provides you with a road map for using *Holt California Mathematics* to teach the concepts and skills required by the California Mathematics Content Standards. This booklet provides a **Minimum Course of Study** to ensure that all standards are covered in the course of the year. In addition, it lists available resources for each standard that enable you to adapt the curriculum to provide access to all of your students.

California Premier Online Edition includes the complete *Student Edition*, **Homework Help Online**, *Lesson Tutorial Videos*, Interactivities with feedback, parent resources, and much more!

California Review for Mastery Workbook includes lesson-by-lesson intervention with instruction, new examples, and practice exercises.

California Standards Virtual File Cabinet CD-ROM enables you to quickly find resources based on your search criteria, including California Mathematics Content Standards, chapter, lesson, and resource type. In addition, you can mark your favorites and even add your own content to the database. In the end, you have a customizable catalog of your favorite resources!

California Standards Practice CD-ROM contains banks of **ExamView®** items organized for teacher convenience in building tests and practice worksheets that reflect the California Mathematics Content Standards.

California Student One Stop CD-ROM solves the backpack problem. The entire *Student Edition*, workbooks, and intervention and enrichment worksheets can be found on one CD-ROM.

California Teacher's One-Stop Planner® CD-ROM is a convenient tool for planning and managing lessons and contains all print-based teaching resources, plus customizable lesson plans.

HOLT
Mathematics
Course 2: Pre-Algebra

Jennie M. Bennett

Edward B. Burger

David J. Chard

Audrey L. Jackson

Paul A. Kennedy

Freddie L. Renfro

Tom W. Roby

Janet K. Scheer

Bert K. Waits

HOLT, RINEHART AND WINSTON

A Harcourt Education Company

Orlando • Austin • New York • San Diego • London

Cover photo: redwood trees (Sequoia sempervirens), Big Basin National Park, California; © Ulf Sjostedt/Getty Images

Cover photo: Sacramento Bridge; © Image Source Limited

Cover photo: Point Reyes National Seashore, California; © Edgar Callaert

Cover photo: Old Chinatown, Los Angeles, California; © Robert Landau/Corbis

Cover photo: surfer on a wave, Imperial Beach, California; © Rick Doyle/Corbis

ISBN 978-0-03-092319-7

ISBN 0-03-092319-0

2 3 4 5 048 10 09 08

California Course 2: Pre-Algebra
Teacher's Edition
Contents in Brief

Chapter Teacher Material

Student Handbook

CALIFORNIA TEACHER ADVISORY PANEL

Kay Barrie
Math Department Chair
Rio Vista MS
Fresno, CA

Youshi Berry
Math Teacher
Emerson MS
Pomona, CA

Charlie Bialowas
Math Curriculum
    Specialist
Anaheim Union HS
    District
Anaheim, CA

**Lorrie Wineberg
Buehler**
Principal
Baldy View Elementary
    School
Upland, CA

Mary Chiaverini
Math Teacher
Plaza Vista MS
Irvine, CA

Dennis Deets
Assistant Principal
AB Miller HS
Fontana, CA

Pauline Embree
Math Department Chair
Rancho San Joaquin MS
Irvine, CA

Sandi Enochs
Math Lead Teacher
Desert Hot Springs HS
Desert Hot Springs, CA

Tricia Gough
Math Department Chair
Emerson MS
Pomona, CA

Lee Haines
IB Coordinator/Math
    Coach
San Bernardino City
    Schools
San Bernardino, CA

Shannon Kelly
Math Teacher
Centennial HS
Corona, CA

Lisa Kernaghan
Math Teacher/
    Administrator
Oak Creek Intermediate
    School
Oakhurst, CA

Mary Ann Kremenliev
Math Teacher
Foothill MS
Walnut Creek, CA

Carole Kuck
Math Department Chair
Jean Farb MS
San Diego, CA

David V. Mattoon
Math Teacher
Potter Junior HS
Fallbrook, CA

Lynette McClintock
Math/Science Teacher
Thompson MS
Murrieta, CA

**Nancy Nazarian-
Carroll**
Math Teacher
Curtiss MS
Carson, CA

John (Jack) P. Nunes
Math Teacher and
    Department Leader
Fern Bacon MS
Sacramento, CA

Suzanne O'Rourke
Math Teacher
Antioch MS
Antioch, CA

Jong Sun Park
Math Teacher
Holmes International MS
Northridge, CA

Barbara Parr
Math Teacher
Emerson MS
Bakersfield, CA

Donna Phair
Math Department Chair
William Hopkins Junior HS
Fremont, CA

Donald R. Price
Math Teacher
Alvarado Intermediate
    School
Irvine, CA

Jennifer Randel
Math/Science Teacher,
    Grade Level Chair
Thompson MS
Murrieta, CA

Wendy Taub-Hoglund
Teacher Expert Secondary
    Math
Los Angeles USD
Los Angeles, CA

Matthew Ting
Math Coach
Peary MS
Gardena, CA

CALIFORNIA REVIEWERS

CALIFORNIA FIELD TEST PARTICIPANTS

California
the golden state

The State Capitol in Sacramento

Big Sur coastline

California palm tree

Correlation to the California Mathematics Content Standards for Grade 7

The following is a correlation of *Holt California Mathematics Course 2: Pre-Algebra* to the California Mathematics Content Standards for Grade 7. The correlation breaks down standards, when appropriate, to show where specific parts of the standards are addressed.

The symbol 🔑 designates key standards.

The state bird is the California Quail

The Poppy is the state flower

California Mathematics Content Standards for Grade 7

Standard		Taught	Reinforced
Number Sense			
1.0 **Students know the properties of, and compute with, rational numbers expressed in a variety of forms:**		pp. 14–17, 18–21, 66–69, 74–77, 274–277, 283–287	pp. 30, 53, 55, 92, 107, 109, 292, 312, 313, 315
1.1 Read, write, and compare rational numbers in scientific notation (positive and negative powers of 10), compare rational numbers in general.	*read and write rational numbers in scientific notation*	pp. 184–188	pp. 190, 195, 215, 218, 219, 227, 372, 419, 524, EP8
	compare rational numbers in scientific notation	pp. 184–188	pp. 190, 215, EP8
	compare rational numbers in general	pp. 14–17, 70–73, 274–277	pp. 30, 59, 68, 77, 92, 106, 109, 110, 133, 139, 163, 218, 292, EP2, EP4, EP12
1.2 Add, subtract, multiply, and divide rational numbers (integers, fractions, and terminating decimals) and take positive rational numbers to whole-number powers.	*add rational numbers*	pp. 18–21, 53, 74–77, 87–91, 107	pp. 29, 30, 36, 53, 69, 81, 92, 107, 139, 143, 162, 171, 502, EP2, EP4, EP5
	subtract rational numbers	pp. 22–25, 53, 74–77, 87–91, 107	pp. 29, 30, 40, 53, 69, 73, 92, 107, 139, 143, 502, EP3, EP4, EP5
	multiply rational numbers	pp. 26–29, 53, 78–81, 107	pp. 30, 36, 47, 53, 69, 92, 101, 107, 147, 227, 251, EP3, EP4
	divide rational numbers	pp. 26–29, 53, 82–86, 107	pp. 30, 36, 47, 53, 92, 107, 119, 236, EP3, EP5
	take positive rational numbers to whole-number powers	pp. 168–171	pp. 190, 203, 205–209, 214, 216, 217

Standard		Taught	Reinforced
1.3 Convert fractions to decimals and percents and use these representations in estimations, computations, and applications.	*convert fractions to decimals*	pp. 66–69	pp. 71–73, 92, 106, 109, 111, 171, 291, 312, EP4
	convert fractions to percents	pp. 274–277	pp. 292, 294–297, 312, 315, EP12
	use these representations in estimations	pp. 278–282	pp. 292, 312, 315, 329, 449, 584, EP12
	use these representations in computations	pp. 283–287, 288–291	pp. 292, 297, 315, 402, EP12
	use these representations in applications	pp. 278–282, 283–287, 288–291, 298–301	pp. 292, 313, 315, 631, EP12
1.4 Differentiate between rational and irrational numbers.		pp. 200–203	pp. 210, 216, 218, 428, 438, 461, 472, 584, EP9
1.5 Know that every rational number is either a terminating or a repeating decimal and be able to convert terminating decimals into reduced fractions.	*know that every rational number is either a terminating or a repeating decimal*	pp. 64–65, 66–69	pp. 200–203, 210, 216, 217
	convert terminating decimals into reduced fractions	pp. 66–69	pp. 86, 92, 106, 109, 119, 195, 536, EP4
1.6 Calculate the percentage of increases and decreases of a quantity.		pp. 294–297	pp. 301, 308, 313, 315, 316, 341, 372, EP13

Standard		Taught	Reinforced
🔑 **1.7** Solve problems that involve discounts, markups, commissions, and profit and compute simple and compound interest.	*discounts*	pp. 294–297	pp. 308, 309, 313, 317, 370–371, 373, 429, 524, 585, 631, EP13
	markups	pp. 294–297	pp. 308, 316, 373, EP13
	commissions	pp. 298–301	pp. 308, 314, 315, 316, 371, 429, EP13
	profit	pp. 298–301	pp. 308, 314, 315, 316, EP13
	simple interest	pp. 302, 303–307	pp. 308, 314, 315, 317, 361, 371, 373, 472, 541, EP13
	compound interest	pp. 302, 303–307	pp. 308, 314, 315, EP13
2.0 Students use exponents, powers, and roots and use exponents in working with fractions:		pp. 168–171, 172–175, 176–179, 192–195, 196–199, 205–209	pp. 190, 210, 214–216, 217
2.1 Understand negative whole-number exponents. Multiply and divide expressions involving exponents with a common base.	*understand negative whole-number exponents*	pp. 172–175	pp. 176–179, 190, 218, 559, EP8
	multiply expressions involving exponents with a common base	pp. 176–179	pp. 190, 215, 241, 453, EP8
	divide expressions involving exponents with a common base	pp. 176–179	pp. 190, 215, 218, 241, 453, EP8

Los Angeles skyline

Standard		Taught	Reinforced
2.2 Add and subtract fractions by using factoring to find common denominators.		pp. 87–91	pp. 92, 97, 107, 109, 143, 356
2.3 Multiply, divide, and simplify rational numbers by using exponent rules.		pp. 168–171, 176–179	p. 175, 183, 188, 190, 203, 214, 215, 217, 218, 241, 282, 453, EP8
2.4 Use the inverse relationship between raising to a power and extracting the root of a perfect square integer; for an integer that is not square, determine without a calculator the two integers between which its square root lies and explain why.	*use the inverse relationship between raising to a power and extracting the root of a perfect square integer*	pp. 192–195	pp. 210, 216, 511, 546, EP9
	for an integer that is not square, determine without a calculator the two integers between which its square root lies and explain why	pp. 196–199	pp. 209, 210, 216, 218, 255, 291, 396, EP9
2.5 Understand the meaning of the absolute value of a number; interpret the absolute value as the distance of the number from zero on a number line; and determine the absolute value of real numbers.		pp. 14–17	pp. 21, 23–25, 30, 53, 59, 81, 110, 111, 356, 428, EP2, EP3

Algebra and Functions

Standard		Taught	Reinforced
1.0 Students express quantitative relationships by using algebraic terminology, expressions, equations, inequalities, and graphs:		pp. 6–9, 10–13, 32–36, 136–139, 349–352	pp. 30, 48, 52, 54, 55, 152, 428
1.1 Use variables and appropriate operations to write an expression, an equation, an inequality, or a system of equations or inequalities that represents a verbal description (e.g., three less than a number, half as large as area A).	*write an expression*	pp. 10–13	pp. 17, 25, 29, 30, 52, 58, 59, 97, 110, 123, 372, EP2
	write an equation	pp. 43–47	pp. 59, 100, 111, 163, 585, EP3
	write an inequality	pp. 136–139, 140–143, 144–147	pp. 152, 157, 158, 163, EP7
	write a system of equations	pp. 129–133	p. 134, EP6
	write a system of inequalities	pp. 136–139	p. 152, EP7

Standard		Taught	Reinforced
1.2 Use the correct order of operations to evaluate algebraic expressions such as $3(2x + 5)^2$.		pp. 6–9, 168–171	pp. 13, 17, 21, 29, 30, 52, 58, 59, 69, 86, 91, 110, 174, 373, 525, EP2, EP8, EP24
1.3 Simplify numerical expressions by applying properties of rational numbers (e.g., identity, inverse, distributive, associative, commutative) and justify the process used.	*identity properties*	pp. 32–36, 37–40, 120–123	pp. 54, 134, 151
	inverse properties	pp. 82–86	pp. 92, 94–97, 98–101, 102, 107, 108, 109, EP5
	distributive property	pp. 116–119, 120–123	pp. 134, 151, 156, 175, EP6
	associative properties	pp. 116–119	pp. 134, 151, 156, 159, 180, EP6
	commutative properties	pp. 116–119, 120–123	pp. 127, 151, 156, 159, 180, EP6
1.4 Use algebraic terminology (e.g., **variable, equation, term, coefficient, inequality, expression, constant**) correctly.		pp. 6–9, 32–36, 120–123, 136–139	pp. 52, 59, 156
1.5 Represent quantitative relationships graphically and interpret the meaning of a specific part of a graph in the situation represented by the graph.		pp. 349–352, 353–356	pp. 362, 368, 369, 428, 524, EP15
2.0 **Students interpret and evaluate expressions involving integer powers and simple roots:**		pp. 168–171, 172–175, 180–183, 192–195	pp. 179, 190, 203, 210, 214, 215, 216, 251, 282, 301, 352, 387
2.1 Interpret positive whole-number powers as repeated multiplication and negative whole-number powers as repeated division or multiplication by the multiplicative inverse. Simplify and evaluate expressions that include exponents.	*positive whole-number powers*	pp. 168–171	pp. 190, 203, 214, 218, EP8
	negative whole-number powers	pp. 172–175	pp. 179, 190, 214, EP8
	simplify and evaluate expressions that include exponents	pp. 168–171, 172–175	pp. 190, 214, 251, 282, 352, 584, EP8

Standard		Taught	Reinforced
2.2 Multiply and divide monomials; extend the process of taking powers and extracting roots to monomials when the latter results in a monomial with an integer exponent.	*multiply monomials*	pp. 180–183	pp. 190, 215, 218, EP8
	divide monomials	pp. 180–183	pp. 190, 215, 301, EP8
	taking powers of monomials	pp. 180–183	pp. 190, 215, 387, EP8
	extracting roots of monomials	pp. 192–195	pp. 210, 216, 219, EP9
3.0 **Students graph and interpret linear and some nonlinear functions:**		pp. 330–333, 334–337, 338–341	pp. 342, 350, 367, 369, 428, 484
3.1 Graph functions of the form $y = nx^2$ and $y = nx^3$ and use in solving problems.	$y = nx^2$	pp. 334–337	pp. 342, 367, 369, 391, EP14
	$y = nx^3$	pp. 338–341	pp. 367, 369, 419, EP14
3.2 Plot the values from the volumes of three-dimensional shapes for various values of the edge lengths (e.g., cubes with varying edge lengths or a triangle prism with a fixed height and an equilateral triangle base of varying lengths).		p. 484	
3.3 Graph linear functions, noting that the vertical change (change in y-value) per unit of horizontal change (change in x-value) is always the same and know that the ratio ("rise over run") is called the slope of a graph.		pp. 330–333, 344–348	pp. 340, 342, 350–351, 358, 362, 367, 369, 373, 391, 429, EP14, EP15
3.4 Plot the values of quantities whose ratios are always the same (e.g., cost to the number of an item, feet to inches, circumference to diameter of a circle). Fit a line to the plot and understand that the slope of the line equals the ratio of the quantities.		pp. 349–352	pp. 358, EP15
4.0 **Students solve simple linear equations and inequalities over the rational numbers:**		pp. 94–97, 140–143, 144–147	pp. 101, 102, 108, 109, 152, 158, 159, 231, 277, 329, EP3, EP5, EP7

Standard		Taught	Reinforced
4.1 Solve two-step linear equations and inequalities in one variable over the rational numbers, interpret the solution or solutions in the context from which they arose, and verify the reasonableness of the results.	*solve two-step equations*	pp. 41–42, 43–47, 54, 98–101, 108	pp. 48, 54, 58, 59, 77, 102, 108, 109, 111, 123, 127, 133, 438, 493, 585, EP3, EP5
	solve two-step inequalities	pp. 148–151, 158	pp. 152, 158, 159, 209, 372, EP7
4.2 Solve multistep problems involving rate, average speed, distance, and time or a direct variation.	*rate, average speed, distance, time*	pp. 124–127, 232–236, 237–241	pp. 242, 247, 263, 317, 333, 373, 429, EP10
	direct variation	pp. 357–361	pp. 362, 368, 369, 449, EP15

Measurement and Geometry

Standard		Taught	Reinforced
1.0 **Students choose appropriate units of measure and use ratios to convert within and between measurement systems to solve problems:**		pp. 237–241, 252–255	pp. 243, 373, SB15
1.1 Compare weights, capacities, geometric measures, times, and temperatures within and between measurement systems (e.g., miles per hour and feet per second, cubic inches to cubic centimeters).		pp. 237–241	pp. 243, 373, EP10, SB15
1.2 Construct and read drawings and models made to scale.		pp. 252–255, 256–257	pp. 258, 259, 264, 317, EP11
1.3 Use measures expressed as rates (e.g., speed, density) and measures expressed as products (e.g., person-days) to solve problems; check the units of the solutions; and use dimensional analysis to check the reasonableness of the answer.	*measures expressed as rates (e.g., speed, density)*	pp. 228–231, 237–241	pp. 242, 263, 472, EP10
	measures expressed as products (e.g., person-days)	pp. 37–40	pp. 48, 55
	check the units of the solutions; and use dimensional analysis to check the reasonableness of the answer	pp. 237–241	pp. 242, 263, EP10

Standard		Taught	Reinforced
2.0 **Students compute the perimeter, area, and volume of common geometric objects and use the results to find measures of less common objects. They know how perimeter, area, and volume are affected by changes of scale:**		pp. 434–438, 439–443, 450–453, 454–457, 458–461, 485–489, 498–502, 512–515	pp. 444, 445, 462, 466–468, 469, 472, 494, 525
2.1 Use formulas routinely for finding the perimeter and area of basic two-dimensional figures and the surface area and volume of basic three-dimensional figures, including rectangles, parallelograms, trapezoids, squares, triangles, circles, prisms, and cylinders.	*perimeter and area of rectangles and squares*	pp. 434–438	pp. 444, 466, 469, 489, 525, EP18
	perimeter and area of parallelograms	pp. 434–438	pp. 444, 466, 469, EP18
	perimeter and area of trapezoids	pp. 439–443	pp. 444, 467, 469, 524, 536, EP18
	perimeter and area of triangles	pp. 439–443	pp. 444, 445, 467, 469, 536, EP18

San Diego Beach

Standard		Taught	Reinforced
2.1 *(continued)*	*perimeter and area of circles*	pp. 450–453	pp. 457, 462, 467, 469, 525, 552, EP19
	surface area and volume of prisms	pp. 485–489, 498–502	pp. 494, 507, 516, 520, 521, 523, EP20, EP21
	surface area and volume of cylinders	pp. 485–489, 498–502	pp. 494, 516, 521, 522, 523, 584, EP20, EP21
2.2 Estimate and compute the area of more complex of irregular two- and three-dimensional figures by greaking the figures down into more basic objects.		pp. 434–438, 454–457, 458–461, 498–502	pp. 444, 462, 466, 468, 469, 472, 523, 525, 585, EP18, EP19
2.3 Compute the length of the perimeter, the surface area of the faces, and the volume of a three-dimensional object built from rectangular solids. Understand that when the lengths of all dimensions are multiplied by a scale factor, the surface area is multipled by the square of the scale factor and the volume is multiplied by the cube of the scale factor.		pp. 484, 498–502, 512–515	pp. 516, 522, 523, EP20, EP21
2.4 Relate the changes in measurement with a change of scale to the units used (e.g., square inches, cubic feet) and to conversions between units (1 square foot = 144 square inches or [1 ft.^{2}] = [144 in.^{2}]; 1 cubic inch is approximately 16.38 cubic centimeters or [1 in.^{3}] = [16.38 cm^3]).		pp. 434–438, 485–489	pp. 493, 507
3.0 **Students know the Pythagorean theorem and deepen their understanding of plane and solid geometric shapes by constructing figures that meet given conditions and by identifying attributes of figures:**		pp. 205–209, 382–383, 397, 403, 446–449	pp. 405, 439, 462, 467, 525
3.1 Identify and construct basic elements of geometric figures (e.g., altitudes, midpoints, diagonals, angle bisectors, and perpendicular bisectors; central angles; radii, diameters, and chords of circles) by using a compass and straightedge.	*identify basic elements of geometric figures*	pp. 397, 403, 446–449	pp. 462, 467, 469, 525, EP18
	construct basic elements of geometric figures	pp. 382–383, 397	

Standard		Taught	Reinforced
3.2 Understand and use coordinate graphs to plot simple figures, determine lengths and areas related to them, and determine their image under translations and reflections.	*use coordinate graphs to plot simple figures*	pp. 398–402, 410–414, 434–438, 439–443, 450–453	pp. 404, 420, 426, 429, 444, 453, 462, 469, 584, EP17, EP18
	determine lengths and areas related to plotted figures	pp. 434–438, 439–443, 450–453	pp. 444, 453, 462, 469, EP18
	determine images under translations and reflections	pp. 410–414, 415	pp. 420, 426, 427, 429, 489, EP17
⚷ **3.3** Know and understand the Pythagorean theorem and its converse and use it to find the length of the missing side of a right triangle and the lengths of other line segments and, in some situations, empirically verify the Pythagorean theorem by direct measurement.	*know and understand the Pythagorean theorem and empirically verify the theorem by direct measurement*	pp. 204, 205–209	pp. 210, 216, 348, 394, 439, 443, 444, 467, EP9, EP18
	converse of the Pythagorean theorem	pp. 205–209	pp. 210, 216, 231, EP9
	find the length of the missing side of a right triangle and the lengths of other line segments	pp. 205–209, 392–396	pp. 210, 216, 395, 404, 425, 427, 439, 443, 525, 584, EP9, EP16, EP18
⚷ **3.4** Demonstrate an understanding of conditions that indicate two geometrical figures are congruent and what congruence means about the relationships between the sides and angles of the two figures.		pp. 406–409	pp. 414, 420, 426, 427, 585, EP17
3.5 Construct two-dimensional patterns for three-dimensional models, such as cylinders, prisms, and cones.		pp. 496–497, 503	p. 502
⚷ **3.6** Identify elements of three-dimensional geometric objects (e.g., diagonals of rectangular solids) and describe how two or more objects are related in space (e.g., skew lines, the possible ways three planes might intersect).		pp. 384–387	pp. 396, 404, 425, 427, 429, EP16

Standard		Taught	Reinforced
Statistics, Data Analysis, and Probability			
1.0 Students collect, organize, and represent data sets that have one or more variables and identify relationships among variables within a data set by hand and through the use of an electronic spreadsheet software program:		pp. 530–531, 532–536, 542–546	pp. 547, 553, 554, 575, 578–579, 581, EP22, SB18–SB21
1.1 Know various forms of display for data sets, including a stem-and-leaf plot or box-and-whisker plot; use the forms to display a single set of data or to compare two sets of data.	*various forms of display*	pp. 532–536	pp. 110, 530–531, 538, 540, 541, 554, 575, 578, 581, EP22, SB18–SB21
	stem-and-leaf plot	pp. 532–536	pp. 541, 554, 575, 581, EP22
	box-and-whisker plot	pp. 542–546	pp. 547, 554, 579, 581, EP22
1.2 Represent two numerical variables on a scatterplot and informally describe how the data points are distributed and any apparent relationship that exists between the two variables (e.g., between time spent on homework and grade level).		pp. 548–552	pp. 553, 554, 563, 575, 579, 581, 585, EP22
1.3 Understand the meaning of, and be able to compute, the minimum, the lower quartile, the median, the upper quartile, and the maximum of a data set.		pp. 537–541, 542–546	pp. 546, 547, 568, 573, 579, 581, EP22

Mathematical reasoning is inherently embedded in all strands of mathematics. Therefore, the standards listed under the Mathematical Reasoning strand are addressed through the presentation of the standards listed under the other strands. The following table gives selected examples of these instances.

Standard	Selected References
Mathematical Reasoning	
1.0 Students make decisions about how to approach problems:	Embedded throughout text. For example, see pp. 84 (NS1.2), 99 (AF4.1), 191 (NS1.1), 206 (MG3.3), 343 (NS1.7), 454–455 (MG2.2).
1.1 Analyze problems by identifying relationships, distinguishing relevant from irrelevant information, identifying missing information, sequencing and prioritizing information, and observing patterns.	Embedded throughout text. For example, see pp. 31 (NS1.2), 72 (NS1.1), 135 (AF1.1), 191 (NS1.1), 243 (MG1.1), 495 (MG1.1).
1.2 Formulate and justify mathematical conjectures based on a general description of the mathematical question or problem posed.	Embedded throughout text. For example, see pp. 64 (NS1.5), 337 (AF3.1), 348 (AF3.3), 361 (AF4.2), 484 (MG2.3).
1.3 Determine when and how to break a problem into simpler parts.	Embedded throughout text. For example, see pp. 43 (AF4.1), 88 (NS1.2), 148 (AF4.1), 303 (NS1.7), 454 (MG2.2).
2.0 Students use strategies, skills, and concepts in finding solutions:	Embedded throughout text. For example, see pp. 40 (AF4.0), 206 (MG3.3), 452 (MG2.1), 550 (SDAP1.2).
2.1 Use estimation to verify the reasonableness of calculated results.	Embedded throughout text. For example, see pp. 83 (NS1.2), 280 (NS1.3).
2.2 Apply strategies and results from simpler problems to more complex problems.	Embedded throughout text. For example, see pp. 40 (AF4.0), 452 (MG2.1), 541 (SDAP1.3).
2.3 Estimate unknown quantities graphically and solve for them by using logical reasoning and arithmetic and algebraic techniques.	Embedded throughout text. For example, see pp. 359 (AF4.2), 550 (SDAP1.2).
2.4 Make and test conjectures by using both inductive and deductive reasoning.	Embedded throughout text. For example, see pp. 172 (NS2.1), 195 (AF2.2), 286 (NS1.3), 341 (AF3.1), 403 (MG3.1).
2.5 Use a variety of methods, such as words, numbers, symbols, charts, graphs, tables, diagrams, and models, to explain mathematical reasoning.	Embedded throughout text. For example, see pp. 71 (NS1.1), 98–99 (AF4.1), 204 (MG3.3), 302 (NS1.7).

Standard	Selected References
2.6 Express the solution clearly and logically by using the appropriate mathematical notation and terms and clear language; support solutions with evidence in both verbal and symbolic work.	Embedded throughout text. For example, see pp. 95 (AF4.0), 148 (AF4.1), 300 (NS1.7).
2.7 Indicate the relative advantages of exact and approximate solutions to problems and give answers to a specified degree of accuracy.	Embedded throughout text. For example, see pp. 298 (NS1.7), 450 (MG2.1), 508 (MG2.0).
2.8 Make precise calculations and check the validity of the results from the context of the problem.	Embedded throughout text. For example, see pp. 140 (AF4.0), 206 (MG3.3).
3.0 Students determine a solution is complete and move beyond a particular problem by generalizing to other situations:	Embedded throughout text. For example, see pp. 79 (NS1.2), 295 (NS1.7), 550 (SDAP1.2).
3.1 Evaluate the reasonableness of the solution in the context of the original situation.	Embedded throughout text. For example, see pp. 45 (AF4.1), 84 (NS1.2), 93 (NS1.2), 239 (MG1.3), 445 (MG2.1).
3.2 Note the method of deriving the solution and demonstrate a conceptual understanding of the derivation by solving similar problems.	Embedded throughout text. For example, see pp. 79 (NS1.2), 295 (NS1.7), 550 (SDAP1.2).
3.3 Develop generalizations of the results obtained and the strategies used and apply them to new problem situations.	Embedded throughout text. For example, see pp. 13 (AF1.1), 119 (AF1.3), 150 (AF4.1), 234 (AF4.2), 297 (NS1.7), 341 (AF3.1).

Using Your Book to Master the Standards

Holt California Mathematics provides many opportunities for you
to master the California Mathematics Content Standards for Grade 7.

Countdown to Mastery

Countdown to Mastery provides practice
with the standards every day.

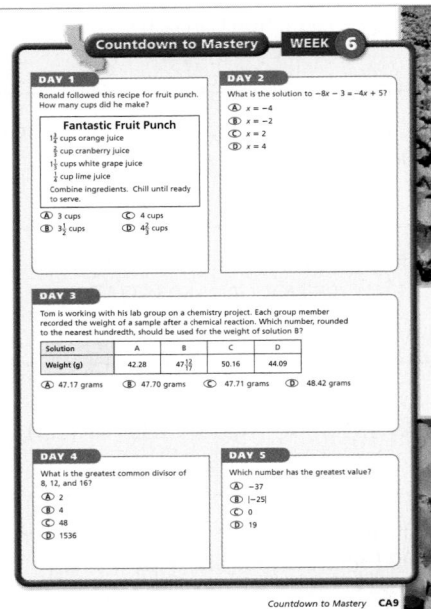

Step 1

✔ **Complete one item each day
before you start the lesson.**

There are 24 pages of standards practice.
Each page has five questions, one for
each day of the week.

California Standards

The **California Standards** taught in each
lesson are listed at the start of the lesson.

Step 2

✔ **Preview the standards
before you start the lesson.**

Complete standards are shown.
The words in bold tell you which
part of the standard is the focus
of the lesson.

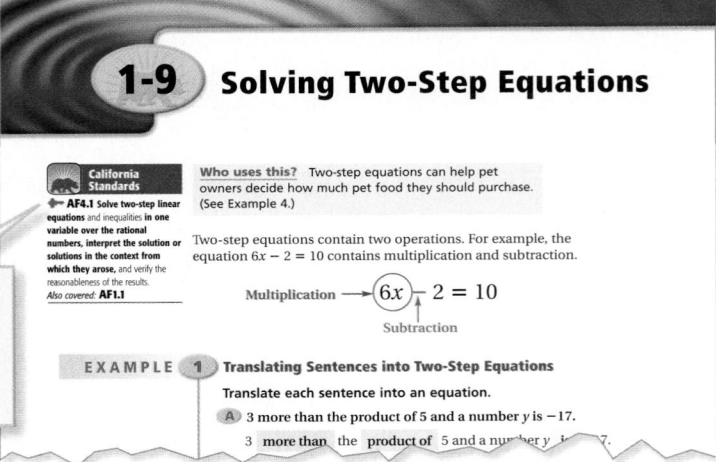

1-9 Solving Two-Step Equations

California Standards

◀ **AF4.1 Solve two-step linear equations and inequalities in one variable over the rational numbers, interpret the solution or solutions in the context from which they arose,** and verify the reasonableness of the results.
Also covered: **AF1.1**

Who uses this? Two-step equations can help pet owners decide how much pet food they should purchase. (See Example 4.)

Two-step equations contain two operations. For example, the equation $6x - 2 = 10$ contains multiplication and subtraction.

Multiplication → $6x - 2 = 10$
Subtraction

EXAMPLE 1 **Translating Sentences into Two-Step Equations**

Translate each sentence into an equation.

A) 3 more than the product of 5 and a number y is -17.

3 more than the product of 5 and a number y is -17.

SPIRAL STANDARDS REVIEW

Use the Spiral Standards Review for constant review of standards taught in the current and previous lessons.

Step 3

✔ Keep your skills fresh by practicing the standards daily.

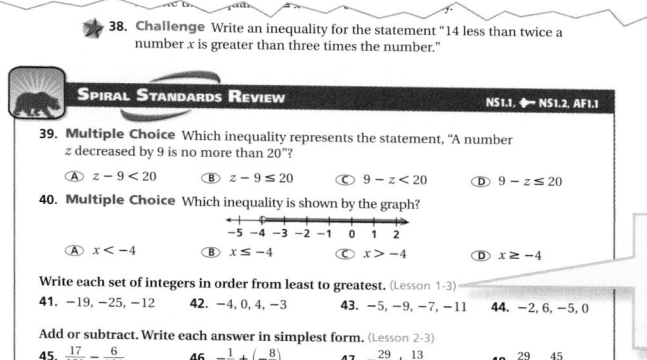

38. Challenge Write an inequality for the statement "14 less than twice a number x is greater than three times the number."

SPIRAL STANDARDS REVIEW
NS1.1, ← NS1.2, AF1.1

39. Multiple Choice Which inequality represents the statement, "A number z decreased by 9 is no more than 20"?

Ⓐ $z - 9 < 20$ Ⓑ $z - 9 \leq 20$ Ⓒ $9 - z < 20$ Ⓓ $9 - z \leq 20$

40. Multiple Choice Which inequality is shown by the graph?

Ⓐ $x < -4$ Ⓑ $x \leq -4$ Ⓒ $x > -4$ Ⓓ $x \geq -4$

Write each set of integers in order from least to greatest. (Lesson 1-3)

41. $-19, -25, -12$ **42.** $-4, 0, 4, -3$ **43.** $-5, -9, -7, -11$ **44.** $-2, 6, -5, 0$

Add or subtract. Write each answer in simplest form. (Lesson 2-3)

45. $\frac{17}{121} - \frac{6}{121}$ **46.** $-\frac{1}{7} + \left(-\frac{8}{7}\right)$ **47.** $-\frac{29}{12} + \frac{13}{12}$ **48.** $\frac{29}{5} - \frac{45}{5}$

3-5 Inequalities **139**

If you need help with a problem, go to the lesson referenced at the end of the problem.

MASTERING THE STANDARDS

Use the Mastering the Standards for review of standards taught in the current and previous chapters.

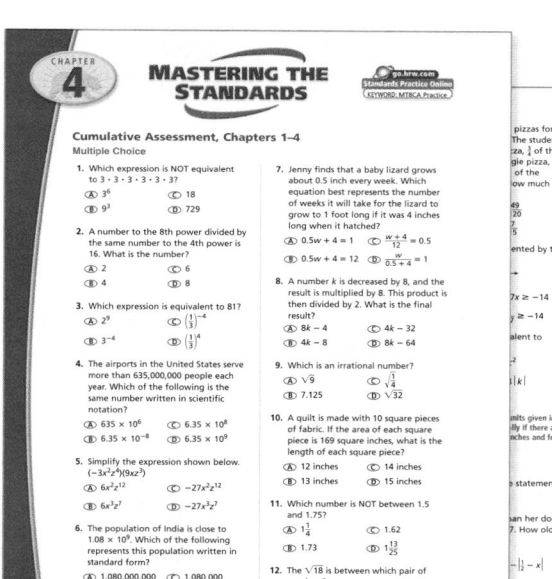

Step 4

✔ After finishing each chapter, review your knowledge of the standards.

There are multiple choice, gridded response, short response, and extended response questions to help you check your knowledge of the Grade 7 standards.

COUNTDOWN TO MASTERY

Each problem in the *Countdown to Mastery* is correlated to the California Mathematics Content Standards for Grade 7. These correlations are shown at the bottom of each page. For the full text of the standards, see pages CAvi – CAxix.

DAY 1

What information does the circle graph **not** tell you about Chris?

(A) Chris spends more time at soccer practice than at the library.

(B) Chris spends the most amount of time doing his chores.

(C) Chris spends less time at guitar lessons than at soccer practice.

(D) Chris spends more time doing chores than studying at the library.

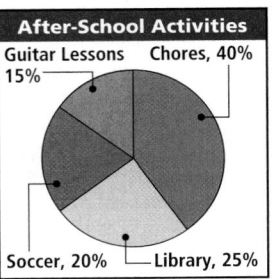

After-School Activities

Guitar Lessons 15%   Chores, 40%

Soccer, 20%   Library, 25%

DAY 2

If these two figures are similar, what is the missing length of figure *B*?

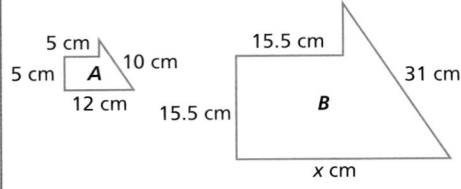

5 cm

5 cm   *A*   10 cm

12 cm   15.5 cm

15.5 cm

B

31 cm

x cm

(A) 3.1 centimeters

(B) 22.5 centimeters

(C) 25.2 centimeters

(D) 37.2 centimeters

DAY 3

Beth saved $2200. A laptop costs $2199.99, extra memory for the computer is $149.50, and an extra battery is $59.95. Beth also has a coupon for $300 off one purchase at the store. Which of the following expressions shows that Beth has saved enough for all of these items?

(A) $2200 - 300 + 150 - 60 = 1890$

(B) $2200 - 150 - 60 - 300 = 1690$

(C) $2200 + 150 + 60 = 2410$

(D) $2200 + 150 + 60 - 300 = 2110$

DAY 4

What value of *n* makes the following equation true? $n \div 13 = 4$

(A) 3.25   (C) 17

(B) 9   (D) 52

DAY 5

What is the value of $3[2^2 - (-4 + 5^2)]$?

(A) -51 (C) 75

(B) -9 (D) 99

Day	California Standards
1	6SDAP2.5
2	6NS1.3
3	6NS2.3
4	6AF1.1
5	6AF1.4

DAY 1

What is the value of the expression $5x - 2(4x - 3)^2$ when $x = -3$?

(A) −465

(B) −177

(C) −147

(D) 885

DAY 2

What is the number 7 called in the expression $3z + 7$?

(A) coefficient

(B) constant

(C) sum

(D) variable

DAY 3

A manufacturer of doll clothes produces more white dresses than blue dresses by a factor of 3.5. Given b, the number of blue dresses produced, which equation shows w, the number of white dresses produced?

(A) $w = b \div 3.5$

(B) $w = \frac{3.5}{b}$

(C) $w = 3.5b$

(D) $w = 3.5 + b$

DAY 4

What is the value of $|3 - 9| + |2 - 5|$?

(A) −9

(B) −3

(C) 3

(D) 9

DAY 5

Which is the greatest number in the list?

$$3.3, \ 3\tfrac{1}{4}, \ 3.1, \ 3.13, \ 3.11, \ 3.31$$

(A) 3.13

(B) $3\tfrac{1}{4}$

(C) 3.3

(D) 3.31

Day	California Standards
1	AF1.2
2	AF1.4
3	AF1.1
4	NS2.5 🔑
5	NS1.1

Countdown to Mastery — WEEK 3

DAY 1

When Kit woke up, it was –15°C outside. By that afternoon, the temperature had risen 20 degrees. What was the afternoon temperature?

(A) –5°C (C) 20°C
(B) 5°C (D) 35°C

DAY 2

Annie needs 500 mini muffins to make gift baskets. She already has 44 muffins. Which equation can be solved to find how many dozens of muffins Annie still needs?

(A) $44 + 12d = 500$
(B) $44 + 500 = 12d$
(C) $12(44 + d) = 500$
(D) $500 - d = 12(44)$

DAY 3

Which expression is equivalent to $5x - 35$?

(A) $5(x - 35)$
(B) $5(x - 7)$
(C) $5(x + 35)$
(D) $5(x + 7)$

DAY 4

Which fraction is equivalent to a repeating decimal?

(A) $\frac{1}{2}$
(B) $\frac{1}{3}$
(C) $\frac{1}{4}$
(D) $\frac{1}{5}$

DAY 5

Simon is shopping for a new mountain bike. He finds one that costs $179.95, but he has a coupon. By which number should Simon multiply the price of the bike to calculate how much money he will save?

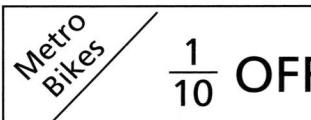

Metro Bikes $\frac{1}{10}$ OFF
the purchase of any bike
offer good until 9/1

(A) 0.01 (C) 1.0
(B) 0.1 (D) 10.0

Day	California Standards
1	NS1.2
2	AF4.1
3	AF1.3
4	NS1.5
5	NS1.3

DAY 1

Sandra uses 3.6 meters of ribbon to weave a small rug and 4.2 meters of ribbon to weave a large rug. She used a total of 118.8 meters of ribbon to make 12 small rugs and x large rugs. Which equation can be used to find the number of large rugs she made?

Ⓐ $12(3.6) + x(4.2) = 118.8$

Ⓑ $x(3.6) + 12(4.2) = 118.8$

Ⓒ $12 + x(3.6 \cdot 4.2) = 118.8$

Ⓓ $12 + x + 3.6 + 4.2 = 118.8$

DAY 2

Which property is used in the equation below?

$3(x + 5) = 3x + 15$

Ⓐ Associative Property of Addition

Ⓑ Commutative Property of Addition

Ⓒ Distributive Property

Ⓓ Inverse Property

DAY 3

Rita is playing a board game. If she had 13 points before landing on the spot shown, how many points does she have now?

LOSE 20 POINTS!

Ⓐ −33   Ⓑ −7   Ⓒ 7   Ⓓ 33

DAY 4

What is the value of $xy - y + 5$ if $x = 3$ and $y = -1$?

Ⓐ −7

Ⓑ −3

Ⓒ 1

Ⓓ 3

DAY 5

Which of the following shows use of the least common denominator to simplify $\frac{2}{6} + \frac{3}{4}$?

Ⓐ $\left(\frac{2}{6} \times \frac{2}{2}\right) + \left(\frac{3}{4} \times \frac{3}{3}\right)$

Ⓑ $\left(\frac{2}{6} \times \frac{4}{4}\right) + \left(\frac{3}{4} \times \frac{6}{6}\right)$

Ⓒ $\left(\frac{2}{6} \times \frac{3}{3}\right) + \left(\frac{3}{4} \times \frac{2}{2}\right)$

Ⓓ $\left(\frac{2}{6} \times \frac{6}{6}\right) + \left(\frac{3}{4} \times \frac{4}{4}\right)$

Day	California Standards
1	AF4.1
2	AF1.3
3	NS1.2
4	AF1.2
5	NS2.2

COUNTDOWN TO MASTERY

DAY 1

Jake is a reporter for a local newspaper. He has rewritten $\frac{7}{12}$ of an interview that lasted 89 minutes. Which expression can Jake use to estimate the number of minutes he has transcribed?

(A) 0.07×90

(B) 0.25×90

(C) 0.7×90

(D) 2×90

DAY 2

Name the property that is illustrated by the following:

$$a + (-a) = 0$$

(A) Associative Property of Addition

(B) Additive Identity Property

(C) Additive Inverse Property

(D) Multiplicative Inverse Property

DAY 3

Chandra is paid 1.5 times her hourly wage of $12.50 per hour when she works overtime. This month she worked 80 regularly paid hours and x hours of overtime. She was paid a total of $1375. Which equation can be used to find the number of overtime hours that Chandra worked this month?

(A) $12.50(80) + 1.5(12.50) + 20 = 1375$

(B) $12.50(80 + 20) + 1.5(12.50) = 1375$

(C) $12.50(80) + (1.5)(12.50)x = 1375$

(D) $1.5(12.50)(80 + 20) = 1375$

DAY 4

The Gordon family is driving to the Grand Canyon from Lubbock, Texas. If they drive an average of 55 miles per hour for h hours, which equation shows d, the distance they traveled?

(A) $d = 55h$

(B) $d = 55 \div h$

(C) $d = \frac{h}{55}$

(D) $d = 55 + h$

DAY 5

The original price of a value meal was $5.49. The meal is discounted this week by 25%. What is the price of the meal after the discount?

(A) $1.37

(B) $4.12

(C) $5.24

(D) $6.86

Day	California Standards
1	NS1.3
2	AF1.3
3	AF4.1
4	AF1.1
5	NS1.7

DAY 1

Ronald followed this recipe for fruit punch. How many cups did he make?

Fantastic Fruit Punch

$1\frac{3}{4}$ cups orange juice

$\frac{2}{3}$ cup cranberry juice

$1\frac{1}{3}$ cups white grape juice

$\frac{1}{4}$ cup lime juice

Combine ingredients. Chill until ready to serve.

Ⓐ 3 cups　　Ⓒ 4 cups
Ⓑ $3\frac{1}{2}$ cups　　Ⓓ $4\frac{2}{3}$ cups

DAY 2

What is the solution to $-8x - 3 = -4x + 5$?

Ⓐ $x = -4$
Ⓑ $x = -2$
Ⓒ $x = 2$
Ⓓ $x = 4$

DAY 3

Tom is working with his lab group on a chemistry project. Each group member recorded the weight of a sample after a chemical reaction. Which number, rounded to the nearest hundredth, should be used for the weight of solution B?

Solution	A	B	C	D
Weight (g)	42.28	$47\frac{12}{17}$	50.16	44.09

Ⓐ 47.17 grams　　Ⓑ 47.70 grams　　Ⓒ 47.71 grams　　Ⓓ 48.42 grams

DAY 4

What is the greatest common divisor of 8, 12, and 16?

Ⓐ 2
Ⓑ 4
Ⓒ 48
Ⓓ 1536

DAY 5

Which number has the greatest value?

Ⓐ -37
Ⓑ $|-25|$
Ⓒ 0
Ⓓ 19

Day	California Standards
1	NS1.2
2	AF4.1
3	NS1.3
4	NS2.2
5	NS2.5

DAY 1

Name the property that is illustrated by the following:

$$3 + 5 = 5 + 3$$

- (A) Associative Property of Addition
- (B) Commutative Property of Addition
- (C) Additive Inverse Property
- (D) Multiplicative Inverse Property

DAY 2

Which expression has the same value as y^5?

- (A) $y + 5$
- (B) $5y$
- (C) $y \cdot y \cdot y \cdot y \cdot y$
- (D) $5y \cdot 5y \cdot 5y \cdot 5y \cdot 5y$

DAY 3

Which of the following has the same value as $3^{-2} \cdot 3^4$?

- (A) 3^{-8}
- (B) 3^{-2}
- (C) 3^2
- (D) 3^6

DAY 4

Which of the following has the same value as $\frac{4^{-2}}{5^{-3}}$?

- (A) $\frac{5^3}{4^2}$
- (B) $\frac{4^3}{5^2}$
- (C) $\frac{-4^2}{-5^3}$
- (D) 5

DAY 5

Which expression has the same value as $2x^3 \cdot 4x^2y^3$?

- (A) $6x^5y^3$
- (B) $6x^6y^3$
- (C) $8x^5y^3$
- (D) $8x^6y^3$

Day	California Standards
1	AF1.3 🔑
2	AF2.1
3	NS2.1
4	NS2.3 🔑
5	AF2.2

DAY 1

The drama club charges $3 admission to its one-act play. The club's expenses are $115. In order for the club to make exactly $110 after expenses, how many people must attend the play?

- (A) 39
- (B) 75
- (C) 114
- (D) 152

DAY 2

Which expression shows use of the least common denominator to simplify $\frac{5}{6} - \frac{2}{3}$?

- (A) $\left(\frac{5}{6} \times \frac{1}{1}\right) - \left(\frac{2}{3} \times \frac{2}{2}\right)$
- (B) $\left(\frac{5}{6} \times \frac{2}{2}\right) - \left(\frac{2}{3} \times \frac{5}{5}\right)$
- (C) $\left(\frac{5}{6} \times \frac{3}{3}\right) - \left(\frac{2}{3} \times \frac{6}{6}\right)$
- (D) $\left(\frac{5}{6} \times \frac{5}{5}\right) - \left(\frac{2}{3} \times \frac{2}{2}\right)$

DAY 3

Which of the following has the same value as $\frac{2^2 \cdot 3^6 \cdot 4^4}{2^3 \cdot 3^6 \cdot 4^3}$?

- (A) $\frac{1}{2}$
- (B) $\frac{1}{4}$
- (C) 1
- (D) 2

DAY 4

How many feet of wood molding would Jeremy need to trim all of the walls of his bedroom?

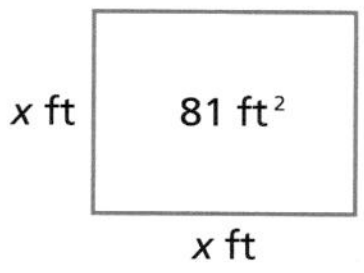

```
        x ft    ┌──────────┐
                │          │
                │  81 ft²  │
                │          │
                └──────────┘
                    x ft
```

- (A) 4 feet
- (C) 72 feet
- (B) 36 feet
- (D) 320 feet

DAY 5

A computer's hard drive spins at 5400 revolutions per minute. If the hard drive has been running for m minutes, which expression shows r, the number of revolutions?

- (A) $r = m \div 5400$
- (B) $r = 5400 \cdot m$
- (C) $r = 5400 + m$
- (D) $r = \frac{5400}{m}$

Day	California Standards
1	AF4.1 🔑
2	NS2.2 🔑
3	NS2.3 🔑
4	NS2.4
5	AF1.1

DAY 1

Which number is irrational?

(A) −2

(B) 1.25

(C) √7

(D) √16

DAY 2

Which of the following has the same value as $\frac{5^3 x^3}{5^2 x^{-1}}$?

(A) $\frac{x^2}{5}$

(B) $\frac{5^3}{x^2}$

(C) $5^3 x^2$

(D) $5x^4$

DAY 3

Which measurement is equivalent to 3 square feet?

(A) 0.0625 in²

(B) 36 in²

(C) 432 in²

(D) 1296 in²

DAY 4

Carolyn is building an isosceles triangle headboard for her bed. What is its height? Round your answer to the nearest tenth.

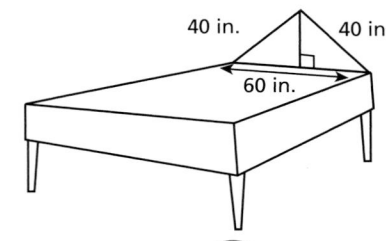

40 in.   40 in.

60 in.

(A) 8.3 inches   (C) 26.5 inches

(B) 10.0 inches   (D) 100.0 inches

DAY 5

Jimmy buys 44 feet of wood to build a square frame for a sandbox. He decides to make the sandbox smaller and reduces its perimeter by $\frac{1}{5}$. How much wood will be left over?

(A) 8.8 feet   (C) 26.4 feet

(B) 17.6 feet   (D) 35.2 feet

Day	California Standards
1	NS1.4
2	NS2.3
3	MG2.4
4	MG3.3
5	NS1.3

Countdown to Mastery WEEK 10

DAY 1

The table shows the typing rates of four applicants for a job. Based on typing rates, which applicant is the best choice to hire?

Applicant	Words	Minute
Ann	112	6
Theo	206	8
June	195	7
Andy	120	5

Ⓐ June
Ⓑ Ann
Ⓒ Andy
Ⓓ Theo

DAY 2

Which expression has the same value as x^{-5}?

Ⓐ $x + 5$
Ⓑ $-5x$
Ⓒ $\frac{1}{5x}$
Ⓓ $\frac{1}{x} \cdot \frac{1}{x} \cdot \frac{1}{x} \cdot \frac{1}{x} \cdot \frac{1}{x}$

DAY 3

Mr. Bryce bought a hybrid car that can travel 240 miles on 8 gallons of gas. How far can Mr. Bryce travel on 10 gallons of gas?

Ⓐ 280 miles
Ⓑ 300 miles
Ⓒ 480 miles
Ⓓ 2400 miles

DAY 4

How many millimeters are in 5 centimeters?

Ⓐ 0.05 mm
Ⓑ 0.5 mm
Ⓒ 50 mm
Ⓓ 500 mm

DAY 5

Mrs. Weyland is making 7 cups of juice for her children's friends. If she wants to serve each guest $\frac{3}{4}$ cup of juice, how many children will the juice serve?

Ⓐ 8
Ⓑ 9
Ⓒ 10
Ⓓ 11

Day	California Standards
1	MG1.3
2	AF2.1
3	AF4.2
4	MG1.1
5	NS1.2

DAY 1

Gina is drawing a scale model of a park. If the scale factor is 1 inch = 4 feet, what is the perimeter of the actual park?

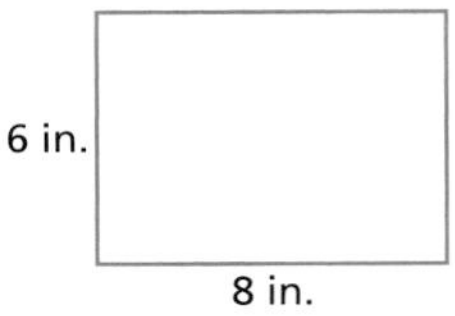

6 in. [ ]

8 in.

(A) 28 feet (B) 56 feet (C) 112 feet (D) 768 feet

DAY 2

Which of the following has the same value as $\dfrac{\left(\frac{1}{5}\right)^{-2} \times \left(\frac{1}{5}\right)^{8}}{\left(\frac{1}{5}\right)^{3}}$?

(A) $\left(\frac{1}{5}\right)^{-3}$

(B) $\left(\frac{1}{5}\right)^{-2}$

(C) $\left(\frac{1}{5}\right)^{2}$

(D) $\left(\frac{1}{5}\right)^{3}$

DAY 3

Which expression has the same value as $\dfrac{12n^{3}}{4n^{4}}$?

(A) $\frac{1}{3n}$

(B) $\frac{3}{n}$

(C) $\frac{n}{3}$

(D) $3n$

DAY 4

Which of the following has the same value as $\dfrac{\left(\frac{1}{2}\right)^{2} \times \left(\frac{1}{2}\right)^{3}}{\left(\frac{1}{2}\right)^{3}}$?

(A) $\dfrac{1}{\left(\frac{1}{2}\right)^{3}}$

(B) $\left(\frac{1}{2}\right)^{2}$

(C) $\left(\frac{1}{2}\right)^{3}$

(D) 1

DAY 5

What is the value of $3(x + 2y) - 2x$ if $x = -5$ and $y = 2$?

(A) -15

(B) -7

(C) -1

(D) 7

Day	California Standards
1	MG1.2
2	NS2.1
3	AF2.2
4	NS2.3 🔑
5	AF1.2

DAY 1

Which expression has the least value?

(A) 0

(B) |4 − 8|

(C) |9 − 17|

(D) |16 − 31|

DAY 2

Television screen size is measured on the diagonal. What is the height of this screen to the nearest tenth?

42 in.

37.5 in.

h

(A) 4.5 inches

(B) 9.0 inches

(C) 18.9 inches

(D) 20.3 inches

DAY 3

Every 2 hours, a hive of honeybees can produce 150 grams of honey. How many grams of honey does the hive produce in 5 hours?

(A) 300 grams

(B) 375 grams

(C) 450 grams

(D) 750 grams

DAY 4

Marty's cell phone bill is usually $39.50. Under a new calling plan, his bill will be $44.24. What is the percent of increase in Marty's cell phone bill?

(A) 0.12%

(B) 11%

(C) 12%

(D) 89%

DAY 5

A sports shop buys tennis rackets from a supplier for $21.00. The shop owner marks the price up by 250% when he prices them for sale to his customers. What must a customer pay for a tennis racket?

(A) $26.25

(B) $47.25

(C) $52.50

(D) $73.50

Day	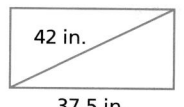 California Standards
1	NS2.5
2	MG3.3
3	AF4.2
4	NS1.6
5	NS1.7

DAY 1

Missy's car can travel 30 miles per gallon. If Missy fills up her tank with 16 gallons of gas, which expression can be used to show how many gallons of gas are left in Missy's tank after she has traveled 90 miles?

Ⓐ $16(90 \div 30)$

Ⓑ $16 - \frac{90}{30}$

Ⓒ $30 + 30 + 30 - 16$

Ⓓ $90 \cdot 16 - 30$

DAY 2

Candace is building a bookcase with shelves that are right triangles. What is the approximate measure across the front of the bookcase?

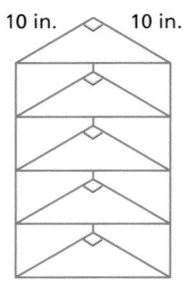

10 in.   10 in.

Ⓐ 4 inches   Ⓒ 50 inches

Ⓑ 14 inches   Ⓓ 72 inches

DAY 3

Casey bought a new video game for $30. He later sold it at a yard sale for $5. What was the percent of decrease in the price of the game? Round your answer to the nearest percent.

Ⓐ 5%

Ⓑ 6%

Ⓒ 17%

Ⓓ 83%

DAY 4

An office-supply company packs 192 boxes of paper clips in 2 cases. How many boxes are packed in 5 cases?

Ⓐ 384

Ⓑ 480

Ⓒ 500

Ⓓ 672

DAY 5

The science club is raising money for a trip. It needs to raise $240.50 so that the entire club can go. So far it has raised $169.75. How much more money does the club need to raise?

Ⓐ $70.50   Ⓒ $70.85

Ⓑ $70.75   Ⓓ $71.75

Day	California Standards
1	MG1.3
2	MG3.3
3	NS1.6
4	AF4.2
5	NS1.2

DAY 1

What is the slope of the line?

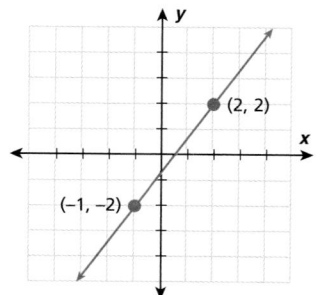

(2, 2)

(−1, −2)

Ⓐ $\frac{3}{4}$ Ⓒ $\frac{4}{3}$

Ⓑ $-\frac{3}{4}$ Ⓓ $-\frac{4}{3}$

DAY 2

Which graph shows $y = 2x^2$?

Ⓐ 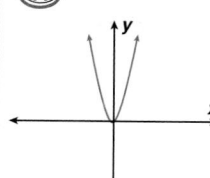 Ⓒ

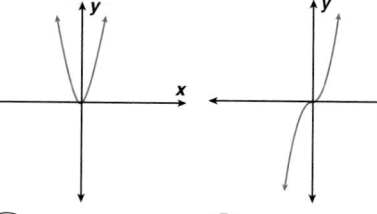

Ⓑ Ⓓ

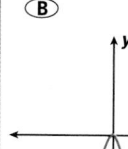 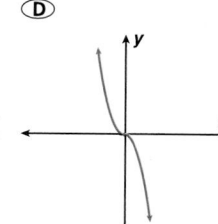

DAY 3

Brandon is paid a 20% commission on his sales of electric guitars. Last month, his sales total was $5600. How much commission was Brandon paid last month?

Ⓐ $112 Ⓒ $4480

Ⓑ $1120 Ⓓ $6720

DAY 4

What is the value of $|6 - 13|^2$?

Ⓐ −49

Ⓑ $\frac{1}{49}$

Ⓒ 7

Ⓓ 49

DAY 5

A job advertisement states that the position pays $12 an hour. Which graph shows the relationship between the number of hours worked and the amount earned?

Ⓐ 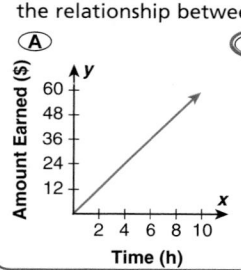 Ⓑ 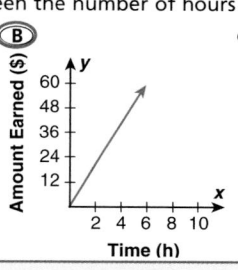 Ⓒ 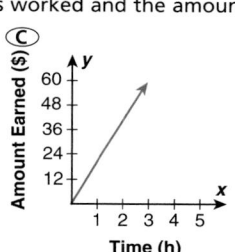 Ⓓ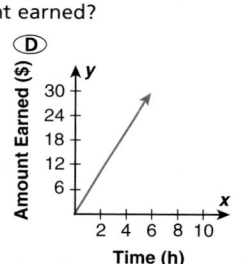

Day	California Standards
1	AF3.3
2	AF3.1
3	NS1.7
4	NS2.5
5	AF3.4

DAY 1

Which rate is approximately equal to 60 mi/h?

(A) 0.03 km/h   (C) 37.5 km/s

(B) 0.03 km/s   (D) 88 ft/min

DAY 2

The cost that taxicab companies charge per ride is shown on the graph.

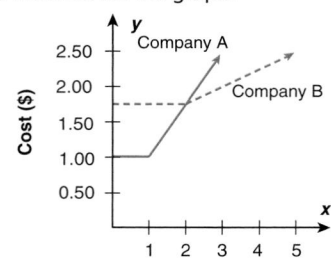

Company A costs less than Company B when the ride lasts

(A) less than 1 minute.

(B) less than 2 minutes.

(C) exactly 2 minutes.

(D) more than 2 minutes.

DAY 3

Between which two integers does the side length of the square lie?

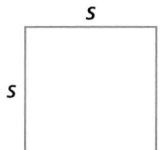

Area = 51 square units

(A) 7 and 8

(B) 8 and 9

(C) 9 and 10

(D) 10 and 11

DAY 4

Kendall can knit 3 hats in 8 hours. Rhonda can knit 2 hats in 4 hours. Meghan can knit $\frac{1}{2}$ hat in $1\frac{1}{2}$ hours. Jordan can knit $\frac{1}{3}$ hat in 30 minutes. Who knits hats fastest?

(A) Kendall

(B) Rhonda

(C) Meghan

(D) Jordan

DAY 5

Mary bought 8 tickets to a hockey game for $19.20. How much would 10 tickets cost?

(A) $21.60

(B) $24.00

(C) $29.20

(D) $32.00

Day	California Standards
1	MG1.1
2	AF1.5
3	NS2.4
4	MG1.3 🔑
5	AF4.2 🔑

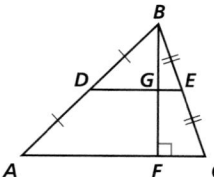

COUNTDOWN TO MASTERY

DAY 1

Which figure is the altitude of the triangle?

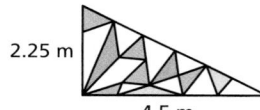

Ⓐ angle *ABC*

Ⓑ segment *DE*

Ⓒ segment *BF*

Ⓓ point *G*

DAY 2

Which situation is not possible in three-dimensional space?

Ⓐ Three lines intersect in exactly one point.

Ⓑ Two planes never intersect.

Ⓒ Two planes intersect in a line.

Ⓓ Two planes intersect in exactly one point.

DAY 3

Audrey sold 12 beaded shawls for $45.50 each. She spent $60.27 on supplies to make the shawls. What was her profit?

Ⓐ $14.77

Ⓑ $485.73

Ⓒ $546.00

Ⓓ $677.74

DAY 4

Katie wants to frame this stained-glass window with wood. What length of wood does she need to buy? Round your answer to the nearest tenth.

2.25 m

4.5 m

Ⓐ 5.0 meters

Ⓑ 6.8 meters

Ⓒ 11.8 meters

Ⓓ 13.5 meters

DAY 5

What is the solution set of $-3 \geq -4x + 5$?

Ⓐ $\{x : x \leq -2\}$

Ⓑ $\{x : x \leq 2\}$

Ⓒ $\{x : x \geq -2\}$

Ⓓ $\{x : x \geq 2\}$

Day	California Standards
1	MG3.1
2	MG3.6
3	NS1.7
4	MG3.3
5	AF4.1

COUNTDOWN TO MASTERY

DAY 1

What is the value of $\left(\frac{2}{3}\right)^3$?

Ⓐ $\frac{6}{9}$

Ⓑ $\frac{8}{9}$

Ⓒ $\frac{6}{27}$

Ⓓ $\frac{8}{27}$

DAY 2

If figure *LMNO* is reflected across the x-axis, which point(s) will **not** change locations?

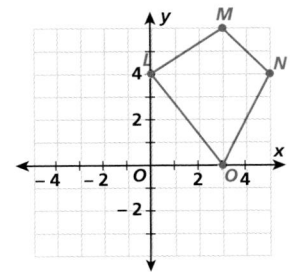

Ⓐ *L* and *O*   Ⓒ *O*

Ⓑ *L*   Ⓓ *L* and *N*

DAY 3

Which graph best represents the graph of $y = 2x + 3$?

Ⓐ 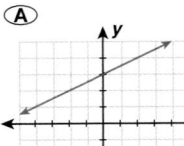   Ⓑ 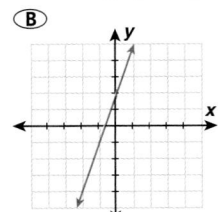   Ⓒ 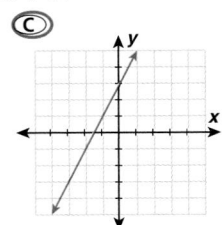   Ⓓ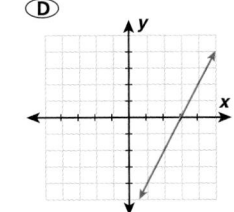

DAY 4

Based on the information in the diagram, which two figures are congruent?

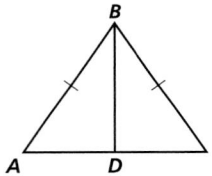

Ⓐ angle *ABC* and angle *BAC*

Ⓑ angle *BDA* and angle *BDC*

Ⓒ segment *AB* and segment *BC*

Ⓓ segment *AD* and segment *DC*

DAY 5

Name the property that is illustrated by the following:

$$x \cdot 1 = x$$

Ⓐ Associative Property of Multiplication

Ⓑ Commutative Property of Multiplication

Ⓒ Multiplicative Inverse Property

Ⓓ Multiplicative Identity Property

Day	California Standards
1	NS1.2 🔑
2	MG3.2
3	AF3.3 🔑
4	MG3.4 🔑
5	AF1.3 🔑

DAY 1

Which graph shows $y = x^3$?

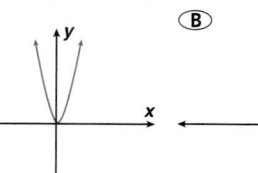

Ⓐ Ⓑ Ⓒ Ⓓ

DAY 2

Ivy's Fresh Eggs needs to send out 3 delivery trucks to deliver 120 crates of eggs. How many crates will 8 trucks carry?

Ⓐ 220

Ⓑ 280

Ⓒ 320

Ⓓ 360

DAY 3

Freida borrowed $500 at 14% simple interest for one year. If she makes no payments during that year, how much interest will she owe at the end of the loan period?

Ⓐ $70

Ⓑ $570

Ⓒ $840

Ⓓ $7000

DAY 4

The graph compares Claire's age to her father's age. Approximately how old will Claire's dad be when Claire is 25 years old?

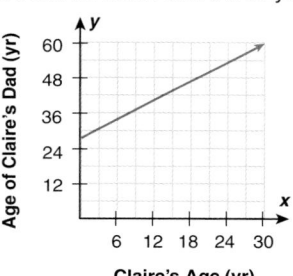

Age of Claire's Dad (yr)

Claire's Age (yr)

Ⓐ 40 years   Ⓒ 54 years

Ⓑ 48 years   Ⓓ 58 years

DAY 5

Ronnie ties his dog to an 8-foot length of rope attached to a pole. What is the distance that the dog can run around the circle? Use 3.14 for π.

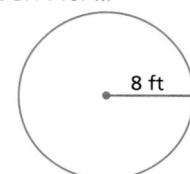

8 ft

Ⓐ 25.12 feet   Ⓒ 100.48 feet

Ⓑ 50.24 feet   Ⓓ 200.96 feet

Day	California Standards
1	AF3.1
2	AF4.2 🔑
3	NS1.7 🔑
4	AF1.5
5	MG2.1

DAY 1

The roof of the greenhouse, which forms half a cylinder, is covered in glass. Estimate the surface area of the glass roof.

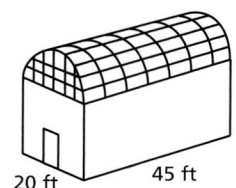

20 ft   45 ft

(A) 1727 ft²   (C) 3140 ft²

(B) 2041 ft²   (D) 3454 ft²

DAY 2

Which of the following correctly shows the length of Earth's equator?

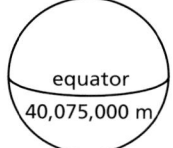

equator
40,075,000 m

(A) 0.40075×10^7 meters

(B) 4.0075×10^7 meters

(C) 40.075×10^7 meters

(D) 4007.5×10^7 meters

DAY 3

Samuel invested $1000 in a savings account that pays him 3.5% interest, compounded annually. If Samuel makes no deposits or withdrawals, approximately how much will the balance of his account be at the end of 4 years?

(A) $1001.04

(B) $1035.00

(C) $1140.00

(D) $1147.52

DAY 4

What is the slope of the line?

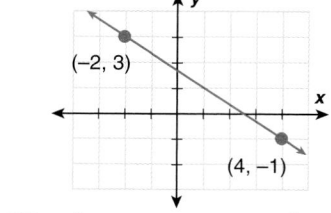

(−2, 3)

(4, −1)

(A) $-\frac{2}{3}$ (C) $-\frac{3}{2}$

(B) $\frac{2}{3}$ (D) $\frac{3}{2}$

DAY 5

Which graph shows the relationship between inches and feet?

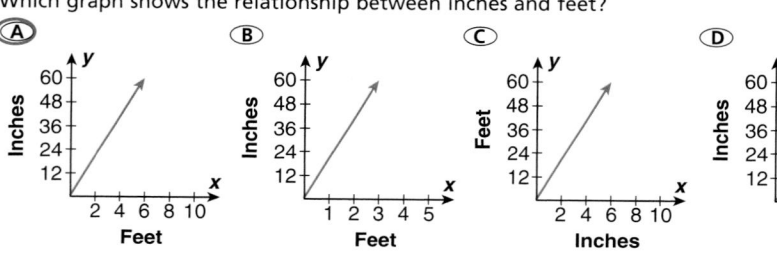

(A) Inches / Feet

(B) Inches / Feet

(C) Feet / Inches

(D) Inches / Feet

Day	California Standards
1	MG2.2
2	NS1.1
3	NS1.7 🔑
4	AF3.3 🔑
5	AF3.4 🔑

DAY 1

What percent of the larger rectangle's area is the smaller rectangle's area?

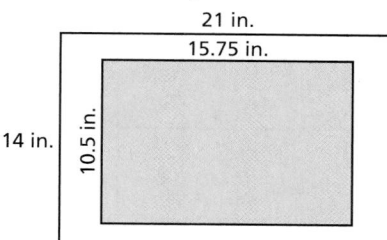

21 in.
15.75 in.
14 in.
10.5 in.

Ⓐ 0.75%   Ⓒ 56.25%

Ⓑ 5.25%   Ⓓ 103%

DAY 2

A bus company sells an annual bus pass for $8.50 and then charges a rider $0.25 per ride. Use the equation $c = 0.25b + 8.5$ to find the number of times a person rode the bus if his or her total cost was $18.00.

Ⓐ 438

Ⓑ 46

Ⓒ 38

Ⓓ 4

DAY 3

The dimensions of this prism are multiplied by a scale factor of 3. What is the volume of the larger figure?

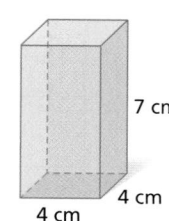

7 cm
4 cm
4 cm

Ⓐ 112 cm³   Ⓒ 1008 cm³

Ⓑ 336 cm³   Ⓓ 3024 cm³

DAY 4

Ben is building a wall. What length of wood does Ben need to buy to create two cross beams for the frame? Round your answer to the nearest tenth.

Ⓐ 4.3 meters

Ⓑ 5.8 meters

Ⓒ 8.5 meters

Ⓓ 11.6 meters

2.1 m
3.7 m

DAY 5

Which fraction is equivalent to 0.15 and in lowest terms?

Ⓐ $\frac{3}{20}$

Ⓑ $\frac{3}{200}$

Ⓒ $\frac{15}{100}$

Ⓓ $\frac{15}{1000}$

Day	California Standards
1	MG2.1
2	AF4.1 🔑
3	MG2.3
4	MG3.3 🔑
5	NS1.5 🔑

Countdown to Mastery — WEEK 21

DAY 1

Mia made this net of a triangular prism. What is the surface area of the prism?

- (A) 615 square centimeters
- (B) 840 square centimeters
- (C) 877.5 square centimeters
- (D) 915 square centimeters

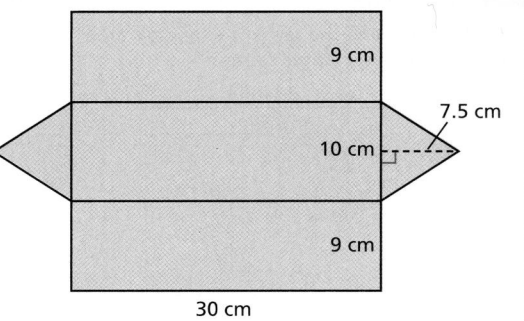

9 cm

7.5 cm

10 cm

9 cm

30 cm

DAY 2

Blake works in a cheese store. He has made 234 cheese tidbits at the end of 2 hours. If he continues at the same pace, how many tidbits will Blake have made at the end of 6 hours?

- (A) 585
- (B) 702
- (C) 819
- (D) 1404

DAY 3

Which equation shows the basic formula for adding and subtracting fractions?

- (A) $\frac{a}{b} \pm \frac{c}{d} = \frac{ac}{bd}$
- (B) $\frac{a}{b} \pm \frac{c}{d} = \frac{ac}{b \pm d}$
- (C) $\frac{a}{b} \pm \frac{c}{d} = \frac{ad \pm bc}{bd}$
- (D) $\frac{a}{b} \pm \frac{c}{d} = \frac{a \pm c}{b \pm d}$

DAY 4

Steve's wood-burning stove can heat his house 6°F an hour. If he lights the stove at 6:00 A.M. and the temperature of the house is 52°F, in how many hours will the temperature reach 82°F?

Hour	0	1	2	3	4
Temperature (°F)	52	58	64		

- (A) 3
- (B) 4
- (C) 5
- (D) 6

DAY 5

Paula drew a circle with four congruent circles inside it. The diameter of the large circle is 14.6 m. Which is closest to the area of the shaded region? Use 3.14 for π.

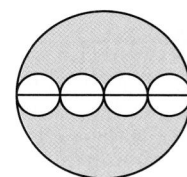

- (A) 41.8 m²
- (B) 125.5 m²
- (C) 156.9 m²
- (D) 167.3 m²

Day	California Standards
1	MG2.1
2	AF4.2
3	NS2.2
4	MG1.3
5	MG2.2

DAY 1

Which situation might be represented by the graph?

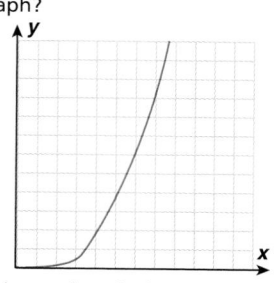

- (A) volume of a cube based on edge length
- (B) area of a square based on side length
- (C) volume of a cylinder based on height
- (D) volume of a sphere based on radius

DAY 2

Which graph best represents the graph of $y = 3x - 1$?

(A)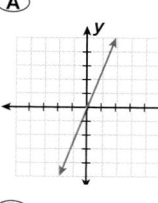

(C)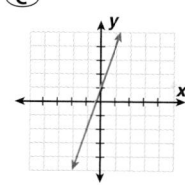

(B)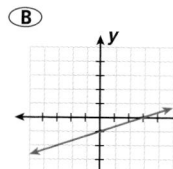

(D)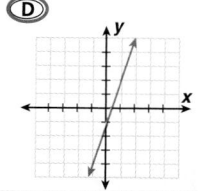

DAY 3

The radius and height of this cylinder are multiplied by a scale factor of 2. What is the surface area of the larger figure? Use 3.14 for π.

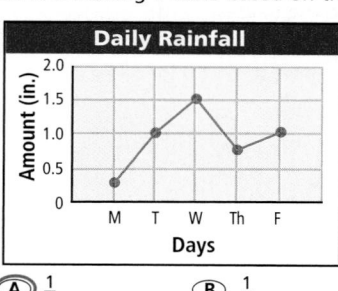

2 in.

6 in.

- (A) 100.48 in²
- (B) 200.96 in²
- (C) 351.68 in²
- (D) 401.92 in²

DAY 4

Kyle is studying the speed of cars as they drive by his house. Which of the following is the most appropriate way for Kyle to display his data?

- (A) circle graph
- (B) bar graph
- (C) stem-and-leaf plot
- (D) line graph

DAY 5

Carla is making a table based on the graph. Complete the table for Monday.

Daily Rainfall

Day	M	T	W	Th	F
Inches		1	$1\frac{1}{2}$		1

- (A) $\frac{1}{4}$
- (B) $\frac{1}{2}$
- (C) $\frac{3}{4}$
- (D) 1

Day	California Standards
1	AF3.2
2	AF3.3 🔑
3	MG2.3
4	SDAP1.1
5	SDAP1.1

COUNTDOWN TO MASTERY

DAY 1

What is the mode of these test scores?

92 85 89 93 74 94

A 74

B 91

C 94

D no mode

DAY 2

The data represents the weight in pounds of 10 sixth grade girls.

89, 95, 100, 103, 112,
117, 120, 122, 125, 130

What is the lower quartile of the data?

A 89 pounds

B 95 pounds

C 100 pounds

D 114.5 pounds

DAY 3

Which of the following can be used to find the range of a set of data?

A the upper quartile and the minimum

B the upper quartile and the lower quartile

C the maximum and the minimum

D the lower quartile and the maximum

DAY 4

Which method can be used to find the range of the middle half of a data set?

A Find the difference between the maximum and the median.

B Find the median.

C Subtract the lower quartile from the upper quartile.

D Subtract the minimum from the maximum.

DAY 5

Megan recorded the weight in grams of each tomato in her garden this week. What is the mean of this data? Round your answer to the nearest tenth.

220, 225, 213, 140, 210, 209

A 85.0

B 202.8

C 211.5

D 1217.0

Day	California Standards
1	6SDAP1.1
2	SDAP1.3 🔑
3	SDAP1.3 🔑
4	SDAP1.3 🔑
5	6SDAP1.1

DAY 1

Which conclusion about worker productivity can you draw based on the scatter plot?

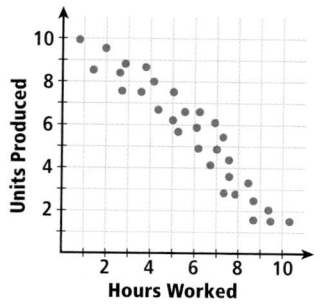

Ⓐ Productivity increases during the day.

Ⓑ There is no trend for productivity in the scatter plot.

Ⓒ As the day progresses, productivity declines.

Ⓓ Productivity remains constant during the day.

DAY 2

Which conclusion can you draw based on the data in this scatter plot?

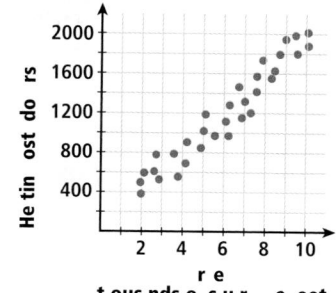

Ⓐ The smaller the area, the more expensive the heating costs.

Ⓑ Heating costs remain constant.

Ⓒ The plot does not show a trend.

Ⓓ The larger the area, the greater the heating costs.

DAY 3

Billy's drawer contains 6 black socks, 4 brown socks, and 8 white socks. Billy picks two socks out of the drawer without looking. What is the probability that he picks a pair of black socks? Round your answer to the nearest tenth.

Ⓐ 0.5%   Ⓑ 1.1%   Ⓒ 9.8%   Ⓓ 11.1%

DAY 4

Juan must pick a drink and a side order. Which list shows all of the possible choices of one drink and one side order?

Drinks	Side Orders
Milk	Salad
Juice	Fruit

Ⓐ {(milk, juice), (milk, salad), (milk, fruit)}

Ⓑ {(milk, salad), (milk, fruit)}

Ⓒ {(milk, salad), (milk, fruit), (juice, salad), (juice, fruit)}

Ⓓ {(milk, salad), (juice, fruit)}

DAY 5

Which events are dependent?

Ⓐ rolling a 5 on a number cube and flipping a coin that lands showing heads

Ⓑ a spinner landing on red on the first spin and landing on blue on the second spin

Ⓒ randomly drawing a marble from a bag, replacing it, and then randomly drawing another marble from the bag

Ⓓ randomly drawing a marble from a bag, setting it aside, and then randomly drawing another marble from the bag

Day	California Standards
1	SDAP1.2
2	SDAP1.2
3	6SDAP3.3
4	6SDAP3.1
5	6SDAP3.5

CALIFORNIA MATHEMATICS CONTENT STANDARDS FOR GRADE 7

California
the golden state

The state bird is the California Quail

The Poppy is the state flower

The State Capitol in Sacramento

Big Sur coastline

California palm tree

California Mathematics Content Standards for Grade 7

Number Sense

1.0 *Students know the properties of, and compute with, rational numbers expressed in a variety of forms:*

1.1 Read, write, and compare rational numbers in scientific notation (positive and negative powers of 10), compare rational numbers in general.

1.2 Add, subtract, multiply, and divide rational numbers (integers, fractions, and terminating decimals) and take positive rational numbers to whole-number powers.

1.3 Convert fractions to decimals and percents and use these representations in estimations, computations, and applications.

1.4 Differentiate between rational and irrational numbers.

1.5 Know that every rational number is either a terminating or a repeating decimal and be able to convert terminating decimals into reduced fractions.

1.6 Calculate the percentage of increases and decreases of a quantity.

1.7 Solve problems that involve discounts, markups, commissions, and profit and compute simple and compound interest.

2.0 *Students use exponents, powers, and roots and use exponents in working with fractions:*

2.1 Understand negative whole-number exponents. Multiply and divide expressions involving exponents with a common base.

2.2 Add and subtract fractions by using factoring to find common denominators.

2.3 Multiply, divide, and simplify rational numbers by using exponent rules.

2.4 Use the inverse relationship between raising to a power and extracting the root of a perfect square integer; for an integer that is not square, determine without a calculator the two integers between which its square root lies and explain why.

2.5 Understand the meaning of the absolute value of a number; interpret the absolute value as the distance of the number from zero on a number line; and determine the absolute value of real numbers.

Algebra and Functions

1.0 *Students express quantitative relationships by using algebraic terminology, expressions, equations, inequalities, and graphs:*

1.1 Use variables and appropriate operations to write an expression, an equation, an inequality, or a system of equations or inequalities that represents a verbal description (e.g., three less than a number, half as large as area A).

1.2 Use the correct order of operations to evaluate algebraic expressions such as $3(2x + 5)^2$.

1.3 Simplify numerical expressions by applying properties of rational numbers (e.g., identity, inverse, distributive, associative, commutative) and justify the process used.

1.4 Use algebraic terminology (e.g., variable, equation, term, coefficient, inequality, expression, constant) correctly.

1.5 Represent quantitative relationships graphically and interpret the meaning of a specific part of a graph in the situation represented by the graph.

2.0 *Students interpret and evaluate expressions involving integer powers and simple roots:*

2.1 Interpret positive whole-number powers as repeated multiplication and negative whole-number powers as repeated division or multiplication by the multiplicative inverse. Simplify and evaluate expressions that include exponents.

2.2 Multiply and divide monomials; extend the process of taking powers and extracting roots to monomials when the latter results in a monomial with an integer exponent.

3.0 *Students graph and interpret linear and some nonlinear functions:*

3.1 Graph functions of the form $y = nx^2$ and $y = nx^3$ and use in solving problems.

3.2 Plot the values from the volumes of three-dimensional shapes for various values of the edge lengths (e.g., cubes with varying edge lengths or a triangle prism with a fixed height and an equilateral triangle base of varying lengths).

3.3 Graph linear functions, noting that the vertical change (change in y-value) per unit of horizontal change (change in x-value) is always the same and know that the ratio ("rise over run") is called the slope of a graph.

3.4 Plot the values of quantities whose ratios are always the same (e.g., cost to the number of an item, feet to inches, circumference to diameter of a circle). Fit a line to the plot and understand that the slope of the line equals the ratio of the quantities.

Continued

CA28

CA29

California
the golden state

4.0 *Students solve simple linear equations and inequalities over the rational numbers:*

4.1 Solve two-step linear equations and inequalities in one variable over the rational numbers, interpret the solution or solutions in the context from which they arose, and verify the reasonableness of the results.

4.2 Solve multistep problems involving rate, average speed, distance, and time or a direct variation.

Measurement and Geometry

1.0 *Students choose appropriate units of measure and use ratios to convert within and between measurement systems to solve problems:*

1.1 Compare weights, capacities, geometric measures, times, and temperatures within and between measurement systems (e.g., miles per hour and feet per second, cubic inches to cubic centimeters).

1.2 Construct and read drawings and models made to scale.

1.3 Use measures expressed as rates (e.g., speed, density) and measures expressed as products (e.g., person-days) to solve problems; check the units of the solutions; and use dimensional analysis to check the reasonableness of the answer.

2.0 *Students compute the perimeter, area, and volume of common geometric objects and use the results to find measures of less common objects. They know how perimeter, area, and volume are affected by changes of scale:*

2.1 Use formulas routinely for finding the perimeter and area of basic two-dimensional figures and the surface area and volume of basic three-dimensional figures, including rectangles, parallelograms, trapezoids, squares, triangles, circles, prisms, and cylinders.

2.2 Estimate and compute the area of more complex or irregular two- and three-dimensional figures by breaking the figures down into more basic geometric objects.

2.3 Compute the length of the perimeter, the surface area of the faces, and the volume of a three-dimensional object built from rectangular solids. Understand that when the lengths of all dimensions are multiplied by a scale factor, the surface area is multiplied by the square of the scale factor and the volume is multiplied by the cube of the scale factor.

2.4 Relate the changes in measurement with a change of scale to the units used (e.g., square inches, cubic feet) and to conversions between units (1 square foot = 144 square inches or [1 ft.²] = [144 in.²]; 1 cubic inch is approximately 16.38 cubic centimeters or [1 in.³] = [16.38 cm³]).

3.0 *Students know the Pythagorean theorem and deepen their understanding of plane and solid geometric shapes by constructing figures that meet given conditions and by identifying attributes of figures:*

3.1 Identify and construct basic elements of geometric figures (e.g., altitudes, midpoints, diagonals, angle bisectors, and perpendicular bisectors; central angles, radii, diameters, and chords of circles) by using a compass and straightedge.

3.2 Understand and use coordinate graphs to plot simple figures, determine lengths and areas related to them, and determine their image under translations and reflections.

3.3 Know and understand the Pythagorean theorem and its converse and use it to find the length of the missing side of a right triangle and the lengths of other line segments and, in some situations, empirically verify the Pythagorean theorem by direct measurement.

Continued

Bay Bridge

CA30

CA31

CA28–CA31 *California Mathematics Content Standards for Grade 7*

← **3.4** Demonstrate an understanding of conditions that indicate two geometrical figures are congruent and what congruence means about the relationships between the sides and angles of the two figures.

3.5 Construct two-dimensional patterns for three-dimensional models, such as cylinders, prisms, and cones.

← **3.6** Identify elements of three-dimensional geometric objects (e.g., diagonals of rectangular solids) and describe how two or more objects are related in space (e.g., skew lines, the possible ways three planes might intersect).

Statistics, Data Analysis, and Probability

1.0 *Students collect, organize, and represent data sets that have one or more variables and identify relationships among variables within a data set by hand and through the use of an electronic spreadsheet software program:*

1.1 Know various forms of display for data sets, including a stem-and-leaf plot or box-and-whisker plot; use the forms to display a single set of data or to compare two sets of data.

San Diego Beach

CA32

1.2 Represent two numerical variables on a scatterplot and informally describe how the data points are distributed and any apparent relationship that exists between the two variables (e.g., between time spent on homework and grade level).

← **1.3** Understand the meaning of, and be able to compute, the minimum, the lower quartile, the median, the upper quartile, and the maximum of a data set.

Mathematical Reasoning

1.0 *Students make decisions about how to approach problems:*

1.1 Analyze problems by identifying relationships, distinguishing relevant from irrelevant information, identifying missing information, sequencing and prioritizing information, and observing patterns.

1.2 Formulate and justify mathematical conjectures based on a general description of the mathematical question or problem posed.

1.3 Determine when and how to break a problem into simpler parts.

2.0 *Students use strategies, skills, and concepts in finding solutions:*

2.1 Use estimation to verify the reasonableness of calculated results.

2.2 Apply strategies and results from simpler problems to more complex problems.

2.3 Estimate unknown quantities graphically and solve for them by using logical reasoning and arithmetic and algebraic techniques.

2.4 Make and test conjectures by using both inductive and deductive reasoning.

2.5 Use a variety of methods, such as words, numbers, symbols, charts, graphs, tables, diagrams, and models, to explain mathematical reasoning.

2.6 Express the solution clearly and logically by using the appropriate mathematical notation and terms and clear language; support solutions with evidence in both verbal and symbolic work.

2.7 Indicate the relative advantages of exact and approximate solutions to problems and give answers to a specified degree of accuracy.

2.8 Make precise calculations and check the validity of the results from the context of the problem.

3.0 *Students determine a solution is complete and move beyond a particular problem by generalizing to other situations:*

3.1 Evaluate the reasonableness of the solution in the context of the original situation.

3.2 Note the method of deriving the solution and demonstrate a conceptual understanding of the derivation by solving similar problems.

3.3 Develop generalizations of the results obtained and the strategies used and apply them to new problem situations.

CA33

Count on **Holt California Mathematics** for

Mastering the California Standards

A program created exclusively for California

Holt California Mathematics is specifically designed for California students and teachers. The California Mathematics Content Standards are unpacked, taught, and then reinforced throughout our program so that teachers can plan, diagnose, teach, assess, and intervene with the standards in mind.

UNDERSTANDING THE STANDARDS

A special **Unpacking the Standards** section at the start of each chapter helps students understand the new concepts they will learn, defines the Academic Vocabulary, and shows how the standards are applied in the chapter.

CHAPTER **4** **Unpacking the Standards**

The information below "unpacks" the standards. The Academic Vocabulary is highlighted and defined to help you understand the language of the standards. Refer to the lessons listed after each standard for help with the math terms and phrases. The Chapter Concept shows how the standard is applied in this chapter.

California Standard	Academic Vocabulary	Chapter Concept
NS1.1 Read, write, and compare rational numbers in scientific notation (positive and negative powers of 10), compare rational numbers in general. (Lesson 4-5)	**compare** determine how items are the same or different **notation** a way of showing something by a special system of marks or characters	You use scientific notation to express very large and very small numbers.
NS1.4 Differentiate between rational and irrational numbers. (Lesson 4-8)	**differentiate** to tell the difference between	You determine the special groups that numbers belong to.
NS2.4 Use the inverse relationship	**inverse** opposite	You multiply an integer by ... square it. You will also ... t whole number can be ... d by itself to get a ... mber. When a whole ... can not be found, you ... what two whole ... the value is between.

Math Background: Teaching the Standards

supports the professional development of teachers. This feature addresses the mathematic theory underlying each lesson and also provides greater depth and complexity for each standard by showing how the math will be used in future courses.

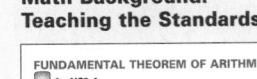

Math Background: Teaching the Standards

Professional Development

FUNDAMENTAL THEOREM OF ARITHMETIC ← NS2.4
Lesson 3-1
The Fundamental Theorem of Arithmetic states that every positive integer greater than 1 is either prime or can be expressed in exactly one way as the product of two or more positive prime numbers. In other words, every positive integer greater than 1 has a unique prime factorization. For example, 84 can be factored as shown.

$$84 = 2 \cdot 42 = 2 \cdot 2 \cdot 21 = 2 \cdot 2 \cdot 3 \cdot 7 = 2^2 \cdot 3 \cdot 7$$
$$84 = 6 \cdot 14 = 2 \cdot 3 \cdot 14 = 2 \cdot 3 \cdot 2 \cdot 7 = 2^2 \cdot 3 \cdot 7$$

In each case, the result is the same. Once the prime factorizations of two numbers are known, it is easy to determine the numbers' greatest common divisor and least common multiple.

GREATEST COMMON DIVISOR ← NS2.4
Lesson 3-2
The greatest common divisor (GCD), sometimes called the *greatest common factor* (GCF), of a set of positive integers is the greatest whole number by which each integer in the set can be divided evenly. The notation GCD (*a*, *b*) represents the GCD of two positive integers *a* and *b*.

In Lesson 3-2, students are taught to find the GCD by listing factors and by using prime factorizations. For ...sider the prime factorizations of 54

... 3 · 3   72 = 2 · 2 · 3 · 3

...prime factors are 2, 3, and 3. The ...ese is the GCD, 18.

...od of finding the GCD is called *Euclid's* ...hich is based on the following fact: ...sitive integers *a* and *b* where *a* > *b*, ...GCD (*b*, *a* − *b*).

This fact can be applied repeatedly to generate simpler problems that eventually result in GCD (*b*, *b*) = *b*. For example, the GCD of 120 and 75 can be found as follows.

$$GCD (120, 75) = GCD (75, 45)$$
$$= GCD (45, 30)$$
$$= GCD (30, 15)$$
$$= GCD (15, 15)$$
$$= 15$$

Therefore, the GCD of 120 and 75 is 15.

An alternate version of the algorithm replaces repeated subtraction with division with a remainder, as shown on page 134.

LEAST COMMON MULTIPLE ← NS2.4
Lesson 3-3
The least common multiple (LCM) of a set of positive integers is the smallest whole number, other than 0, that is a multiple of each integer in the set. In Lesson 3-3, students are taught to find the LCM by listing multiples and by using prime factorizations.

An alternate method of finding the LCM of two positive integers can be taught to students after they have learned to simplify fractions. Given two positive integers *a* and *b*, LCM (*a*, *b*) = $\frac{a \cdot b}{GCD (a, b)}$. For example, the LCM of 72 and 270 can be found as follows.

$$72 = 2 \cdot 2 \cdot 2 \cdot 3 \cdot 3$$
$$270 = 2 \cdot 3 \cdot 3 \cdot 3 \cdot 5$$
$$GCD (72, 270) = 2 \cdot 3 \cdot 3 = 18$$
$$LCM (72, 270) = \frac{72 \cdot 270}{GCD (72,270)}$$
$$= \frac{(2 \cdot 2 \cdot 2 \cdot 3 \cdot 3) \cdot (2 \cdot 3 \cdot 3 \cdot 3 \cdot 5)}{2 \cdot 3 \cdot 3}$$
$$= 1,080$$

As shown above, the LCM of two positive integers is equal to the product of the integers divided by their common prime factors.

128B

Holt's standards-driven content is easy to manage using Holt's **California On-Course Mapping Instruction: A Teacher's Guide for Planning**. Teachers and administrators can see at a glance which lessons and resources address each of the standards.

On-Course Mapping Instruction A Teacher's Guide for Planning

HOLT **CALIFORNIA**
Mathematics
Course 2

HOLT, RINEHART AND WINSTON

CALIFORNIA STANDARDS

PRACTICING THE STANDARDS

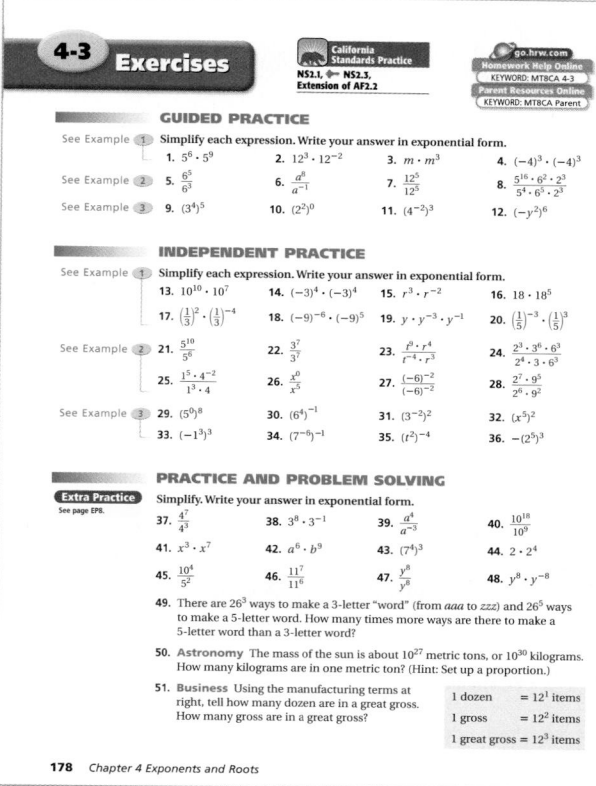

Lesson Exercises include correlations to the
California standards.

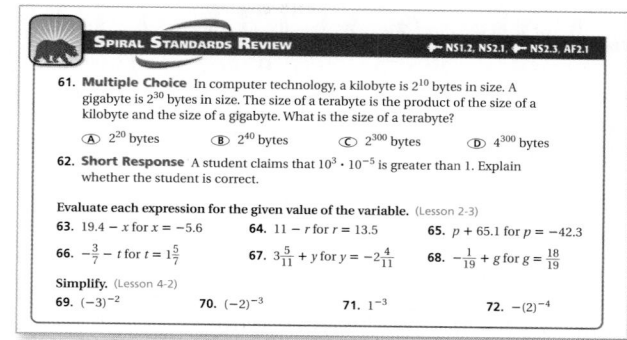

Correlated **Spiral Standards Review** at the end of
each lesson keeps previously learned skills sharp.

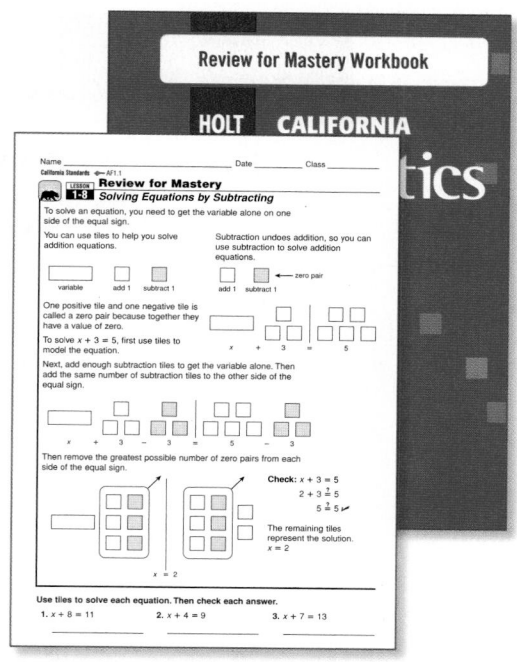

**Review for
Mastery Workbook**
provides reteaching
and additional practice
for every lesson.

Standards Practice for Grades 6 and 7 CD-ROM, powered by
ExamView® Version 5 Assessment Suite, provides a bank of practice
items searchable by California Mathematics Content Standard, so that
you can customize assignments.

California Standards Virtual File Cabinet CD-ROM gives
you access to standards-based content in a database that is
adaptable, searchable, and expandable.

**Only from
Holt!**

> " *Students can master the California standards by learning
> mathematics as a coherent collection of related ideas
> that fit together naturally.* "
> — Tom Roby, Holt author

Program Highlights

Count on **Holt California Mathematics** for

Assessment and Strategic Intervention

Holt's at-a-glance system makes it easy to keep students on track.

You need to know how well your students understand the lesson BEFORE they take the test. With *Holt California Mathematics*, informal and formal assessment options are given at every stage within the chapter. Intervention resources allow you to reteach or review material without merely sending students back to previous lessons in the book.

Program Highlights

- **Assess Prior Knowledge** to make sure all students begin the chapter on solid footing.

  Intervene with alternate teaching strategies and basic skills review in *Are You Ready? Intervention and Enrichment.*

- **Formative Assessment** diagnoses skill development within the chapter.

  Intervene with *Ready to Go On? Intervention and Enrichment, Lesson Tutorial Videos*, **Homework Help Online,** and more.

- **Summative Assessment** allows students to demonstrate their mastery of the concepts.

  Intervene with *Review for Mastery Workbook.*

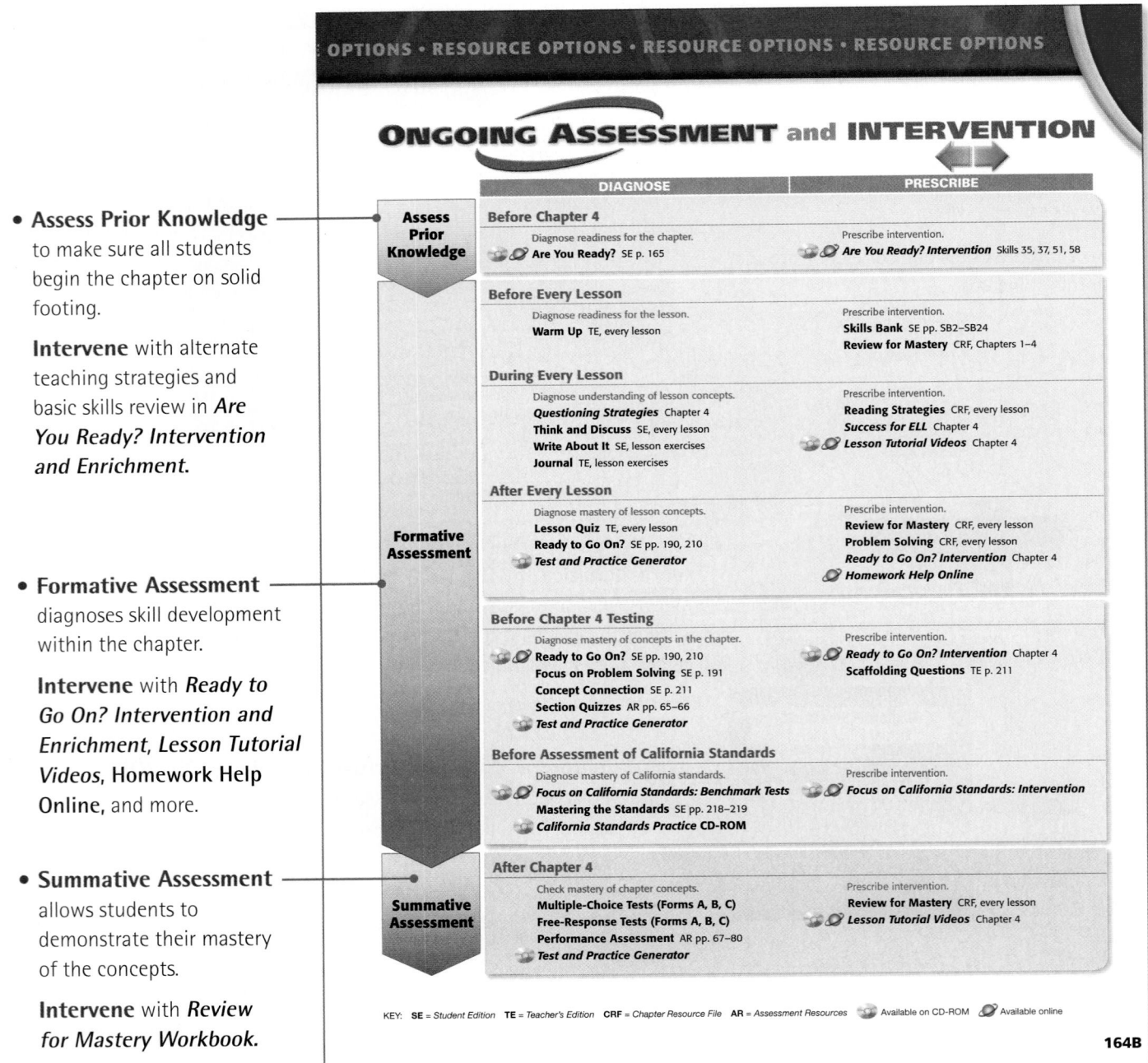

164B

ASSESSMENT AND INTERVENTION

HOLT MATH

When students struggle, rereading the same text hoping that it will eventually make sense is a discouraging task. Research shows that they need to try a new approach to the lesson. That's at the core of the assessment and intervention system in *Holt California Mathematics*.

Only from Holt!

Are You Ready?
Intervention and Enrichment

- Diagnoses mastery of prerequisite skills
- Strengthens student weaknesses with direct instruction, conceptual models, and scaffolded practice
- Enriches every chapter with critical thinking activities
- Available in print, on CD-ROM, and online

Only from Holt!

Ready to Go On?
Intervention and Enrichment

- Diagnoses mastery of newly taught skills
- Addresses deficiencies with alternative instruction and practice
- Checks student progress with post-tests
- Available in print, on CD-ROM, and online

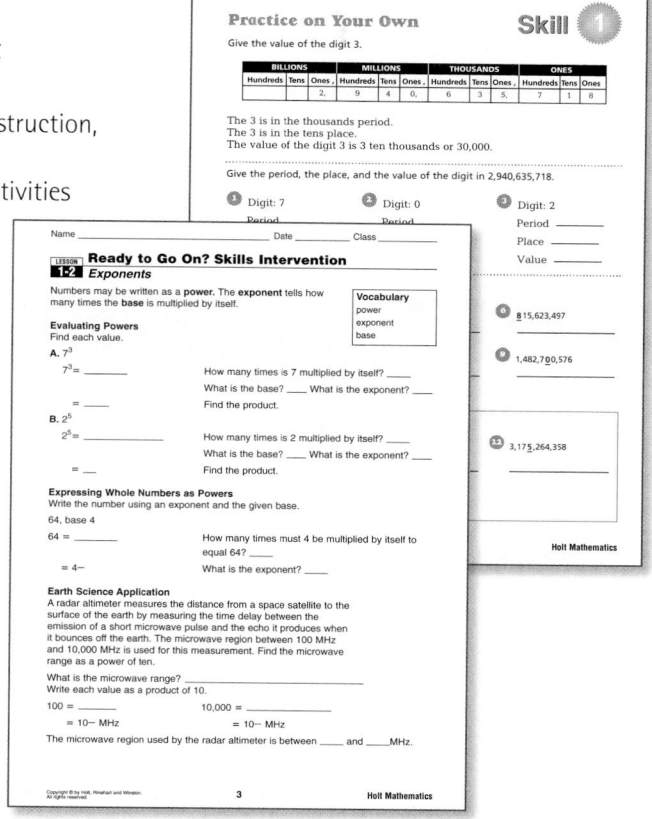

Focus on California Standards: Benchmark Tests
- Pre-tests and post-tests for each of the standards
- Emphasis on the key standards
- Complete solutions and error analysis of incorrect answers

Only from Holt!

Focus on California Standards: Intervention Workbook

Only from Holt!

- Alternative teaching strategies for every standard.
- Scaffolded intervention for skills and problem solving
- Skills and problem-solving practice worksheets
- Key vocabulary worksheets
- Standards review with practice

> *"The right support structure can empower every teacher to be highly confident and every student to succeed."*
>
> — Lee Haines, Holt author

Program Highlights

HOLT CALIFORNIA MATHEMATICS CA37

Count on **Holt California Mathematics** for
Universal Access

Reach all learners in your classroom
every day – no matter what their skill levels.

Not all students "get it" at the same time or in the same way. *Holt California Mathematics* accommodates the students in your classroom with different skill levels and those who benefit from different approaches.

With leveled practice and tests, content presented in a variety of media, and teaching strategies built in at point-of-use, helping all of your students succeed has never been easier.

Program Highlights

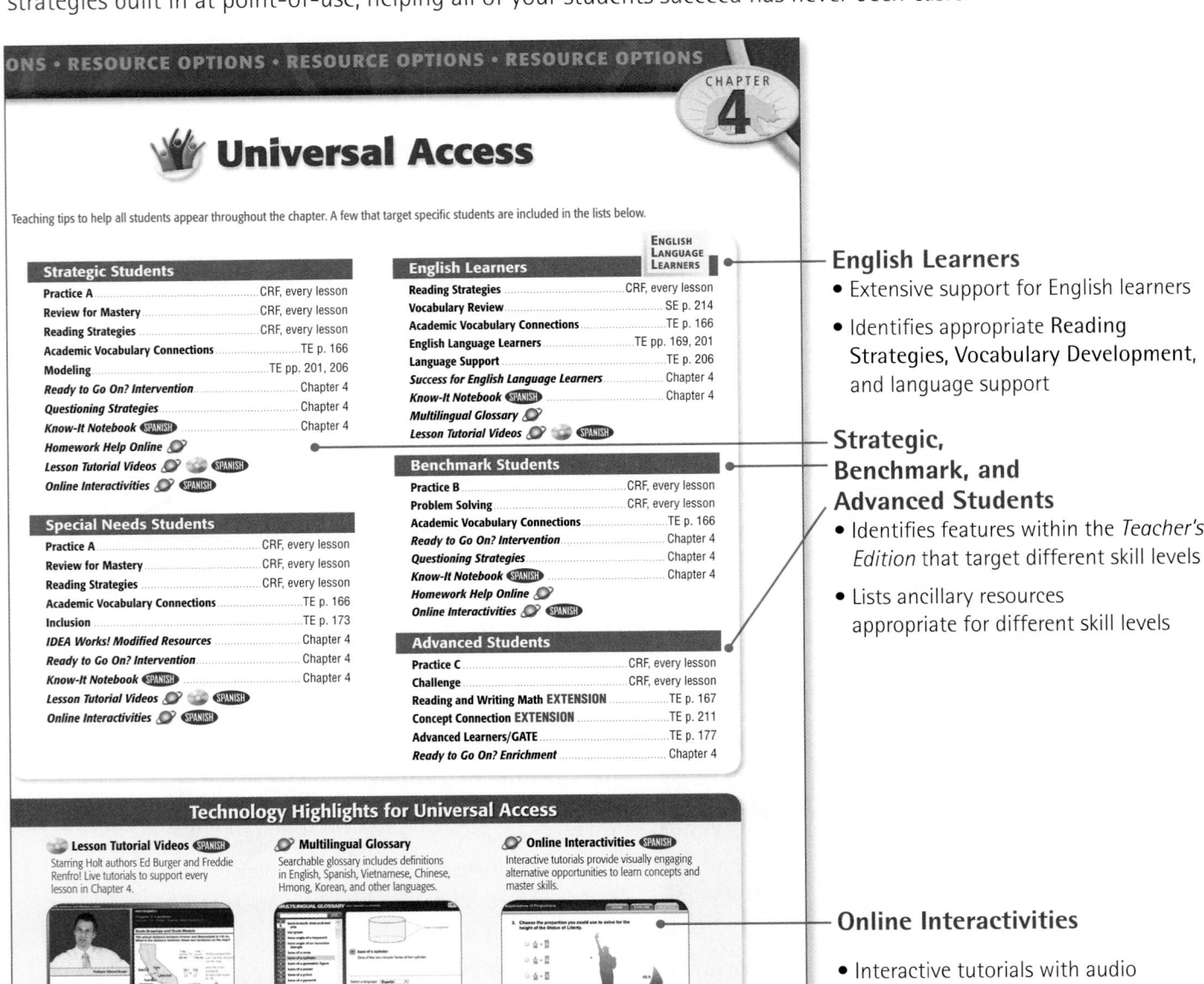

English Learners
- Extensive support for English learners
- Identifies appropriate **Reading Strategies, Vocabulary Development,** and language support

Strategic, Benchmark, and Advanced Students
- Identifies features within the *Teacher's Edition* that target different skill levels
- Lists ancillary resources appropriate for different skill levels

Online Interactivities
- Interactive tutorials with audio
- Interactive **Explore** and **Practice** items

Multilingual Glossary
- Illustrated glossary in twelve languages
- Audio for English and Spanish terms

UNIVERSAL ACCESS

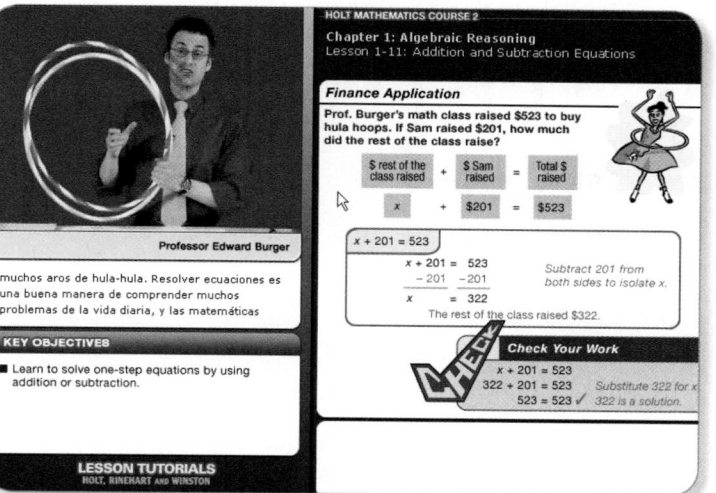

Lesson Tutorial Videos

- Illustrate every example!
- Your students' personal take-home tutor
- Closed captioning in English and Spanish
- Available online or on CD-ROM

Math Builders

- Illustrates important standards through a step-by-step layered approach
- Transparent pages in the *Student Edition*

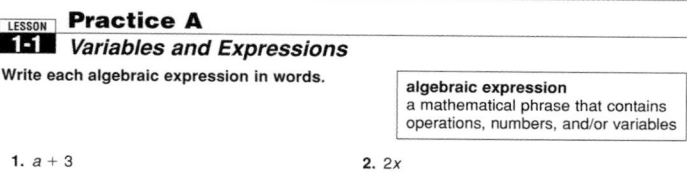

Practice A
1-1 Variables and Expressions

Write each algebraic expression in words.

> **algebraic expression**
> a mathematical phrase that contains operations, numbers, and/or variables

1. $a + 3$ 2. $2x$

Success for English Language Learners
4-3 Properties of Exponents

Steps for Success

Step I These ideas can be used to help students understand multiplying and dividing powers with the same base.

- Ask students what is meant by "powers with the same base." Refer students back to Lesson 4.1 if they cannot recall the definition of the base of a power.

Step II Teach the lesson.

Step III Ask English Language Learners to complete the worksheet for this lesson. Point out the following.

- Problem 1 on the worksheet supports the lesson opener in the student textbook. Remind students that factors without an exponent can be rewritten with an exponent of 1, which can then be added or subtracted with the other powers in the expression.
- Problem 2 on the worksheet supports Example 3A in the student

IDEA Works!®
Modified Worksheets and Tests

- Adapted format for students with special needs
- Modified practice and problem solving for every lesson
- Modified tests and quizzes for every chapter
- Vocabulary flashcards

Success for English Language Learners

- Same concepts as the student lesson, but fewer words and more visuals
- Alternate teaching strategies for English-language learners

> *"Thoughtfully designed and supported instruction demystifies mathematics for all students and enhances their understanding of core foundational knowledge and skills."*
>
> — Dr. Edward Burger, Holt author

Technology to make your life easier!

The right tools to accomplish your goals

Holt California Mathematics empowers you with key management and presentation tools that help you inspire your students and meet their needs while saving you time.

Interactive Answers and Solutions CD-ROM
- Show complete solutions for any exercise at the click of a button!
- Customize answer keys
- Make answer transparencies

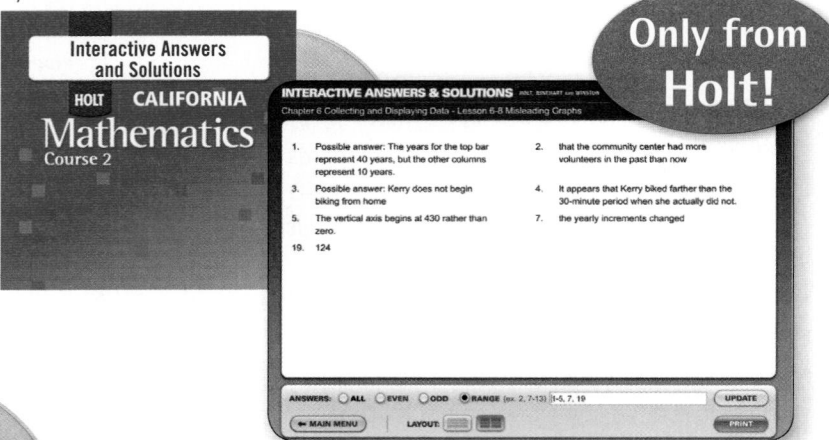

Only from Holt!

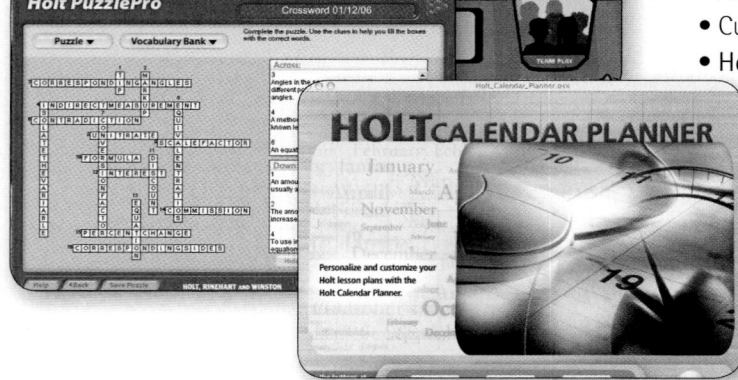

California Teacher's One-Stop Planner® CD-ROM
Everything a math teacher needs to plan and manage lessons is available in one place.
- Complete *Teacher's Edition*
- All print ancillaries and transparencies
- Customizable lesson plans
- Holt Calendar Planner
  - Holt PuzzlePro®
  - MindPoint® Quiz Show
  - ExamView® Version 5 Assessment Suite

California Student One Stop
- Entire *Student Edition*
- All workbooks
- *Are You Ready? Intervention and Enrichment*
- *Ready to Go On? Intervention and Enrichment*

HOLT MATH

California Premier Online Edition

Go home empty-handed and get online.

For students:

• Entire *Student Edition*
• *Lesson Tutorial Videos*
• Homework Help Online
• Extra practice broken out by lesson and chapter
• Interactive quizzes and tests
• All workbooks
• Graphing calculator
• Virtual manipulatives
• Parent resources

For teachers:

• Editable lesson plans
• Lesson transparencies
• PowerPoint® presentations for every lesson
• Leveled practice worksheets for every lesson
• Modified worksheets, quizzes, and tests for special needs students
• *Are You Ready?* and *Ready to Go On? Intervention and Enrichment*
• *Success for English Language Learners* teaching strategies and worksheets

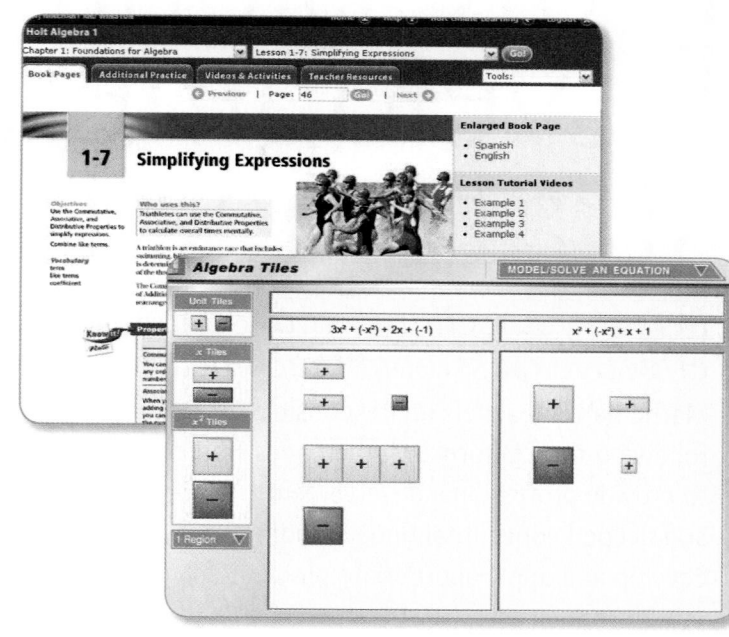

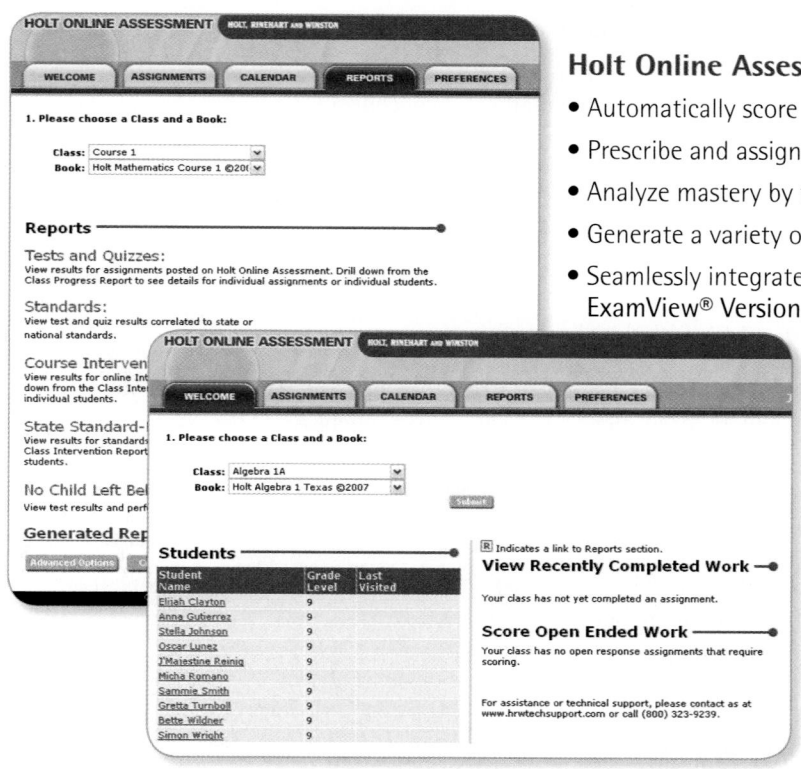

Holt Online Assessment

• Automatically score online assessments
• Prescribe and assign intervention
• Analyze mastery by topic or standard
• Generate a variety of reports
• Seamlessly integrated with ExamView® Version 5 Assessment Suite

California Standards Virtual File Cabinet CD-ROM

• Search for resources by standard, lesson topic, resource type, and other criteria
• Mark your favorites for quick access in the future
• Add your own content to this expandable database

Program Highlights

Count on **Action Learning Systems** for

Professional Development strategies that work

Inspire yourself and your students with effective classroom teaching strategies.

Mathematics teachers are responsible for bringing each lesson to life for their students while following the California Mathematics Framework. Holt has partnered with Action Learning Systems to provide professional development that includes engaging opportunities for students to establish and deepen conceptual understanding, to master specific computational and procedural skills, and to develop and apply appropriate problem-solving skills.

Professional Development Strategies from Action Learning Systems:

INSTRUCTIONAL CONVERSATION Builds Conceptual Understanding

Instructional Conversation provides a structure for students to explain their work to a partner using appropriate mathematical vocabulary. Students clarify their understanding of the mathematical process while helping each other explain the steps to the solution.

- Have students read their text to develop an initial understanding of the mathematical concept.
- Generate a class list of students' vocabulary words.
- Choose five to seven words from the class list and have students write the selected words as "Target Vocabulary."
- Organize students into pairs (Student A and Student B).
- Assign a practice problem to the pairs and have them complete the problem using the designated roles:

Student A	Student B
1. Solve the problem. 2. Explain the work using the Target Vocabulary words. The goal is to use each word at least once.	1. Check the work of Student A. Student B cannot do the work for Student A but can assist Student A. 2. While Student A explains the work, Student B gives a point to Student A for each Target Vocabulary word used.

- Once pairs have completed the first problem, ask them to share how many points Student A earned. Students enjoy sharing their success and being challenged to do better next time.
- Post the solution so students can check and correct their work.
- Assign a second problem and direct partners to switch roles.
- Continue the process until the practice problems are completed.

> **>> What does *conceptual understanding* mean?**
> - Students not only know how to apply skills but also when to apply them and why they are being applied.
> - Students are able to apply their knowledge to new problems and to recognize when they have made procedural errors.

PROFESSIONAL DEVELOPMENT

QUICK DRAW FOR POINTS Builds Computational and Procedural Skills

Quick Draw for Points clarifies the procedure for solving a multi-step problem. Students are given positive reinforcement as they complete the problems and show all work. The criteria for success are clearly delineated, and as students complete more problems, their level of success increases.

- Introduce the mathematical concept either through modeling a few sample problems or reading the text.

- Generate a class list of how points will be rewarded when the practice problems are completed. For example, if multiplying decimal numbers, a point could be given for each of the following: lining the numbers up vertically starting from the right, counting the number of decimal places in each factor, predicting the number of places to move the decimal in the product, multiplying correctly, and writing the product in words using the correct mathematical vocabulary.

- Give students a set amount of time to complete the first problem. Remind them to show all work to receive the maximum points.

- Assign the first problem. When time is up, have students exchange papers with a partner.

- Identify the key components of the solution and ask students to give their partners points for each part that they included.

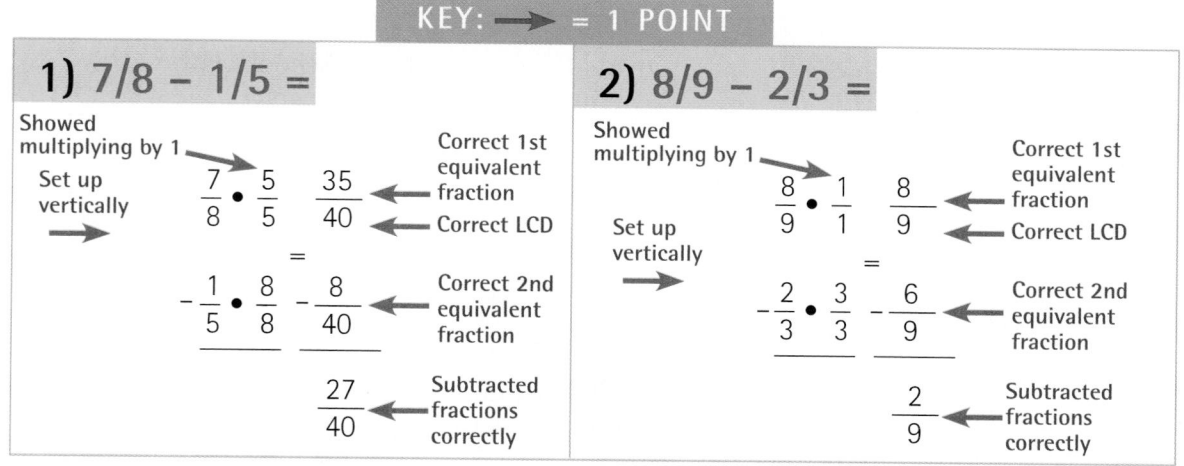

- Give students a prompt to discuss with their partner: for example, "What is one thing that your partner could do next time to get more points?"

- Continue the process for three additional problems. When students have completed four problems, have them summarize the essential steps in solving this type of problem.

> **> What should I know about** *computational and procedural skills?*
- Students should learn to use these skills routinely and automatically.
- Students must practice these skills frequently enough to commit them to memory.
- These skills develop over time and increase in depth and complexity through the years.
- Beware—computational skills can be taught in the absence of conceptual understanding.

Action Learning Systems helps schools and districts focus on—and meet—their ultimate goal of increasing student achievement by offering research-based teaching strategies, training and coaching, and intervention programs. Action Learning Systems and Holt, Rinehart and Winston are working in partnership to provide exceptional professional development services to California schools.

You may download blackline masters of these instructional strategies at www.actionlearningsystems.com. Just click on "Resources."

Count on **Holt California Mathematics** to be

Grounded in research, built by experts, proven in classrooms

Holt California Mathematics is built on a solid foundation of research, proven to work in the classroom, and built to meet the California Mathematics Content Standards. This research is backed by the expertise of a world-class team of authors who have executed a program that makes students want to learn, helps them *actually* learn, and ensures their success in mastering the California standards.

Students show major gains on national standardized tests!**

ERIA, a national research group, found that students using Holt Middle School Math consecutively for two years show a significant improvement in performance on the SAT 10, a national standardized test. *

In this study, pre-test scores both for Group 1 and Group 2 were below Grade Level Expectations (GLE). After two years of using Holt Middle School Math, the scores exceeded GLE.

	Expected GLE Scores	Actual GLE Scores
Group 1	7.8**	8.8
Group 2	8.8**	10.6

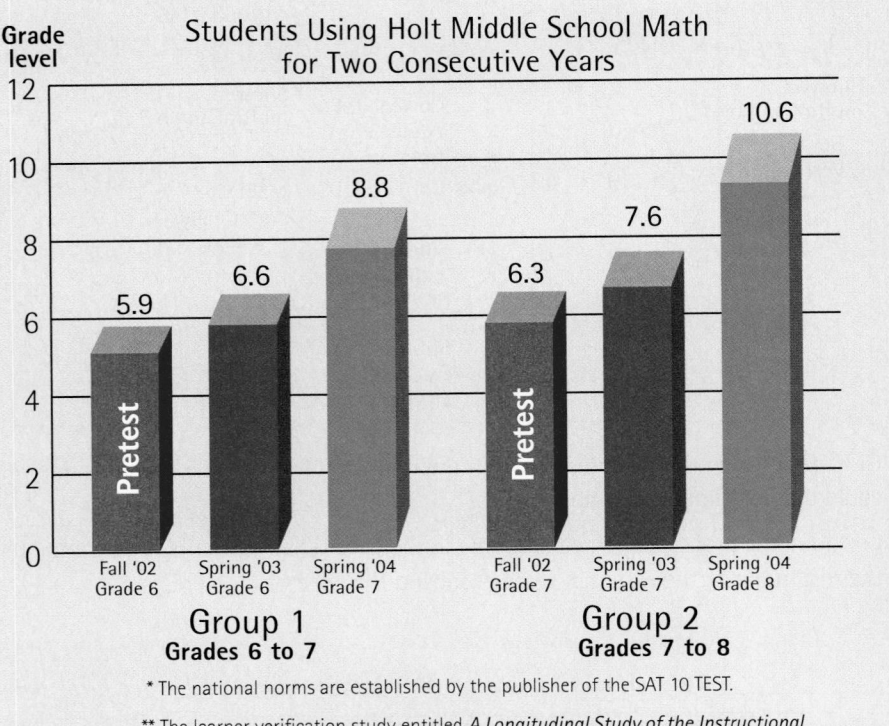

Students Using Holt Middle School Math for Two Consecutive Years

Grade level

Group 1 — Fall '02 Grade 6: 5.9 (Pretest); Spring '03 Grade 6: 6.6; Spring '04 Grade 7: 8.8

Group 2 — Fall '02 Grade 7: 6.3 (Pretest); Spring '03 Grade 7: 7.6; Spring '04 Grade 8: 10.6

Group 1 Grades 6 to 7

Group 2 Grades 7 to 8

* The national norms are established by the publisher of the SAT 10 TEST.

** The learner verification study entitled *A Longitudinal Study of the Instructional Effectiveness of Holt Middle School Math: Year 3* was conducted by Educational Research Institute of America. For a copy of the study, please contact your Holt sales rep.

The Research Underlying the Program

Holt established a pattern of interaction with the educational community throughout all stages of the program's development.

Needs Assessment
- Teacher Interviews
- University Faculty Interviews
- Federal, State, and Local Agencies
- Advisory Panels
- Task Forces
- Academic Conferences
- Surveys with Teachers, Sales, Administrators

Pedagogical Research
- Thorough
- Effective
- Scientifically-Based

Program Development
- Classroom Observation
- Field Testing of Prototypes
- Reviewed by Program and Field Consultants
- Reviewed by Teachers and Administrators

Program Validation
- User Surveys
- Student and Teacher Appraisals
- Field Consultant and Sales Reports

Program Effectiveness
- Post-Implementation Effectiveness Studies
- Valid and Reliable Tests

Count on Holt California Mathematics for a

World-class author team

Meet the experts who make Holt California Mathematics a success.

With a broad range of expertise, award-winning dedication, and a passion for developing strong, effective teaching and learning strategies, our *Holt California Mathematics* author team is unsurpassed.

Jennie M. Bennett, Ed.D.
Mathematics Teacher, Hartman Middle School | Houston , TX

Strategic Problem Solving

"Problem solving plays a pivotal role in mathematics learning and is an integral part of the *Holt California Mathematics* program. Problem solving should strengthen and stretch students' thinking and build students' confidence in their ability to solve challenging problems.

Reading mathematics is a necessary skill for all students to master. Students who have English as a second language will face words that may be confusing to them. For example, a table in mathematics can mean something different in a student's native language than in the context of mathematics. *Holt California Mathematics* provides reading and writing opportunities at the chapter level as well as at the lesson level."

SUPPORTING RESEARCH
Artzt, Alice F., and Shirel Yaloz–Femia. (1999).
Mathematical reasoning during small-group problem solving.
In *Developing mathematical reasoning in grades K-12.*
Reston, Va: National Council of Teachers of Mathematics.

Jensen, Eric. (1998).
Teaching with the brain in mind. Alexandria, Va:
Association for Supervision and Curriculum Development.

Edward B. Burger, Ph.D.
Professor of Mathematics and Chair | Williams College, MA

Student Engagement

"Deep and abstract ideas are challenging to all, but the challenge should be a pleasurable one that students want to conquer. Thus, the mathematics in *Holt California Mathematics* is developed in a meaningful manner with student readers in mind. While maintaining the integrity of the mathematics, questions such as "What would resonate with real middle school students today?" were asked at every stage of the writing and video production.

Holt California Mathematics doesn't just stress the mechanics, it also teaches the ideas behind the mechanics so that students understand not only how the mathematics works but also why. The instruction reflects a balance of computational and procedural basic skills, conceptual understanding, and problem solving. It is designed to stress the deep and profound ideas of mathematics. This emphasis is accomplished through various instructional approaches, including the *Lesson Tutorial Videos,* in order to engage all students and capture their imaginations."

SUPPORTING RESEARCH
Ames, R., & Ames, C. (Eds.). (1984). *Research on motivation in education:*
Vol. 1. Student motivation. New York: Academic Press.

Brewster, Cori, and Jennifer Fager. (2000).
Increasing Student Engagement and Motivation: From Time-on-Task to Homework. Portland, Ore.: Northwest Regional Educational Laboratory.

Program Research

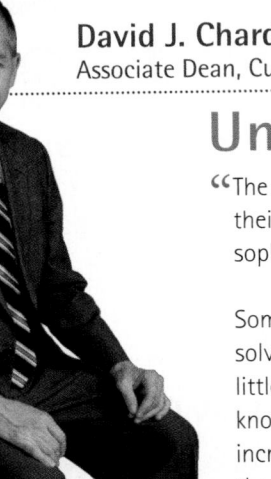

David J. Chard, Ph.D.
Associate Dean, Curriculum and Academic Programs | University of Oregon

Universal Access

"The *Holt California Mathematics* series is designed to assist teachers in helping all their students learn conceptual knowledge, skills, and strategies essential to understanding sophisticated mathematics.

Some students often require substantial assistance in developing strategies for problem solving, while others may already have the knowledge necessary to solve problems with little support. In this program, the instructional framework builds the background knowledge essential for ensuring that all students are able to understand and solve increasingly complex problems. Scaffolding in this program takes many forms. For example, the program presents content starting with simple examples and progressing to more difficult content and applications. In addition, the program offers frequent opportunities to review, alternative lessons to help students who did not master content in introductory lessons, and additional examples for extended instruction."

SUPPORTING RESEARCH

Bransford, J. D., Brown, A. L., & Cocking, R. R. (Eds.). (2000). *How people learn: Brain, mind, experience, and school.* Washington, DC: National Research Council.

Gersten, R., Chard, D. J., Baker, S., et al. (2005). *A meta-analysis of research on mathematics instruction for students with learning disabilities.* Signal Hill, CA: Instructional Research Group.

Audrey Jackson
Program Coordinator for Leadership Development | St. Louis, MO

Learning and the Classroom Environment

" The fundamental goal of *Holt California Mathematics* is to provide teachers with the necessary tools and understanding of mathematics to ensure student success at all levels.

Highly qualified teachers of mathematics establish and create cultures for learning for all students within their classroom. *Holt California Mathematics* promotes successful learning by supporting numerous teaching strategies, including direct instruction and cooperative learning."

SUPPORTING RESEARCH

National Council of Teachers of Mathematics (2000). *Principles and Standards for School Mathematics.* Reston, VA: National Council of Teachers of Mathematics.

Tomlinson, C. (1995). *How to differentiate instruction in mixed ability classrooms.* Alexander, VA: Association for Supervision and Curriculum Development.

Wiggins, G. and J. McTighe (1998). *Understanding by design.* Alexander, VA: Association for Supervision and Curriculum Development.

Program Research

HOLT MATH

Paul A. Kennedy, Ph.D.
Professor, Department of Mathematics | Colorado State University

Algebraic Thinking

" When students enter the middle grades, they are beginning the preparation for the transition to more advanced mathematical topics such as algebra and geometry, while enhancing their basic arithmetic knowledge. It is crucial that they develop abstract reasoning as well as symbolic manipulation skills.

In *Holt California Mathematics,* content is carefully developed using methods aligned with standard best practices. The idea of "doing and undoing" is developed early in the program and carried throughout the series. In addition, students need to see the relationships between the math they are learning and real-world scenarios. "

SUPPORTING RESEARCH

Vygotsky, L.S. (1978). *Mind and society: The development of higher mental processes.* Cambridge, MA: Harvard University Press.

Driscoll, Mark J. (1997). *Fostering algebraic thinking.* Portsmouth, NH.: Heinemann.

Freddie L. Renfro
Former Director of Mathematics Instruction K–12 | Texas City Independent School District

Universal Access

" Imagine a classroom where diversity in learning is the norm, and the teacher responds to the learners' needs with flexible strategies, open dialogue, and ongoing assessment.

Every child is unique. Finding ways to tailor instruction to meet individual student needs in the classroom can be a manageable task with the right support. In the *Holt California Mathematics* series, we promote universal access by including activities that provide a variety of learning approaches: the use of technology, hands-on manipulatives, and student interaction, to name a few.

The *Teacher's Edition* offers suggestions for differentiated assessment as well so that students have the opportunity to demonstrate their understanding in a manner that reflects their skills and abilities. "

SUPPORTING RESEARCH

Tomlinson, C. (1999). *The differentiated classroom: Responding to the needs of all learners.* Alexandria, VA: Association for Supervision and Curriculum Development.

Willis, S. and Mann, Larry. (2000). *Differentiating instruction.* Alexandria, VA: Association for Supervision and Curriculum Development.

Program Research

Tom Roby, Ph.D.
Associate Professor | University of Connecticut

Mathematical Coherence

" The middle grades mark a key transition for students, from basic arithmetical knowledge to the more abstract topics of algebra and geometry. Students need to understand the fundamental properties of numbers, not just the procedures of arithmetic, in order to become comfortable when numbers are replaced by variables. This transition from the concrete to the abstract can be facilitated by using manipulatives and pictures (such as fraction bars and algebra tiles), as is done systematically in *Holt California Mathematics*. These manipulatives function like training wheels on a bicycle, helping students to make sense of the procedures, which ultimately helps them develop computational fluency alongside strong conceptual understanding.

The program is carefully designed to address the California Mathematics Content Standards in such a way that topics fit together naturally. Just addressing each topic is not enough, since students can easily find themselves memorizing many specific individual procedures without ever seeing the bigger picture. Ensuring that the mathematics is not only accurate and aligned with a standard, but also coherent within the grade and well articulated from one grade to the next, is key to helping students succeed at this level and in those to come. "

SUPPORTING RESEARCH

National Research Council. (2001). *Adding it up: Helping children learn mathematics.* J. Kilpatrick, J. Swafford, and B. Findell (Eds.). Mathematics Learning Study Committee, Center for Education, Division of Behavioral and Social Sciences and Education: Washington, DC: National Academy Press.

Wu, H. H. (2001). *How to prepare students for algebra.* American Educator 25 (2): 10-17.

Jan Scheer, Ph.D.
Executive Director, Create-A-Vision

Concrete Understanding

" *Holt California Mathematics* makes use of mathematical modeling and provides many options for the use of manipulatives to enhance student understanding of abstract concepts.

Educational research demonstrates the effectiveness of hands-on learning in supplementing understanding of mathematical ideas for students. This is especially important in the middle grades, when students are exposed to increasingly abstract concepts. This program provides numerous **Hands-On Labs,** in which students use algebra tiles, pattern blocks, two-color counters, and other materials as concrete methods for learning selected topics. "

SUPPORTING RESEARCH

Bohan, Harry J., and Peggy Bohan Shawaker (1994). Using manipulatives effectively: A drive down rounding road. *Arithmetic Teacher 41 (5): 246-48.*

Stein, Mary Kay, and Jane W. Bovalino. (2001). Manipulatives: One piece of the puzzle. *Mathematics Teaching in the Middle School, 6 (6): 356-59.*

Program Research

HOLT MATH

Bert K. Waits, Ph.D.
Professor Emeritus of Mathematics | The Ohio State University

Technology to Enhance Learning

" Research has demonstrated that technology, when used appropriately, can improve students' mathematical understanding and problem-solving skills. Similarly, technological tools can help teachers challenge students to use and understand mathematics in real-world scenarios.

The *Holt California Mathematics* series presents a balanced approach to learning. We stress that students must utilize all available tools, including mental and paper-and-pencil skills and technology, in the mathematics-learning process. This series uses technology not as an end in itself, but rather as a means for understanding and application. Current research supports this use of computer software including spreadsheets, dynamic geometry software, and graphing calculators. "

SUPPORTING RESEARCH

Graham, A.T., & J.O.J. Thomas. (2000). Building a versatile understanding of algebraic variables with a graphic calculator. *Educational Studies in Mathematics*, 41 (3), 265-282.

Hallar, Jeannie C., & Karen Norwood. (1999). The effects of a graphing-approach intermediate algebra curriculum on students' understanding of function. *Journal for Research in Mathematics Education*, 30 (2), 220-226.

CONTRIBUTING AUTHORS

Lee Haines, M.A.
Math Academic Coach, San Bernardino City Schools | San Bernardino, CA

Mastering the California Standards

" Moving all students to proficiency on mathematics standards requires accessible content, motivated students, and confident teachers. Holt's *Focus on California Standards: Benchmark Tests* and *Focus on California Standards: Intervention* were designed to provide all three elements.

By deconstructing the standards, emphasizing vocabulary development, and providing sufficient practice, Holt has created a user-friendly intervention program that is custom-made for California, targets the key standards, and motivates students. Since intervention lessons are taught by instructors with a wide range of mathematics backgrounds, teacher support materials were developed to empower every intervention instructor to teach at the level of a highly qualified mathematics teacher. "

Robin Scarcella, Ph.D.
Associate Professor and Director of Academic English and ESL Program
University of California, Irvine

Teaching English Learners in the Math Classroom

" Mathematics vocabulary includes content words that are found only in mathematics lessons and are not reinforced in other disciplines or in everyday conversation. Many new words are introduced in a small amount of text, and the grammar can be complex. Fortunately, a variety of motivating and effective means are available to teach reading in the mathematics classroom.

Holt California Mathematics incorporates vocabulary development and reading comprehension strategies that enable students to make sense of and remember concepts. Some of these strategies include assessments of prerequisite vocabulary at the start of the chapter, the use of graphic organizers to help students identify and understand critical concepts, and activities that use additional resources like the glossary and index in the *Student Edition*. Additionally, the series encourages students to use the language they are learning through a multitude of opportunities to discuss and write about the mathematics. Language instruction is extended through teaching strategies such as **Language Support Tips** and **ELL Teaching Tips**. "

Program Research

CHAPTER 1

Principles of Algebra

go.hrw.com
Online Resources
KEYWORD: MT8CA TOC

Tools for Success

Reading Math 5
Writing Math 9, 13, 17, 21, 25, 29, 36, 40
Vocabulary 6, 14, 18, 32, 37, 52

Know-It Notebook Chapter 1
Homework Help Online 8, 12, 16, 20, 24, 28, 35, 39, 45
Student Help 6, 10, 11, 14, 18, 26, 32, 34, 38, 44

Countdown to Mastery Weeks 1, 2, 3
Spiral Standards Review 9, 13, 17, 21, 25, 29, 36, 40, 47
Ready to Go On? 30, 48
Mastering the Standards 58

Rational Numbers

go.hrw.com
Online Resources
KEYWORD: MT8CA TOC

Table of Contents

Tools for Success

CHAPTER 3

Multi-Step Equations and Inequalities

go.hrw.com
Online Resources
KEYWORD: MT8CA TOC

Tools for Success

Reading Math 115, 137
Writing Math 119, 123, 127, 133, 139, 143, 147, 151
Vocabulary 116, 120, 136, 156

Know-It Notebook Chapter 3
Homework Help Online 118, 122, 126, 132, 138, 142, 146, 150
Student Help 117, 120, 125, 129, 130, 137, 140, 144, 148, 149

Countdown to Mastery Weeks 5, 6
Spiral Standards Review 119, 123, 127, 133, 139, 143, 147, 151
Ready to Go On? 134, 152
Mastering the Standards 162

Exponents and Roots

Tools for Success

Reading Math 168, 177
Writing Math 171, 179, 183, 188, 192, 195, 199, 203, 209
Vocabulary 168, 180, 184, 192, 200, 205, 214

Know-It Notebook Chapter 4
Homework Help Online 170, 174, 178, 182, 186, 194, 198, 202, 207
Student Help 168, 169, 177, 180, 181, 192, 193, 200, 205, 207

MASTERING THE STANDARDS

Countdown to Mastery Weeks 7, 8, 9
Spiral Standards Review 171, 175, 179, 183, 188, 195, 199, 203, 209
Ready to Go On? 190, 210
Mastering the Standards 218

CHAPTER 5

Ratios, Proportions, and Similarity

go.hrw.com
Online Resources
KEYWORD: MT8CA TOC

Tools for Success

 **Reading and Writing Math**

Reading Math 244, 252
Writing Math 223, 227, 231, 236, 241, 247, 251, 255
Vocabulary 224, 232, 237, 244, 248, 252, 262

 **Study Skills**

Know-It Notebook Chapter 5
Homework Help Online 226, 230, 234, 239, 246, 250, 254
Student Help 224, 233, 234, 237, 244, 245, 249, 252

 **MASTERING THE STANDARDS**

Countdown to Mastery Weeks 9, 10, 11
Spiral Standards Review 227, 231, 236, 241, 247, 251, 255
Ready to Go On? 242, 258
Mastering the Standards 268

Percents

Tools for Success

 Reading and Writing Math

 Study Skills

MASTERING THE STANDARDS

Reading Math 273, 274

Writing Math 277, 282, 297, 307

Vocabulary 274, 278, 294, 303, 312

Know-It Notebook Chapter 6

Homework Help Online 276, 280, 285, 290, 296, 300, 305

Student Help 274, 275, 285, 298, 304

Countdown to Mastery Weeks 11, 12, 13

Spiral Standards Review 277, 282, 287, 291, 297, 301, 307

Ready to Go On? 292, 308

Mastering the Standards 316

CHAPTER 7

Graphs and Functions

go.hrw.com
Online Resources
KEYWORD: MT8CA TOC

Tools for Success

Reading Math 326, 349
Writing Math 321, 325, 329, 333, 337, 341, 348, 352, 356, 361
Vocabulary 322, 326, 330, 334, 338, 344, 357, 366

Know-It Notebook Chapter 7
Homework Help Online 324, 328, 332, 336, 340, 346, 351, 355, 360
Student Help 326, 330, 334, 339, 345, 349, 350

Countdown to Mastery Weeks 13, 14, 15
Spiral Standards Review 325, 329, 333, 337, 341, 348, 352, 356, 361
Ready to Go On? 342, 362
Mastering the Standards 372

Foundations of Geometry

go.hrw.com
Online Resources
KEYWORD: MT8CA TOC

Plane Geometry

Congruence and Transformations

Tools for Success

Reading and Writing Math

Study Skills

MASTERING THE STANDARDS

Two-Dimensional Geometry

Tools for Success

Reading Math 440, 446
Writing Math 438, 442, 449, 453, 457, 461
Vocabulary 434, 446, 450, 466

Know-It Notebook Chapter 9
Homework Help Online 437, 441, 448, 452, 456, 460
Student Help 435, 436, 440, 450, 458

MASTERING THE STANDARDS

Countdown to Mastery Weeks 18, 19
Spiral Standards Review 438, 443, 449, 453, 457, 461
Ready to Go On? 444, 462
Mastering the Standards 472

Three-Dimensional Geometry

Tools for Success

Reading Math 486
Writing Math 477, 489, 493, 502, 507, 515
Vocabulary 480, 485, 498, 504, 508, 520

Know-It Notebook Chapter 10
Homework Help Online 482, 488, 492, 500, 506, 510, 514
Student Help 480, 486

Countdown to Mastery Weeks 19, 20, 21, 22
Spiral Standards Review 483, 489, 493, 502, 507, 511, 515
Ready to Go On? 494, 516
Mastering the Standards 524

CHAPTER 11

Data, Statistics, and Probability

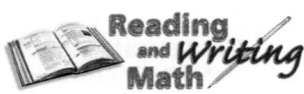
go.hrw.com
Online Resources
KEYWORD: MT8CA TOC

Tools for Success

Reading and Writing Math
Reading Math 529
Writing Math 536, 541, 546, 552, 556, 559, 566, 573
Vocabulary 532, 537, 542, 548, 556, 560, 564, 569, 578

Study Skills
Know-It Notebook Chapter 11
Homework Help Online 534, 540, 544, 550, 558, 562, 567, 572
Student Help 533, 537, 538, 539, 566, 571

MASTERING THE STANDARDS
Countdown to Mastery Weeks 22, 23, 24
Spiral Standards Review 536, 541, 546, 552, 559, 563, 568, 573
Ready to Go On? 554, 574
Mastering the Standards 584

Preview of Algebra 1
Polynomials

go.hrw.com
Online Resources
KEYWORD: MT8CA TOC

Introduction to Polynomials

Polynomial Operations

Tools for Success

Reading and Writing Math

Writing Math 593, 606, 611, 615, 621
Vocabulary 590, 618, 626

Study Skills

Know-It Notebook Chapter 12
Homework Help Online 592, 598, 605, 610, 614, 620
Student Help 591, 596, 612, 618

MASTERING THE STANDARDS

Spiral Standards Review 593, 599, 606, 611, 615, 621
Ready to Go On? 600, 622
Mastering the Standards 630

Focus on Problem Solving

The Problem Solving Plan

In order to be a good problem solver, you first need a good problem-solving plan. A plan or strategy will help you to understand the problem, to work through a solution, and to check that your answer makes sense. The plan used in this book is detailed below.

UNDERSTAND the Problem

■ **What are you asked to find?**	Restate the problem in your own words.
■ **What information is given?**	Identify the important facts in the problem.
■ **What information do you need?**	Determine which facts are needed to solve the problem.
■ **Is all the information given?**	Determine whether all the facts are given.

Make a PLAN

■ **Have you ever solved a similar problem?**	Think about other problems like this that you successfully solved.
■ **What strategy or strategies can you use?**	Determine a strategy that you can use and how you will use it.

SOLVE

■ **Follow your plan.**	Show the steps in your solution. Write your answer as a complete sentence.

LOOK BACK

■ **Have you answered the question?**	Be sure that you answered the question that is being asked.
■ **Is your answer reasonable?**	Your answer should make sense in the context of the problem.
■ **Is there another strategy you could use?**	Solving the problem using another strategy is a good way to check your work.
■ **Did you learn anything while solving this problem that could help you solve similar problems in the future?**	Try to remember the problems you have solved and the strategies you used to solve them.

Using the Problem Solving Plan

During summer vacation, Ricardo will go to space camp and then to visit his relatives. He will be gone for 5 weeks and 4 days and will spend 11 more days with his relatives than at space camp.
How long will Ricardo stay at each place?

UNDERSTAND the Problem

List the important information.

- Ricardo will be gone for 5 weeks and 4 days.
- He will spend 11 more days with his relatives than at space camp.

The answer will be how long Ricardo stays at each place.

Make a PLAN

You can **draw a diagram** to show how long he will stay at each place. Use boxes for the length of each stay. The length of each box will represent the length of each stay.

SOLVE

Think: There are 7 days in a week, so 5 weeks and 4 days is a total of 39 days. Your diagram might look like this:

Relatives	? days	11 days

Space camp	? days

$\Big\}$ = 39 days

$39 - 11 = 28$ *Subtract 11 days from the total number of days.*
$28 \div 2 = 14$ *Divide this number by 2 for the 2 places he visits.*

Relatives	14 days	11 days

= 25 days

Space camp	14 days

= 14 days

So Ricardo will stay with his relatives for 25 days and at space camp for 14 days.

LOOK BACK

Twenty-five days is 11 days longer than 14 days. The total length of the two stays is $25 + 14 = 39$ days, or 5 weeks and 4 days. This solution fits the information given in the problem.

Using Your Book for Success

Holt California Mathematics has many features designed to help you learn and study math. Becoming familiar with these features will prepare you for greater success.

Learn

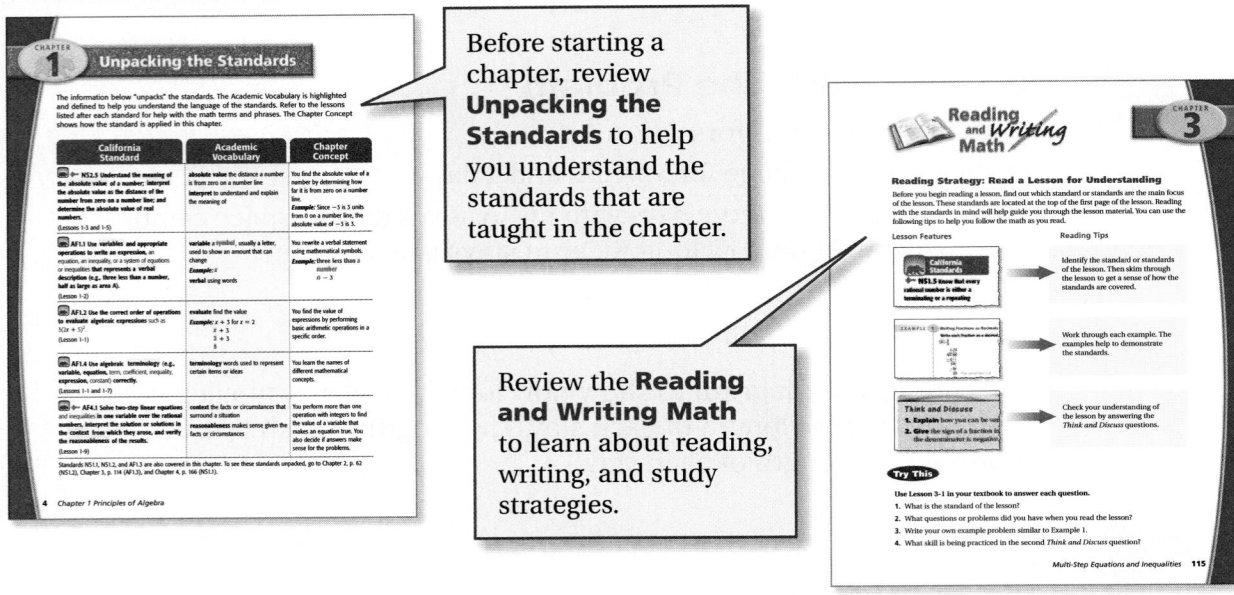

Before starting a chapter, review **Unpacking the Standards** to help you understand the standards that are taught in the chapter.

Review the **Reading and Writing Math** to learn about reading, writing, and study strategies.

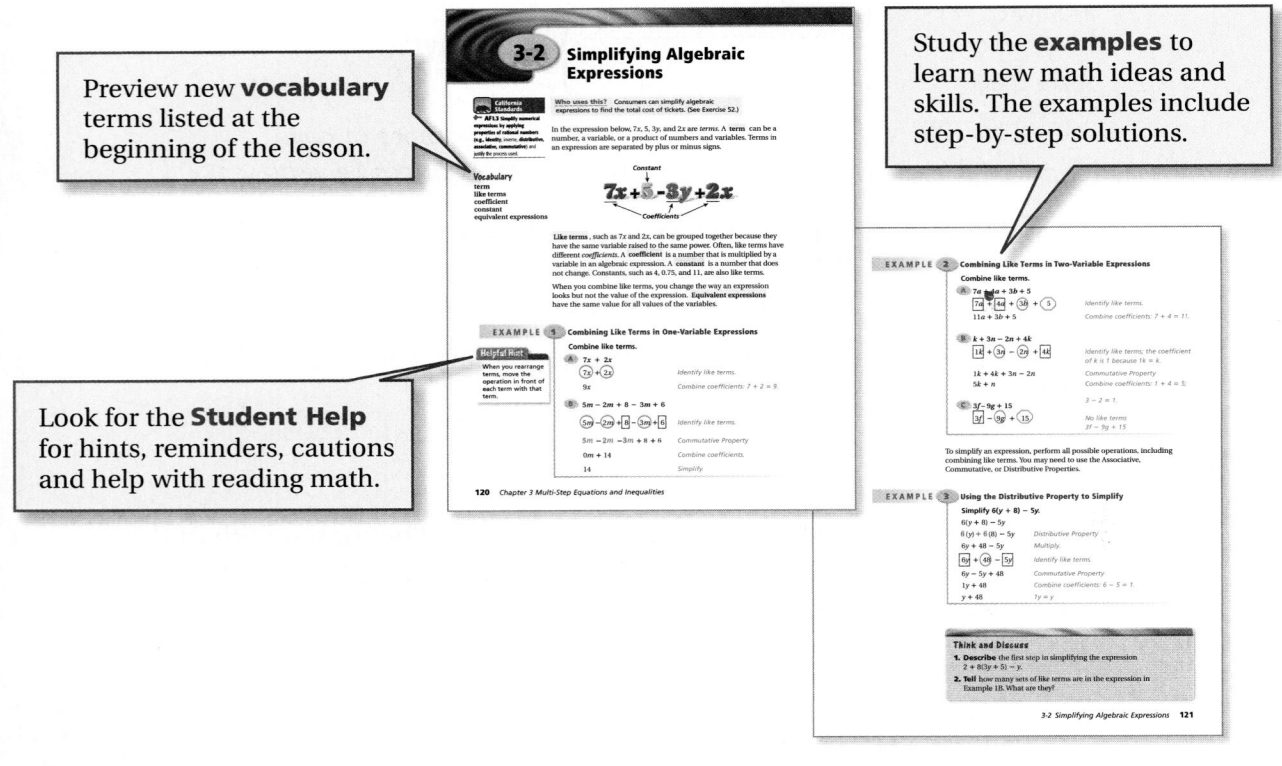

Preview new **vocabulary** terms listed at the beginning of the lesson.

Look for the **Student Help** for hints, reminders, cautions and help with reading math.

Study the **examples** to learn new math ideas and skills. The examples include step-by-step solutions.

Practice

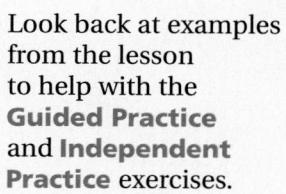

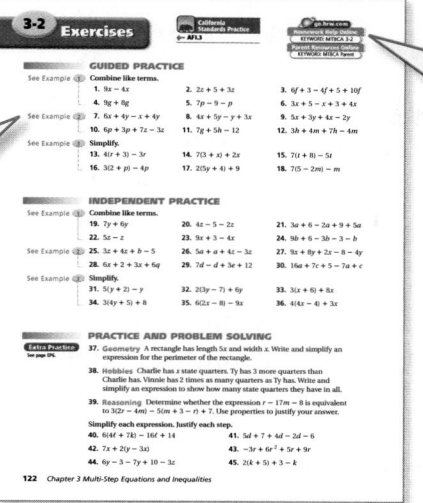

Look back at examples from the lesson to help with the **Guided Practice** and **Independent Practice** exercises.

Use the internet for **Homework Help Online**.

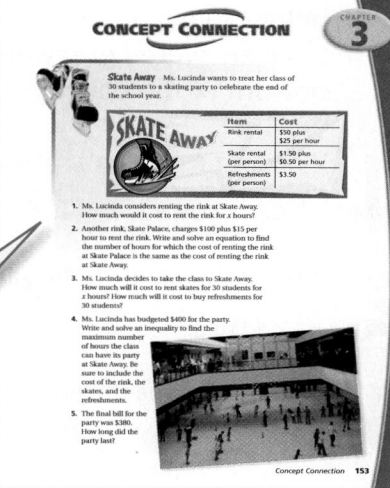

Complete the **Concept Connection** to practice skills from the chapter in a real-world context.

Review

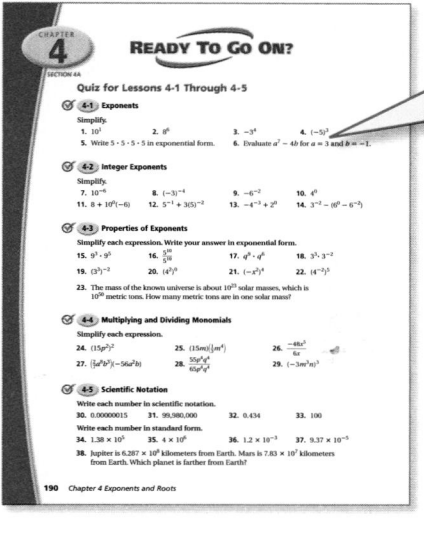

As you finish each section, test your knowledge with **practice problems** before you continue.

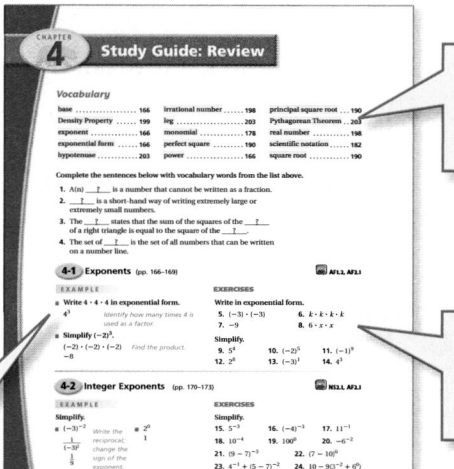

Study and review the **vocabulary** from the entire chapter.

Review important **examples** from every lesson in the chapter.

Test your knowledge with **practice problems**.

Scavenger Hunt

Holt California Mathematics is your resource to help you succeed. Use this scavenger hunt to discover some of the many tools Holt provides to help you be an independent learner.

On a separate sheet of paper, fill in the blanks to answer each question below. In each answer, one letter will be in a yellow box. When you have answered every question, use the letters to fill in the blank at the bottom of the page.

1. What is the first key **vocabulary** term in the Study Guide: Review for Chapter 6?

◼◼◼◼◼◼◼◼◼◼ commiSsion

2. What is the name of the game at the bottom of Chapter 4 **Game Time**?

◼◼◼◼◼◼◼◼ ◼◼◼◼◼ EQUATION BINGO

3. What strategy is the focus of Chapter 1 **Strategies for Success**?

◼◼◼◼◼◼◼◼◼ ◼◼◼◼◼◼ ◼◼◼◼◼◼◼ eLIMINATE ANSWER CHOICES

4. What is the focus of Chapter 8 **Focus on Problem Solving**?

◼◼◼◼◼◼◼◼◼◼ ◼◼◼ ◼◼◼◼◼◼◼ UNDERSTAND THE PROBLEM

5. What is the first word of the fourth question in Chapter 5 **Mastering the Standards**?

◼◼◼◼◼◼◼◼ EVALUATE

6. What is the location of the **Science Link** on page 91?

◼◼◼◼◼◼◼ ◼◼◼◼◼ nIagara FALLS

7. What is the third key vocabulary term in the **Study Guide: Review** for Chapter 3?

◼◼◼◼◼◼◼◼◼◼◼ cOefficient

8. What keyword would you use for Lesson 3-1 **Parent Resources Online**?

◼◼◼◼◼ ◼◼◼◼◼◼ MT8CA PARENt

Math Humor

What do "$x = 4$" and salt water have in common?

◼◼◼◼◼◼◼◼ SOLUTION

They can both be called a "solution."

Math Builders

The Math Builders section in the Student Edition uses transparent pages to allow students to learn important standards through a step-by-step, layered approach. At key points in the text, these pages are referenced in the side margin. The Math Builders are also available on overhead transparencies in *Lesson Transparencies*.

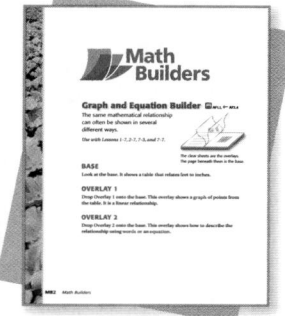

Use with Lessons 1-7, 2-7, 7-3, and 7-7.

Graph and Equation Builder

This Math Builder shows how the same mathematical relationship can often be shown in several different ways.

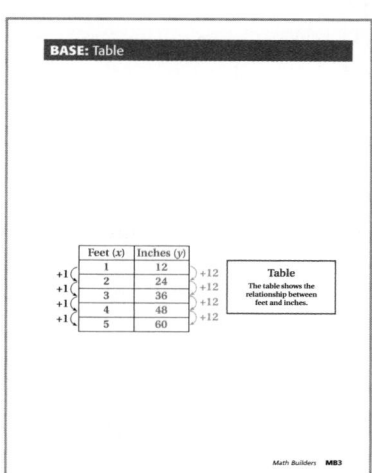

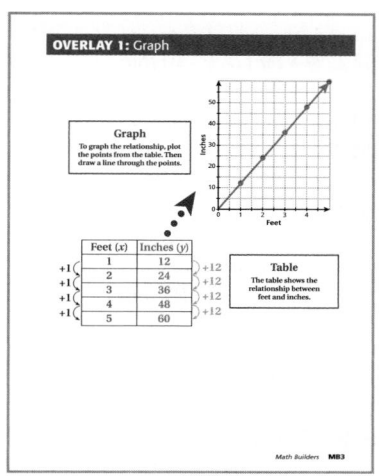

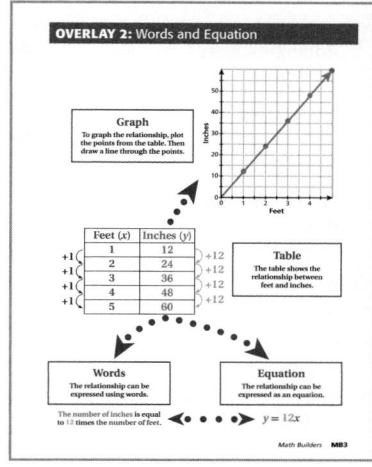

Use with Lessons 1-9, 2-8, and 3-8.

Step-by-Step Solution Builder

This Math Builder shows you the steps involved in solving two-step equations and inequalities.

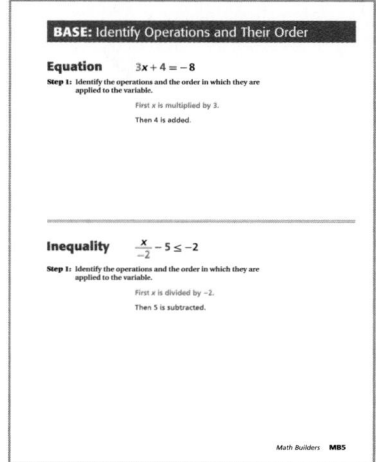

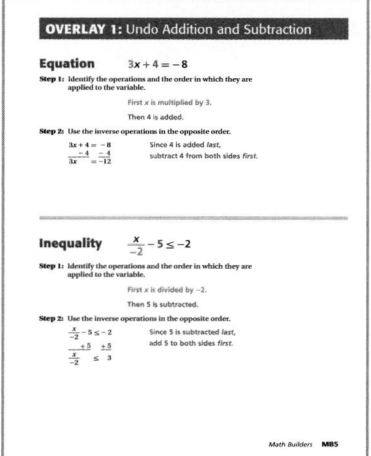

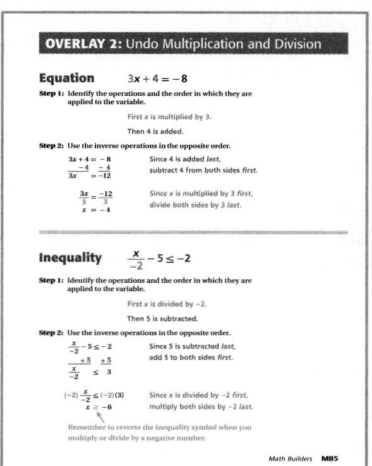

CHAPTER 1

Principles of Algebra

	Grade-level Standard
◀	Review
▶	Beyond the Standards
A	Assessment
O	Optional

Pacing Guide

Calendar Planner
Teacher's **One-Stop** Planner®

Lesson/Lab		California Standards	Time	Advanced Students	Benchmark* Students	Strategic** Students
1-1	Evaluating Algebraic Expressions	AF1.2, AF1.4	50 min	✔	✔	✔
1-2	Writing Algebraic Expressions	AF1.1	50 min	✔	✔	✔
1-3	Integers and Absolute Value	NS1.1, ⟻ NS2.5	50 min	✔	✔	✔
1-4	Adding Integers	⟻ NS1.2, ⟻ AF1.3	50 min	✔	✔	✔
1-5	Subtracting Integers	⟻ NS1.2, ⟻ NS2.5	50 min	✔	✔	✔
1-6	Multiplying and Dividing Integers	⟻ NS1.2	50 min	✔	✔	✔
Ready to Go On?			25 min	A	A	A
Focus on Problem Solving			25 min	A	A	O
1-7	Solving Equations by Adding or Subtracting	AF1.4, Prep for ⟻ AF4.0	50 min	O	◀	◀
1-8	Solving Equations by Multiplying or Dividing	AF1.3, Prep for ⟻ AF4.0	50 min	O	◀	◀
LAB	Model Two-Step Equations	⟻ AF4.1	50 min	✔	✔	✔
1-9	Solving Two-Step Equations	AF1.1, ⟻ AF4.1	100 min	✔	✔	✔
Ready to Go On?			25 min	A	A	A
Concept Connection			25 min	A	A	O
Study Guide: Review			50 min	✔	✔	✔
Chapter Test			50 min	A	A	A

* **Benchmark students** are achieving at or near grade level.

** **Strategic students** may be a year or more below grade level and may require additional time for intervention.

Countdown to Mastery, Weeks ❶, ❷

ONGOING ASSESSMENT and INTERVENTION

	DIAGNOSE	PRESCRIBE

Assess Prior Knowledge

Before Chapter 1

Diagnose readiness for the chapter.
Are You Ready? SE p. 3

Prescribe intervention.
Are You Ready? Intervention Skills 5, 34, 51, 54, 57

Formative Assessment

Before Every Lesson

Diagnose readiness for the lesson.
Warm Up TE, every lesson

Prescribe intervention.
Skills Bank SE pp. SB2–SB24
Review for Mastery CRF, Chapter 1

During Every Lesson

Diagnose understanding of lesson concepts.
Questioning Strategies Chapter 1
Think and Discuss SE, every lesson
Write About It SE, lesson exercises
Journal TE, lesson exercises

Prescribe intervention.
Reading Strategies CRF, every lesson
Success for ELL Chapter 1
Lesson Tutorial Videos Chapter 1

After Every Lesson

Diagnose mastery of lesson concepts.
Lesson Quiz TE, every lesson
Ready to Go On? SE pp. 30, 48
Test and Practice Generator

Prescribe intervention.
Review for Mastery CRF, every lesson
Problem Solving CRF, every lesson
Ready to Go On? Intervention Chapter 1
Homework Help Online

Before Chapter 1 Testing

Diagnose mastery of concepts in the chapter.
Ready to Go On? SE pp. 30, 48
Focus on Problem Solving SE p. 31
Concept Connection SE p. 49
Section Quizzes AR pp. 5–6
Test and Practice Generator

Prescribe intervention.
Ready to Go On? Intervention Chapter 1
Scaffolding Questions TE p. 49

Before Assessment of California Standards

Diagnose mastery of California standards.
Focus on California Standards: Benchmark Tests
Mastering the Standards SE pp. 58–59
California Standards Practice CD-ROM

Prescribe intervention.
Focus on California Standards: Intervention

Summative Assessment

After Chapter 1

Check mastery of chapter concepts.
Multiple-Choice Tests (Forms A, B, C)
Free-Response Tests (Forms A, B, C)
Performance Assessment AR pp. 7–20
Test and Practice Generator

Prescribe intervention.
Review for Mastery CRF, every lesson
Lesson Tutorial Videos Chapter 1

KEY: **SE** = *Student Edition*   **TE** = *Teacher's Edition*   **CRF** = *Chapter Resource File*   **AR** = *Assessment Resources*   Available on CD-ROM   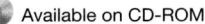 Available online

2B

Supporting the Teacher

Chapter 1 Resource File

Family Involvement
pp. 1–4, 53–56

Practice A, B, C
pp. 5–7, 13–15, 21–23, 29–31, 37–39, 45–47, 57–59, 65–67, 73–75

Review for Mastery
pp. 8, 16, 24, 32, 40, 48, 60, 68, 76

Challenge
pp. 9, 17, 25, 33, 41, 49, 61, 69, 77

Problem Solving
pp. 10, 18, 26, 34, 42, 50, 62, 70, 78

Reading Strategies ELL
pp. 11, 19, 27, 35, 43, 51, 63, 71, 79

Puzzles, Twisters, and Teasers
pp. 12, 20, 28, 36, 44, 52, 64, 72, 80

Hands-On Lab
pp. 81–83, 86–91

Technology Lab
pp. 84–85

Workbooks

Homework and Practice Workbook SPANISH
Teacher's Guide ....pp. 1–9

Know-It Notebook SPANISH
Teacher's Guide .... Chapter 1

Review for Mastery Workbook SPANISH
Teacher's Guide ....pp. 1–9

Focus on California Standards: Intervention Workbook SPANISH
Teacher's Guide

Teacher Tools

Power Presentations
Complete PowerPoint® presentations for Chapter 1 lessons

Lesson Tutorial Videos SPANISH
Holt authors Ed Burger and Freddie Renfro present tutorials to support the Chapter 1 lessons.

Teacher's One-Stop Planner SPANISH
Easy access to all Chapter 1 resources and assessments, as well as software for lesson planning, test generation, and puzzle creation

IDEA Works!
Key Chapter 1 resources and assessments modified to address special learning needs

Questioning Strategies .... Chapter 1

Solutions Key .... Chapter 1

Interactive Answers and Solutions

TechKeys   **Lab Resources**

Project Teacher Support   **Parent Resources**

Transparencies

Lesson Transparencies, Volume 1 .... Chapter 1
• Teacher Tools
• Warm Ups
• Teaching Transparencies
• Lesson Quizzes

Know-It Notebook .... Chapter 1
• Vocabulary   • Chapter Review
• Additional Examples   • Big Ideas

Alternate Openers: Explorations .... pp. 1–9

Countdown to Mastery .... pp. 1–5

Technology Highlights for the Teacher

Power Presentations
Dynamic presentations to engage students. Complete PowerPoint® presentations for every lesson in Chapter 1.

One-Stop Planner SPANISH
Easy access to Chapter 1 resources and assessments. Includes lesson-planning, test-generation, and puzzle-creation software.

Premier Online Edition SPANISH
Includes Tutorial Videos, Lesson Activities, Lesson Quizzes, Homework Help, Chapter Project and more.

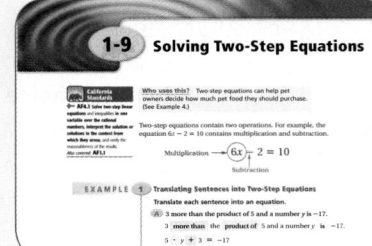

KEY: **SE** = *Student Edition*   **TE** = *Teacher's Edition*   English Language Learners   Spanish available   Available on CD-ROM  Available online

CHAPTER 1

CHAPTER
1

Universal Access

Teaching tips to help all students appear throughout the chapter. A few that target specific students are included in the lists below.

Strategic Students

Practice A	CRF, every lesson
Review for Mastery	CRF, every lesson
Reading Strategies	CRF, every lesson
Academic Vocabulary Connections	TE p. 4
Visual	TE p. 15
Ready to Go On? Intervention	Chapter 1
Questioning Strategies	Chapter 1
Know-It Notebook SPANISH	Chapter 1
Homework Help Online	
Lesson Tutorial Videos SPANISH	
Online Interactivities SPANISH	

Special Needs Students

Practice A	CRF, every lesson
Review for Mastery	CRF, every lesson
Reading Strategies	CRF, every lesson
Academic Vocabulary Connections	TE p. 4
Inclusion	TE pp. 19, 23, 38
IDEA Works! Modified Resources	Chapter 1
Ready to Go On? Intervention	Chapter 1
Know-It Notebook SPANISH	Chapter 1
Lesson Tutorial Videos SPANISH	
Online Interactivities SPANISH	

English Learners

ENGLISH LANGUAGE LEARNERS

Reading Strategies	CRF, every lesson
Vocabulary Review	SE p. 52
Academic Vocabulary Connections	TE p. 4
English Language Learners	TE pp. 6, 15
Language Support	TE p. 20
Success for English Language Learners	Chapter 1
Know-It Notebook SPANISH	Chapter 1
Multilingual Glossary	
Lesson Tutorial Videos SPANISH	

Benchmark Students

Practice B	CRF, every lesson
Problem Solving	CRF, every lesson
Academic Vocabulary Connections	TE p. 4
Ready to Go On? Intervention	Chapter 1
Questioning Strategies	Chapter 1
Know-It Notebook SPANISH	Chapter 1
Homework Help Online	
Online Interactivities SPANISH	

Advanced Students

Practice C	CRF, every lesson
Challenge	CRF, every lesson
Reading and Writing Math EXTENSION	TE p. 5
Concept Connection EXTENSION	TE p. 49
Advanced Learners/GATE	TE pp. 23, 27
Ready to Go On? Enrichment	Chapter 1

Technology Highlights for Universal Access

 Lesson Tutorial Videos SPANISH

Starring Holt authors Ed Burger and Freddie Renfro! Live tutorials to support every lesson in Chapter 1.

 Multilingual Glossary

Searchable glossary includes definitions in English, Spanish, Vietnamese, Chinese, Hmong, Korean, and other languages.

 Online Interactivities SPANISH

Interactive tutorials provide visually engaging alternative opportunities to learn concepts and master skills.

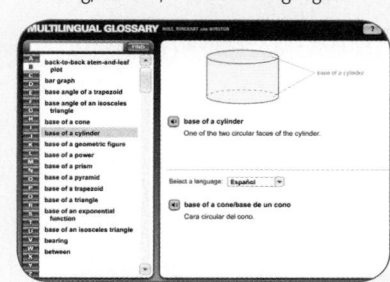

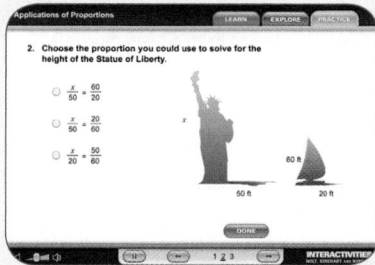

KEY: **SE** = *Student Edition*   **TE** = *Teacher's Edition*   **CRF** = *Chapter Resource File*   SPANISH Spanish available   Available on CD-ROM   Available online

Ongoing Assessment

Assessing Prior Knowledge

Determine whether students have the prerequisite concepts and skills for success in Chapter 1.

Are You Ready? SPANISH .... SE p. 3
Warm Up .... TE, every lesson

Chapter and Standards Assessment

Provide review and practice for Chapter 1 and standards mastery.

Concept Connection .... SE p. 49
Study Guide: Review .... SE pp. 52–54
Strategies for Success .... SE pp. 56–57
Mastering the Standards .... SE pp. 58–59
Countdown to Mastery Transparencies .... pp. 1–4
Focus on California Standards: Benchmark Tests
Focus on California Standards: Intervention Workbook SPANISH
California Standards Practice CD-ROM SPANISH
IDEA Works! Modified Worksheets and Tests

Alternative Assessment

Assess students' understanding of Chapter 1 concepts and combined problem-solving skills.

Performance Assessment .... AR pp. 19–20
Portfolio Assessment .... AR p. xxxvi
Chapter 1 Project

Daily Assessment

Provide formative assessment for each day of Chapter 1.

Think and Discuss .... SE, every lesson
Write About It .... SE, lesson exercises
Journal .... TE, lesson exercises
Lesson Quiz .... TE, every lesson
Questioning Strategies .... Chapter 1
IDEA Works! Modified Lesson Quizzes .... Chapter 1

Weekly Assessment

Provide formative assessment for each week of Chapter 1.

Focus on Problem Solving .... SE p. 31
Concept Connection .... SE p. 49
Ready to Go On? SPANISH .... SE pp. 30, 48
Cumulative Assessment .... SE pp. 58–59
Test and Practice Generator SPANISH ...*One-Stop Planner*

Formal Assessment

Provide summative assessment of Chapter 1 mastery.

Section Quizzes .... AR pp. 5–6
Chapter 1 Test SPANISH .... SE p.55
Chapter Test (Levels A, B, C) .... AR pp. 7–18
      • Multiple-Choice • Free-Response
Cumulative Test .... AR pp. 21–24
Test and Practice Generator SPANISH ...*One-Stop Planner*
IDEA Works! Modified Tests .... Chapter 1

Technology Highlights for the Teacher

Are You Ready? SPANISH

Automatically assess readiness and prescribe intervention for Chapter 1 prerequisite skills.

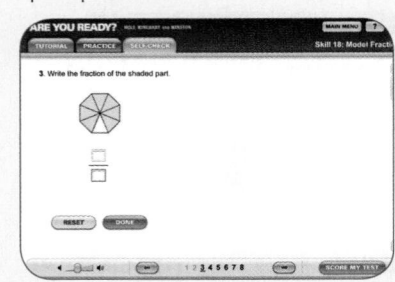

Ready to Go On? SPANISH

Automatically assess understanding of and prescribe intervention for Sections 1A and 1B.

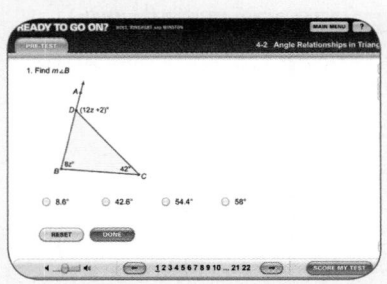

Focus on California Standards: Benchmark Tests and Intervention SPANISH

Automatically assess proficiency with California Grade 7 Standards and provide intervention.

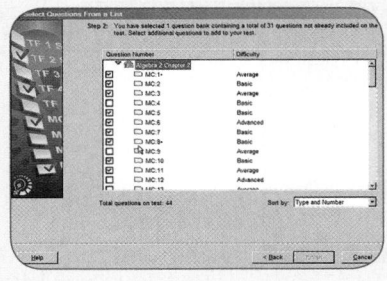

KEY: **SE** = *Student Edition*   **TE** = *Teacher's Edition*   **AR** = *Assessment Resources*   SPANISH Spanish available    Available on CD-ROM    Available online

Formal Assessment

Three levels (A, B, C) of multiple-choice and free-response chapter tests are available in the *Assessment Resources*.

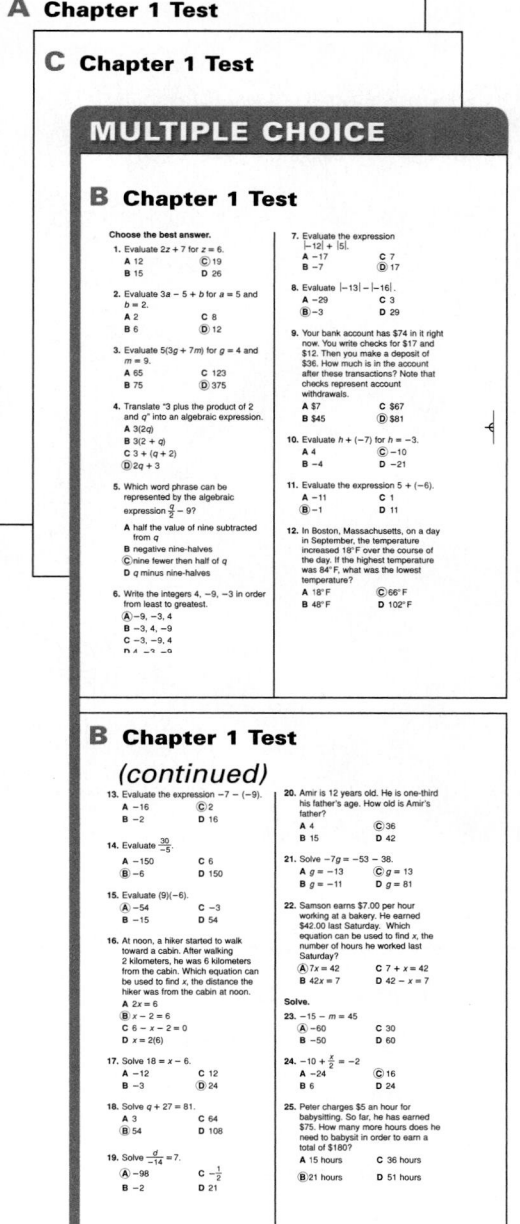

A Chapter 1 Test

C Chapter 1 Test

MULTIPLE CHOICE

B Chapter 1 Test

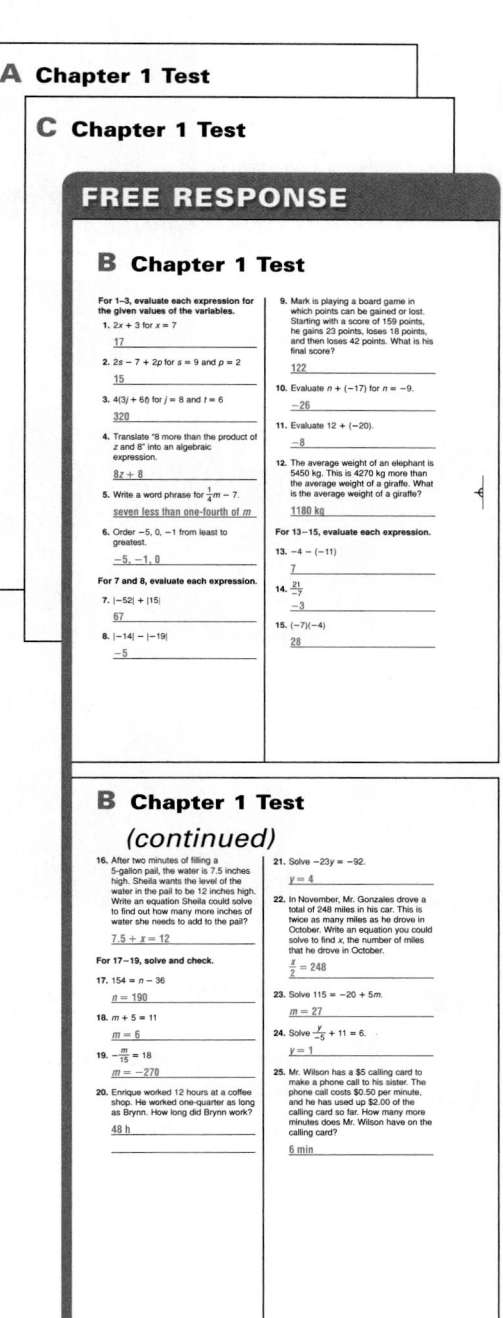

A Chapter 1 Test

C Chapter 1 Test

FREE RESPONSE

B Chapter 1 Test

Modified tests and worksheets found in *IDEA Works!*

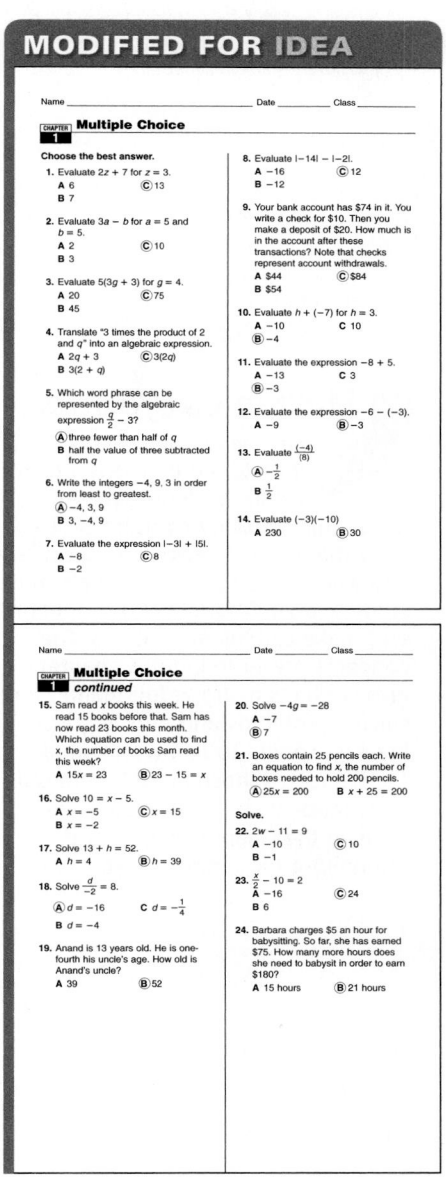

MODIFIED FOR IDEA

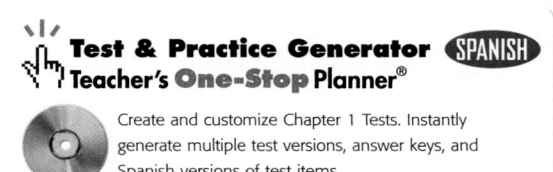

Test & Practice Generator SPANISH
Teacher's One-Stop Planner®

Create and customize Chapter 1 Tests. Instantly generate multiple test versions, answer keys, and Spanish versions of test items.

Focus on Problem Solving

On page 31, students focus on choosing addition or subtraction for the operation used to solve real-world problems.

 **CONCEPT CONNECTION** On page 49, students use addition, subtraction, multiplication, and division of integers to model scores in a basketball game.

Math in *California*

Each year California is threatened by thousands of wildfires. Putting the fires out requires solving complex problems that involve geography, weather, and available resources. Officials must analyze large amounts of information and make careful calculations. The concepts presented in this chapter give students a strong foundation for solving problems and applying algebraic reasoning to real-world situations, such as those faced by fire officials. Students will use these concepts in the Chapter Project and throughout the entire course.

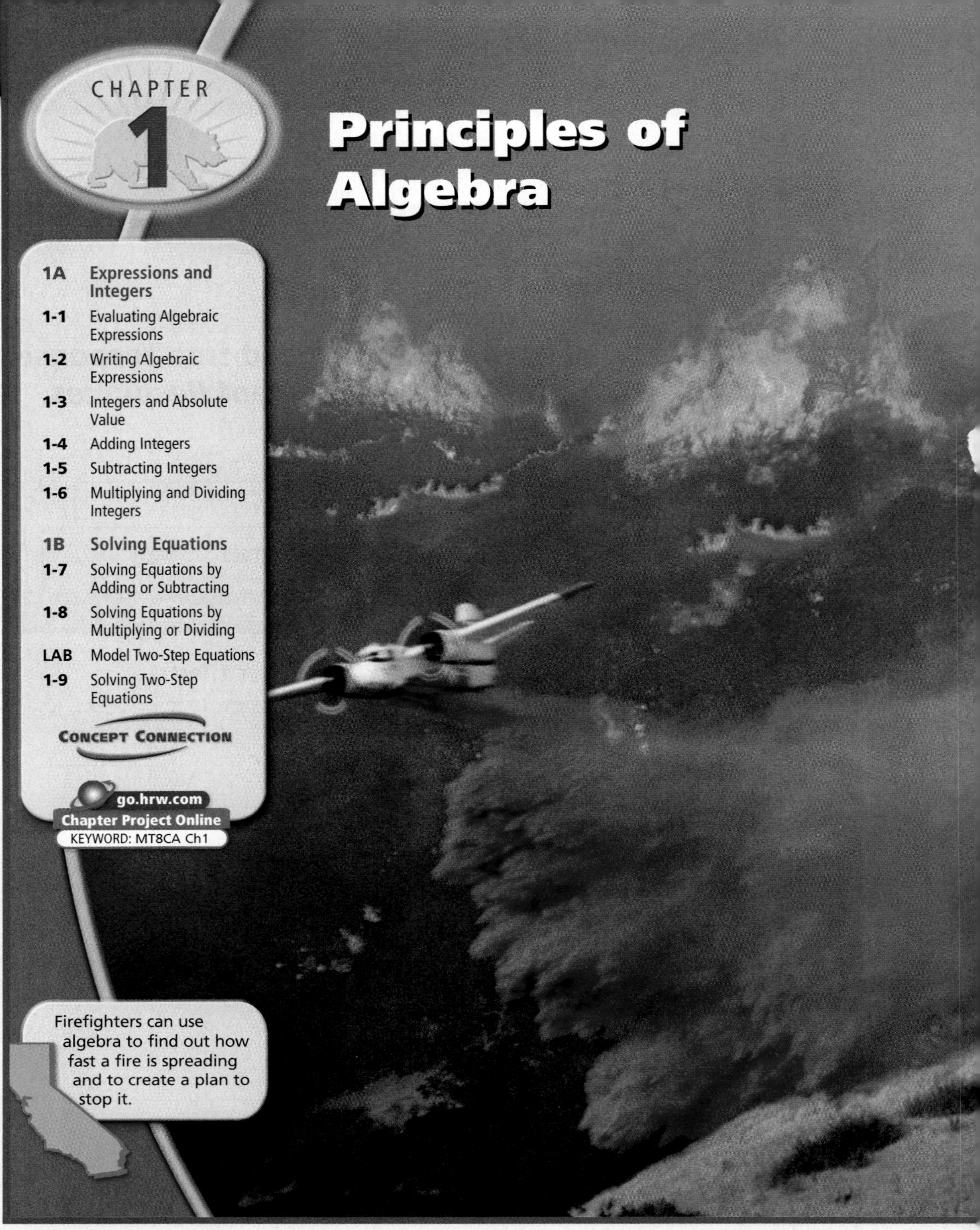

go.hrw.com
Chapter Project Online
KEYWORD: MT8CA Ch1

Firefighters can use algebra to find out how fast a fire is spreading and to create a plan to stop it.

Problem Solving Project

Understand, Plan, Solve, and Look Back

Have students:

- Complete the Firefighter worksheet to discover the relationships among toxic gases.

- Determine an algebraic expression that relates phosgene, carbon monoxide, hydrogen chloride, and hydrogen cyanide.

- Create a graph comparing the danger levels of the gases.

- Research the effects of toxic gases on the human body.

Science Connection

Project Resources

All project resources for teachers and students are provided online.

Materials:

- Firefighter worksheet

go.hrw.com
Project Teacher Support
KEYWORD: MT8CA PSProject1

ARE YOU READY?

Vocabulary
Choose the best term from the list to complete each sentence.

1. __?__ is the __?__ of addition. *subtraction; opposite operation*
2. The expressions $3 \cdot 4$ and $4 \cdot 3$ are equal by the __?__. *Commutative Property*
3. The expressions $1 + (2 + 3)$ and $(1 + 2) + 3$ are equal by the __?__. *Associative Property*
4. Multiplication and __?__ are opposite operations. *division*
5. __?__ and __?__ are commutative. *addition; multiplication*

addition
Associative Property
Commutative Property
division
multiplication
opposite operation
subtraction

Complete these exercises to review skills you will need for this chapter.

Whole Number Operations
Simplify each expression.

6. $8 + 116 + 43$ **167**
7. $2431 - 187$ **2244**
8. $204 \cdot 38$ **7752**
9. $6447 \div 21$ **307**

Compare and Order Whole Numbers
Order each sequence of numbers from least to greatest.

10. 1050; 11,500; 105; 150
    105; 150; 1050; 11,500
11. 503; 53; 5300; 5030
    53; 503; 5030; 5300
12. 44,400; 40,040; 40,400; 44,040
    40,040; 40,400; 44,040; 44,400

Inverse Operations
Rewrite each expression using the inverse operation.

13. $72 + 18 = 90$
    $90 - 18 = 72$
14. $12 \cdot 9 = 108$
    $108 \div 9 = 12$
15. $100 - 34 = 66$
    $66 + 34 = 100$
16. $56 \div 8 = 7$
    $7 \cdot 8 = 56$

Order of Operations
Simplify each expression.

17. $2 + 3 \cdot 4$ **14**
18. $50 - 2 \cdot 5$ **40**
19. $6 \cdot 3 \cdot 3 - 3$ **51**
20. $(5 + 2)(5 - 2)$ **21**
21. $5 - 6 \div 2$ **2**
22. $16 \div 4 + 2 \cdot 3$ **10**
23. $(8 - 3)(8 + 3)$ **55**
24. $12 \div 3 \div 2 + 5$ **7**

Evaluate Expressions
Determine whether the given expressions are equal.

25. $(4 \cdot 7) \cdot 2$ and $4 \cdot (7 \cdot 2)$ **yes**
26. $(2 \cdot 4) \div 2$ and $2 \cdot (4 \div 2)$ **yes**
27. $2 \cdot (3 - 3)$ and $(2 \cdot 3) - 3$ **no**
28. $5 \cdot (50 - 44)$ and $5 \cdot 50 - 44$ **no**
29. $9 - (4 \cdot 2)$ and $(9 - 4) \cdot 2$ **no**
30. $2 \cdot 3 + 2 \cdot 4$ and $2 \cdot (3 + 4)$ **yes**
31. $(16 \div 4) + 4$ and $16 \div (4 + 4)$ **no**
32. $5 + (2 \cdot 3)$ and $(5 + 2) \cdot 3$ **no**

Organizer

Objective: Assess students' understanding of prerequisite skills.

Prerequisite Skills

Whole Number Operations
Compare and Order Whole Numbers
Inverse Operations
Order of Operations
Evaluate Expressions

Assessing Prior Knowledge
INTERVENTION
Diagnose and Prescribe
Use this page to determine whether intervention is necessary or whether enrichment is appropriate.

Resources

 Are You Ready? Intervention and Enrichment Worksheets

 Are You Ready? CD-ROM

 Are You Ready? Online

my.hrw.com

ARE YOU READY?
Diagnose and Prescribe

NO INTERVENE

YES ENRICH

	ARE YOU READY? Intervention, Chapter 1		
☑ Prerequisite Skill	📄 Worksheets	💿 CD-ROM	🪐 Online
☑ Whole Number Operations	Skill 34	Activity 34	
☑ Compare and Order Whole Numbers	Skill 5	Activity 5	Diagnose and Prescribe Online
☑ Inverse Operations	Skill 57	Activity 57	
☑ Order of Operations	Skill 51	Activity 51	
☑ Evaluate Expressions	Skill 54	Activity 54	

ARE YOU READY?
Enrichment, Chapter 1
📄 Worksheets
💿 CD-ROM
🪐 Online

Objective: Help students understand the new concepts they will learn in Chapter 1.

Academic Vocabulary Connections

In addition to the academic vocabulary listed on the student page, it may help students to become familiar with some of the vocabulary terms in the chapter. Possible answers are given.

1. The word **equation** looks like the word *equal,* which means "having the same value." How do you think this meaning applies to an equation? The values of the expressions on either side of the equals sign are the same.

2. The word *opposite* means "at the other end or side." What numbers do you think are the **opposite** of the whole numbers (that is, 0, 1, 2, 3, and so on)? The opposites of the whole numbers are the numbers on the left side of zero, for example, −1, −2, −3 and so on.

3. The word *vary,* which is the root of **variable,** means "to change." How do you think this applies to math? A variable often represents an unknown quantity. Therefore, a variable's value can change from one problem to another.

CHAPTER
1

Unpacking the Standards

The information below "unpacks" the standards. The Academic Vocabulary is highlighted and defined to help you understand the language of the standards. Refer to the lessons listed after each standard for help with the math terms and phrases. The Chapter Concept shows how the standard is applied in this chapter.

California Standard	Academic Vocabulary	Chapter Concept
NS2.5 Understand the meaning of the absolute value of a number; interpret the absolute value as the distance of the number from zero on a number line; and determine the absolute value of real numbers. (Lessons 1-3 and 1-5)	**absolute value** the distance a number is from zero on a number line **interpret** to understand and explain the meaning of	You find the absolute value of a number by determining how far it is from zero on a number line. *Example:* Since −3 is 3 units from 0 on a number line, the absolute value of −3 is 3.
AF1.1 Use variables and appropriate operations to write an expression, an equation, an inequality, or a system of equations or inequalities **that represents a verbal description (e.g., three less than a number, half as large as area A).** (Lesson 1-2)	**variable** a **symbol,** usually a letter, used to show an amount that can change *Example:* x **verbal** using words	You rewrite a verbal statement using mathematical symbols. *Example:* three less than a number $n - 3$
AF1.2 Use the correct order of operations to evaluate algebraic expressions such as $3(2x + 5)^2$. (Lesson 1-1)	**evaluate** find the value *Example:* $x + 3$ for $x = 2$ $x + 3$ $2 + 3$ 5	You find the value of expressions by performing basic arithmetic operations in a specific order.
AF1.4 Use algebraic terminology (e.g., variable, equation, term, coefficient, inequality, **expression,** constant) **correctly.** (Lessons 1-1 and 1-7)	**terminology** words used to represent certain items or ideas	You learn the names of different mathematical concepts.
AF4.1 Solve two-step linear equations and inequalities **in one variable over the rational numbers, interpret the solution or solutions in the context from which they arose, and verify the reasonableness of the results.** (Lesson 1-9)	**context** the facts or circumstances that surround a situation **reasonableness** makes sense given the facts or circumstances	You perform more than one operation with integers to find the value of a variable that makes an equation true. You also decide if answers make sense for the problems.

Standards NS1.1, NS1.2, and AF1.3 are also covered in this chapter. To see these standards unpacked, go to Chapter 2, p. 62 (NS1.2), Chapter 3, p. 114 (AF1.3), and Chapter 4, p. 166 (NS1.1).

Looking Back

Previously, students
- wrote algebraic expressions for word phrases.
- used a number line to add integers.
- used concrete models to solve one- and two-step equations.

In This Chapter

Students will study
- writing and evaluating algebraic expressions.
- using absolute value to add integers.
- using inverse operations to solve one- and two-step equations.

Looking Forward

Students can use these skills
- to write and evaluate complex algebraic expressions in word problems.
- to solve equations involving absolute value.
- to use inverse operations to solve equations involving taking the square root.

Reading Strategy: Use Your Book for Success

Understanding how your textbook is organized will help you locate and use helpful information.

As you read through an example problem, pay attention to the **margin notes**, such as Helpful Hints, Reading Math notes, and Caution notes. These notes will help you understand concepts and avoid common mistakes.

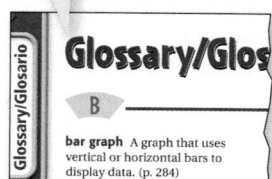
Reading Math
Read $(-4)^3$ as "-4 to the 3rd power" or "-4 cubed."

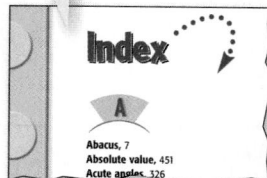
Writing Math
A repeating decimal can be written with a bar over the digits that repeat...

Helpful Hint
In Example 1A, parentheses are not needed because multiplication is...

Caution!
An open circle means that the corresponding value... not a solution. A sol...

The **glossary** is found in the back of your textbook. Use it to find definitions and examples of unfamiliar words or properties.

The **index** is located at the end of your textbook. Use it to find the page where a particular concept is taught.

The **Skills Bank** is found in the back of your textbook. These pages review concepts from previous math courses.

Glossary/Glos

Glossary/Glosario

B

bar graph A graph that uses vertical or horizontal bars to display data. (p. 284)

Index

A

Abacus, 7
Absolute value, 451
Acute angles, 326

Skills Bank

**Place Value—Hu
Hundred-thousa**

You can use a place-value ch

Try This

Use your textbook for the following problems.

1. Use the glossary to find the definition of *absolute value*.

2. Where can you review the order of operations?

3. On what page can you find answers to exercises in Chapter 2?

4. Use the index to find the page numbers where *algebraic expressions*, *monomials*, and *volume of prisms* are explained.

 Reading and Writing Math CHAPTER 1

Organizer

Objective: Help students apply strategies to understand and retain key concepts.

Online Edition

Resources

Chapter 1 Resource File
Reading Strategies

Reading Strategy:
Use Your Book for Success

Discuss When students are aware of the various components of their book, and how to use them, they are able to become more independent learners.

Extend As students work through Chapter 1, have them answer their own questions by discussing where they might find the answer in their book. Have students find the answer and share with the class.

Have students discuss other resources they might use to find answers to math questions. Answers may include Internet sites and dictionaries.

Answers to *Try This*

1. The distance of a number from zero on a number line

2. Skills Bank p. SB14

3. Selected Answers p. SA2

4. pp. 6, 180, and 485

SECTION 1A

Expressions and Integers

One-Minute Section Planner

Lesson	Lab Resources	Materials
Lesson 1-1 Evaluating Algebraic Expressions • Evaluate algebraic expressions. 🐻 **AF1.0, AF1.2, AF1.4**		**Optional** Index cards
Lesson 1-2 Writing Algebraic Expressions • Translate between algebraic expressions and word phrases. 🐻 **AF1.0, AF1.1**		**Optional** Index cards
Lesson 1-3 Integers and Absolute Value • Compare and order integers and simplify expressions containing absolute values. 🐻 **NS1.0, NS1.1, 🔑 NS2.5**		
Lesson 1-4 Adding Integers • Add integers. 🐻 **NS1.0, 🔑 NS1.2, 🔑 AF1.3**	**Hands-On Lab 1-4** In *Chapter 1 Resource File*	**Optional** Integer chips (MK)
Lesson 1-5 Subtracting Integers • Subtract integers. 🐻 🔑 **NS1.2, 🔑 NS2.5**		**Optional** Number line transparency
Lesson 1-6 Multiplying and Dividing Integers • Multiply and divide integers. 🐻 🔑 **NS1.2**	**Technology Lab 1-6** In *Chapter 1 Resource File*	

MK = *Manipulatives Kit*

Notes

_____

_____

_____

_____

_____

_____

_____

_____

_____

_____

Math Background: Teaching the Standards

THE TRANSITION FROM ARITHMETIC TO ALGEBRA
AF1.1, AF1.2, AF1.3, AF1.4
Lessons 1-1, 1-2

In the middle grades, students make the transition from arithmetic to algebra. An essential component of this transition is the understanding that a *variable,* such as the symbol *x,* represents a real number.

Students should begin to recognize the various ways in which variables are used. In Section A of Chapter 1, a variable is a placeholder that stands for a real number in an algebraic expression. If fabric costs $6 per yard, then the expression 6*x* gives the total cost of buying *x* yards of fabric. In this case, the expression may be evaluated by substituting any nonnegative real number for *x.*

Later, students begin to solve equations, such as 6*x* = 42. In these situations, students should understand that *x* represents a specific real number that when multiplied by 6 equals 42. One of the major objectives in the transition to algebra is to develop techniques to find the value or values of the variable that make an equation true.

ORDER OF OPERATIONS AF1.2
Lesson 1-1

The *order of operations* is a convention that ensures that every numerical expression has a unique, agreed-upon value. In particular, the operations in an expression must be carried out in the following order:
1. Parentheses (or other grouping symbols)
2. Exponents
3. Multiplication and division from left to right
4. Addition and subtraction from left to right

Thus, to simplify 5 + 3 · 4, the operation of multiplication takes precedence over addition, and the value of the expression is 5 + 12 = 17, not 8 · 4 = 32.

When the order of operations is followed, the expressions 5 + 3 · 4, 5 + 4 · 3, 3 · 4 + 5, and 4 · 3 + 5 all have the same value. If the operations are simply carried out left to right, the expressions yield different results.

ABSOLUTE VALUE NS2.5
Lesson 1-3

The *absolute value* of a real number is the number's distance from 0 on a number line. Since distance is always nonnegative, absolute value is always nonnegative. Students sometimes think of absolute value as "a number without its sign." While this gives a viable means of finding the absolute value of a real number, students should understand the concept's broader applications, which will be useful when they learn about complex numbers.

Because absolute value measures *magnitude* (that is, how far a real number is from 0), it can be used to measure how far apart two numbers are from each other. For two numbers *a* and *b*, |*a* − *b*| gives the distance between *a* and *b*. Thus, absolute value measures the "closeness" of two numbers, and the statement "*a* and *b* are close to each other" may be expressed mathematically by stating that |*a* − *b*| is small.

INTEGER OPERATIONS NS1.2
Lessons 1-4 through 1-6

Students can develop rules for integer arithmetic by modeling the operations on a number line. However, students should also realize that the rules arise from basic principles. For example, the fact that negative times positive is negative may be derived from the fundamental idea that for any number *x*, the *opposite* of *x*, written −*x*, is the unique number for which $x + (-x) = 0$.

For any positive numbers *a* and *b*, the Distributive Property (*Lesson 3-1*) shows that

$$a \cdot b + (-a \cdot b) = [a + (-a)] \cdot b = 0 \cdot b = 0.$$

Since the sum of *a* · *b* and −*a* · *b* is 0, −*a* · *b* must be the opposite of *a* · *b*. In other words, $-a \cdot b = -(a \cdot b)$. Applying the rule with specific numbers shows that $-2 \cdot 7 = -(2 \cdot 7) = -14$.

Other rules of integer arithmetic may be derived in a similar fashion.

Objective: Students evaluate algebraic expressions.

 Online Edition
Tutorial Videos, Interactivities

 Countdown to Mastery Week 1

Power Presentations
with PowerPoint®

Warm Up

Simplify.
1. $21 - 2(3)$ — 15
2. $4 + 3 \cdot 9$ — 31
3. $2(9) + (3)$ — 21
4. $6(1.4) + 12$ — 20.4
5. $7(2.9) - 5$ — 15.3

Also available on transparency

Math Humor

Overheard in math class:
Teacher: What is $7Q$ plus $3Q$?
Student: $10Q$
Teacher: You're welcome!

 California Standards

AF1.2 Use the correct order of operations to evaluate algebraic expressions such as $3(2x + 5)^2$.
AF1.4 Use algebraic terminology (e.g., **variable**, equation, term, coefficient, inequality, **expression**, constant) **correctly.**

Vocabulary
expression
variable
numerical expression
algebraic expression
evaluate

Why learn this? You can evaluate an expression to convert a temperature from degrees Celsius to degrees Fahrenheit. (See Example 3.)

An **expression** is a mathematical phrase that contains operations, numbers, and/or *variables*. A **variable** is a letter that represents a value that can change or vary. There are two types of expressions: *numerical* and *algebraic*.

A **numerical expression** does not contain variables.

An **algebraic expression** contains one or more variables.

Numerical Expressions		Algebraic Expressions	
$3 + 2$	$4(5)$	$x + 2$	$4n$
$27 - 18$	$\frac{3}{4}$	$p - r$	$\frac{x}{4}$

To **evaluate** an algebraic expression, substitute a given number for the variable. Then use the order of operations to find the value of the resulting numerical expression.

EXAMPLE 1 Evaluating Algebraic Expressions with One Variable

Evaluate each expression for the given value of the variable.

A $x + 5$ for $x = 11$
$11 + 5$ — *Substitute 11 for x.*
16 — *Add.*

Remember!

Order of Operations
PEMDAS:
1. Parentheses
2. Exponents
3. Multiply and Divide from left to right.
4. Add and Subtract from left to right.

See Skills Bank p. SB14.

B $2a + 3$ for $a = 4$
$2(4) + 3$ — *Substitute 4 for a.*
$8 + 3$ — *Multiply.*
11 — *Add.*

C $4(3 + n) - 2$ for $n = 0, 1, 2$

n	Substitute	Parentheses	Multiply	Subtract
0	$4(3 + 0) - 2$	$4(3) - 2$	$12 - 2$	10
1	$4(3 + 1) - 2$	$4(4) - 2$	$16 - 2$	14
2	$4(3 + 2) - 2$	$4(5) - 2$	$20 - 2$	18

---

1 Introduce
Alternate Opener

EXPLORATION

1-1 Evaluating Algebraic Expressions

Catherine's dance team is planning a spring trip to the coast. Catherine is saving money in a bank account to pay for the trip. Her parents started her account with $100. She sells Christmas plants and adds $2.50 to her account for each plant she sells.
How much will be in her account if she sells 50 plants?

(Initial amount) (Price × number of plants)
$100 + 2.5n$

Evaluate the expression $100 + 2.5n$ by substituting 50 for n.
$100 + 2.5(50)$
$100 + 125$
225

There will be $225.00 in Catherine's account if she sells 50 plants.

Evaluate the expression $100 + 2.5n$ for each value of n.
1. $n = 10$ — $100 + 2.5(10)$
2. $n = 25$ — $100 + 2.5(\ \ )$
3. $n = 75$ — $100 + 2.5(\ \ )$

Think and Discuss
4. **Explain** what n represents.
5. **Describe** how you evaluated the expression for different values of n.

Motivate

ENGLISH LANGUAGE LEARNERS

Ask students for the meaning of the word *variable* in a context such as the following: "The air temperature in the desert was quite *variable* yesterday; it was cold overnight and warm during the day." Explain that the word *variable* has the same meaning in mathematics. A variable is a symbol for a quantity that is not fixed or not yet known, such as x.

Explorations and answers are provided in *Alternate Openers: Explorations Transparencies.*

 **California Standards**

Algebra and Functions 1.2 and 1.4
Also covered:
Algebra and Functions
1.0 Students express quantitative relationships by using algebraic terminology, expressions, equations, inequalities, and graphs.

EXAMPLE 2 Evaluating Algebraic Expressions with Two Variables

Evaluate each expression for the given values of the variables.

A $5x + 2y$ for $x = 13$ and $y = 11$

$5(13) + 2(11)$	*Substitute 13 for x and 11 for y.*
$65 + 22$	*Multiply.*
87	*Add.*

B $p(24 - q)$ for $p = 8$ and $q = 17$

$8(24 - 17)$	*Substitute 8 for p and 17 for q.*
$8(7)$	*Simplify within parentheses.*
56	*Multiply.*

EXAMPLE 3 *Science Application*

If c is a temperature in degrees Celsius, then $1.8c + 32$ can be used to find the temperature in degrees Fahrenheit. Convert each temperature from degrees Celsius to degrees Fahrenheit.

A freezing point of water: 0°C

$1.8c + 32$	
$1.8(0) + 32$	*Substitute 0 for c.*
$0 + 32$	*Multiply.*
32	*Add.*

$0°C = 32°F$

Water freezes at 32°F.

B highest recorded temperature in the United States: 57°C

$1.8c + 32$	
$1.8(57) + 32$	*Substitute 57 for c.*
$102.6 + 32$	*Multiply.*
134.6	*Add.*

$57°C = 134.6°F$

The highest recorded temperature in the United States is 134.6°F.

Think and Discuss

1. **Give an example** of a numerical expression and of an algebraic expression.

2. **Tell** how to evaluate an algebraic expression for a given value of a variable.

3. **Explain** why you cannot find a numerical value for the expression $4x - 5y$ for $x = 3$.

Possible answers to
Think and Discuss:

1. algebraic: $x + 1$; not algebraic: $25 + 9$

2. Substitute the given value for the variable, and then find the value of the resulting numerical expression.

3. The y-value is not given.

2 Teach

Guided Instruction

In this lesson, students learn to evaluate algebraic expressions. Explain that to evaluate an algebraic expression, students must replace variables with given numbers and then evaluate the resulting expression by using the order of operations.

 **Reading Math** Remind students that when there is a number in front of a variable, multiplication is indicated. Therefore, when they replace the variable with a value, they need to insert parentheses. For example, the expression $3x + 4$ should be written $3(5) + 4$ if x is replaced with 5.

Universal Access

 Through Cooperative Learning

Have students work in pairs. Each student should write an algebraic expression, such as $3x - 1$ or $x + 5$, on a sheet of paper. The students should evaluate their partner's expression when the variable is equal to 0, 1, 2, 3, 4, and 5. Have them check each other's work and compare the values to determine whether the expressions have the same value for the given value of the variable.

3 Close

Summarize

Ask the students to decide which of the following is a variable: your age (variable); the year in which you were born (not a variable).

Have the students suggest additional examples of variables.

Ask the students if an algebraic expression contains one or more variables (yes).

Ask the students if they would expect to see any variables in an expression after evaluating that expression. Why or why not?

Possible answer: No; because to evaluate an algebraic expression, you must replace the variables with numbers.

1-1 Exercises

California Standards Practice
AF1.2, AF1.4

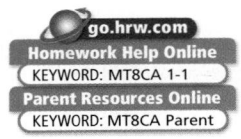
go.hrw.com
Homework Help Online
KEYWORD: MT8CA 1-1
Parent Resources Online
KEYWORD: MT8CA Parent

Assignment Guide

If you finished Example **1** assign:
Proficient 1–3, 10–12, 19–23, 50, 53–64
Advanced 10–12, 21–27, 50, 53–64

If you finished Example **2** assign:
Proficient 1–5, 10–14, 19–23, 28–36, 50, 53–64
Advanced 10–14, 24–27, 36–43, 48–50, 53–64

If you finished Example **3** assign:
Proficient 1–23, 28–36, 46–48, 50–64
Advanced 10–18, 24–27, 36–64

Homework Quick Check

Quickly check key concepts.
Exercises: 10, 12, 14, 16, 36

Math Background

François Viète (1540–1603) was a lawyer in France who devoted his spare time to mathematics. In his book *In Artem,* he introduced the idea of representing unknown quantities using vowels and constants using consonants. He also used our present symbols + and − but had no symbol for equality. To write "equals" he would use the Latin word *aequatur.*

Viète is sometimes called the Father of Algebra.

GUIDED PRACTICE

See Example **1** Evaluate each expression for the given value of the variable.
  1. $x + 4$ for $x = 11$ **15**
  2. $2a + 7$ for $a = 7$ **21**
  3. $2(4 + n) - 5$ for $n = 0$ **3**

See Example **2** Evaluate each expression for the given values of the variables.
  4. $3x + 2y$ for $x = 8$ and $y = 10$ **44**
  5. $5r - (12 + p)$ for $p = 15$ and $r = 9$ **18**

See Example **3** If c is the number of cups of water needed to make papier-mâché paste, then $\frac{1}{4}c$ can be used to find the number of cups of flour needed. Find the number of cups of flour needed for each number of cups of water.
  6. 12 cups **3 c**
  7. 8 cups **2 c**
  8. 7 cups **$1\frac{3}{4}$ c**
  9. 10 cups **$2\frac{1}{2}$ c**

INDEPENDENT PRACTICE

See Example **1** Evaluate each expression for the given value of the variable.
  10. $x + 7$ for $x = 23$ **30**
  11. $7t + 2$ for $t = 5$ **37**
  12. $4(3 + k) - 7$ for $k = 0$ **5**

See Example **2** Evaluate each expression for the given values of the variables.
  13. $4x + 7y$ for $x = 9$ and $y = 3$ **57**
  14. $4m - 2n$ for $m = 25$ and $n = 2.5$ **95**

See Example **3** If c is the number of cups, then $\frac{1}{2}c$ can be used to find the number of pints. Find the number of pints for each of the following.
  15. 26 cups **13 pt**
  16. 12 cups **6 pt**
  17. 20 cups **10 pt**
  18. 34 cups **17 pt**

PRACTICE AND PROBLEM SOLVING

Extra Practice
See page EP2.

Evaluate each expression for the given value of the variable.
19. $30 - n$ for $n = 8$ **22**
20. $x + 4.3$ for $x = 6$ **10.3**
21. $5t + 5$ for $t = 1$ **10**

22. $11 - 6m$ for $m = 0$ **11**
23. $3a - 4$ for $a = 8$ **20**
24. $4g + 5$ for $g = 12$ **53**

25. $4y + 2$ for $y = 3.5$ **16**
26. $18 - 3y$ for $y = 6$ **0**
27. $3(z + 9)$ for $z = 6$ **45**

Evaluate each expression for $t = 0, x = 1.5, y = 6,$ and $z = 23$.
28. $3z - 3y$ **51**
29. yz **138**
30. $1.4z - y$ **26.2**
31. $4.2y - 3x$ **20.7**

32. $4(y - x)$ **18**
33. $4(3 + y)$ **36**
34. $3(y - 6) + 8$ **8**
35. $4(2 + z) + 5$ **105**

36. $5(4 + t)$ **6** **14**
37. $y(3 + t)$ **7** **11**
38. $x + y + z$ **30.5**
39. $10x + z - y$ **32**

40. $4(z - 5t) + 3$ **95**
41. $2y + 6(x + t)$ **21**
42. $8txz$ **0**
43. $2z - 3xy$ **19**

44. A rectangular shape has a length-to-width ratio of approximately 5 to 3. A designer can use the expression $\frac{1}{3}(5w)$ to find the length of such a rectangle with a given width w. Find the length of such a rectangle with width 6 inches. **10 in.**

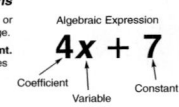

45. Finance A bank charges interest on money it loans. Interest is sometimes a fixed amount of the loan. The expression $a(1 + i)$ gives the total amount due for a loan of a dollars with interest rate i, where i is written as a decimal. Find the amount due for a loan of $100 with an interest rate of 10%. (*Hint:* 10% = 0.1) **$110**

46. Entertainment There are 24 frames, or still shots, in one second of movie footage. To determine the number of frames in a movie, you can use the expression $(24)(60)m$, where m is the running time in minutes. Using the running time of *E.T. the Extra-Terrestrial* shown at right, determine how many frames are in the movie. **165,600 frames**

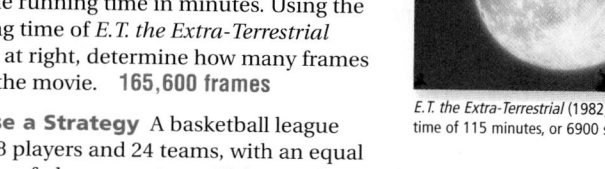

E.T. the Extra-Terrestrial (1982) has a running time of 115 minutes, or 6900 seconds.

47. Choose a Strategy A basketball league has 288 players and 24 teams, with an equal number of players per team. If the number of teams is reduced by 6 but the total number of players stays the same, there will be ____?____ players per team.

Ⓐ 6 more   Ⓑ 4 more   Ⓒ 4 fewer   Ⓓ 6 fewer

48. Write About It A student says that the algebraic expression $5 + x \cdot 7$ can also be written as $5 + 7x$. Is the student correct? Explain.

49. Challenge Can the expressions $2x$ and $x + 2$ ever have the same value? If so, what must the value of x be?
Yes; when $x = 2$, both expressions have a value of 4.

SPIRAL STANDARDS REVIEW
AF1.2

50. Multiple Choice What is the value of the expression $3x + 4$ for $x = 2$?

Ⓐ 4   Ⓑ 6   Ⓒ 9   Ⓓ 10

51. Multiple Choice A bakery charges $7 for a dozen muffins and $2 for a loaf of bread. If a customer bought 2 dozen muffins and 4 loaves of bread, how much did she pay?

Ⓐ $22   Ⓑ $38   Ⓒ $80   Ⓓ $98

52. Gridded Response What is the value of $5(x - y)$ for $x = 19$ and $y = 6$? **65**

Identify the odd number(s) in each list of numbers. (Previous course)

53. 15, 18, 22, 34, 21, 61, 71, 100   **15, 21, 61, 71**   **54.** 101, 114, 122, 411, 117, 121
                                                           101, 411, 117, 121

55. 4, 6, 8, 16, 18, 20, 49, 81, 32   **49, 81**   **56.** 9, 15, 31, 47, 65, 93, 1, 3, 43   **All are odd.**

Find each sum, difference, product, or quotient. (Previous course)

57. 200 + 2   **202**   **58.** 200 ÷ 2   **100**   **59.** 200 · 2   **400**   **60.** 200 − 2   **198**

61. 200 + 0.2   **200.2**   **62.** 200 ÷ 0.2   **1000**   **63.** 200 · 0.2   **40**   **64.** 200 − 0.2   **199.8**

CHALLENGE 1-1

LESSON 1-1 Challenge
Etaulave: Evaluate Backwards

Expression	Value for Variable	Substitution	Value of Expression
2x + 5	1	2(1) + 5	7
2x + 5	2	2(2) + 5	9
2x + 5	3	2(3) + 5	11

In the table above you use the values of the variable to evaluate the given expression. What if you are given the values of the expression and the values of the variable? How can you work backward to determine the expression?

Expression	Value for Variable	Substitution	Value of Expression
	1		5
	2		8
	3		11

Complete the following statements.

1. As the values of the variable increase by 1, the values of the expression increase _____**by 3**_____.

2. Because the values of the expression depend on the values of the variables, your answer to Question 1 tells you the ____**coefficient**____ of the variable.

3. Using the coefficient and the variable x, you know that ___**3x**___ is part of the expression.

4. After each value of the variable is multiplied by ___**3**___, you still need to ___**add 2**___ to get the value of the expression.

Write the expression given the values of x and their corresponding values of the expression.

5. The values of the expression are 12, 14, 16, 18, 20 when x = 10, 11, 12, 13, and 14.
___**2x − 8**___

6. The values of the expression are 50, 45, 40, 35, 30 when x = 2, 3, 4, 5, and 6.
___**60 − 5x**___

PROBLEM SOLVING 1-1

LESSON 1-1 Problem Solving
Evaluating Algebraic Expressions

Write the correct answer.

1. If *l* is the length of a room and *w* is the width, then *lw* can be used to find the area of the room. Find the area of a room with *l* = 10 ft and *w* = 15 ft.

___**150 square feet**___

2. If *l* is the length of a room and *w* is the width, 2*l* + 2*w* can be used to find the perimeter of the room. Find the perimeter of a room with *l* = 12 ft and *w* = 16 ft.

___**56 feet**___

3. Jaime earns 20% commission on her sales. If *s* is her total sales, then 0.2*s* can be used to find the amount she earns in commission. Find her commission if her sales are $1200.

___**$240**___

4. If *p* is the regular hourly rate of pay, then 1.5*p* can be used to find the overtime rate of pay. Find the overtime rate of pay if the regular hourly rate of pay is $6.00 per hour.

___**$9.00 per hour**___

Choose the letter for the best answer.

5. A plumber charges a fee of $75 per service call plus $15 per hour. If *h* is the number of hours the plumber works, then 75 + 15*h* can be used to find the total charges. Find the total charges if the plumber works 2.5 hours.
   A $37.50
   Ⓑ $112.50
   C $225
   D $1127.50

6. Tickets to the movies cost $4 for students and $6 for adults. If *s* is the number of students and *a* is the number of adults, 4*s* + 6*a* can be used to find the cost of the tickets. Find the cost of the tickets for 3 students and 2 adults.
   F $15
   G $17
   Ⓗ $24
   J $26

7. If *c* is the number of cricket chirps in a minute, then the expression 0.25*c* + 20 can be used to estimate the temperature in degrees Farenheit. If there are 92 cricket chirps in a minute, find the temperature.
   Ⓐ 43 degrees
   B 33 degrees
   C 102 degrees
   D 75 degrees

8. Flowers are sold in flats of 6 plants each. If *f* is the number of flats, then 6*f* can be used to find the number of flowers. Find the number of flowers in 18 flats.
   F 3 flowers
   Ⓖ 108 flowers
   H 24 flowers
   J 12 flowers

Answers

48. Possible answer: The student is correct. In both expressions, *x* and 7 would be multiplied before adding 5.

Teaching Tip **Multiple Choice** For **Exercise 50**, remind students that a number and a variable written next to one another without an operation symbol imply *multiplication*. Students who answered **C** used addition; they added 3, 2, and 4, as opposed to multiplying 3 by 2, and then adding 4. Ask students to determine which terms are multiplied and which are added or subtracted in similar expressions, such as in **Exercise 52.**

Journal

Have students write at least three examples of variables (quantities that change value) from their everyday lives.

Power Presentations with PowerPoint®

1-1 Lesson Quiz

Evaluate each expression for the given value(s) of the variables.

1. $6x + 9$ for $x = 3$ 27
2. $x + 14$ for $x = 8$ 22
3. $4x + 3y$ for $x = 2$, $y = 3$ 17
4. $y(27 - x)$ for $x = 19$, $y = 6$ 48
5. If *n* is the amount of money in a savings account, then the expression $n + 0.03n$ can be used to find the amount in the account after it has earned interest for one year. Find the total in the account after one year if $500 is the initial amount. **$515**

Also available on transparency

Online Edition
Tutorial Videos

Countdown to Mastery Week 1

Power Presentations
with PowerPoint®

Warm Up

Evaluate each expression for the given values of the variables.

1. $9y - 13$ for $y = 4$ 23

2. $6n + 2p$ for $n = 2$ and $p = 3$ 18

3. $3x - y$ for $x = 1$ and $y = 2$ 1

Which operation symbol goes with each word?

4. Sum $+$ **5.** Product $\times$

6. Quotient $\div$ **7.** Difference $-$

Also available on transparency

Math Humor

It was impossible to know what sort of mood the equation was in; it had a variable expression.

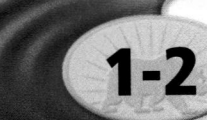

1-2 Writing Algebraic Expressions

Who uses this? Advertisers can write an algebraic expression to represent the cost of airing a commercial a given number of times. (See Example 3.)

To use algebra to solve real-world problems, you may need to translate word phrases into mathematical symbols.

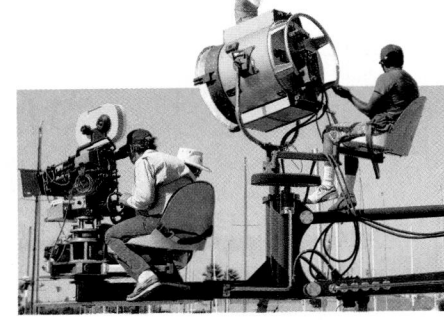

Sixty-eight different commercials aired during the 2005 Super Bowl.

	Word Phrases	Expression
+	• add 5 to a number • sum of a number and 5 • 5 more than a number	$n + 5$
−	• subtract 11 from a number • difference of a number and 11 • 11 less than a number	$x - 11$
✕	• 3 multiplied by a number • product of 3 and a number	$3 \cdot m$ or $3m$
÷	• 7 divided into a number • quotient of a number and 7	$\frac{a}{7}$ or $a \div 7$

EXAMPLE 1   **Translating Word Phrases into Math Expressions**

Write an algebraic expression for each word phrase.

A 4 times the difference of a number n and 2

   4 **times** the **difference of** n and 2

   4    $\cdot$ $(n - 2)$

   $4(n - 2)$

B 1 more than the product of 12 and p

   1 **more than** the **product of** 12 and p

   $(12 \cdot p)$ $+$ 1

   $12p + 1$

Caution! //////

Addition is commutative, so order does not matter in Example 1B. $1 + 12p$ and $12p + 1$ are both correct. Subtraction is not commutative, so "1 less than the product of 12 and p" is written as $12p - 1$, not $1 - 12p$.

---

1 Introduce

Alternate Opener

EXPLORATION

1-2 Writing Algebraic Expressions

The table shows the prices for different activities at a park.

Activity	Price
Park ride	$1.25 per ride
Jet ski rental	$25.00 + $5.00 per hour
Scooter rental	$10.00 + $2.50 per hour
Bike rental	$5.00 + $2.00 per hour
Bay cruise	$25.00 per person

An algebraic expression for this cost is 1.25r.

Use a variable to write an expression for each cost.

	Activity	Cost	Variable	Expression
	Park ride	$1.25 per ride	r (rides)	1.25r
1.	Jet ski rental	$25.00 + $5.00 per hour	h (hours)	
2.	Scooter rental	$10.00 + $2.50 per hour	h (hours)	
3.	Bike rental	$5.00 + $2.00 per hour	h (hours)	
4.	Bay cruise	$25.00 per person	p (people)	

To find the cost of renting a jet ski for 5 hours, evaluate the expression $25 + 5h$ by substituting 5 for h.

$$25 + 5(5) = 25 + 25 = 50$$

5. Use your expressions from above to evaluate the cost of a 5-hour scooter rental and of a 5-hour bike rental.

Think and Discuss

6. Describe a real-world situation in which you might use the expression $50 + 2x$.

7. Explain why $50 + 2x$ is an algebraic expression.

Motivate

Ask the students if any of them speak a language other than English. Ask volunteers to translate simple expressions, such as "hello" or "how are you?" into another language. Explain that in this lesson, they will learn how to "translate" words into algebraic expressions.

Explorations and answers are provided in *Alternate Openers: Explorations Transparencies.*

EXAMPLE 2 Translating Math Expressions into Word Phrases

Write a word phrase for the algebraic expression $4 - 7b$.

$$4 \quad - \quad 7 \quad \cdot \quad b$$

4 **minus** the **product of** 7 and b

4 minus the product of 7 and b

To solve a word problem, first interpret the action you need to perform and then choose the correct operation for that action.

EXAMPLE 3 Writing and Evaluating Expressions in Word Problems

Helpful Hint

When a word problem involves groups of equal size, use multiplication or division. Otherwise, use addition or subtraction.

A company aired its 30-second commercial during Super Bowl XXXIX at a cost of $2.4 million each time. Write an algebraic expression to determine what the cost would be if the commercial had aired n times. Then evaluate the expression for 2, 3, and 4 times.

$2.4 million \cdot n$ *Combine n equal amounts of $2.4 million.*

$2.4n$ *Cost in millions of dollars*

n	$2.4n$	Cost
2	2.4(2)	$4.8 million
3	2.4(3)	$7.2 million
4	2.4(4)	$9.6 million

Evaluate for n = 2, 3, and 4.

EXAMPLE 4 Writing a Word Problem from a Math Expression

Write a word problem that can be evaluated by the algebraic expression $14,917 + m$. Then evaluate the expression for $m = 633$.

At the beginning of the month, Benny's car had 14,917 miles on the odometer. If Benny drove m miles during the month, how many miles were on the odometer at the end of the month?

$14,917 + m$

$14,917 + 633 = 15,550$ *Substitute 633 for m.*

The car had 15,550 miles on the odometer at the end of the month.

Possible answers to Think and Discuss

1. plus, add; less than, minus; times, multiplied by; divided by; quotient of

2. the sum of 5 and 7 times n; 5 plus the product of 7 and n

Think and Discuss

1. **Give** two words or phrases that can be used to express each operation: addition, subtraction, multiplication, and division.

2. **Express** $5 + 7n$ in words in at least two different ways.

---

2 Teach

Guided Instruction

In this lesson, students learn to write algebraic expressions. Review the table of phrases and expressions with students (Teaching Transparency). Point out that there are several different words for each operation.

While reviewing the word problems in **Examples 3** and **4**, make sure students can identify the action that determines the operation(s) that will be used to solve the problem. You may want to spend extra time to review the additional examples, as well.

Universal Access
Through Concrete Manipulatives

Give each pair of students a few flash cards with a word phrase on one side and the corresponding algebraic expression on the other (Lesson Transparencies). Have them place the cards, word phrase side up, between them. Students then take turns writing an algebraic expression for the word phrase. If the expression is correct, the student keeps the card. If not, the card is returned to the bottom of the deck. When the entire deck is gone, or when time is called, the student with the most cards wins.

3 Close

Summarize

Write the four operational symbols $(+, -, \times, \div)$ on the board, and ask students to think of as many words as they can to represent each one. Remind students that "translating" will help them solve many types of word problems.

Possible answers: addition: sum, added, more than, total, increased, plus; subtraction: difference, less than, minus, decrease, take away; multiplication: times, product, multiplied, each; division: divided, split, quotient, separated

---

Assignment Guide

If you finished Example ① assign:
Proficient 1–4, 11–15, 22–31, 41–42, 44–48
Advanced 11–15, 22–31, 44–48, 37–38, 40–42

If you finished Example ② assign:
Proficient 1–8, 11–19, 22–35, 41–42, 44–48
Advanced 11–19, 22–35, 44–48, 37–38, 40–42

If you finished Example ③ assign:
Proficient 1–9, 11–20, 22–36, 41–48
Advanced 11–20, 22–38, 40–48

If you finished Example ④ assign:
Proficient 1–36, 41–48
Advanced 11–48

Homework Quick Check

Quickly check key concepts.
Exercises: 12, 14, 16, 18, 20

Answers

5. 18 plus the product of 43 and s
6. 37 less than the quotient of 22 and r
7. 10 plus the quotient of y and 31
8. the product of 29 and b minus 93
10. Possible answer: Calvin has 450 fewer songs on his MP3 player than his friend Brian. How many songs does Calvin have on his MP3 player if Brian has 1325 songs? 875 songs
20. $\frac{1680}{n}$; $168, $140, $120, $105
16–19, 21. See p. A1.

Math Background

The Egyptians had different symbols for addition and subtraction than those that are used today. The symbol for addition was two feet walking from right to left, which was the direction in which the Egyptians wrote. The symbol for subtraction was a pair of legs walking in the opposite direction, left to right.

California Standards

Standard	Exercises
NS1.2 🔑	44–46
AF1.1	1–43
AF1.2	36, 47–48

California Standards Practice
AF1.1, AF1.2

go.hrw.com
Homework Help Online
KEYWORD: MT8CA 1-2
Parent Resources Online
KEYWORD: MT8CA Parent

GUIDED PRACTICE

See Example ① Write an algebraic expression for each word phrase.
1. 5 less than the product of 3 and p $3p - 5$
2. 77 more than the product of 2 and u $2u + 77$
3. 16 more than the quotient of d and 7 $\frac{d}{7} + 16$
4. 6 minus the quotient of u and 2 $6 - \frac{u}{2}$

See Example ② Write a word phrase for each algebraic expression.
5. $18 + 43s$ **6.** $\frac{22}{r} - 37$ **7.** $10 + \frac{y}{31}$ **8.** $29b - 93$

See Example ③ **9.** Mark is going to work for his father's pool cleaning business during the summer. Mark's father will pay him $5 for each pool he helps clean. Write an algebraic expression to determine how much Mark will earn if he cleans n pools. Then evaluate the expression for 15, 25, 35, or 45 pools. $5n$; $75, $125, $175, $225

See Example ④ **10.** Write a word problem that can be evaluated by the algebraic expression $x - 450$. Then evaluate the expression for $x = 1325$.

INDEPENDENT PRACTICE

See Example ① Write an algebraic expression for each word phrase.
11. $\frac{5}{n} + 1$
11. 1 more than the quotient of 5 and n
12. 2 minus the product of 3 and p $2 - 3p$
13. 45 less than the product of 78 and j $78j - 45$
14. 4 plus the quotient of r and 5 $4 + \frac{r}{5}$
15. 14 more than the product of 59 and q $59q + 14$

See Example ② Write a word phrase for each algebraic expression.
16. $142 - 19t$ **17.** $16g + 12$ **18.** $14 + \frac{5}{d}$ **19.** $\frac{w}{182} - 51$

See Example ③ **20.** A community center is trying to raise $1680 to purchase exercise equipment. The center is hoping to receive equal contributions from members of the community. Write an algebraic expression to determine how much will be needed from each person if n people contribute. Then evaluate the expression for 10, 12, 14, or 16 people.

See Example ④ **21.** Write a word problem that can be evaluated by the algebraic expression $372 + r$. Then evaluate the expression for $r = 137$.

PRACTICE AND PROBLEM SOLVING

Extra Practice
See page EP2.

Write an algebraic expression for each word phrase.
22. 6 times the sum of 4 and y $6(4 + y)$
23. the product of 6 and y increased by 9 $6y + 9$
24. $\frac{1}{3}$ of the sum of 4 and p $\frac{1}{3}(4 + p)$
25. 1 divided by the sum of 3 and g $\frac{1}{3 + g}$
26. half the sum of m and 5 $\frac{1}{2}(m + 5)$
27. 6 less than the product of 13 and y $13y - 6$
28. 2 less than m divided by 8 $\frac{m}{8} - 2$
29. twice the quotient of m and 35 $2\left(\frac{m}{35}\right)$
30. $\frac{3}{4}$ of the difference of p and 7 $\frac{3}{4}(p - 7)$
31. 8 times the sum of $\frac{2}{3}$ and x $8\left(\frac{2}{3} + x\right)$

REVIEW FOR MASTERY 1-2

LESSON 1-2 Review for Mastery
Writing Algebraic Expressions

What words tell you to add, subtract, multiply, or divide?

Add $n + 6$	Subtract $n - 6$	Multiply $6n$	Divide $n \div 6$
n plus 6	n minus 6	n times 6	n divided by 6
the sum of n and 6	the difference between n and 6	the product of n and 6	the quotient of n and 6
6 added to n	6 subtracted from n	6 multiplied by n	6 equal shares of n
n increased by 6	6 less than n		
	n decreased by 6		

Write the algebraic expression that represents the word expression.

1. the quotient of n and 3 $n \div 3$
2. 3 more than n $n + 3$
3. the product of 3 and n $3n$
4. n decreased by 3 $n - 3$
5. 3 less than n $n - 3$
6. the product of n and 3 $3n$
7. n increased by 3 $n + 3$
8. one-third times n $\frac{1}{3}n$ or $n \div 3$

Write a word phrase for each algebraic expression.
Phrases may vary. Possible answers are shown.

9. $4n$ the product of 4 and n
10. $2 + n$ 2 increased by n
11. $n - 5$ 5 less than n
12. $n \div 3$ n divided by 3
13. $n + 9$ 9 more than n
14. $\frac{n}{2}$ the quotient of n and 2

PRACTICE 1-2

LESSON 1-2 Practice B
Writing Algebraic Expressions

Write an algebraic expression for each word phrase.

1. 6 less than twice x $2x - 6$
2. 1 more than the quotient of 21 and b $1 + \frac{21}{b}$
3. 3 times the sum of b and 5 $3(b + 5)$
4. 10 times the difference of d and 3 $10(d - 3)$
5. the sum of 11 times s and 3 $11s + 3$
6. 7 minus the product of 2 and x $7 - 2x$

Write a word phrase for each algebraic expression. Phrases may vary. Possible answers are shown.

7. $2n + 4$ 4 more than twice n
8. $3r - 1$ 1 less than the product of 3 and r
9. $10 - 6n$ the difference of 10 and 6 times n
10. $7 + \frac{2}{c}$ 7 more than 2 divided by c
11. $15x - 12$ 12 less than the product of 15 and x
12. $\frac{x}{5} + 8$ 8 more than the quotient of y and 5

13. Maddie earns $8 per hour. Write an algebraic expression to evaluate how much money Maddie will earn if she works for 15, 20, 25, or 30 hours.

n	8n	Earnings
15	8(15)	$120
20	8(20)	$160
25	8(25)	$200
30	8(30)	$240

14. Write a word problem that can be evaluated by the algebraic expression $y - 95$, and evaluate it for $y = 125$.

Possible answer: Marco has saved y dollars. He wants to buy a skateboard that costs $95. How much money will Marco have left after he buys the skateboard? $30

---

32. 3 less than the product of 4 and b

33. 8 times the sum of m and 5

34. 7 divided by the difference of 8 and x

35. 17 times the quotient of 16 and w

Translate each algebraic expression into words.

32. $4b - 3$ **33.** $8(m + 5)$ **34.** $\dfrac{7}{8 - x}$ **35.** $17\left(\dfrac{16}{w}\right)$

36. At age 2, a cat or a dog is considered 24 "human" years old. Each year after age 2 is equivalent to 4 "human" years. Let a represent the age of a cat or dog. Fill in the expression $[24 + \blacksquare(a - 2)]$ so that it represents the age of a cat or dog in "human" years. Copy the chart and use your expression to complete it. $24 + 4(a - 2)$; 24, 28, 32, 36, 40

Age	$24 + \blacksquare(a - 2)$	Age (human years)
2		
3		
4		
5		
6		

DO NOT WRITE IN BOOK

37. Reasoning Write two different algebraic expressions for the word phrase "$\frac{1}{4}$ the sum of x and 7." $\frac{1}{4}(x + 7)$ or $\dfrac{x + 7}{4}$

38. What's the Error? A student wrote an algebraic expression for "5 less than the quotient of n and 3" as $\frac{n-5}{3}$. What error did the student make?

39. Write About It Paul used addition to solve a word problem about the weekly cost of commuting by toll road for $1.50 each day. Fran solved the same problem by multiplying. They both got the correct answer. How is this possible?

40. Challenge Write an expression for the sum of 1 and twice a number n. If you let n be any number, will the result always be an odd number? Explain.

SPIRAL STANDARDS REVIEW   ⬅ NS1.2, AF1.1, AF1.2

41. Multiple Choice Which expression means "3 times the difference of y and 4"?

ⓐ $3 \cdot y - 4$ ⓑ $3 \cdot (y + 4)$ Ⓒ $3 \cdot (y - 4)$ ⓓ $3 - (y - 4)$

42. Multiple Choice Which expression represents the product of a number n and 32?

ⓐ $n + 32$ ⓑ $n - 32$ Ⓒ $n \cdot 32$ ⓓ $32 \div n$

43. Short Response A company prints n books at a cost of $9 per book. Write an expression to represent the total cost of printing n books. What is the total cost if 1050 books are printed? $9n$; $9450

Simplify. (Previous course)

44. $32 + 8 \div 4$ **34**   **45.** $24 - 2 \cdot 3 \div 6 + 1$ **24**   **46.** $(20 - 8) \cdot 2 + 2$ **26**

Evaluate each expression for the given value of the variable. (Lesson 1-1)

47. $2(4 + x) - 3$ for $x = 1$ **7**   **48.** $3(8 - x) - 2$ for $x = 2$ **16**

CHALLENGE 1-2

LESSON 1-2 Challenge
Amazing Math

Write an algebraic expression for each word phrase on the board. Evaluate each expression for $x = 2$.

Then find a path from the top row to the bottom row that gives a total of 22.

3 times x	1 less than twice x	6 more than x	x increased by 3	the quotient of twice x and 2
$3x = 6$	$2x - 1 = 3$	$x + 6 = 8$	$x + 3 = 5$	$\frac{2x}{2} = 2$
1 more than x	the product of 3 and x	x decreased by 1	half of x	twice x increased by 3
$x + 1 = 3$	$3x = 6$	$x - 1 = 1$	$\frac{x}{2} = 1$	$2x + 3 = 7$
1 less than 3 times x	the difference between 3 and x	the difference between 2 and x	the product of 4 and x	the sum of 6 and twice x
$3x - 1 = 5$	$3 - x = 1$	$2 - x = 0$	$4x = 8$	$6 + 2x = 10$
twice x	the difference between x and 1	the sum of x and 5	1 more than half of x	the product of 4 and 3 times x
$2x = 4$	$x - 1 = 1$	$x + 5 = 7$	$\frac{x}{2} + 1 = 2$	$4(3x) = 24$
x increased by 2	the quotient of x and 2	7 increased by x	the quotient of 6 and x	5 times x divided by 2
$x + 2 = 4$ 22	$\frac{x}{2} = 1$	$7 + x = 9$	$\frac{6}{x} = 3$	$\frac{5x}{2} = 5$

PROBLEM SOLVING 1-2

LESSON 1-2 Problem Solving
Writing Algebraic Expressions

Write the correct answer.

1. Morton bought 15 new books to add to his collection of books b. Write an algebraic expression to evaluate the total number of books in Morton's collection if he had 20 books in his collection.

$15 + b$; 35 books

2. Paul exercises m minutes per day 5 days a week. Write an algebraic expression to evaluate how many minutes Paul exercises each week if he exercises 45 minutes per day.

$5m$; 225 minutes

3. Helen bought 3 shirts that each cost s dollars. Write an algebraic expression to evaluate how much Helen spent in all if each shirt cost $22.

$3s$; $66

4. Claire makes b bracelets to divide evenly among four friends and herself. Write an algebraic expression to evaluate the number of bracelets each person will receive if Claire makes 15 bracelets.

$\frac{b}{5}$; 3 bracelets

Choose the letter for the best answer.

5. Jonas collects baseball cards. He has 245 cards in his collection. For his birthday, he received r more cards, then he gave his brother g cards. Which algebraic expression represents the total number of cards he now has in his collection?

A $245 + r + g$
B $245 - r - g$
Ⓒ $245 + r - g$
D $r + g - 245$

6. Monique is saving money for a computer. She has m dollars saved. For her birthday, her dad doubled her money, but then she spent s dollars on a shirt. Which algebraic expression represents the amount of money she has now saved for her computer?

F $m + 2 - s$
Ⓖ $2m - s$
H $2m + s$
J $m + 2s$

7. Which algebraic expression represents the number of years in m months?

A $12m$
Ⓑ $\frac{m}{12}$
C $12 + m$
D $12 - m$

8. Which algebraic expression represents how many minutes are in h hours?

Ⓕ $60h$
G $\frac{h}{60}$
H $h + 60$
J $h - 60$

FORMATIVE ASSESSMENT
and INTERVENTION ⬅ ➡

Diagnose Before the Lesson
1-2 Warm Up, TE p. 10

Monitor During the Lesson
1-2 Know-It Notebook
1-2 Questioning Strategies

Assess After the Lesson
1-2 Lesson Quiz, TE p. 13

Answers

38. Possible answer: The student wrote an expression for "the quotient of n minus 5 and 3." The correct expression is $\frac{n}{3} - 5$.

39. Possible answer: Multiplication is repeated addition, so either operation can be used to solve the problem. Adding the cost 5 times or multiplying the cost by 5 will give the correct answer.

40. $1 + 2n$; yes; twice any number is always an even number, and adding 1 to an even number always results in an odd number.

Teaching Tip **Short Response** Students may misinterpret "per" in **Exercise 43** and write the expression $9 \div n$. Explain that the total cost is the cost per book multiplied by the number of books.

Journal

Ask students to write why they think that mathematics is often called the universal language.

Power Presentations with PowerPoint®

✓ 1-2 Lesson Quiz

Write an algebraic expression for each word phrase.

1. 5 less than a number k $k - 5$

2. a number x divided by 11 $\frac{x}{11}$

3. 4 times the sum of n and 5 $4(n + 5)$

Write an algebraic expression to evaluate the word problem.

4. Karen buys n raffle tickets for $0.50 each. If she buys 13 of them, how much will they cost? $0.50n$; $6.50

Also available on transparency

Objective: Students compare and order integers and simplify expressions containing absolute values.

 Online Edition
Tutorial Videos

 Countdown to Mastery Week 1

Power Presentations with PowerPoint®

Warm Up

Evaluate each expression for the given values of the variables.

1. $2x - 3y$ for $x = 17$ and $y = 6$ **16**

2. $5(x + 3) + 4y$ for $x = 3$ and $y = 2$ **38**

3. $6.9(x - 2.7) + 7.1$ for $x = 5.1$ **23.66**

4. $5x - 4y$ for $x = 0.3$ and $y = 0.2$ **0.7**

Also available on transparency

Math Humor

Teacher: Why are you looking at the back of your paper?

Student: I'm looking for the opposite side of the number line!

 **California Standards**

Number Sense 2.5

Also covered:

Number Sense

1.1 Read, write, and compare rational numbers in scientific notation (positive and negative powers of 10), **compare rational numbers in general.**

Number Sense

1.0 Students know the properties of, and compute with, **rational numbers expressed in a variety of forms.**

 1-3 Integers and Absolute Value

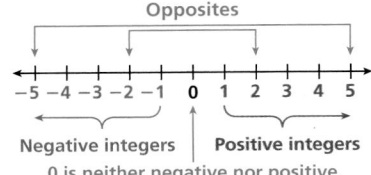 **California Standards**

NS2.5 Understand the meaning of the absolute value of a number; interpret the absolute value as the distance of the number from zero on a number line; and determine the absolute value of real numbers.
Also covered: **NS1.1**

Vocabulary
integer
opposite
absolute value

Why learn this? You can use integers to represent scores in disc golf.

In disc golf, a player throws a disc toward a target, or "hole," in as few throws as possible. The expected number of throws to complete an entire course is called "par." A player's score can be written as an *integer* to show how many throws he or she is above or below par.

If you complete a course in 5 fewer throws than par your score is 5 under par, or −5. If you complete the same course in 4 more throws than par your score is 4 over par, or 4.

Integers are the set of whole numbers and their *opposites*. **Opposites** are numbers that are the same distance from 0 on a number line, but on opposite sides of 0.

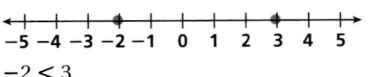

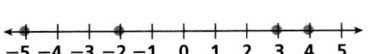

0 is neither negative nor positive.

EXAMPLE 1 **Sports Application**

After one round of disc golf, the scores are Fred −5, Trevor 3, Monique 4, and Julie −2.

Remember!

Numbers on a number line increase in value as you move from left to right.

A Use <, >, or = to compare Trevor's and Julie's scores.

Trevor's score is 3, and Julie's score is −2.

Place the scores on a number line.

$-2 < 3$ *−2 is to the left of 3.*

Julie's score is less then Trevor's.

B List the golfers in order from the lowest score to the highest.

The scores are −5, 3, 4, and −2.

Place the scores on a number line and read them from left to right.

In order from the lowest score to the highest, the golfers are Fred, Julie, Trevor, and Monique.

---

1 Introduce
Alternate Opener

EXPLORATION

1-3 Integers and Absolute Value

You can use a number line to find the distance of a number from 0. For example, to find the distance of −3 from 0, start at −3 and count the number of units until you get to 0.

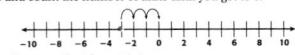

The distance of −3 from 0 is 3.

1. Use a number line to find the distance of each number from 0.
   a. 2
   b. 5
   c. 8
   d. 10
   e. 0

2. Use a number line to find the distance of each number from 0.
   a. −2
   b. −5
   c. −8
   d. −10

Think and Discuss

3. **Describe** any patterns you notice in your results.
4. **Explain** whether it is possible for the distance of a number from 0 to be negative.

Motivate

Ask students to identify situations that involve integers in everyday life. Possible answers: bank deposits/withdrawals; gained/lost yards in football; winter/summer temperatures. Draw and label a number line from −5 to 5. To introduce opposites and absolute value, ask students to find the distance between −4 and 0 and between 0 and 4. 4; 4 Elicit that both integers are the same distance from 0 and that, therefore, distance is always positive.

Explorations and answers are provided in *Alternate Openers: Explorations Transparencies.*

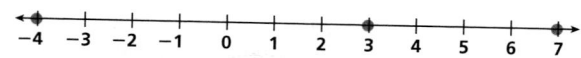

EXAMPLE **Ordering Integers**

Write the integers 7, −4, and 3 in order from least to greatest.

Graph the integers on a number line. Then read them from left to right.

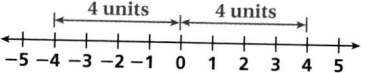

The integers in order from least to greatest are −4, 3, and 7.

A number's **absolute value** is its distance from 0 on a number line. Absolute value of a nonzero number is always positive because distance is always positive. "The absolute value of −4" is written as |−4|. Opposites have the same absolute value.

$|-4| = 4$ 4 units   4 units $|4| = 4$

−5 −4 −3 −2 −1 0 1 2 3 4 5

EXAMPLE **Simplifying Absolute-Value Expressions**

Simplify each expression.

Ⓐ |−6|

6 units

−6 −5 −4 −3 −2 −1 0 1 2 3 4

−6 is 6 units from 0, so |−6| = 6.

Ⓑ |20 − 20|
$|20 - 20| = |0|$ *Subtract first: 20 − 20 = 0.*
$= 0$ *Then find the absolute value: 0 is 0 units from 0.*

Ⓒ |−9| + |7|
$|-9| + |7| = 9 + 7$ *Find the absolute values first: −9 is 9 units*
$= 16$ *from 0. 7 is 7 units from 0. Then add.*

Ⓓ |9 − 3| − |2 + 3|
$|9 - 3| - |2 + 3| = |6| - |5|$ *9 − 3 = 6; 2 + 3 = 5*
$= 6 - 5$ *6 is 6 units from 0. 5 is 5 units from 0.*
$= 1$

Possible answers to
Think and Discuss
1. First find the absolute values of 5 and −2. Then subtract. $|5| - |-2| = 5 - 2 = 3.$

2. No, an absolute value is a distance, and distance cannot be negative.

Think and Discuss

1. **Explain** the steps you would take to simplify |5| − |−2|.

2. **Explain** whether an absolute value is ever negative.

COMMON ERROR ALERT

When ordering positive and negative integers from least to greatest, students sometimes write a greater negative integer as being less than a smaller negative integer, because they look at the number without its sign to order the integers.

Power Presentations
with PowerPoint®

Additional Examples

Example ①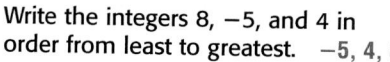

A. Aaron's score is 4, and Felicity's score is −1. Use <, >, or = to compare the scores. $-1 < 4$

B. List the golfers' scores in order from the lowest to the highest. The scores are −4, 2, 5, and −3.   −4, −3, 2, 5

Example ②

Write the integers 8, −5, and 4 in order from least to greatest.   −5, 4, 8

Example ③

Simplify each expression.

A. |−3| 3
B. |17 − 6| 11
C. |−8| + |−5| 13
D. |5 + 1| + |8 − 6| 8

Also available on transparency

---

2 **Teach**

Guided Instruction   ENGLISH LANGUAGE LEARNERS

First, show students how to use the number line (Teaching Transparency) to compare integers. Then show how to compare two integers at a time when ordering a set of integers. Use the number line to show the meanings of *absolute value* and *opposite*.

 **Visual** Suggest that students think of the < and > symbols as arrows that point to the smaller number.

Universal Access
Through Graphic Organizers

Have students work in groups of three. Students draw one number line from −50 to 50, with intervals of 10. Then, each student names an integer from −50 to 50. Students locate their integers on the number line and then compare and order the integers. They can repeat the activity if time permits.

3 **Close**

Summarize   ENGLISH LANGUAGE LEARNERS

Have students choose a positive and a negative integer, compare them, and give their opposites and their absolute values.

Possible answer: −7, 3; −7 < 3; opposite of −7 is 7, opposite of 3 is −3; |−7| = 7, |3| = 3.

1-3 Exercises

California Standards Practice
NS1.1, ⚷ NS2.5

go.hrw.com
Homework Help Online
KEYWORD: MT8CA 1-3
Parent Resources Online
KEYWORD: MT8CA Parent

Assignment Guide

If you finished Example **1** assign:
Proficient 1, 14, 27–30, 59, 61–66
Advanced 14, 27–30, 54, 59, 61–66

If you finished Example **2** assign:
Proficient 1–5, 14–18, 27–30,
35–37, 58–59, 61–66
Advanced 14–18, 27–30, 35–37,
53–54, 58–59, 61–66

If you finished Example **3** assign:
Proficient 1–45, 53–54, 58–66
Advanced 14–66

Homework Quick Check

Quickly check key concepts.
Exercises: 14, 16, 18, 22, 26

GUIDED PRACTICE

See Example **1**
1. After the first round of the 2005 Masters golf tournament, scores relative to par were Tiger Woods 2, Vijay Singh −4, Phil Mickelson −2, and Justin Leonard 5. Use <, >, or = to compare Vijay Singh's and Phil Mickelson's scores. Then list the golfers in order from the lowest score to the highest.
−4 < −2; Vijay Singh, Phil Mickelson, Tiger Woods, Justin Leonard

See Example **2**
Write the integers in order from least to greatest.
2. −5, 2, −3   **3.** −17, 6, −8   **4.** −9, −21, −14   **5.** 3, −7, 0
   −5, −3, 2   **−17, −8, 6**   **−21, −14, −9**   **−7, 0, 3**

See Example **3**
Simplify each expression.
6. $|-9|$ **9**   **7.** $|22-7|$ **15**   **8.** $|-3|+|11|$ **14**   **9.** $|-10|-|4+1|$ **5**

10. $|0|$ **0**   **11.** $|-12|+|-9|$ **21** **12.** $|28-18|$ **10**   **13.** $|8+7|-|6-5|$ **14**

INDEPENDENT PRACTICE

See Example **1**
14. During a very cold week, the temperature in Philadelphia was −7°F on Monday, 4°F on Tuesday, 2°F on Wednesday, and −3°F on Thursday. Use <, >, or = to compare the temperatures on Wednesday and Thursday. Then list the days in order from the coldest to the warmest.
−3°F < 2°F; Monday, Thursday, Wednesday, Tuesday

See Example **2**
Write the integers in order from least to greatest.
15. −6, 5, −2   **16.** 8, −11, −5   **17.** −25, −30, −27   **18.** 4, −2, −1
   −6, −2, 5   **−11, −5, 8**   **−30, −27, −25**   **−2, −1, 4**

See Example **3**
Simplify each expression.
19. $|6+3|$ **9**   **20.** $|3|$ **3**   **21.** $|-6|+|8-3|$ **11**   **22.** $|7-2|-|9-8|$ **4**

23. $|-5|$ **5**   **24.** $|7|+|-14|$ **21**   **25.** $|8-8|$ **0**   **26.** $|-19|+|-13|$ **32**

PRACTICE AND PROBLEM SOLVING

Extra Practice
See page EP2.

46. Possible answer: No, $|A|$ is not always less than $|B|$ when A is less than B. For example, −5 < 2, but $|-5|$, or 5, is greater than $|2|$, or 2.

Compare. Write <, >, or =.
27. −9 ▦ 15 **<**   **28.** 13 ▦ −17 **>**   **29.** −23 ▦ −23 **=**   **30.** −14 ▦ 0 **<**

31. $-|-7|$ ▦ $|6|$ **<** **32.** $|-3|$ ▦ $|3|$ **=** **33.** $|-13|$ ▦ $-|2|$ **>** **34.** $|20|$ ▦ $|-21|$ **<**

Write the integers in order from least to greatest.
35. 24, −16, −12   **36.** −46, −31, −52   **37.** −45, 35, −25
   −16, −12, 24   **−52, −46, −31**   **−45, −25, 35**

Simplify each expression.
38. $|17|+|-24|$ **41** **39.** $|-22|+|-28|$ **50** **40.** $|53-37|$ **16** **41.** $|21-20|$ **1**

42. $|7|\cdot|-9|$ **63** **43.** $|-6|\cdot|-12|$ **72** **44.** $|72|\div|8|$ **9** **45.** $|3|+|-3|$ **6**

46. Reasoning Two integers A and B are graphed on a number line. If A is less than B, is $|A|$ always less than $|B|$? Explain your answer.

REVIEW FOR MASTERY 1-3

LESSON 1-3 Review for Mastery
Integers and Absolute Value

Use a number line to compare and order integers.
To compare 2 and −4, place each integer on a number line.

-5 -4 -3 -2 -1 0 1 2 3 4 5

Because −4 lies to the left of 2, −4 is less than 2: −4 < 2.
Because 2 lies to the right of −4, 2 is greater than −4: 2 > −4.
To order −1, 3, −2, and 0, place each integer on a number line.

-5 -4 -3 -2 -1 0 1 2 3 4 5

To order the integers from least to greatest, read the numbers as they appear in order from left to right on the number line.
From least to greatest: −2, −1, 0, 3.

Place the integers on the number line. Then use < or > to compare.
1. 3 and −1   **2.** −1 and −4
-5 -4 -3 -2 -1 0 1 2 3 4 5   -5 -4 -3 -2 -1 0 1 2 3 4 5
3 **>** −1   −1 **>** −4

3. −2 and 0   **4.** −5 and 2
-5 -4 -3 -2 -1 0 1 2 3 4 5   -5 -4 -3 -2 -1 0 1 2 3 4 5
−2 **<** 0   −5 **<** 2

Place the integers on the number line. List in order from least to greatest.
5. −3, 4, −5, 2   **6.** 0, 1, −4, −1
-5 -4 -3 -2 -1 0 1 2 3 4 5   -5 -4 -3 -2 -1 0 1 2 3 4 5
−5, −3, 2, 4   **−4, −1, 0, 1**

PRACTICE 1-3

LESSON 1-3 Practice B
Integers and Absolute Value

Compare. Write <, >, or =.
1. −6 **<** 6   **2.** 12 **>** 10   **3.** 18 **>** 5

Write the integers in order from least to greatest.
4. −8, 2, −11   **5.** −12, −15, 0   **6.** −24, −17, 30
   −11, −8, 2   **−15, −12, 0**   **−24, −17, 30**

7. 16, −14, −7   **8.** −9, −7, −16   **9.** −19, −23, −10
   −14, −7, 16   **−16, −9, −7**   **−23, −19, −10**

Simplify each expression.
10. $|-17|$ **11.** $|-35|$ **12.** $|19|$
   17   **35**   **19**

13. $|-8|+|-4|$ **14.** $|-12|+|12|$ **15.** $|19|+|-8|$
   12   **24**   **27**

16. $|29-16|$ **17.** $|35-9|$ **18.** $|14-14|$
   13   **26**   **0**

19. $|-15|+|10|$ **20.** $|-9|+|30|$ **21.** $|24|+|-8|$
   25   **39**   **32**

22. Natalie keeps track of her bowling scores. The scores for the games she played this Saturday relative to her best score last Saturday are Game A, 6; Game B, -3; Game C, 8; and Game D, −5. Use <, >, or = to compare her first two games. Then list her games in order from the lowest score to the highest.
6 > −3; Game D, Game B, Game A, Game C

California Standards

Standard	Exercises
NS1.1	1–5, 14–18, 27–37, 46, 53–54, 57–59
NS2.5 ⚷	6–13, 19–26, 38–52, 55–57, 60
AF1.1	65–66
AF1.2	62–64

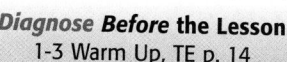

Science

The Ice Hotel in Jukkasjärvi, Sweden, is rebuilt every winter from 30,000 tons of snow and 4000 tons of ice.

Simplify each expression.

47. $|51 - 23| - |8 + 11|$ **9**   48. $|61| - |28 - 9|$ **42**   49. $|37 - 14| + |25 - \frac{38}{10}|$

50. $|-24| + |13 - 5|$ **32**   51. $|35 - 11| - |15 - 7|$ **16**   52. $|17 + 26| - |-29|$ **14**

53. **Science** The table shows the lowest recorded temperatures for each continent. Write the continents in order from the lowest recorded temperature to the highest recorded temperature.

54. **Chemistry** The boiling point of nitrogen is $-196°C$. The boiling point of oxygen is $-183°C$. Which element has the greater boiling point? Explain your answer. **oxygen**

55. **Reasoning** Write rules for using absolute value to compare two integers. Be sure to take all of the possible combinations into account.

Lowest Recorded Temperatures	
Continent	**Temperature**
Africa	$-11°F$
Antarctica	$-129°F$
Asia	$-90°F$
Australia	$-9°F$
Europe	$-67°F$
North America	$-81°F$
South America	$-27°F$

 56. **Write About It** Explain why there is no number that can replace n to make the equation $|n| = -1$ true.

57. **Challenge** List the integers that can replace n to make the statement $-|8| < n \le -|-5|$ true. $-7, -6, -5$

53. Antarctica, Asia, North America, Europe, South America, Africa, Australia

56. The absolute value of a number is always positive.

SPIRAL STANDARDS REVIEW   NS1.1, ← NS2.5, AF1.1, AF1.2

58. **Multiple Choice** Which set of integers is in order from greatest to least?

Ⓐ $-10, 8, -5$ Ⓑ $8, -5, -10$ Ⓒ $-5, 8, -10$ Ⓓ $-10, -5, 8$

59. **Multiple Choice** Which integer is between -4 and 2?

Ⓐ 0 Ⓑ 3 Ⓒ 4 Ⓓ -5

60. **Multiple Choice** Which expression has the greatest value?

Ⓐ $|12|$ Ⓑ $|-15|$ Ⓒ $|18|$ Ⓓ $|-21|$

Evaluate each expression for $a = 3$, $b = 2.5$, and $c = 24$. (Lesson 1-1)

61. $c - 15$ **9**   62. $9a + 8$ **35**   63. $8(a + 2b)$ **64**   64. $bc - a$ **57**

Write an algebraic expression for each word phrase. (Lesson 1-2)

65. 8 more than the product of 7 and a number t $7t + 8$

66. A pizzeria delivered p pizzas on Thursday. On Friday, it delivered 3 more than twice the number of pizzas delivered on Thursday. Write an expression to show the number of pizzas delivered on Friday. $2p + 3$

CHALLENGE 1-3

LESSON **1-3** **Challenge**
Opposite Opposites

You can think of a negative sign as signifying the opposite of an integer.

For example, you can write the opposite of 4 as -4. You can write the opposite of -4 as $-(-4)$ or 4.

Simplify by writing an integer for each expression.

1. $-(-8)$ **8**
2. $-(27)$ **-27**
3. $-|36|$ **-36**
4. $|-45|$ **45**
5. $-|-14|$ **-14**
6. $-|0|$ **0**
7. $|-(-12)|$ **12**
8. $-(-57)$ **57**
9. $|-(-20)|$ **20**
10. $-|51|$ **-51**
11. $-|-25|$ **-25**
12. $-|-(-16)|$ **-16**

Complete.

13. Is there a least positive integer? Explain.

Yes. Possible answer: You can not find a positive integer on the number line to the left of 1.

14. Is there a greatest positive integer? Explain.

No. Possible answer: You can always find an integer on the number line to the right of any given positive integer.

15. Is there a least negative integer? Explain.

No. Possible answer: You can always find an integer on the number line to the left of any given negative integer.

16. Is there a greatest negative integer? Explain.

Yes. Possible answer: You can not find a negative integer on the number line to the right of -1.

PROBLEM SOLVING 1-3

LESSON **1-3** **Problem Solving**
Integers and Absolute Value

Write the correct answer.

1. In Africa, Lake Asal reaches a depth of -153 meters. In Asia, the Dead Sea reaches a depth of -408 meters. Which reaches a greater depth, Lake Asal or the Dead Sea?

Dead Sea

2. Jeremy's scores for four golf games are: $-1, 2, -3,$ and 1. Order his golf scores from least to greatest.

$-3, -1, 1, 2$

3. The lowest point in North America is Death Valley with an elevation of -282 feet. South America's lowest point is the Valdes Peninsula with an elevation of -131 feet. Which continent has the lowest point?

North America

4. Two undersea cameras are taking time lapse photos in a coral reef. The first camera is mounted at -45 feet. The second camera is mounted at -25. Which camera is closer to the surface?

the second camera

Use the table to answer Exercises 5–7. Choose the letter of the best answer.

5. Which state had the coldest temperature?

A Alabama   C Massachusetts
Ⓑ Indiana   D Texas

6. Which is the greatest temperature listed?

F $-27°F$ H $-35°F$
G $-36°F$ Ⓙ $-23°F$

State Low Temperature Records	
State	**Temperature (°F)**
Alabama	-27
Indiana	-36
Massachusetts	-35
Texas	-23

7. The lowest temperature recorded in Connecticut was between the lowest temperatures recorded in Alabama and Massachusetts. Which could be the lowest temperature recorded in Connecticut?

A $-40°F$ Ⓒ $-32°F$
B $-37°F$ D $-40°F$

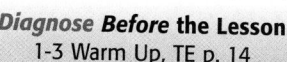

and INTERVENTION ←◆→

Diagnose Before the Lesson
1-3 Warm Up, TE p. 14

Monitor During the Lesson
1-3 Know-It Notebook
1-3 Questioning Strategies

Assess After the Lesson
1-3 Lesson Quiz, TE p. 17

Answers

55. Possible answer:
If a and b are both positive and $|a| > |b|$, then $a > b$.
If a and b are both positive and $|a| < |b|$, then $a < b$.
If a and b are both negative and $|a| > |b|$, then $a < b$.
If a and b are both negative and $|a| < |b|$, then $a > b$.
If a is positive and b is negative and $|a| > |b|$ or $|a| < |b|$, then $a > b$.
If a is negative and b is positive and $|a| > |b|$, or $|a| < |b|$, then $a < b$.

Teaching Tip   **Multiple Choice** Remind students that they must read the directions carefully. For **Exercise 58,** the directions ask the student to list the integers from greatest to least. In previous exercises, the students listed integers from *least* to *greatest*. Students may answer this question incorrectly if they do not read the directions carefully.

 Journal

Have students explain how absolute value helps to order integers. Ask them to use real-world situations involving integers in their explanation.

Power Presentations
with PowerPoint®

✓ **1-3 Lesson Quiz**

1. At the end of the course, your golf score was -2. Your friend's score was 7. Use $<$, $>$, or $=$ to compare your scores. $-2 < 7$

Write the integers in order from least to greatest.

2. $-17, -26, 23$ $-26, -17, 23$

3. $0, 5, -4$ $-4, 0, 5$

Simplify each expression.

4. $|-4| + |-2|$ **6**

5. $|6 + 13| - |7 - 5|$ **17**

Also available on transparency

Objective: Students add integers.

 Hands-On Lab
In *Chapter 1 Resource File*

 Online Edition
Tutorial Videos, Interactivities

 Countdown to Mastery Week 1

Power Presentations
with PowerPoint®

Warm Up

Graph each number on a number line.

1. −5   **2.** 7

3. −4   **4.** 0

−5 −3 −1 0 1 2 3 4 5 6 7

Also available on transparency

Math Humor

No wonder his company went bankrupt. He tried to make larger negative profits because they had a greater absolute value.

California Standards

Number Sense ◆ **1.2**
Algebra and Functions ◆ **1.3**

Also covered:
Number Sense
1.0 Students know the properties of, and **compute** with, rational numbers expressed in a variety of forms.

1-4 Adding Integers

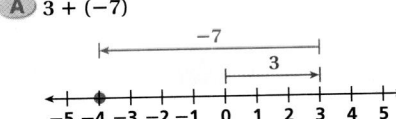

California Standards

◆ **NS1.2 Add,** subtract, multiply, and divide **rational numbers (integers,** fractions, and terminating decimals) and take positive rational numbers to whole-number powers.
◆ **AF1.3 Simplify numerical expressions** by applying properties of rational numbers (e.g., identity, inverse, distributive, associative, commutative) and justify the process used.

Vocabulary
additive inverse

Why learn this? You can track your daily calorie count by adding integers. (See Example 4.)

Suppose you eat a piece of grapefruit that contains 35 calories. Then you walk 2 laps around a track and burn 35 calories. Using opposites, you can represent this situation as $35 + (−35) = 0$. When you add two opposites, or **additive inverses**, the sum is zero.

You can model integer addition on a number line.

EXAMPLE 1 Using a Number Line to Add Integers

Use a number line to find each sum.

Helpful Hint

To add a positive number, move to the right. To add a negative number, move to the left.

A $3 + (−7)$

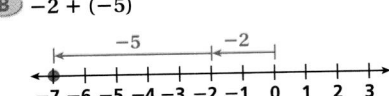

Start at 0. Move right 3 units. From 3, move left 7 units.

You finish at −4, so $3 + (−7) = −4$.

B $−2 + (−5)$

Start at 0. Move left 2 units. From −2, move left 5 units.

You finish at −7, so $−2 + (−5) = −7$.

Another way to add integers is to use absolute value.

ADDING TWO INTEGERS	
If the signs are the same. . .	**If the signs are different. . .**
. . . find the sum of the absolute values. Use the same sign as the integers.	. . . find the difference of the absolute values. Use the sign of the integer with the greater absolute value.

---

1 Introduce

Alternate Opener

EXPLORATION

1-4 Adding Integers

You can use a thermometer to model addition of integers.

1. Suppose the temperature starts at −50°F and increases 40° during the day. Complete the addition statement to show the new temperature.

   $−50° + 40° = $ ___

2. Suppose the temperature starts at 40°F and drops 70° overnight. Complete the addition statement to show the new temperature.

   $40° + (−70°) = $ ___

Complete the addition statement modeled by each number line.

3. $−4 + $ ___ $ = 5$

4. $−1 + ($ ___ $) = −8$

Think and Discuss

5. **Explain** how to add integers on a number line.

Motivate

To introduce students to adding integers, ask for examples of real-world situations that could be represented by integers (e.g., receiving $2 for allowance could be represented by +2; giving away three cookies could be represented by −3). Suggest a set of integers such as {−3, 1, −5, 2}. Ask students to order the integers from least to greatest.

Explorations and answers are provided in *Alternate Openers: Explorations Transparencies.*

EXAMPLE 2 Using Absolute Value to Add Integers

Add.

A $-4 + (-6)$

$-4 + (-6)$ *Think: Find the sum of $|-4|$ and $|-6|$.*

-10 *Same sign; use the sign of the integers.*

B $8 + (-9)$

$8 + (-9)$ *Think: Find the difference of $|8|$ and $|-9|$.*

-1 *$9 > 8$; use the sign of 9.*

C $-5 + 11$

$-5 + 11$ *Think: Find the difference of $|-5|$ and $|11|$.*

6 *$11 > 5$; use the sign of 11.*

EXAMPLE 3 Evaluating Expressions with Integers

Evaluate $b + 11$ for $b = -6$.

$b + 11 = -6 + 11$ *Replace b with -6.*

    Think: Find the difference of $|11|$ and $|-6|$.

$-6 + 11 = 5$ *$11 > 6$; use the sign of 11.*

When finding the sum of three or more integers, you may want to group opposites, or additive inverses. You may also want to group positive integers together and negative integers together.

EXAMPLE 4 *Health Application*

Melanie wants to check her calorie count after breakfast and exercise. Use information from the journal entry to find her total.

Use **positive** for calories eaten and **negative** for calories burned.

$145 + 62 + 110 + (-110) + (-40) + (-65)$

$145 + 62 + (110 + -110) + (-40) + (-65)$ *Group opposites.*

$145 + 62 + 0 + (-40) + (-65)$

$(145 + 62) + (-40 + -65)$ *Group integers with same signs.*

$207 + (-105)$ *Add integers within each group.*

102 *$207 > 105$; use the sign of 207.*

Melanie's calorie count after breakfast and exercise is 102 calories.

Monday Morning

Calories

Oatmeal	145
Toast w/jam	62
8 fl oz juice	110

Calories burned

Walked six laps	110
Swam six laps	40
Jogged two laps	65

Think and Discuss

1. **Compare** the sums of $10 + (-22)$ and $-10 + 22$.

2. **Describe** how to add the following expressions on a number line: $9 + (-13)$ and $-13 + 9$. Then compare the sums.

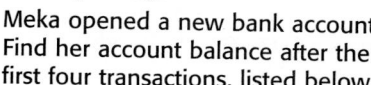
Example 1

Use a number line to find each sum.

A. $(-6) + 2$ -4

B. $-3 + (-6)$ -9

Example 2

Add.

A. $1 + (-2)$ -1

B. $(-8) + 5$ -3

C. $(-2) + (-4)$ -6

Example 3

Evaluate $c + 4$ for $c = -8$. -4

Example 4

Meka opened a new bank account. Find her account balance after the first four transactions, listed below.

Deposits: $200, $20

Withdrawals: $166, $38

Meka's account balance after the first four transactions is $16.

Also available on transparency

Possible answers to Think and Discuss

1. $10 + (-22) = -12$; $-10 + 22 = 12$; The sums are opposites.

2. Start at 0 and draw an arrow to 9, then draw an arrow left 13 units; Start at 0 and draw an arrow to -13, then draw an arrow right 9 units; Both arrows end at -4, so both sums are equal to -4.

2 Teach

Guided Instruction

In this lesson, students learn to add integers. Show students how to use a number line (Teaching Transparency) to add. Starting at zero, move to the first number in the addition expression. From there, move the number of spaces indicated by the second number, moving left for a negative number or right for a positive number. After students have mastered this method, show them that the same results are obtained by using the rules for adding integers.

Teaching Tip   **Inclusion** When adding two integers, suggest that students first determine the sign of the sum, which is always the sign of the number with the greater absolute value.

Reaching All Learners
Through Concrete Manipulatives

Have students complete the following addition problems using integer chips (in Manipulatives Kit) to represent the numbers. Have students use yellow for positive numbers and red for negative numbers. (Pennies can also be used, with heads representing positive and tails representing negative.) Remind students that a positive chip and a negative chip are opposites and their sum is zero.

1. $-3 + 2$ -1

2. $5 + (-4)$ 1

3. $(-1) + (-5)$ -6

3 Close

Summarize

Have students write, in their own words, the rules for adding integers. Discuss how students can check their answers.

Possible answers: If the signs are the same, add the absolute values of the numbers and place the same sign in the answer. If the signs are different, determine which number is greater without the signs. The sign of the greater number (ignoring signs) will be the sign for the answer. Subtract the absolute values of the numbers. You can check your answer using a number line.

Assignment Guide

If you finished Example **1** assign:
Proficient 1–4, 13–16, 29–30, 51–56
Advanced 13–16, 29–30, 47, 51–56

If you finished Example **2** assign:
Proficient 1–8, 13–24, 29–30,
31–34, 51–56
Advanced 13–24, 29–30, 35–38,
47–48, 51–56

If you finished Example **3** assign:
Proficient 1–11, 13–27, 29–30,
32–44 even, 45–46,
49–56
Advanced 13–27, 29–30, 31–45
odd, 46–56

If you finished Example **4** assign:
Proficient 1–30, 32–44 even,
45–46, 49–56
Advanced 13–30, 31–45 odd, 46–56

Homework Quick Check

Quickly check key concepts.
Exercises: 14, 18, 22, 24, 26, 28

 ## Math Background

To find the sum of any two integers, exactly one of the following will apply:

Case 1 Add two numbers with the same sign. This requires two jumps in the same direction on the number line. Because both jumps are in the same direction, you add absolute values to get the final distance from zero.

Case 2 Add two numbers with different signs. This requires two jumps in opposite directions on the number line. Because the jumps are in opposite directions, you subtract absolute values to get the final distance from zero.

Teaching Tip **Language Support** Explain to students that the amount of money in a bank account is called the balance. The balance increases when money is added, or deposited, into the account. The balance decreases when money is taken out, or withdrawn, from the account.

California Standards

Standard	Exercises
NS1.2	1–8, 12, 13–24, 28, 29–38, 45, 47–48
NS2.5	53–56
AF1.2	51–52
AF1.3	12, 28

1-4 Exercises

California Standards Practice
NS1.2, AF1.3

Homework Help Online
KEYWORD: MT8CA 1-4
Parent Resources Online
KEYWORD: MT8CA Parent

GUIDED PRACTICE

See Example **1** Use a number line to find each sum.

1. $5 + 1$ **6**
2. $6 + (-4)$ **2**
3. $-7 + 9$ **2**
4. $-4 + (-2)$ **-6**

See Example **2** Add.

5. $-12 + 5$ **-7**
6. $7 + (-3)$ **4**
7. $-11 + 17$ **6**
8. $-6 + (-8)$ **-14**

See Example **3** Evaluate each expression for the given value of the variable.

9. $t + 16$ for $t = -5$ **11**
10. $m + 7$ for $m = -5$ **2**
11. $p + (-5)$ for $p = -5$ **-10**

See Example **4** 12. Lee opens a checking account. In the first month, he makes two deposits and writes three checks, as shown at right. Find what his balance is at the end of the month. (*Hint:* Checks count as negative amounts.) **$333**

Checks	Deposits
$134	$600
$56	$225
$302	

INDEPENDENT PRACTICE

See Example **1** Use a number line to find each sum.

13. $5 + (-7)$ **-2**
14. $-7 + 7$ **0**
15. $4 + (-9)$ **-5**
16. $-4 + 7$ **3**

See Example **2** Add.

17. $8 + 14$ **22**
18. $-6 + (-7)$ **-13**
19. $-8 + (-8)$ **-16**
20. $19 + (-5)$ **14**
21. $22 + (-15)$ **7**
22. $17 + 9$ **26**
23. $-20 + (-12)$ **-32**
24. $-18 + 7$ **-11**

See Example **3** Evaluate each expression for the given value of the variable.

25. $q + 13$ for $q = 10$ **23**
26. $x + 21$ for $x = -7$ **14**
27. $z + (-7)$ for $z = 16$ **9**

See Example **4** 28. On Monday morning, a mechanic has no cars in her shop. The table at right shows the number of cars dropped off and picked up each day. Find the total number of cars left in her shop on Friday. **12 cars**

	Cars Dropped Off	Cars Picked Up
Monday	8	4
Tuesday	11	6
Wednesday	9	12
Thursday	14	9
Friday	7	6

PRACTICE AND PROBLEM SOLVING

Extra Practice
See page EP2.

Write an addition equation for each number line diagram.

$5 + (-9) = -4$

$-3 + (-4) = -7$

29. (number line −8 to 2)

30. (number line −5 to 5)

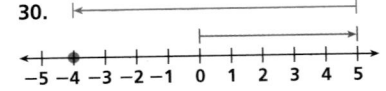

REVIEW FOR MASTERY 1-4

LESSON 1-4 Review for Mastery
Adding Integers

You can model integer addition using two-color counters. Use the yellow side for 1 and the red side for −1. Remember that one yellow counter and one red counter are opposites, so their sum is zero.

$7 + 5 =$ = 12 yellow counters = 12

$7 + (-5) =$ = 2 yellow counters = 2

$-7 + (-5) =$ = 12 red counters = −12

$-7 + 5 =$ = 2 red counters = −2

If the given integers were added, state whether the result would be positive or negative.

1. $-4 + (-6)$ **negative**
2. $-3 + 8$ **positive**
3. $-5 + 2$ **negative**

Notice if the counters are the same color, you add the absolute values of the integers. The answer is the sign of the integers. If the counters are both colors, you subtract the absolute values of the integers. Use the sign of the integer with the greater absolute value.

To add the given integers, state whether you need to add or subtract absolute values.

4. $8 + 3$ **add**
5. $-4 + (-1)$ **add**
6. $3 + (-6)$ **subtract**

Complete to find each sum.

7. $5 + (-9) = ?$
8. $-6 + (-4) = ?$

Are the signs the same or different?   **different** | **same**

Which sign will you use for the sum?   **negative** | **negative**

Will you add or subtract absolute values?   **subtract** | **add**

Write the sum.   **−4** | **−10**

PRACTICE 1-4

LESSON 1-4 Practice B
Adding Integers

Use a number line to find each sum.

1. $3 + 1$ **4**
2. $-3 + 2$ **-1**

Add.

3. $-5 + 18$ **13**
4. $-10 + 17$ **7**
5. $-22 + (-9)$ **-31**
6. $24 + (-15)$ **9**

Evaluate each expression for the given value of the variable.

7. $r + 7$ for $r = 3$ **10**
8. $m + 5$ for $m = 9$ **14**
9. $x + 9$ for $x = 4$ **13**
10. $-6 + t$ for $t = -8$ **-14**
11. $-7 + y$ for $y = -4$ **-11**
12. $x + 9$ for $x = -8$ **1**
13. $-5 + d$ for $d = -2$ **-7**
14. $x + (-4)$ for $x = -4$ **-8**
15. $k + (-3)$ for $k = -5$ **-8**
16. $-8 + b$ for $b = 13$ **5**
17. $-10 + d$ for $d = -2$ **-12**
18. $t + (-3)$ for $t = 3$ **0**

19. Joleen has 2560 trading cards in her collection. She buys 165 new cards for the collection. How many trading cards does she have now?
2725 trading cards

20. The running back for the Bears carries the ball twice in the first quarter. The first run he gained fifteen yards and the second run he lost eight yards. How many yards did the two runs total?
7 yards

Economics

The number one category of imported goods in the United States is industrial supplies, including petroleum and petroleum products. In 2004, this category accounted for over $412 million of imports.

Find each sum.

31. $-9 + (-3)$ **−12**   **32.** $16 + (-22)$ **−6**   **33.** $-34 + 17$ **−17**   **34.** $44 + 39$ **83**

35. $45 + (-67)$ **−22**   **36.** $-14 + 85$ **71**   **37.** $52 + (-9)$ **43**   **38.** $-31 + (-31)$ **−62**

Evaluate each expression for the given value of the variable.

39. $c + 17$ for $c = -9$ **8**   **40.** $k + (-12)$ for $k = 4$ **−8**   **41.** $b + (-6)$ for $b = -24$ **−30**

42. $13 + r$ for $r = -19$ **−6**   **43.** $-9 + w$ for $w = -6$ **−15**   **44.** $3 + n + (-8)$ for $n = 5$ **0**

45. **Economics** Refer to the data at right about U.S. international trade for the year 2004. Consider values of exports as positive quantities and values of imports as negative quantities.

	Exports	Imports
Goods	$807,584,000,000	$1,473,768,000,000
Services	$338,553,000,000	$290,095,000,000

Source: U.S. Census Bureau

  a. What was the total of U.S. exports in 2004? **$1,146,137,000,000**

  b. What was the total of U.S. imports in 2004? **−$1,763,863,000,000**

  c. The sum of exports and imports is called the *balance of trade*. Approximate the 2004 U.S. balance of trade to the nearest billion dollars. **about −$618,000,000,000 or −$618 billion**

 46. What's the Error? A student evaluated $-4 + d$ for $d = -6$ and gave an answer of 2. What might the student have done wrong? Give the correct answer.

 47. Write About It Explain the different ways it is possible to add two integers and get a negative answer.

 48. Challenge What is the sum of $3 + (-3) + 3 + (-3) + \ldots$ when there are 10 terms? 19 terms? 24 terms? 25 terms? Explain any patterns that you find.

SPIRAL STANDARDS REVIEW   NS1.2, NS2.5, AF1.2

49. Multiple Choice Which of the following is the value of $-7 + 3h$ when $h = 5$?

  Ⓐ −22   Ⓑ −8   Ⓒ 8   Ⓓ 22

50. Gridded Response Evaluate the expression $35 + y$ for $y = -8$. **27**

Evaluate each expression for the given values of the variables. (Lesson 1-1)

51. $2x - 3y$ for $x = 8$ and $y = 4$ **4**   **52.** $6s - t$ for $s = 7$ and $t = 12$ **30**

Simplify each expression. (Lesson 1-3)

53. $|-3| + |-9|$ **12**   **54.** $|22 - 9|$ **13**   **55.** $|18| - |-5|$ **13**   **56.** $|-27| - |-5|$ **22**

Objective: Students subtract integers.

 Online Edition
Tutorial Videos, Interactivities

 Countdown to Mastery Week 1

Power Presentations
with PowerPoint®

Warm Up

Add.

1. $-7 + 2$ -5
2. $-12 + (-9)$ -21
3. $32 + (-19)$ 13
4. $-6 + (-28)$ -34
5. $104 + (-87)$ 17
6. $-18 + (-24)$ -42

Also available on transparency

Math Fact

A number and its opposite are called *additive inverses* of each other. The sum of additive inverses is always zero.

California Standards

NS1.2 Add, **subtract**, multiply, and divide **rational numbers (integers,** fractions, and terminating decimals) and take positive rational numbers to whole-number powers.

NS2.5 Understand the meaning of the absolute value of a number; interpret the absolute value as the distance of the number from zero on a number line; **and determine the absolute value of real numbers.**

Why learn this? You can represent the differences between the drops and climbs of a roller coaster by subtracting integers. (See Example 3.)

In Lesson 1-4 you modeled integer addition on a number line. You can also model integer subtraction on a number line. The model below shows how to find $8 - 10$.

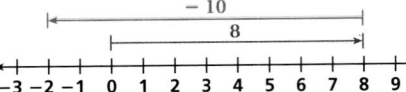

Start at 0. Move right 8 units. From 8, move left 10 units.

When you subtract a positive integer, the difference is *less* than the original number. Therefore, you move to the *left* on the number line. To subtract a negative integer, you move to the *right*.

You can also subtract an integer by adding its opposite. You can then use the rules for addition of integers.

SUBTRACTING TWO INTEGERS		
Words	**Numbers**	**Algebra**
To subtract an integer, add its opposite.	$3 - 7 = 3 + (-7)$ $5 - (-8) = 5 + 8$	$a - b = a + (-b)$ $a - (-b) = a + b$

EXAMPLE 1   **Subtracting Integers**

Subtract.

A $-7 - 7$
$-7 - 7 = -7 + (-7)$ *Add the opposite of 7.*
$\qquad\qquad = -14$ *Same sign; add; use the sign of the integers.*

B $2 - (-4)$
$2 - (-4) = 2 + 4$ *Add the opposite of −4.*
$\qquad\qquad = 6$ *Same sign; add; use the sign of the integers.*

C $-13 - (-5)$
$-13 - (-5) = -13 + 5$ *Add the opposite of −5.*
$\qquad\qquad\qquad = -8$ *Unlike signs; subtract; 13 > 5; use the sign of 13.*

---

1 Introduce

Alternate Opener

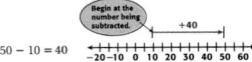

1-5 Subtracting Integers

You can use a number line to model subtracting integers.

To subtract 10 from 50, begin at the number being subtracted, 10, and count the number of units to the number 50.

$50 - 10 = 40$

The direction is **right,** so the difference is **positive.**

To subtract −10 from −70, begin at the number being subtracted, −10, and count the number of units to the number −70.

$-70 - (-10) = -60$

The direction is **left,** so the difference is **negative.**

Use the number line to complete each subtraction statement.

1. $5 - (-4) =$ ___
2. $-8 - (-1) =$ ___

Think and Discuss

3. **Discuss** a different strategy for subtracting integers.

Motivate

To introduce students to subtraction of integers, review with them how to determine the opposite of a number. You may want to use a number line to demonstrate this (Teacher Tools in Lesson Transparencies).

Review with students how to add integers. Have them recite the rules and apply them to several addition problems.

Explorations and answers are provided in *Alternate Openers: Explorations Transparencies.*

 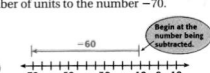

EXAMPLE 2 Evaluating Expressions with Integers

Evaluate each expression for the given value of the variable.

A $-4 - s$ for $s = -9$

$-4 - s$

$-4 - (-9)$ *Substitute −9 for s.*

$-4 + 9$ *Add the opposite of −9.*

5 *9 > 4; use the sign of 9.*

B $-3 - x$ for $x = 5$

$-3 - x$

$-3 - 5$ *Substitute 5 for x.*

$-3 + (-5)$ *Add the opposite of 5.*

-8 *Same sign; use the sign of the integers.*

C $|6 - t| + 5$ for $t = -4$

$|6 - t| + 5$

$|6 - (-4)| + 5$ *Substitute −4 for t.*

$|6 + 4| + 5$ *Add the opposite of −4.*

$|10| + 5$ *6 + 4 = 10*

$10 + 5$ *The absolute value of 10 is 10.*

15 *Add.*

EXAMPLE 3 *Architecture Application*

The roller coaster Desperado has a maximum height of 209 feet and a maximum drop of 225 feet. How far underground does the roller coaster go?

$209 - (225)$ *Subtract the drop from the height.*

$209 + (-225)$ *Add the opposite of 225.*

-16 *225 > 209; use the sign of 225.*

Desperado goes 16 feet underground.

Desperado Roller Coaster

209 ft
225 ft
Ground level, 0 ft
? ft

Possible answers to *Think and Discuss*

1. The differences are not the same because $10 - (-10)$ is positive and $-10 - 10$ is negative.

2. The answer is negative. For example, $12 - 15 = -3$.

Think and Discuss

1. **Explain** why $10 - (-10)$ does not equal $-10 - 10$.

2. **Describe** the answer that you get when you subtract a greater number from a lesser number. Then give an example.

Power Presentations with PowerPoint®

Additional Examples

Example 1

Subtract.

A. $-7 - 4$ -11

B. $8 - (-5)$ 13

C. $-6 - (-3)$ -3

Example 2

Evaluate each expression for the given value of the variable.

A. $-9 - y$ for $y = -4$ -5

B. $n - 6$ for $n = -2$ -8

C. $|8 - j| + |-2|$ for $j = -6$ 16

Example 3

The top of the Sears Tower, in Chicago, is 1454 feet above street level, while the lowest level is 43 feet below street level. How far is it from the lowest level to the top?

It is 1497 feet from bottom to top.

Also available on transparency

---

2 Teach

Guided Instruction

In this lesson, students learn to subtract integers. Explain to students that a subtraction sign can be read as "plus the opposite of." For example, $5 - 2$ can be read "5 minus 2" or "5 plus the opposite of 2." Stress that the answer is the same for either interpretation. You may want to use the Teaching Transparency.

**Teaching Tip**   **Inclusion** Point out that subtraction is not commutative. In fact, if the order in a subtraction expression is reversed, the value of the new expression is the opposite of the original value. For example, $5 - 2 = 3$, and $2 - 5 = -3$.

Universal Access
For Advanced Learners/GATE

Have students compare the following expressions and determine which pairs have the same value.

$3 + 3$ $3 - 3$

$3 + (-3)$ $3 - (-3)$

Both $3 + 3$ and $3 - (-3)$ equal 6.
Both $3 - 3$ and $3 + (-3)$ equal 0.

3 Close

Summarize

Have the students describe how to express a subtraction as an addition. Then have them state the rules for addition. Emphasize the importance of the rules for adding and subtracting integers.

Possible answers: To write a subtraction as an addition, change the subtraction sign to addition and change the sign of the second number. To add two integers with the same sign, add the absolute values of the integers and use the same sign. To add two integers with different signs, subtract the absolute values of the integers and use the sign of the number with the greater absolute value.

California Standards Practice
NS1.2, NS2.5

go.hrw.com
Homework Help Online
KEYWORD: MT8CA 1-5
Parent Resources Online
KEYWORD: MT8CA Parent

Assignment Guide

If you finished Example **1** assign:
Proficient 1–4, 9–12, 17–24, 39–44
Advanced 9–12, 19–24, 39–44

If you finished Example **2** assign:
Proficient 1–7, 9–15, 17–30, 38–44
Advanced 9–15, 19–30, 38–44

If you finished Example **3** assign:
Proficient 1–31, 38–44
Advanced 9–44

Homework Quick Check

Quickly check key concepts.
Exercises: 10, 14, 16, 22, 28

Math Background

The ancient Egyptians used the following symbols for the given numbers:

1,000   100   10   1

The number 118 would look like this:

If a subtraction required regrouping, the Egyptians replaced one symbol with ten symbols. The subtraction problem $118 - 95 = 23$, written with Egyptian symbols, might look like this:

GUIDED PRACTICE

See Example **1**   Subtract.

1. $-5 - 9$ **−14**   2. $-8 - (-6)$ **−2**   3. $8 - (-4)$ **12**   4. $-11 - (-6)$ **−5**

See Example **2**   Evaluate each expression for the given value of the variable.

5. $9 - h$ for $h = -8$ **17**   6. $-7 - m$ for $m = -5$ **−2**   7. $|-3 - k| + |-3|$ for $k = 12$ **18**

See Example **3**   8. The temperature rose from $-4°F$ to $45°F$ in Spearfish, South Dakota, on January 22, 1943, in only 2 minutes! By how many degrees did the temperature change?   **49°F**

INDEPENDENT PRACTICE

See Example **1**   Subtract.

9. $-3 - 7$ **−10**   10. $14 - (-9)$ **23**   11. $11 - (-6)$ **17**   12. $-8 - (-2)$ **−6**

See Example **2**   Evaluate each expression for the given value of the variable.

13. $14 - b$ for $b = -3$ **17**   14. $-7 - q$ for $q = -15$ **8**   15. $|-5 - f| - 7$ for $f = 12$ **10**

See Example **3**   16. A submarine cruising at 27 m below sea level, or -27 m, descends 14 m. What is its new depth?   **−41 m**

PRACTICE AND PROBLEM SOLVING

Extra Practice
See page EP3.

Write a subtraction equation for each number line diagram.

17.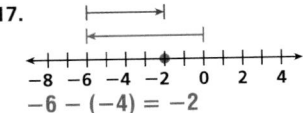
$-6 - (-4) = -2$

18.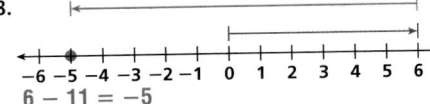
$6 - 11 = -5$

Perform the given operations.

19. $-8 - (-11)$ **3**   20. $24 - (-27)$ **51**   21. $-43 - 13$ **−56**

22. $-26 - 26$ **−52**   23. $-13 - 7 + (-6)$ **−26**   24. $-11 - (-4) + (-9)$ **−16**

Evaluate each expression for the given value of the variable.

25. $x - 16$ for $x = -4$ **−20**   26. $8 - t$ for $t = -5$ **13**

27. $-16 - y$ for $y = 8$ **−24**   28. $s - (-22)$ for $s = -18$ **4**

29. $|r + 11| + |-9|$ for $r = -7$ **13**   30. $4 - |2 - p|$ for $p = 15$ **−9**

31. **Estimation** A roller coaster starts with a 160-foot climb and then plunges 228 feet down a canyon wall. It then climbs a gradual 72 feet before a steep climb of 189 feet. Approximately how far is the coaster above or below its starting point?   **≈ 190 ft above the starting point**

REVIEW FOR MASTERY 1-5

LESSON 1-5 Review for Mastery
Subtracting Integers

To subtract one integer from another, rewrite the subtraction as the addition of an opposite. Then use the rules for adding integers.

| $4 - (-5)$ | **Subtracting a Negative** Change subtraction to addition of a positive. | $4 - 5$ | **Subtracting a Positive** Change subtraction to addition of a negative. |
| $4 + (+5)$ | | $4 + (-5)$ | |

$4 - (-5) = 4 + 5 = 9$

$4 - 5 = 4 + (-5) = -1$

On a calculator, $-$ means subtract and $+/-$ will enter a negative number.

To do $4 - (-5)$ on a calculator:
Input: 4 $-$ 5 $+/-$ $=$
Display: 9

To do $4 - 5$ on a calculator:
Input: 4 $-$ 5 $=$
Display: -1

Complete to find the difference. Remember to change two signs.

1. $7 - (-6)$ is the same as $7 \; + \; + \; 6 = \underline{13}$
2. $-4 - 3$ is the same as $-4 \; + \; - \; 3 = \underline{-7}$
3. $-2 - (-9)$ is the same as $-2 \; + \; + \; 9 = \underline{7}$
4. $14 - 16$ is the same as $14 \; + \; - \; 16 = \underline{-2}$
5. $7 - (-10)$ is the same as $7 \; + \; + \; 10 = \underline{17}$
6. $-8 - (-19)$ is the same as $-8 \; + \; + \; 19 = \underline{11}$
7. $-5 - 12$ is the same as $-5 \; + \; - \; 12 = \underline{-17}$

Find each difference. Use a calculator to check.

8. $7 - 12 = \underline{-5}$ 9. $-3 - 8 = \underline{-11}$ 10. $17 - (-4) = \underline{21}$
11. $-14 - (-3) = \underline{-11}$ 12. $5 - 8 = \underline{-3}$ 13. $-6 - 4 = \underline{-10}$

PRACTICE 1-5

LESSON 1-5 Practice B
Subtracting Integers

Subtract.

1. $8 - 2$ **6**   2. $10 - 5$ **5**   3. $7 - 12$ **−5**   4. $16 - 10$ **6**
5. $3 - 10$ **−7**   6. $16 - 9$ **7**   7. $-4 - 9$ **−13**   8. $-8 - 10$ **−18**
9. $33 - 57$ **−24**   10. $16 - 49$ **−33**   11. $-114 - 19$ **−133**   12. $-88 - (-10)$ **−78**

Evaluate each expression for the given value of the variable.

13. $x - 8$ for $x = 10$ **2**   14. $w - 10$ for $w = 15$ **5**   15. $12 - t$ for $t = -8$ **20**
16. $15 - x$ for $x = -12$ **27**   17. $w - 20$ for $w = -15$ **−35**   18. $-15 - x$ for $x = -10$ **−5**
19. $-9 - x$ for $x = -20$ **−5**   20. $y - (-10)$ for $y = -10$ **4**   21. $x - (-15)$ for $x = -5$ **10**
22. $|w - 8| + 6$ for $w = 9$ **7**   23. $16 - |t + 8|$ for $t = 10$ **−2**   24. $|14 - x| - 9$ for $x = 8$ **−3**

25. The altitude of Mt. Blackburn in Alaska is 16,390 feet. The altitude of Mt. Elbert in Colorado is 14,433 feet. What is the difference in the altitudes of the two mountains?
1957 feet

26. In January, Jesse weighed 230 pounds. By November, he weighed 185 pounds. How much did Jesse's weight change?
−45 pounds

California Standards

Standard	Exercises
NS1.2	1–39, 41–44
NS2.5	7, 15, 29–30, 38
AF1.1	40

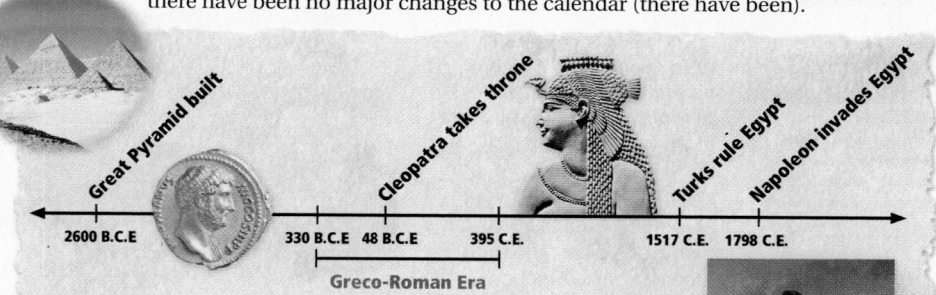

Use the timeline to answer the questions. Use negative numbers for years B.C.E. Assume that there was a year 0 (there wasn't) and that there have been no major changes to the calendar (there have been).

32. How long was the Greco-Roman era, when Greece and Rome ruled Egypt? **725 years**

33. Which was a longer period of time: from the Great Pyramid to Cleopatra, or from Cleopatra to the present? By how many years?
Great Pyramid to Cleopatra; about 500 years

34. Queen Neferteri ruled Egypt about 2900 years before the Turks ruled. In what year did she rule? **1383 B.C.E.**

35. There are 1846 years between which two events on this timeline?
Cleopatra takes the throne and Napoleon invades Egypt.

36. ✏ **Write About It** What is it about years B.C.E. that make negative numbers a good choice for representing them?

37. ⭐ **Challenge** How would your calculations differ if you took into account the fact that there was no year 0?

go.hrw.com
Web Extra!
KEYWORD: MT8CA Egypt

← NS1.2, ← NS2.5, AF1.1

38. Multiple Choice Which of the following is equivalent to $|7 - (-3)|$?

Ⓐ $|7| - |-3|$ Ⓑ $|7| + |-3|$ Ⓒ -10 Ⓓ 4

39. Gridded Response Subtract: $-4 - (-12)$. **8**

Write an algebraic expression to evaluate the word problem. (Lesson 1-2)

40. Tate bought a compact disc for $17.99. The sales tax on the disc was t dollars. What was the total cost including sales tax? **$17.99 + t$**

Evaluate each expression for $m = -3$. (Lesson 1-4)

41. $m + 6$ **3**   **42.** $m + (-5)$ **-8**   **43.** $-9 + m$ **-12**   **44.** $m + 3$ **0**

Diagnose Before the Lesson
1-5 Warm Up, TE p. 22

Monitor During the Lesson
1-5 Know-It Notebook
1-5 Questioning Strategies

Assess After the Lesson
1-5 Lesson Quiz, TE p. 25

Interdisciplinary LINK

Social Studies

Exercises 32–37 involve reading a timeline. Reading and interpreting timelines is a prerequisite skill for middle school social studies courses.

Answers
36–37. See p. A1.

Teaching Tip **Multiple Choice** For **Exercise 38,** students should realize that they do not have to rewrite the given expression in order to correctly answer the problem. Students can eliminate **A, C,** and **D** as the correct answer choices by simplifying the choices and comparing them with the value of the given expression.

 **Journal**

Have students write about a situation involving a vertical change, such as traveling on an elevator. Also have them write about another situation that might involve subtraction of integers.

LESSON 1-5 Challenge
Teeter Totter

Joel wants his math average for 6 tests to be at least 85. So far, his grades on the first 5 tests were 82, 91, 73, 83, and 88.

Complete the following table to help Joel figure out what grade he has to get on the 6th test in order to achieve his goal.

Grade	73	82	83	88	91
Grade − Average	73 − 85 =	82 − 85 =	83 − 85 =	88 − 85 =	91 − 85 =
	−12	−3	−2	3	6

After calculating the differences between the existing grades and the desired average of 85, notice that some of the differences are negative and some are positive. Add the positive and negative differences separately.

1. Sum of negative differences   2. Sum of positive differences

$-12 + (-3) + (-2) = -17$ $3 + 6 = 9$

Joel thinks that since the average is the "middle" grade, the differences below the average should balance the differences above the average. If Joel's reasoning is correct:

3. Should the 6th grade be higher or lower than the average? **higher**

4. By how many points? **8 points**

5. What must the 6th grade be in order to achieve an average of at least 85? **93**

6. Verify your answer by using it as the 6th grade. Find the average by your usual method: add the 6 grades and divide by 6.

$\dfrac{73 + 82 + 83 + 88 + 91 + 93}{6} = 85$

Use Joel's method to find the necessary 6th grade for each set of grades if the given average is to be achieved.

7. 80, 93, 75, 82, 85; average to be 81
6th grade should be ___ **71**

8. 85, 80, 90, 100, 80; average to be 88
6th grade should be ___ **93**

LESSON 1-5 Problem Solving
Subtracting Integers

Write the correct answer.

1. In Fairbanks, Alaska, the average January temperature is −13°F, while the average April temperature is 30°F. What is the difference between the average temperatures?
43°F

2. The highest point in North America is Mt. McKinley, Alaska, at 20,320 ft above sea level. The lowest point is Death Valley, California, at 282 ft below sea level. What is the difference in elevations?
20,602 ft

3. The temperature fell from 44°F to −56°F in 24 hours in Browning, Montana, on January 23–24, 1916. By how many degrees did the temperature change?
100°F

4. The boiling point of chlorine is −102°C, while the melting point is −34°C. What is the difference between the melting and boiling points of chlorine?
68°C

Use the table below to answer Exercises 5–7. The table shows the first and fifth place finishers in a golf tournament. In golf, the winner has the lowest total for all five rounds. Choose the letter for the best answer.

5. By how many points did Mickelson beat Kelly in Round 2?
Ⓐ 2   C 5
B 3   D 8

Bob Hope Chrysler Classic
January 20, 2002

Round	J. Kelly	P. Mickelson
1	−8	−8
2	−3	−5
3	−7	−2
4	−4	−7
5	−5	−8

6. By how many points did Kelly beat Mickelson in Round 3?
F 2   Ⓗ 5
G 3   J 9

7. Who won the Bob Hope Chrysler Classic and how many points difference was there between first and fifth place?
A Kelly; 4   C Kelly; 3
B Mickelson; 4   Ⓓ Mickelson; 3

Power Presentations
with PowerPoint®

✓ **1-5**
Lesson Quiz
Subtract.

1. $-6 - (-4)$ -2

2. $-3 - 3$ -6

3. $4 - (-5)$ 9

Evaluate each expression for the given value of the variable.

4. $9 - s$ for $s = -5$ 14

5. $-4 - w + 5$ for $w = 21$ -20

6. Suretta is flying in an airplane and rises an additional 20 feet. Then she descends 190 feet toward the ground. How far below her original height did Suretta go? **170 feet**

Also available on transparency

Objective: Students multiply and divide integers.

 Technology Lab
In *Chapter 1 Resource File*

 Online Edition
Tutorial Videos

 Countdown to Mastery Week 2

Power Presentations
with PowerPoint®

Warm Up
Multiply or divide.
1. 5(8) 40
2. 6(12) 72
3. $\frac{36}{9}$ 4
4. $\frac{49}{7}$ 7
5. 18(7) 126
6. $\frac{192}{16}$ 12

Also available on transparency

 Math Humor

Who invented algebra? a clever X-pert

 **Math Background**

Inductive reasoning involves examining a set of data to determine a pattern and then making a conjecture about the data. Inductive reasoning is used in this lesson to develop the rule for multiplying two integers. For more on inductive reasoning, see page SB24.

 **California Standards**

Number Sense 🐾 1.2

 1-6 **Multiplying and Dividing Integers**

 **California Standards**

🐾 **NS1.2** Add, subtract, multiply, and divide rational numbers (integers, fractions, and terminating decimals) and take positive rational numbers to whole-number powers.

Who uses this? Football players can multiply integers to represent the total change in yards during several plays. (See Example 3.)

If a football team loses 10 yards in each of 3 plays, the total change in yards can be represented by 3(−10). You can write this product as repeated addition.

$$3(-10) = -10 + (-10) + (-10) = -30$$

Notice that a positive integer multiplied by a negative integer gives a negative product.

You already know that the product of two positive integers is a positive integer. The pattern shown at right can help you understand that the product of two negative integers is also a positive integer.

$$3(-10) = -30$$
$$2(-10) = -20$$
$$1(-10) = -10$$
$$0(-10) = 0$$
$$-1(-10) = 10$$
$$-2(-10) = 20$$
$$-3(-10) = 30$$

+ 10 (between each)

MULTIPLYING AND DIVIDING TWO INTEGERS
If the signs are the same, the sign of the answer is positive.
If the signs are different, the sign of the answer is negative.

EXAMPLE 1 **Multiplying and Dividing Integers**

Multiply or divide.

 Caution!
The *sum* of two negative integers is always negative, but the *product* or *quotient* of two negative integers is always positive.

A 5(−8)   *Signs are different.*
−40   *Answer is negative.*

B $\frac{-45}{-9}$ *Signs are the same.*
5   *Answer is positive.*

C 4(−2)(−3)   *Multiply two integers.*
4(−2)(−3)   *Signs are different.*
−8(−3)   *Answer is negative.*
−8(−3)   *Signs are the same.*
24   *Answer is positive.*

D $\frac{32}{-8}$ *Signs are different.*
−4   *Answer is negative.*

 **1 Introduce**
Alternate Opener

EXPLORATION
1-6 Multiplying and Dividing Integers

Imagine a person walking on a number line. If the person faced a positive direction, it would be to the right. If the person faced a negative direction, it would be to the left.

(number line from −10 to 10)

Suppose each step is 2 units long.

1. A person who is standing at 0 and facing a positive direction takes 3 steps backward. Complete the multiplication statement to find the person's location.
$$3 \cdot (-2) = \_\_\_$$

2. A person who is standing at 0 and facing a negative direction takes 4 steps forward. Complete the multiplication statement to find the person's location.
$$-4 \cdot 2 = \_\_\_$$

3. A person who is standing at 0 and facing a negative direction takes 5 steps backward. Complete the multiplication statement to find the person's location.
$$-5 \cdot (-2) = \_\_\_$$

Think and Discuss

4. **Describe** a situation for the multiplication statement 6 · (−3) = −18 by using a number line.

Motivate

To introduce students to multiplication and division of integers, point out that multiplication of whole numbers is repeated addition. Give examples of repeated addition, such as 6 + 6 + 6 = 3 · 6. Review the rules for adding integers.

Explorations and answers are provided in *Alternate Openers: Explorations Transparencies.*

EXAMPLE 2 Using the Order of Operations with Integers

Simplify.

A $-3(2 - 8)$

$-3(2 - 8)$	*Subtract inside the parentheses.*
$-3(2 + -8)$	*Add the opposite of 8 inside the parentheses.*
$-3(-6)$	*Think: The signs are the same.*
18	*The answer is positive.*

B $4(-7) - 2$

$4(-7) - 2$	*Multiply first.*
$-28 - 2$	*Think: The signs are different; answer is negative.*
-30	*Same sign; use the sign of the integers.*

C $-2(14 + 6)$

$-2(14 + 6)$	*Add inside the parentheses.*
$-2(20)$	*Think: The signs are different.*
-40	*The answer is negative.*

EXAMPLE 3 Sports Application

A football team runs 10 plays. On 6 plays, it has a gain of 4 yards each. On 4 plays, it has a loss of 5 yards each. Each gain in yards can be represented by a positive integer, and each loss can be represented by a negative integer. Find the total net change in yards.

$6(4) + 4(-5)$	*Add the losses to the gains.*
$24 + (-20)$	*Multiply.*
4	*Add.*

The team gained 4 yards.

Possible answers to Think and Discuss

1. $5 \cdot 6 = 30$,
$(-5) \cdot 6 = -30$,
$5 \cdot (-6) = -30$,
$(-5) \cdot (-6) = 30$,
$6 \cdot 5 = 30$,
$(-6) \cdot 5 = -30$,
$6 \cdot (-5) = -30$,
$(-6) \cdot (-5) = 30$,
$30 \div 5 = 6$,
$30 \div 6 = 5$,
$(-30) \div 5 = -6$,
$(-30) \div (-6) = 5$,
$30 \div (-5) = -6$,
$30 \div (-6) = -5$,
$(-30) \div (-5) = 6$,
$(-30) \div 6 = -5$

Think and Discuss

1. **List** all possible multiplication and division statements for the integers with absolute values of 5, 6, and 30. For example, $5 \cdot 6 = 30$.

2. **Compare** the sign of the product of two negative integers with the sign of the sum of two negative integers.

3. **Suppose** the product of two integers is positive. What do you know about the signs of the integers?

Power Presentations
with PowerPoint®

Additional Examples

Example 1

Multiply or divide.

A. $-6(4)$ $\quad -24$ **B.** $-8(-5)(2)$ $\quad 80$

C. $\dfrac{-18}{2}$ $\quad -9$ **D.** $\dfrac{-25}{-5}$ $\quad 5$

Example 2

Simplify.

A. $3(-6 - 12)$ $\quad -54$

B. $-5(-5 + 2)$ $\quad 15$

C. $-2(14) - 5$ $\quad -33$

Example 3

A golfer plays 5 holes. On 3 holes, he is 4 strokes over par. On 2 holes, he is 4 strokes under par. Each score over par can be represented by a positive integer, and each score under par can be represented by a negative integer. Find the total score relative to par. 4

Also available on transparency

Possible answers to Think and Discuss

2. The product of two negative integers is positive, while the sum of two negative integers is negative.

3. The sign of the integers is the same; that is, either both are positive or both are negative.

---

2 Teach

Guided Instruction

In this lesson, students learn to multiply and divide integers. Review with students the pattern given in the lesson. They should be able to determine the sign rules for multiplication and division (Teaching Transparency). Point out that the sign rules are the same for both operations.

Teaching Tip
Communicating Math Remind students of the order of operations. Ask students to explain each step in **Example 2**, referring to both the rules for multiplication and division of integers and the order of operations.

Universal Access
For Advanced Learners/GATE

Have students answer True or False to the following statements, and then provide an example and an explanation for each.

If a product is negative, then there must be an odd number of negative factors in the expression. True; $-3(-2)(-1) = -6$. Because every two negative factors make a positive, an odd number results in one extra negative.

If a quotient is negative, there must be an even number of positive factors in the numerator and denominator combined. False; $\dfrac{-3(6)(2)}{(4)} = -9$. The sign of the quotient is determined only by the number of negative factors.

3 Close

Summarize

Review the rules for the four operations. Discuss why the rules for multiplication and division are the same, while the rules for addition and subtraction are different.

Possible answers: The rules for multiplication and division are the same because one can rewrite division as multiplication without changing any of the signs. The rules for addition and subtraction are different because to change subtraction into addition, the sign of the second number must change.

1-6 Exercises

California Standards Practice
← NS1.2, AF1.2

go.hrw.com
Homework Help Online
KEYWORD: MT8CA 1-6
Parent Resources Online
KEYWORD: MT8CA Parent

Assignment Guide

If you finished Example **1** assign:
Proficient 1–4, 11–18, 45, 47–53
Advanced 15–18, 26–33, 45, 47–53

If you finished Example **2** assign:
Proficient 1–8, 11–22, 45, 47–53
Advanced 15–22, 26–33, 45, 47–53

If you finished Example **3** assign:
Proficient 1–25, 34–40 even, 45–53
Advanced 15–24, 26–33, 35–41 odd, 42–53

Homework Quick Check
Quickly check key concepts.
Exercises: 16, 18, 20, 22, 24

Math Background

One situation that illustrates multiplication of integers is as follows:

Imagine a road that is laid out like a number line. Mile markers to the north are positive and to the south negative. A car moving south at 30 mi/h can be represented by −30 mi/h. If the car starts at mile marker 0, its position after 2 hours would be at mile marker −60 ($2 \times -30 = -60$). The car's position 2 hours before it reached mile marker 0 would have been at mile marker 60 ($-2 \times -30 = 60$). Similar examples can be created using a northbound car traveling at +30 mi/h.

California Standards

Standard	Exercises
NS1.2 🔑	1–33, 40–46, 50–53
AF1.1	47–49
AF1.2	34, 36, 39

GUIDED PRACTICE

See Example **1** Multiply or divide.
1. $8(-4)$ **−32**
2. $\frac{-54}{9}$ **−6**
3. $-7(-4)(3)$ **84**
4. $\frac{32}{-8}$ **−4**

See Example **2** Simplify.
5. $-7(5 - 12)$ **49**
6. $4(-3) - 9$ **−21**
7. $-6(-5 + 9)$ **−24**
8. $3 + 11(-7 + 3)$ **−41**

See Example **3** **Business** An investor buys shares of stock A and stock B. Stock A loses $8 per share, and stock B gains $5 per share. Given the number of shares, how much does the investor lose or gain?

9. stock A: 20 shares, stock B: 35 shares **gains $15**

10. stock A: 30 shares, stock B: 20 shares **loses $140**

INDEPENDENT PRACTICE

See Example **1** Multiply or divide.
11. $-3(-7)$ **21**
12. $\frac{72}{-6}$ **−12**
13. $12(-7)$ **−84**
14. $\frac{-42}{6}$ **−7**
15. $\frac{-3(4)(2)}{-8}$ **3**
16. $-13(-9)$ **117**
17. $5(-7)(4)$ **−140**
18. $\frac{-63}{-3(-21)}$ **−1**

See Example **2** Simplify.
19. $12(9 - 14)$ **−60**
20. $-13(-2) - 8$ **18**
21. $13(8 - 11)$ **−39**
22. $10 + 4(5 - 8)$ **−2**

See Example **3** **Banking** A student puts $50 in the bank each time he makes a deposit. He takes $20 each time he makes a withdrawal. Given the number of transactions, what is the net change in the student's account?

23. deposits: 4, withdrawals: 5 **+$100**
24. deposits: 3, withdrawals: 8 **−$10**

PRACTICE AND PROBLEM SOLVING

Extra Practice
See page EP3.

25. $\frac{15}{3}$; 5
$\frac{-6}{3}$; −2
$\frac{9}{3}$; 3
$\frac{-15}{3}$; −5

25. **Science** Ocean tides are the result of the gravitational force between the sun, the moon, and the earth. When ocean tides occur, the earth's crust also moves. This is called an earth tide. The formula for the height of an earth tide is $y = \frac{x}{3}$, where x is the height of the ocean tide. Fill in the table.

Ocean Tide Height (x)	$\frac{x}{3}$	Earth Tide Height (y)
15		
−6		
9		
−15		

Perform the given operations.
26. $-7(6)$ **−42**
27. $\frac{-144}{12}$ **−12**
28. $-7(-7)$ **49**
29. $\frac{160}{-40}$ **−4**
30. $2(-3)(-5)$ **30**
31. $\frac{-96}{-12}$ **8**
32. $12(3)(-2)$ **−72**
33. $\frac{-18(6)}{-3}$ **36**

REVIEW FOR MASTERY 1-6

LESSON 1-6 Review for Mastery
Multiplying and Dividing Integers

Since multiplication is a shortcut for addition, a pattern becomes apparent when you multiply or divide integers. Look at the two multiplication problems written as repeated addition.

$8 \times 3 = 8 + 8 + 8 = 24$ $-8 \times 3 = -8 + -8 + -8 = -24$
$8 \times 3 = 24$ $-8 \times 3 = -24$
$8 \times 2 = 16$ *Notice the product* $-8 \times 2 = -16$ *Notice the product*
$8 \times 1 = 8$ *is decreasing by 8.* $-8 \times 1 = -8$ *is increasing by 8.*
$8 \times 0 = 0$ $-8 \times 0 = 0$
$8 \times -1 = -8$ *Keep decreasing* $-8 \times -1 = 8$ *Keep increasing by*
$8 \times -2 = -16$ *by 8 even though* $-8 \times -2 = 16$ *8 even though both*
$8 \times -3 = -24$ *one factor is negative.* $-8 \times -3 = 24$ *factors are negative.*

Multiplication and division have the same rules for multiplying integers.
Positive × Positive = Positive   Positive × Negative = Negative
Negative × Positive = Negative   Negative × Negative = Positive

Tell if the signs are the same or different and if the result will be positive or negative.

1. $9 \times (-5)$
signs are **different**
product is **negative**

2. $-14 \div (-2)$
signs are **the same**
quotient is **positive**

3. $27 \div 3$
signs are **the same**
quotient is **positive**

4. $50 \div (-2)$
signs are **different**
quotient is **negative**

Enter + or − for the product or quotient.

5. $(-14) \div (-2) = \underline{+}\ 7$
6. $8 \times 7 = \underline{+}\ 56$
7. $(-3) \times 5 = \underline{-}\ 15$
8. $16 \times (-3) = \underline{-}\ 48$
9. $25 \div (-5) = \underline{-}\ 5$
10. $(-100) \div 50 = \underline{-}\ 2$

Find the product or quotient.

11. $7 \times (-2) = \underline{-14}$
12. $-99 \div (-11) = \underline{9}$
13. $8 \times (-6) = \underline{-48}$
14. $64 \div 16 = \underline{4}$
15. $-12 \times (-3) = \underline{36}$
16. $-48 \div 12 = \underline{-4}$

PRACTICE 1-6

LESSON 1-6 Practice B
Multiplying and Dividing Integers

Multiply or divide.

1. $6 \cdot 7$ **42**
2. $\frac{-15}{5}$ **−3**
3. $-7 \cdot 3$ **−21**
4. $\frac{20}{-4}$ **−5**
5. $\frac{-36}{-4}$ **9**
6. $-8(-9)$ **72**
7. $\frac{-48}{-6}$ **8**
8. $7(-7)$ **−49**
9. $5(-8)$ **−40**
10. $(-6)(-9)$ **54**
11. $\frac{-36}{4}$ **−9**
12. $\frac{42}{-7}$ **−6**
13. $-9(-3)$ **27**
14. $(-4)(8)$ **−32**
15. $\frac{-54}{-9}$ **6**
16. $\frac{-72}{8}$ **−9**

Simplify.

17. $-5(3 + 7)$ **−50**
18. $10(8 - 2)$ **60**
19. $-4(12 - 3)$ **−36**
20. $9(15 - 8)$ **63**
21. $12(-9 + 4)$ **−60**
22. $-11(7 - 13)$ **66**
23. $15(-12 + 8)$ **−60**
24. $-10(-8 - 6)$ **140**
25. $6(-12 + 1)$ **−66**
26. $-5(3 - 12)$ **45**
27. $-8(-5 - 5)$ **80**
28. $7(12 - 3)$ **63**
29. $10(-7 - 1)$ **−80**
30. $12(2 - 5)$ **−36**
31. $-15(-2 - 1)$ **45**
32. $9(8 - 20)$ **−108**

33. Kristin and her three friends buy a pizza with twelve slices and split it equally. How many slices will each person receive?
3 slices

34. The temperature was −1°F, −5°F, 8°F, and −6°F on four consecutive days. What was the average temperature for those days?
−1°F

Science

Anoplogaster cornuta, often called a fangtooth or ogrefish, is a predatory fish that reaches a maximum length of 15 cm. It can be found in tropical and temperate waters at −16,000 ft.

Evaluate the expressions for the given value of the variable.

34. $-4t - 5$ for $t = 3$ **−17**   **35.** $-x + 2$ for $x = -9$ **11**   **36.** $6(s + 9)$ for $s = -1$ **48**

37. $\frac{-r}{8}$ for $r = 64$ **−8**   **38.** $\frac{-42}{t}$ for $t = -6$ **7**   **39.** $\frac{y - 11}{-4}$ for $y = 35$ **−6**

40. Science The ocean floor is extremely uneven. It includes underwater mountains, ridges, and extremely deep areas called *trenches*. To the nearest foot, find the average depth of the trenches shown. **−32,148 ft**

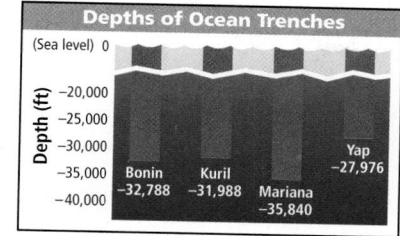

Depths of Ocean Trenches

(Sea level) 0
−20,000
−25,000
−30,000
−35,000
−40,000

Depth (ft)

Bonin −32,788   Kuril −31,988   Mariana −35,840   Yap −27,976

41. Reasoning A football team runs 11 plays. There are 3 plays that result in a loss of 2 yards each and 8 plays that result in a gain of 4 yards each. To find the total yards gained, Art simplifies the expression $3(-2) + 8(4)$. Bella first finds the total yards lost, 6, and the total yards gained, 32. Then she subtracts 6 from 32. Compare these two methods.

41. Possible answer: Both methods give the correct result. Art is adding negative yardage. Bella is subtracting total yards lost.

42. Choose a Strategy P is the set of positive factors of 30, and Q is the set of negative factors of 18. If x is a member of set P and y is a member of set Q, what is the greatest possible value of $x \cdot y$?

Ⓐ 540   Ⓑ 180   Ⓒ 90   Ⓓ −1

43. Write About It If you know that the product of two integers is negative, what can you say about the two integers? Give examples.

44. Challenge A visiting player is positioned on his own 30-yard line. The player loses 3 yards after a gain of 12 yards. What is the player's position if 4 yards are lost on the next two plays? **The player is on his own 31-yard line.**

SPIRAL STANDARDS REVIEW

🔑 NS1.2, AF1.1

45. Multiple Choice What is the product of −7 and −10?

Ⓐ −70   Ⓑ −17   Ⓒ −3   Ⓓ 70

46. Short Response Brenda donates part of her salary to the local children's hospital each month by having $15 taken out of her monthly paycheck. Write an integer to represent the amount taken out of each paycheck. Find an integer to represent the change in the amount of money in Brenda's paychecks after 1.5 years. **−$15, −$270**

Write an algebraic expression for each word phrase. (Lesson 1-2)

47. j decreased by 18 **$j - 18$**   **48.** twice b less 12 **$2b - 12$**   **49.** 22 less than y **$y - 22$**

Find each sum or difference. (Lessons 1-4 and 1-5)

50. $-7 + 3$ **−4**   **51.** $5 - (-4)$ **9**   **52.** $-3 + (-6)$ **−9**   **53.** $-513 - (-259)$ **−254**

CHALLENGE 1-6

LESSON 1-6 Challenge
Pearls of Wisdom

For security, bead bracelets are strung with knots between beads.

Starting to the right of the equals-sign clasp and moving clockwise, write × or ÷ as the knots between numbered beads to make the expression around the bracelet true.

Example
③ ÷ 1 × 4 ÷ −2 × −2 × 8 × −1 ÷ −4 ÷ 2 = ③

1.   **2.**   **3.**

PROBLEM SOLVING 1-6

LESSON 1-6 Problem Solving
Multiplying and Dividing Integers

Write the correct answer.

1. A submersible started at the surface of the water and was moving down at −12 meters per minute toward the ocean floor. The submersible traveled at this rate for 32 minutes before coming to rest on the ocean floor. What is the depth of the ocean floor?

−384 m

2. For the first week in January, the daily high temperatures in Bismarck, North Dakota, were 7°F, −10°F, −10°F, −7°F, 8°F, 12°F, and 14°F. What was the average daily high temperature for the week?

2°F

3. Sally went golfing and recorded her scores as −2 on the first hole, −2 on the second hole, and 1 on the third hole. What is her average for the first three holes?

−1

4. The ocean floor is at −96 m. Tom has reached −15 m. If he continues to move down at −3 m per minute, how far will he be from the ocean floor after 7 minutes?

60 m

Use the table below to answer Exercises 5–7. Choose the letter for the best answer.

5. What is the caloric impact of 2 hours of in-line skating?

A −477 Cal   C −583 Cal
B −479 Cal   D −954 Cal

6. What is the caloric impact of eating a hamburger and then playing Frisbee for 3 hours?

F 220 Cal   H 190 Cal
G −190 Cal   J −220 Cal

7. Tim plays basketball for 1 hour, skates for 5 hours, and plays Frisbee for 4 hours. What is the average amount of calories Tim burns per hour?

Ⓐ −375 Cal   C −545 Cal
B −1250 Cal   D −409 Cal

Calories Consumed or Burned	
Food or Exercise	Calories
Apple	125
Pepperoni pizza (slice)	181
Hamburger	425
Basketball (1hr)	−545
In-line skating (1 hr)	−477
Frisbee (1 hr)	−205

FORMATIVE ASSESSMENT and INTERVENTION ↔

Diagnose Before the Lesson
1-6 Warm Up, TE p. 26

Monitor During the Lesson
1-6 Know-It Notebook
1-6 Questioning Strategies

Assess After the Lesson
1-6 Lesson Quiz, TE p. 29

Answers

43. Possible answer: If the product of two integers is negative, then the integers have opposite signs; for example, $2 \cdot (-3) = -6$ and $-2 \cdot 3 = -6$.

Teaching Tip **Short Response** For **Exercise 46,** remind students that multiplication is also repeated addition. Encourage students to create a table of values to determine the change in the amount of money in Brenda's paychecks if they are struggling with calculating the change by using multiplication.

📝 Journal

Have students write about a career or activity in which someone might want to find an average (mean) of negative integers. One possibility is meteorology; a meteorologist might need an average winter temperature.

Power Presentations with PowerPoint®

✓ **1-6 Lesson Quiz**

Multiply or divide.

1. $-8(4)$ **−32**

2. $\frac{-12(5)}{-10}$ **6**

Simplify.

3. $-2(13 - 4)$ **−18**

4. $6(-5 - 3)$ **−48**

5. Evin completes 11 transactions in his bank account. In 6 transactions, he withdraws $10. In 5 transactions, he deposits $20. Find the total net change in dollars. **$40**

Also available on transparency

Organizer

Objective: Assess students' mastery of concepts and skills in Lessons 1-1 through 1-6.

Resources

 Assessment Resources
Section 1A Quiz

 Test & Practice Generator
One-Stop Planner®

INTERVENTION ◀▬▶

Resources

 **Ready to Go On?
Intervention and
Enrichment** Worksheets

◉ **Ready to Go On? CD-ROM**

🪐 **Ready to Go On? Online**

my.hrw.com

CHAPTER
1

READY TO GO ON?

SECTION 1A

Quiz for Lessons 1-1 Through 1-6

☑ **1-1** **Evaluating Algebraic Expressions**

Evaluate each expression for the given values of the variables.

1. $5x + 6y$ for $x = 8$ and $y = 4$ **64**   **2.** $6(r - 7t)$ for $r = 80$ and $t = 8$ **144**

☑ **1-2** **Writing Algebraic Expressions**

5. 46 less than the product of 7 and y
6. 2 times the sum of 18 and t

Write an algebraic expression for each word phrase.

3. one-sixth the sum of r and 7 $\frac{1}{6}(r + 7)$ **4.** 10 plus the product of 16 and m $10 + 16m$

Write a word phrase for each algebraic expression.

5. $7y - 46$ **6.** $2(18 + t)$ **7.** $\frac{x - 10}{3}$ **8.** $15 + \frac{p}{32}$

7. one-third the difference of x and 10
8. 15 plus the quotient of p and 32

☑ **1-3** **Integers and Absolute Value**

Write the integers in order from least to greatest.

9. $-17, 25, 18, -2$ $-17, -2, 18, 25$ **10.** $0, -8, 9, 1$ $-8, 0, 1, 9$

Simplify each expression.

11. $|14 - 7|$ **7**   **12.** $|-15| - |-12|$ **3**   **13.** $|26| + |-14|$ **40**

☑ **1-4** **Adding Integers**

Evaluate each expression for the given value of the variable.

14. $p + 14$ for $p = -8$ **6**   **15.** $w + (-9)$ for $w = -4$ **−13**

16. In Loma, Montana, on January 15, 1972, the temperature increased 103 degrees in a 24-hour period. If the lowest temperature on that day was $-54°F$, what was the highest temperature?   **49°F**

☑ **1-5** **Subtracting Integers**

Subtract.

17. $12 - (-8)$ **20**   **18.** $-7 - (-5)$ **−2**   **19.** $-5 - (-16)$ **11**   **20.** $-22 - 5$ **−27**

21. The point of highest elevation in the United States is on Mount McKinley, Alaska, at 20,320 feet. The point of lowest elevation is in Death Valley, California, at -282 feet. What is the difference in the elevations?   **20,602 ft**

☑ **1-6** **Multiplying and Dividing Integers**

Multiply or divide.

22. $(-8)(-6)$ **48**   **23.** $\frac{-28}{7}$ **−4**   **24.** $\frac{39}{-3}$ **−13**   **25.** $(-2)(-5)(-6)$ **−60**

READY TO GO ON?
Diagnose and Prescribe

NO
INTERVENE

YES
ENRICH

READY TO GO ON? Intervention, Section 1A			
Ready to Go On? Intervention	🦫 **Worksheets**	◉ **CD-ROM**	🪐 **Online**
☑ Lesson 1-1 🦫 **AF1.2**	1-1 Intervention	Activity 1-1	
☑ Lesson 1-2 🦫 **AF1.1**	1-2 Intervention	Activity 1-2	
☑ Lesson 1-3 🦫 🗝 **NS2.5**	1-3 Intervention	Activity 1-3	Diagnose and Prescribe Online
☑ Lesson 1-4 🦫 🗝 **NS1.2**	1-4 Intervention	Activity 1-4	
☑ Lesson 1-5 🦫 🗝 **NS1.2**	1-5 Intervention	Activity 1-5	
☑ Lesson 1-6 🦫 🗝 **NS1.2**	1-6 Intervention	Activity 1-6	

**READY TO GO ON?
Enrichment, Section 1A**
🦫 **Worksheets**
◉ **CD-ROM**
🪐 **Online**

Focus on Problem Solving

 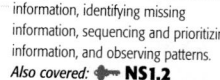

California Standards

MR1.1 Analyze problems by identifying relationships, distinguishing relevant from irrelevant information, identifying missing information, sequencing and prioritizing information, and observing patterns.

Also covered: ← **NS1.2**

Solve

• **Choose an operation: Addition or Subtraction**

To decide whether to add or subtract to solve a word problem, you need to determine what action is taking place in the problem. If you are combining numbers or putting numbers together, you need to add. If you are taking away or finding out how far apart two numbers are, you need to subtract.

Action	Operation	Illustration
Combining or putting together	Add	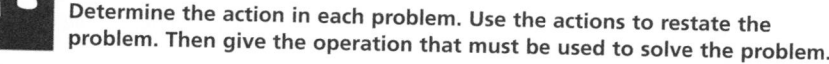
Removing or taking away	Subtract	
Finding the difference	Subtract	

Jan has 10 red marbles. Joe gives her 3 more. How many marbles does Jan have now? The action is combining marbles. Add 10 and 3.

Determine the action in each problem. Use the actions to restate the problem. Then give the operation that must be used to solve the problem.

1 Lake Superior is the largest of the Great Lakes and contains approximately 3000 mi³ of water. Lake Michigan is the second largest Great Lake by volume and contains approximately 1180 mi³ of water. Approximately how much more water is in Lake Superior?

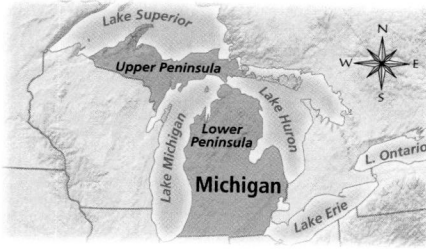

2 The average temperature in Homer, Alaska, is approximately 53°F in July and approximately 24°F in December. How much hotter is the average temperature in Homer in July than in December?

3 Einar has $18 to spend on his friend's birthday presents. He buys one present that costs $12. How much does he have left to spend?

4 Dinah got 87 points on her first test and 93 points on her second test. What is her point total for the first two tests?

Answers

1. 3000 − 1180 = 1820 mi³

2. 53 − 24 = 29°F

3. 18 − 12 = $6

4. 87 + 93 = 180 points

 Focus on Problem Solving

Organizer

Objective: Focus on choosing an operation: addition or subtraction.

 Online Edition

Resources

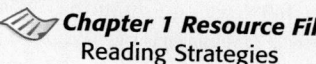 **Chapter 1 Resource File** Reading Strategies

Problem Solving Process

This page focuses on the third step of the problem-solving process: **Solve**

Discuss

Have students discuss the action that is taking place in each exercise and the operation that they chose to perform that action.

Possible answers:

1. Finding the difference; find the difference between the volumes of Lake Superior and Lake Michigan: 3000 − 1180.

2. Finding the difference; find the difference between the average temperatures in Homer in July and in December: 53 − 24.

3. Taking away; if Einar took away $12 from $18, find how much he has left: 18 − 12.

4. Combining; combine the point totals 87 and 93 to find the total points for the first two tests: 87 + 93.

 California Standards

Mathematical Reasoning 1.1
Also covered:
Number Sense
← **1.2 Add, subtract,** multiply, and divide **rational numbers** (integers, fractions, and terminating decimals) and take positive rational numbers to whole-number powers.

Solving Equations

 **One-Minute Section Planner**

Lesson	Lab Resources	Materials
Lesson 1-7 Solving Equations by Adding or Subtracting • Solve equations using addition and subtraction. 🐻 **AF1.0, AF1.4, Preparation for** 🔑 **AF4.0**	**Hands-On Lab 1-7** In *Chapter 1 Resource File*	**Optional** Algebra tiles (MK), balance scale
Lesson 1-8 Solving Equations by Multiplying or Dividing • Solve equations using multiplication and division. 🐻 **AF1.3, Preparation for** 🔑 **AF4.0**	**Hands-On Lab 1-8** In *Chapter 1 Resource File*	**Optional** Square and circle cutouts
1-9 Hands-On Lab Model Two-Step Equations • Use algebra tiles to model and solve two-step equations. 🐻 🔑 **AF4.1**		**Required** Algebra tiles (MK)
Lesson 1-9 Solving Two-Step Equations • Solve two-step equations. 🐻 **AF1.1,** 🔑 **AF4.1**		**Optional** Paper clips, paper cups

MK = *Manipulatives Kit*

Notes

_____

_____

_____

_____

_____

_____

_____

_____

_____

_____

_____

_____

Math Background:
Teaching the Standards

Professional Development

SOLVING SIMPLE EQUATIONS 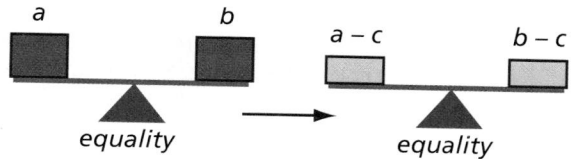 AF4.0
Lessons 1-7, 1-8

Understanding how to solve an equation begins with understanding what is meant by a solution. A *solution* of an equation that contains a variable is a value of the variable that makes the equation true. For the equation $x + 9 = 15$, the value 6 is a solution since the equation $6 + 9 = 15$ is true. The value 7 is not a solution since the equation $7 + 9 = 15$ is not true. Students should recognize that this is the idea behind "checking a solution."

Often, simple equations such as $x + 9 = 15$ can be solved immediately by inspection, and students may feel that any other methods are unnecessarily cumbersome. Students should realize, however, that the basic techniques can be extended to more complex equations and, even more important, that the general process of solving equations is part of the logical system upon which all mathematics is based. Thus, as students learn to solve equations, they begin to build logically sound mathematical arguments.

Solving the equation $x + 9 = 15$ requires the essential understanding that 9 is added to the variable and that the variable can be isolated by using the inverse operation to "undo" the addition, that is, by subtracting 9. However, the equation states that two quantities are equal, and to preserve this "balance," the subtraction must be performed on both sides. This is justified by the Subtraction Property of Equality, which says that if a, b, and c are real numbers and $a = b$, then $a - c = b - c$. The property can be visualized using a balance scale.

```
  a           b          a − c        b − c
 [■]         [■]        [▭]          [▭]
    ▲                      ▲
  equality              equality
```

Even the simplest equations can be written such that the variable appears in a variety of positions. Also, the variable may be represented by any letter, not only by x. With experience, students should recognize the commonalities among the equations $x + 9 = 15$, $13 + j = 20$, $11 = 8 + m$, and $s + 6 = 16$. In all of

these equations, a number is added to the variable, and the equation can be solved by subtracting that same number from both sides of the equation.

TWO-STEP EQUATIONS AF4.1
Lesson 1-9

A *two-step equation* is an equation that involves two operations, such as $5x - 7 = 23$, which involves multiplication and subtraction. Solving a two-step equation requires students to use a sequence of mathematical properties to isolate the variable. At each stage of the process, students write an *equivalent equation;* that is, an equation that has the same solution(s) as the original equation.

When confronted with a two-step equation, a student may have difficulty deciding which operations to use and the order in which to use them. Begin by analyzing the operations in the original equation. For example, in $5x - 7 = 23$, the order of operations tells us that the variable x is first multiplied by 5 and that 7 is then subtracted from the resulting quantity. To undo this process, apply the inverse of each operation *in the reverse order.* In other words, add 7 and then divide by 5, as shown below.

$$5x - 7 = 23$$
$$\underline{+ 7 \quad\quad + 7} \quad\quad \textit{Addition Property of Equality}$$
$$5x \quad\quad = 30$$

$$\frac{5x}{5} = \frac{30}{5} \quad\quad \textit{Division Property of Equality}$$
$$x = 6$$

Notice that the equations $5x = 30$ and $x = 6$ are equivalent to the given equation because they were obtained through a series of steps in which properties of equality were used.

The above example illustrates how solving an equation involves careful decision making. In particular, the process of solving an equation is a process of writing a finite sequence of equivalent equations such that the final equation has the variable isolated on one side. The tools for generating this sequence of equivalent equations are the properties of equality and the properties that are used to simplify expressions, such as the Identity Property of Multiplication (*Lesson 1-8*).

Objective: Students solve equations using addition and subtraction.

 Hands-On Lab
In *Chapter 1 Resource File*

 Online Edition
Tutorial Videos, Interactivities

 Countdown to Mastery Week 2

 **Power Presentations**
with PowerPoint®

Warm Up

Add, subtract, multiply, or divide.

1. $24 + 17$ 41   **2.** $23 - 19$ 4

3. $12 \cdot 3$ 36   **4.** $6(-7)$ -42

5. $\frac{-64}{8}$ -8 **6.** $-250 + (-85)$
   -335

Also available on transparency

Math Humor

After he put his algebra homework in a jar of hot water, the student explained, "I thought you told us to *dissolve* the equations!"

California Standards

Algebra and Functions 1.4 and Prep for AF4.0

Also covered:

**Algebra and Functions
1.0** Students express quantitative relationships by using algebraic terminology, expressions, **equations,** inequalities, and graphs.

California Standards

Preparation for AF4.0
Students solve simple linear equations and inequalities **over the rational numbers.**
AF1.4 Use algebraic terminology (**e.g.,** variable, **equation,** term, coefficient, inequality, expression, constant) **correctly.**

Vocabulary
equation
inverse operations

Why learn this? You can use an equation to represent the forces acting on an object. (See Example 3.)

3 + 8   11

An **equation** is a mathematical statement that uses an equal sign to show that two expressions have the same value. All of these are equations.

$$3 + 8 = 11 \qquad r + 6 = 14 \qquad -24 = x - 7 \qquad \frac{-100}{2} = -50$$

To *solve* an equation that contains a variable, find the value of the variable that makes the equation true. This value of the variable is called the *solution* of the equation.

> **EXAMPLE 1** **Determining Whether a Number Is a Solution of an Equation**
>
> Determine which value of x is a solution of the equation.
>
> $x - 7 = 13; x = 12$ or 20
>
> Substitute each value for x in the equation.
>
> $x - 7 = 13$ $x - 7 = 13$
> $12 - 7 \overset{?}{=} 13$ *Substitute 12 for x.* $20 - 7 \overset{?}{=} 13$ *Substitute 20 for x.*
> $5 \overset{?}{=} 13$ ✗ $13 \overset{?}{=} 13$ ✓
>
> So 12 **is not** a solution.   So 20 **is** a solution.

Helpful Hint

The phrase "subtraction 'undoes' addition" can be understood with this example: If you start with 3 and add 4, you can get back to 3 by subtracting 4.

$$\begin{array}{r} 3 + 4 \\ -\ 4 \\ \hline 3 \end{array}$$

Adding and subtracting by the same number are **inverse operations**. Inverse operations "undo" each other. To solve an equation, use inverse operations to *isolate the variable*. In other words, get the variable alone on one side of the equal sign.

The properties of equality allow you to perform inverse operations. These properties show that you can perform the same operation on both sides of an equation.

You can use the properties of equality along with the Identity Property of Addition to solve addition and subtraction equations.

IDENTITY PROPERTY OF ADDITION		
Words	**Numbers**	**Algebra**
The sum of any number and zero is that number.	$5 + 0 = 5 \qquad -2 + 0 = -2$	$a + 0 = a$

---

1 Introduce

Alternate Opener

> **EXPLORATION**
>
> **1-7 Solving Equations by Adding or Subtracting**
>
> Evaluate the expressions for each given value of x.
>
> 1.
> | x | x + 1 |
> |---|---|
> | 0 | |
> | 1 | |
> | 2 | |
> | 3 | |
>
> 2.
> | x | x − 2 |
> |---|---|
> | 3 | |
> | 4 | |
> | 5 | |
> | 6 | |
>
> Each expression below has been evaluated. Find the value of x.
>
> 3.
> | x | x + 2 |
> |---|---|
> | | 3 |
> | | 4 |
> | | 5 |
> | | 6 |
>
> 4.
> | x | x − 5 |
> |---|---|
> | | 0 |
> | | 1 |
> | | 2 |
> | | 3 |
>
> **Think and Discuss**
> 5. **Explain** how you evaluated the expressions in Problems 1 and 2.
> 6. **Explain** how you found the values of x in Problems 3 and 4.

Motivate

Ask students what makes a scale stay in balance. Have students place various objects on a two-pan scale, removing some, and observing the results. Explain to students that an equation is like a balanced scale, so they must add and subtract carefully.

Explorations and answers are provided in *Alternate Openers: Explorations Transparencies.*

EXAMPLE 2 Solving Equations Using Addition and Subtraction Properties

Solve.

A $6 + t = 28$

$$
\begin{array}{rl}
6 + t = & 28 \\
\underline{-6} & \underline{-6} \\
0 + t = & 22 \\
t = & 22
\end{array}
$$

Since 6 is added to t, subtract 6 from both sides to undo the addition.

Identity Property of Addition: $0 + t = t$

Check

$$
\begin{array}{r}
6 + t = 28 \\
6 + 22 \overset{?}{=} 28 \\
28 \overset{?}{=} 28 \checkmark
\end{array}
$$

To check your solution, substitute 22 for t in the original equation.

B $m - 8 = -14$

$$
\begin{array}{rl}
m - 8 = & -14 \\
\underline{+8} & \underline{+8} \\
m + 0 = & -6 \\
m = & -6
\end{array}
$$

Since 8 is subtracted from m, add 8 to both sides to undo the subtraction.

Identity Property of Addition: $m + 0 = m$

Check

$$
\begin{array}{r}
m - 8 = -14 \\
-6 - 8 \overset{?}{=} -14 \\
-14 \overset{?}{=} -14 \checkmark
\end{array}
$$

To check your solution, substitute -6 for m in the original equation.

C $15 = w + (-14)$

$$
\begin{array}{rl}
15 = & w + (-14) \\
15 - (-14) = & w + (-14) - (-14) \\
29 = & w + 0 \\
29 = & w \\
w = & 29
\end{array}
$$

Since -14 is added to w, subtract -14 from both sides to undo the addition.

Identity Property of Addition

Definition of Equality

PROPERTIES OF EQUALITY

Words	Numbers	Algebra
Addition Property of Equality You can add the same number to both sides of an equation, and the statement will still be true.	$\begin{array}{rl} 2 + 3 = & 5 \\ \underline{+4} & \underline{+4} \\ 2 + 7 = & 9 \end{array}$	If $x = y$, then $x + z = y + z$.
Subtraction Property of Equality You can subtract the same number from both sides of an equation, and the statement will still be true.	$\begin{array}{rl} 4 + 7 = & 11 \\ \underline{-3} & \underline{-3} \\ 4 + 4 = & 8 \end{array}$	If $x = y$, then $x - z = y - z$.

2 Teach

Guided Instruction

In this lesson, students learn to solve equations using addition and subtraction. Before actually solving an equation, review with students how to determine whether a given value is a solution of an equation. Stress the importance of writing all of the steps when solving equations. Share with students the reason for developing the habit—that they will solve equations later that require more steps.

Universal Access

Through Cooperative Learning

Have students work in pairs. Each student writes an addition or subtraction equation, such as $8 + x = 32$ and $x - 3 = 12$, on a sheet of paper. Each student solves the equation and then gives the paper to his or her partner to check the solution. If both solutions are correct, they exchange again to get their original papers and write and solve another equation. If a solution is not correct, the two students work together to find the correct solution.

Possible answers to
Think and Discuss

1. The dog on the left is pulling with more force, so the rope would move to the left.

2. Add 5 to each side to isolate y. The numerical expression on the right side of the equation is the value of y.
   $y = 21$.
   Check the answer:
   $21 − 5 = 16$.

EXAMPLE 3 **PROBLEM SOLVING APPLICATION**

Net force is the sum of all forces acting on an object. Expressed in newtons (N), it tells you in which direction and how quickly the object will move. If two dogs are playing tug-of-war, and the dog on the right pulls with a force of 12 N, what force is the dog on the left exerting on the rope if the net force is 2 N?

1 **Understand the Problem**

The **answer** is the force that the left dog exerts on the rope.

List the **important information:**
• The dog on the right pulls with a force of 12 N.
• The net force is 2 N.

Show the **relationship** of the information:

| net force | = | left dog's force | + | right dog's force |

2 **Make a Plan**

Write **an equation** and solve it. Let f represent the left dog's force on the rope, and use the equation model.

$$2 = f + 12$$

3 **Solve**

$$\begin{aligned} 2 &= f + 12 \\ \underline{-12 \quad\quad -12} & \quad\quad \text{Subtract 12 from both sides.} \\ -10 &= f \end{aligned}$$

The left dog is exerting a force of −10 newtons on the rope.

4 **Look Back**

The problem states that the net force is 2 N, which means that the dog on the right must be pulling with more force. The absolute value of the left dog's force is less than the absolute value of the right dog's force, $|-10| < |12|$, so the answer is reasonable.

Helpful Hint

Force is measured in newtons (N). The number of newtons tells the size of the force and the sign tells its direction. Positive is to the right and up, and negative is to the left and down.

Math Builders

For more on writing equations from words, see the Graph and Equation Builder on page MB2.

Think and Discuss

1. **Explain** what the result would be in the tug-of-war match in Example 3 if the dog on the left pulled with a force of −7 N and the dog on the right pulled with a force of 6 N.

2. **Describe** the steps to solve $y − 5 = 16$.

---

3 **Close**

Summarize

Show students a group of several addition equations. For example:

$$x + 4 = 9 \quad\quad 12 + y = 15$$
$$10 = n + 3 \quad\quad 16 = 4 + z$$

Point out the plus sign in each of the equations. Ask students what operation they would use to solve each of those equations. subtraction Show the solutions and point out the subtraction step in each one. Repeat the procedure with a group of subtraction equations.

California Standards Practice
NS1.2, AF1.4, Preparation for AF4.0

go.hrw.com
Homework Help Online
KEYWORD: MT8CA 1-7
Parent Resources Online
KEYWORD: MT8CA Parent

GUIDED PRACTICE

See Example 1 — Determine which value of x is a solution of each equation.

1. $x + 6 = 18$; $x = 10, 12,$ or 25 **12**   **2.** $x - 7 = 14$; $x = 2, 7,$ or 21 **21**

See Example 2 — Solve.

3. $m - 9 = -23$ **−14**   **4.** $8 + t = 13$ **5**   **5.** $p - (-13) = -10$ **−23**

6. $q + (-25) = 81$ **106**   **7.** $26 = t - 13$ **39**   **8.** $52 = p + (-41)$ **93**

See Example 3 — **9.** A team of mountain climbers descended 3600 feet to a camp that was at an altitude of 12,035 feet. At what altitude did they start?   **15,635 ft**

INDEPENDENT PRACTICE

See Example 1 — Determine which value of x is a solution for each equation.

10. $x - 14 = 8$; $x = 6, 22,$ or 32 **22**   **11.** $x + 23 = 55$; $x = 15, 28,$ or 32 **32**

See Example 2 — Solve.

12. $9 = w + (-8)$ **17**   **13.** $m - 11 = 33$ **44**   **14.** $4 + t = 16$ **12**

15. $z + (-22) = -96$ **−74**   **16.** $102 = p - (-130)$ **−28**   **17.** $27 = h + (-8)$ **35**

See Example 3 — **18.** Olivia owns 43 CDs. This is 15 more CDs than Angela owns. How many CDs does Angela own?   **28**

PRACTICE AND PROBLEM SOLVING

Extra Practice
See page EP3.

Solve. Check your answer.

19. $7 + t = 12$ **5**   **20.** $h - 21 = -52$ **−31**   **21.** $15 = m + (-9)$ **24**

22. $m - 5 = -10$ **−5**   **23.** $h + 8 = 11$ **3**   **24.** $-6 + t = -14$ **−8**

25. $1785 = t - (-836)$ **949**   **26.** $m + 35 = -172$ **−207**   **27.** $x - 29 = 81$ **110**

28. $p + 8 = 23$ **15**   **29.** $n + (-14) = -31$ **−17**   **30.** $20 = -8 + w$ **28**

31. $8 + t = -130$ **−138**   **32.** $57 = c - 28$ **85**   **33.** $-987 = w + 797$ **−1784**

34. Social Studies In 1990, the population of Cheyenne, Wyoming, was 73,142. By 2000, the population had increased to 81,607. Write and solve an equation to find n, the increase in Cheyenne's population from 1990 to 2000.   **73,142 + n = 81,607; 8465**

35. Astronomy Mercury's surface temperature has a range of 600°C. This range is the broadest of any planet in the solar system. Given that the lowest temperature on Mercury's surface is −173°C, write and solve an equation to find the highest temperature.   **t − 600 = −173; 427°C**

Assignment Guide

If you finished Example **1** assign:
Proficient 1–2, 10–11, 36–41, 46, 48–56
Advanced 10–11, 37–41, 43, 46, 48–56

If you finished Example **2** assign:
Proficient 1–8, 10–17, 19–27, 36–41, 46, 48–56
Advanced 10–17, 26–33, 39–41, 43–46, 48–56

If you finished Example **3** assign:
Proficient 1–27, 34–41, 46–52
Advanced 10–18, 28–35, 39–56

Homework Quick Check

Quickly check key concepts.
Exercises: 10, 12, 16, 18, 34

Math Background

An equation with a variable is sometimes called an open sentence. To find a solution to an equation is to find a number that makes an open sentence a true sentence. For example, $x + 5 = 7$ is an open sentence. If you substitute the solution 2 for x, you get the true sentence $2 + 5 = 7$.

Two properties used in solving equations in this lesson are the Addition and Subtraction Properties of Equality. After discussing negative numbers in Chapter 2, the Addition Property of Equality alone can serve the purpose of both properties. To solve the equation $x + 5 = 7$, you can either subtract 5 from both sides or add −5 to both sides.

REVIEW FOR MASTERY 1-7

LESSON 1-7 Review for Mastery
Solving Equations by Adding or Subtracting

To solve an addition equation, use subtraction.

Solve $x + 5 = 12$.
$x + 5 = 12$
$\underline{-5 \quad -5}$ Subtract the number added to the variable.
$x = 7$

To solve a subtraction equation, use addition.

Solve $9 = w - 3$.
$9 = w - 3$
$\underline{+3 \quad +3}$ Add the number subtracted from the variable.
$12 = w$

Tell what you would add or subtract to solve the equation.

1. $a + 2 = 7$ subtract 2   **2.** $x - 2 = 4$ add 2   **3.** $6 + y = 9$ subtract 6   **4.** $34 = b + 13$ subtract 13

5. $21 = z - 9$ add 9   **6.** $14 + r = 20$ subtract 14   **7.** $18 = d - 11$ add 11   **8.** $6 = 5 + p$ subtract 5

Complete to solve the equation. In Exercises 9–11 check the solution.

9. $x - 2 = 15$
$\underline{+2 \quad +2}$
$x - \underline{0} \pm \underline{17}$
$x \pm \underline{17}$
Check: $x - 2 = 15$
$\underline{17} - 2 \pm 15$
$\underline{15} \pm 15 \checkmark$

10. $z + 6 = 14$
$\underline{-6 \quad -6}$
$z + \underline{0} \pm \underline{8}$
$z \pm \underline{8}$
Check: $z + 6 = 14$
$\underline{8} + 6 \pm 14$
$\underline{14} \pm 14 \checkmark$

11. $7 = 4 + n$
$\underline{-4 \quad -4}$
$\underline{3} \pm \underline{0} + n$
$\underline{3} \pm n$
Check: $7 = 4 + n$
$7 \pm 4 + \underline{3}$
$7 \pm \underline{7} \checkmark$

12. $t + 5 = 16$
$\underline{-5 \quad -5}$
$t + \underline{0} = \underline{11}$
$t = \underline{11}$

13. $a - 7 = 13$
$\underline{+7 \quad +7}$
$a - \underline{0} = \underline{20}$
$a = \underline{20}$

14. $28 = 9 + b$
$\underline{-9 \quad -9}$
$\underline{19} = \underline{0} + b$
$\underline{19} = b$

PRACTICE 1-7

LESSON 1-7 Practice B
Solving Equations by Adding or Subtracting

Determine which value is a solution of the equation.

1. $x - 6 = 12$; $x = 6, 8,$ or 18
$x = 18$

2. $9 + x = 17$; $x = 6, 8,$ or 26
$x = 8$

3. $x - 12 = 26$; $x = 14, 38,$ or 40
$x = 38$

4. $x + 18 = 59$; $x = 37, 41,$ or 77
$x = 41$

Solve.

5. $n - 8 = 11$
$n = 19$

6. $9 + g = 13$
$g = 4$

7. $y + 6 = 2$
$y = -4$

8. $-6 + j = -12$
$j = -6$

9. $s - 8 = 11$
$s = 19$

10. $-16 + r = -2$
$r = 14$

11. $a + 35 = 51$
$a = 16$

12. $m - 6 = -13$
$m = -7$

13. $d - 12 = -5$
$d = 7$

14. $7.5 + c = 10.6$
$c = 3.1$

15. $y - 1.7 = 0.6$
$y = 2.3$

16. $m - 2.25 = 4.50$
$m = 6.75$

17. Two sisters, Jenny and Penny, play on the same basketball team. Last season they scored a combined total of 458 points. Jenny scored 192 of the points. Write and solve an equation to find the number of points Penny scored.
$192 + p = 458; p = 266$

18. After his payment, Mr. Weber's credit card balance was $245.76. His payment was for $75.00. Write and solve an equation to find the amount of his credit card bill.
$x - 75.00 = 245.76; x = 320.76$

California Standards

Standard	Exercises
NS1.2 🔑	43, 49–56
AF1.4	1–2, 10–11, 34–42, 44–48
Prep for AF4.0 🔑	1–42, 44–48

Answers

44. Possible answer: If the equation has a plus sign in it, subtract the number after the sign from both sides. If the equation has a minus sign in it, add the number following the sign to both sides.

Journal

Have students explain why they think addition and subtraction equations are often used to find the amount of increase or decrease in a problem.

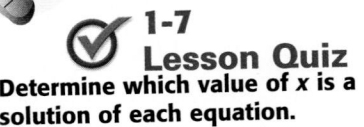

1-7 Lesson Quiz

Determine which value of x is a solution of each equation.

1. $x + 9 = 17$; $x = 6, 8,$ or 26 **8**

2. $x - 3 = 18$; $x = 15, 18,$ or 21 **21**

Solve.

3. $a + 4 = 22$ $a = 18$

4. $n - 6 = 39$ $n = 45$

5. The price of your favorite cereal is now $4.25. In prior weeks, the price was $3.69. Write and solve an equation to find n, the increase in the price of the cereal. $3.69 + n = 4.25$; 0.56

Also available on transparency

42.
$13 + c = 3$; -10
$9 + c = -1$; -10
$8 + c = -2$; -10
$11 + c = 1$; -10

43. Possible answer: The student either subtracted 3 from -7 or added -3 to -7; $-7 - (-3) = -4$.

Determine which value of the variable is a solution of the equation.

36. $d + 4 = 24$; $d = 6, 20,$ or 28 **20**

37. $k + (-13) = 27$; $k = 40, 45,$ or 50 **40**

38. $d - 17 = -36$; $d = 19, 17,$ or -19 **-19**

39. $k + 3 = 4$; $k = 1, 7,$ or 17 **1**

40. $12 = -14 + s$; $s = 20, 26,$ or 32 **26**

41. $-32 = 27 + g$; $g = 58, -25, -59$ **-59**

42. **Science** An ion is a charged particle. Each proton in an ion has a charge of $+1$ and each electron has a charge of -1. The ion charge is the electron charge plus the proton charge. Write and solve an equation to find the electron charge for each ion.

Hydrogen sulfate ion (HSO_4^-)

Name of Ion	Proton Charge	Electron Charge	Ion Charge
Aluminum ion (Al^{3+})	+13	▦	+3
Hydroxide ion (OH^-)	+9	▦	-1
Oxide ion (O^{2-})	+8	▦	-2
Sodium ion (Na^+)	+11	▦	+1

43. **What's the Error?** A student evaluated the expression $-7 - (-3)$ and came up with the answer -10. What did the student do wrong?

44. **Write About It** Write a set of rules to use when solving addition and subtraction equations.

45. **Challenge** Explain how you could solve for h in the equation $14 - h = 8$ using algebra. Then find the value of h.   Possible answers: Subtract 14 from both sides, and then divide by -1, or add h to both sides, and then subtract 8; $h = 6$

SPIRAL STANDARDS REVIEW   ← NS1.2, Prep for ← AF4.0

46. **Multiple Choice** Which value of x is the solution of the equation $x - (-5) = 8$?

   Ⓐ $x = 3$ Ⓑ $x = 11$ Ⓒ $x = 13$ Ⓓ $x = 15$

47. **Multiple Choice** Len bought a pair of $12 flip-flops and a shirt. He paid $30 in all. Which equation can you use to find the price p he paid for the shirt?

   Ⓐ $12 - p = 30$ Ⓑ $12 + p = 30$ Ⓒ $30 + p = 12$ Ⓓ $p - 12 = 30$

48. **Gridded Response** What value of x is the solution of the equation $x - 23 = -19$?   **4**

Add. (Lesson 1-4)

49. $-5 + (-9)$ **-14**   **50.** $16 + (-22)$ **-6**   **51.** $-64 + 51$ **-13**   **52.** $82 + (-75)$ **7**

Multiply or divide. (Lesson 1-6)

53. $7(-8)$ **-56**   **54.** $-63 \div (-7)$ **9**   **55.** $\frac{38}{-19}$ **-2**   **56.** $-8(-13)$ **104**

CHALLENGE 1-7

LESSON 1-7 Challenge
What's Next?

Integers that differ by one, such as 7, 8, 9, are called *consecutive integers*.
Find three consecutive integers whose sum is -12.

   Let $x =$ the 1st of the consecutive integers.

   Let $x + 1 =$ the 2nd of the consecutive integers.

   Let $x + 2 =$ the 3rd of the consecutive integers.

     $(x) + (x + 1) + (x + 2) = -12$ Write an equation.

        $3x + 3 = -12$ Combine like terms.

        $\underline{\,-3 = -3\,}$ Add -3 to each side.

        $3x = -15$

        $\frac{3x}{3} = \frac{-15}{3}$ Divide each side by 3.

        $x = -5$

        $x + 1 = -5 + 1 = -4$

        $x + 2 = -5 + 2 = -3$

So, -5, -4, -3 are the three consecutive integers whose sum is -12.

Write and solve an equation to find the three consecutive integers that satisfy the given condition.

1. Three consecutive integers whose sum is 33 are $\underline{\ 10\ }$, $\underline{\ 11\ }$, $\underline{\ 12\ }$.

   Equation $\underline{(x) + (x + 1) + (x + 2) = 33}$

   $x = \underline{\ 10\ }$

2. Three consecutive integers whose sum is -60 are $\underline{-21}$, $\underline{-20}$, $\underline{-19}$.

   Equation $\underline{(x) + (x + 1) + (x + 2) = -60}$

   $x = \underline{-21}$

3. Three consecutive integers whose sum is -96 are $\underline{-33}$, $\underline{-32}$, $\underline{-31}$.

   Equation $\underline{(x) + (x + 1) + (x + 2) = -96}$

   $x = \underline{-33}$

PROBLEM SOLVING 1-7

LESSON 1-7 Problem Solving
Solving Equations by Adding or Subtracting

Write the correct answer.

1. The 1954 elevation of Mt. Everest was 29,028 ft. In 1999, that elevation was revised to be 29,035 ft. Write an equation to find the change c in elevation of Mt. Everest.

   $\underline{29{,}028 + c = 29{,}035}$
   $\underline{}$

2. The difference between the boiling and melting points of fluorine is 32°C. If the boiling point of fluorine is -188°C, write an equation and solve to find the melting point m of fluorine.

   $\underline{-188 - m = 32;}$
   $\underline{m = -220°C}$

3. Lisa sold her old bike for $140 less than she paid for it. She sold the bike for $85. Write and solve an equation to find how much Lisa paid for her bike.

   $\underline{p - 140 = 85;}$
   $\underline{p = \$225}$

4. The average January temperature in Fairbanks, Alaska, is -13°F. The April average is 43°F higher than the January average. Write an equation to find the average April temperature.

   $\underline{a - (-13) = 43;}$
   $\underline{a = 30°F}$

Choose the letter for the best answer.

5. A survey found that female teens watched 3 hours of TV per week less than male teens. The female teens reported watching an average of 18 hours of TV. Find the number of hours h the male teens watched.

   A $h = 6$ C $h = 18$

   B $h = 15$ Ⓓ $h = 21$

6. It costs about $125 more per year to feed a hamster than it does to feed a bird. If it costs $256 per year to feed a hamster, find the cost c to feed a bird.

   Ⓕ $c = \$131$ H $c = \$256$

   G $c = \$125$ J $c = \$381$

7. Naples, Florida, is the second fastest growing U.S. metropolitan area. From 1990 to 2000, the population increased by 99,278. If the 2000 population was 251,377, find the population p in 1990.

   A $p = 253,377$ C $p = 249,377$

   B $p = 350,655$ Ⓓ $p = 152,099$

8. In 1940, the life expectancy for a female was 65 years. In 1999, the life expectancy for a female was 79 years. Find the increase in the life expectancy for females.

   Ⓕ 14 yrs   H -14 yrs

   G 1.2 yrs   J 144 yrs

Solving Equations by Multiplying or Dividing

California Standards

Preparation for ➤ **AF4.0**
Students solve simple linear **equations** and inequalities **over the rational numbers.**
Also covered: **AF1.3**

Why learn this? You can write a multiplication equation to solve problems about person-hours. (See Example 3.)

Just as with addition and subtraction equations, you can use an identity property to solve multiplication and division equations.

Vocabulary
Identity Property of
  Multiplication
Division Property of
  Equality

IDENTITY PROPERTY OF MULTIPLICATION			
Words	**Numbers**		**Algebra**
The product of any number and one is that number.	$5 \cdot 1 = 5$	$-2 \cdot 1 = -2$	$a \cdot 1 = a$

You can use the properties of equality along with the Identity Property of Multiplication to solve multiplication and division equations.

DIVISION PROPERTY OF EQUALITY		
Words	**Numbers**	**Algebra**
You can divide both sides of an equation by the same nonzero number, and the statement will still be true.	$4 \cdot 3 = 12$ $\dfrac{4 \cdot 3}{2} = \dfrac{12}{2}$ $\dfrac{12}{2} = 6$	If $x = y$ and $z \neq 0$, then $\dfrac{x}{z} = \dfrac{y}{z}$.

EXAMPLE **1** **Solving Equations Using Division**

Solve.

A $8x = 32$

$8x = 32$ *Since x is multiplied by 8, divide both sides*
$\dfrac{8x}{8} = \dfrac{32}{8}$ *by 8 to undo the multiplication.*

$1x = 4$

$x = 4$ *Identity Property of Multiplication: 1 · x = x*

B $-7y = -91$

$-7y = -91$ *Since y is multiplied by −7, divide both sides by*
$\dfrac{-7y}{-7} = \dfrac{-91}{-7}$ *−7 to undo the multiplication.*

$1y = 13$

$y = 13$ *Identity Property of Multiplication: 1 · y = y*

Organizer  1-8

Objective: Students solve equations using multiplication and division.

 Hands-On Lab
In *Chapter 1 Resource File*

 Online Edition
Tutorial Videos, Interactivities

 Countdown to Mastery Week 2

Power Presentations
  with PowerPoint®

Warm Up

Write an algebraic expression for each word phrase.

1. a number x decreased by 9
                    $x - 9$

2. 5 times the sum of p and 6
                    $5(p + 6)$

3. 2 plus the product of 8 and n
                    $2 + 8n$

4. the quotient of 4 and a number c $\dfrac{4}{c}$

Also available on transparency

Math Fact ❗

One of the first mathematical achievements was the equation. Equations can be found in written texts of the Babylonians as far back as 3000 B.C.

---

1 Introduce

Alternate Opener

Motivate

In Lesson 1–7, students may have learned that an equation is like a balanced scale. As with addition and subtraction, remind students to be vigilant about multiplying and dividing by constants.

Explorations and answers are provided in *Alternate Openers: Explorations Transparencies.*

 **California Standards**

Preparation for ➤ **AF4.0**
Also covered:
Algebra and Functions
1.3 Simplify numerical expressions by applying properties of rational numbers (e.g., identity, inverse, distributive, associative, commutative) **and justify the process used.**

Power Presentations
with PowerPoint®

Additional Examples

Example 1

Solve.

A. $6x = 48$ $x = 8$

B. $-9y = 45$ $y = -5$

Example 2

Solve $\frac{b}{-4} = 5$. $b = -20$

Example 3

It takes 450 person-hours to prepare a convention center for a conference. The director of the convention center assigns 25 people to the job. If each person works the same number of hours, how long does each person work? **18 hr**

Also available on transparency

Possible answers to *Think and Discuss*

1. Multiply both sides of the equation by 2.5 to undo the division. $\frac{k}{2.5} = 6$, $2.5 \cdot \frac{k}{2.5} = 2.5 \cdot 6$, $k = 15$

2. All four properties tell you that if you perform the same operation on both sides of an equation, the equality will still hold.

MULTIPLICATION PROPERTY OF EQUALITY		
Words	Numbers	Algebra
You can multiply both sides of an equation by the same number, and the statement will still be true.	$2 \cdot 3 = 6$ $4 \cdot 2 \cdot 3 = 4 \cdot 6$ $8 \cdot 3 = 24$	If $x = y$, then $zx = zy$.

EXAMPLE 2   **Solving Equations Using Multiplication**

Solve $\frac{h}{-3} = 6$.

$$\frac{h}{-3} = 6$$ *Since h is divided by −3, multiply both sides by −3 to undo the division.*

$$-3 \cdot \frac{h}{-3} = -3 \cdot 6$$

$$1h = -18$$

$$h = -18$$ *Identity Property of Multiplication: $1 \cdot h = h$*

EXAMPLE 3   *Sports Application*

It takes 96 person-hours to prepare a baseball stadium for a playoff game. The stadium's manager assigns 6 people to the job. Each person works the same number of hours. How many hours does each person work?

Helpful Hint

A person-hour is a unit of work. It represents the amount of work that can be completed by one person in one hour.

Let x represent the number of hours each person works.

number of people	·	number of hours each person works	=	total number of person-hours
6	·	x	=	96

$$6x = 96$$ *Write the equation.*

$$\frac{6x}{6} = \frac{96}{6}$$ *Since x is multiplied by 6, divide both sides by 6 to undo the multiplication.*

$$1x = 16$$

$$x = 16$$ *Identity Property of Multiplication: $1 \cdot x = x$*

Each person works for 16 hours.

Think and Discuss

1. **Explain** the steps you would use to solve $\frac{k}{2.5} = 6$.

2. **Tell** how the Multiplication and Division Properties of Equality are similar to the Addition and Subtraction Properties of Equality.

2 Teach

Guided Instruction

In this lesson, students learn to solve equations using multiplication and division. Point out that the process is similar to solving equations using addition or subtraction. Review the multiplication and division properties of equality before working through the examples.

 **Teaching Tip**   **Inclusion** Encourage students to check their work by substituting the solution into the original equation.

Universal Access

Through Concrete Manipulatives

Use squares and circles to solve the equation $x + 2 = 5$. Have a square represent x and a circle represent 1. Draw or place a square and two circles on the left side of the equal sign and five circles on the right side. Take two circles away from each side to isolate the variable. Students should see that $x = 3$. Ask students to solve $4x = 12$ using squares and circles and explain how they solved this equation.

Students should draw four squares on the left side and twelve circles on the right. They should group the twelve circles into four groups of three each. $x = 3$

3 Close

Summarize

Review the properties used in solving equations. Have students state the rules for add subtracting, multiplying, and dividing two in gers. Stress the importance of working equa tions one step at a time, writing out each s and checking each solution.

Possible answers: Addition: If the signs are the same, add the absolute values and kee the sign. If the signs are different, subtract the absolute values and use the sign of th number with the greater absolute value. Subtraction: Add the opposite. Multiplicati and division: If the signs are the same, the answer is positive; if the signs are differen the answer is negative.

1-8 Exercises

California Standards Practice
AF1.1, Preparation for ➤ AF4.0

go.hrw.com
Homework Help Online
KEYWORD: MT8CA 1-8
Parent Resources Online
KEYWORD: MT8CA Parent

1-8 Exercises

GUIDED PRACTICE

See Example **1** Solve.

1. $-4x = 28$ **−7**   2. $3y = 42$ **14**   3. $-12q = -24$ **2**   4. $25m = -125$ **−5**

See Example **2** 5. $\frac{l}{-15} = 4$ **−60**   6. $\frac{h}{19} = -3$ **−57**   7. $\frac{m}{-6} = 1$ **−6**   8. $\frac{t}{13} = 52$ **676**

See Example **3** 9. **Business** It takes 270 person-days to prepare one issue of a magazine for publication. Each week, it takes 5 days to prepare an issue of the magazine. Assuming each person works the same number of days, how many people work on the magazine? **54 people**

INDEPENDENT PRACTICE

See Example **1** Solve.

10. $3d = 57$ **19**   11. $-7x = 105$ **−15**   12. $-4g = -40$ **10**   13. $16y = 112$ **7**

14. $-8p = 88$ **−11**   15. $17n = 34$ **2**   16. $-212b = -424$ **2**   17. $41u = -164$ **−4**

See Example **2** 18. $\frac{n}{9} = -63$ **−567** 19. $\frac{h}{-27} = -2$ **54**   20. $\frac{a}{6} = 102$ **612**   21. $\frac{j}{8} = 12$ **96**

22. $\frac{y}{-9} = 11$ **−99**   23. $\frac{d}{7} = -23$ **−161**   24. $\frac{t}{5} = 60$ **300**   25. $\frac{p}{-84} = 3$ **−252**

See Example **3** 26. A kilowatt-hour is one kilowatt of power that is supplied for one hour. The lighting for a 3-hour concert uses a total of 210 kilowatt-hours of electricity. How many kilowatts of electricity do the lights require? **70 kilowatts**

PRACTICE AND PROBLEM SOLVING

Extra Practice
See page EP3.

Solve.

27. $-2x = 14$ **−7**   28. $4y = -80$ **−20**   29. $6y = 12$ **2**   30. $-9m = -9$ **1**

31. $\frac{k}{8} = 7$ **56**   32. $\frac{x}{5} = 121$ **605**   33. $\frac{b}{6} = -12$ **−72**   34. $\frac{n}{15} = 1$ **15**

35. $3x = 51$ **17**   36. $15g = 75$ **5**   37. $r - 92 = 115$ **207**   38. $-23 = x + 36$ **−59**

39. $\frac{b}{-4} = 12$ **−48**   40. $\frac{m}{24} = -24$ **−576**   41. $a + 31 = 16$ **−15**   42. $y - 25 = -5$ **20**

43. **Nutrition** One serving of milk contains 8 grams of protein, and one serving of steak contains 32 grams of protein. Write and solve an equation to find the number of servings of milk n needed to get the same amount of protein as there is in one serving of steak. **$8n = 32$; $n = 4$ servings**

44. **Reasoning** Will the solution of $\frac{x}{-5} = 11$ be greater than 11 or less than 11? Explain how you know.

45. **Multi-Step** Joy earns $8 per hour at an after-school job. Each month she earns $128. How many hours does she work each month? After six months, she gets a $2 per hour raise. How much money does she earn per month now? **16 hr; $160**

44. Possible answer: The solution will be less than 11 because the solution must be negative. Both the divisor and the dividend must be negative because the quotient is positive.

Assignment Guide

If you finished Example **1** assign:
Proficient 1–4, 10–17, 35–38, 57, 59–66
Advanced 10–17, 27–30, 52, 54, 57, 59–66

If you finished Example **2** assign:
Proficient 1–8, 10–25, 35–42, 46–50, 57, 59–66
Advanced 10–34, 46–50, 52, 54, 57, 59–66

If you finished Example **3** assign:
Proficient 1–26, 35–43, 45–51, 53, 57–66
Advanced 10–34, 44–66

Homework Quick Check
Quickly check key concepts.
Exercises: 14, 16, 22, 26, 46

Math Background

Solving equations by using the properties of equality is an essential skill students need in order to develop a strong foundation for algebra. The principles learned here will be useful for other mathematical topics, such as inequalities and formulas. In addition, these skills will aid students in the sciences, including chemistry, physics, and computer science.

California Standards

Standard	Exercises
NS1.2 🔑	59–62
AF1.1	46–50
Prep for AF4.0 🔑	1–58, 63–66

Multiple Choice If students have trouble deciding between answer choices **C** and **D** in **Exercise 57,** remind them that the result of dividing a negative number by a positive number is a negative number. Therefore, they can eliminate choice **D** as the correct answer.

Journal

Have students write about how an equation is like a scale or a balance and what is meant when an equation is "out of balance."

Power Presentations
with PowerPoint®

1-8
Lesson Quiz

Solve.

1. $3t = 9$ $t = 3$

2. $-15 = 3b$ $b = -5$

3. $\frac{x}{-4} = -7$ $x = 28$

4. $z \div 4 = 22$ $z = 88$

5. A roller coaster descends a hill at a rate of 80 feet per second. The bottom of the hill is 400 feet from the top. How long will it take the coaster rides to reach the bottom? **5 seconds**

6. A lot must be cleared so that a new building can be constructed. A crew of 7 workers is assigned to the task and each person works the same number of hours. It takes 525 person-hours to complete the job. How many hours does each person work? **75 hr**

Also available on transparency

Translate each sentence into an equation. Then solve the equation.

46. The quotient of a number d and 4 is -3. $d \div 4 = -3$; $d = -12$

47. The sum of 7 and a number n is 15. $7 + n = 15$; $n = 8$

48. The product of a number b and 5 is 250. $5b = 250$; $b = 50$

49. Twelve is the difference of a number q and -8. $12 = q - (-8)$; $q = 4$

50. Zero is the product of -38 and a number t. $0 = -38t$; $t = 0$

51. **Recreation** While on vacation, Milo drove his car a total of 370 miles. This was 5 times as many miles as he drives in a normal week. How many miles does Milo drive in a normal week?   **74 mi**

52. No. For any value of a, the left side of the equation equals 0 when $x = 0$, but the right side is 12, so $x = 0$ cannot be a solution.

52. **Reasoning** In the equation $ax = 12$, a is an integer. Is it possible to choose a value of a so that the solution of the equation is $x = 0$? Why or why not?

53. **Music** Jason wants to buy the trumpet advertised in the classified ads. He has saved $156. Using the information from the ad, write and solve an equation to find how much more money he needs to buy the trumpet. $195 = 156 + m$; $m = 39$

TICKETS, Friday10/5, Ampitheatre, 7:30 p.m. Good seats. $100/both. Will deliver tickets to you! Jason.123-456-7852.

TICKETS, Rafael Mendoza in concert, Escamillo's ... Haney Island, 10/4, two great seats, row 17. $75 123-567-1234.

TRUMPET, Coronado, mint condition with immaculate finish, asking only $195, Dave, 987-654-3210.

TURNTABLES, 2, Traject 6700 ... Rush M-888 ... needles, great condition. Must sell fast, $1000/best. First buyer takes all. Chad, 321-321-3211.

KCV, Ultrasonic 16-33-45-78 rpm, $100. ... Shure V-15, Mesto, Lancud ...

54. **Write a Problem** Write a problem that can be solved by using the equation $15x = 75$. What is the solution of the problem?   **Possible answer: CDs cost $15 each. Carolyn spent $75 on CDs. How many CDs did she buy? Solution: 5**

55. The solution is $m = 8 \cdot 97$, which is approximately $8 \cdot 100 = 800$.

55. **Write About It** Explain how to estimate the solution of $\frac{m}{8} = 97$.

56. **Challenge** During a winter storm, the temperature dropped $-3°F$ every hour. The overall change in the temperature was $-18°F$. Write and solve an equation to determine how long the storm lasted. $-3x = -18$; 6 hr

SPIRAL STANDARDS REVIEW   NS1.2, Prep for AF4.0

57. **Multiple Choice** Solve the equation $7x = -42$.

   Ⓐ $x = -49$ Ⓑ $x = -35$ Ⓒ $x = -6$ Ⓓ $x = 6$

58. **Gridded Response** On a game show, Paul missed q questions, each worth -100 points. Paul received a total of -900 points. How many questions did he miss?   **9**

Subtract. (Lesson 1-5)

59. $-8 - 8$ -16 60. $-3 - (-7)$ 4   61. $-10 - 2$ -12 62. $11 - (-9)$ 20

Solve each equation. (Lesson 1-7)

63. $4 + x = 13$ $x = 9$ 64. $x - 4 = -9$ $x = -5$ 65. $-17 = x + 9$ $x = -26$ 66. $19 = x + 11$ $x = 8$

CHALLENGE 1-8

Challenge
1-8 *Mathematical Medals*

Each clue will help you determine the number of medals that a country won at the 2004 Summer Olympics. For each clue, write and solve an equation that contains multiplication or division. As you solve each clue, fill in the correct number of medals in the table.

1. You can multiply the number of medals that Kenya won by 8 to get a product of 56.

   $8x = 56$; 7

2. If you divide the number of medals that China won by 9, the result is the number of medals that Kenya won.

   $\frac{x}{9} = 7$; 63

3. China won 21 times as many medals as Morocco.

   $63 = 21x$; 3

4. Divide the number of medals that Great Britain won by 10. The result is the number of medals that Morocco won.

   $\frac{x}{10} = 3$; 30

5. Great Britain won 6 times as many medals as Jamaica.

   $30 = 6x$; 5

6. The number of medals that Cuba won divided by 9 equals the number of medals that Morocco won.

   $\frac{x}{9} = 3$; 27

Country	Number of Medals
China	63
Great Britain	30
Cuba	27
Kenya	7
Jamaica	5
Morocco	3

PROBLEM SOLVING 1-8

Problem Solving
1-8 *Solving Equations by Multiplying or Dividing*

Write the correct answer.

1. Brett is preparing to participate in a 250-kilometer bike race. He rides a course near his house that is 2 km long. Write an equation to determine how many laps he must ride to equal the distance of the race.

   $2l = 250$

2. The average life span of a duck is 10 years, which is one year longer than three times the average life span of a guinea pig. Write and solve an equation to determine the lifespan of a guinea pig.

   $3y + 1 = 10$; $y = 3$

3. The speed of a house mouse is one-fourth that of a giraffe. If a house mouse can travel at 8 mi/h, what is the speed of a giraffe? Write an equation and solve.

   $\frac{g}{4} = 8$; $g = 32$;

   32 mi/h

4. In 2005, the movie with the highest box office sales was *Titanic*, which made about 3 times the box office sales of *Charlie and the Chocolate Factory*. If *Titanic* made about $600 million, about how much did *Charlie and the Chocolate Factory* make? Write an equation and solve.

   $3s = 600$; $s = 200$;

   about $200 million

Choose the letter for the best answer.

5. Farmland is often measured in acres. A farm that is 1920 acres covers 3 square miles. Find the number of acres a in one square mile.

   A 9 acres   Ⓒ 640 acres
   B 213 acres   D 4860 acres

6. When Maria doubles a recipe, she uses 8 cups of flour. How many cups of flour are in the original recipe?

   F 2 cups   H 8 cups
   Ⓖ 4 cups   J 16 cups

7. The depth of water is often measured in fathoms. A fathom is six feet. If the maximum depth of the Gulf of Mexico is 2395 fathoms, what is the maximum depth in feet?

   Ⓐ 14,370 ft   C 29,250 ft
   B 98,867 ft   D 175,464 ft

8. Four times as many pet birds have lived in the White House as pet goats. Sixteen pet birds have lived in the White House. How many pet goats have there been?

   Ⓕ 4   H 12
   G 20   J 64

Model Two-Step Equations

Use with Lesson 1-9

go.hrw.com
Lab Resources Online
KEYWORD: MT8CA Lab1

California Standards

AF4.1 Solve two-step **linear equations** and inequalities **in one variable over the rational numbers,** interpret the solution or solutions in the context from which they arose, **and verify the reasonableness of the results.**

KEY
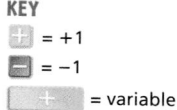 = +1
= −1
= variable

REMEMBER
+ = 0
• You can perform the same operation with the same numbers on both sides of an equation without changing the value of the equation.

You can use algebra tiles to model and solve two-step equations. To solve a two-step equation, you use two different operations.

Activity

① Use algebra tiles to model and solve $3s + 4 = 10$.

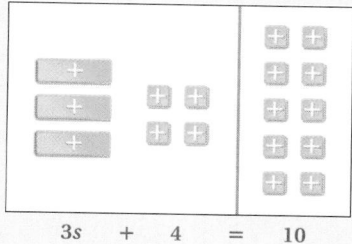

$$3s \quad + \quad 4 \quad = \quad 10$$

Two steps are needed to solve this equation.

Step 1: Remove 4 yellow tiles from each side.

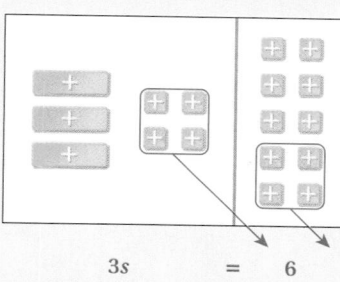

$$3s \quad = \quad 6$$

Step 2: Divide each side into 3 equal groups.

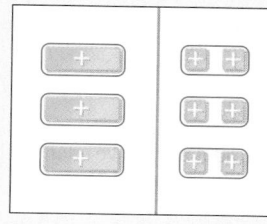

$$s \quad = \quad 2$$

Substitute to check:

$$3s + 4 = 10$$
$$3(2) + 4 \stackrel{?}{=} 10$$
$$6 + 4 \stackrel{?}{=} 10$$
$$10 \stackrel{?}{=} 10 \checkmark$$

Lab continued on next page.

Objective: Use algebra tiles to model and solve two-step equations.

Materials: Algebra tiles

Online Edition
Algebra Tiles

Countdown to Mastery Week 2

Teach
Discuss

Have students use the guess-and-check method to find the solution of the equation $3x + 4 = 10$. Then have them use algebra tiles to model and solve the equation.

Close
Key Concept

When you use algebra tiles to model and solve an equation, you can see how the numbers in the equation are grouped to calculate the final answer.

Assessment

Use algebra tiles to solve each equation.
1. $3x + 4 = 7$ $x = 1$
2. $2x - 9 = 3$ $x = 6$
3. $5x + 6 = 1$ $x = -1$

Teacher to Teacher

Students learn a lot about solving equations by using algebra tiles. Be sure to remind students that because the sum of a number and its opposite is zero, we call opposites "zero pairs." Encourage students to discuss how they use "zero pairs" and inverse operations to solve each of the equations.

Debbie Brown
Austin, Texas

Possible answers to *Think and Discuss*

1. Adding zero pairs in a model is equivalent to adding zero on one side of an algebraic equation. The equation remains balanced.

2.

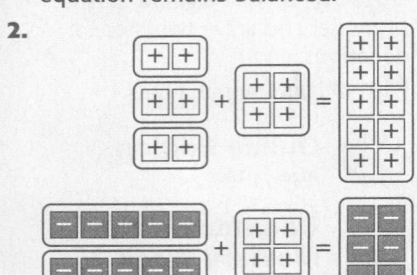

Answers to *Try This*

1.
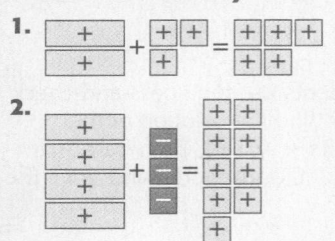

2.
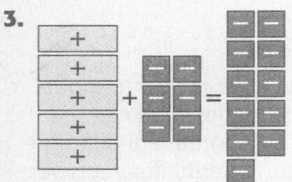

3.
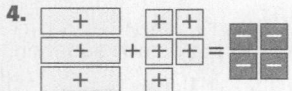

4.
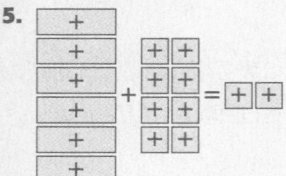

5.
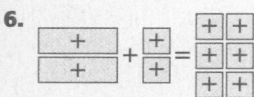

6.
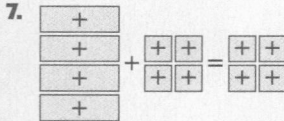

7.

8.
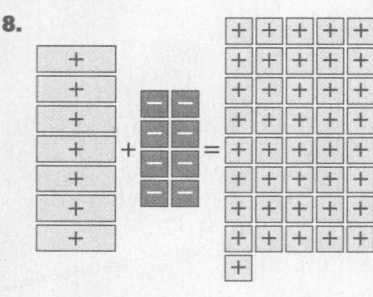

---

② Use algebra tiles to model and solve $2r + 4 = -6$.

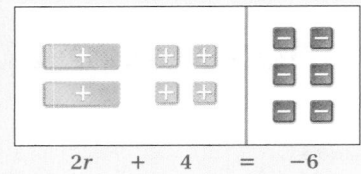

$2r \quad + \quad 4 \quad = \quad -6$

Step 1: Since 4 is being added to $2r$, add 4 red tiles to both sides and remove the zero pairs on the left side.

Add −4 to both sides.

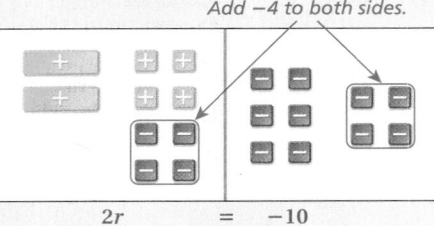

$2r \qquad = \qquad -10$

Step 2: Divide each side into 2 equal groups.

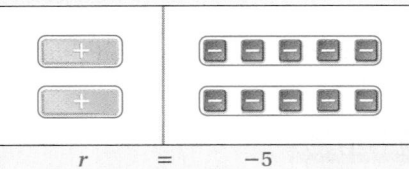

$r \qquad = \qquad -5$

Substitute to check:

$$2r + 4 \overset{?}{=} -6$$
$$2(-5) + 4 \overset{?}{=} -6$$
$$-10 + 4 \overset{?}{=} -6$$
$$-6 \overset{?}{=} -6 \checkmark$$

Think and Discuss

1. Why can you add zero pairs to one side of an equation without having to add them to the other side as well?

2. Show how you could have modeled to check your solution for each equation.

Try This

Use algebra tiles to model and solve each of the following equations.

1. $2x + 3 = 5$ $x = 1$ 2. $4p - 3 = 9$ $p = 3$ 3. $5r - 6 = -11$ $r = -1$ 4. $3n + 5 = -4$
  $n = -3$

5. $6b + 8 = 2$ 6. $2a + 2 = 6$ $a = 2$ 7. $4m + 4 = 4$ $m = 0$ 8. $7h - 8 = 41$
  $b = -1$ $h = 7$

9. Gerry walked dogs five days a week and got paid the same amount each day. One week his boss added on a $15 bonus. That week Gerry earned $90. What was his daily salary?   **$15**

California Standards

AF4.1 Solve two-step linear equations and inequalities in one variable over the rational numbers, interpret the solution or solutions in the context from which they arose, and verify the reasonableness of the results.

Also covered: **AF1.1**

Who uses this? Two-step equations can help pet owners decide how much pet food they should purchase. (See Example 4.)

Two-step equations contain two operations. For example, the equation $6x - 2 = 10$ contains multiplication and subtraction.

$$\text{Multiplication} \longrightarrow \boxed{6x} - 2 = 10$$
$$\underset{\text{Subtraction}}{\uparrow}$$

EXAMPLE 1 **Translating Sentences into Two-Step Equations**

Translate each sentence into an equation.

A 3 more than the product of 5 and a number y is −17.

3 **more than** the **product of** 5 and a number y **is** −17.

$5 \cdot y + 3 = -17$

$5y + 3 = -17$

B The quotient of a number n and −4, minus 8, is −42.

The **quotient of** a number n and −4, **minus** 8, **is** −42.

$[n \div (-4)] - 8 = -42$

$\dfrac{n}{-4} - 8 = -42$

Equations that contain two operations require two steps to solve. Identify the operations and the order in which they are applied to the variable. Then use inverse operations to undo them in the reverse order.

Math Builders

For more on solving two-step equations, see the Step-by-Step Solution Builder on page MB4.

$$6x - 2 = 10$$

Operations in the Equation	To Solve
❶ First x is **multiplied** by 6.	❶ **Add** 2 to both sides of the equation.
❷ Then 2 is **subtracted**.	❷ Then **divide** both sides by 6.

Objective: Solve two-step equations.

 Online Edition
Tutorial Videos

 Countdown to Mastery Weeks 2 and 3

 Power Presentations
with PowerPoint®

Warm Up
Add or subtract.
1. $-6 + (-5)$ −11
2. $4 - (-3)$ 7 **3.** $-2 + 11$ 9
Multiply or divide.
4. $-5(-4)$ 20
5. $\dfrac{18}{-3}$ −6 **6.** $7(-8)$ −56

Also available on transparency

Math Humor

Question: How was the solution of the equation like a toddler?
Answer: It took several steps.

Math Background

Deductive reasoning involves reaching a conclusion by using logical reasoning based on given statements, properties, or premises that you assume to be true. Deductive reasoning is used to solve equations by using the properties of equality. For more on deductive reasoning, see page SB24.

1 Introduce
Alternate Opener

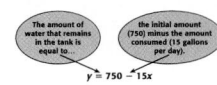
Motivate

Before class, place 3 paper clips into each of 4 paper cups. Show students the cups as well as a pile of 6 additional paper clips. Tell students that each cup contains the same number of paper clips and that there are 18 paper clips altogether. Ask students to determine how many paper clips are in each cup and have them explain their reasoning. Tell students they will be learning a systematic method to solve this type of problem.

Explorations and answers are provided in *Alternate Openers: Explorations Transparencies.*

California Standards

Algebra and Functions **4.1**
Also covered:
Algebra and Functions

1.1 Use variables and appropriate operations to write an expression, an equation, an inequality, or a system of equations or inequalities **that represents a verbal description** (e.g., three less than a number, half as large as area A).

Power Presentations
with PowerPoint®

Additional Examples

Example 1

Translate each sentence into an equation.

A. 17 less than the quotient of a number x and 2 is 21.
$\qquad \frac{x}{2} - 17 = 21$

B. Twice a number m increased by -4 is 0. $\qquad 2m + (-4) = 0$

Example 2

Solve.

A. $3x + 4 = -11 \qquad x = -5$

B. $8 = -5y - 2 \qquad x = -2$

Example 3

Solve.

A. $4 + \frac{m}{7} = 9 \qquad m = 35$

B. $14 = \frac{z}{2} - 3 \qquad z = 34$

Also available on transparency

EXAMPLE 2 Solving Two-Step Equations Using Division

Solve.

Helpful Hint
Reverse the order of operations when solving equations that have more than one operation.

A $2x + 1 = -7$

Step 1: $2x + 1 = -7$
$\qquad \underline{-1 = -1}$
$\qquad 2x \quad = -8$

Note that x is multiplied by 2. Then 1 is added. Work backward: Since 1 is added to 2x, subtract 1 from both sides.

Step 2: $\qquad \frac{2x}{2} = \frac{-8}{2}$
$\qquad x = -4$

Since x is multiplied by 2, divide both sides by 2 to undo the multiplication.

Check

$2x + 1 = -7$
$2(-4) + 1 \overset{?}{=} -7$
$-8 + 1 = -7$
$-7 \overset{?}{=} -7$ ✔

To check your solution, substitute -4 for x in the original equation.

-4 is a solution.

B $18 = -7n - 3$

$18 = -7n - 3$
$\underline{+3 = \qquad +3}$
$21 = -7n$

Since 3 is subtracted from $-7n$, add 3 to both sides to undo the subtraction.

$\frac{21}{-7} = \frac{-7n}{-7}$
$-3 = n$

Since n is multiplied by -7, divide both sides by -7 to undo the multiplication.

EXAMPLE 3 Solving Two-Step Equations Using Multiplication

Solve.

A $5 + \frac{k}{6} = 13$

Step 1: $\quad 5 + \frac{k}{6} = 13$
$\qquad \underline{-5 \qquad = -5}$
$\qquad \frac{k}{6} = \quad 8$

Note that k is divided by 6. Then 5 is added. Work backward: Since 5 is added to $\frac{k}{6}$, subtract 5 from both sides.

Step 2: $\quad (6)\frac{k}{6} = (6)8$
$\qquad k = 48$

Since k is divided by 6, multiply both sides by 6 to undo the division.

B $1 = \frac{v}{9} - 10$

$1 = \frac{v}{9} - 10$
$\underline{+10 = \quad +10}$
$11 = \frac{v}{9}$

Since 10 is subtracted from $\frac{v}{9}$, add 10 to both sides to undo the subtraction.

$(9)11 = (9)\frac{v}{9}$
$99 = v$

Since v is divided by 9, multiply both sides by 9 to undo the division.

---

2 Teach

Guided Instruction

In this lesson, students learn to solve two-step equations. Begin with a brief review of solving one-step equations, emphasizing the use of inverse operations. Then present **Examples 2** and **3**. Help students see that they can "undo" the operations in any order, but it is easier to undo addition or subtraction first.

Universal Access
Through Graphic Organizers

Work with students to create a simple flowchart that shows the process of solving a sample two-step equation. Each item in the flowchart should show one stage of the solution process and give a brief explanation of the mathematics that were used.

3 Close

Summarize

Revisit the situation involving cups and paper clips that was presented at the beginning of the lesson in Motivate. Have students write and solve an equation to find the number of paper clips in each cup.
$4x + 6 = 18; x = 3$

EXAMPLE **4** *Consumer Math Application*

 **Reasoning**

Tyrell is ordering cat food online. Shipping is $12 no matter how many cases he orders. Each case of cat food costs $16. Tyrell has $130 to spend. How many cases of cat food can he order?

Let *c* represent the number of cases that Tyrell can order. That means Tyrell can spend $16c$ plus the cost of shipping.

cost of shipping	+	cost of cat food	=	total cost
$12	+	$16c$	=	$130

$$12 + 16c = 130$$
$$\underline{-12 \qquad\quad = -12} \qquad \text{\textit{Subtract 12 from both sides.}}$$
$$16c = 118$$
$$\frac{16c}{16} = \frac{118}{16} \qquad \text{\textit{Divide both sides by 16.}}$$
$$c = 7.375$$

Since you cannot order part of a case, Tyrell can order 7 cases.

Answers to *Think and Discuss*

1. First add or subtract a quantity on both sides of the equation to isolate the term with the variable in it.

2. Add 5 to both sides of the equation. Then divide both sides of the equation by 7.

Think and Discuss

1. Explain how you decide which operation to use first when solving a two-step equation.

2. Describe the steps you would follow to solve $-5 + 7x = 16$.

Additional Examples

Example **4**

Donna buys a portable DVD player that costs $120. She also buys several DVDs that cost $14 each. She spends a total of $204. How many DVDs does she buy? **6**

Also available on transparency

Teaching Tip **Communicating Math**
After students have read the problem in **Example 4,** help them identify and paraphrase the essential information that will be needed to solve the problem.

1-9 Exercises

 **GUIDED PRACTICE**

See Example **1** Translate each sentence into an equation.

1. 6 more than 9 times a number *x* is −12. $9x + 6 = -12$

2. The quotient of a number *t* and 7, plus 2, is −4. $\frac{t}{7} + 2 = -4$

See Example **2** Solve.

3. $4x + 7 = 15$ **2**

4. $8 + 5s = 53$ **9**

5. $-3n - 18 = 6$ **−8**

6. $12 = -5p + 2$ **−2**

7. $-6 = 2y + 4$ **−5**

8. $6w - 8 = -20$ **−2**

See Example **3** Solve.

9. $4 + \frac{m}{3} = 12$ **24**

10. $7 + \frac{x}{7} = 9$ **14**

11. $\frac{w}{6} - 2 = 5$ **42**

12. $\frac{x}{3} - 13 = 11$ **72**

13. $6 = -5 + \frac{r}{8}$ **88**

14. $-8 = -15 + \frac{z}{2}$ **14**

California Standards Practice
AF1.1, AF4.1

go.hrw.com
Homework Help Online
KEYWORD: MT8CA 1-9
Parent Resources Online
KEYWORD: MT8CA Parent

Assignment Guide

If you finished Example **1** assign:
Proficient 1–2, 16–18, 57–64
Advanced 16–18, 57–64

If you finished Example **2** assign:
Proficient 1–8, 16–24, 39, 42–43, 45, 48–49, 57–64
Advanced 16–18, 22–27, 39, 42–43, 45, 48–49, 57–64

If you finished Example **3** assign:
Proficient 1–14, 16–24, 28–33, 38–43, 55–64
Advanced 16–18, 22–27, 31–36, 44–49, 55–64

If you finished Example **4** assign:
Proficient 1–24, 28–33, 37–43, 50, 55–64
Advanced 16–18, 22–27, 31–64

Homework Quick Check

Quickly check key concepts.
Exercises: 16, 18, 22, 32, 38

After you put on your socks and put on your shoes, you can undo the process by taking off your shoes and taking off your socks. That is, you do the inverse operations and you do them in the opposite order. In the same way, solving an equation can be thought of as undoing operations on a variable. For example, in the equation $3x + 1 = 16$, the variable x is multiplied by 3 and then 1 is added to this quantity. To solve the equation, do the inverse operations in the opposite order: subtract 1 from both sides, and then divide both sides by 3.

See Example 4   15. **Consumer Math** A Web site that rents DVDs charges a one-time fee of $7 to become a member of the site. It costs $3 to rent each DVD. Diana joined the site and spent a total of $61. How many DVDs did she rent?   **18 DVDs**

INDEPENDENT PRACTICE

See Example 1   **Translate each sentence into an equation.**

16. 11 less than the quotient of a number b and 12 is -5. $\frac{b}{12} - 11 = -5$

17. 18 more than the product of 4 and a number z is -54. $4z + 18 = -54$

18. The difference of twice a number n and 9 is 17. $2n - 9 = 17$

See Example 2   **Solve.**

19. $5y + 16 = 21$ **1**   20. $14 = 2x + 16$ **-1**   21. $-6 = 5t + 24$ **-6**

22. $-10w + 3 = 53$ **-5**   23. $-7q + 8 = -27$ **5**   24. $12 = 5m - 13$ **5**

25. $-9 = 6g + 3$ **-2**   26. $16y - 41 = 7$ **3**   27. $-3z + 11 = 38$ **-9**

See Example 3   **Solve.**

28. $2 + \frac{w}{5} = 9$ **35**   29. $10 + \frac{r}{2} = 8$ **-4**   30. $4 = \frac{y}{9} - 4$ **72**

31. $17 = \frac{x}{8} + 12$ **40**   32. $\frac{w}{4} - 5 = 16$ **84**   33. $-3 + \frac{n}{5} = 8$ **55**

34. $\frac{t}{7} + 8 = -5$ **-91**   35. $\frac{g}{-3} - 8 = 2$ **-30**   36. $\frac{x}{-8} + 2 = -3$ **40**

See Example 4   37. Bob's Auto Shop charges $375 to replace the timing belt in a car. The belt costs $50 and the labor to install the belt costs $65 per hour. How many hours does it take to install the timing belt?   **5 hr**

PRACTICE AND PROBLEM SOLVING

Extra Practice
See page EP3.

38. A number divided by 6 plus 5 equals 12; 42

Translate each equation into words. Then solve the equation.

38. $\frac{x}{6} + 5 = 12$

39. $4y - 9 = 3$ Nine less than 4 times a number is 3; 3

40. $7 = \frac{w}{2} - 4$ Seven is equal to a number divided by 2 minus 4; 22

Solve and check.

41. $11 + \frac{m}{3} = 4$ **-21**

42. $-6 + 4p = -2$ **1**

43. $-7j - 12 = 9$ **-3**

44. $4 = \frac{x}{-3} + 1$ **-9**

45. $-5 = 2z - 5$ **0**

46. $\frac{r}{4} - 3 = -8$ **-20**

Translate each sentence into an equation. Then solve the equation.

47. Three less than the quotient of a number x and 9 is 8. $\frac{x}{9} - 3 = 8; x = 99$

48. Thirteen plus the product of -15 and a number a is 58.
    $13 + (-15)a = 58; a = -3$

49. If 5 is decreased by 3 times a number m, the result is -4.
    $5 - 3m = -4; m = 3$

50. **Hobbies** Mike has 60 baseball cards in his collection. Each week he buys a pack of cards to add to the collection. Each pack contains the same number of cards. After 12 weeks, Mike has 156 cards. Write and solve an equation to find the number of cards in a pack. $60 + 12x = 156; x = 8$ cards

REVIEW FOR MASTERY 1-9

LESSON 1-9 Review for Mastery
Solving Two-Step Equations

You can solve two-step equations by undoing one operation at a time. First undo any addition or subtraction, then undo any multiplication or division.

Complete the steps to solve each equation.

1. $4d + 7 = 39$

$4d + 7 - \underline{7} = 39 - \underline{7}$ ← Subtract $\underline{7}$ from both sides to undo addition.
$4d = 32$
$\frac{4d}{4} = \frac{32}{4}$ ← Divide both sides by $\underline{4}$ to undo multiplication.
$d = 8$

Check

$4d + 7 = 39$
$4(\underline{8}) + 7 \stackrel{?}{=} 39$ ← Substitute $\underline{8}$ for d.
$\frac{32}{} + 7 \stackrel{?}{=} 39$
$39 \stackrel{?}{=} 39$ ✔   ← 8 is a solution.

2. $\frac{x}{3} - 5 = 2$ 3. $2m - 8 = 10$ 4. $4 + \frac{a}{5} = 7$
$\frac{x}{3} - 5 + \underline{5} = 2 + \underline{5}$ $2m - 8 + \underline{8} = 10 + \underline{8}$ $4 - \underline{4} + \frac{a}{5} = 7 - \underline{4}$
$\frac{x}{3} = \underline{7}$ $2m = \underline{18}$ $\frac{a}{5} = \underline{3}$
$3 \cdot \frac{x}{3} = \underline{3} \cdot 7$ $\frac{2m}{2} = \frac{18}{2}$ $5 \cdot \frac{a}{5} = \underline{5} \cdot 3$
$x = \underline{21}$ $m = \underline{9}$ $a = \underline{15}$

Solve.

5. $6t + 15 = 33$ 6. $\frac{b}{4} - 7 = 9$ 7. $2 - 8y = -14$

$t = 8$ $b = 64$ $y = 2$

PRACTICE 1-9

LESSON 1-9 Practice B
Solving Two-Step Equations

Solve. Check each answer.

1. $5g + 9 = 24$ 2. $-6w - 3 = 9$ 3. $2d - 16 = 12$

$g = 3$ $w = -2$ $d = 14$

4. $7t - 3 = 11$ 5. $4n + 1 = 13$ 6. $3k - 15 = 6$

$t = 2$ $n = 3$ $k = 7$

Solve.

7. $\frac{y}{6} - 7 = 2$ 8. $\frac{m}{2} + 8 = 5$ 9. $1 + \frac{s}{5} = 8$

$y = 54$ $m = -6$ $s = 35$

10. $-3 + \frac{b}{7} = -6$ 11. $6 + \frac{x}{3} = 13$ 12. $\frac{t}{5} - 9 = -7$

$b = -21$ $x = 21$ $t = 10$

13. $-4 + \frac{v}{2} = 5$ 14. $\frac{a}{7} + 1 = 9$ 15. $\frac{w}{-5} + 8 = 2$

$v = 18$ $a = 56$ $w = 30$

16. Two years of local phone service costs $883, including the installation fee of $55. What is the monthly fee?

$23

California Standards

Standard	Exercises
NS1.2 🔑	54, 57–60
AF1.1	1–2, 16–18, 38–40, 47–53
Prep for AF4.0 🔑	61–64
AF4.1 🔑	3–15, 19–53

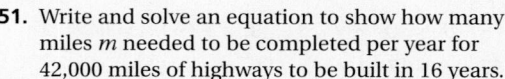

In 1956, during President Eisenhower's term, construction began on the United States interstate highway system. The original plan was for 42,000 miles of highways to be completed within 16 years. It actually took 37 years to complete. The last part, Interstate 105 in Los Angeles, was completed in 1993.

51. Write and solve an equation to show how many miles m needed to be completed per year for 42,000 miles of highways to be built in 16 years.

52. Interstate 35 runs north and south from Laredo, Texas, to Duluth, Minnesota, covering 1568 miles. There are 505 miles of I-35 in Texas and 262 miles in Minnesota. Write and solve an equation to find m, the number of miles of I-35 that are not in either state.
$m + (505 + 262) = 1568$; $m = 801$ miles

53. A portion of I-476 in Pennsylvania, known as the Blue Route, is about 22 miles long. The length of the Blue Route is about one-sixth the total length of I-476. Write and solve an equation to calculate the length of I-476 in miles m. $\frac{1}{6}m = 22$; $m = 132$ miles

54. ⭐ **Challenge** Interstate 80 extends from California to New Jersey. At right are the number of miles of Interstate 80 in each state the highway passes through.

a. __?__ has 134 more miles than __?__. **Iowa; Indiana**

b. __?__ has 174 fewer miles than __?__. **Ohio; Nevada**

Number of I-80 Miles

State	Miles
California	195
Nevada	410
Utah	197
Wyoming	401
Nebraska	455
Iowa	301
Illinois	163
Indiana	167
Ohio	236
Pennsylvania	314
New Jersey	68

SPIRAL STANDARDS REVIEW 🠔 AF4.1

55. Multiple Choice Solve the equation $4 + \frac{t}{5} = -8$.

Ⓐ $t = -60$ Ⓑ $t = -40$ Ⓒ $t = -20$ Ⓓ $t = -10$

56. Multiple Choice For which equation is $m = -3$ a solution?

Ⓐ $5m + 6 = -21$ Ⓑ $\frac{m}{3} + 1 = -1$ Ⓒ $-2 + 3m = -11$ Ⓓ $12 + \frac{m}{3} = 15$

Multiply or divide. (Lesson 1-6)

57. $-4(-11)$ **44**   **58.** $\frac{-12}{3}$ **−4**   **59.** $6(-5)$ **−30**   **60.** $\frac{42}{-7}$ **−6**

Solve. (Lesson 1-8)

61. $\frac{y}{-8} = 9$ **−72**   **62.** $-16m = 48$ **−3**   **63.** $\frac{p}{7} = 21$ **147**   **64.** $12g = -108$ **−9**

CHALLENGE 1-9

LESSON 1-9 **Challenge**
Which Square is Magic?

A *magic square* has the same sum for every row, column, and diagonal. In the magic square below, the solution of each equation is a number of the magic square. But, one of the equations has a solution that does not fit in this magic square.

Solve each equation. Find the magic sum. Circle the equation that does not fit in this magic square. Write a new equation with a solution that completes the magic square. Replacement for the equation in the center box will vary; but, its solution should be 5. Possible replacement: $2x + 15 = 25$.

The magic sum is ___15___.

$8x - 15 = 17$	$6x + 24 = 78$	$\frac{x}{2} + 23 = 24$
$x = $ __4__	$x = $ __9__	$x = $ __2__
$3x - 1 = 8$	$\frac{x}{5} + 23 = 25$	$13x - 2 = 89$
$x = $ __3__	$x = $ __10__	$x = $ __7__
$\frac{x}{2} + 33 = 37$	$9x + 84 = 93$	$\frac{x}{3} - 1 = 1$
$x = $ __8__	$x = $ __1__	$x = $ __6__

PROBLEM SOLVING 1-9

LESSON 1-9 **Problem Solving**
Solving Two-Step Equations

Write the correct answer.

1. Last week, Susan had several bananas and 4 apples as snacks. The snacks contained a total of 760 calories. If each apple had 80 calories and each banana had 110 calories, how many bananas did she have?
4 bananas

2. Beth eats 2,300 calories per day. She eats 600 calories at breakfast and 1.5 times as many at lunch. If she eats three meals with no snacks, which meal will contain the most calories?
dinner

3. Greta is following a 2,500 calorie-per-day diet. She eats 10 servings of fruit, averaging 100 calories per serving. She also eats 6 servings of vegetables. If the rest of her daily intake is 780 calories, what is the average number of calories in each serving of vegetables?
120 calories

4. Linus follows a 2,900 calorie-per-day diet. He has 9 servings of grains, which average 160 calories each. He has a combined 12 servings of fruits and milk, averaging 90 calories each. How many 190-calorie servings of meat and vegetables did he have to complete his diet?
2 servings

Choose the letter for the best answer.

The table shows calories burned by a person performing different activities.

Calories Used in Activities

Activity	Calories (per min)
Hiking	8.4
Kayaking	7.1
Tennis	8.6
Walking	5.9

5. Melinda walks for 0.75 hour. How many calories does she burn?
Ⓐ 4.425 calories Ⓒ 265.5 calories
Ⓑ 378 calories Ⓓ 6.45 calories

6. Sam hikes at a rate of 3 mi/h. How far must he hike to burn 756 calories?
Ⓕ 1.5 mi Ⓕ 90 mi
Ⓖ 4.5 mi Ⓙ 30 mi

7. Joy kayaks for 50 minutes and plays tennis for 1.5 hours. How many calories does she burn?
Ⓐ 1,129 calories C 886 calories
B 1,194 calories D 367.9 calories

8. How many hours would you have to hike to burn 882 calories?
Ⓕ 105 hr Ⓗ 1.75 hr
Ⓖ 123.5 hr Ⓙ 2.07 hr

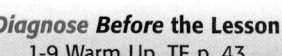
Answers

51. $16 \cdot m = 42{,}000$; 2625 miles per year

Teaching Tip **Multiple Choice** In **Exercise 55,** students who chose **C** may have added 4 to both sides of the equation rather than subtracted 4. Remind students to use inverse operations to isolate the variable. Also encourage them to check their answer choice by substituting the value into the equation.

 Journal

Have students explain how to solve a two-step equation by writing an annotated step-by-step solution to the equation $7y - 12 = 23$.

Power Presentations
with PowerPoint®

✓ **1-9**
Lesson Quiz

Translate the sentence into an equation.

1. The product of −3 and a number c, plus 14, is −7. $-3c + 14 = -7$

Solve.

2. $17 = 2x - 3$ **10**

3. $-4m + 3 = 15$ **−3**

4. $\frac{w}{2} - 5 = 1$ **12**

5. $2 = 3 - \frac{x}{4}$ **4**

6. A discount movie pass costs $14. With the pass, movie tickets cost $6 each. Fern spent a total of $68 on the pass and movie tickets. How many movies did he see? **9**

Also available on transparency

Organizer

Objective: Assess students' mastery of concepts and skills in Lessons 1-7 through 1-9.

Resources

 **Assessment Resources**
Section 1B Quiz

 **Test & Practice Generator**
One-Stop Planner®

INTERVENTION ◀▶

Resources

 Ready to Go On? Intervention and Enrichment Worksheets

 Ready to Go On? CD-ROM

 Ready to Go On? Online

my.hrw.com

Quiz for Lessons 1-7 Through 1-9

☑ **1-7** Solving Equations by Adding or Subtracting

Solve.

1. $p - 12 = -5$ $p = 7$ 2. $w + (-9) = 14$ $w = 23$ 3. $t + (-14) = 8$ $t = 22$
4. $23 + k = -5$ $k = -28$ 5. $-52 + p = 17$ $p = 69$ 6. $y - (-6) = -74$
$y = -80$

7. The approximate surface temperature of Pluto is $-391°F$. This is approximately 1255 degrees cooler than the approximate surface temperature of Venus. What is the approximate surface temperature of Venus? 864°F

☑ **1-8** Solving Equations by Multiplying or Dividing

Solve.

$x = 7$ $y = -6$ $y = -864$
8. $\frac{x}{6} = -48$ $x = -288$ 9. $3x = 21$ 10. $14y = -84$ 11. $\frac{y}{12} = -72$
12. $-5p = 75$ 13. $\frac{r}{-7} = 3$ $r = -21$ 14. $\frac{d}{12} = -10$ 15. $8y = -96$
$p = -15$ $d = -120$ $y = -12$

16. Ahmed's baseball card collection consists of 228 cards. This is 4 times as many cards as Ming has. How many baseball cards are in Ming's collection?

17. It takes 72 person-hours to clean an office building each night. A crew of 12 people cleans the building and each person works the same number of hours. How many hours does each person work?   6 hr

16. 57 baseball cards

☑ **1-9** Solving Two-Step Equations

Solve.

18. $3x + 1 = -8$ $x = -3$ 19. $2 = \frac{y}{5} - 8$ $y = 50$ 20. $-7n - 4 = 24$ $n = -4$
21. $6 + \frac{k}{4} = 14$ $k = 32$ 22. $-13 + \frac{y}{9} = -24$ $y = -99$ 23. $27 = 5x + 2$ $x = 5$
24. $-41 = -2 - 13n$ $n = 3$ 25. $3 + \frac{x}{7} = 3$ $x = 0$ 26. $-15 = 5 + \frac{k}{-6}$ $k = 120$

27. Richard is collecting bottle caps for a school fundraiser. He has collected 335 caps toward his goal of 500 caps. If he collects 15 bottle caps per week, how many more weeks will it take before he reaches his goal? 11 weeks

28. One week Ella worked 36 hours as a prep chef. Her earnings for the week totaled $210, which included $30 in tips that she made as a waitress. How much money does Ella make per hour? $5/hr

---

NO INTERVENE

READY TO GO ON?
Diagnose and Prescribe

YES ENRICH

READY TO GO ON? Intervention, Section 1B			
Ready to Go On? Intervention	Worksheets	CD-ROM	Online
☑ Lesson 1-7 Prep for AF4.0	1-7 Intervention	Activity 1-7	Diagnose and Prescribe Online
☑ Lesson 1-8 Prep for AF4.0	1-8 Intervention	Activity 1-8	
☑ Lesson 1-9 AF4.1	1-9 Intervention	Activity 1-9	

READY TO GO ON? Enrichment, Section 1B
 Worksheets
 CD-ROM
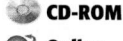 Online

---

CONCEPT CONNECTION

Have a Ball A physical education class is playing a variation of basketball. When a team makes a basket from inside the three-point line, the team gets a "Climb" (C), or 2 points. When a team makes a basket from outside the three-point line, the other team gets a "Slide" (S), or −1 point.

1. During the first 20 minutes of the game, a team gets the following: C, C, S, S, C, S, C, C, and S. Simplify the expression $2 + 2 + (-1) + (-1) + 2 + (-1) + 2 + 2 + (-1)$ to determine the team's score. **6 points**

2. The points scored by two teams during a game are shown in the table. Which team won the game? What was the difference in the teams' scores? **Team 1 won the game; 3 points**

3. Diego's team gets 3 Climbs and 2 Slides, but not necessarily in that order. Find his team's score by substituting $S = -1$ and $C = 2$ in the expression $3C + 2S$. **4 points**

4. After four consecutive baskets are made, Leann's team's score is −8. After the next basket is made, the team's score is −6. Write and solve an equation for the last made basket. $-8 + x = -6; x = 2$

5. Daryl's team finishes the game with a score of 12. If his team scored 9 times, how many Climbs did the team get? **7**

6. Is it possible to finish with a score of 2 after five baskets are made? Explain your reasoning.

Game Results	
Team 1	**Team 2**
C	C
S	C
S	C
S	S
S	S
C	S
C	S
C	S

CONCEPT CONNECTION

Organizer

Objective: Assess students' ability to apply concepts and skills in Chapter 1 in a real-world format.

 **Online Edition**

Problem	Text reference
1	Lesson 1-4
2	Lesson 1-5
3	Lesson 1-6
4	Lesson 1-7
5	Lesson 1-8
6	Lesson 1-9

Answers

6. The only possible scores after 5 baskets are −5, −2, 1, 4, 7, and 10. It is not possible to finish at 2. The table shows all the possibilities.

Climb	Slide	Score
0(2)	5(−1)	−5
1(2)	4(−1)	−2
2(2)	3(−1)	1
3(2)	2(−1)	4
4(2)	1(−1)	7
5(2)	0(−1)	10

INTERVENTION

Scaffolding Questions

1. As you add from left to right, is the sum of 2 and 2 positive or negative? **Positive** What is this sum? **4** How do you add $4 + (-1)$? Find the difference of the absolute values (3) and use the sign of the greater absolute value (+).

2. How can you group Team 1's shots to write the expression compactly? $4(2) + 4(-1)$ or $4C + 4S$

3. What expression do you get by substituting the values of C and S? $3(2) + 2(-1)$ What is the order of operations in evaluating the expression? Multiply, and then add.

4. If x represents the value of the next shot, what equation can you write? $-8 + x = -6$ How do you solve this equation? Add 8 to both sides.

5. Did Daryl's team get mostly Slides or mostly Climbs? Why? Mostly Climbs since the team's score is greater than the number of times it scored.

6. What strategies can you use to find all the possible final positions? Make a table, make an organized list, etc.

Extension

1. Suppose the teams each take 7 shots. What would be the best and worst final positions in this case? 14 and −7

2. The teams decide on a new rule: After a team gets 2 slides in a row, it multiplies its current score by −3 and then continues the game as before. Mei's team scores C C S S C C C. What is the team's final score? 0

California Standards

➡ **NS1.2 Add, subtract, multiply, and divide rational numbers (integers,** fractions, and terminating decimals) **and take positive rational numbers to whole-number powers.**

Organizer

Objective: Participate in games to practice and apply skills learned in Chapter 1.

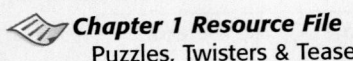
Online Edition

Resources

Chapter 1 Resource File
Puzzles, Twisters & Teasers

Math Magic

Purpose: To apply the problem-solving skill of translating words into math to perform a fun trick

Discuss Ask students to explain how the trick works. What does the variable *n* represent?
Possible answer: Operations are performed on the variable in such a way that the result is a constant. The variable *n* represents whatever number a person begins with.

Extend Challenge students to create their own math magic tricks. Have them explain how their tricks work by using variables.
Possible answer: Think of a number. Multiply the number by 10. Divide the result by 5. Add 7. Subtract 2 times the original number. Your answer is 7. The algebraic representation is as follows: n, $10n$, $\frac{10n}{5}$, $2n + 7$, $2n + 7 - 2n = 7$.

Crazy Cubes

Purpose: To apply the problem-solving skill of guess and check to a classic brainteaser

Discuss Discuss some strategies that students can use to begin the game.
Possible answer: Set the first cube, and then try to place the other cubes, one at a time, so that no number is repeated along the front, back, top, and bottom.

Ask students why this game is a challenge. Possible answer: because you can't see all the sides at once and because the order of the cubes might change as you go along

Extend Have students explore the number of possible ways to position a cube. There are 24 possible ways to position each cube (6 faces to serve as base, with 4 options for the front).

Game Time

Math Magic

You can guess what your friends are thinking by learning to "operate" your way into their minds! For example, try this math magic trick.

> **Think of a number. Multiply the number by 8, divide by 2, add 5, and then subtract 4 times the original number.**

No matter what number you choose, the answer will always be 5. Try another number and see. You can use what you know about variables to prove it. Here's how:

	What you say:	What the person thinks:	What the math is:
Step 1:	Pick any number.	6 (for example)	n
Step 2:	Multiply by 8.	$8(6) = 48$	$8n$
Step 3:	Divide by 2.	$48 \div 2 = 24$	$8n \div 2 = 4n$
Step 4:	Add 5.	$24 + 5 = 29$	$4n + 5$
Step 5:	Subtract 4 times the original number.	$29 - 4(6) = 29 - 24 = 5$	$4n + 5 - 4n = 5$

Invent your own math magic trick that has at least five steps. Show an example using numbers and variables. Try it on a friend!

Crazy Cubes

This game, called The Great Tantalizer around 1900, was reintroduced in the 1960s as "Instant Insanity™." Make four cubes with paper and tape, numbering each side as shown.

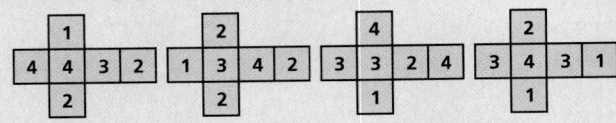
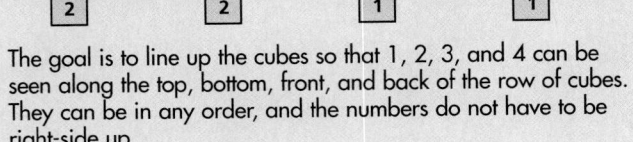

The goal is to line up the cubes so that 1, 2, 3, and 4 can be seen along the top, bottom, front, and back of the row of cubes. They can be in any order, and the numbers do not have to be right-side up.

Materials
- sheet of decorative paper ($8\frac{1}{2}$ by 11 in.)
- ruler
- pencil
- scissors
- glue
- markers

PROJECT Note-Taking
Taking Shape

Make this notebook to help you organize examples of algebraic expressions.

Directions

1 Hold the sheet of paper horizontally. Make two vertical lines $3\frac{5}{8}$ inches from each end of the sheet. **Figure A**

2 Fold the sheet in half lengthwise. Then cut it in half by cutting along the fold. **Figure A**

3 On one half of the sheet, cut out rectangles A and B. On the other half, cut out rectangles C and D. **Figure B**

Rectangle A: $\frac{3}{4}$ in. by $3\frac{5}{8}$ in.

Rectangle B: $1\frac{1}{2}$ in. by $3\frac{5}{8}$ in.

Rectangle C: $2\frac{1}{4}$ in. by $3\frac{5}{8}$ in.

Rectangle D: 3 in. by $3\frac{5}{8}$ in.

4 Place the piece with the taller rectangular panels on top of the piece with the shorter rectangular panels. Glue the middle sections of the two pieces together. **Figure C**

5 Fold the four panels into the center, starting with the tallest panel and working your way down to the shortest.

Taking Note of the Math

Write "Addition," "Subtraction," "Multiplication," and "Division" on the tabs at the top of each panel. Use the space below the name of each operation to list examples of verbal, numerical, and algebraic expressions.

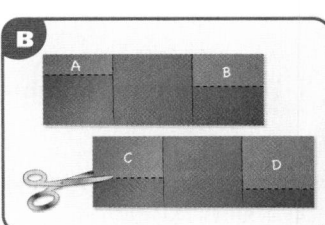

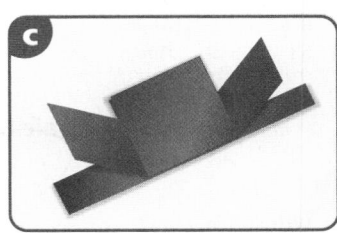

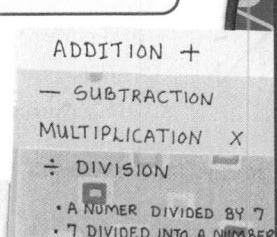

DIVISION EXPRESSION

$\frac{a}{7}$ or $a \div 7$

ADDITION +

— SUBTRACTION

MULTIPLICATION X

÷ DIVISION

- A NUMBER DIVIDED BY 7
- 7 DIVIDED INTO A NUMBER
- QUOTIENT OF A NUMBER AND 7

Organizer

Objective: Make a notebook in which to record examples of algebraic expressions.

Materials: sheet of decorative paper ($8\frac{1}{2}$ by 11 in.), ruler, pencil, scissors, glue, markers

PREMIER **Online Edition**

Using the Page

Preparing the Materials
If class time is limited, you may wish to photocopy $8\frac{1}{2}$ by 11 in. sheets of paper that have preprinted lines for making the necessary cuts.

Making the Project
This project incorporates a hands-on review of measurement skills. Have students work in pairs to ensure accurate measurements.

Extending the Project
Challenge students to make similar notebooks that have six or eight panels. Students will need to plan carefully to calculate the appropriate dimensions for the panels.

Tips from the Bag Ladies!

We've found that the project works especially well when students begin with sheets of paper in different colors. Once students have cut their sheets in half, they can swap one of the halves with a partner. By doing so, each student's booklet will have panels in two different colors!

Organizer

Objective: Help students organize and review key concepts and skills presented in Chapter 1.

Online Edition
Multilingual Glossary

Resources

PuzzlePro®
One-Stop Planner®

Multilingual Glossary Online

go.hrw.com
KEYWORD: MT8CA Glossary

Lesson Tutorial Videos
CD-ROM

Test & Practice Generator
One-Stop Planner®

Answers

1. equation
2. opposite
3. absolute value
4. 147
5. 152
6. 278
7. $2(k + 4)$
8. $4t + 5$
9. 10 less than the product of 5 and b
10. 32 plus the product of 23 and s
11. 12 less than the quotient of 10 and r
12. 16 more than the quotient of y and 8

Vocabulary

absolute value 15	equation 32	integer 14
Addition Property of Equality 33	evaluate 6	inverse operations 32
additive inverse 8	expression 6	numerical expression 6
algebraic expression 6	Identity Property of Addition 32	opposite 14
Division Property of Equality 37	Identity Property of Multiplication 37	Subtraction Property of Equality 33
		variable 6

Complete the sentences below with vocabulary words from the list above.

1. A(n) ___?___ is a statement that two expressions have the same value.

2. ___?___ is another word for "additive inverse."

3. The ___?___ of 3 is 3.

1-1 Evaluating Algebraic Expressions (pp. 6–9)  AF1.2, AF1.4

EXAMPLE

■ Evaluate $4x + 9y$ for $x = 2$ and $y = 5$.

$4x + 9y$
$4(2) + 9(5)$ *Substitute 2 for x and 5 for y.*
$8 + 45$ *Multiply.*
53 *Add.*

EXERCISES

Evaluate each expression.

4. $9a + 7b$ for $a = 7$ and $b = 12$
5. $17m - 3n$ for $m = 10$ and $n = 6$
6. $1.5r + 19s$ for $r = 8$ and $s = 14$

1-2 Writing Algebraic Expressions (pp. 10–13) AF1.1

EXAMPLE

■ Write an algebraic expression for the word phrase "2 less than a number n."
$n - 2$ *Write as subtraction.*

■ Write a word phrase for $25 + 13t$.
25 plus the product of 13 and t

EXERCISES

Write an algebraic expression for each phrase.

7. twice the sum of k and 4
8. 5 more than the product of 4 and t

Write a word phrase for each algebraic expression.

9. $5b - 10$
10. $32 + 23s$
11. $\frac{10}{r} - 12$
12. $16 + \frac{y}{8}$

1-3 Integers and Absolute Value (pp. 14–17)

 NS1.1, NS2.5

EXAMPLE

■ Simplify the expression $|-9| - |3|$.

$|-9| - |3|$

$9 - 3$ $|-9| = 9$ and $|3| = 3$

6 *Subtract.*

EXERCISES

Simplify each expression.

13. $|7 - 6|$
14. $|-8| + |-7|$
15. $|15| + |19|$
16. $|14 + 7|$
17. $|16 - 2|$
18. $|-7| - |-8|$

1-4 Adding Integers (pp. 18–21)

 NS1.2, AF1.3

EXAMPLE

■ Add.

$-8 + 2$ *Find the difference of $|-8|$ and $|2|$.*

-6 *$8 > 2$; use the sign of the 8.*

■ Evaluate.

$-4 + a$ for $a = -7$

$-4 + (-7)$ *Substitute.*

-11 *Same sign*

EXERCISES

Add.

19. $-6 + 4$
20. $-3 + (-9)$
21. $4 + (-7)$
22. $4 + (-3)$
23. $-11 + (-5) + (-8)$

Evaluate.

24. $k + 11$ for $k = -3$
25. $-6 + m$ for $m = -2$

1-5 Subtracting Integers (pp. 22–25)

 NS1.2, NS2.5

EXAMPLE

■ Subtract.

$-3 - (-5)$

$-3 + 5$ *Add the opposite of -5.*

2 *$5 > 3$; use the sign of the 5.*

■ Evaluate.

$-9 - d$ for $d = 2$

$-9 - 2$ *Substitute.*

$-9 + (-2)$ *Add the opposite of 2.*

-11 *Same sign*

EXERCISES

Subtract.

26. $-7 - 9$
27. $8 - (-9)$
28. $-2 - (-5)$
29. $13 - (-2)$
30. $-5 - 17$
31. $16 - 20$

Evaluate.

32. $9 - h$ for $h = -7$
33. $12 - z$ for $z = 17$

1-6 Multiplying and Dividing Integers (pp. 26–29)

 NS1.2

EXAMPLE

Multiply or divide.

■ $4(-9)$ *The signs are **different**.*

-36 *The answer is **negative**.*

■ $\dfrac{-33}{-11}$ *The signs are the **same**.*

3 *The answer is **positive**.*

EXERCISES

Multiply or divide.

34. $7(-5)$
35. $\dfrac{72}{-4}$
36. $-4(-13)$
37. $\dfrac{-100}{-4}$
38. $8(-3)(-5)$
39. $\dfrac{10(-5)}{-25}$

Answers

13. 1
14. 15
15. 34
16. 21
17. 14
18. -1
19. -2
20. -12
21. -3
22. 1
23. -24
24. 8
25. -8
26. -16
27. 17
28. 3
29. 15
30. -22
31. -4
32. 16
33. -5
34. -35
35. -18
36. 52
37. 25
38. 120
39. 2

1-7 Solving Equations by Adding or Subtracting (pp. 32–36)

 AF1.4, Prep for ⟵ AF4.0

EXAMPLE

Solve.

■ $x + 7 = 12$

$\quad \dfrac{-7 \quad -7}{x + 0 = \quad 5}$ *Subtract 7 from both sides.*

$\quad\quad\quad x = \quad 5$ *Identity Property of Zero*

■ $y - 3 = 1.5$

$\quad \dfrac{+3 \quad +3}{y + 0 = \quad 4.5}$ *Add 3 to both sides.*

$\quad\quad\quad y = 4.5$ *Identity Property of Zero*

EXERCISES

Solve and check.

40. $z - 9 = 14$ **41.** $t + 3 = 11$

42. $6 + k = 21$ **43.** $x + 2 = -13$

Write an equation and solve.

44. A polar bear weighs 715 lb, which is 585 lb less than a sea cow. How much does the sea cow weigh?

45. The Mojave Desert, at 15,000 mi^2, is 11,700 mi^2 larger than Death Valley. What is the area of Death Valley?

1-8 Solving Equations by Multiplying or Dividing (pp. 37–40)

Prep for ⟵ AF4.0

EXAMPLE

Solve.

■ $4h = 24$

$\quad \dfrac{4h}{4} = \dfrac{24}{4}$ *Divide both sides by 4.*

$\quad 1h = 6$ *$4 \div 4 = 1$*

$\quad\ h = 6$ *$1 \cdot h = h$*

■ $\dfrac{t}{4} = 16$

$\quad 4 \cdot \dfrac{t}{4} = 4 \cdot 16$ *Multiply both sides by 4.*

$\quad 1t = 64$ *$4 \div 4 = 1$*

$\quad\ t = 64$ *$1 \cdot t = t$*

EXERCISES

Solve and check.

46. $-7g = 56$ **47.** $108 = 12k$

48. $0.1p = -8$ **49.** $-\dfrac{w}{4} = 12$

50. $-20 = \dfrac{y}{2}$ **51.** $\dfrac{z}{24} = 8$

52. The Lewis family drove 235 mi toward their destination. This was $\frac{1}{3}$ of the total distance. What was the total distance?

53. Luz will pay a total of $9360 on her car loan. Her monthly payment is $390. For how many months is the loan?

1-9 Solving Two-Step Equations (pp. 43–47)

⟵ AF4.1

EXAMPLE

Solve $6 + \dfrac{k}{3} = 5$.

$\quad 6 + \dfrac{k}{3} = \quad 5$

$\quad \dfrac{-6 \quad\quad\quad = -6}{}$ *Subtract 6 from both sides.*

$\quad\quad\quad \dfrac{k}{3} = -1$

$\quad (3)\left(\dfrac{k}{3}\right) = (3)(-1)$ *Multiply both sides by 3.*

$\quad\quad\quad\ k = -3$

EXERCISES

Solve.

54. $-15 = 3 + 3x$ **55.** $\dfrac{y}{6} + 9 = 25$

56. $1 + \dfrac{n}{-7} = 8$ **57.** $8x + 10 = 42$

58. $17 = \dfrac{n}{2} + 29$ **59.** $5y - 12 = -67$

60. A home computer repair service charges $68 for the first hour and $48 for each additional hour of service. If a repair bill is $212, how many additional hours did the repair take?

Evaluate each expression for the given value of the variable.

1. $16 - p$ for $p = -12$ **28**

2. $t - 7$ for $t = -14$ **−21**

3. $13 - x + (-2)$ for $x = 4$ **7**

4. $-8y + 27$ for $y = -9$ **99**

Write an algebraic expression for each word phrase.

5. 15 more than the product of 33 and y **$33y + 15$**

6. 18 less than the quotient of x and 7 **$\frac{x}{7} - 18$**

7. 4 times the sum of -7 and h **$4(-7 + h)$**

8. 18 divided by the difference of t and 9 **$\frac{18}{t-9}$**

Write each set of integers in order from least to greatest.

9. $-7, 7, 2, -3, 0, 1$ **$-7, -3, 0, 1, 2, 7$**

10. $-12, -45, 13, 100, 20$ **$-45, -12, 13, 20, 100$**

11. $120, -7, 54, 41, 7$ **$-7, 7, 41, 54, 120$**

Simplify each expression.

12. $|12 - 5| + |-7|$ **14**

13. $|-21| - |9|$ **12**

14. $|-16| - |8 + 3|$ **5**

Perform the given operations.

15. $-9 + (-12)$ **−21**

16. $11 - 17$ **−6**

17. $6(-22)$ **−132**

18. $(-20) \div (-4)$ **5**

19. $42 - (-5)$ **47**

20. $-18 \div 3$ **−6**

21. $-9 - (-13)$ **4**

22. $12 - (-6) + (-5)$ **13**

23. $-2(-21 - 17)$ **76**

24. $(-15 + 3) \div (-4)$ **3**

25. $(54 \div 6) - (-1)$ **10**

26. $-(16 + 4) - 20$ **−40**

27. The temperature on a winter day increased 37°F. If the beginning temperature was −9°F, what was the temperature after the increase? **28°F**

Solve.

28. $y + 19 = 9$ **$y = -10$**

29. $4z = -32$ **$z = -8$**

30. $52 = p - 3$ **$p = 55$**

31. $\frac{w}{3} = 9$ **$w = 27$**

32. $\frac{t}{7} = 12$ **$t = 84$**

33. $-9p = -27$ **$p = 3$**

34. $\frac{q}{-5} = 18$ **$q = -90$**

35. $\frac{g}{4} = -11$ **$g = -44$**

36. Acme Sporting Products manufactures 3216 tennis balls a day. Each container holds 3 balls. How many tennis ball containers are needed daily? **1072 containers**

37. It takes 105 person-hours to set up new computers in an office. A crew sets up the computers and each person works the same number of hours. It takes 7 hours to complete the job. How many people are on the crew? **15 people**

Solve.

38. $9x + 11 = 110$ **$x = 11$**

39. $8 - 6x = 62$ **$x = -9$**

40. $14 = \frac{n}{3} - 4$ **$n = 54$**

41. $2 + \frac{y}{6} = -13$ **$y = -90$**

42. $35 = 27 - 4n$ **$n = -2$**

43. $40 = 53 + \frac{y}{-5}$ **$y = 65$**

44. A round-trip ticket to a soccer camp costs $250. If the total cost for the ticket and 5 days at camp is $715, what is the cost to attend the camp per day? **$93**

45. Group rates at Putt-Putt Pfun include charges of $4 per person and entry to the game room at $10 per group. How many people are in a group that pays $74 for putt-putt and games? **16 people**

Organizer

Objective: Assess students' mastery of concepts and skills in Chapter 1.

 Online Edition

Resources

 Assessment Resources

Chapter 1 Tests
• Free Response
  (Levels A, B, C)
• Multiple Choice
  (Levels A, B, C)
• Performance Assessment

 IDEA Works! CD-ROM
Modified Chapter 1 Test

 **Test & Practice Generator**
One-Stop Planner®

 California Standards

Standard	Items
NS1.1	9–11
NS1.2	15–27
NS2.5	12–14
AF1.1	5–7
AF1.2	1–4
AF1.4	1–4
Prep for AF4.0	28–36
AF4.1	37–44

Organizer

Objective: Provide opportunities to learn and practice common test-taking strategies.

 Online Edition

 **Multiple Choice** When students are faced with a test item that they do not know how to solve, encourage them to eliminate some options and then make an educated guess. Help them identify which options are distracters. In **Example 1,** show students that **B** is a distracter; it is a common student error to subtract instead of add.

Multiple Choice: Eliminate Answer Choices

With some multiple-choice test items, you can use logical reasoning or estimation to eliminate some of the answer choices. Test writers often create the incorrect choices, called *distracters,* using common student errors.

EXAMPLE 1

Which expression represents "4 times the sum of x and 8"?

Ⓐ $4 \cdot (x + 8)$ Ⓒ $4 \cdot x + 8$
Ⓑ $4 \cdot (x - 8)$ Ⓓ $4 \div (x + 8)$

Read the question. Then try to eliminate some of the answer choices.

Use logical reasoning.

Times means "to multiply," and *sum* means "to add." You can eliminate any option without a multiplication symbol and an addition symbol. You can eliminate B and D.

The sum of x and 8 is being multiplied by 4, so you need to add before you multiply. Because multiplication comes before addition in the order of operations, $x + 8$ should be in parentheses. The correct answer is A.

EXAMPLE 2

Which value for k is a solution of the equation $k - 3.5 = 12$?

Ⓐ $k = 8.5$ Ⓒ $k = 42$
Ⓑ $k = 15.5$ Ⓓ $k = 47$

Read the question. Then try to eliminate some of the answer choices.

Use estimation.

You can eliminate C and D immediately because they are too large. Estimate by rounding 3.5 to 4. If $x = 47$, then $47 - 4 = 43$. This is not even close to 12. Similarly, if $x = 42$, then $42 - 4 = 38$, which is also too large to be correct.

Choice A is called a *distracter* because it was created using a common student error, subtracting 3.5 from 12 instead of adding 3.5 to 12. Therefore, A is also incorrect. The correct answer is B.

Even if the answer you calculated is an answer choice, it may not be the correct answer. It could be a distracter. Always check your answers!

Read each test item and answer the questions that follow.

Item A

The table shows average high temperatures for Nome, Alaska. Which answer choice lists the months in order from coolest to warmest?

Month	Temperature (°C)
Jan	−11
Feb	−10
Mar	−8
Apr	−3
May	6
Jun	12
Jul	15
Aug	13
Sep	9
Oct	1
Nov	−5
Dec	−9

(A) Jul, Aug, Jun, Sep, May, Oct, Apr, Nov, Mar, Dec, Feb, Jan

(B) Jul, Jun, Aug, Jan, Feb, Sep, Dec, Mar, May, Nov, Apr, Oct

(C) Jan, Apr, Jun, Jul, Sep, Nov, Feb, Mar, May, Jul, Sep, Nov

(D) Jan, Feb, Dec, Mar, Nov, Apr, Oct, May, Sep, Jun, Aug, Jul

1. Which two choices can you eliminate by using logic? Explain your reasoning.

2. What common error does choice A represent?

Item B

Which value for p is a solution of the equation $p + 5.2 = 15$?

(A) $p = -30.2$ (C) $p = 20.2$
(B) $p = 9.8$ (D) $p = 78$

3. Which choices can you eliminate by using estimation? Explain your reasoning.

4. What common error does choice C represent?

Item C

Solve $\frac{x}{-4} + 20 = -8$ for x.

(A) $x = -112$ (C) $x = 12$
(B) $x = 112$ (D) $x = -48$

5. Which two choices can you eliminate by using logic?

6. What common error does choice C represent?

Item D

Which word phrase can be translated into the algebraic expression $2x - 6$?

(A) six more than twice a number
(B) the sum of twice a number and six
(C) twice the difference of a number and six
(D) six less than twice a number

7. Can you eliminate any of the choices immediately by using logic? Explain your reasoning.

8. Describe how you can determine the correct answer from the remaining choices.

Answers

Possible answers:

1. Both Option A and Option B can be eliminated because they are not reasonable. Both options begin with July, which is the warmest month, not the coolest month.

2. Distracter A was created by listing the months from warmest to coolest.

3. Both Option A and Option D can be eliminated using estimation. Round 5.2 to 5. If $p = -30.2$, estimate $-30 + 5 = -25$. If $p = 78$, estimate $80 + 5 = 85$. Neither answer is close to 15.

4. Distracter C was created by adding 5.2 instead of subtracting it.

5. Since choices A and D will result in a positive quotient, they can be eliminated. The quotient must be negative so that when positive 20 is added to it, the answer will be a negative number.

6. Instead of first using subtraction to move 20 to the right side of the equation, both sides of the equation were multiplied by −4 omitting the term "20" from the process. Then 20 was subtracted from both sides of the equation, resulting in 12 for the solution.

7. Both Option A and Option B can be eliminated because they use the words *six more* and *sum*. Because there is a subtraction symbol, the addition concept cannot be included.

8. Option C is incorrect because "Twice the difference of a number and six" would correspond to the expression $2(x - 6)$. The correct answer is Option D.

Answers To Test Items

A. D
B. B
C. B
D. D

California Standards

NS1.1, AF1.1, ◆ AF4.0, ◆ AF4.1

Organizer

Objective: Provide review and practice for Chapter 1.

 Online Edition

Resources

 Assessment Resources
Chapter 1 Cumulative Test

 Focus on California Standards Benchmark Tests and Intervention

 California Standards Practice CD-ROM

go.hrw.com
KEYWORD: MT8CA Practice

Cumulative Assessment, Chapter 1
Multiple Choice

1. Which expression has a value of 12 when $x = 2$, $y = 3$, and $z = 1$?
   - Ⓐ $3xyz$
   - Ⓑ $2x + 3y + z$
   - Ⓒ $3xz + 2y$
   - Ⓓ $4xyz + 2$

2. The word phrase "10 less than 4 times a number" can be represented by which expression?
   - Ⓐ $10 - 4x$
   - Ⓑ $4x - 10$
   - Ⓒ $10 + 4x$
   - Ⓓ $10x - 4$

3. A copy center prints c copies at a cost of $0.10 per copy. What is the total cost of the copies?
   - Ⓐ $0.10c$
   - Ⓑ $0.10 + c$
   - Ⓒ $\frac{0.10}{c}$
   - Ⓓ $\frac{c}{0.10}$

4. If both x and y are negative, which expression is always negative?
   - Ⓐ $x \cdot y$
   - Ⓑ $x + y$
   - Ⓒ $x \div y$
   - Ⓓ $x - y$

5. What is the solution of $s + (-12) = 16$?
   - Ⓐ $s = 4$
   - Ⓑ $s = 8$
   - Ⓒ $s = 28$
   - Ⓓ $s = 192$

6. Carlos owes his mother money. His paycheck is $105. If he pays his mother the money he owes her, he will have $63 left. Which equation represents this situation?
   - Ⓐ $-x + 63 = 105$
   - Ⓑ $x - 63 = 105$
   - Ⓒ $105 - x = 63$
   - Ⓓ $x - 105 = 63$

7. Which equation uses the Identity Property of Addition?
   - Ⓐ $|-5| = 5$
   - Ⓑ $-8 + 0 = -8$
   - Ⓒ $-6 + 3 = 3 + (-6)$
   - Ⓓ $4 + (1 + 7) = (4 + 1) + 7$

8. Which addition equation represents the number line diagram below?

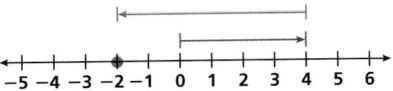

   - Ⓐ $4 + (-2) = 2$
   - Ⓑ $4 + (-6) = -2$
   - Ⓒ $4 + 6 = 10$
   - Ⓓ $-4 + (-6) = -10$

9. Which equation has the solution $x = 16$?
   - Ⓐ $x - 16 = 4$
   - Ⓑ $\frac{x}{2} = 32$
   - Ⓒ $2x = 32$
   - Ⓓ $x + 2 = 16$

10. Solve $6x - 6 = -12$ for x.
    - Ⓐ $x = 1$
    - Ⓑ $x = 3$
    - Ⓒ $x = -3$
    - Ⓓ $x = -1$

11. A scuba diver swimming at a depth of 35 ft below sea level, or -35 ft, dives another 15 ft deeper to get a closer look at a fish. Which integer represents the diver's new depth?
    - Ⓐ -50 ft
    - Ⓑ -20 ft
    - Ⓒ 20 ft
    - Ⓓ 50 ft

Teaching Tip For **item 5,** students who answered **A** subtracted 12 from both sides instead of adding 12 to both sides.

Answers

20. **b.** $42; Substitute 6 for t in the expression $7t$.
    c. $18; Three $20 bills is $60, which is $18 more than the price of the tickets.

21. **a.** $C = 0.15w$
    b. 80; Substitute 12 for C and solve $C = 0.15w$ for w.

22. See 4-Point Response work sample.

California Standards

Standard	Items
NS1.1	12
NS1.2	7, 11, 18, 19
NS2.5	11, 13
AF1.1	2, 3, 6, 8, 20, 21, 22
AF1.2	1, 15, 17, 20
AF1.3	4
AF1.4	22
Prep for AF4.1	5, 9, 16, 21
AF4.1	10, 14, 22

 **HOT TIP!** The incorrect answer choices in a multiple-choice test item are called distracters. They are the results of common mistakes. Be sure to check your work!

12. Which set of numbers is in order from least to greatest?

Ⓐ −15, 13, −10   Ⓒ −10, −15, 13

Ⓑ 13, −10, −15   Ⓓ −15, −10, 13

13. Which expression is equivalent to $|9 - (-5)|$?

Ⓐ $|9| + |-5|$ Ⓒ −14

Ⓑ $|9| - |-5|$ Ⓓ 4

14. Dennis spent a total of $340 on flowers and bushes for his yard. He spent $116 on flowers, and the bushes cost $28 each. To find how many bushes b Dennis bought, solve the equation $28b + 116 = 340$.

Ⓐ 3 bushes   Ⓒ 10 bushes

Ⓑ 8 bushes   Ⓓ 16 bushes

Gridded Response

15. What is the value of the expression $2xy - y$ when $x = 3$ and $y = 5$? **25**

16. What is the solution of the equation $x - 27 = -16$? **11**

17. Evaluate $m + 11 + (-3)$ for $m = -5$. **3**

18. Nora collects 15 magazines every week for 6 weeks to use for an art project. After 6 weeks, she still does not have enough magazines to complete the project. If Nora needs 20 more magazines, how many total magazines does she need? **110**

19. Patricia works twice as many days as Laura works each month. Laura works 3 more days than Jaime. If Jaime works 10 days each month, how many days does Patricia work? **26**

Short Response

20. The Hun family plans to visit the Sea Center. Admission tickets cost $7 each.

a. Write an expression to represent the cost of t tickets. **7t**

b. How much will it cost the Hun family if they buy 6 tickets? Explain your answer.

c. Mrs. Hun pays with three $20 bills. How much change should she get back? Explain your answer.

21. It costs $0.15 per word to place an advertisement in the school newspaper. Let w represent the number of words in an advertisement and C represent the cost of the advertisement.

a. Write an equation that relates the number of words to the cost of the advertisement.

b. If Bernard has $12.00, how many words can he use in his advertisement? Explain your answer.

Extended Response

22. Student Council members at a school are either elected members or work-on members. The number of elected student council members at a school is ten times the number of officers. The 55-member student council includes 5 work-on members.

a. Write an equation to represent the number of student council officers x. Explain the meaning of each term in the equation.

b. Solve the equation in part **a**. Check your answer.

c. At the beginning of the school year, the school's enrollment is 1106 students. By the end of the year, 6 students have transferred out of the school. Write and solve an equation to find the number of students each student council member represented at the end of the year.

Short Response Rubric

Items 20–21

2 Points = The student's answer is an accurate and complete execution of the task or tasks.

1 Point = The student's answer contains attributes of an appropriate response but is flawed.

0 Points = The student's answer contains no attributes of an appropriate response.

Extended Response Rubric

Item 22

4 Points = The student demonstrates a thorough understanding of all concepts and shows all work correctly.

3 Points = The student demonstrates a basic understanding of all concepts, but the work shows some flaws reflecting inattentive execution of mathematical procedures or some misunderstanding of the underlying mathematics.

2 Points = The student demonstrates only a partial understanding of the concepts or procedures embodied in the tasks. The approach may be correct but the work shows a misunderstanding of one or more important concepts.

1 Point = The student demonstrates a very limited understanding of the concepts or procedures embodied in the tasks. The response may show some understanding but exhibits many flaws or is incomplete.

0 Points = The student provides no response at all or a completely incorrect or uninterpretable response.

Student Work Samples for Item 22

4-Point Response

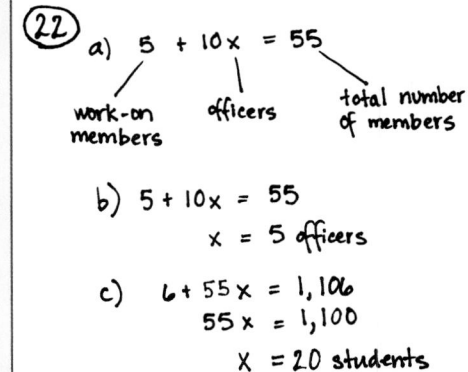

The student thoroughly explained the terms in part **a,** then correctly wrote and solved the equations in parts **b** and **c** showing all work.

3-Point Response

All answers are correct, but the terms are not clearly described in part **a,** not all work shown in part **b,** nor is the answer explained in part **c.**

2-Point Response

The answer to part **a** is correct but incomplete, the answer in part **b** is incorrect as well as incomplete; part **c** is incomplete.

CHAPTER 2

Rational Numbers

		Grade-level Standard
	◄	Review
	►	Beyond the Standards
	A	Assessment
	O	Optional

Pacing Guide

Calendar Planner
Teacher's **One-Stop** Planner®

Lesson/Lab	California Standards	Time	Advanced Students	Benchmark* Students	Strategic** Students
LAB Explore Rational Numbers	🔑 NS1.5	25 min	O	◄	◄
2-1 Rational Numbers	NS1.3, 🔑 NS1.5	50 min	✔	✔	✔
2-2 Comparing and Ordering Rational Numbers	NS1.1, NS1.3	50 min	✔	✔	✔
2-3 Adding and Subtracting Rational Numbers	🔑 NS1.2	50 min	✔	✔	✔
2-4 Multiplying Rational Numbers	🔑 NS1.2	50 min	✔	✔	✔
2-5 Dividing Rational Numbers	🔑 NS1.2, 🔑 AF1.3	75 min	✔	✔	✔
2-6 Adding and Subtracting with Unlike Denominators	🔑 NS1.2, 🔑 NS2.2	50 min	✔	✔	✔
Ready to Go On?		25 min	A	A	A
Focus on Problem Solving		25 min	A	A	O
2-7 One-Step Equations with Rational Numbers	🔑 AF4.0	50 min	O	✔	✔
2-8 Two-Step Equations with Rational Numbers	🔑 AF4.1	50 min	✔	✔	✔
Ready to Go On?		25 min	A	A	A
Concept Connection		25 min	A	A	O
Study Guide: Review		50 min	✔	✔	✔
Chapter Test		50 min	A	A	A

* **Benchmark students** are achieving at or near grade level.

** **Strategic students** may be a year or more below grade level and may require additional time for intervention.

Countdown to Mastery, Weeks 3, 4, 5

ONGOING ASSESSMENT and INTERVENTION

DIAGNOSE	PRESCRIBE

Assess Prior Knowledge

Before Chapter 2

Diagnose readiness for the chapter.
Are You Ready? SE p. 61

Prescribe intervention.
Are You Ready? Intervention Skills 19, 21, 22, 24

Formative Assessment

Before Every Lesson

Diagnose readiness for the lesson.
Warm Up TE, every lesson

Prescribe intervention.
Skills Bank SE pp. SB2–SB24
Review for Mastery CRF, Chapters 1–2

During Every Lesson

Diagnose understanding of lesson concepts.
Questioning Strategies Chapter 2
Think and Discuss SE, every lesson
Write About It SE, lesson exercises
Journal TE, lesson exercises

Prescribe intervention.
Reading Strategies CRF, every lesson
Success for ELL Chapter 2
Lesson Tutorial Videos Chapter 2

After Every Lesson

Diagnose mastery of lesson concepts.
Lesson Quiz TE, every lesson
Ready to Go On? SE pp. 92, 102
Test and Practice Generator

Prescribe intervention.
Review for Mastery CRF, every lesson
Problem Solving CRF, every lesson
Ready to Go On? Intervention Chapter 2
Homework Help Online

Before Chapter 2 Testing

Diagnose mastery of concepts in the chapter.
Ready to Go On? SE pp. 92, 102
Focus on Problem Solving SE p. 93
Concept Connection SE p. 103
Section Quizzes AR pp. 25–26
Test and Practice Generator

Prescribe intervention.
Ready to Go On? Intervention Chapter 2
Scaffolding Questions TE p. 103

Before Assessment of California Standards

Diagnose mastery of California standards.
Focus on California Standards: Benchmark Tests
Mastering the Standards SE pp. 110–111
California Standards Practice CD-ROM

Prescribe intervention.
Focus on California Standards: Intervention

Summative Assessment

After Chapter 2

Check mastery of chapter concepts.
Multiple-Choice Tests (Forms A, B, C)
Free-Response Tests (Forms A, B, C)
Performance Assessment AR pp. 27–38
Test and Practice Generator

Prescribe intervention.
Review for Mastery CRF, every lesson
Lesson Tutorial Videos Chapter 2

KEY: **SE** = *Student Edition*   **TE** = *Teacher's Edition*   **CRF** = *Chapter Resource File*   **AR** = *Assessment Resources*   Available on CD-ROM    Available online

RESOURCE OPTIONS · RESOURCE OPTIONS · RESOURCE OPTIONS · RES

Supporting the Teacher

Chapter 2 Resource File

Family Involvement
pp. 1–4, 53–56

Practice A, B, C
pp. 5–7, 13–15, 21–23, 29–31, 37–39, 45–47, 57–59, 65–67

Review for Mastery
pp. 8, 16, 24, 32, 40, 48, 60, 68

Challenge
pp. 9, 17, 25, 33, 41, 49, 61, 69

Problem Solving
pp. 10, 18, 26, 34, 42, 50, 62, 70

Reading Strategies ELL
pp. 11, 19, 27, 35, 43, 51, 63, 71

Puzzles, Twisters, and Teasers
pp. 12, 20, 28, 36, 44, 52, 64, 72

Hands-On Lab
pp. 75–80

Technology Lab
pp. 73–74

Workbooks

Homework and Practice Workbook SPANISH

Teacher's Guide... pp. 10–17

Know-It Notebook SPANISH
Teacher's Guide.. Chapter 2

Review for Mastery Workbook SPANISH
Teacher's Guide.. pp. 10–17

Focus on California Standards: Intervention Workbook SPANISH
Teacher's Guide

Teacher Tools

Power Presentations 🖸
Complete PowerPoint® presentations for Chapter 2 lessons

Lesson Tutorial Videos SPANISH 💿 🖸
Holt authors Ed Burger and Freddie Renfro present tutorials to support the Chapter 2 lessons.

Teacher's One-Stop Planner SPANISH 🖸
Easy access to all Chapter 2 resources and assessments, as well as software for lesson planning, test generation, and puzzle creation

IDEA Works! 🖸
Key Chapter 2 resources and assessments modified to address special learning needs

Questioning Strategies................................ Chapter 2

Solutions Key.. Chapter 2

Interactive Answers and Solutions 🖸

TechKeys 🪐   **Lab Resources** 🪐

Project Teacher Support 🪐   **Parent Resources** 🪐

Transparencies

Lesson Transparencies, Volume 1 .... Chapter 2
• Teacher Tools
• Warm Ups
• Teaching Transparencies
• Lesson Quizzes

Know-It Notebook.. Chapter 2
• Vocabulary   • Chapter Review
• Additional Examples   • Big Ideas

Alternate Openers: Explorations ....pp. 10–17

Countdown to Mastery ....pp. 5–9

Technology Highlights for the Teacher

🖸 **Power Presentations**

Dynamic presentations to engage students. Complete PowerPoint® presentations for every lesson in Chapter 2.

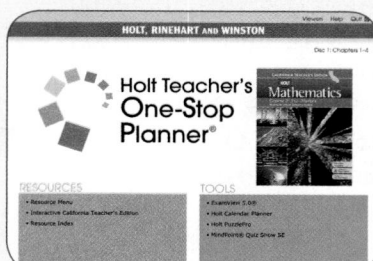

🖸 **One-Stop Planner** SPANISH

Easy access to Chapter 2 resources and assessments. Includes lesson-planning, test-generation, and puzzle-creation software.

🪐 **Premier Online Edition** SPANISH

Includes Tutorial Videos, Lesson Activities, Lesson Quizzes, Homework Help, Chapter Project and more.

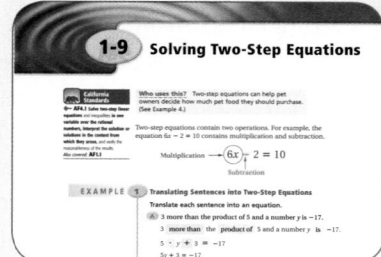

KEY: **SE** = *Student Edition*   **TE** = *Teacher's Edition*   English Language Learners   Spanish available   Available on CD-ROM    Available online

Universal Access

Teaching tips to help all students appear throughout the chapter. A few that target specific students are included in the lists below.

Strategic Students

Practice A	CRF, every lesson
Review for Mastery	CRF, every lesson
Reading Strategies	CRF, every lesson
Academic Vocabulary Connections	TE p. 62
Visual	TE p. 72
Questioning Strategies	Chapter 2
Know-It Notebook SPANISH	Chapter 2
Homework Help Online	
Lesson Tutorial Videos SPANISH	
Online Interactivities SPANISH	

Special Needs Students

Practice A	CRF, every lesson
Review for Mastery	CRF, every lesson
Reading Strategies	CRF, every lesson
Academic Vocabulary Connections	TE p. 62
Inclusion	TE pp. 84, 99
IDEA Works! Modified Resources	Chapter 2
Ready to Go On? Intervention	Chapter 2
Know-It Notebook SPANISH	Chapter 2
Lesson Tutorial Videos SPANISH	
Online Interactivities SPANISH	

English Learners

ENGLISH LANGUAGE LEARNERS

Reading Strategies	CRF, every lesson
Vocabulary Review	SE p. 46
Academic Vocabulary Connections	TE p. 62
English Language Learners	TE pp. 67, 83
Language Support	TE pp. 72, 93
Success for English Language Learners	Chapter 2
Know-It Notebook SPANISH	Chapter 2
Multilingual Glossary	
Lesson Tutorial Videos SPANISH	

Benchmark Students

Practice B	CRF, every lesson
Problem Solving	CRF, every lesson
Academic Vocabulary Connections	TE p. 62
Ready to Go On? Intervention	Chapter 2
Questioning Strategies	Chapter 2
Know-It Notebook SPANISH	Chapter 2
Homework Help Online	
Online Interactivities SPANISH	

Advanced Students

Practice C	CRF, every lesson
Challenge	CRF, every lesson
Reading and Writing Math EXTENSION	TE p. 63
Concept Connection EXTENSION	TE p. 103
Advanced Learners/GATE	TE p. 75
Ready to Go On? Enrichment	Chapter 2

Technology Highlights for Universal Access

Lesson Tutorial Videos SPANISH

Starring Holt authors Ed Burger and Freddie Renfro! Live tutorials to support every lesson in Chapter 2.

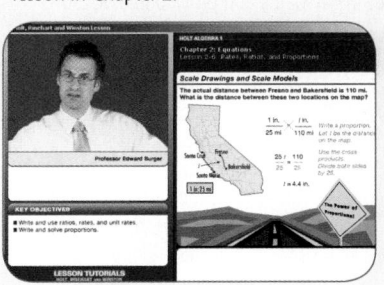

Multilingual Glossary

Searchable glossary includes definitions in English, Spanish, Vietnamese, Chinese, Hmong, Korean, and other languages.

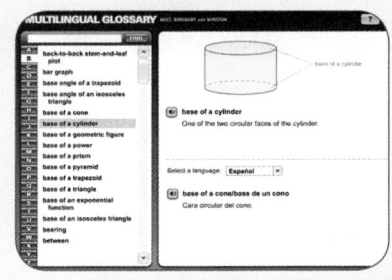

Online Interactivities SPANISH

Interactive tutorials provide visually engaging alternative opportunities to learn concepts and master skills.

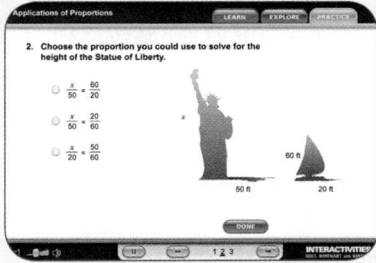

KEY: **SE** = *Student Edition*   **TE** = *Teacher's Edition*   **CRF** = *Chapter Resource File*   SPANISH Spanish available   Available on CD-ROM   Available online

60D

CHAPTER
2

Ongoing Assessment

Assessing Prior Knowledge

Determine whether students have the prerequisite concepts and skills for success in Chapter 2.

Are You Ready? SPANISH 🪐 💿 .... SE p. 61
Warm Up 🔳 💿 .... TE, every lesson

Chapter and Standards Assessment

Provide review and practice for Chapter 2 and standards mastery.

Concept Connection .... SE p. 103
Study Guide: Review .... SE pp. 106–108
Mastering the Standards .... SE pp. 110–111
Countdown to Mastery Transparencies 🔳 💿 ....pp. 5–9
Focus on California Standards: Benchmark Tests 🪐 💿
Focus on California Standards: Intervention Workbook SPANISH
California Standards Practice **CD-ROM** 💿 SPANISH
IDEA Works! Modified Worksheets and Tests

Alternative Assessment

Assess students' understanding of Chapter 2 concepts and combined problem-solving skills.

Performance Assessment .... AR pp. 39–40
Portfolio Assessment .... AR p. xxxvi
Chapter 2 Project 🪐

Daily Assessment

Provide formative assessment for each day of Chapter 2.

Think and Discuss .... SE, every lesson
Write About It .... SE, lesson exercises
Journal .... TE, lesson exercises
Lesson Quiz 🔳 💿 .... TE, every lesson
Questioning Strategies .... Chapter 2
IDEA Works! Modified Lesson Quizzes .... Chapter 2

Weekly Assessment

Provide formative assessment for each week of Chapter 2.

Focus on Problem Solving .... SE p. 93
Concept Connection .... SE p. 103
Ready to Go On? SPANISH 🪐 💿 .... SE pp. 92, 102
Cumulative Assessment .... SE pp. 110–111
Test and Practice Generator SPANISH 💿 ...One-Stop Planner

Formal Assessment

Provide summative assessment of Chapter 2 mastery.

Section Quizzes .... AR pp. 25–26
Chapter 2 Test SPANISH .... SE p.109
Chapter Test (Levels A, B, C) .... AR pp. 27–38
             • Multiple-Choice   • Free-Response
Cumulative Test .... AR pp. 41–44
Test and Practice Generator SPANISH 💿 ...One-Stop Planner
IDEA Works! Modified Tests .... Chapter 2

Technology Highlights for the Teacher

🪐 **Are You Ready?** SPANISH

Automatically assess readiness and prescribe intervention for Chapter 2 prerequisite skills.

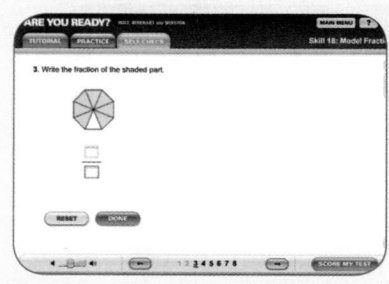

🪐 **Ready to Go On?** SPANISH

Automatically assess understanding of and prescribe intervention for Sections 2A and 2B.

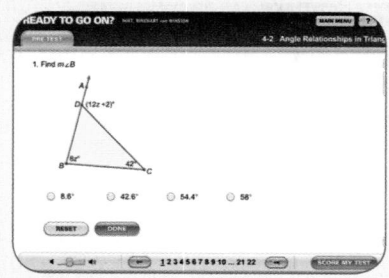

🪐 💿 **Focus on California Standards: Benchmark Tests and Intervention** SPANISH

Automatically assess proficiency with California Grade 7 Standards and provide intervention.

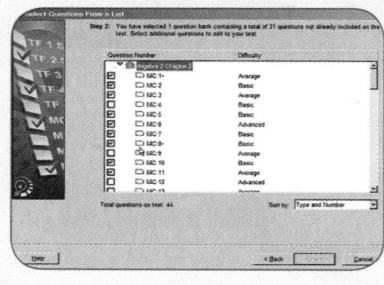

KEY: **SE** = *Student Edition*   **TE** = *Teacher's Edition*   **AR** = *Assessment Resources*   SPANISH Spanish available   💿 Available on CD-ROM   🪐 Available online

60E   Chapter 2

Formal Assessment

Three levels (A, B, C) of multiple-choice and free-response chapter tests are available in the *Assessment Resources.*

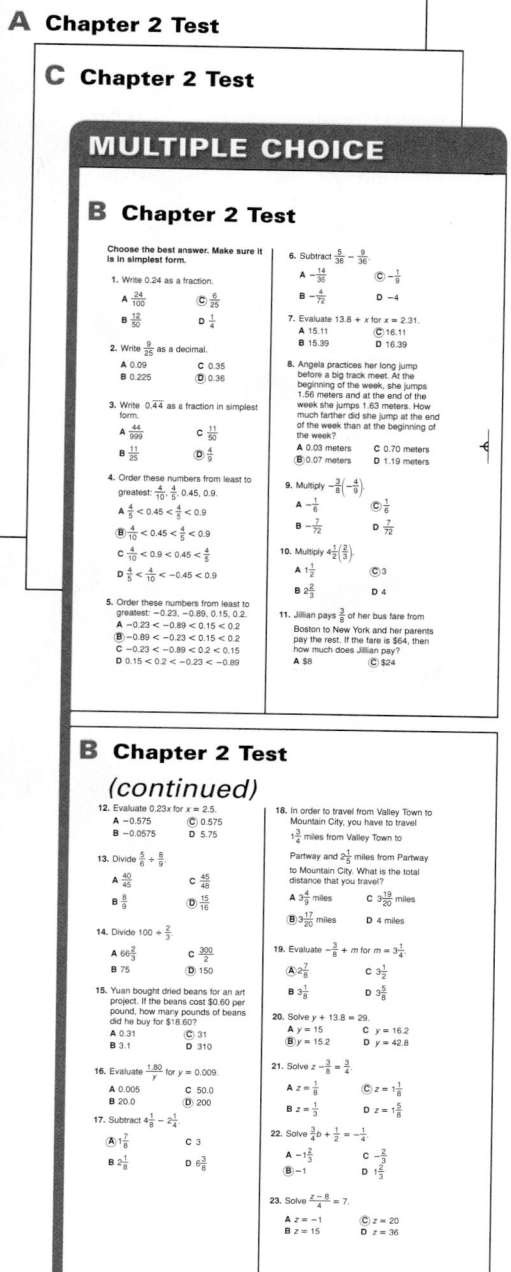

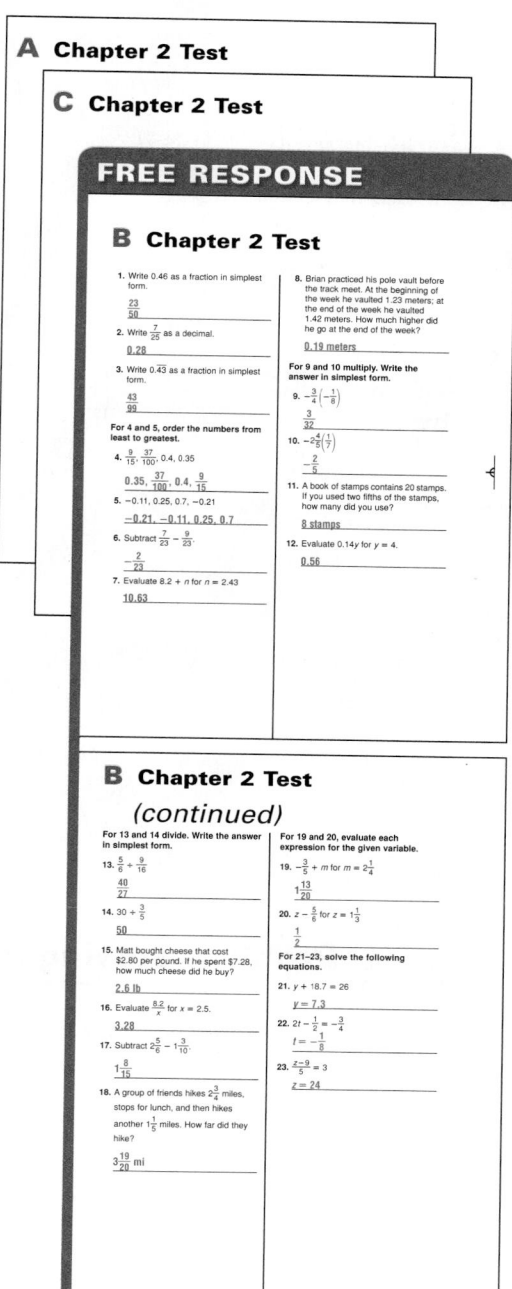

Modified tests and worksheets found in *IDEA Works!*

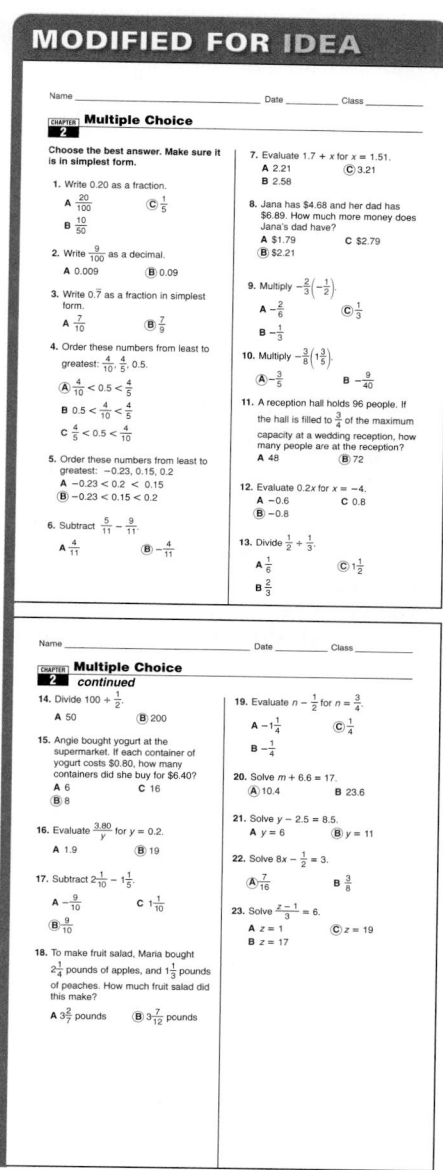

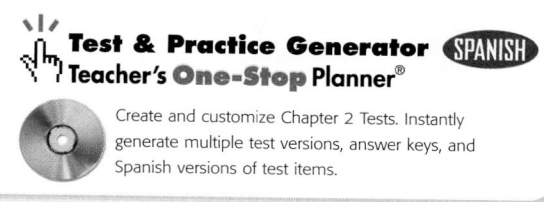

Test & Practice Generator SPANISH
Teacher's One-Stop Planner®

Create and customize Chapter 2 Tests. Instantly generate multiple test versions, answer keys, and Spanish versions of test items.

CHAPTER 2

Focus on Problem Solving

On page 93, students focus on checking for a reasonable answer when solving real-world problems.

CONCEPT CONNECTION On page 103, students use addition, subtraction, multiplication, and division of rational numbers to convert temperatures.

Math in *California*

Castroville is the home of California's annual Artichoke Festival, which includes festivities such as cooking demonstrations and a parade. The nutritional content of artichokes and other foods can be represented by rational numbers, which students will study in this chapter.

CHAPTER 2 — Rational Numbers

CONCEPT CONNECTION

go.hrw.com
Chapter Project Online
KEYWORD: MT8CA Ch2

Rational numbers can be used to describe the amount of nutrients in certain foods.

Problem Solving Project

Understand, Plan, Solve, and Look Back

Have students:

- Complete the Food for Thought worksheet to learn how foods can provide varying amounts of the daily-required nutrients.
- Research why the human body needs the nutrients in the table. What happens when a body is deficient in one of them?
- Bring in some labels from food products. Compare the nutrients on the labels with those in the tables and calculate the fraction of the daily requirements a serving of each food contains.

Life Science and Health Connection

Project Resources
All project resources for teachers and students are provided online.

Materials:
- Food for Thought worksheet

go.hrw.com
Project Teacher Support
KEYWORD: MT8CA PSProject2

ARE YOU READY?

☑ Vocabulary

Choose the best term from the list to complete each sentence.

1. A number that consists of a whole number and a fraction is called a(n) __?__. **mixed number**

2. A(n) __?__ is a number that represents a part of a whole. **fraction**

3. A fraction in which the numerator is greater than or equal to the denominator is called a(n) __?__. **improper fraction; proper fraction**

4. __?__ represent the same value. **equivalent fractions**

equivalent fractions

fraction

improper fraction

mixed number

Complete these exercises to review skills you will need for this chapter.

☑ Simplify Fractions

Write each fraction in simplest form.

5. $\frac{6}{10}$ $\frac{3}{5}$ 6. $\frac{5}{15}$ $\frac{1}{3}$ 7. $\frac{14}{8}$ $1\frac{3}{4}$ 8. $\frac{8}{12}$ $\frac{2}{3}$

9. $\frac{10}{100}$ $\frac{1}{10}$ 10. $\frac{12}{144}$ $\frac{1}{12}$ 11. $\frac{33}{121}$ $\frac{3}{11}$ 12. $\frac{15}{17}$ $\frac{15}{17}$

☑ Write a Fraction as a Mixed Number

Write each improper fraction as a mixed number.

13. $\frac{22}{7}$ $3\frac{1}{7}$ 14. $\frac{18}{5}$ $3\frac{3}{5}$ 15. $\frac{104}{25}$ $4\frac{4}{25}$ 16. $\frac{65}{9}$ $7\frac{2}{9}$

17. $\frac{37}{3}$ $12\frac{1}{3}$ 18. $\frac{48}{5}$ $9\frac{3}{5}$ 19. $\frac{61}{4}$ $15\frac{1}{4}$ 20. $\frac{37}{8}$ $4\frac{5}{8}$

☑ Write a Mixed Number as a Fraction

Write each mixed number as an improper fraction.

21. $7\frac{1}{4}$ $\frac{29}{4}$ 22. $10\frac{3}{7}$ $\frac{73}{7}$ 23. $5\frac{3}{8}$ $\frac{43}{8}$ 24. $11\frac{1}{11}$ $\frac{122}{11}$

25. $3\frac{5}{6}$ $\frac{23}{6}$ 26. $2\frac{4}{5}$ $\frac{14}{5}$ 27. $1\frac{7}{9}$ $\frac{16}{9}$ 28. $3\frac{11}{12}$ $\frac{47}{12}$

☑ Write Equivalent Fractions

Supply the missing information.

29. $\frac{3}{8} = \frac{\blacksquare}{24}$ 9   30. $\frac{5}{13} = \frac{\blacksquare}{52}$ 20   31. $\frac{7}{12} = \frac{\blacksquare}{36}$ 21   32. $\frac{8}{15} = \frac{\blacksquare}{45}$ 24   33. $\frac{3}{5} = \frac{\blacksquare}{75}$ 45

Organizer

Objective: Assess students' understanding of prerequisite skills.

Prerequisite Skills

Simplify Fractions

Write a Fraction as a Mixed Number

Write a Mixed Number as a Fraction

Write Equivalent Fractions

Assessing Prior Knowledge
INTERVENTION

Diagnose and Prescribe

Use this page to determine whether intervention is necessary or whether enrichment is appropriate.

Resources

 **Are You Ready? Intervention and Enrichment Worksheets**

 Are You Ready? CD-ROM

Are You Ready? Online

my.hrw.com

ARE YOU READY?
Diagnose and Prescribe

☑ Prerequisite Skill	🖘 Worksheets	💿 CD-ROM	🪐 Online
☑ Simplify Fractions	Skill 19	Activity 19	Diagnose and Prescribe Online
☑ Write a Fraction as a Mixed Number	Skill 21	Activity 21	
☑ Write a Mixed Number as a Fraction	Skill 22	Activity 22	
☑ Write Equivalent Fractions	Skill 24	Activity 24	

Are You Ready? Intervention, Chapter 2

NO INTERVENE

YES ENRICH

ARE YOU READY? Enrichment, Chapter 2
🖘 **Worksheets**
 **CD-ROM**
🪐 **Online**

Organizer

Objective: Help students understand the new concepts they will learn in Chapter 2.

Academic Vocabulary Connections

In addition to the academic vocabulary listed on the student page, it may help students to become familiar with some of the vocabulary terms in the chapter. Possible answers given.

1. The word *rational* has as its root the word *ration* and sounds somewhat like the word *fraction*. What do you think a **rational number** is in math? A rational number is a number that can be written as a fraction.

2. The word *least* means "smallest," and the word *common* means "the same." What do you think these words mean in combination in **least common denominator**? The least common denominator is the smallest factor that is the same for every denominator.

3. The word *terminate* means "to bring to an end." What do you think a **terminating decimal** might be? A terminating decimal is a decimal number that ends (for example, 0.35).

The information below "unpacks" the standards. The Academic Vocabulary is highlighted and defined to help you understand the language of the standards. Refer to the lessons listed after each standard for help with the math terms and phrases. The Chapter Concept shows how the standard is applied in this chapter.

California Standard	Academic Vocabulary	Chapter Concept
NS1.2 Add, subtract, multiply, and divide rational numbers (integers, fractions, and terminating decimals) and take positive rational numbers to whole-number powers. (Lessons 2-3, 2-4, 2-5, and 2-6)	**terminating** ending; does not repeat	You perform operations with positive and negative fractions and decimals.
NS1.3 Convert fractions to decimals and percents and use these representations in estimations, computations, and applications. (Lesson 2-1)	**convert** change from one form to another	You change fractions into decimals. **Example:** $\frac{1}{4} = 0.25$
NS1.5 Know that every rational number is either a terminating or a repeating decimal and be able to convert terminating decimals into reduced fractions. (Lesson 2-1)	**terminating** ending; does not repeat **convert** change from one form to another	You change decimals that do not contain a repeating pattern into fractions. **Example:** $0.25 = \frac{1}{4}$
NS2.2 Add and subtract fractions by using factoring to find a common denominator. (Lesson 2-6)	**common** the same	You add and subtract fractions with the same denominator. **Example:** $\frac{1}{5} + \frac{2}{5} = \frac{3}{5}$
AF4.0 Students solve simple linear equations and inequalities **over the rational numbers.** (Lesson 2-7)	**solve** find the value of a variable that makes the left side of an equation equal to the right side of the equation (makes the equation true) **Example:** $2x = 6$ $2(3) = 6$ The value that makes $2x = 6$ true is 3.	You perform one operation with rational numbers to find the value of a variable that makes an equation true.

Standards NS1.1, AF1.3, and AF4.1 are also covered in this chapter. To see these standards unpacked, go to Chapter 1, p. 4 (AF4.1), Chapter 3, p. 114 (AF1.3), and Chapter 4, p. 166 (NS1.1).

Looking Back

Previously, students

- compared and ordered positive rational numbers.
- added, subtracted, multiplied, and divided integers.
- solved two-step equations with integers.

In This Chapter

Students will study

- comparing and ordering positive and negative fractions and decimals.
- using appropriate operations to solve problems involving fractions and decimals.
- solving two-step equations with rational numbers.

Looking Forward

Students can use these skills

- to compare and manipulate measurements.
- to find the size of a fraction of a group or an item.
- to solve problems about consumer math.

Writing Strategy: Translate Between Words and Math

When reading a real-world math problem, look for key ideas to help you translate between the words and the math.

There are several different ways to indicate a mathematical operation in words.

Key Ideas for Translating Between Words and Math			
+	−	×	÷
Put parts together	Take away	Put equal parts together	Separate into equal groups
Combine	Find the difference	Repeatedly add the same quantity	Distribute evenly

Identify the mathematical operation(s) described in the word problem below. Explain your choice.

The Montez family went to the state fair over the weekend. They spent $52.50 on rides, food, and drinks, in addition to the $5.50-per-person admission price. How much money did the Montez family spend at the fair?

There are two key ideas in this problem. One is finding the total cost of admission for the family. The other idea is to find the total amount spent at the fair.

They spent $52.50 **in addition to** $5.50 **per person** .

Let p represent the number of people.

$52.50 \quad + \quad \$5.50 \quad \times \quad p$

$52.5 + 5.5p$

 **Try This**

Identify the mathematical operation(s) described in each word problem. Explain your choice.

1. Tyler spent $45 at the convenience store. He paid $6 for food plus $3 per gallon for gas. How many gallons of gas did Tyler buy?

2. Ellen purchased 75 party favors to be divided evenly into sacks to give to her guests. Each sack contained 5 favors. How many sacks did Ellen prepare?

Reading and Writing Math
CHAPTER 2

Organizer

Objective: Help students apply strategies to understand and retain key concepts.

 Online Edition

Resources

 **Chapter 2 Resource File**
Reading Strategies

ENGLISH LANGUAGE LEARNERS

Writing Strategy: Translate Between Words and Math

Discuss Students find it useful to be aware of key terms that will help them translate between words and math.

Extend As students work through Chapter 2, encourage them to make a list of key terms from each lesson to help them solve problems. Have them practice translating sentences using the terms.

Students can work in pairs to write sentences and translate them into mathematical statements.

Answers to *Try This*

1. Add and multiply; the cost of the food must be added to the cost of the gasoline; multiply the number of gallons by 3.

2. Division; the party favors must be separated into equal parts.

Operations with Rational Numbers

 **One-Minute Section Planner**

Lesson	Lab Resources	Materials
2-1 Hands-On Lab Explore Rational Numbers • Classify the decimal expansion of a rational number as terminating or repeating. 🐻 🔑 **NS1.5**		**Required** Index cards
Lesson 2-1 Rational Numbers • Write rational numbers in equivalent forms. 🖥 **NS1.0, NS1.3,** 🔑 **NS1.5**	**Technology Lab 2-1** In *Chapter 2 Resource File*	**Required** Fraction bars (MK)
Lesson 2-2 Comparing and Ordering Rational Numbers • Compare and order positive and negative rational numbers written as fractions, decimals, and integers. 🖥 **NS1.1, NS1.3**		**Optional** Fraction bars (MK) Socket sets
Lesson 2-3 Adding and Subtracting Rational Numbers • Add and subtract decimals and rational numbers with like denominators. 🖥 **NS1.0,** 🔑 **NS1.2**	**Hands-On Lab 2-3** In *Chapter 2 Resource File*	
Lesson 2-4 Multiplying Rational Numbers • Multiply fractions, mixed numbers, and decimals. 🖥 🔑 **NS1.2**		
Lesson 2-5 Dividing Rational Numbers • Divide fractions and decimals. 🐻 🔑 **NS1.2,** 🔑 **AF1.3**	**Hands-On Lab 2-5** In *Chapter 2 Resource File*	
Lesson 2-6 Adding and Subtracting with Unlike Denominators • Add and subtract fractions with unlike denominators. 🐻 🔑 **NS1.2,** 🔑 **NS2.2**		**Optional** Graph paper Fraction bars (MK)

MK = *Manipulatives Kit*

Notes

_____

_____

_____

_____

_____

_____

_____

_____

Math Background: Teaching the Standards

Professional Development

RATIONAL NUMBERS 🐻 🗝 NS1.4, 🗝 NS1.5
Lesson 2-1

A rational number is any number that can be written as a fraction $\frac{n}{d}$, where n and d are integers and $d \neq 0$. When written as a decimal, every rational number either terminates, such as 2.4, or has some finite number of digits that repeat, such as 1.838383... (also written as $1.\overline{83}$). Technically, however, *every* rational number is a repeating decimal because every terminating decimal has an infinite string of repeating zeros: 2.4 = 2.400000....

The fact that all rational numbers are either terminating or repeating decimals may be understood by considering the process of long division. Consider the first few stages in using long division to write $\frac{3}{22}$ as a decimal.

$$
\begin{array}{r}
136 \\
22\overline{)3.0000} \\
\underline{2\ 2} \\
80 \\
\underline{66} \\
140 \\
\underline{132} \\
8
\end{array}
$$

Notice that the last remainder shown, 8, is one that has already appeared earlier in the process. From this point, the remainders will repeat the pattern of the last two steps, so $\frac{3}{22} = 0.1\overline{36}$. The key observations are: (1) the decimal terminates if there is ever a remainder of 0 and (2) if the remainder is never 0, then at some point we *must* see a remainder that has appeared earlier since there are a finite number of possible remainders ($\{0, 1, 2, ..., (d - 1)\}$, where d is the divisor). Thus, the decimal either terminates or repeats.

Students should generate examples of irrational numbers by creating non-repeating, non-terminating decimals. One way to do this is to write the decimal that has zeros in all the places to the right of the decimal point except for the first, fourth, ninth, and sixteenth places and all other places that are perfect squares:

0.1001000010000001000000001000...

FRACTIONS 🐻 NS1.1
Lessons 2-1, 2-2

In Grade 7, negative fractions are formally introduced for the first time. A fraction $\frac{a}{b}$ may be defined as the integer a divided by the integer b. Using this definition and knowing that $-2 \div 3 = 2 \div (-3) = -(2 \div 3)$, students should see that $\frac{-2}{3} = \frac{2}{-3} = -\frac{2}{3}$.

In order to do arithmetic with fractions, students must also understand equivalent fractions. Two fractions $\frac{a}{b}$ and $\frac{c}{d}$ are *equivalent* if and only if there is a number k such that $c = ka$ and $d = kb$. For example, $\frac{5}{8}$ and $\frac{10}{16}$ are equivalent because $\frac{5 \cdot 2}{8 \cdot 2} = \frac{10}{16}$. In this case, $k = 2$, but this value need not be an integer.

FRACTION OPERATIONS 🐻 🗝 NS1.2, 🗝 NS2.2
Lessons 2-3 through 2-6

The sum $a + b$ can be understood as the combined length of a segment that is a units long adjoined to a segment that is b units long. In the same way, students should recognize that $\frac{a}{b} + \frac{c}{d}$ represents the combined length of a segment that is $\frac{a}{b}$ units long adjoined to a segment that is $\frac{c}{d}$ units long. To find the sum, the fractions must first be written as equivalent fractions that have the same denominator. This is simple when $b = d$. To perform the addition when b and d are different, students can use what they know about factoring integers to find a common multiple of b and d.

The formula for the sum of the fractions, $\frac{a}{b} + \frac{c}{d} = \frac{ad + bc}{bd}$, is derived by writing $\frac{a}{b}$ as the equivalent fraction $\frac{ad}{bd}$, writing $\frac{c}{d}$ as the equivalent fraction $\frac{bc}{bd}$, and adding. It is worthwhile to encourage students to find the least common denominator in cases where doing so simplifies calculations. However, there are situations in which finding the least common denominator is cumbersome (e.g., $\frac{2}{51} + \frac{7}{85}$), and in these cases it may be best to use the formula.

Objective: Classify the decimal expansion of a rational number as terminating or repeating.

Materials: Index cards

 Online Edition

 Countdown to Mastery Week 3

Teach
Discuss

Begin by defining rational numbers. Then ask students to give some examples of rational numbers. Be sure to point out that integers are rational numbers because they can be written as fractions with a denominator of 1. For example, $6 = \frac{6}{1}$. Tell students that the most familiar examples of numbers that are not rational numbers are $\sqrt{2}$ and π.

Close
Key Concept

Every rational number can be written as either a terminating decimal or a repeating decimal.

Assessment

1. Tell whether the decimal expansion of each rational number terminates or repeats.

$\frac{7}{10}$ terminates

$\frac{8}{9}$ repeats

A *rational number* is a number that can be written as a fraction $\frac{n}{d}$, where n and d are integers and $d \neq 0$. You can use long division to write the decimal expansion of a rational number.

For example, to write the decimal expansion of $\frac{7}{11}$, divide 7 by 11 as shown at right.

Notice that the division process could be continued forever.

You write $\frac{7}{11} = 0.636363\ldots$ to show that the decimal continues, repeating 63 over and over.

```
        0.6 3 6 3 6 ...
   11)7.0 0 0 0 0
      6 6
        4 0
        3 3
          7 0
          6 6
            4 0
            3 3
              7 0
              6 6
```

California Standards

NS1.5 Know that every rational number is either a **terminating or repeating decimal** and be able to convert terminating decimals into reduced fractions.

Activity 1

1. Use long division to find the decimal expansion of each rational number.

$\frac{3}{5} = 0.6$; $\frac{1}{6} = 0.1\overline{6}$; $\frac{1}{7} = 0.\overline{142857}$; $\frac{2}{7} = 0.\overline{285714}$; $\frac{3}{8} = 0.375$; $\frac{5}{12} = 0.41\overline{6}$; $\frac{7}{16} = 0.4375$; $\frac{3}{20} = 0.15$

$\frac{3}{5}$ $\frac{1}{6}$ $\frac{1}{7}$ $\frac{2}{7}$ $\frac{3}{8}$ $\frac{5}{12}$ $\frac{7}{16}$ $\frac{3}{20}$

2. Write each rational number and its decimal expansion on an index card as shown at right.

$$\frac{7}{11} = 0.636363\ldots$$

3. Sort the index cards into three stacks:

   • Decimals that terminate, or end (for example, $\frac{1}{2} = 0.5$, which is a terminating decimal)

   • Decimals that repeat (for example, $\frac{7}{11} = 0.636363\ldots$, which is a repeating decimal)

   • Decimals that neither terminate nor repeat

4. Which rational numbers are in each stack?

   Terminating: $\frac{3}{5}$, $\frac{3}{8}$, $\frac{7}{16}$, $\frac{3}{20}$; **Repeating:** $\frac{1}{6}$, $\frac{1}{7}$, $\frac{2}{7}$, $\frac{5}{12}$; **Neither terminating nor repeating: none**

California Standards

Number Sense 1.5

Think and Discuss

1. When you use long division to write a decimal expansion, how can you tell   The decimal
that the decimal terminates? How can you tell that the decimal repeats?   terminates when there
is a remainder of 0. The decimal repeats when you get a remainder that you have already seen.
2. What do you notice about your stacks of index cards? Are there any
cards in the stack for decimals that neither terminate nor repeat?
There are no cards in the stack for decimals that neither terminate nor repeat.
3. What can you say about the decimal expansion of any rational number?
The decimal expansion of any rational number must terminate or repeat.

Try This

Determine whether the decimal expansion of each rational number
terminates or repeats.

1. $\frac{4}{7}$ repeats   2. $\frac{7}{8}$ terminates   3. $\frac{2}{9}$ repeats   4. $\frac{4}{5}$ terminates

Activity 2

1. The *period* of a repeating decimal is the shortest set
of digits that repeats over and over. For example, in
the decimal 0.636363 . . ., the shortest set of digits
that repeats over and over is 63, so the period is 63.

2. On each of your index cards that contains a
repeating decimal, circle the period.

3. Write the length of the period on the card.

$$\frac{7}{11} = 0.\overline{63}6363...$$

Length of period: 2

$\frac{1}{6}$: period 6, length 1
$\frac{1}{7}$: period 142857, length 6
$\frac{2}{7}$: period 285714, length 6
$\frac{5}{12}$: period 6, length 1

Think and Discuss

1. What is the longest period that you found?
Which of the rational numbers have the longest period?
Longest periods are 142857 and 285714 for $\frac{1}{7}$ and $\frac{2}{7}$
2. For a rational number $\frac{n}{d}$, do you think that the period can ever have
more than d digits? Explain. No

3. A student writes the decimal expansion of $\frac{3}{7}$ and claims that the
period has 12 digits. Explain why the student is incorrect. What
mistake do you think the student made?   The period cannot have more than 7 digits.
The actual period has 6 digits and the student
counted it twice.

Try This

Find the period of the decimal expansion of each rational number.

1. $\frac{5}{9}$ 5   2. $\frac{9}{11}$ 81   3. $\frac{4}{7}$ 571428   4. $\frac{1}{13}$ 076923

Find the length of the period of the decimal expansion of each
rational number.

5. $\frac{8}{11}$ 2   6. $\frac{7}{9}$ 1   7. $\frac{6}{7}$ 6   8. $\frac{1}{99}$ 2

Objective: Students write rational numbers in equivalent forms.

Technology Lab
In *Chapter 2 Resource File*

Online Edition
Tutorial Videos

Countdown to Mastery Week 3

Power Presentations
with PowerPoint®

Warm Up
Divide.

1. $36 \div 3$ 12

2. $144 \div 6$ 24

3. $68 \div 17$ 4

4. $345 \div 115$ 3

5. $1024 \div 64$ 16

Also available on transparency

Math Humor

Numbers like $\frac{1}{6}$ and $\frac{2}{3}$ in decimal form are like people who make sense but say the same thing over and over. They're rational, but they repeat!

California Standards

Number Sense 🔑 1.5 and 1.3

Also covered:

Number Sense
1.0 Students know the properties of, and compute with, **rational numbers expressed in a variety of forms.**

2-1 Rational Numbers

California Standards

➡ **NS1.5** Know that every rational number is either a terminating or a repeating decimal and be able to convert terminating decimals into reduced fractions.
NS1.3 Convert fractions to decimals and percents and use these representations in estimations, computations, and applications.

Vocabulary
rational number
terminating decimal
repeating decimal

Why learn this? Rational numbers can be used to represent the thickness of a surfboard. (See Exercise 61.)

A **rational number** is any number that can be written as a fraction $\frac{n}{d}$, where n and d are integers and $d \neq 0$. Some examples of rational numbers are shown below.

$$\frac{12}{15} \quad 14 \quad -3 \quad 7.2 \quad -5.81 \quad -4\frac{1}{2}$$

Any fraction can be written as a decimal by dividing the numerator by the denominator. If the division ends, or terminates, because the remainder is zero, then the decimal is a **terminating decimal**.

If the division leads to a repeating block of one or more digits (where all digits are not zeros) after the decimal point, then the decimal is a **repeating decimal**. A repeating decimal can be written with a bar over the digits that repeat. So $0.13333\ldots = 0.1\overline{3}$.

EXAMPLE 1 **Writing Fractions as Decimals**

Write each fraction as a decimal.

A $\frac{5}{4}$ **B** $-\frac{1}{6}$

Writing Math

$-\frac{1}{6}$ can be written as $\frac{-1}{6}$ or as $\frac{1}{-6}$.

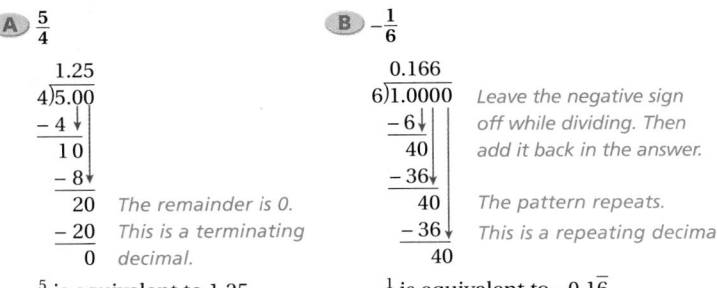

$\frac{5}{4}$ is equivalent to 1.25. $-\frac{1}{6}$ is equivalent to $-0.1\overline{6}$.

To write a terminating decimal as a fraction, identify the place value of the digit farthest to the right. Then write all of the digits after the decimal point as the numerator with the place value as the denominator.

---

1 Introduce
Alternate Opener

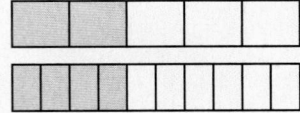

EXPLORATION

2-1 Rational Numbers

Comparing numbers with $\frac{1}{2}$ is useful in many situations.

Phil surveyed 317 voters and found that 156 supported his reelection. He reasoned the following way to determine whether he had a majority.
$156 \times 2 = 150 \times 2 + 6 \times 2$
      $= 300 + 12$
      $= 312$

Phil concluded that he did not have a majority. Look at how Phil checked his estimate with a calculator.

Double the numerator and compare it with the denominator of each fraction to determine whether the fraction is greater than or less than $\frac{1}{2}$. Check your work with a calculator.

Fraction	$> \frac{1}{2}$?	$< \frac{1}{2}$?
1. $\frac{51}{101}$		
2. $\frac{221}{425}$		
3. $\frac{260}{513}$		
4. $\frac{578}{1152}$		

Think and Discuss
5. Explain how you checked your work with a calculator.

Motivate

Show students this diagram:

Ask students: "What fraction of each bar is shaded? Is there a way to write one of these fractions as a decimal?" The responses should illustrate that there are three equivalent forms of the same rational number: $\frac{2}{5}$, $\frac{4}{10}$, and 0.4.

Explorations and answers are provided in *Alternate Openers: Explorations Transparencies.*

The following table shows some decimal place values and their equivalent fractions. You can use this information to write a terminating decimal as a fraction.

Tenths	Hundredths	Thousandths
$0.1 = \frac{1}{10}$	$0.01 = \frac{1}{100}$	$0.001 = \frac{1}{1000}$

EXAMPLE 2 **Writing Terminating Decimals as Fractions**

Write each decimal as a fraction in simplest form.

A -5.59

$$-5.59 = -5\frac{59}{100}$$

9 is in the hundredths place, so write hundredths as the denominator.

Remember!

A fraction is in reduced, or simplest, form when the numerator and the denominator have no common divisor other than 1.

B 0.5714

$$0.5714 = \frac{5714}{10{,}000}$$

4 is in the ten-thousandths place, so write ten-thousandths as the denominator.

$$= \frac{5714 \div 2}{10{,}000 \div 2}$$

Simplify by dividing by the greatest common divisor.

$$= \frac{2857}{5000}$$

EXAMPLE 3 **Writing Repeating Decimals as Fractions**

Write $0.\overline{27}$ as a fraction in simplest form.

$x = 0.272727\ldots$	*Let x represent the number.*
$100x = 100(0.272727\ldots)$	*Multiply both sides by 100 because 2 digits repeat*
$100x = 27.272727\ldots$	*Subtract x from both sides to eliminate the*
$\underline{-x = -0.272727\ldots}$	*repeating part. Since x = 0.272727. . ., use*
$99x = 27$	*0.272727. . . for x on the right side of the equation*
$\frac{99x}{99} = \frac{27}{99}$	*Since x is multiplied by 99, divide both sides by 99*
$x = \frac{27}{99} = \frac{3}{11}$	*Write in simplest form.*

Helpful Hint

Remember that an equation stays balanced if you perform the same operation on both sides. Since $x = 0.272727. . .$, you can subtract x from one side of the equation and $0.272727. . .$ from the other.

In Example 3, you multiplied by 100 because $0.\overline{27}$ has two repeating digits. For one repeating digit, multiply by 10. For three repeating digits, multiply by 1000.

Think and Discuss

1. **Explain** how you know that a fraction is completely simplified.

2. **Give** the sign of a fraction in which the numerator is negative and the denominator is negative. **Positive; a negative number divided by a negative number gives a positive quotient.**

Answers to *Think and Discuss:*
1. Possible answer: When the numerator and denominator have no common factors other than 1, the fraction is in simplest form.

Power Presentations with PowerPoint®

Additional Examples

Example 1

Write each fraction as a decimal.

A. $\frac{11}{9}$ $1.\overline{2}$ **B.** $\frac{7}{20}$ 0.35

Example 2

Write each decimal as a fraction in simplest form.

A. 5.37 $5\frac{37}{100}$ **B.** 0.622 $\frac{311}{500}$

Example 3

Write $0.\overline{4}$ as a fraction in simplest form. $\frac{4}{9}$

Also available on transparency

2 Teach

Guided Instruction

ENGLISH LANGUAGE LEARNERS

In this lesson, students learn to write rational numbers in equivalent forms. Review the definition of *rational number*. Discuss how to simplify a fraction. Review the place-value chart (Teaching Transparency) to prepare students for writing decimals as fractions. Explain that the fraction bar indicates division of the numerator by the denominator. Work **Example 1B** out a few extra places so that students can see the pattern developing. Point out that many fractions will have a repeating pattern of digits when written as decimals.

 **Universal Access**

Through Multiple Representations

Give each student a set of fractions (e.g., $\frac{1}{2}, \frac{2}{3}, \frac{3}{4}, \frac{4}{5}$) in random order. Have students write each fraction as a decimal and use the values to write the fractions in order from least to greatest. Have students analyze the pattern, and then see if they can put other fractions in a set in ascending order without writing them as decimals.

3 Close

Summarize

Remind students that a fraction, such as $\frac{3}{4}$, is another way of showing a division problem (3 divided by 4). To write a fraction as a decimal, solve the division problem. Point out that fractions and decimals are two ways to show numbers that are less than 1. Ask students to write the value of 0.20 in as many ways as they can, and write their responses on the chalkboard. Point out that all correct responses have the same value and lie at the same point on the number line.

Possible answers:
$0.2; 0.200; \frac{20}{100}; \frac{2}{10}; \frac{1}{5}; 20 \div 100; 100\overline{)20}$; twenty-hundredths; two-tenths

California Standards Practice
NS1.3, 🔑 NS1.5

go.hrw.com
Homework Help Online
KEYWORD: MT8CA 2-1
Parent Resources Online
KEYWORD: MT8CA Parent

Assignment Guide

If you finished Example **1** assign:
Proficient 1–10, 28–36 even, 69–81
Advanced 27–36, 63, 66, 68–81

If you finished Example **2** assign:
Proficient 1–18, 28–44 even,
53–56, 69–81
Advanced 27–44, 57–60, 63, 66,
68–81

If you finished Example **3** assign:
Proficient 1–26, 28–52 even,
53–56, 61–62, 64, 66,
69–81
Advanced 27–52, 57–81

Homework Quick Check
Quickly check key concepts.
Exercises: 28, 34, 40, 42, 48, 50

Math Background

A fraction can be written in simplest form as either a mixed number or an improper fraction. Students may prefer a mixed number because they will probably have a clearer concept of its value if it can be easily compared to integers. For example, students may understand that $5\frac{3}{7}$ is between 5 and 6, but they may have difficulty making the same conclusion about the equivalent improper fraction $\frac{38}{7}$. For this reason, the answers to the Exercises have been given as mixed numbers. In more advanced courses, however, improper fractions may prove more useful.

GUIDED PRACTICE

See Example **1** Write each fraction as a decimal.
1. $\frac{5}{8}$ 0.625
2. $-\frac{3}{5}$ −0.6
3. $\frac{5}{12}$ 0.41$\overline{6}$
4. $\frac{1}{4}$ 0.25
5. $\frac{1}{9}$ 0.$\overline{1}$
6. $-\frac{18}{9}$ −2
7. $\frac{3}{8}$ 0.375
8. $-\frac{14}{5}$ −2.8
9. $\frac{7}{20}$ 0.35
10. $\frac{2}{3}$ 0.$\overline{6}$

See Example **2** Write each decimal as a fraction in simplest form.
11. 0.75 $\frac{3}{4}$
12. 1.125 $1\frac{1}{8}$
13. 0.4 $\frac{2}{5}$
14. 0.35 $\frac{7}{20}$
15. −2.2 $-2\frac{1}{5}$
16. 0.625 $\frac{5}{8}$
17. 3.21 $3\frac{21}{100}$
18. −0.3175 $-\frac{127}{400}$

See Example **3** Write each repeating decimal as a fraction in simplest form.
19. 0.$\overline{81}$ $\frac{9}{11}$
20. 0.$\overline{5}$ $\frac{5}{9}$
21. 0.$\overline{345}$ $\frac{115}{333}$
22. 0.$\overline{3}$ $\frac{1}{3}$
23. 0.$\overline{73}$ $\frac{73}{99}$
24. 0.$\overline{2}$ $\frac{2}{9}$
25. 0.$\overline{58}$ $\frac{58}{99}$
26. 0.$\overline{126}$ $\frac{14}{111}$

INDEPENDENT PRACTICE

See Example **1** Write each fraction as a decimal.
27. $-\frac{3}{8}$ −0.375
28. $\frac{7}{12}$ 0.58$\overline{3}$
29. $-\frac{9}{5}$ −1.8
30. $\frac{13}{20}$ 0.65
31. $\frac{8}{5}$ 1.6
32. $\frac{18}{40}$ 0.45
33. $-\frac{23}{5}$ −4.6
34. $\frac{28}{25}$ 1.12
35. $\frac{4}{3}$ 1.$\overline{3}$
36. $-\frac{7}{4}$ −1.75

See Example **2** Write each decimal as a fraction in simplest form.
37. 0.6 $\frac{3}{5}$
38. 3.5 $3\frac{1}{2}$
39. 0.72 $\frac{18}{25}$
40. −0.183 $-\frac{183}{1000}$
41. 1.377 $1\frac{377}{1000}$
42. 1.450 $1\frac{9}{20}$
43. −1.4 $-1\frac{2}{5}$
44. −2.9 $-2\frac{9}{10}$

See Example **3** Write each repeating decimal as a fraction in simplest form.
45. 0.$\overline{15}$ $\frac{5}{33}$
46. 0.$\overline{121}$ $\frac{121}{999}$
47. 0.$\overline{36}$ $\frac{4}{11}$
48. 0.$\overline{1}$ $\frac{1}{9}$
49. 0.$\overline{27}$ $\frac{3}{11}$
50. 0.$\overline{8}$ $\frac{8}{9}$
51. 0.$\overline{453}$ $\frac{151}{333}$
52. 0.$\overline{009}$ $\frac{1}{111}$

PRACTICE AND PROBLEM SOLVING

Extra Practice
See page EP4.

Determine whether the numbers in each pair are equivalent.
53. $\frac{1}{9}$ and 0.$\overline{1}$ yes
54. 0.6 and $\frac{3}{5}$ yes
55. 0.625 and $\frac{7}{8}$ no
56. $\frac{2}{3}$ and 0.6 no
57. $\frac{13}{40}$ and 0.325 yes
58. 0.13 and $\frac{1}{7}$ no
59. 0.45 and $\frac{9}{20}$ yes
60. $\frac{1}{11}$ and 0.09 no

61. **Sports** The thickness of a surfboard is often matched to the weight of the rider. For example, a person weighing 170 pounds might need a surfboard that is 3.375 inches thick. Write 3.375 as a fraction in simplest form. $3\frac{3}{8}$

62. Bondi weighed his mobile phone and found it to be approximately $\frac{7}{25}$ pound. What is the weight of Bondi's phone written as a decimal? 0.28 pound

California Standards

Standard	Exercises
NS1.1	53–60
NS1.2 🔑	74–81
NS1.3	1–10, 27–36, 62–64, 71
NS1.5 🔑	11–26, 37–52, 61, 67, 70
AF1.2	72–73

REVIEW FOR MASTERY 2-1

LESSON 2-1 Review for Mastery
Rational Numbers

To write a fraction as a decimal, divide numerator by denominator.
A decimal may terminate.
$$\frac{3}{4} = 4\overline{)3.00} \quad \begin{array}{r} 0.75 \\ -2\,8 \\ \hline 20 \\ -20 \\ \hline 0 \end{array}$$

A decimal may repeat.
$$\frac{1}{3} = 3\overline{)1.00} \quad \begin{array}{r} 0.\overline{3} \\ -9 \\ \hline 10 \\ -9 \\ \hline 1 \end{array}$$

Write each fraction as a decimal.
1. $\frac{5}{2}$ = ___2.5___
2. $\frac{15}{8}$ = ___1.875___
3. $\frac{28}{6}$ = ___4.$\overline{6}$___
4. $\frac{22}{4}$ = ___5.5___
5. $\frac{62}{12}$ = ___5.1$\overline{6}$___
6. $\frac{105}{10}$ = ___10.5___

Complete to write each fraction as a decimal.
7. $\frac{15}{4}$ = $4\overline{)15.00}$ 3.75
8. $\frac{5}{6}$ = $6\overline{)5.00}$ 0.83
9. $\frac{11}{3}$ = $3\overline{)11.00}$ 3.6$\overline{6}$

PRACTICE 2-1

LESSON 2-1 Practice B
Rational Numbers

Write each fraction as a decimal.
1. $\frac{1}{8}$ 0.125
2. $\frac{8}{3}$ 2.666
3. $\frac{14}{15}$ 0.933
4. $\frac{16}{5}$ 3.2
5. $\frac{11}{16}$ 0.6875
6. $\frac{7}{9}$ 0.777
7. $\frac{4}{5}$ 0.8
8. $\frac{31}{25}$ 1.24

Write each decimal as a fraction in simplest form.
9. 0.72 $\frac{18}{25}$
10. 0.058 $\frac{29}{500}$
11. −1.65 $-1\frac{13}{20}$
12. 2.1 $2\frac{1}{10}$
13. 0.036 $\frac{9}{250}$
14. −4.06 $-4\frac{3}{50}$
15. 2.305 $2\frac{61}{200}$
16. 0.0064 $\frac{4}{625}$
17. −0.60 $-\frac{3}{5}$
18. 6.95 $6\frac{19}{20}$
19. 0.016 $\frac{2}{125}$
20. 0.0005 $\frac{1}{2000}$

Write each repeating decimal as a fraction in simplest form.
21. 0.$\overline{8}$ $\frac{8}{9}$
22. 0.$\overline{84}$ $\frac{28}{33}$
23. 0.$\overline{841}$ $\frac{841}{999}$
24. 0.$\overline{4}$ $\frac{4}{9}$
25. 0.$\overline{28}$ $\frac{28}{99}$
26. 0.$\overline{2}$ $\frac{2}{9}$
27. 0.$\overline{54}$ $\frac{6}{11}$
28. 0.$\overline{774}$ $\frac{86}{111}$

29. Make up a fraction that cannot be simplified that has 24 as its denominator.
Possible answer: $\frac{5}{24}$

63. a. Simplify each fraction.

$$\frac{8}{18} \quad \frac{4}{9} \qquad \frac{8}{48} \quad \frac{1}{6} \qquad \frac{5}{20} \quad \frac{1}{4} \qquad \frac{21}{45} \quad \frac{7}{15} \qquad \frac{18}{32} \quad \frac{9}{16} \qquad \frac{24}{50} \quad \frac{12}{25} \qquad \frac{45}{72} \quad \frac{5}{8} \qquad \frac{36}{96} \quad \frac{3}{8}$$

b. Write the denominator of each simplified fraction as the product of prime factors.

c. Write each simplified fraction as a decimal. Label each as a terminating or repeating decimal.

d. Examine the prime factors in the denominators of the simplified fractions that are equivalent to terminating decimals. Then examine the prime factors in the denominators of the simplified fractions that are equivalent to repeating decimals. What pattern do you see?

65. GCD = 2; $\frac{21}{34}$; No, the fraction cannot be further simplified because the numerator and denominator have no common factors other than 1.

67. Possible answer: Identify the place value of the digit farthest to the right. Use this place value as the denominator of the fraction. Then write all of the digits after the decimal point as the numerator of the fraction.

64. Measurement The ruler is marked at every $\frac{1}{16}$ in. Do the labeled measurements convert to terminating or repeating decimals? **terminating**

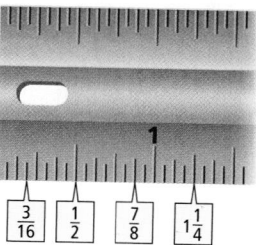

$\boxed{\frac{3}{16}} \quad \boxed{\frac{1}{2}} \quad \boxed{\frac{7}{8}} \quad \boxed{1\frac{1}{4}}$

65. Reasoning The greatest common divisor, GCD, is the largest common factor of two or more given numbers. Find the GCD of 42 and 68 from the fraction $\frac{42}{68}$. Then reduce the fraction by the GCD. Can the resulting fraction be further simplified? Explain.

66. What's the Error? A student simplified a fraction in this manner: $\frac{-25}{-30} = -\frac{5}{6}$. What error did the student make?

67. Write About It Explain how can you use place value to write a terminating decimal in fraction form.

68. Challenge A student simplified a fraction to $-\frac{2}{9}$ by removing the common factors, which were 2 and 9. What was the original fraction? $-\frac{36}{162}$

FORMATIVE ASSESSMENT
and **INTERVENTION**

Diagnose Before the Lesson
2-1 Warm Up, TE p. 66

Monitor During the Lesson
2-1 Know-It Notebook
2-1 Questioning Strategies

Assess After the Lesson
2-1 Lesson Quiz, TE p. 69

Answers

63b–d. See p. A1.

66. Possible answer: The student did not follow the rule for dividing a negative number by a negative number. The simplified fraction should be positive.

Teaching Tip **Multiple Choice** For **Exercise 70,** encourage students to read the problem and examine the answers carefully. If students select **B** as the answer, they either did not realize that the answer must be in simplest form, or they did not realize that answer **B** is not in simplest form. If they simplify this fraction, they will obtain the correct answer, **A**.

Journal

Have students write some real-world situations that involve fractions and/or decimals. Examples might include cooking recipes, distance measurements, and monetary calculations.

Power Presentations
with PowerPoint®

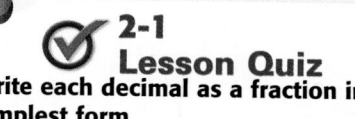

2-1 Lesson Quiz
Write each decimal as a fraction in simplest form.

1. 0.27 $\frac{27}{100}$ **2.** −0.625 $-\frac{5}{8}$

3. Write $\frac{13}{6}$ as a decimal. $2.1\overline{6}$

4. Tommy had 13 hits in 40 at bats for his baseball team. What is his batting average? (Batting average is the number of hits divided by the number of at bats, expressed as a decimal.) 0.325

Also available on transparency

SPIRAL STANDARDS REVIEW ← NS1.2, NS1.3, ← NS1.5, AF1.2

69. Multiple Choice If $y = -\frac{3}{9}$, which of the following is NOT equal to y?

Ⓐ $\frac{-1}{3}$ Ⓑ $-\frac{1}{3}$ Ⓒ $-\left(\frac{-1}{3}\right)$ Ⓓ $-\left(\frac{-1}{-3}\right)$

70. Multiple Choice Which shows 0.68 as a fraction in simplest form?

Ⓐ $\frac{17}{25}$ Ⓑ $\frac{34}{50}$ Ⓒ $\frac{3}{4}$ Ⓓ $\frac{6}{8}$

71. Gridded Response What is the decimal equivalent of the fraction $\frac{79}{8}$? **9.875**

Evaluate each expression for the given values of the variable. (Lesson 1-1)

72. $3x + 5$ for $x = 2$ and $x = 3$ **11; 14** **73.** $4(x + 1)$ for $x = 6$ and $x = 11$ **28; 48**

Simplify. (Lesson 1-6)

74. $-3(6 - 8)$ **6** **75.** $4(-3 - 2)$ **−20** **76.** $-5(3 + 2)$ **−25** **77.** $-3(1 - 8)$ **21**

78. $-12(4 - 9)$ **156** **79.** $15(11 - (-1))$ **180** **80.** $6(-5 - (-4))$ **−6** **81.** $-7(1 - (-17))$ **−126**

CHALLENGE 2-1

LESSON 2-1 Challenge
Encore, Encore, ...

Explore some patterns with repeating decimals. Use a calculator to write each decimal equivalent.

1. $\frac{1}{9} = $ _0.$\overline{1}$_ 2. $\frac{2}{9} = $ _0.$\overline{2}$_ 3. $\frac{3}{9} = $ _0.$\overline{3}$_

Predict the decimal equivalent of each fraction. Verify your results on a calculator.

4. $\frac{4}{9} = $ _0.$\overline{4}$_ 5. $\frac{6}{9} = $ _0.$\overline{6}$_, 6. $\frac{8}{9} = $ _0.$\overline{8}$_

Write each fractional equivalent.

7. $0.\overline{5} = $ _$\frac{5}{9}$_ 8. $0.\overline{7} = $ _$\frac{7}{9}$_ 9. $0.\overline{9} = $ _$\frac{9}{9} = 1$_

Use a calculator to write each decimal equivalent.

10. $\frac{42}{99} = $ _0.$\overline{42}$_ 11. $\frac{358}{999} = $ _0.$\overline{358}$_ 12. $\frac{4276}{9999} = $ _0.$\overline{4276}$_

Predict the decimal equivalent of each fraction.

13. $\frac{76}{99} = $ _0.$\overline{76}$_ 14. $\frac{732}{999} = $ _0.$\overline{732}$_ 15. $\frac{1957}{9999} = $ _0.$\overline{1957}$_

Write each fractional equivalent.

16. $0.\overline{45} = $ _$\frac{45}{99}$_ 17. $0.\overline{148} = $ _$\frac{148}{999}$_ 18. $0.\overline{7213} = $ _$\frac{7213}{9999}$_

19. Summarize your observations.

A single digit repeating decimal equates to a fraction with denominator 9, a 2-digit repeating decimal to denominator 99, and so on.

PROBLEM SOLVING 2-1

LESSON 2-1 Problem Solving
Rational Numbers

Write the correct answer.

1. Fill in the table below which shows the sizes of drill bits in a set.

2. Do the drill bit sizes convert to repeating or terminating decimals?

Terminating decimals

13-Piece Drill Bit Set

Fraction	Decimal	Fraction	Decimal	Fraction	Decimal
$\frac{1}{4}$	0.25	$\frac{11}{64}$	0.171875	$\frac{3}{32}$	0.09375
$\frac{15}{64}$	0.234375	$\frac{5}{32}$	0.15625	$\frac{5}{64}$	0.078125
$\frac{7}{32}$	0.21875	$\frac{9}{64}$	0.140625	$\frac{1}{16}$	0.0625
$\frac{13}{64}$	0.203125	$\frac{1}{8}$	0.125		
$\frac{3}{16}$	0.1875	$\frac{7}{64}$	0.109375		

Use the table at the right that lists the world's smallest nations. Choose the letter for the best answer.

3. What is the area of Vatican City expressed as a fraction in simplest form?

A $\frac{8}{50}$ C $\frac{17}{1000}$ B $\frac{4}{25}$ D $\frac{17}{100}$

World's Smallest Nations

Nation	Area (square miles)
Vatican City	0.17
Monaco	0.75
Nauru	8.2

4. What is the area of Monaco expressed as a fraction in simplest form?

F $\frac{75}{100}$ H $\frac{3}{4}$ G $\frac{15}{20}$ J $\frac{2}{3}$

5. What is the area of Nauru expressed as a mixed number?

A $8\frac{1}{50}$ C $8\frac{2}{100}$ B $8\frac{2}{50}$ D $8\frac{1}{5}$

6. The average annual precipitation in Miami, FL is 57.55 inches. Express 57.55 as a mixed number.

F $57\frac{11}{20}$ H $57\frac{5}{100}$ G $57\frac{55}{1000}$ J $57\frac{1}{20}$

7. The average annual precipitation in Norfolk, VA is 45.22 inches. Express 45.22 as a mixed number.

A $45\frac{11}{50}$ C $45\frac{11}{20}$ B $45\frac{22}{1000}$ D $45\frac{1}{5}$

 **2-2 Organizer**

Objective: Students compare and order positive and negative rational numbers written as fractions, decimals, and integers.

 Online Edition
Tutorial Videos

 Countdown to Mastery Week 3

Power Presentations with PowerPoint®

 **Warm Up**
Write each fraction as a decimal.

1. $\frac{1}{3}$ $0.\overline{3}$ 2. $\frac{4}{5}$ 0.8

3. $\frac{3}{4}$ 0.75 4. $\frac{2}{3}$ $0.\overline{6}$

Also available on transparency

 Math Humor

Parent: Why are you stirring that paper with a spoon?

Student: It's my homework. I'm supposed to create some *mixed* numbers.

 **2-2 Comparing and Ordering Rational Numbers**

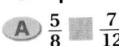 **California Standards**

NS1.1 Read, write, and compare rational numbers in scientific notation (positive and negative powers of 10), **compare rational numbers in general.**
Also covered: **NS1.3**

Vocabulary
least common denominator (LCD)

Why learn this? You can use rational numbers to compare changes in populations. (See Example 3.)

To compare fractions with unlike denominators, you can find a common denominator. This could be the **least common denominator** (LCD), which is the least common multiple of the denominators.

EXAMPLE 1 Comparing Fractions by Finding a Common Denominator

Compare. Write <, >, or =.

A $\frac{5}{8}$ ■ $\frac{7}{12}$

Method 1: Multiply denominators to find a common denominator.

$8 \cdot 12 = 96$ *Multiply 8 and 12 to find a common denominator.*

$\frac{5}{8} \cdot \frac{12}{12} = \frac{5 \cdot 12}{8 \cdot 12} = \frac{60}{96}$ *Write the fractions with a common denominator.*

$\frac{7}{12} \cdot \frac{8}{8} = \frac{7 \cdot 8}{12 \cdot 8} = \frac{56}{96}$

$\frac{60}{96} > \frac{56}{96}$ *Compare the fractions.*

$\frac{5}{8} > \frac{7}{12}$

Remember!
The least common multiple (LCM) of two numbers is the smallest number, other than 0, that is a multiple of both numbers.

B $\frac{3}{4}$ ■ $\frac{5}{6}$

Method 2: Find the least common denominator.

4: 4, 8, ⑫ . . .
6: 6, ⑫ . . .   *List multiples of 4 and 6. The LCM is 12.*

$\frac{3}{4} \cdot \frac{3}{3} = \frac{3 \cdot 3}{4 \cdot 3} = \frac{9}{12}$ *Write the fractions with a common denominator.*

$\frac{5}{6} \cdot \frac{2}{2} = \frac{5 \cdot 2}{6 \cdot 2} = \frac{10}{12}$

$\frac{9}{12} < \frac{10}{12}$ *Compare the fractions.*

$\frac{3}{4} < \frac{5}{6}$

1 Introduce

Alternate Opener

EXPLORATION

2-2 Comparing and Ordering Rational Numbers

You can use a number line to compare rational numbers. For example, the number line shows that $\frac{1}{8} < \frac{1}{4}$ because $\frac{1}{8}$ is to the left of $\frac{1}{4}$.

Use the number line to compare each pair of fractions by writing < or >. Then convert the fractions to decimals and use < or > to compare the decimals.

1. $\frac{5}{8}$ ☐ $\frac{2}{3}$

2. $\frac{3}{8}$ ☐ $\frac{1}{3}$

3. $\frac{7}{8}$ ☐ $\frac{3}{4}$

4. $\frac{3}{8}$ ☐ $\frac{2}{3}$

5. $\frac{3}{4}$ ☐ $\frac{2}{3}$

6. $\frac{1}{4}$ ☐ $\frac{1}{3}$

Think and Discuss

7. **Explain** how you know that $\frac{3}{8} < \frac{5}{8}$ without using the number line.

8. **Describe** how you could use the number line to compare $5\frac{3}{8}$ and $5\frac{1}{2}$.

Motivate

Have students discuss how they have compared and ordered integers. Then discuss the different forms in which a rational number can be expressed (integer, fraction, mixed number, decimal). Have students represent the same rational number in different forms (e.g., $2\frac{1}{2} = 2.5 = \frac{5}{2}$).

Explorations and answers are provided in *Alternate Openers: Explorations Transparencies.*

 **California Standards**

Number Sense 1.1

Also covered:

Number Sense

1.3 Convert fractions to decimals and percents and use these representations in estimations, computations, and applications.

EXAMPLE 2 Comparing by Using Decimals

Compare. Write <, >, or =.

A $3\frac{3}{8}$  $3\frac{3}{5}$

$3\frac{3}{8} = 3.375$ and $3\frac{3}{5} = 3.6$ *Write the fractions as decimals.*

$3.375 < 3.6$, so $3\frac{3}{8} < 3\frac{3}{5}$.   *Compare the decimals.*

B -0.53 ▆ $-\frac{6}{10}$

$-\frac{6}{10} = -0.6$ *Write $-\frac{6}{10}$ as a decimal.*

$-0.53 > -0.6$, so $-0.53 > -\frac{6}{10}$.   *Compare the decimals.*

C $\frac{9}{11}$ ▆ 0.8

$\frac{9}{11} = 0.\overline{81}$ *Write $\frac{9}{11}$ as a decimal.*

$0.\overline{81} > 0.8$, so $\frac{9}{11} > 0.8$.   *Compare the decimals.*

For help with comparing decimals, see page SB3 in the Skills Bank.

Answers to Think and Discuss

1. No; to compare two fractions, you can write them as fractions with a common denominator or as decimals.

To order fractions and decimals, you can either write them all in the same form and then compare them, or place them on a number line. Recall that numbers increase in value as you move from left to right along a number line.

EXAMPLE 3 Social Studies Application

 Reasoning

From 2000 to 2003, the percent changes in populations for three states and the District of Columbia were as follows: $2\frac{2}{5}\%$ for Maine, -1.3% for North Dakota, 4.0% for Washington, and $-1\frac{1}{2}\%$ for Washington, D.C. List these numbers in order from least to greatest.

Place the numbers on a number line and read them from left to right.

The percent changes in population from least to greatest are $-1\frac{1}{2}\%$, -1.3%, $2\frac{2}{5}\%$, and 4.0%.

2. Possible answer: Line up the decimal points and compare the digits in each number from left to right. Look for the first place where the digits are different.

3. Possible answer: $-\frac{5}{8}$ lies to the left of $-\frac{1}{8}$ on the number line.

Think and Discuss

1. **Explain** whether you need to find a common denominator to compare $\frac{2}{3}$ and $\frac{1}{2}$.

2. **Describe** the steps you would use to compare 0.235 and 0.239.

3. **Explain** why $-\frac{5}{8}$ is less than $-\frac{1}{8}$ even though 5 is greater than 1.

Teaching Tip **Visual** When comparing decimals, some students may find it helpful to use zeros as placeholders so that all decimals being compared have the same number of decimal places.

Power Presentations with PowerPoint®

Additional Examples

Example 1

Compare. Write <, >, or =.

A. $\frac{5}{6}$ ▆ $\frac{7}{10}$ >

B. $\frac{2}{3}$ ▆ $\frac{4}{5}$ <

Example 2

Compare. Write <, >, or =.

A. $5\frac{2}{9}$ ▆ $5\frac{2}{7}$ <

B. -0.44 ▆ $-\frac{2}{5}$ <

C. $\frac{1}{9}$ ▆ 0.1 >

Example 3

The numbers $\frac{14}{4}$, -3.4, 6.0, and -2.5 represent the percent changes in populations for four states. List these numbers in order from least to greatest. $-3.4, -2.5, \frac{14}{4}, 6.0$

Also available on transparency

---

2 Teach

Guided Instruction

In this lesson, students learn to compare rational numbers in fractional form by finding a common denominator or by converting the fractions to decimals. Students also learn to order rational numbers on a number line. First, introduce rewriting fractions by using an LCD and comparing the numerators. Next, demonstrate how to change a fraction and a mixed number to a decimal, and compare decimals. Then use a number line to order rational numbers.

 **Teaching Tip** **Number Sense** Have students look at the numerator and denominator of each fraction in **Think and Discuss 1.** In $\frac{1}{2}$, 1 is one-half of 2. In $\frac{2}{3}$, 2 is more than one-half of 3. This shows that $\frac{2}{3}$ is greater than $\frac{1}{2}$.

Universal Access

Through Concrete Manipulatives

Have students research the sizes in a customary-measure socket set. Socket sizes are given in sixteenths of an inch, reduced to simplest form. If students can obtain a socket set, have students put the sockets in order from least to greatest size. The students should then write the socket sizes in order from least to greatest.

3 Close

Summarize

Ask students to describe how to compare two fractions. Then ask them to describe how to compare a fraction and a decimal.

Possible answers: To compare two fractions, rewrite them with their LCD and compare numerators; to compare a fraction and a decimal, change the fraction to a decimal by dividing, line up the decimal points, find first decimal place where digits differ, compare those digits.

2-2 Exercises

California Standards Practice
NS1.1, NS1.3

go.hrw.com
Homework Help Online
KEYWORD: MT8CA 2-2
Parent Resources Online
KEYWORD: MT8CA Parent

Assignment Guide

If you finished Example **1** assign:
Proficient 1–4, 10–17, 44–53
Advanced 10–17, 36, 44–53

If you finished Example **2** assign:
Proficient 1–8, 10–25, 27–28, 31–32, 42–53
Advanced 10–25, 29–30, 33–34, 36, 44–53

If you finished Example **3** assign:
Proficient 1–28, 31–32, 37–39, 42–53
Advanced 10–26, 29–30, 33–53

Homework Quick Check
Quickly check key concepts.
Exercises: 14, 16, 20, 22, 24

Teaching Tip
Visual Comparing negative rational numbers is similar to comparing negative integers. If two negative rational numbers are placed on a number line, the one to the right has the greater value.

Teaching Tip
Language Support The root of the word *relative* is *relate*. In **Exercise 26,** help students understand that "relative to the fastest speed" means how the other speeds relate to the fastest speed.

Math Background

An alternative way to compare two fractions, $\frac{a}{b}$ and $\frac{c}{d}$, is to find the cross products ad and bc. If $ad > bc$, then $\frac{a}{b} > \frac{c}{d}$. This shortcut works because $\frac{a}{b} = \frac{a \cdot d}{b \cdot d}$ and $\frac{c}{d} = \frac{c \cdot b}{d \cdot b}$. So essentially, you are comparing $\frac{a \cdot d}{b \cdot d}$ with $\frac{c \cdot b}{d \cdot b}$. So comparing ad with bc is the same as finding the common denominator and comparing the rewritten fractions.

California Standards

Standard	Exercises
NS1.1	1–43
NS1.2	44–48
NS1.3	5–9, 18–26, 37–43, 49–53

GUIDED PRACTICE

See Example **1** Compare. Write $<$, $>$, or $=$.

1. $\frac{3}{8}$ ▨ $\frac{3}{7}$ $<$ 2. $\frac{9}{11}$ ▨ $\frac{9}{10}$ $<$ 3. $\frac{6}{15}$ ▨ $\frac{2}{5}$ $=$ 4. $-\frac{7}{10}$ ▨ $-\frac{5}{8}$ $<$

See Example **2** 5. $\frac{7}{8}$ ▨ $\frac{9}{11}$ $>$ 6. 4.2 ▨ $4\frac{1}{5}$ $=$ 7. $-\frac{3}{7}$ ▨ -0.375 $<$ 8. $-1\frac{1}{2}$ ▨ $-1\frac{7}{9}$ $>$

See Example **3** 9. **School** In Mr. Corsetti's shop class, students were instructed to measure and cut boards to a length of 8 inches. In checking four students' work, Mr. Corsetti found that one board was 8.25 inches, the second was $8\frac{1}{8}$ inches, the third was 7.5 inches, and the fourth was $7\frac{5}{16}$ inches. List these measurements in order from least to greatest.

$7\frac{5}{16}$ in., 7.5 in., $8\frac{1}{8}$ in., 8.25 in.

INDEPENDENT PRACTICE

See Example **1** Compare. Write $<$, $>$, or $=$.

10. $\frac{2}{3}$ ▨ $\frac{16}{21}$ $<$ 11. $\frac{13}{11}$ ▨ $\frac{8}{7}$ $>$ 12. $-\frac{1}{3}$ ▨ $-\frac{1}{4}$ $<$ 13. $-\frac{3}{4}$ ▨ $-\frac{9}{12}$ $=$

14. $-\frac{2}{3}$ ▨ $-\frac{5}{7}$ $>$ 15. $-\frac{16}{9}$ ▨ $-\frac{8}{3}$ $>$ 16. $\frac{17}{20}$ ▨ $\frac{5}{6}$ $>$ 17. $-\frac{2}{9}$ ▨ $-\frac{1}{8}$ $<$

See Example **2** 18. $5\frac{8}{9}$ ▨ $5\frac{7}{8}$ $>$ 19. $-\frac{1}{6}$ ▨ $-\frac{1}{5}$ $>$ 20. $-\frac{4}{7}$ ▨ $-\frac{2}{5}$ $<$ 21. $\frac{6}{7}$ ▨ 0.87 $<$

22. $-\frac{9}{7}$ ▨ $-\frac{10}{8}$ $<$ 23. $1\frac{2}{3}$ ▨ $1\frac{8}{12}$ $=$ 24. $\frac{15}{22}$ ▨ $0.68\overline{1}$ $=$ 25. $\frac{13}{20}$ ▨ 0.65 $=$

See Example **3** 26. **Sports** During the qualifying for the first NASCAR event at Texas Motor Speedway in 2005, the fastest speed was 192.582 mi/h. The next four fastest speeds, relative to the fastest speed, were approximately $-\frac{17}{25}$ mi/h, -0.15 mi/h, -1.15 mi/h, and $-1\frac{1}{40}$ mi/h. List these relative speeds in order from least to greatest.

-1.15 mi/h, $-1\frac{1}{40}$ mi/h, $-\frac{17}{25}$ mi/h, -0.15 mi/h

PRACTICE AND PROBLEM SOLVING

Extra Practice
See page EP4.

Compare. Write $<$, $>$, or $=$.

27. $-\frac{5}{7}$ ▨ $-\frac{6}{10}$ $<$ 28. -5.00 ▨ $-\frac{20}{5}$ $<$ 29. 7.2 ▨ $7\frac{2}{9}$ $<$ 30. 14.7 ▨ 14.6885 $>$

Write a fraction or decimal that has a value between the given numbers.

31. $\frac{1}{4}$ and $\frac{1}{3}$ $\frac{3}{10}$ 32. 0.89 and 0.9 0.899 33. $-\frac{2}{3}$ and 0.5 $-\frac{1}{3}$ 34. 0.27 and $\frac{4}{5}$ 0.5

31–34. Possible answers given.

35. Possible answer: A reasonable answer is -0.54 because $-0.56 <$ stock C < -0.50 and $-0.56 < -0.54 < -0.50$.

35. Reasoning On Tuesday, stock A's price fell -0.56 and stock B's price fell -0.50. Stock C's price did not fall as much as stock A's, but it fell more than stock B's. What is a reasonable answer for how much stock C's price fell? Explain.

36. Reasoning A positive fraction has a numerator whose value is twice the value of its denominator. Is the fraction less than or greater than 1? Give an example to support your answer.

greater than; Possible answer: $\frac{4}{2} = 2 > 1$

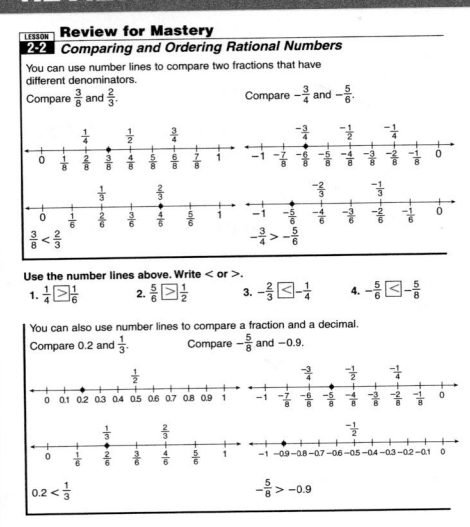

REVIEW FOR MASTERY 2-2

LESSON 2-2 **Review for Mastery**
Comparing and Ordering Rational Numbers

You can use number lines to compare two fractions that have different denominators.

Compare $\frac{3}{8}$ and $\frac{2}{3}$.   Compare $-\frac{3}{4}$ and $-\frac{5}{6}$.

$\frac{3}{8} < \frac{2}{3}$ $-\frac{3}{4} > -\frac{5}{6}$

Use the number lines above. Write $<$ or $>$.

1. $\frac{1}{4}$ ▷ $\frac{1}{6}$ 2. $\frac{5}{6}$ ▷ $\frac{1}{2}$ 3. $-\frac{2}{3}$ ◁ $-\frac{1}{4}$ 4. $-\frac{5}{6}$ ◁ $-\frac{5}{8}$

You can also use number lines to compare a fraction and a decimal.

Compare 0.2 and $\frac{1}{3}$.   Compare $-\frac{5}{8}$ and -0.9.

$0.2 < \frac{1}{3}$ $-\frac{5}{8} > -0.9$

Use the number lines above. Write $<$ or $>$.

5. $\frac{5}{6}$ ▷ 0.5 6. 0.6 ◁ $\frac{2}{3}$ 7. -0.4 ◁ $-\frac{1}{4}$ 8. $-\frac{7}{8}$ ◁ -0.8

PRACTICE 2-2

LESSON 2-2 **Practice B**
Comparing and Ordering Rational Numbers

Compare. Write $<$, $>$, or $=$.

1. $\frac{1}{8}$ ▷ $\frac{1}{10}$ 2. $\frac{3}{5}$ ◁ $\frac{7}{10}$ 3. $-\frac{1}{3}$ ▷ $-\frac{3}{4}$

4. $\frac{5}{6}$ ▷ $\frac{3}{4}$ 5. $-\frac{2}{7}$ ▷ $-\frac{1}{2}$ 6. $\frac{2}{9}$ ◁ $1\frac{1}{3}$

7. $-\frac{8}{9}$ ◁ $-\frac{3}{10}$ 8. $-\frac{4}{5}$ ▯ $-\frac{8}{10}$ 9. 0.08 ◁ $\frac{3}{10}$

10. $\frac{11}{15}$ ▯ 0.73 11. $2\frac{4}{9}$ ◁ $2\frac{3}{4}$ 12. $-\frac{5}{8}$ ◁ -0.58

13. $3\frac{1}{4}$ ◁ 3.3 14. $-\frac{1}{6}$ ▷ $-\frac{1}{9}$ 15. 0.75 ▯ $\frac{3}{4}$

16. $-2\frac{1}{8}$ ◁ -2.1 17. $1\frac{1}{2}$ ▷ 1.456 18. $-\frac{3}{5}$ ▯ -0.6

19. On Monday, Gina ran 1 mile in 9.3 minutes. Her times for running 1 mile on each of the next four days, relative to her time on Monday, were $-1\frac{2}{5}$ minutes, -1.45 minutes, -1.8 minutes, and $-1\frac{3}{8}$ minutes. List these relative times in order from least to greatest.
-1.8 minutes, $-1\frac{2}{5}$ minutes, -1.45 minutes, $-1\frac{3}{8}$ minutes

20. Trail A is 3.1 miles long. Trail C is $3\frac{1}{4}$ miles long. Trail B is longer than Trail A but shorter than Trail C. What is a reasonable distance for the length of Trail B?
Possible answer: 3.2 miles

37. Life Science The lengths of some butterflies' wingspans are shown in the table.

a. List the butterflies in order from smallest to largest wingspan.

b. The pink-spotted swallowtail's wingspan can measure $3\frac{5}{16}$ inches. Between which two butterflies should the pink-spotted swallowtail be in your list from part **a**?

Butterfly	Wingspan (in.)
Great white	3.75
Large orange sulphur	$3\frac{3}{8}$
Apricot sulphur	2.625
White-angled sulphur	3.5

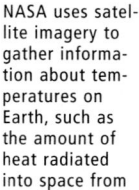
Meteorology

NASA uses satellite imagery to gather information about temperatures on Earth, such as the amount of heat radiated into space from Earth's surface and atmosphere.

38. Meteorology One measure of average global temperature shows how each year varies from a base measure. The table shows results for several years.

Year	1958	1964	1965	1978	2002
Difference from Base	0.10°C	−0.17°C	−0.10°C	$\frac{1}{50}$°C	0.54°C

a. Order the five years from coldest to warmest. 1964, 1965, 1978, 1958, 2002

b. In 1946, the average temperature varied by −0.03°C from the base measure. Between which two years should 1946 fall when the years are ordered from coldest to warmest? between 1965 and 1978

37a.
apricot sulphur, large orange sulphur, white-angled sulphur, great white

37b. between the apricot sulphur and the large orange sulphur

39. What's the Error? A student compared $-\frac{1}{4}$ and −0.3. He changed $-\frac{1}{4}$ to the decimal −0.25 and wrote, "Since 0.3 is greater than 0.25, −0.3 is greater than −0.25." What was the student's error?

40. Write About It Describe two methods to compare $\frac{13}{17}$ and 0.82. Which do you think is easier? Why?

41. Challenge Write $\left|-\frac{2}{3}\right|$, $|-0.75|$, $|0.62|$, and $\left|\frac{5}{6}\right|$ in order from least to greatest. $|0.62|$, $\left|-\frac{2}{3}\right|$, $|-0.75|$, $\left|\frac{5}{6}\right|$

SPIRAL STANDARDS REVIEW   NS1.1, NS1.2, NS1.3

42. Multiple Choice Which pair of numbers does $\frac{3}{7}$ NOT lie between?

(A) 0.3 and 0.45   (B) $\frac{9}{25}$ and $\frac{1}{2}$ (C) 0.2 and $\frac{1}{3}$ (D) $\frac{2}{5}$ and 0.65

43. Multiple Choice Which list of numbers is in order from least to greatest?

(A) 0.3, $\frac{4}{5}$, $\frac{1}{4}$, 0   (B) $\frac{4}{5}$, 0.3, 0, $\frac{1}{4}$ (C) $\frac{1}{4}$, $\frac{4}{5}$, 0, 0.3   (D) 0, $\frac{1}{4}$, 0.3, $\frac{4}{5}$

Simplify. (Lesson 1-5)

44. −5 − (−4)   **45.** 8 − (−2)   **46.** −19 − 13   **47.** 72 − 119   **48.** 24 − 37
        −1   10   −32   −47   −13

Write each fraction as a decimal. (Lesson 2-1)

49. $\frac{3}{4}$ 0.75   **50.** $\frac{1}{8}$ 0.125   **51.** $\frac{10}{4}$ 2.5   **52.** $\frac{9}{15}$ 0.6   **53.** $\frac{19}{20}$ 0.95

CHALLENGE 2-2

LESSON 2-2 **Challenge**
From Repeating Decimal to Fraction

You can use an equation to write a repeating decimal as a fraction.

Write 0.3333... as a fraction.	Write 0.363636... as a fraction.
Let x = 0.3333...	Let x = 0.363636...
Then 10x = 3.3333...	Then 100x = 36.363636...
10x = 3.3333...	100x = 36.3636...
$\underline{-x = 0.3333...}$	$\underline{-x = 0.3636...}$
9x = 3 Subtract.	99x = 36 Subtract.
$\frac{9x}{9} = \frac{3}{9}$ Solve the equation.	$\frac{99x}{99} = \frac{36}{99}$ Solve the equation.
$x = \frac{1}{3}$ Simplify.	$x = \frac{4}{11}$ Simplify.
So, 0.3333... = $\frac{1}{3}$.	So, 0.3636... = $\frac{4}{11}$.

Write each repeating decimal as a fraction.

1. 0.6666... = $\frac{2}{3}$ **2.** 0.8888... = $\frac{8}{9}$

3. 0.454545... = $\frac{5}{11}$ **4.** 0.090909... = $\frac{1}{11}$

5. 0.636363... = $\frac{7}{11}$ **6.** 0.16666... = $\frac{1}{6}$

7. 0.2222... = $\frac{2}{9}$ **8.** 0.83333... = $\frac{5}{6}$

9. 0.41666... = $\frac{5}{12}$ **10.** 0.58333... = $\frac{7}{12}$

PROBLEM SOLVING 2-2

LESSON 2-2 **Problem Solving**
Comparing and Ordering Rational Numbers

Write the correct answer.

1. Carl Lewis won the gold medal in the long jump in four consecutive Summer Olympic games. He jumped 8.54 meters in 1984, 8.72 meters in 1988, 8.67 meters in 1992, 8.5 meters in 1996. Order the length of his winning jumps from least to greatest.
8.5 m, 8.54 m, 8.67 m, 8.72 m

2. The depth of a lake is measured at three different points. Point A is −15.8 meters, Point B is −17.3 meters, and Point C is −16.9 meters. Which point has the greatest depth?
Point B

3. Scientists aboard a submarine are gathering data at an elevation of $-42\frac{1}{2}$ feet. Scientists aboard a submersible are taking photographs at an elevation of $-45\frac{1}{3}$ feet. Which scientists are closer to the surface of the ocean?
scientists aboard the submarine

4. At a swimming meet, Gail's time in her first heat was $42\frac{3}{8}$ seconds. Her time in the second heat was 42.25 seconds. Which heat did she swim faster?
the second heat

The table shows the top times in a 5 K race. Choose the letter of the best answer.

5. Who had the fastest time in the race?
A Marshall
B Renzo
C Dan
D Aaron

Name	Time (minutes)
Marshall	18.09
Renzo	17.38
Dan	17.9
Aaron	18.61

6. Which is the slowest time in the table?
F 18.09 minutes
G 17.38
H 17.9 minutes
J 18.61 minutes

7. Aaron's time in a previous race was less than his time in this race but greater than Marshall's time in this race. How fast could Aaron have run in the previous race?
A 19.24 min   C 18.35 min
B 18.7 min   D 18.05 mi

FORMATIVE ASSESSMENT
and INTERVENTION

Diagnose Before the Lesson
2-2 Warm Up, TE p. 70

Monitor During the Lesson
2-2 Know-It Notebook
2-2 Questioning Strategies

Assess After the Lesson
2-2 Lesson Quiz, TE p. 73

Answers

39. Possible answer: When ordering negative numbers, the number with the greater absolute value is *less than*, not greater than, the number with the smaller absolute value.

40. Possible answer: Method 1: Convert both numbers to decimals. Method 2: Convert both numbers to fractions. To make and compare two fractions, the least common denominator is very large, so it is easier to convert $\frac{13}{17}$ to a decimal and compare the decimals on a number line.

Teaching Tip
Multiple Choice Students may find it helpful to draw one or more number lines to help them determine the answer to **Exercise 42.** Have them plot the pairs of points given in the answer choices, and then decide whether $\frac{3}{7}$ comes between those values.

Journal

Have students explain how ordering rational numbers can be used in everyday life. Ask them to use an inequality in their explanation.

Power Presentations
with PowerPoint®

2-2 Lesson Quiz
Compare. Write <, >, or =.

1. $\frac{1}{4}$ ☐ $\frac{1}{3}$ <

2. $-\frac{2}{9}$ ☐ −0.29   >

3. $-2\frac{6}{7}$ ☐ $-2\frac{7}{8}$ >

4. Sarah competed in a long-jump contest. Her first jump was 3.75 m, her second jump was $3\frac{8}{9}$ m, and her third jump was $3\frac{9}{11}$ m. Which jump was the longest? second

Also available on transparency

Objective: Students add and subtract decimals and rational numbers with like denominators.

 Hands-On Lab
In *Chapter 2 Resource File*

 Online Edition
Tutorial Videos

 Countdown to Mastery Week 3

Power Presentations
with PowerPoint®

Warm Up

Simplify.

1. $\frac{21}{14}$ $1\frac{1}{2}$ 2. $\frac{12}{30}$ $\frac{2}{5}$

3. $\frac{24}{56}$ $\frac{3}{7}$

Write each decimal as a fraction in simplest form.

4. 1.15 $1\frac{3}{20}$ 5. -0.22 $-\frac{11}{50}$

Also available on transparency

Math Humor

How do we know that the fractions $\frac{3}{c}$, $\frac{6}{c}$, and $\frac{8}{c}$ are not from the United States? Because their numerators are all over c's!

California Standards

Number Sense  **1.2**

Also covered:

Number Sense

1.0 Students know the properties of, and **compute** with, rational numbers expressed in a variety of forms.

California Standards

← **NS1.2 Add, subtract,** multiply, and divide **rational numbers** (integers, **fractions, and terminating decimals**) and take positive rational numbers to whole-number powers.

Why learn this? You can subtract rational numbers to find how much faster one athlete is than another. (See Example 2.)

Previously you added and subtracted positive rational numbers and positive and negative integers. You can apply these rules to adding and subtracting positive and negative rational numbers.

$$\begin{array}{r} \mathbf{66.8} \\ \mathbf{+\ 4.0} \\ \hline \mathbf{70.8} \end{array}$$

Use zero as a placeholder so that both numbers have the same number of digits after their decimal points.

Add each column just as you would add integers.

Line up the decimal points.

EXAMPLE 1 **Adding and Subtracting Decimals**

Add or subtract.

A $-7.43 + (-35.8)$

For help with adding and subtracting rational numbers, see pages SB10 and SB12 in the Skills Bank.

$$\begin{array}{r} 7.43 \\ +\ 35.80 \\ \hline -\ 43.23 \end{array}$$

Line up the decimal points. Find the sum of the absolute values.
Use a zero as a placeholder.
Same sign; use the sign of the integers.

B $10.5 - 8.315$

$$\begin{array}{r} 10.500 \\ -\ 8.315 \\ \hline 2.185 \end{array}$$

Line up the decimal points. Use zeros as placeholders.
Subtract.

EXAMPLE 2 **Sports Application**

In the Athens 2004 Summer Olympic Games, Aaron Peirsol of the United States won the gold medal in the 100-meter backstroke with a time of 54.06 seconds. The eighth place finisher, Marco di Carli, completed the race in 55.27 seconds. How much faster was the first-place finisher than the eighth-place finisher?

$$\begin{array}{r} 55.27 \\ -\ 54.06 \\ \hline 1.21 \end{array}$$

Line up the decimal points.

The first-place finisher was 1.21 seconds faster.

---

1 **Introduce**

Alternate Opener

EXPLORATION

2-3 **Adding and Subtracting Rational Numbers**

Beckie has $454.96 in a checking account. She needs to pay bills in the amounts $25.95, $313.00, $45.76, and $87.95.

Beckie estimates the following:

Account: $454.96 ≈ $455.00

Bills: $25.95 ≈ $ 25.00
$313.00 ≈ $310.00
$45.76 ≈ $ 45.00
$87.95 ≈ $ 90.00
$470.00

Beckie determines that she does not have enough money in her account to pay her bills. She then checks her estimate with a calculator.

Estimate the solution to each expression in the table. Then use a calculator to solve.

		Estimate	Actual
1.	$120 - 9.8$		
2.	$45 - 17.8 + 15.9 + 16.1 - 1.07$		
3.	$88.10 + 109.85$		
4.	$34.12 - 18.30 + 65.25$		

Think and Discuss

5. Describe the estimation strategies you used.

Motivate

Use the following examples to review the rules for adding signed numbers (Lesson 1-4):

Same signs: $5 + 2 = 7$, $-5 + (-2) = -7$

Opposite signs: $5 + (-2) = 3$, $-5 + 2 = -3$

Review how to use a number line to perform these additions. Remind students that to subtract a number, you add its opposite (Lesson 1-5).

Explorations and answers are provided in *Alternate Openers: Explorations Transparencies.*

ADDING AND SUBTRACTING WITH LIKE DENOMINATORS		
Words	**Numbers**	**Algebra**
To add or subtract fractions with the same denominator, add or subtract the numerators and keep the denominator.	$\frac{1}{5} + \left(-\frac{4}{5}\right) = \frac{1 + (-4)}{5}$ $= \frac{-3}{5}, \text{ or } -\frac{3}{5}$	$\frac{a}{d} + \frac{b}{d} = \frac{a + b}{d}$

E X A M P L E ③ **Adding and Subtracting Fractions with Like Denominators**

Add or subtract. Write each answer in simplest form.

Ⓐ $\frac{7}{13} + \frac{11}{13}$

$\frac{7}{13} + \frac{11}{13} = \frac{7 + 11}{13}$ *Add numerators. Keep the denominator.*

$= \frac{18}{13}, \text{ or } 1\frac{5}{13}$

> **Remember!**
> Subtracting a number is the same as adding its opposite.

Ⓑ $-\frac{3}{8} - \frac{5}{8}$

$-\frac{3}{8} - \frac{5}{8} = \frac{-3}{8} + \frac{-5}{8}$ $-\frac{5}{8} \text{ can be written as } \frac{-5}{8}.$

$= \frac{-3 + (-5)}{8} = \frac{-8}{8} = -1$

E X A M P L E ④ **Evaluating Expressions with Rational Numbers**

Evaluate each expression for the given value of the variable.

Ⓐ $33.5 + x$ for $x = -48.2$

$33.5 + (-48.2)$ *Substitute −48.2 for x.*

-14.7 *Think: 48.2 > 33.5. Use the sign of 48.2.*

Ⓑ $-\frac{3}{8} + c$ for $c = 1\frac{7}{8}$

$-\frac{3}{8} + 1\frac{7}{8}$ *Substitute $1\frac{7}{8}$ for c.*

$\frac{-3}{8} + \frac{15}{8}$ $1\frac{7}{8} = \frac{1(8) + 7}{8} = \frac{15}{8}$

$\frac{-3 + 15}{8} = \frac{12}{8}$ *Add numerators. Keep the denominator.*

$\frac{3}{2}, \text{ or } 1\frac{1}{2}$ *Simplify.*

Think and Discuss

1. **Give an example** of an addition problem that involves simplifying an improper fraction in the final step.

2. **Explain** why $\frac{7}{9} + \frac{7}{9}$ does NOT equal $\frac{14}{18}$.

Power Presentations
with PowerPoint®

Additional Examples

Example ①

Add or subtract.

A. $0.3 + (-1.2)$ −0.9
B. $17.2 - 4.39$ 12.81

Example ②

In August 2001, at the World University Games in Beijing, China, Jimyria Hicks ran the 200-meter dash in 24.08 seconds. Her best time at the U.S. Senior National Meet in June of the same year was 23.35 seconds. How much faster did she run in June?   0.73 second

Example ③

Add or subtract. Write each answer in simplest form.

A. $-\frac{2}{9} - \frac{5}{9}$ $-\frac{7}{9}$ **B.** $\frac{6}{7} + \left(-\frac{3}{7}\right)$ $\frac{3}{7}$

Example ④

Evaluate each expression for the given value of the variable.

A. $12.1 - x$ for $x = -0.1$ 12.2

B. $\frac{7}{10} + m$ for $m = 3\frac{1}{10}$ $3\frac{4}{5}$

Also available on transparency

Possible answers to Think and Discuss:

1. $\frac{5}{8} + \frac{5}{8} = \frac{10}{8} = \frac{5}{4} = 1\frac{1}{4}$

2. To add fractions with like denominators, add the numerators, but keep the same denominator.
$\frac{7}{9} + \frac{7}{9} = \frac{14}{9} = 1\frac{5}{9}$

---

② Teach

Guided Instruction

In this lesson, students learn to add and subtract decimals and fractions with like denominators. Review with students how to align decimals for addition and subtraction. Explain that you can't add or subtract digits that are in different places because they don't share the same value. In **Example 3,** remind students to write their answers in simplest form.

Universal Access
For Advanced Learners/GATE

Give each pair of students a set of related exercises, such as those shown below.

1. $2.51 + 4.2$ 6.71
2. $-2.51 + (-4.2)$ −6.71
3. $-2.51 + 4.2$ 1.69
4. $2.51 + (-4.2)$ −1.69

Have students compare the answers in each set, and make a generalization about the rules for adding positive and negative numbers. Have students compare generalizations until a consensus is reached.

③ Close

Summarize

Remind students that decimal points must be aligned when adding or subtracting decimals. Remind students that to add or subtract fractions with like denominators, they should add or subtract the numerators and keep the same denominator. Ask students if it's possible to add a decimal and a fraction, and ask them how they would do it.

Possible answer: Yes; you can write the fraction as a decimal and then add the decimals together, or you can write the decimal as a fraction and add the fractions together.

California Standards Practice
NS1.2

go.hrw.com
Homework Help Online
KEYWORD: MT8CA 2-3
Parent Resources Online
KEYWORD: MT8CA Parent

Assignment Guide

If you finished Example **1** assign:
Proficient 1–4, 14–16 even, 43, 46–53
Advanced 13–16, 43, 46–53

If you finished Example **2** assign:
Proficient 1–5, 14–16 even, 17, 43–44, 46–53
Advanced 13–17, 38–40, 43–44, 46–53

If you finished Example **3** assign:
Proficient 1–9, 14–16 even, 17, 18–20 even, 29–39 odd, 43–44, 46–53
Advanced 13–21, 29, 30–40 even, 41–44, 46–53

If you finished Example **4** assign:
Proficient 1–12, 14–16 even, 17, 18–24 even, 25–39 odd, 43–53
Advanced 13–24, 29, 26–40 even, 41–53

Homework Quick Check

Quickly check key concepts.
Exercises: 14, 16, 18, 20, 24

Math Background

The Commutative Property of Addition states that $a + b = b + a$ for all real numbers a and b (e.g., $0.21 + 3.4 = 3.4 + 0.21 = 3.61$). There is no commutative property for subtraction, because $a - b = b - a$ is *not* true for all real numbers a and b (e.g., $\frac{2}{3} - \frac{1}{3} = \frac{1}{3}$, but $\frac{1}{3} - \frac{2}{3} = -\frac{1}{3}$). The Associative Property of Addition states that $a + (b + c) = (a + b) + c$. It holds for all real numbers a, b, and c. However, there is no associative property for subtraction [(e.g., $1.2 - (0.8 - 0.3) = 0.7$, but $(1.2 - 0.8) - 0.3 = 0.1$)].

California Standards

Standard	Exercises
NS1.1	50–53
NS1.2	1–45
AF4.1	46–49

GUIDED PRACTICE

See Example **1** Add or subtract.
1. $21.74 + 8.27$ **30.01**   2. $17 - 9.54$ **7.46**   3. $6.125 + 18$ **24.125**   4. $-3.95 + (-1.7)$ **−5.65**

See Example **2** 5. **Sports** In the Athens 2004 Olympic Games, Jodie Henry of Australia won the gold medal in the 100-meter freestyle swim with a time of 53.84 seconds. The bronze medal winner, Natalie Coughlin of the United States, completed the race in 54.4 seconds. What was the difference between the two times? **0.56 s**

See Example **3** Add or subtract. Write each answer in simplest form.
6. $\frac{1}{6} - \frac{5}{6}$ $-\frac{2}{3}$ 7. $-\frac{3}{10} - \frac{9}{10}$ $-1\frac{1}{5}$ 8. $\frac{3}{12} + \frac{7}{12}$ $\frac{5}{6}$ 9. $\frac{9}{25} + \left(-\frac{4}{25}\right)$ $\frac{1}{5}$

See Example **4** Evaluate each expression for the given value of the variable.
10. $3.7 + x$ for $x = -9.3$ **−5.6**   11. $-\frac{4}{9} + x$ for $x = \frac{8}{9}$ $\frac{4}{9}$ 12. $-\frac{14}{15} + x$ for $x = 1$ $\frac{1}{15}$

INDEPENDENT PRACTICE

See Example **1** Add or subtract.
13. $4.67 + 29$ **33.67**   14. $5 - 3.11$ **1.89**   15. $-3.83 + (-9.072)$ **−12.902**   16. $4.54 - 2.98$ **1.56**

See Example **2** 17. **Sports** Reaction time measures how quickly a runner reacts to the starter pistol. In the 100-meter dash at the 2004 Olympic Games, Lauryn Williams had a reaction time of 0.214 second. Her total race time, including reaction time, was 11.03 seconds. How long did it take her to run the actual distance? **10.816 s**

See Example **3** Add or subtract. Write each answer in simplest form.
18. $\frac{7}{13} - \frac{5}{13}$ $\frac{2}{13}$ 19. $-\frac{1}{17} - \frac{13}{17}$ $-\frac{14}{17}$ 20. $\frac{9}{17} + \frac{16}{17}$ $1\frac{8}{17}$ 21. $\frac{11}{33} + \left(-\frac{19}{33}\right)$ $-\frac{8}{33}$

See Example **4** Evaluate each expression for the given value of the variable.
22. $47.3 + x$ for $x = -18.6$ 23. $\frac{11}{12} + x$ for $x = -\frac{7}{12}$ 24. $-\frac{23}{25} + x$ for $x = \frac{7}{25}$

PRACTICE AND PROBLEM SOLVING

Extra Practice
See page EP4.

22. 28.7
23. $\frac{1}{3}$
24. $-\frac{16}{25}$
25. 7.9375 or $7\frac{15}{16}$
26. 1.9 or $1\frac{9}{10}$
27. $4\frac{69}{200}$ or 4.345

Evaluate each expression for the given value of the variable.
25. $8.25 - x$ for $x = \frac{5}{16}$ 26. $-1.7 + x$ for $x = 3\frac{3}{5}$ 27. $x + \left(-\frac{3}{8}\right)$ for $x = 4.72$
28. Yes; Possible answer: $\frac{8}{9} < 1$ and $-\frac{7}{9} > -1$, $\frac{8}{9} + \left|-\frac{7}{9}\right| = \frac{8}{9} + \frac{7}{9} = \frac{15}{9}$ or $1\frac{2}{3}$.

28. **Reasoning** A positive fraction is less than 1. A negative fraction is greater than -1. Can the sum of the positive fraction and the absolute value of the negative fraction be greater than 1? Explain your reasoning with an example.

29. **Sports** The circumference of a women's NCAA college softball must be between $11\frac{7}{8}$ inches and $12\frac{1}{8}$ inches. What is the greatest possible difference in circumference between two softballs that meet the standards? $\frac{1}{4}$ in.

REVIEW FOR MASTERY 2-3

LESSON 2-3 Review for Mastery
Adding and Subtracting Rational Numbers

To add fractions that have the same denominator:
- Use the common denominator for the sum.
- Add the numerators to get the numerator of the sum.
- Write the sum in simplest form.

$\frac{1}{8} + \frac{3}{8} = \frac{1+3}{8} = \frac{4}{8} = \frac{1}{2}$

To subtract fractions that have the same denominator:
- Use the common denominator for the difference.
- Subtract the numerators.
  Subtraction is addition of an opposite.
- Write the difference in simplest form.

$\frac{3}{6} - \left(-\frac{1}{6}\right) = \frac{3+1}{6} = \frac{4}{6} = \frac{2}{3}$

Complete to add the fractions.
1. $\frac{3}{14} + \frac{4}{14} = \frac{7}{14} = \frac{1}{2}$ 2. $\frac{2}{10} + \left(-\frac{4}{10}\right) = \frac{-2}{10} = -\frac{1}{5}$
3. $-\frac{5}{12} + \left(-\frac{3}{12}\right) = \frac{-8}{12} = -\frac{2}{3}$

Complete to subtract the fractions.
4. $\frac{8}{9} - \frac{2}{9} = \frac{6}{9} = \frac{2}{3}$ 5. $\frac{9}{15} - \left(-\frac{3}{15}\right) = \frac{12}{15} = \frac{4}{5}$
6. $-\frac{10}{24} - \left(-\frac{2}{24}\right) = \frac{-8}{24} = -\frac{1}{3}$

To add or subtract decimals, line up the decimal points and then add or subtract from right to left as usual.

```
  12.83        35.78
+ 24.17      - 14.55
-------      -------
  37.00        21.23
```

Complete to add the decimals.
7. $14.23 + 3.56 = $ __17.79__   8. $44.02 + 8.07 = $ __52.09__
9. $1.39 + 13.6 = $ __14.99__

Complete to subtract the decimals.
10. $124.33 - 13.16 = $ __111.17__   11. $33.47 - 0.6 = $ __32.87__
12. $25.15 - 25.06 = $ __0.09__

PRACTICE 2-3

LESSON 2-3 Practice B
Adding and Subtracting Rational Numbers

1. $47.8 + 25.37$ __73.17__   2. $60.15 - 3.8$ __56.35__

3. Gretchen bought a sweater for $23.89. In addition, she had to pay $1.43 in sales tax. She gave the sales clerk $30. How much change did Gretchen receive from her total purchase?   __$4.68__

4. Jacob is replacing the molding around two sides of a picture frame. The measurements of the sides of the frame are $4\frac{3}{16}$ in. and $2\frac{5}{16}$ in. What length of molding will Jacob need?   __$6\frac{1}{2}$ in.__

Add or subtract. Simplify.
5. $\frac{3}{8} + \frac{5}{8}$ __1__   6. $-\frac{1}{10} + \frac{7}{10}$ __$\frac{3}{5}$__   7. $\frac{5}{14} - \frac{3}{14}$ __$\frac{1}{7}$__   8. $\frac{4}{15} + \frac{7}{15}$ __$\frac{11}{15}$__
9. $\frac{5}{18} - \frac{7}{18}$ __$-\frac{1}{9}$__   10. $-\frac{8}{17} - \frac{2}{17}$ __$-\frac{10}{17}$__   11. $-\frac{1}{16} + \frac{5}{16}$ __$\frac{1}{4}$__   12. $\frac{3}{20} + \frac{1}{20}$ __$\frac{1}{5}$__

Evaluate each expression for the given value of the variable.
13. $38.1 + x$ for $x = -6.1$ __32__   14. $18.7 + x$ for $x = 8.5$ __27.2__   15. $\frac{8}{15} + x$ for $x = -\frac{4}{15}$ __$\frac{4}{15}$__
16. $\frac{13}{20} + x$ for $x = \frac{4}{20}$ __$\frac{17}{20}$__   17. $21.6 + x$ for $x = -11.2$ __10.4__   18. $\frac{8}{13} + x$ for $x = \frac{2}{13}$ __$\frac{10}{13}$__

California LINK
Energy

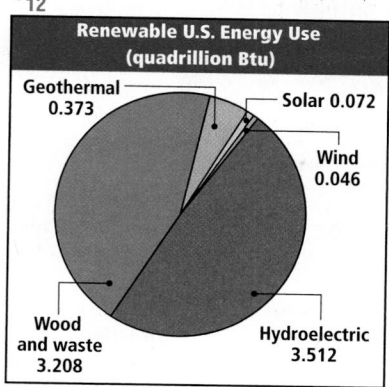

Electricity is generated by this solar power station in the Mojave Desert, California.

Simplify. Write each answer in simplest form.

30. $\frac{4}{9} - \frac{1}{9}$ $\frac{1}{3}$

31. $-\frac{7}{11} + \frac{3}{11} - \frac{2}{11}$ $-\frac{6}{11}$

32. $\frac{13}{5} + \frac{8}{5}$ $4\frac{1}{5}$

33. $-\frac{17}{18} - \frac{29}{18}$ $-2\frac{5}{9}$

34. $\frac{11}{25} - \left(-\frac{19}{25}\right)$ $1\frac{1}{5}$

35. $-\frac{13}{21} + \left(-\frac{8}{21}\right)$ -1

36. $\frac{5}{12} - \frac{7}{12} + \left(-\frac{11}{12}\right)$ $-1\frac{1}{12}$

37. $-\frac{15}{16} + \left(-\frac{9}{16}\right)$ $-1\frac{1}{2}$

Energy The circle graph shows the sources of renewable energy and their use in the United States in British thermal units (Btu).

38. How many quadrillion Btu's from geothermal, wood and waste, and hydroelectric sources combined were used? **7.093 quadrillion Btu**

39. How many more Btu's from hydroelectric sources were used than those from wind, solar, and wood and waste sources combined? **0.186 quadrillion Btu**

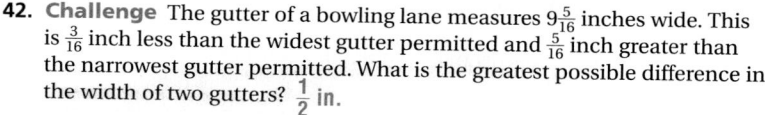

Renewable U.S. Energy Use (quadrillion Btu)

Geothermal 0.373
Solar 0.072
Wind 0.046
Wood and waste 3.208
Hydroelectric 3.512

40. **Write a Problem** Write a math problem that requires a decimal to be converted to a fraction and that also involves addition or subtraction of fractions.

41. **Write About It** Explain how to subtract fractions with like denominators.

42. **Challenge** The gutter of a bowling lane measures $9\frac{5}{16}$ inches wide. This is $\frac{3}{16}$ inch less than the widest gutter permitted and $\frac{5}{16}$ inch greater than the narrowest gutter permitted. What is the greatest possible difference in the width of two gutters? $\frac{1}{2}$ in.

SPIRAL STANDARDS REVIEW

NS1.1, ⬅ NS1.2, ⬅ AF4.1

43. **Multiple Choice** Evaluate the expression $25.18 - x$ for $x = -18.7$.

Ⓐ 6.48   Ⓑ 23.31   Ⓒ 27.05   Ⓓ 43.88

44. **Multiple Choice** Gregory filled a fish tank with $4\frac{5}{12}$ gallons of water. Linda added $3\frac{11}{12}$ more gallons of water. How many total gallons of water were in the tank?

Ⓐ $7\frac{2}{3}$ gal   Ⓑ $8\frac{1}{3}$ gal   Ⓒ $8\frac{5}{12}$ gal   Ⓓ $8\frac{2}{3}$ gal

45. **Gridded Response** Evaluate $\frac{7}{15} - x$ for $x = -\frac{4}{15}$. $\frac{11}{15}$

Solve. (Lessons 1-7 and 1-9)

46. $3x + 13 = 22$ $x = 3$

47. $-7b + 5 = -2$ $b = 1$

48. $2y + 9 = 19$ $y = 5$

49. $4a + 2 = -18$ $a = -5$

Compare. Write <, >, or =. (Lesson 2-2)

50. $0.25 \; \blacksquare \; \frac{1}{3}$ $<$

51. $-0.5\overline{3} \; \blacksquare \; -0.5$ $<$

52. $\frac{4}{7} \; \blacksquare \; 0.57$ $>$

53. $-\frac{9}{11} \; \blacksquare \; -0.8\overline{1}$ $=$

CHALLENGE 2-3

LESSON 2-3 Challenge
Number Code

Each sum is the code for a letter. As you find a sum, write its letter code in the message below. Write the sum in simplest form. Some letters appear more than once. An example is done for you.

$4.5 + (-6.5)$ $\underline{-2}$, T

1. $14.56 + (-10.09)$ $\underline{4.47}$, V

2. $\frac{7}{8} + \left(-1\frac{3}{8}\right)$ $\underline{-\frac{1}{2}}$, M

3. $\frac{6}{8} + \left(-\frac{3}{8}\right)$ $\underline{\frac{3}{8}}$, N

4. $-1.05 + 0.85$ $\underline{-0.2}$, I

5. $\frac{-2}{4} + \left(\frac{-3}{4}\right)$ $\underline{-1\frac{1}{4}}$, U

6. $-7.08 + (-12.02)$ $\underline{-19.1}$, S

7. $-9.5 + 3.1$ $\underline{-6.4}$, E

8. $\frac{-4}{5} + 1$ $\underline{\frac{1}{5}}$, E

9. $-1\frac{1}{2} + \left(-1\frac{1}{2}\right)$ $\underline{-3}$, H

10. $1\frac{2}{4} + \left(\frac{-3}{4}\right)$ $\underline{\frac{3}{4}}$, P

11. $5 + \left(-4\frac{1}{10}\right)$ $\underline{\frac{9}{10}}$, I

12. $8 + (-6.4)$ $\underline{1.6}$, Y

13. $-3\frac{1}{4} + 3\frac{1}{4}$ $\underline{0}$, S

14. $\frac{7}{8} + \left(-1\frac{7}{8}\right)$ $\underline{-1}$, L

15. $6.52 + (-5)$ $\underline{1.52}$, Z

16. $-62.3 + 23.9$ $\underline{-38.4}$, A

17. $9\frac{1}{8} + (-10)$ $\underline{-\frac{7}{8}}$, R

18. $-2.9 + 0.85$ $\underline{-2.05}$, O

19. $2.7 + (-0.9)$ $\underline{1.8}$, O

$\underset{-19.1}{S} \underset{-1\frac{1}{4}}{U} \underset{-\frac{7}{8}}{R} \underset{-6.4}{E}$ $\underset{}{Y} \underset{1.6}{O} \underset{-0.2}{U}$ $\underset{-38.4}{A} \underset{-\frac{7}{8}}{'R} \underset{\frac{1}{5}}{E}$

$\underset{\frac{3}{8}}{N} \underset{1.8}{O} \underset{-2}{T}$ $\underset{-1}{L} \underset{\frac{1}{5}}{E} \underset{-19.1}{S} \underset{0}{S}$ $\underset{-2}{T} \underset{-3}{H} \underset{-38.4}{A} \underset{\frac{3}{8}}{N}$

$\underset{1.52}{Z} \underset{-6.4}{E} \underset{-\frac{7}{8}}{R} \underset{-2.05}{O}?$

$\underset{-0.2}{I'} \underset{-\frac{1}{2}}{M}$ $\underset{\frac{3}{4}}{P} \underset{-2.05}{O} \underset{0}{S} \underset{\frac{9}{10}}{I} \underset{-2}{T} \underset{-0.2}{I} \underset{4.47}{V} \underset{\frac{1}{5}}{E}!$

PROBLEM SOLVING 2-3

LESSON 2-3 Problem Solving
Adding and Subtracting Rational Numbers

Write the correct answer.

1. In 2004, Yuliya Nesterenko of Belarus won the Olympic Gold in the 100-m dash with a time of 10.93 seconds. In 2000, American Marion Jones won the 100-m dash with a time of 10.75 seconds. How many seconds faster did Marion Jones run the 100-m dash?

   0.18 s

2. The snowfall in Rochester, NY in the winter of 1999–2000 was 91.5 inches. Normal snowfall is about 76 inches per winter. How much more snow fell in the winter of 1999–2000 than is normal?

   15.5 inches

3. In a survey, $\frac{76}{100}$ people indicated that they check their e-mail daily, while $\frac{23}{100}$ check their e-mail weekly, and $\frac{1}{100}$ check their e-mail less than once a week. What fraction of people check their e-mail at least once a week?

   $\frac{99}{100}$

4. To make a small amount of play dough, you can mix the following ingredients: 1 cup of flour, $\frac{1}{2}$ cup of salt and $\frac{1}{2}$ cup of water. What is the total amount of ingredients added to make the play dough?

   2 cups

Choose the letter for the best answer.

5. How much more expensive is it to buy a ticket in Boston than in Minnesota?

A $20.95   C $5.40
B $55.19   D $26.35

Baseball Ticket Prices	
Location	Average Price
Minnesota	$14.42
League Average	$19.82
Boston	$40.77

6. How much more expensive is it to buy a ticket in Boston than the league average?

F $60.59
G $20.95
H $5.40
J $26.35

7. What is the total cost of a ticket in Boston and a ticket in Minnesota?

A $55.19
B $34.24
C $60.59
D $54.19

FORMATIVE ASSESSMENT and INTERVENTION ⬅➡

Diagnose Before the Lesson
2-3 Warm Up, TE p. 74

Monitor During the Lesson
2-3 Know-It Notebook
2-3 Questioning Strategies

Assess After the Lesson
2-3 Lesson Quiz, TE p. 77

Answers

40. Possible answer: Ed had a board 8.75 feet in length. He sawed off a piece that was $3\frac{1}{4}$ feet long. What is the length of the remaining board? Answer: $5\frac{1}{2}$ feet

41. Subtract the numerators, and use the common denominator for the answer. Simplify the answer if necessary.

Teaching Tip **Multiple Choice** In **Exercise 43,** encourage students to be careful with the signs when evaluating the expression. If students chose **A,** they may have subtracted 18.7. Instead, remind them to subtract -18.7.

Journal

Have students write a word problem that requires addition or subtraction of rational numbers for the solution.

Power Presentations with PowerPoint®

✓ 2-3 Lesson Quiz

Add or subtract.

1. $-1.2 + 8.4$ 7.2

2. $2.5 + (-2.8)$ -0.3

3. $\frac{3}{4} + \left(-\frac{5}{4}\right)$ $-\frac{1}{2}$

4. Evaluate $62.1 + x$ for $x = -127.0$. -64.9

5. Sarah's best broad jump is 1.6 meters, and Jill's best is 1.47 meters. How much farther can Sarah jump than Jill?   0.13 m

Also available on transparency

Objective: Students multiply fractions, mixed numbers, and decimals.

 Online Edition
Tutorial Videos

 Countdown to Mastery Week 4

Power Presentations
with PowerPoint®

Warm Up

Write each number as an improper fraction.

1. $2\frac{1}{3}$ $\frac{7}{3}$ **2.** $1\frac{7}{8}$ $\frac{15}{8}$ **3.** $3\frac{2}{5}$ $\frac{17}{5}$

4. $6\frac{2}{3}$ $\frac{20}{3}$ **5.** $5\frac{3}{8}$ $\frac{43}{8}$

 **Also available on transparency**

Math Humor

5 out of 4 people have trouble with fractions.

 **California Standards**

Number Sense 🔑 1.2

California Standards

🔑 **NS1.2** Add, subtract, **multiply**, and divide **rational numbers (integers, fractions, and terminating decimals)** and take positive rational numbers to whole-number powers.

Why learn this? You can multiply rational numbers to determine how far you walk your dog. (See Example 2.)

Recall from Lesson 1–6 that the product of two integers with the same sign is positive and the product of two integers with different signs is negative. When multiplying negative fractions, you can use the same rules you used for multiplying integers.

MULTIPLYING RATIONAL NUMBERS IN FRACTION FORM		
Words	**Numbers**	**Algebra**
To multiply two fractions, multiply the numerators to get the numerator and multiply the denominators to get the denominator.	$\frac{3}{5}\left(\frac{1}{4}\right) = \frac{3 \cdot 1}{5 \cdot 4}$	$\frac{a}{b}\left(\frac{c}{d}\right) = \frac{a \cdot c}{b \cdot d}$

EXAMPLE 1 Multiplying Fractions

Multiply. Write each answer in simplest form.

For help with multiplying rational numbers, see pages SB11 and SB13 in the Skills Bank.

A $-\frac{3}{5}\left(-\frac{1}{4}\right)$

$-\frac{3}{5}\left(-\frac{1}{4}\right) = \frac{-3}{5}\left(\frac{-1}{4}\right)$

$= \frac{(-3)(-1)}{5(4)}$ *Multiply numerators.*
Multiply denominators.

$= \frac{3}{20}$ *Simplify.*

B $-\frac{5}{12}\left(2\frac{2}{5}\right)$

$-\frac{5}{12}\left(2\frac{2}{5}\right) = -\frac{5}{12}\left(\frac{12}{5}\right)$ *Rewrite $2\frac{2}{5}$ as an improper fraction:*
$2\frac{2}{5} = \frac{2(5) + 2}{5} = \frac{12}{5}$.

$= \frac{\overset{1}{\cancel{5}}(-\cancel{12})^{1}}{{}_{1}\cancel{12}(\cancel{5})_{1}}$ *Look for common factors: 12, 5.*
Multiply numerators.
Multiply denominators.

$= \frac{1(-1)}{1(1)}$

$= \frac{-1}{1} = -1$ *Simplify.*

---

1 Introduce

Alternate Opener

EXPLORATION

 2-4 Multiplying Rational Numbers

You can use paper folding to find products of mixed numbers. To find $\frac{1}{2} \cdot 1\frac{1}{2}$, first fold two sheets of paper in half vertically to represent $1\frac{1}{2}$. To represent $\frac{1}{2}$ of $1\frac{1}{2}$, fold both sheets in half again horizontally.

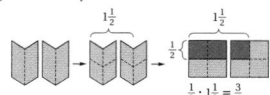

$$\frac{1}{2} \cdot 1\frac{1}{2} = \frac{3}{4}$$

Use paper folding to find each product. Sketch a picture for each product.

1. $\frac{2}{3} \cdot 1\frac{1}{2}$ **2.** $\frac{1}{3} \cdot 1\frac{3}{4}$

Think and Discuss

3. Explain how to multiply a fraction times a mixed number.
4. Explain why the product of a proper fraction and a mixed number is less than the mixed number.

Motivate

Ask students if they have ever mixed ingredients for a recipe. Ask them if they have had to use fractions to measure the ingredients. Ask them if they would have known how much of each ingredient to use to make a double batch, a half batch, or a batch and a half. Tell the students that it is helpful to be able to multiply rational numbers for such purposes.

Explorations and answers are provided in *Alternate Openers: Explorations Transparencies.*

To multiply a fraction by an integer, first write the integer as a fraction with a denominator of 1. Then multiply as you would with two fractions.

EXAMPLE 2 *Recreation Application*

Andrew usually walks his dog 4 miles each Saturday. Last Saturday, Andrew walked only $\frac{2}{3}$ of his usual distance because it started raining. How far did Andrew walk his dog last Saturday?

Andrew walked $\frac{2}{3}$ of 4 miles.

$$\frac{2}{3}(4) = \frac{2}{3}\left(\frac{4}{1}\right) \qquad \text{\textit{Write the integer as a fraction: } } 4 = \frac{4}{1}.$$

$$= \frac{2(4)}{3(1)} = \frac{8}{3} \qquad \text{\textit{Multiply numerators and denominators.}}$$

$$= 2\frac{2}{3} \qquad \text{\textit{Simplify.}}$$

Andrew walked his dog $2\frac{2}{3}$ miles last Saturday.

To multiply decimals, first multiply as you would with integers. The number of decimal places in the product is equal to the sum of the number of decimal places in the factors.

EXAMPLE 3 **Multiplying Decimals**

Multiply.

A $-5.2(-5)$

$$\begin{array}{r} -5.2 \\ \times \ \ -5 \\ \hline 26.0 \end{array} \qquad \begin{array}{l} \textit{1 decimal place} \\ \underline{\textit{+ 0 decimal places}} \\ \textit{1 decimal place} \end{array}$$

B $-0.07(4.6)$

$$\begin{array}{r} -0.07 \\ \times \ \ 4.6 \\ \hline 42 \\ 28 \ \ \\ \hline -0.322 \end{array} \qquad \begin{array}{l} \textit{2 decimal places} \\ \underline{\textit{+ 1 decimal place}} \\ \ \\ \ \\ \textit{3 decimal places} \end{array}$$

Answers to *Think and Discuss*

1. 5 decimal places; the number of decimal places is the sum of the decimal places in the factors.

2. Possible answer: $\frac{3}{2} \cdot \frac{4}{3} = 2$

Think and Discuss

1. Determine the number of decimal places in the product of 5.625 and 2.75.

2. Give an example of two fractions whose product is an integer.

Power Presentations with PowerPoint®

Additional Examples

Example 1

Multiply. Write each answer in simplest form.

A. $\frac{1}{8}\left(\frac{6}{7}\right)$ $\frac{3}{28}$ **B.** $-\frac{2}{3}\left(4\frac{1}{2}\right)$ -3

Example 2

Joy completes $\frac{1}{20}$ of her painting each day. How much of her painting does she complete in a 7-day week?
$\frac{7}{20}$

Example 3

Multiply.

A. $2(-0.51)$ -1.02

B. $(-0.4)(-3.75)$ 1.5

Also available on transparency

Teaching Tip   **Number Sense** Explain to students that multiplying two fractions or two decimals does not necessarily result in a product that is greater than the factors, as shown in **Example 1**.

---

2 Teach

Guided Instruction

In this lesson, students learn to multiply fractions and mixed numbers. Review the concept of multiplication as repeated addition and the rules for multiplying signed numbers (Teaching Transparency). Review **Example 1** and point out that students may "cancel out" common factors between numerators and denominators. For multiplying decimals, remind students that the number of decimal places in the product should be the total number of decimal places in the two factors.

Universal Access

Through Multiple Representations

Show students two ways to evaluate $\frac{1}{2}(0.7)$:

$$\frac{1}{2}(0.7) = 0.5 \cdot 0.7 = 0.35$$

$$\frac{1}{2}(0.7) = \frac{1}{2} \cdot \frac{7}{10} = \frac{7}{20}$$

Show that $\frac{7}{20} = 0.35$ by dividing:

$$20\overline{)7.00} \quad 0.35$$

Have students find each of the following products both ways and show that the results are equal in each case.

1. $\frac{1}{2}(0.3)$ $\frac{3}{20}$, 0.15   **2.** $\frac{1}{5}(0.4)$ $\frac{2}{25}$, 0.08

3. $\frac{3}{4}(0.1)$ $\frac{3}{40}$, 0.075   **4.** $1\frac{1}{2}(0.2)$ $\frac{3}{10}$, 0.3

---

3 Close

Summarize

Ask students to explain how to multiply each of the following:

1) a fraction and a mixed number
2) two decimals
3) a decimal and a fraction

Possible answers:

1. Change the mixed number to an improper fraction, multiply numerators, multiply denominators, and write in simplest form.

2. Multiply the numbers and count the total number of decimal places in the two factors.

3. Either write the decimal as a fraction or the fraction as a decimal, and then multiply.

2-4 **Exercises**

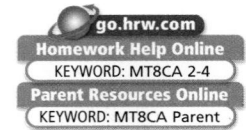

California Standards Practice
← NS1.2

go.hrw.com
Homework Help Online
KEYWORD: MT8CA 2-4
Parent Resources Online
KEYWORD: MT8CA Parent

Assignment Guide

If you finished Example **1** assign:
Proficient 1–4, 10–17, 48, 50–57
Advanced 10–17, 29, 31, 37, 39, 48, 50–57

If you finished Example **2** assign:
Proficient 1–5, 10–19, 41–43, 47–48, 50–57
Advanced 10–19, 29, 31, 37, 39, 41–48, 50–57

If you finished Example **3** assign:
Proficient 1–27, 28–40 even, 41–43, 47–57
Advanced 10–19, 20–26 even, 29–39 odd, 40–57

Homework Quick Check

Quickly check key concepts.
Exercises: 10, 12, 14, 18, 22

Math Background

The expression $3 \cdot \frac{1}{2}$ is read "three times one-half," and it means $\frac{1}{2} + \frac{1}{2} + \frac{1}{2}$.

The expression $\frac{1}{2} \cdot 3$ is read "one-half times three," and it means "one-half of three."

By the Commutative Property of Multiplication, $3 \cdot \frac{1}{2} = \frac{1}{2} \cdot 3$.

GUIDED PRACTICE

See Example **1** Multiply. Write each answer in simplest form.

1. $-\frac{1}{4}\left(-\frac{5}{8}\right)$ $\frac{5}{32}$ 2. $\frac{3}{8}\left(-\frac{7}{10}\right)$ $-\frac{21}{80}$ 3. $6\frac{3}{7}\left(\frac{7}{8}\right)$ $5\frac{5}{8}$ 4. $-\frac{3}{5}\left(-\frac{5}{9}\right)$ $\frac{1}{3}$

See Example **2** 5. Tran jogs $\frac{3}{4}$ mile each day. What is the total distance Tran jogs in 6 days? $4\frac{1}{2}$ miles

See Example **3** Multiply.

6. $-2.1(-7)$ 14.7 7. $0.03(5.4)$ 0.162 8. $-4.8(-2)$ 9.6 9. $-0.15(2.8)$ -0.42

INDEPENDENT PRACTICE

See Example **1** Multiply. Write each answer in simplest form.

10. $-\frac{2}{3}\left(-\frac{5}{6}\right)$ $\frac{5}{9}$ 11. $\frac{2}{9}\left(-\frac{7}{8}\right)$ $-\frac{7}{36}$ 12. $5\frac{7}{8}\left(\frac{5}{11}\right)$ $2\frac{59}{88}$ 13. $-\frac{1}{3}\left(-\frac{7}{8}\right)$ $\frac{7}{24}$

14. $\frac{3}{7}\left(-\frac{5}{6}\right)$ $-\frac{5}{14}$ 15. $2\frac{1}{7}\left(\frac{7}{10}\right)$ $1\frac{1}{2}$ 16. $-\frac{2}{3}\left(-\frac{1}{9}\right)$ $\frac{2}{27}$ 17. $\frac{7}{8}\left(\frac{3}{5}\right)$ $\frac{21}{40}$

See Example **2** 18. There was $\frac{3}{4}$ of a pizza left over from a family gathering. The next day, Tina ate $\frac{1}{2}$ of what was left. How much of the whole pizza did Tina eat? $\frac{3}{8}$

19. **School** The school Community Service Club has 45 members. Of these 45 members, $\frac{3}{5}$ are boys. How many boys are members of the Community Service Club? **27 boys**

See Example **3** Multiply.

20. $-1.7(-4)$ 6.8 21. $-0.05(4.7)$ -0.235 22. $-6.2(-7)$ 43.4 23. $-0.75(5.5)$ -4.125

24. $-6.2(-9)$ 55.8 25. $-0.08(6.2)$ -0.496 26. $-2.4(-9)$ 21.6 27. $-0.04(9.2)$ -0.368

PRACTICE AND PROBLEM SOLVING

Extra Practice
See page EP4.

Multiply.

28. $6\left(\frac{3}{7}\right)$ $2\frac{4}{7}$ 29. $-5\left(1\frac{8}{11}\right)$ $-8\frac{7}{11}$ 30. $7\left(\frac{4}{5}\right)$ $5\frac{3}{5}$ 31. $5\left(3\frac{1}{9}\right)$ $15\frac{5}{9}$

32. $-5.9(-7)$ 41.3 33. $0.7(2.6)$ 1.82 34. $-3.6(-4)$ 14.4 35. $-0.06(9.3)$ -0.558

36. $\frac{4}{11}\left(-\frac{4}{7}\right)$ $-\frac{16}{77}$ 37. $3\frac{5}{6}\left(\frac{7}{9}\right)$ $2\frac{53}{54}$ 38. $-\frac{8}{9}\left(-\frac{3}{5}\right)$ $\frac{8}{15}$ 39. $\frac{5}{12}\left(-\frac{11}{16}\right)$ $-\frac{55}{192}$

40. **Multi-Step** Alejandro, Becky, Marcus, and Kathy ate lunch at a restaurant. The total amount of the bill, including tax and tip, was $34.20. Alejandro paid $10.00, Becky paid $\frac{1}{4}$ of the total bill, Marcus paid 0.2 of the total bill, and Kathy paid the rest. Who paid the greatest portion of the bill? Show your work. **Alejandro**

41. **Consumer Economics** At a bookstore, the ticketed price of a book is $\frac{1}{4}$ off the original price. Kayla has a discount coupon for $\frac{1}{2}$ off the ticketed price. What fraction of the original price is Kayla's discount? $\frac{3}{8}$

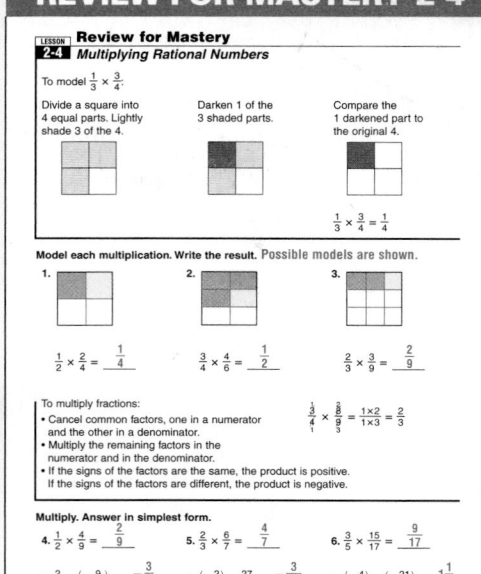

REVIEW FOR MASTERY 2-4

Review for Mastery
2-4 *Multiplying Rational Numbers*

To model $\frac{1}{3} \times \frac{3}{4}$:

Divide a square into 4 equal parts. Lightly shade 3 of the 4.

Darken 1 of the 3 shaded parts.

Compare the 1 darkened part to the original 4.

$\frac{1}{3} \times \frac{3}{4} = \frac{1}{4}$

Model each multiplication. Write the result. Possible models are shown.

1. $\frac{1}{2} \times \frac{2}{4} = \frac{1}{4}$ 2. $\frac{3}{4} \times \frac{4}{6} = \frac{1}{2}$ 3. $\frac{2}{3} \times \frac{3}{9} = \frac{2}{9}$

To multiply fractions:
• Cancel common factors, one in a numerator and the other in a denominator.
• Multiply the remaining factors in the numerator and in the denominator.
• If the signs of the factors are the same, the product is positive. If the signs of the factors are different, the product is negative.

$\frac{3}{4} \times \frac{2}{9} = \frac{1 \times 2}{1 \times 3} = \frac{2}{3}$

Multiply. Answer in simplest form.

4. $\frac{1}{2} \times \frac{4}{9} = \frac{2}{9}$ 5. $\frac{2}{3} \times \frac{6}{7} = \frac{4}{7}$ 6. $\frac{3}{5} \times \frac{15}{17} = \frac{9}{17}$

7. $\frac{2}{3} \times \left(-\frac{9}{10}\right) = -\frac{3}{5}$ 8. $\left(-\frac{2}{9}\right) \times \frac{27}{40} = -\frac{3}{20}$ 9. $\left(-\frac{4}{7}\right) \times \left(-\frac{21}{8}\right) = 1\frac{1}{2}$

PRACTICE 2-4

Practice B
2-4 *Multiplying Rational Numbers*

Multiply. Write each answer in simplest form.

1. $\frac{14}{8}\left(\frac{17}{121}\right)$ $\frac{17}{12}$ or $1\frac{5}{12}$ 2. $-\frac{12}{20}\left(\frac{9}{18}\right)$ $-\frac{3}{10}$ 3. $-\frac{12}{30}\left(-\frac{42}{72}\right)$ $\frac{7}{30}$ 4. $-\frac{13}{35}\left(-\frac{5}{26}\right)$ $\frac{1}{14}$

5. $-\frac{5}{18}\left(\frac{8}{15}\right)$ $-\frac{4}{27}$ 6. $\frac{7}{12}\left(\frac{14}{21}\right)$ $\frac{7}{18}$ 7. $-\frac{1}{9}\left(\frac{27}{24}\right)$ $-\frac{1}{8}$ 8. $-\frac{1}{11}\left(-\frac{3}{2}\right)$ $\frac{3}{22}$

9. $\frac{7}{20}\left(-\frac{15}{28}\right)$ $-\frac{3}{16}$ 10. $\frac{16}{25}\left(-\frac{18}{32}\right)$ $-\frac{9}{25}$ 11. $\frac{1}{9}\left(-\frac{18}{17}\right)$ $-\frac{2}{17}$ 12. $\frac{17}{20}\left(-\frac{12}{34}\right)$ $-\frac{3}{10}$

13. $-4\left(2\frac{1}{6}\right)$ $-8\frac{2}{3}$ 14. $\frac{3}{4}\left(1\frac{3}{8}\right)$ $1\frac{1}{32}$ 15. $3\frac{1}{5}\left(\frac{2}{3}\right)$ $2\frac{2}{15}$ 16. $-\frac{5}{6}\left(2\frac{1}{2}\right)$ $-2\frac{1}{12}$

Multiply.

17. $-2(-5.2)$ 10.4 18. $0.53(0.04)$ 0.0212 19. $(-7)(-3.9)$ 27.3 20. $-2(8.13)$ -16.26

21. $0.02(-4.62)$ -0.0924 22. $0.5(-7.8)$ -3.9 23. $(-0.41)(-8.5)$ 3.485 24. $(-8)(6.3)$ -50.4

25. $15(-0.05)$ -0.75 26. $(-3.04)(-1.7)$ 5.168 27. $10(-0.09)$ -0.9 28. $(-0.8)(-0.15)$ 0.12

29. Travis painted for $6\frac{2}{3}$ hours. He received $27 an hour for his work. How much was Travis paid for doing this painting job? **$180**

California Standards

Standard	Exercises
NS1.1	50–53
NS1.2 🔑	1–49, 54–57
NS2.5 🔑	50, 52–53

Animals

There are fewer than 30 veterinary colleges in the United States.

42. **Health** The directions for a pain reliever recommend that children 96 pounds and over take 4 tablets every 4 hours as needed, and children who weigh between 60 and 71 pounds take only $2\frac{1}{2}$ tablets every 4 hours as needed. Each tablet is $\frac{4}{25}$ gram.

   a. A child takes 4 tablets. How many grams of pain reliever did he receive? $\frac{16}{25}$ g

   b. How many grams of pain reliever is the recommended dose for a child weighing 65 pounds? $\frac{2}{5}$ g

43. **Animals** The label on a bottle of pet vitamins lists dosage guidelines. What dosage would you give to each of these animals?

   a. a 50 lb adult dog $1\frac{1}{4}$ tsp

   b. a 12 lb cat $1\frac{1}{2}$ tsp

   c. a 40 lb pregnant dog   2 tsp

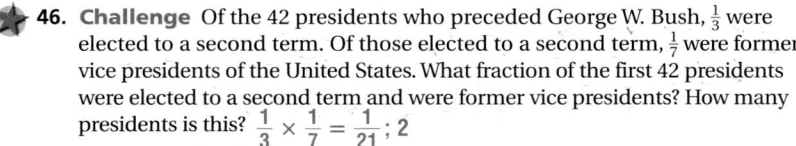

Do-Good Pet Vitamins

- Adult dogs:
  $\frac{1}{2}$ tsp per 20 lb body weight
- Puppies, pregnant dogs, or nursing dogs:
  $\frac{1}{2}$ tsp per 10 lb body weight
- Cats:
  $\frac{1}{4}$ tsp per 2 lb body weight

44. **What's the Error?** A student incorrectly multiplied two mixed numbers in the following fashion: $2\frac{4}{7} \cdot 3\frac{1}{4} = 6\frac{1}{7}$. What's the error?

45. **Write About It** In the pattern $\frac{1}{3} + \frac{1}{4} + \frac{1}{5} + \ldots$, which fraction first makes the sum greater than 1? Explain.

46. **Challenge** Of the 42 presidents who preceded George W. Bush, $\frac{1}{3}$ were elected to a second term. Of those elected to a second term, $\frac{1}{7}$ were former vice presidents of the United States. What fraction of the first 42 presidents were elected to a second term and were former vice presidents? How many presidents is this? $\frac{1}{3} \times \frac{1}{7} = \frac{1}{21}$; 2

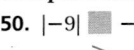

SPIRAL STANDARDS REVIEW   NS1.1, ← NS1.2, ← NS2.5

47. **Multiple Choice** Lindsay walked $\frac{3}{4}$ mile on Monday. She walked $1\frac{5}{8}$ of Monday's distance on Tuesday. How far did she walk on Tuesday?

   Ⓐ $1\frac{7}{32}$ miles   Ⓑ $1\frac{15}{32}$ miles   Ⓒ $2\frac{3}{8}$ miles   Ⓓ $2\frac{15}{32}$ miles

48. **Multiple Choice** What is the product of $-5\frac{1}{3}$ and $3\frac{3}{4}$?

   Ⓐ -20 Ⓑ $-15\frac{1}{4}$ Ⓒ $15\frac{1}{4}$ Ⓓ 20

49. **Multiple Choice** Multiply: $-0.98 \cdot (-8.4)$.

   Ⓐ -82.83 Ⓑ -8.232 Ⓒ 8.232 Ⓓ 82.83

Compare. Write <, >, or =. (Lesson 1-3)

50. $|-9| \blacksquare -9$ 51. $-13 \blacksquare -22$ 52. $|5| \blacksquare |-5|$ 53. $|-17| \blacksquare |-13|$
     >   >   =   >

Find each sum. (Lesson 2-3)

54. $-1.7 + 2.3$ 0.6   55. $-\frac{4}{6} + \left(-\frac{1}{6}\right)$ $-\frac{5}{6}$ 56. $23.75 + (-25.15)$ -1.4 57. $-\frac{4}{9} + \frac{2}{9}$ $-\frac{2}{9}$

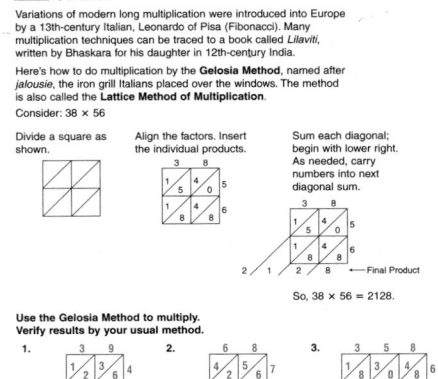

Answers

44. Possible answer: The student multiplied the whole numbers together and then multiplied the fractions together instead of writing both mixed numbers as improper fractions and then multiplying.
$2\frac{4}{7} \cdot 3\frac{1}{4} = \frac{18}{7} \cdot \frac{13}{4} = \frac{234}{28} = 8\frac{5}{14}$

45. $\frac{1}{7}$; the sum through $\frac{1}{6}$ is $\frac{19}{20}$, which is less than 1. Adding the $\frac{1}{7}$ makes the sum $\frac{153}{140}$, which is greater than 1.

Teaching Tip

Multiple Choice Be sure students understand that the product of a negative number and a positive number is a negative number. For **Exercise 48, C** and **D** are incorrect because they are positive numbers. Similarly, the product of two negative numbers is a positive number. For **Exercise 49,** students should eliminate **A** and **B**.

Journal

Remind students that recipes use fractions. Ask students how they can use math to make a half batch of something.

Power Presentations
with PowerPoint®

✓ **2-4 Lesson Quiz**

Multiply.

1. $9\left(\frac{1}{7}\right)$ $1\frac{2}{7}$

2. $\frac{2}{3}\left(-\frac{5}{8}\right)$ $-\frac{5}{12}$

3. $-0.47(2.2)$ -1.034

4. Evaluate $2\frac{1}{2}(x)$ for $x = \frac{4}{5}$.   2

5. Edgar runs $\frac{8}{9}$ mile each day. What is the total distance that Edgar runs in a 7-day week? $6\frac{2}{9}$ miles

Also available on transparency

Objective: Students divide fractions and decimals.

Hands-On Lab
In *Chapter 2 Resource File*

Online Edition
Tutorial Videos

Countdown to Mastery Week 4

Power Presentations
with PowerPoint®

Warm Up

Multiply.

1. $-3\left(\frac{5}{6}\right)$ $-2\frac{1}{2}$

2. $-15\left(-\frac{2}{3}\right)$ 10

3. $0.05(2.8)$ 0.14

4. $-0.9(16.1)$ -14.49

Also available on transparency

Math Humor

Teacher: Do you know how many quarters go into a half?

Student: No, but I know how many go into a video game!

California Standards

Number Sense 1.2
Algebra and Functions 1.3

California Standards

NS1.2 Add, subtract, multiply, and **divide rational numbers** (integers, fractions, and **terminating decimals**) and take positive rational numbers to whole-number powers.

AF1.3 Simplify numerical expressions by applying properties of rational numbers (e.g., identity, **inverse**, distributive, associative, commutative) and justify the process used.

Vocabulary
multiplicative inverse
reciprocal

Why learn this? You can divide rational numbers to determine how many calories are in part of a serving of food. (See Example 4.)

Two numbers whose product is 1 are called **multiplicative inverses**, or **reciprocals**.

INVERSE PROPERTY OF MULTIPLICATION		
Words	**Numbers**	**Algebra**
The product of a nonzero number and its multiplicative inverse is 1.	$\frac{3}{4}\left(\frac{4}{3}\right)=1$ $-6\left(-\frac{1}{6}\right)=1$	$\frac{a}{b}\left(\frac{b}{a}\right)=1$, where $a\neq 0$ and $b\neq 0$

Dividing by a number gives the same result as multiplying by the reciprocal of that number.

$6 \div 2 = 3$

$6 \cdot \frac{1}{2} = \frac{\overset{3}{\cancel{6}}}{1} \cdot \frac{1}{\cancel{2}_1} = 3$

A division problem can always be rewritten as a multiplication problem by using the reciprocal of the divisor.

Reading Math

Multiplicative inverse and *reciprocal* have the same meaning.

DIVIDING RATIONAL NUMBERS IN FRACTION FORM		
Words	**Numbers**	**Algebra**
To divide by a fraction, multiply by the reciprocal of the divisor.	$\frac{1}{7} \div \frac{4}{5} = \frac{1}{7} \cdot \frac{5}{4}$	$\frac{a}{b} \div \frac{c}{d} = \frac{a}{b} \cdot \frac{d}{c}$

EXAMPLE 1 **Dividing Fractions**

Divide. Write each answer in simplest form.

(A) $\frac{7}{15} \div \frac{4}{5}$

$\frac{7}{15} \div \frac{4}{5} = \frac{7}{15} \cdot \frac{5}{4}$ *Multiply by the reciprocal.*

$= \frac{7 \cdot \overset{1}{\cancel{5}}}{\underset{3}{\cancel{15}} \cdot 4}$ *Remove common factors.*

$= \frac{7}{12}$ *Simplest form*

---

1 Introduce

Alternate Opener

EXPLORATION

2-5 **Dividing Rational Numbers**

You can use your calculator to investigate division of rational numbers.

1. Use your calculator to complete the table by dividing the rational numbers. The first one has been filled in as an example.

$\frac{16.8}{0.7} = 24$	$\frac{168}{7} =$	$\frac{1680}{70} =$
$\frac{4.1}{0.5} =$	$\frac{41}{5} =$	$\frac{410}{50} =$
$\frac{0.026}{0.04} =$	$\frac{0.26}{0.4} =$	$\frac{2.6}{4} =$
$\frac{75}{0.06} =$	$\frac{750}{0.6} =$	$\frac{7500}{6} =$
$\frac{16.32}{1.02} =$	$\frac{163.2}{10.2} =$	$\frac{1632}{102} =$

2. How are the division problems in each row related to each other?

Think and Discuss

3. **Show** how you can use the pattern in the first row of the table to write a new division problem whose quotient is equal to 24.

4. **Explain** how to write a division problem that is equivalent to $145 \div 16.5$ but that involves dividing by a whole number.

Motivate

Write the following problems on the board: $12 \div 3 = ?$ and $12 \cdot \frac{1}{3} = ?$. Ask for volunteers to solve both problems and to show the solutions on the board. Both equal 4. Point out that 3 can be expressed as $\frac{3}{1}$. Ask students to describe the relationship between $\frac{3}{1}$ and $\frac{1}{3}$. Explain that these numbers are called *reciprocals*. Tell students that in this lesson, they will see that division is the same as multiplication by the reciprocal.

Explorations and answers are provided in *Alternate Openers: Explorations Transparencies.*

Divide. Write each answer in simplest form.

 $5\frac{1}{3} \div (-7)$

$$5\frac{1}{3} \div (-7) = \frac{16}{3} \div \left(-\frac{7}{1}\right)$$ *Write as improper fractions.*

$$= \frac{16}{3}\left(-\frac{1}{7}\right)$$ *Multiply by the reciprocal.*

$$= \frac{16 \cdot (-1)}{3 \cdot 7}$$ *No common factors*

$$= -\frac{16}{21}$$ *Simplest form*

When dividing a decimal by a decimal, multiply both numbers by a power of 10 so you can divide by a whole number. To decide which power of 10 to multiply by, look at the divisor. The number of decimal places represents the number of zeros after the 1 in the power of 10.

EXAMPLE 2 Dividing Decimals

 Reasoning

Find 1.48 ÷ 0.3. Estimate the reasonableness of your answer.

$$0.3\overline{)1.48}$$

$$\begin{array}{r} 4.933 \\ 3\overline{)14.800} \\ -12 \\ \hline 28 \\ -27 \\ \hline 10 \\ -9 \\ \hline 10 \\ -9 \\ \hline 1 \end{array}$$

0.3 has 1 decimal place, so multiply both numbers by 10 to make the divisor an integer.
Then divide as with whole numbers.

$1.48 \div 0.3 = 4.9\overline{3}$

Estimate: $15 \div 3 = 5$

The 3 repeats, so draw a bar over it.
The answer is reasonable.

EXAMPLE 3 Evaluating Expressions with Rational Numbers

Evaluate $\frac{7.2}{n}$ for $n = -0.24$.

$$\frac{7.2}{n} = \frac{7.2}{-0.24}$$ *Substitute −0.24 for n.*

$$-0.24\overline{)7.20}$$ *−0.24 has 2 decimal places, so multiply both numbers by 100 to make the divisor an integer.*

$$\begin{array}{r} -30 \\ -24\overline{)720} \\ -72 \\ \hline 0 \end{array}$$

Then divide as with whole numbers.

When $n = -0.24$, $\frac{7.2}{n} = -30$.

COMMON ERROR ALERT

Some students will want to cancel common factors out of numerators and denominators in a *division* problem. Remind students that they can only cross out common factors after they have rewritten the division problem as multiplication by the reciprocal of the divisor.

Power Presentations
with PowerPoint®

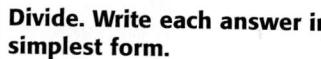

Additional Examples

Example 1

Divide. Write each answer in simplest form.

A. $\frac{5}{11} \div \frac{1}{2}$ $\frac{10}{11}$ **B.** $2\frac{3}{8} \div 2$ $1\frac{3}{16}$

Example 2

Find $0.384 \div 0.24$. Estimate the reasonableness of your answer. **1.6**

Example 3

Evaluate $\frac{5.25}{n}$ for $n = 0.15$. **35**

Also available on transparency

② Teach

Guided Instruction

ENGLISH LANGUAGE LEARNERS

 **Universal Access**
Through Cognitive Strategies

In this lesson, students learn to divide fractions. Define and discuss *reciprocals* (Teaching Transparency). Show that dividing by a number and multiplying by the reciprocal of the number give the same result. Remind students that they may "cancel out" common factors once they have changed the division into multiplication by a reciprocal.

Explain to students that a quart contains 32 oz. Ask students to find out how many servings are in a quart if the serving size is 8 oz. 4 servings Ask students to describe how they found the answer. division Have students find out how many servings one quart contains for the following serving sizes.

Teaching Tip

Number Sense For **Example 2,** show students how to choose which power of 10 to use to clear the decimal from the denominator. You may want to review place value.

1. 5 oz	6.4	**2.** 4 oz	8
3. 3 oz	$10\frac{2}{3}$	**4.** 1 oz	32
5. $\frac{2}{3}$ oz	48	**6.** $\frac{1}{2}$ oz	64

Example 4

A muffin recipe calls for $\frac{1}{2}$ cup of oats. You have $\frac{3}{4}$ cup of oats. How many batches of the muffins can you bake?

You can bake $1\frac{1}{2}$ batches of the muffins.

Also available on transparency

Teaching Tip

Inclusion In **Example 4,** you may want to replace the fractions with whole numbers first to show how to set up the division. For example, "If you pour 8 cups into a container and the serving size is 2 cups, how many servings did you pour?"

$$8 \div 2 = 4$$

amount poured	÷	serving size	=	number of servings

Possible answers to *Think and Discuss*

1. When you divide a fraction by itself, you multiply it by its reciprocal, and the answer is 1. For example:
   $$\frac{4}{5} \div \frac{4}{5} = \frac{4}{5} \cdot \frac{5}{4} = \frac{20}{20} = 1$$

2. Round the decimals to integers so that they divide without leaving a remainder.

EXAMPLE 4 **PROBLEM SOLVING APPLICATION**

Ella ate $\frac{2}{3}$ cup of lowfat yogurt. How many servings did Ella eat? How many calories did Ella eat?

1 **Understand the Problem**

The number of calories Ella ate is the number of calories in the fraction of a serving.

List the **important information:**
- Ella ate $\frac{2}{3}$ cup.
- A full serving is $\frac{3}{4}$ cup.
- There are 100 calories in one serving.

2 **Make a Plan**

Set up an equation to find the number of servings Ella ate.

amount Ella ate	÷	serving size	=	number of servings

Using the number of servings, find the number of calories Ella ate.

number of servings	·	calories per serving	=	total calories

3 **Solve**

Let n = number of servings. Let c = total calories.

Servings: $\frac{2}{3} \div \frac{3}{4} = n$	**Calories:** $\frac{8}{9} \cdot 100 = c$
$\frac{2}{3} \cdot \frac{4}{3} = n$	$\frac{8 \cdot 100}{9} = c$
$\frac{8}{9} = n$	$\frac{800}{9} \approx 88.9$

Ella ate $\frac{8}{9}$ of a serving, which is about 88.9 calories.

4 **Look Back**

Ella did not eat a full serving, so $\frac{8}{9}$ of a serving is a reasonable answer. Since $\frac{8}{9}$ is less than 1 and 88.9 calories is less than 100, the calories in a full serving, 88.9 calories is a reasonable answer.

Think and Discuss

1. **Tell** what happens when you divide a fraction by itself. Show that you are correct using multiplication by the reciprocal.

2. **Explain** how you can check your answer for reasonableness when dividing with decimals.

---

3 **Close**

Summarize

Ask students to explain how multiplication and division of fractions are the same and how they are different. Review the process for dividing decimals. Ask the students what power of 10 they would use when finding the quotient of 22.5 ÷ 1.125.

Possible answer: Division of fractions is the same as multiplication, except that in division, you multiply by the reciprocal; 1000.

California Standards Practice
◆ NS1.2, ◆ AF1.3

go.hrw.com
Homework Help Online
KEYWORD: MT8CA 2-5
Parent Resources Online
KEYWORD: MT8CA Parent

2-5 Exercises

GUIDED PRACTICE

See Example ❶ Divide. Write each answer in simplest form.

1. $\frac{1}{2} \div \frac{3}{4}$ $\frac{2}{3}$ **2.** $4\frac{1}{5} \div 5\frac{2}{3}$ $\frac{63}{85}$ **3.** $-\frac{6}{7} \div 3$ $-\frac{2}{7}$ **4.** $\frac{5}{6} \div \frac{3}{8}$ $2\frac{2}{9}$

5. $5\frac{1}{18} \div 4\frac{4}{9}$ $1\frac{11}{80}$ **6.** $-\frac{5}{8} \div 12$ $-\frac{5}{96}$ **7.** $\frac{14}{15} \div \frac{2}{3}$ $1\frac{2}{5}$ **8.** $4\frac{3}{10} \div \frac{3}{5}$ $7\frac{1}{6}$

See Example ❷ Find each quotient. Estimate the reasonableness of your answer.

9. $3.72 \div 0.3$ 12.4 **10.** $2.1 \div 0.07$ 30 **11.** $10.71 \div 0.7$ 15.3 **12.** $1.72 \div 0.2$ 8.6

13. $2.54 \div 0.6$ 4.23 **14.** $11.04 \div 0.4$ 27.6 **15.** $2.45 \div 0.005$ 490 **16.** $4.41 \div 0.7$ 6.3

See Example ❸ Evaluate each expression for the given value of the variable.

17. $\frac{9.7}{x}$ for $x = -0.5$ −19.4 **18.** $\frac{6.2}{x}$ for $x = 0.2$ 31 **19.** $\frac{40.5}{x}$ for $x = 0.9$ 45

20. $\frac{9.2}{x}$ for $x = 2.3$ 4 **21.** $\frac{32.4}{x}$ for $x = -1.8$ −18 **22.** $\frac{14.7}{x}$ for $x = 0.07$ 210

See Example ❹ 23. You eat $\frac{1}{4}$ ounce of cheddar cheese. One serving of cheddar cheese is $1\frac{1}{2}$ ounces. How much of a serving did you eat? $\frac{1}{6}$ serving

INDEPENDENT PRACTICE

See Example ❶ Divide. Write each answer in simplest form.

24. $\frac{1}{6} \div \frac{3}{4}$ $\frac{2}{9}$ **25.** $4\frac{2}{5} \div 3\frac{1}{2}$ $1\frac{9}{35}$ **26.** $-\frac{5}{12} \div \frac{2}{3}$ $-\frac{5}{8}$ **27.** $\frac{4}{5} \div \frac{1}{2}$ $1\frac{3}{5}$

28. $1\frac{2}{3} \div 2\frac{1}{6}$ $\frac{10}{13}$ **29.** $-\frac{2}{9} \div \frac{7}{12}$ $-\frac{8}{21}$ **30.** $\frac{2}{3} \div \frac{3}{10}$ $2\frac{2}{9}$ **31.** $2\frac{3}{8} \div 1\frac{1}{6}$ $2\frac{1}{28}$

See Example ❷ Find each quotient. Estimate the reasonableness of your answer.

32. $12.11 \div 0.7$ 17.3 **33.** $2.49 \div 0.03$ 83 **34.** $6.64 \div 0.4$ 16.6 **35.** $4.85 \div 0.5$ 9.7

36. $5.49 \div 0.003$ 1830 **37.** $32.44 \div 0.8$ 40.55 **38.** $9.36 \div 0.03$ 312 **39.** $12.24 \div 0.9$ 13.6

See Example ❸ Evaluate each expression for the given value of the variable.

40. $\frac{7.2}{x}$ for $x = -0.4$ −18 **41.** $\frac{9.6}{x}$ for $x = 0.8$ 12 **42.** $\frac{15}{x}$ for $x = -0.05$ −300

43. $\frac{15.4}{x}$ for $x = -1.4$ −11 **44.** $\frac{4.24}{x}$ for $x = 0.8$ 5.3 **45.** $\frac{22.2}{x}$ for $x = 0.06$ 370

See Example ❹ 46. The platform on the school stage is $8\frac{3}{4}$ feet wide. Each chair is $1\frac{5}{12}$ feet wide. How many chairs will fit across the platform? **6 chairs**

PRACTICE AND PROBLEM SOLVING

Extra Practice
See page EP5.

47. Maya is drinking her favorite juice. There are $2\frac{3}{4}$ servings remaining in the bottle. Maya pours only $\frac{1}{4}$ of a serving into her glass at a time. How many glasses can Maya have before the bottle is empty? **11 glasses**

Assignment Guide

If you finished **Example ❶** assign:
Proficient 1–8, 24–30 even, 57–63
Advanced 24–31, 52, 57–63

If you finished **Example ❷** assign:
Proficient 1–16, 24–38 even, 57–63
Advanced 24–39, 52, 57–63

If you finished **Example ❸** assign:
Proficient 1–22, 24–44 even, 54, 57–63
Advanced 24–45, 52, 54, 57–63

If you finished **Example ❹** assign:
Proficient 1–23, 24–46 even, 47, 49, 54–63
Advanced 24–46, 47–63

Homework Quick Check

Quickly check key concepts.
Exercises: 26, 28, 34, 38, 42, 46

Math Background

A division expression containing fractions can be written as a *complex fraction*.

$\frac{1}{2} \div \frac{3}{4}$ can be written as $\dfrac{\frac{1}{2}}{\frac{3}{4}}$.

To find the quotient, multiply the numerator and denominator of the complex fraction by the reciprocal of the fraction in the denominator. The denominator then becomes one, and the numerator is a multiplication expression that can be simplified:

$$\frac{\frac{1}{2}}{\frac{3}{4}} = \frac{\frac{1}{2} \cdot \frac{4}{3}}{\frac{3}{4} \cdot \frac{4}{3}} = \frac{\frac{2}{3}}{1} = \frac{2}{3}.$$

REVIEW FOR MASTERY 2-5

LESSON 2-5 Review for Mastery
Dividing Rational Numbers

To write the **reciprocal** of a fraction, interchange the numerator and denominator.
The product of a number and its reciprocal is 1.

$\frac{2}{3} \bowtie \frac{3}{2}$
Fraction Reciprocal

$\frac{2}{3} \times \frac{3}{2} = 1$

Write the reciprocal of each rational number.

1. The reciprocal of $\frac{3}{5}$ is: **2.** The reciprocal of 6 is: **3.** The reciprocal of $2\frac{1}{3}$ is:
$\frac{5}{3}$ $\frac{1}{6}$ $\frac{3}{7}$

To divide by a fraction, multiply by its reciprocal.

$\frac{2}{3} \div 6$ $\frac{3}{5} \div \frac{9}{10}$
$\frac{2}{3} \times \frac{1}{6}$ $\frac{3}{5} \times \frac{10}{9}$
$\frac{1 \times 1}{3 \times 3} = \frac{1}{9}$ $\frac{\cancel{3}}{\cancel{5}} \times \frac{\cancel{10}}{\cancel{9}} = \frac{2}{3}$

Complete to divide and simplify.

4. $\frac{3}{8} \div 12 = \frac{3}{8} \times \frac{1}{12} = \frac{3}{96} = \frac{1}{32}$ **5.** $\frac{4}{3} \div 16 = \frac{4}{3} \times \frac{1}{16} = \frac{4}{48} = \frac{1}{12}$

6. $\frac{5}{7} \div \frac{20}{21} = \frac{5}{7} \times \frac{21}{20} = \frac{3}{4}$ **7.** $-\frac{3}{4} \div \left(\frac{9}{8}\right) = -\frac{3}{4} \times \left(\frac{8}{9}\right) = -\frac{2}{3}$

Change a decimal divisor to a whole number.
Using the number of places in the divisor, move the decimal point to the right in both the divisor and the dividend.

$0.7\overline{)4.34} \rightarrow 7.\overline{)43.4} \rightarrow 7\overline{)43.4}$ 6.2

Rewrite each division with a whole-number divisor. Then, do the division.

8. $0.6\overline{)11.4} \rightarrow 6\overline{)11.4} = 1.9$ **9.** $0.3\overline{)4.56} \rightarrow 3\overline{)45.6} = 15.2$

10. $0.02\overline{)7.12} \rightarrow 2\overline{)712} = 356$ **11.** $0.08\overline{)57.28} \rightarrow 8\overline{)5728} = 716$

PRACTICE 2-5

LESSON 2-5 Practice B
Dividing Rational Numbers

Divide. Write each answer in simplest form.

1. $\frac{1}{5} \div \frac{3}{10}$ $\frac{2}{3}$ **2.** $-\frac{5}{8} \div \frac{3}{4}$ $-\frac{5}{6}$ **3.** $\frac{1}{4} \div \frac{1}{8}$ 2 **4.** $-\frac{2}{3} \div \frac{4}{15}$ $-2\frac{1}{2}$

5. $1\frac{2}{9} \div 1\frac{2}{3}$ $\frac{11}{15}$ **6.** $-\frac{7}{10} \div \left(\frac{2}{5}\right)$ $-1\frac{3}{4}$ **7.** $\frac{6}{11} \div \frac{3}{22}$ 4 **8.** $\frac{4}{9} \div \left(-\frac{8}{15}\right)$ $-\frac{5}{6}$

9. $\frac{3}{8} \div -15$ $-\frac{1}{40}$ **10.** $-\frac{5}{6} \div 12$ $-\frac{5}{72}$ **11.** $6\frac{1}{2} \div 1\frac{5}{8}$ 4 **12.** $-\frac{9}{10} \div 6$ $-\frac{3}{20}$

Divide.

13. $24.35 \div 0.5$ 48.7 **14.** $2.16 \div 0.04$ 54 **15.** $3.16 \div 0.02$ 158 **16.** $7.32 \div 0.3$ 24.4

17. $87.36 \div 0.6$ 145.6 **18.** $79.36 \div 0.8$ 99.2 **19.** $4.27 \div 0.007$ 610 **20.** $63.81 \div 0.9$ 70.9

21. $1.23 \div 0.003$ 410 **22.** $62.46 \div 0.09$ 694 **23.** $21.12 \div 0.4$ 52.8 **24.** $82.68 \div 0.06$ 1378

Evaluate each expression for the given value of the variable.

25. $\frac{18}{x}$ for $x = 0.12$ 150 **26.** $\frac{10.8}{x}$ for $x = 0.03$ 360 **27.** $\frac{9.18}{x}$ for $x = -1.2$ −7.65

28. A can of fruit contains $3\frac{1}{2}$ cups of fruit. The suggested serving size is $\frac{1}{2}$ cup. How many servings are in the can of fruit? 7 servings

California Standards

Standard	Exercises
NS1.2 ◆	1–56
NS1.5 ◆	59–63
AF1.2	57–58
AF1.3 ◆	1–8, 23–31, 46–53, 55

52. Possible answer: The quotient will have an even denominator. When the division is changed to multiplication by the reciprocal, the factor 5 will be in the numerator. This factor can be divided out with the 10 in the denominator, leaving the factor 2 in the denominator. Because the quotient will have a factor of 2, it must be even.

Multiple Choice Encourage students to read the problem carefully. For **Exercise 55,** Betty is dividing the amount of each ingredient in the recipe by 3. Be sure students realize that the answer should be less than the original amount of each ingredient. Students can eliminate **D** because the number of cups is greater than it is in the original recipe.

 Journal

Ask students to write about a situation from their everyday lives in which they might need to divide by a fraction.

Power Presentations
with PowerPoint®

2-5
Lesson Quiz

Divide.

1. $2\frac{5}{6} \div \left(-1\frac{1}{2}\right)$ $-1\frac{8}{9}$

2. $-14 \div 1.25$ -11.2

3. $3.9 \div 0.65$ 6

4. Evaluate $\frac{112}{x}$ for $x = 6.3$. $17.\overline{7}$

5. A penny weighs 2.5 grams. How many pennies would it take to equal one pound (453.6 grams)?
   182

Also available on transparency

---

48. The width of a DVD case is about $\frac{1}{3}$ inch. How many DVD cases are in a box set if the set is about $1\frac{2}{3}$ inches thick?   **5 cases**

49. Social Studies Nesting dolls called *matrushkas* are a well-known type of Russian folk art. Use the information in the picture to find the height of the largest doll.

$3\frac{31}{48}$ in. $\frac{6}{25}x = \frac{7}{8}$ in.

x in.

50. Estimation Leo's bowl contains 16 ounces of cereal. His spoon can hold $1\frac{1}{8}$ ounces. Approximately how many spoonfuls are in the bowl?   **about 14 spoonfuls**

 **51. Choose a Strategy** Before 2000, the prices of all stocks traded on the New York Stock Exchange were given in fractions. When a stock is split 2-for-1, the price of the stock is halved and the number of shares doubles. A stock trading at $20\frac{1}{4}$ was split 2-for-1. What was the price of the stock after the split?

51. Possible answer:
$20\frac{1}{4} \div 2 =$
$\frac{81}{4} \cdot \frac{1}{2} = \frac{81}{8} =$
$10\frac{1}{8}$; after the split, the price of the stock was $10\frac{1}{8}$.

52. Write About It A proper fraction has an odd number as the numerator and 10 as the denominator. This fraction is divided by a proper fraction with denominator 5. Will the denominator of the quotient be odd or even? Explain.

53. Challenge In 2003, the U.S. Census Bureau estimated that about $\frac{1}{25}$ of the U.S. population resided in Los Angeles County. At that time, about $\frac{3}{25}$ of the U.S. population resided in California. Approximately what fraction of the California population resided in Los Angeles County?   **about $\frac{1}{3}$**

SPIRAL STANDARDS REVIEW
NS1.2, NS1.5, AF1.2

54. Multiple Choice Evaluate the expression $\frac{7.92}{x}$ for $x = 3.3$.

Ⓐ 2.4   Ⓑ 4.62   Ⓒ 11.22   Ⓓ 26.136

55. Multiple Choice A recipe calls for $2\frac{1}{2}$ cups of sugar to make a batch of cookies. To make one-third of a batch, Betty needs to divide the amount of each ingredient in the recipe by 3. How many cups of sugar will she use?

Ⓐ $\frac{3}{4}$ cup   Ⓑ $\frac{5}{6}$ cup   Ⓒ $1\frac{1}{5}$ cups   Ⓓ $7\frac{1}{2}$ cups

56. Gridded Response Frank bought 12.6 gallons of gasoline for $35.91. Find, to the nearest cent, the cost per gallon of gasoline.   **2.85**

Evaluate each expression for the given values of the variables. (Lesson 1-1)

57. $7x - 4y$ for $x = 5$ and $y = 6$ **11**   **58.** $6.5p - 9.1q$ for $p = 2.5$ and $q = 0$ **16.25**

Write each decimal as a fraction or mixed number in simplest form. (Lesson 2-1)

59. 0.65 $\frac{13}{20}$ **60.** -1.25 $-1\frac{1}{4}$ **61.** 0.723 $\frac{723}{1000}$ **62.** 11.17 $11\frac{17}{100}$ **63.** -0.8 $-\frac{4}{5}$

CHALLENGE 2-5

LESSON 2-5 Challenge
A New License to Operate

You can invent new operations based on the familiar operations of addition, subtraction, multiplication, and division, and the familiar order of operations.

If $a \triangle b = \frac{a + b}{2}$ where *a* and *b* represent any rational numbers,

then $3 \triangle 5 = \frac{3 + 5}{2} = 4$.

Use the given definition of operation $\triangle$ to evaluate each expression.

1. $\frac{1}{2} \triangle (-10) =$ __-4.75__   2. $\frac{100 \triangle (-10)}{10} =$ __4.5__

3. $4 \triangle 6 \triangle 3 =$ __4__   4. $[5.5 \triangle (-6)] + [-6 \triangle 5.5] =$ __-0.5__

Use the operation shown to answer each question. $\begin{array}{|c|c|} \hline a & b \\ \hline c & d \\ \hline \end{array} = ac - bd$

5. $\begin{array}{|c|c|} \hline \frac{1}{3} & \frac{1}{4} \\ \hline \end{array} =$ __-29__   6. $\begin{array}{|c|c|} \hline -2 & 3 \\ \hline 3 & -2 \\ \hline \end{array} =$ __0__

7. If $\begin{array}{|c|c|} \hline \frac{1}{x} & \frac{3}{2} \\ \hline \end{array} = 18$, then $x =$ __24__   8. If $\begin{array}{|c|c|} \hline \frac{6}{x} & \frac{2}{x} \\ \hline \end{array} = 12$, then $x =$ __3__

Use the operation shown to answer each question. $a \triangleright b = \frac{a^2}{b^2}$

9. $(3 \triangleright 5) =$ __$\frac{9}{25}$__   10. $(1 \triangleright 8) - (5 \triangleright 8) =$ __$\frac{3}{8}$__

11. $(1 \triangleright 3) \times (3 \triangleright 6) =$ __$\frac{1}{36}$__   12. $(1 \triangleright 10)^2 =$ __$\frac{1}{10,000}$__

If $\lfloor n \rfloor$ means 1 less than the number of digits in the integer *n*, then, for example, $\lfloor 77 \rfloor = 1$ since 77 has 2 digits.

Use the definition of $\lfloor n \rfloor$ to answer each question.

13. If *n* is a positive integer less than 100, what is the greatest value for $\lfloor n \rfloor$?   __1__

14. If *n* is a positive integer less than 1001, what is the greatest value for $\lfloor n \rfloor$?   __3__

15. If *n* has 100 digits, what is the value of $\lfloor \lfloor n \rfloor \rfloor$? Explain.

By definition, $\lfloor 100\text{-digit number} \rfloor = 99$. Then, since 99 has 2 digits, $\lfloor 99 \rfloor = 1$.

PROBLEM SOLVING 2-5

LESSON 2-5 Problem Solving
Dividing Rational Numbers

Use the table at the right that shows the maximum speed over a quarter mile of different animals. Find the time it takes each animal to travel one-quarter mile at top speed. Round to the nearest thousandth.

1. Quarter horse
   0.005 hours
2. Greyhound
   0.006 hours
3. Human
   0.009 hours
4. Giant tortoise
   1.471 hours
5. Three-toed sloth
   1.667 hours

Maximum Speeds of Animals

Animal	Speed (mph)
Quarter Horse	47.50
Greyhound	39.35
Human	27.89
Giant Tortoise	0.17
Three-toed sloth	0.15

Choose the letter for the best answer.

6. A piece of ribbon is $1\frac{7}{8}$ inches long. If the ribbon is going to be divided into 15 pieces, how long should each piece be?
   Ⓐ $\frac{1}{8}$ in.
   B $\frac{1}{15}$ in.
   C $\frac{2}{3}$ in.
   D $28\frac{1}{8}$ in.

7. The recorded rainfall for each day of a week was 0 in., $1\frac{1}{4}$ in., $\frac{3}{8}$ in., 1 in., 0 in., $1\frac{1}{4}$ in., $1\frac{1}{4}$ in. What was the average rainfall per day?
   F $\frac{9}{10}$ in.
   Ⓖ $\frac{9}{14}$ in.
   H $\frac{7}{8}$ in.
   J $4\frac{1}{2}$ in.

8. A drill bit that is $\frac{7}{32}$ in. means that the hole the bit makes has a diameter of $\frac{7}{32}$ in. Since the radius is half of the diameter, what is the radius of a hole drilled by a $\frac{7}{32}$ in. bit?
   A $\frac{14}{32}$ in.
   B $\frac{7}{32}$ in.
   C $\frac{9}{16}$ in.
   Ⓓ $\frac{7}{64}$ in.

9. A serving of a certain kind of cereal is $\frac{2}{3}$ cup. There are 12 cups of cereal in the box. How many servings of cereal are in the box?
   Ⓕ 18
   G 15
   H 8
   J 6

2-6 Adding and Subtracting with Unlike Denominators

Why learn this? You can subtract fractions to find the number of miles remaining in a hike. (See Example 3.)

To add and subtract fractions with unlike denominators, first find a common denominator using one of these methods:

Method 1	Find a common denominator by multiplying the two denominators.
Method 2	Find the least common denominator (LCD).

EXAMPLE 1 Adding and Subtracting Fractions with Unlike Denominators

Add or subtract. Write each answer in simplest form.

Ⓐ $\frac{4}{5} + \frac{1}{6}$

Method 1: $\frac{4}{5} + \frac{1}{6}$ *Find a common denominator: 5(6) = 30.*

$= \frac{4}{5}\left(\frac{6}{6}\right) + \frac{1}{6}\left(\frac{5}{5}\right)$ *Multiply by fractions equal to 1.*

$= \frac{24}{30} + \frac{5}{30}$ *Rewrite with a common denominator.*

$= \frac{24 + 5}{30} = \frac{29}{30}$ *Add numerators. Keep the denominator.*

Ⓑ $2\frac{1}{6} - 2\frac{2}{9}$

Method 2: $2\frac{1}{6} - 2\frac{2}{9}$

$= \frac{13}{6} - \frac{20}{9}$ *Write as improper fractions.*

Multiples of 6: 6, 12, ⑱ . . .   *List the multiples of each denominator*
Multiples of 9: 9, ⑱, 27, . . .   *and find the LCD.*

$= \frac{13}{6}\left(\frac{3}{3}\right) - \frac{20}{9}\left(\frac{2}{2}\right)$ *Multiply by fractions equal to 1.*

$= \frac{39}{18} - \frac{40}{18}$ *Rewrite with the LCD.*

$= \frac{39 - 40}{18} = -\frac{1}{18}$ *Subtract numerators. Keep the denominator.*

Listing the multiples of the denominators is not always the easiest way to find the LCD. For example, if you list the multiples of large numbers such as 78 and 110, you would have to list fifty-five multiples of 78 and thirty-nine multiples of 110 to find the LCD. In cases such as this one, you may want to use factoring.

Power Presentations with PowerPoint®

Warm Up
Add or subtract.
1. $1\frac{3}{5} + \left(-\frac{2}{5}\right)$ $1\frac{1}{5}$
2. $3\frac{11}{12} - 2\frac{7}{12}$ $1\frac{1}{3}$
3. $6.5 + (-1.2)$ 5.3
4. $3.4 - 0.9$ 2.5

Also available on transparency

Math Humor

Clerk: That $2.50 pen is on sale for $2.00.

Customer: But the sign says, "Half off everything."

Clerk: That's right. It was $2\frac{1}{2}$ dollars, so I took off the $\frac{1}{2}$.

---

1 Introduce

Alternate Opener

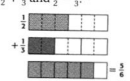 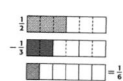
Motivate

To introduce adding and subtracting with unlike denominators, ask students to list the multiples of 5 and the multiples of 2. Then ask the students to identify the *least common multiple*. Show them that although there are many common multiples (10, 20, 30, etc.), there is only one least common multiple (10).

5, ⑩, 15, <u>20</u>, 25, <u>30</u>, . . .

2, 4, 6, 8, ⑩, 12, 14, 16, 18, <u>20</u>, 22, 24, 26, 28, <u>30</u>, . . .

Explorations and answers are provided in *Alternate Openers: Explorations Transparencies.*

Example 1

Add or subtract.

A. $\frac{1}{8} + \frac{2}{7}$ $\frac{23}{56}$ **B.** $1\frac{1}{6} - 1\frac{5}{8}$ $-\frac{11}{24}$

Example 2

Find $\frac{25}{56} + \frac{37}{84}$. Write the answer in simplest form. $\frac{149}{168}$

Example 3

Two dancers are making necklaces from ribbon for their costumes. They need pieces measuring $13\frac{3}{4}$ inches and $12\frac{7}{8}$ inches. How much ribbon will be left over after the pieces are cut from a 36-inch length?

There will be $9\frac{3}{8}$ inches left.

Example 4

Evaluate $t - \frac{4}{5}$ for $t = \frac{5}{6}$. $\frac{1}{30}$

Also available on transparency

EXAMPLE 2 Using Factoring to Find the LCD

Find $\frac{25}{78} + \frac{33}{110}$. Write the answer in simplest form.

Factors of 78: 2 · 3 · 13	*Write the prime factorization of each denominator. Circle the common factors.*
Factors of 110: 2 · 5 · 11	
2, 3, 13, 5, 11	*List all the prime factors of the denominators, using the circled factors only once.*
2 · 3 · 13 · 5 · 11 = 4290	*Multiply.*

The LCD is 4290.

$$4290 \div 78 = 55 \qquad 4290 \div 110 = 39$$

$\frac{25}{78}\left(\frac{55}{55}\right) + \frac{33}{110}\left(\frac{39}{39}\right)$	*Multiply by fractions equal to 1 to get a common denominator.*
$\frac{1375}{4290} + \frac{1287}{4290}$	*Rewrite using the LCD.*
$\frac{2662}{4290}$	*Add numerators. Keep the denominator.*
$\frac{1331}{2145}$	*Simplify.*

EXAMPLE 3 *Recreation Application*

Two hikers begin hiking the North Dome trail in Yosemite National Park, which is $5\frac{3}{4}$ miles to the summit. The hikers cover $2\frac{1}{8}$ miles before taking a break. They then hike another $1\frac{1}{2}$ miles before taking a second break. How many more miles do the hikers have to go before reaching the summit?

$2\frac{1}{8} + 1\frac{1}{2}$	*Add to find the distance hiked.*
$= \frac{17}{8} + \frac{3}{2}$	*Write mixed numbers as improper fractions.*
$= \frac{17}{8} + \frac{12}{8}$	*The LCD is 8.*
$= \frac{29}{8}$, or $3\frac{5}{8}$	

The hikers have hiked $3\frac{5}{8}$ miles. Now find the number of miles remaining.

$5\frac{3}{4} - 3\frac{5}{8}$	*Subtract the distance hiked from the total distance.*
$= \frac{23}{4} - \frac{29}{8}$	*Write as improper fractions.*
$= \frac{46}{8} - \frac{29}{8}$	*The LCD is 8.*
$= \frac{17}{8}$, or $2\frac{1}{8}$	*Simplify.*

The hikers have $2\frac{1}{8}$ miles to go before reaching the summit.

Abraham Lincoln established Yosemite National Park as a natural preserve in 1864.

---

2 Teach

Guided Instruction

In this lesson, students learn to add and subtract fractions with unlike denominators. Discuss the two methods for finding a common denominator. To help students understand why fractions must have common denominators before adding across the numerators, you may want to compare the denominators of fractions with units of measure. For example, just as you cannot add 2 inches and 3 centimeters without first writing them in terms of the same unit, you cannot add $\frac{2}{5}$ and $\frac{3}{10}$ without first writing them in terms of the same denominator.

Universal Access

Through Concrete Manipulatives

Have students use fraction bars (MK) to complete the following exercises.

1. $\frac{1}{2} + \frac{1}{3}$ $\frac{5}{6}$ 2. $\frac{1}{4} + \frac{1}{3}$ $\frac{7}{12}$

3. $\frac{1}{4} + \frac{1}{6}$ $\frac{5}{12}$ 4. $\frac{1}{12} + \frac{1}{6}$ $\frac{1}{4}$

5. $\frac{1}{3} + \frac{1}{12}$ $\frac{5}{12}$ 6. $\frac{1}{4} + \frac{1}{12}$ $\frac{1}{3}$

7. $\frac{1}{2} + \frac{1}{6}$ $\frac{2}{3}$ 8. $\frac{1}{2} + \frac{1}{12}$ $\frac{7}{12}$

EXAMPLE 4 Evaluating Expressions with Rational Numbers

Evaluate $n - \frac{11}{16}$ for $n = -\frac{1}{3}$.

$$n - \frac{11}{16} = \left(-\frac{1}{3}\right) - \frac{11}{16}$$ 　　Substitute $-\frac{1}{3}$ for n.

$$= \left(-\frac{1}{3}\right)\left(\frac{16}{16}\right) - \frac{11}{16}\left(\frac{3}{3}\right)$$ 　Multiply by fractions equal to 1.

$$= -\frac{16}{48} - \frac{33}{48}$$ 　　Rewrite with a common denominator: $3(16) = 48$.

$$= -\frac{49}{48}, \text{ or } -1\frac{1}{48}$$ 　　Simplify.

Think and Discuss

1. **Give an example** of two denominators with no common factors.
2. **Tell** if $-2\frac{1}{5} - \left(-2\frac{3}{16}\right)$ gives a positive or a negative answer. Explain.
3. **Explain** how to add $2\frac{2}{5} + 9\frac{1}{3}$ without first writing them as improper fractions.

Possible answers to Think and Discuss

1. 3 and 7; 4 and 9; 27 and 16
2. Negative; $\left|-2\frac{1}{5}\right| = 2\frac{1}{5}$, and $\left|-2\frac{3}{16}\right| = 2\frac{3}{16}$; since $2\frac{3}{15} > 2\frac{3}{16}$, the answer takes the sign of $-2\frac{1}{5}$.
3. Using the Commutative Property, add the whole number portions, add the fractional portions by finding a common denominator, and combine the two results. $2\frac{2}{5} + 9\frac{1}{3} = 2 + 9 + \frac{2}{5} + \frac{1}{3} = 11\frac{11}{15}$

2-6 Exercises

California Standards Practice
◆— NS1.2, ◆— NS2.2

go.hrw.com
Homework Help Online
KEYWORD: MT8CA 2-6
Parent Resources Online
KEYWORD: MT8CA Parent

GUIDED PRACTICE

See Example 1 Add or subtract. Write each answer in simplest form.

1. $\frac{4}{7} + \frac{1}{3}$ $\frac{19}{21}$
2. $\frac{1}{2} - \frac{7}{8}$ $-\frac{3}{8}$
3. $3\frac{1}{2} + \left(-7\frac{4}{5}\right)$ $-4\frac{3}{10}$
4. $3\frac{7}{12} + \left(-2\frac{4}{5}\right)$ $\frac{47}{60}$

5. $\frac{9}{10} - \frac{7}{8}$ $\frac{1}{40}$
6. $\frac{1}{2} + \frac{3}{7}$ $\frac{13}{14}$
7. $2\frac{1}{12} + \left(-10\frac{2}{3}\right)$ $-8\frac{7}{12}$
8. $3\frac{9}{10} - 1\frac{2}{5}$ $2\frac{1}{2}$

See Example 2 9. $\frac{12}{63} + \frac{13}{42}$ $\frac{1}{2}$
10. $\frac{8}{21} - \frac{21}{70}$ $\frac{17}{210}$
11. $\frac{11}{26} + \frac{7}{65}$ $\frac{69}{130}$
12. $\frac{11}{60} - \frac{5}{90}$ $\frac{23}{180}$

See Example 3 13. Gavin needs $2\frac{5}{8}$ yards of fabric each to make two shirts. This amount is cut from a bolt containing $9\frac{1}{4}$ yards of fabric. How much fabric remains on the bolt? **4 yd**

14. Samantha used $13\frac{5}{8}$ feet of jeweler's wire to make bracelets. The wire was cut off of a spool containing $30\frac{1}{3}$ feet of wire. How much wire remained on the spool? $16\frac{17}{24}$ **feet**

See Example 4 Evaluate each expression for the given value of the variable.

15. $4\frac{3}{8} + x$ for $x = -3\frac{2}{9}$ $1\frac{11}{72}$
16. $n - \frac{3}{8}$ for $n = -\frac{4}{5}$ $-1\frac{7}{40}$
17. $\frac{3}{7} + y$ for $y = \frac{1}{2}$ $\frac{13}{14}$

2-6 Exercises

Assignment Guide

If you finished Example 1 assign:
Proficient 1–8, 18–24 even, 41–43, 56–62
Advanced 18–25, 41–46, 56–62

If you finished Example 2 assign:
Proficient 1–12, 18–28 even, 41–43, 56–62
Advanced 18–29, 41–46, 56–62

If you finished Example 3 assign:
Proficient 1–14, 18–30 even, 41–43, 47, 49, 54–62
Advanced 18–31, 38–40, 41–46, 48, 50–62

If you finished Example 4 assign:
Proficient 1–17, 18–36 even, 41–43, 47, 49–62
Advanced 18–40, 41–46, 48, 50–62

Homework Quick Check
Quickly check key concepts.
Exercises: 20, 22, 26, 30, 34, 36

3 Close

Summarize

Review both methods of finding common denominators. Remind students that fractions can only be added or subtracted when the denominators are the same. Ask them if this is true for multiplication or division. no Ask the students to find the sum of $-1\frac{1}{4}$ and $\frac{5}{6}$ by both of the methods presented in the lesson. Remind students to give the answer in simplest form.

$$-1\frac{1}{4} + \frac{5}{6} = -\frac{5}{4} + \frac{5}{6} = -\frac{30}{24} + \frac{20}{24}$$
$$= -\frac{10}{24} = -\frac{5}{12}$$

$$-1\frac{1}{4} + \frac{5}{6} = -\frac{5}{4} + \frac{5}{6} = -\frac{15}{12} + \frac{10}{12} = -\frac{5}{12}$$

Math Background

Another method for finding the least common multiple of a set of numbers involves prime factors. To find the LCM of 60 and 45, factor each number into its prime factors, using exponents: $60 = 2^2 \cdot 3 \cdot 5$ and $45 = 3^2 \cdot 5$. The LCM is the product of the greatest powers of all the prime factors: $LCM = 2^2 \cdot 3^2 \cdot 5 = 180$. This method is useful for rational expressions as well. To find the sum $\frac{1}{6ab^2} + \frac{1}{4a^2b}$, you would need the LCM of the denominators.

$6ab^2 = 2 \cdot 3 \cdot a \cdot b^2$

$4a^2b = 2^2 \cdot a^2 \cdot b$

$LCM = 2^2 \cdot 3 \cdot a^2 \cdot b^2 = 12\,a^2\,b^2$

INDEPENDENT PRACTICE

See Example 1 Add or subtract. Write each answer in simplest form.

18. $\frac{7}{13} + \frac{2}{7}$ $\frac{75}{91}$

19. $\frac{1}{3} + \frac{4}{7}$ $\frac{19}{21}$

20. $\frac{11}{12} - \frac{4}{5}$ $\frac{7}{60}$

21. $\frac{2}{5} + \frac{14}{15}$ $1\frac{1}{3}$

22. $5\frac{4}{5} + \left(-3\frac{2}{7}\right)$ $2\frac{18}{35}$

23. $\frac{5}{9} - \frac{11}{14}$ $-\frac{29}{126}$

24. $2\frac{1}{4} - 4\frac{3}{7}$ $-2\frac{5}{28}$

25. $\frac{1}{5} + \frac{8}{9}$ $1\frac{4}{45}$

See Example 2 26. $\frac{7}{25} + \frac{13}{150}$ $\frac{11}{30}$

27. $\frac{6}{49} - \frac{9}{119}$ $\frac{39}{833}$

28. $\frac{9}{52} - \frac{3}{22}$ $\frac{21}{572}$

29. $\frac{9}{200} + \frac{7}{150}$ $\frac{11}{120}$

See Example 3 30. An oxygen tank contained $212\frac{2}{3}$ liters of oxygen before $27\frac{1}{3}$ liters were used. If the tank can hold $240\frac{3}{8}$ liters, how much space in the tank is unused? $55\frac{1}{24}$ L

31. Rick rides a bicycle along a $15\frac{1}{2}$ mile route, of which $5\frac{1}{8}$ miles is paved road, $9\frac{1}{4}$ miles is gravel road, and the rest is sidewalk. How many miles of the route is sidewalk? $1\frac{1}{8}$ miles

See Example 4 Evaluate each expression for the given value of the variable.

32. $2\frac{3}{4} + x$ for $x = -3\frac{2}{3}$ $-\frac{11}{12}$

33. $n - \frac{2}{3}$ for $n = \frac{3}{4}$ $\frac{1}{12}$

34. $r - \frac{4}{5}$ for $r = \frac{3}{4}$ $-\frac{1}{20}$

35. $3\frac{1}{6} + x$ for $x = -2\frac{5}{7}$ $\frac{19}{42}$

36. $n - \frac{11}{13}$ for $n = \frac{2}{3}$ $-\frac{7}{39}$

37. $\frac{12}{17} - n$ for $n = \frac{1}{2}$ $\frac{7}{34}$

PRACTICE AND PROBLEM SOLVING

Extra Practice
See page EP5.

38. **Multi-Step** The heights of the starting players for the Davis High School boy's basketball team are $78\frac{1}{8}$ in., 74 in., $71\frac{5}{8}$ in., $70\frac{3}{4}$ in., and $69\frac{1}{2}$ in. Find the average height of the starting players. $72\frac{4}{5}$ in.

39. **Measurement** A water pipe has an outside diameter of $1\frac{1}{4}$ inches and a wall thickness of $\frac{5}{16}$ inch. What is the inside diameter of the pipe? $\frac{5}{8}$ in.

40. **Estimation** Georgia is making a gift box with a rectangular bottom. She plans to glue ribbon along the bottom edge. The length of the box is $7\frac{3}{8}$ inches, and the width is $5\frac{1}{16}$ inches. She has 2 feet of ribbon. Does she have enough for the bottom edge? Explain your reasoning.

Add or subtract. Write each answer in simplest form.

41. $\frac{3}{8} + \left(-\frac{4}{7}\right) + \left(-\frac{2}{3}\right)$ $-\frac{145}{168}$

42. $1\frac{1}{5} + 1\frac{1}{6} - \left(-1\frac{1}{7}\right)$ $3\frac{107}{210}$

43. $\frac{1}{8} + \frac{5}{12} + \frac{7}{18}$ $\frac{67}{72}$

44. $\left(-\frac{2}{9}\right) + \frac{1}{3} + \left(-\frac{1}{6}\right)$ $-\frac{1}{18}$

45. $1\frac{1}{3} + \left(-2\frac{1}{2}\right) + \left(-3\frac{1}{6}\right)$ $-4\frac{1}{3}$

46. $\frac{1}{3} - \left(-\frac{3}{7}\right) + \left(-\frac{5}{42}\right)$ $\frac{9}{14}$

47. The bread that Lynn is baking requires $4\frac{1}{2}$ cups of flour. She has $1\frac{3}{4}$ cups of flour in a canister and $\frac{1}{8}$ cup of flour in a measuring cup. How much more flour does she need to have enough flour to bake the bread? $2\frac{5}{8}$ cups

48. **Reasoning** If n is a positive integer, express the mixed number $1\frac{1}{n}$ as an improper fraction. Show your work.

49. **Multi-Step** Karl rode his bike $16\frac{3}{8}$ miles. Neeka rode her bike m fewer miles.
   a. Write an expression to represent the number of miles Neeka rode. $16\frac{3}{8} - m$
   b. How far did Neeka ride if she rode $5\frac{1}{4}$ fewer miles? $11\frac{1}{8}$ mi
   c. Elda rode as far as Karl and Neeka combined. How far did Elda ride? $27\frac{1}{2}$ mi

40.
Possible answer: No; $7\frac{3}{8}$ is about $7\frac{1}{2}$, and $5\frac{1}{16}$ is about 5.
$7\frac{1}{2} + 7\frac{1}{2} + 5 + 5 = 25$ inches.
She has only 24 inches of ribbon.

48.
Possible answer: First multiply the whole number 1 by n to get $1n$. Then add 1 to get $1n + 1$ for the numerator. Keep the denominator, n. The improper fraction is $\frac{n+1}{n}$.

REVIEW FOR MASTERY 2-6

Review for Mastery
2-6 Adding and Subtracting with Unlike Denominators

To model $\frac{1}{2} + \frac{1}{3}$, use two rectangles of the same size and shape.

A. 1st rectangle: Shade $\frac{1}{2}$ vertically.

B. 2nd rectangle: Shade $\frac{1}{3}$ horizontally.

$\frac{1}{2}$ $\frac{1}{3}$

C. Separate the shaded portions into parts of equal size.

D. Use a new rectangle to show the sum.

$\frac{1}{2} = \frac{3}{6}$ $\frac{1}{3} = \frac{2}{6}$

$\frac{1}{2} + \frac{1}{3} = \frac{3}{6} + \frac{2}{6} = \frac{5}{6}$

Model $\frac{1}{2} + \frac{2}{5}$. Write the result. Possible model.

1.

$\frac{1}{2}$ $\frac{2}{5}$ $\frac{1}{2} + \frac{2}{5} = \frac{5}{10} + \frac{4}{10} = \frac{9}{10}$

Model $\frac{1}{3} + \frac{3}{5}$. Write the result. Possible model.

2.

$\frac{1}{3}$ $\frac{3}{5}$ $\frac{1}{3} + \frac{3}{5} = \frac{5}{15} + \frac{9}{15} = \frac{14}{15}$

PRACTICE 2-6

Practice B
2-6 Adding and Subtracting with Unlike Denominators

Add or subtract.

1. $\frac{2}{3} + \frac{1}{2}$ $1\frac{1}{6}$

2. $\frac{3}{5} + \frac{1}{3}$ $\frac{14}{15}$

3. $\frac{3}{4} - \frac{1}{3}$ $\frac{5}{12}$

4. $\frac{1}{2} - \frac{5}{9}$ $-\frac{1}{18}$

5. $\frac{5}{16} - \frac{5}{8}$ $-\frac{5}{16}$

6. $\frac{7}{9} + \frac{5}{6}$ $1\frac{11}{18}$

7. $\frac{7}{8} - \frac{1}{4}$ $\frac{5}{8}$

8. $\frac{5}{6} - \frac{3}{8}$ $\frac{11}{24}$

9. $2\frac{7}{8} + 3\frac{5}{12}$ $6\frac{7}{24}$

10. $1\frac{2}{9} + 2\frac{1}{18}$ $3\frac{5}{18}$

11. $3\frac{2}{3} - 1\frac{3}{5}$ $2\frac{1}{15}$

12. $1\frac{5}{6} + \left(-2\frac{3}{4}\right)$ $-\frac{11}{12}$

13. $\frac{5}{72} + \frac{68}{90}$ $\frac{33}{40}$

14. $\frac{81}{140} - \frac{67}{105}$ $-\frac{5}{84}$

15. $\frac{11}{45} + \frac{21}{96}$ $\frac{667}{1440}$

16. $\frac{56}{70} - \frac{107}{198}$ $\frac{257}{990}$

Evaluate each expression for the given value of the variable.

17. $2\frac{3}{8} + x$ for $x = 1\frac{5}{6}$ $4\frac{5}{24}$

18. $x - \frac{2}{5}$ for $x = \frac{1}{3}$ $-\frac{1}{15}$

19. $x - \frac{3}{10}$ for $x = \frac{3}{7}$ $\frac{9}{70}$

20. $1\frac{5}{8} + x$ for $x = -2\frac{1}{6}$ $-\frac{13}{24}$

21. $x - \frac{3}{4}$ for $x = \frac{1}{6}$ $-\frac{7}{12}$

22. $x - \frac{3}{10}$ for $x = \frac{1}{2}$ $\frac{1}{5}$

23. Ana worked $6\frac{1}{2}$ h on Monday, $5\frac{3}{4}$ h on Tuesday and $7\frac{1}{3}$ h on Friday. How many total hours did she work these three days? $19\frac{5}{12}$ h

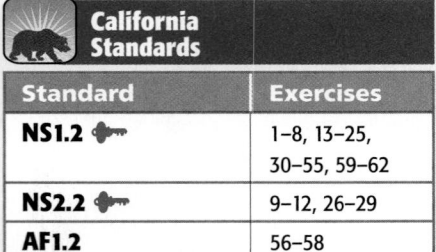

California Standards

Standard	Exercises
NS1.2 🔑	1–8, 13–25, 30–55, 59–62
NS2.2 🔑	9–12, 26–29
AF1.2	56–58

Niagara Falls, on the border of Canada and the United States, has two major falls, Horseshoe Falls on the Canadian side and American Falls on the U.S. side. Surveys of the erosion of the falls began in 1842. From 1842 to 1905, Horseshoe Falls eroded $239\frac{2}{5}$ feet.

Greetings from NIAGARA FALLS

50. In 1986, Thomas Martin noted that American Falls eroded $7\frac{1}{2}$ inches and Horseshoe Falls eroded $2\frac{4}{25}$ feet. What is the difference, in inches, between the two measurements? $18\frac{21}{50}$ in.

51. From 1842 to 1875, the yearly erosion of Horseshoe Falls varied from a minimum of $\frac{61}{100}$ meter to a maximum of $1\frac{17}{50}$ meters. By how much did these rates of erosion differ? $\frac{73}{100}$ meter

52. **Multi-Step** In the 48 years between 1842 and 1890, the average rate of erosion at Horseshoe Falls was $\frac{33}{50}$ meter per year. In the 22 years between 1905 and 1927, the rate of erosion was $\frac{7}{10}$ meter per year. Approximately how much total erosion occurred during these two time periods? $47\frac{2}{25}$ meters

53. ★ **Challenge** Rates of erosion of American Falls have been recorded as $\frac{23}{100}$ meter per year for 33 years, $\frac{9}{40}$ meter per year for 48 years, and $\frac{1}{5}$ meter per year for 4 years. What is the total amount of erosion during these three time spans? $19\frac{19}{100}$ meters

SPIRAL STANDARDS REVIEW
◆— NS1.2

54. **Multiple Choice** A $4\frac{5}{8}$ ft section of wood was cut from a $7\frac{1}{2}$ ft board. How much of the original board remained?

Ⓐ $3\frac{5}{8}$ ft   Ⓑ $3\frac{9}{16}$ ft   Ⓒ $2\frac{7}{8}$ ft   Ⓓ $2\frac{3}{8}$ ft

55. **Extended Response** A rectangular swimming pool measured $75\frac{1}{2}$ feet by $25\frac{1}{4}$ feet. Schmidt Pool Supply computed the perimeter of the pool to be $200\frac{1}{3}$ feet. Explain what the company did incorrectly when computing the perimeter. What is the correct perimeter? **The company did not find a common denominator when adding $\frac{1}{2}$ and $\frac{1}{4}$. The correct perimeter is $201\frac{1}{2}$ feet.**

Evaluate each expression for the given value of the variable. (Lesson 1-4)

56. $\frac{1}{2}c + 4$ for $c = -8$ **0**   57. $-2m - 2$ for $m = 13$ **−28** 58. $5 + \frac{1}{5}d$ for $d = -10$ **3**

Divide. Write each answer in simplest form. (Lesson 2-5)

59. $-\frac{4}{11} \div \frac{2}{7}$ $-1\frac{3}{11}$ 60. $\frac{4}{9} \div 8$ $\frac{1}{18}$ 61. $-\frac{7}{15} \div \frac{14}{25}$ $-\frac{5}{6}$ 62. $3\frac{1}{3} \div \frac{7}{9}$ $4\frac{2}{7}$

CHALLENGE 2-6

LESSON 2-6 Challenge
Please Repeat That.

A decimal that repeats one digit is equivalent to a fraction with denominator 9. $0.\overline{1} = \frac{1}{9}$ $0.\overline{2} = \frac{2}{9}$ $0.\overline{5} = \frac{5}{9}$

A decimal that repeats two digits is equivalent to a fraction with denominator 99. $0.\overline{43} = \frac{43}{99}$ $0.\overline{61} = \frac{61}{99}$ $0.\overline{38} = \frac{38}{99}$

The pattern continues so that $0.\overline{681} = \frac{681}{999}$ and $0.\overline{24793} = \frac{24,793}{99,999}$.

Use a calculator to write each decimal equivalent.

1. $\frac{1}{90} = $ __0.01__   2. $\frac{21}{990} = $ __0.021__   3. $\frac{358}{9990} = $ __0.0358__

Predict the decimal equivalent of each fraction. Verify your results on a calculator.

4. $\frac{4}{90} = $ __0.04__   5. $\frac{62}{990} = $ __0.062__   6. $\frac{617}{9990} = $ __0.0617__

Write each fractional equivalent and simplify.

7. $0.\overline{7} = $ 8. $0.0\overline{8} = $ 9. $0.00\overline{24} = $

$\frac{7}{9}$ $\frac{8}{90} = \frac{4}{45}$ $\frac{24}{9900} = \frac{2}{825}$

When one digit repeats but does not begin in the first decimal place, and the digit in the first place is other than 0, you must add fractions.

$0.3\overline{7} = 0.3 + 0.0\overline{7}$
$= \frac{3}{10} + \frac{7}{90}$
$= \frac{27}{90} + \frac{7}{90} = \frac{34}{90} = \frac{17}{45}$

Write each repeating decimal as the sum of two fractions. Find the sum and simplify. Verify.

10. $0.2\overline{8} = $ 11. $0.25\overline{32} = $

$\frac{2}{10} + \frac{8}{90} = \frac{26}{90} = \frac{13}{45}$ $\frac{25}{100} + \frac{32}{9900} = \frac{2507}{9900}$

12. $0.12\overline{7} = $ 13. $0.75\overline{483} = $

$\frac{1}{10} + \frac{27}{990} = \frac{126}{990} = \frac{7}{55}$ $\frac{75}{100} + \frac{483}{99,900} = \frac{75,408}{99,900} = \frac{6284}{8325}$

PROBLEM SOLVING 2-6

LESSON 2-6 Problem Solving
Adding and Subtracting with Unlike Denominators

Write the correct answer.

1. Nick Hysong of the United States won the Olympic gold medal in the pole vault in 2000 with a jump of 19 ft $4\frac{1}{4}$ inches, or $232\frac{1}{4}$ inches. In 1900, Irving Baxter of the United States won the pole vault with a jump of 10 ft $9\frac{7}{8}$ inches, or $129\frac{7}{8}$ inches. How much higher did Hysong vault than Baxter?

$102\frac{3}{8}$ inches

2. In the 2000 Summer Olympics, Ivan Pedroso of Cuba won the Long jump with a jump of 28 ft $\frac{3}{8}$ inches, or $336\frac{3}{8}$ inches. Alvin Kraenzlein of the United States won the long jump in 1900 with a jump of 23 ft $6\frac{7}{8}$ inches, or $282\frac{7}{8}$ inches. How much farther did Pedroso jump than Kraenzlein?

$53\frac{7}{8}$ inches

3. A recipe calls for $\frac{1}{8}$ cup of sugar and $\frac{3}{4}$ cup of brown sugar. How much total sugar is added to the recipe?

$\frac{7}{8}$ cup

4. The average snowfall in Norfolk, VA for January is $2\frac{3}{5}$ inches, February $2\frac{9}{10}$ inches, March 1 inch, and December $\frac{9}{10}$ inches. If these are the only months it typically snows, what is the average snowfall per year?

$7\frac{2}{5}$ inches

Use the table at the right that shows the average snowfall per month in Vail, Colorado.

5. What is the average annual snowfall in Vail, Colorado?

A $15\frac{13}{20}$ in.   C $187\frac{1}{10}$ in.
B 153 in.   Ⓓ $187\frac{4}{5}$ in.

6. The peak of the skiing season is from December through March. What is the average snowfall for this period?

F $30\frac{19}{20}$ in.   Ⓗ $123\frac{4}{5}$ in.
G $123\frac{3}{5}$ in.   J 127 in.

Average Snowfall in Vail, CO

Month	Snowfall (in.)	Month	Snowfall (in.)
Jan	$36\frac{7}{10}$	July	0
Feb	$35\frac{7}{10}$	August	0
March	$25\frac{2}{5}$	Sept	1
April	$21\frac{1}{5}$	Oct	$7\frac{4}{5}$
May	4	Nov	$29\frac{7}{10}$
June	$\frac{3}{10}$	Dec	26

Interdisciplinary LINK

Science

Exercises 50–53 involve using facts about the erosion of Niagara Falls. Water flow and erosion are studied in middle school Earth science programs, such as *Holt California Life Science*.

Teaching Tip **Multiple Choice** Suggest that students estimate before looking at the answer choices. For **Exercise 54**, students can subtract 4 ft from 7 ft to get 3 ft. Students also need to subtract the fractional parts of the measurements. Since $\frac{5}{8}$ is slightly more than $\frac{1}{2}$, the final answer should be a little *less than* 3 ft, so they can eliminate **A** and **B** as possible answers.

Journal

Ask students to consider the two methods for finding a common denominator, multiplying the denominators or finding the least common denominator. Ask them to describe situations in which it would be better to use one method over the other.

Power Presentations
with PowerPoint®

✓ 2-6 Lesson Quiz

Add or subtract.

1. $\frac{5}{14} + \frac{1}{7}$ $\frac{1}{2}$

2. $8\frac{2}{3} - 1\frac{1}{2}$ $7\frac{1}{6}$

3. $\frac{3}{5} + \left(-2\frac{2}{3}\right)$ $-2\frac{1}{15}$

4. Evaluate $1\frac{3}{8} - n$ for $n = \frac{9}{16}$. $\frac{13}{16}$

5. Robert is 5 feet $6\frac{1}{2}$ inches tall. Judy is 5 feet $3\frac{3}{4}$ inches tall. How much taller is Robert than Judy? $2\frac{3}{4}$ in.

Also available on transparency

Organizer

Objective: Assess students' mastery of concepts and skills in Lessons 2-1 through 2-6.

Resources

 Assessment Resources
Section 2A Quiz

 Test & Practice Generator
One-Stop Planner®

INTERVENTION

Resources

 Ready to Go On?
Intervention and
Enrichment **Worksheets**

🖿 *Ready to Go On?* **CD-ROM**

🪐 *Ready to Go On?* **Online**

my.hrw.com

SECTION 2A

Quiz for Lessons 2-1 Through 2-6

⊘ **2-1** Rational Numbers

Write each fraction as a decimal.

1. $\frac{3}{8}$ 0.375   2. $-\frac{18}{9}$ -2 3. $\frac{2}{3}$ $0.\overline{6}$ 4. $\frac{14}{5}$ 2.8

Write each decimal as a fraction in simplest form.

5. 0.625 $\frac{5}{8}$ 6. $0.\overline{2}$ $\frac{2}{9}$ 7. 5.35 $5\frac{7}{20}$ 8. $0.\overline{126}$ $\frac{14}{111}$

⊘ **2-2** Comparing and Ordering Rational Numbers

Write the numbers in order from least to greatest.

9. $-1.2, \frac{2}{3}, 0.5, -\frac{3}{4}$

10. $2.3, -\frac{3}{2}, -3, -3\frac{8}{9}$

11. $2\frac{10}{13}, 1.3, \frac{33}{8}, 2.99$

9. $-1.2, -\frac{3}{4}, 0.5, \frac{2}{3}$

10. $-3\frac{8}{9}, -3, -\frac{3}{2}, 2.3$

11. $1.3, 2\frac{10}{13}, 2.99, \frac{33}{8}$

⊘ **2-3** Adding and Subtracting Rational Numbers

Add or subtract. Write each answer in simplest form.

12. $65.8 - 24.24$ 41.56   13. $-\frac{3}{7} + 2\frac{4}{7}$ $2\frac{1}{7}$ 14. $\frac{5}{6} + \left(-2\frac{1}{6}\right)$ $-1\frac{1}{3}$ 15. $-9.25 + 3.72$ -5.53

16. On Monday, it took Darius and Jamal about 0.25 hour to ride their bicycles home from school. Today, it took them $\frac{3}{10}$ hour. How much longer did it take today? $\frac{1}{20}$ hour or 0.05 hour

⊘ **2-4** Multiplying Rational Numbers

Multiply. Write each answer in simplest form.

17. $2\left(4\frac{2}{3}\right)$ $9\frac{1}{3}$ 18. $2\frac{2}{5}\left(\frac{7}{36}\right)$ $\frac{7}{15}$ 19. 3.8(4) 15.2   20. $\frac{-1}{7}\left(\frac{-3}{4}\right)$ $\frac{3}{28}$

21. Robert has a piece of twine that is $\frac{3}{4}$ yard long. He needs a piece of twine that is $\frac{2}{3}$ of this length. How long of a piece of twine does Robert need? $\frac{1}{2}$ yd

⊘ **2-5** Dividing Rational Numbers

Divide. Write each answer in simplest form.

22. $\frac{3}{5} \div \frac{4}{15}$ $2\frac{1}{4}$ 23. $2.7 \div 3$ 0.9   24. $-\frac{2}{3} \div 1$ $-\frac{2}{3}$ 25. $-4\frac{6}{7} \div 2\frac{5}{6}$ $-1\frac{5}{7}$

⊘ **2-6** Adding and Subtracting with Unlike Denominators

Add or subtract. Write each answer in simplest form.

26. $\frac{2}{7} + \frac{1}{4}$ $\frac{15}{28}$ 27. $1\frac{2}{3} + 3\frac{5}{9}$ $5\frac{2}{9}$ 28. $6\frac{4}{7} - 3\frac{1}{5}$ $3\frac{13}{35}$ 29. $3\frac{1}{6} - 1\frac{3}{4}$ $1\frac{5}{12}$

READY TO GO ON?
Diagnose and Prescribe

NO
INTERVENE

YES
ENRICH

Ready to Go On? Intervention, Section 2A			
Ready to Go On? Intervention	🖉 **Worksheets**	💿 **CD-ROM**	🪐 **Online**
⊘ Lesson 2-1 🐻 NS1.3, 🔑 NS1.5	2-1 Intervention	Activity 2-1	
⊘ Lesson 2-2 🐻 NS1.1, NS1.3	2-2 Intervention	Activity 2-2	
⊘ Lesson 2-3 🐻 🔑 NS1.2	2-3 Intervention	Activity 2-3	Diagnose and Prescribe Online
⊘ Lesson 2-4 🐻 🔑 NS1.2	2-4 Intervention	Activity 2-4	
⊘ Lesson 2-5 🐻 🔑 NS1.2, 🔑 AF1.3	2-5 Intervention	Activity 2-5	
⊘ Lesson 2-6 🐻 🔑 NS1.2, 🔑 NS2.2	2-6 Intervention	Activity 2-6	

READY TO GO ON?
Enrichment, Section 2A

🖉 **Worksheets**
💿 **CD-ROM**
🪐 **Online**

Focus on Problem Solving

 California Standards

MR2.1 Use estimation to verify the reasonableness of calculated results.

Also covered: **NS1.2, MR3.1**

Look Back

• Is your answer reasonable?

After you solve a word problem, ask yourself if your answer makes sense. You can round the numbers in the problem and estimate to find a reasonable answer. It may also help to write your answer in sentence form.

 Read the problems below and tell which answer is most reasonable.

1 Tonia calculates that she needs $47\frac{2}{3}$ pounds of compost to spread on her garden. There are 38.9 pounds of compost in her compost pile. How much compost does Tonia need to purchase?

  Ⓐ about 9 pounds   **Ⓒ** about 6 pounds
  Ⓑ about 87 pounds   **Ⓓ** about 15 pounds

2 The Qin Dynasty in China began about 2170 years before the People's Republic of China was formed in 1949. When did the Qin Dynasty begin?

  Ⓐ before 200 B.C.E.
  Ⓑ between 200 B.C.E. and 200 C.E.
  Ⓒ between 200 C.E. and 1949 C.E.
  Ⓓ after 1949 C.E.

3 On Mercury, the coldest temperature is about 600°C below the hottest temperature of 430°C. What is the coldest temperature on the planet?

  Ⓐ about 1030°C
  Ⓑ about −1030°C
  Ⓒ about −170°C
  Ⓓ about 170°C

4 Julie is balancing her checkbook. Her beginning balance is $325.46, her deposits total $285.38, and her withdrawals total $683.27. What is her ending balance?

  Ⓐ about −$70
  Ⓑ about −$600
  Ⓒ about $700
  Ⓓ about $1300

 **Language Support** Some students may not have seen B.C.E. and C.E. before. Explain to students that B.C.E. means "Before the Common Era" and C.E. means "Common Era."

 Focus on Problem Solving

Organizer

Objective: Focus on checking for a reasonable answer.

 Online Edition

Resources

Chapter 2 Resource File
Reading Strategies

Problem Solving Process

This page focuses on the last step of the problem-solving process: **Look Back**

Discuss

Have students discuss how they determined which answer was the most reasonable. How does estimation help eliminate some of the answer choices?

Possible answer: Estimation can help you decide whether the answer should be positive or negative and approximately what the answer should be. Answer choices that are not close to the estimate can be eliminated.

1. $50 - 40 = 10$; 9 is the only answer choice close to 10.

2. $1950 - 2200 = -250$; since the difference is negative, the positive (C.E.) choices can be eliminated.

3. $400 - 600 = -200$; −170 is the only answer choice close to −200.

4. $300 + 300 - 700 = -100$; C and D are positive and can be eliminated; B is too low of a balance.

 California Standards

Mathematical Reasoning 2.1
Also covered:
Number Sense 1.2 Add, subtract, multiply, and divide **rational numbers** (integers, fractions, and terminating decimals) and take positive rational numbers to whole-number powers.

Mathematical Reasoning 3.1 Evaluate the reasonableness of the solution in the context of the original situation.

SECTION 2B

Equations with Rational Numbers

One-Minute Section Planner

Lesson	Lab Resources	Materials
Lesson 2-7 One-Step Equations with Rational Numbers • Solve one-step equations with rational numbers. 🐻 🔑 **AF4.0**		
Lesson 2-8 Two-Step Equations with Rational Numbers • Solve two-step equations with rational numbers. 🐻 🔑 **AF4.1**	**Hands-On Lab 2-8** In *Chapter 2 Resource File*	**Optional** Box, wrapping paper, ribbon

Notes

Math Background: Teaching the Standards

MORE ON TWO-STEP EQUATIONS

 **AF4.1**

Lesson 2-8

A two-step linear equation may be written in the form $ax + b = c$, where a, b, and c are real numbers, $a \neq 0$ or 1, and $b \neq 0$. For example, the equation $60 = 100 - 5x$ may be written as the equivalent equation $-5x + 100 = 60$ and so $a = -5$, $b = 100$, and $c = 60$. The equation $\frac{x-4}{3} = 2.5$ is equivalent to $\frac{x}{3} - \frac{4}{3} = 2.5$ or $\frac{1}{3}x - \frac{4}{3} = 2.5$, so $a = \frac{1}{3}$, $b = -\frac{4}{3}$, and $c = 2.5$.

Every equation of the form $ax + b = c$ with $a \neq 0$ has one solution, namely $\frac{c-b}{a}$. Recall that a solution is a value of the variable that makes the equation true. Substituting this value for x in the left side of the equation gives the following.

$$a\left(\frac{c-b}{a}\right) + b = c - b + b = c$$

In other words, $x = \frac{c-b}{a}$ makes the equation true and therefore is a solution.

It is worth noting that $x = \frac{c-b}{a}$ may be considered the "Linear Formula" because it gives the solution to any equation of the form $ax + b = c$, with $a \neq 0$, much in the same way the Quadratic Formula gives the solutions of any equation of the form $ax^2 + bx + c = 0$ and $a \neq 0$.

It still remains to be shown that $ax + b = c$ has *only one* solution. To do so, suppose that the values x_1 and x_2 are both solutions. Then it must be true that $ax_1 + b = c$ and $ax_2 + b = c$. Thus,

$$\begin{array}{ll} ax_1 + b = ax_2 + b & \\ \underline{\quad -b \qquad\qquad -b} & \text{\textit{Subtraction Property of Equality}} \\ ax_1 \quad = ax_2 & \\ \dfrac{ax_1}{a} = \dfrac{ax_2}{a} & \text{\textit{Division Property of Equality}} \\ x_1 = x_2 & \end{array}$$

The preceding discussion shows that every two-step linear equation has one and only one solution. Students are unlikely to question this fact, but they should realize that they will soon encounter equations that have no solution, two solutions, and even infinitely many solutions. Examples of such equations are shown below.

> No solution: $x + 7 = x - 5$
> Two solutions: $x^2 = 9$
> Infinitely many solutions: $6x + 4 = 2(3x + 2)$

EQUATIONS WITH RATIONAL NUMBERS

 **AF4.1**

Lessons 2-7, 2-8

In this chapter, students solve one-step and two-step linear equations that involve fractions and decimals. They should understand that the algebraic processes are exactly the same as those used to solve equations involving integers.

When solutions to equations are fractions or decimals, it is especially important that students evaluate the reasonableness of their solutions to real-world problems. For example, consider the following problem.

> It costs $6.50 to become a member of a store that rents DVDs. With a membership, it costs $2.40 to rent each DVD. Paul wants to become a member and rent DVDs, and he plans to spend a total of $20. How many DVDs can he rent?

The first step in solving the problem is choosing a variable, such as x, to represent the number of DVDs Paul can rent. Then students should write the verbal statements as an algebraic equation: $6.5 + 2.4x = 20$. The usual process may be used to solve this two-step equation, resulting in the solution $x = 5.625$.

At this point, many students will consider the problem solved. However, they should get in the habit of revisiting the original problem to see if the solution makes sense. In this situation, it is not possible to rent part of a DVD, so the correct solution is 5 DVDs. Notice that 5.625 is *not* simply rounded to the nearest whole number. Rather, the solution must be interpreted thoughtfully in the context of the original problem.

Online Edition
Tutorial Videos, Interactivities

Countdown to Mastery Week 4

Power Presentations
with PowerPoint®

Warm Up

Add or subtract.

1. $\frac{7}{10} + \frac{5}{10}$ $1\frac{1}{5}$

2. $2\frac{3}{8} - 1\frac{5}{16}$ $1\frac{1}{16}$

3. $4.8 + 3.6$ 8.4

4. $2.4 - 0.05$ 2.35

Also available on transparency

Math Humor

Math teachers never die; they just reduce to lowest terms.

2-7 One-Step Equations with Rational Numbers

California Standards

AF4.0 Students solve **simple linear equations** and inequalities **over the rational numbers.**

Why learn this? You can solve equations with rational numbers to determine how long it will take to paint a house. (See Example 3.)

In Lessons 1-7 and 1-8 you solved one-step equations involving integers. Similarly, you can use inverse operations to solve one-step equations with rational numbers.

EXAMPLE 1 Solving Equations with Decimals

Solve.

A $y - 17.5 = 11$

$$y - 17.5 = 11$$
$$\underline{+ 17.5 \quad + 17.5}$$
$$y = 28.5$$

Since 17.5 is subtracted from y, add 17.5 to both sides to undo the subtraction.

Remember!

Once you have solved an equation, it is a good idea to check your answer. To check your answer, substitute your answer for the variable in the original equation.

B $-4.2p = 12.6$

$$-4.2p = 12.6$$
$$\frac{-4.2p}{-4.2} = \frac{12.6}{-4.2}$$
$$p = -3$$

Since p is multiplied by −4.2, divide both sides by −4.2.

C $\frac{t}{7.5} = 4$

$$\frac{t}{7.5} = 4$$
$$7.5 \cdot \frac{t}{7.5} = 7.5 \cdot 4$$
$$t = 30$$

Since t is divided by 7.5, multiply both sides by 7.5.

EXAMPLE 2 Solving Equations with Fractions

Solve.

A $x + \frac{1}{9} = -\frac{4}{9}$

$$x + \frac{1}{9} = -\frac{4}{9}$$
$$\underline{-\frac{1}{9} \quad -\frac{1}{9}}$$
$$x = -\frac{5}{9}$$

Since $\frac{1}{9}$ is added to x, subtract $\frac{1}{9}$ from both sides.

---

1 Introduce

Alternate Opener

EXPLORATION

2-7 One-Step Equations with Rational Numbers

A box of cereal has 6 servings. Each serving contains 110.5 calories. How many calories are in the whole box?

110.5	110.5	= 221
110.5	110.5	= 221
110.5	110.5	= $\frac{221}{663}$

Equation
$110.5 \cdot 6 = c$
$663 = c$

Estimate the solution for each equation. Then use a calculator to solve.

	Equation	Estimate	Actual
1.	$124.75 - x = 50$		
2.	$x + 16.9 = 15.5$		
3.	$0.6x = 15$		
4.	$\frac{x}{1.25} = 8$		

Think and Discuss

5. **Describe** how you estimated the solutions for the equations in Problems 1–4.
6. **Discuss** whether it is easier to estimate the solutions of some equations than the solutions of others.

Motivate

Show the students equations such as $n + 4 = 9$, $3x = 12$, and $\frac{y}{5} = 4$.

Remind students that they learned how to solve these equations in Chapter 1. Have the students solve and check these equations. Tell the students that they will solve equations in the new lesson by the same methods.
$n = 5, x = 4, y = 20$

Explorations and answers are provided in *Alternate Openers: Explorations Transparencies.*

California Standards

Algebra and Functions **4.0**

Solve.

B $x - \frac{1}{8} = \frac{9}{16}$

$$x - \frac{1}{8} = \frac{9}{16}$$

Since $\frac{1}{8}$ is subtracted from x, add $\frac{1}{8}$ to both sides.

$$x - \frac{1}{8} + \frac{1}{8} = \frac{9}{16} + \frac{1}{8}$$

$$x = \frac{9}{16} + \frac{2}{16}$$

Find a common denominator, 16.

$$x = \frac{11}{16}$$

C $\frac{3}{5}w = \frac{3}{16}$

$$\frac{3}{5}w = \frac{3}{16}$$

$$\frac{3}{5}w \div \frac{3}{5} = \frac{3}{16} \div \frac{3}{5}$$

Since w is multiplied by $\frac{3}{5}$, divide both sides by $\frac{3}{5}$.

$$\frac{\cancel{3}^1}{\cancel{5}}w \cdot \frac{\cancel{5}^1}{\cancel{3}_1} = \frac{\cancel{3}^1}{16} \cdot \frac{5}{\cancel{3}_1}$$

Multiply by the reciprocal. Simplify.

$$w = \frac{5}{16}$$

For more on writing equations from words, see the Graph and Equation Builder on page MB2.

EXAMPLE 3 Solving Word Problems Using Equations

 Reasoning

Sully has agreed to paint 3 houses. He knows that he can paint $\frac{2}{5}$ of a house in one day. How many days will it take him to paint all 3 houses?

Write an equation:

number of days	·	houses per day	=	number of houses
d	·	$\frac{2}{5}$	=	3

$$d \cdot \frac{2}{5} = 3$$

$$d \cdot \frac{2}{5} \div \frac{2}{5} = 3 \div \frac{2}{5}$$

Since d is multiplied by $\frac{2}{5}$, divide both sides by $\frac{2}{5}$.

$$d \cdot \frac{2}{5} \cdot \frac{5}{2} = 3 \cdot \frac{5}{2}$$

Multiply by the reciprocal.

$$d = \frac{15}{2}, \text{ or } 7\frac{1}{2}$$

Simplify.

Sully can paint 3 houses in $7\frac{1}{2}$ days.

Think and Discuss

1. **Explain** the first step in solving an addition equation with fractions having *like* denominators.

2. **Explain** the first step in solving an addition equation with fractions having *unlike* denominators.

Possible answers to Think and Discuss

1. Subtract the same fraction from both sides of the equation to isolate the variable on one side.

2. Find the least common denominator, or subtract the same fraction from both sides of the equation to isolate the variable on one side.

---

2 Teach

Guided Instruction

In this lesson, students learn to solve one-step equations with rational numbers. To begin, remind students of the methods they used to solve one-step equations with whole numbers and integers (Lessons 1-7 and 1-8). Demonstrate the similarity between solving those equations and solving equations in which the numbers are decimals and fractions. Emphasize that the algebra procedures are the same as those used to solve whole number and integer equations.

Universal Access
Through Cooperative Learning

Have students work in pairs. Each pair should have a sheet of paper with an incomplete equation such as $x + \underline{\hspace{0.5cm}} = \underline{\hspace{0.5cm}}$. Tell students to take turns replacing the blanks with rational numbers and then having their partner solve the equation. It may be helpful to provide students with a list of rational numbers to use, such as 3.4, 1.2, 4.2, 5.3, 0.3, -2.9, $\frac{1}{2}$, $\frac{2}{3}$, $-\frac{3}{5}$, and $\frac{5}{8}$.

3 Close

Summarize

Remind students that one-step equations are solved the same way whether the numbers in the equations are whole numbers, integers, or rational numbers. Ask students what steps they would take to solve the equations that follow: $x + 8 = 12$, $x + 6 = -3$, $x + 2.4 = 1.5$, and $x + \frac{3}{4} = \frac{7}{8}$.

Possible answers: Subtract 8 from both sides; subtract 6 from both sides; subtract 2.4 from both sides; subtract $\frac{3}{4}$ from both sides.

Point out that these equations are all addition equations and that they all should be solved by subtraction.

2-7 Exercises

California Standards Practice
AF4.0

go.hrw.com
Homework Help Online
KEYWORD: MT8CA 2-7
Parent Resources Online
KEYWORD: MT8CA Parent

Assignment Guide

If you finished Example 1 assign:
Proficient 1–6, 14–18 even, 34, 35, 38, 39, 56–61
Advanced 14–19, 41, 45, 48, 49, 52, 56–61

If you finished Example 2 assign:
Proficient 1–12, 14–26 even, 33–40, 54, 56–61
Advanced 14–27, 41–49, 52, 54, 56–61

If you finished Example 3 assign:
Proficient 1–13, 14–28 even, 29–40, 54–61
Advanced 14–28, 41–61

Homework Quick Check
Quickly check key concepts.
Exercises: 14, 16, 22, 24, 26, 28

Math Background

It is important for students to be able to solve equations that contain fractions and decimals as well as integers. They may find it helpful if they can begin to recognize equations by the included operation(s), rather than by the types of numbers they contain. For example, $x + \frac{3}{4} = -\frac{1}{2}$ should be recognized as a one-step equation that involves addition rather than a fraction problem. When teaching the Guided Practice exercises, you may want to have students first identify the operations involved in the equation before they solve it.

California Standards

Standard	Exercises
NS1.2	58–61
AF1.1	13, 28–32, 50–51, 53, 55, 56–57
AF4.0	1–55

GUIDED PRACTICE

See Example 1 **Solve.**

1. $y + 17.3 = -65$
$y = -82.3$

2. $-5.2f = 36.4$ $f = -7$

3. $\frac{m}{3.2} = -6$ $m = -19.2$

4. $r - 15.8 = 24.6$
$r = 40.4$

5. $\frac{s}{15.42} = 6.3$ $s = 97.146$

6. $0.06g = 0.474$ $g = 7.9$

See Example 2 **7.** $x + \frac{1}{9} = -\frac{4}{9}$ $x = -\frac{5}{9}$

8. $-\frac{3}{8} + k = -\frac{7}{8}$ $k = -\frac{1}{2}$

9. $\frac{5}{6}w = -\frac{7}{18}$ $w = -\frac{7}{15}$

10. $m - \frac{4}{3} = -\frac{4}{3}$ $m = 0$

11. $\frac{7}{17}y = -\frac{56}{17}$ $y = -8$

12. $t + \frac{4}{13} = \frac{12}{39}$ $t = 0$

See Example 3 **13.** Alonso runs a company called Speedy House Painters. His workers can paint $\frac{3}{4}$ of a house in one day. How many days would it take them to paint 6 houses? **8 days**

INDEPENDENT PRACTICE

See Example 1 **Solve.**

14. $y + 16.7 = -49$
$y = -65.7$

15. $4.7m = -32.9$ $m = -7$

16. $-\frac{h}{7.8} = 2$ $h = -15.6$

17. $k - 3.2 = -6.8$
$k = -3.6$

18. $\frac{z}{11.4} = 6$ $z = 68.4$

19. $c + 5.98 = 9.1$
$c = 3.12$

See Example 2 **20.** $j + \frac{1}{3} = \frac{3}{4}$ $j = \frac{5}{12}$

21. $\frac{5}{6}d = \frac{3}{15}$ $d = \frac{6}{25}$

22. $7h = \frac{14}{33}$ $h = \frac{2}{33}$

23. $\frac{2}{3} + x = \frac{5}{8}$ $x = -\frac{1}{24}$

24. $x - \frac{1}{16} = \frac{7}{16}$ $x = \frac{1}{2}$

25. $r + \frac{4}{7} = -\frac{1}{7}$ $r = -\frac{5}{7}$

26. $\frac{5}{6}c = \frac{7}{24}$ $c = \frac{7}{20}$

27. $\frac{7}{8}d = \frac{11}{12}$ $d = 1\frac{1}{21}$

See Example 3 **28.** A professional lawn care service can mow $2\frac{3}{4}$ acres of lawn in one hour. How many hours would it take them to mow a lawn that is $6\frac{7}{8}$ acres? **$2\frac{1}{2}$ hours**

PRACTICE AND PROBLEM SOLVING

Extra Practice
See page EP5.

Science The largest of all known diamonds, the Cullinan diamond, weighed 3106 carats before it was cut into 105 gems. The largest cut, Cullinan I, or the Great Star of Africa, weighs $530\frac{1}{3}$ carats. Another cut, Cullinan II, weighs $317\frac{2}{5}$ carats. Cullinan III weighs $94\frac{2}{5}$ carats, and Cullinan IV weighs $63\frac{3}{5}$ carats.

29. How many carats of the original Cullinan diamond were left after the Great Star of Africa and Cullinan II were cut? **$2258\frac{4}{15}$ carats**

30. How much more does Cullinan II weigh than Cullinan IV? **$253\frac{4}{5}$ carats**

31. Which diamond weighs 223 carats less than Cullinan II? **Cullinan III**

32. **Nutrition** An entire can of chicken noodle soup has 6.25 grams of total fat. There are 2.5 servings per can. How many grams of total fat are in a single serving of chicken noodle soup? **2.5 g**

REVIEW FOR MASTERY 2-7

LESSON 2-7 Review for Mastery
One-Step Equations with Rational Numbers

Solving equations with rational numbers is basically the same as solving equations with integers or whole numbers:
Use inverse operations to isolate the variable.

$\frac{1}{4}z = -16$

$4 \cdot \frac{1}{4}z = -16 \cdot 4$ — Multiply each side by 4.

$z = -64$

$y - \frac{3}{8} = \frac{7}{8}$

$+\frac{3}{8}$ $+\frac{3}{8}$ — Add $\frac{3}{8}$ to each side.

$y = \frac{10}{8} = 1\frac{2}{8} = 1\frac{1}{4}$

$x + 3.5 = -17.42$
-3.5 -3.5 — Subtract 3.5 from each side.
$x = -20.92$

$-26t = 317.2$
$\frac{-26t}{-26} = \frac{317.2}{-26}$ — Divide each side by -26.
$t = -12.2$

Tell what you would do to isolate the variable.

1. $x - 1.4 = 7.82$
add 1.4

2. $\frac{1}{4} + y = \frac{7}{4}$
subtract $\frac{1}{4}$

3. $3z = 5$
divide by 3

Solve each equation.

4. $14x = -129.5$
$x = -9.25$

5. $\frac{1}{3}y = 27$
$y = 81$

6. $265.2 = \frac{z}{22.1}$
$5860.92 = z$

7. $x + 53.8 = -1.2$
$x = -55$

8. $25 = \frac{1}{5}k$
$125 = k$

9. $m - \frac{2}{3} = \frac{3}{5}$
$m = 1\frac{4}{15}$

PRACTICE 2-7

LESSON 2-7 Practice B
One-Step Equations with Rational Numbers

Solve.

1. $x + 6.8 = 12.19$
$x = 5.39$

2. $y - 10.24 = 5.3$
$y = 15.54$

3. $0.05w = 6.25$
$w = 125$

4. $\frac{a}{9.05} = 8.2$
$a = 74.21$

5. $-12.41 + x = -0.06$
$x = 12.35$

6. $\frac{d}{-8.4} = -10.2$
$d = 85.68$

7. $-2.89 = 1.7m$
$m = -1.7$

8. $n - 8.09 = -11.65$
$n = -3.56$

9. $\frac{x}{5.4} = -7.18$
$x = -38.772$

10. $\frac{7}{9} + x = 1\frac{1}{9}$
$x = \frac{1}{3}$

11. $\frac{6}{11}y = -\frac{18}{22}$
$y = -1\frac{1}{2}$

12. $\frac{7}{10}d = \frac{21}{20}$
$d = 1\frac{1}{2}$

13. $x - \left(-\frac{9}{14}\right) = \frac{5}{7}$
$x = \frac{1}{14}$

14. $x - \frac{15}{21} = 2\frac{6}{7}$
$x = 3\frac{4}{7}$

15. $-\frac{8}{15}a = \frac{9}{10}$
$a = -1\frac{11}{16}$

16. A recipe calls for $2\frac{1}{3}$ cups of flour and $1\frac{1}{4}$ cups of sugar. If the recipe is tripled, how much flour and sugar will be needed?
7 cups of flour and $3\frac{3}{4}$ cups of sugar

17. Daniel filled the gas tank in his car with 14.6 gal of gas. He then drove 284.7 mi before needing to fill up his tank with gas again. How many miles did the car get to a gallon of gasoline?
19.5 mi

Solve.

33. $z - \frac{2}{9} = \frac{1}{9}$ $z = \frac{1}{3}$ **34.** $-5f = -1.5$ $f = 0.3$ **35.** $\frac{j}{7.2} = -3$ $j = -21.6$ **36.** $\frac{2}{5} + x = 0.25$ $x = -\frac{3}{20}$

37. $t - \frac{3}{4} = 6\frac{1}{4}$ $t = 7$ **38.** $\frac{x}{0.5} = \frac{7}{8}$ $x = \frac{7}{16}$ **39.** $\frac{6}{7}d = -\frac{3}{7}$ $d = -\frac{1}{2}$ **40.** $-4.7g = -28.2$ $g = 6$

41. $\frac{v}{5.5} = -5.5$ $v = -30.25$ **42.** $r + \frac{5}{6} = -3\frac{1}{6}$ $r = -4$ **43.** $y + 2.8 = -1.4$ $y = -4.2$

44. $-\frac{1}{15} + r = \frac{3}{5}$ $r = \frac{2}{3}$ **45.** $-3c = \frac{3}{20}$ $c = -\frac{1}{20}$ **46.** $m - 2.34 = 8.2$ $m = 10.54$

47. $y - 57 = -2.8$ $y = 54.2$ **48.** $-18 = -9.6 + f$ $f = -8.4$ **49.** $\frac{4m}{0.8} = -7$ $m = -1.4$

51.
Possible answer: The salesperson multiplied 60 by 1.8 instead of dividing by 1.8 to get about 33 seconds.

52. Possible answer: No, a is $\frac{1}{3}$ of b describes the equation $a = \frac{1}{3}b$, but $\frac{1}{3}a = b$ means that b is $\frac{1}{3}$ of a.

50. Multi-Step Jack is tiling along the walls of the rectangular kitchen with the tile shown. The kitchen has a length of $243\frac{3}{4}$ inches and a width of $146\frac{1}{4}$ inches.

a. How many tiles will fit along the length of the room? 15 tiles

b. How many tiles will fit along its width? 9 tiles

c. Jack is tiling along the bases of all four walls of the kitchen. How many boxes of ten tiles must he buy? (*Hint:* He must buy whole boxes of tile.) 5 boxes

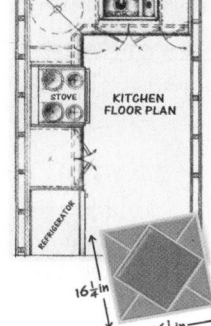
KITCHEN FLOOR PLAN

51. What's the Error? Janice is thinking about buying a CD writer that burns 1.8 megabytes of data per second. A computer salesperson told her that if she had 60 megabytes of data to burn, she could burn it in about 2 minutes with this writer. What was his error?

52. Write About It If a is $\frac{1}{3}$ of b, is it correct to say $\frac{1}{3}a = b$? Explain.

53. Challenge A jeweler cut a 200-carat diamond in half. Then he cut one of the halves, reducing it by $\frac{1}{5}$ of its weight. Then he cut it again, reducing it by $\frac{1}{4}$ of its new weight. How many carats was the resulting diamond? 60 carats

SPIRAL STANDARDS REVIEW ➡ NS1.2, AF1.1, ➡ AF4.0

54. Multiple Choice If $\frac{12}{36} = 2w$, what is the value of w?

Ⓐ $\frac{24}{36}$ Ⓑ $\frac{24}{72}$ Ⓒ $\frac{1}{3}$ Ⓓ $\frac{1}{6}$

55. Short Response The performance of a musical arrangement lasted $6\frac{1}{4}$ minutes. The song consisted of 3 verses that each lasted the same number of minutes. Write and solve an equation to find the length of each verse.

$3v = 6\frac{1}{4}$; $2\frac{1}{12}$ minutes

Write an algebraic expression for each word phrase. (Lesson 1-2)

56. 15 less than a number p $p - 15$ **57.** half of the sum of m and 19 $\frac{1}{2}(m + 19)$

Add or subtract. Write each answer in simplest form. (Lesson 2-6)

58. $\frac{7}{8} + \frac{1}{6}$ $1\frac{1}{24}$ **59.** $4\frac{2}{3} + 5\frac{3}{4}$ $10\frac{5}{12}$ **60.** $6\frac{5}{8} - 2\frac{1}{20}$ $4\frac{23}{40}$ **61.** $2\frac{8}{9} - \frac{4}{5}$ $2\frac{4}{45}$

2-8 Organizer

Objective: Students solve two-step equations with rational numbers.

 Hands-On Lab
In *Chapter 2 Resource File*

 Online Edition
Tutorial Videos, Interactivities

 Countdown to Mastery Week 5

Power Presentations
with PowerPoint®

Warm Up

Solve.

1. $x + 12 = 35$ $x = 23$
2. $8x = 120$ $x = 15$
3. $\frac{y}{9} = 7$ $y = 63$
4. $-34 = y + 56$ $y = -90$

Also available on transparency

Math Humor

Several surgeries only made the author's condition worse. So he wrote his new novel from the end to the beginning. He hoped to undo the operations by working backward.

2-8 Two-Step Equations with Rational Numbers

California Standards

AF4.1 Solve two-step linear equations and inequalities in one variable over the rational numbers, interpret the solution or solutions in the context from which they arose, and verify the reasonableness of the results.

Why learn this? You can solve two-step equations with rational numbers to determine how many circus tickets you can purchase.

Recall that two-step equations contain two operations, and therefore, require two inverse operations to solve. Before solving, ask yourself, "What is being done to the variable and in what order?" One method to solve the equation is to work backward to undo the operations.

EXAMPLE 1 PROBLEM SOLVING APPLICATION

The Kuhr family spent $52.00 for circus tickets. This cost included a $3.25 service fee for the order, and the circus tickets cost $9.75 each. How many tickets did the Kuhrs buy? Justify your answer.

1 Understand the Problem

The **answer** is the number of tickets that the Kuhrs bought. List the **important information:** The service fee is $3.25 per order, the tickets cost $9.75 each, and the total cost is $52.

Let t represent the number of tickets bought.

Total cost	=	Tickets	+	Service Fee
52.00	=	9.75t	+	3.25

2 Make a Plan

Think: First the variable is multiplied by 9.75, and then 3.25 is added to the result. Work backward to solve the equation. Undo the operations in reverse order: First subtract 3.25 from both sides of the equation, and then divide both sides of the new equation by 9.75.

3 Solve

$$52.00 = 9.75t + 3.25$$
$$\underline{-3.25 \qquad -3.25}$$
$$48.75 = 9.75t$$
$$\frac{48.75}{9.75} = \frac{9.75t}{9.75}$$
$$5 = t$$

Since 3.25 is added to 9.75t, subtract 3.25 from both sides.

Since t is multiplied by 9.75, divide both sides by 9.75.

The Kuhrs bought 5 tickets.

Math Builders
For more on solving two-step equations, see the Step-by-Step Solution Builder on page MB4.

1 Introduce

Alternate Opener

EXPLORATION

2-8 Two-Step Equations with Rational Numbers

A hot-air balloon is 15.5 feet above the ground. When the pilot heats the air in the balloon, the balloon begins to rise at 1.25 feet per second.

1. Let s be the number of seconds since the pilot began heating the air. The height h of the balloon, in feet, is given by the equation
$$h = 15.5 + 1.25s$$
Substitute $s = 0$ in the equation. What is the value of h? Why does this make sense?

2. Complete the table.

s	0	1	2	3	4	5	6	7	8	9	10
h											

3. How many seconds does it take for the balloon to reach a height of 23 feet?

4. You can use the table to solve the equation $28 = 15.5 + 1.25s$. First find the value 28 in the h row of the table. Then find the corresponding value of s. What is the solution of the equation?

Think and Discuss

5. **Discuss** what your solution of the equation $28 = 15.5 + 1.25s$ represents.

6. **Explain** how you could check your solution of the equation $28 = 15.5 + 1.25s$.

Motivate

Show the students a box wrapped in paper with a string or ribbon wrapped around it. You may want to wrap a small box in front of the class. Demonstrate that to open it, the ribbon is removed, then the wrapping paper is removed, and then the box is opened. Ask the students to think about the steps that were taken when the gift was wrapped. Point out that to unwrap the gift, the steps must be reversed.

Explorations and answers are provided in *Alternate Openers: Explorations Transparencies.*

California Standards
Algebra and Functions **4.1**

4 Look Back

You can use a table to decide whether your answer is reasonable.

Tickets	Cost of Tickets	Service Charge	Total Cost
1	$9.75	$3.25	$13.00
2	$19.50	$3.25	$22.75
3	$29.25	$3.25	$32.50
4	$39.00	$3.25	$42.25
5	$48.75	$3.25	$52.00

Five tickets is a reasonable answer.

EXAMPLE 2 **Solving Two-Step Equations**

Solve $\frac{2}{3}p - \frac{1}{5} = \frac{2}{5}$.

A **Method 1: Use fraction operations.**

$$\frac{2}{3}p - \frac{1}{5} = \frac{2}{5}$$

$$\frac{2}{3}p - \frac{1}{5} + \frac{1}{5} = \frac{2}{5} + \frac{1}{5}$$

Since $\frac{1}{5}$ is subtracted from $\frac{2}{3}p$, add $\frac{1}{5}$ to both sides to undo the subtraction.

$$\frac{2}{3}p = \frac{3}{5}$$

$$\frac{3}{2} \cdot \frac{2}{3}p = \frac{3}{5} \cdot \frac{3}{2}$$

Since p is multiplied by $\frac{2}{3}$, multiply both sides by the reciprocal of $\frac{2}{3}$.

$$p = \frac{9}{10}$$

B **Method 2: Multiply by the LCD to clear the fractions.**

$$\frac{2}{3}p - \frac{1}{5} = \frac{2}{5}$$

$$15\left(\frac{2}{3}p - \frac{1}{5}\right) = \left(\frac{2}{5}\right)15$$

Multiply both sides by 15, the LCD of the fractions.

$$15\left(\frac{2}{3}p\right) - 15\left(\frac{1}{5}\right) = \left(\frac{2}{5}\right)15$$

Distribute 15 on the left side.

$$10p - 3 = 6$$

Since 3 is subtracted from 10p, add 3 to both sides to undo the subtraction.

$$10p - 3 + 3 = 6 + 3$$

$$10p = 9$$

Since p is multiplied by 10, divide both sides by 10.

$$\frac{10p}{10} = \frac{9}{10}$$

$$p = \frac{9}{10}$$

Simplify.

Think and Discuss

1. **Describe** how you would solve $4.1(x - 2) = 19.68$.

2. **Explain** how to check your solution to an equation.

Power Presentations
with PowerPoint®

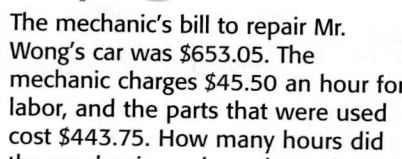

Additional Examples

Example 1

The mechanic's bill to repair Mr. Wong's car was $653.05. The mechanic charges $45.50 an hour for labor, and the parts that were used cost $443.75. How many hours did the mechanic work on the car? **4.6 hr**

Example 2

Solve.

A. $\frac{n}{3} + 7 = 22$ $n = 45$

B. $\frac{y - 4}{3} = 9$ $y = 31$

Also available on transparency

Possible answers to Think and Discuss

1. Divide both sides by 4.1, and then add 2 to both sides.

2. Substitute the solution for the variable in the original equation to see if it makes the equation true.

---

2 Teach

Guided Instruction

In this lesson, students learn to solve two-step equations with rational numbers. Remind students of the order of operations for evaluating expressions. Tell students that to solve an equation, the order of operations must be reversed. Point out that they should usually undo addition and subtraction first and then undo multiplication and division.

Teaching Tip

Inclusion Remind students to check solutions by substituting the value into the original equation and simplifying to make sure both sides are equal.

Universal Access
Through Cooperative Learning

Give each student the following situations:

1. Car repair: $45 per hour labor, $430.35 parts, $722.85 total cost. How many hours of labor? 6.5 hours

2. T-shirt printing: $120 set up fee, $3.19 per shirt, total cost $273.12. How many shirts were ordered? 48 shirts

3. Salesman's salary: $9.50 per hour, $250 in sales commissions, total weekly salary $582.50. How many hours of work this week? 35 hours

Have each student write an equation for each situation and pass them to the student on their left, who solves the equations. Then the next student checks the solutions.

---

3 Close

Summarize

Remind students to reverse the order of operations to solve equations. Point out that addition and subtraction are not always the operations that should be undone first. For an equation such as the one in **Example 2B,** division should be undone first.

2-8 Exercises

go.hrw.com
Homework Help Online
KEYWORD: MT8CA 2-8
Parent Resources Online
KEYWORD: MT8CA Parent

California Standards Practice
AF1.1, ⟜ AF4.1

Assignment Guide

If you finished Example **1** assign:
Proficient 1, 8, 30–34, 39, 41–48
Advanced 8, 34–39, 41–48

If you finished Example **2** assign:
Proficient 1–23, 30–34, 39–48
Advanced 8–14, 21–29, 34–48

Homework Quick Check

Quickly check key concepts.
Exercises: 8, 10, 12, 14, 34

Math Background

The method of reversing the order of operations suggested in the lesson is not the only possible method for solving equations. Some equations may be solved with different steps in different orders as long as deductive reasoning and algebraic properties are applied correctly. For example, the equation in the first Think and Discuss can be solved in at least two different ways:

$4.1(x-2) = 19.68$
$4.1x - 8.2 = 19.68$
$+ 8.2 = + 8.2$
$4.1x = 27.88$
$\frac{4.1x}{4.1} = \frac{27.88}{4.1}$
$x = 6.8$

$4.1(x-2) = 19.68$
$\frac{4.1(x-2)}{4.1} = \frac{19.68}{4.1}$
$x - 2 = 4.8$
$+ 2 = + 2$
$x = 6.8$

GUIDED PRACTICE

See Example **1**
1. Adele is paid a weekly salary of $685. She is paid an additional $23.50 for every hour of overtime she works. This week her total pay, including regular salary and overtime, was $849.50. Write and solve an equation to find how many hours of overtime Adele worked this week. **7 hours**

See Example **2** Solve.

2. $\frac{1}{3}x - 5 = 30$ **$x = 105$**
3. $\frac{1}{6}y + \frac{1}{6} = 2$ **$y = 11$**
4. $\frac{1}{3}t - 1 = \frac{3}{5}$ **$t = 4\frac{4}{5}$**

5. $\frac{2}{7} - \frac{1}{7}x = -\frac{3}{7}$ **$x = 5$**
6. $\frac{1}{3} + \frac{1}{6}j = \frac{7}{18}$ **$j = \frac{1}{3}$**
7. $3 - \frac{1}{8}a = \frac{1}{4}$ **$a = 22$**

INDEPENDENT PRACTICE

See Example **1**
8. The cost of a family membership at a health club is $58 per month plus a one-time $129 start-up fee. A family spent $651 on their membership. Write and solve an equation to find how many months they were members. **9 months**

See Example **2** Solve.

9. $\frac{1}{3} + \frac{5}{6}y = \frac{2}{3}$ **$y = \frac{2}{5}$**
10. $\frac{1}{9}x - \frac{2}{9} = -\frac{5}{9}$ **$x = -3$**
11. $\frac{1}{3}m - 4 = \frac{1}{10}$ **$m = 12\frac{3}{10}$**

12. $\frac{2}{3}t + \frac{1}{5} = 3$ **$t = 4\frac{1}{5}$**
13. $6 - \frac{2}{3}r = 1\frac{1}{2}$ **$r = 6\frac{3}{4}$**
14. $\frac{2}{7} - \frac{1}{7}a = \frac{1}{8}$ **$a = 1\frac{1}{8}$**

PRACTICE AND PROBLEM SOLVING

Extra Practice
See page EP5.

Solve and check.

15. $5w + 2.7 = 12.8$ **2.02**
16. $15 - 3.2x = -6.8$ **6.8125**
17. $\frac{1}{5}m + 6.3 = 9.8$ **17.5**

18. $\frac{z+9}{4} = 2.1$ **−0.6**
19. $2x + \frac{2}{3} = \frac{4}{5}$ **$\frac{1}{15}$**
20. $9.2 = -5g - 23.3$ **−6.5**

21. $6z - \frac{1}{3} = 0$ **$\frac{1}{18}$**
22. $\frac{5}{2}d - \frac{3}{2} = -\frac{1}{2}$ **$\frac{2}{5}$**
23. $600 - 58.1k = 19$ **10**

24. $8.125 = 6.5 + \frac{1}{2}p$ **3.25**
25. $\frac{3}{8}w - 14 = 10$ **64**
26. $\frac{17+s}{15} = -4$ **−77**

27. $9y - 7.2 = 4.5$ **1.3**
28. $\frac{2}{3} - 6h = -\frac{13}{6}$ **$\frac{17}{36}$**
29. $-1 = \frac{5}{8}b + \frac{3}{8}$ **$-\frac{11}{5}$**

33.
Possible answer:
Method 1: Work backward to isolate the variable.
$\frac{m}{2} - \frac{3}{2} = 37$
$\frac{m}{2} - \frac{3}{2} + \frac{3}{2} = 37 + \frac{3}{2}$
$(2)\frac{m}{2} = \frac{77}{2}(2)$
$m = 77$

Method 2: Multiply both sides by the denominator.
$(2)\frac{m-3}{2} = 37(2)$
$m - 3 = 74$
$m = 77$

Translate each sentence into an equation. Then solve the equation.

30. One-half of a number, minus 9, is 14. **$\frac{1}{2}n - 9 = 14$; 46**

31. A number decreased by 7 and then divided by 5 is 13. **$\frac{n-7}{5} = 13$; 72**

32. The sum of one-half and one-seventh of a number is one. **$\frac{1}{2} + \frac{1}{7}n = 1$; $3\frac{1}{2}$**

33. Show two ways to solve the equation $\frac{m-3}{2} = 37$. Check your answer.

34. **Consumer Math** A long distance phone company charges $19.95 per month plus $0.05 per minute for calls. If a family's monthly long distance bill is $23.74, how many minutes of long distance did they use? **75.8 minutes**

REVIEW FOR MASTERY 2-8

Review for Mastery
LESSON 2-8 *Two-Step Equations with Rational Numbers*

To solve an equation, it is important to first note how it is formed.
Then, work backward to undo each operation.

$4z + 3 = 15$
The variable is multiplied by 4 and then 3 is added.
To solve, first subtract 3 and then divide by 4.

$\frac{z}{4} - 3 = 7$
The variable is divided by 4 and then 3 is subtracted.
To solve, first add 3 and then multiply by 4.

$\frac{1}{3}s + \frac{8}{12} = \frac{9}{12}$
The variable is multiplied by $\frac{1}{3}$ and then $\frac{8}{12}$ is added.
To solve, first subtract $\frac{8}{12}$ and then multiply by the reciprocal of $\frac{1}{3}$.

Describe how each equation is formed. Then, tell the steps needed to solve.

1. $3x - 5 = 7$
The variable is ___multiplied by 3___ and then ___5 is subtracted___.
To solve, first ___add 5___ and then ___divide by 3___.

2. $\frac{x}{3} + 5 = 7$
The variable is ___divided by 3___ and then ___5 is added___.
To solve, first ___subtract 5___ and then ___multiply by 3___.

3. $\frac{2}{5}s + \frac{1}{3} = \frac{5}{3}$
The variable is ___multiplied by $\frac{2}{5}$___ and then ___$\frac{1}{3}$ is added___.
To solve, first ___subtract $\frac{1}{3}$___ and then ___multiply by the reciprocal of $\frac{2}{5}$___.

4. $10 = -3x - 2$
The variable is ___multiplied by −3___ and then ___2 is subtracted___.
To solve, first ___add 2___ and then ___divide by −3___.

5. $\frac{3}{8} = \frac{2}{3}s - \frac{1}{8}$
The variable is ___multiplied by $\frac{2}{3}$___ and then ___$\frac{1}{8}$ is subtracted___.
To solve, first ___add $\frac{1}{8}$___ and then ___multiply by the reciprocal of $\frac{2}{3}$___.

PRACTICE 2-8

Practice B
LESSON 2-8 *Two-Step Equations with Rational Numbers*

Write and solve a two-step equation to answer the following questions.

1. The school purchased baseball equipment and uniforms for a total cost of $1762. The equipment costs $598 and the uniforms were $24.25 each. How many uniforms did the school purchase?

$x =$ # of uniforms
$1762 = 598 + 24.25x$
$1762 - 598$
$= 598 - 598 + 24.25x$
$1164 = 24.25x$
$\frac{1164}{24.25} = \frac{24.25x}{24.25}$
$48 = x$

2. Carla runs 4 miles every day. She jogs from home to the school track, which is $\frac{3}{4}$ mile away. She then runs laps around the $\frac{1}{4}$-mile track. Carla then jogs home. How many laps does she run at the school?

$x =$ # of laps
$4 = \frac{3}{4} + \frac{1}{4}x + \frac{3}{4}$
$4 - \frac{6}{4} = \frac{6}{4} - \frac{6}{4} + \frac{1}{4}x$
$\frac{5}{2} = \frac{1}{4}x$
$4\left(\frac{5}{2}\right) = \left(\frac{1}{4}x\right)4$
$10 = x$

Solve.

3. $\frac{a}{3} + \frac{5}{3} = 6$ **$a = 13$**
4. $\frac{x}{4} + \frac{2}{3} = \frac{-2}{3}$ **$x = -\frac{16}{3}$**
5. $\frac{y}{6} - \frac{2}{3} = -3$ **$y = -14$**
6. $\frac{k}{8} + \frac{1}{4} = \frac{7}{4}$ **$k = 12$**

7. $0.5x - 6 = -4$ **$x = 4$**
8. $\frac{x}{3} + 3 = -4$ **$x = -14$**
9. $\frac{1}{5}n + 3 = 6$ **$n = 15$**
10. $2a - 7 = -9$ **$a = -1$**

11. $\frac{3x}{4} - \frac{1}{2} = 4$ **$x = 6$**
12. $-7.8 = 4.4 + 2r$ **$r = -6.1$**
13. $\frac{4w}{5} - \frac{5}{8} = -12$ **$w = -\frac{7}{8}$**
14. $1.3 - 5r = 7.4$ **$r = -1.22$**

15. A phone call costs $0.58 for the first 3 minutes and $0.15 for each additional minute. If the total charge for the call was $4.78, how many minutes was the call? **31 minutes**

16. Seventeen less than four times a number is twenty-seven. Find the number. **11**

California Standards

Standard	Exercises
NS1.2 ⟜	41–44
AF1.1	8, 30–39
AF4.0 ⟜	45–48
AF4.1 ⟜	1–34, 36–37, 39–40

About 20% of the more than 2500 species of snakes are venomous. The United States has 20 domestic venomous snake species.

35. The inland taipan of central Australia is the world's most toxic venomous snake. Just 1 mg of its venom can kill 1000 mice. One bite contains up to 110 mg of venom. About how many mice could be killed with just one inland taipan bite? **110,000**

36. A rattlesnake grows a new rattle segment each time it sheds its skin. Rattlesnakes shed their skin an average of three times per year. However, segments often break off. If a rattlesnake had 44 rattle segments break off in its lifetime and it had 10 rattles when it died, approximately how many years did the rattlesnake live? **18 yr**

37. All snakes shed their skin. The shed skin of a snake is an average of 10% longer than the actual snake. If the shed skin of a coral snake is 27.5 inches long, about how long is the coral snake? **25 in.**

38. ⭐ **Challenge** Black mambas feed mainly on small rodents and birds. Suppose a black mamba is 100 feet away from an animal that is running at 8 mi/h. About how long will it take for the mamba to catch the animal? (*Hint:* 1 mile = 5280 feet) **approximately 17 s**

go.hrw.com
Web Extra!
KEYWORD: MT8CA Snakes

Venom is collected from snakes and injected into horses, which develop antibodies. The horses' blood is sterilized to make antivenom.

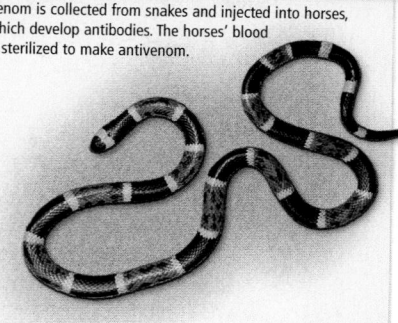

Records of World's Most Venomous Snakes		
Category	Record	Type of Snake
Fastest	12 mi/h	Black mamba
Longest	18 ft 9 in.	King cobra
Heaviest	34 lb	Eastern diamondback rattlesnake
Longest fangs	2 in.	Gaboon viper

 **SPIRAL STANDARDS REVIEW**  NS1.2, AF4.0, AF4.1

39. Multiple Choice A plumber charges $75 for a house call plus $45 per hour. How many hours did the plumber work if he charged $210?

Ⓐ 2 hours   Ⓑ 3 hours   Ⓒ 4 hours   Ⓓ 6 hours

40. Gridded Response What value of y makes the equation $4.4y + 1.75 = 43.99$ true? **9.6**

Multiply. Write each answer in simplest form. (Lesson 2-4)

41. $\frac{5}{6}\left(-\frac{3}{4}\right)$ $-\frac{5}{8}$

42. $4\frac{1}{2}\left(\frac{1}{3}\right)$ $\frac{3}{2}$ or $1\frac{1}{2}$

43. $-\frac{3}{16}\left(-\frac{4}{9}\right)$ $\frac{1}{12}$

44. $-\frac{42}{11}$ or $-3\frac{9}{11}$ $-7\left(\frac{6}{11}\right)$

Solve. (Lesson 2-7)

45. $y - 27.6 = -32$ $y = -4.4$

46. $-5.3f = 74.2$ $f = -14$

47. $\frac{m}{3.2} = -8$ $m = -25.6$

48. $x + \frac{1}{8} = -\frac{5}{8}$ $x = -\frac{3}{4}$

Interdisciplinary

Life Science

Exercises 35–38 involve using data about venomous snakes to solve two-step equations. Snakes and other reptiles are studied in middle school life science programs, such as *Holt California Life Science*.

 **Teaching Tip**

Multiple Choice For **Exercise 39,** encourage students to work backwards. Instead of trying to guess the number of hours or writing an equation, students can find the answer by subtracting the cost for a house call from the total charge, and then dividing the result by the hourly cost. Encourage students to check their answer.

Journal

Ask students to write about how they would explain the process of solving two-step equations to a friend who has not seen them yet.

Power Presentations with PowerPoint®

2-8 Lesson Quiz

Solve.

1. $-\frac{1}{9}x - 3 = 10$ $x = -117$

2. $7y + 25.68 = -26.12$ $y = -7.4$

3. $-8.3 = -3.5x + 13.4$ $x = 6.2$

4. $\frac{y + 5}{11} = 3.1$ $y = 29.1$

5. The cost for a new cell phone plan is $39.79 per month plus a one-time start-up fee of $78. If you are charged $1032.96, how many months will the contract last? **24 months**

Also available on transparency

READY TO GO ON?

Organizer

Objective: Assess students' mastery of concepts and skills in Lessons 2-7 through 2-8.

Resources

 Assessment Resources
Section 2B Quiz

Test & Practice Generator
One-Stop Planner®

INTERVENTION ⬅➡

Resources

Ready to Go On?
Intervention and
Enrichment Worksheets

Ready to Go On? CD-ROM

Ready to Go On? Online

my.hrw.com

READY TO GO ON?

SECTION 2B

Quiz for Lessons 2-7 Through 2-8

2-7 One-Step Equations with Rational Numbers

Solve.

1. $p - 1.2 = -5$ $\quad -3.8$
2. $-9w = 13.5$ $\quad -1.5$
3. $\frac{m}{3.7} = -8$ $\quad -29.6$
4. $x + \frac{1}{9} = -\frac{4}{7}$ $\quad -\frac{43}{63}$
5. $m - \frac{3}{4} = -\frac{4}{3}$ $\quad -\frac{7}{12}$
6. $\frac{7}{33}y = -\frac{56}{3}$ $\quad -88$
7. $\frac{y}{-2.6} = 3.2$ $\quad -8.32$
8. $s + 0.45 = 10.07$ $\quad 9.62$
9. $p + 2.7 = 4.5$ $\quad 1.8$
10. $\frac{h}{2.5} = 3.8$ $\quad 9.5$
11. $y - \frac{7}{8} = -\frac{25}{12}$ $\quad -1\frac{5}{24}$
12. $\frac{8}{11}k = \frac{29}{44}$ $\quad \frac{29}{32}$

13. The Montegro Flooring Company can replace 200 square feet of carpet with tile in one day. They accept a job replacing carpet with tile in an apartment that measures 977.5 square feet. How many days will it take the Montegro Flooring Company to complete this job? **4.89 days**

14. From start to finish, Ellen took $15\frac{2}{3}$ days to write a research paper for her literature class. This was $\frac{9}{10}$ the time it took Rebecca to write her paper. How long did it take Rebecca to write her research paper? **$17\frac{11}{27}$ days**

2-8 Two-Step Equations with Rational Numbers

Solve.

15. $\frac{1}{6}x + 1\frac{1}{6} = -48$ $\quad -295$
16. $3x + 4.2 = 21$ $\quad 5.6$
17. $\frac{1}{4}y - \frac{2}{3} = \frac{5}{6}$ $\quad 6$
18. $\frac{y}{12} + 6 = -72$ $\quad -936$
19. $-5.7p + 10.16 = -65.08$ $\quad 13.2$
20. $\frac{r-2}{-7} = 3$ $\quad -19$
21. $2w + 7.1 = 2.85$ $\quad -2.125$
22. $-8.9y - 10.11 = 74.44$ $\quad -9.5$
23. $\frac{p+17}{25} = 4$ $\quad 83$

24. Marvin sold newspaper subscriptions during summer break. He earned $125.00 per week plus $5.75 for each subscription that he sold. During the last week of the summer, Marvin earned $228.50. How many subscriptions did he sell that week? **18 subscriptions**

25. A cell phone company charges $13.50 per month plus $0.035 for each minute used. If Angelina's cell phone bill was $17.70 last month, how many minutes did she use? **120 minutes**

NO
INTERVENE

READY TO GO ON?
Diagnose and Prescribe

YES
ENRICH

READY TO GO ON? Intervention, Section 2B			
Ready to Go On? Intervention	📜 **Worksheets**	💿 **CD-ROM**	🪐 **Online**
☑ Lesson 2-7 🔑 **AF4.0**	2-7 Intervention	Activity 2-7	Diagnose and Prescribe Online
☑ Lesson 2-8 🔑 **AF4.1**	2-8 Intervention	Activity 2-8	

READY TO GO ON?
Enrichment, Section 2B
📜 **Worksheets**
💿 **CD-ROM**
🪐 **Online**

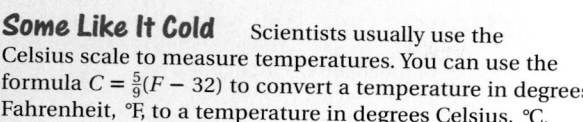

CONCEPT CONNECTION

CHAPTER 2

Organizer

Objective: Assess students' ability to apply concepts and skills in Chapter 2 in a real-world format.

PREMIER **Online Edition**

Some Like It Cold   Scientists usually use the Celsius scale to measure temperatures. You can use the formula $C = \frac{5}{9}(F - 32)$ to convert a temperature in degrees Fahrenheit, °F, to a temperature in degrees Celsius, °C.

1. Water freezes at 32 degrees Fahrenheit (32°F) and boils at 212 degrees Fahrenheit (212°F). Use the formula to convert 32°F and 212°F to degrees Celsius. Why do you think scientists prefer the Celsius scale?

2. When temperatures are converted from Fahrenheit to Celsius, an interesting thing happens as the Fahrenheit temperature decreases. Convert −4°F, −22°F, and −40°F to degrees Celsius. What do you notice?

3. Use the above formula to write an equation to find the temperature in degrees Fahrenheit that corresponds to 40°C. Then solve the equation.

4. The formula $F = \frac{9}{5}C + 32$ converts a temperature in degrees Celsius to a temperature in degrees Fahrenheit. Use this formula to convert $-\frac{5}{18}$°C to degrees Fahrenheit.

5. The table shows the temperature in Nome, Alaska, recorded at several different times during a day in April. At which time was the lowest temperature recorded? Explain.

Temperature in Nome, Alaska	
Time	Temperature
1:00 P.M.	25.7°F
3:00 P.M.	$25\frac{2}{5}$°F
5:00 P.M.	−3.5°C
7:00 P.M.	$-3\frac{4}{5}$°C

Problem	Text reference
1	Lesson 2-4
2	Lesson 2-4
3	Lesson 2-8
4	Lesson 2-4
5	Lesson 2-4

Answers

1. 0°C; 100°C; It is easy to work with numbers such as 0 and 100.

2. −20; −30; −40; They are all multiples of 10.

3. $40 = \frac{5}{9}(F - 32)$; 104°F

4. $31\frac{1}{2}$°F

5. 7:00 P.M.; since $-3.5 > -3\frac{4}{5}$ and $-3\frac{4}{5}$°C $< 25\frac{2}{5}$°F.

Wisconsin high school students participate in the annual Polar Plunge for Special Olympics.

INTERVENTION

Scaffolding Questions

1. What steps should you take to evaluate $\frac{5}{9}(F - 32)$ for a particular value of F? Subtract 32 first, then multiply by $\frac{5}{9}$.

2. When you convert negative degrees Fahrenheit, will you always get negative degrees Celsius? Why? Yes, because you subtract 32 from the negative number, which gives a negative value, and then you multiply by the positive number $\frac{5}{9}$, which also gives a negative value.

3. What value should you substitute into the formula to get the equation? $C = 40$ How can you solve the equation? Multiply both sides by $\frac{9}{5}$. Then add 32 to both sides.

4. What expression do you get when you substitute $C = -\frac{5}{18}$? $\frac{9}{5}\left(\frac{-5}{18}\right) + 32$ How can you simplify the expression? First multiply the fractions, then add 32.

5. How can you compare the temperatures? Convert them all to degrees Celsius or degrees Fahrenheit. Then convert them all to decimals.

Extension

The Kelvin scale is a third way to measure temperatures. To convert degrees Celsius to degrees Kelvin, you add 273.16 to the Celsius temperature. Convert 36.5°F to degrees Celsius and then to degrees Kelvin. 2.5°C; 275.66 Kelvin

California Standards

Number Sense 1.1 Read, write, and compare rational numbers in scientific notation (positive and negative powers of 10), **compare rational numbers in general.**

Algebra and Functions 4.1 Solve two-step linear equations and inequalities in one variable over the rational number, interpret the solution or solutions in the context from which they arose, and verify the reasonableness of the results.

Organizer

Objective: Participate in games to practice and apply skills learned in Chapter 2.

 Online Edition

Resources

📄 **Chapter 2 Resource File**
Puzzles, Twisters & Teasers

Egyptian Fractions

Purpose: To apply operations with fractions to a historical activity

Discuss Ask students: What fraction would you subtract first in order to express the fraction $\frac{3}{8}$ as the Egyptians would have? Explain. You subtract $\frac{1}{3}$ from $\frac{3}{8}$ first, because it is the largest unit fraction that is less than $\frac{3}{8}$. How do you know when to stop? when the difference is a unit fraction

Extend Have students determine how many fractions can be written using the fractions $\frac{1}{2}, \frac{1}{3}, \frac{1}{4}$, and/or $\frac{1}{5}$ as addends a maximum of one time each. Have them write all the fractions.

11 fractions:
$\frac{1}{2} + \frac{1}{3} = \frac{5}{6}$

$\frac{1}{2} + \frac{1}{4} = \frac{3}{4}$

$\frac{1}{2} + \frac{1}{5} = \frac{7}{10}$

$\frac{1}{3} + \frac{1}{4} = \frac{7}{12}$

$\frac{1}{3} + \frac{1}{5} = \frac{8}{15}$

$\frac{1}{4} + \frac{1}{5} = \frac{9}{20}$

$\frac{1}{2} + \frac{1}{3} + \frac{1}{4} = \frac{13}{12}$

$\frac{1}{2} + \frac{1}{3} + \frac{1}{5} = \frac{31}{30}$

$\frac{1}{2} + \frac{1}{4} + \frac{1}{5} = \frac{19}{20}$

$\frac{1}{3} + \frac{1}{4} + \frac{1}{5} = \frac{47}{60}$

$\frac{1}{2} + \frac{1}{3} + \frac{1}{4} + \frac{1}{5} = \frac{77}{60}$

Egg Fractions

Purpose: To practice adding fractions in a game format

Discuss Have students give a combination of fractions with a sum of $\frac{2}{3}$.
Possible answer: $\frac{7}{12}$ and $\frac{1}{12}$

Game Time

Egyptian Fractions

If you were to divide 9 loaves of bread among 10 people, you would give each person $\frac{9}{10}$ of a loaf. The answer was different on the ancient Egyptian Ahmes papyrus, because ancient Egyptians used only *unit fractions*, which have a numerator of 1. All other fractions were written as sums of different unit fractions. So $\frac{5}{6}$ could be written as $\frac{1}{2} + \frac{1}{3}$, but not as $\frac{1}{6} + \frac{1}{6} + \frac{1}{6} + \frac{1}{6} + \frac{1}{6}$.

Method	Example
Suppose you want to write a fraction as a sum of different unit fractions.	$\frac{9}{10}$
Step 1. Choose the largest fraction of the form $\frac{1}{n}$ that is less than the fraction you want.	$0 \quad \frac{1}{5}\frac{1}{4}\frac{1}{3} \quad \frac{1}{2} \quad \frac{9}{10}\frac{1}{1}$
Step 2. Subtract $\frac{1}{n}$ from the fraction you want.	$\frac{9}{10} - \frac{1}{2} = \frac{2}{5}$ remaining
Step 3. Repeat steps 1 and 2 using the difference of the fractions until the result is a unit fraction.	$0 \quad \frac{1}{5}\frac{1}{4} \frac{1}{3}\frac{2}{5} \frac{1}{2} \qquad \frac{1}{1}$ $\frac{2}{5} - \frac{1}{3} = \frac{1}{15}$ remaining
Step 4. Write the fraction you want as the sum of the unit fractions.	$\frac{9}{10} = \frac{1}{2} + \frac{1}{3} + \frac{1}{15}$

Write each fraction as a sum of different unit fractions. **Possible answers:**

1. $\frac{3}{4}$ $\frac{1}{2} + \frac{1}{4}$ **2.** $\frac{5}{8}$ $\frac{1}{2} + \frac{1}{8}$ **3.** $\frac{11}{12}$ $\frac{1}{2} + \frac{1}{4} + \frac{1}{6}$ **4.** $\frac{3}{7}$ $\frac{1}{4} + \frac{1}{7} + \frac{1}{28}$ **5.** $\frac{7}{5}$ $1 + \frac{1}{3} + \frac{1}{15}$

Egg Fractions

This game is played with an empty egg carton. Each compartment represents a fraction with a denominator of 12. The goal is to place tokens in compartments with a given sum.

A complete copy of the rules is available online.

go.hrw.com
Game Time Extra
KEYWORD: MT8CA Games

Extend Have students play the game again, but this time they must make each sum using 3 tokens instead of 2. (Students should replace $\frac{1}{6}$ with $\frac{11}{12}$.)

Materials
- film canister with lid
- adding-machine tape
- ruler
- markers
- self-stick label

It's in the Bag!

PROJECT Canister Carry-All

Turn a film canister into a handy carrying case for a number line and notes about rational numbers.

Directions

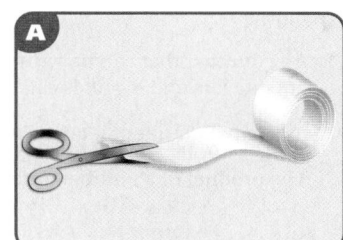
A

1 If necessary, cut off a strip along the bottom edge of the adding-machine tape so that the tape will fit into the film canister when it is rolled up. When you're done, the tape should be about $1\frac{3}{4}$ inches wide. **Figure A**

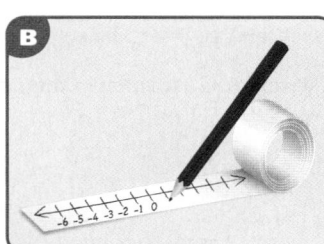
B

2 Use a ruler to make a long number line on one side of the adding-machine tape. **Figure B**

3 Write the number and title of the chapter on a self-stick label. Then peel the backing off the label and place the label on the outside of the canister.

Taking Note of the Math

Place examples of rational numbers on the number line. Choose examples that will help you remember how to compare and order rational numbers. Then turn the adding-machine tape over, and use the other side to write notes and sample problems from the chapter.

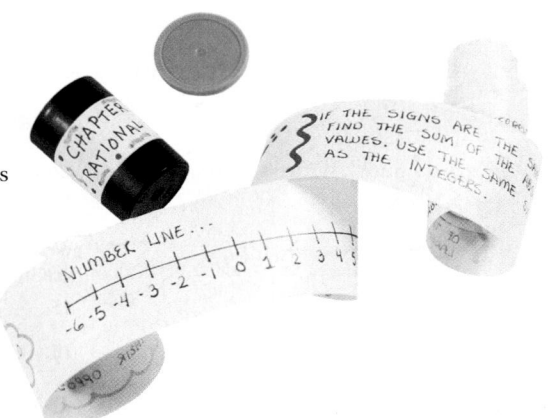

Organizer

Objective: Make a carrying case for a number line that serves as a study guide for the chapter.

Materials: empty film canister with lid, adding-machine tape, ruler, markers, self-stick label

PREMIER Online Edition

Using the Page

Preparing the Materials
Photo-developing centers may have empty 35 mm film canisters that they can donate to your class. Alternatively, you can do the project with any type of cylindrical containers, such as the containers used to package peanuts or other foods.

Making the Project
Have students make simple number lines at first, perhaps making marks only for integers. Later, students can add additional marks as they place rational numbers in the appropriate spots along the line.

Extending the Project
Students can save their number lines and add information to them throughout the course. For example, students might add examples of square roots (Chapter 4) and percents (Chapter 6).

Tips from the Bag Ladies!

To add a fun twist to the project, have students cut a slit in the side of the film canister. When the rolled-up adding-machine tape is placed inside the canister, students can pull it out through the slit to read their notes.

We've used film canisters to store all kinds of things. For instance, when we teach probability we have students keep coins and number cubes in the canisters. Students can even put an eye screw in the lid and attach a short plastic cord. This makes it easy to tie the canister to a spiral notebook for quick access.

Organizer

Objective: Help students organize and review key concepts and skills presented in Chapter 2.

 **Online Edition**
Multilingual Glossary

Resources

 PuzzlePro®
One-Stop Planner®

Multilingual Glossary Online

go.hrw.com
KEYWORD: MT8CA Glossary

Lesson Tutorial Videos
CD-ROM

 Test & Practice Generator
One-Stop Planner®

Answers

1. rational number
2. terminating decimal
3. reciprocal or multiplicative inverse
4. $\frac{3}{5}$
5. $\frac{1}{4}$
6. $\frac{21}{40}$
7. $\frac{5}{11}$
8. $\frac{1}{3}$
9. $\frac{212}{999}$
10. 1.75
11. $0.2\overline{6}$
12. $0.\overline{7}$
13. <
14. =
15. $-0.9, -\frac{2}{3}, 0.25, \frac{1}{2}$
16. $-0.11, 0, 0.67, \frac{9}{10}$

Vocabulary

least common denominator (LCD) 70
multiplicative inverse 82
rational number 66
reciprocal 82
repeating decimal 66
terminating decimal 66

Complete the sentences below with vocabulary words from the list above.

1. Any number that can be written as a fraction $\frac{n}{d}$ (where n and d are integers and $d \neq 0$) is called a ___?___.

2. A decimal number that ends is called a ___?___.

3. The product of a number and its ___?___ is 1.

2-1 Rational Numbers (pp. 66–69) NS1.3, ← NS1.5

EXAMPLE

■ Write 0.8 as a fraction in simplest form.
$0.8 = \frac{8}{10}$ *8 is in the tenths place.*
$= \frac{8 \div 2}{10 \div 2}$ *Divide numerator and denominator by 2.*
$= \frac{4}{5}$

EXERCISES

Write each decimal as a fraction in simplest form.

4. 0.6
5. 0.25
6. 0.525
7. $0.\overline{45}$
8. $0.\overline{3}$
9. $0.\overline{212}$

Write each fraction as a decimal.

10. $\frac{7}{4}$
11. $\frac{4}{15}$
12. $\frac{7}{9}$

2-2 Comparing and Ordering Rational Numbers (pp. 70–73) NS1.1, NS1.3

EXAMPLE

■ Compare $\frac{2}{3}$ and $\frac{5}{8}$. Write <, >, or =.
$\frac{2}{3} \ \blacksquare\ \frac{5}{8}$
$\frac{2 \cdot 8}{3 \cdot 8} = \frac{16}{24}$ *24 is the LCD.*
$\frac{5 \cdot 3}{8 \cdot 3} = \frac{15}{24}$
$\frac{16}{24} > \frac{15}{24}$, so $\frac{2}{3} > \frac{5}{8}$

EXERCISES

Compare. Write <, >, or =.

13. $\frac{5}{7} \ \blacksquare\ \frac{9}{10}$
14. $\frac{7}{8} \ \blacksquare\ \frac{28}{32}$

Write the numbers in order from least to greatest.

15. $-\frac{2}{3}, 0.25, \frac{1}{2}, -0.9$

16. $0.67, \frac{9}{10}, 0, -0.11$

2-3 Adding and Subtracting Rational Numbers (pp. 74–77)  NS1.2

EXAMPLE

Add or subtract.

■ $\frac{3}{7} + \frac{4}{7}$

$= \frac{3+4}{7} = \frac{7}{7} = 1$

■ $\frac{8}{11} - \left(-\frac{2}{11}\right)$

$= \frac{8-(-2)}{11} = \frac{8+2}{11} = \frac{10}{11}$

EXERCISES

Add or subtract.

17. $\frac{-8}{13} + \frac{2}{13}$ 18. $\frac{3}{5} - \left(\frac{-4}{5}\right)$

19. $\frac{-2}{9} + \frac{7}{9}$ 20. $\frac{-5}{12} - \left(\frac{-7}{12}\right)$

21. $\frac{-9}{11} + \frac{10}{11}$ 22. $\frac{5}{13} - \frac{(-7)}{13}$

2-4 Multiplying Rational Numbers (pp. 78–81) NS1.2

EXAMPLE

■ Multiply. Write the answer in simplest form.

$5\left(3\frac{1}{4}\right) = \left(\frac{5}{1}\right)\left(\frac{3(4)+1}{4}\right)$

$= \left(\frac{5}{1}\right)\left(\frac{13}{4}\right)$ *Write as improper fractions.*

$= \frac{65}{4}$, or $16\frac{1}{4}$ *Multiply and simplify.*

EXERCISES

Multiply. Write each answer in simplest form.

23. $3\left(-\frac{2}{5}\right)$ 24. $2\left(3\frac{4}{5}\right)$

25. $\frac{-2}{3}\left(\frac{-4}{5}\right)$ 26. $\frac{8}{11}\left(\frac{-22}{4}\right)$

27. $5\frac{1}{4}\left(\frac{3}{7}\right)$ 28. $2\frac{1}{2}\left(1\frac{3}{10}\right)$

29. $4\frac{7}{8}\left(2\frac{2}{3}\right)$ 30. $-\frac{8}{9}\left(\frac{7}{16}\right)$

2-5 Dividing Rational Numbers (pp. 82–86) NS1.2, AF1.3

EXAMPLE

■ Divide. Write the answer in simplest form.

$\frac{7}{8} \div \frac{3}{4} = \frac{7}{8} \cdot \frac{4}{3}$ *Multiply by the reciprocal.*

$= \frac{7 \cdot \overset{1}{4}}{\underset{2}{8} \cdot 3}$ *Remove common factors.*

$= \frac{7 \cdot 1}{2 \cdot 3}$

$= \frac{7}{6}$, or $1\frac{1}{6}$

EXERCISES

Divide. Write each answer in simplest form.

31. $\frac{3}{4} \div \frac{1}{8}$ 32. $\frac{3}{10} \div \frac{4}{5}$

33. $\frac{2}{3} \div 3$ 34. $4 \div \frac{-1}{4}$

35. $3\frac{3}{4} \div 3$ 36. $1\frac{1}{3} \div \frac{2}{3}$

2-6 Adding and Subtracting with Unlike Denominators (pp. 87–91) NS1.2, NS2.2

EXAMPLE

■ Add.

$\frac{3}{4} + \frac{2}{5}$ *Multiply denominators, $4 \cdot 5 = 20$.*

$\frac{3 \cdot 5}{4 \cdot 5} = \frac{15}{20}$ $\frac{2 \cdot 4}{5 \cdot 4} = \frac{8}{20}$

$\frac{15}{20} + \frac{8}{20} = \frac{15+8}{20} = \frac{23}{20}$, or $1\frac{3}{20}$ *Add and simplify.*

EXERCISES

Add or subtract.

37. $\frac{5}{6} + \frac{1}{3}$ 38. $\frac{5}{6} - \frac{5}{9}$

39. $3\frac{1}{2} + 7\frac{4}{5}$ 40. $7\frac{1}{10} - 2\frac{3}{4}$

41. $\frac{19}{20} + \frac{7}{3}$ 42. $-1\frac{5}{9} - 7\frac{3}{4}$

Answers

17. $-\frac{6}{13}$

18. $\frac{7}{5}$

19. $\frac{5}{9}$

20. $\frac{1}{6}$

21. $\frac{1}{11}$

22. $\frac{12}{13}$

23. $-1\frac{1}{5}$

24. $7\frac{3}{5}$

25. $\frac{8}{15}$

26. -4

27. $2\frac{1}{4}$

28. $3\frac{1}{4}$

29. 13

30. $-\frac{7}{18}$

31. 6

32. $\frac{3}{8}$

33. $\frac{2}{9}$

34. -16

35. $\frac{5}{4}$

36. 2

37. $1\frac{1}{6}$

38. $\frac{5}{18}$

39. $11\frac{3}{10}$

40. $4\frac{7}{20}$

41. $3\frac{17}{60}$

42. $-9\frac{11}{36}$

2-7 One-Step Equations with Rational Numbers (pp. 94–97)  AF4.0

EXAMPLE

Solve.

■ $x - 13.7 = -22$

$\underline{+13.7 = +13.7}$ *Add 13.7 to each side.*

$x = -8.3$

■ $\frac{7}{9}x = \frac{2}{5}$

$\frac{9}{7} \cdot \frac{7}{9}x = \frac{9}{7} \cdot \frac{2}{5}$ *Multiply both sides by $\frac{9}{7}$*

$x = \frac{18}{35}$

EXERCISES

Solve.

43. $y + 7.8 = -14$ **44.** $2.9z = -52.2$

45. $w + \frac{3}{4} = \frac{1}{8}$ **46.** $\frac{3}{8}p = \frac{3}{4}$

47. $x - \frac{7}{9} = \frac{2}{11}$ **48.** $7.2x = -14.4$

49. $y - 18.7 = 25.9$ **50.** $\frac{19}{21}t = -\frac{38}{7}$

51. Freda paid $\$126$ for groceries for her family. This was $1\frac{1}{6}$ as much as she paid the previous time she shopped. How much did Freda pay on her previous shopping trip?

2-8 Two-Step Equations with Rational Numbers (pp. 98–101) AF4.1

EXAMPLE

Solve.

■ $7x + 12 = 33$

Think: First the variable is **multiplied by 7**, and then **12 is added**. To isolate the variable, subtract 12, and then **divide by 7**.

$7x + 12 = 33$

$\underline{-12 \quad -12}$ *Subtract 12 from both sides.*

$7x = 21$

$\frac{7x}{7} = \frac{21}{7}$ *Divide both sides by 7.*

$x = 3$

■ $\frac{z}{3} - 8 = 5$

Think: First the variable is **divided by 3**, and then **8 is subtracted**. To isolate the variable, add 8, and then **multiply by 3**.

$\frac{z}{3} - 8 = 5$

$\underline{+8 \quad +8}$ *Add 8 to both sides.*

$\frac{z}{3} = 13$

$3 \cdot \frac{z}{3} = 3 \cdot 13$ *Multiply both sides by 3.*

$z = 39$

EXERCISES

Solve.

52. $3m + 5 = 35$ **53.** $55 = 7 - 6y$

54. $2c + 1 = -31$ **55.** $5r + 15 = 0$

56. $\frac{t}{2} + 7 = 15$ **57.** $\frac{w}{4} - 5 = 11$

58. $-25 = \frac{r}{3} - 11$ **59.** $\frac{h}{5} - 9 = -19$

60. $\frac{x + 2}{3} = 18$ **61.** $\frac{d - 3}{4} = -9$

62. $21 = \frac{a - 4}{3}$ **63.** $14 = \frac{c + 8}{7}$

64. A music club charges an annual membership fee of $\$20.50$ plus $\$12.99$ for each CD purchased. If Naomi's total bill for the year was $\$163.39$, how many CDs did she purchase?

Write each decimal as a fraction in simplest form.

1. 0.225 $\frac{9}{40}$
2. 0.04 $\frac{1}{25}$
3. −0.101 $-\frac{101}{1000}$
4. 0.875 $\frac{7}{8}$
5. $0.0\overline{9}$ $\frac{1}{11}$
6. $0.\overline{12}$ $\frac{4}{33}$
7. $0.\overline{4}$ $\frac{4}{9}$
8. $0.1\overline{35}$ $\frac{5}{37}$

Write each fraction as a decimal.

9. $\frac{5}{8}$ 0.625
10. $-\frac{13}{25}$ −0.52
11. $\frac{5}{12}$ $0.41\overline{6}$
12. $\frac{4}{33}$ $0.\overline{12}$

Write the numbers in order from least to greatest.

13. $\frac{2}{3}$, −0.36, 0.2, $-\frac{1}{4}$ $-0.36, -\frac{1}{4}, 0.2, \frac{2}{3}$
14. 0.55, $-\frac{7}{8}$, −0.8, $\frac{5}{6}$ $-\frac{7}{8}, -0.8, 0.55, \frac{5}{6}$
15. $\frac{9}{10}$, 0.7, 1.6, $\frac{7}{5}$ $0.7, \frac{9}{10}, \frac{7}{5}, 1.6$

Add or subtract. Write each answer in simplest form.

16. $\frac{-3}{11} - \left(\frac{-4}{11}\right)$ $\frac{1}{11}$
17. 7.25 − 2.75 4.5
18. $\frac{5}{6} + \frac{7}{18}$ $1\frac{2}{9}$
19. $\frac{5}{6} - \frac{8}{9}$ $-\frac{1}{18}$
20. 4.5 + 5.875 10.375
21. $8\frac{1}{5} - 1\frac{2}{3}$ $6\frac{8}{15}$

Multiply or divide. Write each answer in simplest form.

22. 9(0.63) 5.67
23. $\frac{7}{8} \div \frac{5}{24}$ $4\frac{1}{5}$
24. $\frac{2}{3}\left(\frac{-9}{20}\right)$ $-\frac{3}{10}$
25. $3\frac{3}{7}\left(1\frac{5}{16}\right)$ $4\frac{1}{2}$
26. 34 ÷ 3.4 10
27. $-4\frac{2}{3} \div 1\frac{1}{6}$ −4

28. Kory is making Thai food for several friends. She needs to triple her recipe. The recipe calls for $\frac{3}{4}$ teaspoon of curry. How much curry does she need? $2\frac{1}{4}$ tsp

29. Lucie drank $\frac{3}{4}$ pint of bottled water. One serving of the water is $\frac{7}{8}$ pint. How much of a serving did Lucie drink? $\frac{6}{7}$

Solve.

30. $x - \frac{1}{4} = -\frac{3}{8}$ $-\frac{1}{8}$
31. −3.14y = 53.38 −17
32. $\frac{x+7}{12} = 11.9$ 135.8
33. $-2k = \frac{1}{4}$ $-\frac{1}{8}$
34. 2h − 3.24 = −1.1 1.07
35. 4m = −29 $-7\frac{1}{4}$
36. $\frac{4}{7}y + 7 = 31$ 42
37. $\frac{x-18}{32} = -3$ −78
38. $s - \frac{2}{3} = \frac{7}{8}$ $1\frac{13}{24}$

39. Rachel walked to a friend's house, then to the store, and then back home. The distance from Rachel's house to her friend's house is $1\frac{5}{6}$ miles. This is twice the distance from Rachel's house to the store. How far does Rachel live from the store? $\frac{11}{12}$ mi

40. Tickets to an orchestra concert cost $25.50 apiece plus a $2.50 handling fee for each order. If Jamal spent $79, how many tickets did he purchase? 3 tickets

Organizer

Objective: Assess students' mastery of concepts and skills in Chapter 2.

 Online Edition

Resources

 Assessment Resources

Chapter 2 Tests
• Free Response
  (Levels A, B, C)
• Multiple Choice
  (Levels A, B, C)
• Performance Assessment

IDEA Works! CD-ROM
Modified Chapter 2 Test

Test & Practice Generator
One-Stop Planner®

Standard	Items
NS1.1	13–15
NS1.2	16–29, 39
NS1.3	9–12
NS1.5	1–8
AF4.0	30–31, 33, 35, 38
AF4.1	32, 34, 36–37, 40

California Standards

Organizer

Objective: Provide review and practice for Chapters 1–2.

 Online Edition

Resources

 Assessment Resources
Chapter 2 Cumulative Test

 Focus on California Standards Benchmark Tests and Intervention

 California Standards Practice CD-ROM

go.hrw.com
KEYWORD: MT8CA Practice

California Standards	
Standard	**Items**
NS1.1	7
NS1.2 🔑	5, 9, 12, 13, 16, 18, 21, 22
NS1.3	6, 14–15
NS1.5 🔑	14
NS2.5 🔑	3, 17, 23
AF1.1	8, 20, 23
AF1.2	2
AF4.0 🔑	4, 10, 11
AF4.1 🔑	19, 20, 21
SDAP1.1	9

Cumulative Assessment, Chapters 1–2
Multiple Choice

1. What is the value of the expression $12 - k$ for $k = -3$?
- Ⓐ −15
- Ⓒ 9
- Ⓑ −9
- Ⓓ 15

2. Evaluate $2x - 5$ for $x = -4$.
- Ⓐ −13
- Ⓒ 3
- Ⓑ −3
- Ⓓ 13

3. Simplify $|10 - (-5)|$.
- Ⓐ −15
- Ⓒ 5
- Ⓑ −5
- Ⓓ 15

4. Which value of x is the solution of the equation $\frac{x}{3} = -12$?
- Ⓐ $x = -36$
- Ⓒ $x = -4$
- Ⓑ $x = -15$
- Ⓓ $x = 9$

5. A pitcher contains $\frac{3}{4}$ gallon of juice. If each glass will hold $\frac{1}{8}$ gallon of juice, how many glasses can be filled from the pitcher?
- Ⓐ $\frac{3}{32}$ glass
- Ⓒ 6 glasses
- Ⓑ $\frac{3}{4}$ glass
- Ⓓ 8 glasses

6. Skip drove 55.6 miles. Then he drove another $42\frac{1}{5}$ miles. How many miles did he drive in all?
- Ⓐ 97.7 miles
- Ⓒ 97.8 miles
- Ⓑ 98.5 miles
- Ⓓ 13.4 miles

7. Which number is greater than $\frac{3}{4}$?
- Ⓐ $\frac{4}{5}$
- Ⓒ $\frac{5}{8}$
- Ⓑ 0.75
- Ⓓ $0.\overline{6}$

8. Which expression represents 10 less than the quotient of a number and 3?
- Ⓐ $10 - \frac{n}{3}$
- Ⓒ $3n - 10$
- Ⓑ $10 - 3n$
- Ⓓ $\frac{n}{3} - 10$

9. According to the graph, what fraction of games resulted in something other than a tie?

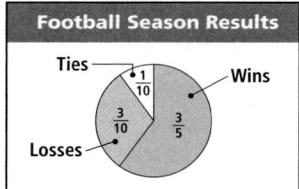
Football Season Results
Ties — $\frac{1}{10}$
Wins — $\frac{3}{5}$
Losses — $\frac{3}{10}$

- Ⓐ $\frac{9}{10}$
- Ⓒ $\frac{6}{15}$
- Ⓑ $\frac{3}{10}$
- Ⓓ $\frac{9}{50}$

10. Which value of x makes the equation $\frac{2}{3}x = -\frac{5}{6}$ true?
- Ⓐ $x = -\frac{5}{9}$
- Ⓒ $x = -1\frac{1}{4}$
- Ⓑ $x = \frac{1}{6}$
- Ⓓ $x = 1\frac{1}{4}$

11. If $\frac{3}{5} = 9s$, what is the value of s?
- Ⓐ 15
- Ⓒ $\frac{5}{3}$
- Ⓑ $\frac{27}{5}$
- Ⓓ $\frac{1}{15}$

12. Jeremy has started drinking $\frac{1}{4}$ cup of grape juice every Wednesday at lunch. If he has consumed a total of 5 cups of juice so far, how many Wednesdays has Jeremy had grape juice?
- Ⓐ 4
- Ⓒ 20
- Ⓑ 5
- Ⓓ 80

Multiple Choice For **Item 3**, students who answered **A** may think that the absolute value of a number and the opposite of a number are the same. Students who answered **B** or **C** may need to review subtraction of negative numbers.

For **Item 4**, students who answered **C** divided both sides by 3 instead of multiplying both sides by 3. If they make a similar mistake on **Item 10**, review solving equations by multiplying and dividing.

Answers

20. a. $C = 39m + 99$
  b. 18 months

22. $21\frac{1}{4} \div \frac{3}{4}$
  $\frac{85}{4} \cdot \frac{4}{3} = \frac{85}{3} = 28.\overline{3}$
  She can cut 28 pieces that are $\frac{3}{4}$ in. long.

23. See 4-Point Response work sample.

HOT TIP! Make sure you look at all the answer choices before making your decision. Try substituting each answer choice into the problem if you are unsure of the answer.

13. Oscar bought a bag of almonds. He ate $\frac{3}{8}$ of the bag on Sunday. On Monday, he ate $\frac{2}{3}$ of the almonds left. What fraction of the entire bag did he eat on Monday?

Ⓐ $\frac{9}{16}$ Ⓒ $\frac{1}{4}$

Ⓑ $\frac{5}{12}$ Ⓓ $\frac{1}{12}$

14. Which fraction converts to a terminating decimal?

Ⓐ $\frac{1}{6}$ Ⓒ $\frac{1}{8}$

Ⓑ $\frac{1}{7}$ Ⓓ $\frac{1}{9}$

15. Which fraction is the same as $18.\overline{6}$?

Ⓐ $\frac{93}{5}$ Ⓒ $\frac{55}{3}$

Ⓑ $\frac{54}{3}$ Ⓓ $\frac{56}{3}$

Gridded Response

16. The diameter of a standard CD is $4\frac{3}{4}$ in. The diameter of the circular hole in the middle is $\frac{1}{2}$ in. Find the distance from the edge of the hole to the outer edge of the CD. **2.125**

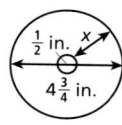

17. Simplify the expression $|-3 - 8|$. **11**

18. Alana has three times as many pairs of shoes as Marie. If Alana has 18 pairs of shoes, how many pairs of shoes does Marie have? **6**

19. What is the solution to the equation $\frac{2}{3}x - \frac{1}{6} = \frac{1}{3}$? **$\frac{3}{4}$**

Short Response

20. A health club charges a one-time fee of $99 and then $39 per month for membership. Let m represent the number of months, and let C represent the total amount of money spent on the health club membership.

a. Write an equation that relates m and C.

b. If Jillian has spent $801 on her membership, how many months has she been a member of the club?

21. Marla purchased a salad at the school cafeteria salad bar. She placed her salad on a plastic plate to be weighed. The scale read $7\frac{1}{8}$ ounces. **$6\frac{7}{8}$ oz**

a. Each plate weights $\frac{1}{4}$ ounce. What was the weight of Marla's salad?

b. Medium drinks cost $0.75. Marla paid a total of $3.50 for her salad and a medium drink. Write and solve an equation to find the cost per ounce of her salad.

$0.75 + 6\frac{7}{8}x = 3.50$; $0.40 per oz

22. Brigid has a $21\frac{1}{4}$ in. long ribbon. For a project she is cutting it into $\frac{3}{4}$ in. pieces. Into how many $\frac{3}{4}$ in. pieces can she cut the ribbon? Show or explain how you found your answer.

Extended Response

23. The sum of 7 and the absolute value of a number is equal to 12.

a. Write an equation that can be used to solve for the number.

b. Describe the first step of solving the equation.

c. Determine how many values make the equation true. Explain your reasoning.

Short Response Rubric
Items 20–22

2 Points = The student's answer is an accurate and complete execution of the task or tasks.

1 Point = The student's answer contains attributes of an appropriate response but is flawed.

0 Points = The student's answer contains no attributes of an appropriate response.

Extended Response Rubric
Item 23

4 Points = The student demonstrates a thorough understanding of all concepts and shows all work correctly.

3 Points = The student demonstrates a basic understanding of all concepts, but the work shows some flaws reflecting inattentive execution of mathematical procedures or some misunderstanding of the underlying mathematics.

2 Points = The student demonstrates only a partial understanding of the concepts or procedures embodied in the tasks. The approach may be correct, but the work shows a misunderstanding of one or more important concepts.

1 Point = The student demonstrates a very limited understanding of the concepts or procedures embodied in the tasks. The response may show some understanding but exhibits many flaws or is incomplete.

0 Points = The student has provided no response at all or a completely incorrect or uninterpretable response.

Student Work Samples for Item 23

4-Point Response

19 a) $7 + |x| = 12$

b) Subtract 7 from both sides so that the equation is $|x| = 5$.

$$\begin{array}{c} 7 + |x| = 12 \\ \underline{-7 \qquad -7} \\ |x| = 5 \end{array}$$

c) Two numbers make the sentence true, 5 and -5. This is because both 5 and -5 are 5 units from zero on the number line.

$\leftarrow$ 5 units $\rightarrow$|$\leftarrow$ 5 units $\rightarrow$|

-6 -4 -2 0 2 4 6

The student correctly wrote the equation, described the first step, found the number of solutions, and explained their reasoning.

3-Point Response

a) $|x| + 7 = 12$

b) $|x| + 7 = 12$
$\quad\ -7\ -7$
$\quad\ |x| = 5$

c) 2; They are both 5 units from 0.

All answers are correct, but the student did not describe the first step in part **b,** and the explanation in part **c** lacks clarity.

2-Point Response

a.) $|x| + 7 = 12$

b.) $12 - 7 = 5$

c.) one.

The answer to part **a** is correct, but the response in part **b** is inadequate and in part **c** shows a misunderstanding of the concept.

CHAPTER 3

Multi-Step Equations and Inequalities

✔	Grade-level Standard	
◀	Review	
▶	Beyond the Standards	
A	Assessment	
○	Optional	

Pacing Guide

Calendar Planner
Teacher's One-Stop Planner®

Lesson/Lab	California Standards	Time	Advanced Students	Benchmark* Students	Strategic** Students
3-1 Properities of Rational Numbers	⚷ AF1.3	50 min	✔	✔	✔
3-2 Simplifying Algebraic Expressions	⚷ AF1.3	50 min	✔	✔	✔
3-3 Solving Multi-Step Equations	Ext. of ⚷ AF4.1	50 min	○	○	▶
LAB Model Equations with Variables on Both Sides	Ext. of ⚷ AF4.1	25 min	○	▶	▶
3-4 Solving Equations with Variables on Both Sides	AF1.1, Ext. of ⚷ AF4.1	50 min	○	▶	▶
Ready to Go On?		25 min	A	A	A
Focus on Problem Solving		25 min	A	A	○
3-5 Inequalities	AF1.1	50 min	✔	✔	✔
3-6 Solving Inequalities by Adding or Subtracting	⚷ AF4.0	50 min	✔	✔	✔
3-7 Solving Inequalities by Multiplying or Dividing	AF1.1, ⚷ AF4.0	50 min	✔	✔	✔
3-8 Solving Two-Step Inequalities	⚷ AF4.1	75 min	✔	✔	✔
Ready to Go On?		25 min	A	A	A
Concept Connection		25 min	A	A	○
Study Guide: Review		50 min	✔	✔	✔
Chapter Test		50 min	A	A	A

* **Benchmark students** are achieving at or near grade level.

** **Strategic students** may be a year or more below grade level and may require additional time for intervention.

Countdown to Mastery, Weeks ⑤, ⑥

ONGOING ASSESSMENT and INTERVENTION

DIAGNOSE	PRESCRIBE

Assess Prior Knowledge

Before Chapter 3

Diagnose readiness for the chapter.
Are You Ready? SE p. 113

Prescribe intervention.
Are You Ready? Intervention Skills 42, 56, 58

Formative Assessment

Before Every Lesson

Diagnose readiness for the lesson.
Warm Up TE, every lesson

Prescribe intervention.
Skills Bank SE pp. SB2–SB24
Review for Mastery CRF, Chapters 1–3

During Every Lesson

Diagnose understanding of lesson concepts.
Questioning Strategies Chapter 3
Think and Discuss SE, every lesson
Write About It SE, lesson exercises
Journal TE, lesson exercises

Prescribe intervention.
Reading Strategies CRF, every lesson
Success for ELL Chapter 3
Lesson Tutorial Videos Chapter 3

After Every Lesson

Diagnose mastery of lesson concepts.
Lesson Quiz TE, every lesson
Ready to Go On? SE pp. 134, 152
Test and Practice Generator

Prescribe intervention.
Review for Mastery CRF, every lesson
Problem Solving CRF, every lesson
Ready to Go On? Intervention Chapter 3
Homework Help Online

Before Chapter 3 Testing

Diagnose mastery of concepts in the chapter.
Ready to Go On? SE pp. 134, 152
Focus on Problem Solving SE p. 135
Concept Connection SE p. 153
Section Quizzes AR pp. 45–46
Test and Practice Generator

Prescribe intervention.
Ready to Go On? Intervention Chapter 3
Scaffolding Questions TE p. 153

Before Assessment of California Standards

Diagnose mastery of California standards.
Focus on California Standards: Benchmark Tests
Mastering the Standards SE pp. 162–163
California Standards Practice CD-ROM

Prescribe intervention.
Focus on California Standards: Intervention

Summative Assessment

After Chapter 3

Check mastery of chapter concepts.
Multiple-Choice Tests (Forms A, B, C)
Free-Response Tests (Forms A, B, C)
Performance Assessment AR pp. 47–60
Test and Practice Generator

Prescribe intervention.
Review for Mastery CRF, every lesson
Lesson Tutorial Videos Chapter 3

KEY: **SE** = *Student Edition*   **TE** = *Teacher's Edition*   **CRF** = *Chapter Resource File*   **AR** = *Assessment Resources*   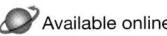 Available on CD-ROM   Available online

Supporting the Teacher

Chapter 3 Resource File

Family Involvement
pp. 1–4, 37–40

Practice A, B, C
pp. 5–7, 13–15, 21–23, 29–31, 41–43, 49–51, 57–59, 65–67

Review for Mastery
pp. 8, 16, 24, 32, 44, 52, 60, 68

Challenge
pp. 9, 17, 25, 33, 45, 53, 61, 69

Problem Solving
pp. 10, 18, 26, 34, 46, 54, 62, 70

Reading Strategies ELL
pp. 11, 19, 27, 35, 47, 55, 63, 71

Puzzles, Twisters, and Teasers
pp. 12, 20, 28, 36, 48, 56, 64, 72

Hands-On Lab
pp. 73–76, 84–85

Technology Lab
pp. 77–83

Workbooks

Homework and Practice Workbook SPANISH
Teacher's Guide .... pp. 18–25

Know-It Notebook SPANISH
Teacher's Guide .... Chapter 3

Review for Mastery Workbook SPANISH
Teacher's Guide .... pp. 18–25

Focus on California Standards: Intervention Workbook SPANISH
Teacher's Guide

Teacher Tools

Power Presentations
Complete PowerPoint® presentations for Chapter 3 lessons

Lesson Tutorial Videos SPANISH
Holt authors Ed Burger and Freddie Renfro present tutorials to support the Chapter 3 lessons.

Teacher's One-Stop Planner SPANISH
Easy access to all Chapter 3 resources and assessments, as well as software for lesson planning, test generation, and puzzle creation

IDEA Works!
Key Chapter 3 resources and assessments modified to address special learning needs

Questioning Strategies .... Chapter 3

Solutions Key .... Chapter 3

Interactive Answers and Solutions

TechKeys   ***Lab Resources***

Project Teacher Support   ***Parent Resources***

Transparencies

Lesson Transparencies, Volume 1 .... Chapter 3
• Teacher Tools
• Warm Ups
• Teaching Transparencies
• Lesson Quizzes

Know-It Notebook .... Chapter 3
• Vocabulary   • Chapter Review
• Additional Examples   • Big Ideas

Alternate Openers: Explorations .... pp. 18–25

Countdown to Mastery .... pp. 9–12

Technology Highlights for the Teacher

 Power Presentations
Dynamic presentations to engage students. Complete PowerPoint® presentations for every lesson in Chapter 3.

 One-Stop Planner SPANISH
Easy access to Chapter 3 resources and assessments. Includes lesson-planning, test-generation, and puzzle-creation software.

 Premier Online Edition SPANISH
Includes Tutorial Videos, Lesson Activities, Lesson Quizzes, Homework Help, Chapter Project and more.

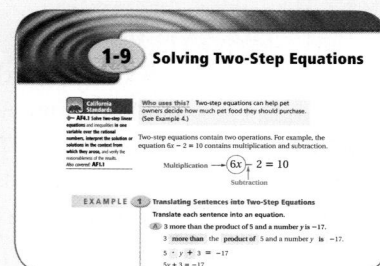

KEY: **SE** = *Student Edition*   **TE** = *Teacher's Edition*   English Language Learners   Spanish available   Available on CD-ROM    Available online

CHAPTER 3

Universal Access

Teaching tips to help all students appear throughout the chapter. A few that target specific students are included in the lists below.

Strategic Students

Practice A	CRF, every lesson
Review for Mastery	CRF, every lesson
Reading Strategies	CRF, every lesson
Academic Vocabulary Connections	TE p. 114
Visual	TE pp. 121, 137
Ready to Go On? Intervention	Chapter 3
Questioning Strategies	Chapter 3
Know-It Notebook SPANISH	Chapter 3
Homework Help Online 🪐	
Lesson Tutorial Videos 🪐 💿 SPANISH	
Online Interactivities 🪐 SPANISH	

Special Needs Students

Practice A	CRF, every lesson
Review for Mastery	CRF, every lesson
Reading Strategies	CRF, every lesson
Academic Vocabulary Connections	TE p. 114
Inclusion	TE p. 125
IDEA Works! Modified Resources	Chapter 3
Ready to Go On? Intervention	Chapter 3
Know-It Notebook SPANISH	Chapter 3
Lesson Tutorial Videos 🪐 💿 SPANISH	
Online Interactivities 🪐 SPANISH	

English Learners
ENGLISH LANGUAGE LEARNERS

Reading Strategies	CRF, every lesson
Vocabulary Review	SE p. 156
Academic Vocabulary Connections	TE p. 114
English Language Learners	TE pp. 120, 144
Language Support	TE p. 117
Success for English Language Learners	Chapter 3
Know-It Notebook SPANISH	Chapter 3
Multilingual Glossary 🪐	
Lesson Tutorial Videos 🪐 💿 SPANISH	

Benchmark Students

Practice B	CRF, every lesson
Problem Solving	CRF, every lesson
Academic Vocabulary Connections	TE p. 114
Ready to Go On? Intervention	Chapter 3
Questioning Strategies	Chapter 3
Know-It Notebook SPANISH	Chapter 3
Homework Help Online 🪐	
Online Interactivities 🪐 SPANISH	

Advanced Students

Practice C	CRF, every lesson
Challenge	CRF, every lesson
Reading and Writing Math **EXTENSION**	TE p. 115
Concept Connection **EXTENSION**	TE p. 153
Advanced Learners/GATE	TE p. 149
Ready to Go On? Enrichment	Chapter 3

Technology Highlights for Universal Access

💿 **Lesson Tutorial Videos** SPANISH

Starring Holt authors Ed Burger and Freddie Renfro! Live tutorials to support every lesson in Chapter 3.

🪐 **Multilingual Glossary**

Searchable glossary includes definitions in English, Spanish, Vietnamese, Chinese, Hmong, Korean, and other languages.

🪐 **Online Interactivities** SPANISH

Interactive tutorials provide visually engaging alternative opportunities to learn concepts and master skills.

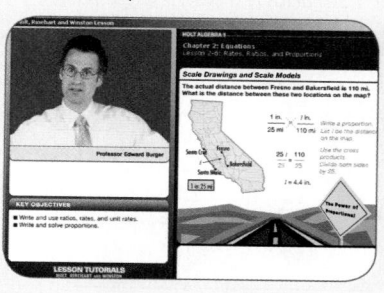

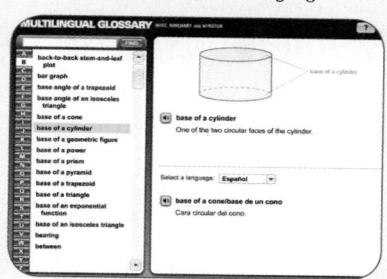

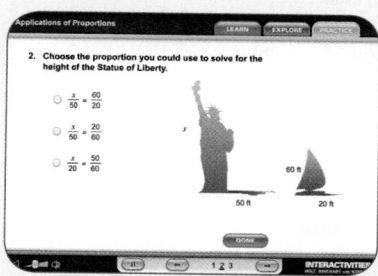

KEY: **SE** = *Student Edition* **TE** = *Teacher's Edition* **CRF** = *Chapter Resource File* SPANISH Spanish available 💿 Available on CD-ROM 🪐 Available online

CHAPTER 3

Ongoing Assessment

Assessing Prior Knowledge

Determine whether students have the prerequisite concepts and skills for success in Chapter 3.

Are You Ready? SPANISH .... SE p. 113
Warm Up .... TE, every lesson

Chapter and Standards Assessment

Provide review and practice for Chapter 3 and standards mastery.

Concept Connection .... SE p. 153
Study Guide: Review .... SE pp. 156–158
Strategies for Success .... SE pp. 160–161
Mastering the Standards .... SE pp. 162–163
Countdown to Mastery Transparencies ......pp. 9–12
Focus on California Standards: Benchmark Tests
Focus on California Standards: Intervention Workbook SPANISH
California Standards Practice CD-ROM SPANISH
IDEA Works! Modified Worksheets and Tests

Alternative Assessment

Assess students' understanding of Chapter 3 concepts and combined problem-solving skills.

Performance Assessment .... AR pp. 59–60
Portfolio Assessment .... AR p. xxxvi
Chapter 3 Project

Daily Assessment

Provide formative assessment for each day of Chapter 3.

Think and Discuss .... SE, every lesson
Write About It .... SE, lesson exercises
Journal .... TE, lesson exercises
Lesson Quiz .... TE, every lesson
Questioning Strategies .... Chapter 3
IDEA Works! Modified Lesson Quizzes .... Chapter 3

Weekly Assessment

Provide formative assessment for each week of Chapter 3.

Focus on Problem Solving .... SE p. 135
Concept Connection .... SE p. 153
Ready to Go On? SPANISH .... SE pp. 134, 152
Cumulative Assessment .... SE pp. 162–163
Test and Practice Generator SPANISH ...One-Stop Planner

Formal Assessment

Provide summative assessment of Chapter 3 mastery.

Section Quizzes .... AR pp. 45–46
Chapter 3 Test SPANISH .... SE p.159
Chapter Test (Levels A, B, C) .... AR pp. 47–58
    • Multiple-Choice • Free-Response
Cumulative Test .... AR pp. 61–64
Test and Practice Generator SPANISH ...One-Stop Planner
IDEA Works! Modified Tests .... Chapter 3

Technology Highlights for the Teacher

Are You Ready? SPANISH

Automatically assess readiness and prescribe intervention for Chapter 3 prerequisite skills.

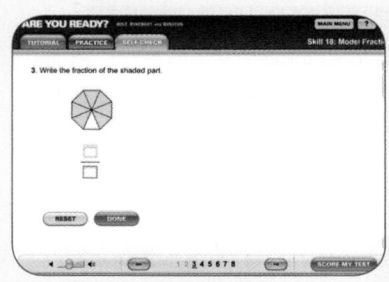

Ready to Go On? SPANISH

Automatically assess understanding of and prescribe intervention for Sections 3A and 3B.

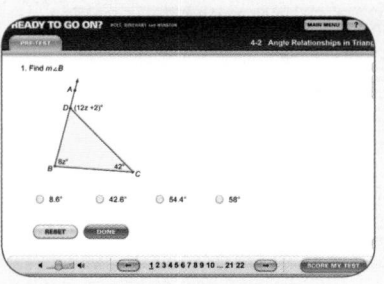

Focus on California Standards: Benchmark Tests and Intervention SPANISH

Automatically assess proficiency with California Grade 7 Standards and provide intervention.

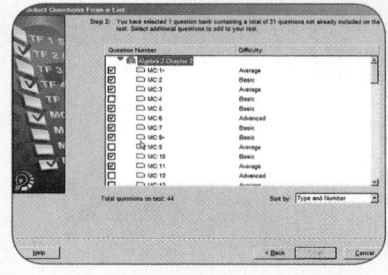

KEY: **SE** = *Student Edition* **TE** = *Teacher's Edition* **AR** = *Assessment Resources* SPANISH Spanish available Available on CD-ROM Available online

Formal Assessment

Three levels (A, B, C) of multiple-choice and free-response chapter tests are available in the *Assessment Resources.*

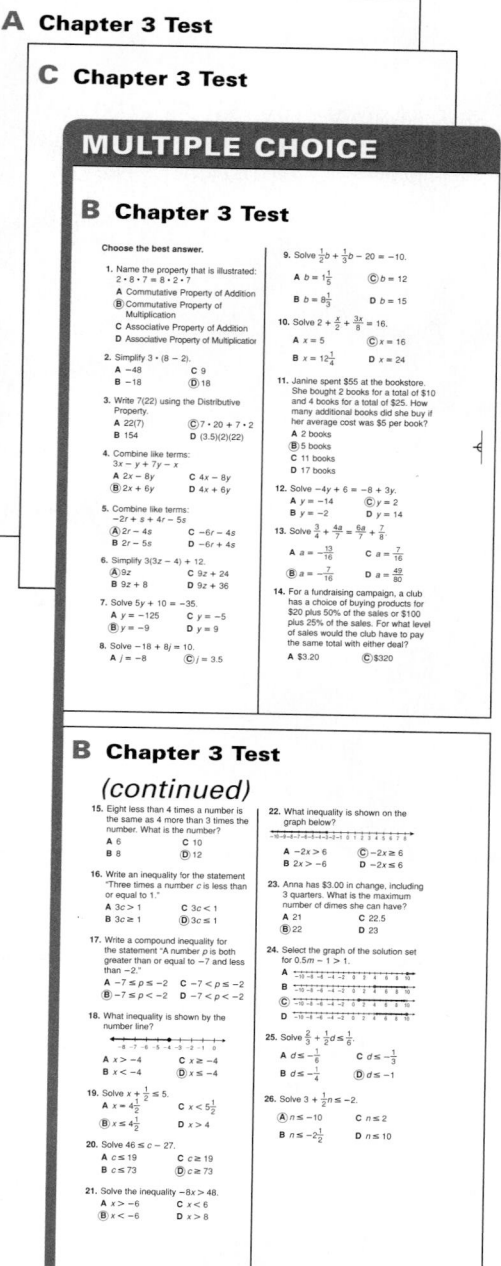

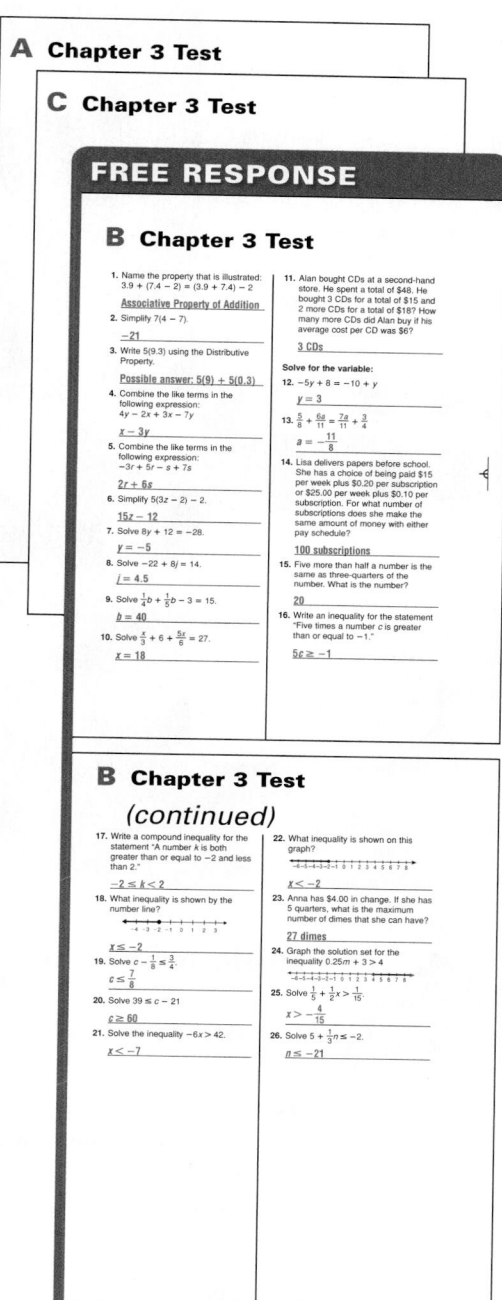

Modified tests and worksheets found in IDEA Works!

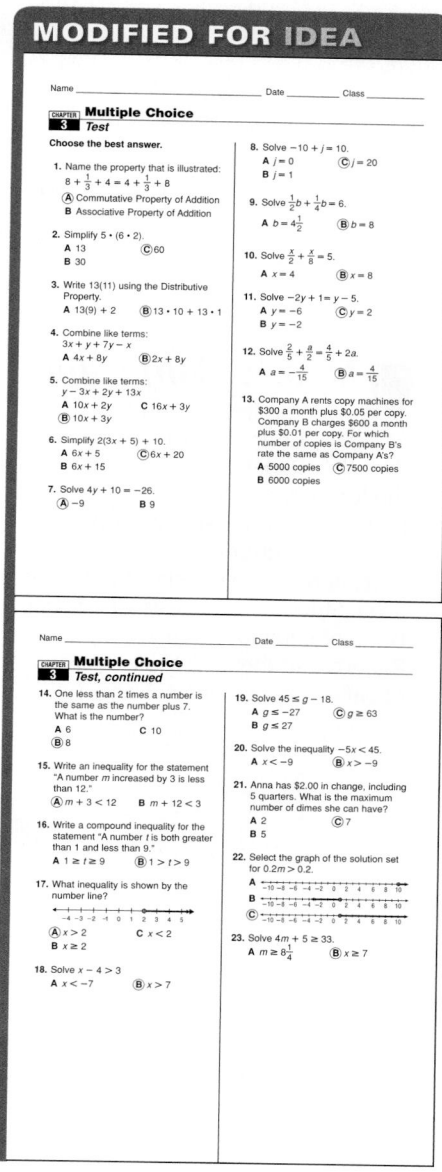

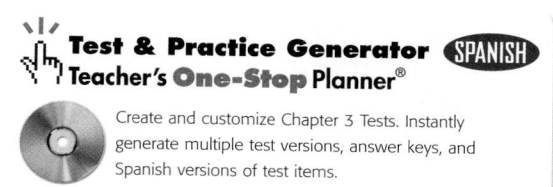

Test & Practice Generator SPANISH
Teacher's One-Stop Planner®

Create and customize Chapter 3 Tests. Instantly generate multiple test versions, answer keys, and Spanish versions of test items.

112F

Multi-Step Equations and Inequalities

 **Focus on Problem Solving**

On page 135, students focus on solving real-world problems by writing an equation that represents the steps.

CONCEPT CONNECTION On page 153, students write inequalities to model different scenarios for the cost of renting an ice rink.

CONCEPT CONNECTION

go.hrw.com
Chapter Project Online
KEYWORD: MT8CA Ch3

Equations and inequalities can describe how fast water is flowing in streams and rivers.

Merced River, Yosemite National Park

Math in *California*

The flow rate of the Merced River in Yosemite National Park varies depending on the location and time of year. Hydrologists can use equations to model the current speed, water volume, and discharge rate of the Merced River. Students will investigate these types of equations in the Chapter Project, and they will solve similar equations in Lessons 3-3 and 3-4.

 **PROBLEM SOLVING**

Problem Solving Project

Understand, Plan, Solve, and Look Back

Have students:

• Complete the Water Flows Downhill worksheet.

• Create an equation for calculating river discharge by relating water velocity (m/s) and stream cross section (m^2).

• Draw a picture to visualize the equation, showing river discharge, water velocity, and stream cross section.

• Research to discover facts about a local river.

Science Connection

Project Resources
All project resources for teachers and students are provided online.

Materials:
• Water Flows Downhill worksheet

go.hrw.com
Project Teacher Support
KEYWORD: MT8CA PSProject3

ARE YOU READY?

✓ Vocabulary

Choose the best term from the list to complete each sentence.

1. A letter that represents a value that can change is called a(n) __?__. **variable**

2. A(n) __?__ has one or more variables. **algebraic expression**

3. A(n) __?__ is a mathematical sentence that uses an equal sign to show that two expressions have the same value. **equation**

4. A mathematical phrase that contains operations and numbers is called a(n) __?__. It does not have an equal sign. **numerical expression**

algebraic expression
equation
numerical expression
variable

Complete these exercises to review skills you will need for this chapter.

✓ Operations with Fractions

Evaluate each expression.

5. $\frac{2}{3} - \frac{1}{2}$ $\frac{1}{6}$ 6. $\frac{13}{18} + \frac{19}{24}$ $1\frac{37}{72}$ 7. $\frac{7}{8}\left(\frac{6}{11}\right)$ $\frac{21}{44}$ 8. $\frac{9}{10} \div \frac{9}{13}$ $1\frac{3}{10}$

9. $\frac{5}{6}\left(\frac{8}{15}\right)$ $\frac{4}{9}$ 10. $\frac{11}{12} \div \frac{121}{144}$ $1\frac{1}{11}$ 11. $\frac{1}{6} + \frac{5}{8}$ $\frac{19}{24}$ 12. $\frac{19}{20} - \frac{4}{5}$ $\frac{3}{20}$

✓ Solve One-Step Equations

Use mental math to solve each equation.

13. $x - 7 = -21$ -14 14. $p + 3 = 22$ 19   15. $14 + v = 30$ 16

16. $b - 5 = 6$ 11   17. $t + 33 = -14$ -47 18. $w + 7 = -7$ -14

✓ Connect Words and Equations

Write an equation to represent each situation.

19. The perimeter P of a rectangle is the sum of twice the length ℓ and twice the width w. $P = 2\ell + 2w$

20. The volume V of a rectangular prism is the product of its three dimensions: length ℓ, width w, and height h. $V = \ell wh$

21. The surface area S of a sphere is the product of 4π and the square of the radius r. $S = 4\pi r^2$

22. The cost c of a telegram of 18 words is the cost f of the first 10 words plus the cost a of each additional word. $c = f + 8a$

Organizer

Objective: Help students understand the new concepts they will learn in Chapter 3.

Academic Vocabulary Connections

Becoming familiar with the academic vocabulary on this student page will be helpful to students. Discussing some of the vocabulary terms in the chapter also may be helpful. Possible answers given.

1. The word *equivalent* contains the same root as the word *equal*. What do you think **equivalent expressions** are? Equivalent expressions are expressions that are equal.

2. The word *simplify* means "make less complicated." What do you think it means to **simplify** an expression? To simplify an expression is to make it less complicated.

3. The adjective *like* means "alike." What do you suppose **like terms** are? Like terms are terms that are alike or similar.

Unpacking the Standards

The information below "unpacks" the standards. The academic vocabulary is highlighted and defined to help you understand the language of the standards. Refer to the lessons listed after each standard for help with the math terms and phrases. The Chapter Concept shows how the standard is applied in this chapter.

California Standard	Academic Vocabulary	Chapter Concept
AF1.1 Use variables and appropriate operations to write an expression, an equation, **an inequality, or a system of** equations or **inequalities that represents a verbal description** (e.g., three less than a number, half as large as area A). (Lesson 3-5)	**variable** a **symbol**, usually a letter, used to show an amount that can change **Example:** *x* **verbal** using words	You rewrite a verbal statement using mathematical symbols. **Example:** a number is greater than −5 $n > -5$
AF1.3 Simplify numerical expressions by applying properties of rational numbers (e.g., identity, inverse, **distributive, associative, commutative) and justify the process used.** (Lessons 3-1 and 3-2)	**property** a characteristic of numbers, operations, or equations **Example:** One property of addition is that you can add numbers in any order without changing the sum. **justify** give a reason for	You use mathematical properties to simplify expressions. You give reasons for each step when you simplify expressions.
AF4.0 Students solve simple linear equations and **inequalities over the rational numbers.** (Lessons 3-6 and 3-7)	**solve** find the value or values of an unknown quantity that make one side of an equation equal to the other side (make the equation true)	You find the values of a variable that make an inequality true.
AF4.1 Solve two-step linear equations and **inequalities in one variable over the rational numbers, interpret the solutions in the context from which they arose,** and verify the reasonableness of the results. (Lesson 3-8)	**interpret** to understand and explain the meaning of **context** in this case, a real-world situation	You understand and can explain the meaning of solutions to inequalities.

Looking Back

Previously, students

- wrote and evaluated algebraic expressions in word problems.
- solved two-step equations with rational numbers.
- compared and ordered rational numbers.

In This Chapter

Students will study

- finding solutions to application problems using algebraic equations.
- solving multi-step equations.
- solving inequalities.

Looking Forward

Students can use these skills

- to write an inequality that represents a verbal description.
- to solve equations and inequalities involving absolute values.

 **Reading and Writing Math**

Reading Strategy: Read a Lesson for Understanding

Before you begin reading a lesson, find out which standard or standards are the main focus of the lesson. These standards are located at the top of the first page of the lesson. Reading with the standards in mind will help guide you through the lesson material. You can use the following tips to help you follow the math as you read.

Lesson Features

Reading Tips

Identify the standard or standards of the lesson. Then skim through the lesson to get a sense of how the standards are covered.

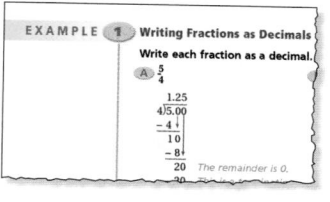

Work through each example. The examples help to demonstrate the standards.

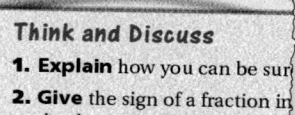 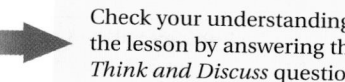

Check your understanding of the lesson by answering the *Think and Discuss* questions.

 **Try This**

Use Lesson 3-1 in your textbook to answer each question.

1. What is the standard of the lesson?

2. What questions or problems did you have when you read the lesson?

3. Write your own example problem similar to Example 1.

4. What skill is being practiced in the second *Think and Discuss* question?

Organizer

Objective: Help students apply strategies to understand and retain key concepts.

 Online Edition

Resources

 Chapter 3 Resource File
Reading Strategies

Reading Strategy: Read a Lesson for Understanding

Discuss Students that do not understand why they are learning certain math skills will often become frustrated.

Remind students that paying attention to the standard or standards of the lesson will help them remember when and how to apply what they learn.

Extend Each time students complete a lesson in Chapter 3, ask whether they have met the lesson standards. Discuss how meeting the standards will help them in a real-life situation, pointing out word problems from the exercises or the examples.

Answers to *Try This*

1. Simplify numerical expressions by applying properties of rational numbers (e.g., identity, inverse, distributive, associative, commutative) and justify the process used.

2. Students' answers will vary.

3. Check students' work.

4. Possible answer: Using the Distributive Property to simplify numerical expressions.

SECTION
3A

Solving Multi-Step Equations

One-Minute Section Planner

Lesson	Lab Resources	Materials
Lesson 3-1 Properties of Rational Numbers • Identify properties of rational numbers and use them to simplify numerical expressions. 🐻 🔑 **AF1.3**		
Lesson 3-2 Simplifying Algebraic Expressions • Combine like terms in an expression. 🐻 🔑 **AF1.3**	**Hands-On Lab 3-2** In *Chapter 3 Resource File*	**Optional** Cut-out shapes
Lesson 3-3 Solving Multi-Step Equations • Solve multi-step equations. 🐻 **Ext. of 🔑 AF4.1**	**Technology Lab 3-3** In *Chapter 3 Resource File*	Algebra tiles (MK), note cards
3-4 Hands-On Lab Model Equations with Variables on Both Sides • Use algebra tiles to model equations with variables on both sides. 🐻 **Ext. of 🔑 AF4.1**		**Required** Algebra tiles (MK)
Lesson 3-4 Solving Equations with Variables on Both Sides • Solve equations with variables on both sides of the equal sign. 🐻 **AF1.1, Ext. of 🔑 AF4.1**	**Technology Lab 3-4** In *Chapter 3 Resource File*	**Optional** Algebra tiles (MK), index cards

MK = *Manipulatives Kit*

Math Background: Teaching the Standards

PROPERTIES OF NUMBERS AND OPERATIONS 🐻 🔑 AF1.3

Lesson 3-1

A *binary operation* is an arithmetic operation on two numbers. For example, addition, subtraction, multiplication, and division are all binary operations because they give rules for operating on a pair of numbers.

A binary operation is *commutative* if the order of the two numbers does not affect the result. Addition and multiplication are commutative, whereas subtraction and division are not.

Binary operations only tell us how to put two numbers together, so additional information is needed when an operation is used to combine three or more numbers, such as $8 + 4 + 7$. An operation is *associative* if you can group the numbers in any order without affecting the answer. Addition and multiplication are associative. For example, the Associative Property of Addition says that to simplify $8 + 4 + 7$, the 8 and 4 may be added first, or the 4 and 7 may be added first. In other words,

$$(8 + 4) + 7 = 8 + (4 + 7).$$

It is instructive to consider an operation that is not associative, such as subtraction. In this case, the grouping of the numbers affects the result: $(11 - 7) - 3 \neq 11 - (7 - 3)$. Therefore, to simplify an expression without parentheses, such as $11 - 7 - 3$, additional rules are needed and this is where the order of operations comes into play.

A third property, the Distributive Property, explains how addition and multiplication work together. The property can be illustrated through an area model, as shown in the figure.

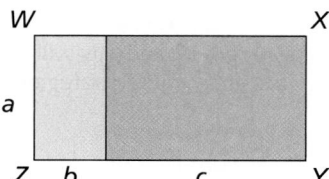

The area of rectangle *WXYZ* is equal to the product of its length and its width, or $a(b + c)$.

The area of rectangle *WXYZ* is also equal to the area of the yellow rectangle plus the area of the blue rectangle, or $ab + ac$. Setting the two area expressions equal gives $a(b + c) = ab + ac$.

Students sometimes wonder why complex names, such as the Commutative Property of Addition, are needed for "obvious" statements, such as $2 + 3 = 3 + 2$. As they begin to develop more-sophisticated algebraic thinking, students should understand that these properties provide the logical foundations of algebra and justify the steps that are used in simplifying algebraic expressions.

SIMPLIFYING EXPRESSIONS 🐻 🔑 AF1.3

Lesson 3-2

In Lesson 3-2, students learn to simplify expressions by combining like terms. The Commutative, Associative, and Distributive Properties make this possible, since they give the justification for rearranging and regrouping terms in an algebraic expression. In particular, combining like terms is nothing more than an application of the Distributive Property. Students may quickly write $4x + 5x = 9x$, but the intermediate step shown below illustrates that the Distributive Property is at work.

$$4x + 5x = (4 + 5)x = 9x$$

SOLVING MORE-COMPLEX EQUATIONS

Lessons 3-3, 3-4

As students learn to solve multi-step equations and equations with variables on both sides, they should be aware that the overall strategy for solving equations is unchanged. That is, the original equation should be transformed into a series of simpler equivalent equations until the variable is isolated. Each stage of this process requires an application of one or more properties of rational numbers or properties of equality. Students must remember to check their solution in the *original* equation. If the solution does not check, at least one of the equations along the way was not equivalent to the original equation. This can happen, for instance, if one squares both sides of an equation.

Online Edition
Tutorial Videos

Countdown to Mastery Week 5

Power Presentations
with PowerPoint®

Warm Up

Add or subtract.

1. $2.5 - 3.7$ -1.2
2. $\frac{1}{5} + \frac{3}{4}$ $\frac{19}{20}$
3. $\frac{5}{6} - \frac{1}{3}$ $\frac{1}{2}$

Multiply or divide.

4. $9\left(\frac{2}{3}\right)$ 6
5. $0.03(4.8)$ 0.144
6. $-12 \div 1.5$ -8

Also available on transparency

Math Humor

Q: Why do math teachers make good real-estate agents?
A: They know lots of properties.

California Standards

AF1.3 Simplify numerical expressions by applying properties of rational numbers (e.g., identity, inverse, **distributive**, **associative**, **commutative**) and justify the process used.

Why learn this? You can use mental math and properties of rational numbers to calculate costs when shopping. (See Exercises 40 and 41.)

In Chapter 2, you performed operations with rational numbers. The following properties are useful when you simplify expressions that contain rational numbers.

Vocabulary
Commutative Property
Associative Property
Distributive Property

PROPERTIES OF ADDITION AND MULTIPLICATION		
Words	**Numbers**	**Algebra**
Commutative Property You can add numbers in any order. You can multiply numbers in any order.	$3 + 4\frac{1}{2} = 4\frac{1}{2} + 3$ $2 \cdot 17 = 17 \cdot 2$	$a + b = b + a$ $ab = ba$
Associative Property When you are only adding or only multiplying, changing the grouping will not affect the sum or product.	$(6 + 8) + 9 = 6 + (8 + 9)$ $\left(2 \cdot \frac{1}{8}\right) \cdot 16 = 2 \cdot \left(\frac{1}{8} \cdot 16\right)$	$(a + b) + c = a + (b + c)$ $(a \cdot b) \cdot c = a \cdot (b \cdot c)$

EXAMPLE 1 Identifying Properties of Addition and Multiplication

Name the property that is illustrated in each equation.

A $3 \cdot (4 \cdot x) = (3 \cdot 4) \cdot x$
$3 \cdot (4 \cdot x) = (3 \cdot 4) \cdot x$ *The factors are grouped differently.*

Associative Property of Multiplication

B $(-9) + 2 = 2 + (-9)$
$(-9) + 2 = 2 + (-9)$ *The order of the numbers changed.*

Commutative Property of Addition

You can use the properties of rational numbers to rearrange or regroup numbers in a way that helps you do math mentally.

---

1 Introduce

Alternate Opener

EXPLORATION

3-1 Properties of Rational Numbers

Look for patterns to explore properties of rational numbers.

1. Find each sum or product.
   a. $3\frac{1}{2} + 1\frac{1}{2}$ b. $1\frac{1}{2} + 3\frac{1}{2}$
   c. $5.1 + 2.8$ d. $2.8 + 5.1$
   e. $\frac{1}{3} \times \frac{1}{4}$ f. $\frac{1}{4} \times \frac{1}{3}$
   g. 2×3.1 h. 3.1×2

2. Complete the following statement: If a and b are rational numbers, then $a + b =$ ___ and $a \times b =$ ___.

3. Find each sum or product. (*Hint:* The order of operations states that you must first simplify expressions in parentheses.)
   a. $3 + (1.2 + 4.1)$ b. $(3 + 1.2) + 4.1$
   c. $\frac{1}{7} + \left(\frac{2}{7} + \frac{4}{7}\right)$ d. $\left(\frac{1}{7} + \frac{2}{7}\right) + \frac{4}{7}$
   e. $2 \times (2 \times 1.1)$ f. $(2 \times 2) \times 1.1$
   g. $3 \times \left(\frac{1}{3} \times 2\right)$ h. $\left(3 \times \frac{1}{3}\right) \times 2$

4. Complete the following statement: If a, b, and c are rational numbers, then $a + (b + c) =$ ___ and $a \times (b \times c) =$ ___.

Think and Discuss
5. **Explain** whether the order of the numbers makes a difference when you subtract two rational numbers. Give an example.
6. **Describe** two different ways to calculate $7 + 5.2 + 3.8$ by adding parentheses to the expression.

Motivate

Write the following sum on the board: $13 + 19 + 7 + 11$. Ask students how they would use mental math to find the sum. If no one suggests it, show students how reordering and regrouping the numbers can make the sum easier to calculate: $(13 + 7) + (19 + 11)$. Explain that the properties students will learn in this lesson provide helpful strategies for mental math.

Explorations and answers are provided in *Alternate Openers: Explorations Transparencies.*

California Standards

Algebra and Functions 1.3

EXAMPLE 2 Using the Commutative and Associative Properties

Simplify each expression. Justify each step.

A 43 + 29 + 7

$$43 + 29 + 7 = 43 + 7 + 29 \qquad \textit{Commutative Property of Addition}$$
$$= (43 + 7) + 29 \qquad \textit{Associative Property of Addition}$$
$$= 50 + 29 = 79 \qquad \textit{Add.}$$

B $15 \cdot 7 \cdot \frac{1}{5}$

$$15 \cdot 7 \cdot \frac{1}{5} = 15 \cdot \frac{1}{5} \cdot 7 \qquad \textit{Commutative Property of Multiplication}$$
$$= \left(15 \cdot \frac{1}{5}\right) \cdot 7 \qquad \textit{Associative Property of Multiplication}$$
$$= 3 \cdot 7 = 21 \qquad \textit{Multiply.}$$

Helpful Hint

Compatible numbers help you do math mentally. Try to make multiples of 5 or 10. They are simpler to use when multiplying.

The Distributive Property is also helpful when you do math mentally.

Possible answers to Think and Discuss

1. Use the Associative Property to regroup the numbers as $(5.8 + 0.2) + 4$.

DISTRIBUTIVE PROPERTY		
Numbers	$7(6 + 12) = 7 \cdot 6 + 7 \cdot 12$	$5(7 - 3) = 5 \cdot 7 - 5 \cdot 3$
Algebra	$a(b + c) = a \cdot b + a \cdot c$	$a(b - c) = a \cdot b - a \cdot c$

When you need to find the product of two numbers, write one of the numbers as a sum or difference. Then use the Distributive Property to help you find the product mentally.

EXAMPLE 3 Using the Distributive Property

Write each product using the Distributive Property. Then simplify.

A 5(43)

$$5(43) = 5(40 + 3) \qquad \textit{Rewrite 43 as a sum.}$$
$$= 5 \cdot 40 + 5 \cdot 3 \qquad \textit{Distributive Property}$$
$$= 200 + 15 = 215 \qquad \textit{Multiply. Then add.}$$

Helpful Hint

Break the larger factor into a sum or difference that contains a multiple of 10.

B 6(28)

$$6(28) = 6(30 - 2) \qquad \textit{Rewrite 28 as a difference.}$$
$$= 6 \cdot 30 - 6 \cdot 2 \qquad \textit{Distributive Property}$$
$$= 180 - 12 = 168 \qquad \textit{Multiply. Then subtract.}$$

2. $8 \cdot 45 = 8(40 + 5) = 8 \cdot 40 + 8 \cdot 5 = 320 + 40 = 360$ or $8 \cdot 45 = 8(50 - 5) = 8 \cdot 50 - 8 \cdot 5 = 400 - 40 = 360$

Think and Discuss

1. **Explain** which property you would use to simplify $5.8 + (0.2 + 4)$.

2. **Describe** two ways to use the Distributive Property to find $8 \cdot 45$.

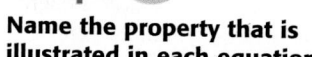

Power Presentations with PowerPoint®

Additional Examples

Example 1

Name the property that is illustrated in each equation.

A. $(-4) \cdot 9 = 9 \cdot (-4)$
Comm. Prop. of Mult.

B. $\left(5 + \frac{3}{4}\right) + \frac{1}{4} = 5 + \left(\frac{3}{4} + \frac{1}{4}\right)$
Assoc. Prop. of Add.

Example 2

Simplify each expression. Justify each step.

A. $29 + 37 + 1$
$= 29 + 1 + 37$ (Comm. Prop. of Add.)
$= (29 + 1) + 37$ (Assoc. Prop. of Add.)
$= 30 + 37$ (Add) $= 67$

B. $7 \cdot \frac{2}{9} \cdot \frac{1}{7}$
$= 7 \cdot \frac{1}{7} \cdot \frac{2}{9}$ (Comm. Prop. of Mult.)
$= \left(7 \cdot \frac{1}{7}\right) \cdot \frac{2}{9}$ (Assoc. Prop. of Mult.)
$= 1 \cdot \frac{2}{9}$ (Mult.) $= \frac{2}{9}$

Example 3

Write each product using the Distributive Property. Then simplify.

A. $9(31)$ $\quad 9 \cdot 30 + 9 \cdot 1 = 279$

B. $8(59)$ $\quad 8 \cdot 60 - 8 \cdot 1 = 472$

Also available on transparency

---

2 Teach

Guided Instruction

In this lesson, students learn to identify properties of rational numbers and use these properties to simplify numerical expressions. As you present each property, show students how to write the property using variables. Then illustrate it with numbers.

 **Language Support** Point out that in everyday language *distribute* means to deliver or share. The Distributive Property describes how one factor is shared among two or more terms in an expression.

 **Universal Access**
Through Cognitive Strategies

Students can remember the properties in this lesson by considering the everyday meanings of *commute* and *associate*. For example, when you commute to work, you go back and forth from home to office. In the same way, the Commutative Property says that numbers can move back and forth. Similarly, the Associative Property describes how numbers may be grouped; that is, how they *associate* with each other.

3 Close

Summarize

Ask students to write their own examples that illustrate each of the following properties.

1. Commutative Property of Addition
Possible answer: $7 + 3.8 = 3.8 + 7$

2. Associative Property of Multiplication
Possible answer: $8 \cdot (5 \cdot 4) = (8 \cdot 5) \cdot 4$

3. Distributive Property
Possible answer: $4(9 + 6) = 4 \cdot 9 + 4 \cdot 6$

California Standards Practice
← AF1.3

go.hrw.com
Homework Help Online
KEYWORD: MT8CA 3-1
Parent Resources Online
KEYWORD: MT8CA Parent

Assignment Guide

If you finished Example **1** assign:
Proficient 1–2, 15–16, 29–34, 52–61
Advanced 15–16, 40–46, 52–61

If you finished Example **2** assign:
Proficient 1–8, 15–20, 29–36, 52–61
Advanced 15–16, 18–22, 37, 40–49, 51–61

If you finished Example **3** assign:
Proficient 1–14, 15–20, 23–26, 29–36, 38–39, 52–61
Advanced 15–16, 18–22, 24–28, 37–61

Homework Quick Check

Quickly check key concepts.
Exercises: 16, 18, 20, 24, 28

Math Background

The Associative Property is needed because addition and multiplication are only defined for pairs of numbers. In order to make sense of an expression such as 7 + 3 + 12, the Associative Property states that the numbers may be grouped as (7 + 3) + 12 or as 7 + (3 + 12). In either case, the grouping restricts each sum to a pair of numbers and the property states that both groupings give the same result.

GUIDED PRACTICE

See Example **1** Name the property that is illustrated in each equation.

1. $y + 16 = 16 + y$ Comm. Prop. of Add. **2.** $(-5) \cdot 12 = 12 \cdot (-5)$ Comm. Prop. of Mult.

See Example **2** Simplify each expression. Justify each step.

3. $17 + 19 + 3$ **39**   **4.** $51 + 48 + 9$ **108**   **5.** $4 \cdot 7 \cdot 25$ **700**

6. $\frac{1}{3} \cdot 8 \cdot 9$ **24**   **7.** $5 \cdot (13 \cdot 2)$ **130**   **8.** $\frac{1}{4} + 3 + \frac{3}{4}$ **4**

See Example **3** Write each product using the Distributive Property. Then simplify.

9. $8(21)$ **168**   **10.** $5(62)$ **310**   **11.** $3(18)$ **54**

12. $6(49)$ **294**   **13.** $4(99)$ **396**   **14.** $(59)5$ **295**

INDEPENDENT PRACTICE

See Example **1** Name the property that is illustrated in each equation.

15. $4x = x \cdot 4$ Comm. Prop. of Mult.   **16.** $(7 \cdot 1.5) \cdot 2 = 7 \cdot (1.5 \cdot 2)$ Assoc. Prop. of Mult.

See Example **2** Simplify each expression. Justify each step.

17. $4 + 89 + 16$ **109**   **18.** $(0.5 \cdot 9) \cdot 2$ **9**   **19.** $2 \cdot 13 \cdot 50$ **1300**

20. $69 + 17 + 1$ **87**   **21.** $8.8 + (15 + 0.2)$ **24**   **22.** $\left(\frac{1}{4} \cdot 9\right) \cdot 12$ **27**

See Example **3** Write each product using the Distributive Property. Then simplify.

23. $7(19)$ **133**   **24.** $(53)4$ **212**   **25.** $12(11)$ **132**

26. $(98)2$ **196**   **27.** $\frac{1}{2}(42)$ **21**   **28.** $\frac{1}{3}(87)$ **29**

PRACTICE AND PROBLEM SOLVING

Extra Practice
See page EP6.

Name the property that is illustrated in each equation.

29. $7(9 - x) = 7 \cdot 9 - 7x$ Distrib. Prop.   **30.** $16 + 0 = 16$ Ident. Prop. of Add.   **31.** $(5 + y) + z = 5 + (y + z)$ Assoc. Prop. of Add.

32. $9 \cdot 1 = 9$ Ident. Prop. of Mult.   **33.** $m + 12n = 12n + m$ Comm. Prop. of Add.   **34.** $3(2 + t) = 3 \cdot 2 + 3t$ Distrib. Prop.

Simplify each expression. Justify each step.

35. $13 + 9 + 7 + 11$ **40**   **36.** $4 \cdot 3 \cdot 25 \cdot 2$ **600**   **37.** $6\frac{1}{2} + 7\frac{2}{5} + \frac{1}{2} + \frac{3}{5}$ **15**

38. **Consumer Math** Mikiko is buying five DVDs at SaveMart. How can she use the Distributive Property to find the total cost of the DVDs before tax? **$90**

39. **Consumer Math** Jerome is buying a DVD, a pair of jeans, and a t-shirt at SaveMart. Show how he can use properties of rational numbers to find the total cost of the items before tax. **$53**

SaveMart Price List	
Item	**Price**
DVD	$18
Jeans	$23
T-Shirt	$12

California Standards

Standard	Exercises
NS1.2 ←	58–61
NS1.5 ←	54–57
AF1.3 ←	1–53

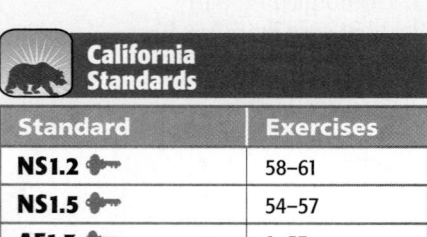

REVIEW FOR MASTERY 3-1

Review for Mastery
3-1 *Properties of Rational Numbers*

You can use the Commutative Property, the Associative Property, and the Distributive Property with mental math to simplify expressions.

$20 \cdot 9 \cdot \frac{1}{4} = 20 \cdot \frac{1}{4} \cdot 9$ Commutative Property of Multiplication
$= \left(20 \cdot \frac{1}{4}\right) \cdot 9$ Associative Property of Multiplication
$= 5 \cdot 9$ Multiply.
$= 45$ Multiply.

$7(22) = 7(20 + 2)$ Rewrite 22 as a sum.
$= 7 \cdot 20 + 7 \cdot 2$ Distributive Property
$= 140 + 14$ Multiply.
$= 154$ Add.

Simplify each expression. Fill in the names of the properties you used.

1. $65 + 17 + 15 = 65 + 15 + \underline{17}$ **Commutative** Property of **Addition**
$= (65 + \underline{15}) + 17$ **Associative** Property of **Addition**
$= \frac{80}{} + \underline{17}$
$= \underline{97}$

2. $18 \cdot 7 \cdot \frac{1}{9} = 18 \cdot \frac{1}{9} \cdot 7$ **Commutative** Property of **Multiplication**
$= \left(18 \cdot \frac{1}{9}\right) \cdot 7$ **Associative** Property of **Multiplication**
$= \frac{2}{} \cdot 7$
$= \underline{14}$

5. $6(49) = 6(50 - \underline{1})$
$= 6 \cdot \underline{50} - 6 \cdot \underline{1}$ **Distributive** Property
$= \frac{300}{} - \underline{6}$
$= \underline{294}$

PRACTICE 3-1

Practice B
3-1 *Properties of Rational Numbers*

Name the property that is illustrated in each equation.

1. $16 + \frac{1}{3} = \frac{1}{3} + 16$
Comm. Prop. of Add.

2. $4 \cdot (3 \cdot p) = (4 \cdot 3) \cdot p$
Assoc. Prop. of Mult.

3. $(11 + m) + 9 = 11 + (m + 9)$
Assoc. Prop. of Add.

4. $6 \cdot 1.5 = 1.5 \cdot 6$
Comm. Prop. of Mult.

Simplify each expression. Write a reason for each step.

5. $38 + 19 + 2$
$38 + 19 + 2 = \underline{38 + 2 + 19}$ Reason: **Comm. Prop. of Add.**
$= \underline{(38 + 2) + 19}$ Reason: **Assoc. Prop. of Add.**
$= \underline{40 + 19}$ Reason: **Add.**
$= \underline{59}$ Reason: **Add.**

6. $\frac{1}{3} \cdot 8 \cdot 18$
$\frac{1}{3} \cdot 8 \cdot 18 = \underline{\frac{1}{3} \cdot 18 \cdot 8}$ Reason: **Comm. Prop. of Mult.**
$= \underline{\left(\frac{1}{3} \cdot 18\right) \cdot 8}$ Reason: **Assoc. Prop. of Mult.**
$= \underline{6 \cdot 8}$ Reason: **Multiply.**
$= \underline{48}$ Reason: **Multiply.**

Write each product using the Distributive Property. Then simplify.

7. $7(31)$
$7(31) = \underline{7(30 + 1)}$
$= \underline{7 \cdot 30 + 7 \cdot 1}$
$= \underline{210 + 7}$
$= \underline{217}$

8. $5(28)$
$5(28) = \underline{5(30 - 2)}$
$= \underline{5 \cdot 30 - 5 \cdot 2}$
$= \underline{150 - 10}$
$= \underline{140}$

Write an example of each property using rational numbers.

40. Distributive Property Possible answer: $8\left(5 + \frac{1}{2}\right) = 8 \cdot 5 + 8 \cdot \frac{1}{2}$

41. Associative Property of Multiplication
Possible answer: $\left(6 \cdot \frac{1}{7}\right) \cdot 14 = 6 \cdot \left(\frac{1}{7} \cdot 14\right)$

42. Commutative Property of Addition
Possible answer: $3.5 + 4.5 = 4.5 + 3.5$

Complete each equation. Then name the property that is illustrated in each.

43. ▦ $(4 + 7) = 8 \cdot 4 + 8 \cdot 7$ 8; Distrib. Prop.

44. $4.8 + 6 = 6 +$ ▦ 4.8; Comm. Prop. of Add.

45. $(x + y) + 12 = x + ($ ▦ $+ 12)$ y; Assoc. Prop. of Add.

46. $9(8 - z) = 9 \cdot$ ▦ $- 9z$ 8; Distrib. Prop.

47. Weather Leann wants to know the total amount of rainfall in Berkeley, California, from 2002 through 2005. Explain how she can use mental math and properties of rational numbers to calculate this amount.

Annual Rainfall, Berkeley, CA

(bar graph: Total rainfall (in.) vs. Year; 2002 = 24, 2003 = 19, 2004 = 26, 2005 = 21)

48. Reasoning Make a conjecture: Is division of rational numbers commutative? Explain your thinking.

49. What's the Error? A student writes, "You can use the Associative Property of Addition to change the order of two numbers before you add them." What is the student's error?

50. Write About It A case of cat food has 24 cans. Explain how to use mental math and the Distributive Property to find the number of cans in 5 cases.

51. Challenge Simplify the expression $12\left(\frac{1}{3} + \frac{1}{6} + \frac{1}{4}\right)$. Justify each step.

SPIRAL STANDARDS REVIEW
⬅ NS1.2, ⬅ NS1.5, ⬅ AF1.3

52. Multiple Choice The equation $3 + (5 + x) = 3 + (x + 5)$ is an example of which property?

Ⓐ Associative Property of Addition
Ⓒ Commutative Property of Multiplication
Ⓑ Commutative Property of Addition
Ⓓ Distributive Property

53. Multiple Choice Which is an example of the Associative Property of Multiplication?

Ⓐ $(-4) \cdot y = y \cdot (-4)$
Ⓒ $\frac{1}{3} \cdot (18 \cdot 6) = \left(\frac{1}{3} \cdot 18\right) \cdot 6$
Ⓑ $2(9 - 1) = 2 \cdot 9 - 2 \cdot 1$
Ⓓ $3 \cdot 5 + 3 \cdot 2 = 3(5 + 2)$

Write each decimal as a fraction in simplest form. (Lesson 2-1)

54. 0.68 $\frac{17}{25}$
55. 1.4 $1\frac{2}{5}$
56. -2.01 $-2\frac{1}{100}$
57. -0.04 $-\frac{1}{25}$

Divide. Write each answer in simplest form. (Lesson 2-5)

58. $\frac{1}{2} \div \frac{3}{8}$ $1\frac{1}{3}$
59. $4\frac{2}{3} \div 2\frac{2}{9}$ $2\frac{1}{10}$
60. $-\frac{5}{8} \div 2$ $-\frac{5}{16}$
61. $2\frac{4}{5} \div \frac{1}{10}$ 28

Objective: Students combine like terms in an expression.

 Hands-On Lab
In *Chapter 3 Resource File*

 Online Edition
Tutorial Videos

 Countdown to Mastery Week 5

Power Presentations
with PowerPoint®

Warm Up
Simplify.
1. $9 + 13 - 5 + 3$ 20
2. $16 - 8 + 4 - 1$ 11
3. $6 + 9 - 10 + 3$ 8
4. $17 + 8 - 20 - 2$ 3

Also available on transparency

Math Fact

From 1939 to 1970, there were more than 30 volumes of mathematics published under the name Nicolas Bourbaki. In fact, there was no such person. The name was used by a group of mathematicians.

California Standards

Algebra and Functions ⬅ 1.3

3-2 Simplifying Algebraic Expressions

California Standards

AF1.3 Simplify numerical expressions by applying properties of rational numbers (e.g., **identity**, inverse, **distributive**, **associative**, **commutative**) and justify the process used.

Vocabulary
term
like terms
coefficient
constant
equivalent expressions

Who uses this? Consumers can simplify algebraic expressions to find the total cost of tickets. (See Exercise 52.)

In the expression below, $7x$, 5, $3y$, and $2x$ are *terms*. A **term** can be a number, a variable, or a product of numbers and variables. Terms in an expression are separated by plus or minus signs.

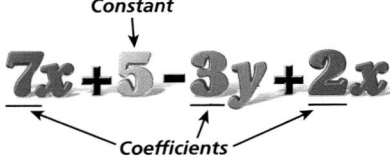

Like terms, such as $7x$ and $2x$, can be grouped together because they have the same variable raised to the same power. Often, like terms have different *coefficients*. A **coefficient** is a number that is multiplied by a variable in an algebraic expression. A **constant** is a number that does not change. Constants, such as 4, 0.75, and 11, are also like terms.

When you combine like terms, you change the way an expression looks but not the value of the expression. **Equivalent expressions** have the same value for all values of the variables.

EXAMPLE 1 Combining Like Terms in One-Variable Expressions

Helpful Hint
When you rearrange terms, move the operation in front of each term with that term.

Combine like terms.

A $7x + 2x$
   $(7x) + (2x)$ *Identify like terms.*
   $9x$ *Combine coefficients: $7 + 2 = 9$.*

B $5m - 2m + 8 - 3m + 6$
   $(5m) - (2m) + 8 - (3m) + 6$ *Identify like terms.*
   $5m - 2m - 3m + 8 + 6$ *Commutative Property*
   $0m + 14$ *Combine coefficients.*
   14 *Simplify.*

1 Introduce
Alternate Opener

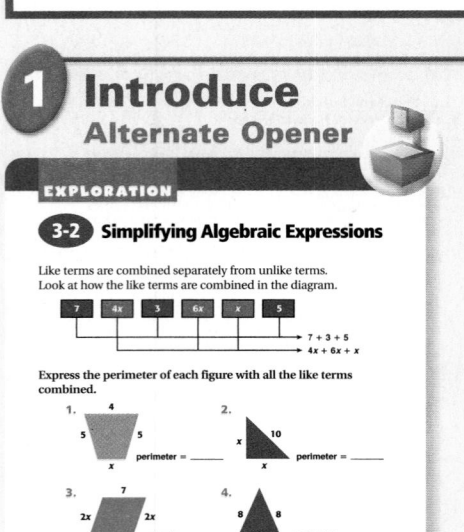

EXPLORATION

3-2 Simplifying Algebraic Expressions

Like terms are combined separately from unlike terms. Look at how the like terms are combined in the diagram.

Express the perimeter of each figure with all the like terms combined.

Think and Discuss
5. **Explain** what it means to combine like terms.
6. **Describe** a real-world situation in which you combine like terms.

Motivate

Ask students if they have ever heard the phrase, "You are trying to compare apples to oranges." Have them tell you what they think it means. Explain that apples and oranges cannot be compared because they are unlike objects.

In this lesson, students will learn that unlike terms cannot be added or subtracted.

ENGLISH LANGUAGE LEARNERS

Explorations and answers are provided in *Alternate Openers: Explorations Transparencies.*

EXAMPLE 2 Combining Like Terms in Two-Variable Expressions

Combine like terms.

A $7a + 4a + 3b + 5$

$\boxed{7a} + \boxed{4a} + \underset{3b}{\textcircled{}} + \underset{5}{\hexagon}$ *Identify like terms.*

$11a + 3b + 5$ *Combine coefficients: 7 + 4 = 11.*

B $k + 3n - 2n + 4k$

$\boxed{1k} + \underset{3n}{\textcircled{}} - \underset{2n}{\textcircled{}} + \boxed{4k}$ *Identify like terms; the coefficient of k is 1 because 1k = k.*

$1k + 4k + 3n - 2n$ *Commutative Property*

$5k + n$ *Combine coefficients: 1 + 4 = 5; 3 − 2 = 1.*

C $3f - 9g + 15$

$\boxed{3f} - \underset{9g}{\textcircled{}} + \underset{15}{\hexagon}$ *No like terms*

$3f - 9g + 15$

To simplify an expression, perform all possible operations, including combining like terms. You may need to use the Associative, Commutative, or Distributive Properties.

EXAMPLE 3 Using the Distributive Property to Simplify

Simplify $6(y + 8) - 5y$.

$6(y + 8) - 5y$

$6(y) + 6(8) - 5y$ *Distributive Property*

$6y + 48 - 5y$ *Multiply.*

$\boxed{6y} + \underset{48}{\textcircled{}} - \boxed{5y}$ *Identify like terms.*

$6y - 5y + 48$ *Commutative Property*

$1y + 48$ *Combine coefficients: 6 − 5 = 1.*

$y + 48$ *1y = y*

Think and Discuss

1. **Describe** the first step in simplifying the expression $2 + 8(3y + 5) - y$.

2. **Tell** how many sets of like terms are in the expression in Example 1B. What are they?

Power Presentations
with PowerPoint®

Additional Examples

Example 1
Combine like terms.
A. $14a - 5a$ $9a$
B. $7y + 8 - 3y - 1 + y$ $5y + 7$

Example 2
Combine like terms.
A. $9x + 3y - 2x + 5$ $7x + 3y + 5$
B. $5t + 7p - 3p - 2t$ $3t + 4p$
C. $4m + 9n - 2$ no like terms

Example 3
Simplify $6(5 + n) - 2n$. $30 + 4n$

Also available on transparency

Possible Answers to Think and Discuss

1. Use the Distributive Property to simplify $8(3y + 5)$ to $24y + 40$.

2. There are two sets of like terms: $5m$, $2m$, and $3m$; and 8 and 6.

---

2 Teach

Guided Instruction

In this lesson, students learn to combine like terms in an expression. Make sure students understand that all constants are like terms and that terms with variables are like terms only if they have the same variable raised to the same power. Point out that unlike terms remain separate in a simplified expression.

 **Teaching Tip**

Visual Students may use one of the following methods to be sure they have included all terms:

- color-coded underlining
- drawing circles, squares, or triangles
- lightly crossing out terms

 **Universal Access**

Through Concrete Manipulatives

Provide students with cut-out shapes like the following: squares labeled with x's, circles labeled with y's, and triangles labeled with 1's. Use the same shapes but different colors for subtracted expressions (e.g., "minus x"). Have students use the cut-outs to simplify expressions, such as $2x + 1 + 3y + 5 + 4x$ ($6x + 3y + 6$) and $5x + 6y - 3 - 2x - 3y$ ($3x + 3y - 3$). Remind students that a pair of cut-outs having the same shape but different colors equals zero.

3 Close

Summarize

Show students the expression $2a + 5b + 5 - a + 3$. Ask students how many terms are in the expression, and to identify the like terms. Ask them to simplify the expression by combining the like terms. Remind students that simplifying like terms is another important step in simplifying expressions and solving equations.

5; $2a$ and a, 5 and 3; $a + 5b + 8$

California Standards Practice
AF1.3

go.hrw.com
Homework Help Online
KEYWORD: MT8CA 3-2
Parent Resources Online
KEYWORD: MT8CA Parent

Assignment Guide

If you finished Example **1** assign:
Proficient 1–9, 20–24 even, 54, 56–61
Advanced 19–24, 41, 46, 51–52, 54, 56–61

If you finished Example **2** assign:
Proficient 1–12, 20–30 even, 46–47, 51, 54, 56–61
Advanced 19–30, 41, 46–47, 51–52, 54, 56–61

If you finished Example **3** assign:
Proficient 1–18, 20–36 even, 37, 40–42 even, 46–48, 51, 54–61
Advanced 19–36, 38–39, 41–45 odd, 46–61

Homework Quick Check
Quickly check key concepts.
Exercises: 24, 28, 30, 32, 34

Answers

39. no; $6r - 12m - 5m - 15 + 5r + 7$, Distrib. Prop.; $6r + 5r - 12m - 5m - 15 + 7$, Comm. Prop.; $6r + 5r - 12m - 5m - 15 + 7$; $11r - 17m - 8$

Math Background

When you combine like terms that have a variable, you are using the Distributive Property.

$5x + 3x = (5 + 3)x = 8x$
$ba + ca = (b + c)a$

So when you simplify expressions like $2(y + 9) + 3y$, you are actually using the Distributive Property twice.

$2(y + 9) + 3y = 2(y) + 2(9) + 3y$
$= 2y + 18 + 3y$
$= 2y + 3y + 18$
$= (2 + 3)y + 18$
$= 5y + 18$

California Standards

Standard	Exercises
AF1.3	1–36, 39–45, 51–52, 59–61
AF4.1	56–58

GUIDED PRACTICE

See Example **1** Combine like terms.
1. $9x - 4x$ $5x$
2. $2z + 5 + 3z$ $5z + 5$
3. $6f + 3 - 4f + 5 + 10f$ $12f + 8$
4. $9g + 8g$ $17g$
5. $7p - 9 - p$ $6p - 9$
6. $3x + 5 - x + 3 + 4x$ $6x + 8$

See Example **2**
7. $6x + 4y - x + 4y$ $5x + 8y$
8. $4x + 5y - y + 3x$ $7x + 4y$
9. $5x + 3y + 4x - 2y$ $9x + y$
10. $6p + 3p + 7z - 3z$ $9p + 4z$
11. $7g + 5h - 12$ $7g + 5h - 12$
12. $3h + 4m + 7h - 4m$ $10h$

See Example **3** Simplify.
13. $4(r + 3) - 3r$ $r + 12$
14. $7(3 + x) + 2x$ $9x + 21$
15. $7(t + 8) - 5t$ $2t + 56$
16. $3(2 + p) - 4p$ $6 - p$
17. $2(5y + 4) + 9$ $10y + 17$
18. $7(5 - 2m) - m$ $35 - 15m$

INDEPENDENT PRACTICE

See Example **1** Combine like terms.
19. $7y + 6y$ $13y$
20. $4z - 5 - 2z$ $2z - 5$
21. $3a + 6 - 2a + 9 + 5a$ $6a + 15$
22. $5z - z$ $4z$
23. $9x + 3 - 4x$ $5x + 3$
24. $9b + 6 - 3b - 3 - b$ $5b + 3$

See Example **2**
25. $3z + 4z + b - 5$ $7z + b - 5$
26. $5a + a + 4z - 3z$ $6a + z$
27. $9x + 8y + 2x - 8 - 4y$ $11x + 4y - 8$
28. $6x + 2 + 3x + 6q$ $9x + 6q + 2$
29. $7d - d + 3e + 12$ $6d + 3e + 12$
30. $16a + 7c + 5 - 7a + c$ $9a + 8c + 5$

See Example **3** Simplify.
31. $5(y + 2) - y$ $4y + 10$
32. $2(3y - 7) + 6y$ $12y - 14$
33. $3(x + 6) + 8x$ $11x + 18$
34. $3(4y + 5) + 8$ $12y + 23$
35. $6(2x - 8) - 9x$ $3x - 48$
36. $4(4x - 4) + 3x$ $19x - 16$

PRACTICE AND PROBLEM SOLVING

Extra Practice
See page EP6.

37. Geometry A rectangle has length $5x$ and width x. Write and simplify an expression for the perimeter of the rectangle. $2(5x + x)$; $12x$

38. Hobbies Charlie has x state quarters. Ty has 3 more quarters than Charlie has. Vinnie has 2 times as many quarters as Ty has. Write and simplify an expression to show how many state quarters they have in all.
$x + x + 3 + 2(x + 3)$; $4x + 9$

39. Reasoning Determine whether the expression $r - 17m - 8$ is equivalent to $3(2r - 4m) - 5(m + 3 - r) + 7$. Use properties to justify your answer.

Simplify each expression. Justify each step.
40. $6(4\ell + 7k) - 16\ell + 14$ $42k + 8\ell + 14$
41. $5d + 7 + 4d - 2d - 6$ $7d + 1$
42. $7x + 2(y - 3x)$ $x + 2y$
43. $-3r + 6r^2 + 5r + 9r$ $6r^2 + 11r$
44. $6y - 3 - 7y + 10 - 3z$ $7 - y - 3z$
45. $2(k + 5) + 3 - k$ $k + 13$

Write and simplify an expression for each situation.

46. Business A promoter charges $7 for each adult ticket, plus an additional $2 per ticket for tax and handling. What is the total cost of x tickets?

$7x + 2x = 9x$

47. Sports Write an expression for the total number of medals won in the 2004 Summer Olympics by the countries shown below. $49g + 53s + 44b$

United States	Great Britain	Brazil	Lithuania
35 Gold	9 Gold	4 Gold	1 Gold
39 Silver	9 Silver	3 Silver	2 Silver
29 Bronze	12 Bronze	3 Bronze	0 Bronze

Write an algebraic expression for each verbal description. Then simplify the expression.

$4(m + p) - 6m; \ -2m + 4p$

48. four times the sum of m and p, decreased by six times m

49. y squared minus twice the sum of x and y squared $y^2 - 2(x + y^2); \ -y^2 - 2x$

50. the product of three and r, increased by the sum of nine, $2r$, and one

$3r + (9 + 2r + 1); \ 5r + 10$

 **51. What's the Error?** A student said that $3x + 4y$ can be simplified to $7xy$ by combining like terms. What error did the student make?

 52. Write About It Write an expression that can be simplified by combining like terms. Then write an expression that cannot be simplified, and explain why it is already in simplest form.

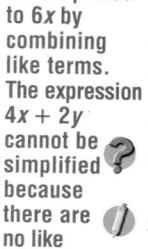 **53. Challenge** Simplify the expression $3\left(\frac{1}{6}x + 4 - \frac{2}{9}x\right) + 5\left(x - \frac{1}{10}\right)$. $4\frac{5}{6}x + 11\frac{1}{2}$

51. Possible answer: The expression $3x + 4y$ does not have any like terms and cannot be simplified further.

52. Possible answer: The expression $4x + 2x$ can be simplified to $6x$ by combining like terms. The expression $4x + 2y$ cannot be simplified because there are no like terms.

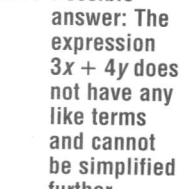

SPIRAL STANDARDS REVIEW   ← AF1.3, ← AF4.1

54. Multiple Choice Which expression is equivalent to $p + 3 - 5t + 4p$?

Ⓐ $5p - 2t$ Ⓑ $7p - 5t$ Ⓒ $5(p - t) + 3$ Ⓓ $3 - 5t + 4p$

55. Gridded Response Simplify $3(2x + 7) + 10x$. What is the coefficient of x?   16

Solve. (Lesson 2-8)

56. $\dfrac{x - 14}{-3} = 8$ $x = -10$ **57.** $\dfrac{a + 35}{5} = -9$ $a = -80$ **58.** $\dfrac{1}{4}w + 7 = 10.7$ $w = 14.8$

Complete each equation. Then name the property that is illustrated in each.
(Lesson 3-1)

59. ▩ $\cdot (x + 3) = 2 \cdot x + 2 \cdot 3$ **60.** $4.8 + 6 = 6 +$ ▩   **61.** $8(5 \cdot 9) = (8 \cdot$ ▩$)9$
      2; Distrib. Prop.   4.8; Comm. Prop. of Add.   5; Assoc. Prop. of Mult.

CHALLENGE 3-2

PROBLEM SOLVING 3-2

Objective: Students solve multi-step equations.

 Technology Lab
In *Chapter 3 Resource File*

 Online Edition
Tutorial Videos

 Countdown to Mastery Week 5

Power Presentations
with PowerPoint®

Warm Up

Solve.
1. $3x = 102$ $x = 34$
2. $\frac{y}{15} = 15$ $y = 225$
3. $z - 100 = 21$ $z = 121$
4. $1.1 + 5w = 98.6$ $w = 19.5$

Also available on transparency

Math Humor

What did one math book say to the other? Leave me alone—I've got my own problems!

3-3 Solving Multi-Step Equations

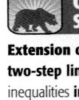

California Standards

Extension of AF4.1 Solve **two-step linear equations** and inequalities **in one variable over the rational numbers**, interpret the solution or solutions in the context from which they arose, and verify the reasonableness of the results.

Why learn this? You can solve problems about average speed by solving multi-step equations. (See Example 3.)

A multi-step equation requires more than two steps to solve. To solve a multi-step equation, you may have to simplify the equation first by combining like terms.

EXAMPLE 1 Solving Equations That Contain Like Terms

Solve $3x + 5 + 6x - 7 = 25$.

$$3x + 5 + 6x - 7 = 25$$
$$3x + 6x + 5 - 7 = 25$$ *Commutative Property of Addition Combine like terms.*
$$9x - 2 = 25$$
$$\underline{+2 \quad +2}$$ *Since 2 is subtracted from 9x, add 2 to both sides.*
$$9x = 27$$
$$\frac{9x}{9} = \frac{27}{9}$$ *Since x is multiplied by 9, divide both sides by 9.*
$$x = 3$$

If an equation contains fractions, it may help to multiply both sides of the equation by the least common denominator (LCD) to clear the fractions before you isolate the variable.

EXAMPLE 2 Solving Equations That Contain Fractions

Solve.

Ⓐ $\frac{3y}{7} + \frac{5}{7} = -\frac{1}{7}$

$$7\left(\frac{3y}{7} + \frac{5}{7}\right) = 7\left(-\frac{1}{7}\right)$$ *Multiply both sides by 7.*
$$7\left(\frac{3y}{7}\right) + 7\left(\frac{5}{7}\right) = 7\left(-\frac{1}{7}\right)$$ *Distributive Property*
$${}^1\!\!\not7\left(\frac{3y}{\not7}\right) + {}^1\!\!\not7\left(\frac{5}{\not7}\right) = \not7\left(-\frac{1}{\not7}\right)$$ *Simplify.*
$$3y + 5 = -1$$
$$\underline{-5 \quad -5}$$ *Since 5 is added to 3y, subtract 5 from both sides.*
$$3y = -6$$
$$\frac{3y}{3} = \frac{-6}{3}$$ *Since y is multiplied by 3, divide both sides by 3.*
$$y = -2$$

---

1 Introduce

Alternate Opener

EXPLORATION

3-3 Solving Multi-Step Equations

José and Rebecca want to rent sports equipment at the city park. José wants to rent inline skates, and Rebecca wants to rent a motor scooter.

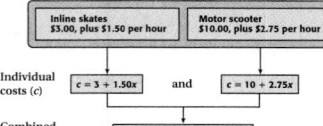

| Inline skates $3.00, plus $1.50 per hour | Motor scooter $10.00, plus $2.75 per hour |

Individual costs (c) $c = 3 + 1.50x$ and $c = 10 + 2.75x$

Combined cost (C) $C = 3 + 1.50x + 10 + 2.75x$

Use the equation $C = 3 + 1.50x + 10 + 2.75x$ to answer each question.
1. How much would José and Rebecca pay for 2 hours' rental?
2. How much would José and Rebecca pay for 3 hours' rental?
3. If their total rental cost is $38.50, for how many hours did they use the equipment?

Think and Discuss
4. **Explain** how to combine like terms in the equation $C = 3 + 1.50x + 10 + 2.75x$.
5. **Discuss** whether it makes sense to combine like terms when each item of sports equipment is rented for a different number of hours.

Motivate

Show students an equation, such as $2x + 1 = 7$, and represent the equation using algebra tiles. You may want to use the overhead algebra tiles provided in the Teacher's Manipulatives Kit.

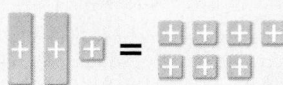

Ask students to solve the equation, always keeping it balanced. $x = 3$

Explorations and answers are provided in *Alternate Openers: Explorations Transparencies*.

California Standards

Ext. of Algebra and Functions 4.1

Solve.

B $\frac{5p}{6} + \frac{p}{3} - \frac{1}{2} = \frac{11}{6}$

$6\left(\frac{5p}{6} + \frac{p}{3} - \frac{1}{2}\right) = 6\left(\frac{11}{6}\right)$ *Multiply both sides by 6, the LCD of the fractions.*

$6\left(\frac{5p}{6}\right) + 6\left(\frac{p}{3}\right) - 6\left(\frac{1}{2}\right) = 6\left(\frac{11}{6}\right)$ *Distributive Property*

$\overset{1}{6}\left(\frac{5p}{\overset{}{6_1}}\right) + \overset{2}{6}\left(\frac{p}{\overset{}{3_1}}\right) - \overset{3}{6}\left(\frac{1}{\overset{}{2_1}}\right) = \overset{1}{6}\left(\frac{11}{\overset{}{6_1}}\right)$ *Simplify.*

$5p + 2p - 3 = 11$

$7p - 3 = 11$ *Combine like terms.*

$\underline{\ +3\ +3}$ *Since 3 is subtracted from 7p, add 3 to both sides.*

$7p = 14$

$\frac{7p}{7} = \frac{14}{7}$ *Since p is multiplied by 7, divide both sides by 7.*

$p = 2$

EXAMPLE **3** *Travel Application*

On the first day of her vacation, Carly drove *m* miles in 4 hours. On the second day, she drove twice as far in 7 hours. If her average speed for the two days was 62.8 mi/h, how far did she drive on the first day? Round your answer to the nearest tenth of a mile.

Carly's average speed is her total distance for the two days divided by the total time.

$$\frac{\text{total distance}}{\text{total time}} = \text{average speed}$$

$\frac{m + 2m}{4 + 7} = 62.8$ *Substitute m + 2m for total distance and 4 + 7 for total time.*

$\frac{3m}{11} = 62.8$ *Simplify.*

$11\left(\frac{3m}{11}\right) = 11(62.8)$ *Multiply both sides by 11.*

$3m = 690.8$

$\frac{3m}{3} = \frac{690.8}{3}$ *Divide both sides by 3.*

$m \approx 230.27$

Carly drove approximately 230.3 miles on the first day.

Think and Discuss

1. List the steps required to solve $3x - 4 + 2x = 7$.

2. Tell how you would clear the fractions in $\frac{3x}{4} - \frac{2x}{3} + \frac{5}{8} = 1$.

Power Presentations
with **PowerPoint®**

Additional Examples

Example 1

Solve.

$8x + 6 + 3x - 2 = 37$ $x = 3$

Example 2

Solve.

A. $\frac{5n}{4} + \frac{7}{4} = \frac{-3}{4}$ $n = -2$

B. $\frac{7x}{9} + \frac{x}{2} - \frac{17}{9} = \frac{2}{3}$ $x = 2$

Example 3

On Monday, David rides his bicycle *m* miles in 2 hours. On Tuesday, he rides three times as far in 5 hours. If his average speed for the two days is 12 mi/h, how far did he ride on Monday? Round your answer to the nearest tenth of a mile. **21.0 miles**

Also available on transparency

Possible answers to
Think and Discuss

1. Combine like terms ($3x$ and $2x$). Add 4 to both sides. Divide both sides by 5. The answer is $x = \frac{11}{5}$.

2. Multiply both sides by 24.

---

2 Teach

Guided Instruction

In this lesson, students learn to solve multi-step equations. Remind students that they can use the Commutative Property of Addition to rearrange terms; this will be helpful for combining like terms. Before discussing the equations that have fractions, review how to find the LCD of a set of fractions.

Teaching Tip
Inclusion Remind students to check each solution by substituting it into the *original equation*. This will help them catch mistakes that were made early in the solution process.

Universal Access
Through Cooperative Learning

Have students work in pairs to play equation tic-tac-toe. Instruct students to draw a large tic-tac-toe grid. Then have them write 9 equations from this lesson on individual note cards and place them face down in the grid. One student chooses a card and solves the equation. Then both students check the solution. If the solution is correct, the solver "wins the square". The first student with 3-across, down, or diagonally wins the game.

3 Close

Summarize

Ask students to write a reasonable first step to solve each of the following equations.

1. $\frac{2a}{5} - \frac{4a}{5} = 3$

2. $\frac{x}{6} - \frac{4x}{3} = \frac{x}{9}$

3. $3t - 1 + t - 5t = 1$

Possible answers:

1. Multiply both sides of the equation by 5.

2. Multiply both sides of the equation by 18.

3. Combine like terms.

3-3 Exercises

 California Standards Practice
Extension of ❖ AF4.1;
❖ AF4.2

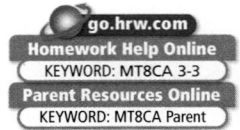 go.hrw.com
Homework Help Online
KEYWORD: MT8CA 3-3
Parent Resources Online
KEYWORD: MT8CA Parent

Assignment Guide

If you finished Example **1** assign:
Proficient 1–6, 12–17, 26, 27, 41–48
Advanced 12–17, 26, 27, 29, 31, 32, 35, 39, 41–48

If you finished Example **2** assign:
Proficient 1–10, 12–23, 25–28, 41–48
Advanced 12–23, 28–32, 35, 38–48

If you finished Example **3** assign:
Proficient 1–28, 33, 34, 41–48
Advanced 12–24, 28–48

Homework Quick Check

Quickly check key concepts.
Exercises: 12, 18, 24, 28

Math Background

Multi-step equations can often be solved using different methods. Clearing fractions is one method of solving equations that contain fractions, but multiplying by the LCD is not the required first step for solving these types of equations. For example, the equation in **Example 2A** can be solved as follows:

$$\frac{3y}{7} + \frac{5}{7} = -\frac{1}{7}$$
$$\frac{3y}{7} + \frac{5}{7} - \frac{5}{7} = -\frac{1}{7} - \frac{5}{7}$$
$$(7)\frac{3y}{7} = -\frac{6}{7}(7)$$
$$3y = -6$$
$$y = -2$$

California Standards

Standard	Exercises
AF1.3 ❖	46–48
AF4.1 ❖	34, 39, 43–45
Ext. of AF4.1 ❖	1–33, 35–38, 40–42
AF4.2 ❖	11, 24

GUIDED PRACTICE

See Example **1** Solve.

1. $7d - 12 + 2d + 3 = 18$ $d = 3$
2. $3y + 4y + 6 = 20$ $y = 2$
3. $10e - 2e - 9 = 39$ $e = 6$
4. $4c - 5 + 14c = 67$ $c = 4$
5. $5h + 6 + 8h - 3h = 76$ $h = 7$
6. $7x - 2x + 3 = -32$ $x = -7$

See Example **2**
7. $\frac{4x}{13} + \frac{3}{13} = -\frac{1}{13}$ $x = -1$
8. $\frac{y}{2} - \frac{5y}{6} + \frac{1}{3} = \frac{1}{2}$ $y = -\frac{1}{2}$
9. $\frac{4}{5} - \frac{2p}{5} = \frac{6}{5}$ $p = -1$
10. $\frac{15}{8}z + \frac{1}{4} = 4$ $z = 2$

See Example **3** **11. Travel** Barry's family drove 843 mi to see his grandparents. On the first day, they drove 483 mi. On the second day, how long did it take to reach Barry's grandparents' house if they averaged 60 mi/h?   **6 hours**

INDEPENDENT PRACTICE

See Example **1** Solve.

12. $5n + 3n - n + 5 = 26$ $n = 3$
13. $-81 = 7k + 19 + 3k$ $k = -10$
14. $36 - 4c - 3c = 22$ $c = 2$
15. $12 + 5w - 4w = 15$ $w = 3$
16. $37 = 15a - 5a - 3$ $a = 4$
17. $30 = 7y - 35 + 6y$ $y = 5$

See Example **2**
18. $\frac{3}{8} + \frac{p}{8} = 3\frac{1}{8}$ $p = 22$
19. $\frac{7h}{12} - \frac{4h}{12} = \frac{18}{12}$ $h = 6$
20. $\frac{4g}{16} - \frac{3}{8} - \frac{g}{16} = \frac{3}{16}$ $g = 3$
21. $\frac{7}{12} = \frac{3m}{6} - \frac{m}{3} + \frac{1}{4}$ $m = 2$
22. $\frac{4}{13} = -\frac{2b}{13} + \frac{6b}{26}$ $b = 4$
23. $\frac{3x}{4} - \frac{21x}{32} = -1\frac{1}{8}$ $x = -12$

See Example **3** **24. Recreation** Lydia rode 243 miles in a three-day bike trip. On the first day, Lydia rode 67 miles. On the second day, she rode 92 miles. How many miles per hour did she average on the third day if she rode for 7 hours?   **12 mi/h**

PRACTICE AND PROBLEM SOLVING

Extra Practice
See page EP6.

Solve and check.

25. $\frac{5n}{8} - \frac{1}{2} = \frac{3}{4}$ $n = 2$
26. $4n + 11 - 7n = -13$ $n = 8$
27. $7b - 2 - 12b = 63$ $b = -13$
28. $\frac{x}{2} + \frac{2}{3} = \frac{5}{6}$ $x = \frac{1}{3}$
29. $-2x - 7 + 3x = 10$ $x = 17$
30. $\frac{3r}{4} - \frac{4}{5} = \frac{7}{10}$ $r = 2$
31. $4y - 3 - 9y = 32$ $y = -7$
32. $7n - 10 - 9n = -13$ $n = \frac{3}{2}$

33. Finance Alessia is paid 1.4 times her normal hourly rate for each hour she works over 30 hours in a week. Last week she worked 35 hours and earned $436.60. What is her normal hourly rate?   **$11.80 per hour**

REVIEW FOR MASTERY 3-3

LESSON 3-3 Review for Mastery
Solving Multi-Step Equations

To combine like terms, add (or subtract) coefficients.
$2m + 3m = (2 + 3)m = 5m$ $x - 3x = (1 - 3)x = -2x$
To solve an equation that contains like terms, first combine the like terms.

$2m + 3m = 35 - 25$ **Check:** Substitute into the original.
 $5m = 10$ Combine like terms. $2m + 3m = 35 - 25$
 $\frac{5m}{5} = \frac{10}{5}$ Divide by 5. $2(2) + 3(2) \stackrel{?}{=} 35 - 25$
 $m = 2$ $4 + 6 \stackrel{?}{=} 10$
                      $10 = 10$ ✔

$x + 6 - 3x + 5 = 13$ **Check:** $x + 6 - 3x + 5 = 13$
 $-2x + 11 = 13$ Combine like terms. $-1 + 6 - 3(-1) + 5 \stackrel{?}{=} 13$
  -11 -11 Subtract 11. $-1 + 6 + 3 + 5 \stackrel{?}{=} 13$
  $-2x = 2$ $-1 + 14 \stackrel{?}{=} 13$
  $\frac{-2x}{-2} = \frac{2}{-2}$ Divide by -2. $13 = 13$ ✔
  $x = -1$

Complete to solve and check each equation.

1. $4z - 7z = -20 - 1$ **Check:** $4z - 7z = -20 - 1$
  -3 $z = -21$ Combine like terms. $4(\underline{7}) - 7(\underline{7}) \stackrel{?}{=} -20 - 1$
  $\frac{-3z}{-3} = \frac{-21}{-3}$ Divide. $\underline{28} - \underline{49} \stackrel{?}{=} -21$
  $z = \underline{7}$ $-21 = -21$ ✔

2. $t + 1 - 4t + 8 = 21$ **Check:** $t + 1 - 4t + 8 = 21$
  -3 $t + 9 = 21$ Combine like terms. $-4 + 1 - 4(-4) + 8 \stackrel{?}{=} 21$
     -9 -9 Subtract. $-4 + 1 + 16 \stackrel{?}{=} 21$
     $-3t = 12$ $-4 + 25 \stackrel{?}{=} 21$
     $\frac{-3t}{-3} = \frac{12}{-3}$ Divide. $21 = 21$ ✔
     $t = -4$

PRACTICE 3-3

LESSON 3-3 Practice B
Solving Multi-Step Equations

Solve.

1. $2x + 5x + 4 = 25$ **2.** $9 + 3y - 2y = 14$ **3.** $16 = 4w + 2w - 2$
  $x = 3$ $y = 5$ $w = 3$
4. $26 = 3b - 2 - 7b$ **5.** $31 + 4t - t = 40$ **6.** $14 - 2x + 4x = 20$
  $b = -7$ $t = 3$ $x = 3$
7. $\frac{5m}{8} - \frac{6}{8} + \frac{3m}{8} = 2$ **8.** $-4\frac{2}{3} = \frac{2n}{3} + \frac{1}{3} + \frac{n}{3}$ **9.** $7a + 16 - 3a = -4$
  $m = 1$ $n = -5$ $a = -5$
10. $\frac{x}{2} + 1 + \frac{3x}{4} = -9$ **11.** $7m + 3 - 4m = -9$ **12.** $\frac{2x}{5} + 3 - \frac{4x}{5} = \frac{1}{5}$
  $x = -8$ $m = -4$ $x = 7$
13. $\frac{7k}{8} - \frac{3}{4} - \frac{5k}{16} = \frac{3}{8}$ **14.** $6y + 9 - 4y = -3$ **15.** $\frac{5a}{6} - \frac{7}{12} + \frac{3a}{4} = -2\frac{1}{6}$
  $k = 2$ $y = -6$ $a = -1$

16. The measure of an angle is 28° greater than its complement. Find the measure of each angle.
  angle = 59°; complement = 31°

17. The measure of an angle is 21° more than twice its supplement. Find the measure of each angle.
  angle = 127°; supplement = 53°

18. The perimeter of the triangle is 126 units. Find the measure of each side.
  $AC = 25$ units; $BC = 50$ units;
  $AB = 51$ units

19. The base angles of an isosceles triangle are congruent. If the measure of each of the base angles is twice the measure of the third angle, find the measure of all three angles.
  36°; 72°; 72°

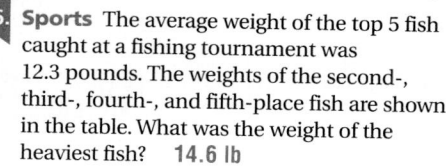

Sports

You can estimate the weight in pounds of a fish that is L inches long and G inches around at the thickest part by using the formula $W \approx \frac{LG^2}{800}$.

34. Geometry The obtuse angle of an isosceles triangle measures 120°. Write and solve an equation to find the measure of the base angles. (*Hint:* An isosceles triangle has two congruent angles. An obtuse angle measures more than 90° but less than 180°.) $180 = 120 + 2x; x = 30°$

35. Reasoning The sum of two consecutive numbers is 63. What are the two numbers? Explain your solution.

 36. Sports The average weight of the top 5 fish caught at a fishing tournament was 12.3 pounds. The weights of the second-, third-, fourth-, and fifth-place fish are shown in the table. What was the weight of the heaviest fish? **14.6 lb**

Winning Entries	
Caught by	Weight (lb)
Wayne S.	
Carla P.	12.8
Deb N.	12.6
Virgil W.	11.8
Brian B.	9.7

37. Science The formula $K = \frac{F - 32}{1.8} + 273$ is used to convert a temperature from degrees Fahrenheit to kelvins. Water boils at 373 kelvins. Use the formula to find the boiling point of water in degrees Fahrenheit. **212°F**

38. What's the Error? A student's work in solving an equation is shown. What error has the student made, and what is the correct answer?

$$\frac{1}{5}x + 5x = 13$$
$$x + 5x = 65$$
$$6x = 65$$
$$x = \frac{65}{6}$$

Possible answer: The student did not multiply $5x$ times 5 to get $25x$. The correct answer is $x = 2.5$.

 39. Write About It Compare the steps you would use to solve the equations $4x - 8 = 16$ and $4(x - 2) = 16$.

40. Challenge Solve the following equation. $x = 6$

$$\frac{4\left(\frac{1}{3}x - \frac{1}{4}\right) + \frac{4}{3}x}{3} + 1 = 6$$

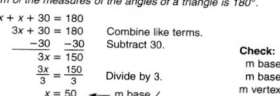
SPIRAL STANDARDS REVIEW ➤ AF1.3, ➤ AF4.1, Ext. of ➤ AF4.1

41. Multiple Choice Solve $4k - 7 + 3 + 5k = 59$.

Ⓐ $k = 6$ Ⓑ $k = 6.6$ Ⓒ $k = 7$ Ⓓ $k = 11.8$

42. Gridded Response Antonio's first four test grades were 85, 92, 91, and 80. What must he score on the next test to have an 88 test average? **92**

Solve. (Lesson 1-9)

43. $-5n + 6 = 21$ $n = -3$ **44.** $17y + 31 = -3$ $y = -2$ **45.** $41 + \frac{x}{-11} = 30$ $x = 121$

Combine like terms. (Lesson 3-2)

46. $9m + 8 - 4m + 7 - 5m$ **47.** $6t + 3k - 15$ **48.** $5a + 3 - b + 1$
    15                 $6t + 3k - 15$ $5a - b + 4$

CHALLENGE 3-3

LESSON 3-3 Challenge
Use the Power of Algebra!

An equation may be used to solve a problem involving angle measure in a triangle.

In isosceles triangle ABC, the measure of vertex angle C is 30° more than the measure of each base angle. Find the measure of each angle of the triangle.

Let x = the number of degrees in m∠A.
Then x = the number of degrees in m∠B.
And $x + 30$ = the number of degrees in m∠C.

The sum of the measures of the angles of a triangle is 180°.

$x + x + x + 30 = 180$
$3x + 30 = 180$ Combine like terms.
$\underline{-30 \quad -30}$ Subtract 30.
$3x = 150$
$\frac{3x}{3} = \frac{150}{3}$ Divide by 3.
$x = 50$ ← m base ∠
$x + 30 = 80$ ← m vertex ∠

Check:
m base ∠ = 50°
m base ∠ = 50°
m vertex ∠ = 80°
180° ✔

So, the measure of each base angle is 50° and the measure of the vertex angle is 80°.

Write and solve an equation to find the measures of the angles of each triangle.

1. The measure of each of the base angles of an isosceles triangle is 9° less than 4 times the measure of the vertex angle.
$x + 4x - 9 + 4x - 9 = 180$
$9x - 18 = 180$
$\underline{+18 \quad +18}$
$9x = 198$
$\frac{9x}{9} = \frac{198}{9}$
$x = 22$
$4x - 9 = 79$
measure of each base angle = __79°__
measure of vertex angle = __22°__

2. The measure of the vertex angle of an isosceles triangle is one-fourth that of a base angle.
$x + x + \frac{x}{4} = 180$
$4 \cdot x + 4 \cdot x + 4 \cdot \frac{x}{4} = 4 \cdot 180$
$9x = 720$
$\frac{9x}{9} = \frac{720}{9}$
$x = 80$
$\frac{x}{4} = 20$
measure of each base angle = __80°__
measure of vertex angle = __20°__

PROBLEM SOLVING 3-3

LESSON 3-3 Problem Solving
Solving Multi-Step Equations

A taxi company charges $2.25 for the first mile and then $0.20 per mile for each mile after the first, or $F = \$2.25 + \$0.20(m - 1)$ where F is the fare and m is the number of miles.

1. If Juan's taxi fare was $6.05, how many miles did he travel in the taxi?
20 miles

2. If Juan's taxi fare was $7.65, how many miles did he travel in the taxi?
28 miles

A new car loses 20% of its original value when you buy it and then 8% of its original value per year, or $D = 0.8V - 0.08Vy$ where D is the value after y years with an original value V.

3. If a vehicle that was valued at $20,000 new is now worth $9,600, how old is the car?
4 years

4. A 6-year old vehicle is worth $12,000. What was the original value of the car?
$37,500

The equation used to estimate typing speed is $S = \frac{1}{5}(w - 10e)$, where S is the accurate typing speed, w is the number of words typed in 5 minutes and e is the number of errors. Choose the letter of the best answer.

5. Jane can type 55 words per minute (wpm). In 5 minutes, she types 285 words. How many errors would you expect her to make?
Ⓐ 0   C 2
Ⓑ 1   D 5

6. If Alex types 300 words in 5 minutes with 5 errors, what is his typing speed?
F 48 wpm   H 59 wpm
Ⓖ 50 wpm   J 60 wpm

7. Johanna receives a report that says her typing speed is 65 words per minute. She knows that she made 4 errors in the 5-minute test. How many words did she type in 5 minutes?
A 285
B 329
Ⓒ 365
D 1825

8. Cecil can type 35 words per minute. In 5 minutes, she types 255 words. How many errors would you expect her to make?
F 2   H 6
G 4   Ⓙ 8

FORMATIVE ASSESSMENT and INTERVENTION ◀ ▶

Diagnose Before the Lesson
3-3 Warm Up, TE p. 124

Monitor During the Lesson
3-3 Know-It Notebook
3-3 Questioning Strategies

Assess After the Lesson
3-3 Lesson Quiz, TE p. 127

Answers

35. 31 and 32; Possible answer: Let n equal one number and $n + 1$ be the next consecutive number. Then $n + (n + 1) = 63$, so $2n + 1 = 63$, or $n = 31$.

39. Possible answer: To solve the first equation, I would add 8 to both sides and then divide both sides by 4 to find that $x = 6$. To solve the second equation, I would divide both sides by 4 and then add 2 to both sides to find that $x = 6$. Alternately, I could distribute the 4 in the second equation and follow the steps for solving the first equation.

 Multiple Choice For **Exercise 41,** have students identify the constants and terms with k as like terms. If students select **D** as the answer, they did not combine like terms correctly.

 Journal

Ask students to compare the process of solving a multi-step equation with the process of checking the solution.

 **Power Presentations with PowerPoint®**

3-3 Lesson Quiz

Solve.

1. $6x + 3x - x + 9 = 33$ $x = 3$

2. $29 = 5x + 21 + 3x$ $x = 1$

3. $\frac{5}{8} + \frac{x}{8} = \frac{33}{8}$ $x = 28$

4. $\frac{6x}{7} - \frac{2x}{21} = \frac{25}{21}$ $x = 1\frac{9}{16}$

5. Linda is paid double her normal hourly rate for each hour she works over 40 hours in a week. Last week she worked 52 hours and earned $544. What is her hourly rate? **$8.50**

Also available on transparency

Organizer

Use with Lesson 3-4

Objective: Use algebra tiles to model equations with variables on both sides.

Materials: Algebra tiles

Online Edition
Algebra Tiles

Countdown to Mastery Week 5

Teach
Discuss

Have students use guess-and-check to solve $2x - 4 = -6 + 3x$. $x = 2$ Then have them use algebra tiles to model and solve the equation.

Close
Key Concept

Using algebra tiles to model an equation helps you to see how the terms can be grouped.

Assessment

1. Model and solve the equation $x - 5 = -x + 3$.

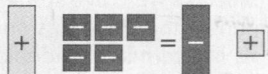 $x = 4$

Possible answers to *Think and Discuss*

1. Replace each yellow *x* bar with 2 yellow unit squares. Replace each red *x* bar with 2 red unit squares. See whether the equation balances.

2. to be able to see what number of unit tiles one variable tile is equal to

California Standards

Ext. of Algebra and Functions 4.1

Model Equations with Variables on Both Sides

Hands-On LAB 3-4

Use with Lesson 3-4

go.hrw.com
Lab Resources Online
KEYWORD: MT8CA Lab3

KEY
Algebra tiles

= x = $-x$

= 1   = -1

REMEMBER
Adding or subtracting zero does not change the value of an expression.

+ = 0   + = 0

California Standards

Extension of AF4.1 Solve two-step linear equations and inequalities **in one variable over the rational numbers,** interpret the solution or solutions in the context from which they arose, and verify the reasonableness of the results.

To solve an equation with the same variable on both sides of the equal sign, you must first add or subtract to eliminate the variable term from one side of the equation.

Activity

1 Model and solve the equation $-x + 2 = 2x - 4$.

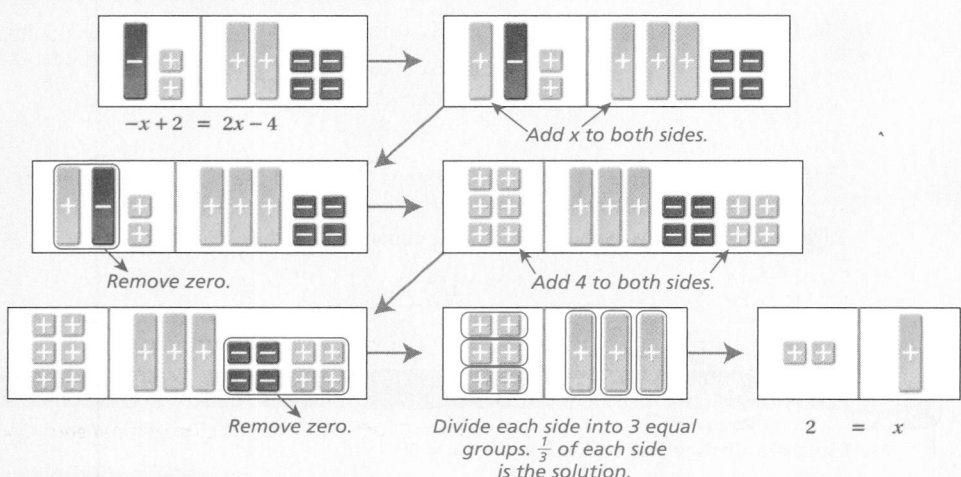

$-x + 2 = 2x - 4$

Add *x* to both sides.

Remove zero.

Add 4 to both sides.

Remove zero.

Divide each side into 3 equal groups. $\frac{1}{3}$ of each side is the solution.

$2 = x$

Think and Discuss

1. How would you check the solution to $-x + 2 = 2x - 4$ using algebra tiles?

2. Why must you isolate the variable terms by having them on only one side of the equation?

Try This

Model and solve each equation. **Check students' models.**

1. $x + 3 = -x - 3$ $x = -3$

2. $3x = -3x + 18$ $x = 3$

3. $6 - 3x = -4x + 8$ $x = 2$

4. $3x + 3x + 2 = x + 17$ $x = 3$

Teacher to Teacher

When we first begin looking at equations with variables on both sides, I have students create their own scenarios to represent the equations. For example, I call the sides of the equation *your yard* and *my yard*. I then explain that I live in a strange community in which I am not allowed to have variables in my yard. However, you are allowed to have variables in your yard, so we want to move all of the variables to your yard.

Wendy Taub-Hoglund
Northridge, CA

3-4 Solving Equations with Variables on Both Sides

Who uses this? Consumers can use equations with variables on both sides to compare costs. (See Example 3.)

The fees for two dog-sitting services are shown at right. To find the number of hours for which the costs will be the same for both services, you can write and solve an equation with variables on both sides of the equal sign.

Happy Paws
$19.00 plus $1.50 per hour

WOOF WATCHERS
$15.00 plus $2.75 per hour

To solve an equation like this, first use inverse operations to "collect" variable terms on one side of the equation.

EXAMPLE 1 Solving Equations with Variables on Both Sides

Solve.

Helpful Hint
You can always check your solution by substituting the value back into the original equation.

$$ A \quad 3a = 2a + 3 $$

$$
\begin{array}{r}
3a = \quad 2a + 3 \\
-2a \quad -2a \\
\hline
a = \quad 3
\end{array}
$$

To collect the variable terms on one side, subtract 2a from both sides.

Check

$$
\begin{array}{r}
3a = 2a + 3 \\
3(3) \stackrel{?}{=} 2(3) + 3 \\
9 \stackrel{?}{=} 6 + 3 \\
9 \stackrel{?}{=} 9 \checkmark
\end{array}
$$

Substitute 3 for a in the original equation.

$$ B \quad 3v - 8 = 7 + 8v $$

$$
\begin{array}{r}
3v - 8 = \quad 7 + 8v \\
-3v \qquad -3v \\
\hline
-8 = \quad 7 + 5v
\end{array}
$$

To collect the variable terms on one side, subtract 3v from both sides.

$$
\begin{array}{r}
-7 \quad -7 \\
\hline
-15 = \qquad 5v
\end{array}
$$

Since 7 is added to 5v, subtract 7 from both sides.

$$ \frac{-15}{5} = \frac{5v}{5} $$

$$ -3 = v $$

Since v is multiplied by 5, divide both sides by 5.

Organizer 3-4

Objective: Students solve equations with variables on both sides of the equal sign.

Technology Lab
In *Chapter 3 Resource File*

Online Edition
Tutorial Videos, Interactivities

Countdown to Mastery Week 6

Power Presentations
with PowerPoint®

Warm Up

Solve.

1. $2x + 9x - 3x + 8 = 16$ $x = 1$

2. $-4 = 6x + 22 - 4x$ $x = -13$

3. $\frac{2}{7} + \frac{x}{7} = 5\frac{1}{7}$ $x = 34$

4. $\frac{9x}{16} - \frac{2x}{4} = 3\frac{1}{8}$ $x = 50$

Also available on transparency

Math Humor

The chef who was taking an algebra class had a flair for creating veggie dishes with a symmetrical look. One day she had to solve the equation $4 - 2p = 3p + 9$. Naturally, she added p's to both sides.

---

1 Introduce

Alternate Opener

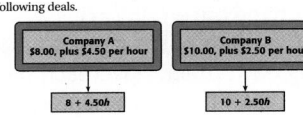

EXPLORATION

3-4 Solving Equations with Variables on Both Sides

Samara wants to rent a kayak. Two rental places offer the following deals.

Company A $8.00, plus $4.50 per hour	Company B $10.00, plus $2.50 per hour
8 + 4.50h	10 + 2.50h

Use the expressions above to solve each problem.

1. Find the cost of a 1-hour rental from company A ($h = 1$).
2. Find the cost of a 1-hour rental from company B ($h = 1$).
3. Find the cost of a 2-hour rental from company A ($h = 2$).
4. Find the cost of a 2-hour rental from company B ($h = 2$).
5. Find the number of hours that a kayak would need to be rented from both companies to make the costs equal by solving $8 + 4.50h = 10 + 2.50h$ for h. (*Hint:* Combine like terms first.)

Think and Discuss

6. **Explain** how you solved the equation in Problem 5.
7. **Discuss** what it means to set $8 + 4.50h$ equal to $10 + 2.50h$.

Motivate

Show students the following algebra tiles modeling an equation.

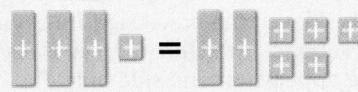

Ask them to write the equation that is represented by the tiles. $3x + 1 = 2x + 5$ Tell them that they will learn how to solve this kind of equation in the new lesson.

Explorations and answers are provided in *Alternate Openers: Explorations Transparencies.*

Power Presentations
with PowerPoint®

Additional Examples

Example 1

Solve.

A. $4x + 6 = x$ $x = -2$

B. $9b - 6 = 5b + 18$ $b = 6$

C. $9w + 3 = 9w + 7$ no solution

Example 2

Solve.

A. $10z - 15 - 4z = 8 - 2z - 15$

   $z = 1$

B. $\dfrac{y}{5} + \dfrac{3y}{5} - \dfrac{3}{4} = y - \dfrac{7}{10}$

   $y = -\dfrac{1}{4}$

Also available on transparency

Helpful Hint

If the variables in an equation are eliminated and the resulting statement is false, the equation has no solution.

Solve.

C $g + 7 = g - 3$

$$g + 7 = \quad g - 3$$
$$\underline{-g \qquad\quad -g}$$
$$7 \neq \qquad -3$$

To collect the variable terms on one side, subtract g from both sides.

There is no solution. There is no number that can be substituted for the variable g to make the equation true.

To solve more complicated equations, you may need to first simplify by combining like terms or clearing fractions. Then add or subtract to collect variable terms on one side of the equation. Finally, use properties of equality to isolate the variable.

EXAMPLE 2 Solving Multi-Step Equations with Variables on Both Sides

Solve.

A $2c + 4 - 3c = -9 + c + 5$

$$2c + 4 - 3c = -9 + c + 5$$
$$-c + 4 = -4 + c \qquad \text{Combine like terms.}$$
$$\underline{+c \qquad\qquad +c} \qquad \text{To collect the variable terms on one}$$
$$4 = -4 + 2c \qquad \text{side, add c to both sides.}$$
$$\underline{+4 \quad +4} \qquad \text{Since } -4 \text{ is add to } 2c, \text{ add 4 to}$$
$$8 = \qquad 2c \qquad \text{both sides.}$$
$$\dfrac{8}{2} = \dfrac{2c}{2} \qquad \text{Since c is multiplied by 2, divide both}$$
$$4 = c \qquad\qquad \text{sides by 2.}$$

B $\dfrac{2w}{3} - \dfrac{5w}{6} + \dfrac{1}{4} = w + \dfrac{11}{9}$

$$\dfrac{2w}{3} - \dfrac{5w}{6} + \dfrac{1}{4} = w + \dfrac{11}{9}$$

$$36\left(\dfrac{2w}{3} - \dfrac{5w}{6} + \dfrac{1}{4}\right) = 36\left(w + \dfrac{11}{9}\right) \qquad \text{Multiply both sides by}$$
$$\text{36, the LCD.}$$

$$^{12}\!\!\cancel{36}\!\left(\dfrac{2w}{\cancel{3}^{1}}\right) - {}^{6}\!\!\cancel{36}\!\left(\dfrac{5w}{\cancel{6}^{1}}\right) + {}^{9}\!\!\cancel{36}\!\left(\dfrac{1}{\cancel{4}^{1}}\right) = 36(w) + {}^{4}\!\!\cancel{36}\!\left(\dfrac{11}{\cancel{9}^{1}}\right) \qquad \text{Distributive Property}$$

$$24w - 30w + 9 = \quad 36w + 44$$
$$-6w + 9 = \quad 36w + 44 \qquad \text{Combine like terms.}$$
$$\underline{+6w \qquad\qquad +6w} \qquad \text{Add 6w to both sides.}$$
$$9 = 42w + 44$$
$$\underline{-44 \qquad\qquad -44} \qquad \text{Subtract 44 from}$$
$$-35 = 42w \qquad\qquad \text{both sides.}$$
$$\dfrac{-35}{42} = \dfrac{42w}{42} \qquad \text{Divide both sides by 42.}$$
$$-\dfrac{5}{6} = w$$

---

2 Teach

Guided Instruction

In this lesson, students solve equations with variables on both sides of the equal sign. In **Example 1,** explain that the variable appears on both sides of the equal sign. They want to add or subtract a variable term so that the variable appears on one side only. The paragraph just before **Example 2** is an excellent summary of the process of solving multi-step equations. (See also Summarize.) Note that in **Example 2A,** there are like terms to combine, and in **Example 2B,** there are fractions to clear.

Universal Access

Through Concrete Manipulatives

Give each student a card containing an expression like $2x + 4$ or $3x - 7$. Have the students form two concentric circles, each with an equal number of students, so that they are facing each other. Have each pair of students facing each other form an equation by setting their expressions equal to each other, and then have them solve that equation. After each pair agrees on their solution, have the circles rotate two students to the right and continue the process.

A *system of equations* is a set of two or more equations that contain two or more variables. To solve a system of two equations, you can reduce the system to one equation that has only one variable.

EXAMPLE 3 *Business Application*

Happy Paws charges a flat fee of $19.00 plus $1.50 per hour to keep a dog. Woof Watchers charges a flat fee of $15.00 plus $2.75 per hour. Find the number of hours for which you would pay the same amount for both services. What is the cost?

Write an equation for each service. Let c represent the total cost and h represent the number of hours.

	total cost	is	flat fee	plus	cost	per hour
Happy Paws:	c	$=$	19.00	$+$	1.5	h
Woof Watchers:	c	$=$	15.00	$+$	2.75	h

Now write an equation showing that the costs are equal.

$$19.00 + 1.5h = 15.00 + 2.75h$$
$$\underline{\quad -1.5h =} \quad \underline{\quad -1.5h} \quad$$ *To collect the variable terms on one*
$$19.00 = 15.00 + 1.25h \quad$$ *side, subtract 1.5h from both sides.*
$$\underline{-15.00} \qquad \underline{-15.00} \quad$$ *Subtract 15.00 from both sides.*
$$4.00 = 1.25h$$
$$\frac{4.00}{1.25} = \frac{1.25h}{1.25} \qquad$$ *Divide both sides by 1.25.*
$$3.2 = h$$

The two services cost the same when used for 3.2 hours.
To find the cost, substitute 3.2 for h in either equation.

Happy Paws:
$c = 19.00 + 1.5h$
$c = 19.00 + 1.5(3.2)$
$c = 19.00 + 4.8$
$c = 23.8$

Woof Watchers:
$c = 15.00 + 2.75h$
$c = 15.00 + 2.75(3.2)$
$c = 15.00 + 8.8$
$c = 23.8$

The cost for 3.2 hours at either service is $23.80.

Think and Discuss

1. **Explain** how you would solve the equation $3x + 4 - 2x = 6x + 2 - 5x + 2$. What do you think the solution means?

2. **Give** a series of steps that you can use to solve any equation with variables on both sides of the equal sign.

Possible answers to Think and Discuss

1. Combine like terms: $x + 4 = x + 4$, subtract x from both sides: $4 = 4$; since this statement is always true, any number you substitute for x is a solution.

2. Simplify both sides if necessary. Collect the variable terms on one side by using inverse operations. Then isolate the variable by using inverse operations.

3 Close

Summarize

Review the process for solving multi-step equations to this point:

- Clear fractions.
- Combine like terms.
- Get the variable on only one side of the equation.
- Undo addition and subtraction.
- Undo multiplication and division.

You may want to create a poster of these steps to display in the classroom.

Assignment Guide

If you finished **Example ① assign:**
Proficient 1–6, 12–17, 23–24, 40–48
Advanced 12–17, 23–24, 28, 30–32, 40–48

If you finished **Example ② assign:**
Proficient 1–10, 12–21, 23–26, 40–48
Advanced 12–21, 25–28, 30–34, 36, 38, 40–48

If you finished **Example ③ assign:**
Proficient 1–26, 30–33, 39–48
Advanced 12–22, 25–48

Homework Quick Check

Quickly check key concepts.
Exercises: 14, 16, 20, 22

Math Background

Solving an equation is a process of writing equivalent equations.

$$x + 2 = x + 3$$
$$\underline{-x \qquad -x}$$
$$2 = \qquad 3$$

Equivalent equations

The first and third lines are equivalent equations, so if $2 = 3$ is false, then $x + 2 = x + 3$ is also false. This means that $x + 2 = x + 3$ has no solutions.

California Standards

Standard	Exercises
NS1.1	45–48
AF1.1	11, 22
AF4.1 🔑	41–44
Ext. of AF4.1 🔑	1–40
MG2.1	33–34

3-4 **Exercises**

California Standards Practice
AF1.1, Extension of ➡ AF4.1; MG2.1

go.hrw.com
Homework Help Online
KEYWORD: MT8CA 3-4
Parent Resources Online
KEYWORD: MT8CA Parent

GUIDED PRACTICE

See Example ① **Solve.**

1. $6x + 3 = x + 8$ $x = 1$

2. $5a - 5 = 7 + 2a$ $a = 4$

3. $2x + 7 = 10x - 9$ $x = 2$

4. $4y - 2 = 6y + 6$ $y = -4$

5. $13x + 15 = 11x - 25$ $x = -20$

6. $5t - 5 = 5t + 7$ no solution

See Example ② **7.** $5x - 2 + 3x = 17 + 12x - 23$ $x = 1$

8. $\frac{3n}{4} + \frac{n}{12} - 6 = 5 + 2n - 18$ $n = 6$

9. $\frac{5}{12} + \frac{11d}{12} - 3 = 3d + 7 - 4d$ $d = 5$

10. $4(x - 5) + 2 = x + 3$ $x = 7$

See Example ③ **11. Business** A long-distance phone company charges $0.027 per minute and a $2 monthly fee. Another long-distance phone company charges $0.035 per minute with no monthly fee. Find the number of minutes for which the charges for both companies would be the same. What is the cost? **250 min; $8.75**

INDEPENDENT PRACTICE

See Example ① **Solve.**

12. $3n + 16 = 7n$ $n = 4$

13. $8x - 3 = 11 - 6x$ $x = 1$

14. $5n + 3 = 14 - 6n$ $n = 1$

15. $3(2x + 11) = 6x + 33$ all real numbers

16. $6x + 3 = x + 8$ $x = 1$

17. $7y - 8 = 5y + 4$ $y = 6$

See Example ② **18.** $\frac{3p}{8} + \frac{7p}{16} - \frac{3}{4} = \frac{1}{4} + \frac{p}{16} + \frac{1}{2}$ $p = 2$

19. $4(x - 5) - 5 = 6x + 7.4 - 4x$ $x = 16.2$

20. $\frac{1}{2}(2n + 6) = 5n - 12 - n$ $n = 5$

21. $\frac{a}{26} - 5.5 + 2a = \frac{9}{13} + \frac{20a}{13} + \frac{4}{13}$ $a = 13$

See Example ③ **22. Business** Al's Rentals charges $25 per hour to rent a Windsurfer™ and a wet suit. Wendy's charges $20 per hour plus $15 extra for a wet suit. Find the number of hours for which the total charges for both would be the same. What is the cost? **3 h; $75**

PRACTICE AND PROBLEM SOLVING

Extra Practice
See page EP6.

Solve and check.

23. $3y - 1 = 13 - 4y$ $y = 2$

24. $4n + 8 = 9n - 7$ $n = 3$

25. $5n + 20n = 5(n + 20)$ $n = 5$

26. $3(4x - 2) = 12x$ no solution

27. $100(x - 3) = 450 - 50x$ $x = 5$

28. $0.2p - 1.2 = 1.2 - 0.2p$ $p = 6$

29. Find two consecutive whole numbers such that $\frac{3}{4}$ of the first number is 5 more than $\frac{1}{2}$ the second number. (*Hint:* Let n represent the first number. Then $n + 1$ represents the next consecutive whole number.) **22, 23**

REVIEW FOR MASTERY 3-4

LESSON **3-4** **Review for Mastery**
Solving Equations with Variables on Both Sides

If there are variable terms on both sides of an equation, first collect them on one side. Do this by adding or subtracting.

If possible, collect the variable terms on the side where the on coefficient will be positive.

$$\frac{5x = 2x + 12}{-2x \quad -2x}$$ To collect on left side, subtract 2x.

$$3x = 12$$
$$\frac{3x}{3} = \frac{12}{3}$$ Divide by 3.
$$x = 4$$

Check: Substitute into the original equation.
$$5x = 2x + 12$$
$$5(4) \stackrel{?}{=} 2(4) + 12$$
$$20 \stackrel{?}{=} 8 + 12$$
$$20 = 20 ✔$$

$$\frac{-6z + 28 = 9z - 2}{+6z \quad +6z}$$ To collect on right side, add 6z.

$$28 = 15z - 2$$
$$\frac{+2 \qquad +2}{}$$ Add 2.
$$30 = 15z$$
$$\frac{30}{15} = \frac{15z}{15}$$ Divide by 15.
$$2 = z$$

Check: $-6z + 28 = 9z - 2$
$$-6(2) + 28 \stackrel{?}{=} 9(2) - 2$$
$$-12 + 28 \stackrel{?}{=} 18 - 2$$
$$16 = 16 ✔$$

Complete to solve and check each equation.

1. $9m = 4m - 25$
$$\frac{-4m \quad -4m}{}$$ To collect on left, subtract.
$$5m = -25$$
$$\frac{5m}{5} = \frac{-25}{5}$$ Divide.
$$m = \underline{-5}$$

Check: $9m = 4m - 25$
$$9(\underline{-5}) \stackrel{?}{=} 4(\underline{-5}) - 25$$
$$\underline{-45} \stackrel{?}{=} \underline{-20} - 25$$
$$\underline{-45} = \underline{-45} ✔$$

2. $3h - 7 = 5h + 1$
$$\frac{-3h \quad -3h}{}$$ To collect on right, subtract.
$$-7 = \underline{2}h + 1$$
$$\frac{-1 \qquad -1}{}$$ Subtract.
$$-8 = \underline{2}h$$
$$\frac{-8}{2} = \frac{2h}{2}$$ Divide.
$$-4 = h$$

Check: $3h - 7 = 5h + 1$
$$3(\underline{-4}) - 7 \stackrel{?}{=} 5(\underline{-4}) + 1$$
$$\underline{-12} - 7 \stackrel{?}{=} \underline{-20} + 1$$
$$\underline{-19} = \underline{-19} ✔$$

PRACTICE 3-4

LESSON **3-4** **Practice B**
Solving Equations with Variables on Both Sides

Solve.

1. $7x - 11 = -19 + 3x$
$x = -2$

2. $11a + 9 = 4a + 30$
$a = 3$

3. $4t + 14 = \frac{6t}{5} + 7$
$t = -2.5$

4. $19c + 31 = 26c - 74$
$c = 15$

5. $\frac{3y}{8} - 9 = 13 + \frac{y}{8}$
$y = 88$

6. $\frac{3k}{5} + 44 = \frac{12k}{25} + 8$
$k = -300$

7. $10a - 37 = 6a + 51$
$a = 22$

8. $5w + 9.9 = 4.8 + 8w$
$w = 1.7$

9. $15 - x = 2(x + 3)$
$x = 3$

10. $15y + 14 = 2(5y + 6)$
$y = -0.4$

11. $14 - \frac{w}{8} = \frac{3w}{4} - 21$
$w = 40$

12. $\frac{1}{2}(6x - 4) = 4x - 9$
$x = 7$

13. $4(3d - 2) = 8d - 5$
$d = \frac{3}{4}$

14. $\frac{y}{3} + 11 = \frac{y}{2} - 3$
$y = 84$

15. $\frac{2x - 9}{3} = 8 - 3x$
$x = 3$

16. Forty-eight decreased by a number is the same as the difference of four times the number and seven. Find the number. **11**

17. The square and the equilateral triangle at the right have the same perimeter. Find the length of the sides of the triangle. **12 units**

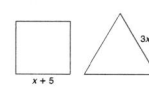

Write an equation to represent each relationship. Then solve the equation.

30. Six plus the product of 3 and a number is the same as the product of 9 and the number. $6 + 3x = 9x; x = 1$

31. A number decreased by 25 is the same as 10 minus 4 times the number. $x - 25 = 10 - 4x; x = 7$

32. Eight less than 2 times a number is the same as the number increased by 24. $2x - 8 = x + 24; x = 32$

The figures in each pair have the same perimeter. Find each perimeter.

33.
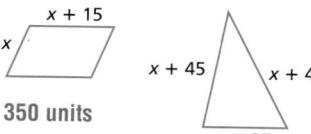
x + 15
x
x + 45
x + 40
350 units
x + 25

34.
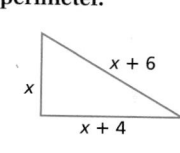
x
x + 2
x
x + 6
x + 4
28 units

35.  **Science** An atom of chlorine (Cl) has 6 more protons than an atom of sodium (Na). The atomic number of chlorine is 5 less than twice the atomic number of sodium. The atomic number of an element is equal to the number of protons per atom.

   a. How many protons are in an atom of chlorine? **17 protons**

   b. What is the atomic number of sodium? **11**

36. Possible answer: Substitute different values for *t*. The equation is true for any value of *t* that is a real number, so the solution is all real numbers.

36. **Choose a Strategy** Solve the following equation for *t*. How can you determine the solution once you have combined like terms?
$$3(t - 24) = 7t - 4(t + 18)$$

37. **Write About It** Two cars are traveling in the same direction. The first car is going 45 mi/h, and the second car is going 60 mi/h. The first car left 2 hours before the second car. Explain how you could solve an equation to find how long it will take the second car to catch up to the first car.

38. **Challenge** Solve the equation $\frac{x + 2}{8} = \frac{6}{7} + \frac{x - 1}{2}$. $x = -\frac{2}{7}$

SPIRAL STANDARDS REVIEW

NS1.1, AF4.1

39. **Multiple Choice** Find three consecutive integers (x, $x + 1$, and $x + 2$) so that the sum of the first two integers is 10 more than the third integer.

   Ⓐ $-7, -6, -5$　　Ⓑ $4, 5, 6$　　Ⓒ $11, 12, 13$　　Ⓓ $35, 36, 37$

40. **Multiple Choice** Solve $6w - 15 = 9w$.

   Ⓐ $w = 3$　　Ⓑ $w = 0$　　Ⓒ $w = -1$　　Ⓓ $w = -5$

Solve. (Lesson 1-9)

41. $6x - 3 = 15$　　42. $7 = -2 + \frac{n}{13}$　　43. $-72 = 5g - 12$　　44. $\frac{y}{4} + 7 = 7$
$x = 3$　　　　　　$n = 117$　　　　　　$g = -12$　　　　　　$y = 0$

Compare. Write <, >, or =. (Lesson 2-2)

45. $\frac{5}{9} \quad \boxed{} \quad \frac{13}{21}$ <　　46. $\frac{13}{11} \quad \boxed{} \quad \frac{8}{7}$ >　　47. $-\frac{1}{7} \quad \boxed{} \quad -\frac{1}{8}$ <　　48. $-\frac{2}{3} \quad \boxed{} \quad -\frac{14}{21}$ =

CHALLENGE 3-4

PROBLEM SOLVING 3-4

Answers

37. Possible answer: When the second car catches the first, the cars will have traveled an equal distance. Since distance can be calculated by multiplying rate and time, the situation can be represented by the equation $45(t + 2) = 60t$. Solving for *t* gives $t = 6$. The second car will catch the first car after 6 hours.

Journal
Have students describe the kind of equation that has no solution.

3-4 Lesson Quiz

Solve.

1. $4x + 16 = 2x$　$x = -8$

2. $8x - 3 = 15 + 5x$　$x = 6$

3. $2(3x + 11) = 6x + 4$　no solution

4. $\frac{1}{4}x = \frac{1}{2}x - 9$　$x = 36$

5. An apple has about 30 more calories than an orange. Five oranges have about as many calories as 3 apples. How many calories are in each? An orange has 45 calories, and an apple has 75.

Also available on transparency

SECTION 3A

READY TO GO ON?

Organizer

Objective: Assess students' mastery of concepts and skills in Lessons 3-1 through 3-4.

Resources

 Assessment Resources
Section 3A Quiz

 **Test & Practice Generator**
One-Stop Planner®

INTERVENTION ⬅➡

Resources

 Ready to Go On?
Intervention and
Enrichment Worksheets

 Ready to Go On? CD-ROM

 Ready to Go On? Online

my.hrw.com

READY TO GO ON?

SECTION 3A

Quiz for Lessons 3-1 Through 3-4

 3-1 **Properties of Rational Numbers**

1. Associative Property of Multiplication
2. Commutative Property of Addition
3. Distributive Property

Name the property that is illustrated in each equation.

1. $3 \cdot \left(\frac{1}{3} \cdot 7\right) = \left(3 \cdot \frac{1}{3}\right) \cdot 7$ **2.** $m + n = n + m$ **3.** $\frac{1}{2}(x - 6) = \frac{1}{2} \cdot x - \frac{1}{2} \cdot 6$

Simplify each expression. Justify each step.

4. $20 \cdot 19 \cdot 5$ **1900**   **5.** $35.5 + 12.7 + 4.5$ **52.7**   **6.** $\frac{1}{4} \cdot 11 \cdot 16$ **44**

Write each product using the Distributive Property. Then simplify.

7. $3(57)$ **171**   **8.** $(42)7$ **294**   **9.** $5(95)$ **475**

3-2 **Simplifying Algebraic Expressions**

Simplify.

10. $5x + 3x$ **8x**   **11.** $6p - 6 - p$ **5p - 6**   **12.** $2t + 3 - t + 4 + 5t$ **6t + 7**

13. $3x + 4y - x + 2y$ **14.** $2(r + 1) - r$ **r + 2**   **15.** $4n + 2m + 8n - 2m$
     2x + 6y   **12n**

3-3 **Solving Multi-Step Equations**

Solve.

16. $2c + 6c + 8 = 32$ **c = 3**   **17.** $\frac{3x}{7} - \frac{2}{7} = \frac{10}{7}$ **x = 4**   **18.** $\frac{t}{4} + \frac{t}{3} = \frac{7}{12}$ **t = 1**

19. $\frac{4m}{3} - \frac{m}{6} = \frac{7}{2}$ **m = 3**   **20.** $\frac{3}{4}b - \frac{1}{5}b = 11$ **b = 20**   **21.** $\frac{r}{3} + 7 - \frac{r}{5} = \frac{-3}{r = -75}$

22. Marlene drove 540 miles to visit a friend. She drove 3 hours and stopped for gas. She then drove 4 hours and stopped for lunch. How many more hours did she drive if her average speed for the trip was 60 miles per hour?   **2 h**

3-4 **Solving Equations with Variables on Both Sides**

Solve.

23. $4x + 11 = x + 2$ **x = -3**   **24.** $q + 5 = 2q + 7$ **q = -2**

25. $6n + 21 = 4n + 57$ **n = 18**   **26.** $2m + 6 = 2m - 1$ **no solution**

27. $-4a - 2a + 11 = 6a$ $a = \frac{11}{12}$ **28.** $\frac{7}{12}y - \frac{1}{4} = 2y - \frac{5}{3}$ **y = 1**

29. The rectangle and the triangle have the same perimeter. Find the perimeter of each figure.   **58 units**

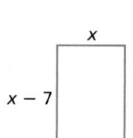 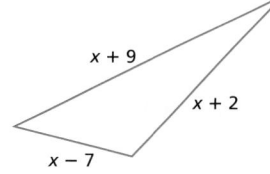

READY TO GO ON?

NO INTERVENE

YES ENRICH

READY TO GO ON? Intervention, Section 3A			
Ready to Go On? Intervention	 **Worksheets**	**CD-ROM**	**Online**
✓ Lesson 3-1 🐢 🔑 **AF1.3**	3-1 Intervention	Activity 3-1	
✓ Lesson 3-2 🐢 🔑 **AF1.3**	3-2 Intervention	Activity 3-2	Diagnose and Prescribe Online
✓ Lesson 3-3 🐢 Ext. of 🔑 **AF4.1**	3-3 Intervention	Activity 3-3	
✓ Lesson 3-4 🐢 **AF1.1,** Ext. of 🔑 **AF4.1**	3-4 Intervention	Activity 3-4	

READY TO GO ON? Enrichment, Section 3A

Worksheets

CD-ROM

Online

134   Chapter 3   Multi-Step Equations and Inequalities

Focus on Problem Solving

Plan

California Standards

MR1.1 Analyze problems by identifying relationships, distinguishing relevant information, identifying missing information, sequencing and prioritizing information, and observing patterns.

Also covered: **AF1.1, Extension of ← AF4.1**

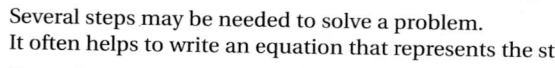

Make a Plan

- **Write an equation**

Several steps may be needed to solve a problem. It often helps to write an equation that represents the steps.

Example:

Juan's first 3 exam scores are 85, 93, and 87. What does he need to score on his next exam to average 90 for the 4 exams?

Let x be the score on his next exam. The average of the exam scores is the sum of the 4 scores, divided by 4. This amount must equal 90.

Write the equation in words:

$$\frac{\text{Exam 1} + \text{Exam 2} + \text{Exam 3} + \text{Exam 4}}{\text{Number of exams}} = 90$$

$$\frac{85 + 93 + 87 + x}{4} = 90$$
$$\frac{265 + x}{4} = 90$$
$$4\left(\frac{265 + x}{4}\right) = 4(90)$$
$$265 + x = 360$$
$$-265 \qquad -265$$
$$x = 95$$

Juan needs a 95 on his next exam.

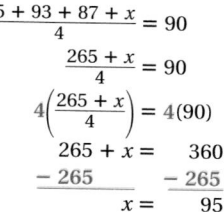

Read each problem and write an equation that could be used to solve it.

① The average of two numbers is 34. The first number is three times the second number. What are the two numbers? **51 and 17**

② Nancy spends $\frac{1}{3}$ of her monthly salary on rent, 0.1 on her car payment, $\frac{1}{12}$ on food, and 20% on other bills. She has $680 left for other expenses. What is Nancy's monthly salary? **$2400**

③ A vendor at a concert sells new and used CDs. The new CDs cost 2.5 times as much as the old CDs. If 4 used CDs and 9 new CDs cost $159, what is the price of each item? **Used CDs cost $6; new CDs cost $15.**

④ Amanda and Rick have the same amount to spend on school supplies. Amanda buys 4 notebooks and has $8.60 left. Rick buys 7 notebooks and has $7.55 left. How much does each notebook cost? **$0.35**

Focus on Problem Solving

Organizer

Objective: Focus on making a plan by writing an equation to solve a problem.

Online Edition

Resources

Chapter 3 Resource File Reading Strategies

Problem Solving Process

This page focuses on the second step of the problem-solving process: **Make a Plan**

Discuss

Have students identify what the variable in each equation represents and give the equation that can be used to solve the problem.

Possible answers:

1. Let x represent the second number; $\frac{3x + x}{2} = 34$

2. Let x represent Nancy's monthly salary; $\frac{1}{3}x + 0.1x + \frac{1}{12}x + 0.2x + 680 = x$

3. Let x represent the cost of an old CD; $4x + 9(2.5x) = 159$

4. Let n represent the cost of each notebook; $4n + 8.6 = 7n + 7.55$

California Standards

Mathematical Reasoning 1.1

Also covered:

Algebra and Functions

1.1 Use variables and appropriate operations **to write** an expression, **an equation,** an inequality, or a system of equations or inequalities that represents a verbal description (e.g., three less than a number, half as large as area A).

Ext. of ← 4.1 Solve two-step linear equations and inequalities in one variable over the rational numbers, interpret the solution or solutions in the context from which they arose, and verify the reasonableness of the results.

Solving Inequalities

One-Minute Section Planner

Lesson	Lab Resources	Materials
Lesson 3-5 Inequalities • Write inequalities that represent verbal descriptions and graph inequalities on a number line. **AF1.0, AF1.1**		
Lesson 3-6 Solving Inequalities by Adding or Subtracting • Solve one-step inequalities by using addition or subtraction. **AF4.0**		
Lesson 3-7 Solving Inequalities by Multiplying or Dividing • Solve one-step inequalities by using multiplication or division. **AF1.1, AF4.0**		
Lesson 3-8 Solving Two-Step Inequalities • Solve two-step inequalities and graph the solutions of an inequality on a number line. **AF4.1**	**Hands-On Lab 3-8** In *Chapter 3 Resource File*	

MK = *Manipulatives Kit*

Notes

_____

_____

_____

_____

_____

_____

_____

_____

_____

_____

_____

_____

_____

Math Background: Teaching the Standards

INEQUALITIES AF1.1

Lesson 3-5

The Law of Trichotomy is the starting point for understanding inequalities. This axiom states that given any two real numbers, a and b, exactly one of the following is true:

$$a = b, \ a < b, \ \text{or} \ a > b.$$

In the first case, a and b are related by an *equality* (a statement that two quantities are equal). In the second and third cases, a and b are related by an *inequality* (a statement that two quantities are *not* equal).

Inequalities are based on the order in which points appear on the real number line. For example, the inequality $-4 < 1$ states that -4 is less than 1. This means that -4 is to the left of 1 on the number line.

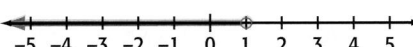

A *solution* of an inequality is any value of the variable that makes the inequality true. For example, every value on the number line to the left of 1 is a solution of $x < 1$ since any of these values, when substituted in the inequality, result in a true statement. The set of all solutions (the *solution set*) is shown as a ray on the number line. The open circle at 1 indicates that $x = 1$ is not itself a solution. Note that any point to the right of 1 is *not* on the ray and therefore is *not* a solution of the inequality.

Some inequalities include an equal sign, such as $x \leq 1$. The solution set of this inequality is the same as that of $x < 1$ but includes the additional solution $x = 1$. This is shown with a closed circle on the number line.

Inequalities that use the symbol $\leq$ or $\geq$ are called *weak inequalities.* Inequalities that use the symbol $<$ or $>$ are called *strong inequalities.*

WRITING INEQUALITIES AF1.1

Lesson 3-5

One of the essential skills of algebra is translating words into mathematics. This can be challenging for many students, especially those for whom English is a second language. Perhaps the most common error is the attempt to make a direct word-to-symbol translation that preserves the order of the words. Although this method works in many cases, it can cause problems. Consider the statement "5 less than a number n is greater than 2." A student making the "word-order" error might translate this incorrectly as $5 - n > 2$. The correct translation is $n - 5 > 2$.

Students should realize that they can check their mathematical translations in much the same way that they can check a solution. In the above example, it is helpful to choose a specific value for n, such as 20, and ask whether "5 less than 20" is represented by $5 - 20$.

SOLVING INEQUALITIES AF4.1

Lessons 3-6 through 3-8

Solving an inequality in one variable is similar to solving an equation in one variable. The goal is to isolate the variable on one side of the inequality by writing a series of equivalent inequalities—that is, a series of inequalities that have the same solution set.

The Addition and Subtraction Properties of Inequality are analogous to their counterparts for equations: the same quantity may be added to or subtracted from both sides of an inequality. For multiplication and division there is a caveat.

Consider the inequality $a > b$. By the Subtraction Property of Inequality, $a - a > b - a$ or $0 > b - a$. Applying the Subtraction Property of Inequality again shows that $0 - b > b - a - b$ or $-b > -a$, which is the same as $-a < -b$. In other words, when both sides of the original inequality are multiplied by -1, the direction of the inequality is reversed. More generally, the direction of the inequality must be reversed when both sides of an inequality are multiplied or divided by a negative number.

Objective: Students write inequalities that represent verbal descriptions and graph inequalities on a number line.

 Online Edition
Tutorial Videos

Countdown to Mastery Week 6

 **Power Presentations**
with PowerPoint®

Warm Up

Order each set of integers from least to greatest.

1. −7, 8, −9   −9, −7, 8

2. −2, 2, 0, −1   −2, −1, 0, 2

3. −11, −13, −10   −13, −11, −10

Write an algebraic expression for each word phrase.

4. 2 less than g $g - 2$

5. 5 minus the product of 3 and m
$5 - 3m$

6. 1 more than the quotient of x and 4 $1 + \frac{x}{4}$

Also available on transparency

 **Math Humor**

Question: What do math superheroes do?

Answer: They fight against inequality.

 California Standards

Algebra and Functions 1.1

Also covered:

Algebra and Functions
1.0 Students express quantitative relationships by using algebraic terminology, expressions, equations, **inequalities,** and graphs.

3-5 Inequalities

 **California Standards**

AF1.1 Use variables and appropriate operations to write an expression, an equation, **an inequality, or a system of** equations or **inequalities that represents a verbal description** (e.g., three less than a number, half as large as area A).

Vocabulary
inequality
algebraic inequality
solution set

Why learn this? You can show the maximum capacity of an elevator using an inequality.

An **inequality** compares two expressions using <, >, ≤, or ≥.

Symbol	Meaning	Word Phrases
<	Is less than	Fewer than, below
>	Is greater than	More than, above
≤	Is less than or equal to	At most, no more than
≥	Is greater than or equal to	At least, no less than

An inequality that contains a variable is an **algebraic inequality** .

EXAMPLE 1 **Translating Word Phrases into Inequalities**

Write an inequality for each situation.

A The capacity of an elevator is at most 12 people.
Let c = the capacity of the elevator.
$c \leq 12$ *"At most" means less than or equal to.*

B There are more than 1000 books in the library.
Let b = the number of books in the library.
$b > 1000$ *"More than" means greater than.*

EXAMPLE 2 **Writing Inequalities**

Write an inequality for each statement.

A A number x plus 14 is greater than or equal to 30.

A number x	plus	14	is greater than or equal to	30
x	+	14	≥	30

$x + 14 \geq 30$

B A number n decreased by 3 is less than 21.

A number n	decreased by	3	is less than	21
n	−	3	<	21

$n - 3 < 21$

---

1 Introduce

Alternate Opener

EXPLORATION

3-5 Inequalities

To raise money for a school trip, Angela sells pencils for $2.50 per box. She has to raise at least $100 from the pencil sales in order to go on the trip.

1. Which of the numbers of boxes of pencils shown gives Angela the following amounts of money?

    | 25 boxes |
    | 30 boxes |
    | 40 boxes |
    | 50 boxes |

    a. Less than her goal of $100
    b. Exactly $100
    c. More than her goal of $100

2. Name another number of boxes that Angela could sell that would give her less than her goal of $100.

3. Name another number of boxes that Angela could sell that would give her more than her goal of $100.

Think and Discuss

4. **Describe** the strategies you used to solve Problem 1.
5. **Explain** how you found numbers of boxes in order to solve Problems 2 and 3.

Motivate

Ask students to give examples of numbers that are no greater than 3. Encourage students to name whole numbers, rational numbers, and negative numbers that fit this description. Make a list of students' responses. Then ask students if they know of a shorthand way to describe *all* of the numbers that fit this description. Tell the class that they will learn how to use inequalities to describe such sets of numbers.

Explorations and answers are provided in *Alternate Openers: Explorations Transparencies.*

A solution of an inequality is any value of the variable that makes the inequality true. All of the solutions of an inequality are called the **solution set**. You can graph the solution set on a number line. The symbols $<$ and $>$ indicate an open circle.

This open circle shows that 5 is not a solution.

The symbols $\leq$ and $\geq$ indicate a closed circle.

This closed circle shows that 3 is a solution.

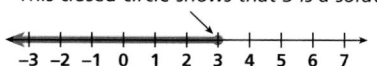

EXAMPLE 3 Graphing Inequalities

Graph each inequality.

A $x > -4$

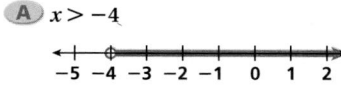

Draw an open circle at −4. The solutions are all values of x greater than −4, so shade to the right of −4.

Reading Math

$1\frac{1}{2} \geq m$ is the same as $m \leq 1\frac{1}{2}$.

B $1\frac{1}{2} \geq m$

Draw a closed circle at $1\frac{1}{2}$. The solutions are $1\frac{1}{2}$ and all values of m less than $1\frac{1}{2}$, so shade to the left of $1\frac{1}{2}$.

A compound inequality is the result of combining two inequalities. The words *and* and *or* are used to describe how the two parts are related.

EXAMPLE 4 Writing Compound Inequalities

Write a compound inequality for each statement.

Helpful Hint

The compound inequality in Example 4B can also be written with the variable between the two endpoints.
$6 \leq n < 9.5$

A A number t is either less than -2 or greater than or equal to 1.
$t < -2$ or $t \geq 1$

B A number n is both greater than or equal to 6 and less than 9.5.
$n \geq 6$ and $n < 9.5$

Think and Discuss

1. Explain how to write "x is no less than 16" as an inequality.

2. Compare the graphs of the inequalities $x < 3$ and $x \leq 3$.

② Teach

Guided Instruction

In this lesson, students learn to write inequalities that represent verbal descriptions and graph inequalities on a number line. Present **Examples 1** and **2**. Next, review number lines, reminding students that lesser values lie to the left of greater values. Then discuss **Example 3**.

Visual Tell students that the smaller side of an inequality symbol always points toward the smaller side of the inequality.

Universal Access
Through Graphic Organizers

Write the equation $x = 5$ and the inequality $x \geq 5$ on the board. Then work with students to make a two-column chart like the one below that lists similarities and differences.

Similarities	Differences
• Both contain a variable.	• $x = 5$ has one solution; $x \geq 5$ has many solutions.
• Both have 5 as a solution.	

③ Close

Summarize

Ask students to write an inequality for each situation and then graph the inequality.

1. There are at least 5 gallons of water in the aquarium. $w \geq 5$

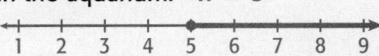

2. The temperature is below 6°C. $t < 6$

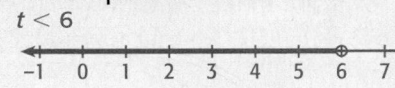

3-5 Exercises

California Standards Practice
AF1.1

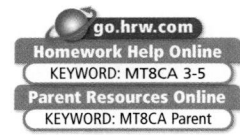

go.hrw.com
Homework Help Online
KEYWORD: MT8CA 3-5
Parent Resources Online
KEYWORD: MT8CA Parent

Assignment Guide

If you finished Example **1** assign:
Proficient 1–2, 11–12, 40–48
Advanced 11–12, 35–37, 40–48

If you finished Example **2** assign:
Proficient 1–4, 11–15, 26–29,
34–36, 39–48
Advanced 11–15, 26–29, 35–48

If you finished Example **3** assign:
Proficient 1–8, 11–19, 26–31,
34–36, 39–48
Advanced 11–23, 26–29, 32–48

If you finished Example **4** assign:
Proficient 1–31, 34–36, 39–48
Advanced 11–29, 32–48

Homework Quick Check

Quickly check key concepts.
Exercises: 12, 14, 16, 18, 24

Answers

5.
$$-5\ -4\ -3\ -2\ -1\ \ 0\ \ 1\ \ 2$$
6.
$$-2\ -1\ \ 0\ \ 1\ \ 2\ \ 3\ \ 4\ \ 5$$

7–8, 16–23. See p. A1.

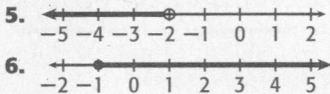

The Law of Trichotomy states that for any real numbers a and b, exactly one of the following three relationships must be true: $a < b$, $a = b$, or $a > b$. This law is the foundation for graphing inequalities because it states that any point on a number line divides the line into three parts: the point itself (equality), the region to the left of the point (less than), and the region to the right of the point (greater than).

GUIDED PRACTICE

See Example **1** Write an inequality for each situation.

1. There are no more than 60 people in the theater. $p \le 60$

2. The temperature of the water is above 72°F. $t > 72$

See Example **2** Write an inequality for each statement.

3. A number m increased by 7 is at least 15. $m + 7 \ge 15$

4. Twice a number x is less than 18. $2x < 18$

See Example **3** Graph each inequality.

5. $x < -2$ 6. $w \ge -1$ 7. $2.5 < y$ 8. $m \le 3\frac{1}{2}$

See Example **4** Write a compound inequality for each statement.

9. A number s is either less than -5 or greater than or equal to 3. $s < -5$ or $s \ge 3$

10. A number t is both greater than -10 and less than 1. $-10 < t < 1$

INDEPENDENT PRACTICE

See Example **1** Write an inequality for each situation.

11. Fewer than 10 students rode their bikes to the game. $s < 10$

12. No more than 18 people may ride the roller coaster at one time. $p \le 18$

See Example **2** Write an inequality for each statement.

13. A number x decreased by 11 is less than 35. $x - 11 < 35$

14. Three times a number n is greater than $4\frac{1}{3}$. $3n > 4\frac{1}{3}$

15. A number y divided by 7 is at most 10. $\frac{y}{7} \le 10$

See Example **3** Graph each inequality.

16. $m \ge -3$ 17. $s < 1.5$ 18. $-2 < x$ 19. $4 \ge y$

20. $b < -1$ 21. $x \ge 0$ 22. $n \le \frac{1}{2}$ 23. $-2\frac{1}{2} < c$

See Example **4** Write a compound inequality for each statement.

24. A number x is both less than 1.5 and greater than or equal to 0. $0 \le x < 1.5$

25. A number c is either greater than or equal to $\frac{1}{2}$ or less than or equal to -7. $c \ge \frac{1}{2}$ or $c \le -7$

PRACTICE AND PROBLEM SOLVING

Extra Practice
See page EP7.

26. Suly earned 87 points on her first test and p points on her second test. She needs a total of at least 140 points on the two tests to pass the class. Write an inequality for this situation. $87 + p \ge 140$

REVIEW FOR MASTERY 3-5

LESSON Review for Mastery
3-5 *Inequalities*

The table summarizes how to graph inequalities.

Inequality	Words	Graph
$x > -2$	All numbers greater than -2	$-5\ -4\ -3\ -2\ -1\ 0\ 1\ 2\ 3\ 4\ 5$ The *open circle* at -2 shows that the value -2 is *not* included in the graph.
$x \ge -2$	All numbers greater than or equal to -2	$-5\ -4\ -3\ -2\ -1\ 0\ 1\ 2\ 3\ 4\ 5$ The *closed circle* at -2 shows that the value -2 *is* included in the graph.
$x < -2$	All numbers less than -2	$-5\ -4\ -3\ -2\ -1\ 0\ 1\ 2\ 3\ 4\ 5$
$x \le -2$	All numbers less than or equal to -2	$-5\ -4\ -3\ -2\ -1\ 0\ 1\ 2\ 3\ 4\ 5$

Graph each inequality.

1. $x > 3$
• Read $x > 3$ as "x is greater than 3."
• Draw an open circle at 3.
• Draw an arrow to the right of 3.
$-5\ -4\ -3\ -2\ -1\ 0\ 1\ 2\ 3\ 4\ 5$

2. $x \le -1$
• Read $x \le -1$ as "x is less than or equal to -1."
• Draw a closed circle at -1.
• Draw an arrow to the left of -1.
$-5\ -4\ -3\ -2\ -1\ 0\ 1\ 2\ 3\ 4\ 5$

3. $x < 5$
$-5\ -4\ -3\ -2\ -1\ 0\ 1\ 2\ 3\ 4\ 5$

4. $x \ge -4$
$-5\ -4\ -3\ -2\ -1\ 0\ 1\ 2\ 3\ 4\ 5$

5. $x > 0$
$-5\ -4\ -3\ -2\ -1\ 0\ 1\ 2\ 3\ 4\ 5$

6. $x < \frac{1}{2}$
$-5\ -4\ -3\ -2\ -1\ 0\ 1\ 2\ 3\ 4\ 5$

PRACTICE 3-5

LESSON Practice B
3-5 *Inequalities*

Write an inequality for each situation.

1. There are no more than 7 peaches in the bowl. $x \le 7$

2. The aquarium contains more than 20 fish. $x > 20$

3. The length of the branch is at most 11 inches. $x \le 11$

4. Mike has at least 6 pencils in his backpack. $x \ge 6$

Write an inequality for each statement.

5. A number s increased by 3 is at least 19. $s + 3 \ge 19$

6. A number m decreased by 10 is less than 25. $m - 10 < 25$

7. Twice a number y is no more than 12. $2y \le 12$

8. The sum of 4 and a number p is greater than 9. $4 + p > 9$

Graph each inequality.

9. $x \ge -3$
$-5\ -4\ -3\ -2\ -1\ 0\ 1\ 2\ 3\ 4\ 5$

10. $n < 4$
$-5\ -4\ -3\ -2\ -1\ 0\ 1\ 2\ 3\ 4\ 5$

11. $g \le -2$
$-5\ -4\ -3\ -2\ -1\ 0\ 1\ 2\ 3\ 4\ 5$

12. $y > \frac{1}{2}$
$-5\ -4\ -3\ -2\ -1\ 0\ 1\ 2\ 3\ 4\ 5$

Write a compound inequality for each statement.

13. A number x is either less than 8 or greater than 15. $x < 8$ or $x > 15$

14. A number t is greater than -4 and less than or equal to -1. $t > -4$ and $t \le -1$

15. A number m is greater than or equal to 0 and less than 6.1. $m \ge 0$ and $m < 6.1$

Write an inequality for each statement.

27. A number w multiplied by 5 is no less than 60. $5w \geq 60$

28. The sum of 10 and a number g is greater than 4.8. $10 + g > 4.8$

29. A number m decreased by $2\frac{2}{5}$ is at most $3\frac{1}{5}$. $m - 2\frac{2}{5} \leq 3\frac{1}{5}$

Write an inequality shown by each graph.

30.
$-4\ -2\ \ 0\ \ 2\ \ 4\ \ 6\ \ 8$
$x < 6$

31.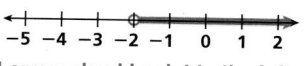
$0\ \ 2\ \ 4\ \ 6\ \ 8\ \ 10\ \ 12$
$x \leq 9$

32.
$-4\ -2\ \ 0\ \ 2\ \ 4\ \ 6\ \ 8$
$x > 4$

33.
$-4\ -2\ \ 0\ \ 2\ \ 4\ \ 6\ \ 8$
$x \geq 4$

34. **Business** A cafe sells fruit smoothies for $3.50 each. The manager of the cafe wants the total daily revenue from the smoothies to be at least $175. Assume the cafe sells n smoothies per day. Write an inequality that represents the manager's goal. $3.50n \geq 175$

35. **Astronomy** The diameter of Jupiter, the largest planet in the Solar System, is 89,000 miles. Let d be the diameter of any planet in the Solar System. Write an inequality for d. $d \leq 89,000$

36. **What's the Error?** A student was asked to graph the inequality $-2 > n$. Explain the student's error in the graph at right. **The shaded arrow should point to the left of -2.**

$-5\ -4\ -3\ -2\ -1\ \ 0\ \ 1\ \ 2$

37. **Switch the order of the 4 and the x, and change the direction of the inequality symbol: $x \geq 4$**

37. **Write About It** In mathematics, the conventional way to write an inequality is with the variable on the left, such as $x > 5$. Explain how to rewrite the inequality $4 \leq x$ in the conventional way.

38. **Challenge** Write an inequality for the statement "14 less than twice a number x is greater than three times the number." $2x - 14 > 3x$

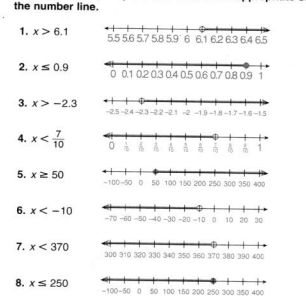

SPIRAL STANDARDS REVIEW

NS1.1, NS1.2, AF1.1

39. **Multiple Choice** Which inequality represents the statement, "A number z decreased by 9 is no more than 20"?

Ⓐ $z - 9 < 20$　　Ⓑ $z - 9 \leq 20$　　Ⓒ $9 - z < 20$　　Ⓓ $9 - z \leq 20$

40. **Multiple Choice** Which inequality is shown by the graph?

$-5\ -4\ -3\ -2\ -1\ \ 0\ \ 1\ \ 2$

Ⓐ $x < -4$　　Ⓑ $x \leq -4$　　Ⓒ $x > -4$　　Ⓓ $x \geq -4$

Write each set of integers in order from least to greatest. (Lesson 1-3)

41. $-19, -25, -12$　42. $-4, 0, 4, -3$　43. $-5, -9, -7, -11$　44. $-2, 6, -5, 0$
　$-25, -19, -12$　　$-4, -3, 0, 4$　　$-11, -9, -7, -5$　　$-5, -2, 0, 6$

Add or subtract. Write each answer in simplest form. (Lesson 2-3)

45. $\frac{17}{121} - \frac{6}{121}$　$\frac{1}{11}$　46. $-\frac{1}{7} + \left(-\frac{8}{7}\right)$　$-1\frac{2}{7}$　47. $-\frac{29}{12} + \frac{13}{12}$　$-1\frac{1}{3}$　48. $\frac{29}{5} - \frac{45}{5}$　$-3\frac{1}{5}$

CHALLENGE 3-5

Challenge
3-5 **A Sense of Scale**

It is important to think about the scale of the number line when you graph an inequality. For example, it is difficult to show the inequality $x < 3.1$ on a number line that goes from -5 to 5 because it is hard to distinguish 3.1 from 3.

$x < 3.1$
$-5-4-3-2-1\ 0\ 1\ 2\ 3\ 4\ 5$

It is better to "zoom in" on the section of the number line near 3. On the number line at right, the spaces between the tick marks represent 0.1.

$x < 3.1$
$2.5\ 2.6\ 2.7\ 2.8\ 2.9\ 3\ 3.1\ 3.2\ 3.3\ 3.4\ 3.5$

When graphing inequalities with large numbers, you might change the scale so that the spaces between the tick marks represent 10, 50, or 100.

$x \leq 700$
$-100\ 0\ 100\ 200\ 300\ 400\ 500\ 600\ 700\ 800\ 900$

Graph each inequality. Be sure to mark an appropriate scale on the number line.

1. $x > 6.1$　5.5 5.6 5.7 5.8 5.9 6 6.1 6.2 6.3 6.4 6.5

2. $x \leq 0.9$　0 0.1 0.2 0.3 0.4 0.5 0.6 0.7 0.8 0.9 1

3. $x > -2.3$　$-2.5\ -2.4\ -2.3\ -2.2\ -2.1\ -2\ -1.9\ -1.8\ -1.7\ -1.6\ -1.5$

4. $x < \frac{7}{10}$

5. $x \geq 50$　$-100\ -50\ 0\ 50\ 100\ 150\ 200\ 250\ 300\ 350\ 400$

6. $x < -10$　$-70\ -60\ -50\ -40\ -30\ -20\ -10\ 0\ 10\ 20\ 30$

7. $x < 370$　300 310 320 330 340 350 360 370 380 390 400

8. $x \leq 250$　$-100\ -50\ 0\ 50\ 100\ 150\ 200\ 250\ 300\ 350\ 400$

PROBLEM SOLVING 3-5

Problem Solving
3-5 **Inequalities**

Write the correct answer.

1. While shopping online, Jenny orders a CD that costs $14 and a book that costs b dollars. If she spends at least $25 she gets free shipping. Write an inequality for this situation.

$14 + b \geq 25$

2. An aquarium is filled with 20 gallons of water. Ernesto removes g gallons of water. He wants to leave more than 12 gallons of water in the aquarium. Write an inequality for this situation.

$20 - g > 12$

3. A chef takes c cartons of eggs from the refrigerator. Each carton contains 12 eggs. The chef wants to have a total of at least 50 eggs. Write an inequality for this situation.

$12c \geq 50$

4. Dee watches 25 minutes of a 90-minute DVD. Then she watches another m minutes, but she still does not reach the end of the DVD. Write an inequality for this situation.

$25 + m < 90$

The table gives the heights of some well-known landmarks. Use the table for Exercises 5-7. Select the best answer.

5. The height s of the Sears Tower in Chicago is not less than the height of the Eiffel Tower. Which inequality represents this situation?
A $s < 984$　　C $s > 984$
B $s \leq 984$　　D $s \geq 984$

6. The height p of the Great Pyramid in Giza, Egypt, is greater than the height of the Statue of Liberty. Which inequality represents this situation?
F $151 < p$　　H $151 > p$
G $151 \leq p$　　J $151 \geq p$

7. The height g of the Gateway Arch in St. Louis is greater than the height of the Washington Monument and no greater than the height of the Hoover Dam. Which compound inequality represents this situation?
A $555 < g < 726$
B $555 < g \leq 726$
C $555 \leq g < 726$
D $555 \leq g \leq 726$

Heights of Famous Landmarks	
Landmark	Height (feet)
Statue of Liberty	151
Washington Monument	555
Hoover Dam	726
Eiffel Tower	984

Source: http://www.infoplease.com/

✓ **3-5**
Lesson Quiz
Write an inequality for each situation.

1. Fewer than 150 people bought tickets. $p < 150$

2. There are at least 20 finches in the cage. $f \geq 20$

Write an inequality for each statement.

3. A number n decreased by 5 is at most 16. $n - 5 \leq 16$

4. The product of 15 and a number z is greater than 100. $15z > 100$

Graph each inequality.

5. $m \leq 1$
$-4\ -3\ -2\ -1\ \ 0\ \ 1\ \ 2\ \ 3\ \ 4$

6. $-3 < y$
$-4\ -3\ -2\ -1\ \ 0\ \ 1\ \ 2\ \ 3\ \ 4$

Also available on transparency

Objective: Students solve one-step inequalities by using addition or subtraction.

Online Edition
Tutorial Videos

Countdown to Mastery Week 6

Power Presentations with PowerPoint®

Warm Up

Compare. Use < or >.

1. 5 ▉ 7   <
2. −3 ▉ −4   >
3. 2.5 ▉ −2.7   >
4. −8 ▉ −7   <

Solve.

5. $4 + y = 16$ 12
6. $m − 7 = 14$ 21
7. $−3 = 8 + w$ −11
8. $7 = t + 10$ −3

Also available on transparency

Math Humor

Question: How do solutions of inequalities buy movie tickets?

Answer: They wait on a number line.

California Standards

← **AF4.0** Students solve simple linear *equations* and *inequalities over the rational numbers.*

Why learn this? You can solve an inequality to find the amount of a nutrient that you should consume. (See Example 2.)

When you add or subtract the same number on both sides of an inequality, the resulting inequality will still be true.

$$-2 < 5$$
$$\underline{+7 \quad +7}$$
$$5 < 12$$

You can use this idea to solve inequalities. You find solution sets of inequalities the same way you find solutions of equations, by isolating the variable.

EXAMPLE 1 **Solving Inequalities by Adding or Subtracting**

Solve and graph.

A $x + 7 < -10$

$x + 7 < -10$

$\underline{-7 \quad -7}$ *Since 7 is added to x, subtract 7 from both sides.*

$x \quad < -17$

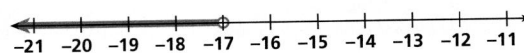

Helpful Hint

When checking your solution, choose numbers that are easy to work with. Remember to substitute the numbers into the original inequality.

Check

According to the graph, −20 should be a solution and 3 should *not* be a solution.

$x + 7 < -10$
$-20 + 7 \overset{?}{<} -10$ *Substitute −20 for x.*
$-13 \overset{?}{<} -10$ ✔

So −20 is a solution.

$x + 7 < -10$
$3 + 7 \overset{?}{<} -10$ *Substitute 3 for x.*
$10 \overset{?}{<} -10$ ✗

So 3 is not a solution.

B $t - 11 < -22$

$t - 11 \leq -22$

$\underline{+11 \quad +11}$ *Since 11 is subtracted from t, add 11 to both sides.*

$t \quad \leq -11$

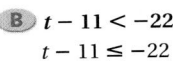

1 Introduce

Alternate Opener

EXPLORATION

3-6 Solving Inequalities by Adding or Subtracting

Ms. Marquez writes numbers on slips of paper and puts them in a hat. Students choose two slips of paper without looking. If the sum of the two numbers is no greater than 7, the student wins a prize.

1. The first number Sara chooses is 5. Suppose the second number is x. The expression $x + 5$ gives the sum of Sara's two numbers. Complete the table.

x	−6	−3.5	−1	0	0.5	1	2	2.5	3	5
$x+5$										

2. Circle all the values of x that result in a sum no greater than 7.

3. Plot the circled x-values on the number line. Then connect the points to form a ray.

4. The ray shows all the values of x that are solutions of the inequality $x + 5 \leq 7$. Describe these values in your own words.

Think and Discuss

5. Explain how the solutions of the inequality $x + 5 \leq 7$ are related to the inequality $x \leq 2$.

6. Describe the solutions of the inequality $x + 5 \geq 7$.

Motivate

Present the following situation to the class. Keith is driving to his cousin's house. He knows that the distance is no more than 75 miles and he knows that he has already driven 40 miles. Ask students how many more miles Keith must drive. Help students see that the problem involves an inequality and tell them that they will learn how to use one-step inequalities to solve the problem.

Explorations and answers are provided in *Alternate Openers: Explorations Transparencies.*

California Standards

Algebra and Functions ← **4.0**

Solve and graph.

C $z + 6 \geq -3$

$$z + 6 \geq -3$$
$$\underline{ -6 \quad -6} \qquad \textit{Since 6 is added to z, subtract 6 from both sides.}$$
$$z \quad\;\; \geq -9$$

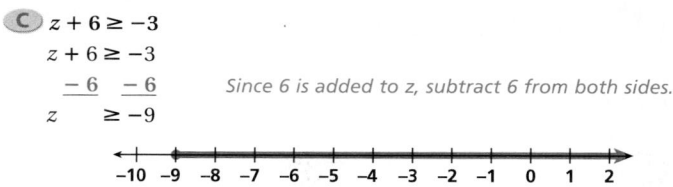

D $4\frac{1}{4} < n - 2\frac{1}{4}$

$$4\frac{1}{4} < n - 2\frac{1}{4}$$
$$\underline{+2\frac{1}{4} \qquad +2\frac{1}{4}} \qquad \textit{Since } 2\frac{1}{4} \textit{ is subtracted from n, add } 2\frac{1}{4} \textit{ to both sides.}$$
$$6\frac{1}{2} < n$$

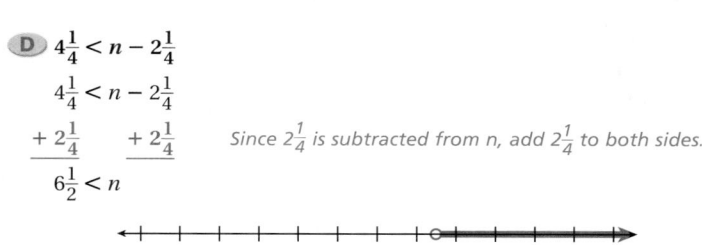

EXAMPLE 2 *Nutrition Application*

Manganese is a mineral that is found in nuts and grains. It is recommended that men consume at least 2.3 mg of manganese each day. Eric has consumed 0.9 mg today. Write and solve an inequality to find how many additional milligrams he should consume.

Let m = the number of additional milligrams of manganese.

0.9 milligrams	plus	additional milligrams	is at least	2.3 milligrams
0.9	+	m	$\geq$	2.3

$$0.9 + m \geq 2.3$$
$$\underline{-0.9 \qquad\;\; -0.9} \qquad \textit{Since 0.9 is added to m,}$$
$$m \geq 1.4 \qquad\qquad \textit{subtract 0.9 from both sides.}$$

Eric should consume at least 1.4 additional milligrams of manganese.

Check

$0.9 + m \geq 2.3$	*2 is greater*
$0.9 + 2 \overset{?}{\geq} 2.3$	*than 1.4.*
$2.9 \overset{?}{\geq} 2.3$ ✔	*Substitute 2 for m.*

$0.9 + m \geq 2.3$	*1 is less*
$0.9 + 1 \overset{?}{\geq} 2.3$	*than 1.4.*
$1.9 \overset{?}{\geq} 2.3$ ✗	*Substitute 1 for m.*

Possible answers to *Think and Discuss*

1. Use the inverse operation that will isolate the variable.

2. Substitute -11 for t and check whether the resulting inequality is true.

Think and Discuss

1. **Explain** how you know whether to use addition or subtraction to solve an inequality.

2. **Describe** how to check whether -11 is a solution of $6 > t - 4$.

Power Presentations with PowerPoint®

Additional Examples

Example 1

Solve and graph each inequality.

A. $x + 3 > -5$. $x > -8$

B. $m - 4 \geq -2$ $m \geq 2$

C. $r + 3 \leq -3$ $r \leq -6$

D. $5\frac{3}{4} > n + 1\frac{1}{4}$ $n < 4\frac{1}{2}$

Example 2

While training for a race, Ann's goal is to run at least 3.5 miles each day. She has already run 1.8 miles today. Write and solve an inequality to find out how many more miles she must run today.

$1.8 + x \geq 3.5$; $x \geq 1.7$

Also available on transparency

2 Teach

Guided Instruction

In this lesson, students learn to solve one-step inequalities by adding or subtracting. Begin by briefly reviewing how to graph inequalities. Then present the examples, emphasizing how the steps for solving an inequality are similar to the steps for solving an equation.

Reading Math Remind students that $x < 3$ is the same as $3 > x$, so the solution of an inequality can be written correctly in more than one way.

Universal Access

Through Auditory Cues

Remind students that certain key words in a problem can give them clues about the inequality symbol that will be used in the solution. For example, have a student read the problem in **Example 2** aloud. Then ask what the phrase "at least 2.3 milligrams of manganese each day" suggests about the solution of the problem.

Possible answer: The solution will involve a "greater than or equal to" inequality.

3 Close

Summarize

Have students solve each inequality.

1. $x + 5 > 12$ $x > 7$
2. $x - 5 > 12$ $x > 17$
3. $5 + x > 12$ $x > 7$
4. $-5 + x > 12$ $x > 17$

3-6 Exercises

California Standards Practice
NS1.2, AF1.1, AF4.0

go.hrw.com
Homework Help Online
KEYWORD: MT8CA 3-6
Parent Resources Online
KEYWORD: MT8CA Parent

Assignment Guide

If you finished Example **1** assign:
Proficient 1–6, 9–14, 23–25, 33, 35–40
Advanced 9–14, 17–25, 33, 35–40

If you finished Example **2** assign:
Proficient 1–16, 23–25, 27, 30, 33–40
Advanced 9–26, 29–40

Homework Quick Check

Quickly check key concepts.
Exercises: 10, 12, 14, 16

Answers

1. $x < -7$
-10 -8 -6 -4 -2 0

2. $b \geq 16$
11 12 13 14 15 16 17 18 19 20 21

3. $f < -24$
-30 -28 -26 -24 -22 -20

4–6, 9–14, 17–22, 26. See p. A1.

Math Background

There may be an infinite number of solutions of an inequality, so it is usually not possible to check all the solutions. You can check the endpoint of the solutions. For example, the solutions of $x + 7 < -10$ are given by $x < -17$. Check the endpoint by substituting -17 for x in the related equation $x + 7 = -10$. The endpoint should be a solution of the equation.

GUIDED PRACTICE

See Example **1** Solve and graph.

1. $x + 3 < -4$ $x < -7$
2. $4 + b \geq 20$ $b \geq 16$
3. $-6 + f < -30$ $f < -24$
4. $z - 8 > 13$ $z > 21$
5. $2.1 \leq k - 7.2$ $k \geq 9.3$
6. $x + \frac{1}{3} < 2$ $x < 1\frac{2}{3}$

See Example **2**

7. $6\frac{1}{2} + x \leq 16;$ $x \leq 9\frac{1}{2}$

7. A measuring cup can hold no more than 16 fluid ounces of liquid. Rosa pours $6\frac{1}{2}$ fluid ounces of water into the cup. Write and solve an inequality to determine how many additional fluid ounces of water she can add.

8. Paul's car can go at most 375 miles on one tank of gas. Paul fills the tank and then drives 167 miles. Write and solve an inequality to find out how many more miles Paul can drive before he will have to refill the tank.
$167 + x \leq 375; x \leq 208$

INDEPENDENT PRACTICE

See Example **1** Solve and graph.

9. $-7 + x \geq 49$ $x \geq 56$
10. $1 < t - 4$ $t > 5$
11. $-3 + x \geq 12$ $x \geq 15$
12. $0.6 + y \geq -0.72$ $y \geq -1.32$
13. $c + 5\frac{1}{3} < 8\frac{2}{3}$ $c < 3\frac{1}{3}$
14. $2 < a + (-5)$ $a > 7$

See Example **2**

15. **Consumer Math** A clothes store gives customers a free gift if they spend at least $50 in the store. Stacey plans to buy a pair of jeans that cost $21.75. Write and solve an inequality to show how much more she must spend in order to get the free gift. $21.75 + x \geq 50; x \geq 28.25$

16. **Consumer Math** Latrell's cell-phone plan allows him to talk for no more than 500 minutes per month. He has already used 288 minutes this month. Write and solve an inequality to determine how many more minutes he can talk on the phone this month. $288 + x \leq 500; x \leq 212$

PRACTICE AND PROBLEM SOLVING

Extra Practice
See page EP7.

Solve and graph.

17. $z - 0.75 > -0.75$ $z > 0$
18. $-\frac{2}{7} + x < 3$ $x < 3\frac{2}{7}$
19. $7 \leq y + 8.8$ $y \geq -1.8$
20. $m + (-12) \geq -6$ $m \geq 6$
21. $\frac{4}{5} \geq k - \frac{1}{5}$ $k \leq 1$
22. $-39.5 > -15.5 + g$ $g < -24$

You can use *set-builder notation* to write the solution of an inequality. For example, $\{x : x < 5\}$ means the set of all real numbers x such that x is less than 5. Solve each inequality and write the solution using set-builder notation.

23. $x + 12 < -8$
$\{x : x < -20\}$
24. $z - 4 \geq -16$
$\{z : z \geq -12\}$
25. $3.5 < b + 7$
$\{b : b > -3.5\}$

26. **Reasoning** When a number is added to -15, the result is greater than -12. What are the possible values of the number? Graph them on a number line. $x > 3$

California Standards

Standard	Exercises
NS1.2	35–38
AF1.1	7–8, 15–16, 27–28, 30, 34, 39–40
AF4.0	1–28, 32–33

27. Business Toshi Business Solutions will make a profit for the current year if their total sales are greater than their operating costs. Their accountants estimate that the company will have operating costs of $201,522 for the entire year. So far this year, the company has sales of $98,200.

a. Write and solve an inequality to find out how much more money Toshi must earn in sales for the remainder of the year to show a profit.

b. Check your answer. Then explain why your answer is reasonable.

28. Language Arts Danielle is reading one of the novels in the graph. She has already read 65 pages. Write and solve two different inequalities to find out how many pages she has left to read. (*Hint:* Write one inequality based on the minimum number of pages and one inequality based on the maximum number of pages.)

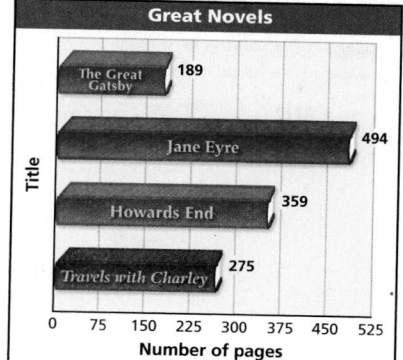

Great Novels

The Great Gatsby — 189
Jane Eyre — 494
Howards End — 359
Travels with Charley — 275

Title

Number of pages
0   75   150   225   300   375   450   525

29. Reasoning Substitute the values 1, 2, 3, 4, 5, and 6 for x in $10 - x \geq 6$. Use the results to make a conjecture about the solution of the inequality. The solution is $x \leq 4$.

 30. Write a Problem Write a word problem that can be answered by solving the inequality $x + 40 \leq 75$.

31. Write About It Explain how to check the solution of an inequality.

32. Challenge The inequality $y - \blacksquare < -3$ is missing a number. The solution of the inequality is shown on the number line. What is the missing number? 7

−2 −1 0 1 2 3 4 5

SPIRAL STANDARDS REVIEW   ⬦ NS1.2, AF1.1, ⬦ AF4.0

33. Multiple Choice Solve $m - 5 > -8$ for m.

Ⓐ $m > -13$ Ⓑ $m > -3$ Ⓒ $m > 3$ Ⓓ $m > 13$

34. Multiple Choice In the inequality $200 < 80 + x$, x is the length of a movie in minutes. Which phrase most accurately describes the length of the movie?

Ⓐ At least 120 minutes   Ⓒ At most 120 minutes

Ⓑ More than 120 minutes   Ⓓ Less than 120 minutes

Add or subtract. (Lesson 2-6)

35. $\frac{1}{4} + \frac{3}{7}$ $\frac{19}{28}$ **36.** $\frac{7}{20} + \frac{5}{8}$ $\frac{39}{40}$ **37.** $\frac{9}{10} - \frac{5}{6}$ $\frac{1}{15}$ **38.** $3\frac{4}{7} - 2\frac{1}{5}$ $1\frac{13}{35}$

Write an inequality for each statement. (Lesson 3-5)

39. A number t increased by 2 is less than 8. $t + 2 < 8$ **40.** Twice a number w is no more than 12. $2w \leq 12$

CHALLENGE 3-6

Challenge
3-6 You Make the Call

Sometimes, an inequality is expressed with words like *no* or *not*. But, the algebraic inequality may be clearer if you avoid those words.

Example
The fire regulation says that this restaurant may seat no more than 350 people.
• the inequality as stated: no more than 350
• the equivalent without *no*: less than or equal to 350
• algebraic inequality: Let x = the number of diners allowed. $x \leq 350$

Sometimes, two conditions of inequality can be expressed as a single inequality.

Example
$x > -9$ and $x < -3$ means that x is between -9 and -3, and can be written as $-9 < x < -3$.

Write an algebraic inequality, identifying what the variable represents.

1. The recipe calls for not less than 15 oz of butter.
   Let x = oz of butter; $x \geq 15$

2. Mr. Valdez says he cannot contribute more than $500.
   Let x = money contributed; $x \leq 500$

3. On his typing test, Philip can have no more than 4 errors to pass.
   Let x = errors allowed; $x \leq 4$

4. The team will have to score no fewer than 20 points to win.
   Let x = points needed; $x \geq 20$

5. This canister can hold at most 5 lb of rice.
   Let x = number of lb; $x \leq 5$

6. The sleeping bag is useful for camping when temperatures are above $-5°$F.
   Let x = degrees farenheit; $x \geq -5$

If x is a whole number, write the solution of each inequality.

7. $7 \leq x < 11$
   7; 8; 9; 10

8. $15 > x \geq 9$
   14; 13; 12; 11; 10; 9

9. $-2 < x < 7$
   -1, 0, 1, 2, 3, 4, 5, 6

10. $-10 \leq x < -5$
    $-10, -9, -8, -7, -6$

PROBLEM SOLVING 3-6

Problem Solving
3-6 Solving Inequalities by Adding or Subtracting

Use the table.

1. Write an inequality that compares the population p of Los Angeles to the population of New York.
   $p < 8,008,278$

2. Write an inequality that compares the population p of Los Angeles to the population of Chicago.
   $p > 2,896,016$

Top 3 U.S. Cities by Population 2000		
Rank	City	Population
1	New York	8,008,278
2	Los Angeles	p
3	Chicago	2,896,016

Write the correct answer.

3. Paul wants to ride his bike at least 30 miles this week to train for a race. He has already ridden 18 miles. How many more miles should Paul ride this week?
   $m \geq 12$ mi

4. To avoid a service charge, Jose must keep more than $500 in his account. His current balance is $536, but he plans to write a check for $157. Find the amount of the deposit d Jose must make to avoid a service charge.
   $d > 121$

Choose the letter for the best answer.

5. Mia wants to spend no more than $10 on an ad in the paper. The first 10 words cost $3. Find the amount of money m she has left to spend on the ad.
   A $m \geq 7$ C $m \leq 7$
   B $m \leq 13$ D $m \geq 13$

6. An auto shop estimates parts and labor for a repair will cost less than $200. Parts will cost $59. Find the maximum cost c of the labor.
   F $c < $141   H $c > $141
   G $c < $259   J $c > $259

7. To advance to the next level of a competition, Rachel must earn at least 180 points. She has already earned 145 points. Find the number of points p she needs to advance to the next level of the competition.
   A $p \leq 35$ C $p \geq 35$
   B $p \leq 325$ D $p \geq 325$

8. The Conway's hiked more than 25 miles on their backpacking trip. If they hiked 8 miles on their last day, find how many miles m they hiked on the rest of the trip.
   F $m > 17$ H $m < 17$
   G $m > 33$ J $m < 33$

Answers
27a. $98,200 + s > 201,522$;
$s > 103,322$
27b, 28, 30, 31. See p. A1.

Teaching Tip **Multiple Choice** If students selected choice **A** for **Exercise 33**, they may have subtracted 5 from both sides of the inequality. Remind students that they should use inverse operations to isolate the variable and that addition is the inverse operation of subtraction.

 Journal

Have students write an original problem that can be solved with an inequality. Then have students write out the steps in solving the problem.

Power Presentations with PowerPoint®

✓ 3-6
Lesson Quiz
Solve and graph each inequality.

1. $g - 7 < -3$ $g < 4$
−1 0 1 2 3 4 5 6 7 8 9

2. $5 + s \geq 4$ $s \geq -1$
−9 −8 −7 −6 −5 −4 −3 −2 −1 0 1

3. $-5.1 \leq x - 5.1$ $x \geq 0$
−1 0 1 2 3 4 5 6 7 8 9

4. $3\frac{1}{5} + y > 4$ $y > \frac{4}{5}$
0 $\frac{1}{5}$ $\frac{2}{5}$ $\frac{3}{5}$ $\frac{4}{5}$ 1 $1\frac{1}{5}$ $1\frac{2}{5}$ $1\frac{3}{5}$ $1\frac{4}{5}$ 2

5. Tasha is folding letters for a fundraiser. She knows there are at least 300 letters, and she has already folded 125 of them. Write and solve an inequality to show how many more letters she must fold. $125 + x \geq 300$; $x \geq 175$

Also available on transparency

Objective: Students solve one-step inequalities by using multiplication or division.

 Online Edition
Tutorial Videos, Interactivities

 Countdown to Mastery Week 6

Power Presentations
with PowerPoint®

Warm Up

Solve.

1. $2x + 8 = x - 7$ $x = -15$

2. $-4(x + 3) = -5x - 2$ $x = 10$

3. $5x + x + (-11) = 25 - 3x$
$x = 4$

4. $6n + 9 - 4n = 3n$ $n = 9$

Also available on transparency

Math Humor

What time is it when a father gives his daughter 15 cents and his son 10 cents? A quarter to two.

 **California Standards**

AF4.0 Students solve simple linear equations and inequalities over the rational numbers.
Also covered: **AF1.1**

Why learn this? You can solve an inequality to determine how many representatives voted on a bill. (See Exercise 18.)

When you multiply (or divide) both sides of an inequality by a negative number, you must reverse the inequality symbol to make the statement true.

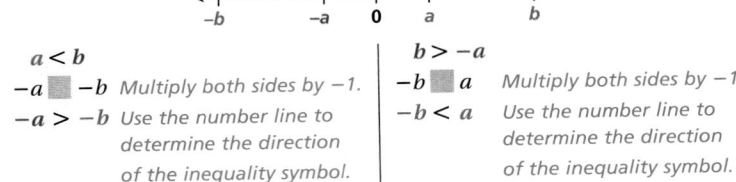

$a < b$
$-a \;\blacksquare\; -b$ *Multiply both sides by −1.*
$-a > -b$ *Use the number line to determine the direction of the inequality symbol.*

$b > -a$
$-b \;\blacksquare\; a$ *Multiply both sides by −1.*
$-b < a$ *Use the number line to determine the direction of the inequality symbol.*

EXAMPLE 1 **Solving Inequalities by Multiplying or Dividing**

Solve and graph.

A $24 > \dfrac{h}{5}$

$5 \cdot 24 > 5 \cdot \dfrac{h}{5}$ *Multiply both sides by 5.*

$120 > h$, or $h < 120$

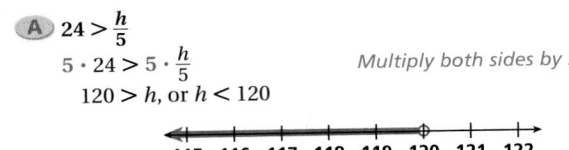

Remember!
When graphing an inequality on a number line, an open circle means that the point is not part of the solution and a closed circle means that the point is part of the solution.

Check
According to the graph, 119 should be a solution and 121 should not be a solution.

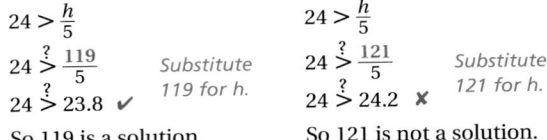

$24 > \dfrac{h}{5}$
$24 \overset{?}{>} \dfrac{119}{5}$ *Substitute 119 for h.*
$24 \overset{?}{>} 23.8$ ✔

So 119 is a solution.

$24 > \dfrac{h}{5}$
$24 \overset{?}{>} \dfrac{121}{5}$ *Substitute 121 for h.*
$24 \overset{?}{>} 24.2$ ✗

So 121 is not a solution.

B $-7x \geq 42$

$\dfrac{-7x}{-7} \leq \dfrac{42}{-7}$ *Divide both sides by −7; ≥ changes to ≤.*

$x \leq -6$

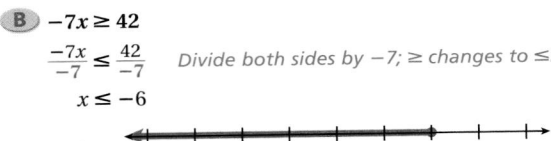

1 Introduce

Alternate Opener

EXPLORATION

3-7 **Solving Inequalities by Multiplying or Dividing**

You can discover an important property of inequalities by looking for patterns.

1. Multiply both sides of each inequality by 2. Write the resulting numbers under the original inequality as shown in 1a. Then insert the correct inequality symbol, < or >, to make the new inequality true.

a. $\dfrac{3}{6} > \dfrac{2}{4}$ b. $-4 < -1$ c. $2 > -3$

2. Multiply both sides of each inequality by −2. Write the resulting numbers under the original inequality as shown in 2a. Then insert the correct inequality symbol, < or >, to make the new inequality true.

a. $\dfrac{3}{-6} > \dfrac{2}{-4}$ b. $-4 < -1$ c. $2 > -3$

Think and Discuss
6. **Describe** any patterns you notice.
7. **Explain** what happens when you multiply both sides of an inequality by a negative number.

Motivate

Explain to students that inequalities are often used in real life to calculate the least amount or the greatest amount of a quantity. Teach students that the phrases, "more than," "less than," "least," and "greatest," are often clues that they are dealing with an inequality.

ENGLISH LANGUAGE LEARNERS

Explorations and answers are provided in *Alternate Openers: Explorations Transparencies.*

 **California Standards**

Algebra and Functions 🔑 **4.0**

Also covered:

Algebra and Functions
1.1 Use variables and appropriate operations to write an expression, an equation, **an inequality,** or a system of equations or inequalities **that represents a verbal description** (e.g., three less than a number, half as large as area A).

EXAMPLE 2 — PROBLEM SOLVING APPLICATION

PROBLEM SOLVING

If all the sheets of paper used by personal computer printers each year were laid end to end, they would circle Earth more than 800 times. Earth's circumference is about 25,120 mi (1,591,603,200 in.), and one letter-size sheet of paper is 11 in. long. About how many sheets of paper are used each year?

1 Understand the Problem

The **answer** is the number of sheets of paper used by personal computer printers in one year. **List the important information:**

• The amount of paper would circle the earth *more than* 800 times.
• Once around Earth is approximately 1.6 billion in.
• One sheet of paper is 11 in. long.

Show the relationship of the information:

| the number of sheets of paper | · | the length of one sheet | > | 800 | · | the distance around Earth |

2 Make a Plan

Use the relationship to *write an inequality*. Let x represent the number of sheets of paper.

| x | · | 11 in. | > | 800 | · | 1.6 billion in. |

3 Solve

$11x > 800 \cdot 1.6$

$11x > 1280$ *Simplify.*

$\dfrac{11x}{11} > \dfrac{1280}{11}$ *Divide both sides by 11.*

$x > 116.36$

More than 116 billion sheets of paper are used by personal computer printers in one year.

4 Look Back

To circle Earth once takes $\frac{1,600,000,000}{11} \approx 145,454,545$ sheets of paper; to circle it 800 times would take $800 \cdot 145,454,545 \approx 116,363,636,000$ sheets.

Think and Discuss

1. Give all the symbols that make $5 \cdot -3 \quad\blacksquare\quad 15$ true. Explain.

2. Explain how you would solve the inequality $-4x \leq 24$.

COMMON ERROR ALERT

Students will sometimes insert the inequality symbol facing the wrong direction. To help students correct this error, have them verbalize what the inequality is expressing.

Power Presentations with PowerPoint®

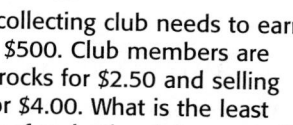

Additional Examples

Example 1

Solve and graph.

A. $12 < \frac{a}{4}$ $a > 48$

43 44 45 46 47 48 49 50 51 52

B. $-9b \leq 45$ $b \geq -5$

−10 −8 −6 −4 −2 0

Example 2

A rock-collecting club needs to earn at least $500. Club members are buying rocks for $2.50 and selling them for $4.00. What is the least number of rocks the club must sell to make the goal? 334 rocks

Also available on transparency

Possible answers to Think and Discuss

1. $<$, $\leq$; Since -15 is less than 15, it can be either sign that includes less than.

2. Divide both sides by -4. Reverse the inequality symbol, since you are dividing by a negative number; $x \geq -6$

---

2 Teach

Guided Instruction

In this lesson, students solve and graph inequalities by using multiplication and division. It is helpful to point out to students that solving inequalities is often similar to solving equations. Show students an example of the number line at the beginning of the lesson using numbers instead of variables. Point out that if you multiply or divide by a negative number on both sides you must reverse the inequality sign.

Universal Access
Through Visual Cues

Have students identify when they multiply or divide by a negative number with a highlighter in their notebook. By making a special effort to identify these instances, they will pay careful attention to when they need to reverse the inequality sign.

3 Close

Summarize

Remind students that to solve and graph inequalities using multiplication and division, they should do the following:

• Reverse the inequality when multiplying or dividing both sides of an inequality by a negative number.

• Use closed endpoints for $\leq$, $\geq$ and open endpoints for $<$ or $>$.

• Check graphs by choosing a number in the solution set of the inequality and make sure it is highlighted in the graph.

3-7 Exercises

Assignment Guide

If you finished Example **1** assign:
Proficient 1–8, 10–17, 19–22, 33–34, 38–44
Advanced 10–17, 22–30, 33–35, 38–44

If you finished Example **2** assign:
Proficient 1–22, 31–34, 38–44
Advanced 10–18, 22–44

Homework Quick Check

Quickly check key concepts.
Exercises: 10, 18, 22, 34

Answers

1. 15 16 17 18 19 20 21 22 23
2. -7 -5 -3 -1 1 3
3. 100 110 120 130 140
4. 1 2 3 4 5 6 7 8 9 10
5. -44 -43 -42 -41 -40 -39 -38 -37
6. 13 14 15 16 17 18 19 20 21 22
7. -68 -66 -64 -62 -60
8. -8 -6 -4 -2 0

10–17, 19–26. See pp. A1–2.

31. Possible answer: The total weight of the cartons cannot exceed 2,200 pounds, so $42w \le 2,200 \to w \le 52.38$. This means that no more than 52 cartons can be carried on the elevator at one time if no people ride with them.

32. Possible answer: Since Marisol spends twice as much time reading as she spends doing homework, $\frac{r}{2} \ge 40 \to r \ge 80$. That means Marisol can spend at least 80 min, or 1 hr 20 min, reading.

California Standards

Standard	Exercises
NS1.2 🔑	40–43
AF1.1	9, 18, 27–32, 36–37, 39, 44
AF4.0 🔑	1–35, 37, 39

3-7 Exercises

California Standards Practice
AF1.1, 🔑 AF4.0
go.hrw.com
Homework Help Online
KEYWORD: MT8CA 3-7
Parent Resources Online
KEYWORD: MT8CA Parent

GUIDED PRACTICE

See Example **1** Solve and graph.

1. $\frac{r}{3} > 6$ $r > 18$
2. $-4w > 12$ $w < -3$
3. $20 \ge \frac{j}{6}$ $120 \ge j$
4. $6r \le 30$ $r \le 5$
5. $10 \le \frac{a}{-4}$ $a \le -40$
6. $-36 < -2m$ $18 > m$
7. $\frac{r}{-3} < 21$ $r > -63$
8. $-20 \ge 5x$ $-4 \ge x$

See Example **2** 9. The owner of a sandwich shop is selling the special of the week for $5.90. At this price, he makes a profit of $3.85 on each sandwich sold. To make a total profit of at least $400 from the special, what is the least number of sandwiches he must sell? **104 sandwiches**

INDEPENDENT PRACTICE

See Example **1** Solve and graph.
10. $-8 < r$

10. $-16 < 2r$
11. $15 < \frac{x}{5}$ $75 < x$
12. $-18w \ge -54$ $w \le 3$
13. $11 \le \frac{p}{-7}$ $-77 \ge p$
14. $\frac{t}{9} > 4$ $t > 36$
15. $9h > 108$ $h > 12$
16. $\frac{a}{-7} < 14$ $a > -98$
17. $-16q \le 64$ $q \ge -4$

See Example **2** 18. **Social Studies** A bill in the U.S. House of Representatives passed because at least $\frac{2}{3}$ of the members present voted in favor of it. If the bill received 284 votes, at least how many members of the House of Representatives were present for the vote? **426 members**

PRACTICE AND PROBLEM SOLVING

Extra Practice
See page EP7.
19. $6 > r$

Solve and graph.
19. $-18 < -3r$
20. $27 < \frac{x}{-3}$ $-81 > x$
21. $17w \ge -51$ $w \ge -3$
22. $101 \le \frac{p}{-7}$ $-707 \ge p$
23. $\frac{t}{-19} > -5$ $t < 95$
24. $3h > 108$ $h > 36$
25. $\frac{a}{10} < 12$ $a < 120$
26. $-6q \le -72$ $q \ge 12$

Write and solve an algebraic inequality.
27. Nine times a number is less than 99. Possible answer: $9x < 99$, $x < 11$
28. The quotient of a number and 6 is at least 8. Possible answer: $\frac{n}{6} \ge 8$, $n \ge 48$
29. The product of -7 and a number is no more than -63. Possible answer: $-7x \le -63$, $x \ge 9$
30. The quotient of some number and 3 is greater than 18. Possible answer: $\frac{n}{3} > 18$, $n > 54$

Write and solve an algebraic inequality. Then explain the solution.
31. A school receives a shipment of books. There are 60 cartons, and each carton weighs 42 pounds. The school's elevator can hold 2200 pounds. What is the greatest number of cartons that can be carried on the elevator at one time if no people ride with them?
32. Each evening, Marisol spends at least twice as much time reading as she spends doing homework. If Marisol works on her homework for 40 minutes, how much time can she spend reading?

REVIEW FOR MASTERY 3-7

Review for Mastery
3-7 *Solving Inequalities by Multiplying or Dividing*

To solve an inequality, multiply and divide the same way you would solve an equation. But, if you multiply or divide by a negative number, you must reverse the inequality sign.

Divide by a Positive Number
$2x < 14$
$\frac{2x}{2} < \frac{14}{2}$
$x < 7$
4 5 6 7 8 9

To check your solution, choose two numbers from the graph and substitute them into the original equation. Choose a number that should be a solution and a number that should not be a solution.

Divide by a Negative Number
$-2x < 14$
$\frac{-2x}{-2} > \frac{14}{-2}$ Reverse the inequality sign.
$x > -7$
-9 -8 -7 -6 -5 -4

Check
According to the graph, -6 should be a solution, but -8 should not be.
$-2x < 14$ $-2x < 14$
$-2 \cdot -8 \stackrel{?}{>} 14$ $-2 \cdot -6 \stackrel{?}{>} 14$
$-8 > -7$ ✗ $-6 > -7$ ✔

Complete to solve. Then graph the equation and check.
1. $-3y \ge 24$
$\frac{-3y}{-3} \le \frac{24}{-3}$
$y \le -8$
-12 -11 -10 -9 -8 -7
Values used to check solution will vary, but should include one number ≤ -8 and one number > -8.

2. $\frac{s}{-9} < 4$
$\frac{s}{-9} \cdot -9 > -9 \cdot 4$
$s > -36$
-38 -37 -36 -35 -34 -33
Values used to check solution will vary, but should include one number ≤ -36 and one number > -36.

PRACTICE 3-7

Practice B
3-7 *Solving Inequalities by Multiplying or Dividing*

Solve and graph.
1. $\frac{m}{-5} \le 4$ $m \ge -20$
-21 -20 -19 -18 -17 -16
2. $-16 < -8n$ $n < 2$
-1 0 1 2 3 4
3. $7p \ge 49$ $p \ge 7$
6 7 8 9 10 11
4. $10 > \frac{q}{2}$ $q < 20$
17 18 19 20 21 22
5. $-\frac{r}{3} \le 15$ $r \ge -45$
-47 -46 -45 -44 -43 -42
6. $22 > -2s$ $s > -11$
-13 -12 -11 -10 -9 -8
7. $-6t < -24$ $t > 4$
3 4 5 6 7 8
8. $\frac{v}{20} \ge 2$ $v \ge 40$
38 39 40 41 42 43

9. On a snorkeling trip, Antonia dove at least 7 times as deep as Lucy did. If Antonia dove 35 feet below the ocean's surface, what was the deepest that Lucy dove?
5 feet
10. Last week, Saul ran more than one-fifth the distance that his friend Omar ran. If Saul ran 14 miles last week, how far did Omar run?
less than 70 miles

146 Chapter 3 Multi-Step Equations and Inequalities

Choose the graph that represents each inequality.

33. $-2y < 14$

A.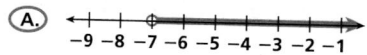
   $-9\ -8\ -7\ -6\ -5\ -4\ -3\ -2\ -1$

B.
   $-12\ -11\ -10\ -9\ -8\ -7\ -6\ -5$

C.
   $5\ \ 6\ \ 7\ \ 8\ \ 9\ \ 10\ \ 11\ \ 12\ \ 13$

34. $6 \geq \dfrac{h}{5}$

A.
   $28\ \ 29\ \ 30\ \ 31\ \ 32\ \ 33\ \ 34\ \ 35\ \ 36$

B.
   $25\ \ 26\ \ 27\ \ 28\ \ 29\ \ 30\ \ 31\ \ 32\ \ 33$

C.
   $25\ \ 26\ \ 27\ \ 28\ \ 29\ \ 30\ \ 31\ \ 32\ \ 33$

35. Possible answer: The student reversed the direction of the inequality sign that should be reversed only when multiplying or dividing by a negative number.

36. Possible answer: The product of 3 and some number is no more than 21; the product of 3 and some number is at most 21; the product of 3 and some number is less than or equal to 21.

35. What's the Error? A student solved $x \div 3 \geq 12$ and got an answer of $x \leq 36$. What error did the student make?

36. Write About It The expressions *no more than*, *at most*, and *less than or equal to* all indicate the same relationship between values. Write a problem that uses this relationship. Write the problem using each of the three expressions.

37. Challenge Angel weighs 5 times as much as his dog. When they stand on a scale together, the scale gives a reading of less than 163 pounds. If both their weights are whole numbers, what is the most each can weigh?
27 lb, 135 lb

 **SPIRAL STANDARDS REVIEW** ← NS1.2, AF1.1, ← AF4.0

38. Multiple Choice Which inequality is shown by the graph?

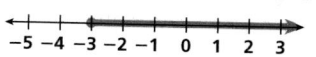
$-5\ -4\ -3\ -2\ -1\ \ 0\ \ 1\ \ 2\ \ 3$

Ⓐ $w \leq -3$ Ⓑ $w > -3$ Ⓒ $w \geq -3$ Ⓓ $-3 < w$

39. Gridded Response In order to have the $200 he needs for a bike, Kevin plans to put money away each week for the next 15 weeks. What is the minimum amount in dollars that Kevin will need to average each week in order to reach his goal? **13.34**

Multiply. Write each answer in simplest form. (Lesson 2-4)

40. $-\dfrac{3}{7}\left(-\dfrac{9}{14}\right)$ $\dfrac{27}{98}$ **41.** $\dfrac{11}{15}\left(-\dfrac{25}{121}\right)$ $-\dfrac{5}{33}$ **42.** $7\dfrac{1}{8}\left(\dfrac{4}{9}\right)$ $3\dfrac{1}{6}$ **43.** $-5\left(1\dfrac{2}{3}\right)$ $-8\dfrac{1}{3}$

44. Frank needs to earn at least $350. He earns $15 for each hour h that he babysits. Write an inequality that represents Frank's goal. (Lesson 3-5) $15h \geq 350$

CHALLENGE 3-7

LESSON 3-7 Challenge
Compounding the Problem

Inequalities that have more than one inequality sign are compound inequalities. You can solve them the same way you solve other inequalities. But, you must check to be sure the solution makes sense.

Example 1
$4 < 2x < 10$
$\dfrac{4}{2} < \dfrac{2x}{2} < \dfrac{10}{2}$ Divide each part by 2.
$2 < x < 5$ This means that $x > 2$ and $x < 5$. That makes sense.

$1\ \ 2\ \ 3\ \ 4\ \ 5\ \ 6$

Example 2
$-4 \geq \dfrac{x}{-3} \geq 2$
$-3 \cdot -4 \leq -3 \cdot \dfrac{x}{-3} \leq -3 \cdot 2$ Multiply each part by -3. Reverse the inequality symbols.
$12 \leq x \leq -6$ This means that $x \geq 12$ and $x \leq -6$. That does not make sense, so the inequality has no solution.

Solve and graph. If the inequality has no solution, write no solution.

1. $5 > \dfrac{x}{5} > 3$
   $25 > x > 15$
   $10\ \ 15\ \ 20\ \ 25\ \ 30\ \ 35$

2. $14 \leq 2y < 18$
   $7 \leq y < 9$
   $6\ \ 7\ \ 8\ \ 9\ \ 10\ \ 11$

3. $20 < -5z < 35$
   $-4 > z > -7$
   $-8\ -7\ -6\ -5\ -4\ -3$

4. $1 \leq \dfrac{b}{-2} < -2$
   $-2 \geq b > 4$; no solution

PROBLEM SOLVING 3-7

LESSON 3-7 Problem Solving
Solving Inequalities by Multiplying or Dividing

Write the correct answer.

1. A bottle contains at least 4 times as much juice as a glass contains. The bottle contains 32 fluid ounces. Write an inequality that shows this relationship.
   $4x \leq 32$

2. Solve the inequality in Exercise 1. What is the greatest amount the glass could contain?
   $x \leq 8$; 8 fluid ounces

3. In the triple jump, Katrina jumped less than one-third the distance that Paula jumped. Katrina jumped 5 ft 6 in. Write an inequality that shows this relationship.
   $\dfrac{x}{3} > 66$

4. Solve the inequality in Exercise 3. How far could Paula could have jumped?
   $x > 198$; more than 198 in., or 16 ft 6 in.

Choose the letter for the best answer.

5. Melinda earned at least 3 times as much money this month as last month. She earned $567 this month. Which inequality shows this relationship?
   A $567 < x$ C $567 > 3x$
   B $567 < 3x$ D $567 \geq 3x$

6. The shallow end of a pool is less than one-quarter as deep as the deep end. The shallow end is 3 feet deep. Which inequality shows this relationship?
   F $4 > 3x$ Ⓗ $\dfrac{x}{4} > 3$
   G $4x < 3$ J $\dfrac{x}{4} < 3$

7. Arthur worked in the garden more than half as long as his brother. Arthur worked 6 hours in the garden. How long did his brother work in the garden?
   A less than 3 hours
   B 3 hours
   Ⓒ less than 12 hours
   D more than 12 hours

8. The distance from Bill's house to the library is no more than 5 times the distance from his house to the park. If Bill's house is 10 miles from the library, what is the greatest distance his house could be from the park?
   Ⓕ 2 miles
   G more than 2 miles
   H 20 miles
   J less than 20 miles

FORMATIVE ASSESSMENT
and INTERVENTION ◄ ►

Diagnose Before the Lesson
3-7 Warm Up, TE p. 144

Monitor During the Lesson
3-7 Know-It Notebook
3-7 Questioning Strategies

Assess After the Lesson
3-7 Lesson Quiz, TE p. 147

Teaching Tip **Gridded Response** If students have difficulty with **Exercise 39**, have them write an inequality to represent the amount Kevin needs to save each week. They should begin with the inequality $200 \leq 15d$, such that d is the amount in dollars saved each week. They should simplify this to $13.33 \leq d$ or $d \geq 13.33$. Kevin should save at least $13.34 per week to make his goal of $200.

 Journal

Ask students to describe some real-world situations in which they might use an inequality.

Power Presentations with PowerPoint®

✓ **3-7 Lesson Quiz**

Solve and graph.

1. $-14x > 28$ $x < -2$
   $-7\ \ -5\ \ -3\ \ -1\ \ \ 1\ \ \ 3$

2. $\dfrac{x}{3} < 15$ $x < 45$
   $41\ 42\ 43\ 44\ 45\ 46\ 47\ 48\ 49\ 50$

3. $18 < -6x$ $-3 > x$
   $-8\ \ -6\ \ -4\ \ -2\ \ \ 0\ \ \ 2$

4. $\dfrac{q}{8} \geq 5$ $q \geq 40$
   $35\ 36\ 37\ 38\ 39\ 40\ 41\ 42\ 43\ 44$

5. Jared isn't supposed to carry more than 35 pounds in his backpack. He has 8 textbooks and each book weighs 5 pounds. What is the greatest amount of textbooks he can carry in his backpack at one time?
   No more than 7

Also available on transparency

Objective: Students solve two-step inequalities and graph the solutions of an inequality on a number line.

 Hands-On Lab
In *Chapter 3 Resource File*

Online Edition
Tutorial Videos

 Countdown to Mastery Week 6

Power Presentations
with PowerPoint®

Warm Up

Solve.

1. $6x + 36 = 2x$ $x = -9$
2. $4x - 13 = 15 + 5x$ $x = -28$
3. $5(x - 3) = 2x + 3$ $x = 6$
4. $\frac{7}{8} + x = \frac{13}{16}$ $x = -\frac{1}{16}$

Also available on transparency

Math Humor

What did the marine biologist call an algebraic expression consisting of 8 terms added together? An *octo-plus*

3-8 Solving Two-Step Inequalities

California Standards

AF4.1 Solve two-step linear equations and **inequalities in one variable over the rational numbers, interpret the solution or solutions in the context from which they arose,** and verify the reasonableness of the results.

Why learn this? Drama club members can use two-step inequalities to determine how many tickets they must sell to a musical to break even. (See Example 3.)

When you solved two-step equations, you used the order of operations in reverse to isolate the variable. You can use the same process when solving two-step inequalities.

EXAMPLE 1 Solving Two-Step Inequalities

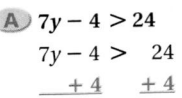
Math Builders

For more on solving two-step inequalities, see the Step-by-Step Solution Builder on page MB4.

Solve and graph.

A $7y - 4 > 24$

$$7y - 4 > 24$$
$$\underline{+ 4 \quad\quad + 4}$$ *Since 4 is subtracted from 7y, add 4 to both sides.*
$$7y > 28$$

$$\frac{7y}{7} > \frac{28}{7}$$ *Since y is multiplied by 7, divide both sides by 7.*

$$y > 4$$

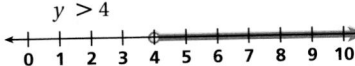

Check
According to the graph, 10 should be a solution and 0 should *not* be a solution.

$$7y - 4 > 24$$
$$7(10) - 4 \overset{?}{>} 24 \quad \text{Substitute}$$
$$66 \overset{?}{>} 24 \;\checkmark \quad \text{10 for y.}$$

So 10 is a solution.

$$7y - 4 > 24$$
$$7(0) - 4 \overset{?}{>} 24 \quad \text{Substitute}$$
$$-4 \overset{?}{>} 24 \;\times \quad \text{0 for y.}$$

So 0 is not a solution.

B $-2x + 4 \le 3$

$$-2x + 4 \le 3$$
$$\underline{\quad - 4 \quad\quad - 4}$$ *Since 4 is added to −2x, subtract 4 from both sides.*
$$-2x \le -1$$

$$\frac{-2x}{-2} \ge \frac{-1}{-2}$$ *Since x is multiplied by −2, divide both sides by −2. Change ≤ to ≥.*

$$x \ge \frac{1}{2}$$

Remember!

If both sides of an inequality are multiplied or divided by a negative number, the inequality symbol must be reversed.

---

1 Introduce

Alternate Opener

EXPLORATION

3-8 Solving Two-Step Inequalities

Rosa is offered two telephone service options when she buys her new cell phone.

Cell phone option A	Cell phone option B
$25, plus 12.5¢ per minute	$90, plus unlimited minutes

1. Complete the table to compare the costs under each option for the given number of minutes.

Minutes	Cost Under Option A	Cost Under Option B
220	$25 + 0.125 \cdot 220 = \$52.50$	$90
320		
420		
520		
620		

2. Solve the inequality $25 + 0.125x < 90$. What does the solution tell you about option A and option B?

3. Solve the inequality $25 + 0.125x > 90$. What does the solution tell you about option A and option B?

Think and Discuss

4. **Explain** how you solved the inequalities in Problems 2 and 3.

Motivate

Tell students that a goal in a fund-raiser is to take in more money than is spent. To reach that goal, you may need to determine the *least number* of items that must be sold to make a profit. One way to determine the least number of items is to write and solve an inequality.

Explorations and answers are provided in *Alternate Openers: Explorations Transparencies.*

California Standards

Algebra and Functions **4.1**

EXAMPLE 2 Solving Inequalities That Contain Fractions

Solve $\frac{-3x}{8} + \frac{5}{6} \le \frac{7}{12}$ and graph the solution.

Remember!

When an inequality contains fractions, you may want to multiply both sides by the LCD to clear the fractions.

$$24\left(\frac{-3x}{8} + \frac{5}{6}\right) \le 24\left(\frac{7}{12}\right) \quad \text{Multiply by the LCD, 24.}$$

$$24\left(\frac{-3x}{8}\right) + 24\left(\frac{5}{6}\right) \le 24\left(\frac{7}{12}\right) \quad \text{Distributive Property}$$

$$-9x + 20 \le 14$$

$$\underline{\quad -20 \quad \quad -20 \quad} \quad \text{Since 20 is added to } -9x, \text{ subtract 20}$$
$$-9x \le -6 \quad \text{from both sides.}$$

$$\frac{-9x}{-9} \ge \frac{-6}{-9} \quad \text{Since x is multiplied by } -9, \text{ divide both}$$
$$\text{sides by } -9. \text{ Change } \le \text{ to } \ge.$$

$$x \ge \frac{6}{9}$$

$$x \ge \frac{2}{3} \quad \text{Simplify.}$$

$$\overset{-1\frac{2}{3}\ -1\frac{1}{3}\ -1\ -\frac{2}{3}\ -\frac{1}{3}\ \ 0\ \ \frac{1}{3}\ \ \frac{2}{3}\ \ 1\ \ 1\frac{1}{3}\ 1\frac{2}{3}}{\longleftarrow\!\!+\!\!+\!\!+\!\!+\!\!+\!\!+\!\!+\!\!\bullet\!\!+\!\!+\!\!+\!\!\longrightarrow}$$

EXAMPLE 3 School Application

Possible answers to
Think and Discuss

1. Use the same steps for both, but if you multiply or divide an inequality by a negative number, you must reverse the inequality symbol.

2. To solve the inequality $-2x + 1 > 7$, subtract 1 from both sides, divide both sides by -2, and reverse the inequality symbol. To solve the inequality $2 - \frac{x}{5} < 3$, subtract 2 from both sides, multiply both sides by -5, and reverse the inequality symbol.

The Drama Club is planning a spring musical. Club members estimate that the entire production will cost $1100.00. If they have $610.75 left from fund-raising, how many tickets must they sell to at least break even?

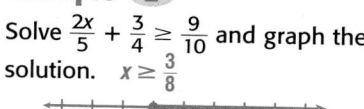

In order to at least break even, ticket sales plus the money in the budget must be greater than or equal to the cost of the production.

$$4.75t + 610.75 \ge 1100.00$$

$$\underline{\quad -610.75 \quad \quad -610.75 \quad} \quad \text{Subtract 610.75 from both sides.}$$
$$4.75t \ge 489.25$$

$$\frac{4.75t}{4.75} \ge \frac{489.25}{4.75} \quad \text{Divide both sides by 4.75.}$$

$$t \ge 103$$

The drama club must sell at least 103 tickets in order to break even.

Think and Discuss

1. Compare solving a multi-step equation with solving a multi-step inequality.

2. Describe two situations in which you would have to reverse the inequality symbol when solving a multi-step inequality.

COMMON ERROR ALERT

Students will sometimes reverse the inequality symbol when they divide a negative number by a positive number.

Incorrect	Correct
$-12 < 3x$	$-12 < 3x$
$\frac{-12}{3} > \frac{3x}{3}$	$\frac{-12}{3} < \frac{3x}{3}$
$-4 > x$	$-4 < x$

Power Presentations
with PowerPoint®

Additional Examples

Example 1
Solve and graph.
A. $4x + 1 > 13$ $x > 3$

$$\overset{-5\ \ \ \ \ \ \ \ 0\ \ \ \ \ 3\ \ \ 5}{\longleftarrow\!\!+\!\!+\!\!+\!\!+\!\!+\!\!+\!\!+\!\!\circ\!\!+\!\!\longrightarrow}$$

B. $-9x + 7 \ge 25$ $x \le -2$

$$\overset{-5\ \ \ \ -2\ \ \ 0\ \ \ \ \ \ \ \ 5}{\longleftarrow\!\!+\!\!+\!\!+\!\!\bullet\!\!+\!\!+\!\!+\!\!+\!\!+\!\!\longrightarrow}$$

Example 2
Solve $\frac{2x}{5} + \frac{3}{4} \ge \frac{9}{10}$ and graph the solution. $x \ge \frac{3}{8}$

$$\overset{0\ \ \ \ \ \ \frac{3}{8}\ \ \ \ \ \ \ \ \ \ 1}{\longleftarrow\!\!+\!\!+\!\!+\!\!\bullet\!\!+\!\!+\!\!+\!\!+\!\!+\!\!\longrightarrow}$$

Example 3
A school's Spanish club is selling bumper stickers. They bought 100 stickers for $55 and have to give the company 15 cents for every sticker that the club sells. If they plan to sell each bumper sticker for $1.25, how many do they have to sell to make a profit?   more than 50

Also available on transparency

---

2 Teach

Guided Instruction

In this lesson, students solve two-step inequalities and graph the solutions of an inequality on a number line. Remind students that the process of solving inequalities is the same as the process of solving equations, with one exception. The exception is that if you multiply or divide both sides of an inequality by a negative number, you must reverse the inequality symbol. (See Math Background.) Remind students how to graph inequalities on a number line.

Universal Access
For Advanced Learners-GATE

Give students inequalities and possible solution sets, such as those given below. Have students graph each solution set and check it by choosing a number from the solution set and substituting it into the inequality. If the solution set is incorrect, have students provide the correct answer.

1. $2x + 17 > 5$; $x < -6$

2. $\frac{2t}{3} + \frac{1}{2} < \frac{1}{6}$; $t < -\frac{1}{2}$

3. $\frac{x}{2} + \frac{x}{4} < \frac{15}{8}$; $x > \frac{5}{2}$

1. incorrect; $x > -6$
2. correct
3. incorrect; $x < \frac{5}{2}$

3 Close

Summarize

Remind students that to solve a multi-step inequality, they should do the following:

- Clear fractions.
- Combine like terms.
- Get the variable on one side of the inequality only.
- Undo addition and subtraction.
- Undo multiplication and division, remembering to reverse the inequality symbol if they multiply or divide both sides of an inequality by a negative number.

3-8 Exercises

3-8 Exercises

California Standards Practice
AF4.1

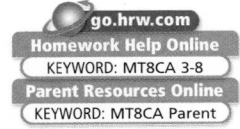
go.hrw.com
Homework Help Online
KEYWORD: MT8CA 3-8
Parent Resources Online
KEYWORD: MT8CA Parent

Assignment Guide

If you finished Example **1** assign:
Proficient 1–6, 14–19, 30–32, 47–54
Advanced 14–19, 33–35, 45, 47–54

If you finished Example **2** assign:
Proficient 1–12, 14–25, 27–32, 47–54
Advanced 14–25, 33–38, 45–54

If you finished Example **3** assign:
Proficient 1–26, 27–32, 40–42, 47–54
Advanced 14–26, 33–54

Homework Quick Check

Quickly check key concepts.
Exercises: 16, 18, 22, 26

Answers

3–12, 14–25, 27–38. See p. A2.

1.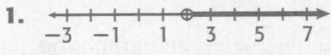
   $-3 \quad -1 \quad 1 \quad 3 \quad 5 \quad 7$

2. $\quad 15\ 16\ 17\ 18\ 19\ 20\ 21\ 22\ 23\ 24$

Math Background

To better understand why an inequality symbol must be reversed when multiplying or dividing by a negative number, use an inequality such as $10 > 8$ to examine the following four possibilities.

- Multiply each side by 2: $20 > 16$ (true)
- Divide each side by 2: $5 > 4$ (true)
- Multiply each side by -2: $-20 < -16$ (The inequality sign must be reversed to make it true.)
- Divide each side by -2: $-5 < -4$ (The inequality sign must be reversed to make it true.)

California Standards

Standard	Exercises
AF1.3 🔑	49–54
AF4.1 🔑	1–48

GUIDED PRACTICE

See Example **1** Solve and graph.

$y < -8$

1. $3k + 5 > 11$ $\quad k > 2$ 2. $2z - 29.5 \le 10.5$ $\quad z \le 20$ 3. $6y + 12 < -36$

4. $-4x + 6 \ge 14$ $\quad x \le -2$ 5. $2y + 2.5 \ge 16.5$ $\quad y \ge 7$ 6. $3k - 2 > 13$ $\quad k > 5$

See Example **2** 7. $\frac{x}{15} + \frac{1}{5} < \frac{2}{5}$ $\quad x < 3$ 8. $\frac{b}{10} - \frac{3}{5} \ge -\frac{1}{2}$ $\quad b \ge 1$ 9. $\frac{h}{3} - 2 \le -\frac{5}{3}$ $\quad h \le 1$

10. $\frac{c}{8} + \frac{1}{2} > \frac{3}{4}$ $\quad c > 2$ 11. $\frac{1}{2} + \frac{d}{6} < \frac{1}{3}$ $\quad d < -1$ 12. $\frac{2}{3} \ge \frac{6m}{9}$ $\quad m \le 1$

See Example **3** 13. The chess club is selling caps to raise $425 for a trip. They have $175 already. If the club members sell caps for $12 each, at least how many caps do they need to sell to make enough money for their trip? **at least 21 caps**

INDEPENDENT PRACTICE

See Example **1** Solve and graph.

$p \ge -13$

14. $8k - 6 > 18$ $\quad k > 3$ 15. $5x + 3 > 23$ $\quad x > 4$ 16. $3p + 3 \ge -36$

17. $13 \ge 11q - 9$ $\quad q \le 2$ 18. $3.6 + 7.2n < 25.2$ $\quad n < 3$ 19. $-7x - 15 \ge 34$ $\quad x \le -7$

See Example **2** 20. $\frac{p}{15} + \frac{4}{5} < \frac{1}{3}$ $\quad p < -7$ 21. $\frac{a}{9} + \frac{2}{3} \ge \frac{1}{3}$ $\quad a \ge -3$ 22. $-\frac{1}{3} + \frac{n}{12} > -\frac{1}{4}$ $\quad n > 1$

23. $-\frac{2}{3} \le \frac{1}{18}k - \frac{5}{6}$ $\quad k \ge 3$ 24. $\frac{4}{7} + \frac{n}{14} \le -\frac{3}{7}$ $\quad n \le -14$ 25. $\frac{1}{3} + \frac{r}{18} < \frac{1}{2}$ $\quad r < 3$

See Example **3** 26. Josef is on the planning committee for the eighth-grade party. The food, decoration, and entertainment costs a total of $350. The committee has $75 already. If the committee sells the tickets for $5 each, at least how many tickets must be sold to cover the remaining cost of the party? **at least 55 tickets**

PRACTICE AND PROBLEM SOLVING

Extra Practice
See page EP7.

Solve and graph.

$w > -1$

27. $3p - 11 \le 11$ $\quad p \le \frac{22}{3}$ 28. $9n + 10 > -17$ $\quad n > -3$ 29. $3 - 5w < 8$

30. $-6x - 18 \ge 6$ $\quad x \le -4$ 31. $12a + 4 > 10$ $\quad a > \frac{1}{2}$ 32. $-4y + 3 \ge 17$ $\quad y \le -\frac{7}{2}$

33. $3q - 5q > -12$ $\quad q < 6$ 34. $\frac{3m}{4} > \frac{5}{8}$ $\quad m > \frac{5}{6}$ 35. $4b - 3.2 < 7.6$ $\quad b < 2.7$

36. $3k + 6 \ge 4$ $\quad k \ge -\frac{2}{3}$ 37. $\frac{90}{4} \le -\frac{5}{6}f$ $\quad f \le -27$ 38. $-\frac{5}{9}v \ge -\frac{1}{3}$ $\quad v \le \frac{3}{5}$

39. **Reasoning** What is the least whole number that is a solution of $2r - 4.4 > 8.6$? **7**

40. **Entertainment** A speech is being given in a gymnasium that can hold no more than 650 people. A permanent bleacher will seat 136 people. The event organizers are setting up 25 rows with an equal number of chairs. At most, how many chairs can be in each row? **at most 20 chairs**

REVIEW FOR MASTERY 3-8

Review for Mastery
3-8 Solving Two-Step Inequalities

To solve an inequality, undo operations the same way you would with an equation. But, when multiplying or dividing by a negative number, reverse the inequality symbol.

$3x + 2 > 11$ To undo addition,
$\underline{-2 \quad -2}$ subtract 2.
$3x > 9$ To undo multiplication,
$\frac{3x}{3} > \frac{9}{3}$ divide by 3.
$x > 3$

The solution set contains all real numbers greater than 3.

$-6\,-5\,-4\,-3\,-2\,-1\ 0\ 1\ 2\ 3\ 4\ 5\ 6$

$-3x + 2 > 11$ To undo addition,
$\underline{-2 \quad -2}$ subtract 2.
$-3x > 9$ To undo multiplication,
$\frac{-3x}{-3} < \frac{9}{-3}$ divide by -3 and
$x < -3$ change > to <.

The solution set contains all real numbers less than -3.

$-6\,-5\,-4\,-3\,-2\,-1\ 0\ 1\ 2\ 3\ 4\ 5\ 6$

Complete to solve and graph.

1. $2t + 1 \le 9$ To undo addition,
   $\underline{-1 \quad -1}$ subtract.
   $2t \le 8$ To undo multiplication,
   $\frac{2t}{2} \le \frac{8}{2}$ divide.
   $t \le 4$

   $-6\,-5\,-4\,-3\,-2\,-1\ 0\ 1\ 2\ 3\ 4\ 5\ 6$

2. $-2t + 1 \le 9$ To undo addition,
   $\underline{-1 \quad -1}$ subtract.
   $-2t \le 8$ To undo multiplication,
   $\frac{-2t}{-2} \ge \frac{8}{-2}$ divide by -2 and
   $t \ge -4$ change $\le$ to $\ge$.

   $-6\,-5\,-4\,-3\,-2\,-1\ 0\ 1\ 2\ 3\ 4\ 5\ 6$

3. $-3z - 2 > 1$
   $\underline{+2 \quad +2}$
   $-3z > 3$
   $\frac{-3z}{-3} > \frac{3}{-3}$
   $z < -1$

   $-6\,-5\,-4\,-3\,-2\,-1\ 0\ 1\ 2\ 3\ 4\ 5\ 6$

4. $3z - 2 > 1$
   $\underline{+2 \quad +2}$
   $3z > 3$
   $\frac{3z}{3} > \frac{3}{3}$
   $z > 1$

   $-6\,-5\,-4\,-3\,-2\,-1\ 0\ 1\ 2\ 3\ 4\ 5\ 6$

PRACTICE 3-8

Practice B
3-8 Solving Two-Step Inequalities

Solve and graph.

1. $4x - 2 < 26$
   $x < 7$
   $-4\,-3\,-2\,-1\ 0\ 1\ 2\ 3\ 4\ 5\ 6\ 7\ 8$

2. $6 - \frac{1}{5}y \le 7$
   $y \ge -5$
   $-6\,-5\,-4\,-3\,-2\,-1\ 0\ 1\ 2\ 3\ 4\ 5\ 6$

3. $2x + 27 \ge 15$
   $x \ge -6$
   $-8\,-7\,-6\,-5\,-4\,-3\,-2\,-1\ 0\ 1\ 2\ 3\ 4$

4. $10x > 14x + 8$
   $x < -2$
   $-6\,-5\,-4\,-3\,-2\,-1\ 0\ 1\ 2\ 3\ 4\ 5\ 6$

5. $7 - 4w \le 19$
   $w \ge -3$
   $-6\,-5\,-4\,-3\,-2\,-1\ 0\ 1\ 2\ 3\ 4\ 5\ 6$

6. $\frac{k}{5} + \frac{3}{20} < \frac{3}{10}$
   $k < \frac{3}{4}$
   $-1 \qquad 0 \qquad 1 \qquad 2$

7. $4.8 - 9.6x \le 14.4$
   $x \ge -1$
   $-6\,-5\,-4\,-3\,-2\,-1\ 0\ 1\ 2\ 3\ 4\ 5\ 6$

8. $\frac{2}{9} + \frac{y}{3} > \frac{1}{3}$
   $y > \frac{1}{3}$
   $-1 \qquad 0 \qquad 1 \qquad 2$

9. One-third of a number, decreased by thirty-six, is at most twenty-two. Find the number. $n \le 174$

10. Jack wants to run at least 275 miles before the baseball season begins. He has already run 25 miles. He plans to run 2.5 miles each day. At this rate, what is the fewest number of days he will need to reach his goal?   **100 days**

41. Katie and April are making a string of beads for *pi* day (March 14). The string already has 70 beads. If there are only 30 more days until *pi* day, and they want to string 1000 beads by then, at least how many beads do they have to string each day? **at least 31 beads**

42. Sports The Astros have won 35 and lost 52 baseball games. They have 75 games remaining. At least how many of the remaining 75 games must the Astros win to have a winning season? (*Hint:* A winning season means they win more than 50% of their games.) **at least 47 games**

43. Economics Satellite TV customers can either purchase a dish and receiver for $249 or pay a $50 fee and rent the equipment for $12 a month.

   a. How much would it cost to rent the equipment for 9 months? **$158**

   b. How many months would it take for the rental charges to be more than the purchase price? **17 mo**

44. Write a Problem Write and solve an inequality using the following shipping rates for orders from a mail-order catalog.

Mail-Order Shipping Rates

Merchandise Amount	$0.01–$25.00	$25.01–50.00	$50.01–75.00	$75.01–125.00	$125.01 and over
Shipping Cost	$3.95	$5.95	$7.95	$9.95	$11.95

45. Write About It Describe two different ways to solve the inequality $-3x - 4 < x$.

46. Challenge Solve the inequality $\frac{x}{5} - \frac{x}{6} \geq \frac{1}{15}$. $x \geq 2$

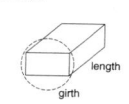

SPIRAL STANDARDS REVIEW   ← AF1.3, ← AF4.1

47. Multiple Choice Solve $3g - 6 > 18$.

   (A) $g > 21$ (B) $g > 8$ (C) $g > 6$ (D) $g > 4$

48. Short Response Solve and graph $\frac{5x}{6} + \frac{1}{2} < \frac{2}{3}$. $x < \frac{1}{5}$

Name the property that is illustrated in each equation. (Lesson 3-1)

49. $12y = y \cdot 12$ **50.** $a + (b + c) = (a + b) + c$ **51.** $x + 13y = 13y + x$
Commutative Property of Multiplication   **Associative Property of Addition**   **Commutative Property of Addition**

Simplify. (Lesson 3-2)

52. $5(x + 1) - 2x$ $3x + 5$ **53.** $6(r - 10) + r$ $7r - 60$ **54.** $3(8 + n) - 21$ $3n + 3$

CHALLENGE 3-8

LESSON 3-8 Challenge
Updated Pony Express

Pat wants to send some copies of her newly published book to friends.

According to the U.S. Postal Service:

Rates are based on the weight of the piece and the zone (distance from origin to destination ZIP code).

The combined length and girth (perimeter of an end) of a package may not exceed 108 inches.

1. Pat wants the box that contains books to be 6 inches high, and twice as long as it is wide.

Let x represent the width of a box that Pat might use.

$2(x) + 2(6) + 2x \leq 108$
$4x + 12 \leq 108$
$4x \leq 96$
$x \leq 24$

Write and solve an inequality to find all possible widths for a box that will satisfy the postal requirements and Pat's conditions.

possible width: **≤ 24 inches**

2. Pat's husband, Mike, suggests that the box be 8 inches high and that the length be 3 times the width.

Let z represent the length of a box that Mike suggests.

$2\left(\frac{z}{3}\right) + 2(8) + z \leq 108$
$2z + 48 + 3z \leq 324$
$5z + 48 \leq 324$
$5z \leq 276$
$z \leq 55.2$

Write and solve an inequality to find, to the nearest inch, the maximum length for a box that will satisfy.

maximum length: **55 inches**

3. On May 1, 2002, Pat shipped a box containing a book to a friend who lives in Zone 4. Pat paid $2.08 to ship this package.

According to the table below, write an inequality to show the weight of this package. **2.5 < x ≤ 3**

Bound Printed Matter Rates

Weight Not Over (pounds)	Local, Zones 1&2	Zone 3	Zone 4	Zone 5	Zone 6	Zone 7	Zone 8
1.0	$1.80	$1.83	$1.87	$1.93	$1.99	$2.06	$2.21
1.5	1.80	1.83	1.87	1.93	1.99	2.06	2.21
2.0	1.84	1.88	1.94	2.02	2.10	2.19	2.38
2.5	1.90	1.95	2.00	2.11	2.21	2.33	2.57
3.0	1.94	2.00	2.08	2.20	2.32	2.46	2.75
3.5	1.99	2.06	2.15	2.29	2.43	2.60	2.93
4.0	2.03	2.11	2.21	2.37	2.55	2.72	3.11

PROBLEM SOLVING 3-8

LESSON 3-8 Problem Solving
Solving Two-Step Inequalities

A school club is selling printed T-shirts to raise $650 for a trip. The table shows the profit they will make on each shirt after they pay the cost of production.

Shirt	Profit
50/50	$5.50
100% cotton	$7.82

1. Suppose the club already has $150, at least how many 50/50 shirts must they sell to make enough money for the trip?

91 shirts

2. Suppose the club already has $100, but it plans to spend $50 on advertising. At least how many 100% cotton shirts must they sell to make enough money for the trip?

77 shirts

3. Suppose the club sold thirty 50/50 shirts on the first day of sales. At least how many more 50/50 shirts must they sell to make enough money for the trip?

89 shirts

For Exercises 4–5, use this equation to estimate typing speed, $S = \frac{w}{5} - 2e$, where S is the accurate typing speed, w is the number of words typed in 5 minutes, and e is the number of errors. Choose the letter for the best answer.

4. One of the qualifications for a job is a typing speed of at least 65 words per minute. If Jordan knows that she will be able to type 350 words in five minutes, what is the maximum number of errors she can make?

  A 0   C 3
  (B) 2   D 4

5. Tanner usually makes 3 errors every 5 minutes while he is typing. If his goal is an accurate typing speed of at least 55 words per minute, how many words does he have to be able to type in 5 minutes?

  F 61 words   (H) 305 words
  G 300 words   J 325 words

6. A taxi charges $2.05 per ride and $0.20 for each mile, which can be written as $F = $2.05 + $0.20m$. How many miles can you travel in the cab and have the fare be less than $10?

  A 15   (C) 39
  B 25   D 43

7. Celia's long distance company charges $5.95 per month plus $0.06 per minute. If Celia has budgeted $30 for long distance, what is the maximum number of minutes she can call long distance per month?

  F 375 minutes   H 405 minutes
  (G) 400 minutes   J 420 minutes

FORMATIVE ASSESSMENT and INTERVENTION ◀▶

Diagnose Before the Lesson
3-8 Warm Up, TE p. 148

Monitor During the Lesson
3-8 Know-It Notebook
3-8 Questioning Strategies

Assess After the Lesson
3-8 Lesson Quiz, TE p. 151

Answers
44–45, 48. See p. A2.

Teaching Tip   **Short Response** Many students are intimidated by fractions in inequalities, such as in **Exercise 48.** Help them find the LCD by pointing out that 2 and 3 are both factors of 6. Emphasize that fractions can be eliminated from most equations and inequalities in just one step by multiplying every term by the LCD.

Journal
Ask students to describe some real-world situations in which an inequality might be more useful than an equation.

Power Presentations with PowerPoint®

3-8 Lesson Quiz

Solve and graph.

1. $4x - 6 > 10$ $x > 4$
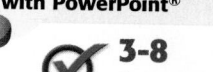

2. $7x + 9 < 3x - 15$ $x < -6$
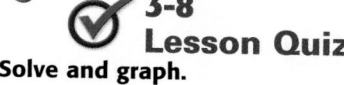

3. $w - 3w < 32$ $w > -16$

4. $\frac{2}{3}w + \frac{1}{4} \leq \frac{1}{2}$ $w \leq \frac{3}{8}$

5. Antonio has budgeted an average of $45 a month for entertainment. For the first five months of the year he has spent $48, $39, $60, $48, and $33. How much can Antonio spend in the sixth month without exceeding his average budget? **no more than $42**

Also available on transparency

SECTION 3B — READY TO GO ON?

Organizer

Objective: Assess students' mastery of concepts and skills in Lessons 3-5 through 3-8.

Resources

 Assessment Resources
Section 3B Quiz

Test & Practice Generator
One-Stop Planner®

INTERVENTION ⟸⟹

Resources

 Ready to Go On?
Intervention and
Enrichment Worksheets

 Ready to Go On? CD-ROM

 Ready to Go On? Online

 **my.hrw.com**

Answers

5–6, 9–20, 22–27. See p. A2.

3.
2 3 4 5 6 7 8 9 10 11 12

4.
–7 –6 –5 –4 –3 –2 –1 0 1

CHAPTER **3**

 **READY TO GO ON?**

SECTION 3B

Quiz for Lessons 3-5 Through 3-8

✓ **3-5 Inequalities**

Write an inequality for each statement.

1. A number n decreased by 15 is no more than 48. $n - 15 \le 48$
2. The product of -7 and a number x is above 49. $-7x > 49$

Graph each inequality.

3. $r \le 7$ 4. $-4 > a$ 5. $c > -\frac{2}{3}$ 6. $h \ge -2$

Write a compound inequality for each statement.

7. A number m is both greater than -15 and less than or equal to 4. $-15 < m \le 4$
8. A number d is either less than $\frac{1}{2}$ or greater than $2\frac{1}{3}$. $d < \frac{1}{2}$ or $d > 2\frac{1}{3}$

✓ **3-6 Solving Inequalities by Adding or Subtracting**

Solve and graph.

9. $n + 1\frac{3}{5} < \frac{4}{5}$ $n < -\frac{4}{5}$ 10. $-15 < -8 + y$ $y > -7$ 11. $-101 + x \le -89$ $x \le 12$
12. $19 < t - 13$ $t > 32$ 13. $27 + d \ge 22$ $d \ge -5$ 14. $5.3 > n - 2.7$ $n < 8$

✓ **3-7 Solving Inequalities by Multiplying or Dividing**

Solve and graph.

15. $-5x > 15$ $x < -3$ 16. $9 \ge \frac{k}{3}$ $k \le 27$ 17. $\frac{y}{-4} < 4$ $y > -16$
18. $-24 \ge 6m$ $m \le -4$ 19. $-n > -10$ $n < 10$ 20. $\frac{h}{2} \le -42$ $h \le -84$

21. Rachael is serving lemonade from a pitcher that holds 60 ounces. What are the possible numbers of 7-ounce juice glasses she can fill from one pitcher? $g \le 8$; 8 glasses or less

✓ **3-8 Solving Two-Step Inequalities**   28. $t \ge 88$; a score of 88 or better

Solve and graph.

22. $2k + 4 > 10$ $k > 3$ 23. $0.5z - 5.5 \le 4.5$ $z \le 20$ 24. $\frac{3x}{5} - \frac{9}{15} \le \frac{3}{5}$ $x \le 2$
25. $\frac{1}{3} + \frac{t}{9} < -2$ $t < -21$ 26. $\frac{1}{3} - \frac{3x}{4} \ge \frac{5}{6}$ $x \le -\frac{2}{3}$ 27. $\frac{3}{7} + \frac{m}{14} \le -\frac{2}{7}$ $m \le -10$

28. Jillian must average at least 90 on two quiz scores before she can move to the next skill level. Jillian got a 92 on her first quiz. What scores could Jillian get on her second quiz in order to move to the next skill level?

READY TO GO ON?
Diagnose and Prescribe

NO INTERVENE

YES ENRICH

READY TO GO ON? Intervention, Section 3B			
Ready to Go On? Intervention	Worksheets	CD-ROM	Online
✓ Lesson 3-5 AF1.1	3-5 Intervention	Activity 3-5	Diagnose and Prescribe Online
✓ Lesson 3-6 AF4.0	3-6 Intervention	Activity 3-6	
✓ Lesson 3-7 AF1.1, AF4.0	3-7 Intervention	Activity 3-7	
✓ Lesson 3-8 AF4.1	3-8 Intervention	Activity 3-8	

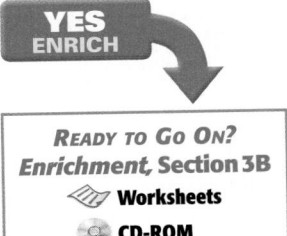

READY TO GO ON? Enrichment, Section 3B
Worksheets
CD-ROM
Online

CONCEPT CONNECTION

Skate Away Ms. Lucinda wants to treat her class of 30 students to a skating party to celebrate the end of the school year.

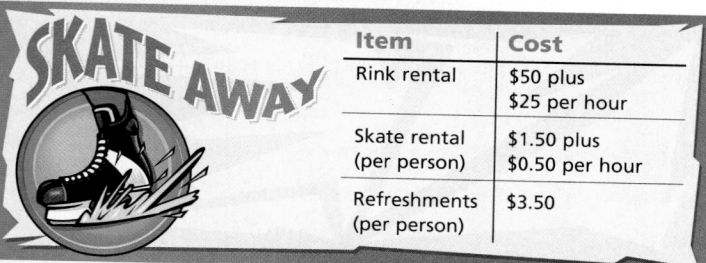

Item	Cost
Rink rental	$50 plus $25 per hour
Skate rental (per person)	$1.50 plus $0.50 per hour
Refreshments (per person)	$3.50

1. Ms. Lucinda considers renting the rink at Skate Away. How much would it cost to rent the rink for *x* hours?

2. Another rink, Skate Palace, charges $100 plus $15 per hour to rent the rink. Write and solve an equation to find the number of hours for which the cost of renting the rink at Skate Palace is the same as the cost of renting the rink at Skate Away.

3. Ms. Lucinda decides to take the class to Skate Away. How much will it cost to rent skates for 30 students for *x* hours? How much will it cost to buy refreshments for 30 students?

4. Ms. Lucinda has budgeted $400 for the party. Write and solve an inequality to find the maximum number of hours the class can have its party at Skate Away. Be sure to include the cost of the rink, the skates, and the refreshments.

5. The final bill for the party was $380. How long did the party last?

CONCEPT CONNECTION

CHAPTER 3

Organizer

Objective: Assess students' ability to apply concepts and skills in Chapter 3 in a real-world format.

PREMIER **Online Edition**

Problem	Text reference
1	Lesson 3-2
2	Lesson 3-3
3	Lesson 3-4
4	Lesson 3-7
5	Lesson 3-8

Answers

1. $50 + 25x$ if x = number of hours

2. $100 + 15x = 50 + 25x$; when the number of hours is 5

3. $30(1.50 + 0.50x)$; $30(3.50) = 105$

4. $50 + 25x + 30(1.50 + 0.50x) + 105 \leq 400$, so $x \leq 5$

5. 4.5 hours

INTERVENTION

Scaffolding Questions

1. What does it cost to rent the rink for 3 hours? $125 for 4 hours? $150 What should you do to figure out the cost for any given number of hours? Multiply the number of hours by $25 and then add $50.

2. What does it cost to rent the rink at Skate Palace for *x* hours? $100 + 15x$ What equation should you solve to find out when the costs are equal? $50 + 25x = 100 + 15x$

3. How much does it cost to rent skates for one student for *x* hours? $1.5 + 0.5x$ How can you use this to write an expression to find the cost for 30 students? Multiply by 30 and simplify.

4. What expression gives the total cost of the party for *x* hours? $50 + 25x + 45 + 15x + 105$ How can you simplify the expression? Combine like terms to write it as $200 + 40x$. What inequality should you solve? $200 + 40x \leq 400$

5. What equation should you solve? $200 + 40x = 380$ What is the first step in solving the equation? Subtract 200 from both sides.

Extension

1. Assume the cost of renting skates and buying refreshments is the same at Skate Palace. How much did Ms. Lucinda save by having the party at Skate Away? $5

California Standards

Algebra and Functions
4.1 Solve two-step linear equations and inequalities **in one variable over the rational numbers**, interpret the solution or solutions in the context from which they arose, and **verify the reasonableness of the results.**

Organizer

Objective: Participate in games to practice and apply skills learned in Chapter 3.

Online Edition

Resources

Chapter 3 Resource File
Puzzles, Twisters & Teasers

Trans-Plants

Purpose: To apply the skill of solving equations to solving a riddle

Discuss Be sure students understand how to decode the message. Work through the first equation with them. Because the solution is $a = -14$, they will place an a above each place where -14 appears in the message.

Extend Have students work in teams of 4 to write new equations for the letters of the alphabet. Have each group write a message in code and trade equations and messages with another group to solve.

Check students' work.

24 Points

Purpose: To practice writing expressions in a game format

Discuss When students get "24," have them write the expression for their teammates to see. Have each team member evaluate the expression to verify that it has a value of 24.

Extend Have students play the game with the target number -24.

Game Time

Trans-Plants

Solve each equation below. Then use the values of the variables to decode the answer to the question.

$3a + 17 = -25 \quad a = -14$

$2b - 25 + 5b = 7 - 32 \quad b = 0$

$2.7c - 4.5 = 3.6c - 9 \quad c = 5$

$\frac{5}{12}d + \frac{1}{6}d + \frac{1}{3}d + \frac{1}{12}d = 6 \quad d = 6$

$4e - 6e - 5 = 15 \quad e = -10$

$420 = 29f - 73 \quad f = 17$

$2(g + 6) = -20 \quad g = -16$

$2h + 7 = -3h + 52 \quad h = 9$

$96i + 245 = 53 \quad i = -2$

$3j + 7 = 46 \quad j = 13$

$\frac{1}{2}k = \frac{3}{4}k - \frac{1}{2} \quad k = 2$

$30l + 240 = 50l - 160 \quad l = 20$

$4m + \frac{3}{8} = \frac{67}{8} \quad m = 2$

$24 - 6n = 54 \quad n = -5$

$8.4o - 6.8 = 14.2 + 6.3o \quad o = 10$

$4p - p + 8 = 2p + 5 \quad p = -3$

$16 - 3q = 3q + 40 \quad q = -4$

$4 + \frac{1}{3}r = r - 8 \quad r = 18$

$\frac{2}{3}s - \frac{5}{6}s + \frac{1}{2} = -\frac{3}{2} \quad s = 12$

$4 - 15 = 4t + 17 \quad t = -7$

$45 + 36u = 66 + 23u + 31 \quad u = 4$

$6v + 8 = -4 - 6v \quad v = -1$

$4w + 3w - 6w = w + 15 + 2w - 3w \quad w = 15$

$x + 2x + 3x + 4x + 5 = 75 \quad x = 7$

$\frac{4 - y}{5} = \frac{2 - 2y}{8} \quad y = -11$

$-11 = 25 - 4.5z \quad z = 8$

What happens to plants that live in a math classroom?

$-7, 9, -10, -11$	$-16, 18, 10, 15$	$12, -4, 4, -14, 18, -10$	$18, 10, 10, -7, 12$
T H E Y	G R O W	S Q U A R E	R O O T S

24 Points

This traditional Chinese game is played using a deck of 52 cards numbered 1–13, with four of each number. The cards are shuffled, and four cards are placed face up in the center. The winner is the first player who comes up with an expression that equals 24, using each of the numbers on the four cards once.

Complete rules and a set of game cards are available online.

go.hrw.com
Game Time Extra
KEYWORD: MT8CA Games

Materials
- magazine
- glue
- scissors
- index cards

It's in the Bag!

PROJECT **Picture Envelopes**

Make these picture-perfect envelopes in which to store your notes on the lessons of this chapter.

Directions

1 Flip through a magazine and carefully tear out eight pages with full-page pictures that you like.

2 Lay one of the pages in front of you with the picture face down. Fold the page into thirds as shown, and then unfold the page. **Figure A**

3 Fold the sides in, about 1 inch, and then unfold. Cut away the four rectangles at the corners of the page. **Figure B**

4 Fold in the two middle flaps. Then fold up the bottom and glue it onto the flaps. **Figure C**

5 Cut the corners of the top section at an angle to make a flap. **Figure D**

6 Repeat the steps to make seven more envelopes. Label them so that there is one for each lesson of the chapter.

Taking Note of the Math

Use index cards to take notes on the lessons of the chapter. Store the cards in the appropriate envelopes.

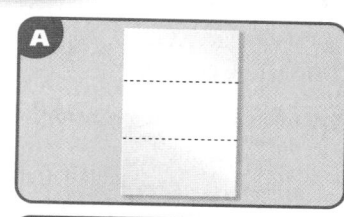
A

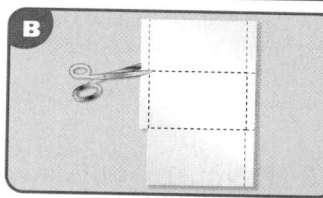
B

C

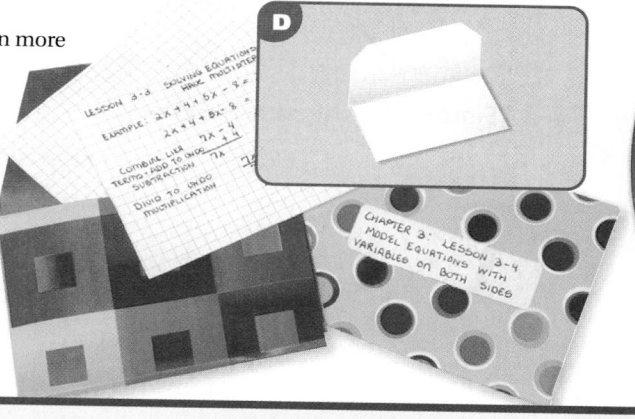
D

It's in the Bag!

Organizer

Objective: Make envelopes in which to store index cards with notes on the chapter.

Materials: magazine, glue, scissors, index cards

PREMIER **Online Edition**

Using the Page

Preparing the Materials
If time is limited, have students select pages from magazines at home and ask them to bring in the detached pages.

Making the Project
Before students glue the bottom flap to the side flaps, have them check that an index card will fit inside the envelope.

Extending the Project
Ask students to use several index cards to write the steps in solving a multi-step equation. Each card should contain one step. Then have students shuffle the cards and put them in an envelope. Students can trade envelopes with a partner and try to order the steps in solving their partner's equation.

Tips from the Bag Ladies!

The envelopes tend to turn out best if students choose magazine pages that do not contain a lot of text. Also, there's no reason to limit the pages to magazines. Our students have done the project with catalogs, calendars, old maps, and posters.

Once students have made their envelopes and filled them with index cards, they can store everything in a small plastic zipper bag.

Organizer

Objective: Help students organize and review key concepts and skills presented in Chapter 3.

 Online Edition
Multilingual Glossary

Resources

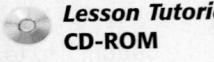 **PuzzlePro®**
One-Stop Planner®

 **Multilingual Glossary** Online

go.hrw.com
KEYWORD: MT8CA Glossary

Lesson Tutorial Videos
CD-ROM

Test & Practice Generator
One-Stop Planner®

Answers

1. inequality
2. Commutative Property
3. terms
4. Commutative Property of Addition
5. Associative Property of Addition
6. Distributive Property
7. Associative Property of Multiplication
8. $19m - 10$
9. $14w + 6$
10. $2x + 3y$
11. $2t^2 - 4t + 3t^3$

Vocabulary

algebraic inequality	136	equivalent expressions	120
Associative Property	116	inequality	136
coefficient	120	like terms	120
Commutative Property	116	solution set	136
constant	120	term	120
Distributive Property	117		

Complete the sentences below with vocabulary words from the list above.

1. A(n) __?__ is a statement that two quantities are not equal.

2. __?__ states that two or more numbers can be added in any order or multiplied in any order.

3. __?__ in an expression are set apart by plus or minus signs.

3-1 Properties of Rational Numbers (pp. 116–119)    AF1.3

EXAMPLE

■ Name the property that is illustrated in the equation.
$10(x + y) = 10 \cdot x + 10 \cdot y$ *Distributive Property*

EXERCISES

Name the property that is illustrated in each equation.

4. $2\frac{1}{2} + 5 = 5 + 2\frac{1}{2}$
5. $x + (8 + y) = (x + 8) + y$
6. $5(3 - n) = 5 \cdot 3 - 5n$
7. $\left(8 \cdot \frac{1}{6}\right) \cdot 7 = 8 \cdot \left(\frac{1}{6} \cdot 7\right)$

3-2 Simplifying Algebraic Expressions (pp. 120–123)    AF1.3

EXAMPLE

■ Simplify.
$3(z - 6) + 2z$
$3z - 3(6) + 2z$ *Distributive Property*
$3z - 18 + 2z$ *3z and 2z are like terms.*
$5z - 18$ *Combine coefficients.*

EXERCISES

Simplify.

8. $5(3m - 2) + 4m$
9. $12w + 2(w + 3)$
10. $4x + 3y - 2x$
11. $2t^2 - 4t + 3t^3$

3-3 Solving Multi-Step Equations (pp. 124–127)

Ext. of ← AF4.1

EXAMPLE

■ Solve.

$$\frac{5x}{9} - \frac{x}{6} + \frac{1}{3} = \frac{3}{2}$$

$18\left(\frac{5x}{9} - \frac{x}{6} + \frac{1}{3}\right) = 18\left(\frac{3}{2}\right)$ *Multiply both sides by 18.*

$18\left(\frac{5x}{9}\right) - 18\left(\frac{x}{6}\right) + 18\left(\frac{1}{3}\right) = 18\left(\frac{3}{2}\right)$ *Distributive Property*

$10x - 3x + 6 = 27$ *Simplify.*

$7x + 6 = 27$ *Combine like terms.*

$\underline{ -6 \quad -6}$ *Subtract 6 from both sides.*

$7x = 21$

$\frac{7x}{7} = \frac{21}{7}$ *Divide both sides by 7.*

$x = 3$

EXERCISES

Solve.

12. $3y + 6 + 4y - 7 = -8$

13. $5h - 6 - h + 10 = 12$

14. $\frac{2t}{3} + \frac{1}{3} = -\frac{1}{3}$

15. $\frac{2r}{5} - \frac{4}{5} = \frac{2}{5}$

16. $\frac{z}{3} - \frac{3z}{4} + \frac{1}{2} = -\frac{1}{3}$

17. $\frac{3a}{8} - \frac{a}{12} + \frac{7}{2} = 7$

3-4 Solving Equations with Variables on Both Sides (pp. 129–133)

Ext. of ← AF4.1

EXAMPLE

■ Solve.

$3x + 5 - 5x = -12 + x + 2$

$-2x + 5 = -10 + x$

$\underline{+2x \qquad\qquad +2x}$ *Combine like terms. Add 2x to both sides.*

$5 = -10 + 3x$

$\underline{+10 \quad +10}$ *Add 10 to both sides.*

$15 = 3x$

$\frac{15}{3} = \frac{3x}{3}$ *Divide both sides by 3.*

$5 = x$

EXERCISES

Solve.

18. $12s = 8 + 2(5s + 3)$

19. $\frac{5c}{8} - \frac{c}{3} = \frac{5c}{6} - 13$

20. $4 - 5x = 3 + x$

21. $4 - 2y = 4y$

22. $2n + 8 = 2n - 5$

23. $\frac{2z}{3} - \frac{3}{2} = \frac{3z}{2} - \frac{17}{3}$

3-5 Inequalities (pp. 136–139)

AF1.1

EXAMPLE

■ **Write an inequality for the situation.**

The capacity of the elevator was at most 2000 pounds.
Let c = capacity of elevator
$c \le 2000$ lb

    "at most" means less than or equal to

■ **Graph** $x < -3$.

EXERCISES

Write an inquality for each situation.

24. It is no more than a one mile walk from home to the school.

25. The cost of the trip will be at least $1500.

26. Fewer than 45 students are expected to attend the workshop.

Graph each inequality.

27. $m \le 0$ **28.** $x \ge 2$

29. $c < \frac{1}{4}$

Answers

12. $y = -1$

13. $h = 2$

14. $t = -1$

15. $r = 3$

16. $z = 2$

17. $a = 12$

18. $s = 7$

19. $c = 24$

20. $x = \frac{1}{6}$

21. $y = \frac{2}{3}$

22. no solution

23. $z = 5$

24. Let d = distance; $d \le 1$ mi

25. Let c = cost; $c \ge 1500$

26. Let s = number of students; $s < 45$

27.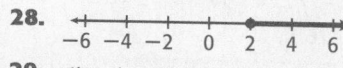

28.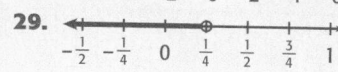

29.

Answers

30. $r \geq 4$

+----+----+----+----+----+----+
 0   2   4   6   8   10   12

31. $n < -\frac{1}{2}$

$-\frac{3}{2}$ -1 $-\frac{1}{2}$ 0 $\frac{1}{2}$ 1 $\frac{3}{2}$

32. $x > 0.2$

-0.2 0 0.2 0.4 0.6 0.8 1

33. $y \leq -5$

-11 -9 -7 -5 -3

34. Let n = the amount of money remaining; $n + 17.75 \leq 20$; $n \leq 2.25$; at most $2.25

35. $m \geq 18$

14 15 16 17 18 19 20 21 22

36. $n \leq -3$

-6 -5 -4 -3 -2 -1 0 1 2

37. $t > -16$

-20 -18 -16 -14 -12

38. $p < -3$

-6 -4 -2 0 2 4

39. $b \geq -27$

-32 -30 -28 -26 -24

40. $a > 8$

3 4 5 6 7 8 9 10 11 12 13

41. $z > 1$

0 1 3 5

42. $h \geq 6$

0 2 4 6 8 10

43. $a < 24$

20 22 24 26 28 30

44. $x \geq -6$

-10 -8 -6 -4 -2 0

45. $k > 3$

-1 0 1 2 3 4 5 6 7 8 9

46. $y > \frac{1}{8}$

-5 -3 -1 1 3 5

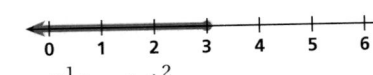 **3-6** Solving Inequalities by Adding or Subtracting (pp. 140–143)

 AF4.0

EXAMPLE

Solve and graph.

■ $n - 5 \leq -2$

$$\begin{array}{r} n - 5 \leq -2 \\ \underline{+5 \quad +5} \\ n \quad \leq \quad 3 \end{array}$$ *Add 5 to both sides.*

0 1 2 3 4 5 6

■ $5\frac{1}{3} > x + 4\frac{2}{3}$

$$\begin{array}{r} 5\frac{1}{3} > x + 4\frac{2}{3} \\ \underline{-4\frac{2}{3} \quad -4\frac{2}{3}} \\ \frac{2}{3} > x \end{array}$$ *Subtract $4\frac{2}{3}$ from both sides.*

$-\frac{1}{3}$ 0 $\frac{1}{3}$ $\frac{2}{3}$ 1 $\frac{4}{3}$ $\frac{5}{3}$

EXERCISES

Solve and graph.

30. $-13 \leq r - 17$

31. $n - 3\frac{1}{6} < -3\frac{2}{3}$

32. $x + 3.8 > 4$

33. $-3 \geq 2 + y$

34. Ellory budgets at most $20 each week for lunch. She has spent $17.75 so far this week. Write and solve an inequality to determine how much more Ellory can spend and stay within her lunch budget.

3-7 Solving Inequalities by Multiplying or Dividing (pp. 144–147)

AF4.0

EXAMPLE

■ Solve and graph.

$$\frac{z}{-13} \leq -10$$

$$(-13)\frac{z}{-13} \geq (-13)-10$$ *Multiply both sides by -13. Change $\leq$ to $\geq$.*

$$z \geq 130$$

60 70 80 90 100 110 120 130 140 150 160

EXERCISES

Solve and graph.

35. $\frac{m}{6} \geq 3$

36. $4n \leq -12$

37. $-8 < \frac{t}{2}$

38. $-5p > 15$

39. $9 \geq -\frac{b}{3}$

40. $-6a < -48$

3-8 Solving Two-Step Inequalities (pp. 148–151)

AF4.1

EXAMPLE

■ Solve and graph $-3x - 3 < 9$.

$$\begin{array}{r} -3x - 3 < 9 \\ \underline{+3 \quad +3} \\ -3x \quad < 12 \end{array}$$ *Add 3 to both sides.*

$$\frac{-3x}{-3} > \frac{12}{-3}$$ *Divide both sides by -3. Change $<$ to $>$.*

$$x > -4$$

-6 -4 -2 0 2

EXERCISES

Solve and graph.

41. $5z - 12 > -7$

42. $2h - 7 \geq 5$

43. $10 > \frac{a}{3} + 2$

44. $\frac{x}{3} - 8 \geq -10$

45. $5 - 3k < -4$

46. $2y + \frac{3}{4} > 1$

Simplify each expression. Justify each step.

1. $12 \cdot 7 \cdot \frac{2}{3}$ 56   **2.** $39 + 52 + 11$ 102   **3.** $(25 \cdot 9) \cdot 4$ 900   **4.** $2.1 + (6.5 + 4.9)$ 13.5

Simplify.

5. $7x + 5x$ $12x$

6. $m + 3m - 3$ $4m - 3$ **7.** $6n + 1 - n + 5n$ $10n + 1$

8. $2y + 2z + 2$ $2y + 2z + 2$ **9.** $3(s + 2) - s$ $2s + 6$ **10.** $10b + 8(b - 1)$ $18b - 8$

Solve.

11. $10x - 2x = 16$ $x = 2$ **12.** $\frac{3y + 5y}{3} = 8$ $y = 3$ **13.** $4c + 6 + 2c = 24$ $c = 3$

14. $\frac{2x}{5} - \frac{3}{5} = \frac{11}{5}$ $x = 7$ **15.** $\frac{2}{5}b - \frac{1}{4}b = 3$ $b = 20$ **16.** $15 - 6g + 8 = 19$ $g = \frac{2}{3}$

17. On her last three quizzes, Elise scored 84, 96, and 88. What grade must she get on her next quiz to have an average of 90 for all four quizzes?   92

Solve.

18. $3x + 13 = x + 1$ $x = -6$ **19.** $q + 7 = 2q + 5$ $q = 2$ **20.** $8n + 24 = 3n + 59$ $n = 7$

21. $m + 5 = m - 3$ no solution   **22.** $-3a + 9 = 3a - 9$ $a = 3$ **23.** $\frac{3z}{2} - \frac{17}{3} = \frac{2z}{3} - \frac{3}{2}$ $z = 5$

24. The square and the equilateral triangle have the same perimeter. Find the perimeter of each figure.   24 units

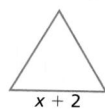

Solve and graph.

25. $-12 \geq \frac{h}{4}$ $h \leq -48$ **26.** $-36 \leq 6y$ $y \geq -6$ **27.** $-56 < -7m$ $m < 8$ **28.** $\frac{b}{-4} < 8$ $b > -32$

29. $n - 14 \leq -3$ $n \leq 11$ **30.** $8 < 22 + p$ $p > -14$ **31.** $-4 + u \leq -20$ $u \leq -16$ **32.** $8 + z > -6$ $z > -14$

33. Glenda has a $40 gift certificate to a café that sells her favorite tuna sandwich for $3.75 after tax. What are the possible numbers of tuna sandwiches that Glenda can buy with her gift certificate?   10 sandwiches or fewer

Solve and graph.

34. $6m + 4 > 2$ $m > -\frac{1}{3}$ **35.** $8 - 3p > 14$ $p < -2$ **36.** $4z + 4 \geq -8$ $z \geq -3$

37. $\frac{x}{10} + \frac{1}{2} \geq \frac{2}{5}$ $x \geq -1$ **38.** $\frac{3}{4} - \frac{c}{8} < \frac{1}{2}$ $c > 2$ **39.** $\frac{2}{3} > \frac{1}{2} - \frac{d}{6}$ $d > -1$

35.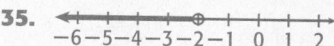

36.

37.

38.

39.

Organizer

Objective: Assess students' mastery of concepts and skills in Chapter 3.

 Online Edition

Resources

 Assessment Resources
Chapter 3 Tests
• Free Response
  (Levels A, B, C)
• Multiple Choice
  (Levels A, B, C)
• Performance Assessment

 IDEA Works! CD-ROM
Modified Chapter 3 Test

 **Test & Practice Generator**
One-Stop Planner®

Answers

25.

26.

27.

28.

29. $n \leq 11$

30. $p > -14$

31. $u \leq -16$

32. $z > -14$

34. $m > -\frac{1}{3}$

 California Standards

Standard	Items
AF1.1	17, 33
AF1.3	1–10
AF4.0	25–32
AF4.1	34–39
Ext. of AF4.1	11–24

Organizer

Objective: Provide opportunities to learn and practice common test-taking strategies.

 **Online Edition**

Teaching Tip **Gridded Response** This Strategies for Success focuses on how to correctly fill in the answer to a gridded-response test item. Students often solve the test item correctly, but get an incorrect answer score because they did not complete the answer grid properly. This strategy reviews the rules for filling in a grid. Students examine filled-in grids and identify why the response was marked as incorrect.

Gridded-response test items appear on many standardized tests, such as the PSAT and the SAT.

Gridded Response: Write Gridded Responses

When responding to a test item that requires you to place your answer in a grid, examine the grid to be sure you know how to fill it in correctly. Grid formats may vary from test to test. The grid in this book is used often, but it is not used on every test that has gridded-response items.

EXAMPLE 1

Gridded Response: Divide. $3000 \div 7.5$

$3000 \div 7.5 = \frac{3000}{7.5}\left(\frac{10}{10}\right)$ *7.5 has 1 decimal place, so multiply by $\frac{10}{10}$.*

$= \frac{30,000}{75}$ *Divide.*

$= 400$ *Simplify.*

- Write your answer in the answer boxes at the top of the grid.
- Put only one digit in each box. Do not leave a blank box in the middle of an answer.
- Shade the bubble for each digit in the column beneath it.

EXAMPLE 2

Gridded Response: Solve $x - \frac{1}{2} = \frac{2}{3}$.

$x - \frac{1}{2} + \frac{1}{2} = \frac{2}{3} + \frac{1}{2}$ *Add $\frac{1}{2}$ to both sides of the equation.*

$x = \frac{4}{6} + \frac{3}{6}$ *Find a common denominator.*

$x = \frac{7}{6}, 1\frac{1}{6},$ **or** $1.1\overline{6}$ *Add.*

- Mixed numbers and repeating decimals cannot be gridded, so you must grid the answer as $\frac{7}{6}$.
- Write your answer in the answer boxes at the top of the grid.
- Put only one digit or symbol in each box. On some grids, the fraction bar and the decimal point have a designated box.
- Shade the bubble for each digit or symbol in the correct column.

HOT TIP! You cannot grid a negative number in a gridded-response item because the grid does not include the negative sign. If you get a negative answer to a test item, recalculate the problem because you probably made a math error.

Read each statement and then answer the questions that follow.

Item A
A student correctly evaluated an expression and got $\frac{9}{13}$ as a result. Then the student filled in the grid as shown.

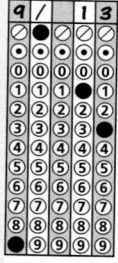

1. What error did the student make when filling in the grid?

2. Explain how to fill in the answer correctly.

Item B
A student added 0.21 and 0.49 and got an answer of 0.7. This answer is displayed in the grid.

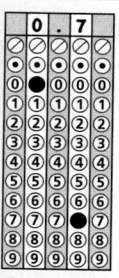

3. What errors did the student make when filling in the grid?

4. Explain how to fill in the answer correctly.

Item C
A student found −0.65 as the answer to −5 · (−0.13). Then the student filled in the grid as shown.

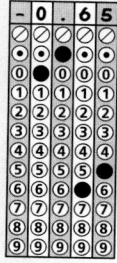

5. What error does the grid show?

6. Another student got an answer of −0.65. Explain why the student knew this answer was wrong.

Item D
A student found that $x = 5\frac{1}{2}$ was the solution to the equation $2x − 3 = 8$. Then the student filled in the grid as shown.

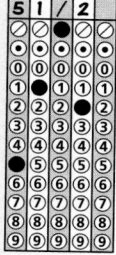

7. What answer does the grid show?

8. Explain why you cannot fill in a mixed number.

9. Write the answer $5\frac{1}{2}$ in two forms that could be entered in the grid correctly.

Teaching Tip

Gridded Response Remind students that they can also write their answer in the grid by placing the last digit of the answer in the far right box. Reassure students that it is okay for the first box to be blank, as long as the last box is filled and there are no blanks between numbers. Use the grid above **Problem 3** to show how the decimal 0.7 could be written by placing the 0 in the third column, the decimal point in the fourth column and the 7 in the last column.

Possible answers

1. The student placed a blank after the fraction bar. Blanks cannot be used in the middle of an answer.

2. The student could correctly fill in the grid in either of these two ways:
   a. 9 in first column, / in the second column, 1 in the third column, and a 3 in the fourth column
   b. 9 in second column, / in the third column, 1 in the fourth column, and a 3 in the fifth column

3. The student centered the answer in the grid, rather than placing the first digit in the far left box or placing the last digit in the far right box. The student also forgot to fill in the dot for the decimal point.

4. The student could correctly fill in the grid in either of these two ways:
   a. 0 in first column, dot in the second column, 7 in the third column
   b. 0 in third column, dot in the fourth column, 7 in the fifth column

5. There is not a negative sign in the grid.

6. You cannot have a negative answer to a gridded response test item.

7. The grid shows the answer $\frac{51}{2}$.

8. You cannot use a blank in the middle of an answer to represent the space between the whole number and the fraction. Without a blank, the answer is read as a fraction, not a mixed number.

9. 5.5; $\frac{11}{2}$

Organizer

Objective: Provide review and practice for Chapters 1–3.

Online Edition

Resources

Assessment Resources
Chapter 3 Cumulative Test

Focus on California Standards Benchmark Tests and Intervention

California Standards Practice CD-ROM

go.hrw.com
KEYWORD: MT8CA Practice

CHAPTER 3
MASTERING THE STANDARDS

go.hrw.com
Standards Practice Online
KEYWORD: MT8CA Practice

Cumulative Assessment, Chapters 1–3
Multiple Choice

1. A cell phone company charges $0.21 per minute for phone calls. Which expression represents the cost of a phone call of m minutes?

(A) $0.21m$ (C) $0.21 - m$
(B) $0.21 + m$ (D) $0.21 \div m$

2. Laurie had $88 in her bank account on Sunday. The table below shows her account activity for the past 5 days. What is the balance in her account on Friday?

Day	Deposit	Withdraw
Monday	$25	—
Tuesday	—	$58
Wednesday	—	$45
Thursday	$32	—
Friday	$91	—

(A) $91 (C) $133
(B) $103 (D) $236

3. Which equation has a solution of $x = -5$?

(A) $2x + 8 = -2$ (C) $\frac{1}{5}x - 6 = -10$
(B) $\frac{1}{5}x + 10 = 5$ (D) $-2x + 10 = -5$

4. You volunteer to bring 4 gallons of juice for a class party. There are 28 students in the class. You plan to give each student an equal amount of juice. Which equation can you use to determine the amount of juice per student?

(A) $4x = 28$ (C) $28 + x = 4$
(B) $\frac{x}{28} = 4$ (D) $28x = 4$

5. In order to apply for a driver's permit in Ohio, you have to be at least 16 years old. Which graph correctly represents the possible ages of Ohioans who can apply for a driver's permit?

(A) ← 12 13 14 15 16 17 18 19
(B) ← 12 13 14 15 16 17 18 19
(C) 12 13 14 15 16 17 18 19 →
(D) ← 12 13 14 15 16 17 18 19 →

6. Which expression represents the Distributive Property?

(A) $2(x + 3) = 2 \cdot x + 2 \cdot 3$
(B) $2x + 3 = 3 + 2x$
(C) $x \cdot y = y \cdot x$
(D) $2(xy) = (2x)y$

7. Which addition equation represents the number line diagram below?

-5 -4 -3 -2 -1 0 1 2 3 4 5 6

(A) $4 + (-2) = 2$ (C) $4 + 6 = 10$
(B) $4 + (-6) = -2$ (D) $-4 + (-6) = -10$

8. A snack package has 4 ounces of mixed nuts, $1\frac{1}{2}$ ounces of wheat crackers, $5\frac{3}{4}$ ounces of pretzels, and $2\frac{1}{8}$ ounces of popcorn. What is the total weight of the snacks?

(A) $13\frac{3}{8}$ ounces (C) $12\frac{5}{8}$ ounces
(B) $13\frac{1}{8}$ ounces (D) $9\frac{3}{8}$ ounces

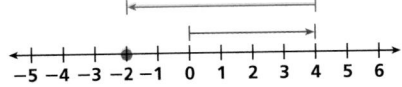
Teaching Tip

Multiple Choice For **items 1** and **4,** students may have trouble choosing a correct operation. Remind students that words such as "each" and "per" usually indicate multiplication or division. Once the students rule out addition and subtraction, they can use basic logic to determine the correct operation. Dividing will usually make a smaller number, whereas multiplying will usually make a larger number.

Answers

16. $4c + 30 = 62$ and $2c + 46 = 62$; $c = 8$

17. a. $-45.25, -40.50, 35.75, 55$
b. The value of the account rose by $5; $130

18. See 4-Point Response work sample.

California Standards	
Standard	**Items**
NS1.1	17
NS1.2 🔑	2, 7–8, 17
NS1.3	15
AF1.1	1, 5, 18
AF1.3 🔑	6, 11
AF4.0 🔑	4, 9, 12, 13, 18
AF4.1 🔑	3, 10, 14, 16

9. Which inequality is the solution of $\frac{2}{3} \geq x - \frac{1}{2}$?

  Ⓐ $x \leq \frac{1}{6}$ Ⓒ $x \leq 1\frac{1}{6}$

  Ⓑ $x \geq \frac{1}{6}$ Ⓓ $x \geq 1\frac{1}{6}$

10. Which value of x is the solution of the equation $\frac{3}{8}x - \frac{3}{4} = \frac{1}{6}$?

  Ⓐ $x = \frac{9}{22}$ Ⓒ $x = 1\frac{5}{9}$

  Ⓑ $x = \frac{5}{9}$ Ⓓ $x = 2\frac{4}{9}$

11. Frank purchased x tickets for a concert. Mark has 1 more ticket than Frank. Karen has twice as many tickets as Mark. Which expression represents how many tickets they have in all?

  Ⓐ $4x + 2$ Ⓒ $3x + 2$

  Ⓑ $3x + 3$ Ⓓ $4x + 3$

 When finding the solution of an equation on a multiple-choice test, work backward by substituting into the equation the answer choices provided.

Gridded Response

12. In 2004, the minimum wage for workers was $5.85 per hour. To find the amount of money someone can make in x hours, use the equation $y = 5.85x$. How much money does a person who works 5 hours earn? **29.25**

13. Solve the equation $\frac{4}{9}x = \frac{1}{3}$ for x. **$\frac{3}{4}$ or 0.75**

14. The sum of two consecutive integers $(x, x + 1)$ is 53. What is the smaller of the two numbers? **26**

15. In a local high school, 15 of the school's 600 students earned National Merit Scholarships. Write as a decimal the number of scholarships earned per total number of students. **0.025**

Short Response

16. Alfred and Eugene each spent $62 on campsite and gasoline expenses during their camping trip. Each campsite they used had the same per-night charge. Alfred paid for 4 nights of campsites and $30 of gasoline. Eugene paid for 2 nights of campsites and $46 of gasoline. Write an equation that could be used to determine the cost of one night's stay at a campsite. What was the cost of one night's stay at a campsite?

17. Omar opened a savings account with a $125 deposit in June. Over the next year, he withdrew $40.50 in September, deposited $35.75 in November, deposited $55 in February, and withdrew $45.25 in May.

  a. List the withdrawals and deposits in order from least to greatest.

  b. Over the 1 year period did the value of the account rise or fall? What value represents the total amount of change in the value of the account? Determine the final value of the account.

Extended Response

18. **Statement 1:** Currently there are 8 more students in student council than there are officers. There are 12 students total in student council.

  Statement 2: In addition, there have to be at least 4 officers in the council.

  a. Write an equation to represent Statement 1 and an inequality to represent Statement 2.

  b. Solve the equation, and plot the solution to the equation on a number line.

  c. Graph the solution set to the inequality.

  d. Explain what the solution sets have in common, and then explain how they are different.

Student Work Samples for Item 18

4-Point Response

a. Statement 1: $x + 8 = 12$
   Statement 2: $x \geq 4$

b. $x + 8 = 12$
   $-8 \quad -8$
   $x = 4$

c. $x \geq 4$

d. They both are equal to 4 but the inequality means more than 4 students are also allowed to be officers.

3-Point Response

a. statement 1: $x + 8 = 12$
   statement 2: $x \geq 4$

b. $x + 8 = 12$
   $x = 4$

c. $x \geq 4$

d. They both are equal to 4 but the inequality means 4 or less students can be officers.

2-Point Response

a. $x - 8 = 12$, $x \geq 4$

b. $x - 8 = 12$
   $+8 \quad +8$
   $x = 20$

c. $x \geq 4$

d. Both solution sets have $x = 20$ but the inequality also has $x \geq 4$ as well.

The student demonstrated an understanding of setting up, solving, and graphing equations and inequalities, and found the correct answers.

The student graphed the solution set incorrectly in part **c.** As a result, the answer and explanation for part **d** are wrong.

Based on the equations given in part **a,** the answers given in parts **b, c,** and **d** appear to be correct and sufficient. However, the student wrote the equation incorrectly in part **a,** so the answers to **a, b,** and **d** are incorrect.

CHAPTER 4

Exponents and Roots

✔	Grade-level Standard
◀	Review
▶	Beyond the Standards
A	Assessment
○	Optional

Pacing Guide

Calendar Planner
Teacher's **One-Stop** Planner®

Lesson/Lab		California Standards	⏱ Time	Advanced Students	Benchmark* Students	Strategic** Students
4-1	Exponents	AF1.2, AF2.1	50 min	✔	✔	✔
4-2	Integer Exponents	NS2.1, AF2.1	50 min	✔	✔	✔
4-3	Properties of Exponents	NS2.1, ◀━ NS2.3	50 min	✔	✔	✔
4-4	Multiplying and Dividing Monomials	◀━ AF1.3, AF2.2	50 min	✔	✔	✔
4-5	Scientific Notation	NS1.1	75 min	✔	✔	✔
LAB	Multiply and Divide Numbers in Scientific Notation	Ext. of NS1.1	25 min	▶	○	○
Ready to Go On?			25 min	A	A	A
Focus on Problem Solving			25 min	A	A	○
4-6	Squares and Square Roots	NS2.4, AF2.2	50 min	✔	✔	✔
4-7	Estimating Square Roots	NS2.4	50 min	✔	✔	✔
4-8	The Real Numbers	◀━ NS1.4	50 min	✔	✔	✔
LAB	Explore the Pythagorean Theorem	◀━ MG3.3	25 min	○	○	✔
4-9	The Pythagorean Theorem	◀━ MG3.3	75 min	✔	✔	✔
Ready to Go On?			25 min	A	A	A
Concept Connection			25 min	A	A	○
Study Guide: Review			50 min	✔	✔	✔
Chapter Test			50 min	A	A	A

* **Benchmark students** are achieving at or near grade level.

** **Strategic students** may be a year or more below grade level and may require additional time for intervention.

Countdown to Mastery, Weeks ❼, ❽, ❾

ONGOING ASSESSMENT and INTERVENTION

DIAGNOSE	PRESCRIBE

Assess Prior Knowledge

Before Chapter 4

Diagnose readiness for the chapter.
Are You Ready? SE p. 165

Prescribe intervention.
Are You Ready? Intervention Skills 35, 37, 51, 58

Formative Assessment

Before Every Lesson

Diagnose readiness for the lesson.
Warm Up TE, every lesson

Prescribe intervention.
Skills Bank SE pp. SB2–SB24
Review for Mastery CRF, Chapters 1–4

During Every Lesson

Diagnose understanding of lesson concepts.
Questioning Strategies Chapter 4
Think and Discuss SE, every lesson
Write About It SE, lesson exercises
Journal TE, lesson exercises

Prescribe intervention.
Reading Strategies CRF, every lesson
Success for ELL Chapter 4
Lesson Tutorial Videos Chapter 4

After Every Lesson

Diagnose mastery of lesson concepts.
Lesson Quiz TE, every lesson
Ready to Go On? SE pp. 190, 210
Test and Practice Generator

Prescribe intervention.
Review for Mastery CRF, every lesson
Problem Solving CRF, every lesson
Ready to Go On? Intervention Chapter 4
Homework Help Online

Before Chapter 4 Testing

Diagnose mastery of concepts in the chapter.
Ready to Go On? SE pp. 190, 210
Focus on Problem Solving SE p. 191
Concept Connection SE p. 211
Section Quizzes AR pp. 65–66
Test and Practice Generator

Prescribe intervention.
Ready to Go On? Intervention Chapter 4
Scaffolding Questions TE p. 211

Before Assessment of California Standards

Diagnose mastery of California standards.
Focus on California Standards: Benchmark Tests
Mastering the Standards SE pp. 218–219
California Standards Practice CD-ROM

Prescribe intervention.
Focus on California Standards: Intervention

Summative Assessment

After Chapter 4

Check mastery of chapter concepts.
Multiple-Choice Tests (Forms A, B, C)
Free-Response Tests (Forms A, B, C)
Performance Assessment AR pp. 67–80
Test and Practice Generator

Prescribe intervention.
Review for Mastery CRF, every lesson
Lesson Tutorial Videos Chapter 4

KEY: **SE** = Student Edition   **TE** = Teacher's Edition   **CRF** = Chapter Resource File   **AR** = Assessment Resources   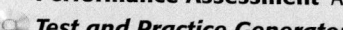 Available on CD-ROM   Available online

Supporting the Teacher

Chapter 4 Resource File

Family Involvement
pp. 1–4, 45–48

Practice A, B, C
pp. 5–7, 13–15, 21–23, 29–31, 37–39, 49–51, 57–59, 65–67, 73–75

Review for Mastery
pp. 8, 16, 24, 32, 40, 52, 60, 68, 76

Challenge
pp. 9, 17, 25, 33, 41, 53, 61, 69, 77

Problem Solving
pp. 10, 18, 26, 34, 42, 54, 62, 70, 78

Reading Strategies ELL
pp. 11, 19, 27, 35, 43, 55, 63, 71, 79

Puzzles, Twisters, and Teasers
pp. 12, 20, 28, 36, 44, 56, 64, 72, 80

Hands-On Lab
pp. 81–82, 86–88, 91–92

Technology Lab
pp. 83–84, 85, 89–90

Workbooks

***Homework and Practice Workbook* SPANISH**
Teacher's Guide.................................pp. 22–26

***Know-It Notebook* SPANISH**
Teacher's Guide.............................Chapter 4

***Review for Mastery Workbook* SPANISH**
Teacher's Guide.................................pp. 43–52

***Focus on California Standards: Intervention Workbook* SPANISH**
Teacher's Guide

Teacher Tools

Power Presentations
Complete PowerPoint® presentations for Chapter 4 lessons

Lesson Tutorial Videos SPANISH
Holt authors Ed Burger and Freddie Renfro present tutorials to support the Chapter 4 lessons.

Teacher's One-Stop Planner SPANISH
Easy access to all Chapter 4 resources and assessments, as well as software for lesson planning, test generation, and puzzle creation

IDEA Works!
Key Chapter 4 resources and assessments modified to address special learning needs

Questioning Strategies.....................Chapter 4

Solutions Key....................................Chapter 4

Interactive Answers and Solutions

TechKeys   ***Lab Resources***

Project Teacher Support   ***Parent Resources***

Transparencies

Lesson Transparencies, Volume 1 ....Chapter 4
• Teacher Tools
• Warm Ups
• Teaching Transparencies
• Lesson Quizzes

Know-It Notebook...............................Chapter 4
• Vocabulary   • Chapter Review
• Additional Examples   • Big Ideas

Alternate Openers: Explorations.............pp. 26–34

Countdown to Mastery........................pp. 13–17

Technology Highlights for the Teacher

Power Presentations
Dynamic presentations to engage students. Complete PowerPoint® presentations for every lesson in Chapter 4.

One-Stop Planner SPANISH
Easy access to Chapter 4 resources and assessments. Includes lesson-planning, test-generation, and puzzle-creation software.

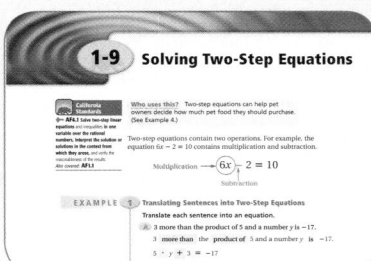

Premier Online Edition SPANISH
Includes Tutorial Videos, Lesson Activities, Lesson Quizzes, Homework Help, Chapter Project and more.

KEY: **SE** = *Student Edition*   **TE** = *Teacher's Edition*   ELL English Language Learners   SPANISH Spanish available   Available on CD-ROM   Available online

CHAPTER
4

Universal Access

Teaching tips to help all students appear throughout the chapter. A few that target specific students are included in the lists below.

Strategic Students

Practice A	CRF, every lesson
Review for Mastery	CRF, every lesson
Reading Strategies	CRF, every lesson
Academic Vocabulary Connections	TE p. 166
Modeling	TE pp. 201, 206
Ready to Go On? Intervention	Chapter 4
Questioning Strategies	Chapter 4
Know-It Notebook SPANISH	Chapter 4
Homework Help Online	
Lesson Tutorial Videos SPANISH	
Online Interactivities SPANISH	

Special Needs Students

Practice A	CRF, every lesson
Review for Mastery	CRF, every lesson
Reading Strategies	CRF, every lesson
Academic Vocabulary Connections	TE p. 166
Inclusion	TE p. 173
IDEA Works! Modified Resources	Chapter 4
Ready to Go On? Intervention	Chapter 4
Know-It Notebook SPANISH	Chapter 4
Lesson Tutorial Videos SPANISH	
Online Interactivities SPANISH	

English Learners

ENGLISH
LANGUAGE
LEARNERS

Reading Strategies	CRF, every lesson
Vocabulary Review	SE p. 214
Academic Vocabulary Connections	TE p. 166
English Language Learners	TE pp. 169, 201
Language Support	TE p. 206
Success for English Language Learners	Chapter 4
Know-It Notebook SPANISH	Chapter 4
Multilingual Glossary	
Lesson Tutorial Videos SPANISH	

Benchmark Students

Practice B	CRF, every lesson
Problem Solving	CRF, every lesson
Academic Vocabulary Connections	TE p. 166
Ready to Go On? Intervention	Chapter 4
Questioning Strategies	Chapter 4
Know-It Notebook SPANISH	Chapter 4
Homework Help Online	
Online Interactivities SPANISH	

Advanced Students

Practice C	CRF, every lesson
Challenge	CRF, every lesson
Reading and Writing Math EXTENSION	TE p. 167
Concept Connection EXTENSION	TE p. 211
Advanced Learners/GATE	TE p. 177
Ready to Go On? Enrichment	Chapter 4

Technology Highlights for Universal Access

 Lesson Tutorial Videos SPANISH

Starring Holt authors Ed Burger and Freddie Renfro! Live tutorials to support every lesson in Chapter 4.

 Multilingual Glossary

Searchable glossary includes definitions in English, Spanish, Vietnamese, Chinese, Hmong, Korean, and other languages.

 Online Interactivities SPANISH

Interactive tutorials provide visually engaging alternative opportunities to learn concepts and master skills.

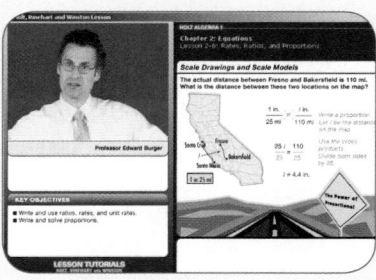

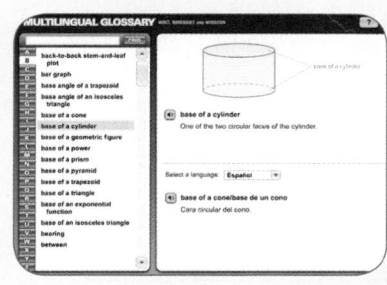

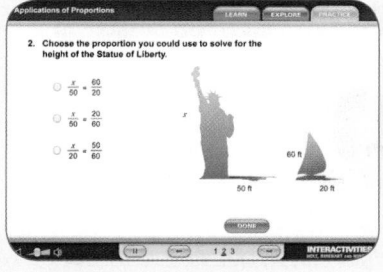

KEY: **SE** = *Student Edition*   **TE** = *Teacher's Edition*   **CRF** = *Chapter Resource File*   SPANISH Spanish available   Available on CD-ROM   Available online

CHAPTER 4

Ongoing Assessment

Assessing Prior Knowledge

Determine whether students have the prerequisite concepts and skills for success in Chapter 4.

Are You Ready? SPANISH .... SE p. 165
Warm Up .... TE, every lesson

Chapter and Standards Assessment

Provide review and practice for Chapter 4 and standards mastery.

Concept Connection .... SE p. 211
Study Guide: Review .... SE pp. 214–216
Mastering the Standards .... SE pp. 218–219
Countdown to Mastery Transparencies .... pp. 13–17
Focus on California Standards: Benchmark Tests
Focus on California Standards: Intervention Workbook SPANISH
California Standards Practice CD-ROM SPANISH
IDEA Works! Modified Worksheets and Tests

Alternative Assessment

Assess students' understanding of Chapter 4 concepts and combined problem-solving skills.

Performance Assessment .... AR pp. 79–80
Portfolio Assessment .... AR p. xxxvi
Chapter 4 Project

Daily Assessment

Provide formative assessment for each day of Chapter 4.

Think and Discuss .... SE, every lesson
Write About It .... SE, lesson exercises
Journal .... TE, lesson exercises
Lesson Quiz .... TE, every lesson
Questioning Strategies .... Chapter 4
IDEA Works! Modified Lesson Quizzes .... Chapter 4

Weekly Assessment

Provide formative assessment for each week of Chapter 4.

Focus on Problem Solving .... SE p. 191
Concept Connection .... SE p. 211
Ready to Go On? SPANISH .... SE pp. 190, 210
Cumulative Assessment .... SE pp. 218–219
Test and Practice Generator SPANISH ...One-Stop Planner

Formal Assessment

Provide summative assessment of Chapter 4 mastery.

Section Quizzes .... AR pp. 65–66
Chapter 4 Test SPANISH .... SE p. 217
Chapter Test (Levels A, B, C) .... AR pp. 67–78
        • Multiple-Choice   • Free-Response
Cumulative Test .... AR pp. 81–84
Test and Practice Generator SPANISH ...One-Stop Planner
IDEA Works! Modified Tests .... Chapter 4

Technology Highlights for the Teacher

Are You Ready? SPANISH

Automatically assess readiness and prescribe intervention for Chapter 4 prerequisite skills.

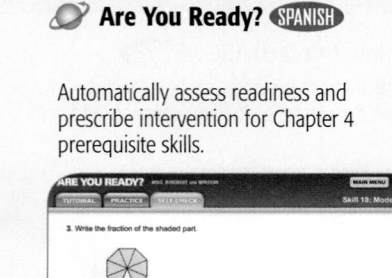

Ready to Go On? SPANISH

Automatically assess understanding of and prescribe intervention for Sections 4A and 4B.

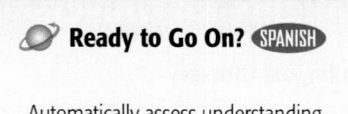
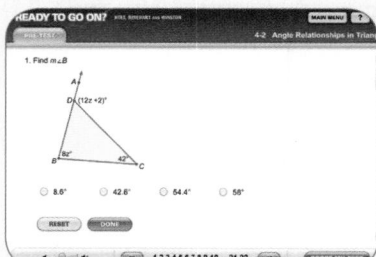

Focus on California Standards: Benchmark Tests and Intervention SPANISH

Automatically assess proficiency with California Grade 7 Standards and provide intervention.

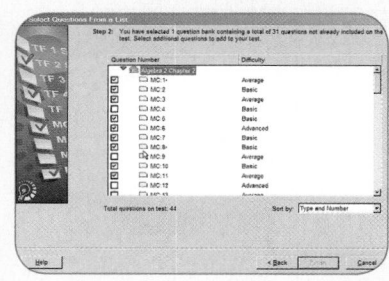

KEY: **SE** = Student Edition **TE** = Teacher's Edition **AR** = Assessment Resources SPANISH Spanish available Available on CD-ROM Available online

CHAPTER 4

Formal Assessment

Three levels (A, B, C) of multiple-choice and free-response chapter tests are available in the *Assessment Resources.*

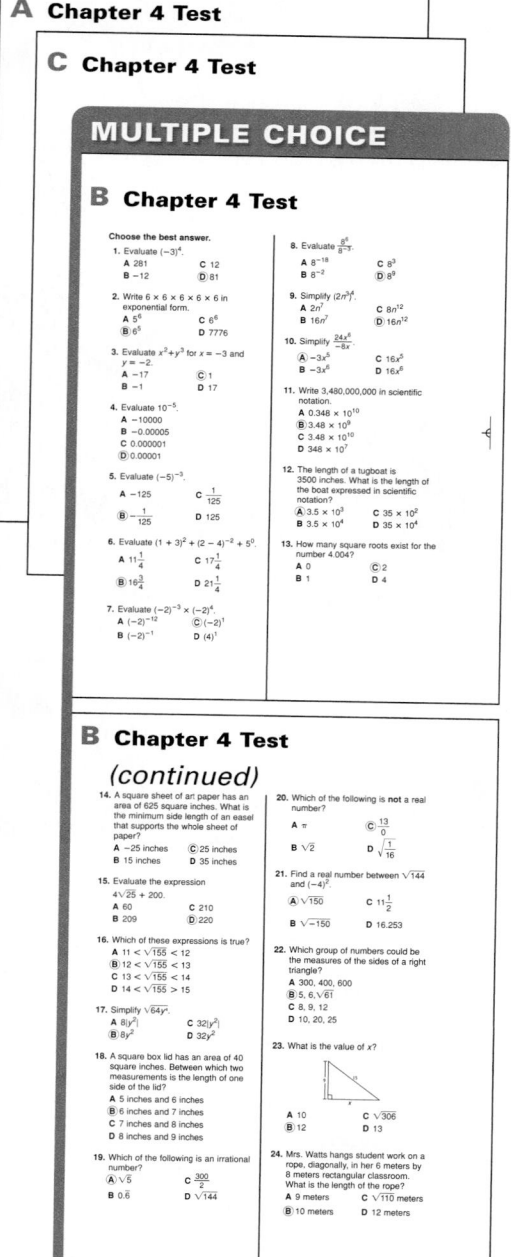

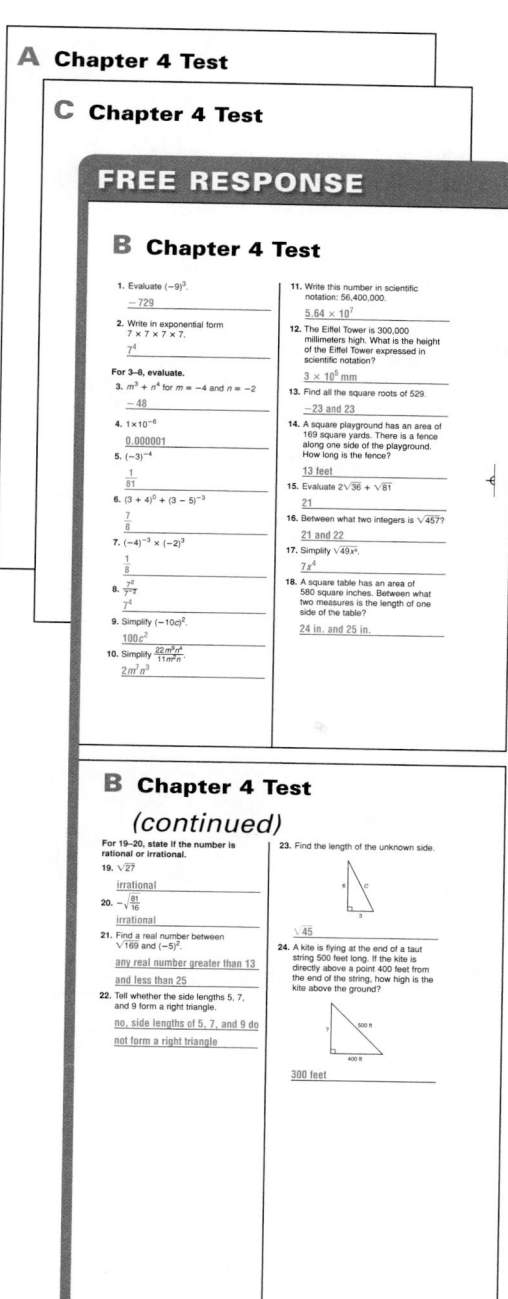

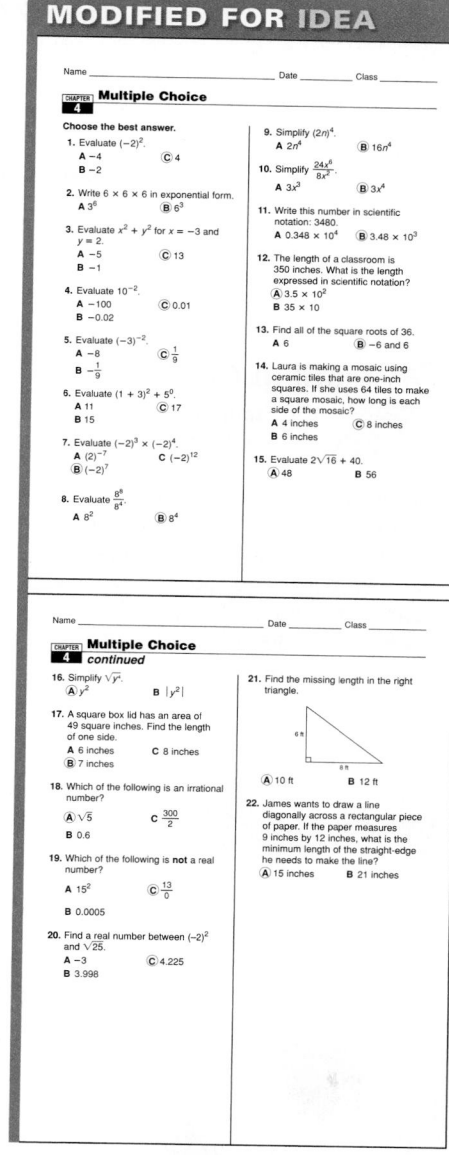

Modified tests and worksheets found in *IDEA Works!*

Test & Practice Generator SPANISH
Teacher's One-Stop Planner®

Create and customize Chapter 4 Tests. Instantly
generate multiple test versions, answer keys, and
Spanish versions of test items.

Exponents and Roots

CHAPTER 4

 **Focus on Problem Solving**

On page 191, students focus on choosing an operation when solving real-world problems.

 **CONCEPT CONNECTION** On page 211, students use exponents and roots to conclude facts about bacterial growth.

Math in *California*

The Stanford Linear Accelerator Center (SLAC) is a particle physics laboratory located south of San Francisco. The scientists and engineers who do research at SLAC use concepts such as exponents and roots to express the sizes and numbers of particles they study. Students will study these concepts in this chapter.

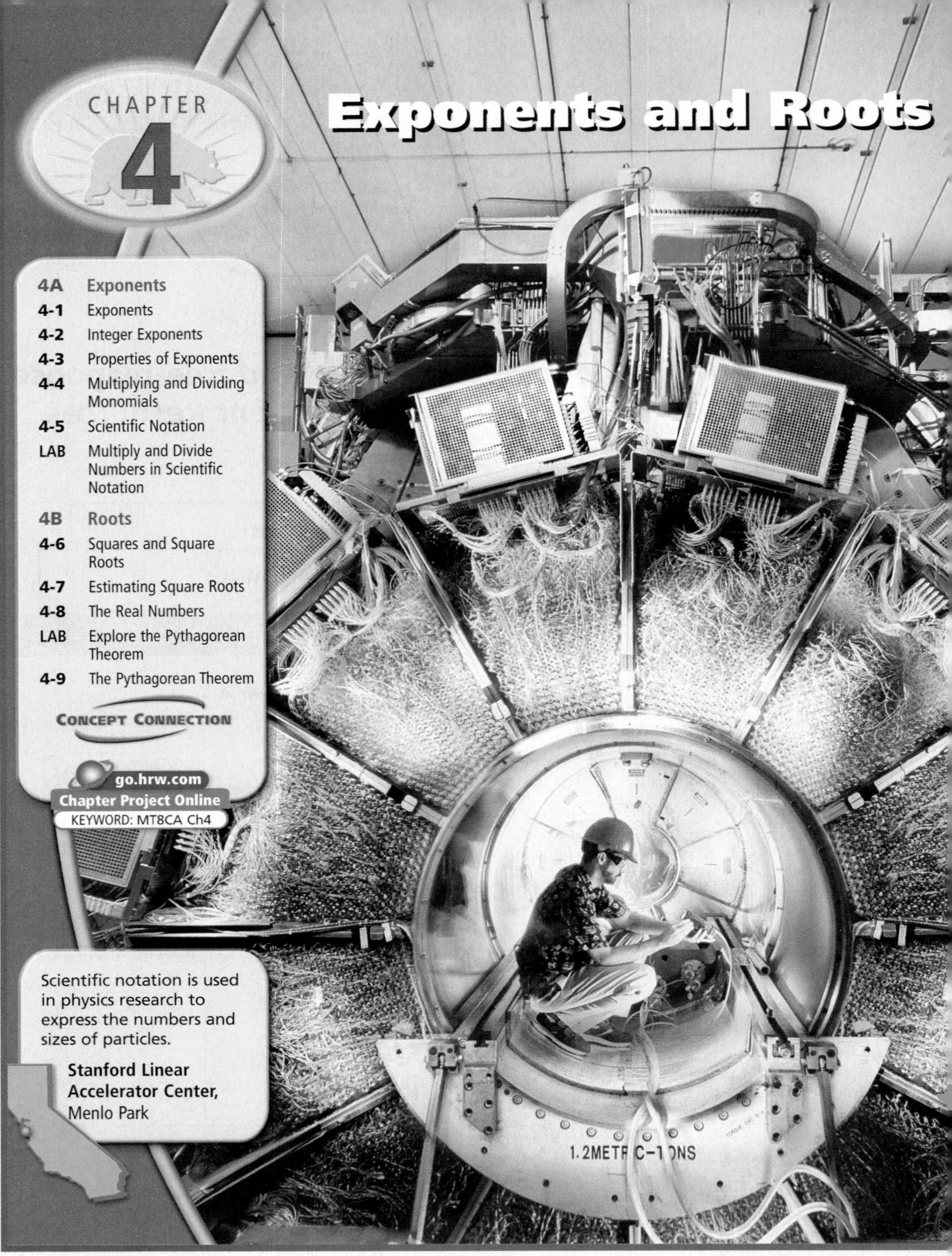

go.hrw.com
Chapter Project Online
KEYWORD: MT8CA Ch4

Scientific notation is used in physics research to express the numbers and sizes of particles.

Stanford Linear Accelerator Center, Menlo Park

 **PROBLEM SOLVING**

Problem Solving Project

Understand, Plan, Solve, and Look Back

Have students:

• Complete The Lives of Particles worksheet to learn about the independent life spans of some atomic particles.

• Construct a drawing or model of the atom and its component particles.

Science Connection

Project Resources
All project resources for teachers and students are provided online.

Materials:

• The Lives of Particles worksheet
• modeling materials

go.hrw.com
Project Teacher Support
KEYWORD: MT8CA PSProject4

ARE YOU READY?

✓ Vocabulary

Choose the best term from the list to complete each sentence.

1. According to the __?__, you must multiply or divide before you add or subtract when simplifying a numerical __?__. **order of operations; expression**

2. An algebraic expression is a mathematical phrase that has at least one __?__. **variable**

3. In a(n) __?__, an equal sign is used to show that two quantities are the same. **equation**

4. You use a(n) __?__ to show that one quantity is greater than another quantity. **inequality**

equation

expression

inequality

order of operations

variable

Complete these exercises to review skills you will need for this chapter.

✓ Order of Operations

Simplify by using the order of operations.

5. $12 + 4(2)$ **20**
6. $12 + 8 \div 4$ **14**
7. $15(14 - 4)$ **150**
8. $(23 - 5) - 36 \div 2$ **0**
9. $12 \div 2 + 10 \div 5$ **8**
10. $40 \div 2 \cdot 4$ **80**

✓ Solve One-Step Equations

Solve.

11. $x + 9 = 21$ $x = 12$
12. $3z = 42$ $z = 14$
13. $\frac{w}{4} = 16$ $w = 64$
14. $24 + t = 24$ $t = 0$
15. $p - 7 = 23$ $p = 30$
16. $12m = 0$ $m = 0$

✓ Use Repeated Multiplication

Find the product.   17. 16,807

20. 14,641

21. 262,144

17. $7 \times 7 \times 7 \times 7 \times 7$
18. $12 \times 12 \times 12$ **1728**
19. $3 \times 3 \times 3 \times 3$ **81**
20. $11 \times 11 \times 11 \times 11$
21. $8 \times 8 \times 8 \times 8 \times 8 \times 8$
22. $2 \times 2 \times 2$ **8**
23. $100 \times 100 \times 100 \times 100$
24. $9 \times 9 \times 9 \times 9 \times 9$
25. $1 \times 1 \times 1 \times 1$ **1**

23. 100,000,000   24. 59,049

✓ Multiply and Divide by Powers of Ten

Multiply or divide.

26. $358(10)$ **3580**
27. $358(1000)$ **358,000**
28. $358(100,000)$ **35,800,000**
29. $\frac{358}{10}$ **35.8**
30. $\frac{358}{1000}$ **0.358**
31. $\frac{358}{100,000}$ **0.00358**

ARE YOU READY?

CHAPTER 4

Organizer

Objective: Assess students' understanding of prerequisite skills.

Prerequisite Skills

Order of Operations

Solve One-Step Equations

Use Repeated Multiplication

Multiply and Divide by Powers of Ten

Assessing Prior Knowledge
INTERVENTION ◀ ▶

Diagnose and Prescribe

Use this page to determine whether intervention is necessary or whether enrichment is appropriate.

Resources

 Are You Ready? Intervention and Enrichment Worksheets

 Are You Ready? CD-ROM

 Are You Ready? Online

my.hrw.com

ARE YOU READY?
Diagnose and Prescribe

NO INTERVENE

YES ENRICH

✓ Prerequisite Skill	📖 Worksheets	💿 CD-ROM	🌐 Online
✓ Order of Operations	Skill 51	Activity 51	
✓ Solve One-Step Equations	Skill 58	Activity 58	Diagnose and Prescribe Online
✓ Use Repeated Multiplication	Skill 35	Activity 35	
✓ Multiply and Divide by Powers of Ten	Skill 37	Activity 37	

ARE YOU READY? Intervention, Chapter 4

ARE YOU READY? Enrichment, Chapter 4
📖 Worksheets
💿 CD-ROM
🌐 Online

Organizer

Objective: Help students understand the new concepts they will learn in Chapter 4.

Academic Vocabulary Connections

Becoming familiar with the academic vocabulary on this student page will be helpful to students. Discussing some of the vocabulary terms in the chapter also may be helpful.
Possible answers given.

1. The word *irrational* contains the prefix *ir–*, which means "not." Knowing what you do about rational numbers, what do you think is true of **irrational numbers?**
   Irrational numbers are numbers that cannot be expressed as the quotient of two integers (a fraction).

2. To *square a number* means "to multiply the number by itself" as in 2 · 2. Keeping this in mind, what do you think a **perfect square** might be? A perfect square is made by multiplying a whole number by itself.

The information below "unpacks" the standards. The Academic Vocabulary is highlighted and defined to help you understand the language of the standards. Refer to the lessons listed after each standard for help with the math terms and phrases. The Chapter Concept shows how the standard is applied in this chapter.

California Standard	Academic Vocabulary	Chapter Concept
NS1.1 Read, write, and compare rational numbers in scientific notation (positive and negative powers of 10), compare rational numbers in general. (Lesson 4-5)	**compare** determine how items are the same or different **notation** a way of showing something by a special system of marks or characters	You use scientific notation to express very large and very small numbers.
NS1.4 Differentiate between rational and irrational numbers. (Lesson 4-8)	**differentiate** to tell the difference between	You determine the special groups that numbers belong to.
NS2.4 Use the inverse relationship between raising to a power and extracting the root of a perfect square integer; for an integer that is not square, determine without a calculator the two integers between which its square root lies and explain why. (Lessons 4-6 and 4-7)	**inverse** opposite **extracting** pulling out	You multiply an integer by itself, or square it. You will also find what whole number can be multiplied by itself to get a given number. When a whole number can not be found, you will find what two whole numbers the value is between.
AF2.1 Interpret positive whole-number powers as repeated multiplication and negative whole-number powers as repeated division or multiplication by the multiplicative inverse. Simplify and evaluate expressions that include exponents. (Lessons 4-1, 4-2, 4-3, and 4-4)	**simplify** make things easier **evaluate** find the value of	You write expressions that contain exponents in a simpler form. You will also find the value of expressions containing variables and exponents.
MG3.3 Know and understand the Pythagorean theorem and its converse and use it to find the length of the missing side of a right triangle and the lengths of other line segments and, **in some situations, empirically verify the Pythagorean theorem by direct measurement.** (Lab 4-9 and Lesson 4-9)	**converse** the opposite or reverse	You learn about the relationship that exists between the three sides of all right triangles.

Standards NS2.1 and AF2.2 are also covered in this chapter.

Looking Back

Previously, students

- simplified expressions containing integers and positive exponents.
- performed operations with integers.
- determined if a decimal is terminating or repeating.

In This Chapter

Students will study

- simplifying expressions that contain rational numbers and negative exponents.
- multiplying and dividing monomials.
- differentiating between rational and irrational numbers.

Looking Forward

Students can use these skills

- to solve equations containing square roots.
- to multiply and divide polynomials.
- to differentiate between real and imaginary numbers.

Reading and Writing Math

Study Strategy: Take Effective Notes

Good note taking is an important study strategy. The Cornell system of note taking is an effective way to organize and review main ideas. This method involves dividing your notebook paper into three main sections. You take notes in the note-taking column during the lecture. You write questions and key phrases in the cue column as you review your notes. You write a brief summary of the lecture in the summary area.

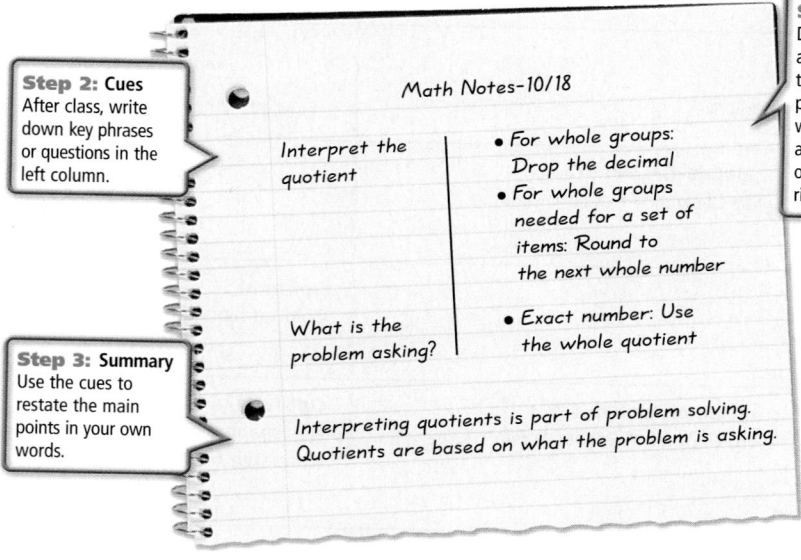

Step 1: Notes Draw a vertical line about 2.5 inches from the left side of your paper. During class, write your notes about the main points of the lecture in the right column.

Step 2: Cues After class, write down key phrases or questions in the left column.

Step 3: Summary Use the cues to restate the main points in your own words.

Math Notes-10/18

Interpret the quotient
- For whole groups: Drop the decimal
- For whole groups needed for a set of items: Round to the next whole number

What is the problem asking?
- Exact number: Use the whole quotient

Interpreting quotients is part of problem solving. Quotients are based on what the problem is asking.

Try This

1. Describe how you can benefit from using the Cornell system of note taking.

2. In your next class, use the Cornell system of note taking. Compare these notes to your notes from a previous lecture. Do you think your old notes or the notes using the Cornell system would better prepare you for tests and quizzes?

Reading and Writing Math

CHAPTER 4

Organizer

Objective: Help students apply strategies to understand and retain key concepts.

 PREMIER **Online Edition**

Resources

Chapter 4 Resource File
Reading Strategies

Study Strategy: Take Effective Notes

Discuss Ask students what methods they use for taking notes. Explain how headings and dates will make their notes easier to reference, and suggest that being able to quickly reference notes will reduce the amount of time it takes them to study. Show them an example of good note taking.

Extend Write the date and a heading on the board at the beginning of every lesson and remind students to write these down. As you progress through the chapter, ask students for definitions or formulas that were taught in previous lessons. Have them use their notes to find the answers instead of using the textbook.

Answers to *Try This*

1. Check students' work.
2. Check students' work.

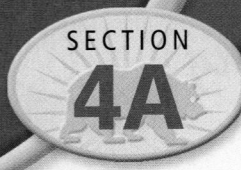
Exponents

One-Minute Section Planner

Lesson	Lab Resources	Materials
Lesson 4-1 Exponents • Simplify expressions with exponents. 🐻 **NS2.0, AF1.2, AF2.1**		**Optional** Calculators, two-color counters (MK)
Lesson 4-2 Integer Exponents • Simplify expressions with negative exponents and the zero exponent. 🐻 **NS2.1, AF2.0, AF2.1**		
Lesson 4-3 Properties of Exponents • Apply the properties of exponents. 🐻 **NS2.1, 🔑 NS2.3**	**Hands-On Lab 4-3** In *Chapter 4 Resource File*	
Lesson 4-4 Multiplying and Dividing Monomials • Multiply and divide monomials and take powers of monomials. 🐻 🔑 **AF1.3, AF2.2**		**Optional** Colored highlighters
Lesson 4-5 Scientific Notation • Express large and small numbers in scientific notation and compare two numbers written in scientific notation. 🐻 **NS1.1**	**Technology Lab 4-5** In *Chapter 4 Resource File*	**Optional** Newspapers or magazines with large numbers
4-5 Technology Lab Multiply and Divide Numbers in Scientific Notation • Use a graphing calculator to multiply and divide numbers written in scientific notation. 🐻 **Extension of NS1.1**		**Required** Graphing calculator

MK = *Manipulatives Kit*

Notes

_____

_____

_____

_____

_____

_____

_____

_____

_____

Math Background:
Teaching the Standards

Professional
Development

EXPONENTS AF2.1

Lessons 4-1, 4-2

When a number is written in exponential form, the exponent represents the number of times the base is to be used as a factor. Thus, the expression 2^4 means $2 \cdot 2 \cdot 2 \cdot 2$. This definition makes sense whenever the exponent is a natural number. For other situations, the definition must be extended.

Students are often puzzled by the fact that any nonzero number raised to the zero power is 1. It makes sense to think of 2^4 as a product where 2 is a factor 4 times, but how does one write a product with 2 as a factor "zero times" to simplify 2^0? Students should understand that 2^0 is *defined* to be 1 in order to make it consistent with the rules of exponent arithmetic. For example, in order for the property $\frac{b^m}{b^n} = b^{m-n}$ (Lesson 4-3) to work in as many situations as possible it must be true that $\frac{2^4}{2^4} = 2^{4-4} = 2^0$, but $\frac{2^4}{2^4} = \frac{16}{16} = 1$. Thus, $2^0 = 1$. In general, $b^0 = 1$ for any nonzero value of b.

A similar line of reasoning is used to define powers in which the exponent is a negative integer. For example, the rule for dividing powers with the same base says that $\frac{2^4}{2^5} = 2^{4-5} = 2^{-1}$. However, $\frac{2^4}{2^5} = \frac{2 \cdot 2 \cdot 2 \cdot 2}{2 \cdot 2 \cdot 2 \cdot 2 \cdot 2} = \frac{1}{2}$. Thus, it is consistent to define 2^{-1} as $\frac{1}{2}$, and, more generally, to define b^{-n} as $\frac{1}{b^n}$ for $b \neq 0$.

PROPERTIES OF EXPONENTS NS2.3

Lessons 4-3, 4-4

Properties of exponents are based on the definition of an exponent and the Commutative and Associative Properties of Multiplication. In fact, the rule for raising a product to a power, which is introduced in Lesson 4-4, is little more than repeated applications of the Commutative and Associative Properties. The rule states that $(ab)^n = a^n \cdot b^n$. To see why this is so, consider the following steps in simplifying $(ab)^2$.

$(ab)^2 = (a \cdot b) \cdot (a \cdot b)$
$\qquad = a \cdot (b \cdot a) \cdot b$ *Associative Property*
$\qquad = a \cdot (a \cdot b) \cdot b$ *Commutative Property*
$\qquad = (a \cdot a) \cdot (b \cdot b)$ *Associative Property*
$\qquad = a^2 \cdot b^2$

It is useful for students to see this type of step-by-step argument so that they can develop the exponent rules from first principles if they forget the formulas. Also, as their mathematical thinking becomes more sophisticated, students should be aware of the role that the Commutative and Associative Properties play in providing the logical underpinnings of many algebraic manipulations.

SCIENTIFIC NOTATION NS1.1

Lesson 4-5

Scientific notation is an efficient way to write very large and very small numbers. The distance from the earth to the sun is approximately 93 million miles, or 93,000,000 miles. The key step in the translation to scientific notation is to recognize that

$$93{,}000{,}000 = 9.3 \times 10{,}000{,}000$$

and to see that 10,000,000 is a power of 10, namely 10^7. Thus, $93{,}000{,}000 = 9.3 \times 10^7$.

In general, every positive real number may be written in scientific notation, $a \times 10^n$, where $1 \leq a < 10$ and n is an integer. The value of a is called the *coefficient.*

Numbers greater than or equal to 1 but less than 10 are written in scientific notation with an exponent of 0 since, for example,

$$3.8 = 3.8 \times 1 = 3.8 \times 10^0.$$

Numbers greater than 0 but less than 1 are written with negative exponents. Again, a specific example shows why this makes sense:

$$0.0041 = 4.1 \times 0.001 = 4.1 \times \tfrac{1}{1000} = 4.1 \times 10^{-3}.$$

 Online Edition
Tutorial Videos, Interactivities

 Countdown to Mastery Week 7

Power Presentations
with PowerPoint®

Warm Up
Find the product.

1. $5 \cdot 5 \cdot 5 \cdot 5$ — 625

2. $3 \cdot 3 \cdot 3$ — 27

3. $(-7)(-7)(-7)$ — -343

4. $9 \cdot 9$ — 81

Also available on transparency

Math Fact !
The modern notation for exponents is believed to have originated with René Descartes around 1637.

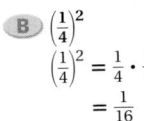

California Standards

Algebra and Functions 2.1
Also covered:
Number Sense
2.0 Students use exponents, powers, and roots and use exponents in working with fractions.
Algebra and Functions
1.2 Use the correct order of operations to evaluate algebraic expressions such as $3(2x + 5)^2$.

4-1 Exponents

California Standards

AF2.1 Interpret positive whole-number powers as repeated **multiplication** and negative whole-number powers as repeated division or multiplication by the multiplicative inverse. **Simplify and evaluate expressions that include exponents.**
Also covered: **AF1.2**

Vocabulary
exponential form
exponent
base
power

Why learn this? You can use exponents to determine how many bacteria exist after one bacterium reproduces multiple times. (See Exercise 41.)

Fold a piece of $8\frac{1}{2}$-by-11-inch paper in half. If you fold it in half again, the paper is 4 sheets thick. After the third fold in half, the paper is 8 sheets thick. How many sheets thick is the paper after 7 folds?

With each fold the number of sheets doubles.

$$2 \cdot 2 \cdot 2 \cdot 2 \cdot 2 \cdot 2 \cdot 2 = 128 \text{ sheets thick after 7 folds}$$

This multiplication problem can also be written in *exponential form.*

$$2 \cdot 2 \cdot 2 \cdot 2 \cdot 2 \cdot 2 \cdot 2 = 2^7 \qquad \text{\textit{The number 2 is a factor 7 times.}}$$

If a number is in **exponential form**, the **exponent** represents the number of times the **base** is to be used as a factor. A number produced by raising a base to an exponent is called a **power**. 128 and 2^7 are equivalent.

Base   Exponent

 **EXAMPLE 1** **Writing Exponents**

Write in exponential form.

A $5 \cdot 5 \cdot 5 \cdot 5 \cdot 5 \cdot 5 \cdot 5$
$5 \cdot 5 \cdot 5 \cdot 5 \cdot 5 \cdot 5 \cdot 5 = 5^7$ *Identify how many times 5 is a factor.*

Reading Math
Read $(-4)^3$ as "-4 to the 3rd power" or "-4 cubed."

B $(-4) \cdot (-4) \cdot (-4)$
$(-4) \cdot (-4) \cdot (-4) = (-4)^3$ *Identify how many times -4 is a factor.*

C $8 \cdot 8 \cdot 8 \cdot 8 \cdot p \cdot p \cdot p$
$8 \cdot 8 \cdot 8 \cdot 8 \cdot p \cdot p \cdot p = 8^4 p^3$ *Identify how many times 8 and p are each used as a factor.*

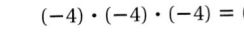 **EXAMPLE 2** **Simplifying Powers**

Simplify.

A 3^4
$3^4 = 3 \cdot 3 \cdot 3 \cdot 3$ *Find the product.*
$= 81$

B $\left(\frac{1}{4}\right)^2$
$\left(\frac{1}{4}\right)^2 = \frac{1}{4} \cdot \frac{1}{4}$
$= \frac{1}{16}$

---

1 Introduce
Alternate Opener

EXPLORATION

4-1 **Exponents**

You can multiply $(-5) \cdot (-5) \cdot (-5) \cdot (-5) \cdot (-5) \cdot (-5)$ using exponents and a calculator.

The number -5 is a factor 6 times, so you can write it as $(-5)^6$.

The expressions are equivalent because they have the same value.

$(-5) \cdot (-5) \cdot (-5) \cdot (-5) \cdot (-5) \cdot (-5) = 15,625$ and $(-5)^6 = 15,625$

Write each of the following using exponents. Then use a calculator to find the value of the expression.

1. $2 \cdot 2 \cdot 2 \cdot 2$
2. $8 \cdot 8 \cdot 8 \cdot 8 \cdot 8 \cdot 8$
3. $(-4) \cdot (-4) \cdot (-4)$
4. $(-5) \cdot (-5)$
5. $3 \cdot 3 \cdot 3 \cdot 3 \cdot 3 \cdot 3 \cdot 3 \cdot 3$
6. $9 \cdot 9 \cdot 9$

 Think and Discuss

7. **Discuss** whether 3^9 is the same as 9^3.
8. **Explain** why 4^6 is greater than 4^5.

Motivate
To introduce the concept of exponents, ask students if there is a simpler expression for the sum $5 + 5 + 5 + 5$. They might suggest the multiplication expression $4 \cdot 5$. Explain that just as repeated addition can be simplified by multiplication, repeated multiplication can be simplified by using exponents. For example, $5 \cdot 5 \cdot 5 \cdot 5 = 5^4$.

Explorations and answers are provided in *Alternate Openers: Explorations Transparencies.*

Simplify.

C $(-8)^2$

$(-8)^2 = (-8) \cdot (-8)$ *Find the product.*
       $= 64$

D -2^3

$-2^3 = -(2 \cdot 2 \cdot 2)$ *Find the product. Then make the*
        $= -8$ *answer negative.*

EXAMPLE 3   **Using the Order of Operations**

Evaluate $x - y(z \cdot y^z)$ for $x = 20$, $y = 4$, and $z = 2$.

$x - y(z \cdot y^z)$

$20 - 4(2 \cdot 4^2)$ *Substitute 20 for x, 4 for y, and 2 for z.*

$20 - 4(2 \cdot 16)$ *Simplify the power.*

$20 - 4(32)$ *Multiply inside the parentheses.*

$20 - 128$ *Multiply from left to right.*

-108 *Subtract from left to right.*

EXAMPLE 4   *Geometry Application*

The number of diagonals of an n-sided figure is $\frac{1}{2}(n^2 - 3n)$. Use the expression to find the number of diagonals in a 6-sided figure.

$\frac{1}{2}(n^2 - 3n)$

$\frac{1}{2}(6^2 - 3 \cdot 6)$ *Substitute the number of sides for n.*

$\frac{1}{2}(36 - 18)$ *Simplify inside the parentheses.*

$\frac{1}{2}(18)$ *Subtract inside the parentheses.*

9 *Multiply.*

A 6-sided figure has 9 diagonals. You can verify your answer by sketching the diagonals.

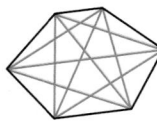

Possible answers to *Think and Discuss*

1. $(-5)^2$ means to find the product of two -5's. -5^2 means to find the product of two 5's and then make the final answer negative.

2. $3 \cdot 2 = 6$; $3^2 = 3 \cdot 3 = 9$; $2^3 = 2 \cdot 2 \cdot 2 = 8$

3. $(4 - 11)^2 = (-7)^2 = 49$; $4^2 - 11^2 = 16 - 121 = -105$; $49 \neq -105$

Think and Discuss

1. Explain the difference between $(-5)^2$ and -5^2.

2. Compare $3 \cdot 2$, 3^2, and 2^3.

3. Show that $(4 - 11)^2$ is not equal to $4^2 - 11^2$.

Teaching Tip   **Reading Math** In **Examples 2C** and **2D,** tell students to read $(-8)^2$ as "the square of negative eight" and to read -2^3 as "the opposite of two cubed."

Power Presentations with PowerPoint®

Additional Examples

Example 1

Write in exponential form.

A. $4 \cdot 4 \cdot 4 \cdot 4$ 4^4

B. $(-6) \cdot (-6) \cdot (-6)$ $(-6)^3$

C. $5 \cdot 5 \cdot d \cdot d \cdot d \cdot d$ $5^2 d^4$

Example 2

Simplify.

A. 3^5 243   **B.** $\left(\frac{1}{3}\right)^3$ $\frac{1}{27}$

C. $(-4)^4$ 256   **D.** -2^8 -256

Example 3

Evaluate $x(y^x - z^y) + x^y$ for $x = 4$, $y = 2$, and $z = 3$.   44

Example 4

Use the expression $\frac{1}{2}(n^2 - 3n)$ to find the number of diagonals in a 7-sided figure.   14 diagonals

Also available on transparency

---

2 Teach

Guided Instruction

In this lesson, students learn to evaluate expressions with exponents. Show students an example, such as 3^4. Point out the *base,* the *exponent,* and the *power.* Show them how to evaluate the power ($3 \cdot 3 \cdot 3 \cdot 3 = 81$). You may want to show that the same result can be obtained by working the multiplications in any order.

Teaching Tip   **Cognitive Strategies** Point out that the sign rules for multiplication still apply. Work the examples containing negative bases step-by-step so students will understand why the result is sometimes positive (when the exponent is even) and sometimes negative (when the exponent is odd).

Universal Access
Through Cooperative Learning

Give each student or group of students a set of 16 counters (provided in the Manipulatives Kit). Ask students to divide the counters into 4 equal groups and to write an addition expression that represents the grouping ($4 + 4 + 4 + 4$). Then have them write a multiplication expression that represents the same grouping ($4 \cdot 4$) and then an expression with an exponent (4^2). After simplifying each expression to get 16, they should begin to see how addition, multiplication, and powers are related.

3 Close

Summarize   **ENGLISH LANGUAGE LEARNERS**

Review the vocabulary terms *power, base,* and *exponent.* Discuss how each term is related to multiplication. You may wish to have students identify the base, exponent, and power in the expression 2^3.

Possible answers: A power is an expression where a number is multiplied by itself a certain number of times. A base is the factor in a power. An exponent is the number of times the factor is used. In the expression 2^3, 2 is the base, 3 is the exponent, and 2^3 is the power.

4-1 Exercises

California Standards Practice
AF1.2, AF2.1

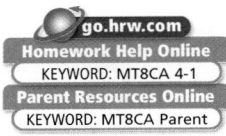

go.hrw.com
Homework Help Online
KEYWORD: MT8CA 4-1
Parent Resources Online
KEYWORD: MT8CA Parent

Assignment Guide

If you finished Example **1** assign:
Proficient 1–4, 15–20, 54–62
Advanced 15–20, 42–45, 54–62

If you finished Example **2** assign:
Proficient 1–9, 15–25, 31–34, 51, 53–62
Advanced 15–25, 35–38, 46, 48–51, 53–62

If you finished Example **3** assign:
Proficient 1–13, 15–29, 31–34, 39–40, 51, 53–62
Advanced 15–29, 35–38, 42–51, 53–62

If you finished Example **4** assign:
Proficient 1–34, 39–41, 51–62
Advanced 15–30, 35–38, 42–62

Homework Quick Check

Quickly check key concepts.
Exercises: 16, 18, 20, 22, 24, 28

Math Background

The second power of a number is commonly called the *square* of the number. This name comes from the fact that the area of a square is given by the formula $A = s^2$, where s is the length of a side of the square.

The third power of a number is called the *cube* of the number because the volume of a cube is given by the formula $V = s^3$, where s is the length of an edge of the cube.

California Standards

Standard	Exercises
NS1.2 🔑	55–58
NS1.3	59–62
AF1.2	10–14, 27–30, 39–40, 46, 48
AF2.1	1–54

GUIDED PRACTICE

See Example **1** — Write in exponential form.
1. 12 12^1 2. $18 \cdot 18$ 18^2 3. $2 \cdot 2 \cdot b \cdot b \cdot b$ $2^2 b^3$ 4. $(-3) \cdot (-3)$ $(-3)^2$

See Example **2** — Simplify.
5. 2^6 64 6. $(-7)^2$ 49 7. $\left(\frac{1}{2}\right)^3$ $\frac{1}{8}$ 8. -7^4 -2401 9. 8^4 4096

See Example **3** — Evaluate each expression for the given values of the variables.
10. $a^5 + 4b$ for $a = 3$ and $b = 12$ 291
11. $2x^9 - (y + z)$ for $x = -1$, $y = 7$, and $z = -4$ -5
12. $s + (t^u - 1)$ for $s = 13$, $t = 5$, $u = 3$ 137
13. $100 - n(p^{q-4})$ for $n = 10$, $p = 3$, and $q = 8$ -710

See Example **4** — 14. The sum of the first n positive integers is $\frac{1}{2}(n^2 + n)$. Check the expression for the first 5 positive integers. Then use the expression to find the sum of the first 14 positive integers. 105

INDEPENDENT PRACTICE

See Example **1** — Write in exponential form.
15. $5 \cdot 5 \cdot 5 \cdot 5 \cdot 5 \cdot 5$ 5^6 16. $(-9) \cdot (-9) \cdot (-9)$ $(-9)^3$ 17. $3 \cdot 3 \cdot d \cdot d$ $3^2 d^2$
18. -8 $(-8)^1$ or -8^1 19. $(-4) \cdot (-4) \cdot c \cdot c \cdot c$ $(-4)^2 c^3$ 20. $x \cdot x \cdot y$ $x^2 y$

See Example **2** — Simplify.
21. 4^4 256 22. $(-3)^6$ 729 23. $\left(\frac{1}{8}\right)^5$ $\frac{1}{32,768}$ 24. -2^9 -512 25. $\left(\frac{1}{6}\right)^2$ $\frac{1}{36}$

See Example **3** — Evaluate each expression for the given values of the variables.
26. b^2 for $b = -7$ 49
27. $2^c + 3d(g + 2)$ for $c = 7$, $d = 5$, and $g = 1$ 173
28. $m + n^p$ for $m = 12$, $n = 11$, and $p = 2$ 133
29. $x \div y^z$ for $x = 9$, $y = 3$, and $z = 2$ 1

See Example **4** — 30. A circle can be divided by n lines into a maximum of $\frac{1}{2}(n^2 + n) + 1$ regions. Use the expression to find the maximum number of regions for 7 lines. 29

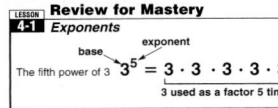

3 lines → 7 regions

PRACTICE AND PROBLEM SOLVING

Extra Practice
See page EP8.

Simplify.
31. $44 - (5 \cdot 4^2)$ -36 32. $(4 + 4^4)$ 260 33. $(6 - 7^1)$ -1 34. $84 - [8 - (-2)^3]$ 68
35. $18 - 7^3$ -325 36. $(3 \cdot 4^2) + 40$ 88 37. $(9 - 10)^5$ -1 38. $16 + (2 + 8^3)$ 530

REVIEW FOR MASTERY 4-1

LESSON 4-1 Review for Mastery *Exponents*

The fifth power of 3 $3^5 = 3 \cdot 3 \cdot 3 \cdot 3 \cdot 3$

base / exponent / 3 used as a factor 5 times

Complete to write each expression using an exponent. State the power.

1. $5 \cdot 5 \cdot 5 \cdot 5 = 5^{\underline{4}}$ the __fourth__ power of 5
2. $(-7) \cdot (-7) \cdot (-7) = (-7)^{\underline{3}}$ the __third__ power of -7

Complete to simplify each expression.

3. $(-2)^3 = (-2)(-2)(-2) = \underline{-8}$
4. $10^4 = \underline{10} \cdot \underline{10} \cdot \underline{10} \cdot \underline{10} = \underline{10,000}$
5. $(-5)^4 = (\underline{-5})(\underline{-5})(\underline{-5})(\underline{-5}) = \underline{625}$

When an expression is a product that includes a power, you simplify the power first.
$3 \cdot 2^3 = 3 \cdot 2 \cdot 2 \cdot 2 = 3 \cdot 8 = 24$

Complete to simplify each expression.

6. $4 \cdot (-2)^3 = 4(\underline{-2})(\underline{-2})(\underline{-2}) = \underline{-32}$
7. $5 \cdot 3^3 = \underline{5} \cdot \underline{3} \cdot \underline{3} \cdot \underline{3} = \underline{135}$
8. $(3 \cdot 2)^3 = 6^3 = \underline{6} \cdot \underline{6} \cdot \underline{6} = \underline{216}$
9. $(-4(-2))^3 = (\underline{8})^3 = (\underline{8})(\underline{8})(\underline{8}) = \underline{512}$
10. $25 - 3(4 \cdot 3^2)$
    $= 25 - 3(4 \cdot \underline{9})$
    $= 25 - 3(\underline{36})$
    $= 25 - \underline{108}$
    $= \underline{-83}$
11. $-100 - 2(3 \cdot 4)^2$
    $= -100 - 2(\underline{12})^2$
    $= -100 - 2(\underline{144})$
    $= -100 - \underline{288}$
    $= \underline{-388}$
12. $15 - 4(3 + 3^2)$
    $= 15 - 4(3 + \underline{9})$
    $= 15 - 4(\underline{12})$
    $= 15 - \underline{48}$
    $= \underline{-33}$

PRACTICE 4-1

LESSON 4-1 Practice B *Exponents*

Write in exponential form.

1. $6 \cdot 6 \cdot 6 \cdot 6 \cdot 6 \cdot 6$ 6^6 2. $7 \cdot 7 \cdot 7 \cdot 7$ 7^4
3. $(-8) \cdot (-8) \cdot (-8) \cdot (-8)$ $(-8)^4$ 4. $5 \cdot 5 \cdot 5 \cdot b \cdot b \cdot b \cdot b$ $5^3 b^4$

Simplify.

5. 10^2 100 6. $(-6)^2$ 36 7. $\left(\frac{1}{8}\right)^2$ $\frac{1}{64}$ 8. $(-7)^2$ 49
9. $(-5)^3$ -125 10. 12^2 144 11. $(-9)^2$ 81 12. $(-4)^3$ -64
13. 2^5 32 14. 5^4 625 15. $(-3)^4$ 81 16. $\left(\frac{1}{6}\right)^3$ $\frac{1}{216}$

Simplify each expression for the given values of the variables.

17. $n^3 - 5$ for $n = 4$ 59
18. $4x^2 + y^3$ for $x = 5$ and $y = -2$ 92
19. $m^p + q^2$ for $m = 5$, $p = 2$, and $q = 4$ 41
20. $a^4 + 2(b - c^2)$ for $a = 2$, $b = 4$, and $c = -1$ 22

21. Write an expression for five times a number used as a factor three times. $5x^3$
22. Find the volume of a regular cube if the length of a side is 10 cm. (Hint: $V = l^3$.) 1000 cm^3

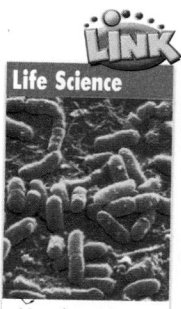

Life Science

Most bacteria reproduce by a type of simple cell division known as binary fission. Each species reproduces best at a specific temperature and moisture level.

Evaluate each expression for the given values of the variable.

39. $m(p - n^q)$ for $m = 2$, $n = 6$, $p = 3$, and $q = 3$ **−426**

40. $r + (t \cdot s^v)$ for $r = 42$, $s = -4$, $t = 3$, and $v = 2$ **90**

 41. Life Science Certain bacteria can divide every 20 minutes, so 1 bacterium can divide into 2 bacteria in 20 minutes, 4 in 40 minutes, and so on. If you begin with 1 bacterium, how many bacteria will there be in 6 hours? Write your answer by using exponents, and then evaluate. $2^{18} = 262,144$ **bacteria**

Write in exponential form.

42. $2b \cdot 2b \cdot 2b$ $(2b)^3$ **43.** $3d \cdot 3d$ $(3d)^2$ **44.** $5a \cdot 5a \cdot 5a$ $(5a)^3$ **45.** $7x \cdot 7x \cdot 7x \cdot 7x$ $(7x)^4$

46. Reasoning For any whole number n, $5^n - 1$ is divisible by 4. Verify this statement for $n = 4$ and $n = 6$.

47. Estimation A gift shaped like a cube has sides that measure 12.3 cm long. What is the approximate volume of the gift? (*Hint:* $V = s^3$) ≈ 1728 cm^3

48. Choose a Strategy Place the numbers 1, 2, 3, 4, and 5 in the boxes to make a true statement: ▨ · ▨^{3} = ▨^{2} − ▨ . $3 \cdot 2^3 = 5^2 - 1^4$

49. Write About It Compare 10^2 and 2^{10}. For any two numbers, make a conjecture about which usually gives the greater number: using the greater number as the base or as the exponent. Give at least one exception.

⭐ **50. Challenge** Write $(4^2)^3$ using a single exponent. 4^6

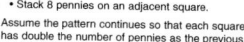 **SPIRAL STANDARDS REVIEW** 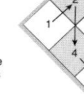 **← NS1.2, NS1.3, AF1.2, AF2.1**

51. Multiple Choice Which expression has the greatest value?

Ⓐ 2^5　　　Ⓑ 3^4　　　Ⓒ 4^3　　　Ⓓ 5^2

52. Multiple Choice The volume of a cube is calculated by using the formula $V = s^3$, where s is the length of the sides of the cube. What is the volume of a cube that has sides 8 meters long?

Ⓐ 24 m^3　　　Ⓑ 512 m^3　　　Ⓒ 888 m^3　　　Ⓓ 6561 m^3

53. Gridded Response What is the value of 5^4? **625**

54. Multiple Choice Which of the following expressions is equivalent to $(-5x)(-5x)(5x)$?

Ⓐ $(-5x)^3$　　　Ⓑ $(-5x)(5x)^2$　　　Ⓒ $(-5x)^2(5x)$　　　Ⓓ $2(-5x)(5x)$

Find each sum. (Lesson 1-4)

55. $-18 + (-65)$ **−83**　**56.** $-123 + 95$ **−28**　**57.** $87 + (-32)$ **55**　**58.** $-74 + (-27)$ **−101**

Write each fraction as a decimal. (Lesson 2-1)

59. $\frac{7}{50}$ **0.14**　**60.** $\frac{4}{15}$ **$0.2\overline{6}$**　**61.** $\frac{3}{8}$ **0.375**　**62.** $\frac{5}{24}$ **$0.208\overline{3}$**

CHALLENGE 4-1

LESSON 4-1 Challenge
Check This Out

Imagine an 8 × 8 checkerboard.
- Put 1 penny on the first square.
- Stack 2 pennies on an adjacent square.
- Stack 4 pennies on an adjacent square.
- Stack 8 pennies on an adjacent square.

Assume the pattern continues so that each square has double the number of pennies as the previous square.

Complete the table.

Square	1	2	3	4	5	6	7	8
1. Number of Pennies	1	2	4	8	16	32	64	128
2. Exponent Form	2^0	2^1	2^2	2^3	2^4	2^5	2^6	2^7

3. Look for a pattern in the table. How many pennies are on the 12th square? the 15th square?

square $n = 2^{n-1}$ pennies; square 12 = 2^{11} or 2048 pennies;

square 15 = 2^{14} or 16,384 pennies

4. Find the number of pennies on the 25th square. How much money is this? Estimate the height of the stack.

2^{24} or 16,777,216 pennies = $167,772.16;

about 1 million in., or over 15 mi

5. Find the number of pennies on the 10th square. Find the total number of pennies on the first nine squares. Which number is greater?

512 pennies on 10th square; 511 pennies on the first nine squares.

512 > 511

6. Explain why it is impossible to stack pennies on every square in the manner described at the top of the page.

Possible answer: By the 25th square, the stack is already over 15 mi high, and there are 39 more squares to stack.

PROBLEM SOLVING 4-1

LESSON 4-1 Problem Solving
Exponents

Write the correct answer.

1. The formula for the volume of a cube is $V = e^3$ where e is the length of a side of the cube. Find the volume of a cube with side length 6 cm.

216 cm^3

2. The distance in feet traveled by a falling object is given by the formula $d = 16t^2$ where t is the time in seconds. Find the distance an object falls in 4 seconds.

256 feet

3. The surface area of a cube can be found using the formula $S = 6e^2$ where e is the length of a side of the cube. Find the surface area of a cube with side length 6 cm.

216 cm^2

4. John's father offers to pay him 1 cent for doing the dishes the first night, 2 cents for doing the dishes the second, 4 cents for the third, and so on, doubling each night. Write an expression using exponents for the amount John will get paid on the tenth night.

2^9 cents

Use the table below for Exercises 5–7, which shows the number of e-mails forwarded at each level if each person continues a chain by forwarding an e-mail to 10 friends. Choose the letter for the best answer.

Forwarded E-mails	
Level	E-mails forwarded
1	10
2	100
3	1000
4	10,000

5. How many e-mails were forwarded at level 5 alone?

A 5^{10}　　C 2^{10}
B 2^5　　D 10^5

6. How many e-mails were forwarded at level 6 alone?

F 100,000　　H 10,000,000
G 1,000,000　　J 100,000,000

7. Forwarding chain e-mails can create problems for e-mail servers. Find out how many total e-mails have been forwarded after 6 levels.

A 1,111,110　　C 1,000,000
B 6,000,000　　D 100,000,000

Answers

46. $\dfrac{5^4 - 1}{4} = \dfrac{624}{4}$
$= 156;$
$\dfrac{5^6 - 1}{4} = \dfrac{15,624}{4}$
$= 3906$

49. Possible answer: using the greater number as the exponent; $10^2 = 100$ and $2^{10} = 1024$, so $10^2 < 2^{10}$; exception: $1^5 = 1$ and $5^1 = 5$, so $1^5 < 5^1$

Teaching Tip **Multiple Choice** For **Exercise 51,** students who answered **A** picked the choice with the greatest exponent. Students who answered **D** picked the choice with the greatest base. Point out to students that expressions with the greatest base or the greatest exponent do not necessarily have the greatest value.

✎ Journal

Have students imagine that they have invested $100 in an account and that their money will double every five years. Have them write about what they would be able to buy with the money after 20 years.

Power Presentations
with PowerPoint®

✓ **4-1**
Lesson Quiz

Write in exponential form.

1. $n \cdot n \cdot n \cdot n$　　n^4
2. $(-8)(-8)(-8)(h)$　　$(-8)^3h$

Simplify.

3. $(-4)^4$　　256
4. $-\left(\dfrac{2}{3}\right)^2$　　$-\dfrac{4}{9}$
5. Evaluate $xz - y^x$ for $x = 5$, $y = 3$, and $z = 6$.　　−213
6. A population of bacteria doubles in size every minute. The number of bacteria after 5 minutes is $15 \cdot 2^5$. How many bacteria are there after 5 minutes?　　480

Also available on transparency

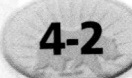

Objective: Students simplify expressions with negative exponents and the zero exponent.

Online Edition
Tutorial Videos

Countdown to Mastery Week 7

Power Presentations
with PowerPoint®

Warm Up

Simplify.

1. 10^3 1000
2. 10^1 10
3. 10^4 10,000
4. 10^5 100,000
5. 10^6 1,000,000

Also available on transparency

Math Humor

Why did the integer get a bad evaluation at work? It had a negative attitude.

California Standards

NS2.1 Understand negative whole-number exponents. Multiply and divide expressions involving exponents with a common base.
AF2.1 Interpret positive whole-number powers as repeated multiplication and **negative whole-number powers as repeated division or multiplication by the multiplicative inverse. Simplify and evaluate expressions that include exponents.**

Why learn this? You can use negative exponents to represent the size of something that is very small, such as the diameter of a white blood cell. (See Exercise 41.)

Look at the pattern shown in the table to extend what you know about exponents to include negative exponents.

10^2	10^1	10^0	10^{-1}	10^{-2}	10^{-3}
$10 \cdot 10$	10	1	$\frac{1}{10}$	$\frac{1}{10 \cdot 10}$	$\frac{1}{10 \cdot 10 \cdot 10}$
100	10	1	$\frac{1}{10} = 0.1$	$\frac{1}{100} = 0.01$	$\frac{1}{1000} = 0.001$

$\div 10 \quad \div 10 \quad \div 10 \quad \div 10 \quad \div 10$

Notice from the chart that as the exponents decrease by 1, the value of the expression decreases by a factor of 10.

EXAMPLE 1 Using a Pattern to Evaluate Negative Exponents

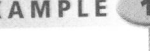
Reasoning

Simplify the powers of 10.

A 10^{-4}

$10^{-4} = \dfrac{1}{10 \cdot 10 \cdot 10 \cdot 10}$ *Extend the pattern from the table.*

$= \dfrac{1}{10,000} = 0.0001$ *Multiply. Write as a decimal.*

B 10^{-5}

$10^{-5} = \dfrac{1}{10 \cdot 10 \cdot 10 \cdot 10 \cdot 10}$ *Extend the pattern from Example 1A.*

$= \dfrac{1}{100,000} = 0.00001$ *Multiply. Write as a decimal.*

NEGATIVE EXPONENTS		
Words	**Numbers**	**Algebra**
Any nonzero number raised to a negative power equals 1 divided by that number raised to a positive power.	$5^{-3} = \frac{1}{5^3} = \frac{1}{125}$	$b^{-n} = \frac{1}{b^n}$, if $b \neq 0$

---

1 Introduce

Alternate Opener

EXPLORATION

4-2 Integer Exponents

Suppose the height of a magic plant doubles every hour, beginning with a height of 1 inch at the "zero hour."

Use the bar graph to think about how tall the plant was 1 hour before (−1) and 2 hours before (−2) the zero hour.

Plant height (in.) / *Time (hr)*

1. Draw and label a bar on the bar graph to show the height at hour −1 and hour −2. (*Hint:* The height doubles each hour.)

2. Use the graph and the pattern in the table to find the value of each exponential expression.

Time, x	Plant Height, 2^x
−3	$2^{-3} = \frac{1}{2^3} = \frac{1}{8}$
−2	
−1	
0	
1	
2	
3	

Think and Discuss

3. **Describe** the pattern in the bar graph.
4. **Describe** the pattern in the table.

Motivate

Prior to beginning this lesson, ask students to simplify the following expressions:

A. 4^5 1024
B. 5^3 125
C. 7^1 7

After they have simplified them, ask them to describe, in their own words, how they got their answers.

Explorations and answers are provided in *Alternate Openers: Explorations Transparencies.*

California Standards

Number Sense 2.1
Algebra and Functions 2.1
Also covered:
Algebra and Functions
2.0 Students interpret and evaluate expressions involving integer powers and simple roots.

EXAMPLE 2 Evaluating Negative Exponents

Simplify.

A $(-2)^{-3}$

$(-2)^{-3} = \dfrac{1}{(-2)^3}$ *Write the power under 1; change the sign of the exponent.*

$= \dfrac{1}{(-2) \cdot (-2) \cdot (-2)}$ *Find the product.*

$= -\dfrac{1}{8}$ *Simplify.*

B 6^{-4}

$6^{-4} = \dfrac{1}{6^4}$ *Write the power under 1; change the sign of the exponent.*

$= \dfrac{1}{6 \cdot 6 \cdot 6 \cdot 6}$ *Find the product.*

$= \dfrac{1}{1296}$ *Simplify.*

Notice from the table on the previous page that $10^0 = 1$. This is true for any nonzero number to the zero power.

THE ZERO POWER

Words	Numbers	Algebra
The zero power of any nonzero number equals 1.	$100^0 = 1$ $(-5)^0 = 1$	$a^0 = 1$, if $a \neq 0$

EXAMPLE 3 Using the Order of Operations

Simplify $2 + (-7)^0 - (4 + 2)^{-2}$.

$2 + (-7)^0 - (4 + 2)^{-2}$

$2 + (-7)^0 - 6^{-2}$ *Add inside the parentheses.*

$2 + (-7)^0 - \dfrac{1}{6^2}$ *Rewrite 6^{-2} as $\dfrac{1}{6^2}$.*

$2 + 1 - \dfrac{1}{36}$ *Simplify the powers.*

$3 - \dfrac{1}{36}$ *Add and subtract from left to right.*

$2\dfrac{35}{36}$

Think and Discuss

1. **Express** $\frac{1}{2}$ using a negative exponent.

2. **Tell** whether an integer raised to a negative exponent can ever be greater than 1. Justify your answer.

Possible answers to Think and Discuss

1. 2^{-1}

2. No, but 1^{-1} is 1. An integer raised to a negative exponent results in the reciprocal of the integer, which is always less than or equal to 1.

---

2 Teach

Guided Instruction

In this lesson, students learn to simplify expressions with negative and zero exponents. Begin by using the pattern shown in the table on the Teaching Transparency to provide a meaningful definition of an expression with a negative exponent. Then give students an opportunity to apply the meaning to simplify powers and expressions containing negative exponents.

 **Teaching Tip**   **Inclusion** Remind students that a negative exponent does not indicate a negative value, but instead a fractional expression.

 **Universal Access**
Through Multiple Representations

Have the class work in pairs. Show students a series of equivalent expressions, such as $5^{-2} = \frac{1}{5^2} = \frac{1}{25}$. Explain that all of the expressions are equal. Have each student create two expressions involving exponents that can be simplified. Encourage students to use negative exponents. Then have the students in each pair exchange problems and solve each other's work.

Sample expressions:

Simplify. **1.** $(-4)^{-2}$ $\dfrac{1}{16}$

2. -3^{-4} $-\dfrac{1}{81}$

3 Close

Summarize

Have students describe how to simplify an expression with a positive exponent and then how to simplify an expression with a negative exponent. Ask students to provide examples of each.

Possible answers: To simplify an expression with a positive exponent, multiply, using the base as a factor the number of times indicated by the exponent. To simplify an expression with a negative exponent, place the expression in the denominator of a fraction with 1 as the numerator and replace the negative exponent with a positive exponent. Then simplify the new expression.

Assignment Guide

If you finished Example **1** assign:
Proficient 1–4, 13–16, 51–59
Advanced 13–16, 44, 48, 51–59

If you finished Example **2** assign:
Proficient 1–8, 13–20, 37–38, 44, 49–59
Advanced 13–20, 39–40, 42–44, 48–59

If you finished Example **3** assign:
Proficient 1–12, 25–35 odd, 37–38, 41, 44–45, 49–59
Advanced 13–24, 26–36 even, 39–59

Homework Quick Check

Quickly check key concepts.
Exercises: 14, 16, 18, 20, 22

Answers

37. $11^{-4} = \frac{1}{11} \cdot \frac{1}{11} \cdot \frac{1}{11} \cdot \frac{1}{11} = \frac{1}{14,641}$

38. $1^{-10} = \frac{1}{1} \cdot \frac{1}{1} \cdot \frac{1}{1} \cdot \frac{1}{1} \cdot \frac{1}{1} \cdot \frac{1}{1} \cdot \frac{1}{1} \cdot \frac{1}{1} \cdot \frac{1}{1} \cdot \frac{1}{1} = 1$

39. $-6^{-3} = -1 \cdot \left(\frac{1}{6}\right) \cdot \left(\frac{1}{6}\right) \cdot \left(\frac{1}{6}\right) = -\frac{1}{216}$

40. $(-6)^{-3} \left(\frac{1}{-6}\right) \cdot \left(\frac{1}{-6}\right) \cdot \left(\frac{1}{-6}\right) = -\frac{1}{216}$

Math Background

Inductive reasoning is used to find the pattern of powers of ten shown at the beginning of this lesson. This pattern is an effective introduction to scientific notation, which will be investigated further in Lesson 4-5.

Because scientists must frequently work with very large and very small numbers, they use powers of ten to keep the numbers simple. Positive exponents are used for very large numbers, such as those used in astronomy and physics. Negative exponents are used for very small numbers, such as those used in chemistry and biology.

California Standards

Standard	Exercises
NS2.1	5–8, 55–59
NS2.3 🔑	9–12, 21–32, 45–47
AF1.2	33–36, 43
AF1.3 🔑	51–54
AF2.1	1–50, 55–59

 **California Standards Practice**
NS2.1, ← NS2.3, AF1.2, AF2.1

 **go.hrw.com**
Homework Help Online
KEYWORD: MT8CA 4-2
Parent Resources Online
KEYWORD: MT8CA Parent

GUIDED PRACTICE

See Example **1** Simplify the powers of 10.
1. 10^{-2} **0.01**   **2.** 10^{-7} **0.0000001**   **3.** 10^{-6} **0.000001**   **4.** 10^{-10} **0.0000000001**

See Example **2** Simplify.
5. $(2)^{-6}$ $\frac{1}{64}$ **6.** $(-3)^{-4}$ $\frac{1}{81}$ **7.** 3^{-3} $\frac{1}{27}$ **8.** $(-2)^{-5}$ $-\frac{1}{32}$

See Example **3** **9.** $4 + 3(4 - 9^0) + 5^{-3}$ $13\frac{1}{125}$ **10.** $7 - 8(2)^{-3} + 13$ **19**

11. $(2 + 2)^{-2} + (1 + 1)^{-4}$ $\frac{1}{8}$ **12.** $2 - (2^{-3})$ $1\frac{7}{8}$

INDEPENDENT PRACTICE

See Example **1** Simplify the powers of 10.
13. 10^{-1} **0.1**   **14.** 10^{-9} **0.000000001**   **15.** 10^{-8} **0.00000001**   **16.** 10^{-12} **0.000000000001**

See Example **2** Simplify.
17. $(-4)^{-1}$ $-\frac{1}{4}$ **18.** 5^{-2} $\frac{1}{25}$ **19.** $(-10)^{-4}$ $\frac{1}{10,000}$, or 0.0001   **20.** $(-2)^{-6}$ $\frac{1}{64}$

See Example **3** **21.** $128(2 + 6)^{-3} + (4^0 - 3)$ $-1\frac{3}{4}$ **22.** $3 + (-3)^{-2} - (9 + 7)^0$ $2\frac{1}{9}$

23. $12 - (-5)^0 + (3^{-3} + 9^{-2})$ $11\frac{4}{81}$ **24.** $5^0 + 49(1 + 6)^{-2}$ **2**

PRACTICE AND PROBLEM SOLVING

Extra Practice
See page EP8.

Simplify.
25. $(18 - 16)^{-5}$ $\frac{1}{32}$ **26.** $25 + (6 \cdot 10^0)$ **31**   **27.** $(1 - 2^{-2})$ $\frac{3}{4}$ **28.** $(3 \cdot 3)^{-3}$ $\frac{1}{729}$

29. $3^{-2} \cdot 2^2 \cdot 4^0$ $\frac{4}{9}$ **30.** $10 + 4^3 \cdot 2^{-2}$ **26**

31. $6^2 - 3^2 + 1^{-1}$ **28**   **32.** $16 - [15 - (-2)^{-3}]$ $\frac{7}{8}$

Evaluate each expression for the given value of the variable.
33. $2(x^2 + x)$ for $x = 2.1$ **13.02**   **34.** $(4n)^{-2} + n$ for $n = 3$ $3\frac{1}{144}$

35. $c^2 + c$ for $c = \frac{1}{2}$ $\frac{3}{4}$ **36.** $m^{-2} \cdot m^0 \cdot m^2$ for $m = 9$ **1**

Write each expression as repeated multiplication. Then simplify the expression.
37. 11^{-4} **38.** 1^{-10} **39.** -6^{-3} **40.** $(-6)^{-3}$

41. Life Science The diameter of a white blood cell in human blood is $\frac{3}{250,000}$ meter $3(500)^{-2}$ meter. Write the diameter of the cell without using an exponent.

42. Patterns Describe the following pattern: $(-1)^{-1} = \blacksquare$; $(-1)^{-2} = \blacksquare$; $(-1)^{-3} = \blacksquare$; $(-1)^{-4} = \blacksquare$. Determine what $(-1)^{-100}$ would be. Justify your thinking.

43. Reasoning Evaluate $n^1 \cdot n^{-1}$ for $n = 1, 2,$ and 3. Then make a conjecture about what $n^1 \cdot n^{-1}$ is for any value of n. Explain your reasoning.

42. Possible answer: The pattern is -1, 1, -1, 1, . . .; $(-1)^{-100} = 1$. -1 raised to an even power is 1; -1 raised to an odd power is -1.

43. Possible answer: 1, 1, 1; for any value of n, $n^1 \cdot n^{-1} = 1$. Any number multiplied by its reciprocal is equal to 1.

REVIEW FOR MASTERY 4-2

Review for Mastery
4-2 Integer Exponents

To rewrite a negative exponent, move the power to the denominator of a unit fraction. $5^{-2} = \frac{1}{5^2}$

Complete to rewrite each power with a positive exponent.
1. $7^{-3} = \frac{1}{7^3}$ 2. $9^{-5} = \frac{1}{9^5}$ 3. $13^{-4} = \frac{1}{13^4}$

Complete each pattern.
4. $10^{-1} = \frac{1}{10} = 0.1$ 5. $5^{-1} = \frac{1}{5}$

$10^{-2} = \frac{1}{10^2} = \frac{1}{100} = 0.01$ $5^{-2} = \frac{1}{5^2} = \frac{1}{5 \cdot 5} = \frac{1}{25}$

$10^{-3} = \frac{1}{10^3} = \frac{1}{1000} = 0.001$ $5^{-3} = \frac{1}{5^3} = \frac{1}{5 \cdot 5 \cdot 5} = \frac{1}{125}$

6. $3^{-1} = \frac{1}{3}$ 7. $(-4)^{-1} = \frac{1}{-4}$

$3^{-2} = \frac{1}{3^2} = \frac{1}{3 \cdot 3} = \frac{1}{9}$ $(-4)^{-2} = \frac{1}{(-4)^2} = \frac{1}{(-4) \cdot (-4)} = \frac{1}{16}$

$3^{-3} = \frac{1}{3^3} = \frac{1}{3 \cdot 3 \cdot 3} = \frac{1}{27}$ $(-4)^{-3} = \frac{1}{(-4)^3} = \frac{1}{(-4) \cdot (-4) \cdot (-4)} = -\frac{1}{64}$

Simplify.
8. $2^{-3} = \frac{1}{\_} = \frac{1}{2^3}; \frac{1}{8}$ 9. $(-6)^{-2} = \frac{1}{\_} = \frac{1}{(-6)^2}; \frac{1}{36}$

10. $4^{-2} = \frac{1}{\_} = \frac{1}{4^2}; \frac{1}{16}$ 11. $(-3)^{-3} = \frac{1}{\_} = \frac{1}{(-3)^3}; -\frac{1}{27}$

12. $6^{-2} = \frac{1}{36}$ 13. $(-2)^{-3} = -\frac{1}{8}$

14. $6^{-3} = \frac{1}{216}$ 15. $(-5)^{-2} = \frac{1}{25}$

16. $2^{-4} = \frac{1}{16}$ 17. $(-9)^{-1} = -\frac{1}{9}$

PRACTICE 4-2

Practice B
4-2 Integer Exponents

Simplify the powers of 10.
1. 10^{-3} $\frac{1}{10,000}$ 2. 10^3 1000   3. 10^{-5} 0.00001   4. 10^{-2} 0.01

5. 10^0 1   6. 10^4 10,000   7. 10^1 10   8. 10^5 100,000

Simplify.
9. $(-6)^{-2}$ $\frac{1}{36}$ 10. $(-9)^{-3}$ $-\frac{1}{729}$ 11. 2^{-5} $\frac{1}{32}$

12. $(-3)^{-4}$ $\frac{1}{81}$ 13. $(-12)^{-1}$ $-\frac{1}{12}$ 14. 6^{-3} $\frac{1}{216}$

15. $10 - (3 + 2)^0 + 2^{-1}$ $9\frac{1}{2}$ 16. $15 + (-6)^0 - 3^{-2}$ $15\frac{8}{9}$

17. $6(8 - 2)^0 + 4^{-2}$ $6\frac{1}{16}$ 18. $2^{-2} + (-4)^{-1}$ 0

19. $3(1 - 4)^{-2} + 9^{-1} + 12^0$ $1\frac{4}{9}$ 20. $9^0 + 64(3 + 5)^{-2}$ 2

21. One milliliter equals 10^{-3} liter. Evaluate 10^{-3}. $\frac{1}{1000}$

22. The volume of a cube is 10^6 cubic feet. Evaluate 10^6. 1,000,000

44. Some whales have been known to dive to depths greater than 10^{12} nanometers. Simplify 10^{12}. **1,000,000,000,000**

45. Blubber makes up 27% of a blue whale's body weight. Davis found the average weight of blue whales and used it to calculate the average weight of their blubber. He wrote the amount as $2^2 \times 3^3 \times 5 \times 71$ pounds. Simplify this amount. **38,340 lb**

46. Most baleen whales migrate an average of $2^5 \times 125$ km each way. The gray whale has the longest known migration of any mammal, a distance of $2^4 \times 3 \times 125$ km farther each way than the average baleen whale migration. How far does the gray whale migrate each way? **10,000 km**

47. A blue whale may eat between 6 and 7 tons of krill each day. Krill are approximately $2^{-5} \times 3^{-1} \times 5^{-1}$ of the length of a blue whale. Simplify this amount. $\frac{1}{480}$

48. ⭐ **Challenge** A cubic centimeter is the same as 1 mL. If a humpback whale has more than 1 kL of blood, how many cubic centimeters of blood does the humpback whale have? **more than 10^6 or 1,000,000 cm^3**

Krill are a food source for different species of baleen whales, such as the humpback whale, pictured above.

SPIRAL STANDARDS REVIEW

NS2.1, 🔑 AF1.3, AF2.1

49. **Multiple Choice** Simplify $(-5)^{-2}$.

Ⓐ -25 Ⓑ $-\frac{1}{25}$ Ⓒ $\frac{1}{25}$ Ⓓ 25

50. **Extended Response** Simplify 8^3, 8^2, 8^1, 8^0, 8^{-1}, and 8^{-2}. Describe a possible pattern that is shown in the values. Use the pattern of the values to predict the value of 8^{-3}. **512, 64, 8, 1, $\frac{1}{8}$, $\frac{1}{64}$; each value is the previous value divided by 8; $\frac{1}{512}$**

Simplify. (Lesson 3-2)

51. $7(x+3) + x$ 52. $4(2y-5) - 6y$ 53. $8(x+3y) - x$ 54. $9(2x-y) + x$
   $8x + 21$ **$2y - 20$**   **$7x + 24y$**   **$19x - 9y$**

Simplify. (Lesson 4-1)

55. $(-3)^4$ **81**   56. 5^2 **25**   57. $(10-15)^3$ **-125**   58. $(-9)^3$ **-729**   59. -2^5 **-32**

CHALLENGE 4-2

LESSON 4-2 Challenge
Stuff It!

$9^{\frac{1}{2}}$ means $\sqrt[2]{9^1}$.

To find the value, first evaluate the root: $\sqrt[2]{9} = 3$.
Then, raise the result to the indicated power: $3^1 = 3$.
So, $9^{\frac{1}{2}}$ is $\sqrt[2]{9^1} = 3^1 = 3$.

In general, here's the way to rewrite a term with a fractional exponent:

$x^{\frac{a}{b}} = \sqrt[b]{x^a}$

Simplify $8^{\frac{2}{3}}$.

$8^{\frac{2}{3}} = \sqrt[3]{8^2}$ Rewrite using radical form.
$= 2^2$ Simplify the root; $\sqrt[3]{8} = 2$ since $2 \cdot 2 \cdot 2 = 8$.
$= 4$ Simplify the power.

Rewrite each term using radical form. Simplify the root. Simplify the power.

1. $64^{\frac{1}{2}} = \underline{\sqrt[2]{64^1}}$ 2. $100^{\frac{1}{2}} = \underline{\sqrt[2]{100^1}}$ 3. $400^{\frac{1}{2}} = \underline{\sqrt[2]{400^1}}$

$= \underline{8^1}$ $= \underline{10^1}$ $= \underline{20^1}$

$= \underline{8}$ $= \underline{10}$ $= \underline{20}$

4. $64^{\frac{2}{3}} = \underline{\sqrt[3]{64^2}}$ 5. $216^{\frac{2}{3}} = \underline{\sqrt[3]{216^2}}$ 6. $1000^{\frac{2}{3}} = \underline{\sqrt[3]{1000^2}}$

$= \underline{4^2}$ $= \underline{6^2}$ $= \underline{10^2}$

$= \underline{16}$ $= \underline{36}$ $= \underline{100}$

7. $625^{\frac{3}{4}} = \underline{\sqrt[4]{625^3}}$ 8. $32^{\frac{2}{5}} = \underline{\sqrt[5]{32^2}}$ 9. $10,000^{\frac{5}{4}} = \underline{\sqrt[4]{10,000^5}}$

$= \underline{5^3}$ $= \underline{2^2}$ $= \underline{10^5}$

$= \underline{125}$ $= \underline{4}$ $= \underline{100,000}$

PROBLEM SOLVING 4-2

LESSON 4-2 Problem Solving
Integer Exponents

Write the correct answer.

1. The weight of 10^7 dust particles is 1 gram. Simplify 10^7.
   10,000,000

2. The weight of one dust particle is 10^{-7} gram. Simplify 10^{-7}.
   0.0000001

3. As of 2001, only 10^6 rural homes in the United States had broadband Internet access. Simplify 10^6.
   1,000,000

4. Atomic clocks measure time in microseconds. A microsecond is 10^{-6} second. Simplify 10^{-6}.
   0.000001

Choose the letter for the best answer.

5. The diameter of the nucleus of an atom is about 10^{-15} meter. Simplify 10^{-15}.
   A 0.000000000000001
   B 0.00000000000001
   C 0.0000000000000001
   Ⓓ 0.000000000000001

6. The diameter of the nucleus of an atom is 0.000001 nanometer. How many nanometers is the diameter of the nucleus of an atom?
   F $(-10)^5$
   G $(-10)^6$
   Ⓗ 10^{-6}
   J 10^{-5}

7. A ruby-throated hummingbird weighs about 3^{-2} ounce. Simplify 3^{-2}.
   A -9
   B -6
   Ⓒ $\frac{1}{9}$
   D $\frac{1}{6}$

8. A ruby-throated hummingbird breathes 2×5^3 times per minute while at rest. Simplify this amount.
   F 1,000
   Ⓖ 250
   H 125
   J 30

FORMATIVE ASSESSMENT and INTERVENTION ◀▶

Diagnose Before the Lesson
4-2 Warm Up, TE p. 172

Monitor During the Lesson
4-2 Know-It Notebook
4-2 Questioning Strategies

Assess After the Lesson
4-2 Lesson Quiz, TE p. 175

Interdisciplinary LINK

Life Science

Exercises 44–48 involve using integer exponents to describe characteristics of some sea creatures. Integer exponents are used throughout middle school science programs such as *Holt California Life Science*.

Teaching Tip | **Multiple Choice** In **Exercise 49,** students who chose **B** probably have trouble remembering the sign rules for raising negative numbers to even powers. Review with students that an expression of the form $(-a)^2$ will have a positive answer, whereas $-a^2$ would have a negative answer. Show them this trend also applies to negative even exponents.

✒ Journal

Have students write about something that is very small, and have them describe the measurement using negative exponents. Examples do not need to be factual but should be realistic. For example: The flea was 2^{-4} inches long.

Power Presentations
with PowerPoint®

✓ 4-2 Lesson Quiz

Simplify the powers of 10.

1. 10^{-3} **0.001**

2. 10^{-7} **0.0000001**

Simplify.

3. $(-6)^{-2}$ $\frac{1}{36}$

4. $4 \cdot 2^{-3} + 10^{-1}$ $\frac{3}{5}$

5. $8^0 - (11 - 2^4)^{-2}$ $\frac{24}{25}$

6. Evaluate $(4w)^{-2} + w^{-1}$ for $w = 4$. $\frac{65}{256}$

Also available on transparency

Objective: Students apply the properties of exponents.

Hands-On Lab
In *Chapter 4 Resource File*

Online Edition
Tutorial Videos

Countdown to Mastery Week 7

Power Presentations
with PowerPoint®

Warm Up

Evaluate.
1. 3^3 27
2. $4 \cdot 4 \cdot 4 \cdot 4$ 256
3. b^2 for $b = 4$ 16
4. $n^2 r$ for $n = 3$ and $r = 2$ 18

Also available on transparency

Math Humor

Teacher: What is a number with a zero power?

Student: A number that didn't pay its electric bill.

California Standards

NS2.1 Understand negative whole-number exponents. Multiply and divide expressions involving exponents with a common base.
← NS2.3 Multiply, divide, and simplify rational numbers by using exponent rules.

Why learn this? You can use properties of exponents to compare distances between planets. (See Exercise 52.)

The following suggests a rule for multiplying powers with the same base.

$$2^4 \cdot 2^2 = (2 \cdot 2 \cdot 2 \cdot 2) \cdot (2 \cdot 2) = 2^6$$
$$a^3 \cdot a^2 = (a \cdot a \cdot a) \cdot (a \cdot a) = a^5$$

Notice that the **sum** of the exponents in each expression equals the exponent in the answer: $4 + 2 = 6$ and $3 + 2 = 5$.

MULTIPLYING POWERS WITH THE SAME BASE		
Words	**Numbers**	**Algebra**
To multiply powers with the same base, keep the base and add the exponents.	$3^5 \cdot 3^8 = 3^{5+8} = 3^{13}$	$b^m \cdot b^n = b^{m+n}$

EXAMPLE 1 **Multiplying Powers with the Same Base**

Simplify each expression. Write your answer in exponential form.

A $5^4 \cdot 5^3$
5^{4+3} *Add exponents.*
5^7

B $(-a)^{12} \cdot (-a)^{-5}$
$(-a)^{12+(-5)}$
$(-a)^7$

The following suggests a rule for dividing powers with the same base.

$$\frac{3^6}{3^2} = \frac{{}^1\!\cancel{3} \cdot {}^1\!\cancel{3} \cdot 3 \cdot 3 \cdot 3 \cdot 3}{{}_1\cancel{3} \cdot {}_1\cancel{3}} = 3 \cdot 3 \cdot 3 \cdot 3 = 3^4$$
$$\frac{x^5}{x^3} = \frac{{}^1\!\cancel{x} \cdot {}^1\!\cancel{x} \cdot {}^1\!\cancel{x} \cdot x \cdot x}{{}_1\cancel{x} \cdot {}_1\cancel{x} \cdot {}_1\cancel{x}} = x \cdot x = x^2$$

Notice that the **difference** between the exponents in each expression equals the exponent in the answer: $6 - 2 = 4$ and $5 - 3 = 2$.

DIVIDING POWERS WITH THE SAME BASE		
Words	**Numbers**	**Algebra**
To divide powers with the same base, keep the base and subtract the exponents.	$\frac{6^9}{6^4} = 6^{9-4} = 6^5$	$\frac{b^m}{b^n} = b^{m-n}$, if $b \neq 0$

1 Introduce

Alternate Opener

EXPLORATION

4-3 Properties of Exponents

You can use patterns to discover properties of exponents.
1. Complete the table.

Product of Powers	Write the Factors	Write As a Single Power
$3^2 \cdot 3^5$	$(3 \cdot 3) \cdot (3 \cdot 3 \cdot 3 \cdot 3 \cdot 3) =$ $3 \cdot 3 \cdot 3 \cdot 3 \cdot 3 \cdot 3 \cdot 3$	3^7
$4^3 \cdot 4^2$		
$7^4 \cdot 7^4$		
$5^2 \cdot 5^4$		

2. Look at the left-hand and right-hand columns of the table. What patterns do you notice?
3. Complete the table.

Product of Powers	Write the Factors	Write As a Single Power
$\frac{3^6}{3^2}$	$\frac{3 \cdot 3 \cdot 3 \cdot 3 \cdot 3 \cdot 3}{3 \cdot 3} = 3 \cdot 3 \cdot 3 \cdot 3$	3^4
$\frac{4^5}{4^3}$		
$\frac{5^4}{5^3}$		
$\frac{8^7}{8^3}$		

4. Look at the left-hand and right-hand columns of the table. What patterns do you notice?

Think and Discuss
5. **Explain** how you can use what you discovered to write $2^7 \cdot 2^{10}$ as a single power.
6. **Explain** how you can use what you discovered to write $\frac{2^{10}}{2^7}$ as a single power.

Motivate

Before introducing students to the properties of exponents, review what an exponent is. Write an expression such as 3^5 on the chalkboard. Have students identify the base and the exponent. Ask them for a step-by-step explanation of how to simplify the expression using multiplication. Encourage students to use the proper vocabulary.
base: 3; exponent: 5; $3 \cdot 3 \cdot 3 \cdot 3 \cdot 3 = 243$

Explorations and answers are provided in *Alternate Openers: Explorations Transparencies.*

California Standards

Number Sense **2.1** and **← 2.3**

EXAMPLE 2 Dividing Powers with the Same Base

Simplify each expression. Write your answer in exponential form.

A $\dfrac{10^8}{10^5}$

10^{8-5} *Subtract exponents.*

10^3

B $\dfrac{3^3 \cdot 2^5 \cdot 5^2}{3^2 \cdot 2^5 \cdot 5^4}$

$3^{3-2} \cdot 2^{5-5} \cdot 5^{2-4}$

$3^1 \cdot 2^0 \cdot 5^{-2}$

$3 \cdot 1 \cdot 5^{-2}$

$\dfrac{3}{5^2}$

To see what happens when you raise a power to a power, use the order of operations.

$(c^3)^2 = (c \cdot c \cdot c)^2$ *Show the power inside the parentheses.*

$= (c \cdot c \cdot c) \cdot (c \cdot c \cdot c)$ *Show the power outside the parentheses.*

$= c^6$ *Simplify.*

Notice that the **product** of the exponents in the power equals the exponent in the answer: $3 \cdot 2 = 6$.

Reading Math

$(9^4)^5$ is read as "nine to the fourth power, to the fifth power."

RAISING A POWER TO A POWER

Words	Numbers	Algebra
To raise a power to a power, keep the base and multiply the exponents.	$(9^4)^5 = 9^{4 \cdot 5} = 9^{20}$	$(b^m)^n = b^{m \cdot n}$

EXAMPLE 3 Raising a Power to a Power

Simplify each expression. Write your answer in exponential form.

A $(7^5)^3$

$7^{5 \cdot 3}$ *Multiply exponents.*

7^{15}

B $(n^9)^{11}$

$n^{9 \cdot 11}$

n^{99}

C $(2^{-7})^{-2}$

$2^{-7 \cdot (-2)}$ *Multiply exponents.*

2^{14}

D $(-12^{10})^{-6}$

$(-12)^{10 \cdot (-6)}$

$(-12)^{-60}$

Think and Discuss

1. Explain why the exponents cannot be added in the product $14^3 \cdot 18^3$.

2. List two ways to express 4^5 as a product of powers.

Power Presentations with PowerPoint®

Additional Examples

Example 1

Simplify each expression. Write your answer in exponential form.

A. $6^6 \cdot 6^3$ 6^9 **B.** $n^5 \cdot n^7$ n^{12}

Example 2

Simplify each expression. Write your answer in exponential form.

A. $\dfrac{7^5}{7^3}$ 7^2 **B.** $\dfrac{x^{10}}{x^9}$ x^1 or x

Example 3

Simplify each expression. Write your answer in exponential form.

A. $(5^4)^2$ 5^8 **B.** $(6^7)^9$ 6^{63}

C. $\left(\left(\dfrac{2}{3}\right)^{12}\right)^{-3}$ $\dfrac{2^{-36}}{3}$ **D.** $(17^2)^{-20}$ 17^{-40}

Also available on transparency

Possible answers to Think and Discuss

1. The exponents cannot be added because the bases are not the same. However, the bases could be multiplied together under the same exponent, for example, $(14 \cdot 18)^3$.

2. $4^5 \cdot 4^0$, $4^3 \cdot 4^2$, $2^5 \cdot 2^5$, $2^8 \cdot 2^2$

---

② Teach

Guided Instruction

In this lesson, students learn to apply the properties of exponents. Help students discover the property $b^m \cdot b^n = b^{m+n}$ by having them write several expressions in expanded form, such as $2^3 \cdot 2^4 = (2 \cdot 2 \cdot 2)(2 \cdot 2 \cdot 2) = 2^7$. Use a similar process for the property $\dfrac{b^m}{b^n} = b^{m-n}$. You may want to display the Teaching Transparency. To discover the property $a^0 = 1$ if $a \neq 0$, have students write several statements, such as $\dfrac{5^2}{5^2}$, and simplify them using the expansion method.

Universal Access
For Advanced Learners/GATE

To reinforce the concepts that $x = x^1$ and $x^0 = 1$ for $x \neq 0$, ask students to simplify the following expressions using both the expansion method and the properties of exponents: $4 \cdot 4^2$ and $4^0 \cdot 4^2$. Have students compare the results.

Possible answers:

$4 \cdot 4^2 = (4)(4 \cdot 4) = 4^3$

$4 \cdot 4^2 = 4^1 \cdot 4^2 = 4^{1+2} = 4^3$

$4^0 \cdot 4^2 = 4^{0+2} = 4^2$

$4^0 \cdot 4^2 = (1)(4 \cdot 4) = 4^2$

---

③ Close

Summarize

Review the rules by showing an example for each and then showing the same example in expanded form. Remind students that if they have trouble remembering the rules, they can use the expansion method to relearn them. Ask students which method would be better for solving a problem with large exponents, such as $\dfrac{7^{23}}{7^{19}}$, and have them explain their answers.

Possible answer: The rules would be better because the expansion would take a lot of time and space to work out.

California Standards Practice
NS2.1, ← NS2.3, Extension of AF2.2

go.hrw.com
Homework Help Online
KEYWORD: MT8CA 4-3
Parent Resources Online
KEYWORD: MT8CA Parent

Assignment Guide

If you finished Example **1** assign:
Proficient 1–4, 13–20, 38, 42, 44, 61–72
Advanced 13–20, 41–42, 48, 57, 61–72

If you finished Example **2** assign:
Proficient 1–8, 13–28, 38–48 even, 61–72
Advanced 13–28, 31–57 odd, 57–72

If you finished Example **3** assign:
Proficient 1–36, 38–48 even, 49, 51, 61–72
Advanced 13–36, 47–72

Homework Quick Check
Quickly check key concepts.
Exercises: 14, 20, 26, 28, 30, 36

Math Background

Some students may have had trouble understanding the rule $a^0 = 1$, if $a \neq 0$ in the previous lesson. To reinforce the rule of the zero exponent, you can now use the rule for dividing powers with the same base, along with rules for simplifying fractions.

$$\frac{2^4}{2^4} = \frac{\cancel{2} \cdot \cancel{2} \cdot \cancel{2} \cdot \cancel{2}}{\cancel{2} \cdot \cancel{2} \cdot \cancel{2} \cdot \cancel{2}} = 1$$

$$\frac{2^4}{2^4} = 2^{4-4} = 2^0$$

Since $\frac{2^4}{2^4}$ equals both 1 and 2^0, it follows that 1 and 2^0 are equal to each other.

California Standards

Standard	Exercises
NS1.1	52
NS1.2 ←	63–68
NS2.1	6, 11, 15, 18–20, 27, 30–31, 34–35, 38–39, 54, 62
NS2.3 ←	1–62
AF2.1	69–72
Ext. of AF2.2	53–56

GUIDED PRACTICE

See Example **1** Simplify each expression. Write your answer in exponential form.

1. $5^6 \cdot 5^9$ $\;5^{15}$
2. $12^3 \cdot 12^{-2}$ $\;12$
3. $m \cdot m^3$ $\;m^4$
4. $(-4)^3 \cdot (-4)^3$ $\;(-4)^6$

See Example **2**
5. $\frac{6^5}{6^3}$ $\;6^2$
6. $\frac{a^8}{a^{-1}}$ $\;a^9$
7. $\frac{12^5}{12^5}$ $\;12^0 = 1$
8. $\frac{5^{16} \cdot 6^2 \cdot 2^3}{5^4 \cdot 6^5 \cdot 2^3}$ $\;\frac{5^{12}}{6^3}$

See Example **3**
9. $(3^4)^5$ $\;3^{20}$
10. $(2^2)^0$ $\;2^0 = 1$
11. $(4^{-2})^3$ $\;\frac{1}{4^6}$
12. $(-y^2)^6$ $\;(-y)^{12}$

INDEPENDENT PRACTICE

See Example **1** Simplify each expression. Write your answer in exponential form.

13. $10^{10} \cdot 10^7$ $\;10^{17}$
14. $(-3)^4 \cdot (-3)^4$ $\;3^8$
15. $r^3 \cdot r^{-2}$ $\;r$
16. $18 \cdot 18^5$ $\;18^6$

17. $\left(\frac{1}{3}\right)^2 \cdot \left(\frac{1}{3}\right)^{-4}$ $\;\left(\frac{1}{3}\right)^{-2}$
18. $(-9)^{-6} \cdot (-9)^5$ $\;(-9)^{-1}$
19. $y \cdot y^{-3} \cdot y^{-1}$ $\;y^{-3}$
20. $\left(\frac{1}{5}\right)^{-3} \cdot \left(\frac{1}{5}\right)^3$ $\;= 1$

See Example **2**
21. $\frac{5^{10}}{5^6}$ $\;5^4$
22. $\frac{3^7}{3^7}$ $\;3^0 = 1$
23. $\frac{t^9 \cdot r^4}{t^{-4} \cdot r^3}$ $\;t^{13}r$
24. $\frac{2^3 \cdot 3^6 \cdot 6^3}{2^4 \cdot 3 \cdot 6^3}$ $\;\frac{3^5}{2}$

25. $\frac{1^5 \cdot 4^{-2}}{1^3 \cdot 4}$ $\;\frac{1}{4^3}$
26. $\frac{x^0}{x^5}$ $\;\frac{1}{x^5}$
27. $\frac{(-6)^{-2}}{(-6)^{-2}}$ $\;6^0 = 1$
28. $\frac{2^7 \cdot 9^5}{2^6 \cdot 9^2}$ $\;2 \cdot 9^3$

See Example **3**
29. $(5^0)^8$ $\;5^0 = 1$
30. $(6^4)^{-1}$ $\;\frac{1}{6^4}$
31. $(3^{-2})^2$ $\;\frac{1}{3^4}$
32. $(x^5)^2$ $\;x^{10}$

33. $(-1^3)^3$ $\;(-1)^9$ or -1
34. $(7^{-6})^{-1}$ $\;7^6$
35. $(t^2)^{-4}$ $\;\frac{1}{t^8}$
36. $-(2^5)^3$ $\;-2^{15}$

PRACTICE AND PROBLEM SOLVING

Extra Practice
See page EP8.

Simplify. Write your answer in exponential form.

37. $\frac{4^7}{4^3}$ $\;4^4$
38. $3^8 \cdot 3^{-1}$ $\;3^7$
39. $\frac{a^4}{a^{-3}}$ $\;a^7$
40. $\frac{10^{18}}{10^9}$ $\;10^9$

41. $x^3 \cdot x^7$ $\;x^{10}$
42. $a^6 \cdot b^9$ cannot combine
43. $(7^4)^3$ $\;7^{12}$
44. $2 \cdot 2^4$ $\;2^5$

45. $\frac{10^4}{5^2}$ cannot combine
46. $\frac{11^7}{11^6}$ $\;11^1$ or 11
47. $\frac{y^8}{y^8}$ $\;y^0 = 1$
48. $y^8 \cdot y^{-8}$ $\;1$

49. There are 26^3 ways to make a 3-letter "word" (from *aaa* to *zzz*) and 26^5 ways to make a 5-letter word. How many times more ways are there to make a 5-letter word than a 3-letter word? $\;26^2$, or 676

50. **Astronomy** The mass of the sun is about 10^{27} metric tons, or 10^{30} kilograms. How many kilograms are in one metric ton? (Hint: Set up a proportion.) $\;10^3$ kg, or 1000 kg

51. **Business** Using the manufacturing terms at right, tell how many dozen are in a great gross. How many gross are in a great gross? $\;12^2$; 12^1

1 dozen	= 12^1 items
1 gross	= 12^2 items
1 great gross	= 12^3 items

REVIEW FOR MASTERY 4-3

Review for Mastery
4-3 *Properties of Exponents*

To multiply powers with the same base, keep the base and add exponents.	To divide powers with the same base, keep the base and subtract exponents.	To raise a power to a power, keep the base and multiply exponents.
$x^a \cdot x^b = x^{a+b}$	$x^a \div x^b = x^{a-b}$	$(x^a)^b = x^{ab}$
$4^5 \cdot 4^2 = 4^{5+2} = 4^7$	$4^5 \div 4^2 = 4^{5-2} = 4^3$	$(4^5)^2 = 4^{5(2)} = 4^{10}$
$8^3 \cdot 8 = 8^{3+1} = 8^4$	$8^3 \div 8 = 8^{3-1} = 8^2$	

Complete to see why the rules for exponents work.

1. $4^5 \cdot 4^2 = (\underline{4})(\underline{4})(\underline{4})(\underline{4})(\underline{4}) \cdot (\underline{4})(\underline{4}) = 4^{\underline{7}}$
2. $8^3 \cdot 8 = (\underline{8})(\underline{8})(\underline{8}) \cdot (\underline{8}) = 8^{\underline{4}}$
3. $4^5 \div 4^2 = \frac{4^5}{4^2} = \frac{\cancel{4} \cdot \cancel{4} \cdot 4 \cdot 4 \cdot 4}{\cancel{4} \cdot \cancel{4}} = 4^{\underline{3}}$
4. $8^3 \div 8 = \frac{8^3}{8} = \frac{8 \cdot 8 \cdot 8}{8} = 8^{\underline{2}}$
5. $(4^2)^3 = 4^2 \cdot 4^2 \cdot 4^2 = 4^{2+2+2} = 4^{2(3)} = 4^{\underline{6}}$

Simplify each expression. Write your answer in exponential form.

6. $12^3 \cdot 12^2 = 12^{3+2} = 12^{\underline{5}}$
7. $9^4 \cdot 9^3 = 9^{4+3} = 9^{\underline{7}}$
8. $\frac{7^6}{7^2} = 7^{6-2} = 7^{\underline{4}}$
9. $\frac{12^6}{12^4} = 12^{6-4} = 12^{\underline{2}}$

Simplify each expression. Write your answer in exponential form.

10. $10^4 \cdot 10^6 = \underline{10^{10}}$
11. $5^5 \cdot 5 = \underline{5^6}$
12. $4^5 \cdot 4 \cdot 4^3 = \underline{4^9}$
13. $\frac{15^6}{15^2} = \underline{15^4}$
14. $\frac{9^5}{9} = \underline{9^4}$
15. $\frac{2^{10}}{2^2} = \underline{2^8}$

Simplify.

16. $(5^3)^4 = 5^{3(4)} = \underline{5^{12}}$
17. $(6^2)^4 = 6^{2(4)} = \underline{6^8}$
18. $(2^5)^2 = \underline{2^{10}}$

PRACTICE 4-3

Practice B
4-3 *Properties of Exponents*

Simplify each expression. Write your answer in exponential form.

1. $10^5 \cdot 10^7$ $\;\underline{10^{12}}$
2. $x^9 \cdot x^8$ $\;\underline{x^{17}}$
3. $14^7 \cdot 14^9$ $\;\underline{14^{16}}$
4. $12^6 \cdot 12^8$ $\;\underline{12^{14}}$

5. $y^{12} \cdot y^{10}$ $\;\underline{y^{22}}$
6. $15^9 \cdot 15^{14}$ $\;\underline{15^{23}}$
7. $(-11)^{20} \cdot (-11)^{10}$ $\;\underline{(-11)^{30}}$
8. $(-a)^6 \cdot (-a)^7$ $\;\underline{(-a)^{13}}$

9. $\frac{12^9}{12^2}$ $\;\underline{12^7}$
10. $\frac{(-11)^{12}}{(-11)^8}$ $\;\underline{(-11)^4}$
11. $\frac{x^{10}}{x^5}$ $\;\underline{x^5}$
12. $\frac{16^{10}}{16^2}$ $\;\underline{16^8}$

13. $\frac{17^{19}}{17^2}$ $\;\underline{17^{17}}$
14. $\frac{14^{16}}{14^{14}}$ $\;\underline{14^2}$
15. $\frac{23^7}{23^5}$ $\;\underline{23^8}$
16. $\frac{(-a)^{12}}{(-a)^7}$ $\;\underline{(-a)^5}$

17. $(6^2)^4$ $\;\underline{6^8}$
18. $(2^4)^{-3}$ $\;\underline{2^{-12}}$
19. $(-9^5)^{-1}$ $\;\underline{(-3^{-5})}$
20. $(y^5)^2$ $\;\underline{y^{10}}$

21. $(9^{-2})^3$ $\;\underline{9^{-6}}$
22. $(10^0)^3$ $\;\underline{10^0}$
23. $(x^4)^{-2}$ $\;\underline{x^{-8}}$
24. $(5^{-2})^0$ $\;\underline{5^0}$

Write the product or quotient as one power.

25. $\frac{w^{12}}{w^3}$ $\;\underline{w^9}$
26. $d^8 \cdot d^5$ $\;\underline{d^{13}}$
27. $(-15)^5 \cdot (-15)^{10}$ $\;\underline{(-15)^{15}}$

28. Jefferson High School has a student body of 6^4 students. Each class has approximately 6^2 students. How many classes does the school have? Write the answer as one power.
$\underline{6^2}$

29. Write the expression for a number used as a factor fifteen times being multiplied by a number used as a factor ten times. Then, write the product as one power.
$\underline{x^{15} \cdot x^{10} = x^{25}}$

52. Estimation The distance from Earth to the moon is about 22^4 miles. The distance from Earth to Neptune is about 22^7 miles. Which distance is greater? About how many times as great? **distance from Earth to Neptune; 22^3, or 10,648 times as great**

Find the missing exponent.

53. $b^{\blacksquare} \cdot b^4 = b^8$ **4** **54.** $(v^2)^{\blacksquare} = v^{-6}$ **−3** **55.** $\dfrac{w^{\blacksquare}}{w^3} = w^{-3}$ **0** **56.** $(a^4)^{\blacksquare} = a$ **$\frac{1}{4}$**

57. A googol is the number 1 followed by 100 zeros.
   a. What is a googol written as a power of 10? **10^{100}**
   b. What is a googol times a googol written as a power of 10? **10^{200}**

 58. What's the Error? A student said that $\dfrac{3^5}{9^5}$ is the same as $\dfrac{1}{3}$. What mistake has the student made? **Possible answer: The student did not consider that the bases must be the same.**

59. Write About It Why do you subtract exponents when dividing powers with the same base?

60. Challenge A number to the 11th power divided by the same number to the 8th power equals 64. What is the number? **4**

 SPIRAL STANDARDS REVIEW ✦ NS1.2, NS2.1, ✦ NS2.3, AF2.1

61. Multiple Choice In computer technology, a kilobyte is 2^{10} bytes in size. A gigabyte is 2^{30} bytes in size. The size of a terabyte is the product of the size of a kilobyte and the size of a gigabyte. What is the size of a terabyte?

   Ⓐ 2^{20} bytes   Ⓑ 2^{40} bytes   Ⓒ 2^{300} bytes   Ⓓ 4^{300} bytes

62. Short Response A student claims that $10^3 \cdot 10^{-5}$ is greater than 1. Explain whether the student is correct. $10^3 \cdot 10^{-5} = 10^{3+(-5)} = 10^{-2} = \dfrac{1}{10^2} = \dfrac{1}{100}$; $\dfrac{1}{100}$ is less than 1.

Evaluate each expression for the given value of the variable. (Lesson 2-3)

63. $19.4 - x$ for $x = -5.6$ **25**   **64.** $11 - r$ for $r = 13.5$ **−2.5**   **65.** $p + 65.1$ for $p = -42.3$ **22.8**

66. $-\dfrac{3}{7} - t$ for $t = 1\dfrac{5}{7}$ **$-2\dfrac{1}{7}$**   **67.** $3\dfrac{5}{11} + y$ for $y = -2\dfrac{4}{11}$ **$1\dfrac{1}{11}$**   **68.** $-\dfrac{1}{19} + g$ for $g = \dfrac{18}{19}$ **$\dfrac{17}{19}$**

Simplify. (Lesson 4-2)

69. $(-3)^{-2}$ **$\dfrac{1}{9}$**   **70.** $(-2)^{-3}$ **$-\dfrac{1}{8}$**   **71.** 1^{-3} **1**   **72.** $-(2)^{-4}$ **$-\dfrac{1}{16}$**

CHALLENGE 4-3

LESSON 4-3 Challenge
Square Dance

Study these patterns.

$1 = 1^2$

$1^2 + 1 + 2 = 4 = 2^2$

$2^2 + 2 + 3 = 9 = 3^2$

$3^2 + 3 + 4 = 16 = 4^2$

So, according to the pattern, 5^2 can be written as the sum of 4^2 and two consecutive integers.

1. Draw a diagram and write an equation to illustrate 5^2.

Equation: $\underline{4^2 + 4 + 5 = 25 = 5^2}$

2. Draw a diagram and write an equation to illustrate 8^2.

Equation: $\underline{7^2 + 7 + 8 = 64 = 8^2}$

3. Use the pattern to write an equation to indicate that, for any integer n, $(n + 1)^2$ can be written as the sum of n^2 and two consecutive integers.

Equation: $\underline{n^2 + (n) + (n + 1) = (n + 1)^2}$

4. If you know that $20^2 = 400$, use the pattern to calculate 21^2.

$21^2 = \underline{400 + 20 + 21 = 441}$

PROBLEM SOLVING 4-3

LESSON 4-3 Problem Solving
Properties of Exponents

Write each answer as a power.

1. Cindy separated her fruit flies into equal groups. She estimates that there are 2^{10} fruit flies in each of 2^2 jars. How many fruit flies does Cindy have in all?

$\underline{2^{12}}$ fruit flies

2. Suppose a researcher tests a new method of pasteurization on a strain of bacteria in his laboratory. If the bacteria are killed at a rate of 8^9 per sec, how many bacteria would be killed after 8^2 sec?

$\underline{8^{11}}$ bacteria

3. A satellite orbits the earth at about 13^4 km per hour. How long would it take to complete 24 orbits, which is a distance of about 13^5 km?

$\underline{13}$ hr

4. The side of a cube is 3^4 centimeters long. What is the volume of the cube? (Hint: $V = s^3$.)

$\underline{3^{12}}$ cm

Use the table to answer Exercises 5–6. The table describes the number of people involved at each level of a pyramid scheme. In a pyramid scheme each individual recruits so many others to participate who in turn recruit others, and so on. Choose the letter of the best answer.

5. Using exponents, how many people will be involved at level 6?
   A 6^6 C 5^5
   B 6^5 Ⓓ 5^6

6. How many times more people will be involved at level 6 than at level 2?
   Ⓕ 5^4 H 5^5
   G 5^3 J 5^6

Pyramid Scheme Each person recruits 5 others.	
Level	Total Number of People
1	5
2	5^2
3	5^3
4	5^4

7. There are 10^3 ways to make a 3-digit combination, but there are 10^6 ways to make a 6-digit combination. How many times more ways are there to make a 6-digit combination than a 3-digit combination?
   A 5^{10} C 2^5
   B 2^{10} Ⓓ 10^3

8. After 3 hours, a bacteria colony has $(25^3)^3$ bacteria present. How many bacteria are in the colony?
   F 25^1 Ⓗ 25^9
   G 25^6 J 25^{33}

FORMATIVE ASSESSMENT
and INTERVENTION ◀ ▶

Diagnose Before the Lesson
4-3 Warm Up, TE p. 176

Monitor During the Lesson
4-3 Know-It Notebook
4-3 Questioning Strategies

Assess After the Lesson
4-3 Lesson Quiz, TE p. 179

Answers

59. Possible answer: Dividing is the same as multiplying by the reciprocal, so when dividing powers with the same base, you add the opposite of the exponent in the denominator. This is the same as subtracting the exponents.

Teaching Tip **Short Response** Some students will see that the expression in **Exercise 62** is positive and agree with the student's claim. Remind students that there are positive numbers that are less than one, and encourage them to write down all of their work.

 Journal

Ask students to write about a topic in science or any other subject that seems likely to make use of large numbers.

Power Presentations with PowerPoint®

4-3 Lesson Quiz

Simplify each expression. Write your answer in exponential form.

1. $n^3 \times n^4$ n^7

2. $8 \cdot 8^8$ 8^9

3. $\dfrac{10^9}{10^5}$ 10^4

4. $\dfrac{t^9}{t^7}$ t^2

5. $3^2 \cdot 3^3 \cdot 3^5$ 3^{10}

6. $(m^2)^{19}$ m^{38}

7. $(9^{-8})^9$ $\dfrac{1}{9^{72}}$

8. $(10^4)^0$ 1

Also available on transparency

4-4 Multiplying and Dividing Monomials

Why learn this? You can multiply monomials to find the volume of an aquarium. (See Exercise 47.)

A **monomial** is a number, variable, or a product of numbers and variables with exponents that are whole numbers.

Monomials	$7x^5$, $-3a^2b^3$, n^2, 8, $\frac{z}{4}$
Not monomials	m^{-3}, $4z^{2.5}$, $5 + y$, $\frac{8}{w^3}$, 2^x

To multiply two monomials, multiply the coefficients and add the exponents that have the same base.

EXAMPLE 1   Multiplying Monomials

Multiply.

A $(2x^3)(5x^2)$
$(2 \cdot 5)(x^3 \cdot x^2)$ *Use the Comm. and Assoc. Properties.*
$2 \cdot 5 \cdot x^{3+2}$ *Multiply coefficients. Add exponents*
$10x^5$ *that have the same base.*

Helpful Hint

When performing operations with monomials, the answer may not be a monomial. Notice that the answer to Example 1B has a variable in the denominator.

B $(8m^5n^3)(4m^2n^{-8})$
$(8 \cdot 4)(m^5 \cdot m^2)(n^3 \cdot n^{-8})$ *Use the Comm. and Assoc. Properties.*
$8 \cdot 4 \cdot m^{5+2} \cdot n^{3+(-8)}$ *Multiply coefficients. Add exponents*
$32m^7n^{-11}$ *that have the same base.*
$\dfrac{32m^7}{n^{11}}$

C $(6a^3b)(-4b^5)$
$(6 \cdot (-4))(a^3)(b \cdot b^5)$ *Use the Comm. and Assoc. Properties.*
$(6 \cdot (-4))(a^3)(b^1 \cdot b^5)$ *Think: $b = b^1$.*
$6 \cdot (-4) \cdot a^3 \cdot b^{1+5}$ *Multiply coefficients. Add exponents*
$-24a^3b^6$ *that have the same base.*

To divide a monomial by a monomial, divide the coefficients and subtract the exponents of the powers in the denominator from the exponents of the powers in the numerator that have the same base.

Motivate

Make a two-column chart on the board. Label the left-hand column *Monomials* and list several examples of monomials. Label the right-hand column *Not Monomials* and list expressions that are not monomials. Encourage students to look for commonalities between the examples of monomials, and then have students offer their own definitions of the term *monomial*.

Explorations and answers are provided in *Alternate Openers: Explorations Transparencies.*

EXAMPLE 2 **Dividing Monomials**

Divide. Assume that no denominator equals zero.

A $\dfrac{12x^7}{2x^3}$

$\dfrac{12}{2}x^{7-3}$ *Divide coefficients. Subtract*

$6x^4$ *exponents that have the same base.*

B $\dfrac{8x^5y^4}{6x^7y^4}$

$\dfrac{4}{3}x^{5-7}y^{4-4}$ *Divide coefficients. Subtract*
exponents that have the same base.

$\dfrac{4}{3}x^{-2}y^0 = \dfrac{4}{3x^2}$ *Think:* $x^{-2} = \dfrac{1}{x^2}$ *and* $y^0 = 1$.

To raise a monomial to a power, you must first understand how to find a power of a product. Notice what happens to the exponents when you find a power of a product.

$$(xy)^3 = xy \cdot xy \cdot xy = x \cdot x \cdot x \cdot y \cdot y \cdot y = x^3y^3$$

RAISING A PRODUCT TO A POWER		
Words	**Numbers**	**Algebra**
To raise a product to a power, raise each factor to that power.	$(2 \cdot 3)^2 = 2^2 \cdot 3^2$ $= 4 \cdot 9$ $= 36$	$(ab)^n = a^n \cdot b^n$

EXAMPLE 3 **Raising a Monomial to a Power**

Answers to *Think and Discuss*

Simplify.

A $(2x)^5$

$2^5 \cdot x^5$ *Raise each factor*

$32x^5$ *to the power.*

B $(-4mn^5)^5$

$(-4)^5 \cdot (m)^5 \cdot (n^5)^5$ *Raise each factor to the power.*

$(-4)^5 \cdot m^{1 \cdot 5} \cdot n^{5 \cdot 5}$ *Multiply*

$-1024m^5n^{25}$ *exponents.*

Remember!

To raise a power to a power, keep the base and multiply the exponents of the bases.

1. The exponent of the variable is not a whole number.

2. The variable m does not appear in the quotient since $m^{3-3} = m^0 = 1$.

Think and Discuss

1. **Explain** why the expression $-5b^{-2}$ is not a monomial.

2. **Tell** what happens to the variable m when you simplify $\dfrac{24m^3n^4}{6m^3n^2}$.

COMMON ERROR ALERT

Students sometimes forget whether they should add or multiply exponents. When this occurs, remind students to go back to the definition of an exponent to write the expression in expanded form.

Power Presentations
with PowerPoint®

Additional Examples

Example 1

Multiply.

A. $(3a^2)(4a^5)$ $12a^7$

B. $(4x^2y^3)(5xy^5)$ $20x^3y^8$

C. $(-3p^2r)(6pr^3s)$ $-18p^3r^4s$

Example 2

Divide. Assume that no denominator equals zero.

A. $\dfrac{15m^5}{3m^2}$ $5m^3$

B. $\dfrac{18a^2b^3}{16ab^3}$ $\dfrac{9}{8}a$

Example 3

Simplify.

A. $(3y)^3$ $27y^3$

B. $(2a^2b^6)^4$ $16a^8b^{24}$

Also available on transparency

Teaching Tip   **Visual** While solving the problems in this lesson, it may be helpful for students to write an exponent of 1 for variables that have no exponent. For example, $3xy^2$ may be written as $3x^1y^2$.

---

2 Teach

Guided Instruction

In this lesson, students multiply and divide monomials. Begin by introducing monomials. Quickly check for understanding by asking students to provide their own examples and nonexamples of monomials. Then show students how to multiply and divide monomials. Point out that these operations are based on the properties of exponents.

Universal Access
Through Visual Cues

Before students begin multiplying a pair of monomials, you may want to have them identify the like variables. They can do so by using colored highlighters or by underlining pairs of like variables as shown below.

$$(4\underline{k}^5\underline{m}^3n)(3\underline{k}\underline{m}^5)$$

3 Close

Summarize

Ask students to describe the rule for each operation in their own words and to provide an example.

1. **Multiply monomials**
Multiply coefficients and add exponents that have the same base.

2. **Divide monomials**
Divide coefficients and subtract exponents that have the same base.

3. **Raise a monomial to a power**
Raise each factor of the monomial to the power.

California Standards Practice
AF1.1, AF1.4, AF2.2

go.hrw.com
Homework Help Online
KEYWORD: MT8CA 4-4
Parent Resources Online
KEYWORD: MT8CA Parent

Assignment Guide

If you finished Example **1** assign:
Proficient 1–6, 20–24 even, 54–61
Advanced 19–24, 44–47, 50–52, 54–61

If you finished Example **2** assign:
Proficient 1–12, 20–30 even, 53–61
Advanced 19–30, 46–47, 50–61

If you finished Example **3** assign:
Proficient 1–18, 20–36 even, 37–39, 44–45, 47–49, 53–61
Advanced 19–36, 40–43, 46–61

Homework Quick Check

Quickly check key concepts.
Exercises: 20, 22, 28, 30, 34, 36

Math Background

Because division by zero is undefined, a monomial that appears as the divisor in a division problem must not be equal to zero. Thus, in general, the quotient makes sense only when the variables that appear in the monomial of the denominator are not equal to zero. Although this restriction may not always be stated explicitly, you can assume that no denominator equals zero in this lesson.

GUIDED PRACTICE

See Example **1** Multiply.

1. $(7y^2)(8y^5)$ $56y^7$
2. $(8m^2)(3m^3)$ $24m^5$
3. $(3a^2b^4)(-2a^3b)$ $-6a^5b^5$
4. $(-3r^2s^7)(2r^9s)$ $-6r^{11}s^8$
5. $(2x)(2y)$ $4xy$
6. $(c^2d^3e)(2c^5d^{12}e^8)$ $2c^7d^{15}e^9$

See Example **2** Divide. Assume that no denominator equals zero.

7. $\frac{15n^5}{5n^2}$ $3n^3$
8. $\frac{-4x^7}{2x^6}$ $-2x$
9. $\frac{18a^2b^8}{12ab^5}$ $\frac{3}{2}ab^3$
10. $\frac{24s^{10}t^{12}}{18s^5}$ $\frac{4}{3}s^5t^{12}$
11. $\frac{42a^4c^7}{7a^4c^2}$ $6c^5$
12. $\frac{16m^5p}{8m^3p}$ $2m^2$

See Example **3** Simplify.

13. $(5a)^3$ $125a^3$
14. $(9m^3)^2$ $81m^6$
15. $(6x^2y^5)^3$ $216x^6y^{15}$
16. $(-7p^5q^3)^2$ $49p^{10}q^6$
17. $(2m^3n^2)^5$ $32m^{15}n^{10}$
18. $(-3x^4yz)^4$ $81x^{16}y^4z^4$

INDEPENDENT PRACTICE

See Example **1** Multiply.

19. $(-11z^3)(2z^9)$ $-22z^{12}$
20. $(5n^7)(12n^3)$ $60n^{10}$
21. $(-x^5)(2x^5)$ $-2x^{10}$
22. $(8p^3r^4)(\frac{1}{2}p^4r^5)$ $4p^7r^9$
23. $(-3a^2b^4)(-2b)$ $6a^2b^5$
24. $(x^4y^{11}z)(7x^2y^4z)$ $7x^6y^{15}z^2$

See Example **2** Divide. Assume that no denominator equals zero.

25. $\frac{35x^9}{7x^7}$ $5x^2$
26. $\frac{20n^{12}}{5n^4}$ $4n^8$
27. $\frac{8pq^8}{4pq^5}$ $2q^3$
28. $\frac{12a^5b^4}{8a^4b^{11}}$ $\frac{3a}{2b^7}$
29. $\frac{15x^2y^7}{10xy^2}$ $\frac{3}{2}xy^5$
30. $\frac{-25a^{10}b^3}{5a^3}$ $-5a^7b^3$

See Example **3** Simplify.

31. $(2y)^8$ $256y^8$
32. $(7x^3)^3$ $343x^9$
33. $(4b^2)^4$ $256b^8$
34. $(5x^4y^5)^3$ $125x^{12}y^{15}$
35. $(2a^3b^{10})^5$ $32a^{15}b^{50}$
36. $(-2p^3r)^4$ $16p^{12}r^4$

PRACTICE AND PROBLEM SOLVING

Extra Practice
See page EP8.

Simplify each expression.

37. $(12m^2)^2$ $144m^4$
38. $(9x^3)(\frac{2}{3}x^7)$ $6x^{10}$
39. $\frac{36a^5b^5}{30a^2}$ $\frac{6}{5}a^3b^5$
40. $(8p^4q^5)(\frac{3}{4}pq^2)$ $6p^5q^7$
41. $\frac{18g^3h^5}{-2g^3h^5}$ -9
42. $(-2xy^2)^6$ $64x^6y^{12}$

43. **Geometry** The volume of a sphere of radius r can be approximated by the monomial $4r^3$. The surface area of the sphere can be approximated by the monomial $12r^2$. Write and simplify an expression for the volume of the sphere divided by the surface area of the sphere. $\frac{r}{3}$

REVIEW FOR MASTERY 4-4

LESSON 4-4 Review for Mastery
Multiplying and Dividing Monomials

To multiply two monomials, multiply the coefficients and add the exponents that have the same base.

$(6x^3)(3x^4)$
$= 6 \cdot 3 \cdot x^{2+4}$
$= 18x^6$

To divide two monomials, divide the coefficients and subtract the exponents of the powers in the denominator from the powers in the numerator that have the same base.

$\frac{24y^7}{3y^5}$
$= \frac{24}{3}y^{7-5}$
$= 8y^2$

To raise a product to a power, raise each factor to that power.

$(4a^3b^2)^2$
$= 4^2 \cdot (a^3)^2 \cdot (b^2)^2$
$= 16 \cdot a^{3 \cdot 2} \cdot b^{2 \cdot 2}$
$= 16a^6b^4$

Complete to find each product.

1. $(5m^2)(2m^8) = \underline{5} \cdot \underline{2} \cdot m^{\underline{2}+\underline{8}} = \underline{10}m^{\underline{10}}$
2. $(12x^3)(4x^4) = \underline{12} \cdot \underline{4} \cdot x^{\underline{3}+\underline{4}} = \underline{48}x^{\underline{7}}$
3. $(2a^2b^3)(3ab^4) = \underline{2} \cdot \underline{3} \cdot a^{\underline{2}+\underline{1}} \cdot b^{\underline{3}+\underline{4}} = \underline{6}a^{\underline{3}}b^{\underline{7}}$

Complete to find each quotient.

4. $\frac{14c^6}{7c^2} = \frac{14}{7}c^{\underline{6}-\underline{2}} = \underline{2}c^{\underline{4}}$
5. $\frac{36m^{10}}{9m^7} = \frac{36}{9}m^{\underline{10}-\underline{7}} = \underline{4}m^{\underline{3}}$
6. $\frac{15r^5s^7}{3r^2s^3} = \frac{15}{3}r^{\underline{5}-\underline{2}}s^{\underline{7}-\underline{3}} = \underline{5}r^{\underline{4}}s^{\underline{4}}$

Complete to simplify each expression.

7. $(7n^4)^2 = 7^2 \cdot (n^4)^2 = \underline{49} \cdot n^{\underline{4} \cdot \underline{2}} = \underline{49}n^{\underline{8}}$
8. $(3c^2d^3)^4 = 3^4 \cdot (c^2)^4 \cdot (d^3)^4 = \underline{81} \cdot c^{\underline{2} \cdot \underline{4}} \cdot d^{\underline{3} \cdot \underline{4}} = \underline{81}c^{\underline{8}}d^{\underline{12}}$

PRACTICE 4-4

LESSON 4-4 Practice B
Multiplying and Dividing Monomials

Multiply.

1. $(3c^5)(12c^3)$
   $36c^8$
2. $(2m^{10})(8m^3)$
   $16m^{13}$
3. $(4r^3s^2)(6rs^2)$
   $24r^4s^4$
4. $(-3ab^4)(2a^3b)$
   $-6a^3b^5$
5. $(2p^2q)(-6pq)$
   $-12p^3q^2$
6. $(x^4)(4x^3y)$
   $4x^7y$

Divide. Assume no denominator equals zero.

7. $\frac{24x^4}{3x^5}$
   $8x^2$
8. $\frac{50c^3}{5c^2}$
   $10c$
9. $\frac{12m^2n^5}{3mn^2}$
   $4mn^3$
10. $\frac{-16x^4y^2}{4x^2y}$
    $-4x^2y$
11. $\frac{18p^5q}{-3pq}$
    $-6p^5$
12. $\frac{60b^6c^4}{12c^6}$
    $5b^2$

Simplify.

13. $(5n^3)^2$
    $25n^6$
14. $(-2c^3)^3$
    $-8c^9$
15. $(3a^2b)^2$
    $9a^4b^2$

A triangle has a base of $4mn$ inches and a height of $5m^2n$ inches.

16. The area of a triangle is one-half the product of its base and height. Write and simplify an expression for the area of the triangle.
    $10m^3n^2$
17. Find the area of the triangle when $m = 2$ and $n = 1$.
    80 in^2

California Standards

Standard	Exercises
NS2.3 🔑	58, 61
AF1.1	43–46, 48
AF1.3 🔑	55–57
AF1.4	50
AF2.2	1–54, 59, 60

The area of a rectangle is the product of the rectangle's length and width. Write and simplify an expression for the area of each rectangle.

44.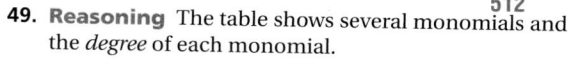
$3xy$

$6x^2y$ $18x^3y^2$

45. $2mn$

$8m^3n^4$

$16m^4n^5$

46. $2ac$

$3abc$ $6a^2bc^2$

47. Hobbies To find the volume of a rectangular prism, such as an aquarium, multiply the length by the width by the height. Find the volume of the aquarium shown. $6x^3y^2$

$2x$

xy $3xy$

49a. The degree of a monomial is the sum of the exponents of the variables in the monomial.

48. Geometry To find the volume of a cube, raise the length of a side to the third power.
  a. The side of a cube is $4x^2y$. Write and simplify an expression for the volume of the cube. $64x^6y^3$
  b. Find the cube's volume when $x = 1$ and $y = 2$. 512

49. Reasoning The table shows several monomials and the *degree* of each monomial.
  a. Make a conjecture about the definition of the degree of a monomial.
  b. What do you think the degree of x^5y^3 is? 8

Monomial	Degree
y^4	4
x^3y^2	5
xyz	3
$x^2y^2z^3$	7

50. The student added the exponents instead of multiplying. The correct answer is $8x^9y^9$.

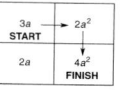 **50. What's the Error?** A student was asked to simplify $(2x^3y^3)^3$. The student's answer was $8x^6y^6$. What error did the student make, and what is the correct answer?

51. $(mn)^3 = m^3n^3$ and $(nm)^3 = n^3m^3$; but $m^3n^3 = n^3m^3$, so the expressions are equivalent.

51. Write About It Explain why $(mn)^3$ is equivalent to $(nm)^3$.

52. Challenge Simplify the expression $(2a^2b^3)^3 \cdot (3ac^2)^2$. $72a^8b^9c^4$

SPIRAL STANDARDS REVIEW   ← NS2.3, ← AF1.3, AF2.2

53. Multiple Choice Which expression is equivalent to $\dfrac{16x^8}{8x^4}$?
  Ⓐ $8x^2$ Ⓑ $8x^4$ Ⓒ $2x^2$ Ⓓ $2x^4$

54. Multiple Choice Which product does NOT equal $8m^2n^2$?
  Ⓐ $(2m^2)(4n^2)$ Ⓑ $(4mn)(2mn)$ Ⓒ $(8mn^2)(m^2n)$ Ⓓ $(mn^2)(8m)$

Simplify. (Lesson 3-2)
55. $3(4y - 6) + 8y$ $20y - 18$ **56.** $4(x + 8) + 9x$ $13x + 32$ **57.** $7(3 + 5k) - 14k$ $21 + 21k$

Simplify. Write your answer in exponential form. (Lesson 4-3)
58. $5^4 \cdot 5^{-2}$ 5^2 **59.** $g^3 \cdot g^8$ g^{11} **60.** $\dfrac{m^6}{m^{-2}}$ m^8 **61.** $\dfrac{7^6}{7^5}$ 7^1 or 7

Teaching Tip   **Multiple Choice** In **Exercise 53,** encourage students to eliminate choices **A** and **B** since the coefficients of the monomials should be divided, not subtracted. Students who chose **C** may have divided rather than subtracted the exponents of the variables.

Journal
Have students write a summary of how to multiply monomials, divide monomials, and raise monomials to a power. Ask them to include a worked-out example of each type of problem.

Power Presentations with PowerPoint®

✓ **4-4 Lesson Quiz**

Multiply.
1. $(3g^2h^3)(-6g^7h^2)$ $-18g^9h^5$
2. $(12m^3)(3mp^3)$ $36m^4p^3$

Divide. Assume that no denominator equals zero.
3. $\dfrac{6a^6b^4}{3a^2b}$ $2a^4b^3$
4. $\dfrac{9x^3y}{6x^2y}$ $\dfrac{3}{2}x$
5. $\dfrac{20p^5q}{-4p^2q}$ $-5p^3$

Simplify.
6. $(-5y^7)^3$ $-125y^{21}$
7. $(3c^2d^3)^4$ $81c^8d^{12}$
8. $(3m^2n)^5$ $243m^{10}n^5$

Also available on transparency

CHALLENGE 4-4

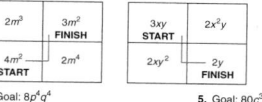

LESSON 4-4 Challenge *Product Puzzles*

To solve these puzzles, find a path from Start to Finish, multiplying the monomials along the way. You must end up with the monomial that is given as the goal. You may only use horizontal or vertical moves, and the path cannot cross itself.

Example
Goal: $24a^5$

Explanation: $(3a)(2a^2) = 6a^3$ and $(6a^3)(4a^2) = 24a^5$.

3a START →	2a²
2a	4a² FINISH

Solve each puzzle.

1. Goal: $24m^9$

2m²	3m² FINISH
4m² START	2m⁴

2. Goal: $12x^2y^4$

3xy START	2x²y
2xy²	2y FINISH

3. Goal: $30a^4b^3$

3ab	5a²b START
2a	3ab² FINISH

4. Goal: $8p^4q^4$

2p START	3p	2q
2p	q²	2pq
2pq	2q²	pq FINISH

5. Goal: $80c^3d^4$

3cd	cd START	2cd
2d³	5cd	5c
2d	2	2d
5cd	2d FINISH	2c²

PROBLEM SOLVING 4-4

LESSON 4-4 Problem Solving *Multiplying and Dividing Monomials*

Write the correct answer.

1. The volume of a rectangular prism is the product of its length, width, and height. A package in the shape of a rectangular prism has length $4x$, width $5xy$, and height $2y$. Write and simplify an expression for the volume of the package.
$40x^2y^2$

2. To find the volume of a cube, raise the length of one side of the cube to the third power. A cube has sides of length $2p^2$. Write and simplify an expression for the volume of the cube.
$8p^6$

3. You can divide the area of a rectangle by the length of the rectangle to find the rectangle's width. A rectangle has area $6m^5$ and length $3m^3$. What is the width of the rectangle?
$2m^2$

4. You can divide the volume of a cylinder by the height of the cylinder to find the area of the cylinder's base. A cylinder has volume $30s^4t^2$ and height $5s^2$. What is the area of the cylinder's base?
$6s^2t^2$

The figure shows the dimensions of a classroom. Use the figure for questions 5–7. Select the best answer.

5. The area of the floor is the length times the width. Which expression gives the area of the floor?
Ⓐ $24p^3q$ C $24p^2q^2$
B $24p^2q$ D $24p^2q^2$

6. The volume of the room is the product of the length, width, and height. Which expression gives the volume of the room?
F $72p^2q^2$ H $72p^4q^4$
Ⓖ $72p^4q^2$ J $17pq$

7. Emma wants to raise the width of the room to the third power. Which expression should she write?
A $12p^5$ C $64p^5$
B $12p^6$ Ⓓ $64p^6$

Height $3pq$
Length $6pq$
Width $4pq$

Objective: Students express large and small numbers in scientific notation and compare two numbers written in scientific notation.

Technology Lab
In *Chapter 4 Resource File*

Online Edition
Tutorial Videos, Interactivities

Countdown to Mastery Weeks 7 and 8

Power Presentations
with PowerPoint®

Warm Up
Order each set of numbers from least to greatest.

1. $10^4, 10^{-2}, 10^0, 10^{-1}$
   $10^{-2}, 10^{-1}, 10^0, 10^4$

2. $8^2, 8^{-2}, 8^3, 8^0$
   $8^{-2}, 8^0, 8^2, 8^3$

3. $2^3, 2^{-6}, 2^{-4}, 2^1$
   $2^{-6}, 2^{-4}, 2^1, 2^3$

4. $5.2^2, 5.2^9, 5.2^{-1}, 5.2^{-2}$
   $5.2^{-2}, 5.2^{-1}, 5.2^2, 5.2^9$

Also available on transparency

Math Fact

For very large and very small numbers, *mega-* indicates 10^6, *giga-* indicates 10^9, *micro-* indicates 10^{-6}, *nano-* indicates 10^{-9}, and *pico-* indicates 10^{-12}.

California Standards
Number Sense 1.1

4-5 Scientific Notation

California Standards
NS1.1 Read, write, and compare rational numbers in scientific notation (positive and negative powers of 10), compare rational numbers in general.

Vocabulary
scientific notation

Why learn this? You can use scientific notation to represent the speed of light. (See Exercise 53.)

The table shows relationships between several powers of 10.

	÷10	÷10	÷10	÷10	÷10	÷10	
Power	10^3	10^2	10^1	10^0	10^{-1}	10^{-2}	10^{-3}
Value	1000	100	10	1	0.1	0.01	0.001
	×10	×10	×10	×10	×10	×10	

- Each time you divide by 10, the exponent in the power decreases by 1 and the decimal point in the value moves one place to the left.

- Each time you multiply by 10, the exponent in the power increases by 1 and the decimal point in the value moves one place to the right.

You can find the product of a number and a power of 10 by moving the decimal point of the number. You may need to write zeros to the right or left of the number in order to move the decimal point.

EXAMPLE 1 Multiplying by Powers of Ten

Multiply.

A 13.7×10^3
  13.7̲0̲0̲
  13,700
  Since the exponent is a positive 3, move the decimal point 3 places to the right.

B 2.3×10^{-4}
  0̲.̲0̲0̲0̲2.3
  0.00023
  Since the exponent is a negative 4, move the decimal point 4 places to the left.

Powers of 10 are used when writing numbers in *scientific notation*. **Scientific notation** is a way to express numbers that are very large or very small. Numbers written in scientific notation are expressed as 2 factors. One factor is a number greater than or equal to 1. The other factor is a power of 10.

---

1 Introduce

Alternate Opener

EXPLORATION

4-5 Scientific Notation

1. Complete the table and look for a pattern.

Power of 10	Factors	Product
10^1	10	10
10^2	10 · 10	100
10^3	10 · 10 · 10	1,000
10^4		
10^5		
10^6		
10^9		

2. Use the pattern you observed in the table to write 10,000,000 as a power of 10.

Think and Discuss

3. **Describe** the pattern you observed in the table.
4. **Explain** how you know that $100,000 = 10^5$ is a true statement.

Motivate

Have students brainstorm about types of data that usually contain very large numbers (e.g., the distance between planets, populations of large countries, age of Earth, and so on). Have students think about why scientists would want to use a more efficient system to express very large numbers (e.g., it is inconvenient to write and compute with such large numbers).

Explorations and answers are provided in *Alternate Openers: Explorations Transparencies.*

The average diameter of an atom is about 0.00000003 cm. A quarter contains about 97,700,000,000,000,000,000,000 atoms. These numbers can be written in scientific notation.

Move the decimal point 8 places to the right.

$$0.00000003 = 3.0 \times 10^{-8}$$

For numbers less than 1, use a negative exponent.

Move the decimal point 22 places to the left.

$$97,700,000,000,000,000,000,000 = 9.77 \times 10^{22}$$

For numbers greater than or equal to 10, use a positive exponent.

EXAMPLE 2 Writing Numbers in Scientific Notation

Write each number in scientific notation.

A 0.0000005

0.0000005   *Think: The decimal point needs to move 7 places to get a number between 1 and 10.*

5×10^{-7} *Think: The number is less than 1, so the exponent will be negative.*

So 0.0000005 written in scientific notation is 5×10^{-7}.

B 2,780,000,000

2,780,000,000   *Think: The decimal point needs to move 9 places to get a number between 1 and 10.*

2.78×10^{9} *Think: The number is greater than 1, so the exponent will be positive.*

So 2,780,000,000 written in scientific notation is 2.78×10^{9}.

EXAMPLE 3 Reading Numbers in Scientific Notation

Write each number in standard form.

A 3.12×10^{9}

3.12×10^{9}

3.120000000   *Think: Move the decimal point right 9 places.*

3,120,000,000

B 1.35×10^{-4}

1.35×10^{-4}

00001.35   *Think: Move the decimal point left 4 places.*

0.000135

Power Presentations with PowerPoint®

Additional Examples

Example 1

Multiply.

A. 14×10^{4} 140,000

B. 3.6×10^{-5} 0.000036

Example 2

Write each number in scientific notation.

A. 0.00709 7.09×10^{-3}

B. 23,000,000,000 2.3×10^{10}

Example 3

Write each number in standard form.

A. 1.35×10^{5} 135,000

B. 2.7×10^{-3} 0.0027

Also available on transparency

2 Teach

Guided Instruction

In this lesson, students learn to express large and small numbers in scientific notation. First, discuss how to write numbers in standard form in scientific notation. Show students how to move the decimal so there is only one digit in front of the decimal point. Then write the correct power of ten by counting the number of decimal spaces moved.

Next, show students how to convert scientific notation to standard form. Review how to multiply by a power of ten by moving the decimal point to the left or right. Move the decimal point to the right for a positive exponent and to the left for a negative exponent.

Universal Access
Through Home Connection

Have students work with an adult to find some real-world examples of very large or very small numbers. They may find these examples in newspapers, books, or magazines, or they may use an example from the adult's workplace. Have students record five numbers and write them in both standard form and scientific notation.

Check students' work.

Possible answers to
Think and Discuss

1. It makes extremely large or extremely small numbers less awkward to use.

2. The exponent is 6 and the sign of the exponent is positive, so move the decimal six places to the right.

3. The speed of a car, because it is usually a 1-, 2-, or 3-digit number.

To compare numbers written in scientific notation, first compare the exponents. If the exponents are equal, then compare the decimals.

E X A M P L E 4 **Comparing Numbers in Scientific Notation**

Mercury is 9.17×10^7 kilometers from Earth. Jupiter is 6.287×10^8 kilometers from Earth. Which planet is closer to Earth?

Mercury: 9.17×10^7 *Compare the exponents.*
Jupiter: 6.287×10^8

Notice that $7 < 8$. So $9.17 \times 10^7 < 6.287 \times 10^8$.

Mercury is closer to Earth than Jupiter.

Think and Discuss

1. Explain the benefit of writing numbers in scientific form.

2. Describe how to write 2.977×10^6 in standard form.

3. Determine which measurement would be least likely to be written in scientific notation: size of bacteria, speed of a car, or number of stars in a galaxy.

4-5 Exercises

Assignment Guide

If you finished Example 1 assign:
Proficient 1–4, 14–20 even, 73–78
Advanced 14–21, 50–52, 73–78

If you finished Example 2 assign:
Proficient 1–8, 14–24 even, 53, 55–62, 72–78
Advanced 14–25, 50–54, 63–70, 72–78

If you finished Example 3 assign:
Proficient 1–12, 14–28 even, 31–41 odd, 44–45, 53, 55–62, 71–78
Advanced 14–29, 32–42 even, 44–45, 50–54, 63–78

If you finished Example 4 assign:
Proficient 1–13, 14–30 even, 31–41 odd, 44–45, 53, 55–62, 71–78
Advanced 14–30, 32–42 even, 43–54, 63–78

Homework Quick Check

Quickly check key concepts.
Exercises: 16, 20, 22, 24, 26, 28

4-5 Exercises

GUIDED PRACTICE

See Example 1 **Multiply.**
  1. $15 \cdot 10^3$ 15,000 **2.** $12 \cdot 10^4$ 120,000 **3.** $208 \cdot 10^3$ **4.** $113 \cdot 10^7$
                                                                208,000   1,130,000,000

See Example 2 **Write each number in scientific notation.**
  5. 0.000057   **6.** 4,000   **7.** 6,980,000   **8.** 0.000000025
       5.7×10^{-5} 4×10^3 6.98×10^6 2.5×10^{-8}

See Example 3 **Write each number in standard form.**
  9. 4.17×10^3 **10.** 1.33×10^{-5} **11.** 6.2×10^7 **12.** 3.9×10^{-7}
       4170   0.0000133   62,000,000   0.00000039

See Example 4 **13.** The maximum length of a particle that can fit through a surgical mask is 1×10^{-4} millimeters. The average length of a dust mite is approximately 1.25×10^{-1} millimeters. Can a dust mite fit through a surgical mask? no

3 Close

Summarize

Discuss with students the meaning and uses of scientific notation. Ask them how many zeros are in a million dollars. Then ask how they would write one million in scientific notation. Repeat the process with one billion dollars. Challenge the class to write one cent in dollars in scientific notation.

Possible answers: Scientific notation is a way to write very large or very small numbers without including a lot of zeros. Scientific notation can make it easier to compare numbers. One million has six zeros, so it can be written as 1×10^6. One billion has nine zeros, so it can be written as 1×10^9. One cent can be written as 1×10^{-2} dollars.

See Example 1 **Multiply.**

14. $21 \cdot 10^2$ **2100** **15.** $8 \cdot 10^4$ **80,000** **16.** $25 \cdot 10^5$ **17.** $40 \cdot 10^4$ **400,000**

2,500,000

18. $268 \cdot 10^3$ **19.** $550 \cdot 10^7$ **20.** $2,115 \cdot 10^5$ **21.** $70,030 \cdot 10^1$
268,000 **5,500,000,000** **211,500,000** **700,300**

See Example 2 **Write each number in scientific notation.**

22. 0.00007 **23.** 6,500,000 **24.** 100,000,000 **25.** 0.00000587
7×10^{-5} 6.5×10^6 1×10^8 5.87×10^{-6}

See Example 3 **Write each number in standard form.**

26. 9.2×10^6 **27.** 6.7×10^{-4} **28.** 3.6×10^{-2} **29.** 5.24×10^8
9,200,000 **0.00067** **0.036** **524,000,000**

See Example 4 **30. Astronomy** The orbits of Neptune and Pluto cross each other. Neptune's average distance from the Sun is approximately 4.5×10^9 kilometers. Pluto's average distance from the Sun is approximately 5.87×10^9 kilometers. Which has the greater average distance from the Sun, Neptune or Pluto? **Pluto**

PRACTICE AND PROBLEM SOLVING

Extra Practice
See page EP8.

Write each number in standard form.

0.0000021
31. 1.4×10^5 **32.** 3.24×10^{-2} **33.** 7.8×10^1 **78** **34.** 2.1×10^{-6}
140,000 **0.0324**
35. 5.3×10^{-8} **36.** 8.456×10^{-4} **37.** 5.59×10^5 **38.** 7.1×10^3
0.000000053 **0.0008456** **559,000** **7100**
39. 7.113×10^6 **40.** 4.5×10^{-1} **41.** 2.9×10^{-4} **42.** 5.6×10^2 **560**
7,113,000 **0.45** **0.00029**

43. Life Science Duckweed plants live on the surface of calm ponds and are the smallest flowering plants in the world. They weigh about 0.00015 g.

a. Write this number in scientific notation. 1.5×10^{-4} g

b. If left unchecked, one duckweed plant, which reproduces every 30–36 hours, could produce 1×10^{30} (a nonillion) plants in four months. How much would one nonillion duckweed plants weigh?

1.5×10^{26} g
44. Life Science The diameter of a human red blood cell ranges from approximately 6×10^{-6} to 8×10^{-6} meters. Write this range in standard form. **0.000006 m to 0.000008 m**

45. History Ancient Egyptians hammered gold into sheets so thin that it took 3.67×10^5 sheets to make a pile 2.5 centimeters high. Write the number of sheets in standard form. **367,000**

46. Astronomy Mars is 7.83×10^7 kilometers from Earth. Venus is 4.14×10^7 kilometers from Earth. Which planet is closer to Earth? **Venus**

Find the missing number or numbers.

47. $24,500 = 2.45 \times 10^{\blacksquare}$ **4** **48.** $16,800 = \blacksquare \times 10^4$ **49.** $\blacksquare = 3.40 \times 10^2$ **340**
1.68
50. $280,000 = 2.8 \times 10^{\blacksquare}$ **5** **51.** $5.4 \times 10^8 = \blacksquare$ **52.** $60,000,000 = \blacksquare \times 10^{\blacksquare}$
540,000,000 **6,0;7**

53. 9.8×10^8 feet per second **53. Science** In a vacuum, light travels at a speed of about nine hundred and eighty million feet per second. Write this speed in scientific notation.

Life Science

This frog is covered with duckweed plants. Duckweed plants can grow both in sunlight and in shade and produce tiny white flowers.

REVIEW FOR MASTERY 4-5

LESSON 4-5 Review for Mastery
Scientific Notation

Standard Form	Scientific Notation	
	(1st factor is between 1 and 10,)	(2nd factor is an integer power of 10.)
430,000	4.3×10^5	positive integer for large number
0.0000057	5.7×10^{-6}	negative integer for small number

To convert from scientific notation, look at the power of 10 to tell how many places and which way to move the decimal point.

Complete to write each in standard form.

	1. 4.12×10^6	2. 3.4×10^{-5}
Is the exponent positive or negative?	positive	negative
Move the decimal point right or left? How many places?	right 6	left 5
Write the number in standard form.	4,120,000	0.000034

Write each number in standard form.

3. 8×10^5 4. 7.1×10^{-4} 5. 3.14×10^8
800,000 0.00071 314,000,000

To convert to scientific notation, determine the factor between 1 and 10. Then determine the power of 10 by counting from the decimal point in the first factor to the decimal point in the given number.

Complete to write each in scientific notation.

	6. 32,000,000	7. 0.0000000712
What is the first factor?	3.2	7.12
From its location in the first factor, which way must the decimal move to its location in the given number? How many places?	right 7	left 8
Write the number in scientific notation.	3.2×10^7	7.12×10^{-8}

Write each number in scientific notation.

8. 41,000,000 9. 0.0000000643 10. 1,370,000,000
4.1×10^7 6.43×10^{-8} 1.37×10^9

PRACTICE 4-5

LESSON 4-5 Practice B
Scientific Notation

Multiply.

1. $115.8 \cdot 10^5$ 2. $1,316 \cdot 10^2$ 3. $21.85 \cdot 10^{-4}$
11,580,000 131,600 0.002185

Write each number in scientific notation.

4. 75,000,000 5. 208 6. 907,100
7.5×10^7 2.08×10^2 9.071×10^5

7. 56 8. 0.093 9. 0.00006
5.6×10^1 9.3×10^{-2} 6.0×10^{-5}

10. 0.00852 11. 0.0505 12. 0.003007
8.52×10^{-3} 5.05×10^{-2} 3.007×10^{-3}

Write each number in standard form.

13. 2.54×10^2 14. 6.7×10^{-2} 15. 1.14×10^3 16. 3.8×10^{-1}
254 0.067 1140 0.38

17. 7.53×10^{-3} 18. 5.6×10^4 19. 9.1×10^5 20. 6.08×10^{-4}
0.00753 56,000 910,000 0.000608

21. 8.59×10^5 22. 3.331×10^6 23. 7.21×10^{-3} 24. 5.88×10^{-4}
859,000 3,331,000 0.00721 0.000588

25. Jupiter is about 778,120,000 kilometers from the Sun. Write this number in scientific notation.
7.7812×10^8

26. The *E. coli* bacterium is about 5×10^{-7} meters wide. A hair is about 1.7×10^{-5} meters wide. Which is wider, the bacterium or the hair?
the hair

Answers

54. a. $\approx 2.21 \times 10^7$; $\approx 1.4 \times 10^4$ mi^2

b. $14,032 \div 22,113,250 \approx$ 0.000635; about 6.35×10^{-4} mi^2/person

72. The decimal needs to move 13 places. The decimal will need to move right to change 2.96 to the original number so the exponent is positive. 2.96×10^{13}

Teaching Tip

Multiple Choice Encourage students to read through the choices for **Exercise 71** and eliminate answers that would be expressed with negative powers of 10. By doing so, students can eliminate choice **D**.

Journal

Have students write a story about traveling from Earth to the Moon. Have them include estimates of the distance in scientific notation and the time it would take to get there.

Power Presentations
with PowerPoint®

4-5 Lesson Quiz

Write each number in standard form.

1. 1.72×10^4 17,200

2. 6.9×10^{-3} 0.0069

Write each number in scientific notation.

3. 0.0053 5.3×10^{-3}

4. 57,000,000 5.7×10^7

5. Order the numbers from least to greatest.
$2 \times 10^{-4}, 9 \times 10^{-5}, 7 \times 10^{-5}$
$7 \times 10^{-5}, 9 \times 10^{-5}, 2 \times 10^{-4}$

6. A human body contains about 5.6×10^6 microliters of blood. Write this number in standard form. 5,600,000

Also available on transparency

---

54. **Social Studies** The diagram shows information about the country of Taiwan.

a. Express the population and area of Taiwan in scientific notation.

b. Divide the number of square miles by the population to find the number of square miles per person in Taiwan. Express your answer in scientific notation.

Taiwan
Population: 22,113,250
Area: 14,032 mi^2
Capital: Taipei
Number of televisions: 10,800,000
Languages: Taiwanese (Min), Mandarin, Hakka dialects

Write each number in scientific notation.

55. 0.00858 8.58×10^{-3}
56. 0.0000063 6.3×10^{-6}
57. 5,900,000 5.9×10^6
58. 7,045,000,000 7.045×10^9
59. 0.0076 7.6×10^{-3}
60. 400 4×10^2
61. 4200 4.2×10^3
62. 0.0000000082 8.2×10^{-9}
63. 0.0000000006 6×10^{-10}
64. 0.000005 5×10^{-6}
65. 7,000,000 7×10^6
66. 0.0095678 9.5678×10^{-3}

67. Order the list of numbers below from least to greatest.
$1.5 \times 10^{-2}, 1.2 \times 10^6, 5.85 \times 10^{-3}, 2.3 \times 10^{-2}, 5.5 \times 10^6$
$5.85 \times 10^{-3}, 1.5 \times 10^{-2}, 2.3 \times 10^{-2}, 1.2 \times 10^6, 5.5 \times 10^6$

68. **Write a Problem** An electron has a mass of about 9.11×10^{-31} kg. Use this information to write a problem. Possible answer: Write the mass of an electron in standard notation.

69. **Write About It** Two numbers are written in scientific notation. How can you tell which number is greater?

69. Possible answer: The number with the greater power of 10 is greater. If the two numbers have equal powers of 10, then the number with the greater factor is greater.

70. **Challenge** Where on a number line does the value of a number in scientific notation with a negative exponent lie? Possible answer: The number would be between 0 and 1. If the power of ten has a negative exponent, the number can be written as a fraction with a denominator that is a positive power of ten. Because the denominator will be larger than the numerator (by the rules of scientific notation), the fraction will be less than one.

SPIRAL STANDARDS REVIEW   NS1.1, NS2.3, AF1.1, AF2.2

71. **Multiple Choice** The distance light can travel in one year is 9.46×10^{12} kilometers. What is this distance in standard form?

(A) 94,600,000,000,000,000 km
(C) 9,460,000,000,000 km
(B) 946,000,000,000 km
(D) 0.000000000946 km

72. **Short Response** Explain how you can determine the sign of the exponent when 29,600,000,000,000 is written in scientific notation.

Write an inequality for each situation. (Lesson 3-5)

73. At least 35 students registered for the photography course.   number of students $\geq$ 35

74. The amount remaining in the savings account was no more than $550.   amount remaining $\leq$ $550

Simplify each expression. Write your answer in exponential form. (Lesson 4-3)

75. $\dfrac{7^4}{7^2}$ 7^2
76. $5^3 \cdot 5^8$ 5^{11}
77. $\dfrac{t^8}{t^5}$ t^3
78. $10^9 \cdot 10^{-3}$ 10^6

CHALLENGE 4-5

LESSON 4-5 Challenge
The Wild Blue Yonder

Astronomers measure distances within our solar system in *astronomical units* (AU).
1 AU $\approx$ 92,956,000 mi or 149,600,000 km
(the distance from Earth to the Sun)

Mean Distance From the Sun

Planet	km	Scientific Notation	AU
Mercury	57,900,000	5.79×10^7	0.4
Venus	108,200,000	1.082×10^8	0.7
Earth	149,600,000	1.496×10^8	1.0
Mars	227,900,000	2.279×10^8	1.5
Jupiter	778,400,000	7.784×10^8	5.2
Saturn	1,429,400,000	1.4294×10^9	9.6
Uranus	2,875,000,000	2.875×10^9	19.2
Neptune	4,504,300,000	4.5043×10^9	30.1

1. The table gives each planet's mean distance from the Sun in kilometers. Write these distances in scientific notation.

2. Convert to AUs by dividing each planet's mean distance from the Sun by 1.496×10^8. Use scientific notation. Round your answers to the nearest tenth of an AU.

Example $\dfrac{5.79 \times 10^7}{1.496 \times 10^8} = \dfrac{5.79}{1.496} \times \dfrac{10^7}{10^8} = 3.87 \times 10^{-1} = 0.387 \approx 0.4$ AU

3. Approximately how many times greater is Saturn's distance from the Sun than is Earth's? Answer to the nearest tenth.
about 9.6 times

4. Approximately how many times greater is the distance of the farthest planet in the table from the Sun than is the distance of the closest planet to the Sun? Answer to the nearest tenth.
Neptune's distance from the Sun is about 77.8 times that of Mercury.

PROBLEM SOLVING 4-5

LESSON 4-5 Problem Solving
Scientific Notation

Write the correct answer.

1. In June 2001, the Intel Corporation announced that they could produce a silicon transistor that could switch on and off 1.5 trillion times a second. Express the speed of the transistor in scientific notation.
1.5×10^{12}

2. With this transistor, computers will be able to do 1×10^9 calculations in the time it takes to blink your eye. Express the number of calculations using standard form.
1,000,000,000

3. The elements in this fast transistor are 20 nanometers long. A nanometer is one-billionth of a meter. Express the length of an element in meters using scientific notation.
2×10^{-8} m

4. The length of the elements in the transistor can also be compared to the width of a human hair. The length of an element is 2×10^{-3} times smaller than the width of a human hair. Express 2×10^{-3} in standard form.
0.002

Use the table to answer Exercises 5–9. Choose the best answer.

5. Express a light-year in miles using scientific notation.
A 58.8×10^{11} C 588×10^{10}
(B) 5.88×10^{12} D 5.88×10^{-13}

6. How many miles is it from Earth to the star Sirius?
F 4.705×10^{12} H 7.35×10^{12}
(G) 4.704×10^{13} J 7.35×10^{11}

7. How many miles is it from Earth to the star Canopus?
(A) 3.822×10^{15} C 3.822×10^{14}
B 1.230×10^{15} D 1.230×10^{14}

8. How many miles is it from Earth to the star Alpha Centauri?
(F) 2.352×10^{13} H 2.352×10^{14}
G 5.92×10^{13} J 5.92×10^{14}

Distance From Earth To Stars Light-Year = 5,880,000,000,000 mi.		
Star	Constellation	Distance (light-years)
Sirius	Canis Major	8
Canopus	Carina	650
Alpha Centauri	Centaurus	4
Vega	Lyra	23

9. How many miles is it from Earth to the star Vega?
A 6.11×10^{13} C 6.11×10^{14}
B 1.3524×10^{13} (D) 1.3524×10^{14}

Technology LAB 4-5

Multiply and Divide Numbers in Scientific Notation

Use with Lesson 4-5

California Standards

Extension of NS1.1 Read, write, and compare rational numbers in scientific notation (positive and negative powers of 10), compare rational numbers in general.

go.hrw.com
Lab Resources Online
KEYWORD: MT8CA Lab4

You can use a graphing calculator to perform operations with numbers written in scientific notation. Use the key combination [2nd] [EE ,] to enter numbers in scientific notation. On a graphing calculator, 9.5×10^{16} is displayed as 9.5E16.

Activity

Use a calculator to find $(4.8 \times 10^{12})(9.4 \times 10^9)$.

Press 4.8 [2nd] [EE ,] 12 [×] 9.4 [2nd] [EE ,] 9 [ENTER].

The calculator displays the answer 4.512E22, which is the same as 4.512×10^{22}.

```
4.8E12*9.4E9
          4.512E22
```

Think and Discuss

1. When you use the Associative and Commutative Properties to multiply 4.8×10^{12} and 9.4×10^9, you get $(4.8 \cdot 9.4)(10^{12} \cdot 10^9) = 45.12 \times 10^{21}$. Explain why this answer is different from the answer you obtained in the activity.

Try This

Use a calculator to simplify each expression.

1. $(5.76 \times 10^{13})(6.23 \times 10^{-20})$

2. $\dfrac{9.7 \times 10^{10}}{2.9 \times 10^7}$

3. $(1.6 \times 10^5)(9.65 \times 10^9)$

4. $\dfrac{5.25 \times 10^{13}}{6.14 \times 10^8}$

5. $(1.1 \times 10^9)(2.2 \times 10^3)$

6. $\dfrac{8.56 \times 10^{97}}{2.34 \times 10^{80}}$

7. $(2.74 \times 10^{11})(3.2 \times 10^{-5})$
   8.768×10^6

8. $\dfrac{5.82 \times 10^{-11}}{8.96 \times 10^{11}}$
   $\approx 6.49553571 \times 10^{-23}$

9. $(4.5 \times 10^{12})(3.7 \times 10^8)$
   1.665×10^{21}

10. The star Betelgeuse, in the constellation of Orion, is approximately 3.36×10^{15} miles from Earth. This is approximately 1.24×10^6 times as far as Pluto's minimum distance from Earth. What is Pluto's approximate minimum distance from Earth? Write your answer in scientific notation.   **approximately 2.71×10^9 mi**

11. If 446 billion telephone calls were placed by 135 million United States telephone subscribers, what was the average number of calls placed per subscriber?   **approximately 3304 calls**

Possible answers to *Think and Discuss*

1. Multiplying 4.8 and 9.4 produced an answer greater than ten, so it is not in scientific notation. In the Activity, the calculator automatically put the answer in scientific notation.

Answers to *Try This*

1. 3.5885×10^{-6}
2. ≈ 3344.83
3. 1.544×10^{15}
4. $\approx 85,504.89$
5. 2.42×10^{12}
6. $\approx 3.658 \times 10^{17}$

Technology LAB

Organizer
Use with Lesson 4-5

Objective: Use a graphing calculator to multiply and divide numbers written in scientific notation.

Materials: Graphing calculator

PREMIER
Online Edition
Scientific Calculator, TechKeys

Countdown to Mastery Week 8

Teach
Discuss

Have students perform some of the operations in the lab using standard form. Ask which notation they think is easiest when multiplying and dividing large numbers.

Close
Key Concept

You can use graphing calculators to quickly multiply or divide numbers in scientific notation.

Assessment

Use a calculator to simplify each expression.

1. $(4.5 \times 10^{12})(1.12 \times 10^9)$
   5.04×10^{21}

2. $\dfrac{9.9 \times 10^{21}}{2.25 \times 10^8}$ 4.4×10^{13}

California Standards

Ext. of Number Sense 1.1

Organizer

Objective: Assess students' mastery of concepts and skills in Lessons 4-1 through 4-5.

Resources

 Assessment Resources
Section 4A Quiz

 Test & Practice Generator
One-Stop Planner®

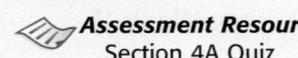

INTERVENTION ◄━━►

Resources

 Ready to Go On?
Intervention and
Enrichment Worksheets

💿 **Ready to Go On? CD-ROM**

🪐 **Ready to Go On? Online**

my.hrw.com

READY TO GO ON?

Quiz for Lessons 4-1 Through 4-5

✅ **4-1** **Exponents**

Simplify.

1. 10^1 10 **2.** 8^6 262,144 **3.** -3^4 −81 **4.** $(-5)^3$ −125

5. Write $5 \cdot 5 \cdot 5 \cdot 5$ in exponential form. 5^4 **6.** Evaluate $a^7 - 4b$ for $a = 3$ and $b = -1$.
2191

✅ **4-2** **Integer Exponents**

Simplify.

7. 10^{-6} $\frac{1}{1,000,000}$ **8.** $(-3)^{-4}$ $\frac{1}{81}$ **9.** -6^{-2} $-\frac{1}{36}$ **10.** 4^0 1

11. $8 + 10^0(-6)$ 2 **12.** $5^{-1} + 3(5)^{-2}$ $\frac{8}{25}$ **13.** $-4^{-3} + 2^0$ $\frac{63}{64}$ **14.** $3^{-2} - (6^0 - 6^{-2})$
$-\frac{31}{36}$

✅ **4-3** **Properties of Exponents**

Simplify each expression. Write your answer in exponential form.

15. $9^3 \cdot 9^5$ 9^8 **16.** $\frac{5^{10}}{5^{10}}$ 1 **17.** $q^9 \cdot q^6$ q^{15} **18.** $3^3 \cdot 3^{-2}$ 3

19. $(3^3)^{-2}$ $\frac{1}{3^6}$ **20.** $(4^2)^0$ 1 **21.** $(-x^2)^4$ x^8 **22.** $(4^{-2})^5$ $\frac{1}{4^{10}}$

23. The mass of the known universe is about 10^{23} solar masses, which is 10^{50} metric tons. How many metric tons are in one solar mass? 10^{27} **metric tons**

✅ **4-4** **Multiplying and Dividing Monomials**

Simplify each expression.

24. $(15p^2)^2$ $225p^4$ **25.** $(15m)(\frac{1}{3}m^4)$ $5m^5$ **26.** $\frac{-48x^5}{6x}$ $-8x^4$

27. $(\frac{2}{7}a^8b^3)(-56a^2b)$ **28.** $\frac{55p^4q^4}{65p^4q^4}$ $\frac{11}{13}$ **29.** $(-3m^3n)^3$ $-27m^9n^3$
$-16a^{10}b^4$

✅ **4-5** **Scientific Notation**

Write each number in scientific notation.

30. 0.00000015 **31.** 99,980,000 **32.** 0.434 **33.** 100
1.5×10^{-7} 9.998×10^7 4.34×10^{-1} 1×10^2
Write each number in standard form.

34. 1.38×10^5 **35.** 4×10^6 **36.** 1.2×10^{-3} **37.** 9.37×10^{-5}
138,000 4,000,000 0.0012 0.0000937
38. Jupiter is 6.287×10^8 kilometers from Earth. Mars is 7.83×10^7 kilometers from Earth. Which planet is farther from Earth? **Jupiter**

READY TO GO ON?

Diagnose and Prescribe

NO
INTERVENE

YES
ENRICH

	READY TO GO ON? Intervention, Section 4A			
Ready to Go On? **Intervention**	📝 **Worksheets**	💿 **CD-ROM**	🪐 **Online**	
✅ Lesson 4-1 🐻 **AF1.2, AF2.1**	4-1 Intervention	Activity 4-1		
✅ Lesson 4-2 🐻 **NS2.1, AF2.1**	4-2 Intervention	Activity 4-2	Diagnose and Prescribe Online	
✅ Lesson 4-3 🐻 **NS2.1,** 🔑 **NS2.3**	4-3 Intervention	Activity 4-3		
✅ Lesson 4-4 🐻 🔑 **AF1.3, AF2.2**	4-4 Intervention	Activity 4-4		
✅ Lesson 4-5 🐻 **NS1.1**	4-5 Intervention	Activity 4-5		

READY TO GO ON?
Enrichment, Section 4A

📝 **Worksheets**

💿 **CD-ROM**

🪐 **Online**

Focus on Problem Solving

California Standards

MR1.1 Analyze problems by identifying relationships, distinguishing relevant from irrelavant information, identifying missing information, sequencing and prioritizing information, and observing patterns.
Also covered: **NS1.1**

Solve

• Choose an operation

To decide whether to add, subtract, multiply, or divide to solve a problem, you need to identify any relationships and determine the action taking place in the problem.

Action	Operation
Combining numbers or putting numbers together	Addition
Taking away or finding out how far apart two numbers are	Subtraction
Combining equal groups	Multiplication
Splitting things into equal groups or finding how many equal groups you can make	Division

Determine the action for each problem. Write the problem using the actions. Then show what operation you used to get the answer.

1 Mary is making a string of beads. If each bead is 7.0×10^{-1} cm wide, how many beads does she need to make a string that is 35 cm long?

2 The total area of the United States is 9.63×10^6 square kilometers. The total area of Canada is 9.98×10^6 square kilometers. What is the total area of both the United States and Canada?

3 Suppose $\frac{1}{3}$ of the fish in a lake are considered game fish. Of these, $\frac{2}{5}$ meet the legal minimum size requirement. What fraction of the fish in the lake are game fish that meet the legal minimum size requirement?

4 Part of a checkbook register is shown below. Find the amount in the account after the transactions shown.

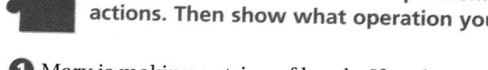

	RECORD ALL CHARGES OR CREDITS THAT AFFECT YOUR ACCOUNT						
TRANSACTION	DATE	DESCRIPTION	AMOUNT	FEE	DEPOSITS	BALANCE	$287.34
Withdrawal	11/16	autodebit for phone bill	$43.16				$43.16
Check 1256	11/18	groceries	$27.56				$27.56
Check 1257	11/23	new clothes	$74.23				$74.23
Withdrawal	11/27	ATM withdrawal	$40.00	$1.25			$41.25

Answers
1. 50
2. 1.961×10^7 km²
3. $\frac{2}{15}$
4. $101.14

Focus on Problem Solving

Organizer

Objective: Focus on choosing an operation.

 Online Edition

Resources

Chapter 4 Resource File
Reading Strategies

Problem Solving Process

This page focuses on the third step of the problem-solving process: **Solve**

Discuss

Have students discuss any relationship that exists and which action is taking place in each problem, rewrite the problem using action words, and then indicate the operation used to get the answer.

Possible answers:

1. Finding how many equal groups you can make; how many equal lengths of 0.7 cm are there in 35 cm?; division.

2. Combining numbers; what is the total area of both countries?; addition.

3. Splitting things into equal groups (multiplying by a fraction is the same as dividing); what is $\frac{1}{3}$ of $\frac{2}{5}$?; multiplication.

4. Taking away; what remains of $287.34 after $43.16, $27.56, $74.23, and $41.25 have been taken away?; subtraction.

California Standards

Mathematical Reasoning 1.1
Also covered:
Number Sense
1.1 Read, write, and compare **rational numbers in scientific notation (positive and negative powers of 10),** compare rational numbers in general.

Roots

One-Minute Section Planner

Lesson	Lab Resources	Materials
Lesson 4-6 Squares and Square Roots • Find square roots of numbers and monomials. **NS2.0, NS2.4, AF2.0, AF2.2**		**Optional** Index cards
Lesson 4-7 Estimating Square Roots • Estimate square roots of numbers. **NS2.4**	**Technology Lab 4-7** In *Chapter 4 Resource File*	**Optional** Index cards **Required** Calculators
Lesson 4-8 The Real Numbers • Determine if a number is rational or irrational. **NS1.4**	**Hands-On Lab 4-8** In *Chapter 4 Resource File*	**Optional** Calculators
4-9 Hands-On Lab Explore the Pythagorean Theorem • Use scissors and paper to explore right triangles. **MG3.3**		**Required** Scissors, straightedges (MK), paper, centimeter ruler **Optional** Graph paper
Lesson 4-9 The Pythagorean Theorem • Use the Pythagorean Theorem and its converse to solve problems. **MG3.0, MG3.3**	**Hands-On Lab 4-9** **Technology Lab 4-9** In *Chapter 4 Resource File*	**Optional** Scissors, string or cord or yarn

MK = *Manipulatives Kit*

Notes

_____

_____

_____

_____

_____

_____

_____

_____

_____

_____

Math Background: Teaching the Standards

SQUARES AND SQUARE ROOTS 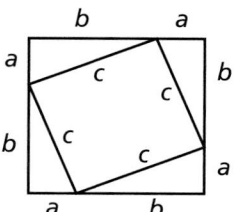 NS2.4

Lessons 4-6, 4-7

Given a square with side length x, the area of the square is x^2. Given a square with area a, the side length of the square is a *square root* of a. Given $a > 0$, if x is a solution of $x^2 = a$, then x is a square root of a. Note that this equation has two solutions that are opposites of each other. For example, $x^2 = 49$ has the solutions 7 and -7. The radical symbol $\sqrt{}$ is used to represent the nonnegative, or principal, square root. Thus, the solutions of $x^2 = a$ are $\sqrt{a}$ and $-\sqrt{a}$.

If $a > 0$, then $\sqrt{a^2} = a$. If $a < 0$, then $\sqrt{a^2} = -a$ because the principal square root must be nonnegative. In general, $\sqrt{a^2} = |a|$.

IRRATIONAL NUMBERS NS1.4

Lesson 4-8

Working with square roots gives students exposure to irrational numbers. The decimal form of an *irrational number* neither terminates nor repeats.

If a positive integer is not a perfect square, then its square root is irrational. For example, $\sqrt{2}$ is irrational. A calculator will give a decimal representation of $\sqrt{2}$ that exhibits no repeating digits, but students should realize that this does not constitute a proof that $\sqrt{2}$ is irrational. (A repeating pattern of digits might be apparent only after the fiftieth decimal place!) The essential idea for students at this level is that there are vast quantities of irrational numbers and that specific examples can be generated using the technique described in the Math Background notes for Section 2A.

THE PYTHAGOREAN THEOREM MG3.3

Lesson 4-9

For most students, the Pythagorean Theorem is the first real theorem that they will see. A *theorem* is a mathematical statement that can be proved. Although students should not be expected to prove the Pythagorean Theorem, the following geometric proof is straightforward and may be of interest to advanced students.

Given a right triangle with legs of length a and b and hypotenuse c, draw a square with sides of length $a + b$ as shown.

The area of the large square is $(a + b)^2$. The Area Addition Postulate states that the area of a region is equal to the sum of the areas of its nonoverlapping parts, so the area of the large square is also equal to the area of the four triangles plus the area of the interior rhombus, $4 \cdot \frac{1}{2} ab + c^2$. (This rhombus can be shown to be a square by noting that along each side of the larger square, the measures of the three angles formed with the vertex of the rhombus must have a sum of 180°. The measures of the other two angles must have a sum of 90° since they are the two acute angles in a right triangle. Therefore, the angle of the rhombus measures 90°.) Now set the two area expressions equal and simplify.

$$(a + b)^2 = 4 \cdot \tfrac{1}{2} ab + c^2$$
$$a^2 + 2ab + b^2 = 2ab + c^2$$
$$a^2 + b^2 = c^2$$

Given a mathematical statement in the form *If p, then q*, the *converse* of the statement is *If q, then p*. In general, a true statement need not have a true converse. Consider this statement: If a natural number is divisible by 10, then it is even. The statement is true, but its converse—If a natural number is even, then it is divisible by 10—is false.

The converse of the Pythagorean Theorem *is* true: if a triangle has sides of length a, b, and c such that $a^2 + b^2 = c^2$, then the triangle is a right triangle. Again, students should not be expected to prove this, but they should recognize that the Pythagorean Theorem works "in both directions" and recognize when they are using the theorem and when they are using the converse.

Objective: Students find square roots of numbers and monomials.

Online Edition
Tutorial Videos, Interactivities

Countdown to Mastery Week 8

Power Presentations
with PowerPoint®

Warm Up

Simplify.

1. 5^2 25   **2.** 8^2 64
3. 12^2 144   **4.** 15^2 225
5. 20^2 400

Also available on transparency

Math Humor

Why wouldn't the tree fit in the round pot? It had square roots!

California Standards

Number Sense 2.4
Also covered:
Number Sense
2.0 Students use exponents, powers, and **roots** and use exponents in working with fractions.
Algebra and Functions
2.0 Students interpret and evaluate expressions involving integer powers and **simple roots**.
Algebra and Functions
2.2 Multiply and divide monomials; **extend the process of taking powers and extracting roots to monomials when the latter results in a monomial with an integer exponent.**

4-6 Squares and Square Roots

California Standards

NS2.4 Use the inverse relationship between raising to a power and extracting the root of a perfect square integer; for an integer that is not square, determine without a calculator the two integers between which its square root lies and explain why.
Also covered: **AF2.2**

Why learn this? When you know the area of a square, you can use square roots to find the length of the square's sides. (See Example 2.)

Because the area of a square can be expressed using an exponent of 2, a number with an exponent of 2 is said to be *squared*. You read 3^2 as "three squared."

3

3
Area = 3^2

The **square root** of a number is one of the two equal factors of that number. Squaring a nonnegative number and finding the square root of that number are inverse operations.

Vocabulary
square root
principal square root
perfect square

Positive real numbers have two square roots, one positive and one negative. The positive square root, or **principal square root**, is represented by $\sqrt{}$. The negative square root is represented by $-\sqrt{}$.

$$4 \cdot 4 = 4^2 = 16 \longrightarrow \sqrt{16} = 4 \longleftarrow \text{Positive square root of 16}$$

$$(-4)(-4) = (-4)^2 = 16 \longrightarrow -\sqrt{16} = -4 \longleftarrow \text{Negative square root of 16}$$

A **perfect square** is a number whose square roots are integers. Some examples of perfect squares are shown in the table.

0	1	4	9	16	25	36	49	64	81	100
0^2	1^2	2^2	3^2	4^2	5^2	6^2	7^2	8^2	9^2	10^2

EXAMPLE **1** **Finding the Positive and Negative Square Roots of a Number**

Find the two square roots of each number.

Writing Math
You can write the square roots of 81 as ± 9, which is read as "plus or minus nine."

A 81
$\sqrt{81} = 9$ *9 is a square root, since 9 · 9 = 81.*
$-\sqrt{81} = -9$ *−9 is also a square root, since −9 · (−9) = 81.*
The square roots of 81 are 9 and −9, or ±9.

B 1
$\sqrt{1} = 1$ *1 is a square root, since 1 · 1 = 1.*
$-\sqrt{1} = -1$ *−1 is also a square root, since −1 · (−1) = 1.*
The square roots of 1 are 1 and −1, or ±1.

---

1 ## Introduce
Alternate Opener

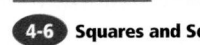

EXPLORATION

4-6 **Squares and Square Roots**

The sequence shows the square numbers 1, 4, 9, and 16.

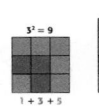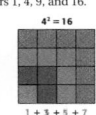

$1^2 = 1$ $2^2 = 4$ $3^2 = 9$ $4^2 = 16$

1   1 + 3   1 + 3 + 5   1 + 3 + 5 + 7

1. Draw a picture to show that $5^2 = 1 + 3 + 5 + 7 + 9$.
2. Add the odd numbers $1 + 3 + 5 + 7 + 9 + \cdots + 17 + 19$. What square number do you get?
3. The table starts with $11^2 = 1 + 3 + 5 + 7 + 9 + 11 + 13 + 15 + 17 + 19 + 21 = 121$. Complete the table by adding the next odd number to this sum.

11^2	12^2	13^2	14^2	15^2	16^2	17^2	18^2	19^2	20^2
121									

Think and Discuss

4. **Explain** how you can determine square numbers using sums of odd numbers.
5. **Demonstrate** that the value of 22^2 can be determined by adding odd numbers.

Motivate

Ask students to explain how addition and subtraction are related to each other. Then have students explain how multiplication and division are related to each other. In each case, they are inverses; one undoes the other. Remind students that when raising a number to an exponent, the exponent tells how many times to use the base as a factor. To square a number means to raise the number to the second power. Just as you can square a number, you can use an inverse process to undo the square. This is known as finding the square root of the number.

Explorations and answers are provided in *Alternate Openers: Explorations Transparencies*.

EXAMPLE 2 *Computer Application*

The square computer icon contains 625 pixels. How many pixels tall is the icon?

Find the square root of 625 to find the length of the side. Use the principal square root; a negative length has no meaning.

$$25^2 = 625$$

So $\sqrt{625} = 25$.

The icon is 25 pixels tall.

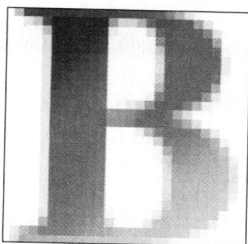

The square computer icon contains 625 colored dots that make up the picture. These dots are called *pixels*.

The symbol $\sqrt{}$ is also used with algebraic expressions. Remember that $\sqrt{}$ represents the nonnegative square root. When you simplify, use absolute value to be sure your answer is not negative. For example, to simplify $\sqrt{x^2}$, write $\sqrt{x^2} = |x|$, since you do not know whether x is positive or negative.

EXAMPLE 3 Finding the Square Root of a Monomial

Simplify each expression.

A $\sqrt{9x^2}$

$\sqrt{9x^2} = \sqrt{(3x)^2}$ *Write the monomial as a square.*

$= 3|x|$ *Use the absolute-value symbol.*

B $\sqrt{m^{10}}$

$\sqrt{m^{10}} = \sqrt{(m^5)^2}$ *Write the monomial as a square: $m^{10} = (m^5)^2$.*

$= |m^5|$ *Use the absolute-value symbol.*

C $\sqrt{36y^4}$

$\sqrt{36y^4} = \sqrt{(6y^2)^2}$ *Write the monomial as a square.*

$= 6y^2$ *$6y^2$ is nonnegative for all values of y. The absolute-value symbol is not needed.*

Helpful Hint

A variable raised to an even power is nonnegative for all values of the variable.

Think and Discuss

1. **Describe** what is meant by a perfect square. Give an example.

2. **Explain** how many square roots a positive number can have. How are these square roots different?

3. **Decide** how many square roots 0 has. Explain whether you can find the square roots of negative numbers.

---

2 Teach

Guided Instruction

In this lesson, students learn to find square roots. Remind students that they are familiar with inverse operations, such as addition and subtraction. Tell students that they will learn about another pair of inverse operations: squaring and finding a square root. Explain that 4 and -4 are the two square roots of 16 because $4^2 = 16$ and $(-4)^2 = 16$. Discuss the fact that the $\sqrt{}$ symbol indicates *principal square root,* which is always either positive or 0. Emphasize that the opposite of a square root is a real number, but that a negative number has no real square roots. For example, $-\sqrt{49} = -7$, but $\sqrt{-49}$ is not a real number.

Universal Access
Through Cooperative Learning

Give each group of students 11 index cards and have them write the integers from -5 to 5 on the cards, one integer per card. Give the class problems involving square roots that have those integers as answers. For example, some questions could be as follows:

• Find $\sqrt{9} + 1$.   4

• Find $-\sqrt{25}$. -5

• Find a square root of 1. ± 1

• What number has exactly one square root?   0

Have groups solve each problem and hold up the card with the correct answer.

3 Close

Summarize

Remind students that every positive number has two square roots, one positive and one negative. The statement that gives the positive, or principal, square root of 9 is $\sqrt{9} = 3$. The statement that gives the negative square root of 9 is $-\sqrt{9} = -3$. Remind students that the square root of a negative number is not a real number. Ask students to help you create a list of the first 15 perfect squares.

1, 4, 9, 16, 25, 36, 49, 64, 81, 100, 121, 144, 169, 196, and 225

4-6 Exercises

California Standards Practice
NS2.4, AF2.2

go.hrw.com
Homework Help Online
KEYWORD: MT8CA 4-6
Parent Resources Online
KEYWORD: MT8CA Parent

Assignment Guide

If you finished Example **1** assign:
Proficient 1–4, 10–13, 19–25 odd,
  38–39, 49, 51–57
Advanced 10–13, 20–26 even,
  40–41, 46–49, 51–57

If you finished Example **2** assign:
Proficient 1–5, 10–14, 19–29 odd,
  38–39, 42–44, 49–57
Advanced 10–14, 20–28 even,
  40–41, 43–44, 46–57

If you finished Example **3** assign:
Proficient 1–18, 19–37 odd, 38–39,
  42–44, 49–57
Advanced 10–18, 20–36 even,
  40–41, 43–57

Homework Quick Check

Quickly check key concepts.
Exercises: 10, 12, 14, 16, 18

Math Background

By agreement among mathematicians, the $\sqrt{\ }$ symbol means *principal* square root, which is nonnegative. Therefore, $\sqrt{36}$ represents just one number, 6. The expression $\pm\sqrt{36}$ represents both square roots of 36.

An important property of square roots is used in **Exercises 38–41.**

Property	Example
$\sqrt{\dfrac{a}{b}} = \dfrac{\sqrt{a}}{\sqrt{b}}, b \neq 0$	$\sqrt{\dfrac{1}{4}} = \dfrac{\sqrt{1}}{\sqrt{4}} = \dfrac{1}{2}$

In the property, a and b represent non-negative real numbers.

GUIDED PRACTICE

See Example **1** **Find the two square roots of each number.**

1. 4 ± 2 **2.** 64 ± 8 **3.** 121 ± 11 **4.** 484 ± 22

See Example **2** **5.** A square court for playing the game four square has an area of 256 ft². How long is one side of the court? **16 ft**

See Example **3** **Simplify each expression.**

6. $\sqrt{4x^2}$ $2|x|$ **7.** $\sqrt{y^6}$ $|y^3|$ **8.** $\sqrt{25n^4}$ $5n^2$ **9.** $\sqrt{49a^8}$ $7a^4$

INDEPENDENT PRACTICE

See Example **1** **Find the two square roots of each number.**

10. 25 ± 5 **11.** 169 ± 13 **12.** 400 ± 20 **13.** 361 ± 19

See Example **2** **14.** Elisa found a square digital image of a famous painting on a Web site. The image contained 256 pixels. How many pixels high is the image? **16 pixels**

See Example **3** **Simplify each expression.**

15. $\sqrt{s^6}$ $|s^3|$ **16.** $\sqrt{100m^2}$ $10|m|$ **17.** $\sqrt{36x^8}$ $6x^4$ **18.** $\sqrt{81y^{12}}$ $9y^6$

PRACTICE AND PROBLEM SOLVING

Extra Practice
See page EP9.

Find the two square roots of each number.

19. 36 ± 6 **20.** 196 ± 14 **21.** 225 ± 15 **22.** 625 ± 25

23. 441 ± 21 **24.** 289 ± 17 **25.** 576 ± 24 **26.** 324 ± 18

27. Possible answer: No, 68.06 ft² is approximately 64 ft². $\sqrt{64}$ is 8, so a better estimate would be 8 ft.

28. The first window is larger. Its sides are 12 in. long and the sides of the second window are 11 in. long.

27. Estimation Mr. Barada bought a square rug. The area of the rug was about 68.06 ft². He estimated that the length of a side was about 7 ft. Is Mr. Barada's estimate reasonable? Explain.

28. Art An artist is making two square stained-glass windows. The first window has a perimeter of 48 inches. The second window has an area of 121 inches. Which window is bigger? Explain.

29. Sports A karate match is held on a square mat that has an area of 676 ft². What is the perimeter of the mat? **104 ft**

Simplify each expression.

30. $\sqrt{9a^{10}}$ $3|a^5|$ **31.** $\sqrt{64x^{16}}$ $8x^8$ **32.** $\sqrt{121n^{20}}$ $11n^{10}$ **33.** $\sqrt{16y^{14}}$ $4|y^7|$

34. $\sqrt{m^2n^6}$ $|mn^3|$ **35.** $\sqrt{a^4b^6}$ $a^2|b^3|$ **36.** $\sqrt{225x^{18}y^{22}}$ $15|x^9y^{11}|$ **37.** $\sqrt{169p^{30}q^{24}}$ $13|p^{15}|q^{12}$

Find the two square roots of each number.

38. $\dfrac{1}{121}$ $\pm\dfrac{1}{11}$ **39.** $\dfrac{81}{16}$ $\pm\dfrac{9}{4}$ **40.** $\dfrac{324}{81}$ ± 2 **41.** $\dfrac{169}{676}$ $\pm\dfrac{1}{2}$

California Standards

Standard	Exercises
NS1.1	55–60
NS1.5 🔑	51–54
NS2.4	1–50
AF2.2	6–9, 15–18, 30–37, 45

REVIEW FOR MASTERY 4-6

LESSON 4-6 Review for Mastery
Squares and Square Roots

A perfect square has two identical factors.
$25 = 5 \times 5 = 5^2$ or $25 = (-5) \times (-5) = (-5)^2$ 25 is a perfect square.

Tell if the number is a perfect square. If yes, write its identical factors.

1. 121 11^2 or $(-11)^2$ **2.** 200 not a perfect square

3. 400 20^2 or $(-20)^2$

Since $5^2 = 25$ and also $(-5)^2 = 25$, both 5 and -5 are **square roots** of 25. $\sqrt{25} = 5$ and $-\sqrt{25} = -5$

The **principal square root** of 25 is 5: $\sqrt{25} = 5$

Write the two square roots of each number.

4. $\sqrt{81} = 9$ **5.** $\sqrt{625} = 25$ **6.** $\sqrt{169} = 13$
$-\sqrt{81} = -9$ $-\sqrt{625} = -25$ $-\sqrt{169} = -13$

Write the principal square root of each number.

7. $\sqrt{144} = 12$ **8.** $\sqrt{6400} = 80$ **9.** $\sqrt{10,000} = 100$

Use the principal square root when evaluating an expression. For the order of operations, do square root first, as you would an exponent.
$5\sqrt{100} - 3$
$5(10) - 3$
$50 - 3$
47

Simplify each expression.

10. $\sqrt{196a^{12}}$ **11.** $\sqrt{100h^{10}}$ **12.** $\sqrt{36s^{16}}$
$14a^6$ $|10h^5|$ $3s^8$

PRACTICE 4-6

LESSON 4-6 Practice B
Squares and Square Roots

Find the two square roots of each number.

1. 36   **2.** 81   **3.** 49   **4.** 100
6, −6   9, −9   7, −7   10, −10

5. 64   **6.** 121   **7.** 25   **8.** 144
8, −8   11, −11   5, −5   12, −12

Simplify each expression.

9. $\sqrt{81m^{10}}$ **10.** $\sqrt{121d^{16}}$ **11.** $\sqrt{49k^6}$ **12.** $\sqrt{9r^8}$
$|9m^5|$ $11d^8$ $|7k^3|$ $3r^4$

13. $\sqrt{144s^{12}}$ **14.** $\sqrt{100p^4}$ **15.** $\sqrt{y^{22}}$ **16.** $\sqrt{r^{36}}$
$12s^6$ $10p^2$ $|y^{11}|$ r^{18}

17. $\sqrt{169s^{18}}$ **18.** $\sqrt{144t^{14}}$ **19.** $\sqrt{36n^6}$ **20.** $\sqrt{49h^{14}}$
$13s^9$ $|12t^7|$ $|6n^3|$ $|7h^7|$

The Pyramids of Egypt are often called the first wonder of the world. This group of pyramids consists of Menkaura, Khufu, and Khafra. The largest of these is Khufu, sometimes called Cheops. During this time in history, each monarch had his own pyramid built to bury his mummified body. Cheops was a king of Egypt in the early 26th century B.C. His pyramid's original height is estimated to have been 482 ft. It is now approximately 450 ft. The estimated completion date of this structure was 2660 B.C.

21. If the area of the base of Cheops' pyramid is 570,025 ft², what is the length of one of the sides of the ancient structure? (Hint: $s = \sqrt{A}$)
755 ft

22. If a replica of the pyramid were built with a base area of 625 in², what would be the length of each side? (Hint: $s = \sqrt{A}$)
25 in.

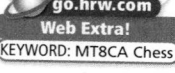
42. Architecture Mr. and Mrs. Garner want to build a house with a square foundation. They want the house to cover 225 square yards. How long should each side of the house be? **15 yd**

43. Games A chessboard contains 32 black and 32 white squares. How many squares are along each side of the game board? **8**

44. Hobbies A quilter wants to use as many of his 65 small fabric squares as possible to make one large square quilt.

  a. How many small squares can the quilter use? How many small squares would he have left? **64; 1**

  b. How many more small squares would the quilter need to make the next largest possible square quilt? **16**

45. Reasoning Simplify the expressions $\sqrt{x^2}$, $\sqrt{x^4}$, $\sqrt{x^6}$, $\sqrt{x^8}$, $\sqrt{x^{10}}$, and $\sqrt{x^{12}}$. Look for a pattern. Make a conjecture about when you do not need to use an absolute value in your answer.

46. What's the Error? A student said that since the square roots of a certain number are 1.5 and -1.5, the number must be their product, -2.25. What error did the student make?

45. $\sqrt{x^2} = |x|$; $\sqrt{x^4} = x^2$; $\sqrt{x^6} = |x^3|$; $\sqrt{x^8} = x^4$; $\sqrt{x^{10}} = |x^5|$; $\sqrt{x^{12}} = x^6$; absolute value is not needed when the original power of x is a multiple of 4.

47. Write About It Explain the difference between finding the square of a number and finding the square root of a number. Use models and numbers in your explanation.

48. Challenge The square root of a number is four less than three times seven. What is the number? **289**

SPIRAL STANDARDS REVIEW
NS1.1, ← NS1.5, NS2.4

49. Multiple Choice Which number does NOT have a square root that is an integer?

Ⓐ 81   Ⓑ 196   Ⓒ 288   Ⓓ 400

50. Short Response Deanna knows that the floor in her kitchen is a square with an area of 169 square feet. The perimeter of her kitchen floor is found by adding the lengths of all its sides. What is the perimeter of her kitchen floor? Explain your answer. **52 feet; the positive square root of 169 is 13, so each side is 13 feet. 13 feet × 4 = 52 feet.**

Write each decimal as a fraction in simplest form. (Lesson 2-1)

51. 0.35 $\frac{7}{20}$ **52.** 2.6 $2\frac{3}{5}$ **53.** -7.18 $-7\frac{9}{50}$ **54.** 0.125 $\frac{1}{8}$

Write each number in scientific notation. (Lesson 4-5)

55. 1,970,000,000 1.97×10^9 **56.** 2,500,000 2.5×10^6 **57.** 31,400,000,000 3.14×10^{10}

58. 0.0000543 5.43×10^{-5} **59.** 0.006 6×10^{-3} **60.** 0.000000088 8.8×10^{-8}

CHALLENGE 4-6

LESSON **4-6** Challenge
Dig It!

Find the **digital root** of a number by adding its digits, adding the digits of the result, and so on, until the result is a single digit.

$358 \rightarrow 3 + 5 + 8 = 16 \rightarrow 1 + 6 = 7$ The digital root of 358 is 7.

1. Complete the table to find the digital roots of the squares of 1–17.

Number	Square	Digital Root Calculation	
1	1		= 1
2	4		= 4
3	9		= 9
4	16	1 + 6	= 7
5	25	2 + 5	= 7
6	36	3 + 6 = 9	= 9
7	49	4 + 9 = 13 → 1 + 3	= 4
8	64	6 + 4 = 10 → 1 + 0	= 1
9	81	8 + 1	= 9
10	100	1 + 0 + 0	= 1
11	121	1 + 2 + 1	= 4
12	144	1 + 4 + 4	= 9
13	169	1 + 6 + 9 = 16 → 1 + 6	= 7
14	196	1 + 9 + 6 = 16 → 1 + 6	= 7
15	225	2 + 2 + 5	= 9
16	256	2 + 5 + 6 = 13 → 1 + 3	= 4
17	289	2 + 8 + 9 = 19 → 1 + 9 = 10 → 1 + 0	= 1

2. Make an observation about the results. Possible answers:
The only results are 1, 4, 7, or 9.

3. Make a conjecture about the digital root of any whole-number perfect square. Verify your conjecture by using at least three more perfect squares.
The result is one of the numbers 1, 4, 7, or 9. Choices vary.

4. A **palindrome** is a number that is the same when read forward or backward, such as 14741. Find two palindromes in the table.
The digital roots of the squares of the numbers 1–8 and then 10–17.

PROBLEM SOLVING 4-6

LESSON **4-6** Problem Solving
Squares and Square Roots

Write the correct answer.

1. For college wrestling competitions, the NCAA requires that the wrestling mat be a square with an area of 1764 square feet. What is the length of each side of the wrestling mat?
42 feet

2. For high school wrestling competitions, the wrestling mat must be a square with an area of 1444 square feet. What is the length of each side of the wrestling mat?
38 feet

3. The Japanese art of origami requires folding square pieces of paper. Elena begins with a large sheet of square paper that is 169 square inches. How many squares can she cut out of the paper that are 4 inches on each side?
9 squares

4. When the James family moved into a new house they had a square area rug that was 132 square feet. In their new house, there are three bedrooms. Bedroom one is 11 feet by 11 feet. Bedroom two is 10 feet by 12 feet and bedroom three is 13 feet by 13 feet. In which bedroom will the rug fit?
Bedroom three

Choose the letter for the best answer.

5. A square picture frame measures 36 inches on each side. The actual wood trim is 2 inches wide. The photograph in the frame is surrounded by a bronze mat that measures 5 inches. What is the maximum area of the photograph?
A 841 sq. inches   B 900 sq. inches
C 1156 sq. inches   D 484 sq. inches

6. To create a square patchwork quilt wall hanging, square pieces of material are sewn together to form a larger square. Which number of smaller squares can be used to create a square patchwork quilt wall hanging?
F 35 squares   G 64 squares
H 84 squares   J 125 squares

7. A can of paint claims that one can will cover 400 square feet. If you painted a square with the can of paint, how long would be each side?
A 200 feet   B 65 feet
C 25 feet   D 20 feet

8. A box of tile contains 12 square tiles. If you tile the largest possible square area using whole tiles, how many tiles will you have left from the box?
F 9   G 6
H 3   J 0

Answers

46. Possible answer: The student multiplied the two square roots together instead of squaring one of them. The number should be 1.5^2 or $(-1.5)^2$, which equal 2.25.

47. Possible answer: Multiply that number by itself. So the square of 6 is $6 \cdot 6 = 36$. To find the square root of a number, you find the number that, when multiplied by itself, equals the first number. So $\sqrt{81}$ is 9 because $9 \cdot 9 = 81$.

Teaching Tip **Short Response** Students who have trouble with **Exercise 50** may benefit from a visual reference. Use a diagram to show students how to calculate area and perimeter. Remind them to discount negative answers since they do not make sense in this context.

 **Journal**

Ask students to list as many perfect squares as they can remember from the lesson.

Power Presentations with PowerPoint®

✓ **4-6 Lesson Quiz**

Find the two square roots of each number.

1. 144 ± 12

2. 2500 ± 50

Simplify each expression.

3. $\sqrt{49p^6}$ $7|p^3|$

4. $\sqrt{z^8}$ z^4

5. Ms. Estefan wants to put a fence around 3 sides of a square garden that has an area of 225 ft². How much fencing does she need? 45 ft

Also available on transparency

Objective: Students estimate square roots of numbers.

 Technology Lab
In *Chapter 4 Resource File*

 Online Edition
Tutorial Videos

 Countdown to Mastery Week 8

Power Presentations
with PowerPoint®

Warm Up

Find the two square roots of each number.

1. 144 ±12 **2.** 256 ±16

Simplify each expression.

3. $8 + \sqrt{144}$ 20 **4.** $7\sqrt{289}$ 119

Also available on transparency

Math Humor

The sum of any number of consecutive odd whole numbers, beginning with 1, is a perfect square (e.g., 1 + 3 = 4, 1 + 3 + 5 = 9, 1 + 3 + 5 + 7 = 16, etc.).

 California Standards

NS2.4 Use the inverse relationship between raising to a power and extracting the root of a perfect square integer; **for an integer that is not square, determine without a calculator the two integers between which its square root lies and explain why.**

Why learn this? By estimating square roots, you can determine approximately how much trim is needed for a square window. (See Exercise 39.)

Recall that a perfect square is a number whose square roots are integers. For example, 25 and 100 are perfect squares.

You can use the square roots of perfect squares to estimate the square roots of other numbers.

EXAMPLE 1 Estimating Square Roots of Numbers

The $\sqrt{30}$ is between two integers. Name the integers. Explain your answer.

$\sqrt{30}$

16, 25, 36, 49 *List perfect squares near 30.*

25 < 30 < 36 *Find the perfect squares nearest 30.*

$\sqrt{25} < \sqrt{30} < \sqrt{36}$ *Find the square roots of the perfect squares.*

5   $< \sqrt{30} < 6$

$\sqrt{30}$ is between 5 and 6 because 30 is between 25 and 36.

EXAMPLE 2 *Recreation Application*

While searching for a lost hiker, a helicopter covers a square area of 150 mi². What is the approximate length of each side of the square area? Round your answer to the nearest mile.

121, 144, 169, 196 *List perfect squares near 150.*

144   < 150   < 169 *Find the perfect squares nearest 150.*

$\sqrt{144} < \sqrt{150} < \sqrt{169}$ *Find the square roots of the perfect squares.*

12   $< \sqrt{150} < 13$

$\sqrt{150} \approx 12$ *150 is closer to 144 than 169, so $\sqrt{150}$ is closer to 12 than 13.*

Each side of the area is about 12 miles long.

1 Introduce

 Alternate Opener

EXPLORATION

4-7 Estimating Square Roots

Knowing the square numbers can help you estimate square roots.

1. Complete the table of squares.

1²	2²	3²	4²	5²	6²	7²	8²	9²	10²
1									

11²	12²	13²	14²	15²	16²	17²	18²	19²	20²
121									

Use the table of squares above to help you estimate each square root to the nearest tenth. Use a calculator to check your estimates. Round to two decimal places.

	Square Root	Estimate	Calculator
2.	$\sqrt{10}$		
3.	$\sqrt{20}$		
4.	$\sqrt{200}$		
5.	$\sqrt{300}$		
6.	$\sqrt{57}$		
7.	$\sqrt{130}$		

Think and Discuss
8. Discuss your strategy for estimating square roots.

Motivate

Ask students to find $\sqrt{4}$ and $\sqrt{9}$. Show the number line diagram:

$\sqrt{4}\ \sqrt{5}$ $\sqrt{8}\ \sqrt{9}$

2 2.24   2.83 3

Ask students where they think $\sqrt{8}$ should be placed on the diagram. If they say "between 2 and 3," ask whether it should be closer to 2 or to 3. Then use a calculator to find the approximation $\sqrt{8} \approx 2.83$. Try the same process with $\sqrt{5}$ (≈ 2.24).

Explorations and answers are provided in *Alternate Openers: Explorations Transparencies.*

 **California Standards**

Number Sense 2.4

You can use the square roots of perfect squares to approximate the square root of a value that is not a perfect square.

 EXAMPLE 3 Approximating Square Roots to the Nearest Hundredth

Approximate $\sqrt{200}$ to the nearest hundredth.

Step 1: Find the value of the whole number.

$196 < 200 < 225$ *Find the perfect squares nearest 200.*
$\sqrt{196} < \sqrt{200} < \sqrt{225}$ *Find the square roots of the perfect squares.*
$14 < \sqrt{200} < 15$ *The number will be between 14 and 15.*

The whole number part of the answer is 14.

Step 2: Find the value of the decimal.

$200 - 196 = 4$ *Find the difference between the given number, 200, and the lower perfect square.*
$225 - 196 = 29$ *Find the difference between the greater perfect square and the lower perfect square.*
$\dfrac{4}{29}$ *Write the difference as a ratio.*
$4 \div 29 \approx 0.137$ *Divide to find the approximate decimal value.*

Step 3: Find the approximate value.

$14 + 0.137 = 14.137$ *Combine the whole number and decimal.*
$14.137 \approx 14.14$ *Round to the nearest hundredth.*

The approximate value of $\sqrt{200}$ to the nearest hundredth is 14.14.

You can also use a calculator to approximate the square root of a value that is not a perfect square.

 EXAMPLE 4 Using a Calculator to Estimate the Value of a Square Root

Use a calculator to find $\sqrt{700}$. Round to the nearest tenth.
$\sqrt{700} \approx 26.45751311$ *Use a calculator.*
$\sqrt{700} \approx 26.5$ *Round to the nearest tenth.*

$\sqrt{700}$ rounded to the nearest tenth is 26.5.

Think and Discuss

1. Discuss whether 9.5 is a good first guess for $\sqrt{75}$.

2. Determine which square root or roots would have 7.5 as a good first guess.

Possible answers to Think and Discuss

1. No; $9^2 = 81$, so $\sqrt{75}$ must be less than 9; 8.5 is a better first guess.

2. Two good choices would be $\sqrt{56}$ and $\sqrt{57}$. $7^2 = 49$ and $8^2 = 64$, so a number that has a square root close to 7.5 is about halfway between 49 and 64. In fact, $7.5^2 = 56.25$.

2 Teach

Guided Instruction

In this lesson, students learn to estimate square roots to a given number of decimal places and solve problems using square roots. Tell students that all positive numbers have square roots, but most of those square roots are not integers. If students have calculators, you may want to ask them to enter $\sqrt{7}$ to see an example. Discuss with students how to identify the two integers that a given square root is between. Show students how to get an approximation of a square root to the nearest tenth.

 **Universal Access**
Through Concrete Manipulatives

Place papers showing the integers 1 to 10 (one per sheet) around the room in order. Give each student a card showing the square root of a positive number between 1 and 100, such as $\sqrt{28}$. Have each student place his or her card between the appropriate pair of integers. For example, $\sqrt{28}$ should be placed between 5 and 6. Continue until all the cards are placed. Then have the class determine if all the placements are correct.

3 Close

Summarize

Remind students that sometimes it is sufficient to approximate a square root by naming the two integers it is between. At other times, they may need to approximate a square root to a given number of decimal places. Emphasize the value of knowing at least the first ten perfect squares: 1, 4, 9, 16, 25, 36, 49, 64, 81, and 100.

Before students begin the Exercises, you may want to clarify the procedure for solving multi-step problems that involve rounding. Answers are given in the most accurate form with rounding as the final step.

4-7 **Exercises**

California Standards Practice
NS2.4

go.hrw.com
Homework Help Online
KEYWORD: MT8CA 4-7
Parent Resources Online
KEYWORD: MT8CA Parent

Assignment Guide

If you finished Example **1** assign:
Proficient 1–5, 17–21, 48–49, 55, 57–64
Advanced 17–21, 33–38, 55, 57–64

If you finished Example **2** assign:
Proficient 1–6, 17–22, 47–50, 55, 57–64
Advanced 17–22, 33–38, 47, 50, 52–53, 55, 57–64

If you finished Example **3** assign:
Proficient 1–11, 17–25, 39, 41–43, 47–50, 55–64
Advanced 17–27, 33–40, 44–47, 50, 51–53, 55–64

If you finished Example **4** assign:
Proficient 1–25, 28–32, 39, 41–43, 47–50, 52, 55–64
Advanced 17–40, 44–47, 50–64

Homework Quick Check

Quickly check key concepts.
Exercises: 18, 20, 22, 24, 32

Answers

1–4, 17–20. See p. A2.

Math Background

In this lesson, students estimate square roots. A reliable method for estimating square roots involves repeated division. For example, to find $\sqrt{28}$, choose the integer whose perfect square is closest to 28 ($5^2 = 25$).

Divide 28 by that integer: $5\overline{)28.0}$ (quotient 5.6).

Find the average of the quotient and the divisor: $(5 + 5.6) \div 2 = 5.3$.

Check the result: $5.3^2 = 28.09$.

You can then repeat the process with your new estimate and continue repeating the algorithm until your estimate has the desired accuracy.

California Standards

Standard	Exercises
NS2.4	1–56
AF1.2	57–60

GUIDED PRACTICE

See Example **1** Each square root is between two integers. Name the integers. Explain your answer.
1. $\sqrt{40}$ 2. $\sqrt{90}$ 3. $\sqrt{156}$ 4. $\sqrt{306}$ 5. $\sqrt{250}$
5. 15 and 16; possible answer: 250 is between 225 and 256.

See Example **2** 6. A Coast Guard ship patrols an area of 125 square miles. The area the ship patrols is a square. About how long is each side of the square?   11 mi

See Example **3** Approximate each square root to the nearest hundredth.
7. $\sqrt{42}$ 6.48   8. $\sqrt{73}$ 8.54   9. $\sqrt{156}$ 12.49 10. $\sqrt{236}$ 15.36 11. $\sqrt{275}$ 16.58

See Example **4** Use a calculator to find each value. Round to the nearest tenth.
12. $\sqrt{74}$ 8.6   13. $\sqrt{34.1}$ 5.8   14. $\sqrt{3600}$ 60.0 15. $\sqrt{190}$ 13.8 16. $\sqrt{5120}$ 71.6

INDEPENDENT PRACTICE

See Example **1** Each square root is between two integers. Name the integers. Explain your answer.
17. $\sqrt{52}$ 18. $\sqrt{3}$ 19. $\sqrt{600}$ 20. $\sqrt{2000}$ 21. $\sqrt{410}$
21. 20 and 21; possible answer: 410 is between 400 and 441.

See Example **2** 22. The area of a square field is 200 ft². What is the approximate length of each side of the field? Round your anwer to the nearest foot.   14 ft

See Example **3** Approximate each square root to the nearest hundredth.
23. $\sqrt{19}$ 4.36   24. $\sqrt{84}$ 9.17   25. $\sqrt{123}$ 11.09 26. $\sqrt{251}$ 15.84 27. $\sqrt{290}$ 17.03

See Example **4** Use a calculator to find each value. Round to the nearest tenth.
28. $\sqrt{58}$ 7.6   29. $\sqrt{91.5}$ 9.6   30. $\sqrt{550}$ 23.5   31. $\sqrt{150}$ 12.2   32. $\sqrt{330}$ 18.2

PRACTICE AND PROBLEM SOLVING

Extra Practice
See page EP9.

Write the letter that identifies the position of each square root.

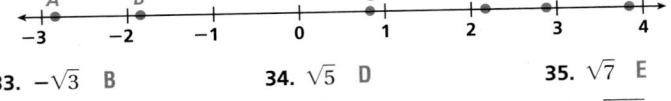

33. $-\sqrt{3}$ B   34. $\sqrt{5}$ D   35. $\sqrt{7}$ E
36. $-\sqrt{8}$ A   37. $\sqrt{14}$ F   38. $\sqrt{0.75}$ C

39. A couple wants to install a square stained-glass window that has an area of 500 square inches. To the nearest tenth of an inch, what length of wood trim is needed to go around the window?   89.6 in.

40. Each square on Laura's chessboard is 13 square centimeters. A chessboard has 8 squares on each side. To the nearest hundredth, what is the width of Laura's chessboard?   ≈28.84 cm

REVIEW FOR MASTERY 4-7

LESSON 4-7 Review for Mastery
Estimating Square Roots

To locate a square root between two integers, refer to the table.

Number	1	2	3	4	5	6	7	8	9	10
Square	1	4	9	16	25	36	49	64	81	100
Number	11	12	13	14	15	16	17	18	19	20
Square	121	144	169	196	225	256	289	324	361	400

Locate $\sqrt{260}$ between two integers.
260 is between the perfect squares 256 and 289: 256 < 260 < 289
So: $\sqrt{256} < \sqrt{260} < \sqrt{289}$
And: 16 < $\sqrt{260}$ < 17

Use the table to complete the statements.
1. $\underline{36}$ < 39 < $\underline{49}$ 2. $\underline{121}$ < 130 < $\underline{144}$
   $\sqrt{36}$ < $\sqrt{39}$ < $\sqrt{49}$ $\sqrt{121}$ < $\sqrt{130}$ < $\sqrt{144}$
   $\underline{6}$ < $\sqrt{39}$ < $\underline{7}$ $\underline{11}$ < $\sqrt{130}$ < $\underline{12}$

After locating a square root between two integers, you can determine which of the two integers the square root is closer to.
27 is between the perfect squares 25 and 36: 25 < 27 < 36
So: $\sqrt{25} < \sqrt{27} < \sqrt{36}$
And: 5 < $\sqrt{27}$ < 6

The difference between 27 and 25 is 2;
the difference between 36 and 27 is 9.
So, $\sqrt{27}$ is closer to 5.

   25 < 27 < 36
   2   9

Complete the statements.
4. 100 < 106 < 121   5. $\underline{225}$ < 250 < $\underline{256}$
   $\sqrt{100} < \sqrt{106} < \sqrt{121}$ $\sqrt{225} < \sqrt{250} < \sqrt{256}$
   $\underline{10}$ < $\sqrt{106}$ < $\underline{11}$ $\underline{15}$ < $\sqrt{250}$ < $\underline{16}$
   106 − 100 = $\underline{6}$ 250 − 225 = $\underline{25}$
   121 − 106 = $\underline{15}$ 256 − 250 = $\underline{6}$
   $\sqrt{106}$ is closer to $\underline{10}$ than $\underline{11}$. $\sqrt{250}$ is closer to $\underline{16}$ than $\underline{15}$.

PRACTICE 4-7

LESSON 4-7 Practice B
Estimating Square Roots

Each square root is between two integers. Name the integers. Explain your answer.
1. $\sqrt{6}$ 2. $\sqrt{20}$
   2 and 3; 6 is between 4 and 9   4 and 5; 20 is between 16 and 25
3. $\sqrt{28}$ 4. $\sqrt{44}$
   5 and 6; 28 is between 25 and 36   6 and 7; 44 is between 36 and 49

Approximate each square root to the nearest hundredth.
5. $\sqrt{130}$ 6. $\sqrt{255}$ 7. $\sqrt{208}$
   11.39   15.97   14.41

Use a calculator to find each value. Round to the nearest tenth.
8. $\sqrt{14}$ 9. $\sqrt{42}$ 10. $\sqrt{21}$ 11. $\sqrt{47}$
   3.7   6.5   4.6   6.9
12. $\sqrt{58}$ 13. $\sqrt{60}$ 14. $\sqrt{35}$ 15. $\sqrt{75}$
   7.6   7.7   5.9   8.7

Police use the formula $r = 2\sqrt{5L}$ to approximate the rate of speed in miles per hours of a vehicle from its skid marks, where L is the length of the skid marks in feet.
16. About how fast is a car going that leaves skid marks of 80 ft?
   40 mi/h
17. About how fast is a car going that leaves skid marks of 245 ft?
   70 mi/h
18. If the formula for finding the length of the skid marks is $L = \frac{r^2}{20}$, what would be the length of the skid marks from a vehicle traveling 80 mi/h?
   320 ft

41. Multi-Step On a baseball field, the infield area created by the baselines is a square. In a youth baseball league for 9- to 12-year-olds, this area is 3600 ft². The distance between each base in a league for 4-year-olds is 20 ft less than it is for 9- to 12-year-olds. What is the distance between each base for 4-year-olds?   **40 ft**

Order the numbers from least to greatest.
42. $\sqrt{49}, \frac{17}{3}, 6.5, 8, \frac{25}{4}$ $\frac{17}{3}, \frac{25}{4}, 6.5, \sqrt{49}, 8$ **43.** $5\frac{2}{3}, \sqrt{25}, 3^2, 7.15, \frac{29}{4}$ $\sqrt{25}, 5\frac{2}{3}, 7.15, \frac{29}{4}, 3^2$

44. Multi-Step Find the perimeter of a square whose area is 49 square inches.   **28 in.**

45. Science The formula $D = 3.56 \cdot \sqrt{A}$ gives the distance D in kilometers to the horizon from an airplane flying at an altitude A meters. If a pilot is flying at an altitude of 1800 m, about how far away is the horizon? Round your answer to the nearest kilometer.   **151 km**

46. Multi-Step For his new room, Darien's grandmother gave him a handmade quilt. The quilt is made of 16 squares set in 4 rows of 4. The area of each square is 324 in². How long is each side of the quilt in inches?   **72 in.**

47.  **Reasoning** Show how two squares can be formed by drawing only 6 lines.

48. Write About It Explain how you know whether $\sqrt{29}$ is closer to 5 or 6 without using a calculator.   **Possible answer:** $\sqrt{29}$ **is closer to 5 than 6 because 29 is closer to 25 than it is to 36.**

49. Challenge The speed of a tsunami in miles per hour can be found using $r = \sqrt{14.88d}$, where d is the water depth in feet. Suppose the water depth is 25,000 ft.

   a. How fast is the tsunami moving in miles per hour?   **approximately 610 mi/h**

   b. How long would it take a tsunami to travel 3000 miles if the water depth were a consistent 10,000 ft?   **approximately 7.8 hr**

SPIRAL STANDARDS REVIEW   NS2.4, AF1.2

50. Multiple Choice Which expression has a value between 14 and 15?

   Ⓐ $\sqrt{188}$ Ⓑ $\sqrt{200}$ Ⓒ $\sqrt{227}$ Ⓓ $\sqrt{324}$

51. Multiple Choice The square of a whole number is between 1000 and 1100. The number must be between which of the following numbers?

   Ⓐ 25 and 30   Ⓑ 30 and 35   Ⓒ 35 and 40   Ⓓ 40 and 45

Evaluate each expression for the given values of the variables. (Lesson 1-1)
52. $4x + 5y$ for $x = 3$ and $y = 9$ **57**   **53.** $7m - 2n$ for $m = 5$ and $n = 7$ **21**
54. $8h + 9j$ for $h = 11$ and $j = 2$ **106**   **55.** $6s - 2t$ for $s = 7$ and $t = 12$ **18**

Find the two square roots of each number. (Lesson 4-5)
56. 100   **±10**   **57.** 64   **±8**   **58.** 484   **±22**   **59.** 1296   **±36**

Objective: Students determine if a number is rational or irrational.

 Hands-On Lab
In *Chapter 4 Resource File*

 Online Edition
Tutorial Videos, Interactivities

 Countdown to Mastery Week 8

Power Presentations
with PowerPoint®

Warm Up

Each square root is between two integers. Name the two integers.

1. $\sqrt{119}$ 10 and 11

2. $\sqrt{15}$ 3 and 4

Use a calculator to find each value. Round to the nearest tenth.

3. $\sqrt{2}$ 1.4

4. $\sqrt{123}$ 11.1

Also available on transparency

Math Humor

When $\frac{2}{0}$ asked if he could join the number line, he was told, "Get real!"

 **California Standards**

Number Sense 🔑 1.4

California Standards

🔑 **NS1.4** Differentiate between rational and irrational numbers.

Vocabulary
real number
irrational number
Density Property

 **Caution!**

A repeating decimal may not appear to repeat on a calculator because calculators show a finite number of digits.

Who uses this? Just as biologists classify living things as plants or animals, mathematicians classify all real numbers as rational or irrational.

Biologists classify animals based on shared characteristics. For example, the horned lizard is an animal, a reptile, a lizard, and a gecko.

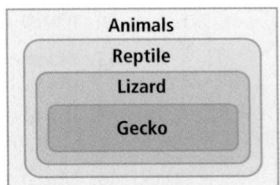

You already know that some numbers can be classified as whole numbers, integers, or rational numbers. The number 2 is a whole number, an integer, and a rational number. It is also a *real* number.

The set of **real numbers** is all numbers that can be written on a number line. It consists of the set of rational numbers and the set of *irrational numbers*.

Recall that rational numbers can be written as the quotient of two integers (a fraction) or as either terminating or repeating decimals.

$$3\tfrac{4}{5} = 3.8 \qquad \tfrac{2}{3} = 0.\overline{6} \qquad \sqrt{1.44} = 1.2$$

Irrational numbers can be written only as decimals that do *not* terminate or repeat. They cannot be written as the quotient of two integers. If a whole number is not a perfect square, then its square root is an irrational number. For example, 2 is not a perfect square, so $\sqrt{2}$ is irrational.

EXAMPLE 1 **Classifying Real Numbers**

Write all classifications that apply to each number.

A $\sqrt{3}$ *3 is a whole number that is not a perfect square.*
irrational, real

B -52.28 *−52.28 is a terminating decimal.*
rational, real

C $-\sqrt{25}$ *$-\sqrt{25} = -5$*
integer, rational, real

---

1 Introduce

Alternate Opener

EXPLORATION

4-8 The Real Numbers

The Set of Real Numbers

Rational numbers can be written as fractions or as decimals that terminate or repeat.	Irrational numbers are decimals that do not terminate or repeat.
Examples: $\frac{1}{4}$ $5 = \frac{5}{1}$ $\sqrt{1.69} = 1.3$ $\frac{1}{6} = 0.1\overline{6}$	Examples: $\sqrt{7} = 2.645751311\ldots$ $\pi = 3.141592654\ldots$

Classify each number as rational or irrational.

		Rational	Irrational
1.	$2\frac{1}{2}$		
2.	$\sqrt{24}$		
3.	$\sqrt{16}$		
4.	$7.\overline{7}$		
5.	$\frac{4}{9}$		

Think and Discuss
6. Explain how to classify numbers as rational.
7. Explain how to classify numbers as irrational.

Motivate

Show students that entering $\sqrt{2}$ on a calculator results in 1.414213562. Then show students that if 1.4142135622 is entered into the calculator, the result is 1.999999999. Explain that because $\sqrt{2}$ is not a perfect square, there is no finite decimal representation for $\sqrt{2}$. The number $\sqrt{2}$ is an example of an *irrational number*.

Also explain that a calculator cannot show more digits than its display will allow. Students should not assume that a result on a calculator is accurate when determining if a number is a terminating decimal.

Explorations and answers are provided in *Alternate Openers: Explorations Transparencies.*

A fraction with a denominator of 0 is undefined because you cannot divide by zero. So it is not a number at all.

EXAMPLE 2 **Determining the Classification of All Numbers**

State if each number is rational, irrational, or not a real number.

A $\sqrt{15}$ *15 is a whole number that is not a perfect square.*

irrational

B $\frac{3}{0}$

undefined, so not a real number

C $\sqrt{\frac{1}{9}}$ $\left(\frac{1}{3}\right)\left(\frac{1}{3}\right) = \frac{1}{9}$

rational

The **Density Property** of real numbers states that between any two real numbers is another real number. This property is not true when you limit yourself to whole numbers or integers. For instance, there is no integer between -2 and -3.

EXAMPLE 3 **Applying the Density Property of Real Numbers**

Find a real number between $1\frac{1}{3}$ and $1\frac{2}{3}$.

There are many solutions. One solution is halfway between the two numbers. To find it, add the numbers and divide by 2.

$$\left(1\frac{1}{3} + 1\frac{2}{3}\right) \div 2$$

$$= \left(2\frac{3}{3}\right) \div 2$$

$$= 3 \div 2 = 1\frac{1}{2}$$

A real number between $1\frac{1}{3}$ and $1\frac{2}{3}$ is $1\frac{1}{2}$.

Check: Use a graph.

(number line from 1 to 2 with marks at $1\frac{1}{3}$, $1\frac{1}{2}$, $1\frac{2}{3}$)

Possible answers to Think and Discuss

2. A number cannot be irrational and whole because all whole numbers can be written as fractions.

3. The Density Property states that there is always another real number between any two real numbers. So, if you find a number x between 0 and 1, there is a number y between 0 and x and a number z between x and 1, and so on.

Think and Discuss

1. **Explain** how rational numbers are related to integers.

2. **Tell** if a number can be irrational and whole. Explain.

3. **Use** the Density Property to explain why there are infinitely many real numbers between 0 and 1.

Power Presentations with PowerPoint®

Additional Examples

Example 1

Write all classifications that apply to each number.

A. $\sqrt{5}$ **B.** -12.75

irrational, real   rational, real

C. $\frac{\sqrt{16}}{2}$ whole, integer, rational, real

Example 2

State if each number is rational, irrational, or not a real number.

A. $\sqrt{21}$ **B.** $\frac{0}{3}$

irrational   rational

C. $\frac{4}{0}$ not a real number

Example 3

Find a real number between $3\frac{2}{5}$ and $3\frac{3}{5}$. Possible answer: $3\frac{1}{2}$

Also available on transparency

Possible answers to Think and Discuss

1. Integers are rational numbers. Rational numbers can be expressed as quotients of two integers.

---

2 Teach

Guided Instruction   ENGLISH LANGUAGE LEARNERS

In this lesson, students learn to determine if a number is rational or irrational. Remind students that a rational number is a number that can be written as a ratio (fraction) of two integers with a nonzero denominator. Describe an *irrational* number as a number that *cannot* be written as a ratio of two integers. Tell students that the set of real numbers consists of the set of all rational numbers together with the set of all irrational numbers (Teaching Transparency).

If students ask about numbers that are not real numbers, tell them they will study *imaginary* and *complex numbers* in later math courses.

Universal Access
Through Modeling

Give students a list of numbers (include terminating and repeating decimals, fractions, integers, and rational and irrational square roots) and a graphic organizer as shown below.

Real number		Not a real number
Rational	Irrational	
Integer		
Whole number		

Ask students to write each number in the list in the correct section of the organizer.

3 Close

Summarize

Remind students that a real number is rational if it can be written as a terminating or repeating decimal. A real number is irrational if it cannot be written as a terminating or repeating decimal.

California Standards Practice
NS1.4

go.hrw.com
Homework Help Online
KEYWORD: MT8CA 4-8
Parent Resources Online
KEYWORD: MT8CA Parent

Assignment Guide

If you finished Example **1** assign:
Proficient 1–4, 16–19, 31–38, 44–52 even, 64–72
Advanced 16–19, 35–42, 45–53 odd, 64–72

If you finished Example **2** assign:
Proficient 1–12, 16–27, 31–38, 44–58 even, 64–72
Advanced 16–27, 31–42, 45–59 odd, 60–62, 64–72

If you finished Example **3** assign:
Proficient 1–38, 43, 44–58 even, 64–72
Advanced 16–42, 43–59 odd, 60–62, 63–72

Homework Quick Check

Quickly check key concepts.
Exercises: 16, 18, 20, 26, 28, 30

Math Background

The only numbers that students at this level have encountered are real numbers. The use of the word *real* implies that there are numbers that are *not* real numbers.

In fact, there are *imaginary* numbers. Imaginary numbers are useful for specific purposes in science and engineering. The imaginary unit is $\sqrt{-1}$; it is represented by the letter *i*.

GUIDED PRACTICE

See Example **1** Write all classifications that apply to each number.

1. $\sqrt{10}$ irrational, real
2. $\sqrt{49}$ whole, integer, rational, real
3. 0.25 rational, real
4. $-\sqrt{16}$ integer, rational, real

See Example **2** State if each number is rational, irrational, or not a real number.

5. $\sqrt{9}$ rational
6. $\frac{17}{0}$ not real
7. $\sqrt{72}$ irrational
8. $-\sqrt{3}$ irrational
9. $-\sqrt{25}$ rational
10. $\sqrt{\frac{2}{3}}$ irrational
11. $\sqrt{\frac{25}{36}}$ rational
12. $\frac{1}{0}$ not real

See Example **3** Find a real number between each pair of numbers. Possible answers given.

13. $3\frac{1}{8}$ and $3\frac{2}{8}$ $3\frac{3}{16}$
14. 4.14 and $\frac{29}{7}$ $\frac{2899}{700}$
15. $\frac{1}{8}$ and $\frac{1}{4}$ $\frac{3}{16}$

INDEPENDENT PRACTICE

See Example **1** Write all classifications that apply to each number.

16. $\sqrt{35}$ irrational, real
17. $\frac{5}{8}$ rational, real
18. 3 whole, integer, rational, real
19. $\frac{\sqrt{81}}{-3}$ integer, rational, real

See Example **2** State if each number is rational, irrational, or not a real number.

20. $\frac{-16}{-4}$ rational
21. $\frac{0}{4}$ rational
22. $\sqrt{81}$ rational
23. $-\sqrt{3}$ irrational
24. $\frac{\sqrt{25}}{8}$ rational
25. $\sqrt{14}$ irrational
26. $\sqrt{\frac{1}{4}}$ rational
27. $\frac{4}{0}$ not real

See Example **3** Find a real number between each pair of numbers.

28. $3\frac{2}{5}$ and $3\frac{3}{5}$
Possible answer: $3\frac{1}{2}$
29. $-\frac{1}{10}$ and 0
Possible answer: $-\frac{1}{20}$
30. 4 and $\sqrt{9}$
Possible answer: 3.5

PRACTICE AND PROBLEM SOLVING

Extra Practice
See page EP9.

Write all classifications that apply to each number.

31. 6 whole, integer, rational, real
32. $-\sqrt{36}$ integer, rational, real
33. $\sqrt{10}$ irrational, real
34. $\frac{1}{3}$ rational, real
35. $\sqrt{2.56}$ rational, real
36. $\sqrt{36} + 6$ whole, integer, rational, real
37. $0.\overline{21}$ rational, real
38. $\frac{\sqrt{100}}{20}$ rational, real
39. -4.3134 rational, real
40. $\sqrt{4.5}$ irrational, real
41. -312 integer, rational, real
42. $\frac{0}{7}$ whole, integer, rational, real

43. $\frac{3}{0}$ is undefined so it is not a real number. $\frac{0}{3}$ is 0 so it is a rational number.

43. Explain the difference between $\frac{3}{0}$ and $\frac{0}{3}$.

Give an example of each type of number.

44. an irrational number that is less than -3 Possible answer: $-\sqrt{30}$

45. a positive rational number that is less than 0.3 Possible answer: 0.2

46. a real number between $\frac{5}{9}$ and $\frac{6}{9}$ Possible answer: $\frac{11}{18}$

47. a real number between $-3\frac{2}{7}$ and $-3\frac{3}{7}$ Possible answer: $-3\frac{5}{14}$

California Standards

Standard	Exercises
NS1.1	63
NS1.4 🔑	1–62, 64, 65
AF1.2	54–59, 65
AF1.3 🔑	66–68
AF2.1	69–72

REVIEW FOR MASTERY 4-8

Review for Mastery
4-8 *The Real Numbers*

The set of **rational numbers** contains all integers, all fractions, and decimals that end or repeat.

Irrational numbers can only be written as decimals that do not end or repeat.

Together, the rational numbers and the irrational numbers form the set of **real numbers**.

Real Numbers
Rational Numbers   Irrational Numbers

Square roots of numbers that are perfect squares are rational.
$\sqrt{25} = 5$

Square roots of numbers that are not perfect squares are irrational.
$\sqrt{3} = 1.732050807\ldots$

Tell if each number is rational or irrational.

1. $\sqrt{7}$ irrational
2. $\sqrt{81}$ rational
3. $\sqrt{169}$ rational
4. $\sqrt{101}$ irrational
5. -8 rational
6. $-\sqrt{8}$ irrational
7. -25 rational
8. $-\sqrt{25}$ rational

Between any two real numbers, there is always another real number. One way to find a number between is to find the number halfway between.

To find a real number between $7\frac{1}{5}$ and $7\frac{2}{5}$, divide their sum by 2: $7\frac{1}{5} + 7\frac{2}{5} = \left(14\frac{3}{5}\right) \div 2 = 7\frac{3}{10}$

Find a real number between each pair. Possible answers are shown.

9. $8\frac{3}{7}$ and $8\frac{4}{7}$ $8\frac{1}{2}$
10. -1.6 and -1.7 -1.65
11. $-3\frac{7}{9}$ and $-3\frac{2}{9}$ $-3\frac{1}{2}$
12. $6\frac{1}{2}$ and $6\frac{3}{4}$ $6\frac{5}{8}$

PRACTICE 4-8

Practice B
4-8 *The Real Numbers*

Write all classifications that apply to each number.

1. $-\frac{7}{8}$ rational; real
2. $\sqrt{0.15}$ irrational; real
3. $\sqrt{\frac{18}{2}}$ whole; integer; rational; real
4. $\sqrt{45}$ irrational; real
5. -25 integer; rational; real
6. -6.75 rational; real

State if the number is rational, irrational, or not a real number.

7. $\sqrt{14}$ irrational
8. $-\sqrt{16}$ rational
9. $\frac{6.2}{0}$ not real
10. $\sqrt{49}$ rational
11. $\frac{7}{20}$ rational
12. $-\sqrt{81}$ rational
13. $\sqrt{\frac{7}{9}}$ irrational
14. -1.3 rational

Find a real number between each pair of numbers.

15. $7\frac{3}{5}$ and $7\frac{4}{5}$ sample answer: $7\frac{7}{10}$
16. 6.45 and $\frac{13}{2}$ sample answer: 6.48
17. $\frac{7}{8}$ and $\frac{9}{10}$ sample answer: $\frac{22}{25}$

18. Give an example of a rational number between $-\sqrt{4}$ and $\sqrt{4}$.
sample answer: 0

19. Give an example of an irrational number less than 0.
sample answer: $-\frac{\sqrt{22}}{7}$

20. Give an example of a number that is not real.
sample answer: $\frac{2}{0}$

48. Find a rational number between $\sqrt{\frac{1}{9}}$ and $\sqrt{1}$. Possible answer: $\frac{2}{3}$

49. Find a real number between $\sqrt{4}$ and $\sqrt{5}$. Possible answer: 2.1

50. Find a real number between $\sqrt{5}$ and $\sqrt{11}$. Possible answer: 3

51. Find a real number between $\sqrt{49}$ and $\sqrt{64}$. Possible answer: 7.2

52. Find a real number between $-\sqrt{25}$ and $-\sqrt{16}$. Possible answer: -4.25

53. a. Find a real number between 1 and $\sqrt{3}$. Possible answer: 1.7
    b. Find a real number between 1 and your answer to part **a**. Possible answer: 1.2
    c. Find a real number between 1 and your answer to part **b**. Possible answer: 1.1

Determine if each expression is rational or irrational when $x = 2$.

54. $\sqrt{2x}$ rational
55. $3 - \sqrt{x}$ irrational
56. $\sqrt{x + 2}$ rational
57. $\sqrt{3x - 6}$ rational
58. $\sqrt{5x + 2}$ irrational
59. $\sqrt{1 - \frac{x}{5}}$ irrational

 60. **What's the Error?** A student said that all integers are whole numbers. What mistake did the student make? Explain.

 61. **Write About It** Can you ever use a calculator to determine if a number is rational or irrational? Explain.

 62. **Challenge** The circumference of a circle divided by its diameter is an irrational number, represented by the Greek letter π (*pi*). Could a circle with a diameter of 2 have a circumference of 6? Why or why not?
Possible answer: no, because the circumference divided by the diameter would be 3, which is rational

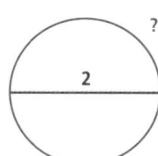

SPIRAL STANDARDS REVIEW   NS1.1, ← NS1.4, AF1.2, ← AF1.3, AF2.1

63. **Multiple Choice** Which value is between 8 and 10?
    Ⓐ 7.12   Ⓑ $\sqrt{61}$ Ⓒ $3 \cdot \pi$ Ⓓ $\frac{123}{11}$

64. **Multiple Choice** Which value is NOT a rational number?
    Ⓐ $0.\overline{7}$ Ⓑ $\frac{11}{13}$ Ⓒ $\sqrt{19}$ Ⓓ $\sqrt{225}$

65. **Multiple Choice** For which values of x is $\sqrt{x - 19}$ a real number?
    Ⓐ $x \geq -19$ Ⓑ $x \leq -19$ Ⓒ $x \geq 19$ Ⓓ $x \leq 19$

Tell which property is represented. (Lesson 3-1)

66. $x + 5 = 5 + x$
Commutative Property of Addition

67. $2(y - 3) = 2y - 2 \cdot 3$
Distributive Property

68. $3(\frac{1}{3} \cdot x) = (3 \cdot \frac{1}{3})x$
Associative Property of Multiplication

Simplify. (Lesson 4-1)

69. 8^5 32,768
70. $(-3)^3$ -27
71. $(-5)^4$ 625
72. 9^2 81

CHALLENGE 4-8

Numbers that are equal to the sum of all their factors (not including the number itself) are called **perfect numbers.**

$6 = 1 + 2 + 3$ 6 is the smallest perfect number.

1. Which of the numbers 24 or 28 is a perfect number? Explain.

24 is not perfect since $1 + 2 + 3 + 4 + 6 + 8 + 12 \neq 24$.

28 is perfect since $1 + 2 + 4 + 7 + 14 = 28$.

The ancient Greek mathematician Euclid devised a method for computing perfect numbers.
- Begin with the number 1 and keep adding powers of 2 until you get a sum that is a *prime number* (only factors are itself and 1).
- Multiply this sum by the last power of 2.

2. Complete the table to write the first three perfect numbers.

	Sum	Prime?	Euclid's Method	Perfect Number
$1 + 2$	= 3	yes	2×3	6
$1 + 2 + 4$	= 7	yes	4×7	28
$1 + 2 + 4 + 8$	= 15	no		
$1 + 2 + 4 + 8 + 16$	= 31	yes	16×31	496

So the first three perfect numbers are   6, 28, 496 .

The next perfect number is tedious to calculate in this manner. If, however, the calculations are written with exponents, a new pattern emerges.

Series	Sum
$1 + 2^1$	$= 2^2 - 1$
$1 + 2^1 + 2^2$	$= 2^3 - 1$
$1 + 2^1 + 2^2 + 2^3$	$= 2^4 - 1$
$1 + 2^1 + 2^2 + 2^3 + 2^4$	$= 2^5 - 1$

3. Complete the table to write the sums using exponents.

Incorporating this information, Euclid proved that for a perfect number of the form $2^n - 1$ is found, a perfect number can be written.

If $2^n - 1$ is prime, then $2^{n-1}(2^n - 1)$ is a perfect number.

4. Find the fourth perfect number. $2^6(2^7 - 1) = 8128$

5. Find the fifth perfect number. $2^{12}(2^{13} - 1) = 33,550,336$

PROBLEM SOLVING 4-8

Write the correct answer.

1. Twin primes are prime numbers that differ by 2. Find an irrational number between twin primes 5 and 7.

Possible answer: $\sqrt{31}$

2. Rounded to the nearest ten-thousandth, $\pi = 3.1416$. Find a rational number between 3 and π.

Possible answer: $\frac{31}{10}$

3. One famous irrational number is e. Rounded to the nearest ten-thousandth $e \approx 2.7183$. Find a rational number that is between 2 and e.

Possible answer: $\frac{5}{2}$

4. Perfect numbers are those that the divisors of the number sum to the number itself. The number 6 is a perfect number because $1 + 2 + 3 = 6$. The number 28 is also a perfect number. Find an irrational number between 6 and 28.

Possible answer: $\sqrt{43}$

Choose the letter for the best answer.

5. Which is a rational number?
   A the length of a side of a square with area 2 cm^2
   B the length of a side of a square with area 4 cm^2
   C a non-terminating decimal
   D the square root of a prime number

6. Which is an irrational number?
   F a number that can be expressed as a fraction
   G the length of a side of a square with area 4 cm^2
   H the length of a side of a square with area 2 cm^2
   J the square root of a negative number

7. Which is an integer?
   A the number half-way between 6 and 7
   B the average rainfall for the week if it rained 0.5 in., 2.3 in., 0 in., 0 in., 0 in., 0.2 in., 0.75 in. during the week
   C the money in an account if the balance was $213.00 and $21.87 was deposited
   D the net yardage after plays that resulted in a 15 yard loss, 10 yard gain, 6 yard gain and 5 yard loss

8. Which is a whole number?
   F the number half-way between 6 and 7
   G the total amount of sugar in a recipe that calls for $\frac{1}{4}$ cup of brown sugar and $\frac{3}{4}$ cup of granulated sugar
   H the money in an account if the balance was $213.00 and $21.87 was deposited
   J the net yardage after plays that resulted in a 15 yard loss, 10 yard gain, 6 yard gain and 5 yard loss

---

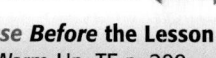
Answers

60. Possible answer: Negative integers are not whole numbers. Integers are the whole numbers and their opposites. All the whole numbers are integers.

61. Possible answer: If the calculator shows a terminating decimal, then the number is rational. If the decimal does not terminate, you cannot tell from the display on the calculator whether it repeats or not because you see only a limited number of digits.

 **Teaching Tip** **Multiple Choice** Students who choose **A** in **Exercise 64** may need reminding that repeating decimals are rational numbers. Show them that $0.\overline{7}$ is the same as $\frac{7}{9}$, which is rational.

 Journal

Have students write about what they think it means when a number is called real. Have them write about what kinds of numbers might not be real.

Power Presentations
with PowerPoint®

4-8 Lesson Quiz

Write all classifications that apply to each number.

1. $\sqrt{2}$ real, irrational

2. $-\frac{\sqrt{16}}{2}$ real, integer, rational

State if each number is rational, irrational, or not a real number.

3. $\frac{\sqrt{25}}{0}$ not a real number

4. $\sqrt{4} \cdot \sqrt{9}$ rational

5. Find a real number between $-2\frac{3}{4}$ and $-2\frac{3}{8}$. Possible answer: $-2\frac{5}{8}$

Also available on transparency

Objective: Use scissors and paper to explore right triangles.

Materials: Scissors, paper, centimeter ruler

Online Edition

Countdown to Mastery Week 9

Teach
Discuss

Before doing the Activity, explain that the area of a square can be used to model square numbers. Draw a 12-inch line on the board, and create a square using the line as one of the sides. The area of the square is 12^2.

Have students do this activity for a triangle that is not a right triangle, so they can see that this property is unique to right triangles.

Close
Key Concept

You can use geometric shapes to observe visual proof of the Pythagorean Theorem.

Assessment

Find the length of the hypotenuse by using the given lengths of the legs.

1. 3 and 4   5
2. 20.5 and 38.9   ≈ 44.0
3. $\frac{1}{20}$ and $\frac{3}{25}$ $\frac{13}{100}$ or 0.13

Hands-On LAB 4-9
Explore the Pythagorean Theorem

Use with Lesson 4-9

The Pythagorean Theorem states that in a right triangle, if the lengths of the legs are a and b and the length of the hypotenuse is c, then $a^2 + b^2 = c^2$. You can use centimeter graph paper and a ruler to verify the Pythagorean Theorem.

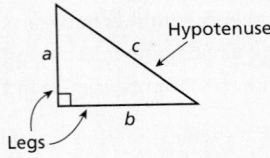

go.hrw.com
Lab Resources Online
KEYWORD: MT8CA Lab4

California Standards

MG3.3 Know and understand the Pythagorean theorem and its converse and use it to find the length of the missing side of a right triangle and the lengths of other line segments and, in some situations, **empirically verify the Pythagorean theorem by direct measurement.**

Activity

1. On centimeter graph paper, draw a right triangle whose legs are 3 cm long and 4 cm long.

2. Use a centimeter ruler to measure the length of the hypotenuse. Copy the table below, and record the length of the hypotenuse as c in the first row of the table.

3. Complete the first row of the table by calculating a^2, b^2, $a^2 + b^2$, and c^2.

4. Repeat the process by drawing right triangles whose legs have lengths a and b as given in the table.

a	b	c	a^2	b^2	$a^2 + b^2$	c^2
3	4	5	9	16	25	25
5	12	13	25	144	169	169
6	8	10	36	64	100	100

Think and Discuss

1. What do you notice about the values of $a^2 + b^2$ and c^2 in your table? **They are equal.**

2. When you have a right triangle and you know the length of the hypotenuse and one leg, how can you find the length of the other leg? **by substituting the known lengths for a and c in the Pythagorean Theorem and solving for b**

Try This

In the right triangle shown, both legs are 2 cm long.

1. Use a centimeter ruler to measure the length of the hypotenuse to the nearest tenth of a centimeter. **2.8 cm**

2. Use the Pythagorean Theorem to calculate the length of the hypotenuse to the nearest tenth of a centimeter. **2.8 cm**

3. How do the results of **1** and **2** compare? **The results are the same.**

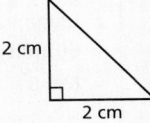
2 cm
2 cm

Miguel Carrizales
San Antonio, Texas

Teacher to Teacher

I find that students have trouble drawing the hypotenuses of length c on regular paper, so I pass out large sheets of graph paper to each student. The students are then able to draw the squares and hypotenuses with ease. I have them find the areas of the squares with side lengths a and b as well as the square with side length c. Doing this helps them to see the Pythagorean Theorem more clearly. After the activity is finished, I display the students' work and use it as a teaching tool for later lessons.

4-9 The Pythagorean Theorem

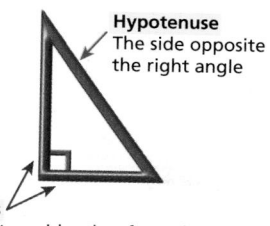

Hypotenuse
The side opposite the right angle

Legs
The two sides that form the right angle in a right triangle

California Standards

⬤ **MG3.3** Know and understand the Pythagorean theorem and its converse and use it to find the length of the missing side of a right triangle and the lengths of other line segments and, in some situations, empirically verify the Pythagorean theorem by direct measurement.

Vocabulary
Pythagorean Theorem
leg
hypotenuse

Why learn this? You can use the Pythagorean Theorem to determine how high a ladder leaning against a wall can safely reach. (See Exercise 23.)

The Pythagorean Theorem shows that a special relationship exists between the sides of a right triangle. You can use the theorem to find the length of any side of a right triangle.

PYTHAGOREAN THEOREM		
Words	**Numbers**	**Algebra**
In a right triangle, the sum of the squares of the lengths of the legs is equal to the square of the length of the hypotenuse.	$6^2 + 8^2 = 10^2$ $36 + 64 = 100$	$a^2 + b^2 = c^2$

EXAMPLE 1 Calculating the Length of a Side of a Right Triangle

Use the Pythagorean Theorem to find each missing measure.

Helpful Hint
Since length can only be positive, use only the principal square root.

A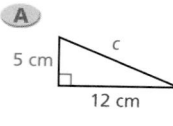

$$a^2 + b^2 = c^2 \quad \text{Use the Pythagorean Theorem.}$$
$$5^2 + 12^2 = c^2 \quad \text{Substitute for } a \text{ and } b.$$
$$25 + 144 = c^2 \quad \text{Simplify the powers.}$$
$$169 = c^2 \quad \text{Add.}$$
$$\sqrt{169} = \sqrt{c^2} \quad \text{Take the square root of}$$
$$13 = c \quad \text{both sides.}$$

The length of the hypotenuse is 13 cm.

B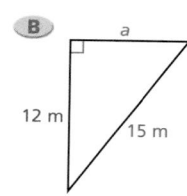

$$a^2 + b^2 = c^2 \quad \text{Use the Pythagorean Theorem.}$$
$$a^2 + 12^2 = 15^2 \quad \text{Substitute for } b \text{ and } c.$$
$$a^2 + 144 = 225 \quad \text{Simplify the powers.}$$
$$\underline{-144 \quad -144} \quad \text{Subtract 144 from both sides.}$$
$$a^2 = 81$$
$$\sqrt{a^2} = \sqrt{81} \quad \text{Take the square root of}$$
$$a = 9 \quad \text{both sides.}$$

The length of the leg is 9 m.

1 Introduce

Alternate Opener

EXPLORATION

4-9 The Pythagorean Theorem

Right triangles have one 90° angle. In the triangles below, each 90° angle is formed by the sides that have lengths a and b.

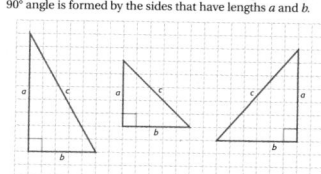

Use the grid to find the side lengths a and b on each triangle. Then square each length (a^2 and b^2) and add the squares ($a^2 + b^2$). Enter this sum in the column labeled c^2. Then use a calculator to find the square root of c^2, or c, the length of the longest side of the triangle. Round your answers to the nearest tenth.

	a	b	a²	b²	a²+b²	c²	c
1.							
2.							
3.							

Think and Discuss

4. Discuss whether only the longest side length of a right triangle can be found using $a^2 + b^2 = c^2$.

Motivate

With a 2 ft long piece of cord, tie one knot 6 in. from one end and another 10 in. from the other end. Hold the ends together. Have two students hold the knots. Pull the cord taut to form a right triangle. Tell students that builders from ancient times to modern times have created right angles this way, which uses the Converse of the Pythagorean Theorem.

Explorations and answers are provided in *Alternate Openers: Explorations Transparencies.*

Organizer 4-9

Objective: Students use the Pythagorean Theorem and its converse to solve problems.

LAB **Hands-On Lab**
In *Chapter 4 Resource File*

Technology Lab
In *Chapter 4 Resource File*

PREMIER **Online Edition**
Tutorial Videos, Interactivities

Countdown to Mastery Week 9

Power Presentations
with PowerPoint®

Warm Up
Estimate each square root to the nearest hundredth.
1. $\sqrt{30}$ 5.48   **2.** $\sqrt{14}$ 3.74
3. $\sqrt{55}$ 7.42   **4.** $\sqrt{48}$ 6.93

Also available on transparency

Math Humor

The right triangle suffered from acute angles. So the mathematical doctor gave it a dose of the Pythagorean serum.

California Standards

Measurement and Geometry ⬤ **3.3**
Also covered:

Measurement and Geometry 3.0 Students know the Pythagorean theorem and deepen their understanding of plane and solid geometric shapes by constructing figures that meet given conditions and by identifying attributes of figures.

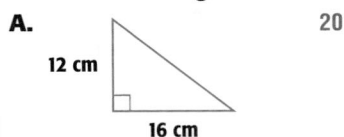
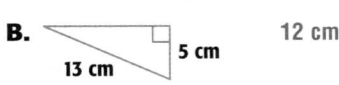

Teaching Tip **Reading Math** Point out that in **Example 2** drawing a segment between home plate and second base divides the figure into two right triangles. This fact should suggest that the Pythagorean Theorem will have something to do with the solution.

Teaching Tip **Language Support** Point out to students that *converse* means "reverse in order." Have students compare the first and last parts of the Pythagorean Theorem to those of its converse to help them see the "reverse order" in their relationship.

EXAMPLE 2 **PROBLEM SOLVING APPLICATION**

A regulation baseball diamond is a square with sides that measure 90 feet. About how far is it from home plate to second base? Round your answer to the nearest tenth.

 Understand the Problem

Rewrite the question as a statement.
• Find the distance from home plate to second base.

List the **important information:**
• Drawing a segment between home plate and second base divides the diamond into two right triangles.
• The angle at first base is the right angle, so the segment between home plate and second base is the hypotenuse.
• The base lines are legs, and they are each 90 feet long.

 Make a Plan

You can use the Pythagorean Theorem to write an equation.

3 Solve

$$a^2 + b^2 = c^2 \quad \text{Use the Pythagorean Theorem.}$$
$$90^2 + 90^2 = c^2 \quad \text{Substitute for the known variables.}$$
$$8{,}100 + 8{,}100 = c^2 \quad \text{Simplify the powers.}$$
$$16{,}200 = c^2 \quad \text{Add.}$$
$$\sqrt{16{,}200} = \sqrt{c^2} \quad \text{Take the square root of both sides.}$$
$$127.279 \approx c$$
$$127.3 \approx c \quad \text{Round.}$$

The distance from home plate to second base is about 127.3 ft.

4 Look Back

The hypotenuse is the longest side of a right triangle. Since the distance from home plate to second base is greater than the distance between the bases, the answer is reasonable.

You can use the Converse of the Pythagorean Theorem to tell whether a triangle is a right triangle. The Converse of the Pythagorean Theorem states that if a triangle has sides of length a, b, and c, and $a^2 + b^2 = c^2$, then the triangle is a right triangle.

2 Teach

Guided Instruction

In this lesson, students learn to use the Pythagorean Theorem and its converse to solve problems. Introduce the Pythagorean Theorem with the Teaching Transparency. Stress that in the equation $a^2 + b^2 = c^2$, c is always the longest side of the triangle, the *hypotenuse*. Explain that the hypotenuse is always the side opposite the right angle. Discuss examples that require finding the hypotenuse and examples that require finding one of the legs.

Universal Access
Through Modeling

Have students draw a right triangle with legs lengths of 3 units and 4 units on grid paper. Have students find the square of each leg, and then find the sum of the squares. Next, have students measure the length of the hypotenuse by finding its length on a string and determining how many units long the string is. Students square this amount and compare it to the sum of the squares of the legs.

EXAMPLE 3 Identifying a Right Triangle

Tell whether the given side lengths form a right triangle.

Helpful Hint

The hypotenuse is always the longest side of a right triangle. Be sure to substitute it only for c.

A 7, 24, 25

$a^2 + b^2 \stackrel{?}{=} c^2$ Compare $a^2 + b^2$ to c^2.

$7^2 + 24^2 \stackrel{?}{=} 25^2$ Substitute the longest side length for c.

$49 + 576 \stackrel{?}{=} 625$ Simplify the powers.

$625 = 625$ ✔   Add.

The side lengths form a right triangle.

B 5, 8, 12

$a^2 + b^2 \stackrel{?}{=} c^2$ Compare $a^2 + b^2$ to c^2.

$5^2 + 8^2 \stackrel{?}{=} 12^2$ Substitute the longest side length for c.

$25 + 64 \stackrel{?}{=} 144$ Simplify the powers.

$89 \neq 144$ ✗   Add.

The side lengths do not form a right triangle.

Think and Discuss

1. **Explain** whether it is ever possible to use the Pythagorean Theorem to find an unknown side length of a scalene triangle.

2. **Explain** if 2, 3, and 4 cm could be side lengths of a right triangle.

4-9 Exercises

California Standards Practice
◆━ MG3.3

go.hrw.com
Homework Help Online
KEYWORD: MT8CA 4-9
Parent Resources Online
KEYWORD: MT8CA Parent

GUIDED PRACTICE

See Example 1 Use the Pythagorean Theorem to find each missing measure.

1.

2.

3.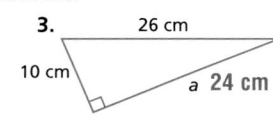

See Example 2 **4.** A 10 ft ladder is leaning against a wall. If the ladder is 5 ft from the base of the wall, how far above the ground does the ladder touch the wall? Round your answer to the nearest tenth. **about 8.7 ft**

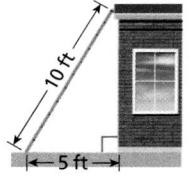

Power Presentations with PowerPoint®

Additional Examples

Example 3

Tell whether the given side lengths form a right triangle.

A. 12, 35, 37   yes

B. 8, 12, 16   no

Also available on transparency

Possible answers to Think and Discuss

1. It is possible if the triangle is a right triangle

2. No, because if 2, 3, and 4 are put into the formula of the Pythagorean Theorem, it is not true; $4 + 9 \neq 16$.

3 Close

Summarize

Draw a right triangle on the board. Have students help you to apply the following labels: hypotenuse, leg, leg, a, b, and c. Then, label the hypotenuse 17 and the longer leg 15. Ask students to write the equation that must be solved to find the missing leg length. Ask students if the missing leg length could be 10, and why or why not.

Possible answers:
$a^2 + 15^2 = 17^2$; a could not be 10 because $10^2 + 15^2 \neq 17^2$. In fact, $a = 8$.

See Example **3**
Tell whether the given side lengths form a right triangle.

5. 3, 4, 5 **yes**   **6.** 8, 10, 14 **no**   **7.** 0.5, 1.2, 1.3 **yes**

INDEPENDENT PRACTICE

See Example **1**
Use the Pythagorean Theorem to find each missing measure.

8. 18 yd, 24 yd, *c* 30 yd

9. 15 ft, 25 ft, *b*, 20 ft

10. 16 in., 30 in., 34 in., *a*

See Example **2**
11. James rides his bike 15 miles west. Then he turns north and rides another 15 miles before he stops to rest. How far is James from his starting point when he stops to rest? Round your answer to the nearest tenth.   **about 21.2 mi**

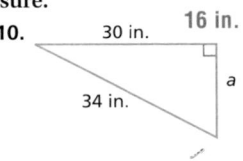

See Example **3**
Tell whether the given side lengths form a right triangle.

12. 8, 15, 17 **yes**   **13.** 5, 6, 9 **no**   **14.** 2.4, 2.5, 3.6 **no**

PRACTICE AND PROBLEM SOLVING

Extra Practice
See page EP9.

Find the missing side length for each right triangle to the nearest tenth.

15. $a = 4$, $b = 3$, $c = \blacksquare$ **5**   **16.** $a = \blacksquare$, $b = 40$, $c = 50$ **30**

17. $a = 5$, $b = 12$, $c = \blacksquare$ **13**   **18.** $a = 10$, $b = \blacksquare$, $c = 26$ **24**

19. $a = \blacksquare$, $b = 40$, $c = 41$ **9**   **20.** $a = 65$, $b = \blacksquare$, $c = 97$ **72**

21. Reasoning The numbers 3, 4, and 5 form a Pythagorean triple because $3^2 + 4^2 = 5^2$. When you double each of these values, does the resulting set of numbers also form a Pythagorean triple? Explain.   **yes; $6^2 + 8^2 = 10^2$**

22. History To determine the boundaries of their fields, ancient Egyptians used a loop of rope that was knotted at 12 equal intervals and stretched around 3 stakes. Explain why the triangle formed by the knotted rope must be a right triangle.

23. For safety reasons, the base of a 24-foot ladder must be placed at least 8 feet from the wall. To the nearest tenth of a foot, how high can a 24-foot ladder safely reach?   **22.6 ft**

24. Write a Problem Use a street map to write and solve a problem that requires the use of the Pythagorean Theorem.   **Check students' work.**

Assignment Guide

If you finished Example **1** assign:
Proficient 1–3, 8, 10, 33–40
Advanced 8, 10, 21–22, 29, 33–40

If you finished Example **2** assign:
Proficient 1–4, 8, 10, 11, 23, 25, 31–40
Advanced 8–11, 21–25, 29, 31–40

If you finished Example **3** assign:
Proficient 1–18, 23, 25, 31–40
Advanced 8–14, 19–40

Homework Quick Check

Quickly check key concepts.
Exercises: 8, 10, 11, 12, 14

Math Background

Every triangle must be either acute, right, or obtuse. You can derive three inequalities from the Pythagorean Theorem to find the type of a triangle, given its side lengths.

Pythagorean Inequalities

For $\triangle ABC$ with c being the length of the longest side:

- If $c^2 < a^2 + b^2$, then $\triangle ABC$ is an acute triangle.
- If $c^2 = a^2 + b^2$, then $\triangle ABC$ is a right triangle.
- If $c^2 > a^2 + b^2$, then $\triangle ABC$ is an obtuse triangle.

Answers

22. The sides have lengths 3, 4, and 5. If you use the Pythagorean Theorem, you find that $3^2 + 4^2 = 5^2$, so the triangle must be a right triangle.

California Standards

Standard	Exercises
NS2.4	37–40
AF4.1 🔑	33–36
MG3.3 🔑	1–32

REVIEW FOR MASTERY 4-9

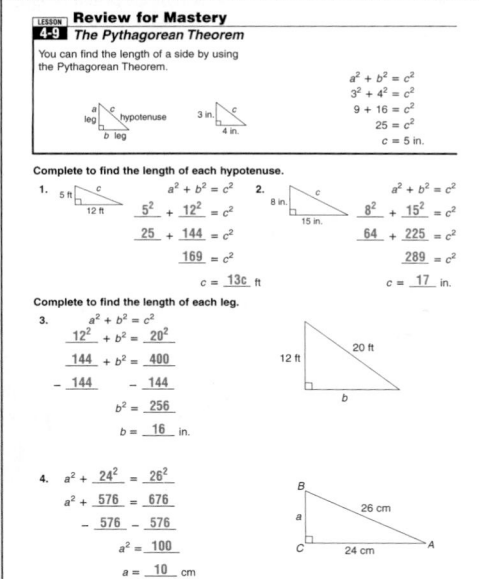

PRACTICE 4-9

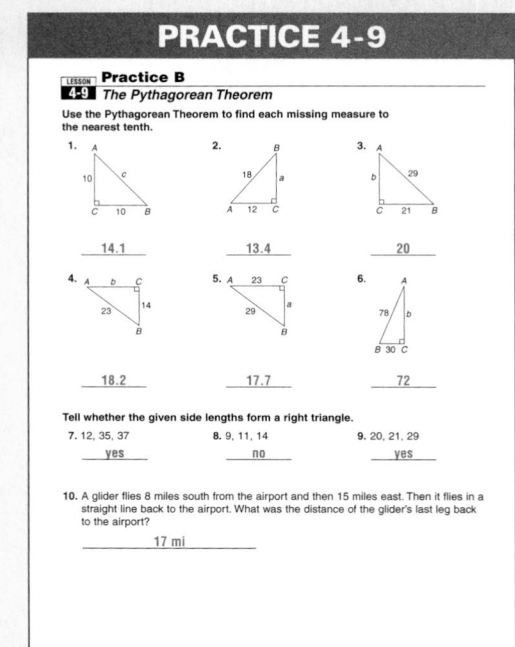

25. Ancient Egyptians built pyramids to serve as tombs for their kings. One pyramid, called Menkaure, has a square base with an area of about 12,100 m².

   a. What is the length of each side of the base?   **110 m**

   b. What is the length of a diagonal of the base? Round your answer to the nearest tenth.   **155.6 m**

26. The photograph shows the Pyramid of Khafre in Egypt. Each side of its square base is about 214 meters long. Each triangular side is an isosceles triangle with a height of about 179 meters. What is the area of one side of the pyramid?   **19,153 m²**

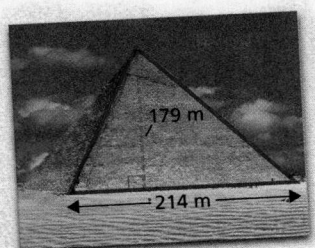
179 m
214 m

27. Use the Pythagorean Theorem to find the distance from one corner of the Pyramid of Khafre to its peak. Round your answer to the nearest tenth.   **208.5 m**

go.hrw.com
Web Extra!
KEYWORD: MT8CA Egypt

28. **Multi-Step** The pyramids were constructed using a unit of measurement called a cubit. There are about 21 inches in 1 cubit. If the height of a pyramid is 471 feet, what is its height in cubits?   **269.1 cubits**

29. ✐ **Write About It** Given a right triangle, explain how you know which values to substitute into the equation $a^2 + b^2 = c^2$.

30. ★ **Challenge** The pyramid at right has a square base. Find the height of the pyramid to the nearest tenth.   **68.8 m**

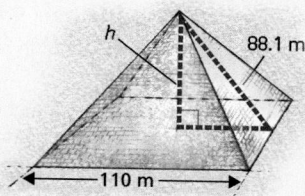
h
88.1 m
110 m

SPIRAL STANDARDS REVIEW

NS2.4, ➤ AF4.1, ➤ MG3.3

31. **Multiple Choice** A flagpole is 24 feet tall. A rope is tied to the top of the flagpole and secured to the ground 9 feet from the base of the flagpole. What is the length of the rope to the nearest foot?

Ⓐ 5 feet   Ⓑ 15 feet   Ⓒ 26 feet   Ⓓ 300 feet

32. **Gridded Response** Brad leans his 13-foot ladder against his house. The base of the ladder is placed 5 feet from the base of the house. How many feet up the house does the ladder reach?   **12 feet**

Solve each inequality. (Lesson 3-8)

$$x > -\frac{1}{4}$$

33. $3 - 7x \le 24$ **34.** $1 - x \ge 11$ **35.** $\frac{-2x}{3} + \frac{1}{6} < \frac{1}{3}$ **36.** $\frac{x}{5} + 0.5 > -0.5$
$x \ge -3$ $x \le -10$ $x > -5$

Each square root is between two integers. Name the integers. (Lesson 4-7)

37. $\sqrt{30}$ **5 and 6**   **38.** $\sqrt{42}$ **6 and 7**   **39.** $\sqrt{55}$ **7 and 8**   **40.** $\sqrt{67}$ **8 and 9**

CHALLENGE 4-9

Challenge
LESSON 4-9 *Triple Play*

Three numbers connected by the Pythagorean relation are called **Pythagorean triples.**

Since $3^2 + 4^2 = 5^2$, the numbers 3-4-5 are a Pythagorean Triple.

Consider the Pythagorean triples shown in the table.

1. Make an observation about the numbers in Column A.

   consecutive odd numbers

2. How are the numbers in Column C related to those in Column B?

   C = B + 1

	Column A	Column B	Column C
row 1	3	4	5
row 2	5	12	13
row 3	7	24	25
row 4	9	40	41
row 5	11	60	61

3. Complete this table by carrying out the indicated calculation. Two calculations are done.

   Compare the results to the Pythagorean triples in Columns A, B, and C of the original table.

   results = Column B

	Column A	row × A + row
row 1	3	1 × 3 + 1 = 4
row 2	5	2 × 5 + 2 = 12
row 3	7	3 × 7 + 3 = 24
row 4	9	4 × 9 + 4 = 40
row 5	11	5 × 11 + 5 = 60

4. In the original table, how do the squares of the numbers in Column A relate to the numbers in Columns B and C?

   $A^2 = B + C$

5. Using the relationships you have observed, calculate rows 6 and 10 of the table of Pythagorean triples. Verify your results by applying the Pythagorean Theorem.

	Column A	Column B	Column C	Verify $A^2 + B^2 = C^2$
row 6	13	84	85	$13^2 + 84^2 \stackrel{?}{=} 85^2$; 7225 = 7225 ✓
row 10	21	220	221	$21^2 + 220^2 \stackrel{?}{=} 221^2$; 48,841 = 48,841 ✓

PROBLEM SOLVING 4-9

Problem Solving
LESSON 4-9 *The Pythagorean Theorem*

Write the correct answer. Round to the nearest tenth.

1. A utility pole 10 m high is supported by two guy wires. Each guy wire is anchored 3 m from the base of the pole. How many meters of wire are needed for the guy wires?

   20.9 m

2. A 12 foot-ladder is resting against a wall. The base of the ladder is 2.5 feet from the base of the wall. How high up the wall will the ladder reach?

   11.7 ft

3. The base-path of a baseball diamond form a square. If it is 90 ft from home to first, how far does the catcher have to throw to catch someone stealing second base?

   127.3 ft

4. A football field is 100 yards with 10 yards at each end for the end zones. The field is 45 yards wide. Find the length of the diagonal of the entire field, including the end zones.

   128.2 yd

Choose the letter for the best answer.

5. The frame of a kite is made from two strips of wood, one 27 inches long, and one 18 inches long. What is the perimeter of the kite? Round to the nearest tenth.

   A 18.8 in.   Ⓒ 65.7 in.
   B 32.8 in.   D 131.2 in.

6. The glass for a picture window is 8 feet wide. The door it must pass through is 3 feet wide. How tall must the door be for the glass to pass through the door? Round to the nearest tenth.

   F 3.3 ft   Ⓗ 7.4 ft
   G 6.7ft   J 8.5 ft

7. A television screen measures approximately 15.5 in. high and 19.5 in. wide. A television is advertised by giving the approximate length of the diagonal of its screen. How should this television be advertised?

   Ⓐ 25 in.   C 12 in.
   B 21 in.   D 6 in.

8. To meet federal guidelines, a wheelchair ramp that is constructed to rise 1 foot off the ground must extend 12 feet along the ground. How long will the ramp be? Round to the nearest tenth.

   F 11.9 ft   H 13.2 ft
   Ⓖ 12.0 ft   J 15.0 ft

FORMATIVE ASSESSMENT
and **INTERVENTION**◀▶

Diagnose Before the Lesson
4-9 Warm Up, TE p. 205

Monitor During the Lesson
4-9 Know-It Notebook
4-9 Questioning Strategies

Assess After the Lesson
4-9 Lesson Quiz, TE p. 209

Answers

29. Possible answer: The longest side is always the side opposite the right angle and labeled side "c". The other two sides are "a" and "b".

Teaching Tip   **Multiple Choice** For **Exercise 31,** suggest that students draw a diagram for triangle problems. With a visual aid, it is more apparent that in this problem, the missing value is a hypotenuse.

✐ **Journal**

Ask students to list some real-world examples of right triangles. Have them write about why it might be important to know the lengths of the sides of these triangles. Examples might include a set of stairs, a sail on a sailboat, or a triangular garden.

Power Presentations
with PowerPoint®

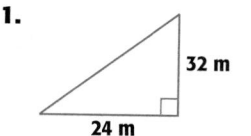
✓ **4-9 Lesson Quiz**

Use the Pythagorean Theorem to find each missing measure.

1.
40 m
32 m
24 m

2.
21 in.
28 in.
35 in.

3. Each rectangular section of a fence is braced by a board nailed on the diagonal of the section. The fence is 6 ft tall and the brace is 10 ft long. What is the length of the section?   8 ft

Tell whether the given side lengths form a right triangle.

4. 2.5, 3, 4.5   no

5. 33, 56, 65   yes

Also available on transparency

Organizer

Objective: Assess students' mastery of concepts and skills in Lessons 4-6 through 4-9.

Resources

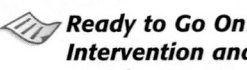
Assessment Resources
Section 4B Quiz

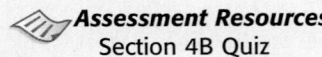
Test & Practice Generator
One-Stop Planner®

INTERVENTION ⬅➡

Resources

Ready to Go On?
Intervention and
***Enrichment* Worksheets**

💿 **Ready to Go On? CD-ROM**

🪐 **Ready to Go On? Online**

my.hrw.com

Answers

11. 14 and 15; 200 is between 196 and 225.

12. 18 and 19; 340 is between 324 and 361.

13. 24 and 25; 610 is between 576 and 625.

Quiz for Lessons 4-6 Through 4-9

✅ **4-6** **Squares and Square Roots**

Find the two square roots of each number.

1. 16 ± 4 **2.** 121 ± 11 **3.** 225 ± 15 **4.** 529 ± 23

5. The Merryweathers want a new square rug for their living room. If the living room is 20 ft × 16 ft, will a square rug with an area of 289 square feet fit? Explain your answer.

Simplify each expression.

6. $\sqrt{64n^2}$ $8|n|$ **7.** $\sqrt{81x^{10}}$ $9|x^5|$ **8.** $\sqrt{9y^{16}}$ $3y^8$ **9.** $\sqrt{b^4}$ b^2

✅ **4-7** **Estimating Square Roots**

Each square root is between two integers. Name the integers. Explain your answer. **10.** 8 and 9; possible answer: 72 is between 64 and 81

10. $\sqrt{72}$ **11.** $\sqrt{200}$ **12.** $\sqrt{340}$ **13.** $\sqrt{610}$

14. The area of a chess board is 110 square inches. Find the length of one side of the board to the nearest hundredth.   **10.49 in.**

✅ **4-8** **The Real Numbers**

Write all classifications that apply to each number.   **17.** whole number, integer, rational, real

15. $\sqrt{12}$ irrational, real   **16.** 0.15 rational, real   **17.** $\sqrt{169}$ **18.** $-\frac{\sqrt{144}}{4}$ integer, rational, real

19. Give an example of an irrational number that is less than −5.   Possible answer: $-\sqrt{30}$

20. Find a real number between 5 and $\sqrt{36}$.   Possible answer: 5.2

✅ **4-9** **The Pythagorean Theorem**

Find the missing side length for each right triangle. Round your answer to the nearest tenth.

21. $a = 3, b = 4, c = $ ▨ 5   **22.** $a = $ ▨ $, b = 24, c = 25$ 7

23. $a = 20, b = $ ▨ $, c = 52$ 48   **24.** $a = $ ▨ $, b = 32, c = 40$ 24

25. A construction company is pouring a concrete foundation. The measures of two sides that meet in a corner are 20 ft and 48 ft. For the corner to be a right angle, what would the length of the diagonal have to be?   **52 ft**

Tell whether the given side lengths form a right triangle.

26. 20, 21, 29 **yes**   **27.** 3.5, 12, 12.5 **yes**   **28.** 3, 7, 9 **no**

5. Possible answer: No; a square rug with an area of 289 ft² is 17 ft long on each side, so it is too long for the 16 ft side of the room.

READY TO GO ON?
Diagnose and Prescribe

NO INTERVENE

READY TO GO ON? Intervention, Section 4B			
Ready to Go On? Intervention	📝 **Worksheets**	💿 **CD-ROM**	🪐 **Online**
✅ Lesson 4-6 🐘 **NS2.4, AF2.2**	4-6 Intervention	Activity 4-6	
✅ Lesson 4-7 🐘 **NS2.4**	4-7 Intervention	Activity 4-7	Diagnose and Prescribe Online
✅ Lesson 4-8 🐘 🔑 **NS1.4**	4-8 Intervention	Activity 4-8	
✅ Lesson 4-9 🐘 🔑 **MG3.3**	4-9 Intervention	Activity 4-9	

YES ENRICH

READY TO GO ON?
***Enrichment*, Section 4B**
📝 **Worksheets**
💿 **CD-ROM**
🪐 **Online**

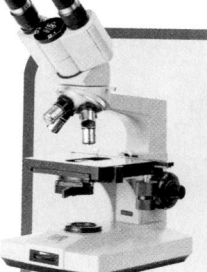

Divide and Conquer

A biologist is growing colonies of two bacteria. As shown in the table, the cells of bacterium A divide in two every hour. The cells of bacterium B divide in two every two hours.

Elapsed Time	Number of Cells	
	Bacterium A	Bacterium B
Start	1	1
1 hour	2^1	—
2 hours	2^2	2^1
3 hours	2^3	—
4 hours	2^4	2^2

1. After 8 hours, how many more cells are there of bacterium A than of bacterium B?

2. How many hours does it take until there are more than 1000 cells of bacterium A?

3. After 24 hours, how many times as many cells are there of bacterium A as bacterium B?

4. At the end of 24 hours, there are about 1.68×10^7 cells of bacterium A. The biologist divides this colony into 3 roughly equal portions. About how many cells are in each portion?

5. As a rule of thumb, if an experiment yields n colonies of bacteria, future experiments are likely to yield between $n - \sqrt{n}$ and $n + \sqrt{n}$ colonies. Suppose an experiment produces 170 colonies of bacterium A. Explain how you can estimate the range of the number of colonies that future experiments will produce.

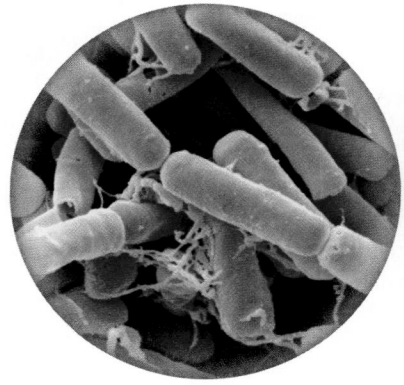
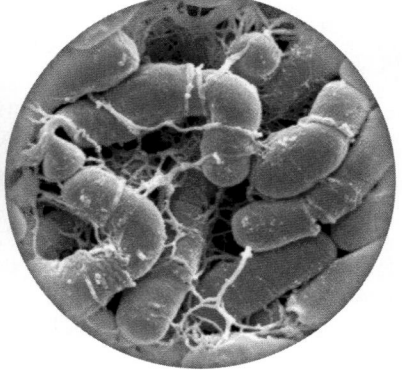

CONCEPT CONNECTION

CHAPTER
4

Organizer

Objective: Assess students' ability to apply concepts and skills in Chapter 4 in a real-world format.

 Online Edition

Problem	Text reference
1	Lesson 4-1
2	Lesson 4-2
3	Lesson 4-3
4	Lesson 4-5
5	Lesson 4-6

Answers

1. 240
2. 10 hours
3. $2^{12} = 4096$
4. 5.6×10^6
5. 157 to 183. $\sqrt{169} = 13$, so $\sqrt{170} \approx 13$ and the approximate range is $170 - 13$ to $170 + 13$.

INTERVENTION

Scaffolding Questions

1. How many cells of Bacterium A are there after n hours? 2^n of Bacterium B? $2^{\frac{n}{2}}$ How many cells of each bacterium are there after 8 hours? 2^8 and 2^4 How can you write these numbers without exponents? 256 and 16

2. What strategy can you use to solve this problem? Possible answer: extend the table How many cells of Bacterium A are there after 10 hours? 1024

3. How many cells of each bacterium are there after 24 hours? 2^{24} and 2^{12} What operation should you use to solve this problem? Division How do you divide 2^{24} by 2^{12}? Subtract the exponents

4. What is 1.68×10^7 in standard notation? 16,800,000 What is this number divided by 3? 5,600,000 How do you write this in scientific notation? 5.6×10^6

5. How can you estimate $\sqrt{170}$? 170 is close to 169 and $\sqrt{169} = 13$, so $\sqrt{170} \approx 13$

Extension

1. How many hours does it take until there are more than 1×10^6 cells of Bacterium B? 40 How many cells are there at this time? 1,048,576

 California Standards

Number Sense

1.1 Read, write, and compare **rational numbers in scientific notation (positive and negative powers of 10)**, compare rational numbers in general.

2.3 Multiply, divide, and simplify rational numbers by using exponent rules.

2.4 Use the inverse relationship between raising to a power and extracting the root of a perfect square integer; for an integer that is not square, determine without a calculator the two integers between which its square root lies and explain why.

Algebra and Functions

2.1 Interpret positive whole-number powers as repeated multiplication and negative whole-number powers as repeated division or multiplication by the multiplicative inverse. Simplify and evaluate expressions that include exponents.

Game Time

Organizer

Objective: Participate in games to practice and apply skills learned in Chapter 4.

Online Edition

Resources

📖 *Chapter 4 Resource File*
Puzzles, Twisters & Teasers

Magic Squares

Purpose: To apply the skill of writing and solving equations to completing a magic square

Discuss Ask students to explain what a magic square is. How can writing and solving equations help you find the missing numbers in a magic square?

Possible answer: In a magic square, the sum of the numbers in any row, column, or diagonal is the same. To find the missing numbers, assign a variable to each. Then write equations and solve them to find the value of one variable. Use that value to find the sum of one row, column, or diagonal. Then use the sum to find the values of the other variables.

Extend Challenge students to create a magic square using the numbers 1–9.

Possible answer:

8	1	6
3	5	7
4	9	2

Equation Bingo

Purpose: To practice solving equations in a game format

Discuss When students get "Bingo," have them demonstrate for the class how the winning solution was obtained.

Extend Have students create new equation cards for each solution on their Bingo cards. Use the new equation cards to play again.

Game Time

Magic Squares

A *magic square* is a square with numbers arranged so that the sums of the numbers in each row, column, and diagonal are the same.

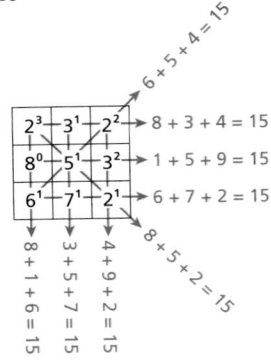

$6 + 5 + 4 = 15$

2^3	3^1	2^2	$\rightarrow 8 + 3 + 4 = 15$
8^0	5^1	3^2	$\rightarrow 1 + 5 + 9 = 15$
6^1	7^1	2^1	$\rightarrow 6 + 7 + 2 = 15$

$8 + 1 + 6 = 15$
$3 + 5 + 7 = 15$
$4 + 9 + 2 = 15$
$8 + 5 + 2 = 15$

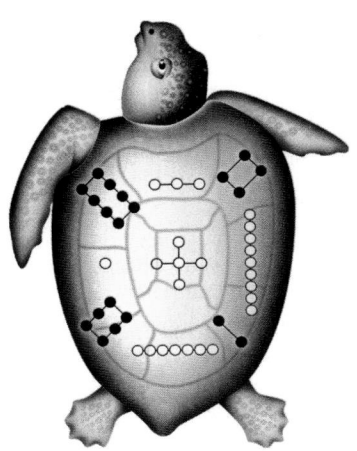

According to an ancient Chinese legend, a tortoise from the Lo river had the pattern of this magic square on its shell.

1 Complete each magic square below.

$\sqrt{36}$	■	2^2
8^0	$\sqrt{9}$	■
■	$3^2 - 2$	■

■	$-(\sqrt{4} + 4)$	$-(9^0)$
$-(\sqrt{16})$	■	0^3
$-(\sqrt{9})$	$2^0 + 1$	■

2 Use the numbers $-4, -3, -2, -1, 0, 1, 2, 3,$ and 4 to make a magic square with row, column, and diagonal sums of 0.

Equation Bingo

Each bingo card has numbers on it. The caller has a collection of equations. The caller reads an equation, and then the players solve the equation for the variable. If players have the solution on their cards, they place a chip on it. The winner is the first player with a row of chips either down, across, or diagonally.

A complete copy of the rules and game boards are available online.

🪐 **go.hrw.com**
Game Time Extra
KEYWORD: MT8CA Games

Answers

1. $-1, 5, 2, 0; 1, -2, 5$

2. Possible answer:

-1	-2	3
4	0	-4
-3	2	1

Materials
- strip of white paper (18 in. by 7 in.)
- piece of decorative paper (6 in. by 6 in.)
- tape
- scraps of decorative paper
- markers
- glue

It's in the Bag!

PROJECT **It's a Wrap**

Design your own energy-bar wrapper to hold your notes on exponents and roots.

Directions

1 Make accordion folds on the strip of white paper so that there are six panels, each about 3 in. wide. **Figure A**

2 Fold up the accordion strip.

3 Wrap the decorative paper around the accordion strip. The accordion strip will stick out on either side. Tape the ends of the decorative paper together to make a wrapper. **Figure B**

4 Write the number and title of the chapter on scraps of decorative paper, and glue these to the wrapper.

Taking Note of the Math

Use the panels of the accordion strip to take notes on the key concepts in this chapter. Include examples that will help you remember facts about exponents, roots, and the Pythagorean Theorem. Fold up the strip and slide it back into the wrapper.

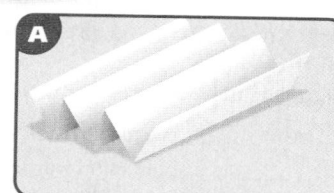

A

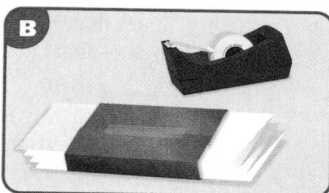

B

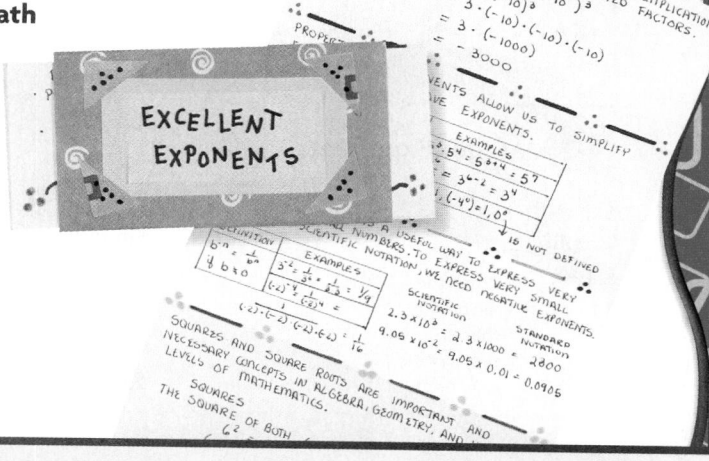

Tips from the Bag Ladies!

Sometimes we have students do this project using actual wrappers from energy bars and other favorite foods. In this case, students can decorate the accordion strip to match the colors of the wrapper.

Many types of paper work well for the wrapper: pieces of wallpaper, construction paper, gift-wrapping paper, and so on. Whatever type of paper students use, you might have them add an ingredients list that shows the contents of the accordion strip.

It's in the Bag!

Organizer

Objective: Make a wrapper for an accordion strip that contains notes on exponents and roots.

Materials: strip of white paper (18 in. by 7 in.), piece of decorative paper (6 in. by 6 in.), tape, scraps of decorative paper, markers, glue

 Online Edition

Using the Page

Preparing the Materials

You can prepare the long strips of white paper by cutting strips from a roll of butcher paper. Alternatively, you might have students tape together shorter pieces of paper until they have a strip of the required length.

Making the Project

Encourage students to fold the accordion strip carefully so that each panel is about the same size. This will make it easier to create a wrapper that fits perfectly.

Extending the Project

Students can start with paper strips of different lengths. Have them calculate the appropriate dimensions of the decorative paper to produce a wrapper that fits snugly.

Organizer

Objective: Help students organize and review key concepts and skills presented in Chapter 4.

Online Edition
Multilingual Glossary

Resources

PuzzlePro®
One-Stop Planner®

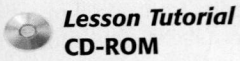
Multilingual Glossary Online

go.hrw.com
KEYWORD: MT8CA Glossary

Lesson Tutorial Videos
CD-ROM

Test & Practice Generator
One-Stop Planner®

Answers

1. irrational number
2. scientific notation
3. Pythagorean Theorem; legs; hypotenuse
4. real numbers
5. $(-3)^2$
6. k^4
7. $(-9)^1$
8. $6x^2$
9. 625
10. -32
11. -1
12. 256
13. -3
14. 64
15. $\frac{1}{125}$
16. $-\frac{1}{64}$
17. $\frac{1}{11}$
18. $\frac{1}{10,000}$
19. 1
20. $-\frac{1}{36}$
21. $\frac{1}{8}$
22. 1
23. $\frac{1}{2}$
24. 0

Vocabulary

base 166
Density Property 199
exponent 166
exponential form 166
hypotenuse 203
irrational number 198
leg 203
monomial 178
perfect square 190
power 166
principal square root ... 190
Pythagorean Theorem .. 203
real number 198
scientific notation 182
square root 190

Complete the sentences below with vocabulary words from the list above.

1. A(n) __?__ is a number that cannot be written as a fraction.

2. __?__ is a short-hand way of writing extremely large or extremely small numbers.

3. The __?__ states that the sum of the squares of the __?__ of a right triangle is equal to the square of the __?__.

4. The set of __?__ is the set of all numbers that can be written on a number line.

4-1 Exponents (pp. 166–169)

 AF1.2, AF2.1

EXAMPLE

- Write $4 \cdot 4 \cdot 4$ in exponential form.

  4^3 *Identify how many times 4 is used as a factor.*

- Simplify $(-2)^3$.

  $(-2) \cdot (-2) \cdot (-2)$ *Find the product.*
  -8

EXERCISES

Write in exponential form.

5. $(-3) \cdot (-3)$
6. $k \cdot k \cdot k \cdot k$
7. -9
8. $6 \cdot x \cdot x$

Simplify.

9. 5^4
10. $(-2)^5$
11. $(-1)^9$
12. 2^8
13. $(-3)^1$
14. 4^3

4-2 Integer Exponents (pp. 170–173)

 NS2.1, AF2.1

EXAMPLE

Simplify.

- $(-3)^{-2}$ *Write the reciprocal; change the sign of the exponent.*

  $\frac{1}{(-3)^2}$
  $\frac{1}{9}$

- 2^0
  1

EXERCISES

Simplify.

15. 5^{-3}
16. $(-4)^{-3}$
17. 11^{-1}
18. 10^{-4}
19. 100^0
20. -6^{-2}
21. $(9 - 7)^{-3}$
22. $(7 - 10)^0$
23. $4^{-1} + (5 - 7)^{-2}$
24. $10 - 9(3^{-2} + 6^0)$

4-3 Properties of Exponents (pp. 174–177)

NS2.1, NS2.3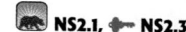

EXAMPLE

Simplify each expression. Write your answer in exponential form.

■ $2^5 \cdot 2^3$

2^{5+3} *Add*
2^8 *exponents.*

■ $\dfrac{10^9}{10^2}$

10^{9-2} *Subtract*
10^7 *exponents.*

EXERCISES

Simplify each expression. Write your answer in exponential form.

25. $4^2 \cdot 4^5$ 26. $9^2 \cdot 9^4$ 27. $p \cdot p^3$

28. $15 \cdot 15^2$ 29. $6^2 \cdot 6^2$ 30. $x^4 \cdot x^6$

31. $\dfrac{8^5}{8^2}$ 32. $\dfrac{9^3}{9}$ 33. $\dfrac{m^7}{m^2}$

34. $\dfrac{3^5}{3^{-2}}$ 35. $\dfrac{4^{-5}}{4^{-5}}$ 36. $\dfrac{y^6}{y^{-3}}$

37. $(4^3)^4$ 38. $(x^{-2})^5$ 39. $(-10^0)^8$

4-4 Multiplying and Dividing Monomials (pp. 178–181)

 AF1.3, AF2.2

EXAMPLE

■ Multiply.

$(-9x^2y)(4x^3y^7)$ *Commutative Property*
$(-9 \cdot 4)(x^2 \cdot x^3)(y^1 \cdot y^7)$ *Multiply coefficients.*
$-9 \cdot 4 \cdot x^{2+3}y^{1+7}$ *Add exponents that*
$-36x^5y^8$ *have the same base.*

■ Divide. Assume that no denominator equals zero.

$\dfrac{-14m^7n}{2m^2}$

$-7m^{7-2}n$ *Divide coefficients. Subtract*
$-7m^5n$ *exponents that have the same base.*

EXERCISES

Multiply.

40. $(-m^9n)(5mn^9)$ 41. $\left(-\tfrac{1}{3}x^2z^6\right)(21xz^5)$

42. $(-a^3b^2)(-a^4)$ 43. $(2rs^5)(10r^5s)$

Divide. Assume that no denominator equals zero.

44. $\dfrac{81p^9}{9p^8}$ 45. $\dfrac{24s^6t^5}{-4s^6t^3}$

46. $\dfrac{-22x^5y^2}{11x^2}$ 47. $\dfrac{14m^{11}n^7}{12m^2n^4}$

Simplify.

48. $(4t^3)^2$ 49. $(-7p^5q^6)^2$

50. $(-6x^4y)^3$ 51. $(10m^2n^5)^4$

4-5 Scientific Notation (pp. 182–186)

NS1.1

EXAMPLE

Write each number in scientific notation.

■ 0.000007

0.000007

7×10^{-6}

■ 62,500

6.2500

6.25×10^4

Write each number in standard form.

■ 3.58×10^4

3.5800

35,800

■ 3.58×10^{-4}

00003.58

0.000358

EXERCISES

Write each number in scientific notation.

52. 0.000000008   53. 73,000,000

54. 0.0000096   55. 56,400,000,000

Write each number in standard form.

56. 1.62×10^3 57. 1.62×10^{-3}

58. 9.1×10^5 59. 9.1×10^{-5}

60. Order 2.3×10^{-5}, -3.1×10^5, 4.9×10^{45}, and -1.7×10^{-4} from least to greatest.

Answers

25. 4^7

26. 9^6

27. p^4

28. 15^3

29. 6^4

30. x^{10}

31. 8^3

32. 9^2

33. m^5

34. 3^7

35. 4^0, or 1

36. y^9

37. 4^{12}

38. $\dfrac{1}{x^{10}}$

39. $(-10)^0 = 1$

40. $-5m^{10}n^{10}$

41. $-7x^3z^{11}$

42. a^7b^2

43. $20r^6s^6$

44. $9p$

45. $-6t^2$

46. $-2x^3y^2$

47. $\tfrac{7}{6}m^9n^3$

48. $16t^6$

49. $49p^{10}q^{12}$

50. $-216x^{12}y^3$

51. $10,000m^8n^{20}$

52. 8×10^{-9}

53. 7.3×10^7

54. 9.6×10^{-6}

55. 5.64×10^{10}

56. 1620

57. 0.00162

58. 910,000

59. 0.000091

60. -3.1×10^5, -1.7×10^{-4}, 2.3×10^{-5}, 4.9×10^4

Answers

61. 4 and −4
62. 30 and −30
63. 26 and −26
64. $7m^2$
65. $2|a^3|$
66. x^6
67. 9 and 10
68. 3 and 4
69. 11 and 12
70. 6 and 7
71. 16 and 17
72. 13 and 14
73. rational
74. irrational
75. rational
76. irrational
77. rational
78. not a real number
79. Possible answer: 3.5
80. 10
81. 10
82. no
83. yes
84. no

4-6 Squares and Square Roots (pp. 190–193)   NS2.4, AF2.2

EXAMPLE

■ Find the two square roots of 400.

$\sqrt{400} = 20$ $-\sqrt{400} = -20$

The square roots of 400 are ±20.

■ Simplify the expression $\sqrt{16r^2}$.

$\sqrt{16r^2} = \sqrt{(4r)^2}$ *Write the monomial as a square.*

$= 4|r|$ *Write the nonnegative square root.*

EXERCISES

Find the two square roots of each number.

61. 16   **62.** 900   **63.** 676

Simplify each expression.

64. $\sqrt{49m^4}$ **65.** $\sqrt{4a^6}$ **66.** $\sqrt{x^{12}}$

4-7 Estimating Square Roots (pp. 194–197)   NS2.4

EXAMPLE

■ $\sqrt{53}$ is between two integers. Name the integers.

$\sqrt{49} < \sqrt{53} < \sqrt{64}$

$7 < \sqrt{53} < 8$

$\sqrt{53}$ is between 7 and 8.

EXERCISES

Each square root is between two integers. Name the integers. Explain your answer.

67. $\sqrt{82}$ **68.** $\sqrt{13}$ **69.** $\sqrt{125}$

70. $\sqrt{37}$ **71.** $\sqrt{259}$ **72.** $\sqrt{174}$

4-8 The Real Numbers (pp. 198–201)   NS1.4

EXAMPLE

State if the number is rational, irrational, or not a real number.

■ $-\sqrt{2}$ *The decimal equivalent*
irrational   *does not repeat or end.*

■ $\frac{2}{0}$ *The number is undefined,*
not real   *so it is not real.*

EXERCISES

State if the number is rational, irrational, or not a real number.

73. $\sqrt{81}$ **74.** $\sqrt{122}$ **75.** $-\sqrt{16}$

76. $-\sqrt{5}$ **77.** $\frac{0}{-4}$ **78.** $\frac{7}{0}$

79. Find a real number between $\sqrt{9}$ and $\sqrt{16}$.

4-9 The Pythagorean Theorem (pp. 203–207)   MG3.3

EXAMPLE

■ Find the length of side b in the right triangle where $a = 8$ and $c = 17$.

$a^2 + b^2 = c^2$
$8^2 + b^2 = 17^2$
$64 + b^2 = 289$
$b^2 = 225$
$\sqrt{b^2} = \sqrt{225}$
$b = 15$

EXERCISES

Solve for the unknown side in each right triangle.

80. If $a = 6$ and $b = 8$, find c.

81. If $b = 24$ and $c = 26$, find a.

Tell whether the given side lengths form a right triangle.

82. 1, 1, 2   **83.** 12, 16, 20   **84.** 7, 12, 19

Simplify.

1. 10^9 **1,000,000,000**   **2.** 11^{-3} $\frac{1}{1331}$ **3.** 2^7 **128**   **4.** 3^{-4} $\frac{1}{81}$

Simplify each expression. Write your answer in exponential form.

5. $\frac{3^3}{3^6}$ $\frac{1}{3^3}$ **6.** $7^9 \cdot 7^2$ 7^{11} **7.** $(5^{10})^6$ 5^{60} **8.** $\frac{11^{-7}}{11^7}$ $\frac{1}{11^{14}}$

9. $27^3 \cdot 27^{-18}$ $\frac{1}{27^{15}}$ **10.** $(52^{-7})^{-3}$ 52^{21} **11.** $13^0 \cdot 13^9$ 13^9 **12.** $\frac{8^{12}}{8^7}$ 8^5

Simplify each expression.

13. $(-4a)^3$ $-64a^3$ **14.** $(7y^4)(-9y^5)$ $-63y^9$ **15.** $\frac{72mn^2}{-8mn}$ $-9n$

16. $(12pq^7)(\frac{2}{3}q^2)$ $8pq^9$ **17.** $\frac{12a^8b^3}{9a^5}$ $\frac{4}{3}a^3b^3$ **18.** $(-5x^3y)^2$ $25x^6y^2$

Write each number in standard form.

19. 4.257×10^5 **20.** 4.8×10^8 **21.** 6.09×10^{-3} **22.** 3.5×10^{-4}
    425,700   **480,000,000**   **0.00609**   **0.00035**

Write each number in scientific notation.

23. 19,000,000,000   **24.** 0.0000039   **25.** $\underset{1,980,000,000}{1.98 \times 10^9}$ **26.** 0.00045 4.5×10^{-4}

27. Order 3.7×10^5, 3.7×10^6, 3.7×10^{-5}, and 3.7×10^{-6} from least to greatest. 3.7×10^{-6}, 3.7×10^{-5}, 3.7×10^5, 3.7×10^6

       23. 1.9×10^{10}
       24. 3.9×10^{-6}

Find the two square roots of each number.

28. 196 ± 14 **29.** 1 ± 1 **30.** 225 ± 15 **31.** 625 ± 25

32. The area of a square rug is 144 square feet. What is the length of the rug?   **12 ft**

Simplify each expression.

33. $\sqrt{y^4}$ y^2 **34.** $\sqrt{121s^8}$ $11s^4$ **35.** $\sqrt{9y^6}$ $3\,|y^3|$ **36.** $\sqrt{25m^2}$ $5\,|m|$

Each square root is between two integers. Name the integers. Explain your answer.

37. $\sqrt{230}$ **15 and 16**   **38.** $\sqrt{125}$ **11 and 12**   **39.** $-\sqrt{60}$ **−7 and −8**   **40.** $-\sqrt{3}$ **−1 and −2**

Write all classifications that apply to each number.

41. $-\sqrt{121}$ **42.** $-1.\overline{7}$ **43.** $\frac{7}{0}$ **not a real**   **44.** $\frac{\sqrt{225}}{3}$
integer, rational, real   **rational, real**   **number**   **whole number, integer, rational, real**

Find the missing length for each right triangle.

45. $a = 10$, $b = 24$, $c = $ ▮   **26**   **46.** $a = $ ▮, $b = 15$, $c = 17$ **8**   **47.** $a = 12$, $b = $ ▮, $c = 20$
                                                                              16

Tell whether the given side lengths form a right triangle.

48. 8, 10, 14   **no**   **49.** 30, 40, 50   **yes**   **50.** 2.5, 6, 6.5   **yes**

CHAPTER TEST

Organizer

Objective: Assess students' mastery of concepts and skills in Chapter 4.

 Online Edition

Resources

 Assessment Resources

Chapter 4 Tests
• Free Response
  (Levels A, B, C)
• Multiple Choice
  (Levels A, B, C)
• Performance Assessment

IDEA Works! CD-ROM
Modified Chapter 4 Test

Test & Practice Generator
One-Stop Planner®

 **California Standards**

Standard	Items
NS1.1	19–27
NS1.4 🔑	41–44
NS2.1	2, 4, 8–10
NS2.4	28–32, 34–40
AF2.1	1–12
AF2.2	13–18, 33–36
MG3.3 🔑	45–50

CHAPTER 4

MASTERING THE STANDARDS

CHAPTER 4

MASTERING THE STANDARDS

go.hrw.com
Standards Practice Online
KEYWORD: MT8CA Practice

Organizer

Objective: Provide review and practice for Chapters 1–4.

Online Edition

Resources

Assessment Resources
Chapter 4 Cumulative Test

Focus on California Standards Benchmark Tests and Intervention

Standards Practice CD-ROM

go.hrw.com
KEYWORD: MT8CA Practice

Cumulative Assessment, Chapters 1–4

Multiple Choice

1. Which expression is NOT equivalent to $3 \cdot 3 \cdot 3 \cdot 3 \cdot 3 \cdot 3$?
   - (A) 3^6
   - (B) 9^3
   - (C) 18
   - (D) 729

2. A number to the 8th power divided by the same number to the 4th power is 16. What is the number?
   - (A) 2
   - (B) 4
   - (C) 6
   - (D) 8

3. Which expression is equivalent to 81?
   - (A) 2^9
   - (B) 3^{-4}
   - (C) $\left(\frac{1}{3}\right)^{-4}$
   - (D) $\left(\frac{1}{3}\right)^{4}$

4. The airports in the United States serve more than 635,000,000 people each year. Which of the following is the same number written in scientific notation?
   - (A) 635×10^6
   - (B) 6.35×10^{-8}
   - (C) 6.35×10^8
   - (D) 6.35×10^9

5. Simplify the expression shown below.
   $(-3x^2z^4)(9xz^3)$
   - (A) $6x^2z^{12}$
   - (B) $6x^3z^7$
   - (C) $-27x^2z^{12}$
   - (D) $-27x^3z^7$

6. The population of India is close to 1.08×10^9. Which of the following represents this population written in standard form?
   - (A) $1,080,000,000$
   - (B) $180,000,000$
   - (C) $1,080,000$
   - (D) $108,000$

7. Jenny finds that a baby lizard grows about 0.5 inch every week. Which equation best represents the number of weeks it will take for the lizard to grow to 1 foot long if it was 4 inches long when it hatched?
   - (A) $0.5w + 4 = 1$
   - (B) $0.5w + 4 = 12$
   - (C) $\frac{w+4}{12} = 0.5$
   - (D) $\frac{w}{0.5+4} = 1$

8. A number k is decreased by 8, and the result is multiplied by 8. This product is then divided by 2. What is the final result?
   - (A) $8k - 4$
   - (B) $4k - 8$
   - (C) $4k - 32$
   - (D) $8k - 64$

9. Which is an irrational number?
   - (A) $\sqrt{9}$
   - (B) 7.125
   - (C) $\sqrt{\frac{1}{4}}$
   - (D) $\sqrt{32}$

10. A quilt is made with 10 square pieces of fabric. If the area of each square piece is 169 square inches, what is the length of each square piece?
    - (A) 12 inches
    - (B) 13 inches
    - (C) 14 inches
    - (D) 15 inches

11. Which number is NOT between 1.5 and 1.75?
    - (A) $1\frac{1}{4}$
    - (B) 1.73
    - (C) 1.62
    - (D) $1\frac{13}{25}$

12. The $\sqrt{18}$ is between which pair of numbers?
    - (A) 8 and 9
    - (B) 7 and 8
    - (C) 4 and 5
    - (D) 3 and 4

California Standards

Standard	Items
NS1.1	4, 6, 11, 20
NS1.2	13
NS1.4	9
NS2.1	2–3
NS2.3	2
NS2.4	10, 12, 21
NS2.5	18
AF1.1	7–8, 17
AF1.2	18
AF2.1	1, 16
AF2.2	5, 15
AF4.0	14, 17
MG2.4	21
MG3.3	19, 22

Teaching Tip

For **Item 3**, students who answered **B** or **D** think that $\frac{1}{81}$ is the same as 81 or do not understand negative exponents.

For **Item 13**, students who answered **A** did not subtract the total eaten pizza from the total amount of pizza, 5.

For **Item 22** part **b**, students may miss subtracting 2.5 ft from Marissa's height of 5.5 feet. Remind students to read each item closely.

Answers

20. **a.** 2,100,000 pounds
    b. 2.10×10^2, 1.0×10^4
    c. $(2.1 \times 10^2)(1.0 \times 10^4) = (2.1 \times 1.0)(10^2 \times 10^4) = 2.1 \times 10^6$. You can add the exponents of 10^2 and 10^4 because the bases are the same. This becomes 10^6. The product of 2.1 and 1.0 is 2.1. So the answer is 2.1×10^6.

21. **a.** between 29 feet and 30 feet
    b. Using an estimated length of 30 feet, Jack and his dad need 900 square feet, or 100 square yards, of carpet to make sure that they have enough.

22. See 4-Point Response work sample.

13. Mrs. Graham ordered five pizzas for her top-performing class. The students ate $\frac{7}{8}$ of the pepperoni pizza, $\frac{3}{4}$ of the cheese pizza, $\frac{4}{5}$ of the veggie pizza, $\frac{2}{3}$ of the Hawaiian pizza, and $\frac{1}{2}$ of the barbecue chicken pizza. How much total pizza was left over?

Ⓐ $3\frac{71}{120}$ Ⓒ $1\frac{49}{120}$

Ⓑ $2\frac{1}{8}$ Ⓓ $1\frac{7}{15}$

14. Which inequality is represented by this graph?

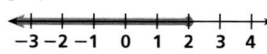

Ⓐ $\frac{x}{-7} \le 14$ Ⓒ $-7x \ge -14$

Ⓑ $-7x \le 14$ Ⓓ $\frac{x}{-7} \ge -14$

15. Which expression is equivalent to $\sqrt{64k^2}$?

Ⓐ $8k$ Ⓒ $8k^2$

Ⓑ $8|k|$ Ⓓ $64|k|$

 Pay attention to the units given in a test question, especially if there are mixed units, such as inches and feet.

Gridded Response

16. What exponent makes the statement $3^? = 27^2$ true?   **6**

17. Chrissy is 25 years older than her dog. The sum of their ages is 37. How old is Chrissy's dog?   **6**

18. Evaluate the expression $\frac{4}{5} - |\frac{1}{2} - x|$ for $x = \frac{1}{5}$.   **1/2**

19. From her house, Lea rode her bike 8 miles north and then 15 miles west to a friend's house. How far in miles was she from her house along a straight path?   **17**

Short Response

20. A bag of pinto beans weighs 210 pounds.

   a. How much does 10,000 bags of pinto beans weigh? Write your answer in standard form.

   b. Write the numbers 210 and 10,000 in scientific notation.

   c. Explain how to use rules of exponents to write the weight of 10,000 bags of pinto beans in scientific notation.

21. Jack works part time with his dad installing carpet. They need to install carpet in a square room that has an area of about 876 square feet. Carpet can only be ordered in whole square yards.

   a. About how many feet long is the room?

   b. About how many square yards of carpet do Jack and his dad need in order to cover the floor of the room? Explain your reasoning.

Extended Response

22. Marissa's cat is stuck in a tree. The cat is on a branch 23 feet from the ground. Marissa is 5.5 feet tall, and she owns a 16-foot ladder.

   a. Create a table that shows how high up on the tree the top of the ladder will reach if Marissa places the base of the ladder 1 foot, 2 feet, 3 feet, 4 feet, and 5 feet from the tree.

   b. How high will Marissa be if she places the base of the ladder the distances from the tree in part **a** and stands on the rung 2.5 feet from the top of the ladder?

   c. Do you think Marissa can use this ladder to reach her cat? Explain your reasoning.

Student Work Samples for Item 22

4-Point Response

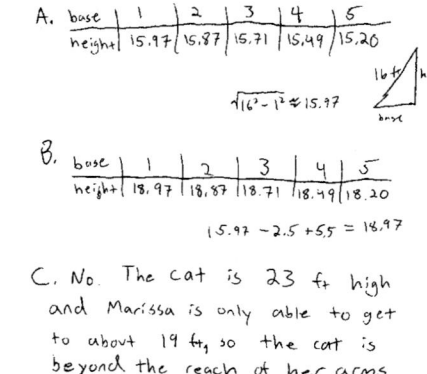

The student calculated both tables correctly and showed work for the first pair of elements in each table. The explanation in part **c** is also correct.

3-Point Response

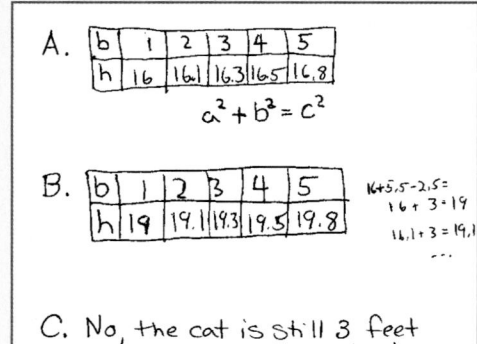

The student knew to use the Pythagorean Theorem, but solved for a hypotenuse instead of a leg.

2-Point Response

a. base	height		b. base	height
1	16		1	13.5
2	15.9		2	13.4
3	15.7		3	13.2
4	15.5		4	13
5	15.2		5	12.7

$\sqrt{16^2 - b^2} = h$

c. No, even with the ladder 1 ft from the base of the tree, she will still be almost 10 ft away from her cat.

The student completed part **a** correctly. However, the student did not account for Marissa's height in part **b**, so answers to parts **b** and **c** are incorrect.

CHAPTER 5

Ratios, Proportions, and Similarity

Pacing Guide

Calendar Planner
Teacher's *One-Stop* Planner®

	Grade-level Standard
◀	Review
▶	Beyond the Standards
A	Assessment
O	Optional

Lesson/Lab	California Standards	Time	Advanced Students	Benchmark* Students	Strategic** Students
5-1 Ratios	Prep for **MG1.1**	50 min	O	◀	◀
5-2 Rates and Unit Rates	⚷ **MG1.3**	50 min	✔	✔	✔
5-3 Proportions	⚷ **AF4.2**	75 min	✔	✔	✔
5-4 Dimensional Analysis	⚷ **AF4.2, MG1.1,** ⚷ **MG1.3**	50 min	✔	✔	✔
Ready to Go On?		25 min	A	A	A
Focus on Problem Solving		25 min	A	A	O
5-5 Similar Figures	Prep for **MG1.2**	50 min	O	◀	◀
5-6 Indirect Measurement	Ext. of **MG1.2**	50 min	▶	O	O
5-7 Scale Drawings and Scale Models	**MG1.2**	50 min	✔	✔	✔
LAB Construct Scale Drawings and Scale Models	**MG1.2**	25 min	O	✔	O
Ready to Go On?		25 min	A	A	A
Concept Connection		25 min	A	A	O
Study Guide: Review		50 min	✔	✔	✔
Chapter Test		50 min	A	A	A

* **Benchmark students** are achieving at or near grade level.

** **Strategic students** may be a year or more below grade level and may require additional time for intervention.

Countdown to Mastery, Weeks ⑨, ⑩, ⑪

ONGOING ASSESSMENT and INTERVENTION

DIAGNOSE	PRESCRIBE

Assess Prior Knowledge

Before Chapter 5

Diagnose readiness for the chapter.
Are You Ready? SE p. 221

Prescribe intervention.
Are You Ready? Intervention Skills 17, 19, 23, 59, 71

Formative Assessment

Before Every Lesson

Diagnose readiness for the lesson.
Warm Up TE, every lesson

Prescribe intervention.
Skills Bank SE pp. SB2–SB24
Review for Mastery CRF, Chapters 1–5

During Every Lesson

Diagnose understanding of lesson concepts.
Questioning Strategies Chapter 5
Think and Discuss SE, every lesson
Write About It SE, lesson exercises
Journal TE, lesson exercises

Prescribe intervention.
Reading Strategies CRF, every lesson
Success for ELL Chapter 5
Lesson Tutorial Videos Chapter 5

After Every Lesson

Diagnose mastery of lesson concepts.
Lesson Quiz TE, every lesson
Ready to Go On? SE pp. 242, 258
Test and Practice Generator

Prescribe intervention.
Review for Mastery CRF, every lesson
Problem Solving CRF, every lesson
Ready to Go On? Intervention Chapter 5
Homework Help Online

Before Chapter 5 Testing

Diagnose mastery of concepts in the chapter.
Ready to Go On? SE pp. 242, 258
Focus on Problem Solving SE p. 243
Concept Connection SE p. 259
Section Quizzes AR pp. 85–86
Test and Practice Generator

Prescribe intervention.
Ready to Go On? Intervention Chapter 5
Scaffolding Questions TE p. 259

Before Assessment of California Standards

Diagnose mastery of California standards.
Focus on California Standards: Benchmark Tests
Mastering the Standards SE pp. 268–269
California Standards Practice CD-ROM

Prescribe intervention.
Focus on California Standards: Intervention

Summative Assessment

After Chapter 5

Check mastery of chapter concepts.
Multiple-Choice Tests (Forms A, B, C)
Free-Response Tests (Forms A, B, C)
Performance Assessment AR pp. 87–98
Test and Practice Generator

Prescribe intervention.
Review for Mastery CRF, every lesson
Lesson Tutorial Videos Chapter 5

KEY: **SE** = *Student Edition* **TE** = *Teacher's Edition* **CRF** = *Chapter Resource File* **AR** = *Assessment Resources* 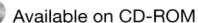 Available on CD-ROM  Available online

Supporting the Teacher

Chapter 5 Resource File

Family Involvement
pp. 1–2, 37–38

Practice A, B, C
pp. 5–7, 13–15, 21–23, 29–31, 41–43, 49–51, 57–59

Review for Mastery
pp. 8, 16, 24, 32, 44, 52, 60

Challenge
pp. 9, 17, 25, 33, 45, 53, 61

Problem Solving
pp. 10, 18, 26, 34, 46, 54, 62

Reading Strategies ELL
pp. 11, 19, 27, 35, 47, 55, 63

Puzzles, Twisters, and Teasers
pp. 12, 20, 28, 36, 48, 56, 64

Hands-On Lab
pp. 67–68, 71–72, 73–74, 75–76, 77–78

Technology Lab
pp. 65–66, 69–70

Workbooks

Homework and Practice Workbook SPANISH
Teacher's Guide...pp. 27–33

Know-It Notebook SPANISH
Teacher's Guide.. Chapter 5

Review for Mastery Workbook SPANISH
Teacher's Guide...pp. 53–66

Focus on California Standards: Intervention Workbook SPANISH
Teacher's Guide

Teacher Tools

Power Presentations
Complete PowerPoint® presentations for Chapter 5 lessons

Lesson Tutorial Videos SPANISH
Holt authors Ed Burger and Freddie Renfro present tutorials to support the Chapter 5 lessons.

Teacher's One-Stop Planner SPANISH
Easy access to all Chapter 5 resources and assessments, as well as software for lesson planning, test generation, and puzzle creation

IDEA Works!
Key Chapter 5 resources and assessments modified to address special learning needs

Questioning Strategies................................... Chapter 5

Solutions Key... Chapter 5

Interactive Answers and Solutions

TechKeys   **Lab Resources**

Project Teacher Support   **Parent Resources**

Transparencies

Lesson Transparencies, Volume 1...................... Chapter 5
 • Teacher Tools
 • Warm Ups
 • Teaching Transparencies
 • Lesson Quizzes

Know-It Notebook.. Chapter 5
 • Vocabulary   • Chapter Review
 • Additional Examples   • Big Ideas

Alternate Openers: Explorations.......................pp. 35–41

Countdown to Mastery....................................pp. 18–21

Technology Highlights for the Teacher

 Power Presentations
Dynamic presentations to engage students. Complete PowerPoint® presentations for every lesson in Chapter 5.

 One-Stop Planner SPANISH
Easy access to Chapter 5 resources and assessments. Includes lesson-planning, test-generation, and puzzle-creation software.

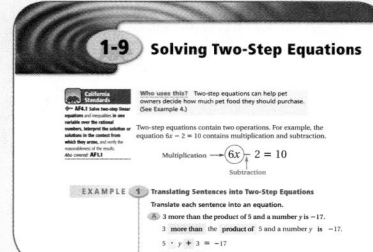 **Premier Online Edition** SPANISH
Includes Tutorial Videos, Lesson Activities, Lesson Quizzes, Homework Help, Chapter Project and more.

KEY: **SE** = *Student Edition*   **TE** = *Teacher's Edition*   ELL English Language Learners   SPANISH Spanish available   Available on CD-ROM   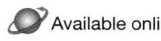 Available online

CHAPTER
5

 **Universal Access**

Teaching tips to help all students appear throughout the chapter. A few that target specific students are included in the lists below.

ENGLISH
LANGUAGE
LEARNERS

Strategic Students

Practice A	CRF, every lesson
Review for Mastery	CRF, every lesson
Reading Strategies	CRF, every lesson
Academic Vocabulary Connections	TE p. 222
Visual	TE p. 249
Ready to Go On? Intervention	Chapter 5
Questioning Strategies	Chapter 5
Know-It Notebook SPANISH	Chapter 5
Homework Help Online	
Lesson Tutorial Videos SPANISH	
Online Interactivities SPANISH	

Special Needs Students

Practice A	CRF, every lesson
Review for Mastery	CRF, every lesson
Reading Strategies	CRF, every lesson
Academic Vocabulary Connections	TE p. 222
Inclusion	TE p. 225
IDEA Works! Modified Resources	Chapter 5
Ready to Go On? Intervention	Chapter 5
Know-It Notebook SPANISH	Chapter 5
Lesson Tutorial Videos SPANISH	
Online Interactivities SPANISH	

English Learners

Reading Strategies	CRF, every lesson
Vocabulary Review	SE p. 262
Academic Vocabulary Connections	TE p. 222
English Language Learners	TE pp. 223, 228
Language Support	TE p. 229
Success for English Language Learners	Chapter 5
Know-It Notebook SPANISH	Chapter 5
Multilingual Glossary	
Lesson Tutorial Videos SPANISH	

Benchmark Students

Practice B	CRF, every lesson
Problem Solving	CRF, every lesson
Academic Vocabulary Connections	TE p. 222
Ready to Go On? Intervention	Chapter 5
Questioning Strategies	Chapter 5
Know-It Notebook SPANISH	Chapter 5
Homework Help Online	
Online Interactivities SPANISH	

Advanced Students

Practice C	CRF, every lesson
Challenge	CRF, every lesson
Reading and Writing Math EXTENSION	TE p. 223
Concept Connection EXTENSION	TE p. 259
Advanced Learners/GATE	TE p. 245
Ready to Go On? Enrichment	Chapter 5

Technology Highlights for Universal Access

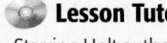 **Lesson Tutorial Videos** SPANISH

Starring Holt authors Ed Burger and Freddie Renfro! Live tutorials to support every lesson in Chapter 5.

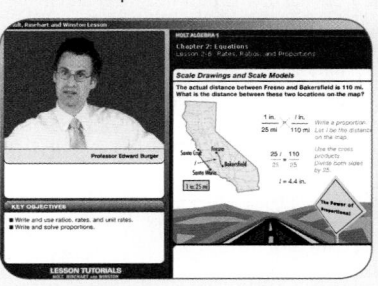

 Multilingual Glossary

Searchable glossary includes definitions in English, Spanish, Vietnamese, Chinese, Hmong, Korean, and other languages.

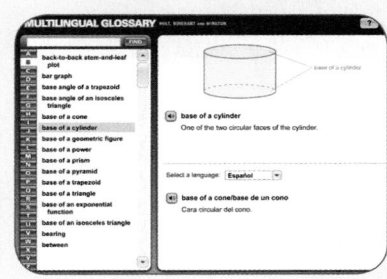

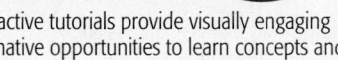 **Online Interactivities** SPANISH

Interactive tutorials provide visually engaging alternative opportunities to learn concepts and master skills.

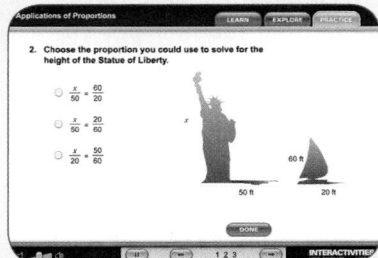

KEY: **SE** = *Student Edition* **TE** = *Teacher's Edition* **CRF** = *Chapter Resource File*  SPANISH Spanish available  Available on CD-ROM  Available online

Ongoing Assessment

Assessing Prior Knowledge

Determine whether students have the prerequisite concepts and skills for success in Chapter 5.

Are You Ready? SPANISH .... SE p. 221
Warm Up .... TE, every lesson

Chapter and Standards Assessment

Provide review and practice for Chapter 5 and standards mastery.

Concept Connection .... SE p. 259
Study Guide: Review .... SE pp. 262–264
Strategies for Success .... SE pp. 266–267
Mastering the Standards .... SE pp. 268–269
Countdown to Mastery Transparencies .....pp. 18–21
Focus on California Standards: Benchmark Tests
Focus on California Standards: Intervention Workbook SPANISH
California Standards Practice CD-ROM SPANISH
IDEA Works! Modified Worksheets and Tests

Alternative Assessment

Assess students' understanding of Chapter 5 concepts and combined problem-solving skills.

Performance Assessment .... AR pp. 99–100
Portfolio Assessment .... AR p. xxxvi
Chapter 5 Project

Daily Assessment

Provide formative assessment for each day of Chapter 5.

Think and Discuss .... SE, every lesson
Write About It .... SE, lesson exercises
Journal .... TE, lesson exercises
Lesson Quiz .... TE, every lesson
Questioning Strategies .... Chapter 5
IDEA Works! Modified Lesson Quizzes .... Chapter 5

Weekly Assessment

Provide formative assessment for each week of Chapter 5.

Focus on Problem Solving .... SE p. 243
Concept Connection .... SE p. 259
Ready to Go On? SPANISH .... SE pp. 242, 258
Cumulative Assessment .... SE pp. 268–269
Test and Practice Generator SPANISH ...One-Stop Planner

Formal Assessment

Provide summative assessment of Chapter 5 mastery.

Section Quizzes .... AR pp. 85–86
Chapter 5 Test SPANISH .... SE p. 265
Chapter Test (Levels A, B, C) .... AR pp. 87–98
  • Multiple-Choice • Free-Response
Cumulative Test .... AR pp. 101–104
Test and Practice Generator SPANISH ...One-Stop Planner
IDEA Works! Modified Tests .... Chapter 5

Technology Highlights for the Teacher

Are You Ready? SPANISH

Automatically assess readiness and prescribe intervention for Chapter 5 prerequisite skills.

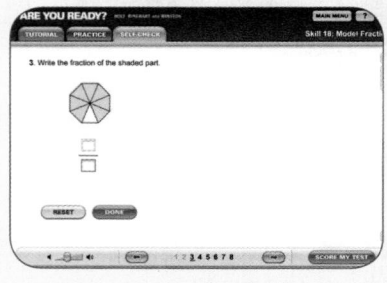

Ready to Go On? SPANISH

Automatically assess understanding of and prescribe intervention for Sections 5A and 5B.

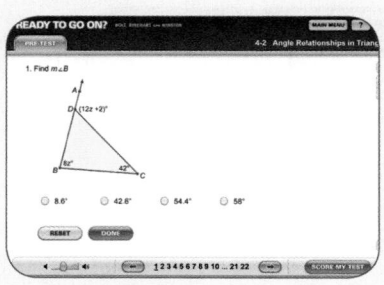

Focus on California Standards: Benchmark Tests and Intervention SPANISH

Automatically assess proficiency with California Grade 7 Standards and provide intervention.

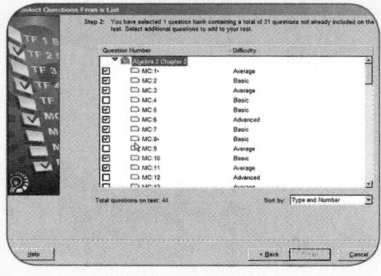

KEY: **SE** = *Student Edition* **TE** = *Teacher's Edition* **AR** = *Assessment Resources* SPANISH Spanish available Available on CD-ROM Available online

Formal Assessment

Three levels (A, B, C) of multiple-choice and free-response chapter tests are available in the *Assessment Resources*.

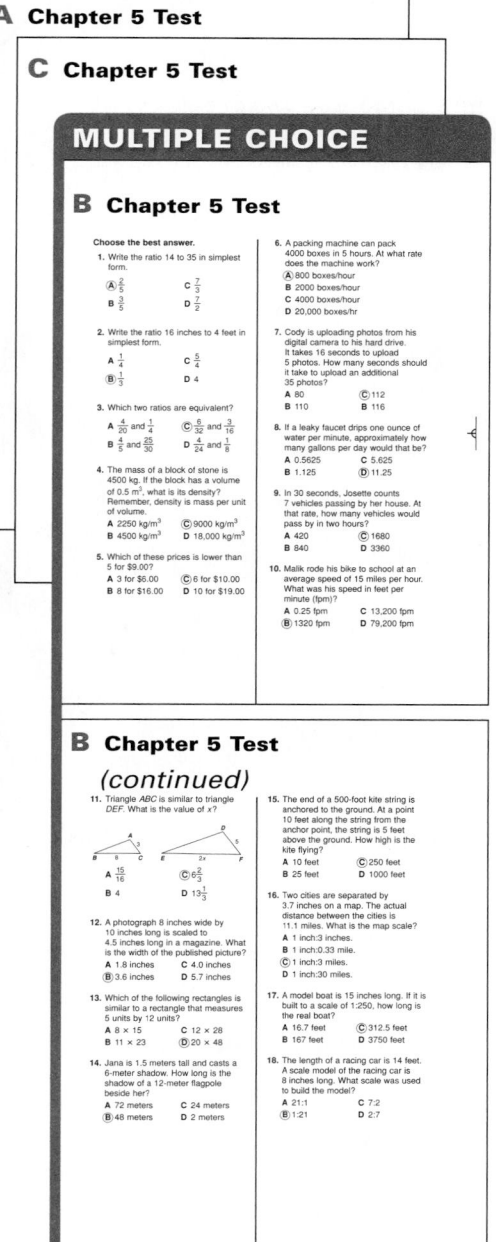

A Chapter 5 Test

C Chapter 5 Test

MULTIPLE CHOICE

B Chapter 5 Test

Choose the best answer.

1. Write the ratio 14 to 35 in simplest form.
   A $\frac{2}{5}$ C $\frac{7}{3}$
   B $\frac{2}{5}$ D $\frac{7}{2}$

2. Write the ratio 16 inches to 4 feet in simplest form.
   A $\frac{1}{4}$ C $\frac{5}{4}$
   B $\frac{1}{3}$ D 4

3. Which two ratios are equivalent?
   A $\frac{4}{20}$ and $\frac{1}{4}$ C $\frac{6}{32}$ and $\frac{3}{16}$
   B $\frac{4}{5}$ and $\frac{25}{30}$ D $\frac{4}{24}$ and $\frac{1}{8}$

4. The mass of a block of stone is 4500 kg. If the block has a volume of 0.5 m³, what is its density? Remember, density is mass per unit of volume.
   A 2250 kg/m³   C 9000 kg/m³
   B 4500 kg/m³   D 18,000 kg/m³

5. Which of these prices is lower than 5 for $9.00?
   A 3 for $6.00   C 6 for $10.00
   B 8 for $16.00   D 10 for $19.00

6. A packing machine can pack 4000 boxes in 5 hours. At what rate does the machine work?
   A 800 boxes/hour
   B 2000 boxes/hour
   C 4000 boxes/hour
   D 20,000 boxes/hr

7. Cody is uploading photos from his digital camera to his hard drive. It takes 16 seconds to upload 5 photos. How many seconds should it take to upload an additional 35 photos?
   A 80   C 112
   B 110   D 116

8. If a leaky faucet drips one ounce of water per minute, approximately how many gallons per day would that be?
   A 0.5625   C 5.625
   B 1.125   D 11.25

9. In 30 seconds, Josette counts 7 vehicles passing by her house. At that rate, how many vehicles would pass by in two hours?
   A 420   C 1680
   B 840   D 3360

10. Malik rode his bike to school at an average speed of 15 miles per hour. What was his speed in feet per minute (fpm)?
    A 0.25 fpm   C 13,200 fpm
    B 1320 fpm   D 79,200 fpm

B Chapter 5 Test
(continued)

11. Triangle *ABC* is similar to triangle *DEF*. What is the value of *x*?
    A $\frac{15}{16}$ C $6\frac{2}{3}$
    B 4   D $13\frac{1}{3}$

12. A photograph 8 inches wide by 10 inches long is scaled to 4.5 inches in a magazine. What is the width of the published picture?
    A 1.8 inches   C 4.0 inches
    B 3.6 inches   D 5.7 inches

13. Which of the following rectangles is similar to a rectangle that measures 5 units by 12 units?
    A 8 × 15   C 12 × 28
    B 11 × 23   D 20 × 48

14. Jana is 1.5 meters tall and casts a 6-meter shadow. How long is the shadow of a 12-meter flagpole beside her?
    A 72 meters   C 24 meters
    B 48 meters   D 2 meters

15. The end of a 500-foot kite string is anchored to the ground. At a point 10 feet along the string from the anchor point, the string is 5 feet above the ground. How high is the kite flying?
    A 10 feet   C 250 feet
    B 25 feet   D 1000 feet

16. Two cities are separated by 3.7 inches on a map. The actual distance between the cities is 11.1 miles. What is the map scale?
    A 1 inch:3 inches.
    B 1 inch:0.33 mile.
    C 1 inch:3 miles.
    D 1 inch:30 miles.

17. A model boat is 15 inches long. If it is built to a scale of 1:250, how long is the real boat?
    A 16.7 feet   C 312.5 feet
    B 167 feet   D 3750 feet

18. The length of a racing car is 14 feet. A scale model of the racing car is 8 inches long. What scale was used to build the model?
    A 21:1   C 7:2
    B 1:21   D 2:7

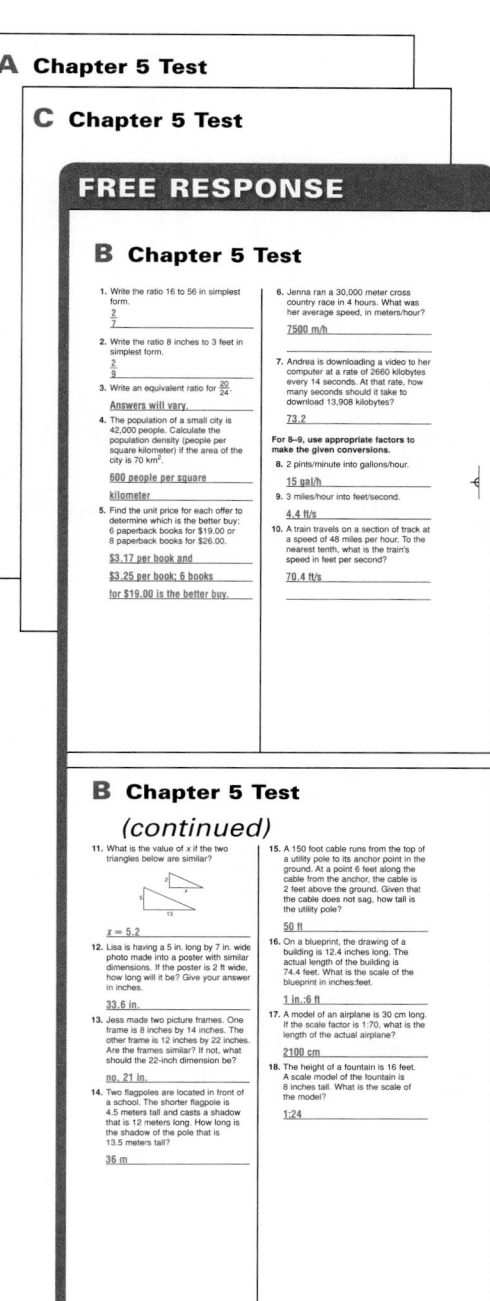

A Chapter 5 Test

C Chapter 5 Test

FREE RESPONSE

B Chapter 5 Test

1. Write the ratio 16 to 56 in simplest form.
   $\frac{2}{7}$

2. Write the ratio 8 inches to 3 feet in simplest form.
   $\frac{2}{9}$

3. Write an equivalent ratio for $\frac{20}{24}$.
   Answers will vary.

4. The population of a small city is 42,000 people. Calculate the population density (people per square kilometer) if the area of the city is 70 km².
   600 people per square kilometer

5. Find the unit price for each offer to determine which is the better buy: 6 paperback books for $19.00 or 8 paperback books for $26.00.
   $3.17 per book and
   $3.25 per book; 6 books
   for $19.00 is the better buy.

6. Jenna ran a 30,000 meter cross country race in 4 hours. What was her average speed, in meters/hour?
   7500 m/h

7. Andrea is downloading a video to her computer at a rate of 2660 kilobytes every 14 seconds. At that rate, how many seconds should it take to download 13,908 kilobytes?
   73.2

For 8–9, use appropriate factors to make the given conversions.

8. 2 pints/minute into gallons/hour.
   15 gal/h

9. 3 miles/hour into feet/second.
   4.4 ft/s

10. A train travels on a section of track at a speed of 48 miles per hour. To the nearest tenth, what is the train's speed in feet per second?
    70.4 ft/s

B Chapter 5 Test
(continued)

11. What is the value of *x* if the two triangles below are similar?
    x = 5.2

12. Lisa is having a 5 in. long by 7 in. wide photo made into a poster with similar dimensions. If the poster is 2 ft wide, how long will it be? Give your answer in inches.
    33.6 in.

13. Jess made two picture frames. One frame is 8 inches by 14 inches. The other frame is 12 inches by 22 inches. Are the frames similar? If not, what should the 22-inch dimension be?
    no, 21 in.

14. Two flagpoles are located in front of a school. The shorter flagpole is 4.5 meters tall and casts a shadow that is 12 meters long. How long is the shadow of the pole that is 13.5 meters tall?
    36 m

15. A 150 foot cable runs from the top of a utility pole to its anchor point in the ground. At a point 6 feet along the cable from the anchor, the cable is 2 feet above the ground. Given that the cable does not sag, how tall is the utility pole?
    50 ft

16. On a blueprint, the drawing of a building is 12.4 inches long. The actual length of the building is 74.4 feet. What is the scale of the blueprint in inches:feet?
    1 in.:6 ft

17. A model of an airplane is 30 cm long. If the scale factor is 1:70, what is the length of the actual airplane?
    2100 cm

18. The height of a fountain is 16 feet. A scale model of the fountain is 8 inches tall. What is the scale of the model?
    1:24

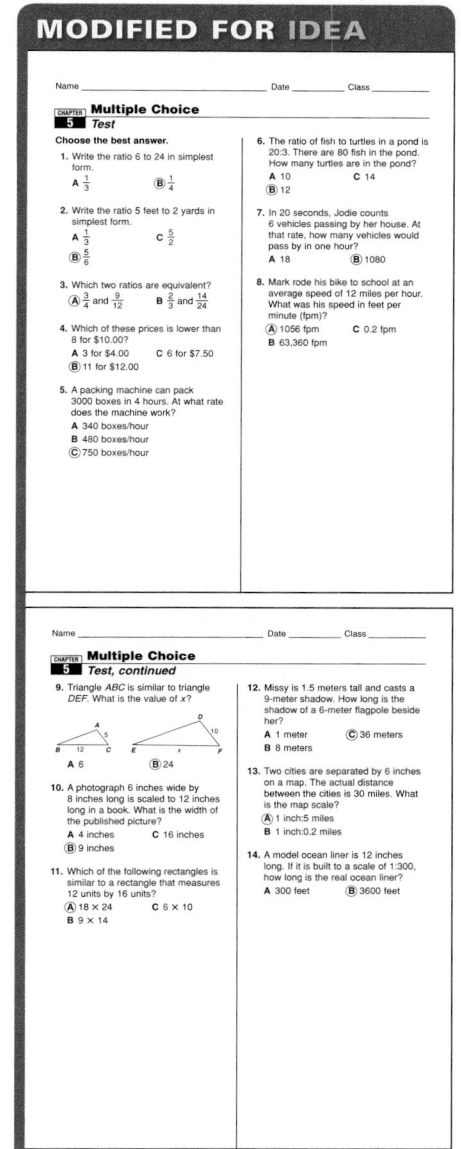

Modified tests and worksheets found in *IDEA Works!*

MODIFIED FOR IDEA

Name _____ Date _____ Class _____

CHAPTER 5 Multiple Choice *Test*

Choose the best answer.

1. Write the ratio 6 to 24 in simplest form.
   A $\frac{1}{3}$ B $\frac{1}{4}$

2. Write the ratio 5 feet to 2 yards in simplest form.
   A $\frac{1}{3}$ C $\frac{5}{2}$
   B $\frac{5}{6}$

3. Which two ratios are equivalent?
   A $\frac{3}{4}$ and $\frac{9}{12}$ B $\frac{2}{3}$ and $\frac{14}{24}$

4. Which of these prices is lower than 8 for $10.00?
   A 3 for $4.00   C 6 for $7.50
   B 11 for $12.00

5. A packing machine can pack 3000 boxes in 4 hours. At what rate does the machine work?
   A 340 boxes/hour
   B 480 boxes/hour
   C 750 boxes/hour

6. The ratio of fish to turtles in a pond is 20:3. There are 80 fish in the pond. How many turtles are in the pond?
   A 10   C 14
   B 12

7. In 20 seconds, Jodie counts 6 vehicles passing by her house. At that rate, how many vehicles would pass by in one hour?
   A 18   B 1080

8. Mark rode his bike to school at an average speed of 12 miles per hour. What was his speed in feet per minute (fpm)?
   A 1056 fpm   C 0.2 fpm
   B 63,360 fpm

Name _____ Date _____ Class _____

CHAPTER 5 Multiple Choice *Test, continued*

9. Triangle *ABC* is similar to triangle *DEF*. What is the value of *x*?
   A 6   B 24

10. A photograph 6 inches wide by 8 inches long is scaled to 12 inches long in a book. What is the width of the published picture?
    A 4 inches   C 16 inches
    B 9 inches

11. Which of the following rectangles is similar to a rectangle that measures 12 units by 16 units?
    A 18 × 24   C 6 × 10
    B 9 × 14

12. Missy is 1.5 meters tall and casts a 9-meter shadow. How long is the shadow of a 6-meter flagpole beside her?
    A 1 meter   C 36 meters
    B 8 meters

13. Two cities are separated by 6 inches on a map. The actual distance between the cities is 30 miles. What is the map scale?
    A 1 inch:5 miles
    B 1 inch:0.2 miles

14. A model ocean liner is 12 inches long. If it is built to a scale of 1:300, how long is the real ocean liner?
    A 300 feet   B 3600 feet

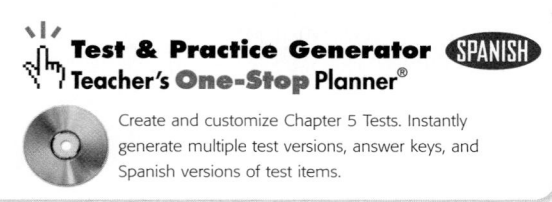

Test & Practice Generator SPANISH
Teacher's One-Stop Planner®

Create and customize Chapter 5 Tests. Instantly generate multiple test versions, answer keys, and Spanish versions of test items.

Focus on Problem Solving

On page 243, students focus on solving real-world problems by choosing an operation to solve the problem.

CONCEPT CONNECTION On page 259, students use scales to calculate the actual dimensions of a scale model.

CHAPTER 5
Ratios, Proportions, and Similarity

5A	**Ratios, Rates, and Proportions**
5-1	Ratios
5-2	Rates and Unit Rates
5-3	Proportions
5-4	Dimensional Analysis
5B	**Similarity and Scale**
5-5	Similar Figures
5-6	Indirect Measurement
5-7	Scale Drawings and Scale Models
LAB	Construct Scale Drawings and Scale Models

CONCEPT CONNECTION

go.hrw.com
Chapter Project Online
KEYWORD: MT8CA Ch5

Proportions are used in the design and construction of scale models like this sculpture of a bow and arrow.

Cupid's Span,
Rincon Park
San Francisco

Math in *California*
This 60-foot-tall sculpture is a scale model of a bow and arrow. The structure is located near San Francisco's Bay Bridge and was created by sculptors Claes Oldenburg and Coosje Van Bruggen. Students will investigate scale models in Lesson 5-7 of this chapter.

Problem Solving Project

Understand, Plan, Solve, and Look Back
Have students:
- Complete the Growing Tiny Trees worksheet to learn more about ratios, proportions, and scale.
- Create a full-size drawing of a small tree that they selected. Divide them into groups to create scale drawings of the tree using different scales that they select. Compare the scale drawings and note their similarities and differences, as well as with the full-size drawing.
- Research the history of bonsai. Invite a bonsai grower to bring some bonsai to class.

Life Science Connection
Project Resources
All project resources for teachers and students are provided online.

Materials:
- Growing Tiny Trees worksheet
- drawing and modeling materials

go.hrw.com
Project Teacher Support
KEYWORD: MT8CA PSProject5

ARE YOU READY?

✓ Vocabulary

Choose the best term from the list to complete each sentence.

1. To solve an equation, you use __?__ to isolate the variable. To solve the __?__ $3x = 18$, divide both sides by 3. inverse operations; multiplication equation

2. For the fractions $\frac{2}{3}$ and $\frac{1}{6}$, 18 is a(n) __?__, but 6 is the __?__.
common denominator; least common denominator

3. Two numbers whose product is 1 are called __?__ or __?__.
multiplicative inverses; reciprocals

common denominator

inverse operations

least common denominator

multiplication equation

multiplicative inverses

reciprocals

Complete these exercises to review skills you will need for this chapter.

✓ Simplify Fractions

Write each fraction in simplest form.

4. $\frac{8}{24}$ $\frac{1}{3}$ 5. $\frac{15}{50}$ $\frac{3}{10}$ 6. $\frac{18}{72}$ $\frac{1}{4}$ 7. $\frac{25}{125}$ $\frac{1}{5}$

✓ Find Common Denominators

Find the least common denominator for each set of fractions.

8. $\frac{2}{3}$ and $\frac{1}{5}$ 15   9. $\frac{3}{4}$ and $\frac{1}{8}$ 8   10. $\frac{5}{7}, \frac{3}{7}$, and $\frac{1}{14}$ 14 11. $\frac{1}{2}, \frac{2}{3}$, and $\frac{3}{5}$ 30

✓ Compare and Order Decimals

Write each set of decimals in order from least to greatest.

12. 4.2, 2.24, 2.4, 0.242   13. 1.1, 0.1, 0.01, 1.11   14. $1.4, 2.53, 1.\overline{3}, 0.\overline{9}$
    0.242, 2.24, 2.4, 4.2   0.01, 0.1, 1.1, 1.11 $0.\overline{9}, 1.\overline{3}, 1.4, 2.53$

✓ Solve Multiplication Equations

Solve.

15. $5x = 60$ 16. $0.2y = 14$ 17. $\frac{1}{2}t = 10$ 18. $\frac{2}{3}z = 9$
    $x = 12$ $y = 70$ $t = 20$ $z = 13.5$

✓ Customary Units

Change each to the given unit.

19. 18 yd = ▓ ft 54   20. 15 gal = ▓ qt 60   21. 30 lb = ▓ oz 480   22. 96 in. = ▓ ft 8

23. 46 c = ▓ pt 23   24. 160 oz = ▓ lb 10   25. 39 ft = ▓ yd 13   26. 108 qt = ▓ gal 27

ARE YOU READY?

Organizer

Objective: Assess students' understanding of prerequisite skills.

Prerequisite Skills

Simplify Fractions

Find Common Denominators

Compare and Order Decimals

Solve Multiplication Equations

Customary Units

Assessing Prior Knowledge

INTERVENTION

Diagnose and Prescribe

Use this page to determine whether intervention is necessary or whether enrichment is appropriate.

Resources

 Are You Ready? Intervention and Enrichment Worksheets

 Are You Ready? CD-ROM

🪐 **Are You Ready? Online**

my.hrw.com

ARE YOU READY?

Diagnose and Prescribe

NO INTERVENE

YES ENRICH

✓ Prerequisite Skill	ARE YOU READY? Intervention, Chapter 5		
	📜 Worksheets	💿 CD-ROM	🪐 Online
✓ Simplify Fractions	Skill 19	Activity 19	
✓ Find Common Denominators	Skill 23	Activity 23	Diagnose and Prescribe Online
✓ Compare and Order Decimals	Skill 17	Activity 17	
✓ Solve Multiplication Equations	Skill 59	Activity 59	
✓ Customary Units	Skill 71	Activity 71	

ARE YOU READY? Enrichment, Chapter 5

📜 **Worksheets**

💿 **CD-ROM**

🪐 **Online**

Organizer

Objective: Help students understand the new concepts they will learn in Chapter 5.

Academic Vocabulary Connections

Becoming familiar with the academic vocabulary on this student page will be helpful to students. Discussing some of the vocabulary terms in the chapter also may be helpful.
Possible answers given.

1. The word *cross* can mean "to intersect," forming an "X" shape. Since a *product* is the result of multiplying, what do you suppose you multiply to find the **cross products** of two fractions? Multiply the values at opposite ends of the X formed by connecting the values.

2. The word *indirect* means "not direct." What do you think it means to find the length of something using **indirect measurement?** Use a method that is not direct, for instance, without using a ruler or tape measure.

3. A **ratio** compares two quantities using a particular operation. Knowing what you do about *rational numbers*, which operation do you think you use in a ratio? division

The information below "unpacks" the standards. The Academic Vocabulary is highlighted and defined to help you understand the language of the standards. Refer to the lessons listed after each standard for help with the math terms and phrases. The Chapter Concept shows how the standard is applied in this chapter.

California Standard	Academic Vocabulary	Chapter Concept
MG1.1 Compare weights, capacities, geometric measures, times, and temperatures, within and between measurement systems (e.g., miles per hour and feet per second, cubic inches to cubic centimeters). (Lessons 5-1 and 5-4)	**compare** decide if items are the same or different **system** method of organizing related things	You write ratios as fractions in simplest form and decide if they are equal. You convert rates within measurement systems.
MG1.2 Construct and read drawings and models made to scale. (Lessons 5-5, 5-6, and 5-7)	**construct** make something a certain way	You draw diagrams that look like actual objects so you can find real measurements.
MG1.3 Use measures expressed as rates (e.g., speed, density) and measures expressed as products (e.g., person-days) **to solve problems;** check the units of the solutions; and use dimensional analysis to check the reasonableness of the answer. (Lesson 5-2)	**expressed** spoken or shown **density** thickness	You use rates to find the cost of one item. Then you compare that unit cost with the unit cost of other items to find the lowest price. You find the density of different substances.
AF4.2 Solve multistep problems involving rate, average speed, distance, and time or a direct variation. (Lesson 5-3)	**solve** find the answer **involving** using	You use properties to show whether two ratios are equal.

Looking Back

Previously, students

- used division to find ratios.
- used proportions to solve problems.
- determined if two figures are similar.

In This Chapter

Students will study

- using ratios to convert within and between measurement systems.
- solving multistep problems involving rate.
- using proportional relationships in similar figures to find missing measurements.

Looking Forward

Students can use these skills

- to use measures expressed as rates to solve problems.
- to use dimensional analysis to find proportional relationships.
- to create scale drawings and scale models.

Reading and Writing Math

CHAPTER 5

Writing Strategy: Write a Convincing Argument

Your ability to write a convincing argument proves that you have a solid understanding of the concept. An effective argument should include the following four parts:

(1) A goal
(2) A response to the goal
(3) Reasoning to support the response
(4) A summary statement

California Standards
English-Language Arts, Writing 1.2

From Lesson 4-1

49. Write About It
Compare 10^2 and 2^{10}. For any two numbers, make a conjecture about which usually gives the greater number: using the greater number as the base or as the exponent. Give at least one exception.

Step 1 **Identify the goal.**

For any two numbers, explain whether using the greater number as the base or as the exponent will generally result in a greater number. Find one exception.

Step 2 **Provide a response to the goal.**

Using the greater number as the exponent usually gives the greater number.

Step 3 **Provide reasoning to support your response.**

For the numbers 10 and 2, using the greater number, 10, as the exponent will result in a greater number.

$$10^2 = 100$$
$$2^{10} = 1024$$
$$100 < 1024$$
$$10^2 < 2^{10}$$

Exception: For the numbers 2 and 3, using the greater number, 3, as the exponent will not result in a greater number.

$$3^2 = 9$$
$$2^3 = 8$$
$$9 > 8$$
$$3^2 > 2^3$$

Step 4 **Summarize your argument.**

Generally, for any two numbers, using the greater number as the exponent instead of as the base will result in a greater number.

Try This

1. A student said a number raised to a negative power is always negative. What error might the student have made? Write a convincing argument or explanation.

Possible answers to *Try This*

1. **Goal:** Find and explain the error.

   Response: A number raised to a negative power is 1 divided by that power with its opposite exponent. So a positive number raised to a negative exponent will always be positive. A negative number raised to a negative even exponent will be positive. A negative number raised to a negative odd exponent will be negative.

   Reasoning:

   $2^{-3} = \frac{1}{2^3} = \frac{1}{8}$;

   $(-3)^{-2} = \frac{1}{(-3)^2} = \frac{1}{9}$;

   $(-2)^{-3} = \frac{1}{(-2)^3} = \frac{1}{-8}$

   Summary: The sign of the number is affected by whether the base is positive or negative and whether the power is odd or even, not whether the power is negative.

Reading and Writing Math

CHAPTER 5

Organizer

Objective: Help students apply strategies to understand and retain key concepts.

 Online Edition

Resources

 Chapter 5 Resource File
Reading Strategies

ENGLISH LANGUAGE LEARNERS

Writing Strategy: Write a Convincing Argument

Discuss Students benefit from explaining math concepts in their own words.

Writing a clear explanation helps them organize their thoughts and identify any misconceptions.

Extend As students work through the *Think and Discuss* exercises in Chapter 5, choose items for which they should write out their explanations, using the strategies presented on this page.

Have students exchange their writing samples to check if others can understand their explanations.

 California Standards

Writing 7.1.2 Support all statements and claims with anecdotes, descriptions, facts and statistics, and specific examples.

Ratios, Rates, and Proportions

 **One-Minute Section Planner**

Lesson	Lab Resources	Materials
Lesson 5-1 Ratios • Write and compare ratios. 🐻 **Prep for MG1.1**	**Hands-On Lab 5-1** **Technology Lab 5-1** *In Chapter 5 Resource File*	
Lesson 5-2 Rates and Unit Rates • Work with rates and unit rates. 🐻 🔑 **MG1.3**	**Technology Lab 5-2** *In Chapter 5 Resource File*	
Lesson 5-3 Proportions • Identify and solve proportions. 🐻 🔑 **AF4.2**		**Optional** Recipe
Lesson 5-4 Dimensional Analysis • Use one or more conversion factors to solve rate problems. 🐻 🔑 **AF4.2, MG1.0, MG1.1,** 🔑 **MG1.3**	**Hands-On Lab 5-4** *In Chapter 5 Resource File*	

MK = *Manipulatives Kit*

Notes

_____

_____

_____

_____

_____

_____

_____

_____

_____

_____

_____

_____

_____

Math Background: Teaching the Standards

RATIOS 🐻 ← AF3.4, ← AF4.2, ← MG1.3
Lessons 5-1 through 5-3

A *ratio* is a comparison of two quantities. The ratio of *a* to *b* can be understood most simply as "*a* divided by *b*." The ratio 8 to 5 may be written as 8:5 or $\frac{8}{5}$, but all of these are the same as 8 ÷ 5, or 1.6.

Strictly speaking, students have divided only rational numbers thus far, and division of irrational numbers has not been defined for them. However, students should realize that this small logical gap will be remedied in later courses and that defining a ratio as a quotient works for any pair of real numbers as long as division by zero is prohibited.

The connection between ratios and slopes is one of the essential understandings of algebra. This is developed more fully in Chapter 7 when students study graphs and functions. However, it is useful to lay the groundwork for this understanding by having students explore quotients of quantities that have a constant ratio.

Consider a store that sells walnuts in bulk at a price of $5 for 4 lb. Because it is possible to multiply or divide the numerator and denominator of a fraction by any nonzero number without changing the value of the fraction, students can generate numerous ratios that are equivalent to $\frac{5}{4}$. Some of these ratios are shown in the table.

Weight (lb)	Cost ($)
1	1.25
2	2.50
4	5.00
8	10.00
10	12.50

Written as the quotient 1.25, the ratio gives the *unit cost* ($1.25 per pound). This connects naturally to students' knowledge of linear equations. For example, to find the amount of walnuts that can be purchased for $9, students can set up and solve the equation 9 = 1.25x.

DIMENSIONAL ANALYSIS 🐻 ← MG1.3
Lesson 5-4

When students are asked to convert 24 feet to inches, they sometimes have difficulty deciding whether to multiply by 12 or divide by 12. *Dimensional analysis* eliminates this dilemma through the use of conversion factors.

A *conversion factor* is simply a fraction that is equal to 1. Since 1 foot = 12 inches, you can write two conversion factors: $\frac{1 \text{ foot}}{12 \text{ inches}}$ and $\frac{12 \text{ inches}}{1 \text{ foot}}$. To convert 24 feet to inches, multiply by the conversion factor that has feet in the denominator so that these units "cancel."

$$24 \text{ ft} = 24 \text{ ft} \cdot \frac{12 \text{ in.}}{1 \text{ ft}} = 288 \text{ in.}$$

Dimensional analysis is especially effective with compound units, such as miles per hour or gallons per minute. As such, it is a valuable tool for checking the reasonableness of answers in problems that deal with ratios or rates. For example, the answer to a problem about the rate of a garden snail may be 0.03 mi/h. However, it would be easier to get a sense of the snail's rate by expressing the answer in feet per minute. Converting miles per hour to feet per minute requires two conversion factors.

$$\frac{0.03 \text{ mi}}{1 \text{ hr}} = \frac{0.03 \text{ mi}}{1 \text{ hr}} \cdot \frac{1 \text{ hr}}{60 \text{ min}} \cdot \frac{5280 \text{ ft}}{1 \text{ mi}} = \frac{2.64 \text{ ft}}{1 \text{ min}}$$

Writing the snail's rate as 2.64 ft/min shows that the answer is reasonable.

Once students are comfortable setting up conversion factors, dimensional analysis offers an efficient way to tackle problems that might otherwise seem overwhelming. To calculate the number of seconds in 3 years, students need only set up a string of conversion factors that link years to days, days to hours, hours to minutes, and minutes to seconds. Each conversion factor is based on a familiar relationship, and the cancellations of intermediate units show that the factors are arranged correctly.

$$3 \text{ yr} = 3 \text{ yr} \cdot \frac{365 \text{ days}}{1 \text{ yr}} \cdot \frac{24 \text{ hr}}{1 \text{ day}} \cdot \frac{60 \text{ min}}{1 \text{ hr}} \cdot \frac{60 \text{ s}}{1 \text{ min}}$$

$$= 94,608,000 \text{ s}$$

5-1 Organizer

Objective: Students write and compare ratios.

 Hands-On Lab
In *Chapter 5 Resource File*

 Technology Lab
In *Chapter 5 Resource File*

 Online Edition
Tutorial Videos

 Countdown to Mastery Week 9

Power Presentations
with PowerPoint®

Warm Up

Write each fraction in lowest terms.

1. $\frac{14}{16}$ $\frac{7}{8}$ 2. $\frac{24}{64}$ $\frac{3}{8}$
3. $\frac{9}{72}$ $\frac{1}{8}$ 4. $\frac{45}{120}$ $\frac{3}{8}$

Also available on transparency

Math Humor

Mathematics is made up of $\frac{1}{2}$ formulas, $\frac{1}{2}$ proofs, and $\frac{1}{2}$ imagination.

 **California Standards**

Prep for Measurement and Geometry 1.1

 **California Standards**

Preparation for MG1.1
Compare weights, capacities, geometric measures, times, and temperatures **within** and between **measurement systems** (e.g., miles per hour and feet per second, cubic inches to cubic centimeters).

Why learn this? You can use ratios to compare the amount of trash you recycle to the average amount recycled in the United States. (See Example 4.)

A **ratio** is a comparison of two quantities. Ratios can be written in several ways. 7 to 5, 7:5, and $\frac{7}{5}$ name the same ratio.

The United States leads the world in both producing and recycling trash.

EXAMPLE 1 **Writing Ratios in Simplest Form**

Write the ratio 18 girls to 12 boys in simplest form.

Vocabulary
ratio
equivalent ratios

$$\frac{\text{girls}}{\text{boys}} = \frac{18}{12} \qquad \textit{Write the ratio as a fraction.}$$
$$= \frac{18 \div 6}{12 \div 6} = \frac{3}{2} \qquad \textit{Simplify.}$$

The ratio of girls to boys is $\frac{3}{2}$, 3:2, or 3 to 2.

When simplifying ratios based on measurements, write the quantities with the same units, if possible.

EXAMPLE 2 **Writing Ratios Based on Measurements**

 Reasoning

Write the ratio 2 feet to 9 inches in simplest form.

First convert feet to inches.

$2 \text{ feet} = 2 \cdot 12 \text{ inches}$ *There are 12 inches in each foot.*
$= 24 \text{ inches}$ *Multiply.*

For help with converting measurements, see p. SB15 in the Skills Bank.

Now write the ratio.

$$\frac{2 \text{ feet}}{9 \text{ inches}} = \frac{24 \text{ inches}}{9 \text{ inches}}$$
$$= \frac{24 \div 3}{9 \div 3} \qquad \textit{Simplify.}$$
$$= \frac{8}{3}$$

The ratio is $\frac{8}{3}$, 8:3, or 8 to 3.

Ratios that make the same comparison are **equivalent ratios**. Equivalent ratios represent the same point on the number line. To check whether two ratios are equivalent, you can write both in simplest form.

---

 1 Introduce

Alternate Opener

 EXPLORATION

5-1 Ratios

Sam and Jill counted the number of foreign cars and the number of domestic cars that entered the parking lot of a movie theater between 5:30 P.M. and 5:45 P.M. for a week. Their results are listed in the table.

	Mon	Tue	Wed	Thu	Fri	Sat	Sun
Foreign	16	25	15	20	40	40	45
Domestic	8	25	10	25	20	50	45

They compared the number of foreign cars to the number of domestic cars by using ratios. For example, the ratio for Monday was $\frac{\text{foreign}}{\text{domestic}} = \frac{16}{8} = \frac{2}{1}$.

1. Write a ratio for each day.
2. Which ratios are greater than the Monday ratio?
3. Which ratios are less than the Monday ratio?
4. Which ratio is the same as the Monday ratio?

Think and Discuss

5. **Explain** what it means if two ratios are equal.
6. **Describe** how the ratios are different if you write them as $\frac{\text{domestic}}{\text{foreign}}$.

Motivate

Pose the following question to the students: "If there are 16 carrots for 8 children, how many carrots will each child receive?"
2 carrots Explain to students that the number of carrots can be compared with the number of students by using the ratio $\frac{16 \text{ carrots}}{8 \text{ children}}$. Show them that the ratio can be simplified to $\frac{2 \text{ carrots}}{1 \text{ child}}$. Explain that the ratios are equivalent because they express the same relationship between the two quantities.

Explorations and answers are provided in *Alternate Openers: Explorations Transparencies.*

EXAMPLE 3 Determining Whether Two Ratios Are Equivalent

Simplify to tell whether the ratios are equivalent.

A $\frac{9}{36}$ and $\frac{2}{8}$

$\frac{9}{36} = \frac{9 \div 9}{36 \div 9} = \frac{1}{4}$

$\frac{2}{8} = \frac{2 \div 2}{8 \div 2} = \frac{1}{4}$

Since $\frac{1}{4} = \frac{1}{4}$, the ratios are equivalent.

B $\frac{9}{12}$ and $\frac{16}{24}$

$\frac{9}{12} = \frac{9 \div 3}{12 \div 3} = \frac{3}{4}$

$\frac{16}{24} = \frac{16 \div 8}{24 \div 8} = \frac{2}{3}$

Since $\frac{3}{4} \neq \frac{2}{3}$, the ratios are *not* equivalent.

EXAMPLE 4 *Environment Application*

On average, each American recycles about 1.08 pounds of trash per day. To see how his family compared, Ahmed weighed his family's recycling on Earth Day and recorded the results in a table. Tell whether Ahmed's family and the U.S. average have the same ratio of trash recycled to number of people. Explain.

Recycling		
	Number of People	Trash Recycled (lb)
Average in the U.S.	1	1.08
Ahmed's Family	4	5.1

$\frac{1}{1.08}$ ← Number of people → $\frac{4}{5.1}$
← Pounds of trash →

$\frac{1}{1.08}$ *Divide.* $\frac{4 \div 4}{5.1 \div 4}$

$\frac{1}{1.08}$ *Simplify.* $\frac{1}{1.275}$

Since $\frac{1}{1.08}$ is not equal to $\frac{1}{1.275}$, the ratio of trash recycled per person in Ahmed's family is not equivalent to the U.S. average.

Possible answers to *Think and Discuss*

1. Two ratios are equivalent if the simplest forms of the ratios are equivalent.

2. 1:2, 4:8, 24:48

3. 2:4 simplifies to 1:2, and 6:10 simplifies to 3:5. Their simplest forms are not equivalent.

4. $\frac{-2}{4} = \frac{5}{-10}$

Think and Discuss

1. **Describe** how to tell if two ratios are equivalent.

2. **Give** three ratios equivalent to 12:24.

3. **Explain** why the ratios 2:4 and 6:10 are not equivalent.

4. **Give an example** of two ratios that are equivalent and have numerators with different signs.

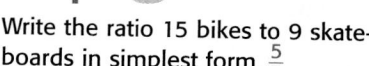
COMMON ERROR ALERT

Some students may want to simplify ratios with a denominator of 1 into whole numbers (e.g., $\frac{3}{1} = 3$). Remind students that ratios are comparisons of two numbers and should be written with both a numerator and a denominator.

Power Presentations with PowerPoint®

Additional Examples

Example 1

Write the ratio 15 bikes to 9 skateboards in simplest form. $\frac{5}{3}$

Example 2

Write the ratio 3 yards to 12 feet in simplest form. $\frac{3}{4}$

Example 3

Simplify to tell whether the ratios are equivalent.

A. $\frac{3}{27}$ and $\frac{2}{18}$ $\frac{1}{9} = \frac{1}{9}$; yes

B. $\frac{12}{15}$ and $\frac{27}{36}$ $\frac{4}{5} \neq \frac{3}{4}$; no

Example 4

At 4°C, four cubic feet of silver has the same mass as 42 cubic feet of water. At 4°C, would 20 cubic feet of silver have the same mass as 210 cubic feet of water? yes

Also available on transparency

---

2 Teach

Guided Instruction

In this lesson, students learn to find equivalent ratios. Explain that ratios are comparisons between two numbers. Point out that ratios are similar to fractions but that ratios can have numbers other than integers in both the numerator and denominator. Teach students to find equivalent ratios by either multiplying or dividing the numerator and denominator by the same number.

 **Teaching Tip** **Inclusion** You may want to use an area model to demonstrate equivalent ratios. For example, shade 3 out of 4 squares on one diagram and 12 out of 16 squares on a second diagram of the same size. Help students see that the ratios represent the same area and are therefore equivalent.

 **Universal Access**
Through Cooperative Learning

Have pairs of students find the missing number to make each pair of ratios equivalent.

1. $\frac{5}{8} = \frac{?}{40}$ 25   2. $\frac{?}{21} = \frac{3}{7}$ 9

3. $\frac{10}{?} = \frac{20}{40}$ 20   4. $\frac{6}{27} = \frac{18}{?}$ 81

Have students explain the strategies they used to find their answers.

3 Close

Summarize

Remind students that a ratio can be expressed with a colon, or as a fraction. Ask students to name two ways to find equivalent ratios. Ask them how many equivalent ratios can be found for the ratio 2:5.

Possible answers: Multiply the numerator and denominator by the same number or divide the numerator and denominator by the same number. Because you can multiply or divide the quantities in a ratio by any number, there are an infinite number of equivalent ratios for 2:5.

5-1 Exercises

California Standards Practice
Preparation for MG1.1

go.hrw.com
Homework Help Online
KEYWORD: MT8CA 5-1
Parent Resources Online
KEYWORD: MT8CA Parent

Assignment Guide

If you finished Example **1** assign:
Proficient 1–3, 12–14, 42–49
Advanced 12–14, 42–49

If you finished Example **2** assign:
Proficient 1–6, 12–17, 26–30, 42–49
Advanced 12–17, 30–34, 36–38, 42–49

If you finished Example **3** assign:
Proficient 1–10, 12–21, 26–30, 39–49
Advanced 12–21, 25, 30–34, 36–49

If you finished Example **4** assign:
Proficient 1–24, 26–30, 39–49
Advanced 12–25, 30–49

Homework Quick Check
Quickly check key concepts.
Exercises: 12, 16, 18, 20, 22

Answers

7. $\frac{4}{11} \neq \frac{2}{11}$; no
8. $\frac{2}{3} \neq \frac{5}{9}$; no
9. $\frac{7}{4} = \frac{7}{4}$; yes
10. $\frac{2}{3} = \frac{2}{3}$; yes
18. $\frac{1}{2} \neq \frac{5}{32}$; no
19. $\frac{3}{5} = \frac{3}{5}$; yes
20. $\frac{1}{3} = \frac{1}{3}$; yes
21. $\frac{1}{3} \neq \frac{1}{4}$; no
23–25. See p. A2.

Math Background

Ratio is an ancient topic in mathematics. For example, ratios were used in early Greek works in arithmetic, geometry, and music.

The word *ratio* comes from the Latin word *ratus*, which means "calculation." During the Middle Ages, the word *pro-portio* was used to indicate what we mean by a ratio today.

California Standards

Standard	Exercises
NS1.1	46–49
NS1.2 🔑	42–45
Prep for MG1.1	1–41

GUIDED PRACTICE

See Example **1** **Write each ratio in simplest form.**

1. 6 lemons to 15 limes $\frac{2}{5}$ 2. 35 cars to 10 trucks $\frac{7}{2}$ 3. 200 men to 140 women $\frac{10}{7}$

See Example **2** 4. 24 inches to 4 feet $\frac{1}{2}$ 5. 10 yards to 2 feet $\frac{15}{1}$ 6. 5 feet to 8 inches $\frac{15}{2}$

See Example **3** **Simplify to tell whether the ratios are equivalent.**

7. $\frac{8}{22}$ and $\frac{2}{11}$ 8. $\frac{6}{9}$ and $\frac{10}{18}$ 9. $\frac{49}{28}$ and $\frac{35}{20}$ 10. $\frac{22}{33}$ and $\frac{18}{27}$

See Example **4** 11. **Entertainment** The table lists prices for movie tickets. Tell whether the ratios of number of tickets to price are equivalent for 1 ticket and 2 tickets. Explain. **Answer: Yes; the ratio $\frac{1}{8.25}$ is equivalent to $\frac{2}{16.50}$.**

Movie Ticket Prices			
Number of Tickets	1	2	3
Price	$8.25	$16.50	$24.75

INDEPENDENT PRACTICE

See Example **1** **Write each ratio in simplest form.**

12. 12 frogs to 42 toads $\frac{2}{7}$ 13. 50 pens to 24 pencils $\frac{25}{12}$ 14. 95 dogs to 150 cats $\frac{19}{30}$

See Example **2** 15. 4 feet to 4 inches $\frac{12}{1}$ 16. 36 inches to 5 feet $\frac{3}{5}$ 17. 2 yards to 15 feet $\frac{2}{5}$

See Example **3** **Simplify to tell whether the ratios are equivalent.**

18. $\frac{8}{16}$ and $\frac{5}{32}$ 19. $\frac{45}{75}$ and $\frac{3}{5}$ 20. $\frac{1}{3}$ and $\frac{15}{45}$ 21. $\frac{16}{48}$ and $\frac{17}{68}$

See Example **4** 22. **Science** A molecule of butane contains 10 atoms of hydrogen to every 4 atoms of carbon. Could a compound containing the number of atoms shown be butane? Explain.
Yes; the ratio $\frac{4}{10}$ is equivalent to $\frac{36}{90}$.

	Hydrogen Atoms	Carbon Atoms
Molecule of Butane	10	4
Compound	90	36

PRACTICE AND PROBLEM SOLVING

Extra Practice
See page EP10.

23. **Cooking** A pancake recipe calls for 2.5 cups of pancake mix to make 10 servings. Carmen uses 3 cups of mix to make 14 servings. Does Carmen have the correct ratio for the recipe? Explain.

24. **Business** Cal pays his employees weekly. He would like to start paying them four times the weekly amount on a monthly basis. Is a month equivalent to four weeks? Explain.

25. **Reasoning** Using the list of ratios shown, create as many pairs of equivalent ratios as you can. Then show an example of two ratios that are *not* equivalent.

$\frac{2}{4}, \frac{2}{5}, \frac{3}{9}, \frac{8}{1}, \frac{2}{10}, \frac{12}{3}, \frac{4}{10}, \frac{4}{1}, \frac{12}{8}, \frac{10}{4}, \frac{9}{6}, \frac{3}{6}$

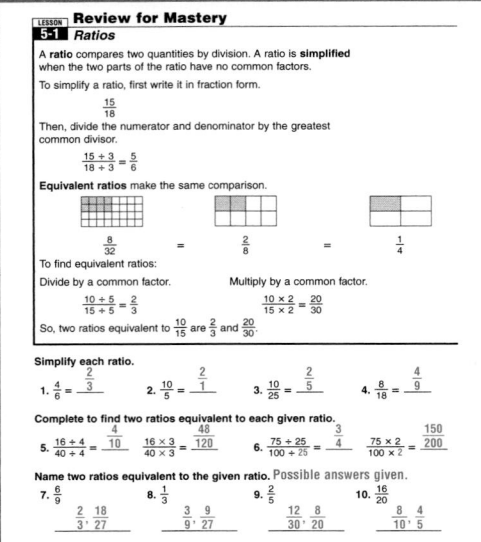

REVIEW FOR MASTERY 5-1

LESSON 5-1 Review for Mastery
Ratios

A **ratio** compares two quantities by division. A ratio is **simplified** when the two parts of the ratio have no common factors.

To simplify a ratio, first write it in fraction form.

$$\frac{15}{18}$$

Then, divide the numerator and denominator by the greatest common divisor.

$$\frac{15 \div 3}{18 \div 3} = \frac{5}{6}$$

Equivalent ratios make the same comparison.

$$\frac{8}{32} = \frac{2}{8} = \frac{1}{4}$$

To find equivalent ratios:
Divide by a common factor.   Multiply by a common factor.

$$\frac{10 \div 5}{15 \div 5} = \frac{2}{3} \qquad \frac{10 \times 2}{15 \times 2} = \frac{20}{30}$$

So, two ratios equivalent to $\frac{10}{15}$ are $\frac{2}{3}$ and $\frac{20}{30}$.

Simplify each ratio.

1. $\frac{4}{6} = \frac{2}{3}$ 2. $\frac{10}{5} = \frac{2}{1}$ 3. $\frac{10}{25} = \frac{2}{5}$ 4. $\frac{8}{18} = \frac{4}{9}$

Complete to find two ratios equivalent to each given ratio.

5. $\frac{16 \div 4}{40 \div 4} = \frac{4}{10} \quad \frac{16 \times 3}{40 \times 3} = \frac{48}{120}$ 6. $\frac{75 \div 25}{100 \div 25} = \frac{3}{4} \quad \frac{75 \times 2}{100 \times 2} = \frac{150}{200}$

Name two ratios equivalent to the given ratio. Possible answers given.

7. $\frac{6}{9}$ 8. $\frac{1}{3}$ 9. $\frac{2}{5}$ 10. $\frac{16}{20}$
$\frac{2}{3}, \frac{18}{27}$ $\frac{3}{9}, \frac{9}{27}$ $\frac{12}{30}, \frac{8}{20}$ $\frac{4}{5}, \frac{8}{10}$

PRACTICE 5-1

LESSON 5-1 Practice B
Ratios

Write the ratio in simplest form.

1. 15 cows to 25 sheep 2. 24 cars to 18 trucks 3. 30 knives to 27 spoons
3:5 4:3 10:9

4. 34 mice to 17 cats 5. 12 notebooks to 20 pens 6. 44 students to 2 teachers
2:1 3:5 22:1

7. 9 feet to 84 inches 8. 6 yards to 18 feet 9. 12 feet to 12 inches
9:7 1:1 12:1

Simplify to tell whether the ratios are equal.

10. $\frac{13}{39}$ and $\frac{16}{48}$ 11. $\frac{21}{49}$ and $\frac{28}{56}$ 12. $\frac{12}{28}$ and $\frac{18}{42}$ 13. $\frac{18}{27}$ and $\frac{10}{15}$
yes, $\frac{1}{3} = \frac{1}{3}$ no, $\frac{3}{7} \neq \frac{1}{2}$ yes, $\frac{3}{7} = \frac{3}{7}$ yes, $\frac{2}{3} = \frac{2}{3}$

14. $\frac{24}{27}$ and $\frac{27}{30}$ 15. $\frac{14}{10}$ and $\frac{35}{25}$ 16. $\frac{10}{32}$ and $\frac{30}{80}$ 17. $\frac{16}{48}$ and $\frac{15}{45}$
no, $\frac{8}{9} \neq \frac{9}{10}$ yes, $\frac{7}{5} = \frac{7}{5}$ yes, $\frac{5}{16} = \frac{5}{16}$ yes, $\frac{1}{3} = \frac{1}{3}$

18. Mrs. Walters wanted one daffodil plant for every 2 tulip plants in her garden. If she planted 20 daffodil bulbs, how many tulip bulbs did she plant?
40 tulip bulbs

19. In a survey, 9 out of 10 doctors recommended a certain medicine. If 80 doctors were surveyed, how many doctors recommended the medicine?
72 doctors

20. A molecule of sodium carbonate contains 2 atoms of sodium to every 3 atoms of oxygen. Could a compound containing 12 atoms of sodium and 15 atoms of oxygen be sodium carbonate? Explain.
No, the ratio $\frac{12}{15}$ is not equivalent to $\frac{2}{3}$.

Tell whether the ratios are equivalent. If not, find a ratio equivalent to the first ratio. **Possible answers:**

26. $\frac{4}{12}$ and $\frac{10}{15}$ no; $\frac{1}{3}$ 27. $\frac{5}{7}$ and $\frac{100}{140}$ yes   28. $\frac{4}{7}$ and $\frac{12}{49}$ no; $\frac{8}{14}$

29. $\frac{30}{36}$ and $\frac{15}{16}$ no; $\frac{5}{6}$ 30. $\frac{15}{14}$ and $\frac{45}{42}$ yes   31. $\frac{12}{25}$ and $\frac{24}{50}$ yes

32. $\frac{18}{84}$ and $\frac{6}{56}$ no; $\frac{3}{14}$ 33. $\frac{22}{12}$ and $\frac{42}{16}$ no; $\frac{11}{6}$ 34. $\frac{22}{242}$ and $\frac{44}{484}$ yes

35. **Hobbies** A bicycle chain moves along two sprockets when you shift gears. The number of teeth on the front sprocket and the number of teeth on the rear sprocket form a ratio. Equivalent ratios provide equal pedaling power. Find a ratio equivalent to the ratio $\frac{52}{24}$. $\frac{39}{18}$

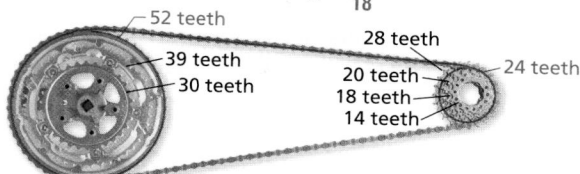

- 52 teeth
- 39 teeth
- 30 teeth
- 28 teeth
- 20 teeth
- 18 teeth
- 14 teeth
- 24 teeth

 36. **What's the Error?** A student said that the ratios $\frac{3}{4}$ and $\frac{9}{16}$ were equivalent. What error did the student make?

37. **Write About It** Describe at least two ways, given a ratio, to write an equivalent ratio.

38. **Challenge** Using each of the numbers 3, 9, 27, and 81 once, write all possible pairs of equivalent ratios.

SPIRAL STANDARDS REVIEW

NS1.1, ← NS1.2, Prep for MG1.1

39. **Multiple Choice** Which of the following ratios is equivalent to the ratio 3:4?

Ⓐ 6:10   Ⓑ 8:6   Ⓒ 9:12   Ⓓ 10:40

40. **Multiple Choice** Which of the following does NOT show equivalent ratios?

Ⓐ $\frac{5}{8} = \frac{10}{16}$ Ⓑ $\frac{15}{24} = \frac{10}{16}$ Ⓒ $\frac{5}{9} = \frac{10}{16}$ Ⓓ $\frac{25}{40} = \frac{10}{16}$

41. **Short Response** One ticket to the aquarium costs $10.50. Three tickets to the aquarium cost $31.50. Are the ratios of number of tickets to price equivalent for 1 ticket and 3 tickets? Explain.   **Yes; the ratio $\frac{1}{10.50}$ is equivalent to $\frac{3}{31.50}$.**

Multiply. (Lesson 2-4)

42. $-2.4(-7)$ **16.8**   43. $3.2(-1.7)$ **-5.44**   44. $-0.03(8.6)$ **-0.258**   45. $-1.07(-0.6)$ **0.642**

Write each number in scientific notation. (Lesson 4-5)

46. 0.0009   **9×10^{-4}**   47. 12,000,000   **1.2×10^{7}**   48. 7,560,000   **7.56×10^{6}**   49. 0.0000011   **1.1×10^{-6}**

CHALLENGE 5-1

LESSON 5-1 Challenge
Mixing It Up

In a pair of equal ratios, there are 4 terms. The 1st and 4th are called **extremes.** $\frac{\text{1st (extreme)}}{\text{2nd (mean)}} = \frac{\text{3rd (mean)}}{\text{4th (extreme)}}$ The 2nd and 3rd are called **means.**

In the following exercises, you will explore some properties of equal ratios.

1. Explain why the ratios $\frac{6}{9}$ and $\frac{8}{12}$ are equal.

Both ratios are equivalent to $\frac{2}{3}$.

2. a. Rewrite $\frac{6}{9} = \frac{8}{12}$ by interchanging the means and extremes. Determine if the resulting statement is true. Explain.

$\frac{9}{6} = \frac{12}{8}$; yes, since each ratio is equivalent to $\frac{3}{2}$

b. Generalize these results by completing this statement:
If $\frac{a}{b} = \frac{c}{d}$, then it is also true that:

$\frac{b}{a} = \frac{d}{c}$

3. a. Consider changing each ratio of $\frac{6}{9} = \frac{8}{12}$ by addition. Determine if the ratios $\frac{6+9}{9}$ and $\frac{8+12}{12}$ are equal. Explain.

yes; each ratio is equivalent to $\frac{5}{3}$

b. Generalize these results by completing this statement:
If $\frac{a}{b} = \frac{c}{d}$, then it is also true that:

$\frac{a+b}{b} = \frac{c+d}{d}$

c. Determine if the ratios $\frac{6-9}{9}$ and $\frac{8-12}{12}$ are equal. Explain.

yes; each ratio is equivalent to $\frac{-1}{3}$

d. Generalize these results. If $\frac{a}{b} = \frac{c}{d}$, then it is also true that:

$\frac{a-b}{b} = \frac{c-d}{d}$

PROBLEM SOLVING 5-1

LESSON 5-1 Problem Solving
Ratios

A medicine for dogs indicates that the medicine should be administered in the ratio 0.5 tsp per 5 lb, based on the weight of the dog. Write the correct answer.

1. Jaime has a 60 lb dog. She plans to give the dog 12 teaspoons of medicine. Is she administering the medicine correctly?

no

2. Jaime also has a 15 lb puppy. She plans to give the puppy 1.5 teaspoons of medicine. Is she administering the medicine correctly?

yes

Sports statistics can be given as ratios. Find the ratios for the given statistics. Reduce each ratio.

3. In 69 games, Darrel Armstrong of the Orlando Magic had 136 steals and 144 turnovers. What is his steals per turnover ratio?

$\frac{17}{18}$

4. In 69 games, Ben Wallace of the Detroit Pistons blocked 234 shots. What is his blocks per game ratio?

$\frac{78}{23}$

Choose the letter for the best answer.

5. There are 675 students and 30 teachers in the middle school. What is the ratio of teachers to students?

Ⓐ $\frac{45}{2}$ Ⓒ $\frac{1}{27}$
Ⓑ $\frac{2}{45}$ Ⓓ $\frac{27}{1}$

6. In a science experiment, out of a sample of seeds, 13 sprouted and 7 didn't. What is the ratio of seeds that sprouted to the number of seeds planted?

Ⓕ $\frac{13}{7}$ Ⓗ $\frac{13}{20}$
Ⓖ $\frac{7}{13}$ Ⓙ $\frac{7}{20}$

7. Many Internet services advertise their customer to modem ratio. One company advertises a 10 to 1 customer to modem ratio. Find a ratio that is equivalent to the $\frac{10}{1}$.

Ⓐ $\frac{40}{4}$ Ⓒ $\frac{400}{4}$
Ⓑ $\frac{20}{2}$ Ⓓ $\frac{50}{10}$

8. A molecule of sulfuric acid contains 2 atoms of hydrogen to every 4 atoms of oxygen. Which combination of hydrogen and oxygen atoms could be sulfuric acid?

Ⓕ 4 atoms of hydrogen and 6 atoms of oxygen
Ⓖ 6 atoms of hydrogen and 10 atoms of oxygen
Ⓗ 6 atoms of hydrogen and 12 atoms of oxygen
Ⓙ 16 atoms of hydrogen and 8 atoms of oxygen

Answers

36. Possible answer: $\frac{3}{4}$ and $\frac{9}{16}$ are both in simplest form and are not equal. $\frac{9}{16} = \left(\frac{3}{4}\right)^2$, so it may appear on first glance that the ratios are equivalent.

37–38. See p. A3.

 Teaching Tip   **Multiple Choice** For **Exercise 39**, remind students that they can quickly eliminate choices **B** and **D**, because the first number of each ratio, 8 and 10, respectively, cannot be divided evenly by 3.

 **Journal**

Have students write about some real-world situations in which ratios are useful. Examples might include figuring the cost of a number of items or changing the quantities of ingredients for a recipe.

Power Presentations with PowerPoint®

✓ **5-1 Lesson Quiz**

Write each ratio in simplest form.

1. 22 tigers to 44 lions $\frac{1}{2}$

2. 5 feet to 14 inches $\frac{30}{7}$

Find two ratios that are equivalent to each given ratio.

3. $\frac{4}{15}$ Possible answer: $\frac{8}{30}$, $\frac{12}{45}$

4. $\frac{8}{21}$ Possible answer: $\frac{16}{42}$, $\frac{24}{63}$

Simplify to tell whether the ratios are equivalent.

5. $\frac{16}{10}$ and $\frac{32}{20}$ $\frac{8}{5} = \frac{8}{5}$; yes

6. $\frac{36}{24}$ and $\frac{28}{18}$ $\frac{3}{2} \neq \frac{14}{9}$; no

7. Kate poured 8 oz of juice from a 64 oz bottle. Brian poured 16 oz of juice from a 128 oz bottle. Are the ratios of poured juice to starting amount of juice equivalent? Yes; $\frac{8}{64}$ and $\frac{16}{128}$ both equal $\frac{1}{8}$.

Also available on transparency

Objective: Students work with rates and unit rates.

Technology Lab
In *Chapter 5 Resource File*

Online Edition
Tutorial Videos, Interactivities

Countdown to Mastery Week 9

Power Presentations
with PowerPoint®

Warm Up

Divide. Round answers to the nearest tenth.

1. $\frac{420}{18}$ 23.3
2. $\frac{73}{21}$ 3.5
3. $\frac{380}{16}$ 23.8
4. $\frac{430}{18}$ 23.9

Also available on transparency

Math Humor

Wow! 9 out of 10 cars this company has built in the past 20 years are still on the road.

Amazing. Except that the company just started manufacturing cars last year!

California Standards

MG1.3 Use measures expressed as rates (e.g., speed, density) and measures expressed as products (e.g., person-days) **to solve problems;** check the units of the solutions; and use dimensional analysis to check the reasonableness of the answer.

Why learn this? You can use unit rates to express speed and density. (See Examples 1 and 2.)

A **rate** is a ratio that compares two quantities measured in different units.

ratio: $\frac{90}{3}$ rate: $\frac{90 \text{ miles}}{3 \text{ hours}}$ ← *Read as "90 miles per 3 hours."*

Unit rates are rates in which the second quantity is 1. The ratio $\frac{90}{3}$ can be simplified by dividing: $\frac{90}{3} = \frac{30}{1}$.

unit rate: $\frac{30 \text{ miles}}{1 \text{ hour}}$, or 30 mi/h

EXAMPLE 1   Finding Unit Rates

Miki can type 120 words in 3 minutes. How many words can she type per minute?

$\frac{120 \text{ words}}{3 \text{ minutes}}$ *Write the rate.*

$\frac{120 \text{ words} \div 3}{3 \text{ minutes} \div 3} = \frac{40 \text{ words}}{1 \text{ minute}}$ *Divide to find words per minute.*

Miki can type 40 words per minute.

Density is a ratio that compares mass and volume. For example, gold has a density of $\frac{19,300 \text{ kg}}{1 \text{ m}^3}$, or 19,300 kilograms per cubic meter. Since density is measured in units of mass per unit of volume, it is a unit rate.

EXAMPLE 2   Science Application

A Four cubic meters of silver has a mass of 41,960 kilograms. What is the density of silver?

$\frac{41,960 \text{ kg}}{4 \text{ m}^3}$ *Write the rate.*

$\frac{41,960 \text{ kg} \div 4}{4 \text{ m}^3 \div 4}$ *Divide to find kilograms per 1 m³.*

$\frac{10,490 \text{ kg}}{1 \text{ m}^3}$

Silver has a density of 10,490 kg/m³.

B Aluminum weighing 1350 kilograms has a volume of 0.5 cubic meters. What is the density of aluminum?

$\frac{1350 \text{ kg}}{0.5 \text{ m}^3}$ *Write the rate.*

$\frac{1350 \text{ kg} \cdot 2}{0.5 \text{ m}^3 \cdot 2}$ *Multiply to find kilograms per 1 m³.*

$\frac{2700 \text{ kg}}{1 \text{ m}^3}$

Aluminum has a density of 2700 kg/m³.

1 Introduce
Alternate Opener

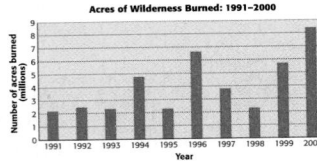

EXPLORATION

5-2 Rates and Unit Rates

The bar graph shows the number of acres of wilderness burned each year from 1991 to 2000. Each bar represents a *unit rate,* because it shows the number of acres burned in *one* year.

Acres of Wilderness Burned: 1991–2000

1. The National Interagency Fire Center reported that an average of 3,647,883 acres were burned per year from 1991 to 2000.
   a. Is the average also a unit rate?
   b. In what years were the number of acres burned above the average?
   c. In what years were the number of acres burned below the average?

Think and Discuss

2. **Explain** why a unit rate such as 40 miles per hour may be more useful than an equivalent rate such as 60 miles per 1.5 hours.

Motivate

ENGLISH LANGUAGE LEARNERS

Present the following problem: A package of 8 rolls costs $2.00. A package of 10 rolls costs $2.79. Which is the better buy?

The 8-roll package; unit prices are 25 cents and 27.9 cents, respectively.

Encourage students to give answers and explain how they got their answers. Explain that one way to compare prices is to use *unit prices,* such as the price per roll. A unit price is a type of *unit rate,* one of the lesson topics.

Explorations and answers are provided in *Alternate Openers: Explorations Transparencies.*

California Standards

Measurement and Geometry **1.3**

EXAMPLE 3 — Estimating Unit Rates

Estimate each unit rate.

A 560 miles in 9 hours

$$\frac{560 \text{ miles}}{9 \text{ hours}} \approx \frac{560 \text{ miles}}{10 \text{ hours}}$$

Choose a number close to 9 that is a factor of 560.

$$\approx \frac{56 \text{ miles}}{1 \text{ hour}}$$

Divide to find miles per hour.

560 miles in 9 hours is approximately 56 miles per hour.

B 143 students to 7 teachers

$$\frac{143 \text{ students}}{7 \text{ teachers}} \approx \frac{140 \text{ students}}{7 \text{ teachers}}$$

Choose a number close to 143 that is divisible by 7.

$$\approx \frac{20 \text{ students}}{1 \text{ teacher}}$$

Divide to find students per teacher.

143 students to 7 teachers is approximately 20 students per teacher.

Unit price is a unit rate used to compare price per item.

EXAMPLE 4 — Finding Unit Prices to Compare Costs

A Blank CDs can be purchased in packages of 3 for $1.99 or 20 for $10.99. Which package has the lower unit price?

$$\frac{\text{price for package}}{\text{number of CDs}} = \frac{\$1.99}{3 \text{ CDs}} \approx \$0.66 \text{ per CD}$$

Divide the price by the number of CDs.

$$\frac{\text{price for package}}{\text{number of CDs}} = \frac{\$10.99}{20 \text{ CDs}} \approx \$0.55 \text{ per CD}$$

The package of 20 has the lower unit price.

B Arnie can buy a 16 oz box of cereal for $5.49 or a 20 oz box for $5.99. Which box has the lower unit price?

$$\frac{\text{price for box}}{\text{number of ounces}} = \frac{\$5.49}{16 \text{ oz}} \approx \$0.34/\text{oz}$$

Divide the price by the number of ounces.

$$\frac{\text{price for box}}{\text{number of ounces}} = \frac{\$5.99}{20 \text{ oz}} \approx \$0.30/\text{oz}$$

The 20 oz box has the lower unit price.

Think and Discuss

1. **Choose** the quantity that has a lower unit price: 6 oz for $1.29 or 15 oz for $3.00. Explain your answer.
2. **Give** two rates by which speed could be measured.

Power Presentations with PowerPoint®

Additional Examples

Example 1

Geoff can type 30 words in half a minute. How many words can he type per minute? 60 words

Example 2

A. Five cubic meters of copper has a mass of 44.800 kilograms. What is the density of copper? 8960 kg/m³

B. A piece of gold with a volume of 0.5 cubic meters weighs 9650 kilograms. What is the density of gold? 19,300 kg/m³

Example 3

Estimate each unit rate.

A. 468 students to 91 computers
5 students per computer

B. 313 feet in 8 seconds
40 feet per second

Example 4

A. Pens can be purchased in a 5-pack for $1.95 or a 15-pack for $6.20. Which pack has the lower unit price? 5-pack

B. Jamie can buy a 15 oz jar of peanut butter for $2.19 or a 20 oz jar for $2.78. Which jar has the lower unit price? 20 oz jar

Also available on transparency

Possible answers to Think and Discuss

1. 15 oz has the lower unit price at $0.20 per ounce. The unit price for 6 oz is $0.22 per ounce.
2. miles per hour; feet per second

---

2 Teach

Guided Instruction

In this lesson, students learn to work with rates. Review simplifying fractions and writing fractions as decimals. Remind students how to order decimals. Use **Example 1** to explain how to convert from a rate to a unit rate. Point out that a *unit price* is a type of unit rate, and use **Example 4** to find and compare unit prices.

 **Teaching Tip** — **Language Support** To help students remember the distinction between rate and ratio, point out that a heart *rate* compares *beats* and *minutes*, two quantities that have different units. A ratio may compare quantities that have no units, such as a ratio of boys to girls.

Universal Access
Through Home Connection

Ask students to go to the grocery store with a family member and make a list of five products. For each product, students should record the brand and quantity they purchase (or would purchase) and its unit price. For each product, students should also record one other brand or quantity they decided not to purchase (or would not purchase) and its unit price. Ask students to give a reason for each decision. Suggest that not all decisions must be based only on cost, but that cost is one consideration along with preference, quality, and other considerations.

3 Close

Summarize

Have the students match each term below with its corresponding example. Ask them to be as specific as possible and to use each term only once. Ask them to explain their choices.

Ratio — 120 miles per 3 hours
Rate — 15 ft/s
Unit rate — $1.15 per pound
Unit price — 4:2

A ratio is a comparison of two quantities. A rate is a ratio that has two different units. A unit rate is a rate in which the second quantity is 1. A unit price is a unit rate involving the cost of an item.

5-2 Exercises

California Standards Practice
◆ **MG1.3**

go.hrw.com
Homework Help Online
KEYWORD: MT8CA 5-2
Parent Resources Online
KEYWORD: MT8CA Parent

Assignment Guide

If you finished Example **1** assign:
Proficient 1, 8, 16–19, 28, 32, 34–41
Advanced 8, 16–19, 28, 29, 32, 34–41

If you finished Example **2** assign:
Proficient 1, 2, 8, 9, 16–19, 28, 32, 34–41
Advanced 8, 9, 16–19, 26, 28, 29, 32, 34–41

If you finished Example **3** assign:
Proficient 1–6, 8–13, 16–23, 27, 28, 32, 34–41
Advanced 8–13, 16–23, 26–29, 31, 32, 34–41

If you finished Example **4** assign:
Proficient 1–25, 27, 28, 32–41
Advanced 8–41

Homework Quick Check

Quickly check key concepts.
Exercises: 8, 9, 10, 14

Math Background

The Pythagoreans, early Greek philosophers, originally believed that all numbers could be written as a ratio of integers. However, they discovered that some numbers could not be written as a ratio of integers. They kept this secret for many years because they thought it was scandalous.

GUIDED PRACTICE

See Example **1** 1. Ana Maria walks 9 miles in 3 hours. How many miles does she walk per hour?
3 mi

See Example **2** 2. A nickel has a mass of 5 g and a volume of approximately 0.689 cm^3. What is the approximate density of a nickel? ≈ **7.26 g/cm^3**

See Example **3** **Estimate each unit rate.**

3. 121 students in 3 buses
about 40 students per bus
4. $31.50 for 4 hours
about $8 per h
5. 4008 Calories for 8 servings of pot pie
about 500 Calories per serving
6. 22 minutes for 10 laps
about 2 min per lap

See Example **4** 7. A 16 oz box of crackers costs $3.99 and a 38 oz box of crackers costs $6.99. Which box has the lower unit price? **38 oz box**

INDEPENDENT PRACTICE

See Example **1** 8. Kenji earns $32 in 4 hours. How much does he earn per hour? **$8**

See Example **2** 9. The mass of a diamond is 1.76 g. The volume is 0.5 cm^3. What is the density of the diamond? **3.52 g/cm^3**

See Example **3** **Estimate each unit rate.**

10. 268 chairs in 9 rows
about 30 chairs per row
11. 9 cups of flour for 4 batches of muffins
about 2 cups per batch
12. $59.95 for 5 CDs
about $12 per CD
13. $2.19 for $\frac{1}{2}$ pound
about $4 per lb

See Example **4** 14. One yard of ribbon costs $0.49 and 3 yards of ribbon costs $1.49. Which has the lower unit price? **1 yard of ribbon**

15. A 16 oz package of brown rice costs $0.79 and a 32 oz package of brown rice costs $3.49. Which package has the lower unit price? **16 oz package**

PRACTICE AND PROBLEM SOLVING

Extra Practice
See page EP10.

Find each unit rate.

16. travel 804 miles in 16 hours
50.25 mi/h
17. score 84 points in 6 games
14 points per game
18. $7.05 for 3 tacos
$2.35 per taco
19. 64 beats in 4 measures of music
16 beats per measure

Estimate each unit rate.

20. $107 for 22 magazines
approximately $5 per magazine
21. 250 heartbeats in 6 minutes
approximately 50 beats per minute
22. 295 words in 6 minutes
approximately 50 words per minute
23. 17 apples weigh 4 pounds
approximately 4 apples per pound

Find each unit price. Then tell which has the lower unit price.
$0.16/fl oz; $0.08/fl oz; 90 fl oz

24. $3.99 for 25 fl oz of detergent or $6.99 for 90 fl oz of detergent

25. $\frac{2}{3}$ pound of walnuts for $2.50 or $\frac{1}{2}$ pound of walnuts for $2.25 **$3.75/lb; $4.50/lb; $\frac{2}{3}$ lb**

REVIEW FOR MASTERY 5-2

LESSON
5-2 **Review for Mastery**
Rates and Unit Rates

A **rate** is a ratio that compares two *different kinds* of quantities.

2 aides for 18 students
$\frac{2 \text{ aides}}{18 \text{ students}}$
135 words in 3 minutes
$\frac{135 \text{ words}}{3 \text{ minutes}}$
7 ads per 4 pages of copy
$\frac{7 \text{ ads}}{4 \text{ pages of copy}}$

Express each comparison as a rate in ratio form.

1. 275 students per 11 teachers
$\frac{275 \text{ students}}{11 \text{ teachers}}$
2. 3 books in 2 months
$\frac{3 \text{ books}}{2 \text{ months}}$
3. 15 strike-outs in 6 innings
$\frac{15 \text{ strike-outs}}{6 \text{ innings}}$

In a **unit** rate, the second quantity is 1.

300 miles in 6 hours
$\frac{300 \text{ miles}}{6 \text{ hours}} = \frac{300 \div 6}{6 \div 6} = \frac{50 \text{ miles}}{1 \text{ hour}}$
81 entries in 4 minutes
$\frac{81 \text{ entries}}{4 \text{ minutes}} = \frac{81 \div 4}{4 \div 4} = \frac{20.25 \text{ entries}}{1 \text{ minute}}$

Express each comparison as a unit rate.

4. 28 patients for 2 nurses
$\frac{28 \text{ patients}}{2 \text{ nurses}} = \frac{28 \div 2}{2 \div 2} = \frac{14 \text{ patients}}{1 \text{ nurse}}$
5. 16 children in 7 families
$\frac{16 \text{ children}}{7 \text{ families}} = \frac{16 \div 7}{7 \div 7} = \frac{2.3 \text{ children}}{1 \text{ family}}$

A **unit price** tells the price per 1 unit.

$2.49 for 3 muffins
$\frac{\$2.49}{3 \text{ muffins}} = \frac{2.49 \div 3}{3 \div 3} = \frac{\$0.83}{1 \text{ muffin}}$
$1.67 for 10 pencils
$\frac{\$1.67}{10 \text{ pencils}} = \frac{1.67 \div 10}{10 \div 10} = \frac{\$0.167}{1 \text{ pencil}}$

$0.83 for 1 muffin
$0.17 for 1 pencil

Find each unit price.

6. $10.74 for 3 reams of paper
$\frac{\$10.74}{3 \text{ reams}} = \frac{10.74 \div 3}{3 \div 3}$
$\frac{\$3.58}{1 \text{ ream}}$
7. $9.99 for 6 blank jewel cased CDs
$\frac{\$9.99}{6 \text{ CDs}} = \frac{9.99 \div 6}{6 \div 6}$
$\frac{\$1.665}{1 \text{ CD}}$
8. $8.99 for a 12-pack of gel pens
$\frac{\$8.99}{12 \text{ pens}} = \frac{8.99 \div 12}{12 \div 12}$
$\frac{\$0.7492}{1 \text{ pen}}$

PRACTICE 5-2

LESSON
5-2 **Practice B**
Rates and Unit Rates

1. Copper weighing 4480 kilograms has a volume of 0.5 cubic meters. What is the density of copper?
8960 kg / **m^3**

2. Yoshi's yogurt contains 15 calories per ounce. How many calories are in an 8-ounce container of Yoshi's yogurt?
120 calories

3. Emily earns $7.50 per hour. How much does she earn in 3 hours?
$22.50

Estimate the unit rate.

4. 43 apples in 5 bags
about 9 apples per bag
5. $71 for 8 hours
about $9 per hour
6. 146 students in 6 classes
about 25 students per class
7. $52.00 for 5 hours
about $10 per hour
8. 7 miles in 64 minutes
about 9 minutes per mile
9. $3.55 for 4 pounds
about $0.90 per pound

Determine the lower unit price.

10. 8.2 oz of toothpaste for $2.99 or 6.4 oz of toothpaste for $2.49
8.2 oz for $2.99

11. a 3 lb bag of apples for $2.99 or a 5 lb bag of apples for $4.99
3 lb bag for $2.99

12. 16 oz bottle of soda for $1.25 or 20 oz bottle of soda for $1.55
20 oz bottle for $1.55

13. Mavis rides the bus every day. She bought a bus pass good for the month of October for $38.75. How much was Mavis charged per day for the bus pass?
$1.25

California Standards

Standard	Exercises
AF4.0 ◆	34–37
MG1.3 ◆	1–33
MG3.3 ◆	38–41

26. Multi-Step Before 1986, a gold bullion in the Federal Reserve Bank was rectangular and had a volume of approximately 727.7 cm^3. The density of gold is 19.3 g/cm^3. A pound is approximately 454 g. Find the weight of one gold bullion to the nearest tenth of a pound.   **30.9 lb**

27. Estimation Maura received $790 for work she did for a catering company during one week. Find Maura's approximate daily rate.   **approximately $110 per day**

28. Entertainment Tom, Cherise, and Tina work as film animators. The circle graph shows the number of frames each rendered, or produced, in an 8-hour day.

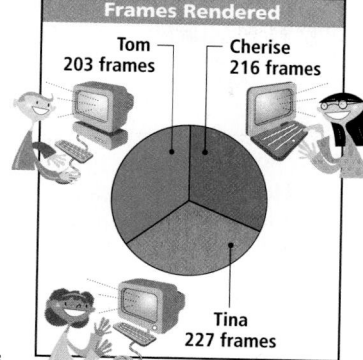

Frames Rendered
Tom 203 frames
Cherise 216 frames
Tina 227 frames

28a. Tom: $25\frac{3}{8}$ frames per hour; Cherise: 27 frames per hour; Tina $28\frac{3}{8}$ frames per hour

a. Find the hourly unit rendering rate for each employee.

b. Who was the most efficient?   **Tina**

c. How many more frames per hour did Cherise render than Tom? $1\frac{5}{8}$ **frames**

d. How many more frames per hour did Tom and Cherise together render than Tina?   **24 frames**

 29. What's the Error? A clothing store charges $25 for 4 T-shirts. A student says that the unit price is $0.16 per T-shirt. What is the error? What is the correct unit price?

 30. Write About It Explain how to find unit rates. Give an example, and explain how consumers can use unit rates to save money.

 31. Challenge The size of a television (13 in., 25 in., 32 in., and so on) represents the length of the diagonal of the television screen. An aspect ratio describes a screen by comparing its width to its height. A 25 in. television has an aspect ratio of 4:3. Find the width and height of the screen.   **width: 20 in.; height: 15 in.**

SPIRAL STANDARDS REVIEW   ← AF4.0, ← MG1.3, ← MG3.3

32. Multiple Choice A 24 lb bag of dog food sells for $10.56. What is the unit price per pound?

(A) $0.44/lb   (B) $0.53/lb   (C) $13.44/lb   (D) $34.56/lb

33. Extended Response Flowers can be purchased in bunches of 4 for $2.48 or bunches of 6 for $3.96. Which has the lower unit price? Explain.   **The unit price of the bunch of 4 is $0.62 per flower. The unit price of the bunch of 6 is $0.66. The bunch of 4 has the lower unit price.**

Solve. (Lesson 2-7)

34. $p - 8.2 = 12.9$ **21.1** **35.** $\frac{4}{7}w = \frac{16}{21}$ $1\frac{1}{3}$ **36.** $x + \frac{1}{15} = -\frac{14}{15}$ **−1** **37.** $\frac{t}{2.1} = -4$ **−8.4**

Tell whether the given side lengths form a right triangle. (Lesson 4-9)
38. 9, 12, 15 **yes**   **39.** 8, 14, 20 **no**   **40.** 16, 30, 34 **yes**   **41.** 4, 7, 8 **no**

CHALLENGE 5-2

Challenge
5-2 All That Glitters

Used by the ancient Greeks around 500 B.C., the **golden rectangle** is thought to have a shape that is most pleasing to the human eye.

Follow these steps to construct a golden rectangle to determine its dimensions.

1. a. Work with square *ABCD* below of side 2 inches.
 Use a ruler to locate *M*, the midpoint of $\overline{AB}$. $AM =$ ___1___

b. Draw $\overline{MC}$. Use the Pythagorean theorem to find *MC*. $MC =$ ___$\sqrt{5}$___

c. Extend $\overline{AB}$ through *B*. Locate *P* on $\overline{AB}$ so that *MP = MC*. $AP =$ ___$1+\sqrt{5}$___

d. Extend $\overline{DC}$ through *C*. At *P*, draw a line perpendicular to $\overline{AB}$. Use *Q* to label the point at which the perpendicular intersects $\overline{DC}$. *APQD* is a golden rectangle.

(diagram: D, 2 in., C, Q, A, M, B, P, with 2 in. on left side)

2. In golden rectangle *APQD*, the ratio $\frac{AP}{AD}$ is called the **golden ratio**.

a. The exact value of the golden ratio is: $\frac{1+\sqrt{5}}{2}$

b. Write an approximation of the golden ratio. Use as many decimal places as your calculator allows.   1.6180339887

3. a. Write the reciprocal of the golden ratio. $\frac{2}{1+\sqrt{5}}$

b. Write an approximation of the reciprocal of the golden ratio.   0.6180339887

c. Comment on the result.
Decimal portions of golden ratio and its reciprocal are the same.

PROBLEM SOLVING 5-2

Problem Solving
5-2 Rates and Unit Rates

Scientists have researched the ratio of brain weight to body size in different animals. The results are in the table below.

1. Order the animals by their brain weight to body weight ratio, from smallest to largest.

hippo, horse, elephant, dog, cat, human, small birds

Animal	Brain Weight / Body Weight
Cat	$\frac{1}{100}$
Dog	$\frac{1}{125}$
Elephant	$\frac{1}{560}$
Hippo	$\frac{1}{2789}$
Horse	$\frac{1}{600}$
Human	$\frac{1}{40}$
Small birds	$\frac{1}{12}$

2. It has been hypothesized that the higher the brain weight to body weight ratio, the more intelligent the animal is. By this measure, which animals listed are the most intelligent?
small birds

3. Name two sets of animals that have approximately the same brain weight to body weight ratio.
elephant and horse; cat & dog

Find the unit rate. Round to the nearest hundredth.

4. A 64-ounce bottle of apple juice costs $1.35.
 A $0.01/oz   C $0.47/oz
 B $0.02/oz   D $47.4/oz

5. Find the unit rate for a 2 lb package of hamburger that costs $3.45.
 F $0.58/lb   (H) $1.73/lb
 G $1.25/b   J $2.28/b

6. 12 slices of pizza cost $9.00.
 A $0.45/slice   (C) $0.75/slice
 B $0.50/slice   D $1.33/slice

7. John is selling 5 comic books for $6.00.
 F $0.83/book   H $1.02/book
 (G) $1.20/book   J $1.45/book

8. There are 64 beats in 4 measures of music.
 (A) 16 beats/measure
 B 12 beats/measure
 C 4 beats/measure
 D 0.06 beats/measure

9. The average price of a 30 second commercial for the 2002 Super Bowl was $1,900,000.
 F $120.82/sec
 G $1,242.50/sec
 H $5,839.02/sec
 (J) $63,333.33/sec

Answers

29. Possible answer: The student divided the number of shirts by the cost instead of the cost by the number of shirts; $6.25 per T-shirt

30. Possible answer; Simplify the ratio so that the second quantity is 1. An example is the cost per pound of fruit. Consumers can use the unit rate to find the better buy.

 Teaching Tip   **Multiple Choice For Exercise 32,** encourage students to look over all answer choices before making any calculations. They can eliminate **C** and **D** by realizing that the unit price per pound of dog food will not be greater than the price of a 24 lb bag.

 Journal
Ask students to describe why they think it is or is not helpful for supermarkets to include unit prices on price labels.

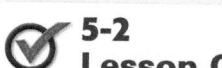 **Power Presentations with PowerPoint®**

5-2 Lesson Quiz

1. Meka can make 6 bracelets per half hour. How many bracelets can she make per hour? **12**

2. A penny has a mass of 2.5 g and a volume of approximately 0.360 cm^3. What is the approximate density of a penny?
 ≈6.94 g/cm^3

Estimate each unit rate.

3. $2.22 for 6 stamps
 $0.37 per stamp

4. 8 heartbeats in 6 seconds
 ≈1.3 beats/s

Find each unit price. Then tell which has the lower unit price.

5. a half dozen carnations for $4.75 or a dozen for $9.24 a dozen

6. 4 pens for $5.16 or a ten-pack for $12.90 They cost the same.

Also available on transparency

Objective: Students identify and solve proportions.

 Online Edition
Tutorial Videos

 Countdown to Mastery Week 10

Power Presentations
with PowerPoint®

Warm Up

Find two ratios that are equivalent to each given ratio.
Possible answers:

1. $\frac{3}{5}$ $\frac{6}{10}, \frac{9}{15}$ 2. $\frac{10}{12}$ $\frac{5}{6}, \frac{20}{24}$

3. $\frac{45}{30}$ $\frac{3}{2}, \frac{90}{60}$ 4. $\frac{8}{9}$ $\frac{16}{18}, \frac{24}{27}$

Also available on transparency

 **Math Humor**

Teacher: Why are you using a first-aid kit to solve a proportion?

Student: The problem is printed in red, so I'm using a Red Cross product.

California Standards

AF4.2 Solve multistep problems involving rate, average speed, distance, and time or a direct variation.

Vocabulary
proportion
cross products

Why learn this? You can use proportions to compare ratios, such as the mass of a child to his or her distance from the fulcrum of a seesaw. (See Example 2.)

Recall from Lesson 5-1 that equivalent ratios are ratios that name the same comparison. An equation that states that two ratios are equivalent is called a **proportion**. For example, the equation, or proportion, $\frac{2}{3} = \frac{4}{6}$ states that the ratios $\frac{2}{3}$ and $\frac{4}{6}$ are equivalent. Ratios that are equivalent are said to be *proportional,* or *in proportion.*

In the proportion $\frac{a}{b} = \frac{c}{d}$, the products $a \cdot d$ and $b \cdot c$ are called **cross products**.

$$\frac{a}{b} = \frac{c}{d} \quad \longleftarrow \text{Proportion}$$
$$a \cdot d = b \cdot c \quad \longleftarrow \text{Cross products}$$

One way to find whether two ratios are equivalent is to find their cross products.

CROSS PRODUCTS	
Cross products in proportions are equal. If the ratios are *not* in proportion, the cross products are not equal.	

Proportions		*Not* Proportions	
$\frac{6}{8} \times \frac{9}{12}$	$\frac{5}{2} \times \frac{15}{6}$	$\frac{1}{6} \not\times \frac{2}{7}$	$\frac{5}{12} \not\times \frac{2}{5}$
$6 \cdot 12 = 8 \cdot 9$	$5 \cdot 6 = 2 \cdot 15$	$1 \cdot 7 \neq 6 \cdot 2$	$5 \cdot 5 \neq 12 \cdot 2$
$72 = 72$	$30 = 30$	$7 \neq 12$	$25 \neq 24$

EXAMPLE 1   **Using Cross Products to Identify Proportions**

A Tell whether the ratios $\frac{5}{6}$ and $\frac{15}{21}$ are proportional.

$$\frac{5}{6} \overset{?}{=} \frac{15}{21}$$

$$\frac{5}{6} \overset{?}{\times} \frac{15}{21} \qquad \textit{Find the cross products.}$$

$$5 \cdot 21 \overset{?}{=} 6 \cdot 15$$

$$105 \neq 90$$

Since the cross products are not equal, the ratios are not proportional.

---

1 Introduce

Alternate Opener

EXPLORATION

5-3 Proportions

The grid shows three rectangles aligned by a diagonal line.

Complete the table. Use the grid to measure the length and width of each rectangle. Divide the length by the width and write this answer as a fraction in simplest form.

		Length	Width	Length ÷ Width
1.	Blue rectangle			
2.	Red rectangle			
3.	Green rectangle			

Think and Discuss
4. **Compare** the fractions you found in Problems 1–3.
5. **Explain** how you wrote each fraction in simplest form.

Motivate
Give students the following two statements: $\frac{2}{3} \overset{?}{=} \frac{6}{10}$ and $\frac{3}{4} \overset{?}{=} \frac{6}{8}$. Ask them to decide whether each statement is true or false. $\frac{2}{3} \neq \frac{6}{10}; \frac{3}{4} = \frac{6}{8}$ Ask students to explain how they decided whether the statements were true or false. Remind students that $\frac{3}{4} = \frac{6}{8}$ is a proportion because it is true. Tell them they will learn to solve proportions with an unknown term in this new lesson.

Explorations and answers are provided in *Alternate Openers: Explorations Transparencies.*

 California Standards

Algebra and Functions 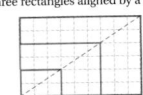 4.2

B A shade of paint is made by mixing 5 parts yellow paint with 7 parts green paint. Will 21 quarts of green paint and 15 quarts of yellow paint make the correct shade? Explain.

$$\frac{5 \text{ parts yellow}}{7 \text{ parts green}} \stackrel{?}{=} \frac{15 \text{ quarts yellow}}{21 \text{ quarts green}}$$ *Set up equal ratios.*

                Find the cross products.

$$5 \cdot 21 \stackrel{?}{=} 7 \cdot 15$$

$$105 = 105$$

The cross products are equal. You will get the correct shade of paint.

To solve a proportion that contains a variable, you must find the value that makes the equation true.

EXAMPLE 2   Using Properties of Equality to Solve Proportions

For most people, the ratio of the length of their head to their total height is 1:7. If a person is 56 inches tall, what should the length of their head be?

$$\frac{\text{head length}}{\text{total height}} \rightarrow \frac{1}{7}$$ *Write a ratio comparing head length to total height.*

$$\frac{1}{7} = \frac{x}{56}$$ *Set up the proportion. Let x represent the length of the person's head.*

$$(56)\frac{1}{7} = (56)\frac{x}{56}$$ *Since x is divided by 56, multiply both sides of the equation by 56.*

$$8 = x$$

The length of the person's head should be 8 inches.

EXAMPLE 3   Using Cross Products to Solve Proportions

Unequal masses can be balanced on a fulcrum only when $\frac{\text{mass 1}}{\text{length 2}} = \frac{\text{mass 2}}{\text{length 1}}$. The children on the seesaw shown are balanced. What is the mass of the child on the right?

Helpful Hint

You can also simplify the ratios in proportions before solving. For example, $\frac{24}{8} = 3$, so $3 = \frac{m}{14}$. Then solve by using the properties of equality.

Set up a proportion using the information given in the diagram. Let m represent the mass of the child on the right.

$$\frac{\text{mass 1}}{\text{length 2}} = \frac{\text{mass 2}}{\text{length 1}}$$

$$\frac{24}{8} = \frac{m}{14}$$

$$24 \cdot 14 = 8m$$ *Find the cross products.*

$$\frac{336}{8} = \frac{8m}{8}$$ *Divide both sides by 8.*

$$42 = m$$ *Simplify.*

The mass of the child on the right is 42 lb.

Power Presentations
with **PowerPoint®**

Additional Examples

Example 1

A. Tell whether the ratios $\frac{6}{15}$ and $\frac{4}{10}$ are proportional. yes

B. A mixture of fuel for a certain small engine should be 4 parts gasoline to 1 part oil. If you combine 5 quarts of oil with 15 quarts of gasoline, will the mixture be correct? no

Example 2

The ratio of the length of the actual height of a person to the length of the shadow cast by the person is 1:3. At the same time, a lighthouse casts a shadow that is 36 meters long. What should the length of its shadow be? 12 meters

Example 3

Allyson weighs 55 pounds and sits on a seesaw 4 feet away from its center. If Marco sits on the seesaw 5 feet away from the center and the seesaw is balanced, how much does Marco weigh? 44 lb

Also available on transparency

---

2   Teach

Guided Instruction

In this lesson, students learn to solve proportions. Remind them that one way to determine whether ratios are equivalent is to simplify the ratios and see whether they are the same (Lesson 5-1). A second method is to find the *cross products*. If the cross products are equal, then the ratios are in proportion (Teaching Transparency). Show students that if they are given a proportion with one value missing, they can write an equation using cross products to find it.

Universal Access
Through Diversity

Ask students to find a recipe at home for a particular number of servings. Ask them to use a proportion to find the amount of each ingredient needed for a different number of servings. Suggest that students use the following proportion:

$$\frac{\text{original amount of ingredient}}{\text{original number of servings}} = \frac{\text{new amount of ingredient}}{\text{new number of servings}}$$

Additional Examples

Example 4

Nate has 225 envelopes to prepare for mailing. He takes 30 minutes to prepare 45 envelopes. If he continues at the same rate, how many more minutes until he has completed the job? **120 minutes**

Also available on transparency

Teaching Tip

Multiple Representations Show students that the proportion $\frac{a}{b} = \frac{c}{d}$ can also be written in the following ways: $\frac{a}{c} = \frac{b}{d}$, $\frac{b}{a} = \frac{d}{c}$, $\frac{c}{a} = \frac{d}{b}$.

Possible answers to Think and Discuss

1. the numerators of the fractions when you find a common denominator by multiplying the denominators

2. The ratios are not equal.

3. Cross multiply, isolate the variable, and solve the equation.

EXAMPLE 4 *School Application*

Lee is reading a 374-page novel for her English class. It takes her 6 days to read the first 132 pages. If she continues to read at the same rate, how many more days will it take her to finish the novel?

Let x represent the number of days it takes Lee to read the entire novel.

$\frac{6}{132} = \frac{x}{374}$	Set up the proportion.
$6 \cdot 374 = 132x$	Find the cross products.
$\frac{2244}{132} = \frac{132x}{132}$	Divide both sides by 132.
$17 = x$	Simplify.

It takes Lee 17 days to read the entire novel. Lee has already read for 6 days, so it will take her $17 - 6 = 11$ more days to finish the novel.

Helpful Hint

You could also set up a proportion using the number of pages that Lee still needs to read: $374 - 132 = 242$.

$$\frac{6}{132} = \frac{x}{242}$$

Then x represents the number of days it takes to read the rest of the novel.

Think and Discuss

1. **Explain** what the cross products of two ratios represent.

2. **Tell** what it means if the cross products are not equal.

3. **Describe** how to solve a proportion. Let x represent the missing value.

California Standards Practice
⬅ AF4.2

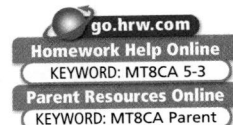

go.hrw.com
Homework Help Online
KEYWORD: MT8CA 5-3
Parent Resources Online
KEYWORD: MT8CA Parent

5-3 Exercises

GUIDED PRACTICE

See Example ① Tell whether the ratios are proportional.

1. $\frac{6}{12} \stackrel{?}{=} \frac{12}{24}$ **yes**   2. $\frac{2}{9} \stackrel{?}{=} \frac{6}{27}$ **yes**   3. $\frac{5}{7} \stackrel{?}{=} \frac{10}{15}$ **no**   4. $\frac{10}{25} \stackrel{?}{=} \frac{6}{15}$ **yes**

5. A bubble solution can be made with a ratio of 1 part detergent to 8 parts water. Would a mixture of 56 oz water and 8 oz detergent represent the same ratio? Explain. **no; $\frac{1}{8} \neq \frac{8}{56}$**

See Example ② 6. **Science** The ratio of an object's weight on Earth to its weight on the Moon is 6:1. The first person to walk on the Moon was Neil Armstrong. He weighed 165 pounds on Earth. How much did he weigh on the Moon? **27.5 pounds**

5-3 Exercises

Assignment Guide

If you finished Example ① assign:
Proficient 1–5, 9–13, 36–39
Advanced 9–13, 19–22, 36–39

If you finished Example ② assign:
Proficient 1–6, 9–14, 17–20, 23, 25, 35–39
Advanced 9–14, 19–22, 26, 28, 35–39

If you finished Example ③ assign:
Proficient 1–7, 9–15, 17–20, 23–25, 29–30, 34–39
Advanced 9–15, 19–22, 26–28, 31–39

If you finished Example ④ assign:
Proficient 1–20, 23–25, 29–30, 34–39
Advanced 9–16, 19–22, 26–39

Homework Quick Check

Quickly check key concepts.
Exercises: 10, 12, 14, 16, 20

---

③ Close

Summarize

Remind students that they can use cross products to determine whether two ratios form a proportion. Ask students to determine whether each of the following is a proportion.

1. $\frac{1}{2} \stackrel{?}{=} \frac{50}{100}$ **yes**   2. $\frac{3}{8} \stackrel{?}{=} \frac{7}{20}$ **no**

3. $\frac{2}{8} \stackrel{?}{=} \frac{6}{24}$ **yes**   4. $\frac{8}{12} \stackrel{?}{=} \frac{2}{3}$ **yes**

California Standards

Standard	Exercises
NS1.2 ⬅	36–38
AF4.2 ⬅	8, 16, 30
MG1.3 ⬅	39

See Example 3 **7.** A 12 lb weight is positioned 8 in. from a fulcrum. At what distance from the fulcrum must an 18 lb weight be positioned to keep the scale balanced? $5\frac{1}{3}$ in.

See Example 4 **8.** Ana is using a photocopier to make 315 copies of a poster. It takes 3 minutes to print the first 63 posters. If the photocopier continues to print at the same rate, how many more minutes will it take to complete the job? **12 min**

INDEPENDENT PRACTICE

See Example 1 **Tell whether the ratios are proportional.**

9. $\frac{22}{42} \overset{?}{=} \frac{3}{7}$ no   **10.** $\frac{17}{51} \overset{?}{=} \frac{2}{6}$ yes   **11.** $\frac{40}{36} \overset{?}{=} \frac{20}{16}$ no   **12.** $\frac{8}{9} \overset{?}{=} \frac{40}{45}$ yes

13. An after-school club had 10 girls and 12 boys. Then 5 more girls and 6 more boys signed up. Did the ratio of girls to boys stay the same? Explain. yes; $\frac{10}{12} = \frac{15}{18}$

See Example 2 **14.** **School** The ratio of seventh graders to eighth graders participating in a science fair is 4:3. There are 18 eighth graders participating in the science fair. How many seventh graders are there?   **24 seventh graders**

See Example 3 **15.** A 150 kg weight is positioned 3 m from a fulcrum. If a 200 kg weight is placed at the opposite end of the balance, how far from the fulcrum should it be positioned?   **2.25 m**

See Example 4 **16.** Jaron is downloading a file. The size of the file is 3200 KB. It takes 3 minutes to download the first 1200 KB of the file. If the file continues downloading at the same rate, how many more minutes will it take to finish downloading?   **5 min**

PRACTICE AND PROBLEM SOLVING

Extra Practice
See page EP10.

For each set of ratios, find the two that are proportional.

17. $\frac{8}{4}, \frac{24}{12}, \frac{55}{27}$ $\frac{8}{4}, \frac{24}{12}$

18. $\frac{1}{4}, \frac{4}{16}, \frac{110}{444}$ $\frac{1}{4}$ and $\frac{4}{16}$

19. $\frac{35}{26}, \frac{81}{39}, \frac{27}{13}$ $\frac{81}{39}, \frac{27}{13}$

20. $\frac{49}{182}, \frac{7}{26}, \frac{45}{160}$ $\frac{49}{182}, \frac{7}{26}$

21. $\frac{0.5}{6}, \frac{0.25}{9}, \frac{1}{12}$ $\frac{0.5}{6}, \frac{1}{12}$

22. $\frac{a}{c}, \frac{a}{b}, \frac{4a}{4b}$ $\frac{a}{b}, \frac{4a}{4b}$

Solve each proportion.

23. $\frac{\$d}{12 \text{ hours}} = \frac{\$96}{8 \text{ hours}}$ $\$144$

24. $\frac{s \text{ students}}{6 \text{ teachers}} = \frac{209 \text{ students}}{11 \text{ teachers}}$ **114 students**

25. $\frac{m \text{ minutes}}{8 \text{ miles}} = \frac{24 \text{ minutes}}{3 \text{ miles}}$ **64 minutes**

26. $\frac{\$d}{4 \text{ tickets}} = \frac{\$72}{6 \text{ tickets}}$ $\$48$

27. $\frac{c \text{ computers}}{15 \text{ students}} = \frac{20 \text{ computers}}{25 \text{ students}}$ **12 computers**

28. $\frac{m \text{ miles}}{6 \text{ hours}} = \frac{110 \text{ miles}}{2 \text{ hours}}$ **330 miles**

29. **Science** One molecule of nitrogen reacting with 3 molecules of hydrogen makes 2 molecules of ammonia. How many molecules of nitrogen must react with 42 molecules of hydrogen to make 28 molecules of ammonia?   **14 molecules**

30. **Multi-Step** Jacob is selling T-shirts at a music festival. Yesterday, he sold 51 shirts and earned $191.25. How many shirts must Jacob sell today and tomorrow to earn a total of $536.25 for all three days?   **92 shirts**

You can see that cross products in a proportion are equal by multiplying both sides of the proportion by a form of 1 using the denominator of the fraction on the opposite side of the proportion. Consider the following demonstration:

For real numbers a, b, c, and d,
$\frac{a}{b} = \frac{c}{d}$.

$\frac{a}{b} \cdot \frac{d}{d} = \frac{ad}{bd}$ $\frac{c}{d} \cdot \frac{b}{b} = \frac{cb}{db}$

Since the fractions to the right of the equal signs have the same denominator, they are equal if and only if their numerators are equal (i.e., if and only if $ad = cb$).

Teaching Tip **Multiple Choice** For **Exercise 34,** point out to students that there are two proportions they can use to solve this problem. However, suggest that they choose the proportion with the smaller numbers, because it will make the calculations easier with less chance for error.

 Journal

An *analogy* is a comparison of pairs of words or ideas that have a similar relationship. For example, in the analogy "*good* is to *bad* as *big* is to *small*," both sets of words have opposite meanings. Have students write about how proportions are like analogies.

 **Health LINK**

A doctor reports blood pressure in millimeters of mercury (mm Hg) as a ratio of *systolic* blood pressure to *diastolic* blood pressure (such as 140 over 80). Systolic pressure is measured when the heart beats, and diastolic pressure is measured when it rests. Refer to the table of blood pressure ranges for adults for Exercise 31.

Blood Pressure Ranges			
	Normal	**Prehypertension**	**Hypertension (very high)**
Systolic	under 120 mm Hg	120–139 mm Hg	140 mm Hg and above
Diastolic	under 80 mm Hg	80–89 mm Hg	90 mm Hg and above

31. **Estimation** Eduardo is a healthy 37-year-old man whose blood pressure is in the normal category.
   a. Calculate an approximate ratio of systolic to diastolic blood pressure in the normal range. **about 3:2**
   b. Eduardo's systolic blood pressure is 102 mm Hg. Use the ratio from part **a** to predict his diastolic blood pressure. **about 68 mm Hg**

32. **Write About It** A ratio related to heart health is LDL cholesterol to HDL cholesterol. The optimal ratio of LDL to HDL is below 3. A patient's total cholesterol is 168 and HDL is 44. Is the patient's ratio optimal? Explain. **Yes; the ratio is less than 2.82:1.**

33. ★ **Challenge** The sum of Ken's LDL and HDL cholesterol is 210, and his LDL to HDL ratio is 2.75. What are his LDL and HDL? **154 and 56**

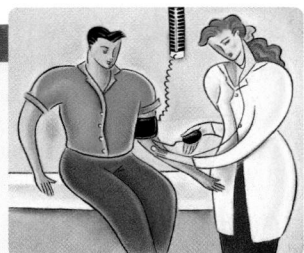
The disc-like shape of red blood cells allows them to pass through tiny capillaries.

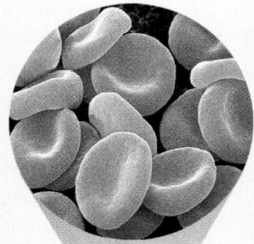

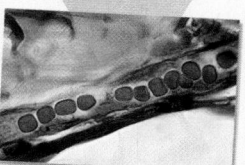

go.hrw.com
Web Extra!
KEYWORD: MT8CA Health

🐻 SPIRAL STANDARDS REVIEW ← NS1.2, ← AF4.2, ← MG1.3

34. **Multiple Choice** A tree was 3.5 feet tall after 2 years and 8.75 feet tall after 5 years. If the tree grew at a constant rate, how tall was it after 3 years?
   Ⓐ 5 feet   Ⓑ 5.25 feet   Ⓒ 5.75 feet   Ⓓ 6.5 feet

35. **Gridded Response** What value of b makes the proportion $\frac{4}{5} = \frac{b}{20}$ true? **16**

Divide. Write each answer in simplest form. (Lesson 2-5)

36. $\frac{3}{4} \div \frac{1}{2}$ $\frac{3}{2}$ 37. $3\frac{1}{7} \div \left(-\frac{2}{21}\right)$ -33 38. $-2\frac{1}{8} \div \left(-2\frac{1}{2}\right)$ $\frac{17}{20}$

39. A 6-ounce can of tuna costs $2.39, and a 12-ounce can of tuna costs $4.89. Which can has the lower unit rate? (Lesson 5-2) **6-ounce can**

CHALLENGE 5-3

LESSON 5-3 Challenge
Meanwhile . . .

In a proportion, there are 4 terms.

The 1st and 4th are called **extremes**.
The 2nd and 3rd are called **means**.

$\frac{1st\ (extreme)}{2nd\ (mean)} = \frac{3rd\ (mean)}{4th\ (extreme)}$

When the means of a proportion are equal, either is a **mean proportional**.

$\frac{2}{6} = \frac{6}{18}$

6 is the mean proportional between 2 and 18.

To find the mean proportional m between 4 and 25:

Check by showing equal ratios.

$\frac{4}{m} = \frac{m}{25}$

$m^2 = 100$

$m = \sqrt{100} = 10$

$\frac{4}{10} \stackrel{?}{=} \frac{10}{25}$

$\frac{4 \div 2}{10 \div 2} \stackrel{?}{=} \frac{10 + 5}{25 + 5}$

$\frac{2}{5} = \frac{2}{5}$

Find the mean proportional m between each pair of numbers. Check by showing equal ratios.

1. 4 and 9   2. 0.3 and 1.2   3. $\frac{1}{2}$ and $\frac{1}{8}$

$\frac{4}{m} = \frac{m}{9}$

$m^2 = 36$

$m = \sqrt{36} = 6$

Check: $\frac{4}{6} \stackrel{?}{=} \frac{6}{9}$

$\frac{4 \div 2}{6 \div 2} \stackrel{?}{=} \frac{6 \div 3}{9 \div 3}$

$\frac{2}{3} = \frac{2}{3}$

$\frac{0.3}{m} = \frac{m}{1.2}$

$m^2 = 0.36$

$m = \sqrt{0.36} = 0.6$

Check: $\frac{0.3}{0.6} \stackrel{?}{=} \frac{0.6}{1.2}$

$\frac{0.3 \times 10}{0.6 \times 10} \stackrel{?}{=} \frac{0.6 \times 10}{1.2 \times 10}$

$\frac{3 \div 3}{6 \div 3} \stackrel{?}{=} \frac{6 + 6}{12 + 6}$

$\frac{1}{2} = \frac{1}{2}$

$\frac{\frac{1}{2}}{m} = \frac{m}{\frac{1}{8}}$

$m^2 = \frac{1}{16}$

$m = \sqrt{\frac{1}{16}} = \frac{1}{4}$

Check: $\frac{\frac{1}{2}}{\frac{1}{4}} \stackrel{?}{=} \frac{\frac{1}{4}}{\frac{1}{8}}$

$\frac{1}{2} \times \frac{4}{1} \stackrel{?}{=} \frac{1}{4} \times \frac{8}{1}$

$2 = 2$

PROBLEM SOLVING 5-3

LESSON 5-3 Problem Solving
Proportions

Use the ratios in the table to answer each question. Round to the nearest tenth.

Body Part	Body Part Height
Femur	$\frac{1}{4}$
Tibia	$\frac{1}{5}$
Hand span	$\frac{2}{17}$
Arm span	1
Head circumference	$\frac{1}{3}$

1. Which body part is the same length as the person's height?
   arm span

2. If a person's tibia is 13 inches, how tall would you expect the person to be?
   65 inches

3. If a person's hand span is 8.5 inches, about how tall would you expect the person to be?
   72.3 inches

4. If a femur is 18 inches long, how many feet tall would you expect the person to be?
   6 feet

5. What would you expect the head circumference to be of a person who is 5.5 feet tall?
   1.8 feet

6. What would you expect the hand span to be of a person who is 5 feet tall?
   0.6 feet

Choose the letter for the best answer.

7. Five milliliters of a children's medicine contains 400 mg of the drug amoxicillin. How many mg of amoxicillin does 25 mL contain?
   A 0.3 mg   Ⓒ 2000 mg
   B 80 mg   D 2500 mg

8. Vladimir Radmanovic of the Seattle Supersonics makes, on average, about 2 three-pointers for every 5 he shoots. If he attempts 10 three-pointers in a game, how many would you expect him to make?
   Ⓕ 4   H 8
   G 5   J 25

9. In 2002, a 30-second commercial during the Super Bowl cost an average of $1,900,000. At this rate, how much would a 45-second commercial cost?
   A $1,266,666   C $3,500,000
   Ⓑ $2,850,000   D $4,000,000

10. A medicine for dogs indicates that the medicine should be administered in the ratio 2 teaspoons per 5 lb, based on the weight of the dog. How much should be given to a 70 lb dog?
   F 5 teaspoons   H 14 teaspoons
   G 12 teaspoons   Ⓙ 28 teaspoons

5-4 Dimensional Analysis

Organizer 5-4

Objective: Students use one or more conversion factors to solve rate problems.

Why learn this? You can use dimensional analysis to find the speed of a car in miles per hour. (See Example 2.)

The process of converting from one unit to another is called *dimensional analysis*, or *unit analysis*. To convert units, multiply by one or more *conversion factors*. A **conversion factor** is a ratio of two quantities that are equal but use different units.

For example, to convert inches to feet use the ratio $\frac{1\,\text{ft}}{12\,\text{in.}}$ as a conversion factor.

Vocabulary
conversion factor

$$\frac{1\,\text{ft}}{12\,\text{in.}} = \frac{12\,\text{in.}}{12\,\text{in.}} = \frac{1\,\text{ft}}{1\,\text{ft}} = 1$$

Multiplying by a conversion factor is like multiplying by 1.

Hands-On Lab
In *Chapter 5 Resource File*

Online Edition
Tutorial Videos, Interactivities

Countdown to Mastery Week 10

EXAMPLE 1 Using Conversion Factors to Solve Problems

A As you go deeper underground, the earth's temperature increases. In some places, it may increase by 25°C per kilometer. Find this rate in degrees per meter.

Convert the rate 25°C per *kilometer* to degrees per *meter*.

$$\frac{25°C}{1\,\text{km}} \cdot \frac{1\,\text{km}}{1000\,\text{m}}$$

To convert the second quantity in a rate, multiply by a conversion factor with that unit in the first quantity.

$$\frac{25°C}{1000\,\text{m}}$$

Divide out like units. $\frac{°C}{\cancel{km}} \cdot \frac{\cancel{km}}{m} = \frac{°C}{m}$

$$\frac{0.025°C}{1\,\text{m}}$$

Divide 25°C by 1000 m.

The rate is 0.025°C per meter.

B In the United States in 2003, the average person drank approximately 22 gallons of milk. Find this rate in quarts per year.

Convert the rate 22 *gallons* per year to *quarts* per year.

$$\frac{22\,\text{gal}}{1\,\text{yr}} \cdot \frac{4\,\text{qt}}{1\,\text{gal}}$$

To convert the first quantity in a rate, multiply by a conversion factor with that unit in the second quantity.

$$\frac{22 \cdot 4\,\text{qt}}{1\,\text{yr}}$$

Divide out like units. $\frac{\cancel{gal}}{yr} \cdot \frac{qt}{\cancel{gal}} = \frac{qt}{yr}$

$$\frac{88\,\text{qt}}{1\,\text{yr}}$$

Multiply 22 by 4 qt.

The rate is 88 quarts per year.

Helpful Hint

In Example 1A, "1 km" appears to divide out, leaving "degrees per meter," which are the units asked for. Use this strategy of "dividing out" units when converting rates.

Math Fact

A *statute mile* is another term for *mile*. A *nautical mile* is 1.15 statute miles. A *knot* is one nautical mile per hour, and is a measure of speed.

---

1 Introduce

Alternate Opener

EXPLORATION

5-4 Dimensional Analysis

The radius of a planet is called the *equatorial radius* and is the imaginary line between the center of the planet and a point on its equator.

The table shows the radius of each planet in our solar system measured in two different units. In the second column, each radius is measured using the radius of Earth. In the third column, each radius is measured in kilometers.

Calculate the equatorial radius of each planet.

	Planet	Equatorial Radius (number of Earth radii)	Equatorial Radius (km)
1.	Mercury	0.38	
2.	Venus	0.95	
3.	Earth	1	6378.14
4.	Mars	0.53	
5.	Jupiter	11	
6.	Saturn	9	
7.	Uranus	4	
8.	Neptune	4	
9.	Pluto	0.19	

Think and Discuss

10. **Explain** how you found the equatorial radius of each planet.
11. **Discuss** whether using Earth's radius or the kilometer makes comparing the radii of the planets easier.

Motivate

Have students determine the missing values.

?	inches = 1 foot	12
?	centimeters = 1 meter	100
?	ounces = 1 pound	16
?	seconds = 1 minute	60
?	minutes = 1 hour	60

Explain that these facts allow people to convert from one measurement to another.

Explorations and answers are provided in *Alternate Openers: Explorations Transparencies.*

COMMON ERROR ALERT

When students are determining a conversion factor, they may write the units in the incorrect place in the ratio. Remind them that for units to cancel, they must be on opposite sides of the fraction bar. Show students an example of placing the units incorrectly $\left(\text{e.g., } \frac{mi}{h} \cdot \frac{mi}{ft} = \frac{mi^2}{h \cdot ft}\right)$.

Power Presentations
with PowerPoint®

 Additional Examples

Example 1

The average American uses 580 pounds of paper per year. Find this rate in pounds per month, to the nearest tenth. **48.3 lb/mo**

Example 2

A car traveled 60 miles on a road in 2 hours. Find this rate in feet per second. **44 ft/s**

Also available on transparency

EXAMPLE 2 PROBLEM SOLVING APPLICATION

A car traveled 330 feet in 5 seconds. How many miles per hour was the car traveling?

 **Reasoning**

1. Understand the Problem

The problem is stated in units of feet and seconds. The question asks for the answer in units of miles and hours. You will need to use several conversion factors.

List the important information:

- The car traveled 330 feet in 5 seconds.
- There are 5280 feet in 1 mile.
- There are 60 seconds in 1 minute.
- There are 60 minutes in 1 hour.

2. Make a Plan

You know the conversion factor that converts feet to miles. So write a conversion factor that converts seconds to hours. Then multiply $\frac{330 \text{ feet}}{5 \text{ seconds}}$ by the appropriate conversion factors.

3. Solve

$$\frac{60 \text{ s}}{1 \text{ min}} \cdot \frac{60 \text{ min}}{1 \text{ h}} = \frac{3600 \text{ s}}{1 \text{ h}} \qquad \textit{Convert seconds to hours.}$$

$$\frac{330 \text{ ft}}{5 \text{ s}} \cdot \frac{1 \text{ mi}}{5280 \text{ ft}} \cdot \frac{3600 \text{ s}}{1 \text{ h}} \qquad \textit{Set up the conversion factors.}$$

$$= \frac{330 \text{ ft}}{5 \text{ s}} \cdot \frac{1 \text{ mi}}{5280 \text{ ft}} \cdot \frac{3600 \text{ s}}{1 \text{ h}} \qquad \textit{Divide out like units.}$$

$$= \frac{330 \cdot 1 \text{ mi} \cdot 3600}{5 \cdot 5280 \cdot 1 \text{ h}} \qquad \textit{Multiply.}$$

$$= \frac{237{,}600 \text{ mi}}{5280 \text{ h}} \qquad \textit{Simplify.}$$

$$= \frac{45 \text{ mi}}{1 \text{ h}} \qquad \textit{Divide.}$$

The car was traveling 45 miles per hour.

4. Look Back

A rate of 45 mi/h is less than 1 mi/min. 5 seconds is $\frac{1}{12}$ minute. A car traveling 45 mi/h would go less than $\frac{1}{12}$ mile in 5 seconds, or less than $\frac{1}{12}$ of 5280 ft in 5 seconds. It goes 330 ft, which is less than $\frac{1}{12}$ of 5280 ft, so 45 mi/h is a reasonable speed.

---

② Teach

Guided Instruction

In this lesson, students learn to use one or more conversion factors to solve rate problems. Show students how to write common rates in fractional form $\left(\text{e.g., 40 miles per hour} = \frac{40 \text{ mi}}{1 \text{ h}}\right)$. Then explain how to choose the correct conversion factors by setting up rates that cancel the appropriate units. In **Examples 1** and **2,** show students how the original units are canceled out by the units in the denominator of the conversion factor. Review **Example 3** with students. You may want to show the work at every step because these concepts may be new for many of them.

Universal Access
Through Curriculum Integration

The speed of sound in air is approximately 770 mi/h. Have students use the conversion factors given below to express the speed of sound in ft/s and m/s to the nearest whole unit. The speed of light is approximately 300,000 km/s. Have students express the speed of light in cm/s, mi/s, and mi/h in scientific notation.

conversion factors: 1 mi = 5280 ft, 1 m = 3.28 ft, 1 km = 10^5 cm, 1 km = 0.62 mi

speed of sound: 1129 ft/s; 344 m/s
speed of light: 3.0×10^{10} cm/s; 1.86×10^5 mi/s; 6.696×10^8 mi/h

EXAMPLE **3** *Sports Application*

A football player runs from his team's 9-yard line to his team's 44-yard line in 7 seconds. Find the player's average speed in yards per second. Use dimensional analysis to check the reasonableness of your answer.

$$\text{Average speed} = \frac{\text{total distance}}{\text{total time}}$$

$$= \frac{35 \text{ yards}}{7 \text{ seconds}}$$ *The player runs $44 - 9 = 35$ yards in 7 seconds.*

$$\frac{35 \text{ yards} \div 7}{7 \text{ seconds} \div 7} = \frac{5 \text{ yards}}{1 \text{ second}}$$ *Divide to find yards per second.*

The player's average speed is 5 yards per second.

Convert yd/s to mi/h to see if the answer is reasonable.

$$\frac{1 \text{ mi}}{5280 \text{ ft}} \cdot \frac{3 \text{ ft}}{1 \text{ yd}} = \frac{3 \text{ mi}}{5280 \text{ yd}} = \frac{1 \text{ mi}}{1760 \text{ yd}}$$ *Convert miles to yards.*

$$\frac{5 \text{ yd}}{1 \text{ s}} \cdot \frac{1 \text{ mi}}{1760 \text{ yd}} \cdot \frac{3600 \text{ s}}{1 \text{ h}}$$ *Set up the conversion factors.*

$$= \frac{5 \text{ yd}}{1 \text{ s}} \cdot \frac{1 \text{ mi}}{1760 \text{ yd}} \cdot \frac{3600 \text{ s}}{1 \text{ h}}$$ *Divide out like units.*

$$= \frac{5 \cdot 1 \text{ mi} \cdot 3600}{1 \cdot 1760 \cdot 1 \text{ h}} \approx 10.2 \text{ mi/h}$$ *Multiply. Then simplify.*

The player's average speed is approximately 10.2 mi/h, which is a reasonable speed for a football player to run a short distance.

Think and Discuss

1. Give the conversion factor for converting $\frac{\text{lb}}{\text{yr}}$ to $\frac{\text{lb}}{\text{mo}}$.

2. Explain how to find whether 10 mi/h is faster than 15 ft/s.

5-4 Exercises

California Standards Practice
← **AF4.2, MG1.1**, ← **MG1.3**

go.hrw.com
Homework Help Online
KEYWORD: MT8CA 5-4
Parent Resources Online
KEYWORD: MT8CA Parent

GUIDED PRACTICE

See Example **1**
1. The maximum speed of the Tupolev Tu-144 airliner is 694 m/s. Find this rate in kilometers per second.   **0.694 km/s**

2. Ali's car uses 12 gallons of gas each week. Find this rate in quarts per year.
                     2496 qt/yr

See Example **2**
3. A model airplane flies 22 feet in 2 seconds. What is its speed in mi/h?
                     7.5 mi/h

See Example **3**
4. Martin begins driving to work at 8:15 A.M. He drives 18 miles and arrives at his office at 8:39 A.M. Find Martin's average speed in miles per minute. Use dimensional analysis to check the reasonableness of your answer.
                     0.75 mi/min (= 45 mi/h)

3 Close

Summarize

Review the process for using conversion factors to convert rates from one set of units to another. Have students choose the correct conversion factor for each conversion:

1. $\frac{\text{mi}}{\text{h}}$ to $\frac{\text{ft}}{\text{h}}$ **A.** $\frac{1 \text{ yr}}{12 \text{ mo}}$ **E.** $\frac{1 \text{ kg}}{1000 \text{g}}$

2. $\frac{\text{g}}{\text{yr}}$ to $\frac{\text{g}}{\text{mo}}$ **B.** $\frac{1 \text{ mi}}{5280 \text{ ft}}$ **F.** $\frac{1 \text{ h}}{3600 \text{ s}}$

3. $\frac{\text{ft}}{\text{h}}$ to $\frac{\text{ft}}{\text{s}}$ **C.** $\frac{1 \text{ h}}{3600 \text{ ft}}$ **G.** $\frac{5280 \text{ ft}}{1 \text{ mi}}$

4. $\frac{\text{g}}{\text{yr}}$ to $\frac{\text{kg}}{\text{yr}}$ **D.** $\frac{12 \text{ mo}}{1 \text{ yr}}$ **H.** $\frac{1000 \text{ g}}{1 \text{ kg}}$

1. G   **2.** A   **3.** F   **4.** E

Power Presentations
with PowerPoint®

Additional Example

Example **3**

A strobe lamp can be used to measure the speed of an object. The lamp flashes every $\frac{1}{100}$ of a second. A camera records the object moving 52 cm between flashes. How fast is the object moving in m/s? Use dimensional analysis to check the reasonableness of your answer. **52 m/s**

Also available on transparency

Answers to
Think and Discuss

1. $\frac{1 \text{ yr}}{12 \text{ mo}}$

2. Possible answer: Convert 10 mi/h to ft/s by multiplying by the conversion factors $\frac{1 \text{ h}}{3600 \text{ s}}$ and $\frac{5280 \text{ ft}}{1 \text{ mi}}$. (10 miles per hour ≈ 14.67 feet per second, so 10 miles per hour is slower than 15 feet per second.)

5-4 Exercises

Assignment Guide

If you finished Example **1** assign:
Proficient 1–2, 5–6, 9–11, 17, 28, 30–41
Advanced 5–6, 12–14, 22–23, 25, 28, 30–41

If you finished Example **2** assign:
Proficient 1–3, 5–7, 9–11, 17, 21, 28–41
Advanced 5–7, 12–17, 19–20, 28–41

If you finished Example **3** assign:
Proficient 1–11, 15–19, 21, 27–41
Advanced 5–8, 12–16, 19–41

Homework Quick Check

Quickly check key concepts.
Exercises: 6, 7, 8, 16

INDEPENDENT PRACTICE

See Example **1**

5. Lydia wrote $4\frac{1}{2}$ pages of her science report in one hour. What was her writing rate in pages per minute?   **0.075 page/min**

6. An Olympic athlete can run 110 yards in 10 seconds. How fast in miles per hour can the athlete run?   **22.5 mi/h**

See Example **2**

7. A yellow jacket can fly 4.5 meters in 9 seconds. How fast in kilometers per hour can a yellow jacket fly?   **1.8 km/h**

See Example **3**

8. There are markers every 1000 feet along the side of a road. While driving, Sonya passes marker number 8 at 3:10 P.M. and marker number 20 at 3:14 P.M. Find Sonya's average speed in feet per minute. Use dimensional analysis to check the reasonableness of your answer.   **3000 ft/min (≈34.1 mi/h)**

PRACTICE AND PROBLEM SOLVING

Extra Practice
See page EP10.

Use conversion factors to find each of the following.

9. cereal boxes assembled in 4 minutes at a rate of 2 boxes per second
480 cereal boxes

10. distance traveled in feet after 12 seconds at 87 miles per hour   **1531.2 ft**

11. fish caught in a day at a rate of 42 fish caught each week   **6 fish**

12. concert tickets sold in an hour at a rate of 6 tickets sold per minute   **360 tickets**

13. miles jogged in 1 hour at an average rate of 8.5 feet per second   **≈ 5.8 mi**

14. calls made in a 3 day telephone fund-raiser at a rate of 10 calls per hour
720 calls

15. There are about 400 cocoa beans in a pound. There are 2.2 pounds in a kilogram. About how many grams does a cocoa bean weigh?   **≈ 0.88 g**

16. Estimation Assume that one dollar is equal to 1.14 euros. If 500 g of an item is selling for 25 euros, what is its approximate price in dollars per kilogram?
$45/kg

17. Food The largest block of cheese on record weighed 920,136 oz. How many tons is this?   **≈ 28.75 tons**

18. Sports Use the graph to find each world-record speed in miles per hour. (*Hint:* 1 mi ≈ 1609 m.)

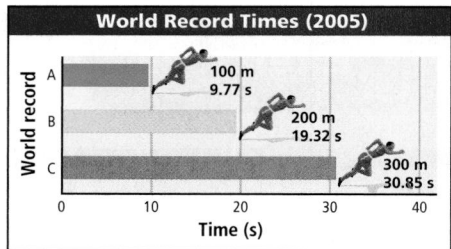

World Record Times (2005)

A — 100 m 9.77 s
B — 200 m 19.32 s
C — 300 m 30.85 s

Time (s): 0 10 20 30 40

19. Transportation The rate of one knot equals one nautical mile per hour. One nautical mile is 1852 meters. What is the speed in meters per second of a ship traveling at 20 knots?   **≈ 10.3 m/s**

20. Life Science The Outer Bay exhibit at the Monterey Bay Aquarium holds about 1,000,000 gallons of sea water. How many days would it take to fill the exhibit at a rate of 1 gallon per second?   **≈ 11.57 days**

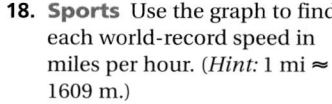

California **LINK**
Food

At the Joe Matos Cheese Factory in Santa Rosa, California, Joe and Mary Matos make 4000 pounds of St. George cheese every month.

18.
A ≈ 22.90 mi/h;
B ≈ 23.16 mi/h;
C ≈ 21.76 mi/h

California Standards

Standard	Exercises
NS2.1	30–37
AF4.2	3, 7, 10, 13, 18, 27
MG1.1	1–29
MG1.3	4, 8, 38–41

Focus on Problem Solving

California Standards

MR1.1 Analyze problems by identifying relationships, distinguishing relevant information, identifying missing information, sequencing and prioritizing information, and observing patterns.
Also covered: **MG1.1** and

MG1.3

Solve

• **Choose an operation: multiplication or division**

When you are converting units, think about whether the number in the answer will be greater or less than the number given in the question. This will help you to decide whether to multiply or divide to convert the units.

For example, if you are converting feet to inches, you know that the number of inches will be greater than the number of feet because each foot is 12 inches. So you know that you should multiply by 12 to get a greater number.

In general, if you are converting from bigger units to smaller units, the number of units will have to be greater to represent the same quantity.

For each problem, determine whether the number in the answer will be greater or less than the number given in the question. Use your answer to decide whether to multiply or divide by the conversion factor. Then solve the problem.

1 The speed a boat travels is usually measured in nautical miles per hour, or knots. The Staten Island Ferry in New York, which provides service between Manhattan and Staten Island, can travel at 15.5 knots. Find the speed in miles per hour. (*Hint:* 1 knot = 1.15 miles per hour)

2 When it is finished, the Crazy Horse Memorial in the Black Hills of South Dakota will be the world's largest sculpture. The sculpture's height will be 563 feet. Find the height in meters. (*Hint:* 1 meter ≈ 3.28 feet)
about 171.65 m

3 The grams of fat per serving of some common foods are given in the table below. Find the number of calories from fat for each serving. (*Hint:* 1 gram of fat = 9 calories)

Food	Fat per Serving (g)
Avocado (1 c, sliced)	22.3
Pretzels (1 oz)	1
Baked Potato (7 oz)	0.4
Plain Bagel (4 oz)	1.8

4 Nearly a quarter of the Texas Gulf Coast is national seashore or state park. The Gulf Coast is 372 miles long. Find the length of the Texas shoreline in kilometers. (*Hint:* 1 mile ≈ 1.61 kilometers)
598.92 km

Answers

1. 17.825 mi/h

3.

Food	Calories per Serving (cal)
Avocado (1 c, sliced)	200.7
Pretzels (1 oz)	9
Baked potato (7 oz)	3.6
Plain bagel (4 oz)	16.2

Focus on Problem Solving

Organizer

Objective: Focus on choosing an operation to solve a problem.

Online Edition

Resources

Chapter 5 Resource File
Reading Strategies

Problem Solving Process

This page focuses on the third step of the problem-solving process:
Solve

Discuss

Discuss whether the number in the answer will be greater or less than the number given in the problem, and discuss how knowing which measurement is less can help determine whether to multiply or divide.

Possible answers:

1. Greater; one mile per hour is smaller than a knot, so you should multiply.

2. Less; a meter is greater than a foot, so you should divide.

3. Greater; a calorie is less than a gram, so you should multiply.

4. Greater; a kilometer is less than a mile, so you should multiply.

California Standards

Mathematical Reasoning 1.1
Also covered:
Measurement and Geometry
1.1 Compare weights, capacities, **geometric measures,** times, and temperatures **within and between measurement systems** (e.g., miles per hour and feet per second, cubic inches to cubic centimeters).
1.3 Use measures expressed as rates (e.g., speed, density) and measures expresssed as products (e.g., person-days) **to solve problems;** check the units of the solutions; and use dimensional analysis to check the reasonableness of the answer.

SECTION 5B

Similarity and Scale

One-Minute Section Planner

Lesson	Lab Resources	Materials
Lesson 5-5 Similar Figures • Determine whether figures are similar and find missing dimensions in similar figures. 🐾 **Prep for MG1.2**	**Hands-On Lab 5-5** In *Chapter 5 Resource File*	
Lesson 5-6 Indirect Measurement • Find measures indirectly by applying the properties of similar figures. 🐾 **Ext. of MG1.2**		**Optional** Materials suitable for building a bridge between two desks in the classroom (card stock, popsicle sticks, balsa wood, etc.)
Lesson 5-7 Scale Drawings and Scale Models • Make comparisons between and find dimensions of scale drawings, models, and actual objects. 🐾 **MG1.2**		**Optional** Meter or yard sticks, tape measures, graph paper, materials for building a scale model (sugar cubes, balsa wood, card stock, etc.)
5-7 Hands-On Lab Construct Scale Drawings and Scale Models • Become familiar with the concept of scale by making scale drawings and scale models. 🐾 **MG1.2**		**Required** Graph paper, card stock, scissors, tape, ruler

MK = *Manipulatives Kit*

Notes

Math Background: Teaching the Standards

PROPORTIONALITY

Lesson 5-6

A *proportion* is a statement that two ratios are equal. In the proportion $\frac{a}{b} = \frac{c}{d}$, where $b \neq 0$ and $d \neq 0$, ad and bc are called the *cross products*. The Cross Products Property states that $\frac{a}{b} = \frac{c}{d}$ if and only if the cross products are equal. This rule is useful for checking whether two ratios form a proportion and for finding an unknown value in a proportion.

Students should recognize that the Cross Products Property is based on multiplying both sides of an equation by a multiplicative inverse. This is illustrated in Steps 2 and 4 of the following proof that $\frac{a}{b} = \frac{c}{d}$ implies $ad = bc$.

1.	$\frac{a}{b} = \frac{c}{d}$	*Given*
2.	$a \cdot \frac{1}{b} = c \cdot \frac{1}{d}$	*Definition of division*
3.	$a \cdot \frac{1}{b} \cdot b = c \cdot \frac{1}{d} \cdot b$	*Mult. Property of Equality*
4.	$a = c \cdot \frac{1}{d} \cdot b$	
5.	$a \cdot d = c \cdot \frac{1}{d} \cdot b \cdot d$	*Mult. Property of Equality*
6.	$a \cdot d = c \cdot b \cdot \frac{1}{d} \cdot d$	*Comm. Property of Mult.*
7.	$a \cdot d = c \cdot b$	
8.	$ad = bc$	*Comm. Property of Mult.*

Note that a few steps have been condensed. For example, going from Step 2 to Step 3 uses the Associative Property as well as the definition of a multiplicative inverse ($\frac{1}{b} \cdot b = 1$) and the Identity Property of Multiplication ($a \cdot 1 = a$). The proof that the Cross Products Property works in the other direction ($ad = bc$ implies $\frac{a}{b} = \frac{c}{d}$) uses a similar sequence of steps.

SIMILARITY

Lesson 5-7

Informally speaking, two figures are *similar* if they have the same shape but not necessarily the same size. Alternatively, two figures are similar if one is an enlargement or reduction of the other.

For polygons, a more formal definition can be given as follows. Consider polygon X with vertices A, B, C, ... and polygon Y with vertices A', B', C', ... Polygon X is *similar* to polygon Y if there is a correspondence between the vertices such that:

$$\angle A \cong \angle A', \angle B \cong \angle B', \angle C \cong \angle C', \dots$$

and

$$\frac{A'B'}{AB} = \frac{B'C'}{BC} = \frac{C'D'}{CD} = \dots$$

In other words, two polygons are similar if corresponding angles are congruent and corresponding sides are proportional.

The ratio $\frac{A'B'}{AB}$ is called the *scale factor*.

- If the scale factor is greater than 1, polygon Y is an enlargement of polygon X.
- If the scale factor is less than 1, polygon Y is a reduction of polygon X.
- If the scale factor is equal to 1, the polygons are congruent. In this way, congruence can be considered a special case of similarity.

SCALE DRAWINGS MG1.2

Lesson 5-8

A *scale drawing* is a two-dimensional drawing that accurately represents an object and is similar to the object. The drawing's *scale* gives the ratio of the dimensions of the drawing to the dimensions of the object. A scale of $\frac{1}{4}$ in:10 ft means that $\frac{1}{4}$ inch on the drawing represents 10 feet of the object.

Units in a scale may be mixed. To get a sense of how much an object has been enlarged or reduced, students may want to change the scale into a scale factor, where all dimensions use the same units. Thus, a scale of $\frac{1}{4}$ in:10 ft is the same as $\frac{1}{4}$ in:120 in., which is a ratio of $\frac{1}{480}$. This scale factor means that the object is reduced by a factor of 480 in the scale drawing.

Objective: Students determine whether figures are similar and find missing dimensions in similar figures.

Hands-On Lab
In *Chapter 5 Resource File*

Online Edition
Tutorial Videos

Countdown to Mastery Week 10

Power Presentations
with PowerPoint®

Warm Up

Solve each proportion.

1. $\frac{3}{9} = \frac{b}{30}$ $b = 10$

2. $\frac{y}{5} = \frac{56}{35}$ $y = 8$

3. $\frac{p}{9} = \frac{4}{12}$ $p = 3$

4. $\frac{28}{26} = \frac{56}{m}$ $m = 52$

Also available on transparency

Math Humor

How many times can you subtract 7 from 22, and what is left afterwards?

I can subtract it as many times as I want, and it leaves 15 every time!

California Standards
Prep for Measurement and Geometry 1.2

5-5 Similar Figures

California Standards
Preparation for **MG1.2** Construct and read drawings and models made to scale.

Why learn this? You can use properties of similar figures to find how wide a photo will be when it is resized for a Web page. (See Example 2.)

Similar figures have the same shape but not necessarily the same size.

Corresponding sides of two figures are in the same relative position, and **corresponding angles** are in the same relative position. Two figures are similar if the lengths of corresponding sides are proportional and the corresponding angles have equal measures.

Vocabulary
similar
corresponding sides
corresponding angles

Reading Math

∠A is read as "angle A." △ABC is read as "triangle ABC." "△ABC ~ △EFG" is read as "triangle ABC is similar to triangle EFG."

SIMILAR POLYGONS		
Words	**Diagram**	**Corresponding Parts**
For two polygons to be similar, corresponding angles must have equal measures, and the ratios of the lengths of the corresponding sides must be proportional.	△ABC ~ △EFG	$m\angle A = m\angle E$ $m\angle B = m\angle F$ $m\angle C = m\angle G$ $\frac{AB}{EF} = \frac{BC}{FG} = \frac{AC}{EG} = \frac{2}{1}$

EXAMPLE 1 Identifying Similar Figures

Which triangles are similar?

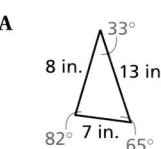
A

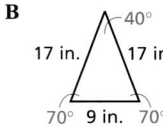
B

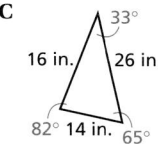
C

Both triangles *A* and *C* have angle measures of 82°, 33°, and 65°, while triangle *B* has angle measures of 70°, 40°, and 70°, so triangle *B* cannot be similar to triangle *A* or *C*.

Compare the ratios of corresponding sides in triangles *A* and *C* to see if they are proportional.

$$\frac{13}{26} = \frac{7}{14} = \frac{8}{16} \text{ or } \frac{1}{2} = \frac{1}{2} = \frac{1}{2}$$

The ratios are equal. So triangle *A* is similar to triangle *C*.

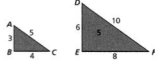
1 Introduce
Alternate Opener

EXPLORATION

5-5 Similar Figures

Similar figures have the same shape but not necessarily the same size. The two triangles shown below are similar.

1. What appears to be true about each pair of angles below?
   ∠A and ∠D   ∠B and ∠E   ∠C and ∠F

2. Calculate each of the ratios shown below. What do you notice?
   $\frac{\text{length of } \overline{AB}}{\text{length of } \overline{DE}}$ $\frac{\text{length of } \overline{BC}}{\text{length of } \overline{EF}}$ $\frac{\text{length of } \overline{AC}}{\text{length of } \overline{DF}}$

3. The two rectangles are similar to each other. What is true about the pairs of angles ∠J and ∠P, ∠K and ∠Q, ∠L and ∠R, and ∠M and ∠S?

4. What is true about all the ratios $\frac{\text{length of } \overline{JK}}{\text{length of } \overline{PQ}}$, $\frac{\text{length of } \overline{KL}}{\text{length of } \overline{QR}}$, $\frac{\text{length of } \overline{LM}}{\text{length of } \overline{RS}}$, and $\frac{\text{length of } \overline{MJ}}{\text{length of } \overline{SP}}$?

Think and Discuss

5. **Describe** what must be true when two polygons are similar to each other.

Motivate

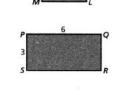
ENGLISH LANGUAGE LEARNERS

Ask students what the word *similar* means in everyday use (showing likeness or resemblance). Show students three rectangles, of which only two are similar in the mathematical sense. Explain that someone might say the three figures are similar in the everyday meaning of the word, but only two of the rectangles are mathematically similar. You may want to review proportions (Lesson 5-3).

Explorations and answers are provided in *Alternate Openers: Explorations Transparencies.*

EXAMPLE 2 **Finding Missing Measures in Similar Figures**

A picture is 10 inches wide and 8 inches tall. To display the picture on a Web page, the picture must be reduced to 3.5 inches tall. How wide should the picture be on the Web page for the two pictures to be similar?

Set up a proportion. Let w be the width of the picture on the Web page.

width of picture → $\frac{10}{w} = \frac{8}{3.5}$ ← *height of picture*
width of Web page → $\phantom{\frac{10}{w}}$ ← *height of Web page*

$10 \cdot 3.5 = w \cdot 8$ *Find the cross products.*

$35 = 8w$

$\frac{35}{8} = \frac{8w}{8}$ *Divide both sides by 8.*

$4.375 = w$

The picture should be 4.375 in. wide.

EXAMPLE 3 **Architecture Application**

 **Reasoning**

Helpful Hint

The proportion can also be set up with ratios that compare the side and base of the small triangle and the side and base of the large triangle:

$\frac{4}{5.1} = \frac{27.8}{x}$

A souvenir model of the pyramid over the entrance of the Louvre in Paris has faces in the shape of a triangle. Two sides are each 4 in. long and the base is 5.1 in. long. On the actual pyramid, each triangular face has two sides that are each 27.8 m long. What is the length of the base of the actual pyramid?

Draw a diagram to help you visualize the problem.

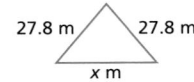

$\frac{\text{Side of small triangle}}{\text{Side of large triangle}} = \frac{\text{Base of small triangle}}{\text{Base of large triangle}}$

$\frac{4 \text{ in.}}{27.8 \text{ m}} = \frac{5.1 \text{ in.}}{x \text{ m}}$ *Set up a proportion.*

$4 \cdot x = 27.8 \cdot 5.1$ *Find the cross products.*

$4x = 141.78$ *Multiply.*

$x = \frac{141.78}{4} = 35.445$ *Solve for x.*

The base of the actual pyramid is about 35.4 m long.

Possible answers to *Think and Discuss*

1. A photograph and an enlarged version of the photograph; a model airplane and a full-size airplane.

Think and Discuss

1. Name a pair of real-world items that appear to be similar figures.

Power Presentations with PowerPoint®

Additional Examples

Example 1

Which rectangles are similar?

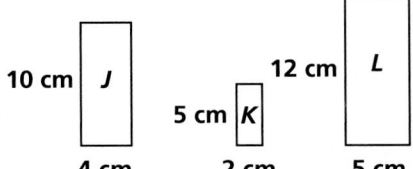

J and K are similar.

Example 2

A picture 10 in. tall and 14 in. wide is to be scaled to 1.5 in. tall to be displayed on a Web page. How wide should the picture be on the Web page for the two pictures to be similar? 2.1 in.

Example 3

A T-shirt design includes an isosceles triangle with side lengths 4.5 in., 4.5 in., and 6 in. An advertisement shows an enlarged version of the triangle with two sides that are each 3 ft long. What is the length of the third side of the triangle in the advertisement? 4 ft

Also available on transparency

---

2 Teach

Guided Instruction

In this lesson, students learn to determine whether figures are similar, to use scale factors, and to find missing dimensions in similar figures. Explain that *similar* figures have the same shape but can be different sizes (Teaching Transparency). For polygons, this means corresponding angles are congruent and corresponding sides are proportional. Point out that the ratio of corresponding sides represents the scale factor.

Teaching Tip **Visual** It will be helpful to draw diagrams when discussing **Examples 1** and **2**.

 **Universal Access**
For Advanced Learners/GATE

Ask students to find the perimeters of the similar rectangles in **Additional Example 1** and the ratio of the perimeters. 28 cm; 14 cm; $\frac{2}{1}$ Ask them to find the areas of the rectangles and the ratio of the areas. 40 cm²; 10 cm²; $\frac{4}{1}$ Then ask them to compare these ratios. ratio of areas is the square of the ratio of perimeters Ask students to find the perimeters of the triangles in **Example 1** and the ratio of the perimeters. 28 cm; 56 cm; $\frac{1}{2}$ Ask them to make a hypothesis about the ratio of the areas of the triangles. The ratio of areas is equal to the ratio of perimeters squared, $\frac{1}{4}$.

3 Close

Summarize

Show students the following sketch, and tell them the triangles are similar.

Ask students to find the measures of angles D and F and the lengths x and y.
$m\angle D = 60°$; $m\angle F = 30°$; $x = 12$; $y = 10.35$

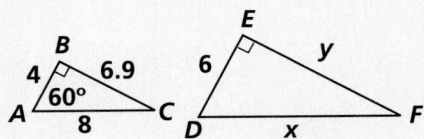

5-5 Exercises

California Standards Practice
Preparation for MG1.2

go.hrw.com
Homework Help Online
KEYWORD: MT8CA 5-5
Parent Resources Online
KEYWORD: MT8CA Parent

Assignment Guide

If you finished Example **1** assign:
Proficient 1, 4, 7–9, 24–25
Advanced 4, 7–10, 20, 24–25

If you finished Example **2** assign:
Proficient 1, 2, 4, 5, 7–9, 12–16, 22, 24–25
Advanced 4, 5, 7–16, 18–20, 22, 24–25

If you finished Example **3** assign:
Proficient 1–9, 12–18, 22–25
Advanced 4–25

Homework Quick Check
Quickly check key concepts.
Exercises: 4, 5, 6, 8, 12

Math Background

Another method of solving the problems in **Examples 2** and **3** uses scale factors. Students will learn about scale factors in Lesson 5-7.

GUIDED PRACTICE

See Example **1**

1. Which triangles are similar?   **triangle A and triangle B**

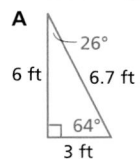

A
26°
6 ft   6.7 ft
64°
3 ft

B
6 ft
64°
13.4 ft   12 ft
26°

C
45°   9.9 ft
7 ft
45°
7 ft

See Example **2**

2. Gwen scans a photo that is 4 in. tall by 6 in. wide into her computer. She scales the width down to 5 in. How tall should the similar photo be?   **≈ 3.3 in.**

See Example **3**

3. A triangle has a base of 11 cm and legs measuring 16 cm. A similar triangle has legs measuring 24 cm. What is the base of the second triangle?   **16.5 cm**

INDEPENDENT PRACTICE

See Example **1**

4. Which triangles are similar?   **triangle A and triangle C**

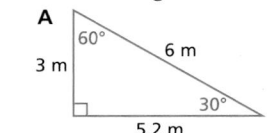

A
60°   6 m
3 m
30°
5.2 m

B
3 m   45°   4.3 m
45°
3 m

C
1.5 m   60°   3 m
30°
2.6 m

See Example **2**

5. A rectangular park measures 6.5 mi wide and 9.1 mi long. On a map, the park is similar and its width is 2.13 in. What is the length of the park on the map?   **≈ 2.98 in.**

See Example **3**

6. Vernon drew an 8 in. wide by 5 in. tall picture that will be turned into a 48 ft wide billboard. How tall will the actual billboard be?   **30 ft**

PRACTICE AND PROBLEM SOLVING

Extra Practice
See page EP11.

Tell whether the figures are similar. If they are not similar, explain.

7. **similar**

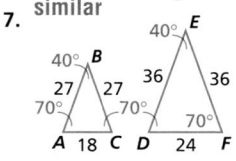

40°   E
40°   B
27   27   36   36
70°   70°
70°
A   18   C   D   24   F

8. **Not similar; corresponding sides are not in proportion.**

6 in.
4 in.
6 in.
2 in.

9. **similar**

9½ cm
2½ cm
19 cm
5 cm

10. The legs of a right triangle measure 4 cm and 6 cm. The legs of another right triangle measure 6 cm and 9 cm. Could the triangles be similar? Explain.   **Yes; the sides are proportional. $\frac{6}{4} = \frac{9}{6}$.**

11. Sari's garden is 12 ft by 16 ft 6 in. Her sketch of the garden is 8 in. by 11 in. Is Sari's sketch similar to the actual garden?   **yes**

REVIEW FOR MASTERY 5-5

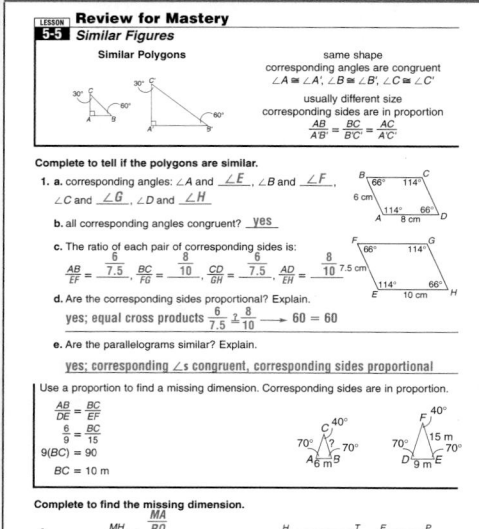

PRACTICE 5-5

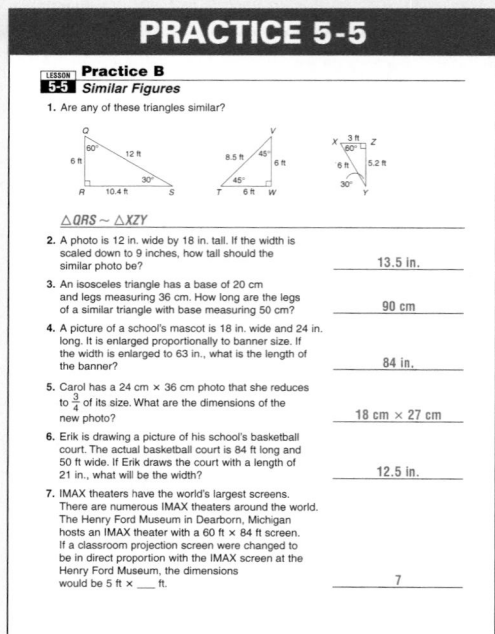

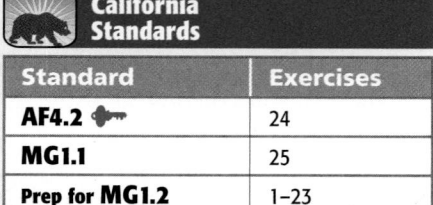

California Standards

Standard	Exercises
AF4.2 🔑	24
MG1.1	25
Prep for MG1.2	1–23

The figures in each pair are similar. Find the missing measure in each pair.

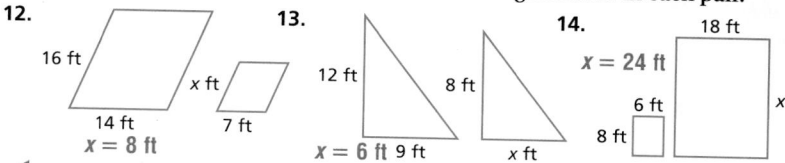

12.
16 ft
14 ft
x ft
$x = 8$ ft

13.
12 ft
8 ft
$x = 6$ ft 7 ft 9 ft

14.
18 ft
$x = 24$ ft
6 ft
8 ft
x ft

15. Art Helen is copying a printed reproduction of the Mona Lisa. The print is 24 in. wide and 36 in. tall. If Helen's canvas is 12 in. wide, how tall should her canvas be? **18 in.**

16. A rectangle is 16 cm long and 7 cm wide. A similar rectangle is 3.5 cm wide and x cm long. Find x. **8 cm**

17. Will is 5 ft tall. He casts a 3 ft shadow at the same time that a tree casts a 9 ft shadow. Use similar triangles to find the height of the tree. **15 ft**

18. Vickie knitted a baby blanket and a similar throw blanket. The baby blanket had a length of 3 ft and a width of 2.5 ft. The throw blanket had a width of 5 ft. What was the length of the throw blanket? **6 ft**

19. Write a Problem A drawing on a sheet of graph paper shows a rectangle 9 cm wide and 12 cm long. The width of the rectangle is labeled 3 ft. Write and solve a problem about the rectangle.

20. Write About It Consider the statement "All similar figures are congruent." Is this statement true or false? Explain.

21. Challenge In right triangle ABC, $\angle B$ is the right angle, $AB = 36$ cm, and $BC = 28$ cm. Right triangle ABC is similar to right triangle DEF. If $DE = 9$ cm, what is the area of triangle DEF? **31.5 cm^2**

SPIRAL STANDARDS REVIEW ← AF4.2, MG1.1, Prep for MG1.2

22. Multiple Choice An isosceles triangle has two sides that are each 4.5 centimeters long and a base that is 3 centimeters long. A similar triangle has a base that is 1.5 centimeters long. How long are each of the other two sides of the similar triangle?

Ⓐ 2.25 cm Ⓑ 3.75 cm Ⓒ 4.5 cm Ⓓ 150 cm

23. Gridded Response A rectangle is 6 feet wide by 35 feet long. A similar rectangle has a width of 12 in. How many inches long is the similar rectangle? **70**

24. A train makes a 700 mile trip. It takes the train 2 hours to travel 400 miles. If the train continues at the same rate, how many more hours will it take before the trip is completed? (Lesson 5-3) $1\frac{1}{2}$ **hours**

25. Carmen uses 16 gallons of gas for her car each week. Find the total number of quarts Carmen uses in a year. (Lesson 5-4) **3328 quarts**

CHALLENGE 5-5

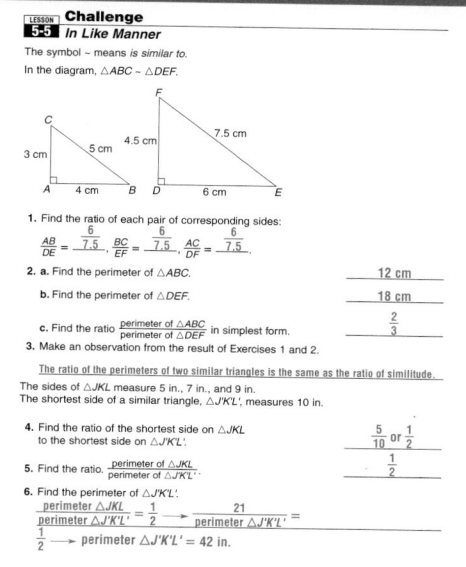

LESSON 5-5 Challenge
In Like Manner

The symbol ~ means *is similar to*.
In the diagram, $\triangle ABC \sim \triangle DEF$.

C 3 cm 5 cm A 4 cm B
F 4.5 cm 7.5 cm D 6 cm E

1. Find the ratio of each pair of corresponding sides:
$\frac{AB}{DE} = \frac{6}{7.5}$, $\frac{BC}{EF} = \frac{6}{7.5}$, $\frac{AC}{DF} = \frac{6}{7.5}$

2. a. Find the perimeter of $\triangle ABC$.   12 cm
   b. Find the perimeter of $\triangle DEF$.   18 cm
   c. Find the ratio $\frac{\text{perimeter of } \triangle ABC}{\text{perimeter of } \triangle DEF}$ in simplest form. $\frac{2}{3}$

3. Make an observation from the result of Exercises 1 and 2.
   The ratio of the perimeters of two similar triangles is the same as the ratio of similitude.

The sides of $\triangle JKL$ measure 5 in., 7 in., and 9 in. The shortest side of a similar triangle, $\triangle J'K'L'$, measures 10 in.

4. Find the ratio of the shortest side on $\triangle JKL$ to the shortest side on $\triangle J'K'L'$. $\frac{5}{10}$ or $\frac{1}{2}$

5. Find the ratio. $\frac{\text{perimeter of } \triangle JKL}{\text{perimeter of } \triangle J'K'L'}$ $\frac{1}{2}$

6. Find the perimeter of $\triangle J'K'L'$.
$\frac{\text{perimeter } \triangle JKL}{\text{perimeter } \triangle J'K'L'} = \frac{1}{2} \rightarrow \frac{21}{\text{perimeter } \triangle J'K'L'} = \frac{1}{2} \rightarrow$ perimeter $\triangle J'K'L' = 42$ in.

PROBLEM SOLVING 5-5

LESSON 5-5 Problem Solving
Similar Figures

Write the correct answer.

1. Until 1929, United States currency measured 3.13 in. by 7.42 in. The current size is 2.61 in. by 6.14 in. Are the bills similar?   no

2. Owen has a 3 in. by 5 in. photograph. He wants to make it as large as he can to fit in a 10 in. by 12.5 in. ad. What will be the new size?   7.5 in. by 12.5 in.

3. A painting is 15 cm long and 8 cm wide. In a reproduction that is similar to the original painting, the length is 36 cm. How wide is the reproduction?   19.2 cm

4. The two shortest sides of a right triangle are 10 in. and 24 in. long. What is the length of the shortest side of a similar right triangle whose two longest sides are 36 in. and 39 in.?   15 in.

The scale on a map is 1 inch = 40 miles. Round to the nearest mile.

5. On the map, it is 5.75 inches from Orlando to Miami. How many miles is it from Orlando to Miami?
   A 46 miles Ⓒ 230 miles
   B 175 miles D 340 miles

6. On the map it is $18\frac{1}{8}$ inches from Norfolk, VA, to Indianapolis, IN. How many miles is it from Norfolk to Indianapolis?
   F 58 miles H 800 miles
   Ⓖ 725 miles J 1025 miles

7. It is 185 miles from Chicago to Indianapolis. On the map it is 2.5 inches from Indianapolis to Terra Haute, IN. How far is it from Chicago to Terra Haute going through Indianapolis?
   A 100 miles C 430 miles
   Ⓑ 285 miles D 7500 miles

8. On the map, it is 7.5 inches from Chicago to Cincinnati. Traveling at 65 mi/h, how long will it take to drive from Chicago to Cincinnati? Round to the nearest tenth of an hour.
   Ⓕ 4.6 hours H 8.7 hours
   G 5.2 hours J 12.0 hours

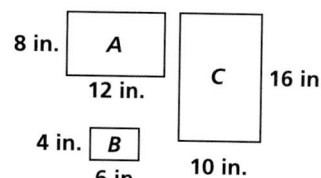

5-5 Lesson Quiz
Use the properties of similar figures to answer each question.

1. Which rectangles are similar?

8 in. [A] 12 in.
[C] 16 in.
4 in. [B] 6 in.
10 in.

A and *B* are similar.

2. Karen enlarged a 3 in. wide by 5 in. tall photo into a poster. If the poster is 2.25 ft wide, how tall should the poster be for the photo and poster to be similar? **3.75 ft**

3. A rectangular house is 32 ft wide and 68 ft long. On a blueprint, the width is 8 in. Find the length on the blueprint. **17 in.**

Also available on transparency

Online Edition
Tutorial Videos

Countdown to Mastery Week 10

Power Presentations
with PowerPoint®

Warm Up
Solve each proportion.

1. $\frac{3}{5} = \frac{x}{75}$ 45
2. $\frac{6}{x} = \frac{2.4}{8}$ 20
3. $\frac{9}{27} = \frac{x}{6}$ 2
4. $\frac{x}{3.5} = \frac{8}{7}$ 4

Also available on transparency

Math Humor

Teacher: Why didn't you finish your math homework?

Student: I have a solar-powered calculator and it was cloudy.

5-6 Indirect Measurement

California Standards

Extension of **MG1.2** Construct and read drawings and models made to scale.

Why learn this? You can use indirect measurement to find the length of something that is hard to measure, such as the width of a river. (See Example 1.)

Vocabulary
indirect measurement

Sometimes, distances cannot be easily measured directly. One way to find such a distance is to use **indirect measurement**, a way of using similar figures and proportions to find a measure.

EXAMPLE 1 *Geography Application*

A scout troop wants to make a temporary bridge across the river. The diagram shows the measurements that the troop knows. The triangles in the diagram are similar. How wide is the river where the troop wants to make the bridge?

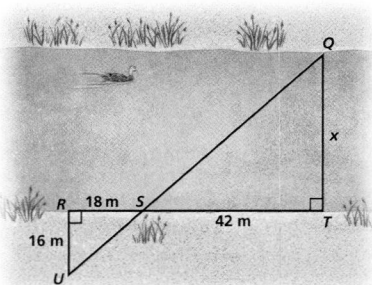

Triangles *RSU* and *TSQ* are similar.

$\dfrac{QT}{UR} = \dfrac{ST}{SR}$ *Set up a proportion.*

$\dfrac{x}{16} = \dfrac{42}{18}$ *Substitute 16 for UR, 42 for ST, and 18 for SR.*

$18x = 672$ *Find the cross products.*

$\dfrac{18x}{18} = \dfrac{672}{18}$ *Divide both sides by 18.*

$x \approx 37.\overline{3}$

The distance across the river is approximately 37.3 meters.

---

1 Introduce
Alternate Opener

EXPLORATION

5-6 Indirect Measurement

Mr. Kelly's science class is tracking the motion of the sun during the year. To do so, they measure the shadow cast by a 120-foot building on four different days of the year. To check the measurements, the students also measure the shadow cast by a 36-inch stick. The table shows their findings.

Day	Height of Building	Length of Building's Shadow	Height of Stick	Length of Stick's Shadow
1	120 ft	20 ft	36 in.	6 in.
2	120 ft	30 ft	36 in.	9 in.
3	120 ft	40 ft	36 in.	12 in.
4	120 ft	80 ft	36 in.	24 in.

1. a. On Day 1, what was the ratio of the height of the building to the length of the building's shadow?
   b. What was the ratio of the height of the stick to the length of the stick's shadow?
   c. What do you notice about these ratios?
2. Does your observation about the ratios also hold for Day 2, Day 3, and Day 4?

Think and Discuss
3. **Describe** how you could find the length of the stick's shadow if you know that the length of the building's shadow is 60 ft.
4. **Explain** what must be true about the building's shadow on a day when the stick's shadow is 36 in.

Motivate
Ask students to identify situations where they would need to know a measurement, but could not measure it directly, such as with a tape measure. Draw two similar figures. Ask students to name the pairs of corresponding sides. Remind students that corresponding sides of similar figures are proportional.

Explorations and answers are provided in *Alternate Openers: Explorations Transparencies*.

California Standards

Ext. of Measurement and Geometry 1.2

EXAMPLE 2 PROBLEM SOLVING APPLICATION

A flagpole casts a 32 ft shadow, while a 6 ft tall man standing nearby casts a 4.5 ft shadow. How tall is the pole?

 Understand the Problem

The **answer** is the height of the flagpole.

List the important information:
• The length of the flagpole's shadow is 32 ft.
• The height of the man is 6 ft.
• The length of the man's shadow is 4.5 ft.

2 Make a Plan

Use the information to *draw a diagram.*

3 Solve

Draw a diagram. Then draw the dashed lines to form triangles. The flagpole and its shadow and the man and his shadow form similar right triangles.

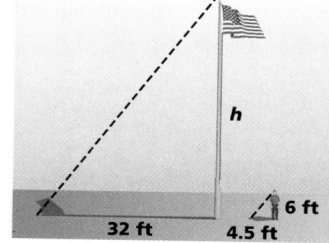

$\frac{32}{4.5} = \frac{h}{6}$ *Corresponding sides of similar figures are proportional.*

$4.5h = 192$ *Find the cross products.*

$\frac{4.5h}{4.5} = \frac{192}{4.5}$ *Divide both sides by 4.5.*

$h \approx 42.\overline{6}$

The height of the flagpole is approximately 42.7 ft.

 Look Back

The ratio $\frac{4.5}{6}$ is equivalent to $\frac{3}{4}$, so the man's shadow is $\frac{3}{4}$ of his height. The flagpole's shadow should be $\frac{3}{4}$ of its height and 32 is approximately $\frac{3}{4}$ of 42.7.

Helpful Hint

The proportion can also be set up with ratios that compare the flagpole's height to its shadow and the man's height to his shadow:

$\frac{h}{32} = \frac{6}{4.5}$

Think and Discuss

1. **Describe** a situation for which it would make sense to use indirect measurement to find the height of an object.

2. **Explain** how you can tell whether the terms of a proportion you have written are in the correct order.

Power Presentations
with PowerPoint®

Additional Examples

Example 1

Triangles *ABC* and *EFG* are similar. Find the length of side *EG*. **12 ft**

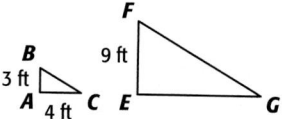

Example 2

A 30-ft building casts a shadow that is 75 ft long. A nearby tree casts a shadow that is 35 ft long. How tall is the tree? **14 ft**

Also available on transparency

Possible answers to *Think and Discuss*

1. To find the height of a tall building, measure its shadow. Then measure the height of a person and their shadow.

2. Use number sense: check that both ratios are in the same order: smaller to larger or larger to smaller.

2 Teach

Guided Instruction

Before solving problems using indirect measurement, review how to solve proportions using the cross products. Then show students which sides of similar figures are proportional. Use the corresponding sides of two similar figures to write proportions.

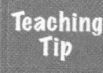 **Teaching Tip**
Visual Suggest that students draw and label the similar figures before writing the proportions.

 **Universal Access**
Through Modeling

Present students with a problem similar to the one in **Example 1.** Have them build a bridge across an open expanse, such as between two desks. Give them three of the measurements and ask them to find the missing one through indirect measurement. Then have students make the bridge using the measurement they calculated to test whether or not it connects the two objects.

3 Close

Summarize

Ask students to explain why similar figures can be used to find a dimension through indirect measurement.

You can find the unknown length by solving a proportion because the side lengths of similar figures are proportional.

5-6 Exercises

California Standards Practice
Extension of MG1.2

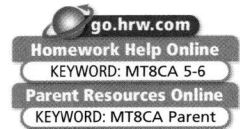
go.hrw.com
Homework Help Online
KEYWORD: MT8CA 5-6
Parent Resources Online
KEYWORD: MT8CA Parent

Assignment Guide

If you finished Example **1** assign:
Proficient 1, 4, 7–9, 16–24
Advanced 4, 7–9, 12, 13, 16–24

If you finished Example **2** assign:
Proficient 1–11, 15–24
Advanced 4–24

Homework Quick Check
Quickly check key concepts.
Exercises: 4, 6, 8, 10

GUIDED PRACTICE

See Example **1**
1. Walter wants to know the width of the pond on his farm. He drew the diagram and labeled it with measurements that he made. The triangles in the diagram are similar. How wide is the pond? **128 yd**

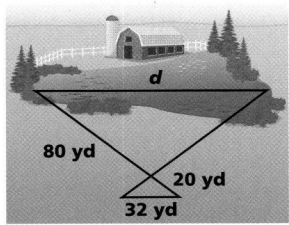
d
80 yd
20 yd
32 yd

See Example **2** **Use the diagram for Exercises 2 and 3.**
2. How tall is the tree? **42 ft**
3. How tall is the girl? **5.6 ft**

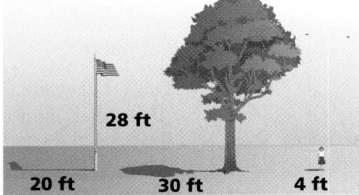
28 ft
20 ft   30 ft   4 ft

Math Background

Surveyors have used scientific instruments to measure distances indirectly as far back as 3000 years ago. Simple instruments were used to reestablish field boundaries after the annual floods of the river Nile and to build tunnels, aqueducts, and other structures throughout the Middle East. The instruments have moved from the simple, such as squares and levels, to the complex, including many forms of theodolite, quadrant, and astrolabe.

INDEPENDENT PRACTICE

See Example **1**
4. The town council has decided to build a footbridge over a pond in the park. An engineer drew a diagram of the pond and labeled it with measurements that she made. The triangles in the diagram are similar. How long will the footbridge *d* be? **100 m**

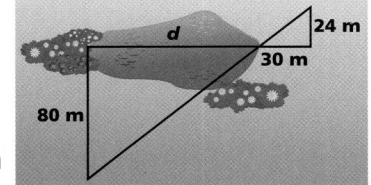
d   24 m
30 m
80 m

See Example **2** **Use the diagram for Exercises 5 and 6.**
5. How tall is the child? **4 ft**
6. The house is 19 ft tall. How long is its shadow? **14.25 ft**

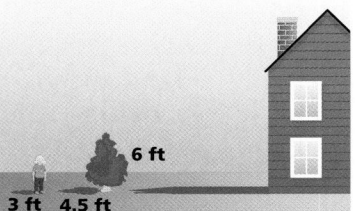
6 ft
3 ft   4.5 ft

REVIEW FOR MASTERY 5-6

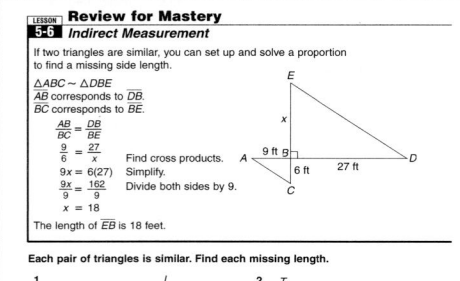

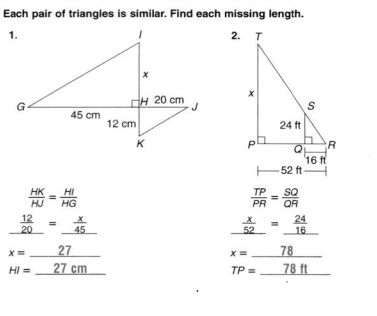

PRACTICE 5-6

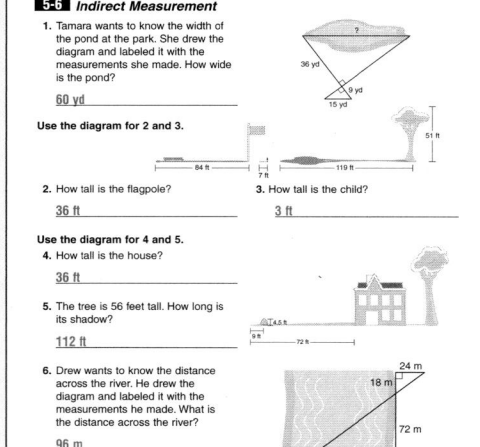

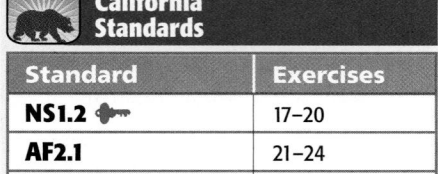

California Standards	
Standard	**Exercises**
NS1.2 🔑	17–20
AF2.1	21–24
Ext. of **MG1.2**	1–16

PRACTICE AND PROBLEM SOLVING

Extra Practice
See page EP11.

8. The tree's shadow will be 20 ft long.

7. A totem pole casts a shadow that is 45 feet long at the same time that a 6-foot-tall man casts a shadow that is 3 feet long. What is the height of the totem pole? **90 ft**

8. Brooke is 5 ft tall. She and her class are walking through a wooded area looking for a tree that is 50 ft tall. If the length of Brooke's shadow is 2 ft, how will the students know when they have found a 50 ft tree?

9. A ramp is built by putting a triangle on top of a trapezoid. How long is the ramp? (Hint: The two triangles in the diagram are similar.) **85 ft**

10. An 11 m tall sign casts a 19 m shadow when the shadow of a boy standing next to it is 3 m long. To the nearest tenth of a meter, how tall is the boy? **1.7 m**

11. A 40 ft tall monument casts a shadow that just reaches the base of a 4 ft tall parking meter. If the parking meter's shadow is 6.5 ft long, how far apart are the monument and the meter? **65 ft**

12. Write a Problem Write a problem using indirect measurement to measure an object at home or school.

13. Write About It Explain how you might use similar rectangles to measure indirectly.

14. Challenge Stanley is 6 ft tall. He wants to stand in the shade of a tree that is 35 ft tall. If the tree casts a 10 ft shadow, what is the farthest Stanley can stand from the tree and be completely in its shadow? Round your answer to the nearest tenth of a foot. **8.3 ft**

SPIRAL STANDARDS REVIEW
➡ NS1.2, AF1.2, AF2.1, Ext. of MG1.2

15. Multiple Choice Triangles *ABC* and *DEF* are similar right triangles. If you know the lengths of sides *AB*, *AC*, *BC*, and *DE*, which other length(s) can you find?

Ⓐ Only *DF*　　Ⓑ Only *EF*　　Ⓒ *DF* and *EF*　　Ⓓ None of them

16. Short Response At the same time that a tree casts a 44 ft shadow, a 3.5 ft girl standing next to the tree casts a 5 ft shadow. How much taller than the girl is the tree? **27.3 ft**

Multiply. Write each answer in simplest form. (Lesson 2-4)

17. $-\frac{1}{4}\left(\frac{4}{5}\right)$ $-\frac{1}{5}$ 　　**18.** $\frac{4}{7}\left(\frac{3}{8}\right)$ $\frac{3}{14}$ 　　**19.** $-\frac{2}{3}\left(-\frac{1}{4}\right)$ $\frac{1}{6}$ 　　**20.** $\frac{3}{8}\left(-\frac{2}{3}\right)$ $-\frac{1}{4}$

Simplify. (Lesson 4-2)

21. $(-7)^{-2}$ $\frac{1}{49}$ 　　**22.** $3^0(2)^5$ **32** 　　**23.** $1^{-1} - (-2)^{-1}$ $1\frac{1}{2}$ 　　**24.** $(-5)^2 + 36(1 + 5)^{-2}$ $\frac{26}{?}$

CHALLENGE 5-6

PROBLEM SOLVING 5-6

Answers

12. Possible answer: A fellow student is 4 ft tall and casts a 1.5 ft shadow. If a flag pole casts a 15 ft shadow, how tall is the flag pole? Answer: 40 ft

13. Possible answer: If you are given any vertical and horizontal measurement, you can then use the same process as you would with triangles.

Teaching Tip **Multiple Choice** For **Exercise 15,** suggest that students draw the two similar triangles and label the sides. This will help them identify the corresponding sides. By looking at the diagram, they should realize they can find the lengths of sides *DF* and *EF*.

Journal

Have students give an example of how they use proportions in a real world situation. Ask them to use real measurements or quantities in their explanation.

5-6 Lesson Quiz

1. Vilma wants to know how wide the river near her house is. She drew a diagram and labeled it with her measurements. The triangles in the diagram are similar. How wide is the river?

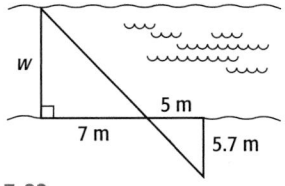

W 　7 m 　5 m 　5.7 m

7.98 m

2. A yardstick casts a 2 ft shadow. At the same time, a tree casts a shadow that is 6 ft long. How tall is the tree? **9 ft**

Also available on transparency

Objective: Students make comparisons between and find dimensions of scale drawings, models, and actual objects.

 Online Edition
Tutorial Videos, Interactivities

Countdown to Mastery Week 11

 **Warm Up**

Evaluate the following for $x = 16$.

1. $3x$ 48   **2.** $\frac{3}{4}x$ 12

Evaluate the following for $x = \frac{2}{5}$.

3. $10x$ 4   **4.** $\frac{1}{4}x$ $\frac{1}{10}$

Also available on transparency

 Math Humor

Teacher: Why did you turn in a picture of a snake?

Student: You said to make a *scale drawing.*

 **5-7** **Scale Drawings and Scale Models**

 California Standards

MG1.2 Construct and **read** drawings and models made to scale.

Vocabulary
scale drawing
scale model
scale
scale factor

Why learn this? Ratios and proportions are used to draw accurate maps. (See Example 1.)

A **scale drawing** is a two-dimensional drawing of an object that is proportional to the object. This map of Yosemite National Park is a *scale drawing.*

A **scale model** is a three-dimensional model that is proportional to the object.

A **scale** gives the ratio of the dimensions in the drawing to the dimensions of the object. All dimensions are reduced or enlarged using the same scale. Scales can use the same units or different units.

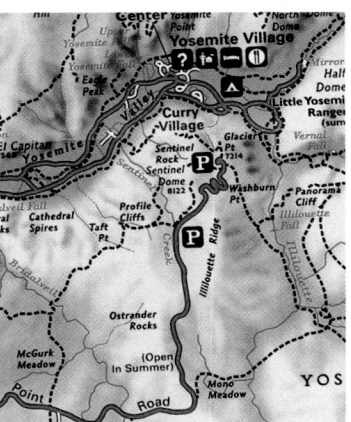
Scale: 1 in:2 mi

EXAMPLE 1 **Finding Actual Measurements**

On the map, the distance between El Capitan and Panorama Cliff is 2 inches. What is the actual distance?

$\dfrac{1 \text{ in.}}{2 \text{ mi}} = \dfrac{2 \text{ in.}}{x \text{ mi}}$ *Write a proportion using the scale. Let x be the actual number of miles from El Capitan to Panorama Cliff.*

$2 \cdot 2 = 1 \cdot x$ *The cross products are equal.*

$4 = x$

The actual distance from El Capitan to Panorama Cliff is 4 miles.

EXAMPLE 2 **Using Proportions to Find Unknown Scales**

 **Reading Math**

The scale *a:b* is read "*a* to *b*." For example, the scale 1 cm:6 m is read "one centimeter to six meters."

The length of an object on a scale drawing is 8 cm, and its actual length is 48 m. The scale is 1 cm:▦ m. What is the scale?

$\dfrac{1 \text{ cm}}{x \text{ m}} = \dfrac{8 \text{ cm}}{48 \text{ m}}$ *Set up a proportion using* $\dfrac{scale\ length}{actual\ length}$.

$1 \cdot 48 = x \cdot 8$ *Find the cross products.*

$x = 6$ *Divide both sides by 8.*

The scale is 1 cm:6 m.

 **1** **Introduce**
Alternate Opener

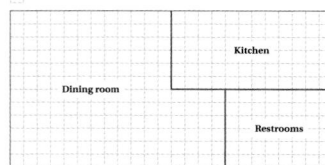
Motivate

On the chalkboard, sketch a rough scale drawing of the classroom floor. (You will need to measure the room ahead of time and decide on a scale; you may want to use a scale of 1:10 or 1:20.) Ask students how much larger they think the actual floor is than the drawing. Have students measure the drawing and the actual floor and determine the scale.

Explorations and answers are provided in *Alternate Openers: Explorations Transparencies.*

The ratio of a length on a scale drawing or model to the corresponding length on the actual object is called the **scale factor**. When finding a scale factor, you must use the same measurement units. You can use a scale factor to find unknown dimensions.

EXAMPLE 3 **Using Scale Factors to find Unknown Dimensions**

A model of a 36 ft tall house was made using the scale 3 in:2 ft. What is the height of the model?

$$\frac{3\text{ in.}}{2\text{ ft}} = \frac{3\text{ in.}}{24\text{ in.}} = \frac{1\text{ in.}}{8\text{ in.}} \qquad \textit{Find the scale factor.}$$

The scale factor for the model is $\frac{1}{8}$. Now set up a proportion.

$$\frac{1}{8} = \frac{h\text{ in.}}{36\text{ ft}} \qquad \textit{Convert: 36 ft = 432 in.}$$

$$\frac{1}{8} = \frac{h\text{ in.}}{432\text{ in.}} \qquad \textit{Convert: 36 ft = 432 in.}$$

$$432 = 8h \qquad \textit{Find the cross products.}$$

$$h = 54 \qquad \textit{Divide both sides by 8.}$$

The height of the model is 54 in.

EXAMPLE 4 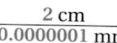 *Life Science Application*

A DNA model was built using the scale 2 cm:0.0000001 mm. If the model of the DNA chain is 17 cm long, what is the length of the actual chain?

$$\frac{2\text{ cm}}{0.0000001\text{ mm}} = \frac{20\text{ mm}}{0.0000001\text{ mm}} = 200{,}000{,}000 \qquad \textit{Find the scale factor.}$$

The scale factor for the model is 200,000,000. This means the model is 200 million times larger than the actual chain.

$$\frac{200{,}000{,}000}{1} = \frac{17\text{ cm}}{x\text{ cm}} \qquad \textit{Set up a proportion.}$$

$$200{,}000{,}000x = 17(1) \qquad \textit{Find the cross products.}$$

$$x = 0.000000085 \qquad \textit{Divide both sides by 200,000,000.}$$

The length of the DNA chain is 0.000000085 or 8.5×10^{-8} cm.

Think and Discuss

1. **Describe** which scale would produce the largest drawing of an object: 1:20, 1 in. = 1 ft, or $\frac{1}{4}$ in. = 1 ft.

2. **Explain** how you could show that the answer to Example 3 is reasonable.

Answers to Think and Discuss

1. The scale 1 in. = 1 ft would produce the largest drawing.

2. Possible answer: Two feet on the house represents 3 in. on the model. Since 2 ft · 18 = 36 ft, you can multiply 3 in. by 18 to get the answer. So 54 in. is reasonable.

2 Teach

Guided Instruction

In this lesson, students learn to make comparisons between and find dimensions of scale drawings, scale models, and actual objects. Explain that a scale drawing represents an actual object that is either larger or smaller than the drawing. Explain that a scale model is similar to a scale drawing except that it shows all three dimensions. Define *scale*, and point out that a scale may contain different units or no units at all. Show students how to simplify scale factors by writing ratios with the same units. You may want to review the use of conversion factors (Lesson 5-4).

Universal Access
Through Modeling

Have students use tape measures (Manipulatives Kit) and graph paper to make a scale drawing of a room in their home. Students will need to measure important lines, walls, or objects, such as a bed or other large furniture, and decide on an appropriate scale. Then, students should work with an adult or family member to create a scale model of the room. Suggest that students design the scale model using materials of their choice (sugar cubes, balsa wood, card stock, etc.). Each student should submit the scale factor and all calculations, along with the model and drawing.

3 Close

Summarize

Review the process of simplifying scale factors. For each scale below, ask students to write the scale factor. Ask them to also write whether the actual object would be larger or smaller than the scale model.

1. 1 in:4 ft
   1/48; actual object is larger

2. 2 ft:6 in.
   4/1; actual object is smaller

3. 2 cm:1 km
   1/50,000; actual object is larger

5-7 Exercises

California Standards Practice
MG1.2

go.hrw.com
Homework Help Online
KEYWORD: MT8CA 5-7
Parent Resources Online
KEYWORD: MT8CA Parent

Assignment Guide

If you finished Example **1** assign:
Proficient 1, 5, 24–32
Advanced 5, 14, 24–32

If you finished Example **2** assign:
Proficient 1, 2, 5, 6, 24–32
Advanced 5, 6, 14, 24–32

If you finished Example **3** assign:
Proficient 1–3, 5–7, 9–13, 16–18, 23–32
Advanced 5–7, 11–20, 23–32

If you finished Example **4** assign:
Proficient 1–14, 16–18, 23–32
Advanced 5–8, 11–32

Homework Quick Check

Quickly check key concepts.
Exercises: 5, 6, 7, 8, 10

Math Background

The Museum of Science in Boston, Massachusetts, recently installed a full-scale version of *Tyrannosaurus rex*. The process used to create the full-scale version involved a reduction followed by an enlargement. First, a scale-model sculpture was created using a 1:12 scale. Then the model was sliced from snout to tail, like a banana. Next, images of each slice were projected using a 12:1 scale. The enlarged images were then traced and cut from foam. The foam pieces were glued together to create a dinosaur display 14 feet tall and 39 feet long.

GUIDED PRACTICE

See Example **1** 1. On the map, the distance between the post office and the fountain is 6 cm. What is the actual distance? **300 ft**

See Example **2** 2. A 10 ft fence is 8 in. long on a scale drawing. What is the scale? **1 in.:1.25 ft**

See Example **3** 3. A model of a 42 ft tall shopping mall was built using the scale 1 in.:3 ft. What is the height of the model? **14 in.**

See Example **4** 4. A molecular model uses the scale 2.5 cm:0.00001 mm. If the model is 7 cm long, how long is the actual molecule? **0.000028 mm**

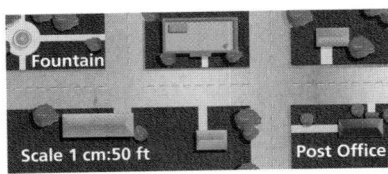
Fountain
Scale 1 cm:50 ft
Post Office

INDEPENDENT PRACTICE

See Example **1** 5. On the map of California, Los Angeles is 1.25 inches from Malibu. What is the actual distance? **25 mi**

See Example **2** 6. What is the scale of a drawing where a 6 m wall is 4 cm long? **1 cm:1.5 m**

See Example **3** 7. A model of a house was built using the scale 5 in.:25 ft. If a window in the model is 1.5 in. wide, how wide is the actual window? **7.5 ft**

See Example **4** 8. To create a model of an artery, a health teacher uses the scale 2.5 cm:0.75 mm. If the diameter of the artery is 2.7 mm, what is the diameter on the model? **9 cm**

Scale 1 in:20 mi

PRACTICE AND PROBLEM SOLVING

Extra Practice
See page EP11.

Find the scale factor.

9. 1 ft model of a 1 in. fossil $\frac{12}{1}$

10. 20 cm model of a 28 m rocket $\frac{1}{140}$

11. 30 cm model of a 6 m tree $\frac{1}{20}$

12. 3 ft model of a 5 yd whale $\frac{1}{5}$

13. **Architecture** Maurice is building a 2 ft tall model of the Gateway Arch in St. Louis, Missouri. If he is using a 3 in:78.75 ft scale, how tall is the actual arch? **630 ft**

14. **Abilene: 317.5 mi; Austin: 145 mi; Dallas: 225 mi; Galveston: 47.5 mi**

14. **Geography** The straight-line distances between Houston and several cities on a map of Texas are shown in the table. The scale is 2 cm:50 mi. Find the actual distances in miles.

15. On a scale drawing, a fence is $6\frac{1}{4}$ in. tall. The scale factor is $\frac{1}{12}$. Find the height of the actual fence in feet. **6.25 ft**

City	Distance from Houston (cm)
Abilene	12.7
Austin	5.8
Dallas	9.0
Galveston	1.9

California Standards

Standard	Exercises
NS2.4	25–29
MG1.2	1–24
MG1.3 🔑	30–32

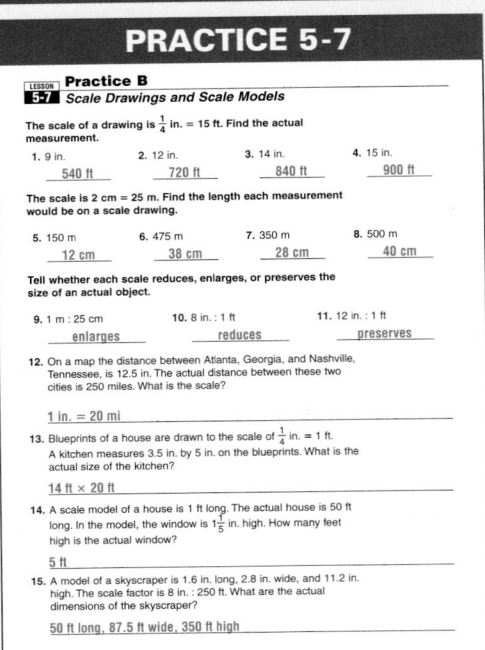

REVIEW FOR MASTERY 5-7

Review for Mastery
5-7 *Scale Drawings and Scale Models*

In a **scale drawing or a scale model**, all the dimensions of the actual object are reduced or enlarged proportionally.

A map is a scale drawing in which actual distance is reduced.

The towns of Ardon and Bacton are on a map with scale 1 cm = 15 km.

If the map distance between Ardon and Bacton is 4.5 cm, what is the actual distance?

$$\frac{\text{actual distance}}{\text{map distance}} = \frac{\text{actual distance}}{\text{map distance}}$$

$$\frac{15 \text{ km}}{1 \text{ cm}} = \frac{x \text{ km}}{4.5 \text{ cm}}$$

$$1(x) = 15(4.5)$$

$$x = 67.5 \text{ km} \leftarrow \text{actual distance between Ardon and Bacton}$$

Complete to find each unknown measure.

1. A map scale is 1 in. = 75 mi. The map distance between two towns is 3.5 in. Find the actual distance *x* between the towns.

$$\frac{\text{actual distance}}{\text{map distance}} = \frac{\text{actual distance}}{\text{map distance}}$$

$$\frac{75 \text{ mi}}{1 \text{ in.}} = \frac{x \text{ mi}}{3.5 \text{ in.}}$$

$$x = \underline{262.5}$$

actual distance = __262.5 mi__

2. The actual distance between two towns is 175 mi. If the distance between them on a map is 7 cm, what is the map scale?

$$\frac{x \text{ km}}{1 \text{ cm}} = \frac{175 \text{ km}}{7 \text{ cm}}$$

$$7x = 175$$

$$x = \underline{25}$$

map scale: 1 cm = __25 km__

3. An archway on a $\frac{1}{2}$ in. scale drawing is 4.5 in. tall. Find the actual height *x*.

$$\frac{\text{actual height}}{\text{scale height}} = \frac{\text{actual height}}{\text{scale height}}$$

$$\frac{1 \text{ ft}}{0.5 \text{ in.}} = \frac{x \text{ ft}}{4.5 \text{ in.}}$$

$$0.5x = 4.5$$

$$x = 9$$

actual height = __9 ft__

4. Under a 7:1 magnification, this letter F appears to be 84 points high. Find the actual height *x*.

$$\frac{\text{actual height}}{\text{scale height}} = \frac{\text{actual height}}{\text{scale height}}$$

$$\frac{1}{7} = \frac{x \text{ points}}{84 \text{ points}}$$

$$7x = 84$$

$$x = 12$$

actual height = __12 points__

PRACTICE 5-7

Practice B
5-7 *Scale Drawings and Scale Models*

The scale of a drawing is $\frac{1}{4}$ in. = 15 ft. Find the actual measurement.

1. 9 in. __540 ft__
2. 12 in. __720 ft__
3. 14 in. __840 ft__
4. 15 in. __900 ft__

The scale is 2 cm = 25 m. Find the length each measurement would be on a scale drawing.

5. 150 m __12 cm__
6. 475 m __38 cm__
7. 350 m __28 cm__
8. 500 m __40 cm__

Tell whether each scale reduces, enlarges, or preserves the size of an actual object.

9. 1 m : 25 cm __enlarges__
10. 8 in. : 1 ft __reduces__
11. 12 in. : 1 ft __preserves__

12. On a map the distance between Atlanta, Georgia, and Nashville, Tennessee, is 12.5 in. The actual distance between these two cities is 250 miles. What is the scale?

__1 in. = 20 mi__

13. Blueprints of a house are drawn to the scale of $\frac{1}{4}$ in. = 1 ft. A kitchen measures 3.5 in. by 5 in. on the blueprints. What is the actual size of the kitchen?

__14 ft × 20 ft__

14. A scale model of a house is 1 ft long. The actual house is 50 ft long. In the model, the window is $1\frac{1}{5}$ in. high. How many feet high is the actual window?

__5 ft__

15. A model of a skyscraper is 1.6 in. long, 2.8 in. wide, and 11.2 in. high. The scale factor is 1 in. : 250 ft. What are the actual dimensions of the skyscraper?

__50 ft long, 87.5 ft wide, 350 ft high__

The blueprint shows the design for the Anderson's new family room. Use a metric ruler to measure the width of the 36-inch-wide door on the blueprint and determine the scale factor. **The scale is about 0.9 cm:36 in.**

For Exercises 16–21, indicate the scale that you used.

16. How wide are the pocket doors (shown by the red line)? ≈ 64 in.

17. What is the distance *s* between two interior studs? ≈ 16 in.

18. How long is the oak mantle? (The right side ends just above the *B* in the word *BRICK*.) ≈ 80 in.

19. What is the area of the tiled hearth in square inches? in square feet? ≈ 960 in²; ≈ 6.7 ft²

20. What is the area of the entire family room in square feet? ≈ 274 ft²

21. ✐ **Write About It** Could a 4 ft wide bookcase fit along the right-hand wall without blocking the pocket doors? Explain.

22. ⭐ **Challenge** Suppose the architect used a $\frac{1}{8}$ in. = 1 ft scale.
   a. What would the dimensions of the family room be? 22 ft by 12 ft
   b. Use the result from part **a** to find the area of the family room. 264 ft²
   c. If the carpet the Andersons want costs $4.99 per square foot, how much would it cost to carpet the family room? $1317.36

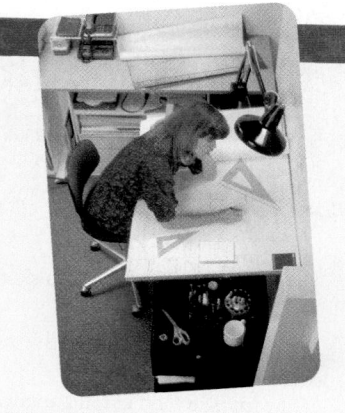

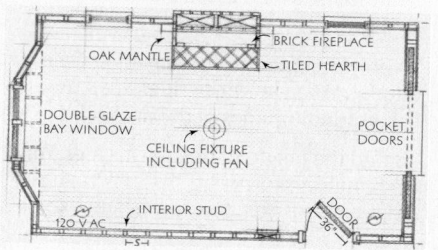

BRICK FIREPLACE
OAK MANTLE
TILED HEARTH
DOUBLE GLAZE BAY WINDOW
POCKET DOORS
CEILING FIXTURE INCLUDING FAN
INTERIOR STUD
120 V AC
DOOR

go.hrw.com
Web Extra!
KEYWORD: MT8CA Scale

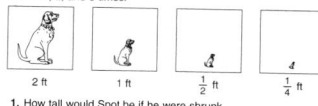 **SPIRAL STANDARDS REVIEW**   NS2.4, MG1.2, 🔑 MG1.3

23. **Multiple Choice** What scale factor was used to create a 10-inch-tall model of a 15-foot-tall statue?
   (A) 1:1.5   (B) 1:3   (C) 1:15   (D) 1:18

24. **Short Response** The height of a building on a $\frac{1}{4}$ in: 1 ft scale drawing is 5 inches tall. How tall is the actual building? Explain. 20 feet; 5 ÷ 0.25 = 20

Each square root is between two integers. Name the integers. Explain your answer. (Lesson 4-7)

25. $\sqrt{27}$ 5 and 6 26. $\sqrt{18}$ 4 and 5 27. $\sqrt{53}$ 7 and 8 28. $\sqrt{39}$ 6 and 7 29. $\sqrt{45}$ 6 and 7

Find each unit rate. (Lesson 5-2)

30. $90 for 8 hours of work
    $11.25 per hour

31. 5 apples for $0.85
    $0.17 per apple

32. 24 players on 2 teams
    12 players per team

Interdisciplinary  LINK

Architecture

Exercises 16–22 involve using a scale drawing, or an architectural blueprint, to find actual dimensions.

Answers

21. No; the bookcase is 48 in. wide, but each wall next to the doors is only about 44 in. wide.

 Teaching Tip **Multiple Choice** For **Exercise 23,** students who answered **A** did not convert the feet to inches. Instead, they divided 15 feet by 10 inches. Students who answered **D** correctly converted the feet to inches before dividing.

✐ **Journal**

Explain to students that one kind of common scale drawing is a highway map. Ask students to write about how the scale on a map could be helpful to them when they are taking a trip.

Objective: Become familiar with the concept of scale by making scale drawings and scale models.

Materials: Graph paper, card stock, scissors, tape, ruler

Online Edition

Countdown to Mastery Week 11

Teach
Discuss

Have students discuss what they would do if they were given a 6 in. square and were asked to draw a square half that size, or twice that size.

Close
Key Concept

Scale drawings accurately represent objects without being drawn full size.

Assessment

Use a square with a height of 4 and the given scale factor to draw a similar figure.

1. scale factor: 2

2. scale factor: $\frac{1}{4}$

California Standards

Measurement and Geometry 1.2

Hands-On LAB 5-7

Construct Scale Drawings and Scale Models

Use with Lesson 5-7

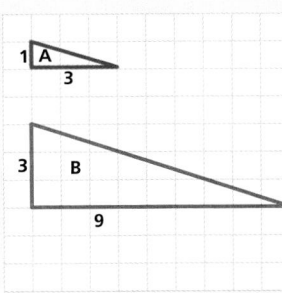

go.hrw.com
Lab Resources Online
KEYWORD: MT8CA Lab5

California Standards

MG1.2 Construct and read **drawings and models made to scale.**

You can use a scale factor to sketch scale drawings.

Activity 1

Draw triangle A on graph paper with height 1 and base 3 as shown.

To draw a similar triangle using a scale factor of 3, draw another triangle whose sides are 3 times as long as the corresponding sides of the original.

To find the height of the new triangle, multiply the height of triangle A by 3.
height = 1 · 3 = 3; the new height will be 3 units.

To find the base of the new triangle, multiply the base of triangle A by 3.
base = 3 · 3 = 9; the new base will be 9 units.

Label the new figure triangle B.

For every 1 unit of length on triangle A, triangle B has 3 units of length.

Think and Discuss

1. How does knowing the scale factor help you find the dimensions of a similar figure?   It helps you find how many units the new figure will be compared to the original.

2. If you use a scale factor of $\frac{3}{2}$, will the new figure be larger or smaller than the original? Explain.
It will be larger; for every 2 units on the original, the new figure will be 3 units.

Try This

Use the given scale factor to draw a figure similar to triangle A.

1. 4   **2.** $\frac{1}{2}$ **3.** 2   **4.** $\frac{3}{2}$

Answers to *Try This*

1.

2.

3.
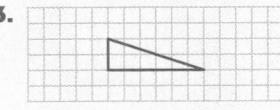

4.

Answers to *Assessment*

1.

2.

You can make a scale model of a solid object, such as a rectangular prism, in many ways; you can make a net and fold it, or you can cut card stock and tape the pieces together. The most important thing is to find a good scale.

Activity 2

The Trump Tower in New York City is a rectangular prism with these approximate dimensions: height, 880 feet; base length, 160 feet; base width, 80 feet.

Make a scale model of the Trump Tower.

First determine the appropriate height for your model and find a good scale.

To use $8\frac{1}{2}$ in. by 11 in. card stock, divide the longest dimension by 11 to find a scale.

$$\frac{880 \text{ ft}}{11 \text{ in.}} = \frac{80 \text{ ft}}{1 \text{ in.}}$$

Use a scale of 1 in:80 ft.

The dimensions of the model using this scale are

$\frac{880}{80} = 11$ in., $\frac{160}{80} = 2$ in., and $\frac{80}{80} = 1$ in.

So you will need to cut the following:

Two 11 in. × 2 in. rectangles

Two 11 in. × 1 in. rectangles

Two 2 in. × 1 in. rectangles

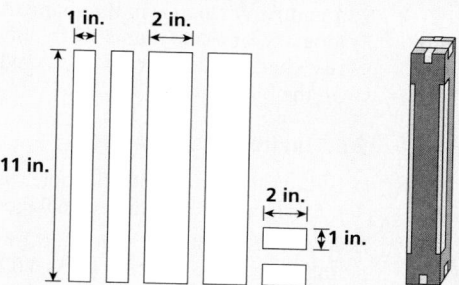

Tape the pieces together to form the model.

Think and Discuss

1. How tall would a model of a 500 ft tall building be if the same scale were used?

2. Why would a building stand more solidly than your model?

3. What could be another scale of the model if the numbers were without units?

Try This

1. Build a scale model of a four-wall handball court. The court is an open-topped rectangular prism 20 feet wide and 40 feet long. Three of the walls are 20 feet tall, and the back wall is 14 feet tall.

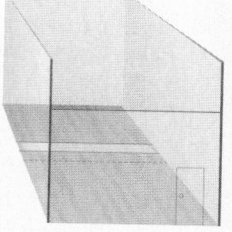

Teach
Discuss

Discuss with students how to choose the best scale, depending upon what size paper the model is being made from.

Close
Key Concept

When you make a scale model, it's important to choose the best scale to use. Use the largest dimension of the material you're using to determine the scale.

Assessment

1. What scale would you use to make a model of a building 850 ft tall with a rectangular base 300 ft by 150 ft out of the following:

   a. 8.5 in. by 11 in. card stock
   Possible answer: 1 in. = 100 ft

   b. 11 in. by 17 in. card stock
   Possible answer: 1 in. = 75 ft

   c. 30 in. by 40 in. poster board
   Possible answer: 1 in. = 28 ft

Activity 2

Answers to *Think and Discuss*

1. 6.25 in. tall

2. Possible answer: The building is made of concrete and has a solid base.

3. 1:960

Answers to *Try This*

1. Check students' work. Possible scale is 1 in. = 5 ft. Then you will need the following pieces:

   Three 8 in. × 4 in. rectangles
   One 4 in. × 4 in. square
   One 4 in. × 2.8 in. rectangle

Organizer

Objective: Assess students' mastery of concepts and skills in Lessons 5-5 through 5-7.

Resources

 Assessment Resources
Section 5B Quiz

 Test & Practice Generator
One-Stop Planner®

INTERVENTION ◄═══►

Resources

 Ready to Go On?
Intervention and
Enrichment Worksheets

💿 **Ready to Go On? CD-ROM**

🪐 **Ready to Go On? Online**

my.hrw.com

Quiz for Lessons 5-5 Through 5-7

✓ **5-5 Similar Figures**

1. Corresponding angles are not congruent; corresponding sides are not proportional.

Tell whether the triangles are similar. If they are not similar, explain.

1. △DEF and △JKL   not similar
2. △PQR and △PRS   similar
3. △UVW and △XYZ   similar

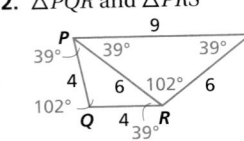
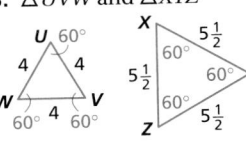

4. A picture that is 4 in. tall and 9 in. wide is to be scaled to 2.5 in. tall. How wide should the picture be for the two pictures to be similar?   **5.625 in.**

5. A company's logo is in the shape of a triangle with two sides that are each 2.4 in. long and one side that is 1.8 in. long. On a billboard, the triangle in the logo has two sides that are each 8 ft long. What is the length of the third side of the triangle on the billboard?   **6 ft**

✓ **5-6 Indirect Measurement**

6. At the same time that a flagpole casts a 4.5 m shadow, a meter stick casts a 1.5 m shadow. How tall is the flagpole?   **3 m**

7. A tree casts a 30 foot shadow. Mi-Ling, standing next to the tree, casts a 13.5 foot shadow. If Mi-Ling is 5 ft tall, how tall is the tree?   **11.1 ft**

8. The Petronas Towers in Malaysia are the tallest buildings in the world. On a sunny day, the Petronas Towers cast shadows that are 4428 feet long. A 6-foot-tall person standing by one building casts an 18-foot-long shadow. How tall are the Petronas Towers?   **1476 ft**

✓ **5-7 Scale Drawings and Scale Models**

9. A model of a ship was built by using a scale of 3 cm:15 m. If the model is 54 cm long, how long is the ship?   **270 m**

10. The model of a 27 ft tall house was made by using the scale 2 in:3 ft. What is the height of the model?   **18 in.**

Use the scale drawing and a metric ruler to answer each question.

11. What is the actual length of the kitchen?   **19.2 ft**

12. What are the actual dimensions of bedroom #1?   **19.2 ft by 11.2 ft**

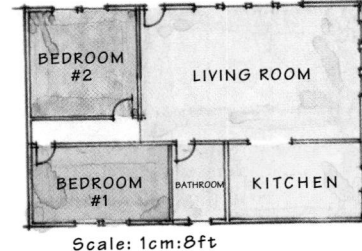

Scale: 1cm:8ft

READY TO GO ON?
Diagnose and Prescribe

NO
INTERVENE

YES
ENRICH

READY TO GO ON? Intervention, Section 5B			
Ready to Go On? Intervention	📝 **Worksheets**	💿 **CD-ROM**	🪐 **Online**
✓ Lesson 5-5 🐘 **Prep for MG1.2**	5-5 Intervention	Activity 5-5	Diagnose and Prescribe Online
✓ Lesson 5-6 🐘 **Ext. of MG1.2**	5-6 Intervention	Activity 5-6	
✓ Lesson 5-7 🐘 **MG1.2**	5-7 Intervention	Activity 5-7	

READY TO GO ON?
Enrichment, Section 5B

📝 **Worksheets**

💿 **CD-ROM**

🪐 **Online**

CONCEPT CONNECTION

CHAPTER 5

Javier Builds a Model Javier, an architect, builds a scale model of the new faculty center at the university. The diagram shows the scale model.

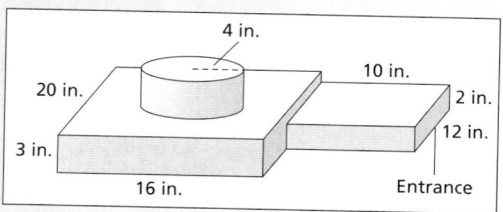

1. In the scale model, the entrance is 12 inches wide. If the entrance is actually 60 feet wide, what scale did Javier use to create the model? Explain your reasoning. $\frac{1}{60}$ or 1 in:5 ft; the entrance in the model is 1 ft wide.

2. Find the actual dimensions of the new faculty center. Use the table to organize your work.

Model Dimensions	Actual Dimensions
2 in.	10 ft
3 in.	15 ft
4 in.	20 ft
10 in.	50 ft
12 in.	60 ft
16 in.	80 ft
20 in.	100 ft

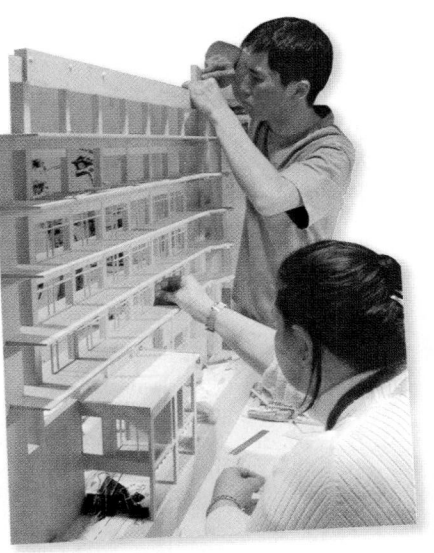

3. Redraw the model and label its actual dimensions.

4. Javier makes a new model of the building using a scale of 1 in:10 ft. What is the width of the entrance in the new model? **6 in.**

5. How does the new model compare with the original one? Is it larger or smaller? Explain. It is smaller because the scale is half that of the original model.

INTERVENTION

Scaffolding Questions

1. What is the ratio of the model's entrance to the actual entrance? 12 in:60 ft

2. Do you have to convert inches to feet in order to complete the table? no What is the scale used to create the model that you found in Problem 1? 1 in:5 ft

3. What is the correct label for the actual width of the entrance? 60 ft Will your redrawn model be labeled in feet or inches? feet

4. What proportion could you use to find the entrance width in the new model?
$\frac{1}{10} = \frac{x}{60}$

5. How many feet does 1 inch represent in the scale you found in Problem 1? 5 ft How many feet does 1 inch represent in the new scale? 10 ft

Extension

1. Javier wants to enlarge the model to twice the size shown in the diagram. What scale should he use? 1 in:2.5 ft

CONCEPT CONNECTION

CHAPTER 5

Organizer

Objective: Assess students' ability to apply concepts and skills in Chapter 5 in a real-world format.

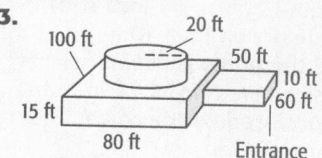 **Online Edition**

Problem	Text reference
1	Lesson 5-4
2	Lesson 5-3
3	Lesson 5-5
4	Lesson 5-6
5	Lesson 5-7

Answers

3.

California Standards

Algebra and Functions
4.2 Solve multistep problems involving **rate**, average speed, distance, and time or a direct variation.

Measurement and Geometry
1.1 Compare weights, **capacities**, geometric measures, times, and temperatures **within** and between **measurement systems** (e.g., miles per hour and feet per second, cubic inches to cubic centimeters).

1.2 Construct and read drawings and models made to scale.

Concept Connection **259**

Game Time

Organizer

Objective: Participate in games to practice and apply skills learned in Chapter 5.

 Online Edition

Resources

📄 **Chapter 5 Resource File**
Puzzles, Twisters & Teasers

Copy-Cat

Purpose: To apply drawing skills to creating similar figures

Discuss What geometry word describes the relationship between the original and the copy? similar If 1-inch square gridlines are drawn on a 10 in. × 13 in. photo and the photo is copied so that its dimensions are 5 in. × $6\frac{1}{2}$ in., what size grid was used on the copy? $\frac{1}{2}$ in. × $\frac{1}{2}$ in. squares

Extend Let students explore how an overhead projector can be used to create similar figures. Have them use an overhead projector to enlarge a drawing or picture for display in the classroom. Check students' work.

Tic-Frac-Toe

Purpose: To practice forming proportions in a game format

Discuss What would a player have to spin in order to win a square containing the equation $\frac{2}{3} = \frac{8}{\blacksquare}$? 12 What would a player have to spin in order to block a square containing the equation $\frac{2}{3} = \frac{\blacksquare}{\blacksquare}$? Possible answer: The player could spin a 10 and place it in the missing denominator.

Extend Have students model each proportion formed in the game using fraction strips or other manipulatives.

Game Time

Copy-Cat

You can use this method to copy a well-known work of art or any drawing. First, draw a grid over the work you want to copy, or draw a grid on tracing paper and tape it over the picture.

Next, on a separate sheet of paper draw a blank grid with the same number of squares. The squares do not have to be the same size. Copy each square from the original exactly onto the blank grid. Do not look at the overall picture as you copy. When you have copied all of the squares, the drawing on your finished grid should look just like the original work.

Suppose you are copying an image from a 12 in. by 18 in. print, and that you use 1-inch squares on the first grid.

❶ If you use 3-inch squares on the blank grid, what size will your finished copy be?

❷ If you want to make a copy that is 10 inches tall, what size should you make the squares on your blank grid? How wide will the copy be?

❸ Choose a painting, drawing, or cartoon, and copy it using the method above.

1. 36 in. by 54 in.   **2.** $\frac{5}{6}$ in.; 15 in.   **3.** Check students' work.

Tic-Frac-Toe

Draw a large tic-tac-toe board. In each square, draw a blank proportion, $\frac{\blacksquare}{\blacksquare} = \frac{\blacksquare}{\blacksquare}$. Players take turns using a spinner with 12 sections or a 12-sided die. A player's turn consists of placing a number anywhere in one of the proportions. The player who correctly completes the proportion can claim that square. A square may also be blocked by filling in three parts of a proportion that cannot be completed with a number from 1 to 12. The first player to claim three squares in a row wins.

🪐 **go.hrw.com**
Game Time Extra
KEYWORD: MT8CA Games

A gameboard is available online.

Materials
- wide duct tape
- ruler
- scissors
- 6 index cards (3 in. by 5 in.)
- markers

Organizer

Objective: Make a duct-tape wallet to store cards that contain notes on ratios, proportions, and similarity.

Materials: wide duct tape, ruler, scissors, 6 index cards (3 in. by 5 in.), markers

 Online Edition

PROJECT **A Worthwhile Wallet**

Make a duct-tape wallet to carry index cards. The index cards will help you study ratios, proportions, and similarity.

Directions

❶ Cut three strips of duct tape at least 9 inches long. Lay the strips next to each other, sticky side up, so that they overlap slightly. The total width should be about $5\frac{1}{2}$ inches. **Figure A**

❷ Lay three more strips of duct tape on top of the first three, sticky side down. Trim the ends. This will make a sheet of duct-tape "fabric."

❸ Fold up the fabric about $3\frac{1}{2}$ inches from the bottom to form a pocket. Use duct tape to seal the sides shut. **Figure B**

❹ Fold the top down. Trim the corners of the flap. **Figure C**

Taking Note of the Math

Review the chapter to identify key concepts. Then write vocabulary, examples, and practice problems on the index cards. Store the cards in the duct-tape wallet.

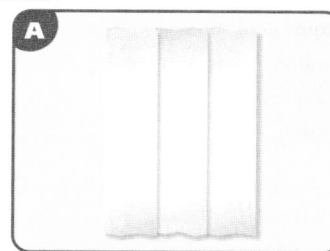
A

B

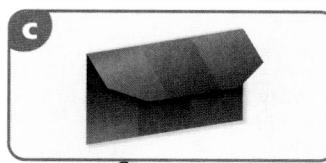
C

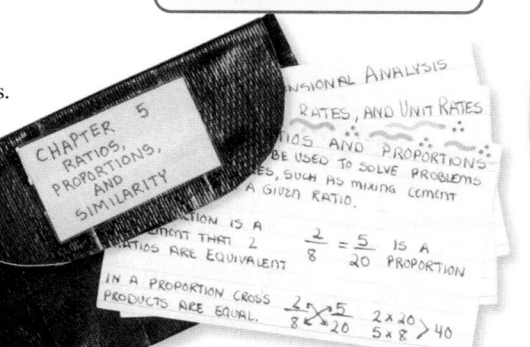

Using the Page

Preparing the Materials
Each student will need approximately 5 feet of duct tape.

Making the Project
Remind students to work carefully as they lay down the strips of duct tape. Students should check that the strips are parallel and that the total width of the side-by-side strips is about $5\frac{1}{2}$ inches.

Extending the Project
Challenge students to design a billfold-style wallet. If necessary, students can trim the index cards to fit inside.

Tips from the Bag Ladies!

After students have prepared the duct-tape "fabric," encourage them to use an index card as a sizing guide. This way students will be sure that the cards fit once the fabric has been folded to form a wallet.

It's fun to make these wallets using different colors of duct tape. Students can make wallets in various colors to hold notes for different chapters.

Organizer

Objective: Help students organize and review key concepts and skills presented in Chapter 5.

Online Edition
Multilingual Glossary

Resources

PuzzlePro®
One-Stop Planner®

***Multilingual Glossary* Online**

go.hrw.com
KEYWORD: MT8CA Glossary

Lesson Tutorial Videos
CD-ROM

Test & Practice Generator
One-Stop Planner®

Answers

1. ratio; proportion
2. rate; unit rate
3. similar; scale factor
4. $\frac{5}{4}$
5. $\frac{27}{40}$
6. $\frac{3}{4}$
7. $\frac{2}{1}$
8. yes
9. no
10. yes
11. no

Vocabulary

conversion factor 237	ratio 224
corresponding angles 244	scale 252
corresponding sides 244	scale drawing 252
cross product 232	scale factor 253
equivalent ratio 224	scale model 252
indirect measurement 248	similar 244
proportion 232	unit price 229
rate 228	unit rate 228

Complete the sentences below with vocabulary words from the list above.

1. A(n) __?__ is a comparison of two quantities. Two ratios that are equivalent are said to be in __?__ .

2. A(n) __?__ is a comparison of two quantities that have different units. A rate in which the second quantity is 1 is called a(n) __?__ .

3. A scale drawing is mathematically __?__ to the actual object. All dimensions are reduced or enlarged using the same __?__ .

5-1 Ratios (pp. 224–227)

Prep for MG1.1

EXAMPLE

■ Write the ratio 12 forks to 45 spoons in simplest form.

$$\frac{\text{forks}}{\text{spoons}} = \frac{12}{45} \qquad \textit{Write the ratio as a fraction.}$$
$$= \frac{12 \div 3}{45 \div 3} \qquad \textit{Simplify.}$$
$$= \frac{4}{15}$$

The ratio of forks to spoons is $\frac{4}{15}$, 4:15, or 4 to 15.

■ Simplify to tell whether $\frac{5}{15}$ and $\frac{6}{24}$ are equivalent.

$$\frac{5 \div 5}{15 \div 5} = \frac{1}{3} \qquad \frac{6 \div 6}{24 \div 6} = \frac{1}{4}$$

Since $\frac{1}{3} \neq \frac{1}{4}$, the ratios are not equivalent.

EXERCISES

Write each ratio in simplest form.

4. 20 bottles to 16 cans
5. 54 books to 80 CDs
6. 1 foot to 16 inches
7. 4 yards to 6 feet

Simplify to tell whether the ratios are equivalent.

8. $\frac{8}{24}$ and $\frac{2}{6}$ 9. $\frac{3}{12}$ and $\frac{6}{18}$

10. $\frac{25}{125}$ and $\frac{5}{25}$ 11. $\frac{6}{8}$ and $\frac{9}{16}$

5-2 Rates and Unit Rates (pp. 228–231)

 MG1.3

EXAMPLE

■ Alex can buy a 4 pack of AA batteries for $2.99 or an 8 pack for $4.98. Which pack has the lower unit price?

$$\frac{\text{price per package}}{\text{number of batteries}} = \frac{\$2.99}{4} \approx \$0.75 \text{ per battery}$$

$$\frac{\text{price per package}}{\text{number of batteries}} = \frac{\$4.98}{8} \approx \$0.62 \text{ per battery}$$

The 8 pack for $4.98 has the lower unit price.

EXERCISES

Find each unit price. Then tell which has the lower unit price.

12. 50 formatted computer disks for $14.99 or 75 disks for $21.50

13. 6 boxes of 3-inch incense sticks for $22.50 or 8 boxes for $30

14. a package of 8 binder dividers for $23.09 or a 25 pack for $99.99

5-3 Proportions (pp. 232–236)

 AF4.2

EXAMPLE

■ Solve the proportion $\frac{18}{12} = \frac{x}{2}$.

$$\frac{18}{12} = \frac{x}{2}$$

$12x = 18 \cdot 2$ *Find the cross products.*

$\frac{12x}{12} = \frac{36}{12}$ *Divide both sides by 12.*

$x = 3$ *Simplify.*

EXERCISES

Solve each proportion.

15. $\frac{3}{5} = \frac{9}{x}$

16. $\frac{24}{h} = \frac{16}{4}$

17. $\frac{w}{6} = \frac{7}{2}$

18. $\frac{3}{8} = \frac{11}{y}$

19. Nancy is folding origami cranes for an art project. She needs to make a total of 54 cranes. It takes her 9 minutes to fold the first 6 cranes. If she continues to work at the same rate, how many more minutes will it take her to complete the project?

5-4 Dimensional Analysis (pp. 237–241)

 MG1.1

EXAMPLE

■ At a rate of 75 kilometers per hour, how many meters does a car travel in 1 minute?

km to m: $\frac{1000 \text{ m}}{1 \text{ km}}$ h to min: $\frac{1 \text{ h}}{60 \text{ min}}$

$$\frac{75 \text{ km}}{1 \text{ h}} \cdot \frac{1000 \text{ m}}{1 \text{ km}} \cdot \frac{1 \text{ h}}{60 \text{ min}} = \frac{75 \cdot 1000 \text{ m}}{60 \text{ min}}$$

$$= \frac{1250 \text{ m}}{1 \text{ min}}$$

The car travels 1250 meters in 1 minute.

EXERCISES

Use conversion factors to find each rate.

20. 90 km/h to m/h

21. 75 feet per second to feet per minute

22. 35 kilometers per hour to meters per minute

23. While driving along a road, Barry passes mile marker 130 at 3:10 P.M. He passes mile marker 170 at 4:00 P.M. Find Barry's average speed in miles per minute. Use dimensional analysis to check the reasonableness of your answer.

Answers

12. $0.30 per disk; $0.29 per disk; 75 disks

13. $3.75 per box; $3.75 per box; unit prices are the same.

14. $2.89 per divider; $4.00 per divider; 8-pack

15. $x = 15$

16. $h = 6$

17. $w = 21$

18. $y = 29\frac{1}{3}$

19. 72 min

20. 90,000 m/h

21. 4500 ft/min

22. $583\frac{1}{3}$ m/min

23. 0.8 mi/min (= 48 mi/h)

5-5 Similar Figures (pp. 244–247)

Prep for **MG1.2**

EXAMPLE

■ A stamp 1.2 in. tall and 1.75 in. wide is to be scaled to 4.2 in. tall. How wide should the new stamp be?

$$\frac{4.2}{1.2} = \frac{w}{1.75}$$

$4.2 \cdot 1.75 = w \cdot 1.2$ *Find the cross products.*

$7.35 = 1.2w$

$\frac{7.35}{1.2} = \frac{1.2w}{1.2}$ *Divide both sides by 1.2.*

$6.125 = w$ *Simplify*

The larger stamp should be 6.125 in. wide.

EXERCISES

24. A picture 3 in. wide by 5 in. tall is to be scaled to 7.5 in. wide to be put on a flyer. How tall should the picture on the flyer be?

25. A picture 8 in. wide by 10 in. tall is to be scaled to 2.5 in. wide to be put on an invitation. How tall should the picture on the invitation be?

5-6 Indirect Measurement (pp. 248–251)

Ext. of **MG1.2**

EXAMPLE

■ A telephone pole casts a 5 ft shadow at the same time that a man standing next to it casts a 1.5 ft shadow. If the man is 6 ft tall, how tall is the telephone pole?

$\frac{1.5}{5} = \frac{6}{x}$ *Set up a proportion.*

$1.5x = 30$ *Find the cross products.*

$\frac{1.5x}{1.5} = \frac{30}{1.5}$ *Divide both sides by 1.5.*

$x = 20$ *Simplify.*

The telephone pole is 20 ft tall.

EXERCISES

26. A flagpole casts a 15 ft shadow at the same time Jon casts a 5 ft shadow. If Jon is 6 ft tall, how tall is the flagpole?

27. April casts a 16.5 ft shadow at the same time that Ron casts an 18.6 ft shadow. If April is 5.5 ft tall, how tall is Ron?

5-7 Scale Drawings and Scale Models (pp. 252–255)

MG1.2

EXAMPLE

■ Find the actual distance from A to B.

A ←— 3 cm —→ B
1 cm:35 m

$\frac{1 \text{ cm}}{35 \text{ m}} = \frac{3 \text{ cm}}{x \text{ m}}$ *Write a proportion.*

$1 \cdot x = 35 \cdot 3$ *Find the cross products.*

$x = 105$

The actual distance is 105 m.

EXERCISES

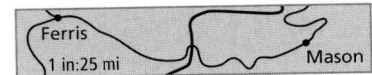

Ferris
1 in:25 mi
Mason

28. Find the actual distance from Ferris to Mason.

29. Renfield is 75 mi from Mason. About how far apart should Renfield and Mason be on the map?

The scale of a map is 1 in:10 mi. How many actual miles does each measurement represent?

30. 4.6 in.   **31.** $5\frac{3}{4}$ in.   **32.** 15.3 in.

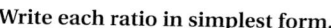

Write each ratio in simplest form.

1. 25 boys to 40 girls $\frac{5}{8}$
2. 32 eggs to 24 hens $\frac{4}{3}$
3. 140 coats to 180 hats $\frac{7}{9}$
4. 6 feet to 9 inches $\frac{8}{1}$
5. 48 inches to 5 feet $\frac{4}{5}$
6. 4 yards to 5 feet $\frac{12}{5}$

Simplify to tell whether the ratios are equivalent.

7. $\frac{4}{5}$ and $\frac{16}{20}$ yes
8. $\frac{33}{60}$ and $\frac{11}{21}$ no
9. $\frac{7}{9}$ and $\frac{35}{45}$ yes
10. $\frac{8}{20}$ and $\frac{4}{25}$ no

Estimate each unit rate.

11. $3.59 for $\frac{1}{2}$ pound   about $7.20 per pound
12. 57 students in 3 classrooms   about 20 students per classroom
13. $46.50 for 5 hours   about $9 per hour
14. 62 books on 5 shelves   about 12 books per shelf
15. You can buy one 10 pack of AAA batteries for $5.49 and get one battery free, or you can buy two 4 packs for $2.98. Which has the lower unit price per battery?   two 4 packs for $2.98

Use conversion factors to find each rate to the nearest hundredth.

16. Change 60 ounces to pounds.   3.75 pounds
17. Change 35 pounds to ounces.   560 ounces
18. Simon bought 5 cans of chili for $10.95. At this rate, how much would 12 cans of chili cost? $26.28

Solve each proportion.

19. $\frac{6}{9} = \frac{n}{72}$ 48
20. $\frac{18}{12} = \frac{3}{x}$ 2
21. $\frac{0.7}{1.4} = \frac{z}{28}$ 14
22. $\frac{12}{y} = \frac{32}{16}$ 6

23. Roberto is printing a 132-page document on his printer. It takes 5 minutes to print the first 60 pages. If the printer continues to work at the same rate, how many more minutes will it take to finish printing the document?   6 min

24. There are markers every 1000 feet along the side of a road. While driving, Mai passes marker number 15 at 10:05 and marker number 39 at 10:11. Find Mai's average speed in feet per minute. Use dimensional analysis to check the reasonableness of your answer.   4000 ft/min ($\approx$45.5 mi/h)

25. Fran scans a document that is 8.5 in. wide by 11 in. long into her computer. If she scales the length down to 7 in., how wide should the similar document be? $\approx$ 5.4 in.

26. Wally has an 18 in. model of a 42 ft. dinosaur, *Tyrannosaurus rex*. Find the scale factor.   1 in:28 in.

27. Margie's school building casts a 12.5 ft shadow at the same time that Margie casts a 2.875 ft shadow. If Margie is 5.75 ft tall, how tall is the school?   25 ft

28. If a wall in a $\frac{1}{4}$ in. scale drawing is 6 in. tall, how tall is the actual wall?   24 in.

Organizer

Objective: Assess students' mastery of concepts and skills in Chapter 5.

 Online Edition

Resources

 Assessment Resources

Chapter 5 Tests
• Free Response (Levels A, B, C)
• Multiple Choice (Levels A, B, C)
• Performance Assessment

 IDEA Works! CD-ROM
Modified Chapter 5 Test

 Test & Practice Generator
One-Stop Planner®

California Standards	
Standard	**Items**
AF4.2 🔑	19–23
Prep for **MG1.1**	1–10
MG1.1	16–18, 24
Prep for **MG1.2**	25
MG1.2	26, 28
Ext. of **MG1.2**	27
MG1.3 🔑	11–15

Organizer

Objective: Provide opportunities to learn and practice common test-taking strategies.

 **Online Edition**

Short Response This Strategies for Success focuses on how short response test items are scored and demonstrates how to write a response worth full credit. Explain that responses to these types of test items are scored and points are awarded based on the completeness and correctness of the response. The scoring guides, or rubrics, are designed so that all test scorers will arrive at the same result for a given student response.

Point out to students that many times, short response test items have several steps. Remind students to answer each part of the test item.

Short Response: Write Short Responses

To answer a short response test item completely, you must show how you solved the problem and explain your answer. Short response test items are scored using a 2-point scoring rubric. A sample scoring rubric is shown below.

EXAMPLE 1

Short Response A carpenter is pouring a concrete foundation for a garden planter in the shape of a right triangle. The length of one leg of the planter is 18 feet, and the length of the diagonal is 22 feet. What is the length of the other leg of the planter? Round your answer to the nearest tenth. Show all of your work.

Here are examples of how different responses were scored using the scoring rubric shown.

2-point response:

Let s = the length of the other leg.

$18^2 + s^2 = 22^2$ Use the Pythagorean Theorem.

$s^2 = 160$

$\sqrt{s^2} = \sqrt{160}$ Find the square root.

$s = 12.64911$ Round to the nearest tenth.

$s \approx 12.6$ ft

The length of the other leg is 12.6 ft.

1-point response:

Let s = the length of the other leg.

$18^2 + s^2 = 22^2$

$324 + s^2 = 484$

$\sqrt{s^2} = \sqrt{160}$

$s = 13$ ft

The length of the other leg is 13 ft.

The student showed all of the work, but there was a minor computation error, which resulted in an incorrect answer.

0-point response:

$s = 12$ *The student's answer is not rounded to the nearest tenth, and there is no explanation.*

Scoring Rubric

2 points: The student demonstrates a thorough understanding of the concept, correctly answers the question, and provides a complete explanation.

1 point: The student correctly answers the question but does not show all work or does not provide an explanation.

1 point: The student makes minor errors, resulting in an incorrect solution, but shows an understanding of the concept through explanation.

0 points: The student gives a response showing no work or giving no explanation, or the student gives no response.

Read short-response test items carefully. If you are allowed to write in the test booklet, underline or circle the parts of the question that tell you what your solution must include. Be sure to use complete sentences in your explanation.

Read each test item, and answer the questions that follow by using the scoring rubric on page 266.

Item A
The actual width of a doghouse is 2 feet. Use the scale drawing of the doghouse to find the actual height.

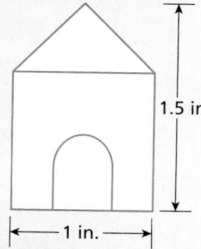

1.5 in.

1 in.

Student's Response

$$\frac{2 \text{ ft}}{1 \text{ in.}} = \frac{h}{1.5 \text{ in.}}$$

$h = 36$ in.
The height is 3 feet.

1. What score should the student's response receive? Explain your reasoning.

2. What additional information, if any, should the student's answer include in order for the student to receive full credit?

Item B
The ratio of the length of a rectangular garden to its width is 12:5. If the width of the garden is 8 feet, find the area of the garden. Show all of your work.

Student's Response

$\frac{l}{w} = \frac{12}{5}$ The ratio of the length to the width is 12:5.

$\frac{12}{5} = \frac{8}{l}$; $12l = 40$; $l = 3.\overline{3}$ The length is 3.3 ft.

$A = lw$: $A = 3.3 \times 8 = 26.4$
The area is 26.4 ft^2.

3. What score should the student's response receive? Explain your reasoning.

4. What additional information, if any, should the student's answer include in order for the student to receive full credit?

Item C
An office supply store charges $24 for 72 file folders. A student says that the unit price is $3 per folder. What is the student's error? What is the correct unit price? Show all of your work.

Student's Response

The student divided wrong. The student should have divided 24 by 72, not 72 by 24.

5. What score should the student's response receive? Explain your reasoning.

6. What additional information, if any, should the student's answer include in order for the student to receive full credit?

Possible answers:

1. 1-point response. The student's answer is correct but the work is not shown and there is no explanation.

2. The student should have included the explanation with the first step that the ratio of the width of the actual doghouse to the width of the model is equal to the height of the actual doghouse, h, to the height of the model. The student's work should have included the following step between the first and second steps that were shown:
$\frac{24 \text{ in.}}{1 \text{ in.}} = \frac{h}{1.5 \text{ in.}}$

3. The response is worth 1 point because the student set up the ratio incorrectly, which resulted in an incorrect measurement for the length.
$\frac{12}{5} = \frac{l}{8}$; $5l = 96$; $l = 19.2$ ft

4. To receive full credit, the student would need to fix the error and find the correct solution.

5. The response is worth 1 point because the responding student correctly identified the error but did not give the correct unit price. The response is incomplete.

6. To receive full credit, the student should include the correct unit price and show the solution. $\frac{\$24}{72 \text{ folders}} = \$0.33/\text{folder}$

California Standards
AF4.2, MG1.2, MG1.3

Organizer

Objective: Provide review and practice for Chapters 1–5.

 Online Edition

Resources

 Assessment Resources
Chapter 5 Cumulative Test

 Focus on California Standards Benchmark Tests and Intervention

California Standards Practice CD-ROM

go.hrw.com
KEYWORD: MT8CA Practice

Cumulative Assessment, Chapters 1–5

Multiple Choice

1. Which inequality describes the graph?

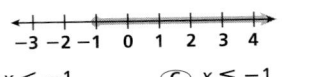

   Ⓐ $x < -1$ Ⓒ $x \le -1$
   Ⓑ $x > -1$ Ⓓ $x \ge -1$

2. Solve $-6x + 20.4 = 48$ for x.

   Ⓐ $x = -11.4$ Ⓒ $x = -4.6$
   Ⓑ $x = 11.4$ Ⓓ $x = -4.2$

3. Which two numbers both have an absolute value of 6?

   Ⓐ 0 and 6   Ⓒ −3 and 3
   Ⓑ −6 and 6   Ⓓ 5 and −1

4. Evaluate $x(7 - y)$ for $x = -3$ and $y = -15$.

   Ⓐ −66   Ⓒ 66
   Ⓑ 24   Ⓓ −24

5. If a drinking glass holds $\frac{1}{16}$ gallon of water, how many gallons of water are contained in 8 drinking glasses?

   Ⓐ $\frac{1}{8}$ gallon   Ⓒ 2 gallons
   Ⓑ $\frac{1}{2}$ gallon   Ⓓ 64 gallons

6. Which of the following inequalities represents the statement "Twice a number x increased by 27 is no more than 45"?

   Ⓐ $2x + 27 \ge 45$
   Ⓑ $2x + 27 \le 45$
   Ⓒ $2x + 27 > 45$
   Ⓓ $2x + 27 < 45$

7. A total of 2080 people entered a zoo. In the first hour, 260 people entered. If people entered at the same rate, how many more hours after the first hour did it take for all of the people to enter the zoo?

   Ⓐ 8 hours   Ⓒ 79 hours
   Ⓑ 7 hours   Ⓓ 6 hours

8. Carl is driving 30 miles per hour. What is his approximate speed in kilometers per hour? (1 mile ≈ 1.6 kilometers)

   Ⓐ 7   Ⓒ 19
   Ⓑ 48   Ⓓ 60

9. During which of the following races did the fastest average speed occur?

Race	Distance (m)	Time (s)
1	100	10
2	240	20
3	800	125
4	5000	800

   Ⓐ 1   Ⓒ 3
   Ⓑ 2   Ⓓ 4

10. Which set of fractions are in order from least to greatest?

   Ⓐ $\frac{3}{8}, \frac{1}{4}, \frac{2}{5}, \frac{1}{3}$ Ⓒ $\frac{1}{4}, \frac{1}{3}, \frac{2}{5}, \frac{3}{8}$
   Ⓑ $\frac{1}{3}, \frac{1}{4}, \frac{2}{5}, \frac{3}{8}$ Ⓓ $\frac{1}{4}, \frac{1}{3}, \frac{3}{8}, \frac{2}{5}$

California Standards

Standard	Items
NS1.1	10
NS1.2 🔑	12, 17
NS2.4	11
NS2.5 🔑	3
AF1.0	1
AF1.1	6, 15
AF1.2	4
AF4.1 🔑	2, 15
AF4.2 🔑	7, 13, 18
MG1.1	8
MG1.2	20
MG1.3 🔑	5, 9, 16, 19
MG3.3 🔑	14

Teaching Tip For **Item 16,** remind students that they must do two conversions to solve this problem. They must change centimeters to meters and seconds to minutes.

Answers

18. **a.** 150; $\frac{5}{7} = \frac{n}{210}$; $\frac{5}{7}(210) = 150 = n$
    b. 360; 150 + 210 = 360

19. **a.** 12 for $1.25; The unit price, $0.10/pencil, is less than the unit price of the box of 8 pencils, which is $0.11/pencil.
    b. $0.34; $\frac{1.25}{12} \times 48 = \$5.00$ and $\frac{0.89}{8} \times 48 = \$5.34$
    $5.34 − $5.00 = $0.34

20. See 4-point Response work sample.

HOT TIP! It is helpful to draw or redraw a figure. Answers to geometry problems may become clearer as you redraw the figure.

11. Which expression has a value between 6 and 7?

Ⓐ $\sqrt{35}$ Ⓒ $\sqrt{41}$

Ⓑ $\sqrt{51}$ Ⓓ $\sqrt{36}$

Gridded Response

12. A football team earns a first down when the team has moved the ball 10 yards forward. If a team has moved the ball forward 15 feet, what is the least number of yards the team needs to earn a first down?   **5**

13. A ballet class has a rule that all productions must have a ratio of 4 boys for every 5 girls. If there are 12 boys in a production, how many girls can be in the same production?   **15**

14. What is the length, in feet, of the base of the sail, x?   **16**

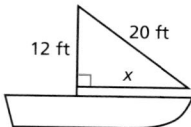
12 ft   20 ft x

15. A 60-yard piece of string is divided into three pieces. The first piece is twice the length of the second piece, and the third piece is three times the length of the second piece. What is the length in yards of the longest piece?   **30**

16. If a snail moves 5 centimeters in 10 seconds, how fast in meters per minute can a snail move?   **3/10**

17. Three friends split the cost of a birthday present and a meal for another friend. The present cost $56.75, and the meal cost $23.65. Find the amount, in dollars, that each friend paid.   **26.80**

Short Response

18. At the student store, the ratio of notebooks sold to three-ring binders sold is 5 to 7.

   a. At this rate, how many notebooks can you predict will be sold if 210 three-ring binders are sold? Show your work.

   b. At the same rate, predict how many total notebooks and three-ring binders will be sold. Explain your reasoning.

19. While shopping for school supplies Sara finds boxes of pencils in two sizes. One box has 8 pencils for $0.89, and the other box has 12 pencils for $1.25.

   a. Which box has the lower unit price? Why? Round your answer to the nearest cent.

   b. How much would Sara save if she bought 48 pencils at the lower unit rate? Show your work.

Extended Response

20. To build an accurate model of the solar system, choose a diameter for the model of the Sun. Then all distances and sizes of the planets can be calculated proportionally using the table below.

   a. What is the diameter of Mars in the model?

   b. What is Mars's distance from the Sun in the model?

   c. What would Mars's distance from the Sun be in the model if the Sun's diameter were changed to 2 ft?

	Sun	Mars	Jupiter
Diameter (mi)	864,000	4200	88,640
Distance from Sun (million mi)		141	483

Student Work Samples for Item 20

4-Point Response

a. diameter of sun = 1 in. in model

$\frac{1}{864,000} = \frac{x}{4,200}$

$864,000x = 4,200$

$x = 0.0048611 \approx 0.0049$ in.

b. $\frac{1}{864,000} = \frac{x}{141,000,000}$

$864,000x = 141,000,000$

$x \approx 163$ in.

c. $\frac{2}{864,000} = \frac{x}{141,000,000}$

$864,000x = 282,000,000$

$x \approx 326$ ft.

3-Point Response

a) $\frac{1}{864,000} = \frac{x}{4,200}$ sun = 1 in.

$864,000x = 4,200$

$x = 0.0048611$

$x = 0.0049$ in.

b) $\frac{1}{864,000} = \frac{x}{141}$

$864,000x = 141$

$x = 0.0016786$

$x = 0.0017$ in.

c) $\frac{2}{864,000} = \frac{x}{4,200}$

$864,000x = 8,400$

$x = 0.0097222 \approx 0.0097$ ft.

2-Point Response

a) $\frac{1}{864,000} = \frac{x}{4200}$

$864,000x = 4200$

$x = 0.0048611 \approx 0.0049$ in.

b)

c) $\frac{2}{864,000} = \frac{x}{4200}$

$864,000 = 8400$

$= 0.0097222 \approx 0.0097$

In part **b,** the student correctly used the calculated answer from part **a** and the correct information in the table to calculate the answer.

The student correctly set up and solved a proportion in part **a,** but used an incorrect proportion to solve part **b.** Part **c** is incomplete.

Though the scale is not given, the student correctly set up and solved a proportion in part **a,** but did not use the given information to correctly answer part **b** and **c.**

Percents

		Grade-level Standard
◀		Review
▶		Beyond the Standards
A		Assessment
O		Optional

Pacing Guide

Calendar Planner
Teacher's **One-Stop** Planner®

Lesson/Lab	California Standards	Time	Advanced Students	Benchmark* Students	Strategic** Students
6-1 Relating Fractions, Decimals, and Percents	NS1.3	50 min	✔	✔	✔
6-2 Estimating with Percents	NS1.3	50 min	✔	✔	✔
6-3 Finding Percents	NS1.3	50 min	✔	✔	✔
6-4 Finding a Number When the Percent Is Known	NS1.3	50 min	✔	✔	✔
Ready to Go On?		25 min	A	A	A
Focus on Problem Solving		25 min	A	A	O
6-5 Applying Percent of Increase and Decrease	NS1.6, ⚊ NS1.7	50 min	✔	✔	✔
6-6 Commission, Sales Tax, and Profit	NS1.3, ⚊ NS1.7	100 min	✔	✔	✔
LAB Explore Compound Interest	⚊ NS1.7	25 min	O	✔	O
6-7 Applying Simple and Compound Interest	⚊ NS1.7	75 min	✔	✔	✔
Ready to Go On?		25 min	A	A	A
Concept Connection		25 min	A	A	O
Study Guide: Review		50 min	✔	✔	✔
Chapter Test		50 min	A	A	A

* **Benchmark students** are achieving at or near grade level.

** **Strategic students** may be a year or more below grade level and may require additional time for intervention.

Countdown to Mastery, Weeks ⑪, ⑫, ⑬

ONGOING ASSESSMENT and INTERVENTION

DIAGNOSE	PRESCRIBE

Assess Prior Knowledge

Before Chapter 6

Diagnose readiness for the chapter.
Are You Ready? SE p. 271

Prescribe intervention.
Are You Ready? Intervention Skills 14, 26, 45, 65

Formative Assessment

Before Every Lesson

Diagnose readiness for the lesson.
Warm Up TE, every lesson

Prescribe intervention.
Skills Bank SE pp. SB2–SB24
Review for Mastery CRF, Chapters 1–6

During Every Lesson

Diagnose understanding of lesson concepts.
Questioning Strategies Chapter 6
Think and Discuss SE, every lesson
Write About It SE, lesson exercises
Journal TE, lesson exercises

Prescribe intervention.
Reading Strategies CRF, every lesson
Success for ELL Chapter 6
Lesson Tutorial Videos Chapter 6

After Every Lesson

Diagnose mastery of lesson concepts.
Lesson Quiz TE, every lesson
Ready to Go On? SE p. 292
Test and Practice Generator

Prescribe intervention.
Review for Mastery CRF, every lesson
Problem Solving CRF, every lesson
Ready to Go On? Intervention Chapter 6
Homework Help Online

Before Chapter 6 Testing

Diagnose mastery of concepts in the chapter.
Ready to Go On? SE pp. 292, 308
Focus on Problem Solving SE p. 293
Concept Connection SE p. 309
Section Quizzes AR pp. 105–106
Test and Practice Generator

Prescribe intervention.
Ready to Go On? Intervention Chapter 6
Scaffolding Questions TE p. 309

Before Assessment of California Standards

Diagnose mastery of California standards.
Focus on California Standards: Benchmark Tests
Mastering the Standards SE pp. 316–317
California Standards Practice CD-ROM

Prescribe intervention.
Focus on California Standards: Intervention

Summative Assessment

After Chapter 6

Check mastery of chapter concepts.
Multiple-Choice Tests (Forms A, B, C)
Free-Response Tests (Forms A, B, C)
Performance Assessment AR pp. 107–118
Test and Practice Generator

Prescribe intervention.
Review for Mastery CRF, every lesson
Lesson Tutorial Videos Chapter 6

KEY: **SE** = *Student Edition* **TE** = *Teacher's Edition* **CRF** = *Chapter Resource File* **AR** = *Assessment Resources*   Available on CD-ROM  Available online

Supporting the Teacher

Chapter 6 Resource File

Family Involvement
pp. 1–2, 37–38

Practice A, B, C
pp. 5–7, 13–15, 21–23, 29–31, 41–43, 49–51, 57–59

Review for Mastery
pp. 8, 16, 24, 32, 44, 52, 60

Challenge
pp. 9, 17, 25, 33, 45, 53, 61

Problem Solving
pp. 10, 18, 26, 34, 46, 54, 62

Reading Strategies ELL
pp. 11, 19, 27, 35, 47, 55, 63

Puzzles, Twisters, and Teasers
pp. 12, 20, 28, 36, 48, 56, 64

Hands-On Lab
pp. 65–66, 67–68, 69–70, 71–72

Teacher Tools

Power Presentations
Complete PowerPoint® presentations for Chapter 6 lessons

Lesson Tutorial Videos SPANISH
Holt authors Ed Burger and Freddie Renfro present tutorials to support the Chapter 6 lessons.

Teacher's One-Stop Planner SPANISH
Easy access to all Chapter 6 resources and assessments, as well as software for lesson planning, test generation, and puzzle creation

IDEA Works!
Key Chapter 6 resources and assessments modified to address special learning needs

Questioning Strategies .... Chapter 6

Solutions Key .... Chapter 6

Interactive Answers and Solutions

TechKeys   **Lab Resources**

Project Teacher Support   **Parent Resources**

Workbooks

Homework and Practice Workbook SPANISH
Teacher's Guide .... pp. 34–40

Know-It Notebook SPANISH
Teacher's Guide .... Chapter 6

Review for Mastery Workbook SPANISH
Teacher's Guide .... pp. 67–80

Focus on California Standards: Intervention Workbook SPANISH
Teacher's Guide

Transparencies

Lesson Transparencies, Volume 1 .... Chapter 6
• Teacher Tools
• Warm Ups
• Teaching Transparencies
• Lesson Quizzes

Know-It Notebook .... Chapter 6
• Vocabulary   • Chapter Review
• Additional Examples   • Big Ideas

Alternate Openers: Explorations .... pp. 42–48

Countdown to Mastery .... pp. 21–25

Technology Highlights for the Teacher

 Power Presentations
Dynamic presentations to engage students. Complete PowerPoint® presentations for every lesson in Chapter 6.

 One-Stop Planner SPANISH
Easy access to Chapter 6 resources and assessments. Includes lesson-planning, test-generation, and puzzle-creation software.

 Premier Online Edition SPANISH
Includes Tutorial Videos, Lesson Activities, Lesson Quizzes, Homework Help, Chapter Project and more.

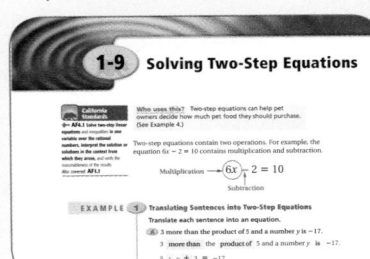

KEY: **SE** = *Student Edition*   **TE** = *Teacher's Edition*   ELL English Language Learners   SPANISH Spanish available   Available on CD-ROM    Available online

270C   Chapter 6

CHAPTER
6

 **Universal Access**

Teaching tips to help all students appear throughout the chapter. A few that target specific students are included in the lists below.

Strategic Students

Practice A	CRF, every lesson
Review for Mastery	CRF, every lesson
Reading Strategies	CRF, every lesson
Academic Vocabulary Connections	TE p. 272
Visual	TE p. 275
Ready to Go On? Intervention	Chapter 6
Questioning Strategies	Chapter 6
Know-It Notebook SPANISH	Chapter 6
Homework Help Online	
Lesson Tutorial Videos SPANISH	
Online Interactivities SPANISH	

Special Needs Students

Practice A	CRF, every lesson
Review for Mastery	CRF, every lesson
Reading Strategies	CRF, every lesson
Academic Vocabulary Connections	TE p. 272
Inclusion	TE p. 279
IDEA Works! Modified Resources	Chapter 6
Ready to Go On? Intervention	Chapter 6
Know-It Notebook SPANISH	Chapter 6
Lesson Tutorial Videos  SPANISH	
Online Interactivities SPANISH	

English Learners
ENGLISH LANGUAGE LEARNERS

Reading Strategies	CRF, every lesson
Vocabulary Review	SE p. 46
Academic Vocabulary Connections	TE p. 272
English Language Learners	TE pp. 273, 275, 284
Language Support	TE pp. 281, 295, 298
Success for English Language Learners	Chapter 6
Know-It Notebook SPANISH	Chapter 6
Multilingual Glossary	
Lesson Tutorial Videos SPANISH	

Benchmark Students

Practice B	CRF, every lesson
Problem Solving	CRF, every lesson
Academic Vocabulary Connections	TE p. 272
Ready to Go On? Intervention	Chapter 6
Questioning Strategies	Chapter 6
Know-It Notebook SPANISH	Chapter 6
Homework Help Online	
Online Interactivities SPANISH	

Advanced Students

Practice C	CRF, every lesson
Challenge	CRF, every lesson
Reading and Writing Math EXTENSION	TE p. 273
Concept Connection EXTENSION	TE p. 309
Advanced Learners/GATE	TE pp. 289, 299
Ready to Go On? Enrichment	Chapter 6

Technology Highlights for Universal Access

Lesson Tutorial Videos SPANISH
Starring Holt authors Ed Burger and Freddie Renfro! Live tutorials to support every lesson in Chapter 6.

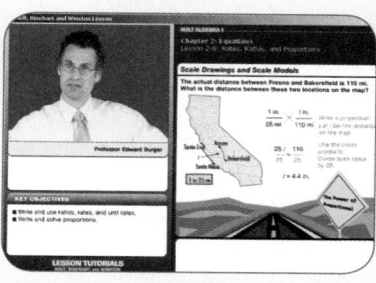

Multilingual Glossary
Searchable glossary includes definitions in English, Spanish, Vietnamese, Chinese, Hmong, Korean, and other languages.

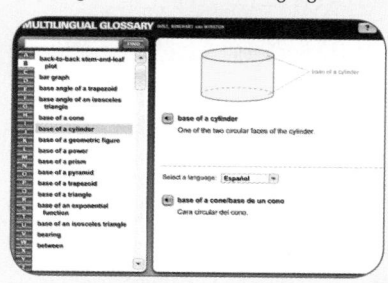

Online Interactivities SPANISH
Interactive tutorials provide visually engaging alternative opportunities to learn concepts and master skills.

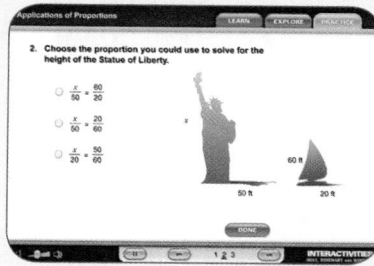

KEY: **SE** = *Student Edition*   **TE** = *Teacher's Edition*   **CRF** = *Chapter Resource File*   SPANISH Spanish available   Available on CD-ROM   Available online

CHAPTER
6

Ongoing Assessment

Assessing Prior Knowledge

Determine whether students have the prerequisite concepts and skills for success in Chapter 6.

Are You Ready? SPANISH .... SE p. 271
Warm Up .... TE, every lesson

Chapter and Standards Assessment

Provide review and practice for Chapter 6 and standards mastery.

Concept Connection .... SE p. 309
Study Guide: Review .... SE pp. 312–314
Mastering the Standards .... SE pp. 316–317
Countdown to Mastery Transparencies ...pp. 21–25
Focus on California Standards: Benchmark Tests
Focus on California Standards: Intervention Workbook SPANISH
California Standards Practice CD-ROM SPANISH
IDEA Works! Modified Worksheets and Tests

Alternative Assessment

Assess students' understanding of Chapter 6 concepts and combined problem-solving skills.

Performance Assessment .... AR pp. 119–120
Portfolio Assessment .... AR p. xxxvi
Chapter 6 Project

Daily Assessment

Provide formative assessment for each day of Chapter 6.

Think and Discuss .... SE, every lesson
Write About It .... SE, lesson exercises
Journal .... TE, lesson exercises
Lesson Quiz .... TE, every lesson
Questioning Strategies .... Chapter 6
IDEA Works! Modified Lesson Quizzes .... Chapter 6

Weekly Assessment

Provide formative assessment for each week of Chapter 6.

Focus on Problem Solving .... SE p. 293
Concept Connection .... SE p. 309
Ready to Go On? SPANISH .... SE pp. 292, 308
Cumulative Assessment .... SE pp. 316–317
Test and Practice Generator SPANISH ...*One-Stop Planner*

Formal Assessment

Provide summative assessment of Chapter 6 mastery.

Section Quizzes .... AR pp. 105–106
Chapter 6 Test SPANISH .... SE p. 315
Chapter Test (Levels A, B, C) .... AR pp. 107–118
        • Multiple-Choice   • Free-Response
Cumulative Test .... AR pp. 121–124
Test and Practice Generator SPANISH ...*One-Stop Planner*
IDEA Works! Modified Tests .... Chapter 6

Technology Highlights for the Teacher

Are You Ready? SPANISH

Automatically assess readiness and prescribe intervention for Chapter 6 prerequisite skills.

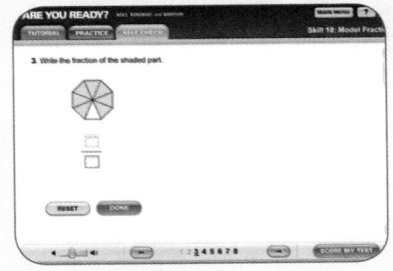

Ready to Go On? SPANISH

Automatically assess understanding of and prescribe intervention for Sections 6A and 6B.

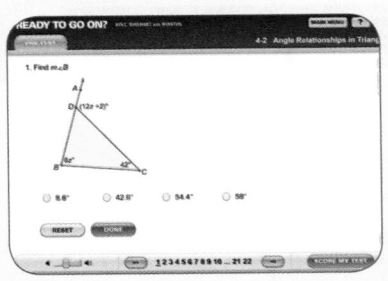

Focus on California Standards: Benchmark Tests and Intervention SPANISH

Automatically assess proficiency with California Grade 7 Standards and provide intervention.

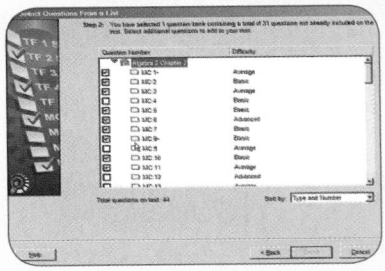

KEY: **SE** = *Student Edition*   **TE** = *Teacher's Edition*   **AR** = *Assessment Resources*   SPANISH Spanish available    Available on CD-ROM   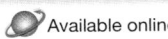 Available online

270E   Chapter 6

CHAPTER
6

Formal Assessment

Three levels (A, B, C) of multiple-choice and free-response chapter tests are available in the *Assessment Resources*.

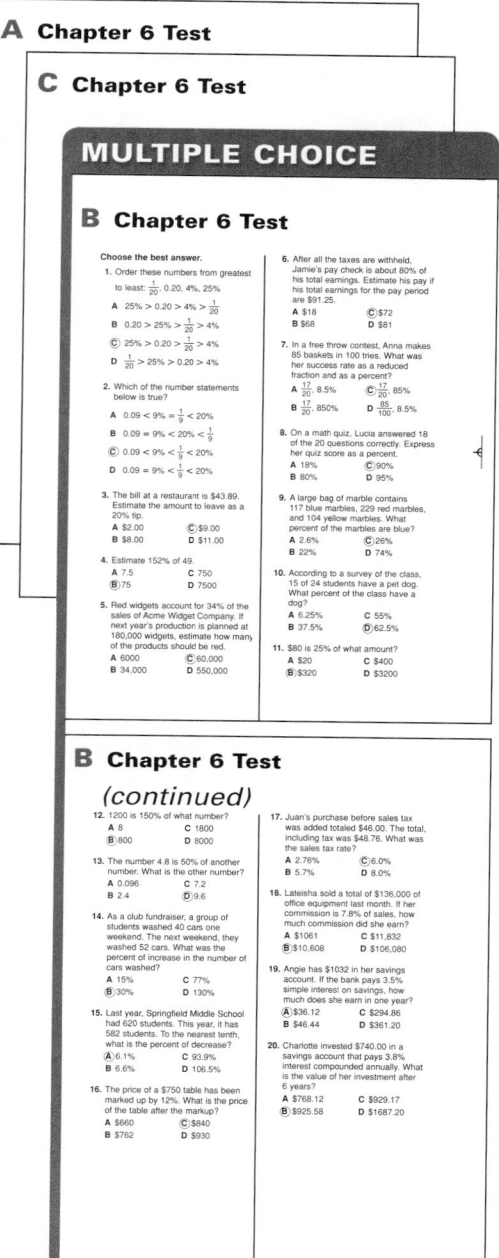

A Chapter 6 Test
C Chapter 6 Test

MULTIPLE CHOICE

B Chapter 6 Test

Choose the best answer.

1. Order these numbers from greatest to least: $\frac{1}{20}$, 0.20, 4%, 25%
   A 25% > 0.20 > 4% > $\frac{1}{20}$
   B 0.20 > 25% > $\frac{1}{20}$ > 4%
   C 25% > 0.20 > $\frac{1}{20}$ > 4%
   D $\frac{1}{20}$ > 25% > 0.20 > 4%

2. Which of the number statements below is true?
   A 0.09 < 9% = $\frac{1}{9}$ < 20%
   B 0.09 = 9% < 20% < $\frac{1}{9}$
   C 0.09 < 9% < $\frac{1}{9}$ < 20%
   D 0.09 = 9% < $\frac{1}{9}$ < 20%

3. The bill at a restaurant is $43.89. Estimate the amount to leave as a 20% tip.
   A $2.00   C $9.00
   B $8.00   D $11.00

4. Estimate 152% of 49.
   A 7.5   C 750
   B 75   D 7500

5. Red widgets account for 34% of the sales of Acme Widget Company. If next year's production is planned at 180,000 widgets, estimate how many of the products should be red.
   A 6000   C 60,000
   B 34,000   D 550,000

6. After all the taxes are withheld, Jamie's pay check is about 80% of his total earnings. Estimate his pay if his total earnings for the pay period are $91.25.
   A $18   C $72
   B $68   D $81

7. In a free throw contest, Anna makes 85 baskets in 100 tries. What was her success rate as a reduced fraction and as a percent?
   A $\frac{17}{20}$, 8.5%   C $\frac{17}{20}$, 85%
   B $\frac{17}{20}$, 850%   D $\frac{85}{100}$, 8.5%

8. On a math quiz, Lucia answered 18 of the 20 questions correctly. Express her quiz score as a percent.
   A 18%   C 90%
   B 80%   D 95%

9. A large bag of marble contains 117 blue marbles, 229 red marbles, and 104 yellow marbles. What percent of the marbles are blue?
   A 2.6%   C 26%
   B 22%   D 74%

10. According to a survey of the class, 15 of 24 students have a pet dog. What percent of the class have a dog?
   A 6.25%   C 55%
   B 37.5%   D 62.5%

11. $80 is 25% of what amount?
   A $20   C $400
   B $320   D $3200

B Chapter 6 Test

(continued)

12. 1200 is 150% of what number?
   A 8   C 1800
   B 800   D 8000

13. The number 4.8 is 50% of another number. What is the other number?
   A 0.096   C 7.2
   B 2.4   D 9.6

14. As a club fundraiser, a group of students washed 40 cars one weekend. The next weekend, they washed 52 cars. What was the percent of increase in the number of cars washed?
   A 15%   C 77%
   B 30%   D 130%

15. Last year, Springfield Middle School had 620 students. This year, it has 582 students. To the nearest tenth, what is the percent of decrease?
   A 6.1%   C 93.9%
   B 6.6%   D 106.5%

16. The price of a $750 table has been marked up by 12%. What is the price of the table after the markup?
   A $660   C $840
   B $762   D $930

17. Juan's purchase before sales tax was added totaled $46.00. The total, including tax was $48.76. What was the sales tax rate?
   A 2.76%   C 6.0%
   B 5.7%   D 8.0%

18. Lateisha sold a total of $136,000 of office equipment last month. If her commission is 7.8% of sales, how much commission did she earn?
   A $1061   C $11,832
   B $10,608   D $106,080

19. Angie has $1032 in her savings account. If the bank pays 3.5% simple interest on savings, how much does she earn in one year?
   A $36.12   C $294.86
   B $46.44   D $361.20

20. Charlotte invested $740.00 in a savings account that pays 3.8% interest compounded annually. What is the value of her investment after 6 years?
   A $768.12   C $929.17
   B $925.58   D $1687.20

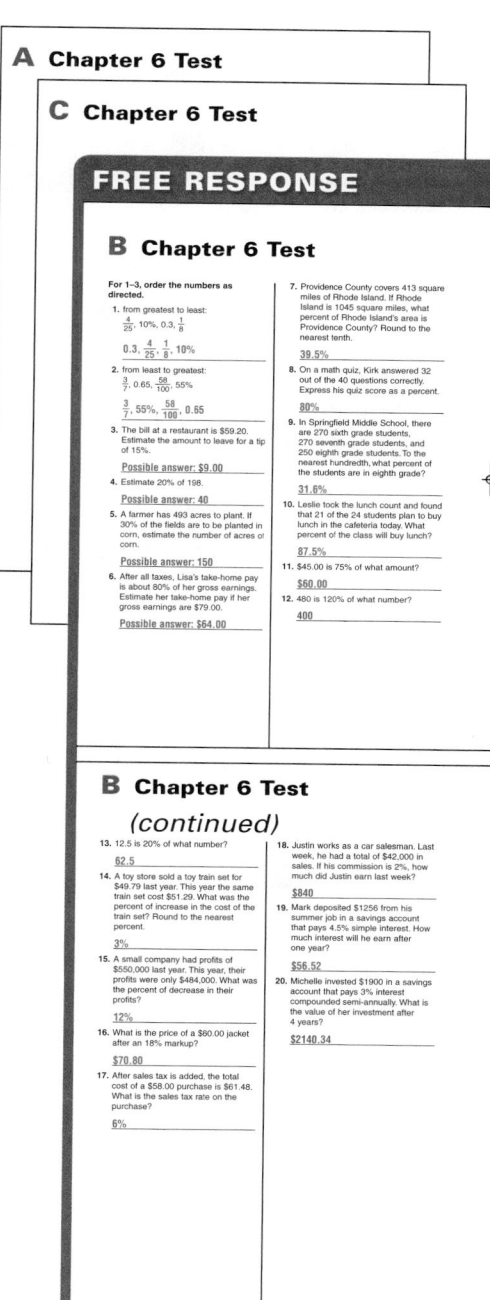

A Chapter 6 Test
C Chapter 6 Test

FREE RESPONSE

B Chapter 6 Test

For 1–3, order the numbers as directed.

1. from greatest to least:
   $\frac{4}{25}$, 10%, 0.3, $\frac{1}{8}$
   0.3, $\frac{4}{25}$, $\frac{1}{8}$, 10%

2. from least to greatest:
   $\frac{3}{7}$, 0.65, $\frac{58}{100}$, 55%
   $\frac{3}{7}$, 55%, $\frac{58}{100}$, 0.65

3. The bill at a restaurant is $59.20. Estimate the amount to leave for a tip of 15%.
   Possible answer: $9.00

4. Estimate 20% of 198.
   Possible answer: 40

5. A farmer has 493 acres to plant. If 30% of the fields are to be planted in corn, estimate the number of acres of corn.
   Possible answer: 150

6. After all taxes, Lisa's take-home pay is about 80% of her gross earnings. Estimate her take-home pay if her gross earnings are $79.00.
   Possible answer: $64.00

7. Providence County covers 413 square miles of Rhode Island. If Rhode Island is 1045 square miles, what percent of Rhode Island's area is Providence County? Round to the nearest tenth.
   39.5%

8. On a math quiz, Kirk answered 32 out of the 40 questions correctly. Express his quiz score as a percent.
   80%

9. In Springfield Middle School, there are 270 sixth grade students, 270 seventh grade students, and 250 eighth grade students. To the nearest hundredth, what percent of the students are in eighth grade?
   31.6%

10. Leslie took the lunch count and found that 21 of the 24 students plan to buy lunch in the cafeteria today. What percent of the class will buy lunch?
   87.5%

11. $45.00 is 75% of what amount?
   $60.00

12. 480 is 120% of what number?
   400

B Chapter 6 Test

(continued)

13. 12.5 is 20% of what number?
   62.5

14. A toy store sold a toy train set for $49.79 last year. This year the same train set cost $51.29. What was the percent of increase in the cost of the train set? Round to the nearest percent.
   3%

15. A small company had profits of $550,000 last year. This year, their profits were only $484,000. What was the percent of decrease in their profits?
   12%

16. What is the price of a $60.00 jacket after an 18% markup?
   $70.80

17. After sales tax is added, the total cost of a $58.00 purchase is $61.48. What is the sales tax on the purchase?
   6%

18. Justin works as a car salesman. Last week, he had a total of $42,000 in sales. If his commission is 2%, how much did Justin earn last week?
   $840

19. Mark deposited $1256 from his summer job in a savings account that pays 4.5% simple interest. How much interest will he earn after one year?
   $56.52

20. Michelle invested $1900 in a savings account that pays 3% interest compounded semi-annually. What is the value of her investment after 4 years?
   $2140.34

Modified tests and worksheets found in *IDEA Works!*

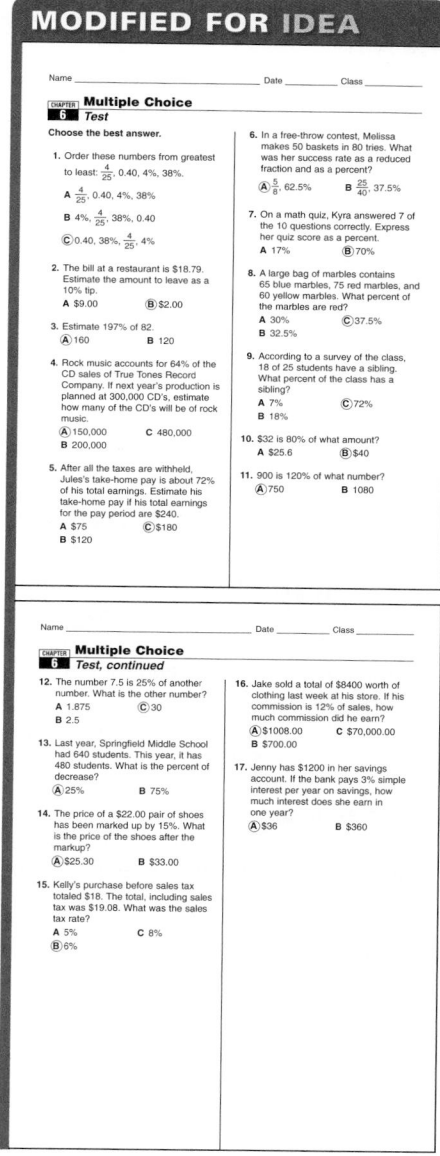

MODIFIED FOR IDEA

Name _____ Date _____ Class _____

CHAPTER 6 **Multiple Choice**
Test

Choose the best answer.

1. Order these numbers from greatest to least: $\frac{4}{25}$, 0.40, 4%, 38%.
   A $\frac{4}{25}$, 0.40, 4%, 38%
   B 4%, $\frac{4}{25}$, 38%, 0.40
   C 0.40, 38%, $\frac{4}{25}$, 4%

2. The bill at a restaurant is $18.79. Estimate the amount to leave as a 10% tip.
   A $9.00   B $2.00

3. Estimate 197% of 82.
   A 160   B 120

4. Rock music accounts for 64% of the CD sales of True Tones Record Company. If next year's production is planned at 300,000 CD's, estimate how many of the CD's will be of rock music.
   A 150,000   C 480,000
   B 200,000

5. After all the taxes are withheld, Jules's take-home pay is about 72% of his total earnings. Estimate his take-home pay if his total earnings for the pay period are $240.
   A $75   C $180
   B $120

6. In a free-throw contest, Melissa makes 50 baskets in 80 tries. What was her success rate as a reduced fraction and as a percent?
   A $\frac{5}{8}$, 62.5%   B $\frac{25}{40}$, 37.5%

7. On a math quiz, Kyra answered 7 of the 10 questions correctly. Express her quiz score as a percent.
   A 17%   B 70%

8. A large bag of marbles contains 65 blue marbles, 75 red marbles, and 60 yellow marbles. What percent of the marbles are red?
   A 30%   C 37.5%
   B 32.5%

9. According to a survey of the class, 18 of 25 students have a sibling. What percent of the class has a sibling?
   A 7%   C 72%
   B 18%

10. $32 is 80% of what amount?
   A $25.6   B $40

11. 900 is 120% of what number?
   A 750   B 1080

Name _____ Date _____ Class _____

CHAPTER 6 **Multiple Choice**
Test, continued

12. The number 7.5 is 25% of another number. What is the other number?
   A 1.875   C 30
   B 2.5

13. Last year, Springfield Middle School had 640 students. This year, it has 480 students. What is the percent of decrease?
   A 25%   B 75%

14. The price of a $22.00 pair of shoes has been marked up by 15%. What is the price of the shoes after the markup?
   A $25.30   B $33.00

15. Kelly's purchase before sales tax totaled $18. The total, including sales tax was $19.08. What was the sales tax rate?
   A 5%   C 8%
   B 6%

16. Jake sold a total of $8400 worth of clothing last week at his store. If his commission is 12% of sales, how much commission did he earn?
   A $1008.00   C $70,000.00
   B $700.00

17. Jenny has $1200 in her savings account. If the bank pays 3% simple interest per year on savings, how much interest does she earn in one year?
   A $36   B $360

Test & Practice Generator SPANISH
Teacher's One-Stop Planner®

Create and customize Chapter 6 Tests. Instantly generate multiple test versions, answer keys, and Spanish versions of test items.

CHAPTER 6

Focus on Problem Solving

On page 293, students focus on determining whether an exact answer is needed or an estimate is sufficient when solving real-world problems.

On page 309, students use percents to calculate the cost of their purchases for a camping trip.

Math in *California*

Statistics are used to compare the records of baseball players, such as Tony Gwynn. For example, in order to determine the hitter with the most frequent home runs, statisticians compare the at bats/home run statistic for each player. These statistics help statisticians find the percent of time that a player who comes up to bat will hit a home run. Point out to students that the player with the best at bats/home run statistic may not be the player with the most home runs. Students will investigate percents in the Chapter Project.

CHAPTER 6

Percents

CONCEPT CONNECTION

go.hrw.com
Chapter Project Online
KEYWORD: MT8CA Ch6

Sports statisticians use percents to make predictions.

San Diego
Home of the Padres

Problem Solving Project

Understand, Plan, Solve, and Look Back

Have students:

- Complete the Home Run Derby worksheet to learn more about working with percents.

- Estimate the number of home runs each player would hit if they each had 500 at bats in a given season.

- Research the number of home runs hit by their favorite players. What percent of their favorite players' total hits were home runs? What other kinds of hits did they have? Create a circle graph to show the results.

Social Studies and Sports Connection

Project Resources
All project resources for teachers and students are provided online.

Materials:
- Home Run Derby worksheet

go.hrw.com
Project Teacher Support
KEYWORD: MT8CA PSProject6

ARE YOU READY?

✓ Vocabulary

Choose the best term from the list to complete each sentence.

cross multiply

equivalent ratios

proportion

ratio

1. A(n) __?__ is a comparison of two numbers or quantities, often expressed as a fraction. **ratio**

2. Ratios that make the same comparison are __?__. **equivalent ratios**

3. An equation that states two ratios are equivalent is called a(n) __?__. **proportion**

4. To solve a proportion, you can __?__. **cross multiply**

Complete these exercises to review skills you will need for this chapter.

✓ Write Fractions as Decimals

Write each fraction as a decimal.

5. $\frac{3}{4}$ **0.75**   6. $\frac{5}{8}$ **0.625**   7. $\frac{2}{5}$ **0.4**   8. $\frac{2}{3}$ **$0.\overline{6}$**

✓ Represent Decimals

Write each decimal as a fraction in simplest form.

9. 0.7 **$\frac{7}{10}$**   10. 0.6 **$\frac{3}{5}$**   11. 0.25 **$\frac{1}{4}$**   12. 0.35 **$\frac{7}{20}$**

13. 0.2 **$\frac{1}{5}$**   14. 0.9 **$\frac{9}{10}$**   15. 0.86 **$\frac{43}{50}$**   16. 0.99 **$\frac{99}{100}$**

✓ Solve Proportions

Solve each proportion.

17. $\frac{x}{3} = \frac{9}{27}$ **$x = 1$**   18. $\frac{7}{8} = \frac{h}{4}$ **$h = 3.5$**   19. $\frac{9}{n} = \frac{2}{3}$ **$n = 13.5$**

20. $\frac{3}{8} = \frac{12}{t}$ **$t = 32$**   21. $\frac{4}{5} = \frac{28}{z}$ **$z = 35$**   22. $\frac{100}{p} = \frac{90}{45}$ **$p = 50$**

✓ Multiply with Fractions and Decimals

Multiply.

23. $\frac{12}{13} \times 8$ **$\frac{96}{13}$**   24. $\begin{array}{r} 18 \\ \times\ 0.45 \end{array}$ **8.1**   25. $20 \times \frac{9}{10}$ **18**

26. $\begin{array}{r} 2.75 \\ \times\ 11 \end{array}$ **30.25**   27. $\frac{1}{5} \times 12$ **$\frac{12}{5}$**   28. $\begin{array}{r} 6 \\ \times\ 0.08 \end{array}$ **0.48**

29. $13 \times \frac{25}{26}$ **$\frac{25}{2}$**   30. $\begin{array}{r} 15.32 \\ \times\ 9 \end{array}$ **137.88**   31. $\frac{2}{9} \times 78$ **$\frac{52}{3}$**

Organizer

Objective: Help students understand the new concepts they will learn in Chapter 6.

Academic Vocabulary Connections

Becoming familiar with the academic vocabulary on this student page will be helpful to students. Discussing some of the vocabulary terms in the chapter also may be helpful. Possible answers given.

1. The word *principal* means "first." What do you suppose **principal** means when referring to interest? the original amount of money from which interest is calculated

2. The word **commission** has the Latin prefix *com-*, which means "with," and the Latin root *mis*, which means "send." What do you think these Latin parts mean together when referring to money? money received with making a sale

3. The word *percent* contains the root word *cent*, which means "one hundred." What do you think a **percent** is? one hundredth of a whole

 CHAPTER 6 Unpacking the Standards

The information below "unpacks" the standards. The Academic Vocabulary is highlighted and defined to help you understand the language of the standards. Refer to the lessons listed after each standard for help with the math terms and phrases. The Chapter Concept shows how the standard is applied in this chapter.

California Standard	Academic Vocabulary	Chapter Concept
NS1.3 **Convert** fractions to decimals and percents and use these **representations** in estimations, computations, and applications. (Lessons 6-1, 6-2, 6-3, 6-4)	**convert** change from one form to another **representation** version or description	You rewrite numbers so that they have the same value, but are in a different form. *Example:* The decimal number 0.5 can be written as a fraction, $\frac{1}{2}$, or as a percent, 50%.
NS1.6 Calculate the percentage of **increases** and **decreases** of a quantity. (Lesson 6-5)	**increases** adds to or grows larger **decreases** takes away from or becomes smaller	You find the percent by which an amount has increased by finding how much was added to the original amount. You find the percent by which an amount has decreased by finding how much was taken away from the original amount.
NS1.7 Solve problems that **involve** discounts, markups, commissions, and profit and **compute** simple and compound interest. (Lessons 6-5, 6-6, 6-7)	**involve** contain or include **compute** calculate or figure out	You find the price of items on sale and how much money a company makes from the sale of the items. *Example:* A store manager buys an item for $40 and marks the price up by 75%. What is the price of the item? $0.75 \cdot 40 = 30$ $40 + 30 = 70$ The price of the item is $70.

Looking Back

Previously, students

- wrote common fractions as decimals and percents.
- investigated the meaning of percent.
- solved real-world problems involving decimals.

In This Chapter

Students will study

- estimating with percents.
- solving problems involving commission, sales tax, and profit.
- calculating percent of increase and decrease.
- simple and compound interest

Looking Forward

Students can use these skills

- to solve problems involving percents greater than 100.
- to apply algebraic techniques to solve percent problems.
- to solve problems involving probability and statistics.

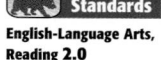

Reading and Writing Math

California Standards
English-Language Arts,
Reading 2.0

Reading Strategy: Read Problems for Understanding

When solving a word problem, first read the problem to identify exactly what the problem asks you to do. Then read the problem again, slowly and carefully, to break the problem into parts. Find the key information. Then make a plan to solve the problem.

From Lesson 5-5

15. **Art** Helen is copying a printed reproduction of the Mona Lisa. The print is 24 in. wide and 36 in. tall. If Helen's canvas is 12 in. wide, how tall should her canvas be?

> Slowly read the exercise again.

Step 1	Identify exactly what the problem asks you to do.	• Find the height of the canvas Helen should use.
Step 2	Break the problem into parts. Highlight or underline the key information.	• The print is **24 in. wide** and **36 in. tall**. • The canvas is **12 in. wide** • The **height** of the canvas is **unknown**. • The print and the copy are **similar rectangles**.
Step 3	Make a plan to solve the problem.	• Set up a proportion using the corresponding sides of the similar rectangles. • Find the cross products, and solve for x. • Check the answer by making sure the cross products are equal.

 Try This

For the problem below:
  a. Identify exactly what the problem asks you to do.
  b. Break the problem into parts. Find the key information.
  c. Make a plan to solve the problem.

1. An 8-pound weight is positioned 2 feet from a fulcrum. Another weight is placed 12 feet from the fulcrum on the opposite end. For the scale to balance, how much should this second weight weigh?

Answers to *Try This*

1. a. Find how much weight is needed to balance a scale.

b. An 8-pound weight is 2 feet from a fulcrum. On the opposite side, an unknown weight is placed 12 feet from the fulcrum. Find the weight needed to balance the scale.

c. For the scale to balance, $\frac{mass\ 1}{length\ 2} = \frac{mass\ 2}{length\ 1}$. Set up the proportion. Find the cross products, and solve for the unknown. Check the answer by making sure the cross products are equal.

Organizer

Objective: Help students apply strategies to understand and retain key concepts.

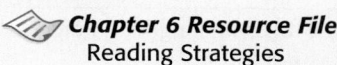 **Online Edition**

Resources

Chapter 6 Resource File
Reading Strategies

Reading Strategy: Read Problems for Understanding

ENGLISH LANGUAGE LEARNERS

Discuss Sometimes word problems can be intimidating. Suggest that students take their time and read through a word problem more than once before trying to solve it.

Remind students to look for information other than numbers, such as words and phrases that can give them a clue about which math operations to use.

Extend As you go through examples that are word problems in the Chapter 6 lessons, ask students to use the strategies presented on this page.

Choose at least one word problem from each lesson. Ask students to highlight the key information, break the problem into parts, and explain their plan to solve it.

California Standards

Reading 2.0 Students read and understand grade-level-appropriate material. They describe and connect the essential ideas, arguments, and perspectives of the text by using their knowledge of text structure, organization, and purpose. The selections in *Recommended Literature, Kindergarten Through Grade Twelve* illustrate the quality and complexity of the materials to be read by students. In addition, by grade eight, students read one million words annually on their own, including a good representation of grade-level-appropriate narrative and expository text (e.g., classic and contemporary literature, magazines, newspapers, online information). In grade seven, students make substantial progress toward this goal.

SECTION 6A

Percents

One-Minute Section Planner

Lesson	Lab Resources	Materials
Lesson 6-1 Relating Fractions, Decimals, and Percents • Compare and order fractions, decimals, and percents. **NS1.3**	**Hands-On Lab 6-1** In *Chapter 6 Resource File*	**Optional** Media advertisements with percents, index cards
Lesson 6-2 Estimating with Percents • Estimate with percents. **NS1.3**		**Optional** Calculators
Lesson 6-3 Finding Percents • Find percents. **NS1.3**	**Hands-On Lab 6-3** In *Chapter 6 Resource File*	**Optional** News article with election results
Lesson 6-4 Finding a Number When the Percent Is Known • Find a number when the percent is known. **NS1.3**		

MK = *Manipulatives Kit*

Notes

_____
_____
_____
_____
_____
_____
_____
_____
_____
_____
_____
_____
_____
_____

Math Background: Teaching the Standards

PERCENTS  NS1.3

Lesson 6-1

According to 2005 data from the U.S. Census Bureau, 42 out of every 400 California residents are 65 or older. In West Virginia, $\frac{3}{20}$ of the residents are 65 or older. When presented in this way, the data from the two states are difficult to compare. Percents are useful because they provide a standardized way to talk about and compare parts of a whole.

42 out of 400 equals 10.5%.

$\frac{3}{20}$ equals 15%.

A percent is a ratio that compares a number to 100. The term *percent* is an abbreviation of the Latin *per centum,* meaning "by the hundred." Students should know how to use this definition as a way of understanding and visualizing percents. For example, 40% means 40 parts out of 100. This relationship is illustrated by shading 40 of the 100 squares on a 10-by-10 grid.

Each square of the grid is 1%. Each column and row of the grid contains 10 squares and represents 10%. The grid makes it easy to see that 40% is equal to $\frac{4}{10}$, or $\frac{2}{5}$.

Since 40% means "the ratio of 40 to 100," the percent can be written directly as the fraction $\frac{40}{100}$. This leads to the decimal representation 0.40 (40 hundredths) or simply 0.4.

A fraction can be converted to a percent by writing it with a denominator of 100. Thus, $\frac{7}{20} = \frac{7 \cdot 5}{20 \cdot 5} = \frac{35}{100}$ and so $\frac{7}{20} = 35\%$. More generally, the fraction $\frac{a}{b}$ can be converted to a percent by solving the proportion $\frac{a}{b} = \frac{n}{100}$. For example, solving the proportion $\frac{3}{8} = \frac{n}{100}$ gives $n = 37.5$, and so $\frac{3}{8} = 37.5\%$.

Finally, decimals can be converted to percents by asking the question "how many hundredths are there?" The decimal 0.57 means 57 hundredths, so 0.57 = 57%. In practice, a decimal may be converted to a percent by multiplying by 100 or simply by moving the decimal point two places to the right. However, students should understand that the rationale for this decimal point movement is based on the definition of percents.

The same definitions and rules apply to percents that are less than 1% or greater than 100%. For example, multiplying 0.005 by 100 shows that this decimal equals 0.5%. This percent can be represented by shading half of one of the squares in the 10-by-10 grid. This shading helps to illustrate the fact that 0.5% is half of one one-hundredth, or $\frac{1}{200}$.

PERCENT PROBLEMS  NS1.3

Lessons 6-2 through 6-4

Percent problems may take a variety of forms.

- What is 28% of 95?
- What percent of 160 is 44?
- 15 is 60% of what number?

Students sometimes view these as unrelated problems that each require their own solution method. It is important for students to recognize that one essential relationship may be used to solve all of these percent problems. The relationship may be written as follows.

$$\frac{n}{100} = \frac{\text{part}}{\text{whole}}$$

In the proportion, n is the value of the percent ($n\%$).

Whether students use the equation or the proportion to solve percent problems, they should realize that every percent problem supplies two of the three required values. Finding the remaining unknown value becomes a matter of solving a simple linear equation or of solving a proportion.

 Hands-On Lab
In *Chapter 6 Resource File*

 Online Edition
Tutorial Videos, Interactivities

 Countdown to Mastery Week 11

Power Presentations
with PowerPoint®

Warm Up

Evaluate.

1. $\frac{2}{15} + \frac{3}{15}$ $\frac{1}{3}$ 2. $\frac{7}{12} - \frac{3}{12}$ $\frac{1}{3}$

3. $\frac{4}{5} \cdot \frac{7}{2}$ $\frac{14}{5}$ or $2\frac{4}{5}$ 4. $3\frac{1}{2} \div \frac{1}{4}$ 14

Also available on transparency

Math Humor

Which of these numbers is under the most stress, 30%, $\frac{1}{3}$, or 0.2? The last, because it's *too tense.*

 **California Standards**

Number Sense 1.3
Also covered:
Number Sense
1.0 Students know the properties of, and compute with, **rational numbers expressed in a variety of forms.**

 **6-1 Relating Fractions, Decimals, and Percents**

 **California Standards**

NS1.3 Convert fractions to decimals and percents and use these representations in estimations, computations, and **applications.**

Vocabulary
percent

Why learn this? You can use fractions, decimals, and percents to show the part of a day that a baby sleeps.

In an average day, a typical newborn baby sleeps 16 out of 24 hours. The part of a day the baby sleeps can be shown in several ways.

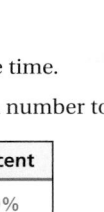

$$\frac{16}{24} = 0.66\overline{6} = 66.\overline{6}\%$$

So newborns sleep over 60% of the time.

Percents are ratios that compare a number to 100.

Reading Math

Think of the % symbol as meaning per 100 or /100.
75% = 75/100 = 0.75

Fraction	Decimal	Percent
$\frac{3}{10} = \frac{30}{100}$	0.30	30%
$\frac{1}{2} = \frac{50}{100}$	0.50	50%
$\frac{3}{4} = \frac{75}{100}$	0.75	75%

To convert a fraction to a decimal, divide the numerator by the denominator.

$\frac{1}{8} = 1 \div 8 = 0.125$

To convert a decimal to a percent, multiply by 100 and insert the percent symbol.

$0.125 \cdot 100 \rightarrow 12.5\%$

EXAMPLE 1   **Finding Equivalent Fractions and Percents**

Find the missing fraction or percent equivalent for each letter on the number line.

0%   b   25% $37\frac{1}{2}$%   e $66\frac{2}{3}$%   100%   h

a $\frac{7}{40}$ c   d $\frac{1}{2}$ f   g $1\frac{1}{5}$

a: $0\% = \frac{0}{100} = 0$ **b:** $\frac{7}{40} = 0.175 = 17.5\% = 17\frac{1}{2}\%$

c: $25\% = \frac{25}{100} = \frac{5}{20} = \frac{1}{4}$ **d:** $37\frac{1}{2}\% = 0.375 = \frac{375}{1000} = \frac{3}{8}$

e: $\frac{1}{2} = 0.5 = 50\%$ **f:** $66\frac{2}{3}\% = 0.66\overline{6} = \frac{2}{3}$

g: $100\% = \frac{100}{100} = 1$ **h:** $1\frac{1}{5} = 1.2 = 120\%$

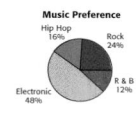 **1 Introduce**

Alternate Opener

EXPLORATION

6-1 Relating Fractions, Decimals, and Percents

A *percent* is a ratio that compares a number to 100. Percents can be modeled on circle graphs. The circle graph below shows the results of a survey in which 25 students were asked which type of music they preferred.

- 16% means 16 per 100.
- 16% as a decimal is 0.16.
- 16% as a fraction is $\frac{16}{100} = \frac{4}{25}$.

Music Preference
Hip Hop 16%
Rock 24%
R & B 12%
Electronic 48%

Use the percents in the circle graph to complete the table.

	Music Type	Percent	Decimal	Fraction
1.	Electronic	48%		
2.	Rock	24%		
3.	Hip Hop	16%		
4.	R & B	12%		

Think and Discuss
5. **Explain** how you wrote each percent as a decimal.
6. **Explain** how you wrote each decimal as a fraction.

Motivate

Show students magazines or newspapers that advertise sales using percents. Ask the students whether they can explain how much money would be saved and what the sale price would be as a result of the percent savings.

Explorations and answers are provided in *Alternate Openers: Explorations Transparencies.*

To compare and order fractions, decimals, and percents, write them in the same form first.

EXAMPLE **2** **Comparing Fractions, Decimals, and Percents**

Remember!
When multiplying a decimal by 100, simply move the decimal point two spaces to the right.

Compare. Write <, >, or =.

A $\frac{1}{2}$ ▓ 37%

$\frac{1}{2} = 0.50 = 50\%$ *Write as a percent.*

$50\% > 37\%$ *Compare.*

$\frac{1}{2} > 37\%$

B 0.125 ▓ 19%

$0.125 = 12.5\%$ *Write as a percent.*

$12.5\% < 19\%$ *Compare.*

$0.125 < 19\%$

EXAMPLE **3** **Ordering Fractions, Decimals, and Percents**

Possible answers to
Think and Discuss
1. (1) money; (2) measurements in recipes; (3) sales tax
2. (1) $\frac{1}{4}$; (2) 25%; (3) 0.25; 0.25 is most common when writing it.

Write 0.25%, $\frac{13}{5}$, 0.57, and 300% in order from least to greatest.

$\frac{13}{5} = 2.6 = 260\%$ *Write the numbers in the same form.*

$0.57 = 57\%$

$0.25\% < 57\% < 260\% < 300\%$ *Compare.*

$0.25\%, 0.57, \frac{13}{5}, 300\%$

EXAMPLE **4** *Science Application*

3. If the number is a decimal, you can find the equivalent percent by multiplying by 100, or the equivalent fraction by writing the value over the correct power of 10. If the number is a fraction, you can find the decimal by dividing the numerator by the denominator. If the number is a percent, you can find the decimal by dividing by 100.

The United States nickel was once made of 100% nickel. Today nickels are 3 parts copper and 1 part nickel. What percent of today's nickel is pure nickel?

$\dfrac{\text{parts pure nickel}}{\text{total parts}} \rightarrow \dfrac{1}{4}$ *Set up a ratio and simplify.*

$\frac{1}{4} = 1 \div 4 = 0.25 = 25\%$ *Find the percent.*

So today's nickel is 25% pure nickel.

Think and Discuss
1. Give an example of a real-world situation in which you would use (1) decimals, (2) fractions, and (3) percents.
2. Show 25 cents as a part of a dollar in terms of (1) a reduced fraction, (2) a percent, and (3) a decimal. Which is most common?
3. Explain how you can find a fraction, decimal, or percent when you have only one form of a number.

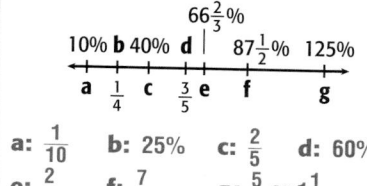

Teaching Tip
Visual When comparing fractions, decimals, and percents, some students may want to place the numbers on a number line. Encourage these students to convert all the numbers to decimals.

2 Teach

Guided Instruction

In this lesson, students learn to relate fractions, decimals, and percents. Demonstrate to students that fractions, decimals, and percents are all ratios. Remind students how to convert between fractions and decimals. Explain that percents are ratios in the form of *parts per hundred.*

Teaching Tip
Reading Math Ask students how many cents there are in a dollar. 100 Then ask what the word *per* means. "for each" or "divided by" Then explain that the word *percent* means "divided by one hundred" (e.g., 20% literally means "20 divided by 100" or "20 for each 100").

ENGLISH LANGUAGE LEARNERS

Universal Access
Through Concrete Manipulatives

Prepare sets of number cards that contain three equivalent numbers, such as $\frac{1}{4}$, 0.25, and 25%. Distribute the numbers randomly so that each student gets a fraction, a decimal, or a percent. Have each student find the two students in the class with the numbers equivalent to his or her number. Once students have formed their groups of three, have the class form a human number line (three deep) so that the numbers are in increasing order.

3 Close

Summarize

Remind students that fractions, terminating or repeating decimals, and percents are all ratios. In a fraction, the denominator can be any nonzero integer. A percent is equivalent to a ratio with a denominator of 100. A terminating decimal is equivalent to a ratio with a denominator of 10, 100, 1000, or some other power of 10. Any of the three forms can be changed to the other two forms.

California Standards Practice
NS1.1, NS1.3

go.hrw.com
Homework Help Online
KEYWORD: MT8CA 6-1
Parent Resources Online
KEYWORD: MT8CA Parent

Assignment Guide

If you finished Example **1** assign:
Proficient 1–4, 12–15, 23–25, 34–40
Advanced 12–15, 23–25, 27, 34–40

If you finished Example **2** assign:
Proficient 1–8, 12–19, 23–25, 34–40
Advanced 12–19, 23–25, 27, 31, 34–40

If you finished Example **3** assign:
Proficient 1–10, 12–21, 23–25, 30, 34–40
Advanced 12–21, 23–27, 34–40

If you finished Example **4** assign:
Proficient 1–25, 28, 30, 32–40
Advanced 12–40

Homework Quick Check
Quickly check key concepts.
Exercises: 12, 16, 20, 21, 24

Math Background

Using 10-by-10 grids is an excellent way to reinforce the meaning of *percent*. On the grid, each square represents 1%, or $\frac{1}{100}$, of the grid's area. You can shade different percents on the grid and then divide the grid into equal areas to show fractional equivalents. The example below shows that 20% is equal to $\frac{1}{5}$.

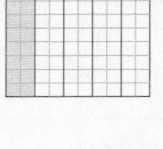

California Standards

Standard	Exercises
NS1.1	1–10, 12–21, 30, 34–37
NS1.3	1–33
AF4.0	38–40

GUIDED PRACTICE

See Example **1** Find the missing fraction or percent equivalent for each letter on the number line.

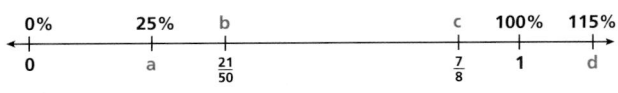

1. a $\frac{1}{4}$ 2. b 42%   3. c 87.5%   4. d $\frac{23}{20}$

See Example **2** Compare. Write <, >, or =.

5. $\frac{3}{4}$ > 70%   6. 42% > $\frac{2}{5}$ 7. 87.5% = 0.875   8. 0.99 < 100%

See Example **3** Order the numbers from least to greatest.

9. 36%, 0.3, $33\frac{1}{3}$%, $\frac{3}{8}$ 0.3, $33\frac{1}{3}$%, 36%, $\frac{3}{8}$ 10. $\frac{4}{5}$, −0.5, 500%, $66\frac{2}{3}$%   −0.5, $66\frac{2}{3}$%, $\frac{4}{5}$, 500%

See Example **4** 11. A molecule of water is made up of 2 atoms of hydrogen and 1 atom of oxygen. What percent of the atoms of a water molecule is oxygen? $33\frac{1}{3}$%

INDEPENDENT PRACTICE

See Example **1** Find the missing fraction or percent equivalent for each letter on the number line.

12. e 20%   13. f $\frac{39}{100}$ 14. g $\frac{4}{5}$ 15. h 125%

See Example **2** Compare. Write <, >, or =.

16. $\frac{2}{3}$ > 66%   17. 37% < $\frac{3}{8}$ 18. 6% < 0.6   19. 0.09 = 9%

See Example **3** Order the numbers from least to greatest.

20. −6%, 0.6, $66\frac{1}{3}$%, $\frac{3}{6}$ −6%, $\frac{3}{6}$, 0.6, $66\frac{1}{3}$%   21. $\frac{2}{5}$, 0.04, 42%, 70%   0.04, $\frac{2}{5}$, 42%, 70%

See Example **4** 22. Sterling silver is an alloy combining 925 parts pure silver and 75 parts of another metal, such as copper. What percent of sterling silver is not pure silver? 7.5%

PRACTICE AND PROBLEM SOLVING

Extra Practice
See page EP12.

Write the labels from each circle graph as percents.

23. 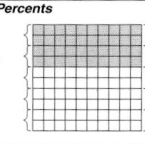 0.4, 0.3, 0.1, 0.2   40%, 30%, 20%, 10%

24. 0.15, 0.08, 0.25, 0.52   15%, 25%, 52%, 8%

25. $\frac{2}{5}$, $\frac{1}{20}$, $\frac{3}{10}$, $\frac{1}{4}$ 40%, 30%, 25%, 5%

REVIEW FOR MASTERY 6-1

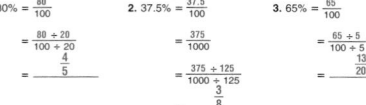
LESSON 6-1 Review for Mastery
Relating Fractions, Decimals, and Percents

A **percent** (symbol %) is a *ratio*, where the comparison is to the number 100.

The ratio is then written as a fraction in simplest form.

$40\% = \frac{40}{100} = \frac{40 \div 20}{100 \div 20} = \frac{2}{5}$

Write each percent as a fraction in simplest form.

1. $80\% = \frac{80}{100}$
$= \frac{80 \div 20}{100 \div 20}$
$= \frac{4}{5}$

2. $37.5\% = \frac{37.5}{100}$
$= \frac{375}{1000}$
$= \frac{375 \div 125}{1000 \div 125}$
$= \frac{3}{8}$

3. $65\% = \frac{65}{100}$
$= \frac{65 \div 5}{100 \div 5}$
$= \frac{13}{20}$

Since a percent compares a number to 100, a percent can be written as a decimal. $40\% = \frac{40}{100} = 0.40$

Write each percent as a decimal.

4. $80\% = \frac{80}{100}$
$= \underline{0.80}$

5. $37.5\% = \frac{37.5}{100}$
$= \frac{375}{1000}$
$= \underline{0.375}$

6. $65\% = \frac{65}{100}$
$= \underline{0.65}$

Use the results of Exercises 1–6 to compare. Write <, >, or =.

7. $\frac{13}{20}$ > 37.5%
8. 80% > 0.65
9. 65% < 0.8
10. 0.375 < 80%
11. 37.5% < 0.65
12. 65% = $\frac{13}{20}$

PRACTICE 6-1

LESSON 6-1 Practice B
Relating Fractions, Decimals, and Percents

Find the missing fraction or percent equivalent for each letter on the number line.

1. a 6%
2. b 36%
3. c $\frac{16}{25}$
4. d 80%
5. m $\frac{11}{50}$
6. r 45%
7. t $\frac{14}{25}$
8. x $\frac{7}{10}$

Compare. Write <, >, or =.

9. $\frac{3}{4}$ > 70%
10. 60% = $\frac{3}{5}$
11. 58% < 0.6
12. 0.09 < 15%
13. $\frac{2}{3}$ > 59%
14. 0.45 > 40.5%

Order the numbers from least to greatest.

15. 99%, 0.95, $\frac{5}{9}$, 9.5%   9.5%, $\frac{5}{9}$, 0.95, 99%
16. $\frac{3}{8}$, 50%, 0.35, 38%   0.35, $\frac{3}{8}$, 38%, 50%
17. $\frac{4}{5}$, 54%, 0.45, 44.5%   44.5%, 0.45, 54%, $\frac{4}{5}$
18. $\frac{1}{3}$, 20%, 0.3, 3%   3%, 20%, 0.3, $\frac{1}{3}$

19. There are 25 students in math class. Yesterday, 6 students were absent. What percent of the students were absent?   24%
20. Albert spends 2 hours a day on his homework and an hour playing video games. What percent of the day is this?   12.5%
21. Ragu ran the first 3 miles of a 5 mile race in 24 minutes. What percent of the race has he run?   60%

26. Multi-Step One-half of the 1100 students at Anderson Middle School are girls. One-tenth of the girls are in the band, and one-fifth of those play the drums. What percent of the students at Anderson are girls who play the drums in the band? **1%**

27. Reasoning Describe a situation when changing a fraction to a percent would be helpful.

28a. $\frac{4}{25}$; 0.16

28b. 23%; Possible answer: Alaska and Texas make up nearly $\frac{1}{4}$ of the total land area in the United States.

28. Geography The graph shows the percents of the total U.S. land area taken up by the five largest states. The sixth section of the graph represents the area of the remaining 45 states.

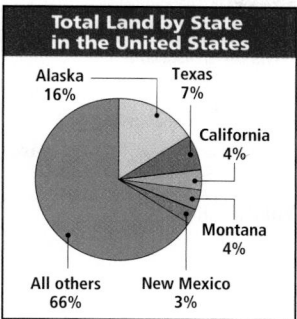

Total Land by State in the United States

Alaska 16%
Texas 7%
California 4%
Montana 4%
New Mexico 3%
All others 66%

a. Alaska is the largest state in total land area. Write Alaska's portion of the total U.S. land area as a fraction and as a decimal.

b. What percent of the total U.S. land area is taken up by Alaska and Texas? How might you describe this percent?

29. What's the Error? An analysis showed that 0.06% of the T-shirts made by one company were defective. A student says this is 6 out of every 100. What is the student's error?

30. Write About It Explain the steps you would take to order $\frac{1}{3}$, 0.33, and 30% from least to greatest.

31. Challenge Wyatt and Allyson were asked to solve a percent problem using the numbers 13 and 38. Wyatt found 13% of 38, and Allyson found 38% of 13. Explain why they both got the same answer. Would this work for other numbers as well? Why or why not?

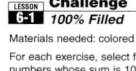
SPIRAL STANDARDS REVIEW

NS1.1, NS1.3, ☞ AF4.0

32. Multiple Choice Of the 32 students in Mr. Smith's class, 12 have jobs during the summer. What percent of the students have a summer job?

Ⓐ 12%   Ⓑ 20%   Ⓒ 37.5%   Ⓓ 62.5%

33. Multiple Choice Claudia has 40 CDs. Of these, 14 are country music CDs. What percent of Claudia's CD collection is country music?

Ⓐ 40%   Ⓑ 35%   Ⓒ 14%   Ⓓ 12%

Compare. Write <, >, =. (Lesson 2-2)

34. $\frac{4}{9}$ ▤ $\frac{21}{25}$ <

35. $\frac{3}{7}$ ▤ $\frac{8}{9}$ <

36. $-\frac{1}{3}$ ▤ $-\frac{2}{5}$ >

37. $-\frac{8}{14}$ ▤ $-\frac{4}{7}$ =

Solve. (Lesson 3-6)

38. $-6 < y + 4.2$ $y > -10.2$

39. $z - 1.5 \geq 4$ $z \geq 5.5$

40. $t - 12 \leq 8.4$ $t \leq 20.4$

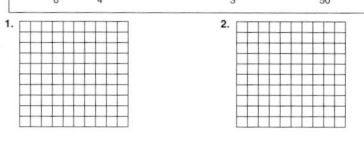

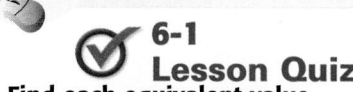

Objective: Students estimate with percents.

Online Edition
Tutorial Videos

Countdown to Mastery Week 11

Power Presentations
with PowerPoint®

Warm Up
Write each percent as a fraction.
1. 33% $\frac{1}{3}$ **2.** 75% $\frac{3}{4}$

3. 20% $\frac{1}{5}$ **4.** 60% $\frac{3}{5}$

Also available on transparency

Math Fact !

One thousand seconds pass in about 17 minutes. One million seconds pass in about 12 days. One billion seconds pass in about 32 years.

6-2 Estimating with Percents

California Standards

NS1.3 Convert fractions to decimals and percents and use these representations in estimations, computations, and applications.

Vocabulary
estimate
compatible numbers

Why learn this? You can use estimation to find the amount you should tip at a restaurant. (See Example 2.)

Some problems require only an **estimate**. Estimates involving percents and fractions can be found by using **compatible numbers**, numbers that go well together because they have common factors.

$\frac{13}{24}$ *13 and 24 are not compatible numbers.*

$\frac{12}{24}$ *12 and 24 are compatible numbers because 12 is a common factor of 12 and 24.*

$\frac{12}{24} = \frac{1}{2}$ *Simplify.*

$\frac{13}{24} \approx \frac{1}{2}$ *$\frac{13}{24}$ is nearly equivalent to $\frac{12}{24}$.*

When estimating with percents, it helps to know some *benchmarks*. Benchmarks are common numbers that serve as points of reference. Some common benchmarks for percents are shown in the table.

Percent	Decimal	Fraction	Percent	Decimal	Fraction
5%	0.05	$\frac{1}{20}$	50%	0.5	$\frac{1}{2}$
10%	0.1	$\frac{1}{10}$	66.$\overline{6}$%	0.$\overline{6}$	$\frac{2}{3}$
25%	0.25	$\frac{1}{4}$	75%	0.75	$\frac{3}{4}$
33.$\overline{3}$%	0.$\overline{3}$	$\frac{1}{3}$	100%	1	1

EXAMPLE **1** **Estimating with Percents**

Estimate.

 A 24% of 44

$24\% \approx 25\%$ *Use a benchmark close to 24%.*

$\approx \frac{1}{4}$ *Write 25% as a fraction.*

$\frac{1}{4} \cdot 44 = 11$ *Use mental math: 44 ÷ 4.*

24% of 44 is about 11.

---

1 Introduce
Alternate Opener

EXPLORATION

6-2 Estimating with Percents

Stores that go out of business often offer big discounts on purchases. In such situations, 50% off sales are common.

Estimate the discount for each item at 50% off. Then calculate the actual discount.

	Item	Price	Estimated Discount	Actual Discount
1.	Shirt	$39.95		
2.	DVD player	$288.95		
3.	Speakers	$239.95		
4.	TV	$1,035.29		
5.	MP3 player	$247.99		

Think and Discuss
6. Discuss the estimation strategies you used.
7. Explain whether a one-time 50% discount is equivalent to two consecutive 25% discounts. (*Hint:* Use $100.00 as the base amount.)

Motivate

Tell students to imagine that a store is celebrating its 19th anniversary, and it is having a sale in which every item is 19% off. Ask students if they know how to estimate the savings on an item priced at $19.99.
About 20% of $20, or $4

Explorations and answers are provided in *Alternate Openers: Explorations Transparencies*.

California Standards

Number Sense 1.3

 **Reasoning**

Estimate.

 **36% of 20**

$36\% \approx 35\%$	*Round.*
$\approx 25\% + 10\%$	*Break 35% into two benchmarks.*
$35\% \cdot 20 = (25\% + 10\%) \cdot 20$	*Set up an equation.*
$= 25\% \cdot 20 + 10\% \cdot 20$	*Use the Distributive Property.*
$= 5 + 2$	*25% of 20 is 5, and 10% of 20 is 2.*

36% of 20 is about 7.

A tip is an amount of money added to a bill for service. Tips are sometimes estimated instead of calculated exactly.

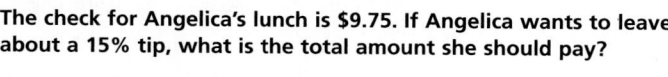

EXAMPLE **2** **PROBLEM SOLVING APPLICATION**

The check for Angelica's lunch is $9.75. If Angelica wants to leave about a 15% tip, what is the total amount she should pay?

 Understand the Problem

The **answer** is the total amount Angelica should pay for her lunch.

List the important information:
• Angelica's lunch check is $9.75.
• Angelica wants to leave about a 15% tip.

2 Make a Plan

Use estimation and mental math to find the tip. Then add the tip to the check amount to find the total amount Angelica should pay.

3 Solve

First round $9.75 to $10.	*Use compatible numbers.*
$15\% = 10\% + 5\%$	*Think: 15% is 10% plus 5%.*

$$10\% \text{ of } \$10 = \$1.00$$
$$5\% \text{ of } \$10 = 10\% \div 2$$
$$= \$1.00 \div 2 = \$0.50$$

$$15\% = 10\% + 5\%$$
$$= \$1.00 + \$0.50 = \$1.50$$

$\$9.75 + \$1.50 = \$11.25$	*Add the tip to the check amount.*

Angelica should pay about $11.25.

 Look Back

Use a calculator to determine whether $1.50 is a reasonable estimate of a 15% tip. $9.75 \cdot 0.15 \approx 1.46$, so $1.50 is a reasonable estimate.

2 Teach

Guided Instruction

In this lesson, students learn to estimate with percents by rounding to compatible numbers. Explain how to determine whether numbers are compatible, and if they are not, how to find compatible numbers that are appropriate.

 **Inclusion** After each estimation, have students decide whether their estimate makes sense. Before students work the exercises, remind them that their estimates may vary.

 **Universal Access**
Through Number Sense

Have each student write the price and sale information for an everyday item. Students should work in groups to estimate each sale price. Then have students exchange papers to find the exact answers. Ask students to compare their answers with their estimates. This activity will give students the opportunity to evaluate their estimates by comparing them with the exact answers.

EXAMPLE 3 *Manufacturing Application*

 Reasoning

A company has found that on average 9% of the radios it manufactures are defective. Out of a production run of 1523 radios, the plant manager assumes that 137 are defective. Estimate to see if the plant manager's number is reasonable. Explain.

$9\% \cdot 1523 \approx 10\% \cdot 1500$ *Use compatible numbers.*

$\approx 0.1 \cdot 1500$ *Write 10% as a decimal.*

≈ 150 *Multiply.*

Because 150 is close to 137, the plant manager's number is reasonable.

Think and Discuss

1. **Determine** the ratios that are nearly equivalent to each of the following percents: 23%, 53%, 65%, 12%, and 76%.

2. **Describe** how to find 35% of a number when you know 10% of the number.

6-2 Exercises

6-2 Exercises

GUIDED PRACTICE

See Example **1**   Estimate.

1. 11% of 507 50   2. 26% of 99 25   3. 34% of 91 30   4. 48% of 124 62

5. 20% of 66 13   6. $12\frac{1}{2}$% of 87 11   7. $66\frac{2}{3}$% of 25 16   8. 47% of 80 37

See Example **2**   9. Arnold ate breakfast at a restaurant. The check for his meal was $6.45. If Arnold wants to leave about a 20% tip, what is the total amount he should pay?
Possible answer: $7.75

See Example **3**   10. Approximately 11% of each batch of yo-yos is defective. Mr. Andersen said that in a batch of 1500 yo-yos, 105 yo-yos would be defective. Estimate to determine if Mr. Andersen's number is reasonable. Explain.   No; Possible answer: 11% of 1500 is a little more than 10% of 1500. 10% of 1500 is 150. 105 is much less than 150.

INDEPENDENT PRACTICE

See Example **1**   Estimate.

11. 48% of 202 100   12. 74% of 39 30   13. 101% of 6 6   14. 20% of 42 8

15. 40% of 81 32   16. $62\frac{1}{2}$% of 239 150   17. $33\frac{1}{3}$% of 26 9   18. 30% of 118 36

Possible answers to
Think and Discuss

1. $\frac{1}{4}, \frac{1}{2}, \frac{2}{3}, \frac{1}{8}, \frac{3}{4}$

2. 35% = 10% + 10% + 10% + 5%
= (3 · 10%) + $\frac{1}{2}$(10%)

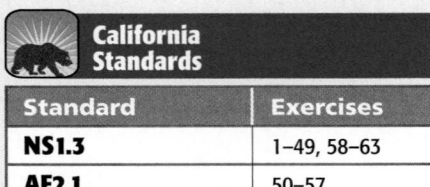

See Example ② **19.** A family's dinner check is $38.82. If they want to leave about a 15% tip, what is the total amount they should pay? **Possible answer: $44.82**

See Example ③ **20.** In a recent election, the leading candidate captured approximately 75% of the 24,082 total votes. The newspaper reported that the winner captured 18,039 votes. Estimate to determine if the newspaper report is reasonable. Explain. **Yes; Possible answer: 75% of 24,000 is about 18,000, which is close to 18,039.**

PRACTICE AND PROBLEM SOLVING

Extra Practice
See page EP12.

Choose the best estimate. Write A, B, or C.

21. 5% of 29.4
   A 0.15
   (B) 1.5
   C 15

22. 50% of 29.85
   A 3
   B 12
   (C) 15

23. 33.3% of 65
   A 2
   (B) 20
   C 30

24. 66% of $357.99
   A $120
   (B) $240
   C $360

25. 75% of $317.99
   A $24
   B $120
   (C) $240

26. 105% of $776.50
   A $80
   B $900
   (C) $800

Estimate.

27. 50% of 297 is about what number?
  150

28. 75% of 76 is about what number?
  60

29. 103% of 40 is about what number?
  40

30. 103% of 885 is about what number?
  900

31. 50% of 1611 is about what number?
  800

32. 50% of 12.42 is about what number?
  6

33. $33\frac{1}{3}$% of 87 is about what number?
  30

34. 9.6% of 77 is about what number?
  8

35. 24% of 402 is about what number?
  100

36. 66% of 1.8 is about what number?
  1.2

37. On a weekday, 911 cars passed through a city intersection. On Saturday, only 33% of that number passed through the intersection. Approximately how many cars passed through the intersection on the weekend? **≈ 300 cars**

38. A jury wants to give an award of about 9% of $695,531. What is a good estimate of the award? **$70,000**

Science

Freezing a light stick may make it glow longer, but not as brightly.

39. Business The daily circulation for a city newspaper was 498,739. After a six-month period, the circulation dropped 5.1%. Approximately what was the daily circulation at the end of the six-month period? **≈ 475,000**

40. Finance Brooke earns $320 a week. After taxes, her paycheck is only 78% of her earnings. Approximately how much is her paycheck each week? **≈ $240**

41. Science When you snap a light stick, you break a barrier between two chemical compounds. This causes a reaction that releases energy as light. An improvement allows a 9-hour light stick to glow for 50% more time. Approximately how long does the improved light stick glow? **≈ 14 hours**

42. Sports Over his ten-year career, Jackie Robinson reached base approximately 41% of his 4877 plate appearances. Approximately how many times did he reach base? **≈ 2000 times**

REVIEW FOR MASTERY 6-2

LESSON 6-2 Review for Mastery
Estimating with Percents

You can estimate the solutions to different types of problems involving percents by rounding numbers.

Type 1: Finding a percent of a number.

Estimate 38% of 470.

First, round the percent to a common percent with an easy fractional equivalent.

$38\% \approx 40\% = \frac{40}{100} = \frac{2}{5}$

Then, round the number to a number divisible by the denominator of the fraction.

470 ≈ 500 ← 500 is divisible by 5.

Use mental math to multiply.

$\frac{2}{5} \cdot 500$ Think: If 500 ÷ 5 = 100, then 100 · 2 = 200

So, 38% of 470 is about 200.

Complete to estimate each percent. *Estimates may vary.*

1. 32% of 872

Round to a percent with an easy fractional equivalent: 32% ≈ $33\frac{1}{3}$% = $\frac{1}{3}$

Round to hundreds place, divisible by 3: 872 ≈ **900**

Do mental math to multiply: $\frac{1}{3}$ × **900** = **300**

So, 32% of 872 is about **300**.

2. 78% of 495

% to easy fraction:

78% ≈ **80** % = $\frac{4}{5}$

divisible by denominator:

495 ≈ **500**

Do mental math to multiply.

$\frac{4}{5}$ × **500** = **400**

So, 78% of 495 is about **400**.

3. 73% of 1175

% to easy fraction:

73% ≈ **75** % = $\frac{3}{4}$

divisible by denominator:

1175 ≈ **1200**

Do mental math to multiply.

$\frac{3}{4}$ × **1200** = **900**

So, 73% of 1175 is about **900**.

PRACTICE 6-2

LESSON 6-2 Practice B
Estimating with Percents

Estimate. *Estimates may vary.*

1. 74% of 99   **about 75**

2. 25% of 39   **about 10**

3. 52% of 10   **about 5**

4. 21% of 50   **about 10**

5. 30% of 61   **about 20**

6. 24% of 48   **about 12**

7. 5% of 41   **about 2**

8. 50% of 178   **about 90**

9. 33% out of 62   **about 20**

Estimate.

10. 48% of 30 is about what number? **about 15**

11. 26% of 36 is about what number? **about 9**

12. 30% of 22 is about what number? **about 7**

13. 21% of 63 is about what number? **about 12**

14. Rodney's weekly gross pay is $91. He must pay about 32% in deductions. Estimate Rodney's weekly take-home pay after deductions. **about $60**

15. In the last school election, 492 students voted. Mary received 48% of the votes. About how many votes did she receive? **about 250**

16. A restaurant bill for lunch is $14.10. Grace wants to leave a 15% tip. About how much will lunch cost Grace in all? **about $16.22**

17. A company has found that on average about 6% of the batteries they manufacture are defective. Out of 1,385 batteries, the supervisor assumes that about 83 are defective. Estimate to determine if the manager's number is reasonable? Explain. **Yes; 6% of 1,385 is about 5% of 1,400; 10% of 1,400 is 140, and half of 140 is 70. Since 5% of 1,400 is 83 and 70 is close to 70, the estimate is reasonable.**

Answers

45. Possible answer: To find 1%, move the decimal point in the number two places left (about 40). To find 10%, move the decimal one place (about 400). 100% is the same as the original number (4027).

Multiple Choice For **Exercise 48,** remind students that to convert from a percent to a decimal, divide the percent by 100 or multiply the percent by 0.01.

 **Journal**

When selling products or services, many businesses give the customer an estimate of the cost of the job before the work is done. Have students write about why businesses provide estimates and about possible problems these estimates could cause.

Power Presentations
with PowerPoint®

6-2 Lesson Quiz

Estimate. Possible answers:

1. 34% of 12   **4**

2. 113% of 80   **90**

3. Ian had dinner with some friends at a restaurant. The check for his dinner was $10.25. If he wants to leave about a 20% tip, what is the total amount Ian should pay? Possible answer: $12.25

4. Approximately 8% of each batch of jeans produced at one factory is defective. Ms. Fleming said that in a batch of 400 jeans, about 35 jeans would be defective. Estimate to determine if her number is reasonable. Explain. Yes, because 8% of 400 is a little less than 10% of 400. 10% of 400 is 40 and 35 is a little less than 40.

Also available on transparency

43a. No; Possible answer: 2% of 570,000 is approximately 11,400, which isn't close to 1045. Rhode Island is approximately 0.02% the area of Alaska.

43b. Yes; Possible answer: 60% of 1,000,000 is about 600,000, which is close to 655,435.

43. Social Studies Alaska is the largest state in the United States in total land area, and Rhode Island is the smallest.

a. The area of Rhode Island is approximately 2% the area of Alaska. Determine if this statement is reasonable. Explain.

b. Although Rhode Island is much smaller than Alaska, it has a larger population. Alaska has approximately 60% the population of Rhode Island. Determine if this statement is reasonable. Explain.

c. Estimate the number of people per square mile in Alaska and in Rhode Island. ≈ 1 per mi²; ≈ 1000 per mi²

Area and Population: 2004		
	Total Land (mi²)	Population
Alaska	571,949	655,435
Rhode Island	1045	1,080,632

Source: U.S. Census Bureau

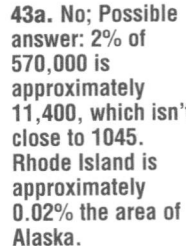 **44. Write a Problem** Write a percent estimation problem using the following data: The equatorial circumference of Earth is approximately 40,075 km. The equatorial circumference of the moon is approximately 25% Earth's equatorial circumference.   **Possible answer: Estimate the equatorial circumference of the moon. Answer: ≈ 10,000 km.**

45. Write About It Explain how you can estimate 1%, 10%, and 100% of 4027.

46. Challenge Explain two ways to estimate 20% of 82.
Possible answer: 20% of 82 is about $\frac{1}{5}$ of 80, or 16. It is also twice 10% of 82, or about 8 + 8 = 16.

SPIRAL STANDARDS REVIEW   NS1.3, AF2.1

47. Multiple Choice 328% of 82 is about what number?

(A) 246   (B) 264   (C) 287   (D) 298

48. Multiple Choice Regina receives a 5% commission on the merchandise she sells. Last week, Regina sold $11,976.57 worth of merchandise. Approximately how much commission does she earn?

(A) $600   (B) $11,400   (C) $550   (D) $10,450

49. Multiple Choice Which is the best estimate for 20% of 703?

(A) 14   (B) 140   (C) 1400   (D) 14,000

Evaluate. (Lesson 4-1)

50. 2^5 **32**   **51.** $(-3)^2$ **9**   **52.** $(-7)^3$ **−343**   **53.** -4^3 **−64**

54. $(-2)^7$ **−128**   **55.** 5^3 **125**   **56.** $(-4)^4$ **256**   **57.** 8^1 **8**

Find the percent, fraction, or decimal equivalent for each of the following.
(Lesson 6-1)

58. $\frac{9}{10}$ as a percent **90%**   **59.** 46% as a fraction $\frac{23}{50}$ **60.** $\frac{3}{8}$ as a decimal **0.375**

61. $\frac{7}{14}$ as a decimal **0.5**   **62.** 0.78 as a fraction $\frac{39}{50}$ **63.** 52.5% as a decimal **0.525**

CHALLENGE 6-2

LESSON 6-2 Challenge
As the Wheel Turns

For each wheel, write a percent problem using estimation. In your problem, use the percent at the center of the wheel and two other numbers on the wheel. The first one in each row is done.

1. [90 / 70 / 63% / 150 / 30]
63% of 150 is about 90.

2. [70 / 60 / 68% / 90 / 31]
68% of 90 is about 60.

3. [62 / 33 / 51% / 48 / 21]
51% of 62 is about 33.

4. [16 / 71 / 23% / 38 / 64]
16 is about 23% of 71.

5. [87 / 16 / 11% / 36 / 4]
4 is about 11% of 36.

6. [53 / 29 / 38% / 21 / 88]
21 is about 38% of 53.

7. [120 / 263 / 141% / 85 / 10]
141% of 85 is about 120.

8. [14 / 8 / 129% / 37 / 6]
129% of 6 is about 8.

9. [62 / 75 / 247% / 31 / 111]
247% of 31 is about 75.

PROBLEM SOLVING 6-2

LESSON 6-2 Problem Solving
Estimating with Percents

Write an estimate.

1. A store requires you to pay 15% up front on special orders. If you plan to special order items worth $74.86, estimate how much you will have to pay up front.
Possible answer: $11

2. A store is offering 25% off of everything in the store. Estimate how much you will save on a jacket that is normally $58.99.
Possible answer: $15

3. A certain kind of investment requires that you pay a 10% penalty on any money you remove from your investment in the first 7 years. If you take $228 out of the investment, estimate how much of a penalty you will have to pay.
Possible answer: $25

4. John notices that about 18% of the earnings from his job go to taxes. If he works 14 hours at $6.25 an hour, about how much of his check will go for taxes?
Possible answer: $18

Choose the letter for the best estimate.

5. In its first week, an infant can lose up to 10% of its body weight in the first few days of life. Which is a good estimate of how many ounces a 5 lb 13 oz baby might lose in the first week of life?
A 0.6 oz   C 18 oz
(B) 9 oz   D 22 oz

6. Jim wants to buy a CD which costs $12.89. He has a coupon for 4.75% off. Which is the best estimate of the cost of the CD with the coupon?
F $13.30   (H) $12.25
G $13.55   J $12.50

7. In a class election, Pedro received 52% of the votes. There were 274 students who voted in the election. Which is the best estimate of the number of students who voted for Pedro?
A 70 students   C 125 students
(B) 100 students   (D) 140 students

8. Mel's family went out for breakfast. The bill was $25. Mel wants to leave a 20% tip. Which is the best estimate of the total bill?
F $25.45   (H) $30.25
G $29.25   J $32.25

6-3 Finding Percents

Who uses this? Statistics from the Nielsen Television Ratings are reported as a percent of all American homes in which television is being watched at a given time. (See Exercise 8.)

Peanuts: © United Feature Syndicate, Inc.

EXAMPLE 1 Finding the Percent One Number Is of Another

What percent of 144 is 64?

Method 1: Set up a proportion.

$$\frac{\text{percent}}{100} = \frac{\text{part}}{\text{whole}}$$ *Set up a proportion.*

$$\frac{n}{100} = \frac{64}{144}$$ *Let n represent the percent.*

$$n \cdot 144 = 100 \cdot 64$$ *Find the cross products.*

$$144n = 6400$$ *Simplify.*

$$\frac{144n}{144} = \frac{6400}{144}$$ *Divide both sides by 144.*

$$n \approx 44.4$$ *Simplify.*

64 is approximately 44.4% of 144.

Method 2: Set up an equation.

$$\text{percent} \cdot \text{whole} = \text{part}$$ *Set up an equation.*

$$n \cdot 144 = 64$$ *Let n represent the percent.*

$$\frac{144n}{144} = \frac{64}{144}$$ *Divide both sides by 144.*

$$n = 0.\overline{4}, \text{ or approximately } 0.444.$$ *Simplify.*

64 is approximately 44.4% of 144. *0.44 is 44%*

Check

$$44.4\% \cdot 144 \overset{?}{=} 64$$ *Substitute 44.4% for n.*

$$0.444 \cdot 144 \overset{?}{=} 64$$ *Write a decimal and multiply.*

$$63.936 \approx 64 ✓$$ *44.4% of 144 is approximately 64.*

Power Presentations
with PowerPoint®

Warm Up
Rewrite each value as indicated.
1. $\frac{24}{50}$ as a percent 48%
2. 25% as a fraction $\frac{1}{4}$
3. $\frac{3}{8}$ as a decimal 0.375
4. 0.16 as a fraction $\frac{4}{25}$

Also available on transparency

Math Humor

Teacher: What is 5% of the power of a 20-watt lightbulb?
Student: A what?
Teacher: Wow, you got that one fast.

---

1 Introduce
Alternate Opener

Motivate
Ask students percent questions about themselves, such as: "What percent of the students in this class have brown hair?" or "What percent of the students are wearing blue jeans?" Tell students that before class is over, they will be able to answer questions like these.

Explorations and answers are provided in
Alternate Openers: Explorations Transparencies.

Example 1

What percent of 92 is 66? ≈72%

Example 2

A. Four friends volunteered to cut the grass around their neighbor's house. Jay cut 23% of the grass, Aimee cut $\frac{1}{5}$ of the grass, Ken cut 0.31 of the grass, and Bryn cut the rest. What percent of the grass did Bryn cut? 26%

B. Jeremy organizes his movie collection by genre. $\frac{2}{5}$ of his collection are dramas, 0.325 are action films, 3% are documentaries, 19.5% are comedies, and the rest of his movies are independent films. What percent of his movie collection are independent films? 5%

Example 3

A. The city of Dallas, Texas has a population of approximately 1,189,000 people. The population of the city of Austin, Texas is 55% of the population of Dallas. To the nearest thousand, what is the population of Austin? 654,000

B. After a drought, a reservoir had only $66\frac{2}{3}\%$ of the average amount of water. If the average amount of water is 57,000,000 gallons, how much water was in the reservoir after the drought? 38,000,000 gal

Also available on transparency

EXAMPLE 2 *Recreation Application*

A A brother and three sisters built a treehouse in their backyard. Mary did $\frac{1}{4}$ of the work, Joshua did 0.28 of the work, Caroline did 30% of the work, and Laura did the rest. What percent of the work on the treehouse did Laura do?

First, find what percent of the work Mary and Joshua did.

Mary: $\frac{1}{4} = 25\%$ Joshua: $0.28 = 28\%$

Next, subtract the percents you know from 100% to find the remaining percent.

$100\% - 25\% - 28\% - 30\% = 17\%$

Laura did 17% of the work.

B Emma is planning a vegetable garden for her backyard. What percent of the garden will have green beans?

First, find what percent of the garden will have broccoli and carrots.

Broccoli: $\frac{3}{8} = 37.5\%$

Carrots: $0.25 = 25\%$

Next, subtract the percents you know from 100% to find the remaining percent.

$100\% - 37.5\% - 25\% - 12.5\% - 15\% = 10\%$

10% of the garden will have green beans.

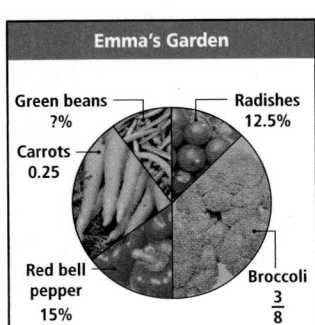

Emma's Garden

Green beans ?%
Radishes 12.5%
Carrots 0.25
Red bell pepper 15%
Broccoli $\frac{3}{8}$

EXAMPLE 3 *Finding the Percent of a Number*

A A domestic pig can run about $33\frac{1}{3}\%$ of the speed of a giraffe. A giraffe can run about 32 mi/h. To the nearest tenth, how fast can a domestic pig run?

Choose a method: Set up an equation.

Think: What speed is $33\frac{1}{3}\%$ of 32 mi/h?

$s = 33\frac{1}{3}\% \cdot 32$ *Set up an equation.*

$s = \frac{1}{3} \cdot 32$ *$33\frac{1}{3}\%$ is equivalent to $\frac{1}{3}$.*

$s = \frac{32}{3} = 10\frac{2}{3} = 10.\overline{6}$ *Simplify.*

$s \approx 10.7$ *Round to the nearest tenth.*

A domestic pig can run about 10.7 miles per hour.

---

2 Teach

Guided Instruction

In this lesson, students learn to find percents. Explain the relationship among a part, a whole, and a percent (percent × whole = part). Show students that percent problems can be solved by using a proportion (**Example 1A**) or by setting up and solving an equation (**Example 1B**). Encourage students to become familiar with both methods.

Universal Access
Through Curriculum Integration

Social Studies Give students the following election results or use election results from a news article.

In an election for mayor, the results were as follows: Garcia, 42%; Jackson, 36%; Shiu, 22%. If 14,000 votes were cast, how many votes did each candidate receive? Garcia: 5880; Jackson: 5040; Shiu: 3080 If a candidate must receive at least 50% of the votes to become mayor, how many votes are needed to become mayor? at least 7000 How many more votes would the leading candidate have needed to become mayor? 1120

Teaching Tip
Reading Math In the application problems, you may want to have students identify the part, whole, and percent before solving the problems. Point out that the word *of* can help students identify the whole.

ENGLISH LANGUAGE LEARNERS

Remind students that in problems like **Example 3** they should fully answer the question asked by adding the appropriate units to their answers.

B Mt. Churchill, in Alaska, is about 15,638 feet high. The height of Mt. McKinley is approximately 130% of the height of Mt. Churchill. To the nearest foot, find the height of Mt. McKinley.

Choose a method: Set up a proportion.

Think: 130 is to 100 as what height is to 15,638 ft?

$$\frac{130}{100} = \frac{h}{15,638}$$ *Set up a proportion.*

$130 \cdot 15,638 = 100 \cdot h$ *Find the cross products.*

$2,032,940 = 100h$ *Simplify.*

$\frac{2,032,940}{100} = \frac{100h}{100}$ *Divide both sides by 100.*

$20,329.4 = h$ *Simplify.*

$20,329 \approx h$ *Round to the nearest whole number.*

Mt. McKinley is about 20,329 feet high.

Think and Discuss

1. **Show** why 5% of a number is less than $\frac{1}{10}$ of the number.
2. **Demonstrate** two ways to find 70% of a number.
3. **Name** fractions in simplest form that are the same as 40% and as 250%.

Possible answers to Think and Discuss

1. 5% is less than $\frac{1}{10}$ because 5% = 0.05 and $\frac{1}{10}$ = 0.10.

2. $0.70 \cdot 50 = 35$; $\frac{70}{100} = \frac{n}{50}$; $n = 35$

3. $\frac{2}{5}, \frac{5}{2}$

6-3 Exercises

6-3 Exercises

California Standards Practice
NS1.3

go.hrw.com
Homework Help Online
KEYWORD: MT8CA 6-3
Parent Resources Online
KEYWORD: MT8CA Parent

GUIDED PRACTICE

See Example 1 1. What percent of 91 is 45? **49.5%**

2. What percent of 1270 is 375? **29.5%**

3. What percent of 240 is 180? **75%**

4. What percent of 186 is 75? **40.3%**

See Example 2 5. Four friends ordered a pizza. Christopher ate $\frac{1}{5}$, Emma ate 30%, Tanya ate 0.27, and Jamie ate the rest. What percent of the pizza did Jamie eat? **23%**

6. Three classmates read and took notes over a chapter in their history textbook. Carly read $\frac{1}{3}$ of the chapter, Jo read 0.25, and Sam read the rest. What percent of the chapter did Sam read? **$41\frac{2}{3}$%**

See Example 3 7. Elijah walks 2 miles to school. If Bailey's walk is 80% of the length of Elijah's walk, find the length of Bailey's walk. **1.6 mi**

8. Jay's term paper is 18 pages long. If Madison's paper is 175% of the length of Jay's paper, find the length of Madison's paper. **31.5 pages**

Assignment Guide

If you finished Example **1** assign:
Proficient 1–4, 9–12, 29, 32, 37–45
Advanced 9–12, 22–24, 29, 30, 32, 34, 37–45

If you finished Example **2** assign:
Proficient 1–6, 9–13, 29, 32, 35, 37–45
Advanced 9–13, 22–24, 29–32, 35, 37–45

If you finished Example **3** assign:
Proficient 1–21, 29, 31–32, 35–45
Advanced 9–15, 20–45

Homework Quick Check

Quickly check key concepts.
Exercises: 10, 13, 14, 20

---

3 Close

Summarize

Review the two types of problems in the lesson: Find what percent a number is of another number, and find a percent of a number. Remind students that there are two methods that can be used to solve each type of problem. Ask students for some real-world situations in which they might solve these types of problems.

Possible answers: finding sales tax or discounts, calculating nutritional information, calculating sports statistics

---

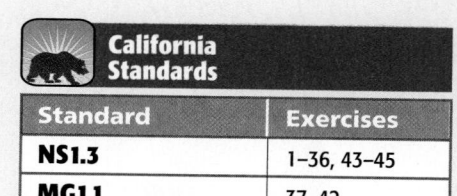

California Standards

Standard	Exercises
NS1.3	1–36, 43–45
MG1.1	37–42

Math Background

Percents are widely used in many disciplines. They are used extensively in business economics to describe many things, including taxes, economic growth, inflation, interest rates, and changes in the stock market. Percents are also useful in consumer economics, including the calculation of sales tax, discounts, withholding tax, and tips. Other applications include sports (e.g., winning percentage, field-goal percentage, and save percentage) and even grading (e.g., 90% or above is an A, etc.). Understanding percents will help students in many areas, including the study of probability (Chapter 11).

Answers

25. Possible answer: When the percent is doubled and the full amount is halved, the answer stays the same, 12.

26. Possible answer: When the percent is halved and the full amount is halved, the answer is reduced by $\frac{1}{4}$.

27. Possible answer: When the percent is halved and the full amount is tripled, the answer increases by a factor of $\frac{3}{2}$, or 1.5.

INDEPENDENT PRACTICE

See Example ①
9. What percent of 56 is 224? **400%**
10. What percent of 180 is 30? **16.7%**
11. 12.5 is what percent of 1250? **1%**
12. 115 is what percent of 40? **287.5%**

See Example ②
13. The Bishop family bought a case of water containing 24 bottles. During one week, Lydia drank $\frac{1}{8}$ of the bottles, Mitchell drank $33\frac{1}{3}$% of the bottles, Alexa drank 0.25 of the bottles, and Todd drank the rest. What percent of the case did Todd drink? $29\frac{1}{6}$%

See Example ③
14. The tallest building in the United States is the Sears Tower in Chicago. The height of the Sears Tower is 1450 feet, which is 240% of the height of the Seattle Space Needle in Washington. Find the height of the Seattle Space Needle to the nearest foot. **604 ft**

15. In Arkansas, the highest elevation is Mount Magazine, and the lowest is the Ouachita River. Mount Magazine is 2753 ft above sea level, which is about 5098% of the elevation of the lowest portion of the state. Find the elevation of the Ouachita River area. **≈ 54 ft above sea level**

PRACTICE AND PROBLEM SOLVING

Extra Practice
See page EP12.

Find each number to the nearest tenth.

16. What number is $33\frac{1}{3}$% of 30? **10**
17. What number is $11\frac{1}{3}$% of 215? **24.4**
18. What number is 77% of 9? **6.9**
19. What number is $3\frac{1}{2}$% of 11,400? **399**
20. What number is 166% of 300? **498**
21. What number is $66\frac{2}{3}$% of 750? **500**

Complete each statement.

22. Since 8 is 16% of 50,
 a. 16 is ▦% of 50. **32**
 b. 24 is ▦% of 50. **48**
 c. 80 is ▦% of 50. **160**

23. Since 8 is 5% of 160,
 a. 8 is ▦% of 80. **10**
 b. 8 is ▦% of 40. **20**
 c. 8 is ▦% of 20. **40**

24. Since 15 is 300% of 5,
 a. 15 is ▦% of 10. **150**
 b. 15 is ▦% of 20. **75**
 c. 15 is ▦% of 40. **37.5**

Patterns Describe a possible pattern for the information shown below.

25. 1% of 1200 = 12
 2% of 600 = 12
 4% of 300 = 12
 8% of 150 = 12
 16% of 75 = 12

26. 400% of 320 = 1280
 200% of 160 = 320
 100% of 80 = 80
 50% of 40 = 20
 25% of 20 = 5

27. 400% of 5 = 20
 200% of 15 = 30
 100% of 45 = 45
 50% of 135 = 67.5
 25% of 405 = 101.25

28. Social Studies In 2003, 14% of the 50 largest U.S. cities were located in Texas. How many of the 50 largest U.S. cities were located in Texas in 2003? **7 cities**

29. Geography About 600 mi² of the 700 mi² of the Okefenokee Swamp is located in Georgia. If Georgia is 57,906 mi², find the percent of that area that is part of the Okefenokee Swamp. **1.0%**

REVIEW FOR MASTERY 6-3

LESSON 6-3 Review for Mastery
Finding Percents

Since a percent is a ratio, problems involving percent can be solved by using a proportion.

$$\frac{\text{symbol number}}{100} = \frac{\text{is number}}{\text{of number}}$$

There are different possibilities for an unknown quantity in this proportion.

Possibility 1: Find the *symbol number.*

What percent of 80 is 16?
$$\frac{\text{symbol number}}{100} = \frac{\text{is number}}{\text{of number}}$$
$$\frac{x}{100} = \frac{16}{80}$$
$$80 \cdot x = 16 \cdot 100$$
$$\frac{80x}{80} = \frac{1600}{80}$$
$$x = 20$$
So, 16 is 20% of 80.

Possibility 2: Find the *is number.*

What is 20% of 80?
$$\frac{\text{symbol number}}{100} = \frac{\text{is number}}{\text{of number}}$$
$$\frac{20}{100} = \frac{x}{80}$$
$$100 \cdot x = 20 \cdot 80$$
$$\frac{100x}{100} = \frac{1600}{100}$$
$$x = 16$$
So, 20% of 80 is 16.

1. What percent of 64 is 16?
$$\frac{x}{100} = \frac{16}{64}$$
$$64 \cdot x = 16 \cdot 100$$
$$\frac{64x}{64} = \frac{1600}{64}$$
$$x = \underline{25}$$
So, 16 is **25%** of 64.

2. What percent of 200 is 150?
$$\frac{x}{100} = \frac{150}{200}$$
$$200 \cdot x = 150 \cdot 100$$
$$\frac{200x}{200} = \frac{15,000}{200}$$
$$x = \underline{75}$$
So, 150 is **75%** of 200.

3. What is 30% of 150?
$$\frac{30}{100} = \frac{x}{150}$$
$$100 \cdot x = 30 \cdot 150$$
$$\frac{100x}{100} = \frac{4500}{100}$$
$$x = \underline{45}$$
So, 30% of 150 is **45**.

4. What is 75% of 205?
$$\frac{75}{100} = \frac{x}{205}$$
$$100 \cdot x = 75 \cdot 205$$
$$\frac{100x}{100} = \frac{15,375}{100}$$
$$x = \underline{153.75}$$
So, 75% of 205 is **153.75**.

PRACTICE 6-3

LESSON 6-3 Practice B
Finding Percents

Find each percent.

1. What percent of 84 is 21? **25%**
2. 24 is what percent of 60? **40%**
3. What percent of 150 is 75? **50%**
4. What percent of 80 is 68? **85%**
5. 36 is what percent of 80? **45%**
6. What percent of 88 is 33? **37.5%**
7. 19 is what percent of 95? **20%**
8. 28.8 is what percent of 120? **24%**
9. What percent of 56 is 49? **87.5%**
10. What percent of 102 is 17? **$16\frac{2}{3}$**
11. What percent of 94 is 42.3? **45%**
12. 90 is what percent of 75? **120%**

13. Daphne bought a used car for $9200. She made a down payment of $1840. Find the percent of the purchase price that is the down payment. **20%**

14. Tricia read $\frac{1}{4}$ of her book on Monday. On Tuesday, she read 36% of the book. On Wednesday, she read 0.27 of the book. She finished the book on Thursday. What percent of the book did she read on Thursday? **12%**

15. An airplane traveled from Boston to Las Vegas making a stop in St. Louis. The plane traveled 2410 miles altogether, which is 230% of the distance from Boston to St. Louis. Find the distance from Boston to St. Louis to the nearest mile. **1048 mi**

16. The first social studies test had 16 questions. The second test had 220% as many questions as the first test. Find the number of questions on the second test. **36 questions**

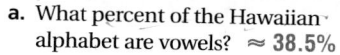

30. **Language Arts** The Hawaiian words shown contain all of the letters of the Hawaiian alphabet. The ` is actually a consonant!

a. What percent of the Hawaiian alphabet are vowels? ≈ 38.5%

b. To the nearest tenth, what percent of the letters in the English alphabet are also in the Hawaiian alphabet? 46.2%

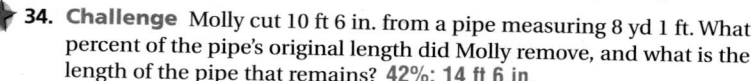

Halakahiki: pineapple

Wai: water

'ekahi: one

Pohaku: rock, stone

Mauna: mountain

33. Possible answer: This answer is not reasonable because 175% of 72 must be greater than 72. The correct answer is 126.

31. **Multi-Step** Joseph, Ana, Lena, and George chipped in money for a friend's gift. The gift cost $45.99 plus $3.45 sales tax. Joseph paid $12.50, Ana paid $\frac{1}{4}$ of the total cost, Lena paid 24% of the total cost, and George paid the rest. Order the people from least amount paid to greatest amount paid. Lena: $11.87, Ana: $12.36, Joseph: $12.50, George: $12.71

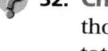 32. **Choose a Strategy** Masco Industries has 285,000 total employees. Of those employees, 85,500 telecommute. What percent of the company's total employees telecommute?

Ⓐ 3%　　　Ⓑ 15%　　　Ⓒ 30%　　　Ⓓ 150%

33. **Reasoning** A question on a math quiz asks, "What is 175% of 72?" Petra calculates 12.6 as the answer. Is this a reasonable answer? Explain.

34. **Challenge** Molly cut 10 ft 6 in. from a pipe measuring 8 yd 1 ft. What percent of the pipe's original length did Molly remove, and what is the length of the pipe that remains? 42%; 14 ft 6 in.

SPIRAL STANDARDS REVIEW

NS1.3, MG1.1

35. **Multiple Choice** Currently, 96 students are enrolled in the Grove City Dance Center. Of those students, 54 study tap dance. The remaining students study ballet. What percentage of the students study ballet?

Ⓐ 42%　　　Ⓑ 43.75%　　　Ⓒ 54%　　　Ⓓ 56.25%

36. **Gridded Response** According to the 2003 U.S. Census, approximately 129 million Americans spend 3.4% of a 24-hour day commuting. How many minutes a day does a person in this group spend commuting? ≈ 49 min

Find the appropriate factor for each conversion. (Lesson 5-3)

37. kilograms to grams 1000 g/1 kg
38. seconds to minutes 1 min/60 s
39. feet to miles 1 mi/5280 ft
40. gallons to quarts 4 qt/1 gal
41. pounds to ounces 16 oz/1 lb
42. centimeters to meters 1 m/100 cm

Estimate. (Lesson 6-2)

43. 26% of 398 100
44. 48% of 746 375
45. 39% of 99 40

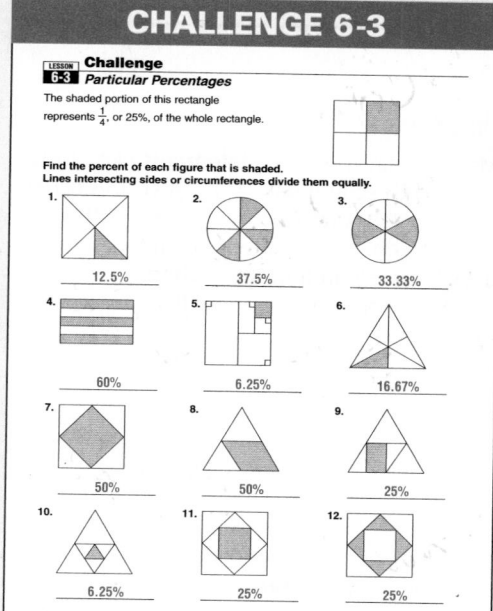

CHALLENGE 6-3

LESSON 6-3 Challenge
Particular Percentages

The shaded portion of this rectangle represents $\frac{1}{4}$, or 25%, of the whole rectangle.

Find the percent of each figure that is shaded.
Lines intersecting sides or circumferences divide them equally.

1. 12.5%　2. 37.5%　3. 33.33%
4. 60%　5. 6.25%　6. 16.67%
7. 50%　8. 50%　9. 25%
10. 6.25%　11. 25%　12. 25%

PROBLEM SOLVING 6-3

LESSON 6-3 Problem Solving
Finding Percents

Write the correct answer.

1. Florida State University in Tallahassee, Florida has 29,820 students. Approximately 60% of the students are women. How many of the students are women?

17,892 students

2. The yearly cost of tuition, room and board at Florida State University for a Florida resident is $10,064. If tuition is $3,208 a year, what percent of the yearly cost is tuition? Round to the nearest tenth of a percent.

31.9%

3. The yearly cost of tuition, room and board at Florida State University for a non-Florida resident is $23,196. If tuition is $16,340 a year, what percent of the yearly cost is tuition for a non-resident? Round to the nearest tenth of a percent.

70.4%

4. Approximately 65% of the students who apply to Florida State University are accepted. If 15,000 students apply to Florida State University, how many would you expect to be accepted?

9750 students

The top four NBA field goal shooters for the 2003–2004 regular season are given in the table below. Choose the letter for the best answer.

5. What percent of field goals did Shaquille O'Neal make? Round to the nearest tenth of a percent.
A 0.6%　Ⓒ 58.4%
B 1.71%　D 59.2%

NBA Field Goal Leaders 2003–2004 Season			
Player	Attempts	Made	Percent
Shaquille O'Neal	948	554	
Donyell Marshall	604		56.6
Elton Brand	950	348	
Dale Davis	913		53.5

6. How many field goals did Donyell Marshall make in the 2003–2004 regular season?
F 38　H 295
G 114　Ⓙ 342

7. What percent of field goals did Elton Brand make? Round to the nearest tenth of a percent.
A 1.87%　C 51.9%
B 50%　Ⓓ 36.6%

8. How many field goals did Dale Davis make in the 2003–2004 regular season?
F 274　H 457
G 378　Ⓙ 488

FORMATIVE ASSESSMENT and INTERVENTION ←→

Diagnose Before the Lesson
6-3 Warm Up, TE p. 283

Monitor During the Lesson
6-3 Know-It Notebook
6-3 Questioning Strategies

Assess After the Lesson
6-3 Lesson Quiz, TE p. 287

Teaching Tip **Multiple Choice** For **Exercise 35,** remind students that they are asked to find the percentage of students studying ballet. Students who chose answer **D** found the percentage studying tap.

Journal

Ask students to compare the two methods for solving percent problems presented in the lesson—writing and solving equations and setting up proportions.

Power Presentations with PowerPoint®

6-3 Lesson Quiz

Find each percent.

1. What percent of 33 is 22? $66\frac{2}{3}$%

2. Of Earth's 197 million mi^2 of surface area, about 139 million mi^2 is water. Find the percent of Earth's surface that is covered by water. 70.6%

3. The Ramirez family bought a large bag of oranges during their trip to Florida. Jorge ate $\frac{2}{5}$ of the oranges, Ana ate 0.18 of the oranges, Mrs. Ramirez ate 22% of the oranges, and Mr. Ramirez ate the rest. What percent of the oranges did Mr. Ramirez eat? 20%

4. Rada is 170% as tall as her brother Raj. Raj is 0.82 m tall. To the nearest tenth of a meter, how tall is Rada? 1.4 m

5. The volume of Lake Superior is 2900 mi^3 and the volume of Lake Erie is 116 mi^3. What percent of the volume of Lake Superior is the volume of Lake Erie? 4%

Also available on transparency

6-4 Organizer

Objective: Students find a number when the percent is known.

Online Edition
Tutorial Videos

Countdown to Mastery Week 12

Power Presentations
with PowerPoint®

Warm Up

1. What percent of 20 is 18? **90%**
2. What percent of 400 is 50? **12.5%**
3. 9 is what percent of 27? **$33\frac{1}{3}$%**
4. 25 is what percent of 4? **625%**

Also available on transparency

Math Humor

The store owner offered to order the new football uniforms if the team would pay $33\frac{1}{3}$% of the cost in advance. The players did not accept the offer. They always passed on a third down.

6-4 Finding a Number When the Percent Is Known

California Standards

NS1.3 Convert fractions to decimals and percents and **use these representations in** estimations, computations, and applications.

Why learn this? You can use known percents to find the maximum size of sharks' teeth. (See Example 3.)

When one number is known, and its relationship to another number is given by a percent, the other number can be found.

Carcharocles megalodon, an extinct giant shark, had a jaw that may have been 6 feet wide.

EXAMPLE 1 Finding a Number When the Percent Is Known

42 is 5% of what number?

Choose a method: Set up an equation.

part = percent · whole	*Set up an equation.*
$42 = 5\% \cdot n$	*Let n represent the whole.*
$42 = 0.05n$	*5% = 0.05*
$\dfrac{42}{0.05} = \dfrac{0.05n}{0.05}$	*Divide both sides by 0.05.*
$840 = n$	*Simplify*

42 is 5% of 840.

EXAMPLE 2 Science Application

In a science lab, a sample of a compound contains 14.5 grams of magnesium. If 72.5% of the sample is magnesium, find the number of grams the entire sample weighs.

Choose a method: Set up a proportion.

$\dfrac{percent}{100} = \dfrac{part}{whole}$	*Set up a proportion.*
$\dfrac{72.5}{100} = \dfrac{14.5}{m}$	*Let m represent the whole.*
$72.5 \cdot m = 100 \cdot 14.5$	*Find the cross products.*
$72.5m = 1450$	*Simplify.*
$\dfrac{72.5m}{72.5} = \dfrac{1450}{72.5}$	*Divide both sides by 72.5.*
$m = 20$	*Simplify.*

The entire sample weighs 20 grams.

---

1 Introduce

Alternate Opener

EXPLORATION

6-4 Finding a Number When the Percent is Known

A CD player is on sale for $15 off the original price. According to the advertisement, this is a 25% discount. You can use what you know about percents to figure out the original price of the CD player.

Think: 25% is $\frac{1}{4}$, so $15 must be $\frac{1}{4}$ of the original price.

You can model the situation as shown.

	25%	50%	75%	100%
$15				
	15	30	45	60

The original price is $60.

Draw a model to find the original price for each of the following.

1. Amount of discount: $8; percent of discount: 20%
2. Amount of discount: $12; percent of discount: $33\frac{1}{3}$%
3. Amount of discount: $17; percent of discount: 50%

Think and Discuss

4. **Explain** how you could find the value of a number given that 7 is 10% of the number.
5. **Describe** what must be true about a number if you know that 45 is 100% of the number.

Motivate

Make a pair of related statements like "Today is the 90th school day of the year. This school year is 50% over." Ask the students if they can tell from those statements how many days there are in a normal school year. about 180 Have them explain how they arrived at their answers.

Explorations and answers are provided in *Alternate Openers: Explorations Transparencies.*

California Standards

Number Sense 1.3

EXAMPLE 3 *Life Science Application*

Life Science LINK

Reticulated means "net-like" or "forming a network." The reticulated python is named for the net-like pattern on its skin.

A The king cobra can reach a length of 18 feet. This is only about 60% of the length of the largest reticulated python. Find the length of the largest reticulated python.

Choose a method: Set up a proportion.

Think: 60 is to 100 as 18 ft is to what length?

$$\frac{60}{100} = \frac{18}{\ell}$$ *Set up a proportion.*

$60 \cdot \ell = 100 \cdot 18$ *Find the cross products.*

$$\frac{60\ell}{60} = \frac{1800}{60}$$ *Divide both sides by 60.*

$\ell = 30$ *Simplify.*

The largest reticulated python is 30 feet long.

B *Carcharocles megalodon* had teeth as large as 7.25 inches along an edge. This is 240% of the maximum size of the teeth of a modern great white shark. To the nearest inch, find the maximum size of the teeth of a great white shark.

Choose a method: Set up an equation.

Think: 7.25 in. is 240% of what length?

$7.25 = 240\% \cdot \ell$ *Set up an equation.*

$7.25 = 2.40 \cdot \ell$ *240% = 2.40*

$$\frac{7.25}{2.40} = \frac{2.40 \cdot \ell}{2.40}$$ *Divide both sides by 2.40.*

$3 \approx \ell$ *Simplify.*

The maximum size is about 3 inches along an edge.

You have now seen all three types of percent problems.

Percent Problem	Equation	Proportion
Finding the percent of a number	15% of 120 = n	$\frac{15}{100} = \frac{n}{120}$
Finding the percent one number is of another	p% of 120 = 18	$\frac{p}{100} = \frac{18}{120}$
Finding a number when the percent is known	15% of n = 18	$\frac{15}{100} = \frac{18}{n}$

Possible answers to *Think and Discuss*

1. In the first case, divide the known number by the decimal equivalent of the percent. In the second case, divide the first number by the second and write the answer as a percent.

2. The number is greater than 36 because 36 is a small part (22%) of a larger whole (the number).

Think and Discuss

1. Compare finding a number when a percent is known to finding the percent one number is of another number.

2. Explain whether a number is greater than or less than 36 if 22% of the number is 36.

Power Presentations with PowerPoint®

Additional Examples

Example 1

60 is 12% of what number? **500**

Example 2

Anna earned 85% on a test by answering 17 questions correctly. If each question was worth the same amount, how many questions were on the test? **20**

Example 3

A. When a giraffe is born, it is approximately 55% as tall as it will be as an adult. If a baby giraffe is 5.2 feet tall when it is born, how tall will it be when it is full grown, to the nearest tenth of a foot? **9.5 ft**

B. A fisherman caught a lobster that weighed 11.5 lb. This was 70% of the weight of the largest lobster that fisherman had ever caught. What was the weight, to the nearest tenth of a pound, of the largest lobster the fisherman had ever caught? **16.4 lb**

Also available on transparency

---

2 Teach

Guided Instruction

In this lesson, students learn to find a number when the percent is known. Explain that in the last lesson, students found the percent and the part (of the whole amount) that the percent represents. In this lesson, they will find the whole amount. Explain that they will use equations and proportions similar to those from the last lesson. For each example, you may want to have students identify the part, the percent, and the whole.

Teaching Tip

Multiple Representations You may want to solve each example using both methods so that students can see that they give the same result.

Universal Access

For Advanced Learners/GATE

Give each student the following set of related percent problems:

1. What percent of 30 is 18? **60%**

2. 18 is 60% of what number? **30**

3. A jacket is on sale for 60% of its original price. The original price was $30. What is the sale price? **$18**

Have students solve the first problem mathematically and then solve the related problems by inspection.

---

3 Close

Summarize

Review the chart at the end of the lesson. Review both methods for solving percent problems—using equations and proportions. Ask students how they can identify the part, the whole, and the percent in a word problem.

Possible answers: The percent is always labeled with the word "percent" or the % symbol. The whole often follows the phrase "percent of" or "% of" and is the total amount. The part is the portion of the total represented by the percent; it is often less than the whole but can be greater.

6-4 Exercises

California Standards Practice
NS1.3

go.hrw.com
Homework Help Online
KEYWORD: MT8CA 6-4
Parent Resources Online
KEYWORD: MT8CA Parent

Assignment Guide

If you finished Example **1** assign:
Proficient 1–4, 7–10, 24–44
Advanced 7–10, 13–15, 24–44

If you finished Example **2** assign:
Proficient 1–5, 7–11, 17–21, 23–44
Advanced 7–11, 13–44

If you finished Example **3** assign:
Proficient 1–12, 17–21, 23–44
Advanced 7–44

Homework Quick Check

Quickly check key concepts.
Exercises: 8, 10, 11, 12

Math Background

As indicated at the end of the lesson, there are three basic types of percent problems. Equations for all three types can be written using a direct translation approach. If a question is stated using the word "what," then an equation can be written with "what" replaced by a variable, "of" by a multiplication symbol, and "is" by an equal sign. Some examples are shown below:

36 is 4% of what number?
$\rightarrow 36 = 0.04 \cdot x$

What is 82.5% of 250?
$\rightarrow x = 0.825 \cdot 250$

What percent of 162 is 90?
$\rightarrow x \cdot 162 = 90$

California Standards

Standard	Exercises
NS1.3	1–24, 35–44
NS2.4	25–34

GUIDED PRACTICE

See Example **1** **Find each number to the nearest tenth.**

1. 6.9 is $11\frac{1}{2}\%$ of what number? **60**   2. 92 is $66\frac{2}{3}\%$ of what number? **138**

3. 12% of what number is 20? **166.7**   4. 30% of what number is 96? **320**

See Example **2**   5. How much water can a 7.4 oz piece of chalk absorb if it can absorb 32% of its weight? **≈ 2.4 oz**

See Example **3**   6. At 2 P.M., a flag pole casts a shadow that is 155% of its actual height. If the shadow is 23.25 ft, what is the actual height of the pole? **15 ft**

INDEPENDENT PRACTICE

See Example **1** **Find each number to the nearest tenth.**

7. 90 is $66\frac{2}{3}\%$ of what number? **135**   8. 63 is 15% of what number? **420**

9. 0.75% of what number is 10? **1333.3**   10. 44% of what number is 37.4? **85**

See Example **2**   11. Isaac sold 58 of his baseball cards at a collectors' show. If this represented $14\frac{1}{2}\%$ of his total collection, how many baseball cards did Isaac have before he sold his cards? **400 cards**

See Example **3**   12. When a tire is labeled "185/70/14," that means it is 185 mm wide, the sidewall height (from the rim to the road) is 70% of its width, and the wheel has a diameter of 14 in. What is the tire's sidewall height? **129.5 mm**

PRACTICE AND PROBLEM SOLVING

Extra Practice
See page EP12.

Complete each statement.

13. Since 2% of 500 is 10,   14. Since 100% of 8 is 8,   15. Since 15% of 60 is 9,

a. 4% of ▮ is 10. **250**   a. 50% of ▮ is 8. **16**   a. 30% of ▮ is 9. **30**

b. 8% of ▮ is 10. **125**   b. 25% of ▮ is 8. **32**   b. 45% of ▮ is 9. **20**

c. 16% of ▮ is 10. **62.5**   c. 10% of ▮ is 8. **80**   c. 60% of ▮ is 9. **15**

16. In a survey of 175 students, 42 said that their favorite cookout food was hamburgers, and 61 said that their favorite was hot dogs. Give these numbers as percents. **24% hamburgers; ≈ 34.9% hot dogs**

17. **Life Science** The Congress Avenue bridge in Austin, Texas, is home to the largest urban bat colony in the world. Nearly 1.5 million Mexican free-tailed bats live under the bridge. This bat population is approximately 228.3% the population of Austin. What is the population of Austin to the nearest thousand people? **657,000**

REVIEW FOR MASTERY 6-4

LESSON 6-4 Review for Mastery
Finding a Number When the Percent Is Known

Since a percent is a ratio, problems involving percent can be solved by using a proportion.

$$\frac{symbol\ number}{100} = \frac{is\ number}{of\ number}$$

To find a number when the percent is known, the variable appears in the *of* position in the proportion

16 is 20% of what number?
$\frac{20}{100} = \frac{16}{x}$
$20 \cdot x = 16 \cdot 100$
$\frac{20x}{20} = \frac{1600}{20}$
$x = 80$
So, 16 is 20% of 80.

Find each number whose percentage is given.

1. 18 is 75% of what number?
$\frac{75}{100} = \frac{18}{x}$
$75 \cdot x = 18 \cdot 100$
$\frac{75x}{75} = \frac{1800}{75}$
$x = \underline{24}$
So, 18 is 75% of __24__.

2. 96 is 40% of what number?
$\frac{40}{100} = \frac{96}{x}$
$40 \cdot x = 96 \cdot 100$
$\frac{40x}{40} = \frac{9600}{40}$
$x = \underline{240}$
So, 96 is 40% of __240__.

3. 7 is 125% of what number
$\frac{125}{100} = \frac{7}{x}$
$125 \cdot x = 7 \cdot 100$
$\frac{125x}{125} = \frac{700}{125}$
$x = \underline{5.6}$
So, 7 is 125% of __5.6__.

4. 40 is about 30% of what number?
$\frac{30}{100} = \frac{40}{x}$
$30 \cdot x = 40 \cdot 100$
$\frac{30x}{30} = \frac{4000}{30}$
$x = \underline{133.3}$
So, 40 is about 30% of __133.3__.

PRACTICE 6-4

LESSON 6-4 Practice B
Finding a Number When the Percent Is Known

Find each number to the nearest tenth.

1. 40% of what number is 18? __45__

2. 28 is 35% of what number? __80__

3. 21 is 60% of what number? __35__

4. 25% of what number is 19? __76__

5. 40% of what number is 22? __55__

6. 41 is 50% of what number? __82__

7. 50 is 15% of what number? __333.3__

8. 0.3% of what number is 24? __8,000__

9. 36 is 30% of what number? __120__

10. 26 is 75% of what number? __34.7__

11. 12.5% of what number is 14? __112__

12. 25% of what number is 28.25? __113__

13. 27 is $33\frac{1}{3}\%$ of what number? __81__

14. 54 is 150% of what number? __36__

15. There were 546 students at a school assembly. This was 65% of all students who attend Content Middle School. How many students attend Content Middle School?
__840 students__

16. On his last test Greg answered 64 questions correctly. This was 80% of the questions. How many questions were on the test?
__80 questions__

17. The price of a jacket at store A is $48. If the price at store B is 5.5% higher, what is the price difference? What is the cost of the jacket at store B?
__price difference is $2.64; cost at store B is $50.64__

18. Carla has finished swimming 14 laps in swim practice. This is 70% of the total number of laps she must swim. How many more laps must Carla swim to complete her practice?
__6 laps__

 ## Social Studies LINK

The U.S. census collects information about state populations, economics, income and poverty levels, births and deaths, and so on. This information can be used to study trends and patterns. For Exercises 18–20, round answers to the nearest tenth.

2000 U.S. Census Data			
	Population	Male	Female
Alaska	626,932	324,112	302,820
New York	18,976,457	9,146,748	9,829,709
Age 34 and Under	139,328,990	71,053,554	68,275,436
Age 35 and Over	142,092,916	67,000,009	75,092,907
Total U.S.	281,421,906	138,053,563	143,368,343

18. What percent of New York's population is male? **48.2%**

19. What percent of the entire country's population is made up of people in New York? **6.7%**

20. Tell what percent of the total U.S. population each represents.
   a. people 34 and under **49.5%** **b.** people 35 and over **50.5%** **c.** male **49.1%** **d.** female **50.9%**

21. American Indians and Native Alaskans make up about 15.6% of Alaska's population. What is their population, to the nearest thousand? **98,000**

22. ⭐ **Challenge** What percent of the total U.S. population lives in either Alaska or New York? Round your answer to the nearest tenth. **7.0%**

go.hrw.com
Web Extra!
KEYWORD: MT8CA Census

SPIRAL STANDARDS REVIEW

NS1.3, NS2.4

23. **Multiple Choice** There are 72 boys in the eighth-grade class at Lincoln Middle School. The other 55% of the class are girls. How many girls are there?

Ⓐ 55   Ⓑ 72   Ⓒ 88   Ⓓ 127

24. **Gridded Response** 25% of what number is 9.6? **38.4**

Each square root is between two integers. Name the integers. (Lesson 4-6)

25. $\sqrt{35}$ **5 and 6** 26. $\sqrt{45}$ **6 and 7** 27. $\sqrt{55}$ **7 and 8** 28. $\sqrt{65}$ **8 and 9** 29. $\sqrt{140}$ **11 and 12**

30. $\sqrt{27}$ **5 and 6** 31. $\sqrt{101}$ **10 and 11** 32. $\sqrt{42}$ **6 and 7** 33. $\sqrt{222}$ **14 and 15** 34. $\sqrt{1011}$ **31 and 32**

Find the decimal equivalent of each. (Lesson 6-1)

35. $\frac{5}{8}$ **0.625** 36. 212% **2.12** 37. 71% **0.71** 38. $4\frac{1}{12}$ **4.08$\overline{3}$** 39. $-\frac{3}{4}$ **−0.75**

40. $\frac{4}{5}$ **0.8** 41. 123% **1.23** 42. 26% **0.26** 43. $3\frac{1}{2}$ **3.5** 44. $27\frac{1}{5}$ **27.2**

CHALLENGE 6-4

LESSON **Challenge**
6-4 *In the Chemistry Laboratory*

When a chemist dilutes pure acid with another substance, the resulting mixture is no longer pure acid.

Consistent with the words, *pure acid* is 100% acid. So, there are 20 grams of pure acid in 20 grams of a pure-acid solution.

Laura, a chemist, has 20 grams of a solution that is only 40% acid.

1. How many grams of pure acid are there in Laura's acid solution?

   40% of 20 grams = 8 grams

Suppose, now, Laura wants to increase the acid content of the 40% acid solution to make it a 50%-acid solution.

2. What do you think Laura has to do to increase the acid content of the solution? Possible answer:

   Add some pure acid; also possible to evaporate.

Laura decides to add *n* ounces of pure acid to increase the acid content of the original 20 grams of 40%-acid solution to make it a 50%-acid solution.

3. Represent in terms of *n* the total number of grams in the new solution. **20 + n**

4. Represent in terms of *n* the number of grams of pure acid in the new solution. **0.50 (20 + n)**

Then, the amount of pure acid in the original solution plus the amount of pure acid added equals the amount of pure acid in the new solution.

5. Use the results of Exercises 1 and 4 to write an equation that will find the number *n* of grams of pure acid that will be added to the original solution to increase its acid content from 40% to 50%. Solve the equation.

   $8 + n = 0.50(20 + n)$
   $8 + n = 10 + 0.50n$
   $n - 0.50n = 10 - 8$
   $0.50n = 2$
   $n = 4$

6. Explain how to check your result. Possible answer:

   There are 24 g in all in the new solution; 50%, or 12 g, are pure acid. This is consistent with adding 4 g of pure acid to the original solution that had 8 g of pure acid.

PROBLEM SOLVING 6-4

LESSON **Problem Solving**
6-4 *Finding a Number When the Percent Is Known*

Write the correct answer.

1. The two longest running Broadway shows are *Cats* and *A Chorus Line*. *A Chorus Line* had 6137, or about 82% of the number of performances that *Cats* had. How many performances of *Cats* were there?

   7484

2. *Titanic* and *Star Wars* have made the most money at the box office. *Star Wars* made about 76.7% of the money that *Titanic* made at the box office. If *Star Wars* made about $461 million, how much did *Titanic* make? Round to the nearest million dollars.

   $601 million

Use the table below. Round to the nearest tenth of a percent.

3. What percent of students are in Pre-K through 8th grade?

   71.2%

4. What percent of students are in grades 9–12?

   28.8%

Public Elementary and Secondary School Enrollment, 2001	
Grades	Population (in thousands)
Pre-K through grade 8	33,952
Grades 9–12	13,736
Total	47,688

Choose the letter for the best answer.

5. In 2000, women earned about 72.2% of what men did. If the average woman's weekly earnings was $491 in 2000, what was the average man's weekly earnings? Round to the nearest dollar.
   A $355   Ⓒ $680
   B $542   D $725

6. The highest elevation in North America is Mt. McKinley at 20,320 ft. The highest elevation in Australia is Mt. Kosciusko, which is about 36% of the height of Mt. McKinley. What is the highest elevation in Australia? Round to the nearest foot.
   F 5480 ft   H 12,825 ft
   Ⓖ 7315 ft   J 56,444 ft

7. The Gulf of Mexico has an average depth of 4,874 ft. This is about 36.2% of the average depth of the Pacific Ocean. What is the average depth of the Pacific Ocean? Round to the nearest foot.
   A 1764 ft   C 10,280 ft
   B 5843 ft   Ⓓ 13,464 ft

8. Karl Malone is the NBA lifetime leader in free throws. He attempted 11,703 and made 8,636. What percent did he make? Round to the nearest tenth of a percent.
   F 1.4%   Ⓗ 73.8%
   G 58.6%   J 135.6%

FORMATIVE ASSESSMENT
and INTERVENTION ⬅➡

Diagnose Before the Lesson
6-4 Warm Up, TE p. 288

Monitor During the Lesson
6-4 Know-It Notebook
6-4 Questioning Strategies

Assess After the Lesson
6-4 Lesson Quiz, TE p. 291

Interdisciplinary LINK

Social Studies

Exercises 18–22 involve using U.S. Census data in percent problems. Students study census data from countries around the world in middle school social studies programs.

Teaching Tip **Multiple Choice** Point out to students that **Exercise 23** is a two-step problem. They must first find the total number of students in the class before calculating the number of girls in the class.

✎ Journal

Ask students to describe the process they would use to solve each of the three types of percent problems.

Power Presentations
with PowerPoint®

✓ 6-4
Lesson Quiz
1. 10 is $12\frac{1}{2}$% of what number? **80**
2. 326 is 25% of what number? **1304**
3. 44% of what number is 11? **25**
4. 290% of what number is 145? **50**
5. Larry has 9 novels about the American Revolutionary War. This represents 15% of his total book collection. How many books does Larry have in all? **60**

Also available on transparency

SECTION
6A

READY TO
GO ON?

Organizer

Objective: Assess students' mastery of concepts and skills in Lessons 6-1 through 6-4.

Resources

 Assessment Resources
Section 6A Quiz

 Test & Practice Generator
One-Stop Planner®

INTERVENTION ◄══►

Resources

 Ready to Go On? Intervention and Enrichment Worksheets

💿 **Ready to Go On? CD-ROM**

🪐 **Ready to Go On? Online**

my.hrw.com

CHAPTER
6

SECTION 6A

READY TO GO ON?

Quiz for Lessons 6-1 Through 6-4

☑ **6-1** **Relating Fractions, Decimals, and Percents**

Compare. Write <, >, or =.

1. $\frac{5}{6}$ ■ 83%   **>**   2. $\frac{4}{9}$ ■ 45%   **<**   3. 0.03 ■ 3%   **=**   4. 6.5 ■ 65%   **>**

Order the numbers from least to greatest.

5. $\frac{1}{4}$, 0.1, 3%, 28%
   3%, 0.1, $\frac{1}{4}$, 28%

6. 130%, $\frac{3}{2}$, 1.25, 10%
   10%, 1.25, 130%, $\frac{3}{2}$

7. $\frac{2}{3}$, 72%, 0.6, $\frac{3}{4}$
   0.6, $\frac{2}{3}$, 72%, $\frac{3}{4}$

8. A molecule of ferric oxide is made up of 2 atoms of iron and 3 atoms of oxygen. What percent of the atoms of a ferric oxide molecule is oxygen?   **60%**

☑ **6-2** **Estimating with Percents**

Estimate.

9. 48% of 52   **25**   10. 33% of 613   **200**   11. $12\frac{1}{2}$% of 57   **7**   12. 60% of 26   **15**

Estimate the tip for each bill.

13. tip: 10% bill: $28.20   **$3**   14. tip: 15% bill: $41.80   **$6**

15. Approximately 9.6% of all daily shipments are returned. Ms. Kui said that in a daily shipment of 12,034 packages, approximately 120 would be returned. Estimate to determine if Ms. Kui's number is reasonable. Explain. **No; Possible answer: 10% of 12,000 is about 1200, which is much greater than 120.**

☑ **6-3** **Finding Percents**

16. What percent of 8 is 2.56?   **32%**   17. What percent of 75 is 63?   **84%**

18. What number is 45% of 94?   **42.3**   19. What number is 8% of 130?   **10.4**

20. Of Canada's total area of 9,976,140 km², 755,170 km² is water. To the nearest tenth of a percent, what part of Canada is water?   **≈ 7.6%**

☑ **6-4** **Finding a Number When the Percent Is Known**

21. 27 is 7.5% of what number?   **360**   22. 30% of what number is 42?   **140**

23. 336 is 375% of what number?   **89.6**   24. 2% of what number is 7.6?   **380**

25. The speed of sound in air at sea level at 32°F is 1088 ft/s. If that represents only 22.04% of the speed of sound in ice-cold water, what is the speed of sound in ice-cold water, to the nearest whole number?   **4936 ft/s**

READY TO GO ON?
Diagnose and Prescribe

NO INTERVENE

YES ENRICH

Ready to Go On? Intervention	READY TO GO ON? Intervention, Section 6A		
	📝 **Worksheets**	💿 **CD-ROM**	🪐 **Online**
☑ Lesson 6-1 🐻 **NS1.3**	6-1 Intervention	Activity 6-1	
☑ Lesson 6-2 🐻 **NS1.3**	6-2 Intervention	Activity 6-2	Diagnose and Prescribe Online
☑ Lesson 6-3 🐻 **NS1.3**	6-3 Intervention	Activity 6-3	
☑ Lesson 6-4 🐻 **NS1.3**	6-4 Intervention	Activity 6-4	

READY TO GO ON? Enrichment, Section 6A
📝 **Worksheets**
💿 **CD-ROM**
🪐 **Online**

Focus on Problem Solving

California Standards

MR1.1 Analyze problems by identifying relationships, distinguishing relevant from irrelevant information, identifying missing information, sequencing and prioritizing information, and observing patterns.
Also covered: **NS1.3**

Make a Plan

• Do you need an estimate or an exact answer?

When you are solving a word problem, ask yourself whether you need an exact answer or whether an estimate is sufficient. For example, if the amounts given in the problem are approximate, only an approximate answer can be given. If an estimate is sufficient, you may wish to use estimation techniques to save time in your calculations.

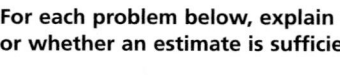

For each problem below, explain whether an exact answer is needed or whether an estimate is sufficient. Then find the answer.

1. In a poll of 5000 registered voters in a certain district, 2800 favored a proposed new library. What percent favored the new library?

2. Albert needs to score 78% on his final exam to get a B in his math class. If the final is worth 300 points, how many points does he need?

3. Mai needs $500 for a trip to Hawaii. If she has saved 23% of what she needs for the trip, about how much money does Mai have?

4. Esteban makes $8.30 per hour at his job. If he receives a 3% raise, how much will he be making per hour?

5. Carmen is planning to tile her kitchen floor. The room is 215 square feet. It is recommended that she buy enough tiles for an area 25% greater than the actual kitchen floor space to account for breakage. How many square feet of tile should she buy?

6. There are about 1,032,000 known species of animals on Earth. Of these, about 751,000 are insects. What percent of known species are insects?

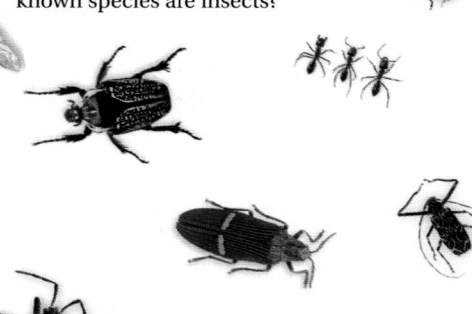

Answers

1. 56%

2. 234 points

3. $125

4. $8.55

5. about 265 ft² of tile

6. about 75%

3. Possible answer: An estimate is sufficient because of the word *about*.

4. An exact answer is needed. 3% of $8.00 is $0.24, so Esteban's new pay rate should be around $8.50.

5. An estimate is sufficient because the 25% extra is an approximation of how many tiles may be broken. Round 215 to 200; 25% of 200 is 50, so she should buy about 215 + 50 = 265 tiles.

6. An estimation is sufficient because of the word *about*. Round each number: $\frac{750,000}{1,000,000} = \frac{3}{4}$. About 75% of the known species are insects.

Focus on Problem Solving

Organizer

Objective: Focus on making a plan to solve a problem by deciding whether an exact answer or an estimate is needed.

 Online Edition

Resources

 Chapter 6 Resource File
Reading Strategies

Problem Solving Process

This page focuses on the second step of the problem-solving process: **Make a Plan**

Discuss

For each problem, have students tell whether an exact answer is needed and then use estimation to check the reasonableness of their answers. If estimation was all that was required, have them explain how they estimated. Point out that words such as "approximately" and "about" usually indicate estimation.

Possible answers:

1. An exact answer is needed. 2800 out of 5000 is a little more than half. The answer should be a little more than 50%.

2. An exact answer is needed. 70% of 300 is 210. 80% of 300 is 240. Albert's score should be between 210 and 240.

California Standards

Mathematical Reasoning 1.1

Also covered:

Number Sense

1.3 Convert fractions to decimals and **percents** and use these representations in estimations, computations, and applications.

Applying Percents

One-Minute Section Planner

Lesson	Lab Resources	Materials
Lesson 6-5 Applying Percent of Increase and Decrease • Find percent increase and decrease. ⬛ NS1.6, ⚷ NS1.7		
Lesson 6-6 Commission, Sales Tax, and Profit • Find commission, sales tax, percent of earnings, profit, and total sales. ⬛ NS1.3, ⚷ NS1.7	**Hands-On Lab 6-6** In *Chapter 6 Resource File*	Optional Calculator
6-7 Hands-On Lab Explore Compound Interest • Explore compound interest using simple interest. ⬛ ⚷ NS1.7		Optional Calculator
Lesson 6-7 Applying Simple and Compound Interest • Compute simple and compound interest. ⬛ ⚷ NS1.7		Optional Credit card applications, bank advertisements, store circulars; Number cubes (MK), calculators

MK = *Manipulatives Kit*

Notes

_____

_____

_____

_____

_____

_____

_____

_____

_____

_____

_____

_____

_____

Math Background: Teaching the Standards

APPLYING PERCENTS 🐻 NS1.6, 🔑 NS1.7

Lessons 6-5 through 6-7

Percents are frequently used in everyday life to describe percent increases and percent decreases. For example, newspapers often report that the price of a company's stock fell by 8% or that the cost of a gallon of gasoline rose by 3%. Despite this widespread use of percents, there are two common misconceptions that should be addressed.

1. An increase of $r\%$ followed by an increase of $p\%$ is not the same as a single increase of $(r + p)\%$. Likewise, a decrease of $r\%$ followed by a decrease of $p\%$ is not the same as a single decrease of $(r + p)\%$. This can be illustrated with a specific example, such as a stereo that costs $100. If the price increases by 10%, the new price is $110. If the price then increases by 20%, the final price is $132. This is not the same as a 30% increase in the original price ($130).

2. A decrease of $r\%$ followed by an increase of $r\%$ does not result in the original amount. Again, a specific example makes this clear. If the price of a $100 stereo decreases by 20%, the new price is $80. If this price is now increased by 20%, the final price is $96.

These misconceptions are discredited by the fact that a percent change is based on a comparison to an original amount. After the first percent change, the original amount changes. Thus, the second percent change is based on a comparison to a different original amount.

SIMPLE AND COMPOUND INTEREST

🐻 🔑 NS1.7

Lesson 6-7

Interest is a fee for borrowing or lending money. For example, when you deposit money in a savings account, you lend the money to the bank, and the bank pays you interest.

The *principal* is the original amount that is borrowed or loaned. *Simple interest* is calculated only on the

principal. In other words, the interest rate is applied only to the original amount that is borrowed or loaned; accumulated interest is not taken into account. Therefore, for each period (generally one year), the interest is simply $P \cdot r$, where P is the principal and r is the interest rate expressed as a decimal. To find the total interest I for t years, the formula becomes $I = P \cdot r \cdot t$. The total amount A after t years is

$$A = P + I = P + Prt = P(1 + rt).$$

The table illustrates simple interest. It shows the growth of a savings account paying 5% simple annual interest on principal of $1000.

Year	Principal	Interest	Balance
1	$1000	$50.00	$1050
2	$1000	$50.00	$1100
3	$1000	$50.00	$1150

With simple interest, the total amount is a linear function of time. That is, the balance grows by a constant (in this case, $50) each year.

Compound interest is calculated on the principal and all the interest that has so far accumulated. For interest that is compounded annually, the amount at the end of the first year is $P(1 + r)$. At the end of the second year, $A = P(1 + r)(1 + r)$ or $A = P(1 + r)^2$. At the end of t years, $A = P(1 + r)^t$.

With compound interest, you can think of the principal being updated each period to include the accrued interest. This is illustrated in the table. It shows the growth of a savings account paying 5% interest that is compounded annually. Because of the compounded interest, the balance grows exponentially.

Year	Principal	Interest	Balance
1	$1000.00	$50.00	$1050.00
2	$1050.00	$52.50	$1102.50
3	$1102.50	$55.13	$1157.63

Interest may be compounded more than once per year. If the interest is compounded n times per year, the rate is divided by n and there are nt periods in t years. Therefore, the formula becomes $A = P(1 + \frac{r}{n})^{nt}$.

Online Edition
Tutorial Videos

Countdown to Mastery Week 12

Power Presentations
with PowerPoint®

Warm Up

1. 14,000 is $2\frac{1}{2}$% of what number?
   560,000

2. 39 is 13% of what number? 300

3. $37\frac{1}{2}$% of what number is 12? 32

4. 150% of what number is 189? 126

Also available on transparency

Math Humor

Salesperson: I had zero sales this week, but next week I'm going after a 100% increase.

Manager: You should be going after a new job instead.

6-5 Applying Percent of Increase and Decrease

California Standards

NS1.6 Calculate the percentage of increases and decreases of a quantity.

⟵ **NS1.7** Solve problems that involve discounts, markups, commissions, and profit and compute simple and compound interest.

Vocabulary
percent of change
percent of increase
percent of decrease
discount
markup

Who uses this? Biologists can use percent of decrease to monitor the heart rates of hibernating animals, such as bears. (See Example 2.)

Percents can be used to describe a change. **Percent of change** is the ratio of the *amount of change* to the *original amount*.

$$\text{percent of change} = \frac{\text{amount of change}}{\text{original amount}}$$

Percent of increase describes how much the original amount increases.
Percent of decrease describes how much the original amount decreases.

EXAMPLE 1 Finding Percent of Increase or Decrease

Find the percent of increase or decrease.

A from 36 to 45

This is a percent of increase.

$45 - 36 = 9$ *First find the amount of change.*

$\frac{\text{amount of increase}}{\text{original amount}} \rightarrow \frac{9}{36}$ *Set up the ratio.*

$\frac{9}{36} = 0.25 = 25\%$ *Find the decimal form. Write as a percent.*

From 36 to 45 is a 25% increase.

B from 55 to 44

This is a percent of decrease.

$55 - 44 = 11$ *First find the amount of change.*

$\frac{\text{amount of decrease}}{\text{original amount}} \rightarrow \frac{11}{55}$ *Set up the ratio.*

$\frac{11}{55} = 0.2 = 20\%$ *Find the decimal form. Write as a percent.*

From 55 to 44 is a 20% decrease.

---

1 Introduce

Alternate Opener

EXPLORATION

6-5 Applying Percent of Increase and Decrease

1. After his first year at a job, Andrew's original hourly wage of $7.95 increased to $9.54.

   a. Subtract the old hourly wage from the new hourly wage to find the amount by which Andrew's hourly wage increased.

   b. Divide the amount in 1a by Andrew's original hourly wage to compare the amount of increase to the original hourly wage.

   c. Write the decimal in 1b as a percent to find the percent of increase in Andrew's hourly wage.

2. An electronics store offers a $100 discount on everything in the store that is priced between $500 and $900. Complete the table to determine the percent of decrease for each price.

Price	$500	$600	$700	$800	$900
Percent of Decrease	$\frac{100}{500} = \_\_$%	$\frac{100}{600} =$	$\frac{100}{700} =$	$\frac{100}{800} =$	$\frac{100}{900} =$

Think and Discuss

3. **Explain** how you wrote the decimal in Problem 1c as a percent.

4. **Compare** the percents of decrease in the table in Problem 2.

Motivate

Ask students to name a salary they would like to earn if they had a job (perhaps a student knows someone with a part-time job and can name an actual amount earned). Tell students to imagine that they received a 12% increase. Ask if anyone can compute the new salary. Point out to students that this lesson is about percent of increase and percent of decrease. You may want to discuss other situations involving various increases or decreases.

Explorations and answers are provided in
Alternate Openers: Explorations Transparencies.

EXAMPLE 2 *Life Science Application*

The heart rate of a grizzly bear slows from 52 to 8 beats per minute during hibernation. What is the percent of decrease, to the nearest tenth of a percent?

$52 - 8 = 44$ *First find the amount of change.*

$\dfrac{\text{amount of decrease}}{\text{original amount}} \rightarrow \dfrac{44}{52}$ *Set up the ratio.*

$\dfrac{44}{52} \approx 0.8461 \approx 84.6\%$ *Find the decimal form. Write as a percent.*

The grizzly bear's heart rate decreases by about 84.6%.

Discount is the difference between the regular price and the sale price of an item. You can use percent of decrease to find discounts. **Markup** is the difference between the wholesale cost and the retail price of an item. You can use percent of increase to find markups.

 EXAMPLE 3 **Finding Discount and Markup**

A Admission to a museum is $8. Students receive a 15% discount. How much do students pay?

Method 1: Multiply, then subtract.

$(8)(0.15) = 1.20$ *Find 15% of 8. This is the amount of discount.*
$8 - 1.20 = 6.80$ *Subtract $1.20 from $8.*

Method 2: Subtract, then multiply.

$100\% - 15\% = 85\%$ *Find the percent the students pay.*
$(8)(0.85) = 6.80$ *Find 85% of 8.*

By either method, students pay $6.80.

B Kaleb buys necklaces at a wholesale price of $48 each. The retail price is marked up by 75%. What is the selling price?

Method 1: Multiply, then add.

$(48)(0.75) = 36$ *Find 75% of 48. This is the amount of markup.*
$48 + 36 = 84$ *Add $36 to $48.*

Method 2: Add, then multiply.

$100\% + 75\% = 175\%$ *Find the total percent of the selling price.*
$(48)(1.75) = 84$ *Find 175% of 48.*

By either method, the selling price is $84.

Possible answers to *Think and Discuss*
1. The amount after a 20% increase is the same as 120% of the original number.

Think and Discuss

1. Compare finding a 20% increase to finding 120% of a number.

---

2 Teach

Guided Instruction

In this lesson, students learn to find percent of increase and decrease. Explain to students that the actual amount of increase or decrease is not the same as the percent of increase or decrease. Emphasize that when calculating the percent, they must compare the amount of increase or decrease with the original amount. Explain that percent of increase or decrease problems often involve two steps: solving a percent problem and addition or subtraction. In **Example 2,** the addition or subtraction is the first step.

 **Universal Access**
Through Diversity

Ask students to find a fact in another subject area that involves a percent of increase or decrease (e.g., social studies: population increase, economics: cost of living increase, health: increase in life expectancy, physical education: decrease in winning times for track events).

Have students prepare a brief report on the topic and include the percent of increase or decrease.

Power Presentations
with PowerPoint®

 Additional Examples

Example 1
Find the percent of increase or decrease.
A. from 16 to 12   25% decrease
B. from 45 to 54   20% increase

Example 2
When Jim was exercising, his heart rate went from 72 beats per minute to 98 beats per minute. What was the percent of increase to the nearest tenth of a percent?
36.1% increase

Example 3
A. Sarah bought a DVD player originally priced at $450 that was on sale for 20% off. What was the discounted price? $360
B. Mr. Olsen has a computer business in which he marks the price of everything up 40% above the wholesale price. If he purchased a printer for $85 wholesale, what will be the retail price? $119

Also available on transparency

 Language Support Some students may not know what *wholesale price* and *retail price* mean. Tell them that the wholesale price is what a store pays for an object, and the retail price is what the store sells the item for.

3 Close

ENGLISH LANGUAGE LEARNERS

Summarize

Remind students that when solving percent of increase or decrease problems, the original amount is always used as the denominator. Ask students to name as many words as possible that indicate an increase or a decrease. Ask students what a 100% increase means and a 100% decrease means.

Possible answers: Increase: *go up, raise, rise, was higher, inflation, marked up, growth;* decrease: *went down, lowered, discount, savings, reduced, decline;* a 100% increase doubles the original amount; a 100% decrease reduces the original amount to zero.

Assignment Guide

If you finished Example **1** assign:
Proficient 1–3, 6–8, 11–13, 21, 22, 34–37
Advanced 6–8, 14–16, 21, 22, 28, 30, 34–37

If you finished Example **2** assign:
Proficient 1–4, 6–9, 11–13, 21, 22, 25, 27, 32, 34–37
Advanced 6–9, 14–16, 21, 22, 27, 28, 30, 32, 34–37

If you finished Example **3** assign:
Proficient 1–13, 17–22, 24, 25, 27, 32–37
Advanced 6–37

Homework Quick Check

Quickly check key concepts.
Exercises: 8, 10, 12, 18

Math Background

If an amount of increase is followed by an equal amount of decrease, the percent of increase and the percent of decrease are not equal. Consider the example:

Find the percent of increase from 40 to 50: $\frac{increase}{original\ amount} = \frac{10}{40} = 25\%$.

Find the percent of decrease from 50 to 40: $\frac{decrease}{original\ amount} = \frac{10}{50} = 20\%$.

The explanation for this is that a percent of change is based on a comparison to an original amount. When the same amount of change (10) is compared with two different original amounts (40 and 50), you get different percents of change.

California Standards

Standard	Exercises
NS1.3	35–37
NS1.6	1–33
NS1.7 🔑	5, 10, 17–22, 23, 26, 28–29, 31–33
MG1.3 🔑	34

6-5 Exercises

California Standards Practice
NS1.6, ← NS1.7

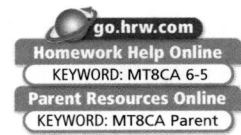

go.hrw.com
Homework Help Online
KEYWORD: MT8CA 6-5
Parent Resources Online
KEYWORD: MT8CA Parent

GUIDED PRACTICE

See Example 1 Find each percent of increase or decrease to the nearest percent.

1. from 40 to 59
48% increase
2. from 85 to 30
65% decrease
3. from 85 to 170
100% increase

See Example 2 4. A population of squirrels rose from 338 to 520 over a period of 3 years. What is the percent of increase, to the nearest tenth of a percent? **53.8%**

See Example 3 5. An automobile dealer agrees to reduce the $10,288 sticker price of a new car by 5% for a customer. What is the discounted price of the car for the customer?
$9773.60

INDEPENDENT PRACTICE

See Example 1 Find each percent of increase or decrease to the nearest percent.

6. from 800 to 1500
88% increase
7. from 0.76 to 0.59
22% decrease
8. from 35 to 19
46% decrease

See Example 2 9. The boiling point of water is lower at higher altitudes. Water boils at 212°F at sea level and 193.7°F at 10,000 ft. What is the percent of decrease in the temperatures, to the nearest tenth of a percent? ≈ **8.6%**

See Example 3 10. Mr. Woodruff owns an automobile parts store and typically marks up merchandise 32% over warehouse cost. How much would he charge customers for a rotor that costs him $62.25? **$82.17**

PRACTICE AND PROBLEM SOLVING

Extra Practice
See page EP13.

Find each percent of increase or decrease to the nearest percent.

11. from $34.70 to $23.20
33% decrease
12. from $72 to $119
65% increase
13. from $320 to $195
39% decrease
14. from $644 to $588
9% decrease
15. from $0.37 to $0.28
24% decrease
16. from $12.50 to $14.75
18% increase

Find each missing number.

17. originally: $400 **$500**
new price: ▪
25% increase
18. originally: 140 **210**
new amount: ▪
50% increase
19. originally: ▪ **120**
new amount: 210
75% increase

20. originally: ▪ **$4.47**
new price: $3.80
15% decrease
21. originally: 28 **50**
new amount: 42
▪ % increase
22. originally: $45 **40**
new price: $27
▪ % decrease

23. **Multi-Step** A pair of $195 boots are discounted 40%.
a. How much is the price decrease? **$78**
b. What is the discounted price of the boots? **$117**
c. If the boots are reduced in price by an additional $66\frac{2}{3}\%$, what will be the discounted price? **$39**
d. What percent of decrease from the original price does this final sale price represent? **80%**

Literature

Harper Lee's *To Kill a Mockingbird* has sold over 10,000,000 copies worldwide and has been translated into more than 25 languages.

24. Science After the Mount St. Helens volcano erupted in 1980, the elevation of the mountain decreased by about 13.6%. Its elevation had been 9677 ft. What was its elevation after the eruption? **about 8361 ft**

25. Literature A signed hard-cover edition of Harper Lee's *To Kill a Mockingbird* is worth $1500. A paperback version of the novel sells for $6. What is the percent of increase in price between the paperback version and the signed hard-cover version? **24,900%**

26. Multi-Step A video game console that is normally priced at $269.99 has been marked down to 70% of its original price. If sales tax is 8%, how much will Marcus pay for the discounted game console, to the nearest cent? **$204.11**

27. Last year, 12,932 people attended an annual convention. This year, 11,245 people are planning to attend. Does this represent a percent of increase or a percent of decrease? Find the percent of change, to the nearest percent. **Percent decrease; 13%**

28. Reasoning Is the percent of change the same when a DVD is marked up from $10 to $15 as when it is discounted from $15 to $10? Explain.

29. Choose a Strategy A digital camera originally sold for $249. Two months later, the price was reduced 40%. During a sale, the camera was discounted an additional 15% off the reduced price. What was the final price of the camera?

Ⓐ $14.94   Ⓑ $22.41   Ⓒ $126.99   Ⓓ $136.95

30. Write About It Describe how to use mental math to find the percent of increase from 75 to 100 and the percent of decrease from 100 to 75.

31. Challenge During a sale, the price of a cell phone was decreased by 20%. By what percent must the sale price be increased to restore the original price? **25%**

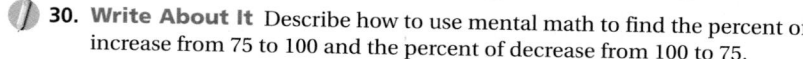

SPIRAL STANDARDS REVIEW   NS1.3, NS1.6, ← NS1.7, ← MG1.3

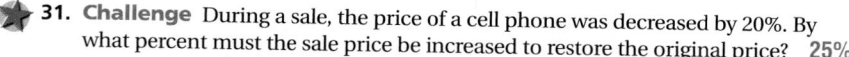

32. Multiple Choice A washing machine that usually sells for $459 is on sale for $379. What is the percent of decrease, to the nearest tenth of a percent?

Ⓐ 17.4%   Ⓑ 21.1%   Ⓒ 32.8%   Ⓓ 82.6%

33. Extended Response Puzzle Place has discounted its puzzles 20%. A puzzle of a giraffe is priced at $20.95, and a puzzle of a mountain is priced at $16.50. How much will Thomas save on both puzzles? If the sales tax rate is 6%, what is the final cost of the puzzles? **$7.49; $31.76**

34. An airliner makes a 2748-mile flight in 6 hours. What is the airliner's average rate of speed in miles per hour? (Lesson 5-2) **458 mi/h**

Find each percent or number. (Lesson 6-3)

35. What percent of 122 is 61? **50%**

36. What is 35% of 2340? **819**

37. What is 145% of 215? **311.75**

CHALLENGE 6-5

 Challenge
6-5 *The Ups and Downs of the Marketplace*

Prices change. The price of a stock can change every few minutes. The price of a house changes over a longer period of time.

The *selling price* of an item is what someone is willing to pay for it. It is a good measure of market value.

Find the current value of each item. Round your answer to the nearest cent

1. a. Amy bought a baseball card for $12. To date, the value of the card increased by 30%, then decreased by 15%, and finally increased by 40%.

Joe bought a baseball card for $12. To date, the value of the card decreased by 10%, then increased by 70%, and finally decreased by 5%.

Whose card is currently worth more? by how much? Explain.

Amy's, by $1.12

$18.56 − $17.44 = $1.12

b. By about what percent must the currently lesser-valued card increase to be of equal value with the greater-valued card? Round your answer to the nearest tenth of a percent.

6.4%

2. a. Jorge's family bought a house for $125,000. To date, the value of the house increased by 5%, then decreased by 25%, and finally increased by 10%.

Gene's family bought a house for $125,000. To date, the value of the house decreased by 5%, then increased by 15%, and finally decreased by 20%.

Whose house is currently worth more? by how much? Explain.

Gene's, by $968.75

$109,250 − $108,281.25
= $968.75

b. By about what percent must the currently lesser-valued house increase to be of equal value with the greater-valued house? Round your answer to the nearest tenth of a percent.

0.9%

PROBLEM SOLVING 6-5

Problem Solving
6-5 *Applying Percent of Increase and Decrease*

Use the table below. Write the correct answer.

1. What is the percent increase in the population of Las Vegas, NV from 1990 to 2000? Round to the nearest tenth of a percent.

83.3%

2. What is the percent increase in the population of Naples, FL from 1990 to 2000? Round to the nearest tenth of a percent.

65.3%

Fastest Growing Metropolitan Areas, 1990–2000			
Metropolitan Area	Population		Percent Increase
	1990	2000	
Las Vegas, NV	852,737	1,563,282	
Naples, FL	152,099	251,377	
Yuma, AZ	106,895		49.7%
McAllen-Edinburg-Mission, TX	383,545		48.5%

3. What was the 2000 population of Yuma, AZ to the nearest whole number?

160,022

4. What was the 2000 population of McAllen-Edinburg-Mission, TX metropolitan area to the nearest whole number?

569,564

For exercises 5–7, round to the nearest tenth. Choose the letter for the best answer.

5. The amount of money spent on automotive advertising in 2000 was 4.4% lower than in 1999. If the 1999 spending was $1812.3 million, what was the 2000 spending?
A $79.7 million   C $1892 million
Ⓑ $1732.6 million   D $1923.5 million

6. In 1967, a 30-second Super Bowl commercial cost $42,000. In 2000, a 30-second commercial cost $1,900,000. What was the percent increase in the cost?
F 1.7%   H 442.4%
G 44.2%   Ⓙ 4423.8%

7. In 1896 Thomas Burke of the U.S. won the 100-meter dash at the Summer Olympics in a time of 12.00 seconds. In 2004, Justin Gatlin of the U.S. won with a time of 9.85 seconds. What was the percent decrease in the winning time?
A 2.15%   C 21.8%
Ⓑ 17.9%   D 45.1%

8. In 1928 Elizabeth Robinson won the 100-meter dash with a time of 12.20 seconds. In 2004, Yuliya Nesterenko won with a time that was about 10.4% less than Robinson's winning time. What was Nesterenko's time, rounded to the nearest hundredth?
F 9.83 seconds   H 12.16 seconds
Ⓖ 10.93 seconds   J 13.47 seconds

Answers

28. Possible answer: No, the amount of change is the same, but the original amounts are different. So the resulting percents are different. The percent of increase is $\frac{5}{10} = 50\%$, but the percent of decrease is $\frac{5}{15} = 33\frac{1}{3}\%$.

30. Possible answer: In both cases, the amount of change is 25. The percent of increase is $\frac{25}{75}$, which reduces to $\frac{1}{3}$, or $33\frac{1}{3}\%$. The percent of decrease is $\frac{25}{100}$, or 25%.

 Teaching Tip   **Multiple Choice** For **Exercise 32,** remind students that they must first find the amount of change by subtracting $379 from $459. Then, they can calculate the percent of increase. Students who chose answer **D** found what percent $379 is of $459.

 Journal

Ask students to describe how they would calculate the percent of increase in their height over the last year.

Power Presentations with PowerPoint®

 **6-5 Lesson Quiz**

Find each percent of increase or decrease to the nearest percent.

1. from 12 to 15   **25% increase**

2. from 1625 to 1400   **14% decrease**

3. from 37 to 125   **238% increase**

4. from 1.25 to 0.85   **32% decrease**

5. A computer game originally sold for $40 but is now on sale for 30% off. What is the discounted price of the computer game? **$28**

Also available on transparency

Objective: Students find commission, sales tax, percent of earnings, profit, and total sales.

Hands-On Lab
In *Chapter 6 Resource File*

Online Edition
Tutorial Videos

Countdown to Mastery Week 12

Power Presentations
with PowerPoint®

Warm Up

Estimate. Possible answers:

1. 20% of 602   120

2. 133 out of 264   50%

3. 151% of 78   120

4. 0.28 out of 0.95   30%

Also available on transparency

Math Humor

Student: Would you ever punish me for something that I didn't do?

Teacher: Of course not.

Student: Good…I didn't do my homework!

Teaching Tip **Language Support** Some students may not know what *salary* means. Tell them that a salary is a fixed amount that is paid to a person for regular work or services.

California Standards

NS1.7 Solve problems that involve discounts, markups, **commissions, and profit** and compute simple and compound interest.
Also covered: **NS1.3**

Who uses this? People who work in sales are often paid a percent of their sales, or a commission. (See Example 1.)

A **commission** is a fee paid to a person who makes a sale. It is usually a percent of the selling price. This percent is called the **commission rate** .

commission rate • sales = commission

EXAMPLE 1 Multiplying by Percents to Find Commission Amounts

Julie is paid a monthly salary of $2100 plus commissions. Last month she sold one car for $39,500, earning a 4% commission on the sale. How much was her commission? What was her total pay for the month?

First find her commission.

4% · $39,500 = c	commission rate · sales = commission
0.04 · 39,500 = c	Change the percent to a decimal.
1580 = c	Solve for c.

She earned a commission of $1580 on the sale.

Now find her total pay for last month.

$1580 + $2100 = $3680	commission + salary = total pay

Her total pay for last month was $3680.

Sales tax is the tax on the sale of an item or service. It is a percent of the purchase price and is collected by the seller.

EXAMPLE 2 Multiplying by Percents to Find Sales Tax Amounts

If the sales tax rate is 7.75%, how much tax would Meka pay if she bought a portable CD player for $45.80 and two CDs for $15.99 each?

Helpful Hint
A 7.75% sales tax rate means that for every $100 you spend, you would pay $7.75 in sales tax.

CD player: 1 at $45.80 →	$45.80	
CDs: 2 at $15.99 →	$31.98	
	$77.78	Total price
0.0775 · 77.78 = 6.02795		Write the tax rate as a decimal and multiply by the total price.

Meka would pay $6.03 in sales tax.

---

1 Introduce
Alternate Opener

EXPLORATION

6-6 Commission, Sales Tax, and Profit

The profit on the sale of a bike is $30.00. This is 20% of the regular price. What is the regular price?

$$0.20x = 30$$
$$x = \frac{30}{0.20}$$
$$x = 150 \quad \text{The regular price is } \$150.$$

Solve each problem.

		Profit	Regular Price	Equation
1.	An airline earns a 30% profit on airfare on weekdays. The profit made on a ticket is $126.00. What is the regular price?	$126.00	x	0.30x = 126
2.	The profit on the sale of a computer is $360.00. This is 40% of the regular price. What is the regular price?	$360.00	x	0.40x = 360

Think and Discuss

3. **Explain** how you solved each problem.
4. **Discuss** what the equation would look like in a problem involving a discount instead of a profit.

Motivate

Ask students if they've ever shopped in a store where the salesperson seemed especially helpful. Explain that in some stores, the amount an employee earns is based on how much merchandise he or she sells. Tell students that an amount earned based on sales is called a *commission*.

Explorations and answers are provided in *Alternate Openers: Explorations Transparencies.*

California Standards

Number Sense 🔑 **1.7**
Also covered:
Number Sense
1.3 Convert fractions to decimals and percents and **use these representations in** estimations, **computations, and applications.**

EXAMPLE 3 **Using Proportions to Find the Percent of Earnings**

Jorge earns $36,000 yearly. Of that, he pays $12,240 for rent. What percent of Jorge's earnings goes to rent?

Think: What percent of $36,000 is $12,240?

$$\frac{n}{100} = \frac{12,240}{36,000}$$ *Set up a proportion.*

$$n \cdot 36,000 = 100 \cdot 12,240$$ *Find the cross products.*

$$36,000n = 1,224,000$$ *Simplify.*

$$\frac{36,000n}{36,000} = \frac{1,224,000}{36,000}$$ *Divide both sides by 36,000.*

$$n = 34$$ *Simplify.*

So 34% of Jorges's earnings goes to rent.

Profit is the difference between total income and total expenses. Profit can be expressed as a percent or as a dollar amount.

EXAMPLE 4 **Finding Profit and Total Sales**

Students in Salim's class sell gift wrap to raise funds for class trips. The class earns 11% profit on all sales.

A If the total sales were $4962, what was the profit?

Think: What is 11% of 4962?

$$x = 0.11 \cdot 4962$$ *Set up an equation.*

$$x = 545.82$$ *Multiply.*

The profit was $545.82.

B If the class earned $647.35, how much were the total sales?

Think: 647.35 is 11% of what number?

Let s = total sales

$$647.35 = 0.11 \cdot s$$ *Set up an equation.*

$$\frac{647.35}{0.11} = \frac{0.11s}{0.11}$$ *Divide each side by 0.11.*

$$5885 = s$$ *Simplify.*

The total sales of gift wrap for Salim's class were $5885.

Possible answers to
Think and Discuss

1. Both are based on percents of the price.

2. Usually, the sales tax would be double. If the tax rate is 8%, the tax on $10 would be $0.80 and the tax on $20 would be $1.60. However, if the tax rate is 8.25%, the tax on $10 would be $0.83 after rounding to the nearest cent, and the tax on $20 would be $1.65.

 Think and Discuss

1. Tell how finding commission is similar to finding sales tax.

2. Explain whether the sales tax on a $20 item would be double the sales tax on a $10 item. Justify your answer.

Power Presentations with PowerPoint®

 Additional Examples

Example 1

A real-estate agent is paid a monthly salary of $900 plus commission. Last month he sold one condominium for $65,000, earning a 4% commission on the sale. How much was his commission? What was his total pay last month? $2600; $3500

Example 2

If the sales tax rate is 6.75%, how much tax would Adrian pay if he bought two CDs at $16.99 each and one DVD for $36.29? $4.74

 Example 3

Anna earns $1500 monthly. Of that, $114.75 is withheld for Social Security and Medicare. What percent of Anna's earnings are withheld for Social Security and Medicare? 7.65%

 Example 4

A furniture store earns 30% profit on all sales.

A. If total sales are $2790, what is the profit? $837

B. If the store earns $10,044, how much are the total sales? $33,480

Also available on transparency

---

 2 Teach

Guided Instruction

In this lesson, students learn to find commission, sales tax, and percent of earnings. Explain the meanings of *commission* and *sales tax.* Explain that each is a percent of some amount of money. Students use given percents to find these amounts in **Examples 1 and 2.** In **Example 3,** students find what percent of earnings a given amount of rent is. In **Example 4,** students use a given percent profit and a given amount of sales to find an amount of profit. Students also find total sales using a given percent profit and a given amount of earnings.

Universal Access
For Advanced Learners/GATE

Have students work in pairs. Tell students that they have been hired to sell cars. They can choose between three salary packages: A) $2500 per month with no commission, B) $1000 per month with 2% commission, or C) no monthly salary and 4% commission. If an average car sells for $20,000, have students calculate the salary they would receive if they sold 1, 3, or 5 cars in a month. Then have them discuss which salary package they would choose.

A) $2500; B) $1400, $2200, or $3000;
C) $800, $2400, or $4000

3 Close

Summarize

Ask for volunteers to define each of the vocabulary terms. Remind students that commissions and sales taxes are based on the price of an item. Explain that many taxes are calculated as a percent of earnings, and that they are generally taken before you get a paycheck.

6-6 Exercises

California Standards Practice
NS1.3, NS1.7

go.hrw.com
Homework Help Online
KEYWORD: MT8CA 6-6
Parent Resources Online
KEYWORD: MT8CA Parent

Assignment Guide

If you finished Example 1 assign:
Proficient 1, 5, 19, 21–26
Advanced 5, 15, 19, 21–26

If you finished Example 2 assign:
Proficient 1, 2, 5, 6, 9–11, 19–26
Advanced 5, 6, 9–11, 15, 19–26

If you finished Example 3 assign:
Proficient 1–3, 5–7, 16, 19–26
Advanced 5–7, 9–11, 15–26

If you finished Example 4 assign:
Proficient 1–14, 16, 19–26
Advanced 5–26

Homework Quick Check

Quickly check key concepts.
Exercises: 6, 8, 10, 12

Answers

15. Deborah should choose the salary option that pays $2100 plus 4% of sales. She would make $2300 to $2500 a month. The other salary option of $1800 plus 6.5% of sales would pay less. For sales totals of $10,000, she would make only $2450 a month.

GUIDED PRACTICE

See Example 1　**1.** Aaron earns a weekly salary of $350 plus a 7% commission on sales. Last week, his sales totaled $3200. What was his total pay? **$574**

See Example 2　**2.** In a state with a sales tax rate of 7%, Hernando buys a radio for $59.99 and a CD for $13.99. How much is the sales tax? **$5.18**

See Example 3　**3.** Last year, Nadia earned $31,025. Of that amount, she spent $3612.59 on food. What percent of her income went to food, to the nearest tenth of a percent? **11.6%**

See Example 4　**4.** A sporting-goods store earns 9% profit on all sales of boxing gloves. If one pair of boxing gloyes sold for $43.00, what was the profit made on the gloves? **$3.87**

INDEPENDENT PRACTICE

See Example 1　**5.** Kayla earns a weekly salary of $290 plus a 5.5% commission on sales at a gift shop. How much would she make in a week if she sold $5700 worth of merchandise? **$603.50**

See Example 2　**6.** The sales tax rate in Brad's town is 4.25%. If he buys 3 lamps for $22.49 each and a sofa for $829.99, how much sales tax does he owe? **$38.14**

See Example 3　**7.** Jada typically earns $1545 each month, of which $47.20 is spent on electricity. What percent of Jada's earnings are spent on electricity each month, to the nearest tenth of a percent? **3.1%**

See Example 4　**8.** A small mail-order company earns a 15% profit on all sales. If the company earned $5250 one month, how much were the total sales? **$35,000**

PRACTICE AND PROBLEM SOLVING

Extra Practice
See page EP13.

Find each sales tax to the nearest cent.

9. total sales: $210.13
sales tax rate: 7.25%
$15.23

10. total sales: $42.99
sales tax rate: 9%
$3.87

11. total sales: $895.75
sales tax rate: 4.25%
$38.07

Find the total sales to the nearest cent.

12. commission: $63.06
commission rate: 5% **$1261.20**

13. commission: $2842
commission rate: 3.5% **$81,200**

14. Consumer Economics A store buys jeans from the manufacturer for $30 each and sells them for a 50% profit. At the end of the season, the store reduces the price of the jeans by 50%. What is the profit on the sale of the jeans during the season? Does the store make a profit on the sale of the jeans at the end of the season? Explain. **$15; no, at the end of the season the jeans sell for $22.50, which is less than the price of $30 paid to the manufacturer.**

15. Reasoning Deborah can choose between a monthly salary of $1800 plus 6.5% of sales or $2100 plus 4% of sales. She expects sales between $5,000 and $10,000 a month. Which salary option should she choose? Explain.

California Standards

Standard	Exercises
NS1.3	2–3, 6–7, 9–11, 16–18, 20
NS1.6	25–26
NS1.7 🔑	1, 4–5, 8, 12–15, 19
AF2.2	21–24

REVIEW FOR MASTERY 6-6

LESSON 6-6 Review for Mastery
Commission, Sales Tax, and Profit

Salespeople often earn a **commission**, a percent of their total sales.

Find the commission on a real-estate sale of $125,000 if the commission rate is 4%.

Write the percent as a decimal and multiply.

commission rate × amount of sale = amount of commission
0.04 × $125,000　　　 = $5000

If, in addition to the commission, the salesperson earns a salary of $1000, what is the total pay?

commission + salary = total pay
$5000 + $1000 = $6000

Complete to find each total monthly pay.

1. total monthly sales = $170,000; commission rate = 3%; salary = $1500

amount of commission = 0.03 × $ <u>170,000</u> = $ <u>5100</u>

total pay = $ <u>5100</u> + $1500 = $ <u>6600</u>

2. total monthly sales = $16,000; commission rate = 5.5%; salary = $1750

amount of commission = <u>0.055</u> × $ <u>16,000</u> = $ <u>880</u>

total pay = $ <u>880</u> + $ <u>1750</u> = $ <u>2630</u>

A **tax** is a charge, usually a percentage, generally imposed by a government.
Sales tax is the tax on the sale of an item or service.

If the sales tax rate is 7%, find the tax on a sale of $9.49.

Write the tax rate as a decimal and multiply.

tax rate × amount of sale = amount of tax
0.07　 × $9.49　　　 = $0.6643 ≈ $0.66

Complete to find each amount of sales tax.

3. item price = $5.19; sales tax rate = 6%

amount of sales tax = 0.06 × $ <u>5.19</u> = $ <u>0.3114</u> ≈ $ <u>0.31</u>

4. item price = $250; sales tax rate = 6.75%

amount of sales tax = <u>0.0675</u> × $ <u>250</u> = $ <u>16.875</u> ≈ $ <u>16.88</u>

PRACTICE 6-6

LESSON 6-6 Practice B
Commission, Sales Tax, and Profit

Complete the table to find the amount of sales tax for each sale amount to the nearest cent.

1.

Sale amount	5% sales tax	8% sales tax	6.5% sales tax
$67.50	$3.38	$5.40	$4.39
$98.75	$4.94	$7.90	$6.42
$399.79	$19.99	$31.98	$25.99
$1250.00	$62.50	$100.00	$81.25

Complete the table to find the commission for each sale amount to the nearest cent.

2.

Sale amount	6% commision	9% commision	8.5% commission
$475.00	$28.50	$42.75	$40.38
$2450.00	$147.00	$220.50	$208.25
$12,500.00	$750.00	$1125.00	$1062.50
$98,900.00	$5934.00	$8901.00	$8406.50

3. Alice makes bracelets and sells them for $5 each. If it costs her $2 to make a bracelet, what percent of the money she makes is profit? **60%**

4. Phillipe works for a computer store that pays a 12% commission and no salary. What will Phillipe's weekly sales have to be for him to earn $360? **$3000**

5. The purchase price of a book is $35.85. The sales tax rate is 6.5%. How much is the sales tax to the nearest cent? What is the total cost of the book?

sales tax is $2.33; total cost is $38.18

6. Who made more commission this month? How much did she make? Salesperson A made 11% of $67,530. Salesperson B made 8% of $85,740.

Salesperson A $7428.30

7. Jon earned $38,000 last year. He paid $6,840 towards entertainment. What percent of his earnings did Jon pay in entertainment expenses? **18%**

8. The Cougars won 62% of their games. They won 93 games. How many games did they lose? **57 games**

Economics LINK

Tax brackets are used to determine how much income tax people pay. Depending upon a person's taxable income, tax is given by the formula base tax + tax rate (amount over). "Amount over" refers only to the income above the amount listed. Refer to the table for Exercises 16–18.

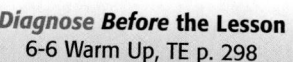

2005 IRS Income Tax Brackets (Single)

Taxable Income Range	Base Tax	Tax Rate	Amount Over
$0–$7,300	$0	10%	$0
$7,300–$29,700	$730	15%	$7,300
$29,700–$71,950	$4,090	25%	$29,700
$71,950–$150,150	$14,652.50	28%	$71,950
$150,150–$326,450	$36,548.50	33%	$150,150
$326,450 and up	$94,727.50	35%	$326,450

16. Tina's pay stub is shown at right. Find the missing numbers.

17. Anna earned $71,458 total in 2005. She was able to deduct $7250 for job-related expenses. This amount is subtracted from her total income to determine her taxable income.
   a. What was Anna's taxable income in 2005? **$64,208**
   b. How much income tax did she owe? **$12,717**
   c. What percent of Anna's total income did the tax represent? **≈ 17.8%**
   d. What percent of her taxable income did the tax represent? **≈ 19.8%**

18. ⭐ **Challenge** Charlena paid $10,050 in taxes in 2005. How much taxable income did she earn that year? **$53,540**

16. **$6.77; $16.25; $12.43; $133.82**

Ellie's Flowers

Hours worked	24
Hourly rate	☐ per hour
Gross pay	$162.50
Federal income tax (10%)	☐
Other federal taxes (7.65%)	☐
NET PAY	☐

SPIRAL STANDARDS REVIEW

NS1.3, NS1.6, ← NS1.7, AF2.2

19. **Short Response** Gabrielle earned a weekly salary of $235 plus 8% commission on sales over $500. What was her weekly pay if she had $6,250 in sales? **$695**

20. **Gridded Response** Rafael buys a video game for $49.95. The sales tax rate is 6.5%. What is the total cost, including tax, to the nearest dollar? **$53.20**

Divide. Assume that no denominator equals zero. (Lesson 4-4)

21. $\frac{x^9}{x^7}$ x^2

22. $\frac{12a^5}{3a^2}$ $4a^3$

23. $\frac{x^4y^8}{x^6y^6}$ $\frac{y^2}{x^2}$

24. $\frac{5m^2n^4}{m^2n}$ $5n^3$

Find each percent increase or decrease to the nearest percent. (Lesson 6-5)

25. from 600 to 300 **50% decrease**

26. from $109.99 to $94.99 **14% decrease**

CHALLENGE 6-6

LESSON 6-6 Challenge
Shoppers' Delight

Shoppers save money by buying items on sale.
The amount by which the regular price is reduced is called a **discount**.

amount of discount = discount rate × regular price
sale price = regular price − amount of discount

Find the sale price after each discount.

1. regular price = $899;
   discount rate = 20%
   amount of discount = __$179.80__
   sale price = __$719.20__

2. regular price = $14.99;
   discount rate = 15%
   amount of discount = __$2.25__
   sale price = __$12.74__

Stores may offer discounts in a variety of ways.

Use **$100 as the regular price for the item to write your explanations**. Possible answers are given:

3. Buy one at regular price. Get a second one for half price. Explain how this is different from getting a 50% discount.
   __50% discount: $50 for 1 item and $100 for 2 items__
   __2nd item half price: $100 for first item and $150 for 2 items__

4. Buy two. Get one free. Explain how this is different from getting a 33⅓% discount.
   __Buy 2, get 1 free: $200 for 3 items__
   __33⅓% discount: $200 for 3 items__

5. This item is marked down by 10%. Use a coupon and get an additional 10% off. Explain how this is different from getting a 20% discount.
   __20% discount on $100 item: pay $80__
   __After first 10% discount, item price is $90.__
   __Now, take 10% off $90 and final price is $81.__

6. An item is marked "50% off — Today Only Get Another 50% off". Explain why the item is not free.
   __The additional 50% is off 50% of the reduced price.__
   __The item is 25% of the original price.__

PROBLEM SOLVING 6-6

LESSON 6-6 Problem Solving
Commission, Sales Tax, and Profit

Write the correct answer.

1. A bakery can sell muffins for $1 each. If it costs the bakery $5 to make 20 muffins, what percent of the money made from muffins sales is profit?
   __75%__

2. A community is considering increasing the sales tax rate 0.5% to fund a new sports arena. If the tax rate is raised, how much more will you pay in sales tax on $500?
   __$2.50__

3. Trent earned $28,500 last year. He paid $8,265 for rent. What percent of his earnings did Trent pay for rent?
   __29%__

4. Julie has been offered two jobs. The first pays $400 per week. The second job pays $175 per week plus 15% commission on her sales. How much will she have to sell in order for the second job to pay as much as the first?
   __$1500__

Choose the letter for the best answer. Round to the nearest cent.

5. Clay earned $2,600 last month. He paid $234 for entertainment. What percent of his earnings did Clay pay in entertainment expenses?
   Ⓐ 9%
   B 11%
   C 30%
   D 90%

6. Susan's parents have offered to help her pay for a new computer. They will pay 30% and Susan will pay 70% of the cost of a new computer. Susan has saved $550 for a new computer. With her parents help, how expensive of a computer can she afford?
   F $165.00   H $1650.00
   Ⓖ $785.71   J $1833.33

7. Kellen's bill at a restaurant before tax and tip is $22.00. If tax is 5.25% and he wants to leave 15% of the bill including the tax for a tip, how much will he spend in total?
   A $22.17   Ⓒ $26.63
   B $26.46   D $27.82

8. The 8th grade class is trying to raise money for a field trip. They need to raise $600 and the fundraiser they have chosen will give them 20% of the amount that they sell. How much do they need to sell to raise the money for the field trip?
   F $120.00   Ⓗ $3000.00
   G $857.14   J $3200.00

FORMATIVE ASSESSMENT and INTERVENTION ← →

Diagnose Before the Lesson
6-6 Warm Up, TE p. 298

Monitor During the Lesson
6-6 Know-It Notebook
6-6 Questioning Strategies

Assess After the Lesson
6-6 Lesson Quiz, TE p. 301

Interdisciplinary LINK

Economics

Exercises 16–18 involve using data from pay stubs and tax tables to solve percent problems. Understanding these types of problems is important in the study of economics.

Teaching Tip **Short Response** For **Exercise 19,** encourage students to read the problem carefully. Point out that the commission is added to the salary only when the weekly sales exceed $500. That means students must first subtract $500 from $6250 before calculating the commission.

🖊 Journal

Ask students to write and explain whether they would prefer to have a job that pays commission or one that pays a straight salary.

Power Presentations with PowerPoint®

✓ 6-6 Lesson Quiz

1. Every month, Gillian makes $1600 plus an 8.9% commission on sales. If her sales last month totaled $18,400, what was her total pay? **$3237.60**

2. The sales tax is 5.75%, and the shirt costs $20. What is the total cost of the shirt? **$21.15**

3. Sheridan has a yearly income of $39,650, and he is advised to invest $4500 every year. What percent of his income should he invest, to the nearest tenth of a percent? **11.3%**

4. A grocery store earns 5% profit on all canned goods. If the store sold $1635 of canned goods, what was the profit? **$81.75**

Also available on transparency

Objective: Explore compound interest using simple interest.

 Online Edition

 Countdown to Mastery Week 12

Teach
Discuss

Work through *Think and Discuss* **item 3** with students, comparing the total compound interest earned with the total simple interest earned. Explain to students that when the same operations are repeated in mathematics, there is often a formula that incorporates these operations.

Close
Key Concept

You can use a calculator to apply the compound interest formula in various situations.

Assessment

1. Suppose $200 is deposited into an account paying 3% interest compounded quarterly for one year. Find the amount in the account at the end of one year. about $206.06

Answers to *Try This*
1a.

Quarter	Beginning Balance	Interest	Amount
1	$200.00	$5.00	$205.00
2	$205.00	$5.13	$210.13
3	$210.13	$5.25	$215.38
4	$215.38	$5.38	$220.76

Hands-On

LAB 6-7 Explore Compound Interest

Use with Lesson 6-7

 go.hrw.com
Lab Resources Online
KEYWORD: MT8CA Lab6

Every time interest is calculated on a bank account with *compound interest*, the interest is added to the principal for future interest calculations.

California Standards

➤ **NS1.7** Solve problems that involve discounts, markups, commissions, and profit **and compute simple and compound interest.**

Activity

Suppose $1000 is deposited into an account paying 5% interest compounded quarterly for one year. Find the amount *A* in the account at the end of one year. Complete the table. Round your answers to the nearest tenth.

Quarter	Beginning Balance	Interest = (P)(r)(t)	Amount = P + I
1	$1000.00	I = (1000.00)(0.05)(0.25) = 12.50	A = 1000.00 + 12.50 = $1012.50
2	$1012.50	I = (1012.50)(0.05)(0.25) = 12.66	A = 1012.50 + **$12.66** = $1025.16
3	**$1025.16**	I = (1025.16)(0.05)(0.25) = 12.81	A = **$1025.16** + 12.81 = $1037.97
4	$1037.97	I = (**$1037.97**)(0.05)(0.25) = 12.97	A = 1037.97 + 12.97 = **$1050.94**

Think and Discuss

1. What is the balance in the account at the end of the four quarters (one year)? **$1050.94**

2. If this account paid only simple interest, what would be the amount in the account at the end of one year using the simple interest formula? **$1050.00**

3. How much more interest was earned by compounding quarterly? **$0.94**

Try This

1. Suppose $200 is deposited into an account paying 10% interest compounded quarterly for one year.

a. Make a table to find the balance in the account at the end of one year. Round your answers to the nearest tenth.

b. If this account paid only simple interest, what would be the amount in the account at the end of one year using the simple interest formula? **$220.00**

c. How much more interest was earned by compounding quarterly? **$0.76**

Nets or Not

Lisa Kernaghan
Oakhurst, CA

Teacher to Teacher

A great time to have a guest speaker is when you are teaching the concept of compound interest! I invite a local financial planner to class (a realtor would work too). Financial planners and realtors have special "financial" or "real estate" calculators that they use to compute interest. Students are amazed to see a different type of calculator and how it works!

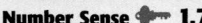

6-7 Applying Simple and Compound Interest

Vocabulary
simple interest
principal
rate of interest
compound interest

Why learn this? You can calculate the amount of money a bank pays you in interest using the simple interest formula.

When you deposit money into a bank, the bank pays you interest. When you borrow money from a bank, you pay interest to the bank.

Simple interest is money paid only on the principal.

Rate of interest is the percent charged or earned.

$$I = P \cdot r \cdot t$$

Principal is the amount of money borrowed or invested.

Time that the money is borrowed or invested (in years)

EXAMPLE **1** **Finding Interest and Total Payment on a Loan**

Tristan borrowed $14,500 from a bank and promised to pay them back over 5 years at an annual simple interest rate of 7%. How much interest will he pay if he pays off the entire loan at the end of the fifth year? What is the total amount he will repay?

First, find the interest he will pay.

$I = P \cdot r \cdot t$	*Use the formula.*
$I = 14{,}500 \cdot 0.07 \cdot 5$	*Substitute. Use 0.07 for 7%.*
$I = 5075$	*Solve for I.*

Tristan will pay $5075 in interest.

The total amount *A* to be repaid is the principal *P* plus the interest *I*.

$P + I = A$	*principal + interest = total amount*
$14{,}500 + 5075 = A$	*Substitute.*
$19{,}575 = A$	*Solve for A.*

Tristan will repay a total of $19,575 on his loan.

EXAMPLE **2** **Determining the Amount of Investment Time**

Isaiah invested $3500 in a mutual fund at a yearly rate of 6%. He earned $945 in interest. For how long was the money invested?

$I = P \cdot r \cdot t$	*Use the formula.*
$945 = 3500 \cdot 0.06 \cdot t$	*Substitute. Use 0.06 for 6%.*
$945 = 210t$	*Simplify.*
$4.5 = t$	*Solve for t.*

The money was invested for 4.5 years, or 4 years and 6 months.

Power Presentations
with PowerPoint®

Warm Up

1. What is 35 increased by 8%? **37.8**

2. What is the percent of decrease from 144 to 120? $16\frac{2}{3}\%$

3. What is 1500 decreased by 75%? **375**

4. What is the percent of increase from 0.32 to 0.64? **100%**

Also available on transparency

Math Humor

Old bankers never die. They just lose their interest.

---

1 Introduce

Alternate Opener

Motivate

Show students some bank advertisements or credit card applications that offer different interest rates. Explain that it is important to understand interest if you want to avoid paying more than necessary for something.

Explorations and answers are provided in *Alternate Openers: Explorations Transparencies.*

Power Presentations
with PowerPoint®

Additional Examples

Example 1

To buy a car, Jessica borrowed $15,000 for 3 years at an annual simple interest rate of 9%. How much interest will she pay if she pays the entire loan off at the end of the third year? What is the total amount that she will repay? $4050; $19,050

Example 2

Nancy invested $6000 in a bond at a yearly rate of 3%. She earned $450 in interest. How long was the money invested? 2.5 yr, or 2 yr 6 mo

Example 3

John's parents deposited $1000 into a savings account as a college fund when he was born. How much will John have in this account after 18 years at a yearly simple interest rate of 3.25%? $1585

Example 4

Mr. Johnson borrowed $8000 for 4 years to make home improvements. If he repaid a total of $10,320, at what interest rate did he borrow the money? 7.25%, or $7\frac{1}{4}$%

Also available on transparency

EXAMPLE 3 **Computing Total Savings**

Nadia's aunt deposited $3000 into a savings account as a college fund for Nadia. How much will be in this account after 5 years if the account earns a yearly simple interest rate of 3.5%?

$I = P \cdot r \cdot t$	Use the formula.
$I = 3000 \cdot 0.035 \cdot 5$	Substitute. Use 0.035 for 3.5%.
$I = 525$	Solve for I.

The interest is $525.

Now you can find the total.

$P + I = A$	Use the formula.
$3000 + 525 = A$	Substitute.
$3525 = A$	Solve for A.

Nadia will have $3525 in her savings account after 5 years.

EXAMPLE 4 **Finding the Rate of Interest**

To pay for her college expenses, Hannah borrows $7000. She plans to repay the loan in 5 years at simple interest. If Hannah repays a total of $9187.50, what is the interest rate?

$P + I = A$	Use the formula.
$7000 + I = 9187.5$	Substitute.
$-7000 \qquad -7000$	Subtract 7000 from both sides.
$I = 2187.5$	Simplify.

She paid $2187.50 in interest. Use the amount of interest to find the interest rate.

$I = P \cdot r \cdot t$	Use the formula.
$2187.5 = 7000 \cdot r \cdot 5$	Substitute.
$2187.5 = 35{,}000r$	Simplify.
$\dfrac{2187.5}{35{,}000} = \dfrac{35{,}000r}{35{,}000}$	Divide both sides by 35,000.
$0.0625 = r$	Simplify.

The simple annual rate is 6.25%, or $6\frac{1}{4}$%.

For more on the compound interest formula, see page 302.

Compound interest is interest paid not only on the principal, but also on the interest that has already been earned. The formula for compound interest is below.

$$A = P\left(1 + \frac{r}{n}\right)^{nt}$$

A is the final dollar value, P is the principal, r is the rate of interest, t is the number of years, and n is the number of *compounding periods* per year.

---

2 Teach

Guided Instruction

In this lesson, students learn to compute simple and compound interest. Begin by discussing *interest*. Explain to students that there are different kinds of interest, but that the principle of simple interest provides the basis for all types of interest. Show them the formula $I = Prt$, and discuss what each of the four variables represents (Teaching Transparency). Emphasize the fact that the time is generally in years and that the rate should be changed to a decimal before using it in the formula. Point out that the formula can be used to solve for any of the four variables.

Universal Access
Through Cooperative Learning

Have the students work in pairs. Give each pair a store circular with an advertised interest rate for credit purchases and a number cube. Have students "buy" items on the store circular. Tell students to roll the number cube to determine the number of years they will take to pay for the item charged on their credit cards. Using the interest rate on the circular and the number of years rolled on the number cube, students are to calculate the interest they will owe on that item.

The table shows some common compounding periods and how many times per year interest is paid for them.

Compounding Periods	Times per year (n)
Annually	1
Semi-annually	2
Quarterly	4
Monthly	12

EXAMPLE **5** **Applying Compound Interest**

Danielle invested $1500 in a savings account that pays 3% interest compounded quarterly. Find the value of the investment after 9 years.

$$A = P\left(1 + \frac{r}{n}\right)^{nt}$$ *Use the compound interest formula.*

$$= 1500\left(1 + \frac{0.03}{4}\right)^{4(9)}$$ *Substitute.*

$$= 1500(1 + 0.0075)^{36}$$ *Simplify.*

$$= 1500(1.0075)^{36}$$ *Add inside the parentheses.*

$$\approx 1500(1.308645)$$ *Find $(1.0075)^{36}$ and round.*

$$\approx 1962.97$$ *Multiply and round to the nearest cent.*

After 9 years, the investment will be worth about $1962.97.

Possible answers to Think and Discuss

1. Since *t* is always written in years, $t = 0.5$ or $\frac{1}{2}$.

2. Interest on $500 at 8% for 1 year is $500 \cdot 0.08 \cdot 1 = \$40$; interest on the same amount at 4% for 2 years is $500 \cdot 0.04 \cdot 2 = \$40$.

Think and Discuss

1. **Tell** what value should be used for *t* when referring to 6 months.

2. **Demonstrate** that doubling the time while halving the interest rate results in the same amount of simple interest.

 **6-7** **Exercises**

California Standards Practice
NS1.7

go.hrw.com
Homework Help Online
KEYWORD: MT8CA 6-7
Parent Resources Online
KEYWORD: MT8CA Parent

GUIDED PRACTICE

See Example **1**   1. Nick borrowed $7150, to be repaid after 5 years at an annual simple interest rate of 6.25%. How much interest will be due after 5 years? How much will Nick have to repay?   **$2234.38; $9384.38**

See Example **2**   2. Mr. Williams invested $4000 in a bond with a yearly interest rate of 4%. His total interest on the investment was $800. What was the length of the investment?   **5 years**

3 Close

Summarize

Remind students that they can earn interest on money that they deposit in the bank or invest in some other way. If they borrow money, they must pay interest as a fee to the lender. As the amount of time that the money is deposited or borrowed increases, so does the amount of interest that is paid.

6-7 **Exercises**

Assignment Guide

If you finished Example **1** assign:
Proficient 1, 6, 11–14, 22, 24, 26–30
Advanced 5, 13–16, 20, 22–24, 26–30

If you finished Example **2** assign:
Proficient 1, 2, 6, 7, 11–14, 17, 22, 24, 26–30
Advanced 6, 7, 15–17, 20, 24, 26–30

If you finished Example **3** assign:
Proficient 1–3, 6–8, 11–14, 17, 22, 24, 26–30
Advanced 6–8, 15–17, 20, 22–24, 26–30

If you finished Example **4** assign:
Proficient 1–4, 6–9, 11–14, 17, 22, 24–30
Advanced 6–9, 11–17, 19–30

If you finished Example **5** assign:
Proficient 1–14, 17, 22, 24–30
Advanced 5–30

Homework Quick Check

Quickly check key concepts.
Exercises: 6, 8, 10, 12

California Standards

Standard	Exercises
NS1.3	29–30
NS1.7	1–25
MG1.1	26–28

Math Background

While the principle of simple interest is mathematically important, compound interest is used for most applications in the real world. Students may benefit from studying compound interest as it will give them a better understanding of how interest works in the real world.

See Example ③ **3.** Paige deposited $1277 in a savings account. How much would she have in the account after 3 years at an annual simple interest rate of 4%? **$1430.24**

See Example ④ **4.** Tom borrowed $35,000 to remodel his house. At the end of the 5-year loan, he had repaid a total of $46,375. At what simple interest rate did he borrow the money? **6.5%**

See Example ⑤ **5.** Mari invested $2000 in a savings account that pays 4% interest compounded semi-annually. Find the value of the investment after 10 years. **about $2,971.89**

INDEPENDENT PRACTICE

See Example ① **6.** A bank offers an annual simple interest rate of 7% on home improvement loans. How much would Billy owe if he borrowed $18,500 over a period of 3.5 years? **$23,032.50**

See Example ② **7.** Eliza deposits $8500 in a college fund. If the fund earns an annual simple interest rate of 6.5%, how long must the money be in the fund to earn $9392.50 in interest? **17 years**

See Example ③ **8.** Jessika gave a security deposit of $1200 to her landlord, Mr. Allen, 8 years ago. Mr. Allen now intends to give her the deposit back with simple interest of 2.85%. How much will he return to her? **$1473.60**

See Example ④ **9.** Premier Bank loaned a construction company $275,000 at an annual simple interest rate. After 5 years, the company repaid the bank $350,625. What was the interest rate on the loan? **5.5%**

See Example ⑤ **10.** Tai invested $300 in a savings account that pays 3.6% interest compounded quarterly. Find the value of the investment after 8 years. **about $399.61**

PRACTICE AND PROBLEM SOLVING

Extra Practice
See page EP13.

Find the simple interest and the total amount to the nearest cent.

11. $315 at 6% per year for 5 years
$94.50, $409.50

12. $800 at 9% per year for 1 year
$72, $872

13. $4250 at 7% per year for 1.5 years
$446.25, $4696.25

14. $550 at 5.5% per year for 3 years
$90.75, $640.75

15. $617 at 6% per year for 3 months
$9.26, $626.26

16. $2975 at 6% per year for 5 years
$892.50, $3867.50

17. Selena borrowed $9500 to buy a used car. The credit union charged 7% simple interest per year. She paid $3325 in interest. For what period of time did she borrow money? **5 years**

18. Aleta invested $10,000 in a savings account for 10 years at a rate of 3%.

  a. What would be the value of the investment if the account is compounded semi-annually? **about $13,468.55**

  b. What would be the value of the investment if the account is compounded quarterly? **about $13,483.49**

  c. What would be the value of the investment if the account is compounded monthly? **about $13,493.54**

  d. Reasoning What can you conclude about the relationship between the compounding period and the amount of interest a savings account will earn? **If the rate of interest and time are the same, then the shorter the compounding period, the greater the amount of interest earned.**

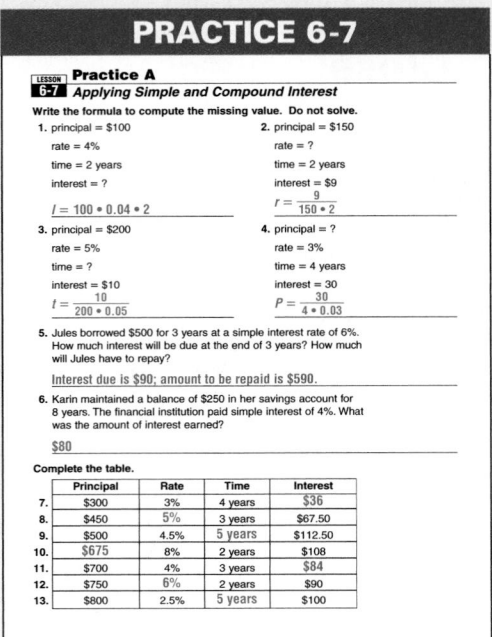

REVIEW FOR MASTERY 6-7

LESSON 6-7 Review for Mastery
Applying Simple and Compound Interest

Interest is money paid on an investment. A borrower pays the interest. An investor earns the interest.

Simple interest, I, is earned when an amount of money, the *principal P*, is borrowed or invested at a *rate of interest r* for a *period of time t*.

| Interest = Principal · Rate · Time |
| $I = P \cdot r \cdot t$ |

Situation 1: Find I given P, r, and t.

Calculate the simple interest on a loan of $3500 for a period of 6 months at a yearly rate of 5%.

Write the interest rate as a decimal.   5% = 0.05
Write the time period in terms of years.   6 months = 0.5 year
$I = P \cdot r \cdot t$
$I = 3500 \cdot 0.05 \cdot 0.5 = \$87.50$ ← interest earned

Find the interest in each case.

1. principal P = $5000; time t = 2 years; interest rate r = 6%
$I = P \cdot r \cdot t = \underline{5000} \cdot 0.06 \cdot \underline{2} = \$\underline{600}$

2. principal P = $2500; time t = 3 months; interest rate r = 8%
$I = P \cdot r \cdot t = \underline{2500} \cdot \underline{0.08} \cdot \underline{0.25} = \$\underline{50}$

Situation 2: Find t given I, P, and r.

An investment of $3000 at a yearly rate of 6.5% earned $390 in interest. Find the period of time for which the money was invested.

$I = P \cdot r \cdot t$
$390 = 3000 \cdot 0.065 \cdot t$
$390 = 195t$
$\frac{390}{195} = \frac{195t}{195}$
$2 = t$

The investment was for 2 years.

Find the time in each case.

3. $I = \$1120; P = \$4000; r = 7\%$
$I = P \cdot r \cdot t$
$1120 = \underline{4000} \cdot 0.07 \cdot t$
$1120 = \underline{280} t$
$\frac{1120}{280} = \frac{280t}{280}$
$\underline{4}$ years $= t$

4. $I = \$812.50; P = \$5000; r = 6.5\%$
$I = P \cdot r \cdot t$
$812.50 = \underline{5000} \cdot 0.065 \cdot t$
$812.50 = \underline{325} t$
$\frac{812.50}{325} = \frac{325t}{325}$
$\underline{2.5}$ years $= t$

PRACTICE 6-7

LESSON 6-7 Practice A
Applying Simple and Compound Interest

Write the formula to compute the missing value. Do not solve.

1. principal = $100
rate = 4%
time = 2 years
interest = ?
$I = 100 \cdot 0.04 \cdot 2$

2. principal = $150
rate = ?
time = 2 years
interest = $9
$r = \frac{9}{150 \cdot 2}$

3. principal = $200
rate = 5%
time = ?
interest = $10
$t = \frac{10}{200 \cdot 0.05}$

4. principal = ?
rate = 3%
time = 4 years
interest = 30
$P = \frac{30}{4 \cdot 0.03}$

5. Jules borrowed $500 for 3 years at a simple interest rate of 6%. How much interest will be due at the end of 3 years? How much will Jules have to repay?

Interest due is $90; amount to be repaid is $590.

6. Karin maintained a balance of $250 in her savings account for 8 years. The financial institution paid simple interest of 4%. What was the amount of interest earned?

$80

Complete the table.

	Principal	Rate	Time	Interest
7.	$300	3%	4 years	$36
8.	$450	5%	3 years	$67.50
9.	$500	4.5%	5 years	$112.50
10.	$675	8%	2 years	$108
11.	$700	4%	3 years	$84
12.	$750	6%	2 years	$90
13.	$800	2.5%	5 years	$100

Money

Many bank ATMs in Bangkok, Thailand, are located in sculptures to attract customers.

19. Reasoning Meghan and Sabrina compared the amount of interest they each earned on their savings accounts. Each had deposited $1000, but Meghan earned $140 interest and Sabrina earned $157.50. Whose savings account had a higher interest rate? Explain.

20. Money The Smiths will borrow $35,500 from a bank to start a business. They have two loan options. Option A is a 5-year loan; option B is a 4-year loan. Use the graph to answer the following questions.

  a. What is the total amount the Smiths would pay under each loan option?

  b. What would be the interest rate under each loan option?

  c. What would be the monthly payment under each loan option?

  d. How much interest will the Smiths save by choosing loan option B?

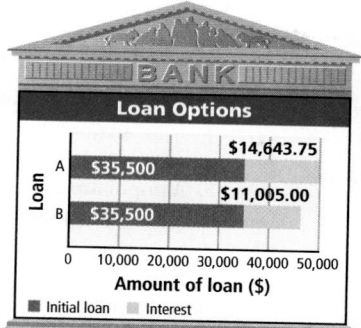

Loan Options

A: $35,500 — $14,643.75
B: $35,500 — $11,005.00

Loan / Amount of loan ($)
0   10,000 20,000 30,000 40,000 50,000
■ Initial loan   □ Interest

 21. What's the Question? Alice places $700 in a savings account with a simple annual interest rate of 4%. When Alice withdraws the money, she has $840. What is the question?

 22. Write About It Which loan would cost a borrower less: $3000 at 6% for 4 years or $3000 at 7.5% for 3 years? How much interest would the borrower save by taking the cheaper loan?

 23. Challenge How would the total payment on a 5-year loan at 3% annual simple interest compare with the total payment on a 5-year loan where one-twelfth of that simple interest, 0.25%, is calculated monthly? Give an example.

SPIRAL STANDARDS REVIEW
NS1.3, ✦ NS1.7, MG1.1

24. Multiple Choice Sam invested $2500 for 2 years in a savings account. The savings account paid an annual simple interest rate of 2.5% How much interest did Sam earn during the 2 years?

  Ⓐ $62.50   **Ⓑ $125**   Ⓒ $1250   Ⓓ $2625

25. Multiple Choice Toni invested $250 in a savings account for 4 years. The total interest earned on the investment was $125. What was the interest rate on the account?

  Ⓐ 3.125%   **Ⓑ 12.5%**   Ⓒ 125%   Ⓓ 1125%

Find the appropriate factor for each conversion. (Lesson 5-4)

26. meters to millimeters
    1000 mm/1 m

27. quarts to gallons
    1 gal/4 qt

28. gallons to pints
    8 pt/1 gal

Find each number. (Lesson 6-4)

29. 19 is 20% of what number? 95

30. 74% of what number is 481? 650

CHALLENGE 6-7

PROBLEM SOLVING 6-7

Organizer

Objective: Assess students' mastery of concepts and skills in Lessons 6-5 through 6-7.

Resources

 Assessment Resources
Section 6B Quiz

 Test & Practice Generator
One-Stop Planner®

INTERVENTION ◀══▶

Resources

 Ready to Go On?
Intervention and
Enrichment Worksheets

 Ready to Go On? CD-ROM

🪐 **Ready to Go On? Online**

my.hrw.com

Quiz for Lessons 6-5 Through 6-7

6-5 Applying Percent of Increase and Decrease

Find each percent of increase or decrease to the nearest percent.

1. from 40 to 55
38% increase

2. from 75 to 150
100% increase

3. from 110 to 82
25% decrease

4. from 87 to 25
71% decrease

5. A population of geese rose from 234 to 460 over a period of two years. What is the percent of increase, to the nearest tenth of a percent? **96.6%**

6. Mr. Simmons owns a hardware store and typically marks up merchandise by 28% over warehouse cost. How much would he charge a customer for a hammer that costs him $13.50? **$17.28**

7. A blouse and skirt that normally sell for $39.55 are on sale for 30% off the normal price. What is the discounted price? **$27.69**

6-6 Commission, Sales Tax, and Profit

Find each commission or sales tax to the nearest cent. **$687.50**

8. total sales: $12,500 **$406.25**
commission rate: 3.25%

9. total sales: $14.23
sales tax rate: 8.25% **$1.17**

10. total sales: $25,000
commission rate: 2.75%

11. total sales: $251.50
sales tax rate: 7.5% **$18.86**

12. total sales: $10,500
commission rate: 4%
$420

13. total sales: $75.99
sales tax rate: 6.125%
$4.65

14. Tom sells sunglasses that he buys wholesale. He earns 75% profit on all sales. If total sales were $5250, what was the profit? **$3937.50**

6-7 Applying Simple and Compound Interest

Find the interest and the total amount to the nearest cent.

15. $225 at 5% per year for 3 years
$33.75; $258.75

16. $775 at 8% per year for 1 year
$62; $837

17. Leroy borrowed $8250 to be repaid after 3 years at an annual simple interest rate of 7.25%. How much interest will be due after 3 years? How much will Leroy have to repay? **$1,794.38; $10,044.38**

18. Hank borrowed $25,000 to remodel his house. At the end of 3 years, he had repaid a total of $29,125. At what simple interest rate did he borrow the money? **5.5%**

19. Akule borrowed $1500 at an annual simple interest rate of 12%. He paid $270 in interest. For what period of time did Akule borrow the money? **1.5 years or 18 months**

20. Erik invested $3000 in a savings account that pays 4% interest compounded quarterly. Find the value of the investment after 5 years. **$3660.57**

READY TO GO ON?
Diagnose and Prescribe

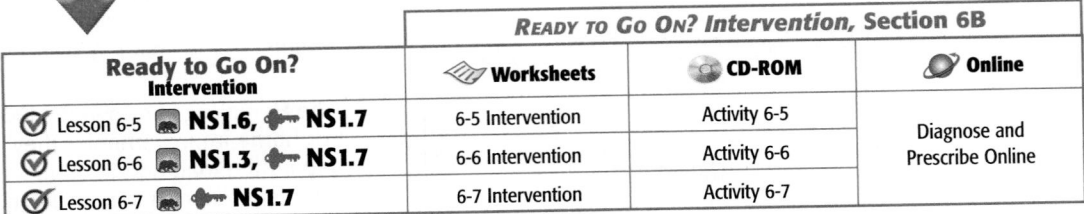

NO INTERVENE				
Ready to Go On? Intervention	🖎 **Worksheets**	💿 **CD-ROM**	🪐 **Online**	
☑ Lesson 6-5 🐻 NS1.6, 🔑 NS1.7	6-5 Intervention	Activity 6-5	Diagnose and Prescribe Online	
☑ Lesson 6-6 🐻 NS1.3, 🔑 NS1.7	6-6 Intervention	Activity 6-6		
☑ Lesson 6-7 🐻 🔑 NS1.7	6-7 Intervention	Activity 6-7		

READY TO GO ON? Intervention, Section 6B

YES ENRICH

READY TO GO ON?
Enrichment, Section 6B
🖎 **Worksheets**
🪐 **CD-ROM**
🪐 **Online**

CONCEPT CONNECTION

Get in Gear Mrs. Okendo's class is planning a camping trip. The students need to buy some camping gear. They use the advertisement from Mitchell's Sporting Goods to help them plan their purchases.

1. What is the discount on the lantern as a percent? How much do you save by buying the lantern during the sale?

2. Jake is looking for a tent for under $100. Explain how he can estimate the dollar amount of the discount on the tent at Mitchell's. Will Jake be able to buy his tent there?

3. Mitchell's advertises that all backpacks are discounted at least 25% during the spring sale. Is the statement true? Why or why not?

4. Li Ming needs to buy a sleeping bag, tent, and lantern. How much will these items cost if she buys them at Mitchell's? How much money will she save altogether?

5. Mrs. Okendo buys a set of 8 compasses for the class at Mitchell's. If the sales tax rate is 8.25%, what is the final cost for the compasses?

MITCHELL'S SPORTING GOODS

SPRING SALE!

18% OFF
COMPASS REG. PRICE $6

$13.75 OFF THE REGULAR PRICE

14% OFF

BACKPACK REG. PRICE $62.50

TENT REG. PRICE $119

10% OFF

$\frac{2}{5}$ OFF

SLEEPING BAG REG. PRICE $42

LANTERN REG. PRICE $15

Organizer

Objective: Assess students' ability to apply concepts and skills in Chapter 6 in a real-world format.

 Online Edition

Problem	Text reference
1	Lesson 6-1
2	Lesson 6-2
3	Lesson 6-3
4	Lesson 6-4
5	Lesson 6-6

Answers

1. 40%, $6.00

2. Possible estimate: $18. Use compatible numbers to estimate the discount as 15% of $120, which is $(10\% + 5\%) \cdot 120 = 12 + 6 = \$18$. Jake will not be able to buy the tent at Mitchell's.

3. The statement is not true. The discount on the backpack in the table is 22%.

4. $37.80, $102.34, $9.00; total saved is $26.86

5. $42.61

INTERVENTION

Scaffolding Questions

1. How do you convert a fraction to a percent? Divide the numerator by the denominator, then multiply by 100.

2. When estimating the cost of an item, is it better to estimate a little higher or a little lower than the actual cost? Why? It's better to estimate a little higher, because that way you can usually tell whether you'll have enough money to make the purchase.

3. What information do you need to answer this question? The percent discount of the backpack shown in the ad.

4. Can you add up the percent discounts to find the percent Li Ming will save? No

   What is one way to find the approximate percent of Li Ming's savings? Find the average percent discount of the items she plans to buy.

5. To solve this problem, what should you do first, add the sales tax or reduce the price of the item by the percent discount? Why? Reduce the price by the percent discount first, because the sales tax is taken from the final sale amount.

Extension

1. Bill's Sporting Goods advertises lanterns at a regular price of $14 each. During their spring sale, if you buy two lanterns at the regular price, you can buy a third at 50% off. Which store offers the better price for three lanterns? Mitchell's

 California Standards

Number Sense

1.3 Convert fractions to decimals and percents and use these representations in estimations, computations, and applications.

1.7 Solve problems that involve discounts, markups, commissions, and profit and compute simple and compound interest.

Organizer

Objective: Participate in games to practice and apply skills learned in Chapter 6.

 Online Edition

Resources

> **Chapter 6 Resource File**
> Puzzles, Twisters & Teasers

Percent Puzzlers

Purpose: To apply the skill of solving percent problems to perplexing puzzles

Discuss Instruct students that it is often helpful to express percents as decimals or fractions in order to solve a problem. In **problem 1,** what fraction of his sheep did the farmer put in each pen? $\frac{1}{5}$ in the first pen, $\frac{3}{10}$ in the second pen, $\frac{3}{8}$ in the third pen, and $1 - (\frac{1}{5} + \frac{3}{10} + \frac{3}{8}) = \frac{5}{40} = \frac{1}{8}$ in the fourth pen

Extend Have students search the Internet for more tricky percent problems. Have them prepare their own percent puzzlers to test on a parent or classmate. Check students' work.

Percent Tiles

Purpose: To practice finding percents in a game format

Discuss When a student collects a card, have him or her write an equation to show that the card has been correctly completed.

Extend Have students play again using tiles containing numbers from 1 to 25.

Game Time

Percent Puzzlers

Prove your precision with these perplexing percent puzzlers!

❶ A farmer is dividing his sheep among four pens. He puts 20% of the sheep in the first pen, 30% in the second pen, 37.5% in the third pen, and the rest in the fourth pen. What is the smallest number of sheep he could have?　**40**

❷ Karen and Tina are on the same baseball team. Karen has hit in 35% of her 200 times at bat. Tina has hit in 30% of her 20 times at bat. If Karen hits in 100% of her next five times at bat and Tina hits in 80% of her next five times at bat, who will have the higher percentage of hits?　**Tina**

❸ Joe was doing such a great job at work that his boss gave him a 10% raise! Then he made such a huge mistake that his boss gave him a 10% pay cut. What percent of his original salary does Joe make now?　**99%**

❹ Suppose you have 100 pounds of saltwater that is 99% water (by weight) and 1% salt. Some of the water evaporates so that the remaining liquid is 98% water and 2% salt. How much does the remaining liquid weigh?　**50 lb**

Percent Tiles

Use cardboard or heavy paper to make 100 tiles with a digit from 0 through 9 (10 of each) on each tile, and print out a set of cards. Each player draws seven tiles. Lay four cards out on the table as shown. The object of the game is to collect as many cards as possible. To collect a card, use numbered tiles to correctly complete the statement on the card.

A complete set of the rules and game cards are available online.

go.hrw.com
Game Time Extra
KEYWORD: MT8CA Games

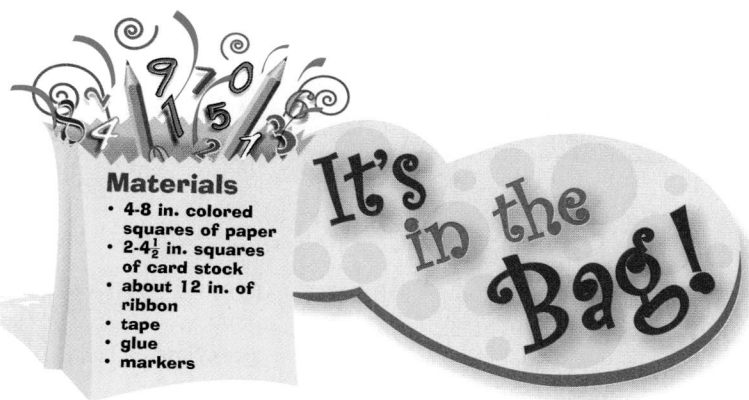

Materials
- 4-8 in. colored squares of paper
- 2-4½ in. squares of card stock
- about 12 in. of ribbon
- tape
- glue
- markers

It's in the Bag!

PROJECT ▶ Origami Percents

Make this spectacular fold-and-hold origami notebook to record facts about percents.

Directions

1 Fold one of the colored squares of paper in half vertically and then horizontally. Unfold the paper. Then fold the square diagonally and unfold the paper. **Figure A**

2 Fold the diagonal crease back and forth so that it is easy to work with. Then bring the two ends of the diagonal together as shown in the figure. **Figure B**

3 Repeat steps 1 and 2 for all of the squares of paper, and set them aside.

4 Lay the squares of card stock in front of you so that they are about ¼ inch apart. Lay the ribbon across the squares as shown, and tape it down. **Figure C**

5 Glue one of the folded squares onto the piece of card stock on the left. Glue the next folded square onto the first one so that their sides match up and they open in the same direction. Continue with the remaining squares, gluing the last one onto the piece of card stock on the right.

Taking Note of the Math

Write notes from the chapter on the various faces of the folded squares.

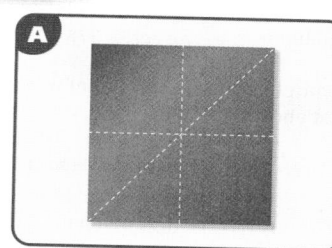

A

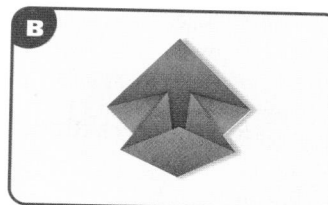

B

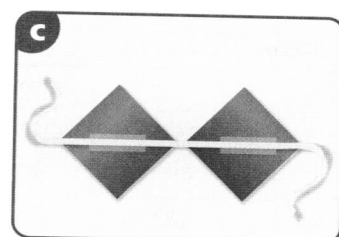

C

Organizer

Objective: Make a folding origami notebook on which to record notes about percents.

Materials: 4 colored squares of paper (8 in. by 8 in.), 2 squares of card stock (4½ in. by 4½ in.), about 12 in. of ribbon, tape, glue, markers

 Online Edition

Using the Page

Preparing the Materials
You can use paper squares that are specifically designed for origami or you can cut squares out of construction paper or copy paper.

Making the Project
To make the project flow more smoothly, demonstrate how to fold the paper squares before students begin folding them on their own.

Extending the Project
Students can make additional folded squares to make a longer chain. Have them use the extra space to write their own practice quiz on percents.

Tips from the Bag Ladies!

This project looks more complicated than it is. If your students are familiar with origami, they may recognize that the paper squares are folded into one of the most basic origami shapes.

As students are gluing the folded squares to each other, emphasize that the squares should all open in the same direction. This will make it much easier to use the resulting booklet.

Organizer

Objective: Help students organize and review key concepts and skills presented in Chapter 6.

 Online Edition
Multilingual Glossary

Resources

 **PuzzlePro®**
One-Stop Planner®

Multilingual Glossary Online

go.hrw.com
KEYWORD: MT8CA Glossary

Lesson Tutorial Videos
CD-ROM

 **Test & Practice Generator**
One-Stop Planner®

Answers

1. percent
2. percent of change
3. commission
4. 0.4375
5. 43.75%
6. $1\frac{1}{8}$
7. 112.5%
8. $\frac{7}{10}$
9. 0.7
10. 30
11. 62
12. 3.3
13. 18
14. $7.50
15. $16.00

Vocabulary

commission 298	markup 295	principal 302
commission rate 298	percent 274	profit 299
compatible numbers ..278	percent of change 294	rate of interest 302
discount 295	percent of decrease 294	sales tax 298
estimate 278	percent of increase 294	simple interest 302

Complete the sentences below with vocabulary words from the list above.

1. A ratio that compares a number to 100 is called a(n) ___?___.

2. The ratio $\frac{\text{amount of change}}{\text{original amount}}$ is called the ___?___.

3. Percent is used to calculate ___?___, a fee paid to a person who makes a sale.

6-1 Relating Fractions, Decimals, and Percents (pp. 274–277) NS1.3

EXAMPLE

■ Complete the table.

Fraction	Decimal	Percent
$\frac{3}{4}$	0.75	0.75(100) = 75%
$\frac{625}{1000} = \frac{5}{8}$	0.625	0.625(100) = 62.5%
$\frac{80}{100} = \frac{4}{5}$	0.80	80%

EXERCISES

Complete the table.

Fraction	Decimal	Percent
$\frac{7}{16}$	4.	5.
6.	1.125	7.
8.	9.	70%

6-2 Estimating with Percents (pp. 278–282) NS1.3

EXAMPLE

■ Estimate 6% of 17.

6% · 17 ≈ 5% · 20   *Use compatible numbers.*
≈ 0.05 · 20   *Write 5% as a decimal.*
≈ 1   *Multiply.*

6% of 17 is about 1.

EXERCISES

Estimate.

10. 11% of 303
11. 102% of 62
12. $33\frac{1}{3}$% of 10
13. 60% of 34
14. a 15% tip for $48.90
15. a 20% tip for $82.75

6-3 Finding Percents (pp. 283–287)

NS1.3

EXAMPLE

■ A raw apple weighing 5.3 oz contains about 4.45 oz of water. What percent of an apple is water?

$\frac{number}{100} = \frac{part}{whole}$ *Set up a proportion.*

$\frac{n}{100} = \frac{4.45}{5.3}$ *Substitute.*

$5.3n = 445$ *Cross multiply.*

$n = \frac{445}{5.3} \approx 83.96 \approx 84\%$

An apple is about 84% water.

EXERCISES

16. The length of a year on Mars is about 687 Earth days. The length of a year on Venus is about 225 Earth days. About what percent of the length of Mars's year is Venus's year?

17. The main span of the Brooklyn Bridge is 1595 feet long. The Golden Gate Bridge is about 263% the length of the Brooklyn Bridge. To the nearest hundred feet, how long is the Golden Gate Bridge?

6-4 Finding a Number When the Percent Is Known (pp. 288–291)

NS1.3

EXAMPLE

■ In 2003 the population of Fairbanks, Alaska, was 30,970. This was about 491% of the population of Kodiak, Alaska. To the nearest ten people, find the population of Kodiak in 2003.

$\frac{491}{100} = \frac{30,970}{n}$ *Set up a proportion.*

$491n = 3,097,000$ *Cross multiply.*

$n = \frac{3,097,000}{491} \approx 6307.5356 \approx 6310$

The population of Kodiak was about 6310.

EXERCISES

18. The diameter at the equator of Saturn is 74,897 miles. This is about 945% of the diameter of Earth at its equator. To the nearest ten miles, find the diameter of Earth at its equator.

19. At the age of 20 weeks, Zoe weighed 16 lb 4 oz. Her birth weight was about $33\frac{1}{3}\%$ of her 20-week weight. To the nearest ounce, what was her birth weight?

6-5 Applying Percent of Increase and Decrease (pp. 294–297)

NS1.6, NS1.7

EXAMPLE

■ In 1990 there were 639,270 robberies reported in the United States. This number decreased in 2002 to 420,637. What was the percent of decrease?

$639,270 - 420,637 = 218,633$ *Amount of decrease*

$\frac{amount\ of\ decrease}{original\ amount} = \frac{218,633}{639,270}$ *decrease*

$\approx 0.3420 \approx 34.2\%$

The number of reported robberies decreased by 34.2%.

EXERCISES

20. In 1900 the U.S. public debt was $1.2 billion dollars. This number increased to $5674.2 billion dollars in 2000. Find the percent of increase.

21. At the beginning of a 40-week medically supervised diet, Arnie weighed 276 lb. After the diet, Arnie weighed 181 lb. Find the percent of decrease.

22. A skirt originally priced at $25 was reduced in price by 16%. What was the discounted price?

Answers

16. 33%
17. 4200 ft
18. 7930 mi
19. 5 lb 7 oz
20. 472,750%
21. 34.4%
22. $21

Answers

23. $16,830

24. $3.55

25. $2000

26. $3171.88

27. $400

28. 7%

29. 0.5 yr

30. $1000 at 3.75% for 3 years; $7.50

31. about $574.44

6-6 Commission, Sales Tax, and Profit (pp. 298–301)  NS1.3, NS1.7

EXAMPLE

■ As an appliance salesman, Gavin earns a base pay of $525 per week plus a 6% commission on his weekly sales. Last week, his sales totaled $3250. How much did he earn for the week?

Find the amount of commission.

6% · $3250 = 0.06 · $3250 = $195

Add the commission amount to his base pay.

$195 + $525 = $720

Last week Gavin earned $720.

EXERCISES

23. As a real estate agent, Kensho earns $4\frac{1}{2}$% commission on the houses he sells. In the first quarter of this year, he sold two houses, one for $175,000 and the other for $199,000. How much was Kensho's commission for this quarter?

24. If the sales tax is $8\frac{1}{4}$%, how much tax would Luisa pay for a picture frame that costs $17.99 and a desk calendar that costs $24.99?

25. Members of the Helping Hand Club sell baskets to raise funds. The club earns 12% profit on all sales. If the club earned $240, how much were total sales?

6-7 Applying Simple and Compound Interest (pp. 303–307)  NS1.7

EXAMPLE

■ For home improvements, the Walters borrowed $10,000 for 3 years at simple interest. They repaid a total of $11,050. What was the interest rate of the loan?

Find the amount of interest.

$$P + I = A \quad \text{Use the formula.}$$
$$10{,}000 + I = 11{,}050 \quad \text{Substitute.}$$
$$\underline{-10{,}000 \qquad -10{,}000} \quad \begin{array}{l}\text{Subtract 10,000}\\\text{from both sides.}\end{array}$$
$$I = 1050 \quad \text{Simplify.}$$

Substitute into the simple interest formula.

$$I = P \cdot r \cdot t \quad \text{Use the formula.}$$
$$1050 = 10{,}000 \cdot r \cdot 3 \quad \text{Substitute.}$$
$$1050 = 30{,}000r \quad \text{Simplify.}$$
$$\frac{1050}{30{,}000} = \frac{30{,}000r}{30{,}000} \quad \begin{array}{l}\text{Divide both}\\\text{sides by 30,000.}\end{array}$$
$$0.035 = r \quad \text{Simplify.}$$

The interest rate of the loan was 3.5%.

EXERCISES

Using the simple interest formula, find the missing number.

26. interest = ▮; principal = $14,500; rate = $6\frac{1}{4}$% per year; time = $3\frac{1}{2}$ years

27. interest = $32; principal = ▮; rate = 2% per year; time = 4 years

28. interest = $367.50; principal = $1500; rate per year = ▮; time = $3\frac{1}{2}$ years

29. interest = $1787.50; principal = $55,000; rate = $6\frac{1}{2}$% per year; time = ▮

30. Which simple-interest loan would cost the borrower less, $1000 at 3% for 4 years or $1000 at 3.75% for 3 years? How much less?

31. Ana invested $500 in a savings account that pays 3.5% interest compounded semi-annually. Find the value of the investment after 4 years.

Order the numbers from least to greatest.

1. $\frac{4}{5}$, 75%, 0.82, $\frac{17}{20}$ 2. $\frac{8}{20}$, 0.35, 15%, 0.2   3. 75%, $\frac{7}{9}$, 0.8, $\frac{5}{6}$ 4. 58%, $\frac{33}{60}$, 0.45, 49%

   75%, $\frac{4}{5}$, 0.82, $\frac{17}{20}$ 15%, 0.2, 0.35, $\frac{8}{20}$ 75%, $\frac{7}{9}$, 0.8, $\frac{5}{6}$ 0.45, 49%, $\frac{33}{60}$, 58%

Estimate.

5. 17% of 42 **6**
6. 79% of 122 **96**
7. 32% of 511 **170**
8. 83% of 197 **170**
9. 4% of 1900 **80**
10. 27% of 80 **20**
11. a 15% tip on a $37 bill **$6**
12. a 19% tip on a $53 bill **$10**
13. a 17% tip on a $23 bill **$3**

14. Of the 50 states in the Union, 32% have names that begin with either M or N. How many states have names beginning with either M or N? **16**

15. 30 is 12.5% of what number? **240**
16. 244 is 250% of what number? **97.6**
17. $7\frac{1}{2}$ is 5% of what number? **150**
18. 5.6 is 56% of what number **10**

19. At 3 P.M., a chimney casts a shadow that is 135% its actual height. If the shadow is 37.8 ft, what is the actual height of the chimney? **28 ft**

Find each percent of increase or decrease to the nearest percent.

20. from 125 to 75   21. from 20 to 62   22. from 236 to 125   23. from 11 to 98
24. from 0.5 to 2   25. from 12.2 to 6.1   26. from 18.4 to 3.2   27. from 0.2 to 6

28. The price for a share of XYZ stock went from $32 to $37 in one month. What was the percent of increase to the nearest tenth of a percent? **15.6%**

Find each commission or sales tax to the nearest cent.

29. total sales: $13,600 **$374**   30. total sales: $135.50 **$11.18**   31. total sales: $20,250 **$789.75**
    commission rate: 2.75%   sales tax rate: 8.25%   commission rate: 3.9%

32. A tourist shop earns a 20% profit on all sales of flip-flops. If the total in flip-flop sales was $1280, what was the profit? **$256**

33. All drum sets at a music store earn a 60% profit. If the store earned $12,000 for the sale of drum sets, how much were total sales of the drum sets? **$20,000**

34. Dena borrowed $7500 to buy a used car. The credit union charged 9% simple interest per year. She paid $2025 in interest. For what period of time did she borrow the money? **3 years**

35. Doug invested $2000 in a savings account that pays 3% interest compounded monthly. Find the value of the investment after 5 years. **about $2323.23**

20. **40% decrease**   21. **210% increase**   22. **47% decrease**   23. **791% increase**
24. **300% increase**   25. **50% decrease**   26. **83% decrease**   27. **2900% increase**

Organizer

Objective: Assess students' mastery of concepts and skills in Chapter 6.

 Online Edition

Resources

 Assessment Resources

Chapter 6 Tests
- Free Response (Levels A, B, C)
- Multiple Choice (Levels A, B, C)
- Performance Assessment

IDEA Works! CD-ROM
Modified Chapter 6 Test

Test & Practice Generator
One-Stop Planner®

California Standards	
Standard	**Exercises**
NS1.1	1–4
NS1.3	5–19, 30
NS1.6	20–28
NS1.7 🔑	29, 31–35

Organizer

Objective: Provide review and practice for Chapters 1–6.

 Online Edition

Resources

 Assessment Resources
Chapter 6 Cumulative Test

 Focus on California Standards Benchmark Tests and Intervention

 California Standards Practice CD-ROM

go.hrw.com
KEYWORD: MT8CA Practice

California Standards	
Standard	**Items**
NS1.3	1, 8, 11–12, 16–17
NS1.6	7, 9
NS1.7 🔑	2–4, 10, 19–20
AF1.1	6, 14
AF4.1 🔑	5, 14
MG1.1	13
MG1.2	15
MG2.4	18

Cumulative Assessment, Chapters 1–6

Multiple Choice

1. Stella purchases a meal and beverage at a restaurant for a total cost of $8.75. She wants to leave a 20% tip. Which expression CANNOT be used to estimate the tip?

- (A) $\frac{1}{5} \times \$9$
- (B) $0.2 \times \$9$
- (C) $0.02 \times \$9$
- (D) $2(0.1 \times \$9)$

2. The Lincoln School Booster Club makes a profit of 20% on all sales of bill caps. During one football season, the total sales on bill caps were $2625. How much was the profit?

- (A) $3150
- (B) $2100
- (C) $630
- (D) $525

3. A retail jewelry store marks the price of its jewelry up 50%. What will be the selling price of an item that the store purchased for $95?

- (A) $142.50
- (B) $99.75
- (C) $47.50
- (D) $4.75

4. A sailboat associate makes $2500 per month plus commission. One month she sold one sailboat for $38,000, earning a 3% commission on the sale. What was her total pay for the month?

- (A) $114
- (B) $1140
- (C) $2614
- (D) $3640

5. Which equation is equivalent to the equation $\frac{1}{2}x + 8 = -10$?

- (A) $\frac{1}{2}x = -2$
- (C) $x + 8 = -20$
- (B) $x + 8 = -5$
- (D) $\frac{1}{2}x = -18$

6. Which situation corresponds to the inequality $x < 90$?

- (A) Jerry has at least $90 in his bank account.
- (B) Jerry owes his mom no more than $90 for his car insurance.
- (C) Jerry rented more than 90 videos last year.
- (D) Jerry works fewer than 90 hours each month at the newspaper.

7. A refrigerator that usually sells for $879 goes on sale for $649. What is the percent of decrease, to the nearest tenth of a percent?

- (A) 12.2%
- (C) 35.4%
- (B) 26.2%
- (D) 173.8%

8. The human body is 65% water. Which is NOT an equivalent number?

- (A) 0.65
- (C) 6.5×10^{-1}
- (B) $\frac{13}{20}$
- (D) 6.50

9. A can of soup had 480 mg of sodium per serving. The sodium was reduced to 360 mg per serving so that the soup could be advertised as "low sodium." What was the percent of decrease in sodium content?

- (A) 25%
- (C) 75%
- (B) 33%
- (D) 175%

 **Teaching Tip**

For **item 5,** remind students that in order to simplify the equation, they must subtract 8 from both sides. Students who answer **A** added 8 to the right side of the equation.

For **item 8,** remind students that in order to convert a percent to a decimal, they must divide by 100. Students who answered **D** divided by 10 instead.

Answers

16. 40%; $\frac{p}{100} = \frac{10}{25}$; $p = 40$

17. 40%; Every time Jim fills a jar he puts 1 L of excess into the 10 L jar. After he has filled the 4 L, 3 L, 2 L, and 1 L jars, there are 4 L in the 10 L jar.
$p \cdot 10 = 4$; $p = 0.4$

18–19. See p. A3.

20. See 4-Point Response work sample.

10. Gloria invests $158 in a simple interest account for 4 years at 2% interest. How many dollars did she earn in interest?

Ⓐ $170.64   Ⓒ $12.64
Ⓑ $126.40   Ⓓ $1.26

Underline key words, such as *at least, rounded to,* and *equivalent,* to help you focus on what is being asked.

Gridded Response

11. Heidi, Mike, Brenda, and Luis won 120 tokens in all at a fair. Heidi won $\frac{1}{5}$ of the tokens, Mike won 0.4 of the tokens, Brenda won 25% of the tokens, and Luis won the rest. How many tokens did Luis win?   **18**

12. Yesenia, a real estate agent, has 32 houses on the market. If she sells 5 of the houses this month, what percent of the houses on the market will she sell? Grid your response as a decimal rounded to the nearest thousandth.   **15.625**

13. A bicyclist rides at the rate of 20 feet per second. Give the rate in miles per hour. Round your answer to the nearest tenth.   **13.6**

14. Six more than $\frac{1}{4}$ of a number is 12.1. What is the number?   **24.4**

15. Find the number of km the Steward family will travel sailing from St. Petersburg to Pensacola, Florida. Grid your response to the nearest one hundred kilometers.   **600**

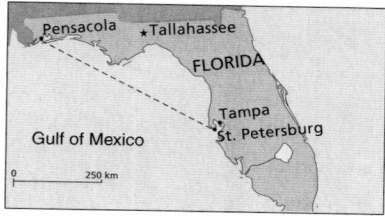

Short Response

16. If 10 kg of acid is added to 15 kg of water, what percent of the resulting solution is acid? Show your work.

17. In the chemistry laboratory, Jim is working with six large jars of capacities 5 L, 4 L, 3 L, 2 L, 1 L, and 10 L. The 5 L jar is filled with an acid mix, and the rest of the jars are empty. Jim uses the 5 L jar to fill the 4 L jar and pours the excess into the 10 L jar. Then he uses the 4 L jar to fill the 3 L jar and pours the excess into the 10 L jar. He repeats the process until all but the 1 L and 10 L jars are empty. What percent of the 10 L jar is now filled? Show your work.

18. One package of decorative paper contains 12 ft^2 of paper. Another package of decorative paper contains 1872 in^2. Which package contains the most paper? Show your work.

19. Four friends equally shared the cost of a $48.80 gift. They got a 20% discount and then paid 7.25% sales tax on the discounted price. How much money did each person pay? Explain.

Extended Response

20. Amanda and Sergio each have $3000 to invest. Amanda invests with her local banker, while Sergio invests his money using an online service. They both invest at a 3% interest rate.

   a. Amanda's banker invests the money using a simple interest plan. If Amanda keeps her money in this plan for 5 years, how much interest will she earn?

   b. What is the value of Sergio's investment if he invests for 5 years compounded annually?

   c. What is the difference in the amount of money earned? Explain your reasoning.

   d. Who earns more money after 5 years?

Student Work Samples for Item 20

4-Point Response

a. $I = Prt$
$I = (3000)(0.03)(5)$
$I = \$450$

b. $A = P\left(1 + \frac{r}{k}\right)^{nk}$
$A = (3000)\left(1 + \frac{0.03}{1}\right)^{5 \cdot 1}$
$A = \$3477.82$

c. $\$3477.82 - \$3450 = \$27.82$
Subtract the amount Amanda earned from the amount Sergio earned.

d. Sergio

The student correctly applied the simple interest and compound interest equations, correctly calculated the amounts, and offered an adequate explanation.

3-Point Response

a. $I = Prt$
$I = (3000)(0.30)(5)$
$I = \$4500$

b. $A = P\left(1 + \frac{r}{k}\right)^{nk}$
$A = (3000)\left(1 + \frac{0.30}{k}\right)^{5 \cdot 1}$
$A = \$11,138.79$

c. $\$11,138.79 - \$4500 = \$6638.79$
Subtract Amanda's total from Sergio's total.

d. Sergio

The student correctly applied the simple interest and compound interest equations, but made a mistake in applying a percent, which caused errors in all calculations.

2-Point Response

a. $I = Prt$
$I = 3000(3)(5)$
$I = \$45,000$

b. $A = (Prt)t$
$A = (3000 \cdot 3 \cdot 5)5$
$A = \$225,000$

c. $\$225,000 - \$45,000 = \$180,000$
Subtract one total from the other.

d. Sergio

The student made a mistake in applying a percent, which caused errors in all calculations. The student also incorrectly applied the compound interest formula.

Graphs and Functions

✔ Grade-level Standard
◀ Review
▶ Beyond the Standards
A Assessment
O Optional

Pacing Guide

Calendar Planner
Teacher's *One-Stop* Planner®

Lesson/Lab	California Standards	Time	Advanced Students	Benchmark* Students	Strategic** Students
7-1 The Coordinate Plane	Prep for AF3.3	50 min	O	O	◀
7-2 Functions	Prep for AF3.3	50 min	O	◀	◀
7-3 Graphing Linear Functions	AF1.1, AF3.3	50 min	✔	✔	✔
7-4 Graphing Quadratic Functions	AF3.1	50 min	✔	✔	✔
7-5 Cubic Functions	AF3.1	50 min	✔	✔	✔
Ready to Go On?		25 min	A	A	A
Focus on Problem Solving		25 min	A	A	O
7-6 Rate of Change and Slope	AF3.3	75 min	✔	✔	✔
7-7 Finding Slope of a Line	AF1.5, AF3.3, AF3.4	50 min	✔	✔	✔
7-8 Interpreting Graphs	AF1.5	50 min	✔	✔	✔
7-9 Direct Variation	AF3.3, AF3.4, AF4.2	75 min	✔	✔	✔
Ready to Go On?		25 min	A	A	A
Concept Connection		25 min	A	A	O
Study Guide: Review		50 min	✔	✔	✔
Chapter Test		50 min	A	A	A

* **Benchmark students** are achieving at or near grade level.

** **Strategic students** may be a year or more below grade level and may require additional time for intervention.

Countdown to Mastery, Weeks 13, 14, 15

ONGOING ASSESSMENT and INTERVENTION

DIAGNOSE	PRESCRIBE

Assess Prior Knowledge

Before Chapter 7

Diagnose readiness for the chapter.
Are You Ready? SE p. 319

Prescribe intervention.
Are You Ready? Intervention Skills 28, 47, 54, 59, 60

Formative Assessment

Before Every Lesson

Diagnose readiness for the lesson.
Warm Up TE, every lesson

Prescribe intervention.
Skills Bank SE pp. SB2–SB24
Review for Mastery CRF, Chapters 1–7

During Every Lesson

Diagnose understanding of lesson concepts.
Questioning Strategies Chapter 7
Think and Discuss SE, every lesson
Write About It SE, lesson exercises
Journal TE, lesson exercises

Prescribe intervention.
Reading Strategies CRF, every lesson
Success for ELL Chapter 7
Lesson Tutorial Videos Chapter 7

After Every Lesson

Diagnose mastery of lesson concepts.
Lesson Quiz TE, every lesson
Ready to Go On? SE pp. 342, 362
Test and Practice Generator

Prescribe intervention.
Review for Mastery CRF, every lesson
Problem Solving CRF, every lesson
Ready to Go On? Intervention Chapter 7
Homework Help Online

Before Chapter 7 Testing

Diagnose mastery of concepts in the chapter.
Ready to Go On? SE pp. 342, 362
Focus on Problem Solving SE p. 343
Concept Connection SE p. 363
Section Quizzes AR pp. 125–126
Test and Practice Generator

Prescribe intervention.
Ready to Go On? Intervention Chapter 7
Scaffolding Questions TE p. 363

Before Assessment of California Standards

Diagnose mastery of California standards.
Focus on California Standards: Benchmark Tests
Mastering the Standards SE pp. 372–373
California Standards Practice CD-ROM

Prescribe intervention.
Focus on California Standards: Intervention

Summative Assessment

After Chapter 7

Check mastery of chapter concepts.
Multiple-Choice Tests (Forms A, B, C)
Free-Response Tests (Forms A, B, C)
Performance Assessment AR pp. 127–140
Test and Practice Generator

Prescribe intervention.
Review for Mastery CRF, every lesson
Lesson Tutorial Videos Chapter 7

KEY: **SE** = *Student Edition* **TE** = *Teacher's Edition* **CRF** = *Chapter Resource File* **AR** = *Assessment Resources*  Available on CD-ROM Available online

318B

Supporting the Teacher

Chapter 7 Resource File

Family Involvement
pp. 1–4, 45–48

Practice A, B, C
pp. 5–7, 13–15, 21–23, 29–31, 37–39, 49–51, 57–59, 65–67, 73–75

Review for Mastery
pp. 8, 16, 24, 32, 40, 52, 60, 68, 76

Challenge
pp. 9, 17, 25, 33, 41, 53, 61, 69, 77

Problem Solving
pp. 10, 18, 26, 34, 42, 54, 62, 70, 78

Reading Strategies ELL
pp. 11, 19, 27, 35, 43, 55, 63, 71, 79

Puzzles, Twisters, and Teasers
pp. 12, 20, 28, 36, 44, 56, 64, 72, 80

Hands-On Lab
pp. 83–84, 87–90

Technology Lab
pp. 81–82, 85–86, 91–92

Workbooks

Homework and Practice Workbook SPANISH
Teacher's Guide..pp. 49–57

Know-It Notebook SPANISH
Teacher's Guide... Chapter 7

Review for Mastery Workbook SPANISH
Teacher's Guide.. pp. 49–57

Focus on California Standards: Intervention Workbook SPANISH
Teacher's Guide

Teacher Tools

Power Presentations
Complete PowerPoint® presentations for Chapter 7 lessons

Lesson Tutorial Videos SPANISH
Holt authors Ed Burger and Freddie Renfro present tutorials to support the Chapter 7 lessons.

Teacher's One-Stop Planner SPANISH
Easy access to all Chapter 7 resources and assessments, as well as software for lesson planning, test generation, and puzzle creation

IDEA Works!
Key Chapter 7 resources and assessments modified to address special learning needs

Questioning Strategies.. Chapter 7

Solutions Key... Chapter 7

Interactive Answers and Solutions

TechKeys   **Lab Resources**

Project Teacher Support   **Parent Resources**

Transparencies

Lesson Transparencies, Volume 2............................ Chapter 7
• Teacher Tools
• Warm Ups
• Teaching Transparencies
• Lesson Quizzes

Know-It Notebook... Chapter 7
• Vocabulary   • Chapter Review
• Additional Examples   • Big Ideas

Alternate Openers: Explorations............................pp. 49–57

Countdown to Mastery..pp. 25–29

Technology Highlights for the Teacher

 **Power Presentations**
Dynamic presentations to engage students. Complete PowerPoint® presentations for every lesson in Chapter 7.

One-Stop Planner SPANISH
Easy access to Chapter 7 resources and assessments. Includes lesson-planning, test-generation, and puzzle-creation software.

Premier Online Edition SPANISH
Includes Tutorial Videos, Lesson Activities, Lesson Quizzes, Homework Help, Chapter Project and more.

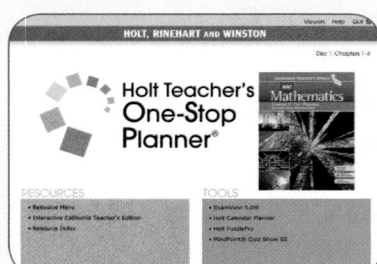

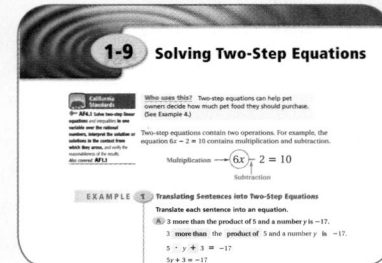

Universal Access

Teaching tips to help all students appear throughout the chapter. A few that target specific students are included in the lists below.

Strategic Students

Practice A	CRF, every lesson
Review for Mastery	CRF, every lesson
Reading Strategies	CRF, every lesson
Academic Vocabulary Connections	TE p. 320
Visual	TE pp. 331, 345
Ready to Go On? Intervention	Chapter 7
Questioning Strategies	Chapter 7
Know-It Notebook SPANISH	Chapter 7
Homework Help Online 🌐	
Lesson Tutorial Videos 🌐 💿 SPANISH	
Online Interactivities 🌐 SPANISH	

Special Needs Students

Practice A	CRF, every lesson
Review for Mastery	CRF, every lesson
Reading Strategies	CRF, every lesson
Academic Vocabulary Connections	TE p. 320
Inclusion	TE p. 350
IDEA Works! Modified Resources	Chapter 7
Ready to Go On? Intervention	Chapter 7
Know-It Notebook SPANISH	Chapter 7
Lesson Tutorial Videos 🌐 💿 SPANISH	
Online Interactivities 🌐 SPANISH	

English Learners

Reading Strategies	CRF, every lesson
Vocabulary Review	SE p. 366
Academic Vocabulary Connections	TE p. 320
English Language Learners	TE pp. 323, 335
Language Support	TE p. 327
Success for English Language Learners	Chapter 7
Know-It Notebook SPANISH	Chapter 7
Multilingual Glossary 🌐	
Lesson Tutorial Videos 🌐 💿 SPANISH	

Benchmark Students

Practice B	CRF, every lesson
Problem Solving	CRF, every lesson
Academic Vocabulary Connections	TE p. 320
Ready to Go On? Intervention	Chapter 7
Questioning Strategies	Chapter 7
Know-It Notebook SPANISH	Chapter 7
Homework Help Online 🌐	
Online Interactivities 🌐 SPANISH	

Advanced Students

Practice C	CRF, every lesson
Challenge	CRF, every lesson
Reading and Writing Math EXTENSION	TE p. 321
Concept Connection EXTENSION	TE p. 363
Advanced Learners/GATE	TE pp. 327, 345
Ready to Go On? Enrichment	Chapter 7

Technology Highlights for Universal Access

💿 Lesson Tutorial Videos SPANISH

Starring Holt authors Ed Burger and Freddie Renfro! Live tutorials to support every lesson in Chapter 7.

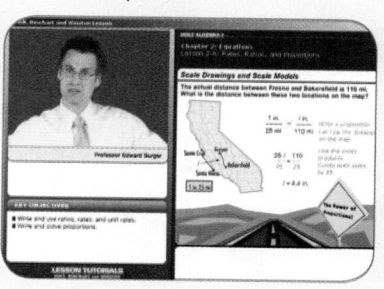

🌐 Multilingual Glossary

Searchable glossary includes definitions in English, Spanish, Vietnamese, Chinese, Hmong, Korean, and other languages.

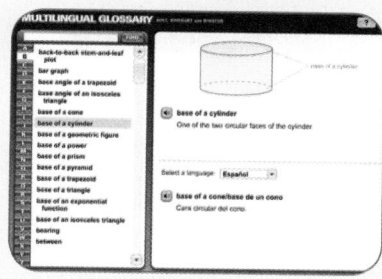

🌐 Online Interactivities SPANISH

Interactive tutorials provide visually engaging alternative opportunities to learn concepts and master skills.

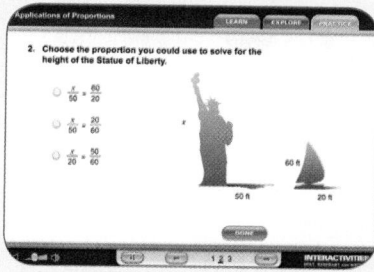

KEY: **SE** = *Student Edition* **TE** = *Teacher's Edition* **CRF** = *Chapter Resource File* SPANISH Spanish available 💿 Available on CD-ROM 🌐 Available online

CHAPTER 7

Ongoing Assessment

Assessing Prior Knowledge

Determine whether students have the prerequisite concepts and skills for success in Chapter 7.

Are You Ready? SPANISH 🪐 💿 .... SE p. 319
Warm Up ✋ 💿 .... TE, every lesson

Chapter and Standards Assessment

Provide review and practice for Chapter 7 and standards mastery.

Concept Connection .... SE p. 363
Study Guide: Review .... SE pp. 366–368
Strategies for Success .... SE pp. 370–371
Mastering the Standards .... SE pp. 372–373
Countdown to Mastery Transparencies ✋ 💿 ..... pp. 25–29
Focus on California Standards: Benchmark Tests 🪐 💿
Focus on California Standards: Intervention Workbook SPANISH
California Standards Practice CD-ROM 💿 SPANISH
IDEA Works! Modified Worksheets and Tests

Alternative Assessment

Assess students' understanding of Chapter 7 concepts and combined problem-solving skills.

Performance Assessment .... AR pp. 139–140
Portfolio Assessment .... AR p. xxxvi
Chapter 7 Project 🪐

Daily Assessment

Provide formative assessment for each day of Chapter 7.

Think and Discuss .... SE, every lesson
Write About It .... SE, lesson exercises
Journal .... TE, lesson exercises
Lesson Quiz ✋ 💿 .... TE, every lesson
Questioning Strategies .... Chapter 7
IDEA Works! Modified Lesson Quizzes .... Chapter 7

Weekly Assessment

Provide formative assessment for each week of Chapter 7.

Focus on Problem Solving .... SE p. 343
Concept Connection .... SE p. 363
Ready to Go On? SPANISH 🪐 💿 .... SE pp. 342, 362
Cumulative Assessment .... SE pp. 372–373
Test and Practice Generator SPANISH 💿 ...One-Stop Planner

Formal Assessment

Provide summative assessment of Chapter 7 mastery.

Section Quizzes .... AR pp. 125–126
Chapter 7 Test SPANISH .... SE p. 369
Chapter Test (Levels A, B, C) .... AR pp. 127–138
  • Multiple-Choice • Free-Response
Cumulative Test .... AR pp. 141–144
Test and Practice Generator SPANISH 💿 ...One-Stop Planner
IDEA Works! Modified Tests .... Chapter 7

Technology Highlights for the Teacher

🪐 **Are You Ready?** SPANISH

Automatically assess readiness and prescribe intervention for Chapter 7 prerequisite skills.

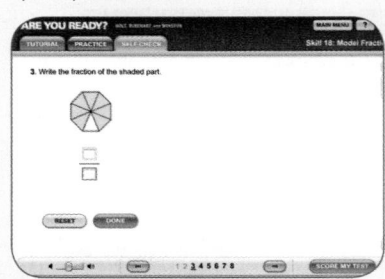

🪐 **Ready to Go On?** SPANISH

Automatically assess understanding of and prescribe intervention for Sections 7A and 7B.

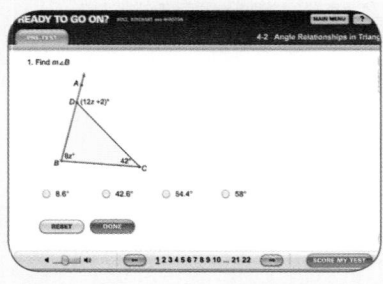

🪐 💿 **Focus on California Standards: Benchmark Tests and Intervention** SPANISH

Automatically assess proficiency with California Grade 7 Standards and provide intervention.

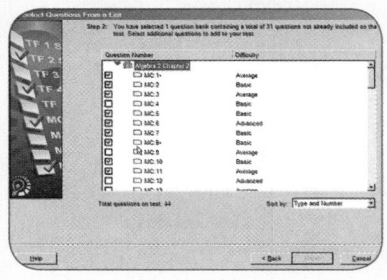
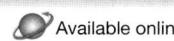

KEY: **SE** = *Student Edition* **TE** = *Teacher's Edition* **AR** = *Assessment Resources* SPANISH Spanish available 💿 Available on CD-ROM 🪐 Available online

Formal Assessment

Three levels (A, B, C) of multiple-choice and free-response chapter tests are available in the *Assessment Resources.*

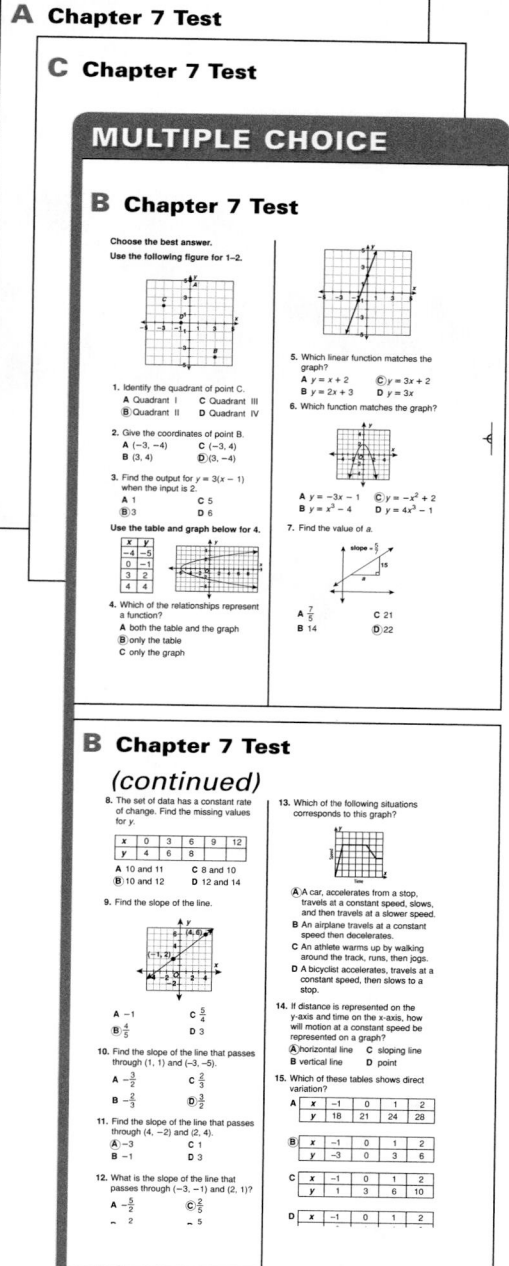

A Chapter 7 Test

C Chapter 7 Test

MULTIPLE CHOICE

B Chapter 7 Test

Choose the best answer.
Use the following figure for 1–2.

1. Identify the quadrant of point C.
   A Quadrant I   C Quadrant III
   B Quadrant II   D Quadrant IV

2. Give the coordinates of point B.
   A (−3, −4)   C (−3, 4)
   B (3, 4)   D (3, 4)

3. Find the output for $y = 3(x − 1)$ when the input is 2.
   A 1   C 5
   B 3   D 6

Use the table and graph below for 4.

x	y
−4	−5
0	−1
3	2
4	4

4. Which of the relationships represent a function?
   A both the table and the graph
   B only the table
   C only the graph

5. Which linear function matches the graph?
   A $y = x + 2$ C $y = 3x + 2$
   B $y = 2x + 3$ D $y = 3x$

6. Which function matches the graph?
   A $y = −3x − 1$ C $y = −x^2 + 2$
   B $y = x^3 − 4$ D $y = 4x^3 − 1$

7. Find the value of a.
   slope = $\frac{5}{9}$
   15
   A $\frac{7}{5}$ C 21
   B 14   D 22

B Chapter 7 Test
(continued)

8. The set of data has a constant rate of change. Find the missing values for y.

x	0	3	6	9	12
y	4	6	8		

   A 10 and 11   C 8 and 10
   B 10 and 12   D 12 and 14

9. Find the slope of the line.
   A −1   C $\frac{5}{4}$
   B $\frac{4}{5}$ D 3

10. Find the slope of the line that passes through (1, 1) and (−3, −5).
    A $−\frac{3}{2}$ C $\frac{2}{3}$
    B $−\frac{2}{3}$ D $\frac{3}{2}$

11. Find the slope of the line that passes through (4, −2) and (2, 4).
    A −3   C 1
    B −1   D 3

12. What is the slope of the line that passes through (−3, −1) and (2, 1)?
    A $−\frac{5}{2}$ C $\frac{2}{5}$
    ~ 2   ~ 5

13. Which of the following situations corresponds to this graph?
    A A car, accelerates from a stop, travels at a constant speed, slows, and then travels at a slower speed.
    B An airplane travels at a constant speed then decelerates.
    C An athlete warms up by walking around the track, runs, then jogs.
    D A bicyclist accelerates, travels at a constant speed, then slows to a stop.

14. If distance is represented on the y-axis and time on the x-axis, how will motion at a constant speed be represented on a graph?
    A horizontal line   C sloping line
    B vertical line   D point

15. Which of these tables shows direct variation?

    A | x | −1 | 0 | 1 | 2 |
      |---|---|---|---|---|
      | y | 18 | 21 | 24 | 28 |

    B | x | −1 | 0 | 1 | 2 |
      |---|---|---|---|---|
      | y | −3 | 0 | 3 | 6 |

    C | x | −1 | 0 | 1 | 2 |
      |---|---|---|---|---|
      | y | 1 | 3 | 6 | 10 |

    D | x | −1 | 0 | 1 | 2 |

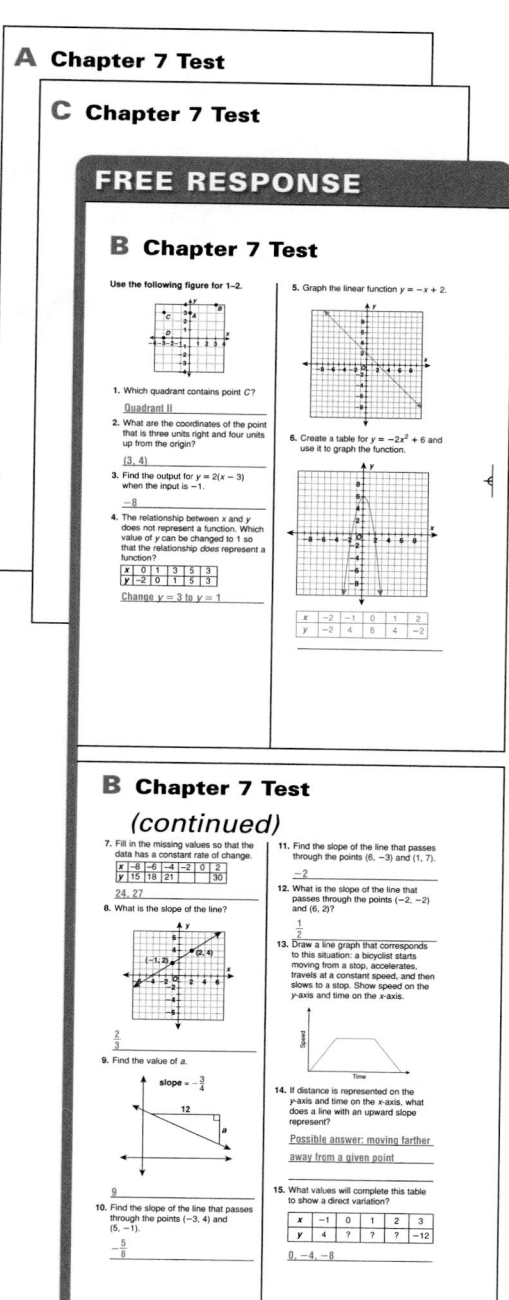

A Chapter 7 Test

C Chapter 7 Test

FREE RESPONSE

B Chapter 7 Test

Use the following figure for 1–2.

5. Graph the linear function $y = −x + 2$.

1. Which quadrant contains point C?
   Quadrant II

2. What are the coordinates of the point that is three units right and four units up from the origin?
   (3, 4)

3. Find the output for $y = 2(x − 3)$ when the input is −1.
   −8

4. The relationship between x and y does not represent a function. Which value of y can be changed to 1 so that the relationship *does* represent a function?

x	0	1	3	5	3
y	−2	0	1	5	3

   Change y = 3 to y = 1

6. Create a table for $y = −2x^2 + 6$ and use it to graph the function.

x	−2	−1	0	1	2
y	−2	4	6	4	−2

B Chapter 7 Test
(continued)

7. Fill in the missing value so that the data has a constant rate of change.

x	−8	−6	−4	−2	0	2
y	15	18	21			30

   24, 27

8. What is the slope of the line?
   $\frac{2}{3}$

9. Find the value of a.
   slope = $−\frac{3}{4}$
   12
   9

10. Find the slope of the line that passes through the points (−3, 4) and (5, −1).
    $−\frac{5}{8}$

11. Find the slope of the line that passes through the points (6, −3) and (1, 7).
    −2

12. What is the slope of the line that passes through the points (−2, −2) and (6, 2)?
    $\frac{1}{2}$

13. Draw a line graph that corresponds to this situation: a bicyclist starts moving from a stop, accelerates, travels at a constant speed, and then slows to a stop. Show speed on the y-axis and time on the x-axis.

14. If distance is represented on the y-axis and time on the x-axis, what does a line with an upward slope represent?
    Possible answer: moving farther away from a given point

15. What values will complete this table to show a direct variation?

x	−1	0	1	2	3
y	4	?	?	?	−12

    0, −4, −8

Modified tests and worksheets found in *IDEA Works!*

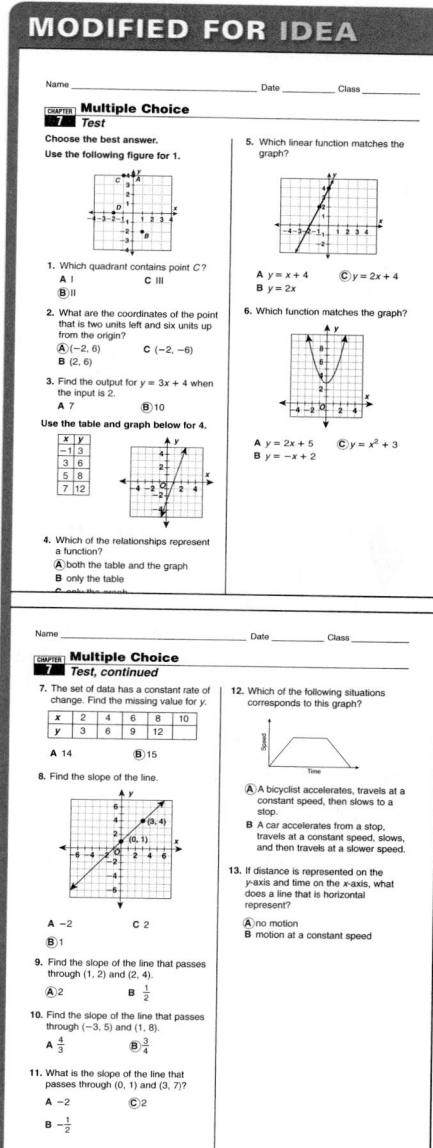

MODIFIED FOR IDEA

Name _____ Date _____ Class _____

CHAPTER 7 **Multiple Choice**
Test

Choose the best answer.
Use the following figure for 1.

1. Which quadrant contains point C?
   A I   C III
   B II

2. What are the coordinates of the point that is two units left and six units up from the origin?
   A (−2, 6)   C (−2, −6)
   B (2, 6)

3. Find the output for $y = 3x + 4$ when the input is 2.
   A 7   B 10

Use the table and graph below for 4.

x	y
−1	3
3	6
5	8
7	12

4. Which of the relationships represent a function?
   A both the table and the graph
   B only the table
   C only the graph

5. Which linear function matches the graph?
   A $y = x + 4$ C $y = 2x + 4$
   B $y = 2x$

6. Which function matches the graph?
   A $y = 2x + 5$ C $y = x^2 + 3$
   B $y = −x + 2$

Name _____ Date _____ Class _____

CHAPTER 7 **Multiple Choice**
Test, continued

7. The set of data has a constant rate of change. Find the missing value for y.

x	2	4	6	8	10
y	3	6	9	12	

   A 14   B 15

8. Find the slope of the line.
   A −2   C 2
   B 1

9. Find the slope of the line that passes through (1, 2) and (2, 4).
   A 2   B $\frac{1}{2}$

10. Find the slope of the line that passes through (−3, 5) and (1, 8).
    A $\frac{4}{3}$ B $\frac{3}{4}$

11. What is the slope of the line that passes through (0, 1) and (3, 7)?
    A −2   C 2
    B $−\frac{1}{2}$

12. Which of the following situations corresponds to this graph?
    A A bicyclist accelerates, travels at a constant speed, then slows to a stop.
    B A car accelerates from a stop, travels at a constant speed, slows, and then travels at a slower speed.

13. If distance is represented on the y-axis and time on the x-axis, what does a line that is horizontal represent?
    A no motion
    B motion at a constant speed

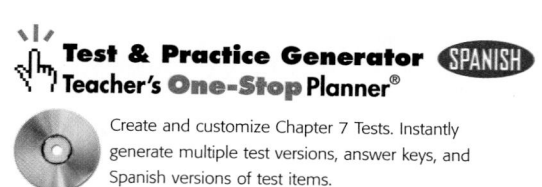

Test & Practice Generator SPANISH
Teacher's One-Stop Planner®

Create and customize Chapter 7 Tests. Instantly generate multiple test versions, answer keys, and Spanish versions of test items.

Graphs and Functions

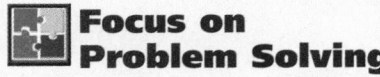

Focus on Problem Solving

On page 343, students focus on choosing a method of computation to solve real-world problems.

CONCEPT CONNECTION On page 363, students write the rule for a function, and then use the function to predict beaver population trends.

CONCEPT CONNECTION

go.hrw.com
Chapter Project Online
KEYWORD: MT8CA Ch7

The slope of a line can be used to model the steepness of a ski slope.

Heavenly Valley Ski Resort,
Lake Tahoe

Math in *California*

Depending upon their abilities and experience, people choose to ski on slopes varying in steepness from the bunny slopes to the black-diamond runs. In Lessons 7-6 and 7-7, students will learn methods for describing the slope of a line. In Lessons 7-6 through 7-9 they will learn how slope can be used to recognize data and interpret graphs that describe real-world relationships.

Problem Solving Project

Understand, Plan, Solve, and Look Back

Have students:

- Examine the table. Ask them what seems to have happened to the whooping crane over the last 60 years. Why did those changes occur?

- Complete the Whooping it Up worksheet.

- Estimate what the whooping crane population will be in 2050. Describe how they reached the conclusion.

- Do research on an endangered species. What environmental issues face the population? What is the prediction of population change in the future?

Science Connection

Project Resources

All project resources for teachers and students are provided online.

Materials:

- Whooping it Up worksheet

go.hrw.com
Project Teacher Support
KEYWORD: MT8CA PSProject7

ARE YOU READY?

✓ Vocabulary

Choose the best term from the list to complete each sentence.

1. A(n) __?__ states that two expressions have the same value. **equation**

2. Any number that can be written as a fraction is a(n) __?__. **rational number**

3. A(n) __?__ serves as a placeholder for a number. **variable**

4. A(n) __?__ can be a whole number or its opposite. **integer**

algebraic expression

equation

integer

rational number

variable

Complete these exercises to review skills you will need for this chapter.

✓ Integer Operations

Simplify.

5. $\frac{7-5}{-2}$ -1
6. $\frac{-8+2}{-2+8}$ -1
7. $\frac{-6+0}{4-2}$ -3
8. $\frac{-2+2}{2}$ 0

✓ Evaluate Expressions

Evaluate each expression for the given value of the variable.

9. $3x - 2$ for $x = -2$ $\;-8$
10. $4y - 8 + \frac{1}{2}y$ for $y = -2$ $\;-17$
11. $3(x + 1)$ for $x = -2$ $\;-3$
12. $-3(y + 2) - y$ for $y = -1$ $\;-2$

✓ Solve Multiplication Equations

Solve.

13. $3p = 4$ $\;1\frac{1}{3}$
14. $18 = -3x$ $\;-6$
15. $\frac{7}{2}a = 21$ $\;6$
16. $-3 = \frac{1}{3}s$ $\;-9$
17. $0.5x = 6.5$ $\;13$
18. $0.04y = 5.2$ $\;130$

✓ Simplify Ratios

Write each ratio in simplest form.

19. $\frac{3}{9}$ $\;\frac{1}{3}$
20. $\frac{-12}{4}$ $\;-3$
21. $\frac{27}{45}$ $\;\frac{3}{5}$
22. $\frac{3}{-45}$ $\;-\frac{1}{15}$
23. $\frac{-20}{8}$ $\;\frac{-5}{2}$

✓ Solve Two-Step Equations

Solve.

24. $3p - 4 = 8$ $\;4$
25. $2(a + 3) = 4$ $\;-1$
26. $9 = -2k + 27$ $\;9$
27. $\frac{s}{3} - 4 = 1$ $\;15$
28. $5x + 8 = 20$ $\;2\frac{2}{5}$
29. $\frac{y}{5} + 7 = 8$ $\;5$

ARE YOU READY?

Organizer

Objective: Assess students' understanding of prerequisite skills.

Prerequisite Skills

Integer Operations

Evaluate Expressions

Solve Multiplication Equations

Simplify Ratios

Solve Two-Step Equations

Assessing Prior Knowledge

INTERVENTION

Diagnose and Prescribe

Use this page to determine whether intervention is necessary or whether enrichment is appropriate.

Resources

 Are You Ready? Intervention and Enrichment Worksheets

 Are You Ready? CD-ROM

🪐 **Are You Ready? Online**

my.hrw.com

ARE YOU READY?

Diagnose and Prescribe

NO INTERVENE

YES ENRICH

✓ Prerequisite Skill	📃 Worksheets	💿 CD-ROM	🪐 Online
✓ Integer Operations	Skill 47	Activity 47	Diagnose and Prescribe Online
✓ Evaluate Expressions	Skill 54	Activity 54	
✓ Solve Multiplication Equations	Skill 59	Activity 59	
✓ Simplify Ratios	Skill 28	Activity 28	
✓ Solve Two-Step Equations	Skill 60	Activity 60	

ARE YOU READY? Intervention, Chapter 7

ARE YOU READY? Enrichment, Chapter 7

📃 Worksheets

💿 CD-ROM

🪐 Online

Organizer

Objective: Help students understand the new concepts they will learn in Chapter 7.

Academic Vocabulary Connections

Becoming familiar with the academic vocabulary on this student page will be helpful to students. Discussing some of the vocabulary terms in the chapter also may be helpful.
Possible answers given.

1. An *origin* is the point at which something begins. Can you describe where to begin when you plot a point on a coordinate plane? Can you guess why the point where the *x*-axis and *y*-axis cross is called the **origin?** You start at the origin; it is the point at which the numbering of both the *x*-axis and *y*-axis begins.

2. The word *linear* means "relating to a line." What do you think the graph of a **linear equation** looks like? The graph of a linear equation would look like a line.

3. The adjective *direct* can mean "passing in a straight line." What do you suppose the graph of an equation with **direct variation** looks like? The graph looks like a straight line.

The information below "unpacks" the standards. The Academic Vocabulary is highlighted and defined to help you understand the language of the standards. Refer to the lessons listed after each standard for help with the math terms and phrases. The Chapter Concept shows how the standard is applied in this chapter.

California Standard	Academic Vocabulary	Chapter Concept
AF1.5 Represent quantitative **relationships graphically and interpret the meaning of a** specific **part of a graph in the situation represented by the graph.** (Lesson 7-8)	**quantitative** can be measured **specific** exact	You learn how to sketch a graph of a real-world event and describe the situation the graph represents.
AF3.1 Graph functions of the form $y = nx^2$ **and** $y = nx^3$ **and use in** solving **problems.** (Lessons 7-4, 7-5)	**solving** finding the answer to a question	You graph functions that contain a variable raised to the second or third power.
AF3.3 Graph linear functions, noting that the vertical **change (change in *y*-value) per unit of** horizontal **change (change in *x*-value) is always the same and know that the ratio ("rise over run") is called the slope of a graph.** (Lessons 7-3, 7-6, 7-7)	**vertical** straight up or down **horizontal** parallel to the horizon	You graph functions that contain a variable whose power is one. You use data to make a graph and learn how to interpret the slope of the line drawn through these points.
AF3.4 Plot the values **of quantities whose ratios are always the same** (e.g., cost to the number of an item, feet to inches, circumference to diameter of a circle). **Fit a line to the plot and understand that the slope of the line** equals **the quantities.** (Lesson 7-7)	**value(s)** amount **equals** has the same value	You plot data points and connect them with a line. Then you find the slope of the line.
AF4.2 Solve multi-step **problems involving** rate, average speed, distance, and time or **a direct** variation. (Lesson 7-9)	**multi-step** more than one part **variation** difference	You make a graph and compare ratios to determine whether a data set shows direct variation.

Looking Back

Previously, students
- used a graph to find the vertical and horizontal change between two points on a line.
- graphed points on a coordinate plane.
- used tables and equations to find missing values and write equations.

In This Chapter

Students will study
- using coordinate pairs to find the slope of a line.
- graphing linear functions.
- generating different representations of data using tables, graphs, and equations.

Looking Forward

Students can use these skills
- to interpret graphs and identify direct variations.
- to graph other functions such as quadratic and cubic functions.
- to use a variety of methods to explain mathematical reasoning.

Reading and Writing Math

Writing Strategy: Keep a Math Journal

By keeping a math journal, you can improve your writing and thinking skills. Use your journal to summarize key ideas and vocabulary from each lesson and to analyze any questions you may have about a concept or your homework.

Journal Entry: Read the entry a student made in her journal.

> January 27
>
> ● I'm having trouble with Lesson 6-5. I can find what percent one number is of another number, but I get confused about finding percent increase and decrease. My teacher helped me think it through:
>
> Find the percent increase or decrease from 20 to 25.
> - First figure out if it is a percent increase or decrease. It goes from a smaller to a larger number, so it is a percent increase because the number is getting larger, or increasing.
>
> ● Then find the amount of increase, or the difference, between the two numbers. $25 - 20 = 5$
>
> - Now find what percent the amount of increase, or difference, is of the original number.
>
> $$\frac{\text{amount of increase}}{\text{original number}} \rightarrow \frac{5}{20} = 0.25 = 25\%$$
>
> So it is a 25% increase.

Try This

Begin a math journal. Write in it each day this week, using these ideas as starters. Be sure to date and number each page.

- In this lesson, I already know …
- In this lesson, I am unsure about …
- The skills I need to complete this lesson are …
- The challenges I encountered were …
- I handled these challenges by …
- In this lesson, I enjoyed/did not enjoy …

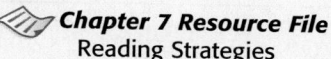

Reading and Writing Math

CHAPTER 7

Organizer

Objective: Help students apply strategies to understand and retain key concepts.

Online Edition

Resources

Chapter 7 Resource File
Reading Strategies

ENGLISH LANGUAGE LEARNERS

Writing Strategy: Keep a Math Journal

Discuss Students will be able to better understand and retain mathematical concepts if they summarize the key ideas they learn in their own words.

Encourage students to make a journal entry after each lesson.

Extend As students work through Chapter 7, select a few each day to read their journal entries to the class.

Encourage students to share with the rest of the class ideas they found challenging and things they enjoyed or did not enjoy about each lesson.

Possible answers to Try This

In this lesson, I already know how to evaluate expressions for given values. I'm unsure about how to identify a function. I handled this challenge by asking my teacher for further explanation and working extra examples.

Functions

One-Minute Section Planner

Lesson	Lab Resources	Materials
Lesson 7-1 The Coordinate Plane • Plot and identify ordered pairs on a coordinate plane. 🐻 **Preparation for** ⟵ **AF3.3**	**Technology Lab 7-1** In *Chapter 7 Resource File*	**Optional** Game markers
Lesson 7-2 Functions • Represent functions with tables and graphs. 🐻 **Preparation for** ⟵ **AF3.3**	**Hands-On Lab 7-2** In *Chapter 7 Resource File*	
Lesson 7-3 Graphing Linear Functions • Identify and graph linear functions. 🐻 **AF1.1, AF3.0,** ⟵ **AF3.3**	**Technology Lab 7-3** In *Chapter 7 Resource File*	**Optional** Graph paper, science textbook
Lesson 7-4 Graphing Quadratic Functions • Identify and graph quadratic functions. 🐻 **AF3.0, AF3.1**	**Hands-On Lab 7-4** In *Chapter 7 Resource File*	
Lesson 7-5 Cubic Functions • Identify and graph cubic functions. 🐻 **AF3.1**		**Optional** Scissors

MK = *Manipulatives Kit*

Notes

Math Background: Teaching the Standards

THE COORDINATE PLANE AF1.5
Lesson 7-1

The study of functions brings together essential ideas from several strands of the curriculum, including number sense, algebra, and geometry. The coordinate plane is the tool that makes it possible to explore these connections.

In one dimension, we use a number line to locate a point. The point on the line that corresponds to 0 is the point of reference from which other points are located. In this way, every point on the line has a unique name, and every real number corresponds to a unique point.

In two dimensions, we locate points using two perpendicular number lines that form a coordinate plane. In this case, the reference point is the origin—the point at which the two number lines intersect. Any point in the plane is uniquely identified by a pair of real numbers called an *ordered pair* written as (x, y).

It is useful to understand the geometric connection between certain pairs of points. The points $(2, 3)$ and $(2, -3)$, for example, are related by a reflection across the x-axis. More generally, for any real numbers a and b, the point $(a, -b)$ is the image of the point (a, b) under a reflection across the x-axis. Equivalently, the x-axis is the perpendicular bisector of the line segment with endpoints (a, b) and $(a, -b)$. Similarly, the point $(-c, d)$ is the image of the point (c, d) under a reflection across the y-axis.

As students work with the coordinate plane, they should begin to recognize and express other geometric relationships. For example, the points $(-5, 3)$, $(0, 3)$, $(4, 3)$, and $(8, 3)$ all lie on a horizontal line. In fact, any point named by an ordered pair of the form $(x, 3)$, where x is a real number, lies on this line, and any point on the line may be named by such an ordered pair.

RELATIONS AND FUNCTIONS AF3.3
Lesson 7-2

A *relation* is simply a set of ordered pairs. In each ordered pair, the first value (or x-value) is the domain, and the second value (or y-value) is the range. The ordered pairs in a relation may be given as a set. For example, the relation described by the set $\{(-1, 2), (4, 0), (4, 3), (7, -5)\}$ consists of four ordered pairs.

A *function* is a relation in which each domain value is paired with exactly one range value. But many students mistakenly think that functions must be described by equations. So, it is helpful to introduce functions by defining them as a set of ordered pairs in which each domain value is paired with exactly one range value, and by giving examples of functions for which no formula is known. Such an example is the temperature at noon at LAX as a function of the date.

LINEAR FUNCTIONS AF1.5, AF3.3
Lesson 7-3

A *solution* of an equation in two variables is an ordered pair that makes the equation true. Thus, $(3, 5)$ is a solution of the equation $y = 2x - 1$ because $5 = 2(3) - 1$. When the set of ordered pairs that are solutions of an equation form a straight line in the coordinate plane, the equation is called a *linear equation*.

A *linear function* is a function that can be described by a linear equation. Note that some linear equations, such as $x = 2$, do not correspond to linear functions.

One of the key understandings of algebra is the idea that the graph of an equation is exactly the set of ordered pairs that are solutions of the equation. In other words, once students have made a table of values, plotted points, and graphed the line $y = 2x - 1$, they should recognize that they can find additional solutions of the equation by finding ordered pairs that lie on the line. Likewise, a point that does *not* lie on the line, such as $(6, 4)$, cannot be a solution of the equation.

Technology Lab
In *Chapter 7 Resource File*

Online Edition
Tutorial Videos

Countdown to Mastery Week 13

Power Presentations
with PowerPoint®

Warm Up

Graph each integer and its opposite on a number line.

1. 4   **2.** −7   **3.** −2

$$\begin{array}{c} -7 \quad -4 -2 \qquad 2 \ 4 \qquad 7 \\ \overset{+}{-8}\overset{+}{-6}\overset{+}{-4}\overset{+}{-2}\ \overset{+}{0}\ \overset{+}{2}\ \overset{+}{4}\ \overset{+}{6}\ \overset{+}{8} \end{array}$$

4. Graph each integer on a number line: 7, −2, 0, 3, −5.

$$\begin{array}{c} -5 \quad -2\ 0 \quad 3 \qquad 7 \\ \overset{+}{-8}\overset{+}{-6}\overset{+}{-4}\overset{+}{-2}\ \overset{+}{0}\ \overset{+}{2}\ \overset{+}{4}\ \overset{+}{6}\ \overset{+}{8} \end{array}$$

Also available on transparency

Math Fact

Archaeologists use a coordinate system at dig sites to record the original location of each artifact found.

7-1 The Coordinate Plane

California Standards

Preparation for ◆ **AF3.3**
Graph linear functions, noting that the vertical change (change in *y*-value) per unit of horizontal change (change in *x*-value) is always the same and know that the ratio ("rise over run") is called the slope of a graph.

Why learn this? You can use a coordinate plane to plot the path of a hurricane. (See Exercise 35.)

A **coordinate plane** is a plane containing a horizontal number line, called the **x-axis**, and a vertical number line, called the **y-axis**. The intersection of these axes is called the **origin**. The axes divide the coordinate plane into four regions called **quadrants**.

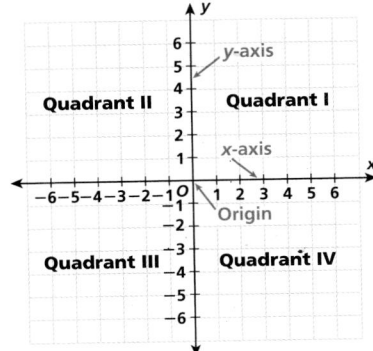

EXAMPLE 1 **Identifying Quadrants on a Coordinate Plane**

Vocabulary
coordinate plane
x-axis
y-axis
origin
quadrant
ordered pair

Identify the quadrant that contains each point.

A *P*
 P lies in Quadrant II.

B *Q*
 Q lies in Quadrant IV.

C *R*
 R lies on the *x*-axis, between Quadrants II and III.

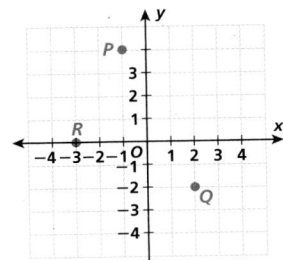

An **ordered pair** is a pair of numbers (x, y) that can be used to locate a point on a coordinate plane. The two numbers that form the ordered pair are called **coordinates**. The origin is identified by the ordered pair (0, 0).

Ordered pair

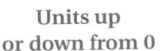

$$(3, 2)$$

x-coordinate   *y*-coordinate
Units right   Units up
or left from 0   or down from 0

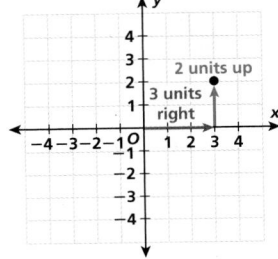

---

1 Introduce

Alternate Opener

EXPLORATION

7-1 The Coordinate Plane

The grid shown has a horizontal number line and a vertical number line that meet in the middle, called the *origin*.

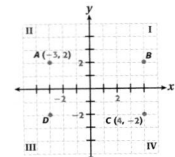

Point *A* is located 3 units to the left of the vertical number line and 2 units above the horizontal number line. Point *A* can be represented with the coordinates (−3, 2).

Point *C* is located 4 units to the right of the vertical number line and 2 units below the horizontal number line. Point *C* can be represented with the coordinates (4, −2).

1. Name the coordinates that represent point *B*.
2. Name the coordinates that represent point *D*.

Think and Discuss

3. **Describe** how points *A, B, C,* and *D* are represented with coordinates.

Motivate

To introduce students to a coordinate plane, have them discuss their experiences with locating a place by using the intersection of two lines (e.g., the streets and avenues in a city or the letters and numbers of a map grid). Students may have played a popular game in which players locate "battleships" by using a letter-number grid.

Explorations and answers are provided in *Alternate Openers: Explorations Transparencies.*

EXAMPLE 2 Plotting Points on a Coordinate Plane

Plot each point on a coordinate plane.

A *G*(2, 5)

Start at the origin. Move 2 units right and 5 units up.

B *N*(−3, −4)

Start at the origin. Move 3 units left and 4 units down.

C *P*(0, 0)

Point P is at the origin.

EXAMPLE 3 Identifying Points on a Coordinate Plane

Give the coordinates of each point.

A *J*

Start at the origin. Point J is 3 units right and 2 units down.
The coordinates of J are (3, −2).

B *K*

Start at the origin. Point K is 2 units left and 4 units up.
The coordinates of K are (−2, 4).

C *L*

Start at the origin. Point L is 3 units left on the x-axis.
The coordinates of L are (−3, 0).

Possible answers to Think and Discuss

1. No, they are not the same point. Point (4, 5) lies 4 units to the right of the origin and 5 units up, while point (5, 4) lies 5 units to the right and 4 units up.

2. The x-coordinate of a point on the y-axis is 0. The y-coordinate of a point on the x-axis is 0.

3. East of the prime meridian is positive, and west is negative. North of the equator is positive, and south is negative.

Think and Discuss

1. **Explain** whether (4, 5) and (5, 4) name the same point.

2. **Name** the x-coordinate of a point on the y-axis. Name the y-coordinate of a point on the x-axis.

3. **Suppose** the equator represents the x-axis on a map of Earth and a line called the *prime meridian*, which passes through England, represents the y-axis. Starting at the origin, which of these directions —east, west, north, and south—are positive? Which are negative?

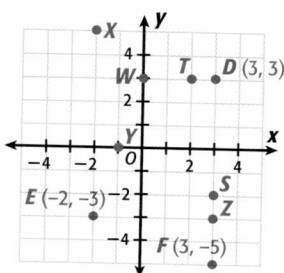

2 Teach

Guided Instruction

In this lesson, students learn to plot points on a coordinate plane and to name the coordinates of a point. Have students identify the components of a coordinate plane: the two number lines, one placed horizontally (the x-axis) and the other placed vertically (the y-axis), dividing the plane into four quadrants. Point out that the quadrants are numbered counterclockwise, beginning at the upper right, with the Roman numerals I, II, III, and IV (Teaching Transparency).

Teaching Tip

Multiple Representations Remind students that the familiar horizontal number line they studied in Lesson 1-3 corresponds to the x-axis.

Universal Access
Through Cooperative Learning

Have students work in three teams to play coordinate tic-tac-toe. Use a coordinate plane that is 5 units from the origin in all directions. Players on each team alternate calling out the coordinates of a point. Another player on the team locates the point. The mark is placed at the coordinates called, even if it is not the intended point. The first team to place three marks in an uninterrupted row horizontally, vertically, or diagonally wins the round.

3 Close

ENGLISH LANGUAGE LEARNERS

Summarize

You may wish to have students write brief definitions of new vocabulary terms in the lesson: *coordinate plane, x-axis, y-axis, origin, quadrant,* and *ordered pair.*

Possible answers: A coordinate plane has a horizontal number line, the x-axis, and a vertical number line, the y-axis. The origin is where the x-axis and the y-axis cross. The x-axis and y-axis divide the plane into four sections called quadrants. An ordered pair is made up of two numbers. The first number shows how far to the right or left to move from the origin, and the second shows how far up or down from the origin.

California Standards Practice
Preparation for ← AF3.3; MG3.2

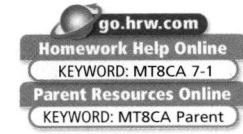

go.hrw.com
Homework Help Online
KEYWORD: MT8CA 7-1
Parent Resources Online
KEYWORD: MT8CA Parent

Assignment Guide

If you finished **Example 1** assign:
Proficient 1–4, 13–16, 41–46
Advanced 13–16, 31–32, 41–46

If you finished **Example 2** assign:
Proficient 1–8, 13–20, 27–33 odd, 41–46
Advanced 13–20, 28–34, 41–46

If you finished **Example 3** assign:
Proficient 1–27, 29–33 odd, 39–46
Advanced 13–46

Homework Quick Check
Quickly check key concepts.
Exercises: 14, 16, 18, 20, 22, 24

Answers

5–8, 17–20, 27, 28. See p. A3.

Math Background

The concept of the rectangular coordinate system is generally credited to French mathematician and philosopher René Descartes (dā • kärt′) and, therefore, is sometimes referred to as the Cartesian plane. Because all real numbers, not just integers, are used, every point on a plane can be located. The points represented by integer coordinates are sometimes called lattice points.

GUIDED PRACTICE

See Example 1 — Identify the quadrant that contains each point.
1. A II
2. B IV
3. C III
4. D I

See Example 2 — Plot each point on a coordinate plane.
5. $E(-1, 2)$
6. $N(2, -4)$
7. $H(-3, -4)$
8. $T(5, 0)$

See Example 3 — Give the coordinates of each point.
9. J $(6, -3)$
10. P $(-3, 2)$
11. S $(-4, 0)$
12. M $(5, 0)$

INDEPENDENT PRACTICE

See Example 1 — Identify the quadrant that contains each point.
13. F I
14. J III
15. K IV
16. E II

See Example 2 — Plot each point on a coordinate plane.
17. $A(-1, 1)$
18. $M(2, -2)$
19. $W(-5, -5)$
20. $G(0, -3)$

See Example 3 — Give the coordinates of each point.
21. Q $(-4, 4)$
22. V $(5, -6)$
23. R $(-5, -4)$
24. P $(0, -4)$
25. S $(5, 6)$
26. L $(2, 2)$

PRACTICE AND PROBLEM SOLVING

Extra Practice
See page EP14.

For Exercises 27 and 28, use graph paper to plot the ordered pairs. Use a different coordinate plane for each exercise.

27. $(-8, 1)$; $(4, 3)$; $(-3, 6)$
28. $(-8, -2)$; $(-1, -2)$; $(-1, 3)$; $(-8, 3)$

29. Geometry Connect the points in Exercise 27. Identify the figure and the quadrants in which it is located. **triangle; Quadrants I and II**

30. Geometry Connect the points in Exercise 28 in the order listed. Identify the figure and the quadrants in which it is located. **rectangle; Quadrants II and III**

Identify the quadrant of each point described below.

31. The x-coordinate and the y-coordinate are both negative. **III**

32. The x-coordinate is negative and the y-coordinate is positive. **II**

REVIEW FOR MASTERY 7-1

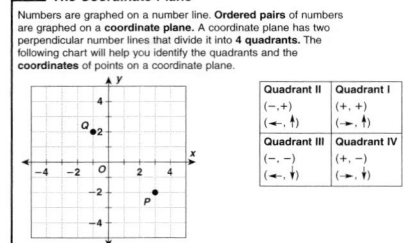

LESSON 7-1 Review for Mastery
The Coordinate Plane

Numbers are graphed on a number line. **Ordered pairs** of numbers are graphed on a **coordinate plane**. A coordinate plane has two perpendicular number lines that divide it into **4 quadrants**. The following chart will help you identify the quadrants and the **coordinates** of points on a coordinate plane.

Quadrant II	Quadrant I
(−,+)	(+, +)
(←, ↑)	(→, ↑)

Quadrant III	Quadrant IV
(−, −)	(+, −)
(←, ↓)	(→, ↓)

To find the coordinates of P, start at $(0, 0)$. Move 3 units →, then 2 units ↓. So the coordinates of P are $(3, -2)$, and P is in quadrant IV.

To plot point Q with coordinates $(-1, 2)$, start at $(0, 0)$. Move 1 unit ←, then 2 units ↑. Q is in quadrant II.

Identify the quadrant and the coordinates of each point on the coordinate plane at the right.

1. A II; $(-4, 2)$
2. B I; $(3, 4)$
3. C III; $(-5, -2)$
4. D I; $(1, 3)$
5. E IV; $(1, -4)$
6. F III; $(-2, -3)$

Plot each point on the coordinate plane above.
7. $G(-4, -3)$
8. $H(0, -2)$
9. $J(3, -5)$
10. $K(-3, 1)$
11. $L(4, -1)$
12. $M(-3, 4)$
13. $N(-1, 3)$
14. $Z(3, 0)$

PRACTICE 7-1

LESSON 7-1 Practice B
The Coordinate Plane

Identify the quadrant that contains each point.
1. A III
2. B IV
3. C II
4. D I

Plot each point on a coordinate plane.
5. $(-4, 0)$
6. $(3, -3)$
7. $(1, 4)$
8. $(-5, -1)$
9. $(-2, 2)$
10. $(-1, -4)$

Give the coordinates of each point.
11. P $(-2, 5)$
12. Q $(3, 0)$
13. R $(4, -3)$
14. S $(-5, -4)$
15. T $(0, 2)$
16. U $(-2, -2)$
17. W $(3, 3)$
18. X $(2, -1)$

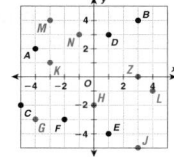

California Standards

Standard	Exercises
NS1.3	44–46
Prep for AF3.3 🔑	1–40
MG1.3 🔑	41–43
MG3.2	27–30

Weather

When the wind speed of a tropical storm reaches 74 mi/h, it is classified as a hurricane.

33. What point is located 9 units right and 3 units up from point (3, 4)? **(12, 7)**

34. Reasoning After being moved 6 units right and 4 units down, a point is located at (6, 1). What were the original coordinates of the point? **(0, 5)**

 35. Weather The map shows the path of Hurricane Andrew. Estimate to the nearest integer the coordinates of the storm for each of the times below.

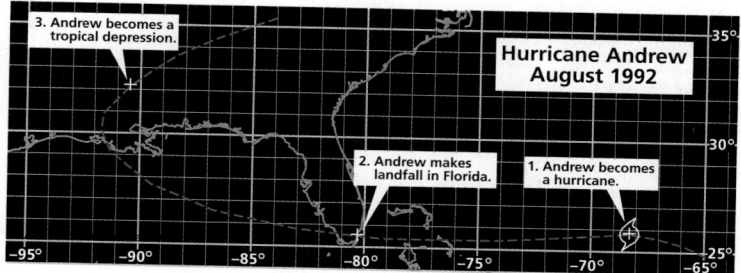

a. when Andrew first became a hurricane   **(−68°, 26°)**
b. when Andrew made landfall in Florida   **(−80°, 26°)**
c. when Andrew weakened to a tropical depression   **(−91°, 32°)**

36. What's the Error? To plot (−12, 1), a student started at (0, 0) and moved 12 units right and 1 unit down. What did the student do wrong?

37. Write About It Why is order important when plotting an ordered pair on a coordinate plane?

 **38. Challenge** Armand and Kayla started jogging from the same point. Armand jogged 4 miles south and then 6 miles east. Kayla jogged west and then 4 miles south. If they were 11 miles apart when they stopped, how far west did Kayla jog? **5 mi**

SPIRAL STANDARDS REVIEW
NS1.3, Prep for ➜ AF3.3, ➜ MG1.3

39. Multiple Choice Which of the following points lie within the circle graphed at right?

Ⓐ (2, 6)   Ⓑ (−4, 4)   Ⓒ (0, −4)   Ⓓ (−6, 6)

40. Multiple Choice Which point on the x-axis is the same distance from the origin as (0, −3)?

Ⓐ (0, 3)   Ⓑ (3, 0)   Ⓒ (3, −3)   Ⓓ (−3, 3)

Estimate each unit rate. (Lesson 5-2)

41. $89 for 4 hours
  about $22 per hour

42. 4 laps in 13 minutes
  about 3 minutes per lap

43. 47 students and 3 teachers
  about 16 students per teacher

Order the numbers from least to greatest. (Lesson 6-1)

44. $\frac{1}{3}$, 0.375, 0.3, 34%
  0.3, $\frac{1}{3}$, 0.34, 0.375

45. $\frac{1}{6}$, 0.14, $\frac{1}{7}$, 15%
  0.14, $\frac{1}{7}$, 15%, $\frac{1}{6}$

46. 12%, $\frac{1}{8}$, 0.13, $\frac{1}{9}$
  $\frac{1}{9}$, 12%, $\frac{1}{8}$, 0.13

Answers

36–37. See p. A3.

Teaching Tip **Multiple Choice** Students who chose **A, C,** or **D** in **Exercise 40** may not have read the problem carefully. The student is to find the point *on the x-axis* that is the same distance from the origin as (0, −3). Only choice **B** names a point on the x-axis.

Journal

Have students render the features of a familiar neighborhood on a coordinate plane. Ask students to supply the coordinates of landmarks, such as a school or library, as well as written directions for traveling from the origin to the landmarks.

Power Presentations with PowerPoint®

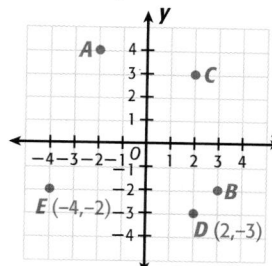

✓ **7-1 Lesson Quiz**

Give the coordinates of each point and identify the quadrant that contains each point.

1. A (−2, 4); II   **2.** B (3, −2); IV

3. C (2, 3); I

Plot each point on a coordinate plane. See points D and E above.

4. D(2, −3)

5. E(−4, −2)

6. To plot (7, −2) a student started at (0, 0) and moved 7 units left and 2 units down. What did the student do wrong? He should have moved 7 units right.

Also available on transparency

Objective: Students represent functions with tables and graphs.

 Hands-On Lab
In *Chapter 7 Resource File*

 Online Edition
Tutorial Videos

 Countdown to Mastery Week 13

 **Power Presentations**
with PowerPoint®

Warm Up

What three terms come next?

1. 9, 12, 15, 18, ☐, ☐, ☐   *21 24 27*

2. −8, −3, 2, 7, ☐, ☐, ☐   *12 17 22*

3. 9, 10, 12, 15, 19, ☐, ☐, ☐   *24 30 37*

Also available on transparency

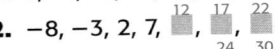 **Math Humor**

The brothers and sisters were always arguing about how many outputs there were for each input. They were truly a *dysfunctional* family.

 **California Standards**

Preparation for ➤ AF3.3
Graph linear functions, noting that the vertical change (change in *y*-value) per unit of horizontal change (change in *x*-value) is always the same and know that the ratio ("rise over run") is called the slope of a graph.

Vocabulary
function
input
output
vertical line test

Who uses this? A business can use functions to determine how many items it needs to sell to break even. (See Exercise 20.)

A **function** is a set of ordered pairs (x, y) so that each x-value corresponds to exactly one y-value.

Some functions can be described by a rule written in words, such as "double a number and then add nine to the result," or by an equation with two variables. One variable (often x) represents the *input*, and the other variable (often y) represents the *output*.

Function Rule
$$y = 2x + 9$$
↑ Output variable   ↑ Input variable

When a function can be written as an equation, the **input** is the value substituted into the function rule. The **output** is the result of that substitution.

EXAMPLE 1 **Finding Output Values**

Find the output for each input.

A $y = 4x - 2$, Input: $-1, 0, 3$

Reading Math

The input values of a function are also called the *domain*. The output values of a function are also called the *range*.

Input	Rule	Output
x	$4x - 2$	y
-1	$4(-1) - 2$	-6
0	$4(0) - 2$	-2
3	$4(3) - 2$	10

Make a table.

Substitute −1 for x. Then simplify.
Substitute 0 for x. Then simplify.
Substitute 3 for x. Then simplify.

The output values are -6, -2, and 10.

B $y = 6x^2$, Input: $-5, 0, 5$

Input	Rule	Output
x	$6x^2$	y
-5	$6(-5)^2$	150
0	$6(0)^2$	0
5	$6(5)^2$	150

Make a table.

Substitute −5 for x. Then simplify.
Substitute 0 for x. Then simplify.
Substitute 5 for x. Then simplify.

The output values are 150 and 0.

1 Introduce

Alternate Opener

EXPLORATION

7-2 Functions

A *function* is a rule that assigns exactly one *output* value for each *input* value. An input/output table is a convenient way of representing functions.

1. Complete the table by applying the rule to each input value.

Input (x)	Rule: 2000 − 25(x)	Output (y)
0	2000 − 25(0) = 2000	2000
1		
2		
3		

2. Determine the rule that produces the following output values from the given input values.

Input (x)	Rule	Output (y)
2		0
4		2
6		4
8		6

Think and Discuss

3. **Explain** the relationship between the input values, a rule, and the output values.

4. **Discuss** whether the output values have to be different from the input values.

Motivate

Use the formula for converting degrees Celsius to degrees Fahrenheit, $F = 1.8C + 32$, to show the students an example of a function. Show them that entering any value of C will determine the value of F, using values for C such as 0° or 100°. Ask the students if it's possible for a temperature in degrees Fahrenheit to be equivalent to two different temperatures in degrees Celsius. no Inform the students that all molecular activity ceases at −273°C and have them enter this value in the formula to determine the lowest value of degrees Fahrenheit. −459.4°F

Explorations and answers are provided in *Alternate Openers: Explorations Transparencies.*

 **California Standards**

Prep for Algebra and Functions ➤ 3.3

Because a function has exactly one output for each input, you can use the **vertical line test** to determine whether a graph is a function. If no vertical line intersects the graph at more than one point, then the graph is a function. One way to perform the vertical line test is to pass a vertical line across a graph.

EXAMPLE 2 Identifying Functions

Determine if each relationship represents a function.

A.

x	y
0	5
1	4
2	3
3	2

Each input value has only one output value.

The relationship is a function.

B.

x	y
−2	0
−1	1
0	2
−1	4

The input value −1 has two output values, 1 and 4.

The relationship is not a function.

C.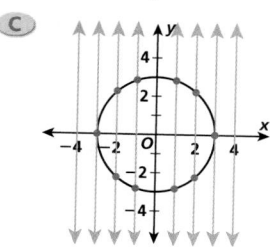

Pass a vertical line across the graph. Many vertical lines intersect the graph at two points.

The relationship is not a function.

D.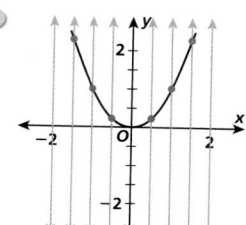

Pass a vertical line across the graph. No vertical lines intersect the graph at more than one point.

The relationship is a function.

Possible answers to Think and Discuss

1. The input values consist of all numbers. The only output value is 2.

2. Verify that each input has only one output.

3. $3x - 4$; {−1, 0, 1}; {−7, −4, −1}

Think and Discuss

1. **Describe** the possible input and output values for $y = 2$.

2. **Describe** how to tell if a relationship is a function.

3. **Identify** the function rule, the inputs, and the outputs.

x	3x − 4	y
−1	3(−1) − 4	−7
0	3(0) − 4	−4
1	3(1) − 4	−1

Additional Examples

Example 1

Find the output for each input: −2, 0, 2.

A. $y = 3 - x^2$ −1, 3, −1

B. $y = -2x - 3$ 1, −3, −7

Example 2

Determine if each relationship represents a function.

A.

x	2	3	3	2	no
y	3	4	5	6	

B.

x	−1	2	5	8	yes
y	−1	−4	−7	−10	

C. 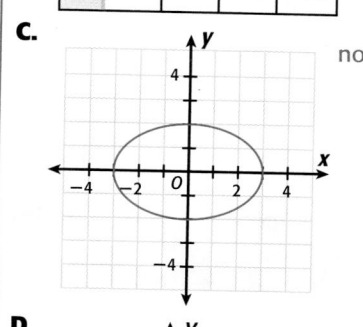 no

D. 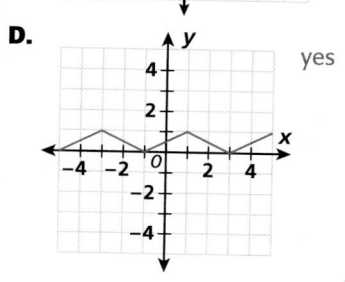 yes

Also available on transparency

② Teach

Guided Instruction

ENGLISH LANGUAGE LEARNERS

In this lesson, students learn to represent functions with tables, graphs, or equations. Introduce the important vocabulary terms in the lesson. You may want to use the example in Motivate to give examples of *input*, *output*, and *function*. Emphasize that a function assigns exactly one *output* to each *input*.

 **Language Support** Explain to students that "to perform a function" means to act in a certain way that leads to a certain result. In mathematics, the word *function* means that for a particular input value, there is one output value.

 Universal Access

For Advanced Learners/GATE

Each function rule below is incomplete. Have students use the given input and output values in each table to complete the function rules.

1. $5x + 7$

Input	Rule	Output
1	5x + ?	12
2	5x + ?	17
3	5x + ?	22

2. $-x^2 + (-3)$

Input	Rule	Output
3	−x² + ?	−12
4	−x² + ?	−19
5	−x² + ?	−28

3. $2x - 3$

Input	Rule	Output
4	?x − 3	5
5	?x − 3	7
6	?x − 3	9

4. $\frac{1}{2}x + 4$

Input	Rule	Output
2	?x + 4	5
3	?x + 4	5.5
4	?x + 4	6

③ Close

Summarize

Review the vocabulary terms with students. Show students the following function table. Ask students to identify the function, an input, and an output.

x	3x − 1	y
3	3(3) − 1	8
4	3(4) − 1	11
5	3(5) − 1	14

$y = 3x - 1$; 3; 8

Assignment Guide

If you finished Example **1** assign:
Proficient 1–4, 8–11, 20, 28–36
Advanced 8–11, 20–22, 28–36

If you finished Example **2** assign:
Proficient 1–14, 16–20, 26–36
Advanced 8–16, 20–36

Homework Quick Check

Quickly check key concepts.
Exercises: 10, 12, 16, 20

Answers

1–4, 8–11. See p. A3.

15. No; 4 has two outputs, 39 and 62.

16. Yes; each input has one output.

17. Yes; each input has one output.

18. No; both 20 and 25 have two outputs.

Math Background

Over 4000 years ago, the Babylonians had a working idea of functions, which is represented in their tablets containing mathematical tables and lists of mathematical problems.

It was not until over 3600 years later that the term *function,* in its Latin equivalent, was used to denote a quantity and its relationship to a curve.

California Standards

Standard	Exercises
NS1.3	31–36
Prep for AF3.3 🔑	1–27
AF4.0 🔑	28–30

7-2 Exercises

California Standards Practice
Preparation for 🔑 AF3.3

go.hrw.com
Homework Help Online
KEYWORD: MT8CA 7-2
Parent Resources Online
KEYWORD: MT8CA Parent

GUIDED PRACTICE

See Example **1** Find the output for each input: −2, 0, 2.

1. $y = 2x − 4$ **2.** $y = 3x + 4$ **3.** $y = 4x^2$ **4.** $y = −x + 1$

See Example **2** Determine if each relationship represents a function.

5.

x	y
−1	−7
9	1
12	8
15	−7

Yes

6.
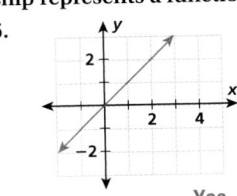
Yes

7.

x	y
−2	−3
−1	−1
0	1
−2	5

No

INDEPENDENT PRACTICE

See Example **1** Find the output for each input: −2, 0, 2.

8. $y = 2x + 5$ **9.** $y = 3(x + 1)$ **10.** $y = −3x^2$ **11.** $y = 2(1 − 2x)$

See Example **2** Determine if each relationship represents a function.

12.

x	y
2	4
5	5
8	6
3	7

Yes

13.
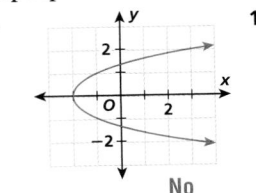
No

14.
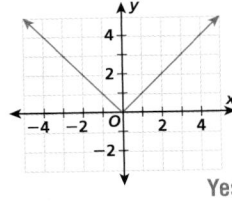
Yes

PRACTICE AND PROBLEM SOLVING

Extra Practice
See page EP14.

Determine if each relationship represents a function. Explain.

15.

x	y
1	27
4	39
8	50
4	62

16.

x	y
100	5.4
120	3.5
150	2.7
170	3.5

17.

x	y
30	60
40	50
50	45
60	32

18.

x	y
20	12
25	15
25	21
20	24

19. Sports A distance runner trains by running 750 meters at a time. Her coach records the distance covered by the runner every 20 seconds. The results of one run are presented in the table.

Time x (s)	0	20	40	60	80	100
Distance y (m)	0	150	300	450	600	750

a. Does the relationship represent a function? **yes**

b. What are the inputs of the function? What are the outputs? Input: {0, 20, 40, 60, 80, 100}; Output: {0, 150, 300, 450, 600, 750}

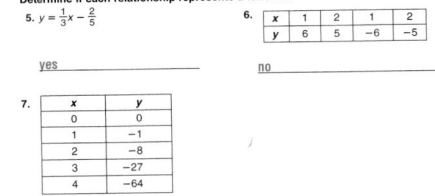

REVIEW FOR MASTERY 7-2

LESSON 7-2 **Review for Mastery**
Functions

A **function** is a relationship in which the value of one quantity depends on the value of another quantity. A function can be represented by a rule or an equation. A *function table* can help you find the output for a function.

Complete the missing values in the table.

	Input x	Rule 3x + 2	Output y
1.	−2	3(−2) + 2 = −6 + 2	−4
2.	−1	3(−1) + 2 = −3 + 2	−1
3.	0	3(0) + 2 = 0 + 2	2
4.	1	3(1) + 2 = 3 + 2	5

A **function** is a relation in which each input corresponds to *exactly* one output.

The relation below is a function.

Input	Output
a	d
b	d
c	e

function: {(a, d), (b, d), (c, e)}
a has only one partner, d.
b has only one partner, d.
c has only one partner, e.

The relation below is not a function.

Input	Output
a	d
b	d
c	d
c	e

relation: {(a, d), (b, d), (c, d), (c, e)}
a has only one partner, d.
b has only one partner, d.
c has two partners, d and e.

Tell if each relation is a function. Explain.

5.

Input	Output
a	d
b	d
c	d

Yes; a, b, c each have one partner, d.

6.

Input	Output
a	d
b	d
c	e
a	e

No; a has two partners, d and e.

PRACTICE 7-2

LESSON 7-2 **Practice B**
Functions

Find the output for each input.

1. $y = 5x − 1$

Input x	Rule 5x − 1	Output y
−2	5(−2) − 1	−11
0	5(0) − 1	−1
3	5(3) − 1	14
6	5(6) − 1	29

2. $y = −2x^2$

Input x	Rule −2x²	Output y
−2	−2(−2)²	−8
2	−2(2)²	−8
3	−2(3)²	−18
4	−2(4)²	−32

3. $y = −2x + 5$

Input x	Rule −2x + 5	Output y
−2	−2(−2) + 5	1
−1	−2(−1) + 5	3
0	−2(0) + 5	5
1	−2(1) + 5	7
2	−2(2) + 5	9

4. $y = x − 2$

Input x	Rule x − 2	Output y
−2	−2 − 2	−4
−1	−1 − 2	−3
0	0 − 2	−2
1	1 − 2	−1
2	2 − 2	0

Determine if each relationship represents a function.

5. $y = \frac{1}{3}x − \frac{2}{5}$

yes

6.

x	1	2	1	2
y	6	5	−6	−5

no

7.

x	y
0	0
1	−1
2	−8
3	−27
4	−64

yes

Home Economics

In 1879, Thomas Edison used a carbonized piece of sewing thread to form a light bulb filament that lasted 13.5 hours before burning out.

20. Health You can burn about 3 calories per minute when paddling a canoe. The function $y = 3x$ gives the total calories burned when you have paddled for x minutes.

   a. How many calories will you burn if you paddle for 3 min., 10 min., and 30 min.? **9; 30; 90**

   b. How many calories will you burn if you paddle for 1 hour? **180**

21. Home Economics The cost of using a 60-watt light bulb is given by the function $y = 0.0036x$. The cost is in dollars, and x represents the number of hours the bulb is lit.

   a. How much does it cost to use a 60-watt light bulb 8 hours a day for a week? **$0.20**

   b. Describe the input values of the function. **any nonnegative number of hours ($x \geq 0$)**

   c. If the total cost of using a 60-watt bulb is $1.98, for how many hours can it be used? **550 hours**

22. What's the Question? The following set of points defines a function: $\{(3, 6), (-4, 1), (5, -5), (9, -6), (10, -2), (-2, 10)\}$. If the answer is 6, 1, -5, -6, -2, and 10, what is the question?
Possible answer: What are the outputs of the function?

23. Write About It Can you tell if a relationship is a function by just looking at the output? Explain why or why not.

24. Challenge What values of x make the ordered pairs $(x, 0)$, $(2, 3)$, $(4, 6)$ a function? Explain. **all real numbers except 2 and 4; input values cannot repeat**

25. Challenge What values of y make the ordered pairs $(-1, -2)$, $(2, y)$, $(3, 2)$ a function? Explain. **all real numbers; output values can repeat**

SPIRAL STANDARDS REVIEW   NS1.3, Prep for AF3.3, AF4.0

26. Multiple Choice Which relationship does NOT represent a function?

  Ⓐ $(0, 8)$, $(3, 8)$, $(1, 6)$

  Ⓑ $y = 3x + 17$

x	4	6	8
y	2	1	9

  Ⓒ (table above)

  Ⓓ $(0, 3)$, $(2, 3)$, $(2, 0)$

27. Multiple Choice Which function matches the function table?

  Ⓐ $y = x + 3$

  Ⓑ $y = x^2 + 7$

  Ⓒ $y = 5x + 1$

  Ⓓ $y = x^3 + 3$

x	0	1	2
y	3	4	11

Solve. Check your answer. (Lesson 2-7)

28. $n + 10.7 = -23$ **−33.7**   **29.** $-6.8x = 47.6$ **−7**   **30.** $-\frac{2}{3}m = -\frac{1}{9}$ $\frac{1}{6}$

Estimate. (Lesson 6-2)

31. 15% of 40 **6**   **32.** $33\frac{1}{3}$% of 100 **33**   **33.** 76% of 148 **100**

34. 23% of $120 **$30**   **35.** 15% of $21 **$3**   **36.** 75% of $218.99 **$165**

CHALLENGE 7-2

LESSON 7-2 Challenge
What's My Rule?

Sometimes you are given a set of ordered pairs and need to find a function rule that describes how to get the outputs from the inputs.

Example Write a function rule for the ordered pairs in the table.

To get each y-value, double the corresponding x-value and then add 1.

The rule is $y = 2x + 1$.

x	y
3	7
5	11
6	13
8	17

Check the rule by making sure each input (x-value) in the table gives the corresponding output (y-value).

$2(3) + 1 = 7$ ✔
$2(5) + 1 = 11$ ✔
$2(6) + 1 = 13$ ✔
$2(8) + 1 = 17$ ✔

Write a function rule for the ordered pairs in each table.

1.
x	y
1	5
2	6
4	8
7	11

Rule: $y = x + 4$

2.
x	y
0	0
2	4
5	10
9	18

Rule: $y = 2x$

3.
x	y
−1	−9
0	−8
4	−4
10	2

Rule: $y = x - 8$

4.
x	y
−2	−10
−1	−5
3	15
7	21

Rule: $y = 5x$

5.
x	y
1	5
2	7
3	9
4	11

Rule: $y = 2x + 3$

6.
x	y
0	1
2	7
5	16
9	28

Rule: $y = 3x + 1$

7.
x	y
−3	−7
0	−1
1	1
4	7

Rule: $y = 2x - 1$

8.
x	y
−1	−1
2	2
6	6
9	9

Rule: $y = x$

9.
x	y
−2	4
2	4
3	9
5	25

Rule: $y = x^2$

PROBLEM SOLVING 7-2

LESSON 7-2 Problem Solving
Functions

Write the correct answer.

1. Film passes through a projector at the rate of 24 frames per second. The equation $y = 24x$ describes the number of frames, y, that have passed over any number of seconds, x. Complete the function table.

Input x	Rule 24x	Output y
2	24 • 2	48
3	24 • 3	72
4	24 • 4	96
5	24 • 5	120
6	24 • 6	144

2. Anne pays $40 a month for cable TV, plus $4 for each movie she watches on pay-per-view channels. Complete the function table, where x is the number of pay-per-view movies she watches each month and y is her monthly cable bill.

Input x	Rule 4x + 40	Output y
3	4(3) + 40	52
5	4(5) + 40	60
7	4(7) + 40	68
9	4(9) + 40	76
11	4(11) + 40	84

Choose the letter of the best answer.

Madeline has a discount coupon for $5 off her next purchase of tennis balls. Tennis balls are on sale for $3 per can. The equation $y = 3x - 5$ gives her final cost, y, to purchase x cans of tennis balls.

3. If $x = 3$, what is the value of y?
  A 15   C 9
  B 14   Ⓓ 4

4. If $x = 5$, what is the value of y?
  F 25   Ⓗ 10
  G 15   J 5

5. If $x = 10$, what is the value of y?
  Ⓐ 25   C 35
  B 30   D 50

6. If $x = 4$, what is the value of y?
  F 5   H 12
  Ⓖ 7   J 17

7. If $x = 9$, what is the ordered pair (x, y)?
  A (5, 9)   Ⓒ (9, 22)
  B (9, 5)   D (9, 10)

8. If $x = 6$, what is the ordered pair (x, y)?
  F (6, 18)   H (12, 31)
  G (6, 30)   Ⓙ (6, 13)

Answers

23. No; you must look at the input and output. A relationship is not a function if an input value corresponds to more than one output value.

Teaching Tip **Multiple Choice** For **Exercise 26,** remind students who answered **A** that it is okay for a function to have multiple x-values with the same y-values. Similarly, make sure that students who answered **D** did so because of the ordered pairs (2, 3) and (2, 0) rather than (0, 3) and (2, 3).

Journal

Ask students to write about how they use a graph to determine whether or not a relationship represents a function.

Power Presentations
with PowerPoint®

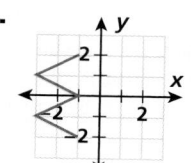

7-2 Lesson Quiz

Find the output for each input: −2, 0, 2.

1. $y = 3x + 3$ **−3, 3, 9**

2. $y = -x^2$ **−4, 0, −4**

Determine if each relationship represents a function.

3.

x	−2	−1	0	1	1
y	3	4	3	5	6

no

4.

no

Also available on transparency

Objective: Students identify and graph linear functions.

 Technology Lab
In *Chapter 7 Resource File*

 Online Edition
Tutorial Videos

 Countdown to Mastery Week 13

Power Presentations
with PowerPoint®

Warm Up

Interpret the graph.
A rocket is fired into the air.

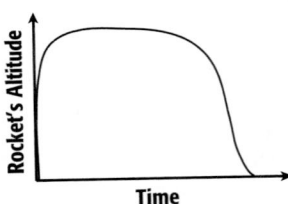

Time

Possible answer: The rocket's speed increases until gravity gradually slows the rocket and causes it to fall to the ground.

Also available on transparency

Math Humor

Why is an equation whose graph is a straight line sillier than an equation whose graph is not straight? It's a *loonier* equation.

7-3 Graphing Linear Functions

Vocabulary
linear equation
linear function

Why learn this? You can use the graph of a linear function to show the relationship between the Celsius and Fahrenheit scales. (See Example 2.)

Recall that the solution of an equation with one variable is the value of the variable that makes the equation true. The solutions of an equation with two variables are the ordered pairs that make the equation true. When these ordered pairs form a line, the equation is called a **linear equation** .

A function described by a linear equation is a **linear function** . To graph a linear function, plot some solutions of the related linear equation, then draw a line through them. The line represents all of the ordered pair solutions of the equation.

For example, the function that relates distance d, rate r, and time t is described by the linear equation $d = rt$. This graph shows solutions of this equation when $r = 2$ feet per second.

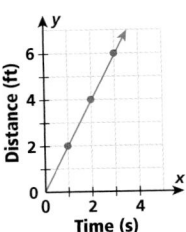

EXAMPLE 1 Graphing Linear Functions

Graph the linear function $y = 2x + 1$.

Helpful Hint
Not all linear equations describe functions. The graphs of some linear equations are vertical lines, which do not pass the vertical line test.

Input	Rule	Output	Ordered Pair
x	$2x + 1$	y	(x, y)
-1	$2(-1) + 1$	-1	$(-1, -1)$
0	$2(0) + 1$	1	$(0, 1)$
1	$2(1) + 1$	3	$(1, 3)$

Make a table.

Substitute positive, negative, and zero values for x.

Plot each ordered pair on the coordinate grid. Then connect the points to form a line.

1 Introduce

Alternate Opener

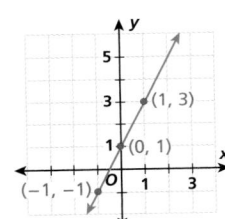

EXPLORATION

7-3 Graphing Linear Functions

The graph of a *linear function* is a nonvertical straight line. A linear function can be represented by a *linear equation* or by a graph.

1. Complete the table of values for the linear equation $y = 2x + 2$.

x	$y = 2x + 2$	(x, y)	Graph
-4	$2(-4) + 2 = -6$	$(-4, -6)$	
-3			
-2			
-1			
0			
1			
2			

2. Plot points on the graph using the *x*- and *y*-values generated in the table. Then draw a line through the points.

Think and Discuss

3. **Explain** how you can find another point on the line.
4. **Discuss** how you can recognize a linear function by its graph.

Motivate

Ask students to demonstrate different paths connecting two points. Discuss the type of path that represents the shortest distance between the two points (a straight line).

Explorations and answers are provided in *Alternate Openers: Explorations Transparencies.*

EXAMPLE 2 *Science Application*

For every degree that temperature increases on the Celsius scale, the temperature increases by 1.8 degrees on the Fahrenheit scale. When the temperature is 0°C, it is 32°F. So a temperature in degrees Fahrenheit is 32 degrees more than 1.8 times a temperature in degrees Celsius.

Math Builders

For more on graphing relationships, see the Graph and Equation Builder on page MB2.

a. Write a linear function that describes the relationship between the Celsius and Fahrenheit scales.

Let *x* represent the input, which is the temperature in degrees Celsius. Let *y* represent the output, which is the temperature in degrees Fahrenheit.

degrees Fahrenheit	is	1.8	times	degrees Celsius	plus	32 degrees
y	$=$	1.8	$\cdot$	x	$+$	32

The function is $y = 1.8x + 32$.

b. Make a graph to show the relationship.

Make a function table. Include a column for the rule.

Input	Rule	Output
x	$1.8x + 32$	y
0	$1.8(0) + 32$	32
15	$1.8(15) + 32$	59
30	$1.8(30) + 32$	86

Multiply the input by 1.8, and then add 32.

Graph the ordered pairs (0, 32), (15, 59), and (30, 86) from your table. Connect the points to form a line.

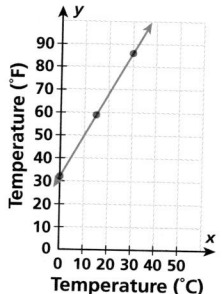

Possible answers to Think and Discuss

1. A linear equation and a linear graph are different representations that describe the same relationship between *x* and *y*.

2. Locate the given input value on the *x*-axis. Move up to find the *y*-value that lies on the line above the given input value.

Think and Discuss

1. **Describe** how a linear equation is related to a linear graph.

2. **Explain** how to use a graph to find the output value of a linear function for a given input value.

Example 1

Graph the linear function $y = 4x - 1$.

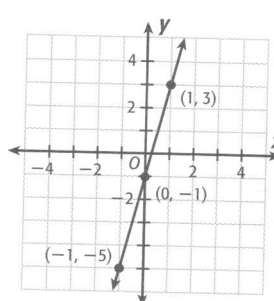

Example 2

The fastest-moving tectonic plates on Earth move apart at a rate of 15 centimeters per year. Scientists began studying two parts of these plates when they were 30 centimeters apart. Write a linear function that describes the movement of the plates over time. Then make a graph to show the movement over 4 years.
$y = 15x + 30$

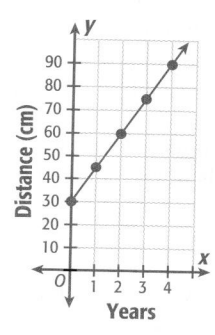

Also available on transparency

---

2 Teach

Guided Instruction

In this lesson, students learn to identify and graph linear equations. You may wish to remind students that they are already familiar with the main concepts of the lesson. Students already know how to use input/output tables, and they know how to plot points on the plane. They also know how to solve equations. Students will now apply these concepts together and relate them to linear equations and their graphs.

Teaching Tip **Visual** Have students use graph paper to sketch the graphs. Some students have trouble making clean graphs on standard notebook paper because there are no vertical lines on notebook paper.

Universal Access
Through Curriculum Integration

Science Have students look through science textbooks for examples of formulas and graphs of linear equations. Ask students to explain how they can recognize a formula of a linear equation.

Possible answer: In a formula of a linear equation, the variable in the formula is not raised to a power.

3 Close

Summarize

Have students graph the equation $y = 3x + 1$ for $x = -1$, 0, and 1.

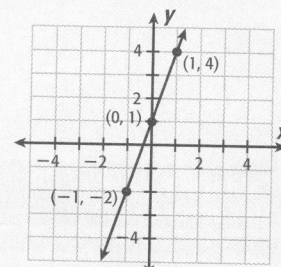

7-3 **Exercises**

California Standards Practice
AF1.1, ⟵ AF3.3

go.hrw.com
Homework Help Online
KEYWORD: MT8CA 7-3
Parent Resources Online
KEYWORD: MT8CA Parent

Assignment Guide

If you finished Example **1** assign:
Proficient 1–2, 4–7, 20–26
Advanced 4–7, 11–13, 20–26

If you finished Example **2** assign:
Proficient 1–10, 20–26
Advanced 4–8, 11–26

Homework Quick Check

Quickly check key concepts.
Exercises: 4, 6, 8

Answers

Complete answers 1–8. See pp. A3–4.

Math Background

Graphs of linear equations of the form $y = a$ are horizontal lines. The line $y = a$ intersects the y-axis at the point $(0, a)$. All horizontal lines are parallel to the x-axis and have a slope of 0. The equation of the x-axis is $y = 0$.

Graphs of linear equations of the form $x = a$ are vertical lines. The line $x = a$ intersects the x-axis at the point $(a, 0)$. All vertical lines are parallel to the y-axis. The slope is not defined. The equation of the y-axis is $x = 0$.

COMMON ERROR ALERT

When graphing, remind students to place arrows at both ends of a line to indicate that it extends indefinitely, unless the problem indicates otherwise.

GUIDED PRACTICE

See Example **1** Graph each linear function.

1. $y = x + 3$

Input	Rule	Output	Ordered Pair
x	x + 3	y	(x, y)
−2	−2 + 3	1	(−2, 1)
0	0 + 3	3	(0, 3)
2	2 + 3	5	(2, 5)

2. $y = 2x - 2$

2(−1) − 2
2(0) − 2
2(1) − 2

Input	Rule	Output	Ordered Pair
x	2x − 2	y	(x, y)
−1		−4	(−1, −4)
0		−2	(0, −2)
1		0	(1, 0)

See Example **2** **3.** A water tanker is used to fill a community pool. The tanker pumps 750 gallons of water per hour, so the amount of water in the pool is 750 times the number of hours.

    a. Write a linear function that describes the amount of water in the pool over time. $y = 750x$

    b. Make a graph to show the amount of water in the pool over the first 6 hours.

INDEPENDENT PRACTICE

See Example **1** Graph each linear function.

    4. $y = -x - 2$ **5.** $y = x - 1$ **6.** $y = 3x - 1$ **7.** $y = 2x + 3$

See Example **2** **8. Science** The temperature of a liquid is increasing at the rate of 3°C per hour. When Joe begins measuring the temperature, it is 40°C, so the temperature of the liquid is 40°C more than 3 times the number of hours.

    a. Write a linear function that describes the temperature of the liquid over time. $y = 3x + 40$

    b. Make a graph to show the temperature over the first 12 hours.

PRACTICE AND PROBLEM SOLVING

Extra Practice
See page EP14.

9. Business A charter bus service charges a $125 transportation fee plus $8.50 per passenger. This is represented by the function $c = 8.5p + 125$, where c is the total cost based on p passengers. What is the total cost of transportation for the following numbers of passengers: 50, 100, 150, 200, and 250? $550; $975; $1400; $1825; $2250

$w = 4d + 5110$;
5118 lb; 5124 lb;
5130 lb

10. Life Science *Tyrannosaurus rex* was one of the largest meat-eaters that ever lived. By 14 years of age, the weight of a *T. rex* was increasing by about 4 pounds every day. Suppose a *T. rex* was 14 years old and weighed 5110 pounds. Write a linear function that describes the relationship between its current weight w and how much it would weigh d days later. How much would it weigh after 2 days? after 3.5 days? after 5 days?

REVIEW FOR MASTERY 7-3

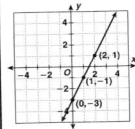

LESSON 7-3 Review for Mastery
Graphing Linear Functions

The graph of a linear equation is a straight line. A **linear function** is a function whose graph is a straight line that is not vertical. To graph a linear equation, first make a function table.

Complete the function table for $y = 2x - 3$.

	Input	Linear Equation	Output	Ordered Pair
	x	y = 2x − 3	y	(x, y)
1.	0	y = 2(0) − 3 = 0 − 3	−3	(0, −3)
2.	1	y = 2(1) − 3 = 2 − 3	−1	(1, −1)
3.	2	y = 2(2) − 3 = 4 − 3	1	(2, 1)

To graph the equation, graph ordered pairs. Then draw a line through the points.

Complete the function table and graph the equation.

4. $y = -x + 1$

Input	Linear Equation	Output	Ordered Pair
x	y = −x + 1	y	(x, y)
0	y = −0 + 1	1	(0, 1)
1	y = −1 + 1	0	(1, 0)
2	y = −2 + 1	−1	(2, −1)

PRACTICE 7-3

LESSON 7-3 Practice B
Graphing Linear Functions

Graph each linear function.

1. $y = -x - 5$

Input	Linear Equation	Output	Ordered Pair
x	y = −x − 5	y	(x, y)
−4	y = −(−4) − 5	−1	(−4, −1)
−2	y = −(−2) − 5	−3	(−2, −3)
0	y = −0 − 5	−5	(0, −5)

2. $y = 2x - 1$

Input	Linear Equation	Output	Ordered Pair
x	y = 2x − 1	y	(x, y)
−2	y = 2(−2) − 1	−5	(−2, −5)
0	y = 2(0) − 1	−1	(0, −1)
1	y = 2(1) − 1	1	(1, 1)

3. The temperature of a swimming pool is 75°F. When the pool heater is turned on, the temperature rises 2°F every hour. What will the temperature be after 3 hours? Make a function table to answer the question.

Input	Equation	Output
x	y = 2x + 75	y
1	y = 2(1) + 75	77
2	y = 2(2) + 75	79
3	y = 2(3) + 75	81

81°F

4. Mel's Pizza Place charges $15.00 for a large cheese pizza plus $1.25 for each additional topping. What will be the cost of a large pizza with 3 additional toppings? Make a function table to answer the question.

Input	Equation	Output
x	y = 1.25x + 15	y
1	y = 1.25(1) + 15	16.25
2	y = 1.25(2) + 15	17.50
3	y = 1.25(3) + 15	18.75

$18.75

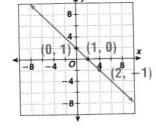

California Standards

Standard	Exercises
NS1.3	23–26
AF1.1	3, 8, 10
AF3.3 ⟵	1–21
AF4.2 ⟵	22

Graph the function $d = rt$ for each value of r.

11. $r = 35$ mi/h

12. $r = 4$ ft/min

13. $r = 10$ ft/s

14. Multi-Step Graph the function $y = -2x + 1$. Use your graph to find the value of x if the ordered pair $(x, -5)$ lies on the graph of the function. **3**

15. Environment The graph shows the amount of carbon dioxide in the atmosphere from 1958 to 1994.

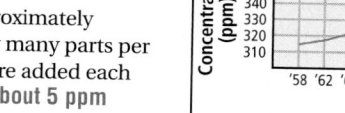

a. The graph is approximately linear. About how many parts per million (ppm) were added each 4-year period? **about 5 ppm**

b. About how many parts per million do you predict there will be after five more 4-year periods, in 2014? **about 382 ppm**

16. The water level in a well is 100 m. Water is seeping into the well and raising the water level by 10 cm per year. Water is also draining out of the well at a rate of 2 m per year. What will the water level be in 10 years? **8100 cm, or 81 m**

 17. What's the Question? Tron used the equation $y = 100 + 25x$ to track his savings y after x months. If the answer is $250, what is the question? **Possible answer: How much money does Tron have after 6 months?**

 18. Write About It Explain how to graph $y = 2x - 5$.

 19. Challenge Certain bacteria divide every 30 minutes. You can use the function $y = 2^x$ to find the number of bacteria after each half-hour period, where x is the number of half-hour periods. Make a table of values for $x = 1, 2, 3, 4,$ and 5. Plot the points, and then connect them. How does the graph differ from those you have seen so far in this lesson? **It is not linear.**

SPIRAL STANDARDS REVIEW NS1.3, ⬅ AF3.3, ⬅ AF4.2

20. Multiple Choice The graph of which linear function passes through the origin?

Ⓐ $y = x + 2$ Ⓑ $y = 3x$ Ⓒ $y = x - 1$ Ⓓ $y = 2x + 4$

21. Short Response Simon graphed the linear function $y = -x + 3$ at right. Explain his error. Then graph $y = -x + 3$ correctly on a coordinate plane.

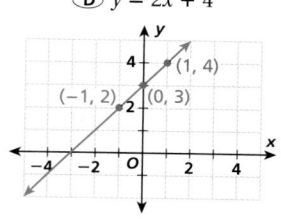

22. Zachary is making 20 decorative place cards for a dinner party. It takes him 15 minutes to make the first 3 place cards. If he continues to work at the same rate, how much longer will it take him to finish making the place cards? (Lesson 5-3) **85 minutes**

Find each number to the nearest tenth. (Lesson 6-3)

23. What number is 75% of 43? **32.3**

24. What number is 12.5% of 70? **8.8**

25. What number is 25% of 9? **2.3**

26. What number is 115% of 57? **65.6**

CHALLENGE 7-3
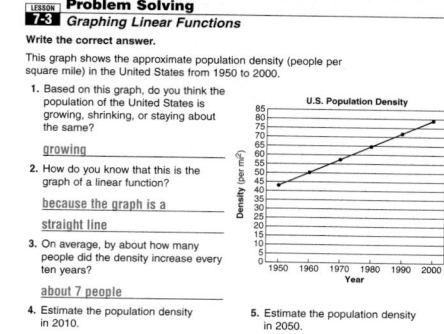

PROBLEM SOLVING 7-3

Answers 11–14, 18, 21. See p. A4.

 Teaching Tip

Multiple Choice For **Exercise 20,** suggest that students think about what point represents the origin. Then students may substitute the coordinates of that point into each function to find the correct choice.

 Journal

Ask students to describe how to sketch the graph of a linear equation.

 **Power Presentations** with PowerPoint®

7-3 Lesson Quiz

Graph the linear functions.

1. $y = 3x - 4$

2. $y = -x + 4$

3. $y = 2$

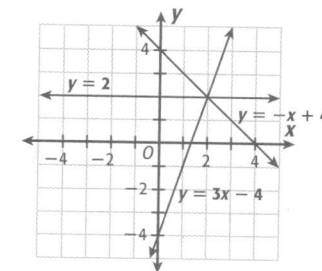

4. The temperature of a liquid is decreasing at a rate of 12°F per hour. Susan begins measuring the liquid at 200°F. Write a linear function that describes the change in temperature over time. Then make a graph to show the temperature over 5 hours. $y = 200 - 12x$

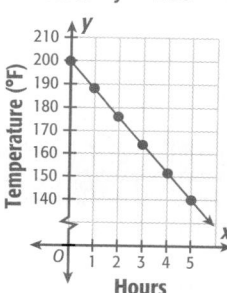

Also available on transparency

 Hands-On Lab
In *Chapter 7 Resource File*

 Online Edition
Tutorial Videos

 Countdown to Mastery Week 14

Power Presentations
with PowerPoint®

Warm Up

For each function, find the value of y for x = 0, x = 4, and x = −5.

1. $y = 6x - 3$ −3, 21, −33

2. $y = 3.8x - 12$ −12, 3.2, −31

3. $y = 1.6x + 5.9$ 5.9, 12.3, −2.1

Also available on transparency

Math Humor

The baseball player understood linear functions but had trouble with quadratic functions. He never knew what to do when someone threw him a *curve*.

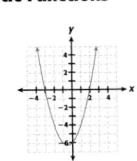 **California Standards**

Algebra and Functions 3.1
Also covered:
Algebra and Functions
3.0 Students graph and interpret linear and some nonlinear functions.

 **7-4** **Graphing Quadratic Functions**

 **California Standards**

AF3.1 Graph functions of the form $y = nx^2$ and $y = nx^3$ and use in solving problems.

Vocabulary
quadratic function
parabola

Why learn this? You can use a graph of a quadratic function to find the size of a parabolic mirror. (See Example 2.)

A **quadratic function** is a function in which the greatest power of the variable is 2. The most basic quadratic function is $y = nx^2$ where $n \neq 0$.

The graphs of all quadratic functions have the same basic shape, called a **parabola**.

The mirror of this telescope is made of liquid mercury that is rotated to form a parabolic shape.

EXAMPLE **1** **Graphing Quadratic Functions**

Create a table for each quadratic function, and use it to graph the function.

A $y = -x^2 - 3$

Helpful Hint

Use the value of *n* to help you decide if your graph is reasonable. If *n* is positive, the graph opens upward. If *n* is negative, the graph opens downward.

x	$-x^2 - 3$	y
−3	$-(-3)^2 - 3$	−12
−2	$-(-2)^2 - 3$	−7
−1	$-(-1)^2 - 3$	−4
0	$-(0)^2 - 3$	−3
1	$-(1)^2 - 3$	−4
2	$-(2)^2 - 3$	−7
3	$-(3)^2 - 3$	−12

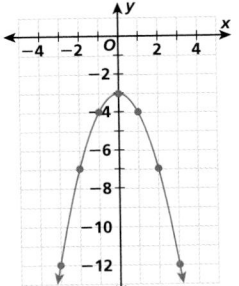

Plot the points and connect them with a smooth curve.

B $y = x^2 + x - 2$

x	$x^2 + x - 2$	y
−3	$(-3)^2 + (-3) - 2$	4
−2	$(-2)^2 + (-2) - 2$	0
−1	$(-1)^2 + (-1) - 2$	−2
0	$(0)^2 + 0 - 2$	−2
1	$(1)^2 + 1 - 2$	0
2	$(2)^2 + 2 - 2$	4
3	$(3)^2 + 3 - 2$	10

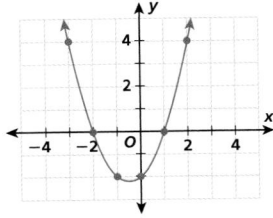

Plot the points and connect them with a smooth curve.

---

1 **Introduce**
Alternate Opener

Motivate

Review the type of function the students have studied so far (linear). Ask students what happens when they throw a ball into the air. Does the ball travel in a straight line like a linear function? no Explain that the ball travels in a path that can be described by a new type of function.

Explorations and answers are provided in *Alternate Openers: Explorations Transparencies*.

EXAMPLE 2 *Astronomy Application*

In a *liquid mirror,* a container of liquid mercury is rotated around an axis. Gravity and centrifugal force cause the liquid to form a parabolic shape. The cross section of a liquid mirror that rotates at 10 revolutions per minute is approximated by the graph of $y = 0.027x^2$ where x and y are measured in meters. If the diameter of the mirror is 3 m, about how much higher are the sides than the center?

Spinning mercury forms a parabolic surface.

First create a table of values. Then graph the cross section.

x	$0.027x^2$	y
-2	$0.027(-2)^2$	0.108
-1	$0.027(-1)^2$	0.027
0	$0.027(0)^2$	0
1	$0.027(1)^2$	0.027
2	$0.027(2)^2$	0.108

Possible answers to
Think and Discuss

1. The graphs have the same shape, but the graph for $y = x^2 + 1$ is translated up one unit.

2. a smooth line with line symmetry that is narrower at the bottom and continues to get wider as the x-values get farther away from 0

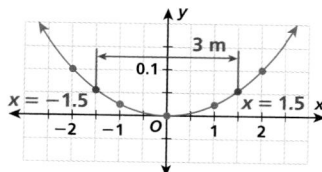

The center of the mirror is at $x = 0$ m where the height is 0 m. The diameter of the mirror is 3 m, so the edges (highest points) are at $x = -1.5$ m and $x = 1.5$ m.

The height of the mirror at $x = 1.5$ is $0.027(1.5)^2 \approx 0.06$ m. The sides are about 0.06 m, or 6 cm, higher than the center.

Think and Discuss

1. **Compare** the graphs of $y = x^2$ and $y = x^2 + 1$.
2. **Describe** the shape of a parabola.

Power Presentations
with PowerPoint®

Additional Examples

Example 1

Create a table for each quadratic function, and use it to graph the function.

A. $y = x^2 + 1$

x	-2	-1	0	1	2
y	5	2	1	2	5

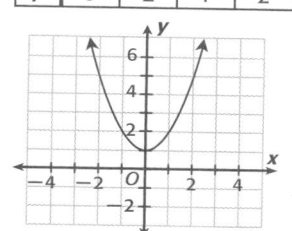

B. $y = x^2 - x + 1$

x	-2	-1	0	1	2
y	7	3	1	1	3

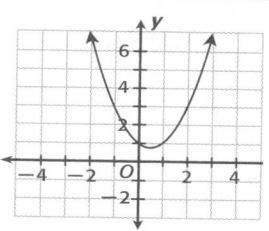

Example 2

A reflecting surface of a television antenna was formed by rotating the parabola $y = 0.1x^2$ about its axis of symmetry. If the antenna has a diameter of 4 feet, about how much higher are the sides than the center?
0.4 ft

Also available on transparency

2 Teach

Guided Instruction

ENGLISH LANGUAGE LEARNERS

In this lesson, students learn to identify and graph quadratic functions. Explain that a *quadratic function* has a squared variable, such as x^2. Show the students that graphs of these functions are in a shape similar to the letter U and are called *parabolas*. Explain that in order to graph the quadratic functions, students will find ordered pairs in the same way they have done with previous functions. Help students recognize that vertical line symmetry exists in each of the parabolas.

Universal Access
Through Visual Cues

Have students graph the following set of parabolas on the same coordinate plane: $y = x^2$, $y = x^2 + 2$, and $y = x^2 + 4$. Ask them to identify any relationship between changes in the equations of the functions and changes in the graphs of the functions. Then ask them to test their hypotheses by guessing how the graphs $y = x^2 - 2$ and $y = x^2 - 4$ will look. Have students discuss their hypotheses and findings.

3 Close

Summarize

Remind students that the graph of a quadratic equation is a parabola with vertical line symmetry. Ask students to classify each function below as linear or quadratic.

a. $y = 2x^2 - 8x$ **b.** $y = 4 - x$

c. $y = 3x^2$ **d.** $y = 3x + 8$

e. $y = x - 7$ **f.** $y = x^2 - 7$

a. quadratic; **b.** linear; **c.** quadratic;
d. linear; **e.** linear; **f.** quadratic

7-4 Exercises

California Standards Practice
AF3.1

go.hrw.com
Homework Help Online
KEYWORD: MT8CA 7-4
Parent Resources Online
KEYWORD: MT8CA Parent

Assignment Guide

If you finished Example **1** assign:
Proficient 1–3, 5–7, 9–17, 27–33
Advanced 5–7, 9–17, 20, 24–25, 27–33

If you finished Example **2** assign:
Proficient 1–20, 26–33
Advanced 5–17, 20–33

Homework Quick Check

Quickly check key concepts.
Exercises: 6, 8, 12, 16

Answers

1–3, 5–7, 19a. See pp. A4–5.

Math Background

Some quadratic functions are given in what is called *factored form.* The benefit of presenting the functions in this way is that the *x*-intercepts can be quickly determined. The property involved is called the *Zero Product Property,* and it states that if the product of two factors is zero, then one or both of the factors must be zero. (If $ab = 0$, then $a = 0$ or $b = 0$.) Applying this property to a quadratic function in factored form yields the *x*-intercept(s). For example:

$$y = (x - 4)(x + 6)$$
$$0 = (x - 4)(x + 6)$$
$$(x - 4) = 0 \text{ or } (x + 6) = 0$$
$$x = 4 \text{ or } \qquad x = -6$$

GUIDED PRACTICE

See Example **1** Create a table for each quadratic function, and use it to graph the function.

1. $y = -x^2 + 5$ **2.** $y = x^2 - 3$ **3.** $y = x^2 + 1.5x$

See Example **2** **4. Sports** The function $y = -0.15t^2 + 2.4t + 5.1$ gives the height in feet of a baseball y seconds after it was thrown. What was the height of the baseball when it was initially thrown ($t = 0$)? **5.1 ft**

INDEPENDENT PRACTICE

See Example **1** Create a table for each quadratic function, and use it to graph the function.

5. $y = x^2 + x + 2$ **6.** $y = -x^2 + 2$ **7.** $y = 3x^2 - 2$

See Example **2** **8. Manufacturing** The function $y = 2x^2 - 300x + 14{,}450$ gives the cost of manufacturing x items per day. Which number of items will give the lowest cost per day: 40, 75, or 90? What will the cost be? **75; $3200**

PRACTICE AND PROBLEM SOLVING

Extra Practice
See page EP14.

Find y when $x = -3$, $x = 0$, and $x = 3$.

9. $y = x^2 + 6$ **15, 6, 15** **10.** $y = \frac{1}{2}x^2$ **4.5, 0, 4.5** **11.** $y = x^2 + 3x$ **0, 0, 18**

12. $y = x^2 + 9$ **18, 9, 18** **13.** $y = 3x^2 - x + 7$ **37, 7, 31** **14.** $y = \frac{x^2}{3} - 1$ **2, −1, 2**

Match each equation with the correct graph.

15. $y = x^2 - 3$ **Graph C** **16.** $y = -2x + 3$ **Graph A** **17.** $y = -x^2 + 3$ **Graph B**

Graph A
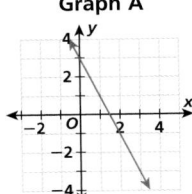

Graph B
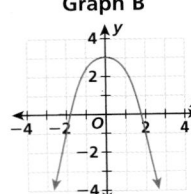

Graph C
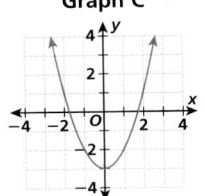

18. Hobbies The height h of a model airplane launched from the top of a 24 ft hill is given by the function $h = -0.08t^2 + 2.6t + 24$, where t is the time in seconds. Find the height of the airplane after 4, 8, and 16 seconds. Round to the nearest tenth of a foot. What can you tell about the direction of the airplane? **33.1 ft, 39.7 ft, 45.1 ft; the airplane is flying up.**

19. Science The height h of a toy rocket launched straight up with an initial velocity of 48 feet per second is given by the function $h = 48t - 16t^2$. The time t is in seconds.

a. Graph the function for $t = 0$, 0.5, 1, 1.5, 2, 2.5, and 3.

b. How many seconds does it take for the rocket to land? **3 s**

California Standards

Standard	Exercises
NS1.3	32–33
AF3.1	1–27
MG1.2	28–31

REVIEW FOR MASTERY 7-4

LESSON 7-4 Review for Mastery
Graphing Quadratic Functions

A quadratic function has a variable that is squared.

general quadratic function $y = ax^2 + bx + c$
square term *y*-intercept

$y = x^2 - 4x + 3$

The graph of a quadratic function is a **parabola**, a curve that falls on one side of a turning point and rises on the other. You can make a table of a function's values and use them to graph the function.

x	$y = x^2 - 4x + 3$
−1	$y = (-1)^2 - 4(-1) + 3 = 8$
0	$y = 0^2 - 4(0) + 3 = 3$
1	$y = 1^2 - 4(1) + 3 = 0$
2	$y = 2^2 - 4(2) + 3 = -1$
3	$y = 3^2 - 4(3) + 3 = 0$
4	$y = 4^2 - 4(4) + 3 = 3$
5	$y = 5^2 - 4(5) + 3 = 8$

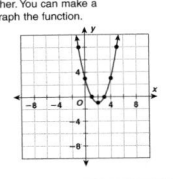

Complete the table for the quadratic function and use it to graph the function.

1. $y = x^2 - 2x - 3$

x	$y = x^2 - 2x - 3$
−2	$y = (-2)^2 - 2(-2) - 3 = 5$
−1	$y = (-1)^2 - 2(-1) - 3 = 0$
0	$y = (0)^2 - 2(0) - 3 = -3$
1	$y = (1)^2 - 2(1) - 3 = -4$
2	$y = (2)^2 - 2(2) - 3 = -3$
3	$y = (3)^2 - 2(3) - 3 = 0$
4	$y = (4)^2 - 2(4) - 3 = 5$

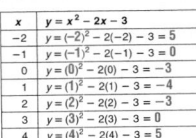

PRACTICE 7-4

LESSON 7-4 Practice B
Graphing Quadratic Functions

Create a table for each quadratic function, and use it to make a graph.

1. $y = x^2 - 5$

x	$y = x^2 - 5$
−3	$y = (-3)^2 - 5 = 4$
−1	$y = (-1)^2 - 5 = -4$
0	$y = (0)^2 - 5 = -5$
2	$y = (2)^2 - 5 = -1$
3	$y = (3)^2 - 5 = 4$

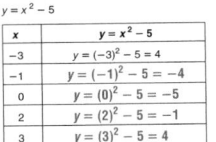

2. $y = x^2 - 2x + 3$

x	$y = x^2 - 2x + 3$
3	$y = (3)^2 - 2(3) + 3 = 6$
2	$y = (2)^2 - 2(2) + 3 = 3$
1	$y = (1)^2 - 2(1) + 3 = 2$
0	$y = (0)^2 - 2(0) + 3 = 3$
−1	$y = (-1)^2 - 2(-1) + 3 = 6$

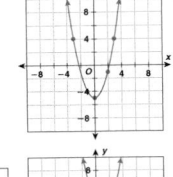

3. Complete the table for the values $x = -3$, $x = 0$, and $x = 3$.

	x = −3	x = 0	x = 3
$y = x^2 - 2x + 1$	16	1	4
$y = x^2 - 6$	3	−6	3
$y = x^2 - x + 3$	15	3	9

4. The function $y = -4.9t^2$ gives the distance in meters that an object will fall toward Earth in t seconds. Find the distance an object will fall in 1, 2, 3, 4, and 5 seconds. (Note that the distance traveled by a falling object is shown as a negative number.)

4.9 m, 19.6 m, 44.1 m, 78.4 m, and 122.5 m

20. The graph of a linear function is a straight line. The graph of a quadratic function is a parabola. The linear equation contains a variable to the first power. The quadratic equation contains a variable squared.

20. Describe the difference between a linear function and a quadratic function in terms of their graphs and their equations.

21. Business A store owner can sell 30 digital cameras a week at a price of $150 each. For every $5 drop in price, she can sell 2 more cameras a week. If x is the number of $5 price reductions, the weekly sales function is
$y = (30 + 2x)(150 - 5x)$.

a. Find y for $x = 3, 4, 5, 6$, and 7.

b. How many $5 price reductions will result in the highest weekly sales? **7**

Predicted Sales			
Price	$150	$145	$140
Number Sold	30	32	34
Weekly Sales	$4500	$4640	$4760

21a.
$4860, $4940, $5000, $5040, $5060

22. Reasoning The height of an object dropped from the top of a 16 ft ladder is given by the function $h = -t^2 + 16$. Find h when t is 4. What does this tell you about $t = 4$ seconds? Does this equation seem more realistic for dropping a rock or a feather? Explain.

 23. Choose a Strategy Suppose the function $y = -5x^2 + 300x + 1250$ gives a company's profit for producing x items. Which of the following numbers of items should be produced to maximize profit?

Ⓐ 25   Ⓑ 30   Ⓒ 35   Ⓓ 40

 24. Write About It Which will grow faster as x gets larger, $y = x^2$ or $y = 2^x$? Check by testing each function for several values of x.

25. Challenge Create a table of values for the quadratic function $y = -3(x^2 + 1)$, and then graph the function. At what points does the graph intersect the x-axis? **It has no x-intercepts.**

SPIRAL STANDARDS REVIEW

NS1.3, AF3.1, MG1.2

26. Multiple Choice The height of a tennis ball thrown straight up with an initial velocity of 64 meters per second is given by the function $h = 64t - 16t^2$. The time t is in seconds. At what time does the tennis ball land?

Ⓐ 1 s   Ⓑ 4 s   Ⓒ 16 s   Ⓓ 64 s

27. Gridded Response What is the value of y when $y = x^2 + 2x - 1$ and x is -4? **7**

The scale of a drawing is 2 in. = 3 ft. Find the actual measurement for each length in the drawing. (Lesson 5-7)

28. 1 in. **1.5 ft**   **29.** 5 in. **7.5 ft**   **30.** 12 in. **18 ft**   **31.** 8.5 in. **12.75 ft**

Find each number to the nearest tenth. (Lesson 6-4)

32. 85% of what number is 1250? **1470.6**   **33.** 560 is 4.5% of what number? **12,444.4**

Answers
22, 24–25. See p. A5.

Teaching Tip **Multiple Choice** For **Exercise 26,** students can eliminate choices **C** and **D** because they will result in a negative height.

Journal
Ask students to write about why a negative x-value will often produce a positive y-value in a quadratic function.

Power Presentations
with PowerPoint®

7-4 Lesson Quiz
Create a table for each quadratic function, and use it to graph the function.

1. $y = x^2 - 2$

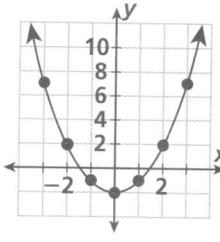

x	y
−3	7
−2	2
−1	−1
0	−2
1	−1
2	2
3	7

2. $y = x^2 + x - 6$

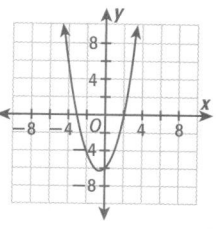

x	y
−3	0
−2	−4
−1	−6
0	−6
1	−4
2	0
3	6

3. The function $y = 40t - 5t^2$ gives the height of an arrow in meters t seconds after it is shot upward. What is the height of the arrow after 5 seconds? **75 m**

Also available on transparency

CHALLENGE 7-4

LESSON 7-4 Challenge
A Piece of This, a Piece of That

A function defined differently over various parts of its domain is called a **piecewise function.**
$y = \begin{cases} x - 2 & \text{when } x < 0 \\ x^2 & \text{when } x \geq 0 \end{cases}$

This function consists of the line $y = x - 2$ when x is negative and the parabola $y = x^2$ when x is nonnegative.

x	x − 2	y		x	x²	y
−4	−4 − 2	−6		0	0²	0
−3	−3 − 2	−5		1	1²	1
−2	−2 − 2	−4		2	2²	4
−1	−1 − 2	−3		3	3²	9

Note the open hole on the line at (0, −2).
When $x = 0$, the point on this graph is on the parabola, not on the line.

Graph each piecewise function.

1. $y = \begin{cases} x & \text{when } x < 0 \\ 2x^2 & \text{when } x \geq 0 \end{cases}$

x	y = x		x	2x²	y
−4	−4		0	2 • 0²	0
−3	−3		1	2 • 1²	2
−2	−2		2	2 • 2²	8
−1	−1		3	2 • 3²	18

2. $y = \begin{cases} x + 2 & \text{when } x < 0 \\ -x^2 & \text{when } x \geq 0 \end{cases}$

x	x + 2	y		x	−x²	y
−4	−4 + 2	−2		0	−(0²)	0
−3	−3 + 2	−1		1	−(1²)	−1
−2	−2 + 2	0		2	−(2²)	−4
−1	−1 + 2	1		3	−(3²)	−9

PROBLEM SOLVING 7-4

LESSON 7-4 Problem Solving
Graphing Quadratic Functions

To find the time it takes an object to fall, you can use the equation $h = -16t^2 - vt + s$ where h is the height in feet, t is the time in seconds, v is the initial velocity, and s is the starting height in feet. Write the correct answer.

1. If a construction worker drops a tool from 240 feet above the ground, how many feet above the ground will it be in 2 seconds? Hint: $v = 0$, $s = 240$.

176 feet

2. How long will it take the tool in Exercise 1 to hit the ground? Round to the nearest hundredth.

3.87 seconds

3. The Gateway Arch in St. Louis, Missouri is the tallest manmade memorial. The arch rises to a height of 630 feet. If you drop a rock down from the top of the arch with a velocity of 20 ft/s, how many feet above the ground will the rock be in 2 seconds?

526 feet

4. Will the rock in exercise 3 hit the ground within 6 seconds of throwing it?

yes

The average monthly rainfall for Seattle, Washington can be approximated by the equation $y = 0.147x^2 - 1.890x + 7.139$ where x is the month (January: $x = 1$, February, $x = 2$, etc.) and y is the monthly rainfall in inches. Choose the letter for the best answer.

5. What is the average monthly rainfall in Seattle for the month of January?
A 3.7 in.   C 7.6 in.
Ⓑ 5.4 in.   D 9.2 in.

6. What is the average monthly rainfall in Seattle for the month of April?
F 0.2 in.   Ⓗ 1.9 in.
G 1.4 in.   J 2.8 in.

7. What is the average monthly rainfall in Seattle for the month of August?
A 1.1 in.   C 5.6 in.
Ⓑ 1.4 in.   D 6.8 in.

8. In what month does it rain the least in Seattle, Washington?
F May   H July
Ⓖ June   J August

Objective: Students identify and graph cubic functions.

Online Edition
Tutorial Videos

Countdown to Mastery Week 14

Power Presentations
with PowerPoint®

Warm Up

Graph each function.

1. $y = 2x + 4$
2. $y = -x - 1$
3. $y = x^2 - 4$
4. $y = \frac{1}{2}x^2$

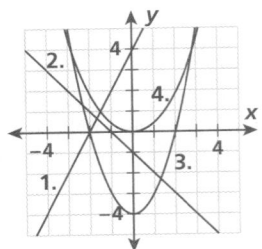

Also available on transparency

Math Humor

Q: Why is it helpful to have some wood, a few nails, and a hammer when you graph a function?

A: So you can first make a table.

California Standards

AF3.1 Graph functions of the form $y = nx^2$ and $y = nx^3$ and use in solving problems.

Vocabulary
cubic function

Why learn this? You can use a cubic function to approximate the growth of a population. (See Exercise 23.)

A **cubic function** is a function in which the greatest power of the variable is 3. The most basic cubic function is $y = nx^3$ where $n \neq 0$.

The graph of $y = x^3$ is shown. When x is negative, y is negative because odd powers of negative numbers are negative. The graphs of all cubic functions have this same basic shape, curving down, then curving up.

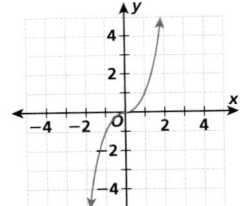

EXAMPLE **1** **Graphing Cubic Functions**

Create a table for each cubic function, and use it to graph the function.

A $y = 2x^3$

x	$2x^3$	y
-2	$2(-2)^3$	-16
-1	$2(-1)^3$	-2
0	$2(0)^3$	0
1	$2(1)^3$	2
2	$2(2)^3$	16

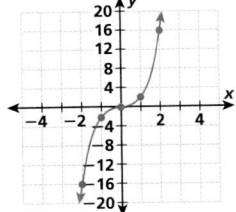

Choose both positive and negative values for x.
Plot the points and connect them with a smooth curve.

B $y = -x^3$

x	$-x^3$	y
-2	$-(-2)^3$	8
-1	$-(-1)^3$	1
0	$-(0)^3$	0
1	$-(1)^3$	-1
2	$-(2)^3$	-8

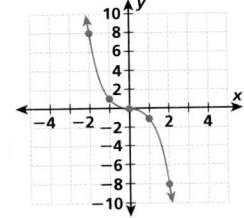

Choose both positive and negative values for x.
Plot the points and connect them with a smooth curve.

---

1 **Introduce**
Alternate Opener

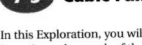

EXPLORATION

7-5 **Cubic Functions**

In this Exploration, you will investigate the graph of the function $y = x^3$.

1. Complete the table of values for the function $y = x^3$.

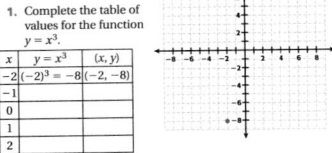

x	$y = x^3$	(x, y)
-2	$(-2)^3 = -8$	$(-2, -8)$
-1		
0		
1		
2		

2. Plot the ordered pairs (x, y) on the graph.
3. Draw a smooth curve through the points.

Think and Discuss

4. **Explain** what you would do to extend the graph by plotting additional points.
5. **Compare** the graph of $y = x^3$ to the graph of $y = x^2$.

Motivate

Write the function $y = 2x + 5$ on the board and label it as a linear function. Then write $y = 3x^2 - 4x + 1$ on the board and label it as a quadratic function. Ask students if they can guess what a cubic function might look like. Have students suggest possible examples of cubic functions.

Explorations and answers are provided in *Alternate Openers: Explorations Transparencies.*

California Standards

Algebra and Functions 3.1

Create a table for each cubic function, and use it to graph the function.

C $y = x^3 + 2$

x	$x^3 + 2$	y
-2	$(-2)^3 + 2$	-6
-1	$(-1)^3 + 2$	1
0	$(0)^3 + 2$	2
1	$(1)^3 + 2$	3
2	$(2)^3 + 2$	10

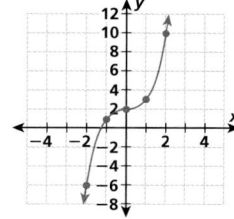

You can identify different types of functions based on their graphs.

EXAMPLE 2 Identifying Types of Functions

Tell whether each function is linear, quadratic, or cubic.

A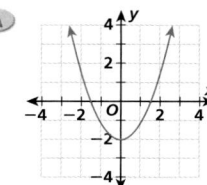

The graph is a parabola.
Quadratic

B

The graph curves down, then up.
Cubic

C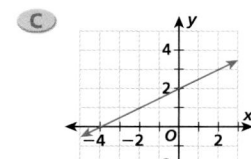

The graph is a line.
Linear

D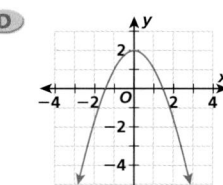

The graph is a parabola.
Quadratic

Possible answers to *Think and Discuss*
1. The graph of $y = 5x^2$ is a parabola in the first and second quadrants. The graph of $y = 5x^3$ is a smooth curve in the first and third quadrants.
2. No; the function does not have a variable raised to the third power; the variable is the exponent.

Think and Discuss

1. Compare the graph of $y = 5x^2$ to the graph of $y = 5x^3$.

2. Explain whether $y = 3^x$ is a cubic function.

Additional Examples

Example 1

Create a table for each cubic function, and use it to graph the function.
A. $y = \frac{1}{4}x^3$
B. $y = -x^3 + 1$
C. $y = x^3 - 2$

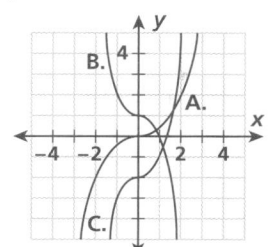

Example 2

Tell whether each function is linear, quadratic, or cubic.

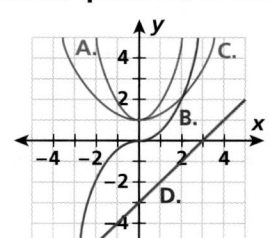

A. quadratic
B. cubic
C. quadratic
D. linear

Also available on transparency

Teaching Tip **Visual** Remind students that the scales on the axes of a coordinate plane can affect the appearance of a graph. The graphs in **Examples 1A and 1B** appear to have the same shape, but the scales on the y-axes are different.

2 Teach

Guided Instruction

In this lesson, students learn to identify and graph cubic functions. Begin by quickly reviewing what it means to cube a number. Then present **Example 1,** emphasizing the characteristic shape of the graph of any function of the form $y = nx^3 + c$. Next, show students how they can use the shape of a graph to identify the type of function.

Universal Access
Through Cooperative Learning

Have students work in pairs to create a matching game. Each pair should graph two linear functions, two quadratic functions, and two cubic functions. Have students cut out the graphs and write the corresponding equations on slips of paper. Then ask students to trade the graphs and equations with another pair of students. Partners should work together to match the equations to the graphs.

3 Close

Summarize

Ask students to graph the following cubic functions.

1. $y = -3x^3$ **2.** $y = x^3 + 3$

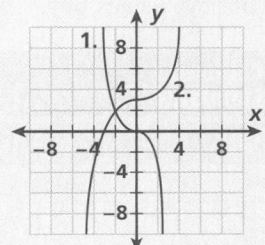

7-5 Exercises

Assignment Guide

If you finished Example **1** assign:
Proficient 1–3, 7–12, 23, 25, 29–35
Advanced 7–12, 22–27, 29–35

If you finished Example **2** assign:
Proficient 1–18, 21, 24, 25, 28–35
Advanced 7–15, 18–35

Homework Quick Check
Quickly check key concepts.
Exercises: 8, 10, 12, 14, 22

Answers
1–3, 7–12, 16–21, 22. See p. A5.

Math Background

A cubic function can be written in the form $y = ax^3 + bx^2 + cx + d$, where a, b, c, and d are real numbers and $a \neq 0$. The graph of a cubic function has one of two basic shapes. It either has a shape similar to that of the graph of $y = x^3$ or has a shape with a "peak" and a "valley" as in the graph of $y = x^3 + 3x^2 - 3$, shown below.

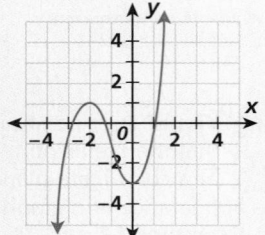

COMMON ERROR ALERT

In **Exercise 2**, students may incorrectly evaluate the function for negative values of x. Remind students that the cube of a negative number is negative. This value is then multiplied by -2, which means that negative values of x result in positive values of y.

California Standards

Standard	Exercises
NS1.6	30–32
AF3.1	1–4, 6, 7–15, 17–19, 23–30, 33–35
AF3.2	22
AF3.3 ←	5, 16, 20–21

GUIDED PRACTICE

See Example **1** Create a table for each cubic function, and use it to graph the function.

1. $y = -\frac{1}{2}x^3$ **2.** $y = -2x^3$ **3.** $y = x^3 - 3$

See Example **2** Tell whether each function is linear, quadratic, or cubic.

4.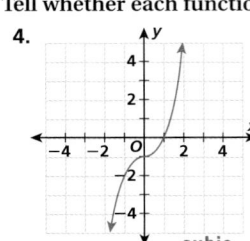
cubic

5.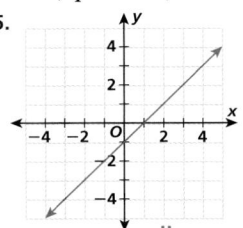
linear

6.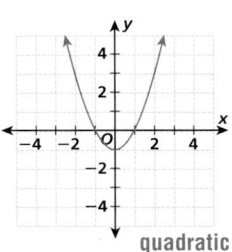
quadratic

INDEPENDENT PRACTICE

See Example **1** Create a table for each cubic function, and use it to graph the function.

7. $y = -\frac{1}{3}x^3$ **8.** $y = 3x^3$ **9.** $y = -3x^3$

10. $y = \frac{1}{2}x^3$ **11.** $y = x^3 + 5$ **12.** $y = x^3 - 4$

See Example **2** Tell whether each function is linear, quadratic, or cubic.

13.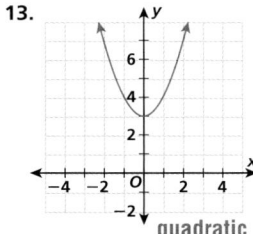
quadratic

14.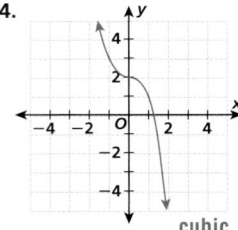
cubic

15.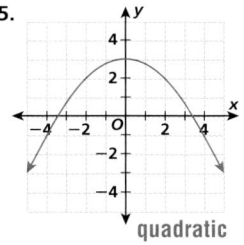
quadratic

PRACTICE AND PROBLEM SOLVING

Extra Practice
See page EP14.

Graph each function.

16. $y = 2x - 4$ **17.** $y = x^2 - 3$ **18.** $y = \frac{1}{3}x^3$

19. $y = \frac{1}{2}x^2 - 1$ **20.** $y = -x + 2$ **21.** $y = -4$

22. Geometry The volume V of a cube with edges x inches long is given by the function $V = x^3$. Make a table of values and use it to graph this function. (*Hint:* Would it make sense to include negative values of x?)

REVIEW FOR MASTERY 7-5

Review for Mastery
7-5 *Cubic Functions*

A cubic function contains a variable that is raised to the third power. In other words, the function has a variable that is cubed.

General cubic function $y = ax^3 + bx^2 + cx + d$, where $a \neq 0$
variable is cubed

You can make a table of values to help you graph a cubic function. For example, here is a table and graph for the cubic function $y = x^3 + 2$.

x	$x^3 + 2$	y
-2	$(-2)^3 + 2$	-6
-1	$(-1)^3 + 2$	1
0	$(0)^3 + 2$	2
1	$(1)^3 + 2$	3
2	$(2)^3 + 1$	10

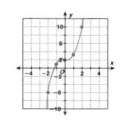

Complete the table for the cubic function and use it to graph the function.

1. $y = x^3 - 5$

x	$x^3 - 5$	y
-2	$(-2)^3 - 5$	-13
-1	$(-1)^3 - 5$	-6
0	$(0)^3 - 5$	-5
1	$(1)^3 - 5$	-4
2	$(2)^3 - 5$	3

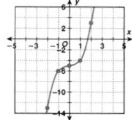

PRACTICE 7-5

Practice B
7-5 *Cubic Functions*

Complete the table for each cubic function, and use it to graph the function.

1. $y = x^3 - 4$

x	$x^3 - 4$	y
-2	$(-2)^3 - 4$	-12
-1	$(-1)^3 - 4$	-5
0	$(0)^3 - 4$	-4
1	$(1)^3 - 4$	-3
2	$(2)^3 - 4$	4

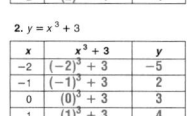

2. $y = x^3 + 3$

x	$x^3 + 3$	y
-2	$(-2)^3 + 3$	-5
-1	$(-1)^3 + 3$	2
0	$(0)^3 + 3$	3
1	$(1)^3 + 3$	4
2	$(2)^3 + 3$	11

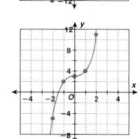

Tell which of the following could be the graph of each equation.

$y = 2x$, $y = 2x^2$, $y = -2x^2$, $y = 2x^3$

3. **4.** **5.** **6.**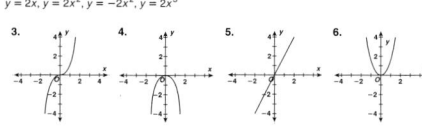

$y = 2x^3$ $y = -2x^3$ $y = 2x$ $y = 2x^2$

23. Reasoning How does the sign of the x^3-term affect the graph of a cubic function? **The sign determines whether the curve rises or falls from left to right.**

24. Life Science A biologist is studying a population of zebra mussels in a river. The number of mussels y is approximated by the cubic function $y = 20t^3 + 10$, where t is the number of weeks since the start of the study.
a. Graph the function.
b. Use your graph to estimate the number of mussels when $t = 2.5$ weeks.

Possible estimate: 320

25. Reasoning The y-intercept of a function is the y-coordinate of the point where the function's graph crosses the y-axis (where $x = 0$).
a. Graph each cubic function in the table.
b. Complete the table by finding the y-intercept for each function.
c. Look for a pattern in your table. Without graphing, what do you think is the y-intercept of $y = x^3 - 15$? **−15**

Function	y-intercept
$y = x^3 + 1$	1
$y = x^3 + 3$	3
$y = x^3 - 2$	−2
$y = x^3 - 4$	−4

26. What's the Error? A student graphed the function $y = -x^3$ so that the graph included the points $(-3, -27)$, $(-2, -8)$, and $(-1, -1)$. Explain the student's error. **The graph should include the points $(-3, 27)$, $(-2, 8)$, and $(-1, 1)$.**

27. Write About It Explain how the graph of $y = 2x^3$ compares to the graph of $y = x^3$.

28. Challenge Graph the cubic function $y = x^3 + 3x^2 - 2$.

27. The graphs have the same basic shape, but compared to the graph of $y = x^3$, the graph of $y = 2x^3$ is stretched vertically by a factor of 2.

SPIRAL STANDARDS REVIEW

NS1.6, AF3.1, AF3.3

29. Multiple Choice Which equation could be shown in the graph at right?
Ⓐ $y = -3x^2$ Ⓒ $y = -3x$
Ⓑ $y = 3x^3$ Ⓓ $y = 3x^2$

30. Multiple Choice The price of a stock in dollars is given by the cubic function $p = 5x^3 + 2$, where x is the number of years since 2002. What was the price of the stock in 2005?
Ⓐ $42   Ⓑ $47   Ⓒ $137   Ⓓ $322

Find the percent of increase or decrease to the nearest percent. (Lesson 6-5)

31. from $64 to $88
38% increase

32. from $95 to $50
47% decrease

33. from $147 to $165
12% increase

Create a table for each quadratic function, and use it to graph the function. (Lesson 7-4)

34. $y = \frac{1}{4}x^2$ **35.** $y = x^2 + x - 6$ **36.** $y = -x^2 + 3$

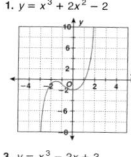
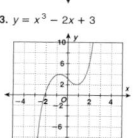
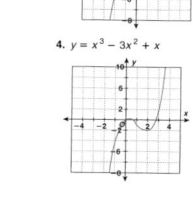

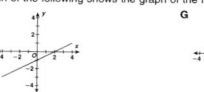
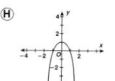
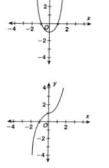

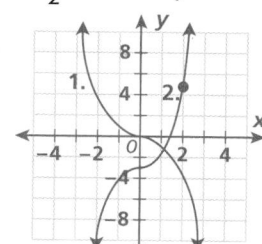
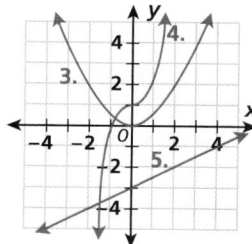

Organizer

Objective: Assess students' mastery of concepts and skills in Lessons 7-1 through 7-5.

Resources

 Assessment Resources
Section 7A Quiz

 Test & Practice Generator
 One-Stop Planner®

INTERVENTION ◀▦▶

Resources

 **Ready to Go On?
Intervention and
Enrichment** Worksheets

 **Ready to Go On? CD-ROM**

🪐 **Ready to Go On? Online**

my.hrw.com

Answers

1–4, 9–16. See p. A6.

Quiz for Lessons 7-1 Through 7-5

☑ **7-1** The Coordinate Plane

Plot each point on a coordinate plane.

1. $W(1, 5)$ **2.** $X(5, -3)$ **3.** $Y(-1, -5)$ **4.** $Z(-8, 2)$

☑ **7-2** Functions

Determine if each relationship represents a function.

5.
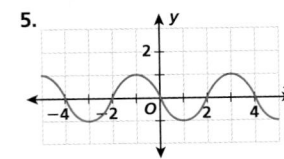
yes

6.

x	y
0	9
1	8
2	7
3	8
4	9

yes

7.

x	y
0	0
1	1
2	2
3	3
1	4

no

8.
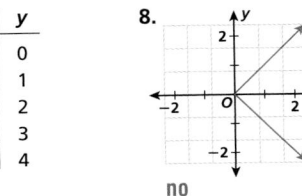
no

☑ **7-3** Graphing Linear Functions

Graph each linear function.

9. $y = x - 4$ **10.** $y = 2x - 5$ **11.** $y = -x + 7$ **12.** $y = -2x + 1$

13. A freight train travels 50 miles per hour. Write a linear function that describes the distance the train travels over time. Then make a graph to show the distance the train travels in 5 hours. $y = 50x$

☑ **7-4** Graphing Quadratic Functions

Create a table for each quadratic function, and use it to graph the function.

14. $y = x^2 + 4$ **15.** $y = x^2 + 2.5x$ **16.** $y = x^2 + x - 1$

17. The function $y = 2x^2 - 300x + 14,450$ gives the cost of manufacturing x items per day. Which number of items will give the lowest cost per day, 50, 70, or 85? What will the cost be?   **70; $3250**

☑ **7-5** Cubic Functions

Tell whether each function is linear, quadratic, or cubic.

18.
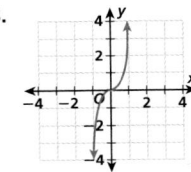
cubic

19.
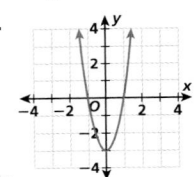
quadratic

20.
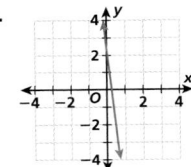
linear

READY TO GO ON?
Diagnose and Prescribe

**NO
INTERVENE**

**YES
ENRICH**

READY TO GO ON? Intervention, Section 7A			
Ready to Go On? Intervention	🖎 **Worksheets**	💿 **CD-ROM**	🪐 **Online**
☑ Lesson 7-1 🐘 Prep for ⟵ AF3.3	7-1 Intervention	Activity 7-1	
☑ Lesson 7-2 🐘 Prep for ⟵ AF3.3	7-2 Intervention	Activity 7-2	
☑ Lesson 7-3 🐘 AF1.1, ⟵ AF3.3	7-3 Intervention	Activity 7-3	Diagnose and Prescribe Online
☑ Lesson 7-4 🐘 AF3.1	7-4 Intervention	Activity 7-4	
☑ Lesson 7-5 🐘 AF3.1	7-5 Intervention	Activity 7-5	

**READY TO GO ON?
Enrichment, Section 7A**

 🖎 **Worksheets**
💿 **CD-ROM**
🪐 **Online**

Focus on Problem Solving

California Standards

MR1.1 Analyze problems by **identifying relationships,** distinguishing relevant from irrelevant information, identifying missing information, sequencing and prioritizing information, **and observing patterns.**

Also covered: ← **NS1.2,** ← **NS1.3,** ← **NS1.7,** ← **AF4.2**

Make a Plan

- **Choose a method of computation**

When solving problems, you must decide which calculation method is best: paper and pencil, calculator, or mental math. Your decision will be based on many factors, such as what the problem asks, the numbers involved, and your own number sense. Use the following table as a guideline.

Paper and Pencil	Calculator	Mental Math
Use when solving multi-step problems so you can see how the steps relate.	Use when working with large or difficult numbers.	Use when performing basic operations or generating simple estimates.

For each problem, tell whether you would use a calculator, mental math, or pencil and paper. Justify your choice, and then solve the problem.

1 The local high school radio station has 500 CDs. Each week, the music manager gets 25 new CDs. How many CDs will the station have in 8 weeks? **700**

2 There are 360 deer in a forest. The population each year is 10% more than the previous year. How many deer will there be after 3 years? **479**

3 Heidi works 8-hour shifts frosting cakes. She has frosted 12 cakes so far, and she thinks she can frost 4 cakes an hour during the rest of her shift. How many more hours will it take for her to frost a total of 32 cakes? **5**

4 Kai has $170 in a savings account that earns 3% simple interest each year. How much interest will he have earned in 14 years? **$71.40**

5 A company's logo is in the shape of a right triangle. On the company's stationery, the triangle has legs measuring 5.1 cm and 6.9 cm. On a poster, the shorter leg of the similar logo measures 14.79 cm. Estimate the length of the longer leg on the poster. **≈ 21 cm**

6 Margo and her friends decided to hike the Wildcat Rock trail. After hiking $\frac{1}{4}$ of the way, they turned back because it began to rain. How far did they hike in all? **$3\frac{1}{8}$ mi**

Trail	Distance (mi)
Meadowlark	$5\frac{3}{8}$
Key Lake	$4\frac{1}{2}$
Wildcat Rock	$6\frac{1}{4}$
Eagle Lookout	8

4. Calculator; Use the formula *I = Prt* to find that Kai will earn *I* = ($170)(0.03)(14) = $71.40.

5. Mental math; The ratio of the bases is about 15 cm to 5 cm, or 3. Therefore, the length of the longer leg of the logo must be about 7 · 3 = 21 cm.

6. Paper and pencil; First, identify the distance being used, $6\frac{1}{4}$ or $\frac{25}{4}$ miles. $\frac{1}{4}$ of $\frac{25}{4}$ is $\frac{1}{4} \cdot \frac{25}{4} = \frac{25}{16}$. Since they hiked $\frac{1}{4}$ out of the way and then had to hike the same distance back to where they started, they hiked $2 \cdot \frac{25}{16} = \frac{25}{8} = 3\frac{1}{8}$ miles in all.

Focus on Problem Solving

Organizer

Objective: Focus on choosing a method of computation.

 Online Edition

Resources

 Chapter 7 Resource File Reading Strategies

Problem Solving Process

This page focuses on the second step of the problem-solving process: **Make a Plan**

Discuss

Have students discuss how they decided whether to use a calculator, mental math, or pencil and paper to solve each problem.

Possible answers:

1. Mental math; 8 multiples of 25 is a total of 200 CDs in 8 weeks, so the total will be 200 + 500 = 700.

2. Calculator; Use a calculator to find 110% of each of the previous years' populations. 360 · 1.1 = 396; 396 · 1.1 = 435.6; 435.6 · 1.1 = 479.16; there will be approximately 479 deer after 3 years.

3. Paper and pencil; First, Heidi has already frosted 12 cakes, so there are 32 − 12 = 20 cakes left to frost. At 4 cakes an hour, it will take her $\frac{20}{4}$ = 5 more hours to frost a total of 32 cakes.

 California Standards

Mathematical Reasoning 1.1
Also covered:
Number Sense
← **1.2** Add, subtract, **multiply,** and divide **rational numbers** (integers, **fractions,** and terminating decimals) and take positive rational numbers to whole-number powers.

1.3 Convert fractions to decimals and **percents** and **use these representations** in estimations, computations, and **applications.**

← **1.7** Solve problems that involve discounts, markups, commissions, and profit and **compute simple** and compound **interest.**

Algebra and Functions
← **4.2 Solve multistep problems involving** rate, average speed, distance, and time or **a direct variation.**

SECTION
7B

Graphs

One-Minute Section Planner

Lesson	Lab Resources	Materials
Lesson 7-6 Rate of Change and Slope ● Find rates of change and slopes. 🐻 🔑 **AF3.3**		
Lesson 7-7 Finding Slope of a Line ● Find the slope of a line and use slope to understand graphs. 🐻 **AF1.0, AF1.5,** 🔑 **AF3.3,** 🔑 **AF3.4**	**Technology Lab 7-7** In *Chapter 7 Resource File*	
Lesson 7-8 Interpreting Graphs ● Relate graphs to situations. 🐻 **AF1.5**		**Optional** Advertisement circulars
Lesson 7-9 Direct Variation ● Recognize direct variation by graphing tables of data and checking for constant ratios. 🐻 🔑 **AF3.3,** 🔑 **AF3.4,** 🔑 **AF4.2**		**Optional** Scale, paper cup, pennies

MK = *Manipulatives Kit*

Notes

_____

_____

_____

_____

_____

_____

_____

_____

_____

_____

_____

_____

_____

Math Background: Teaching the Standards

UNDERSTANDING SLOPE 🐻 🔑 AF3.3

Lessons 7-6, 7-7

The concept of slope of a line is based on the more general idea of rate of change. A *rate of change* is a ratio that compares the amount of change in a dependent variable to the corresponding amount of change in an independent variable.

Consider a situation in which you drive from 1:00 P.M. until 3:00 P.M., and your odometer reading changes from 33,000 miles to 33,120 miles. In this case, the change in the dependent variable, distance, is 120 miles. The change in the independent variable, time, is 2 hours. The rate of change is $\frac{120}{2}$ = 60 mi/h. In real-world situations, rates of change always have compound units, such as miles per hour, dollars per year, or degrees per minute.

A function may or may not have a constant rate of change. For example, if you continue to drive from 3:00 P.M. to 4:00 P.M., and the odometer reads 33,170 at 4:00 P.M., the rate of change for this segment of the trip is $\frac{33,170 - 33,120}{1} = \frac{50}{1}$ = 50 mi/h. Thus, the distance increased more slowly during the second segment of the trip than during the first segment of the trip because you were driving more slowly.

When a function is defined by a set of ordered pairs, students can calculate rates of change by choosing two of the ordered pairs and dividing the amount of change in the dependent variable by the amount of change in the independent variable. It is important for students to see functions for which the rate of change is variable as well as functions for which the rate of change is constant (that is, equal to a particular value no matter which two ordered pairs are chosen).

THE SLOPE OF A LINE 🐻 🔑 AF3.3

Lessons 7-6, 7-7

Every linear function has a constant rate of change. Conversely, if a function has a constant rate of change, the function is a linear function. The constant rate of change of a linear function is called the function's *slope*. The graph of a linear function is a straight line,

and the slope describes the steepness of the line. Lines with positive slopes slant upward from left to right, lines with negative slopes slant downward from left to right, and lines with a slope of 0 are horizontal.

The slope of a line may be calculated by finding the ratio of the rise to the run for any two points on the line. It is possible to prove that the slope of a line is independent of the two points that are chosen by using the fact that sides of similar triangles are proportional. Students may investigate this proof in future geometry courses.

Students sometimes confuse lines that have slopes of 0 with those that have no slope. They should understand that horizontal lines have a slope of 0 since the rise is 0 for any run, and 0 divided by a nonzero number is 0. On the other hand, the slope of a vertical line is undefined because any two points on the line will have a run of 0 and division by 0 is undefined.

DIRECT VARIATION 🐻 🔑 AF3.4

Lesson 7-9

A *direct variation* is a special type of linear function that can be written in the form $y = kx$ where k is a nonzero constant. Equivalently, the phrase "y varies directly with x" means that there exists a nonzero k such that $y = kx$. The constant k is called the *constant of variation* or *constant of proportionality*.

The graph of a direct variation is a straight line through the origin. The line passes through the origin since (0, 0) is a solution of the equation $y = kx$ for all values of k. The slope of the line is k. This can be shown as follows. Suppose the points (x_1, y_1) and (x_2, y_2) lie on the line. Then $y_1 = kx_1$ and $y_2 = kx_2$. The slope is

$$\frac{y_2 - y_1}{x_2 - x_1} = \frac{kx_1 - kx_2}{x_2 - x_1} = \frac{k(x_2 - x_1)}{x_2 - x_1} = k.$$

Direct variations model a wide range of situations, including measurement conversions (e.g., feet to inches) and many geometric relationships (e.g., the relationship between the circumference and diameter of a circle).

Objective: Students find rates of change and slopes.

Objective: Students find rates of change and slopes.

Online Edition
Tutorial Videos

Countdown to Mastery Week 14

Power Presentations
with PowerPoint®

Warm Up

Graph each point on a coordinate plane.

1. (3, 4)   **2.** (4, 0)

3. (−2, −1)   **4.** (−3, 2)

5. (0, 1)   **6.** (2, −4)

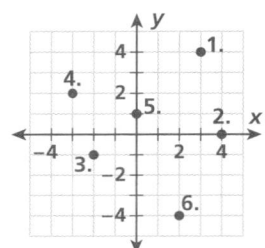

Also available on transparency

Math Humor

Q: Why did the math students put loaves of bread on a ladder?

A: So they could find the ryes over the rung.

California Standards

➤ **AF3.3** Graph linear functions, noting that the vertical change (change in *y*-value) per unit of horizontal change (change in *x*-value) is always the same and know that the ratio ("rise over run") is called the slope of a graph.

Vocabulary
rate of change
rise
run
slope

Why learn this? You can use rates of change to find out how the average price of a movie ticket has increased. (See Exercise 19.)

The input of a function is called the *independent variable*. It is often represented by the letter *x*. The output of a function is called the *dependent variable*. It is often represented by the letter *y*.

A **rate of change** is a ratio that compares the amount of change in a dependent variable to the amount of change in an independent variable.

$$\text{rate of change} = \frac{\text{change in dependent variable}}{\text{change in independent variable}}$$

The rates of change for a set of data may vary or they may be constant.

EXAMPLE 1 **Identifying Constant and Variable Rates of Change in Data**

Determine whether the rates of change are constant or variable.

A

x	0	1	3	6	8
y	0	4	8	8	6

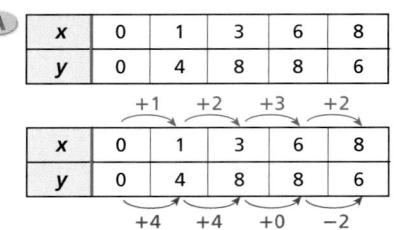

x	0	1	3	6	8
y	0	4	8	8	6

Find the difference between consecutive data points.

$$\frac{4}{1} = 4 \quad \frac{4}{2} = 2 \quad \frac{0}{3} = 0 \quad \frac{-2}{2} = -1$$

Find each ratio of change in y to change in x.

The rates of change are variable.

B

x	0	1	4	6	7
y	1	2	5	7	8

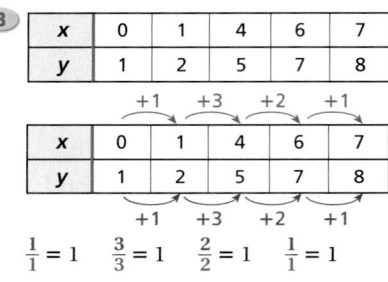

x	0	1	4	6	7
y	1	2	5	7	8

Find the difference between consecutive data points.

$$\frac{1}{1} = 1 \quad \frac{3}{3} = 1 \quad \frac{2}{2} = 1 \quad \frac{1}{1} = 1$$

Find each ratio of change in y to change in x.

The rates of change are constant.

---

1 Introduce

Alternate Opener

EXPLORATION

7-6 Rate of Change and Slope

Speed is a *rate of change* that occurs in many real-world situations.

The graph shows the speed of a cheetah (**red**) and of a lion (**blue**) while chasing prey in the wild for five seconds.

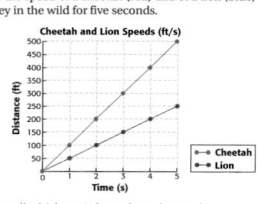

1. How can you tell which cat is faster from the graph?

2. Find the speed in feet per second of each cat.

Think and Discuss

3. **Discuss** what a constant rate of change is.

4. **Explain** what feature of the graph represents that the speed of each cat was constant.

Motivate

Present the following situation to the class. Over a 5-year period, a tree grew a total of 10 feet. Then, over a 3-year period, the tree grew a total of 9 feet. During which period was the tree growing more quickly? 3-year period Have students explain their thinking. The tree grew 3 ft/yr during the 3-year period but only 2 ft/yr during the 5-year period. Tell students they will learn to find rates of change in this lesson.

Explorations and answers are provided in *Alternate Openers: Explorations Transparencies.*

California Standards

Algebra and Functions ➤ **3.3**

To show rates of change on a graph, plot the data points and connect them with line segments. The graphs and rates of change of the data sets in Examples 1A and 1B are shown below.

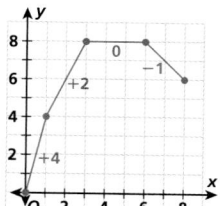

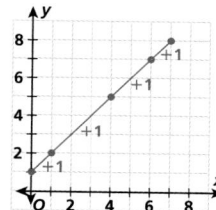

Steeper segments have rates of change with greater absolute values. A horizontal segment has a rate of change of 0. A segment that slants downward from left to right has a negative rate of change.

If all the segments have the same rate of change, then they form a straight line. This is the case when the data set has a constant rate of change.

The constant rate of change of a line is called the *slope* of the line.

SLOPE OF A LINE

The **rise** is the difference in the *y*-values of two points on a line.

The **run** is the difference in the *x*-values of two points on a line.

The **slope** of a line is the ratio of rise to run for any two points on the line.

$$\text{slope} = \frac{\text{rise}}{\text{run}} = \frac{\text{change in } y}{\text{change in } x}$$

(Remember that *y* is the dependent variable and *x* is the independent variable.)

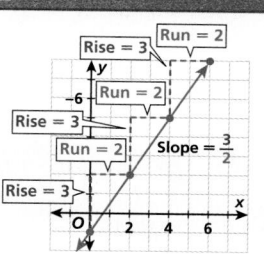

EXAMPLE 2 Finding the Slope of a Line

Find the slope of the line.

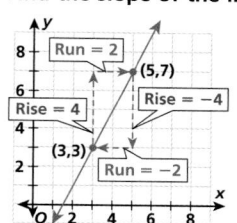

Begin at one point and count vertically to find the rise.

Then count horizontally to the second point to find the run.

$$\text{slope} = \frac{4}{2} = 2$$

$$\text{slope} = \frac{-4}{-2} = 2$$

The slope of the line is 2.

Power Presentations
with PowerPoint®

Additional Examples

Example 1

Determine whether the rates of change are constant or variable.

A.

x	0	1	3	5	8
y	0	2	6	10	16

constant

B.

x	1	3	4	6	9
y	0	2	6	6	3

variable

Example 2

Find the slope of the line. $\frac{1}{2}$

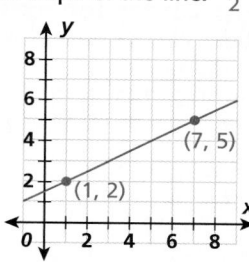

Also available on transparency

---

2 Teach

Guided Instruction

In this lesson, students learn to find rates of change and slopes. Begin by discussing rates of change. Tell students that in real-world situations, rates of change have units like miles per hour, feet per year, or dollars per month. As you present **Example 2,** emphasize that you can find the slope by starting at either of the points on the line. When finding the run, moving to the right is positive and moving to the left is negative. When finding the rise, moving up is positive and moving down is negative.

Universal Access

For Advanced Learners/GATE

Ask students why they think the slope of a line is defined as the rise divided by the run, rather than the run divided by the rise. To explore this question, have students calculate the slope both ways for several lines with a variety of positive slopes. Ask students if they see any advantages in defining the slope as the rise divided by the run. With this definition, steeper lines have greater slopes.

Visual When students are given a line and asked to find the slope, encourage them to imagine walking along the line from left to right. An uphill line has a positive slope. A downhill line has a negative slope.

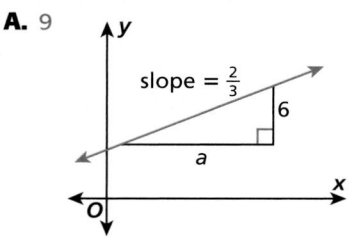
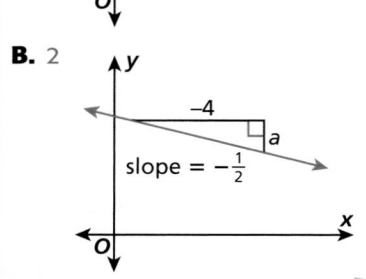
E X A M P L E 3 **Finding a Rise or a Run**

Find the value of *a*.

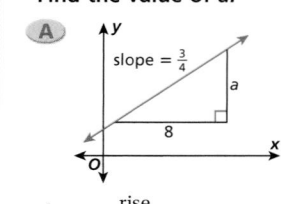

A

slope = $\frac{3}{4}$
a
8

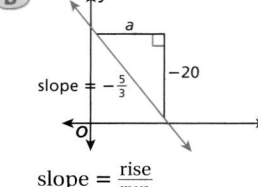

B

a
−20
slope = $-\frac{5}{3}$

slope = $\frac{\text{rise}}{\text{run}}$

$\frac{3}{4} = \frac{a}{8}$

$3 \cdot 8 = 4a$

$24 = 4a$ *Multiply.*

$6 = a$ *Divide both sides by 4.*

slope = $\frac{\text{rise}}{\text{run}}$

$\frac{-5}{3} = \frac{-20}{a}$

$-5a = -20 \cdot 3$

$-5a = -60$ *Multiply.*

$a = 12$ *Divide both sides by −5.*

Answer to
Think and Discuss

1. If the graph is a
straight line, the
data set has a
constant rate
of change.
Otherwise, it has
a variable rate of
change.

Think and Discuss

1. Explain how to use a graph to determine whether a data set has a
constant or variable rate of change.

7-6 **Exercises**

California
Standards Practice

◆ AF3.3

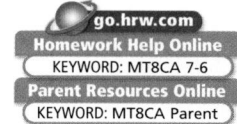

go.hrw.com
Homework Help Online
KEYWORD: MT8CA 7-6
Parent Resources Online
KEYWORD: MT8CA Parent

Assignment Guide

If you finished Example ① assign:
Proficient 1–2, 7–8, 17, 24–32
Advanced 7–8, 17–18, 24–32

If you finished Example ② assign:
Proficient 1–4, 7–10, 13–17, 20,
24–32
Advanced 7–10, 15–22, 24–32

If you finished Example ③ assign:
Proficient 1–17, 20, 23–32
Advanced 7–12, 15–32

Homework Quick Check

Quickly check key concepts.
Exercises: 8, 10, 12, 16, 20

GUIDED PRACTICE

See Example ① Determine whether the rates of change are constant or variable.

1.

x	0	1	3	7	8
y	1	3	7	15	17

constant

2.

x	2	4	5	6	7
y	2	6	7	13	14

variable

See Example ② Find the slope of each line.

3.

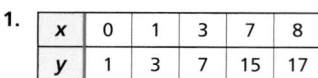

$\frac{1}{3}$

(6, 5)
(0, 3)

4.

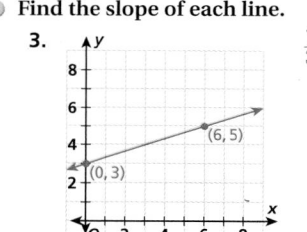

−2

(0, 2)
(2, −2)

3 Close

Summarize

Have students match each slope with one of the
descriptions on the right.

1. slope 2 b **a.** slants downward from left to right
2. slope 0 c **b.** slants upward from left to right
3. slope $-\frac{1}{2}$ a **c.** a horizontal line

See Example 3 Find the value of *a*.

5. 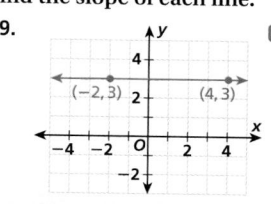 slope = $\frac{2}{3}$ 6

6. 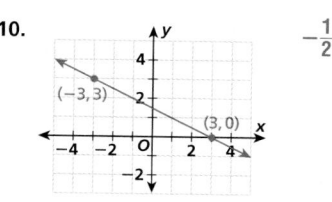   −10

INDEPENDENT PRACTICE

See Example 1 Determine whether the rates of change are constant or variable.

7.

x	−1	0	3	5	9
y	1	3	6	10	4

variable

8.

x	2	4	6	7	8
y	8	4	0	−2	−4

constant

See Example 2 Find the slope of each line.

9. 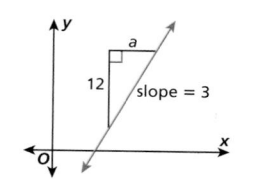   0

10. 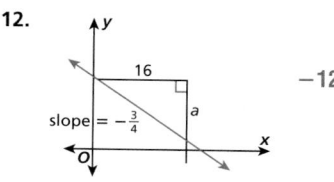 $-\frac{1}{2}$

See Example 3 Find the value of *a*.

11. 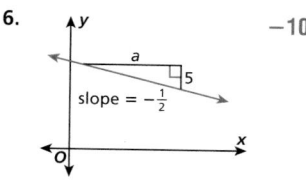 12 slope = 3   4

12. 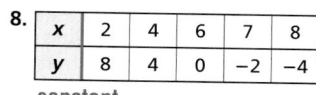 16 slope = $-\frac{3}{4}$ −12

PRACTICE AND PROBLEM SOLVING

Extra Practice
See page EP15.

Graph each set of data. Label the rate of change for each segment. Then tell whether the data set has a constant or variable rate of change.

13.

x	0	3	5	6	7
y	2	5	7	8	9

constant

14.

x	−2	0	1	3	6
y	4	4	4	4	4

constant

15.

x	−4	−1	2	3	4
y	0	3	5	5	2

variable

16.

x	−3	−1	0	3	4
y	−5	−1	1	7	9

constant

17. **Reasoning** The data in the table have a constant rate of change. Find the missing value in the table. 19

x	0	1	3	6
y	1	4	10	

7-6 Rate of Change and Slope **347**

Math Background

The slope of a line is defined as the rise divided by the run so that steeper lines will have slopes with greater absolute values. However, the apparent steepness of a line on a coordinate plane may depend on the scales of the axes. For example, the line shown below appears to be relatively flat, but it has a slope of 1000.

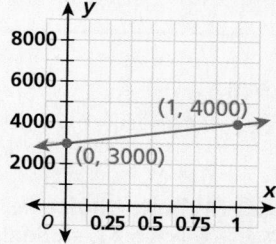

Note that for vertical lines, the run is 0. Since division by 0 is not defined, the slope of a vertical line is also not defined.

Answers

13.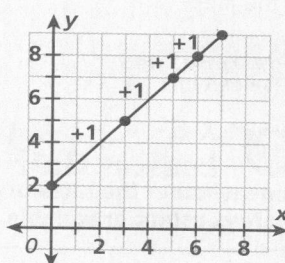

14.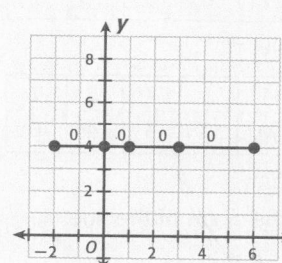

15.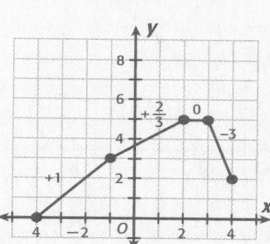

16.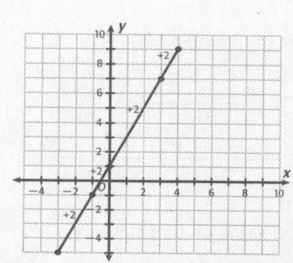

REVIEW FOR MASTERY 7-6

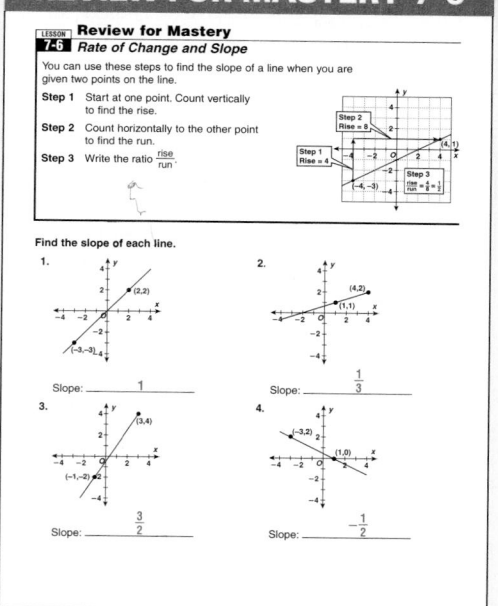

PRACTICE 7-6

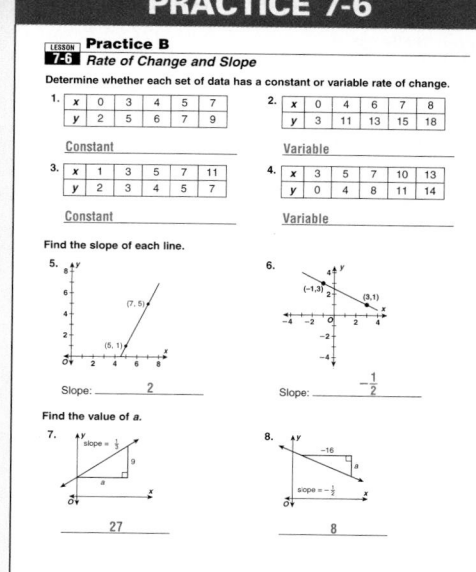

7-6 Rate of Change and Slope **347**

Answers
21–22. See p. A6.

Teaching Tip **Multiple Choice** For **Exercise 23,** students who chose **A** or **B** did not notice that the line has a positive slope.

Journal

Have students explain how to find the slope of a line given its graph and two points on the line.

Power Presentations
with PowerPoint®

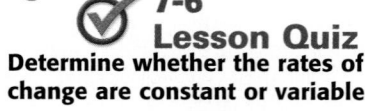

7-6
Lesson Quiz
Determine whether the rates of change are constant or variable.

1.

x	−1	1	2	4	8
y	2	6	8	10	14

variable

2.

x	1	3	4	5	7
y	0	2	3	4	6

constant

3. Find the slope of the line. 3

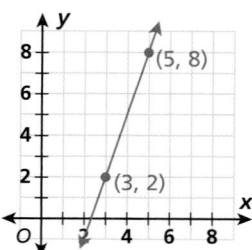

4. Find the value of *a*. −4

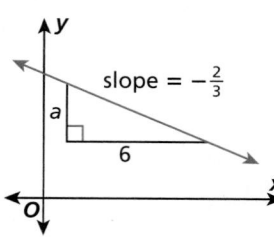

Also available on transparency

Agree; the rate of change is 3.

18. Reasoning In a table of data, every *y*-value is 3 times the corresponding *x*-value. A student makes a conjecture that the data set must have a constant rate of change. Do you agree or disagree with the student's conjecture? Why?

19. Entertainment The table shows the average price of a movie ticket in different years.
a. Find the rate of change per year for 1993 to 1998, for 1998 to 2001, and for 2001 to 2005.

Year	1993	1998	2001	2005
Average Ticket Price ($)	4.14	4.69	5.65	6.41

$0.11/yr; $0.32/yr; $0.19/yr

b. During which period did the price increase at the greatest rate? 1998 to 2001

20. What's the Error? A student was asked to find the slope of the line at right. The student's work is shown below. Explain the error.

slope $= \frac{\text{rise}}{\text{run}} = \frac{6}{3} = 2$ The rise is −6, and the slope is −2.

21. Write About It Explain how you can tell whether the slope of a line is positive, negative, or zero just by looking at the line.

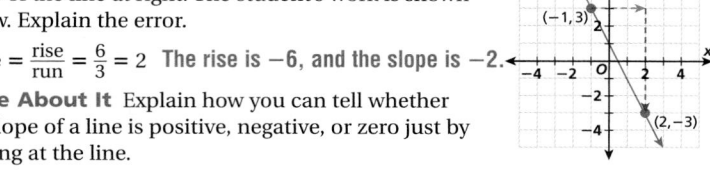

22. Challenge Draw a line with a slope of 2 that passes through the point (2, 1).

SPIRAL STANDARDS REVIEW   NS1.3, AF3.3, MG3.3

23. Multiple Choice The slope of the line shown in the graph is $\frac{4}{3}$. What is the value of *k*?

Ⓐ −16   Ⓒ 9
Ⓑ −9   Ⓓ 16

24. Multiple Choice On a winter day, the temperature changed at a constant rate of −5° per hour. Which could be the graph of this situation?

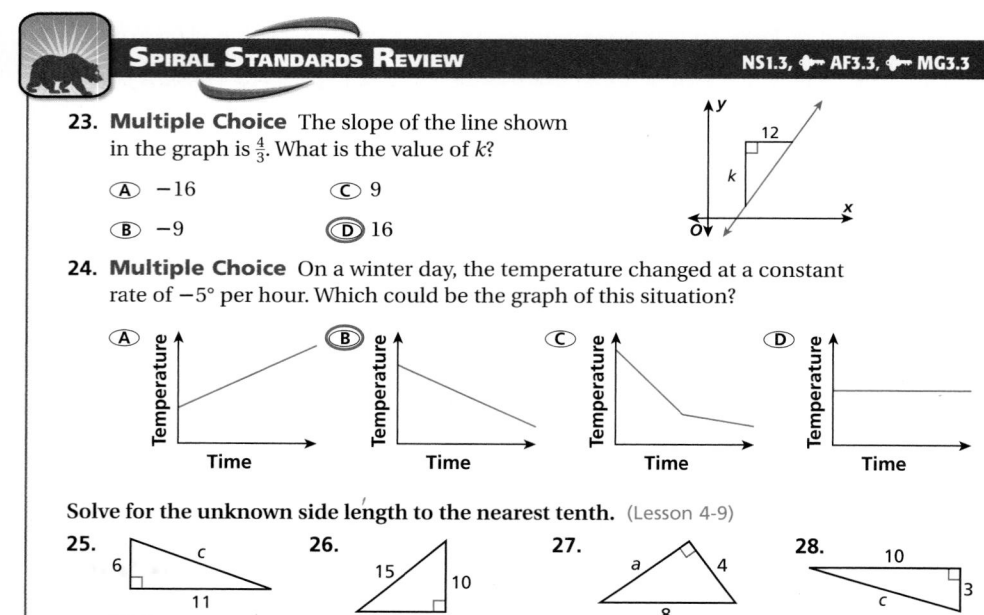

Solve for the unknown side length to the nearest tenth. (Lesson 4-9)

25. 12.5   **26.** 11.2   **27.** 6.9   **28.** 10.4

Estimate. (Lesson 6-2)
29. 34% of 59   20   **30.** 26% of 201   50   **31.** 20% of 98   20   **32.** 51% of 697   350

CHALLENGE 7-6

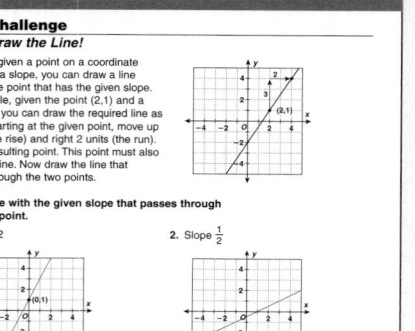

LESSON Challenge
7-6 *Draw the Line!*

If you are given a point on a coordinate plane and a slope, you can draw a line through the point that has the given slope. For example, given the point (2,1) and a slope of $\frac{3}{2}$, you can draw the required line as follows. Starting at the given point, move up 3 units (the rise) and right 2 units (the run). Plot the resulting point. This point must also be on the line. Now draw the line that passes through the two points.

Draw a line with the given slope that passes through the given point.
1. Slope 2   **2.** Slope $\frac{1}{2}$

3. Slope $-\frac{1}{3}$ **4.** Slope $-\frac{2}{3}$

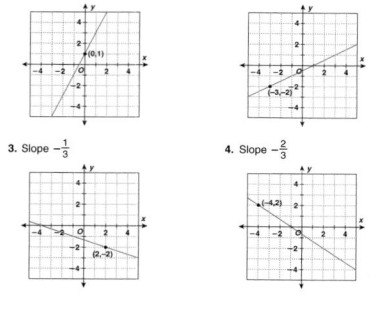

PROBLEM SOLVING 7-6

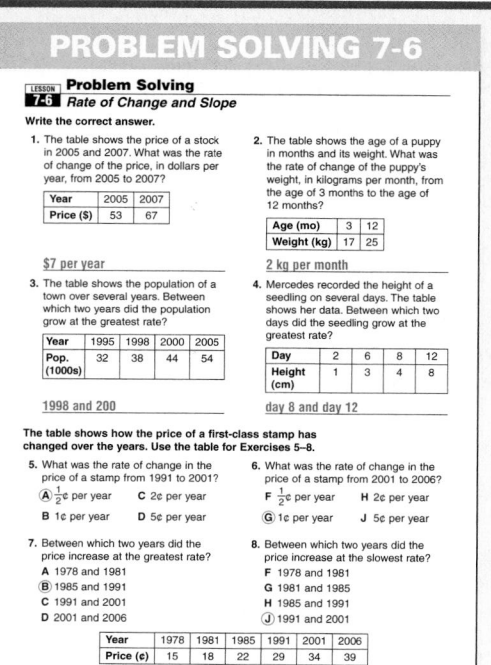

LESSON Problem Solving
7-6 *Rate of Change and Slope*

Write the correct answer.
1. The table shows the price of a stock in 2005 and 2007. What was the rate of change of the price, in dollars per year, from 2005 to 2007?

Year	2005	2007
Price ($)	53	67

$7 per year

2. The table shows the age of a puppy in months and its weight. What was the rate of change of the puppy's weight, in kilograms per month, from the age of 3 months to the age of 12 months?

Age (mo)	3	12
Weight (kg)	17	25

2 kg per month

3. The table shows the population of a town over several years. Between which two years did the population grow at the greatest rate?

Year	1995	1998	2000	2005
Pop. (1000s)	32	38	44	54

1998 and 200

4. Mercedes recorded the height of a seedling on several days. The table shows her data. Between which two days did the seedling grow at the greatest rate?

Day	2	6	8	12
Height (cm)	1	3	4	8

day 8 and day 12

The table shows how the price of a first-class stamp has changed over the years. Use the table for Exercises 5–8.

5. What was the rate of change in the price of a stamp from 1991 to 2001?
Ⓐ $\frac{1}{2}$¢ per year   C 2¢ per year
B 1¢ per year   D 5¢ per year

6. What was the rate of change in the price of a stamp from 2001 to 2006?
F $\frac{1}{2}$¢ per year   H 2¢ per year
Ⓖ 1¢ per year   J 5¢ per year

7. Between which two years did the price increase at the greatest rate?
A 1978 and 1981
Ⓑ 1985 and 1991
C 1991 and 2001
D 2001 and 2006

8. Between which two years did the price increase at the slowest rate?
F 1978 and 1981
G 1981 and 1985
H 1985 and 1991
Ⓙ 1991 and 2001

Year	1978	1981	1985	1991	2001	2006
Price (¢)	15	18	22	29	34	39

California Standards

➤ **AF3.4** Plot the values of quantities whose ratios are always the same (e.g., cost to the number of an item, feet to inches, circumference to diameter of a circle). **Fit a line to the plot and understand that the slope of the line equals the quantities.**

Also covered: **AF1.5,** ➤ **AF3.3**

Why learn this? You can use slope to make sure a wheelchair ramp is not too steep. (See Exercise 18.)

Recall that lines have constant slope. For a line on the coordinate plane, slope is the following ratios:

$$\frac{\text{vertical change}}{\text{horizontal change}} = \frac{\text{change in } y}{\text{change in } x}$$

Reading Math

The small number in x_1 is called a subscript. Read x_1 as "x sub one" and y_2 as "y sub 2."

If you know any two points on a line, you can find the slope of the line without graphing. The slope of a line through the points (x_1, y_1) and (x_2, y_2) is as follows:

$$\text{slope} = \frac{y_2 - y_1}{x_2 - x_1}$$

When finding slope using the ratio above, it does not matter which point you choose for (x_1, y_1) and which point you choose for (x_2, y_2).

EXAMPLE 1 **Finding Slope, Given Two Points**

Find the slope of the line that passes through each pair of points.

A **(1, 7) and (9, 3)**

Let (x_1, y_1) be $(1, 7)$ and (x_2, y_2) be $(9, 3)$.

$\dfrac{y_2 - y_1}{x_2 - x_1} = \dfrac{3 - 7}{9 - 1}$ *Substitute 3 for y_2, 7 for y_1, 9 for x_2, and 1 for x_1.*

$= \dfrac{-4}{8}$

$= -\dfrac{1}{2}$ *Simplify.*

The slope of the line that passes through $(1, 7)$ and $(9, 3)$ is $-\frac{1}{2}$.

B **(−2, 5) and (3, 5)**

Let (x_1, y_1) be $(-2, 5)$ and (x_2, y_2) be $(3, 5)$.

$\dfrac{y_2 - y_1}{x_2 - x_1} = \dfrac{5 - 5}{3 - (-2)}$ *Substitute 5 for y_2, 5 for y_1, 3 for x_2, and −2 for x_1.*

$= \dfrac{5 - 5}{3 + 2}$ *Rewrite subtraction as addition of the opposite.*

$= \dfrac{0}{5}$ *Simplify.*

$= 0$

The slope of the line that passes through $(-2, 5)$ and $(3, 5)$ is 0.

Organizer 7-7

Objective: Students find the slope of a line and use slope to understand graphs.

 Technology Lab In *Chapter 7 Resource File*

 Online Edition Tutorial Videos

 Countdown to Mastery Week 14

Power Presentations with PowerPoint®

Warm Up

Evaluate each equation for $x = -1$, 0, and 1.

1. $y = 3x$ −3, 0, 3
2. $y = x - 7$ −8, −7, −6
3. $y = 2x + 5$ 3, 5, 7
4. $y = 6x - 2$ −8, −2, 4

Also available on transparency

Math Humor

Whenever the teacher mentioned *slope,* the student imagined a revolt in the bread bakery. He would picture all the commotion as the *ryes overrun* the bakery.

---

1 **Introduce**

Alternate Opener

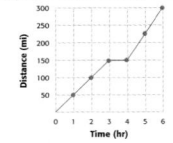

EXPLORATION

7-7 **Finding Slope of a Line**

Joseph plots a graph of his 300-mile trip to the coast.

1. Calculate his average speed for the first 3 hours. (*Hint:* Divide the distance traveled during the first three hours by 3.)
2. What happens between hours 3 and 4?
3. Calculate his average speed for the last 2 hours. (*Hint:* Divide the distance traveled during the last two hours by 2.)

Think and Discuss
4. **Discuss** how you could find Joseph's average speed between hours 3 and 4.
5. **Discuss** how average speed is related to the shape of the graph.

Motivate

Ask students if they have ever been skiing or seen it on television. Discuss the difference between the beginner's trail, often called the *bunny slope,* and the expert's trail, often called the *black diamond slope.* Generally the black diamond slope will be much steeper than the bunny slope.

Explorations and answers are provided in *Alternate Openers: Explorations Transparencies.*

California Standards

Algebra and Functions ➤ **3.4**

Also covered:

Algebra and Functions
1.0 Students express quantitative relationships by using algebraic terminology, expressions, equations, inequalities, and **graphs.**
1.5 Represent quantitative relationships graphically and interpret the meaning of a specific part of a graph in the situation represented by the graph.
➤ **3.3** Graph linear functions, noting that the vertical change (change in y-value) per unit of horizontal change (change in x-value) is always the same and know that the ratio ("rise over run") is called the slope of a graph.

Power Presentations
with PowerPoint®

Additional Examples

Example

Find the slope of the line that passes through each pair of points.

A. $(-2, -3)$ and $(4, 6)$ $\frac{3}{2}$

B. $(1, 3)$ and $(2, 1)$ -2

C. $(3, -2)$ and $(1, -2)$ 0

Example

The table shows the total cost of fruit per pound purchased at the grocery store. Use the data to make a graph. Find the slope of the line and explain what it shows.

Cost of Fruit	
Pounds	**Cost**
0	0
5	15
10	30
15	45

3; For every pound of fruit, you will pay another $3.
See p. A6.

Also available on transparency

Find the slope of the line that passes through each pair of points.

 (1, 0) and **(−3, −4)**

Let (x_1, y_1) be $(1, 0)$ and (x_2, y_2) be $(-3, -4)$.

$\frac{y_2 - y_1}{x_2 - x_1} = \frac{-4 - 0}{-3 - 1}$ *Substitute −4 for y₂, 0 for y₁, −3 for x₂, and 1 for x₁.*

$= \frac{-4}{-4} = 1$ *Simplify.*

The slope of the line that passes through $(1, 0)$ and $(-3, -4)$ is 1.

EXAMPLE 2 *Science Application*

The table shows the volume of water released by Hoover Dam over a certain period of time. Use the data to make a graph. Find the slope of the line and explain what it shows.

Graph the data.

Water Released from Hoover Dam	
Time (s)	**Volume of Water (m³)**
5	75,000
10	150,000
15	225,000
20	300,000

Helpful Hint

You can use any two points to find the slope of the line.

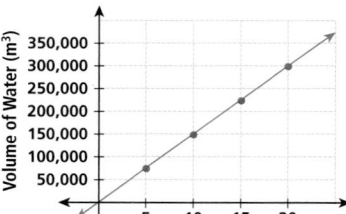

For more on graphing relationships, see the Graph and Equation Builder on page MB2.

Water Released from Hoover Dam

Find the slope of the line.

$\frac{y_2 - y_1}{x_2 - x_1}$

$\frac{150,000 - 75,000}{10 - 5}$ *Substitute.*

$\frac{75,000}{5}$

15,000   *Simplify.*

The slope of the line is 15,000. This means that for every second that passed, 15,000 m³ of water was released from Hoover Dam. The graph shows that the total amount of water released increased as time passed.

The slope of a line may be positive, negative, zero, or undefined. You can tell which of these is the case by looking at the graph of a line—you do not need to calculate the slope.

POSITIVE SLOPE	NEGATIVE SLOPE	ZERO SLOPE	UNDEFINED SLOPE

---

2 Teach

Guided Instruction

In this lesson, students find the slope of a line and use it to understand and draw graphs. Remind students that in linear equations, a constant change in *x*-values corresponds to a constant change in *y*-values. Explain that this relationship is called *slope* (Teaching Transparency). Remind students that they have worked with slope before as $\frac{\text{rise}}{\text{run}}$ (Lesson 7-6).

Teaching Tip
Inclusion Emphasize that any two points on a line will yield the same slope and that the points can be used in the slope formula in either order, but the order must be the same for *y*'s and *x*'s.

 Universal Access
Through Multiple Representations

Give students graphs of four lines (one with positive slope, one with negative slope, one with zero slope, and one with undefined slope) and five pairs of points (one for each line and one extraneous pair). Have students use the slope formula to determine the slope between each pair of points and to match the points with the appropriate graph.

3 Close

Summarize

Remind students that slope describes the steepness of the line and is defined as the ratio of vertical change to horizontal change (rise over run). Show students a coordinate plane, and ask them to describe a line with each type of slope (positive, negative, zero, and undefined). As they describe each line, draw an example on the coordinate plane.

Possible answers to
Think and Discuss

1. Changing the order of the points will change both differences into their opposites. When these opposites are placed into a ratio, however, the ratio will be the same.

Think and Discuss

1. **Explain** why it does not matter which point you choose as (x_1, y_1) and which point you choose as (x_2, y_2) when finding slope.

2. **Give an example** of two points on each of the following: a line with zero slope and a line with an undefined slope.

3. **Explain** whether you think it would be more difficult to run up a hill with a slope of $\frac{1}{3}$ or a hill with a slope of $\frac{3}{4}$.

2. $(-1, 5)$ and $(5, 5)$; $(-3, -2)$ and $(-3, 4)$
3. $\frac{3}{4}$, because it is more steep.

Assignment Guide

If you finished Example **1** assign:
Proficient 1–6, 11–16, 26–32
Advanced 8–16, 23–32

If you finished Example **2** assign:
Proficient 1–7, 11–18, 20, 23, 26–32
Advanced 8–32

Homework Quick Check

Quickly check key concepts.
Exercises: 12, 14, 16, 18, 20

Answers

7, 17. See p. A6.

Math Background

Some important points about slope:

• The slope of a line is constant regardless of which points are used to calculate it.

• The order in which the points are used in the slope formula will not affect the slope.

• Vertical lines have an undefined slope. For any two points on the line, the run is zero, so
$\frac{\text{rise}}{\text{run}} = \frac{\text{(any value)}}{0} = \text{undefined}$.

• Horizontal lines have a slope of zero. For any two points on the line, the rise is zero, so
$\frac{\text{rise}}{\text{run}} = \frac{0}{\text{(any nonzero value)}} = 0$.

7-7 Exercises

 California Standards Practice
AF1.5, AF3.3, AF3.4

 go.hrw.com
Homework Help Online
KEYWORD: MT8CA 7-7
Parent Resources Online
KEYWORD: MT8CA Parent

GUIDED PRACTICE

See Example **1** **Find the slope of the line that passes through each pair of points.**

1. $(2, 5)$ and $(3, 6)$ **1**
2. $(2, 6)$ and $(0, 2)$ **2**
3. $(-2, 4)$ and $(6, 6)$ $\frac{1}{4}$
4. $(4, -2)$ and $(-1, 2)$ $-\frac{4}{5}$
5. $(-3, 4)$ and $(2, 4)$ **0**
6. $(-6, 0)$ and $(-4, -2)$ -1

See Example **2** 7. The table shows how much money Marvin earned while helping his mother with yard work one weekend. Use the data to make a graph. Find the slope of the line and explain what it shows. **The slope of the line is 5. This means that Marvin earned $5 for each hour he worked.**

Time (hr)	3	5	7	9
Money Earned	$15	$25	$35	$45

INDEPENDENT PRACTICE

See Example **1** **Find the slope of the line that passes through each pair of points.**

8. $(-2, -2)$ and $(-4, 1)$ $-\frac{3}{2}$
9. $(0, 0)$ and $(4, -2)$ $-\frac{1}{2}$
10. $(3, -6)$ and $(2, -1)$ -5
11. $(4, 2)$ and $(0, 5)$ $-\frac{3}{4}$
12. $(-2, -3)$ and $(2, 4)$ $\frac{7}{4}$
13. $(0, -4)$ and $(-7, 2)$ $-\frac{6}{7}$
14. $(-1, 7)$ and $(3, 7)$ **0**
15. $(0, 1)$ and $(5, 0)$ $-\frac{1}{5}$
16. $(-3, -6)$ and $(-6, -9)$ **1**

See Example **2** 17. The table shows how water was in a swimming pool as it was being filled. Use the data to make a graph. Find the slope of the line and explain what it shows. **The slope of the line is 4. This means that the amount of water increased by 4 gallons every minute.**

Time (min)	10	13	16	19
Amount of Water (gal)	40	52	64	76

REVIEW FOR MASTERY 7-7

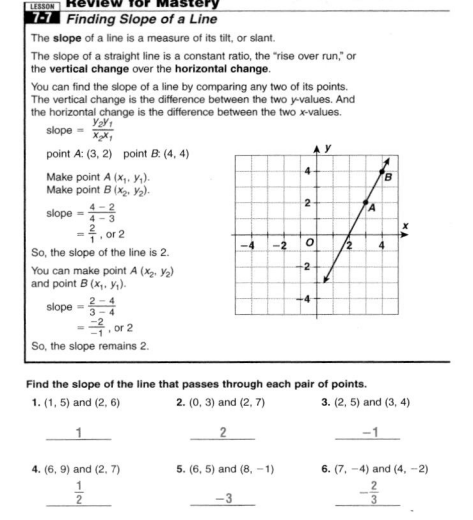

LESSON 7-7 **Review for Mastery**
Finding Slope of a Line

The **slope** of a line is a measure of its tilt, or slant.

The slope of a straight line is a constant ratio, the "rise over run," or the **vertical change** over the **horizontal change**.

You can find the slope of a line by comparing any two of its points. The vertical change is the difference between the two y-values. And the horizontal change is the difference between the two x-values.

$\text{slope} = \frac{y_2 - y_1}{x_2 - x_1}$

point A: (3, 2)   point B: (4, 4)

Make point A (x_1, y_1).
Make point B (x_2, y_2).

$\text{slope} = \frac{4 - 2}{4 - 3}$
$= \frac{2}{1}$, or 2

So, the slope of the line is 2.

You can make point A (x_2, y_2) and point B (x_1, y_1).

$\text{slope} = \frac{2 - 4}{3 - 4}$
$= \frac{-2}{-1}$, or 2

So, the slope remains 2.

Find the slope of the line that passes through each pair of points.

1. (1, 5) and (2, 6)   2. (0, 3) and (2, 7)   3. (2, 5) and (3, 4)
   1   2   −1

4. (6, 9) and (2, 7)   5. (6, 5) and (8, −1)   6. (7, −4) and (4, −2)
   $\frac{1}{2}$ −3 $-\frac{2}{3}$

PRACTICE 7-7

LESSON 7-7 **Practice B**
Finding Slope of a Line

Find the slope of the line that passes through each pair of points.

1. (−2, −8), (1, 4)   2. (−2, 0), (0, 4)   3. (0, 4), (4, 4)
   4   2   0

4. (3, −6), (2, −4)   5. (−3, 4), (3, −4)   6. (3, 0), (0, −6)
   −2 $-\frac{4}{3}$ 2

7. (3, 2), (3, −2)   8. (−4, 4), (3, −1)   9. (−5, −6), (3, −6)
   undefined $-\frac{5}{7}$ 0

10. (−6, −9), (4, −1)   11. (7, −1), (6, 2)   12. (−2, −1), (−3, −6)
    $\frac{4}{5}$ −3   5

13. The table shows the distance Ms. Long had traveled as she went to the beach. Use the data to make a graph. Find the slope of the line and explain what it shows.

Time (min)	Distance (mi)
8	6
12	9
16	12
20	15

The slope is $\frac{3}{4}$, which means that for every 4 minutes Ms. Long drives, she travels 3 miles. She is driving 45 mph.

Distance Traveled (mi)

California Standards

Standard	Exercises
AF1.5	7, 17
AF2.1	30–32
AF3.3	1–6, 8–16, 23–27
AF3.4	7, 17–22
MG1.3	28–29

Answers

19, 23–24. See pp. A6–7.

Journal

Have students write about the difference between a line that has zero slope and a line that has an undefined slope.

Power Presentations
with PowerPoint®

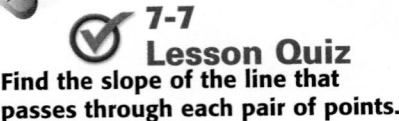

7-7 Lesson Quiz

Find the slope of the line that passes through each pair of points.

1. (4, 3) and (−1, 1) $\frac{2}{5}$

2. (−1, 5) and (4, 2) $-\frac{3}{5}$

3. The table shows how much money Susan earned as a house painter for one afternoon. Use the data to make a graph. Find the slope of the line and explain what it shows.

Time (h)	Money Earned
2	$14
5	$35
8	$56
11	$77

See p. A7.

Also available on transparency

PRACTICE AND PROBLEM SOLVING

 **Extra Practice**
See page EP15.

18. **Safety** For safety reasons, the slope of a wheelchair ramp should never exceed the ratio of 1 to 12. A wheelchair ramp rises 1.5 feet for every 20 feet of horizontal distance it covers. Is this wheelchair ramp considered to be safe? Explain your answer. **Yes; the slope of the ramp is about 1 to 13, which is less than 1 to 12. The ramp is less steep.**

19. **Architecture** The Luxor Hotel in Las Vegas, Nevada, has a 350-foot-tall glass pyramid. The elevator of the pyramid moves at an incline such that its rate of change is −4 feet in the vertical direction for every 5 feet in the horizontal direction. Graph the line that describes the path it travels. (*Hint:* The point (0, 350) is the top of the pyramid.)

20. **Manufacturing** A factory produces widgets at a constant rate. After 3 hours, 2520 widgets have been produced. After 8 hours, 6720 widgets have been produced. At what rate are the widgets being produced? How long will it take to produce 10,080 widgets? **840 widgets per hour; 12 hours**

21. **The vertical rise must be 0, $\frac{0}{12}$, so the roof extends only horizontally. The roof is flat.**

21. **Construction** The angle, or pitch, of a roof is the number of inches it rises vertically for every 12 inches it extends horizontally. Morgan's roof has a pitch of 0. What does this mean?

22. A large container holds 5 gallons of water. It begins leaking at a constant rate. After 10 minutes, the container has 3 gallons of water left. At what rate is the water leaking? After how many minutes will the container be empty? **1 gal every 5 min; 25 min**

23. **What's the Error?** The slope of the line through the points (2, 5) and (−2, −5) is $\frac{2 - (-2)}{5 - (-5)} = \frac{2}{5}$. What is the error in this statement?

24. **Write About It** A vertical line passes through the points (3, 4) and (3, 7). Graph the line. Explain why the slope of the line is undefined.

25. **Challenge** Find the slope of the line containing the points $(2w, z)$ and $(w, 3z)$. $-\frac{2z}{w}$

 **SPIRAL STANDARDS REVIEW**   AF2.1, AF3.3, MG1.3

26. **Multiple Choice** Which best describes the slope of the line that passes through the points (4, −4) and (9, −4)?

Ⓐ positive   Ⓑ negative   Ⓒ zero   Ⓓ undefined

27. **Gridded Response** What is the slope of the line that passes through the points (−5, 4) and (−7, −2)? **3**

Use conversion factors to find each of the following. (Lesson 5-2)

28. The number of movie tickets sold in three hours at a rate of 1 ticket per minute   **180 tickets**

29. The number of miles walked in 1 hour at an average rate of 352 feet per minute   **4 miles**

Simplify. (Lesson 4-1)

30. $(3 \cdot 4)^2 - 2^7$
16

31. $3^0 - (5 + 4^2)$
−20

32. $7 - (-3)^2$
−2

CHALLENGE 7-7

Challenge
7-7 Aligned?

1. Points *A*, *B*, and *C* are on the same line. Draw a conclusion about the slope between *A* and *B* and the slope between *B* and *C*.

slope between *A* and *B* = slope between *B* and *C*

2. Determine if the three points are collinear (lie on the same line).

a. *R*(2, 5), *S*(6, 15), *T*(16, 18)
slope between *R* and *S* =
$\frac{15 - 5}{6 - 2} = \frac{10}{4} = \frac{5}{2}$

slope between *S* and *T* =
$\frac{18 - 15}{16 - 6} = \frac{3}{10}$

R, *S*, *T* __are not__ collinear.

b. *J*(0, −4), *K*(1, −2), *L*(3, 2)
slope between *J* and *K* =
$\frac{-2 - (-4)}{1 - 0} = \frac{-2 + 4}{1} = 2$

slope between *K* and *L* =
$\frac{2 - (-2)}{3 - 1} = \frac{2 + 2}{2} = \frac{4}{2} = 2$

J, *K*, *L* __are__ collinear.

3. Find the value of *k* so that *U*(−5, −1), *V*(−1, −5), and *W*(5, *k*) are collinear.

a. Find the slope between *U* and *V*. $\frac{-5 - (-1)}{-1 - (-5)} = \frac{-5 + 1}{-1 + 5} = \frac{-4}{4} = -1$

b. Find the slope between *V* and *W*. $\frac{k - (-5)}{5 - (-1)} = \frac{k + 5}{5 + 1} = \frac{k + 5}{6}$

c. Set the results of parts a and b equal to each other and solve for *k*. Justify your result.
$\frac{-1}{1} = \frac{k + 5}{6}$

$(k + 5)(1) = (-1)(6)$

$k + 5 = -6$

$k = -11$

Check: When *k* = −11, the

slope between *V* and *W* should

equal −1.
$\frac{k + 5}{6} = \frac{-11 + 5}{6} = \frac{-6}{6} = -1 ✓$

4. The points *P*(2, −3), *Q*(2, 3) and *R*(*k*, 0) are collinear. Find *k*. Justify your result.

Since *P* and *Q* have the same *x*-values, $\overline{PQR}$ is a vertical line. So, *k* = 2.

PROBLEM SOLVING 7-7

Problem Solving
7-7 Finding Slope of a Line

Write the correct answer.

1. The state of Kansas has a fairly steady slope from the east to the west. At the eastern side, the elevation is 771 ft. At the western edge, 413 miles across the state, the elevation is 4039 ft. What is the approximate slope of Kansas?
__−0.0015__

2. The Feathered Serpent Pyramid in Teotihuacan, Mexico, has a square base. From the center of the base to the center of an edge of the pyramid is 32.5 m. The pyramid is 19.4 m high. What is the slope of each face of the pyramid?
$\frac{19.4}{32.5}$

3. On a highway, a 6% grade means a slope of 0.06. If a highway covers a horizontal distance of 0.5 miles and the elevation change is 184.8 feet, what is the grade of the road? (Hint: 5280 feet = 1 mile.)
__7%__

4. The roof of a house rises vertically 3 feet for every 12 feet of horizontal distance. What is the slope, or pitch of the roof?
$\frac{1}{4}$

Use the graph for Exercises 5–8.

5. Find the slope of the line between 1990 and 1992.
Ⓐ $\frac{2}{11}$ Ⓒ $\frac{11}{2}$
Ⓑ $\frac{35}{3982}$ Ⓓ $\frac{11}{1992}$

6. Find the slope of the line between 1994 and 1996.
Ⓕ $\frac{7}{2}$ Ⓗ $\frac{2}{7}$
Ⓖ $\frac{-37}{3990}$ Ⓙ $\frac{7}{1996}$

7. Find the slope of the line between 1998 and 2000.
Ⓐ 1
Ⓑ $\frac{1}{999}$
Ⓒ $\frac{1}{1000}$
Ⓓ 2

8. What does it mean when the slope is negative?
Ⓕ The number of earthquakes stayed the same.
Ⓖ The number of earthquakes increased.
Ⓗ The number of earthquakes decreased.
Ⓙ It means nothing.

Number of Earthquakes Worldwide with a Magnitude of 7.0 or Greater

---

7-8 Interpreting Graphs

California Standards

AF1.5 Represent quantitative relationships graphically and interpret the meaning of a specific part of a graph in the situation represented by the graph.

Why learn this? You can use graphs to analyze the speed of a horse over time.

You can use graphs to show real-world situations visually. For example, the graph below shows the varying speeds at which Emma exercises her horse.

- The horse walks at a constant speed for the first 10 minutes.
- Its speed increases over the next 7 minutes.
- It gallops at a constant rate for 20 minutes.
- Then it slows down over the next 3 minutes.
- It walks at a constant pace for 10 minutes.

Read the graph from left to right. A horizontal line represents no change, a line that slants upward represents an increase, and a line that slants downward represents a decrease. Recall that a steeper line represents a rate of change with a greater absolute value.

EXAMPLE 1 Relating Graphs to Situations

Jenny leaves home and drives to the beach. She stays at the beach all day before driving back home. Which graph best shows the situation?

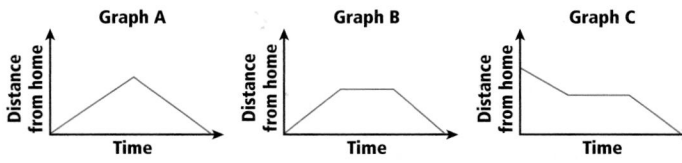

As Jenny drives to the beach, her distance from home *increases*, so the segment slants upward. While she is at the beach, her distance from home *does not change*, so the segment is horizontal. As she drives home, her distance from home *decreases*, so the segment slants downward.
The answer is Graph B.

Organizer

Objective: Students relate graphs to situations.

Online Edition
Tutorial Videos

Countdown to Mastery Week 15

Power Presentations with PowerPoint®

Warm Up

Alessia walked to the store to buy some groceries. Tell whether her distance from home in each situation is best represented by a line with positive, negative, or zero slope.

1. Alessia stopped to tie her shoe. zero

2. Alessia walked from home to the store. positive

3. Alessia ran home from the store. negative

Also available on transparency

Math Humor

Why is a spoof of a coordinate grid just like the start of a flight? It's a take-off on a plane.

1 Introduce

Alternate Opener

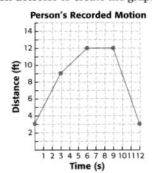

Motivate

Have students describe some of the characteristics of different graphs they have encountered and studied this year. Encourage them to include graphs from areas of study other than math (e.g., social studies and science). Discuss why graphs are used to represent data (e.g., graphs are used to summarize a data set and to show how data change).

Explorations and answers are provided in *Alternate Openers: Explorations Transparencies.*

California Standards

Algebra and Functions 1.5

Additional Examples

Example 1

The height of a tree increases over time, but not at a constant rate. Which graph best shows this? b

a.
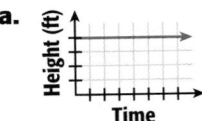

b.
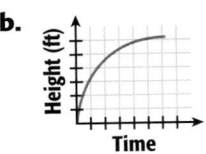

Example 2

Jarod parked his car in the super-market parking lot and walked 40 ft into the store to the customer service counter, where he waited in line to pay his electric bill. Jarod then walked 60 ft to the back of the store to get 2 gallons of milk and walked 50 ft to the checkout near the front of the store to pay for them. After waiting his turn and paying for the milk, he walked 50 ft back to his car. Sketch a graph to show Jarod's distance from his car over time.

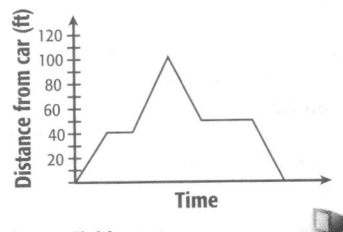

Also available on transparency

EXAMPLE 2 Sketching Graphs for Situations

Maili and Katrina traveled 10 miles from Maili's house to the movie theater. They watched a movie, and then they traveled 5 miles farther to a restaurant to eat lunch. After eating they returned to Maili's house. Sketch a graph to show the distance that the two friends are from Maili's house compared to time.

Step 1 List the different actions you need to show on the graph. Then describe the segment for each action.

- Went to the movies — *Distance from home increased: segment slants upward.*

- Watched the movie — *Distance does not change: horizontal segment.*

- Went to the restaurant — *Distance from home increased: segment slants upward.*

- Ate lunch — *Distance does not change: horizontal segment.*

- Went to Maili's house — *Distance from home decreased: segment slants downward.*

Step 2 Draw the graph.

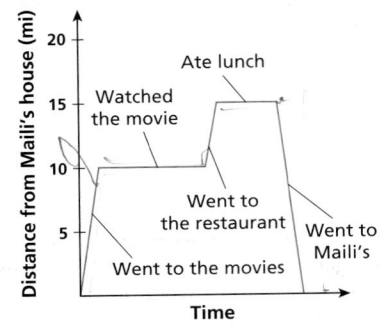

Possible answers to Think and Discuss

1. The distance does not change during that time period.

2. The height of a flag as it is raised up a flagpole

Think and Discuss

1. **Explain** the meaning of a horizontal segment on a graph that compares distance to time.

2. **Describe** a real-world situation that could be represented by a graph that has connected lines or curves.

---

2 Teach

Guided Instruction

In this lesson, students learn to relate graphs to situations. Tell students that a graph is a pictorial representation of a numerical relationship. A graph conveys how data change and relate to each other.

Universal Access
Through Cooperative Learning

Put students in groups of three or four. Have each group write a situation on a piece of paper and draw a corresponding graph on a separate piece of paper. Collect all graphs and shuffle them; then collect all situations and shuffle. Randomly label graphs A, B, C, ..., and situations 1, 2, 3, ... Display all graphs and situations on the wall. Have groups match each graph with the correct description.

3 Close

Summarize

Ask students to describe the relationship shown in the graph below.

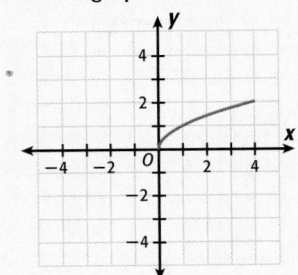

As *x* increases, *y* increases; however, the rate of increase is not constant.

 California Standards Practice
AF1.5

 go.hrw.com
Homework Help Online
KEYWORD: MT8CA 7-8
Parent Resources Online
KEYWORD: MT8CA Parent

GUIDED PRACTICE

See Example ① **Graph A**

1. The temperature of an ice cube increases until it starts to melt. While it melts, its temperature stays constant. Which graph best shows the situation?

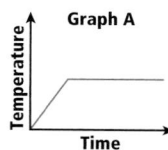 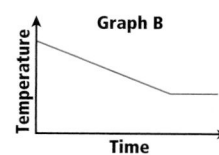 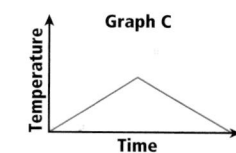

See Example ② **2.** Mike and Claudia rode a bus 15 miles to a wildlife park. They waited in line to ride a train, which took them on a 3-mile ride around the park. After the train ride, they ate lunch, and then they rode the bus home. Sketch a graph to show the distance Mike and Claudia are from home compared to time.

INDEPENDENT PRACTICE

See Example ① **Graph B**

3. The ink in a printer is used until the ink cartridge is empty. The cartridge is refilled, and the ink is used up again. Which graph best shows the situation?

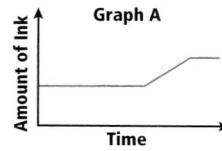 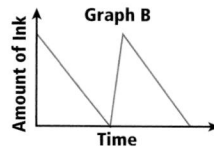 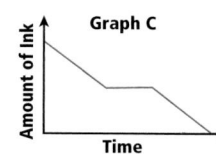

See Example ② **4.** On her way from home to the grocery store, a 6-mile trip, Veronica stopped at a gas station to buy gas. After filling her tank, she continued to the grocery store. She then returned home after shopping. Sketch a graph to show the distance Veronica traveled compared to time.

PRACTICE AND PROBLEM SOLVING

 **Extra Practice**
See page EP15.

5. Describe a situation that fits the graph at right.

6. Lynn jogged for 2.5 miles. Then she walked a little while before stopping to stretch. Sketch a graph to show Lynn's speed compared to time.

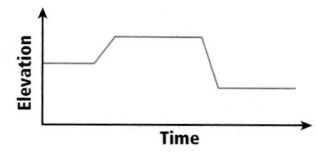

7. On his way to the library, Jeff runs two blocks and then walks three more blocks. Sketch a graph to show the distance Jeff travels compared to time.

REVIEW FOR MASTERY 7-8

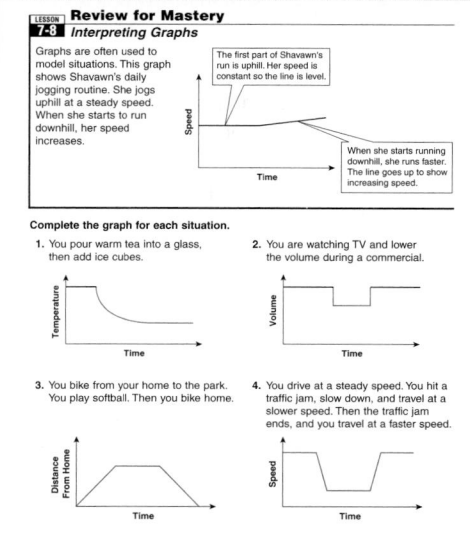

PRACTICE 7-8

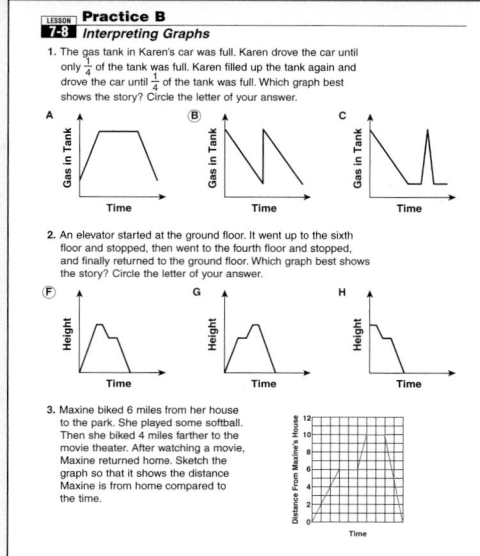

Assignment Guide

If you finished Example ① assign:
Proficient 1, 3, 5, 13, 15–23
Advanced 3, 5, 12, 13, 15–23

If you finished Example ② assign:
Proficient 1–10, 13–23
Advanced 3–23

Homework Quick Check
Quickly check key concepts.
Exercises: 4, 6, 8, 10

Answers

2. Possible graph:
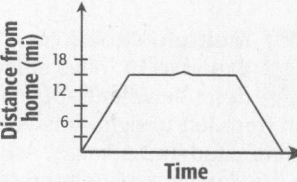

4. Possible graph:
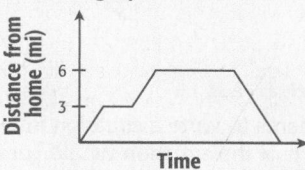

5. Possible answer: Mary walked along a flat trail for some time and then walked up a hill. She walked along the top of the hill for a while and then walked down the hill and continued walking along a flat trail.

6. Possible graph:
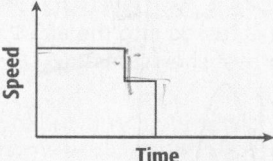

7. Possible graph:
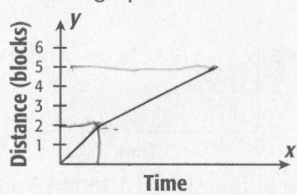

California Standards

Standard	Exercises
NS2.2 🔑	20–23
NS2.5 🔑	15–19
AF1.5	1–14

Answers
12. See p. A7.

Teaching Tip **Multiple Choice** For **Exercise 13,** have students describe what happens to the graph from left to right. Answer **C** can be eliminated immediately. Ask students if a downward line represents an increase or a decrease.

Journal
Ask students to write a situation in which the graph of the situation would contain either a vertical or horizontal line. Then have students draw the graph.

Power Presentations
with PowerPoint®

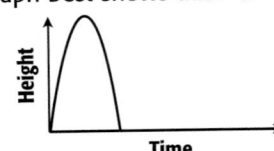

7-8 Lesson Quiz
1. A ball is tossed into the air. Which graph best shows this? a

a.
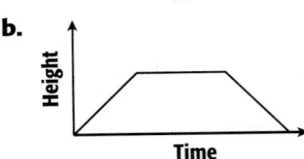

b.

2. Sam in-line skated 1000 m from his home to the park, where he rested on a bench. He then returned home. Sketch a graph to show the distance he in-line skated compared to time.

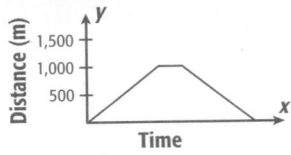

Also available on transparency

The graphs below show the speeds of three dogs at given times during an obstacle course race. Tell which graph corresponds to each situation in Exercises 8–10.

Graph A 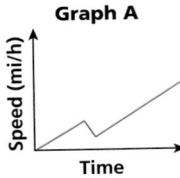 **Graph B** 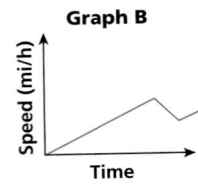 **Graph C**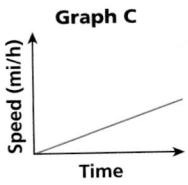

8. Brandy increases her speed throughout the race. Graph C

9. Bruno decreases his speed early in the race to run around cones on the course. After this, he steadily increases his speed. Graph A

10. Max gets off to a fast start and picks up speed for several seconds. He slows down to run through a tunnel but then increases his speed right afterward. Graph B

11. A graph of the car's speed compared to time would be a horizontal line segment. A graph of the distance traveled compared to time would be a line segment that rises steadily from left to right.

11. Write About It A driver sets his car's cruise control to 55 mi/h. Describe a graph that shows the car's speed compared to time. Then describe a second graph that shows the distance traveled compared to time.

12. Challenge The graph at right shows the temperature of an oven after the oven is turned on. Explain what the graph shows.

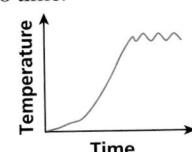

SPIRAL STANDARDS REVIEW
NS2.2, NS2.5, AF1.5

13. Multiple Choice How does speed compare to time in the graph at right?

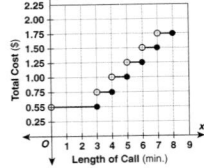

  Ⓐ It increases.   Ⓒ It stays the same.

  Ⓑ It decreases.   Ⓓ It fluctuates.

14. Short Response Keisha takes a big drink from a bottle of water. She sets the bottle down to tie her shoe and then picks up the bottle to take a small sip of water. Sketch a graph to show the amount of water in the bottle over time.
Check students' graphs.

Find each absolute value. (Lesson 1-3)

15. $|9|$ 9   **16.** $|-3|$ 3   **17.** $|-15|$ 15   **18.** $|0|$ 0   **19.** $|5|$ 5

Add or subtract. (Lesson 2-6)

20. $\frac{3}{5} + \left(-\frac{4}{7}\right) + \left(-\frac{2}{3}\right)$ $-\frac{67}{105}$ **21.** $1\frac{1}{7} + 1\frac{1}{6} - \left(-1\frac{1}{3}\right)$ $3\frac{9}{14}$ **22.** $\frac{1}{12} + \frac{5}{8} - \frac{7}{18}$ $\frac{23}{72}$

23. A tabletop has a thickness of $\frac{7}{8}$ of an inch. A glass cover for the table is $\frac{3}{16}$ of an inch thick. Find the total thickness of the tabletop with the glass cover. $1\frac{1}{16}$ inches

---

CHALLENGE 7-8

LESSON 7-8 Challenge
Step Functions

A step graph is a graph that looks like steps. You can use step graphs to represent certain kinds of relationships. The step graph below shows the total cost of calls of different lengths on a particular pay phone system.

The symbol ○—● shows that the segment includes the right endpoint, but not the left endpoint.

Use the graph above to answer the questions.

1. What is the cost of making a 4-minute phone call? $0.75

2. What is the cost of making a 5.5-minute phone call? $1.25

3. Describe how the length of the call is used to determine the total cost.
A call of up to 3 minutes costs $0.50. Each additional minute costs $0.25 more.

4. Find the charge for any phone call with a length (l) that has the following values: 6 minutes < l ≤ 7 minutes. $1.50

5. How does this phone system calculate charges for fractions of minutes?
When a call goes above a whole number of minutes, it charges for the next whole minute. For example, all calls that are greater than 6 minutes and less than or equal to 7 minutes have the same total charge.

PROBLEM SOLVING 7-8

LESSON 7-8 Problem Solving
Interpreting Graphs

Write the correct answer.

Eduardo exercises by doing laps around a track. He sprints the straight-aways and walks the curves.

1. What action is represented by the lower horizontal lines in the graph?
He is walking.

2. What action is represented by the higher horizontal lines in the graph?
He is sprinting at full speed.

3. What action is represented by the dashed lines in the graph?
He begins to sprint.

4. What action is represented by the dotted lines in the graph?
He slows down.

Choose the letter of the best answer.

5. What situation could this graph represent?
Ⓐ cost of birdseed by the pound
B weight of bags of birdseed
C ages of birds eating birdseed
D a buy-one-get-one-free sale

6. What would you expect to pay if you needed $3\frac{1}{2}$ pounds of birdseed?
F $3.50
G $5.00
Ⓗ $7.00
J $7.50

7. What is the price for each pound of birdseed?
A $0.25
B $0.50
C $1.00
Ⓓ $2.00

Vocabulary
direct variation
constant of variation

Why learn this? You can use a direct variation to determine reaction distance. (See Example 3.)

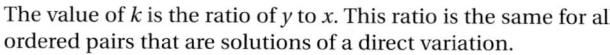

A **direct variation** is a linear function that can be written as $y = kx$, where k is a nonzero constant called the **constant of variation**.

Solve $y = kx$ for k.

$$y = kx$$
$$\frac{y}{x} = \frac{kx}{x} \qquad \textit{Divide both sides by x.}$$
$$\frac{y}{x} = k$$

The value of k is the ratio of y to x. This ratio is the same for all ordered pairs that are solutions of a direct variation.

Since the rate of change k is constant for any direct variation, the graph of a direct variation is always linear. The graph of any direct variation always contains the point $(0, 0)$ because for any value of k, $0 = k0$.

EXAMPLE 1 **Determining Whether a Data Set Varies Directly**

Determine whether the data set shows direct variation.

Ⓐ
Shoe Sizes					
U.S. Size	7	8	9	10	11
European Size	39	41	43	44	45

Method 1 Make a graph.

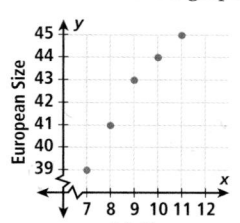

European Size / U.S. Size

The graph is not linear.

Method 2 Compare ratios.

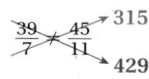
$$\frac{39}{7} \qquad \frac{45}{11}$$
315
429

$315 \neq 429$
The ratios are not equivalent.

Both methods show the relationship is not a direct variation.

Objective: Students recognize direct variation by graphing tables of data and checking for constant ratios.

 Online Edition
Tutorial Videos

 Countdown to Mastery Week 15

Power Presentations
with PowerPoint®

Warm Up

Tell whether the ratios are proportional.

1. $\frac{6}{9} \overset{?}{=} \frac{24}{36}$ yes

2. $\frac{56}{68} \overset{?}{=} \frac{14}{17}$ yes

3. $\frac{12}{13} \overset{?}{=} \frac{60}{78}$ no

4. $\frac{45}{6} \overset{?}{=} \frac{30}{4}$ yes

Also available on transparency

Math Humor

Teacher: Give an example of direct variation in business.

Student: Volume and spending: the *louder* I yell, the more time my parents make me *spend* in my room.

---

1 Introduce
Alternate Opener

Motivate

Give students a few examples of direct variation, for example, "The more groceries I buy, the more money I spend," or "The less sleep I get, the less energy I have." Tell students that if two variables are in direct variation, as one gets larger, the other gets proportionally larger, *or* as one gets smaller, the other gets proportionally smaller.

Explorations and answers are provided in *Alternate Openers: Explorations Transparencies.*

Example ①

Determine whether the data sets show direct variation.

A.

Adam's Growth Chart				
Age (mo)	3	6	9	12
Length (in.)	22	24	25	27

no

B.

Distance Traveled by Train				
Time (min)	10	20	30	40
Distance (mi)	25	50	75	100

yes

Example ②

Rachel rents space in a salon to cut and style hair. She paid the salon owner $24 for 3 cut and styles. Write a direct variation function for this situation. If Rachel does 7 cut and styles, how much will she pay the salon owner? $y = 8x$; $56

Also available on transparency

Determine whether the data set shows direct variation.

 B

Number of Watts of Sound for Watts of Power					
Input Signal Power (W)	6	8	12	20	28
Output Sound Intensity $\left(\frac{W}{m^2}\right)$	4.5	6	9	15	21

Method 1 Make a graph.

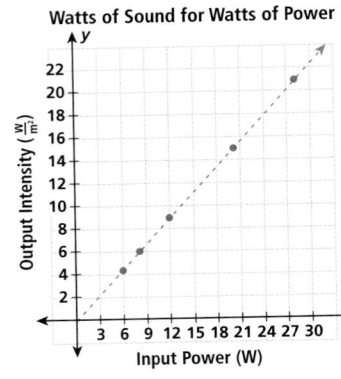

Watts of Sound for Watts of Power

The points lie in a straight line.
(0, 0) is on the line.

Method 2 Compare ratios.

$$\frac{6}{4.5} = \frac{8}{6} = \frac{12}{9} = \frac{20}{15} = \frac{28}{21}$$ *The ratio is constant.*

Both methods show the relationship is a direct variation.

EXAMPLE ② Chelsea's income varies directly with the number of hours she babysits. She earns $11 for 2 hours of babysitting. Write a direct variation function for this situation. If Chelsea babysits for 6 hours, how much will she make?

Step 1 Write the direct variation function.

$x = 2$ and $y = 11$ *Think: Her pay varies directly with time worked.*

$y = kx$

$11 = k \cdot 2$ *Substitute 11 for y and 2 for x.*

$5.5 = k$ *Solve for k.*

$y = 5.5x$ *Substitute 5.5 for k in the original equation.*

Step 2 Find how much Chelsea will make if she babysits for 6 hours.

$y = 5.5(6)$ *Substitute 6 for x in the direct variation function.*

$y = 33$ *Multiply.*

Chelsea will make $33 if she babysits for 6 hours.

---

2 Teach

Guided Instruction

In this lesson, students learn to recognize direct variation by graphing tables of data and checking for constant ratios. Explain that direct variation is very similar to linear equations. In direct variation, the constant of variation k replaces slope, and the y-intercept is always 0 (Teaching Transparency). Show students how to check for constant ratios to identify direct variation. Then show students how to find the constant of variation, given two values.

Universal Access
Through Concrete Manipulatives

Have students work in small groups. Give each group of students a scale, a paper cup, and 30 pennies. Have students adjust the scale so that the weight of the cup registers as zero. Have students weigh five pennies and record the number of pennies and the weight. Then have them repeat the procedure for 10, 15, 20, 25, and 30 pennies. Using the data recorded in this experiment, have students explain whether they believe the variables are in direct variation and explain why. You may want to allow for slight variations in the weights of individual pennies.

EXAMPLE 3 *Science Application*

When a driver applies the brakes, a car's total stopping distance is the sum of the reaction distance and the braking distance. The reaction distance is the distance the car travels between the time the driver decides to apply the brakes and the time the driver actually presses the brake pedal. The braking distance is the distance the car travels after the brakes have been applied.

Determine whether there is a direct variation between each of the following.

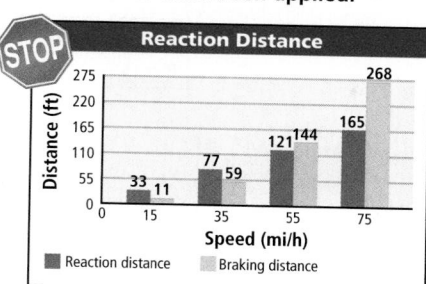

A reaction distance and speed

$$\frac{\text{reaction distance}}{\text{speed}} = \frac{33}{15} = 2.2$$

$$\frac{\text{reaction distance}}{\text{speed}} = \frac{77}{35} = 2.2$$

The first two pairs of data result in a common ratio. In fact, all of the reaction distance to speed ratios are equivalent to 2.2.

$$\frac{\text{reaction distance}}{\text{speed}} = \frac{33}{15} = \frac{77}{35} = \frac{121}{55} = \frac{165}{75} = 2.2$$

The variables are related by a constant ratio of 2.2 to 1.

B braking distance and speed

$$\frac{\text{braking distance}}{\text{speed}} = \frac{11}{15} = 0.7\overline{3}$$

$$\frac{\text{braking distance}}{\text{speed}} = \frac{59}{35} \approx 1.69$$

$$0.7\overline{3} \neq 1.69$$

If any of the ratios are not equal, then there is no direct variation. It is not necessary to compute additional ratios.

Think and Discuss

1. Describe the slope of a direct variation function.

2. Compare and contrast proportional and non-proportional linear relationships.

Example 3

Mrs. Perez has $4000 in a CD and $4000 in a money market account. The amount of interest she has earned since the beginning of the year is organized in the following table. Determine whether there is a direct variation between either data set and time.

Time (mo)	Interest from CD ($)	Interest from Money Market ($)
0	0	0
1	17	19
2	34	37
3	51	55
4	68	73

A. interest from CD and time
direct variation

B. interest from money market and time   no direct variation

Also available on transparency

Answers to Think and Discuss

1. The slope is the constant of variation, k. The y-intercept is always 0.

2. Possible answer: A proportional linear relationship is a direct variation between the variables. However, a non-proportional relationship is not a direct variation and thus will have a y-intercept other than 0.

---

③ Close

Summarize

ENGLISH LANGUAGE LEARNERS

Remind students that direct variation can be determined by checking for constant ratios or by graphing and seeing whether the graph is a straight line that passes through the origin. Point out that the phrase *direct variation* suggests that there is a direct relationship between the changes in the variables (i.e., as one variable increases, the other increases proportionally).

7-9 Exercises

California Standards Practice
AF3.3, AF3.4, AF4.2

go.hrw.com
Homework Help Online
KEYWORD: MT8CA 7-9
Parent Resources Online
KEYWORD: MT8CA Parent

Assignment Guide

If you finished Example **1** assign:
Proficient 1, 4, 27, 28
Advanced 4, 11, 27, 28

If you finished Example **2** assign:
Proficient 1–2, 4–5, 7–10, 12–19, 24–28
Advanced 4–5, 7–11, 15–19, 21–28

If you finished Example **3** assign:
Proficient 1–10, 12–20, 24–28
Advanced 4–28

Homework Quick Check

Quickly check key concepts.
Exercises: 4, 6, 8, 10, 12

GUIDED PRACTICE

See Example **1**
1. The table shows an employee's pay per number of hours worked. Determine whether the data set shows direct variation. **yes**

Hours Worked	0	1	2	3	4	5	6
Pay ($)	0	9.50	19.00	28.50	38.00	47.50	57.00

See Example **2**
2. **Life Science** A moose can be a very fast animal. It can move at speeds up to 4840 feet per minute for short periods of time. Write a direct variation function for the distance y a moose can travel in x minutes. How far could a moose travel in $\frac{1}{4}$ min? $y = 4840x$; **1210 feet**

See Example **3**
3. The table shows how many hours it takes to travel 600 miles, depending on your speed in miles per hour. Determine whether there is direct variation between the two data sets. **no direct variation**

Speed (mi/h)	5	6	7.5	10	15	30	60
Time (h)	120	100	80	60	40	20	10

INDEPENDENT PRACTICE

See Example **1**
4. The table shows the amount of current flowing through a 12-volt circuit with various resistances. Determine whether the data set shows direct variation. **no**

Resistance (ohms)	48	24	12	6	4	3	2
Current (amps)	0.25	0.5	1	2	3	4	6

See Example **2**
5. **Science** Weight varies directly with gravity. *Apollo 11* weighed 5898 kg on Earth but only 983 kg on the Moon. *Apollo 12* weighed 5806 kg on Earth. Write a direct variation function for this situation. About how much did *Apollo 12* weigh on the Moon? Round your answer to the nearest kilogram. $y = \frac{1}{6}x$; **about 968 kg**

See Example **3**
6. The table shows how many hours it takes to drive certain distances at a speed of 30 miles per hour. Determine whether there is direct variation between the two data sets. **yes**

Distance (mi)	15	30	60	90	120	150	180
Time (h)	0.5	1	2	3	4	5	6

REVIEW FOR MASTERY 7-9

LESSON 7-9 Review for Mastery
Direct Variation

Two data sets have **direct variation** if they are related by a constant ratio, the **constant of proportionality**. A graph of the data sets is linear and passes through (0, 0).

$y = kx$ equation of direct variation, where k is the constant ratio

To determine whether two data sets have direct variation, you can compare ratios. You can also graph the data sets on a coordinate grid.

x	3	5	8
y	15	25	40

$\frac{y}{x} = \frac{15}{3} = \frac{25}{5} = \frac{40}{8} = \frac{5}{1}$ ← constant ratio

$k = 5 \rightarrow y = 5x$

The graph of the data sets is linear and passes through (0, 0).
So, the data sets show direct variation.

Determine whether the data sets show direct variation. If there is a constant ratio, identify it and write the equation of direct variation. Plot the points and tell whether the graph is linear.

1.
x	1	2	4	8
y	8	4	2	1

constant ratio? **no**
If yes, equation.
Is the graph linear? **no**

2.
x	0	2	3	5
y	0	20	30	50

constant ratio? **yes, 10**
If yes, equation. $y = 10x$
Is the graph linear? **yes**

PRACTICE 7-9

LESSON 7-9 Practice B
Direct Variation

Make a graph to determine whether the data sets show direct variation.

1.
x	y
6	9
4	6
0	0
−2	−3
−8	−12

The data sets show direct variation.

2. Write the equation of direct variation for Exercise 1.
$y = 1.5x$ or $y = \frac{3}{2}x$

3. Reynaldo ordered 12 large pepperoni pizzas. The total cost was $101.40. Write a direct variation function for the cost of one large pepperoni pizza. How much would 5 large pepperoni pizzas cost?
$y = $8.45x$; 42.25

4. Randall earns $460 for working a 40-hour work week. Write a direct variation function for the amount that Randall earns in one hour. How much money would Randall earn if he only worked 28 hours in one week?
$y = 11.5x$; 322

5. The table shows the length and width of various U.S. flags. Determine whether there is direct variation between the two data sets. If so, find the equation of direct variation.

Length (ft)	2.85	5.7	7.6	9.88	11.4
Width (ft)	1.5	3	4	5.2	6

There is direct variation between the lengths and widths of the flags.
$y = 1.9x$, where y is the length, x is the width, and 1.9 is the constant of proportionality

PRACTICE AND PROBLEM SOLVING

Extra Practice
See page EP15.

Tell whether each equation represents direct variation between x and y.

7. $y = 217x$ **yes**   **8.** $y = -3x^2$ **no**   **9.** $y = \dfrac{k}{x}$ **no**   **10.** $y = 4\pi x$ **yes**

11. Reasoning Is every linear relationship a direct variation? Is every direct variation a linear relationship? Explain.   **No; yes; a direct variation is a linear relationship in which the y-intercept is always 0.**

Find each equation of direct variation, given that y varies directly with x.

12. y is 10 when x is 2 $y = 5x$ **13.** y is 16 when x is 4 $y = 4x$

14. y is 12 when x is 15 $y = \dfrac{4}{5}x$ **15.** y is 3 when x is 6 $y = \dfrac{1}{2}x$

16. y is 220 when x is 2 $y = 110x$ **17.** y is 5 when x is 40 $y = \dfrac{1}{8}x$

18. y is 8 when x is 22 $y = \dfrac{4}{11}x$ **19.** y is 52 when x is 4 $y = 13x$

Life Science

Although snakes shed their skins all in one piece, most reptiles shed their skins in much smaller pieces.

20. Life Science The weight of a person's skin is related to body weight by the equation $s = \frac{1}{16}w$, where s is skin weight and w is body weight.

   a. Does this equation show direct variation between body weight and skin weight?   **yes**

   b. If a person's skin weight is $9\frac{3}{4}$ lb, what is the person's body weight?   **156 lb**

21. Write a Problem The perimeter P of a square varies directly with the length l of a side. Write a direct variation problem about the perimeter of a square.   **Check students' work.**

22. Write About It Describe how the constant of variation k affects the appearance of the graph of a direct variation function.

23. Challenge Watermelons are being sold at 79¢ a pound. What condition would have to exist for the price paid and the number of watermelons sold to represent a direct variation?   **Each watermelon would need to be exactly the same weight.**

SPIRAL STANDARDS REVIEW   ← NS1.7, ← AF4.1, ← AF4.2

24. Multiple Choice Given that y varies directly with x, what is the equation of direct variation if y is 16 when x is 20?

   Ⓐ $y = 1\frac{1}{5}x$ Ⓑ $y = \dfrac{5}{4}x$ Ⓒ $y = \dfrac{4}{5}x$ Ⓓ $y = 0.6x$

25. Gridded Response If y varies directly with x, what is the value of x when $y = 14$ and $k = \frac{1}{2}$?   **28**

26. The school track team is selling pizzas to make money for travel. The supplier charges $100 plus $4 per pizza. If the team sells the pizzas for $10 each, how many pizzas will they need to sell to make a $1250 profit? (Lesson 3-8)   **225 pizzas**

Find the simple interest and the total amount to the nearest cent. (Lesson 6-7)

27. $775 at 4.5% for 10 years   **$348.75; $1123.75**   **28.** $1595 at 8% for 9 months   **$95.70; $1690.70**

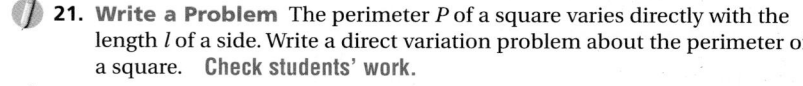
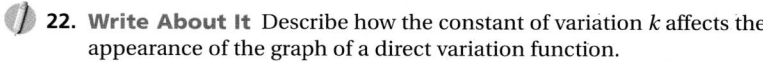
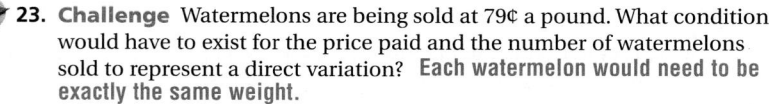

Answers
22. See p. A7.

Teaching Tip   **Multiple Choice** When discussing **Exercise 24,** encourage students to compare the y-value to the x-value. In lowest terms, this is the slope. This should allow them to identify the correct equation as **C**. If students compare the x-value to the y-value, they will choose **B**.

Journal

Ask students to describe a real-world example of direct variation. Examples might include an hourly wage, the cost of renting a video game, or the number of cookies made with various amounts of flour.

Power Presentations
with PowerPoint®

7-9 Lesson Quiz

Determine whether the data sets show direction variation.

1.

Amount of Water in a Rain Gauge					
Time (h)	1	2	3	4	5
Rain (in.)	2	4	6	8	10

direct variation

2.

Driving Time					
Speed (mi/h)	30	40	50	60	80
Time (h)	10	7.5	6	5	3.75

no direct variation

3. Roy's income varies directly with the number of dogs that he walks. He earned $8.50 for walking 2 dogs. Write a direct variation function for this situation. If Roy walks 5 dogs, how much will he earn? $y = 4.25x$; $21.25

Also available on transparency

Organizer

Objective: Assess students' mastery of concepts and skills in Lessons 7-6 through 7-9.

Resources

 Assessment Resources
Section 7B Quiz

 Test & Practice Generator
One-Stop Planner®

INTERVENTION

Resources

 Ready to Go On?
Intervention and
Enrichment Worksheets

💿 **Ready to Go On? CD-ROM**

🪐 **Ready to Go On? Online**

my.hrw.com

Answers

10.

Pay Per Number of Hours Worked

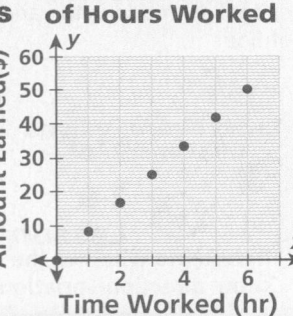

Quiz for Lessons 7-6 Through 7-9

✓ **7-6** Rate of Change and Slope

Determine whether the rates of change are constant or variable.

1.   variable

x	0	1	3	5	7
y	1	3	7	6	8

Find the slope of each line.

2. 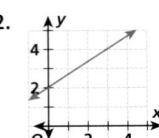 $\frac{2}{3}$ **3.** 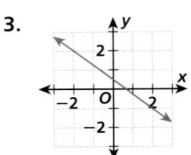 $-\frac{3}{4}$ **4.** 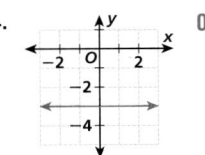 0

✓ **7-7** Finding Slope of a Line

Find the slope of the line that passes through each pair of points.

5. (6, 3) and (2, 4) $-\frac{1}{4}$ **6.** (1, 4) and (−1, −3) $\frac{7}{2}$ **7.** (0, −3) and (−4, 0) $-\frac{3}{4}$

✓ **7-8** Interpreting Graphs

8. Raj climbs to the top of a cliff. He descends a little bit to another cliff and then begins to climb again. Which graph best shows the situation? **Graph A**

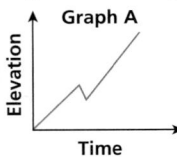   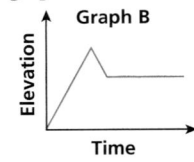   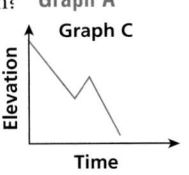

9. Ty walks 1 mile to the mall. An hour later, he walks $\frac{1}{2}$ mile farther to a park and eats lunch. Then he walks home. Sketch a graph to show the distance Ty is from home compared to time.

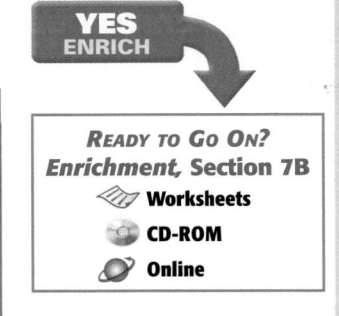

✓ **7-9** Direct Variation

10. The table shows an employee's pay per number of hours worked. Determine whether the data set shows direct variation. **yes**

Time Worked (hr)	0	1	2	3	4	5	6
Amount Earned ($)	0	8.50	17.00	25.50	34.00	42.50	51.00

NO
INTERVENE

READY TO GO ON?
Diagnose and Prescribe

YES
ENRICH

READY TO GO ON? Intervention, Section 7B			
Ready to Go On? **Intervention**	📜 **Worksheets**	💿 **CD-ROM**	🪐 **Online**
✓ Lesson 7-6 🐻 🔑 **AF3.3**	7-6 Intervention	Activity 7-6	
✓ Lesson 7-7 🐻 🔑 **AF3.3,** 🔑 **AF3.4**	7-7 Intervention	Activity 7-7	Diagnose and
✓ Lesson 7-8 🐻 **AF1.5**	7-8 Intervention	Activity 7-8	Prescribe Online
✓ Lesson 7-9 🐻 🔑 **AF3.4,** 🔑 **AF4.2**	7-9 Intervention	Activity 7-9	

READY TO GO ON?
Enrichment, Section 7B
📜 **Worksheets**
💿 **CD-ROM**
🪐 **Online**

Beset by Beavers Greg and Maria are wildlife biologists. They are studying beaver population trends in a national forest. There are currently 200 beavers in the forest. The table shows Greg's and Maria's predictions for the beaver population in future years.

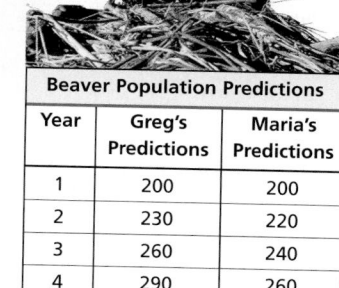

1. Write a function based on Greg's prediction that gives the beaver population in year x. Then use the function to find the population in year 8.

2. According to your function, in what year will the beaver population be 500? Explain.

3. Write a function based on Maria's prediction that gives the beaver population in year x. Then use the function to find the population in year 8.

4. A third biologist, Amir, makes his predictions using the function $y = 5x^2 + 195$, where x is the year number. Use the function to find the beaver population that Amir predicts in year 8.   **515**

5. Which of the three biologists predicts the greatest beaver population in year 12? What is this population?   **Amir; 915**

Beaver Population Predictions

Year	Greg's Predictions	Maria's Predictions
1	200	200
2	230	220
3	260	240
4	290	260

Organizer

Objective: Assess students' ability to apply concepts and skills in Chapter 7 in a real-world format.

 **Online Edition**

Problem	Text reference
1	Lesson 7-3
2	Lesson 7-3
3	Lesson 7-3
4	Lesson 7-4
5	Lesson 7-4

Answers

1. $y = 200 + (x - 1)30$ or $y = 170 + 30x$; 410

2. Year 11. Solve $500 = 200 + (x - 1)30$ to find that $x = 11$.

3. $y = 20x + 180$; 340

INTERVENTION ◄═══►

Scaffolding Questions

1. What type of function is formed by Greg's population predictions? Linear Why? The plotted points (1, 200), (2, 230), (3, 260), and (4, 290) form a line.

2. What equation can you write as a first step in solving this problem? $500 = 200 + (x - 1)30$

3. What type of function is formed by Maria's population predictions? Linear Why? The plotted points (1, 200), (2, 220), (3, 240), and (4, 260) form a line.

4. What is the population when $x = 1$? 200 How can you use the function to find the beaver population in year 8? Find y when $x = 8$.

5. What population does Greg predict in year 12? 530 What population does Maria predict in year 12? 420 What population does Amir predict in year 12? 915

Extension

1. According to Greg's predictions, in what year will the beaver population be greater than 10,000 for the first time? Year 328

 California Standards

Algebra and Functions

1.1 Use variables and appropriate operations to write an expression, **an equation,** an inequality, or a system of equations or inequalities **that represents a verbal description** (e.g., three less than a number, half as large as area A).

3.0 Students graph and **interpret** linear and some nonlinear functions.

Ext. of ☞ 4.1 Solve two-step linear equations and inequalities **in one variable over the rational numbers, interpret the solution or solutions in the context from which they arose,** and verify the reasonableness of the results.

Game Time

Organizer

Objective: Participate in games to practice and apply skills learned in Chapter 7.

 Online Edition

Resources

Chapter 7 Resource File
Puzzles, Twisters & Teasers

Squared Away

Purpose: To apply the problem-solving skill of writing sequences to solve a puzzle

Discuss Ask students to explain how to determine the number of different squares in a square of side length n.

The number of $n \times n$ squares is 1^2, or 1. The number of $(n - 1) \times (n - 1)$ squares is 2^2, or 4. The number of $(n - 2) \times (n - 2)$ squares is 3^2, or 9. The number of $(n - a) \times (n - a)$ squares is $(a + 1)^2$. Add the number of squares of each size to find the total number.

Extend Challenge students to notice other patterns in the tables used to record *Size of Square* and *Number of Squares*. Have them test hypotheses by testing their rule on the tables for 4×4, 5×5, 6×6, and 7×7 squares.

Possible answer: Find the area of each size square and multiply it by the number of squares of that size. The products are square numbers that form a palindrome pattern when listed in order. For example, for a 4×4 square, the products are as follows:

1   4×4 square = 16 square units
4   3×3 squares = 36 square units
9   2×2 squares = 36 square units
16 1×1 squares = 16 square units

What's Your Function?

Purpose: To practice identifying functions in a game format

Discuss When a team guesses a function correctly, have them demonstrate that each input/output pair used is a solution to the function.

Extend Have students create new function cards, including linear, quadratic, and cubic functions. Use the new equation cards to play again.

Game Time

Squared Away

How many squares can you find in the figure at right?

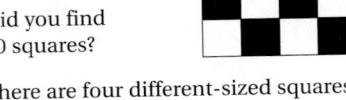

Did you find 30 squares?

There are four different-sized squares in the figure.

Size of Square	Number of Squares
4 × 4	1
3 × 3	4
2 × 2	9
1 × 1	16
Total	**30**

3 × 3 squares

2 × 2 squares

The total number of squares is $1 + 4 + 9 + 16 = 1^2 + 2^2 + 3^2 + 4^2$.

Draw a 5 × 5 grid and count the number of squares of each size. Can you see a pattern?

What is the total number of squares on a 6 × 6 grid? a 7 × 7 grid? Can you come up with a general formula for the sum of squares on an $n \times n$ grid?

What's Your Function?

One member from the first of two teams draws a function card from the deck, and the other team tries to guess the rule of the function. The guessing team gives a function input, and the card holder must give the corresponding output. Points are awarded based on the type of function and number of inputs required.

Complete rules and function cards are available online.

go.hrw.com
Game Time Extra
KEYWORD: MT8CA Games

Answers

$5 \times 5 \to 55$ squares
$6 \times 6 \to 91$ squares
$7 \times 7 \to 140$ squares
$8 \times 8 \to 204$ squares

Possible answer:

$n \times n \to 1^2 + 2^2 + 3^2 + \cdots + n^2 = \dfrac{n(n + 1)(2n + 1)}{6}$

Materials
- small paper bag
- scissors
- tape
- graph paper
- stapler

It's in the Bag!

PROJECT Graphing Tri-Fold

Use this organizer to hold notes, vocabulary, and practice problems related to graphing.

Directions

❶ Hold the bag flat with the flap facing you at the bottom. Fold up the flap. Cut off the part of the bag above the flap. **Figure A**

❷ Unfold the bag. Cut down the middle of the top layer of the bag until you get to the flap. Then cut across the bag just above the flap, again cutting only the top layer of the bag. **Figure B**

❸ Open the bag. Cut away the sides at the bottom of the bag. These sections are shaded in the figure. **Figure C**

❹ Unfold the bag. There will be three equal sections at the bottom of the bag. Fold up the bottom section and tape the sides to create a pocket. **Figure D**

❺ Trim several pieces of graph paper to fit in the middle section of the bag. Staple them to the bag to make a booklet.

Taking Note of the Math

Write definitions of vocabulary words behind the "doors" at the top of your organizer. Graph sample linear equations on the graph paper. Use the pocket at the bottom of the organizer to store notes on the chapter.

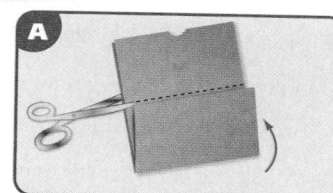

A

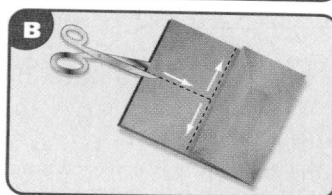

B

C

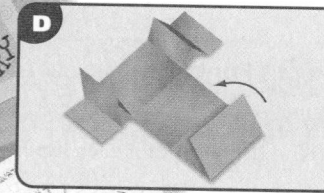

D

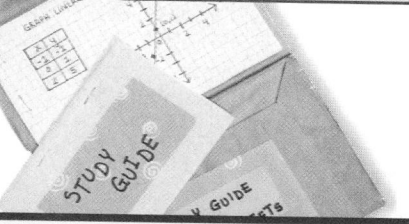

It's in the Bag!

Organizer

Objective: Make an organizer to store notes about graphs of lines.

Materials: small paper bag, scissors, tape, graph paper, stapler

 **Online Edition**

Using the Page

Preparing the Materials

The project works best when students begin with folded, unused paper bags. If students use recycled bags, have them begin by flattening them into their original shape.

Making the Project

You may want to demonstrate each step of the project in front of the class while students make their organizers. In particular, be sure students understand that in **Step 2** they must cut only the top layer of the bag.

Extending the Project

Have students use index cards to make flash cards for the chapter. Students can store the flash cards in the pocket of their organizer.

Tips from the Bag Ladies!

We usually make one of the organizers along with the class. The demonstration helps answer any questions that students may have as they follow the directions. You might even make your organizer out of a large grocery bag so that it's easy for all students to see the demonstration.

This project is infinitely adaptable. Once students have made their organizers, they can add library pockets, plastic zipper bags, and/or small stacks of sticky notes.

Organizer

Objective: Help students organize and review key concepts and skills presented in Chapter 7.

Online Edition
Multilingual Glossary

Resources

PuzzlePro®
One-Stop Planner®

Multilingual Glossary Online

go.hrw.com
KEYWORD: MT8CA Glossary

Lesson Tutorial Videos
CD-ROM

Test & Practice Generator
One-Stop Planner®

Answers

1. direct variation
2. function
3. linear function
4. J(2, −1), IV
5. K(−2, 3), II
6. L(1, 0), x-axis
7. M(−4, −2), III
8. Possible answer:

x	−1	0	1	2	3
y	−11	−4	3	10	17

9. Possible answer:

x	−1	0	1	2	3
y	−2	0	−2	−8	−18

10. yes

11.

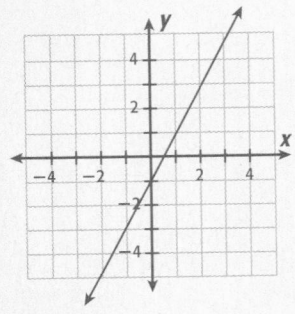

12.

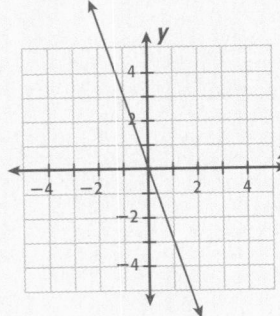

13.

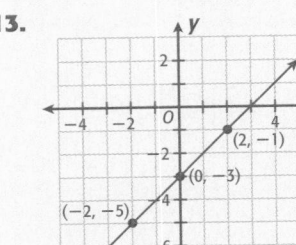

Vocabulary

Complete the sentences below with vocabulary words from the list above.

1. Two variables related by a constant ratio are in ___?___ .

2. A(n) ___?___ gives exactly one output for every input.

3. A(n) ___?___ is a function whose graph is a nonvertical line.

7-1 The Coordinate Plane (pp. 322–325)

Prep for AF3.3

EXAMPLE

Give the coordinates of each point and tell which quadrant contains it.

$A(-3, 2)$; II
$B(2, -3)$; IV
$C(-2, -3)$; III
$D(3, 2)$; I

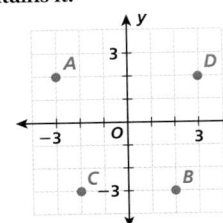

EXERCISES

Give the coordinates of each point and tell which quadrant contains it.

4. J
5. K
6. L
7. M

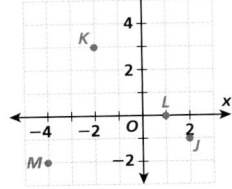

7-2 Functions (pp. 326–329)

Prep for AF3.3

EXAMPLE

■ Find the output for each input.

Input	Rule	Output
x	x − 3	y
−1	−1 − 3	−4
0	0 − 3	−3
1	1 − 3	−2

EXERCISES

Find the output for each input: −1, 0, 1, 2, 3.

8. $y = 7x - 4$ **9.** $y = -2x^2$

10. Determine if the relationship represents a function.

x	1	2	3	4	5
y	17	19	21	23	25

7-3 Graphing Linear Functions (pp. 330–333)

 AF3.3

EXAMPLE

■ Graph the linear function $y = -x + 2$.

x	y
−1	3
0	2
2	0

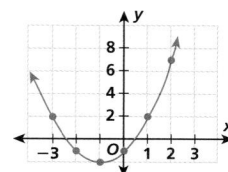

EXERCISES

Graph each linear function.

11. $y = 2x - 1$
12. $y = -3x$
13. $y = x - 3$
14. $y = 2x + 4$
15. $y = x - 6$

7-4 Graphing Quadratic Functions (pp. 334–337)

 AF3.1

EXAMPLE

■ Graph the quadratic function $y = x^2 + 2x - 1$.

x	y
−2	−1
−1	−2
0	−1
1	2

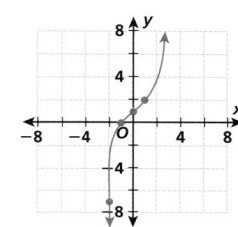

EXERCISES

Graph each quadratic function.

16. $y = 2x^2$
17. $y = x^2 + 3$
18. $y = 2x^2 - x$
19. $y = x^2 + 5x + 6$

7-5 Cubic Functions (pp. 338–341)

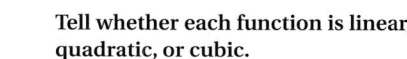 AF3.1

EXAMPLE

■ Graph the cubic function $y = x^3 + 1$.

x	y
−2	−7
−1	0
0	1
1	2

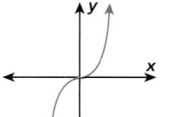

EXERCISES

Graph each cubic function.

20. $y = 2x^3$
21. $y = x^3 - 1$
22. $y = x^3 + 2$

■ Tell whether the function is linear, quadratic, or cubic.

The graph curves down, then up.

Cubic

Tell whether each function is linear, quadratic, or cubic.

23.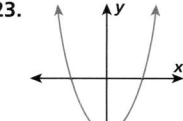

24.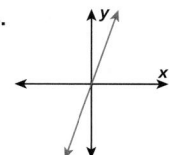

Answers

14.

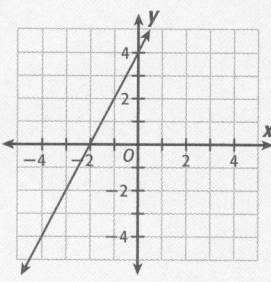

15.

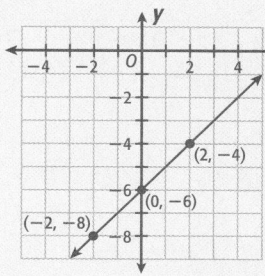

(2, −4)
(0, −6)
(−2, −8)

16.

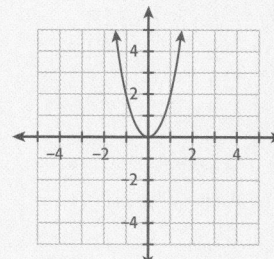

17.

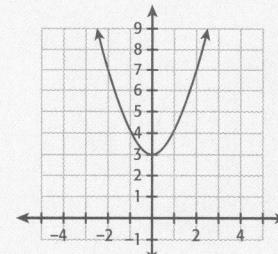

18.

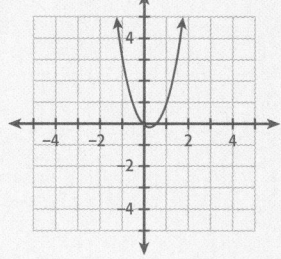

19.

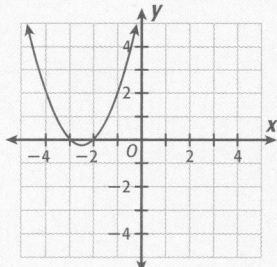

20.

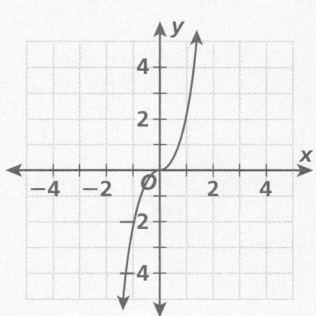

21.

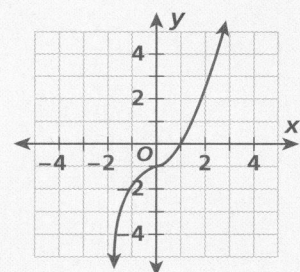

22.

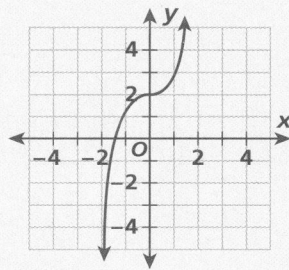

23. quadratic
24. linear

25. constant

26. constant

27. $\frac{3}{4}$

28. -4

29. -1

30.

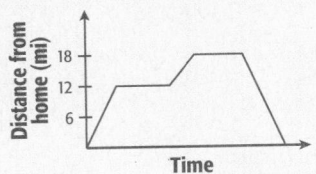

31. $y = 5x$; \$22.50

7-6 **Rate of Change and Slope** (pp. 344–348)

 AF3.3

EXAMPLE

■ Determine whether the rates of change are constant or variable.

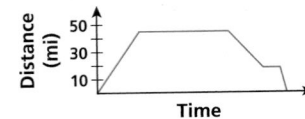

x	y
-3	1
-2	4
0	6
2	6

$+1 \quad +3 \qquad \frac{3}{1} = 3$
$+2 \quad +2 \qquad \frac{2}{2} = 1$
$+2 \quad +0 \qquad \frac{0}{2} = 0$

The data set has a variable rate of change.

EXERCISES

Determine whether the rates of change are constant or variable.

25.

x	-3	-1	0	2	4
y	3	1	0	-2	-4

26.

x	-2	-1	2	4	5
y	3	3	3	3	3

7-7 **Finding Slope of a Line** (pp. 349–352)

 AF3.3, AF3.4

EXAMPLE

■ Find the slope of the line that passes through $(-1, 2)$ and $(1, 3)$.

$$\frac{y_2 - y_1}{x_2 - x_1} = \frac{3 - 2}{1 - (-1)} = \frac{1}{2}$$

EXERCISES

Find the slope of the line that passes through each pair of points.

27. $(4, 2)$ and $(8, 5)$ **28.** $(4, 3)$ and $(5, -1)$

29. $(-3, -3)$ and $(-4, -2)$

7-8 **Interpreting Graphs** (pp. 353–356)

 AF1.5

EXAMPLE

■ Ari drives 45 miles. Then he returns home, stopping for gas along the way. Sketch a graph to show Ari's distance from home compared to time.

EXERCISES

30. Joel rides his bike 12 miles. He then rides an additional 6 miles and returns home. Sketch a graph to show Joel's distance from home compared to time.

7-9 **Direct Variation** (pp. 357–361)

 AF4.2

EXAMPLE

■ Determine whether the data set shows a direct variation.

Time (h)	1	2	3	4	5
Distance (mi)	55	110	165	220	275

$$\frac{1}{55} = \frac{2}{110} = \frac{3}{165} = \frac{4}{220} = \frac{5}{275}$$

Yes; the ratio is constant.

EXERCISE

31. Ben earns \$10 for working 2 hours at his after-school job. The total amount of his paycheck varies directly with the amount of time he works. If he works for 4.5 hours, how much will he make?

Plot each point and identify the quadrant in which it lies.

1. $L(4, -3)$ **IV**   **2.** $M(-5, 2)$ **II**   **3.** $N(7, 1)$ **I**   **4.** $O(-7, -2)$ **III**

Find the output for each input: $-2, -1, 0, 1, 2$.

5. $y = 5x - 3$ **6.** $y = 9x + 2$ **7.** $y = -2x - 5$

Graph each function.

8. $y = 3x - 4$ **9.** $y = 2x + 7$ **10.** $y = x^2 + x + 3$

11. $y = 2x^2 - 1$ **12.** $y = -\frac{1}{2}x^3$ **13.** $y = x^3 + 3$

Tell whether each function is linear, quadratic, or cubic.

14.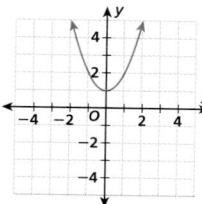
quadratic

15.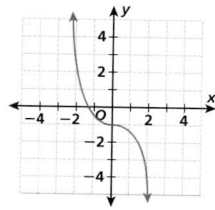
cubic

16.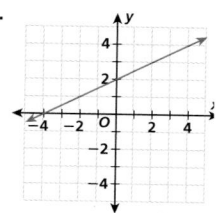
linear

Graph each set of data. Label the rate of change for each segment. Then tell whether the data set has a constant or variable rate of change.

17.

x	1	2	3	4	5
y	2	4	3	6	9

variable

18.

x	0	3	5	6	7
y	2	2	2	2	0

variable

Find the slope of the line that passes through each pair of points.

19. $(0, -8)$ and $(-1, -10)$ **2**   **20.** $(0, -2)$ and $(-5, 0)$ $-\frac{2}{5}$ **21.** $(3, 1)$ and $(0, 3)$ $-\frac{2}{3}$

22. Ian jogs 4 miles to the lake and then rests for 30 minutes before jogging home. Sketch a graph to show Ian's distance from home compared to time.

23. Make a graph to determine whether the data set shows direct variation.

Miles per Gallon in a Hybrid Car					
Gallons (gal)	1	2	3	4	5
Miles (mi)	60	120	180	240	300

24. The number of gallons of water used by a washing machine varies directly as the number of loads of laundry. A new washer saves 45 gallons of water after 3 loads of laundry. Find the number of gallons of water saved after 7 loads of laundry.   **105 gallons**

8.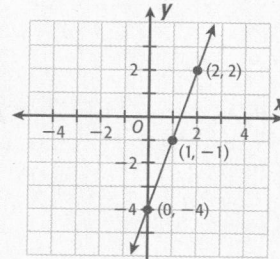

9.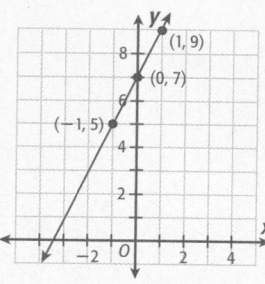

10.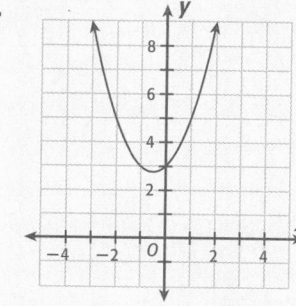

11.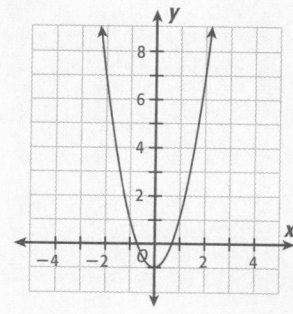

Organizer

Objective: Assess students' mastery of concepts and skills in Chapter 7.

 Online Edition

Resources

 Assessment Resources

Chapter 7 Tests
- Free Response
  (Levels A, B, C)
- Multiple Choice
  (Levels A, B, C)
- Performance Assessment

IDEA Works! CD-ROM
Modified Chapter 7 Test

 Test & Practice Generator
One-Stop Planner®

Answers

1–4.

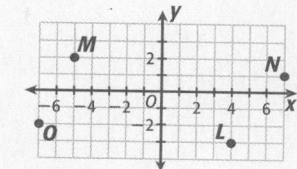

5.

x	−2	−1	0	1	2
y	−13	−8	−3	2	7

6.

x	−2	−1	0	1	2
y	−16	−7	2	11	20

7.

x	−2	−1	0	1	2
y	−1	−3	−5	−7	−9

Answers

12–13, 17–18, 22–23. See p. A7.

Organizer

Objective: Provide opportunities to learn and practice common test-taking strategies.

 Online Edition

Teaching Tip

Extended Response This Strategies for Success focuses on how extended response test items are scored and demonstrates how to write a response worth full credit. Explain that a grader scores responses to these types of test items and awards points based on the completeness and correctness of the response. Point out to students that a full-credit extended response includes not only the correct computation of the answer, but also the ability to clearly explain the reasoning that led to the answer.

Extended Response: Write Extended Responses

Extended response test items often consist of multi-step problems to evaluate your understanding of a math concept. Extended response questions are scored using a 4-point scoring rubric.

EXAMPLE 1

Extended Response Julianna bought a shirt marked down 20%. She had a coupon for an additional 20% off the sale price. Is this the same as getting 40% off the regular price? Explain your reasoning.

4-point response:

> No, the prices are not the same. Suppose the shirt originally cost $40.
> 20% off a 20% markdown: $40 × 20% = $8; $40 − $8 = $32;
> $32 × 20% = $6.40; $32 − $6.40 = $25.60
> 40% off: $40 × 40% = $16; $40 − $16 = $24

The student answers the question correctly and shows all work.

3-point response:

> Yes, it is the same. If the shirt originally cost $25, it would cost $15 after taking 20% off of a 20% discount. A 40% discount off $20 is $15.
>
> Shirt original price = $25
> Shirt at 20% off = $20 $25 × 20% = $5; $25 − $5 = $20
> Shirt at 20% off sales price = $15 $20 × 20% = $4; $20 − $4 = $15
> Shirt at 40% off = $15 $25 × 40% = $10; $25 − $10 = $15

The student makes a minor computation error that results in an incorrect answer.

2-point response:

> No, it is not the same. A $30 shirt with 20% off and then an additional 20% off is $6. A $30 shirt at 40% off is $12.

The student makes major computation errors and does not show all work.

1-point response:

> It is the same.

The student shows no work and has the wrong answer.

Scoring Rubric

4 points: The student answers all parts of the question correctly, shows all work, and provides a complete and correct explanation.

3 points: The student answers all parts of the question, shows all work, and provides a complete explanation that demonstrates understanding, but the student makes minor errors in computation.

2 points: The student does not answer all parts of the question but shows all work and provides a complete and correct explanation for the parts answered, or the student correctly answers all parts of the question but does not show all work or does not provide an explanation.

1 point: The student gives incorrect answers and shows little or no work or explanation, or the student does not follow directions.

0 points: The student gives no response.

To receive full credit, make sure all parts of the problem are answered. Be sure to show all of your work and to write a neat and clear explanation.

Read each test item and answer the questions that follow.

Item A
Janell has two job offers. Job A pays $500 per week. Job B pays $200 per week plus 15% commission on her sales. She expects to make $7500 in sales per month. Which job pays better? Explain your reasoning.

1. A student wrote this response:

> Job A pays better.

What score should the student's response receive? Explain your reasoning.

2. What additional information, if any, should the student's response include in order to receive full credit?

3. Add to the response so that it receives a score of 4-points.

4. How much would Janell have to make in sales per month for job A and job B to pay the same amount?

Item B
A new MP3 player normally costs $97.99. This week, it is on sale for 15% off its regular price. In addition to this, Jasmine receives an employee discount of 20% off the sale price. Excluding sales tax, what percent of the original price will Jasmine pay for the MP3 player?

5. What information needs to be included in a response to receive full credit?

6. Write a response that would receive full credit.

Item C
Three houses were originally purchased for $125,000. After each year, the value of each house either increased or decreased. Which house had the least value after the third year? What was the value of that house? Explain your reasoning.

House	Original Cost ($)	Percent Change in Value		
		Year 1	Year 2	Year 3
A	125,000	1%	1%	1%
B	125,000	4%	−2%	−1%
C	125,000	3%	−2%	2%

7. A student wrote this response:

> House A increased 3% over three years. House B increased 1% over three years. House C increased 3% over three years. So, House B had the least value after the third year. Its value increased 1% of $125,000, or $1250, for a total value of $126,250.

What score should the student's response receive? Explain your reasoning.

8. What additional information, if any, should the student's response include in order to receive full credit?

Item D
Kara is trying to save $4500 to buy a used car. She has $3000 in an account that earns a yearly simple interest of 5%. Will she have enough money in her account after 3 years to buy a car? If not, how much more money will she need? Explain your reasoning.

9. What information needs to be included in a response to receive full credit?

10. Write a response that would receive full credit.

Answers
Possible answers:

1. The student should receive 1 point because the student provides a correct answer without giving any explanation.

2. In order to receive full credit, the student needs to show and explain that Job A pays better than Job B. Job A pays $26,000 a year and Job B pays $23,900 a year. Job A pays better.

Job A: $500 × 52 weeks = $26,000 per year

Job B: $200 × 52 weeks = $10,400 per year salary

$7500 × 12 = $90,000 × 15% = $13,500 in expected commission

$10,400 + $13,500 = $23,900 total per year (salary plus commission)

3. Job A pays better: $500 × 4 = $2000. Job B pays ($200 × 4) + (0.15 × $7500): $800 + 1125 = $1925.

4. ≈$8666.67

5. The students should display calculations for finding the percent amounts of the sales and the final price after the original amount has been reduced by both sales.

6. $97.99 − 0.15($97.99) = $83.29, $83.29 − 0.2($83.29) = $66.63; After both sales it costs $66.63.

7. The student should receive 2 points because the student makes major computation errors resulting in an incorrect response.

8. The student needs to actually calculate the value of houses after each year and then compare the value of each house after 3 years. They will find House B has a total value of $126,126.

9. The student needs to apply the simple interest formula with a rate of 5%, and then point out that the final amount after 3 years is less than $4500. The student should also include the amount of money Kara still needs to buy the car.

10. $A = P + Prt$
= 3000 + 3000(0.05)(3)
= 3450
$4500 − $3450 = $1050
No, she will need $1050 more to buy the car.

Organizer

Objective: Provide review and practice for Chapters 1–7.

 Online Edition

Resources

 Assessment Resources
Chapter 7 Cumulative Test

 Focus on California Standards Benchmark Tests and Intervention

 California Standards Practice CD-ROM

go.hrw.com
KEYWORD: MT8CA Practice

Cumulative Assessment, Chapters 1–7

Multiple Choice

1. Which inequality describes the graph?

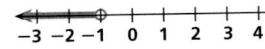
-3 -2 -1 0 1 2 3 4

Ⓐ $-2x + 3 > 5$

Ⓑ $-2x + 3 \geq 5$

Ⓒ $-2x + 3 < 5$

Ⓓ $-2x + 3 \leq 5$

2. A jeweler buys a diamond for $68 and resells it for $298. What is the percent of increase to the nearest percent?

Ⓐ 3%

Ⓑ 33%

Ⓒ 138%

Ⓓ 338%

3. A grocery store sells one dozen ears of white corn for $2.40. What is the unit rate for one ear of corn?

Ⓐ $0.05/ear of corn

Ⓑ $0.20/ear of corn

Ⓒ $1.30/ear of corn

Ⓓ $2.40/ear of corn

4. The people of Ireland drink the most milk in the world. All together, they drink more than 602,000,000 quarts each year. What is this number written in scientific notation?

Ⓐ 60.2×10^5

Ⓑ 602×10^6

Ⓒ 6.02×10^8

Ⓓ 6.02×10^9

5. For which equation is the point a solution to the equation?

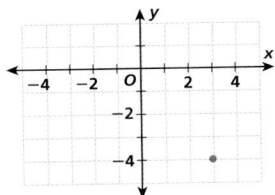

Ⓐ $y = 2x + 1$

Ⓑ $y = 2x - 2$

Ⓒ $y = -x + 1$

Ⓓ $y = -2x + 2$

6. Cara is making a model of a car that is 14 feet long. What other information is needed to find the length of the model?

Ⓐ Car's width

Ⓑ Car's speed

Ⓒ Scale factor

Ⓓ Car's height

7. Which expression represents "twice the difference of a number and 5"?

Ⓐ $2(x + 5)$ Ⓒ $2(x - 5)$

Ⓑ $2x - 5$ Ⓓ $2x + 5$

8. For which equation is $x = -1$ the solution?

Ⓐ $3.3x + 8 = 11.3$

Ⓑ $8.5 - x = 9.5$

Ⓒ $-2.9x + 8 = 5.1$

Ⓓ $8.5 + x = 9.5$

 **California Standards**

Standard	Items
NS1.1	4
NS1.6	2
NS1.7 🔑	10, 13, 15
AF1.1	7
AF1.2	14
AF3.1	17
AF3.3 🔑	5, 11, 16, 18
AF4.0 🔑	8
AF4.1 🔑	1
AF4.2 🔑	12, 18
MG1.1	9
MG1.2	6
MG1.3 🔑	3

 **Teaching Tip**

Multiple Choice Remind students who chose answer **A** or **B** in **item 4** that the first factor of a number written in scientific notation is a number greater than or equal to 1 and less than 10.

Point out to students that **B** and **D** in **item 1** can be eliminated because the graph does not include −1.

Answers

16a.

Chirps/min	100	126	152
Temperature (°F)	63	?	77

18. See 4-Point Response work sample.

9. A pole is 2.5 m tall. About how tall is the pole in feet and inches? (1 m ≈ 39 in.)

  Ⓐ 7 ft 0 in.   Ⓒ 7 ft 6 in.

  Ⓑ 8 ft 0 in.   Ⓓ 8 ft 6 in.

10. Marcus bought a shirt that was discounted 20%. If Marcus paid $20 for the shirt, what was the regular price?

  Ⓐ $25   Ⓒ $16

  Ⓑ $40   Ⓓ $30

 **HOT TIP!** Use logic to eliminate answer choices that are unreasonable. This will help you make an educated guess if you are having trouble with the question.

Gridded Response

11. The slope of the line shown is $\frac{2}{3}$. What is the value of a? **6**

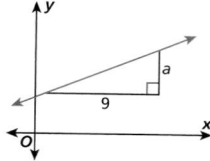

12. Jake is reading a 234-page book. During the past 5 days he has read 90 pages. If he continues reading at the same rate, how many more days will it take him to complete the book? **8 days**

13. Maryann bought a purse that had been marked up 25%. The purse was $36 before markup. What did Maryann pay for the purse? **$45**

14. Evaluate the expression $-2xy + y^2$ when $x = -1$ and $y = 4$. **24**

15. Guillermo invests $180 at a 4% simple interest rate for 6 months. How much money will Guillermo earn in interest? **$3.60**

Short Response

16. Suppose that a linear equation can be used to model the relationship between the outdoor temperature and the number of chirps per minute a bird makes. A bird chirps 100 times per minute at 63°F and 152 times per minute at 77°F.

  a. Create a table to show the given input and output values for the situation.

  b. At what temperature does the bird chirp 126 times per minute? **70°F**

17. The height h that a football is kicked is given by the function $h = -16t^2 + 64t$, where h is in feet and t is in seconds. Find h when t is 0 seconds and when t is 4 seconds. What is the height of the football at these times? *h is 0 when t is 0 and when t is 4; the football is on the ground*

Extended Response

18. A bus travels at an average rate of 50 miles per hour from Nashville, Tennessee, to El Paso, Texas. To find the distance y traveled in x hours, use the equation $y = 50x$.

  a. Make a table of ordered pairs using the input values $x = 1, 2, 3, 4,$ and 5.

  b. Graph the solutions from the table of ordered pairs on a coordinate plane.

  c. Brett leaves Nashville by bus at 6:00 A.M. He needs to be in El Paso by 5:00 A.M. the following day. Nashville is 1100 miles from El Paso. Assuming the bus does not make any stops, will Brett make it on time? Explain how you determined your answer.

Short Response Rubric
Items 16–17

2 Points = The student's answer is an accurate and complete execution of the task or tasks.

1 Point = The student's answer contains attributes of an appropriate response but is flawed.

0 Points = The student's answer contains no attributes of an appropriate response.

Extended Response Rubric
Item 18

4 Points = The student demonstrates a thorough understanding of all concepts and shows all work correctly.

3 Points = The student demonstrates a basic understanding of all concepts, but the work shows some flaws reflecting inattentive execution of mathematical procedures or some misunderstanding of the underlying mathematics.

2 Points = The student demonstrates only a partial understanding of the concepts or procedures embodied in the tasks. The approach may be correct, but the work shows a misunderstanding of one or more important concepts.

1 Point = The student demonstrates a very limited understanding of the concepts or procedures embodied in the tasks. The response may show some understanding but exhibits many flaws or is incomplete.

0 Points = The student provides no response at all or a completely incorrect or uninterpretable response.

Student Work Samples for Item 18

4-Point Response

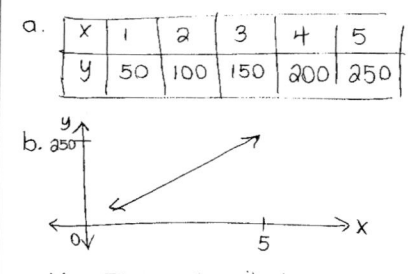

The student correctly made a table of ordered pairs, graphed the solutions, calculated the time the trip will take, and offered an adequate explanation.

3-Point Response

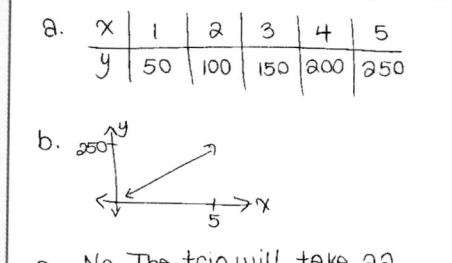

The student answered parts **a** and **b** correctly. However, the student misunderstood the question and therefore the answer to part **c** is incorrect, although adequate.

2-Point Response

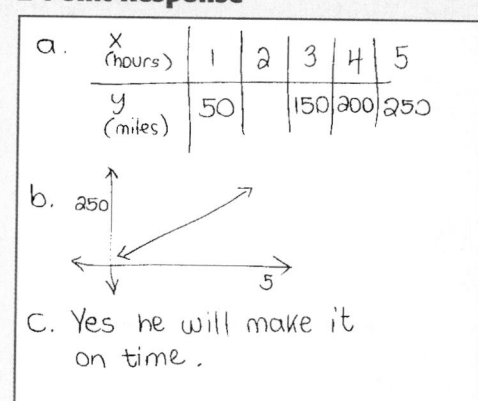

The student correctly made a table in part **a** but it is incomplete. The student did graph the solutions correctly in part **b** but the explanation in part **c** is inadequate.

CHAPTER 8

Foundations of Geometry

✔	Grade-level Standard
◀	Review
▶	Beyond the Standards
A	Assessment
O	Optional

Pacing Guide

☀ **Calendar Planner**
Teacher's **One-Stop** Planner®

Lesson/Lab	California Standards	🕐 Time	Advanced Students	Benchmark* Students	Strategic** Students
8-1 Points, Lines, Planes, and Angles	Prep for MG3.1	50 min	O	◀	◀
LAB Construct Bisectors and Congruent Angles	MG3.1	25 min	✔	✔	✔
8-2 Geometric Relationships	⚿ MG3.6	50 min	✔	✔	✔
8-3 Angle Relationships	Review of 6MG2.1, ⚿ 6MG2.2	50 min	O	O	◀
8-4 Triangles	Review of ⚿ 6MG2.2, ⚿ MG3.3	50 min	O	◀	◀
LAB Identify and Construct Altitudes	MG3.1	25 min	✔	✔	✔
8-5 Coordinate Geometry	⚿ AF3.3, MG3.2	75 min	✔	✔	✔
LAB Angles in Polygons	MG3.1	25 min	✔	✔	✔
Ready to Go On?		25 min	A	A	A
Focus on Problem Solving		25 min	A	A	O
8-6 Congruent Polygons	⚿ MG3.4	50 min	✔	✔	✔
8-7 Transformations	MG3.2	50 min	✔	✔	✔
LAB Combine Transformations	MG3.2	25 min	✔	✔	O
8-8 Tessellations	Ext. of MG3.2	75 min	▶	O	O
Ready to Go On?		25 min	A	A	A
Concept Connection		25 min	A	A	O
Study Guide: Review		50 min	✔	✔	✔
Chapter Test		50 min	A	A	A

* **Benchmark students** are achieving at or near grade level.

** **Strategic students** may be a year or more below grade level and may require additional time for intervention.

Countdown to Mastery, Weeks 15, 16, 17, 18

ONGOING ASSESSMENT and INTERVENTION

DIAGNOSE	PRESCRIBE

Assess Prior Knowledge

Before Chapter 8

Diagnose readiness for the chapter.
Are You Ready? SE p. 375

Prescribe intervention.
Are You Ready? Intervention Skills 58, 60, 68, 82

Formative Assessment

Before Every Lesson

Diagnose readiness for the lesson.
Warm Up TE, every lesson

Prescribe intervention.
Skills Bank SE pp. SB2–SB24
Review for Mastery CRF, Chapters 1–8

During Every Lesson

Diagnose understanding of lesson concepts.
Questioning Strategies Chapter 8
Think and Discuss SE, every lesson
Write About It SE, lesson exercises
Journal TE, lesson exercises

Prescribe intervention.
Reading Strategies CRF, every lesson
Success for ELL Chapter 8
Lesson Tutorial Videos Chapter 8

After Every Lesson

Diagnose mastery of lesson concepts.
Lesson Quiz TE, every lesson
Ready to Go On? SE pp. 404, 420
Test and Practice Generator

Prescribe intervention.
Review for Mastery CRF, every lesson
Problem Solving CRF, every lesson
Ready to Go On? Intervention Chapter 8
Homework Help Online

Before Chapter 8 Testing

Diagnose mastery of concepts in the chapter.
Ready to Go On? SE pp. 404, 420
Focus on Problem Solving SE p. 405
Concept Connection SE p. 421
Section Quizzes AR pp. 145–146
Test and Practice Generator

Prescribe intervention.
Ready to Go On? Intervention Chapter 8
Scaffolding Questions TE p. 421

Before Assessment of California Standards

Diagnose mastery of California standards.
Focus on California Standards: Benchmark Tests
Mastering the Standards SE pp. 428–429
California Standards Practice CD-ROM

Prescribe intervention.
Focus on California Standards: Intervention

Summative Assessment

After Chapter 8

Check mastery of chapter concepts.
Multiple-Choice Tests (Forms A, B, C)
Free-Response Tests (Forms A, B, C)
Performance Assessment AR pp. 147–160
Test and Practice Generator

Prescribe intervention.
Review for Mastery CRF, every lesson
Lesson Tutorial Videos Chapter 8

KEY: **SE** = *Student Edition* **TE** = *Teacher's Edition* **CRF** = *Chapter Resource File* **AR** = *Assessment Resources*  Available on CD-ROM 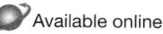 Available online

CHAPTER 8

Supporting the Teacher

Chapter 8 Resource File

Family Involvement
pp. 1–4, 45–48

Practice A, B, C
pp. 5–7, 13–15, 21–23, 29–31, 37–39, 49–51, 57–59, 65–67

Review for Mastery
pp. 8, 16, 24, 32, 40, 52, 60, 68

Challenge
pp. 9, 17, 25, 33, 41, 53, 61, 69

Problem Solving
pp. 10, 18, 26, 34, 42, 54, 62, 70

Reading Strategies ELL
pp. 11, 19, 27, 35, 43, 55, 63, 71

Puzzles, Twisters, and Teasers
pp. 12, 20, 28, 36, 44, 56, 64, 72

Hands-On Lab
pp. 75–80, 84–85

Technology Lab
pp. 73–74, 81–83

Workbooks

Homework and Practice Workbook SPANISH
Teacher's Guide .... pp. 58–65

Know-It Notebook SPANISH
Teacher's Guide .... Chapter 8

Review for Mastery Workbook SPANISH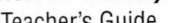
Teacher's Guide .... pp. 58–65

Focus on California Standards: Intervention Workbook SPANISH
Teacher's Guide

Teacher Tools

Power Presentations
Complete PowerPoint® presentations for Chapter 8 lessons

Lesson Tutorial Videos SPANISH
Holt authors Ed Burger and Freddie Renfro present tutorials to support the Chapter 8 lessons.

Teacher's One-Stop Planner SPANISH
Easy access to all Chapter 8 resources and assessments, as well as software for lesson planning, test generation, and puzzle creation

IDEA Works!
Key Chapter 8 resources and assessments modified to address special learning needs

Questioning Strategies .... Chapter 8

Solutions Key .... Chapter 8

Interactive Answers and Solutions

TechKeys   **Lab Resources**

Project Teacher Support   **Parent Resources**

Transparencies

Lesson Transparencies, Volume 2 .... Chapter 8
• Teacher Tools
• Warm Ups
• Teaching Transparencies
• Lesson Quizzes

Know-It Notebook .... Chapter 8
• Vocabulary   • Chapter Review
• Additional Examples   • Big Ideas

Alternate Openers: Explorations .... pp. 58–65

Countdown to Mastery .... pp. 30–35

Technology Highlights for the Teacher

 Power Presentations
Dynamic presentations to engage students. Complete PowerPoint® presentations for every lesson in Chapter 8.

2-1 Solving One-Step Equations

Isolate a variable by using inverse operations which "undo" operations on the variable.

An equation is like a balanced scale. To keep the balance, perform the same operation on both sides.

Inverse Operations	
Operation	**Inverse Operation**
Addition	Subtraction
Subtraction	Addition

 One-Stop Planner SPANISH
Easy access to Chapter 8 resources and assessments. Includes lesson-planning, test-generation, and puzzle-creation software.

 Premier Online Edition SPANISH
Includes Tutorial Videos, Lesson Activities, Lesson Quizzes, Homework Help, Chapter Project and more.

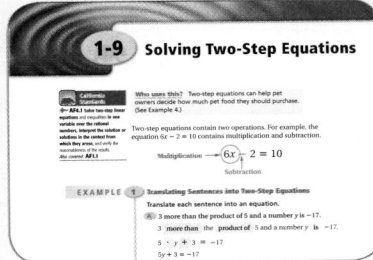

KEY: **SE** = *Student Edition*   **TE** = *Teacher's Edition*   ELL English Language Learners   SPANISH Spanish available   Available on CD-ROM   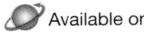 Available online

CHAPTER

8

Universal Access

Teaching tips to help all students appear throughout the chapter. A few that target specific students are included in the lists below.

ENGLISH
LANGUAGE
LEARNERS

Strategic Students

Practice A	CRF, every lesson
Review for Mastery	CRF, every lesson
Reading Strategies	CRF, every lesson
Academic Vocabulary Connections	TE p. 376
Visual	TE p. 385
Ready to Go On? Intervention	Chapter 8
Questioning Strategies	Chapter 8
Know-It Notebook SPANISH	Chapter 8
Homework Help Online	
Lesson Tutorial Videos SPANISH	
Online Interactivities SPANISH	

Special Needs Students

Practice A	CRF, every lesson
Review for Mastery	CRF, every lesson
Reading Strategies	CRF, every lesson
Academic Vocabulary Connections	TE p. 376
Inclusion	TE pp. 385, 393
IDEA Works! Modified Resources	Chapter 8
Ready to Go On? Intervention	Chapter 8
Know-It Notebook SPANISH	Chapter 8
Lesson Tutorial Videos SPANISH	
Online Interactivities SPANISH	

English Learners

Reading Strategies	CRF, every lesson
Vocabulary Review	SE p. 424
Academic Vocabulary Connections	TE p. 376
English Language Learners	TE pp. 379, 389
Language Support	TE p. 379
Success for English Language Learners	Chapter 8
Know-It Notebook SPANISH	Chapter 8
Multilingual Glossary	
Lesson Tutorial Videos SPANISH	

Benchmark Students

Practice B	CRF, every lesson
Problem Solving	CRF, every lesson
Academic Vocabulary Connections	TE p. 376
Ready to Go On? Intervention	Chapter 8
Questioning Strategies	Chapter 8
Know-It Notebook SPANISH	Chapter 8
Homework Help Online	
Online Interactivities SPANISH	

Advanced Students

Practice C	CRF, every lesson
Challenge	CRF, every lesson
Reading and Writing Math EXTENSION	TE p. 377
Concept Connection EXTENSION	TE p. 421
Advanced Learners/GATE	TE p. 393
Ready to Go On? Enrichment	Chapter 8

Technology Highlights for Universal Access

 Lesson Tutorial Videos SPANISH

Starring Holt authors Ed Burger and Freddie Renfro! Live tutorials to support every lesson in Chapter 8.

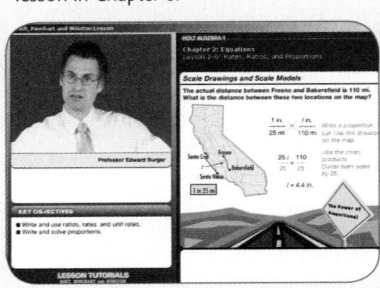

 Multilingual Glossary

Searchable glossary includes definitions in English, Spanish, Vietnamese, Chinese, Hmong, Korean, and other languages.

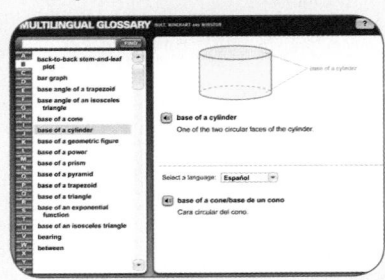

 Online Interactivities SPANISH

Interactive tutorials provide visually engaging alternative opportunities to learn concepts and master skills.

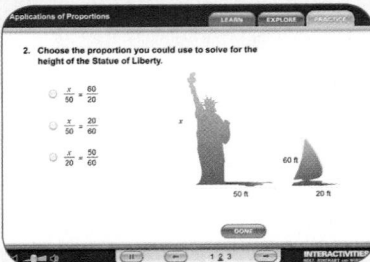

KEY: **SE** = *Student Edition*   **TE** = *Teacher's Edition*   **CRF** = *Chapter Resource File*   SPANISH Spanish available    Available on CD-ROM    Available online

CHAPTER 8

Ongoing Assessment

Assessing Prior Knowledge

Determine whether students have the prerequisite concepts and skills for success in Chapter 8.

Are You Ready? SPANISH .... SE p. 375

Warm Up .... TE, every lesson

Chapter and Standards Assessment

Provide review and practice for Chapter 8 and standards mastery.

Concept Connection .... SE p. 421

Study Guide: Review .... SE pp. 424–426

Mastering the Standards .... SE pp. 428–429

Countdown to Mastery Transparencies .... pp. 30–35

Focus on California Standards: Benchmark Tests

Focus on California Standards: Intervention Workbook SPANISH

***California Standards Practice* CD-ROM** SPANISH

IDEA Works! Modified Worksheets and Tests

Alternative Assessment

Assess students' understanding of Chapter 8 concepts and combined problem-solving skills.

Performance Assessment .... AR pp. 159–160

Portfolio Assessment .... AR p. xxxvi

Chapter 8 Project

Daily Assessment

Provide formative assessment for each day of Chapter 8.

Think and Discuss .... SE, every lesson

Write About It .... SE, lesson exercises

Journal .... TE, lesson exercises

Lesson Quiz .... TE, every lesson

Questioning Strategies .... Chapter 8

IDEA Works! Modified Lesson Quizzes .... Chapter 8

Weekly Assessment

Provide formative assessment for each week of Chapter 8.

Focus on Problem Solving .... SE p. 405

Concept Connection .... SE p. 421

Ready to Go On? SPANISH .... SE pp. 404, 420

Cumulative Assessment .... SE pp. 428–429

Test and Practice Generator SPANISH .... *One-Stop Planner*

Formal Assessment

Provide summative assessment of Chapter 8 mastery.

Section Quizzes .... AR pp. 145–146

Chapter 8 Test SPANISH .... SE p. 427

Chapter Test (Levels A, B, C) .... AR pp. 147–158
　　　　　　　　• Multiple-Choice　• Free-Response

Cumulative Test .... AR pp. 161–164

Test and Practice Generator SPANISH .... *One-Stop Planner*

IDEA Works! Modified Tests .... Chapter 8

Technology Highlights for the Teacher

Are You Ready? SPANISH

Automatically assess readiness and prescribe intervention for Chapter 8 prerequisite skills.

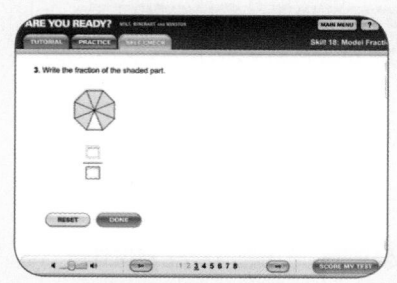

Ready to Go On? SPANISH

Automatically assess understanding of and prescribe intervention for Sections 8A and 8B.

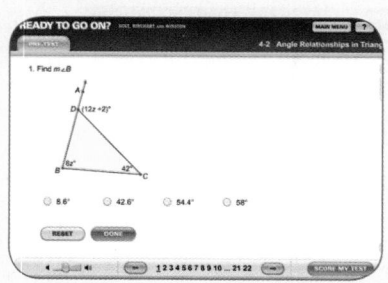

Focus on California Standards: Benchmark Tests and Intervention SPANISH

Automatically assess proficiency with California Grade 7 Standards and provide intervention.

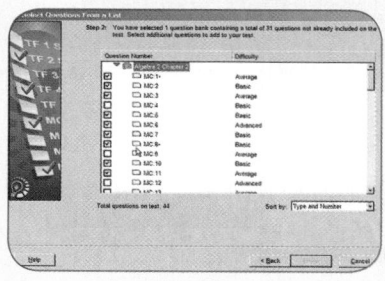

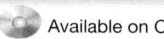
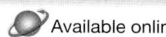

KEY:　**SE** = *Student Edition*　**TE** = *Teacher's Edition*　**AR** = *Assessment Resources*　SPANISH Spanish available　　Available on CD-ROM　　Available online

CHAPTER
8

Formal Assessment

Three levels (A, B, C) of multiple-choice and free-response chapter tests are available in the *Assessment Resources.*

A Chapter 8 Test

C Chapter 8 Test

MULTIPLE CHOICE

A Chapter 8 Test

C Chapter 8 Test

FREE RESPONSE

Modified tests and worksheets found in *IDEA Works!*

MODIFIED FOR IDEA

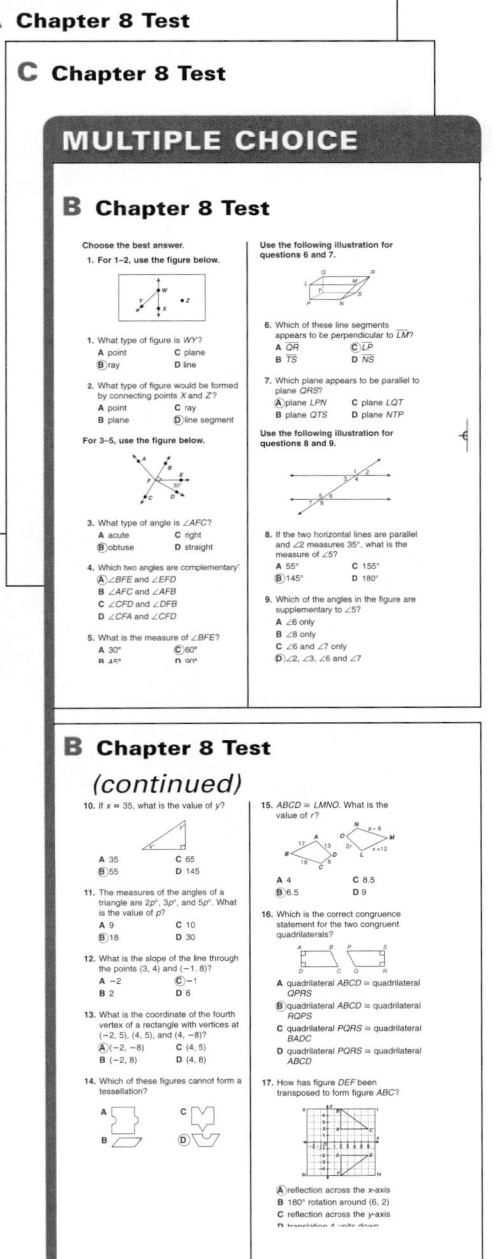

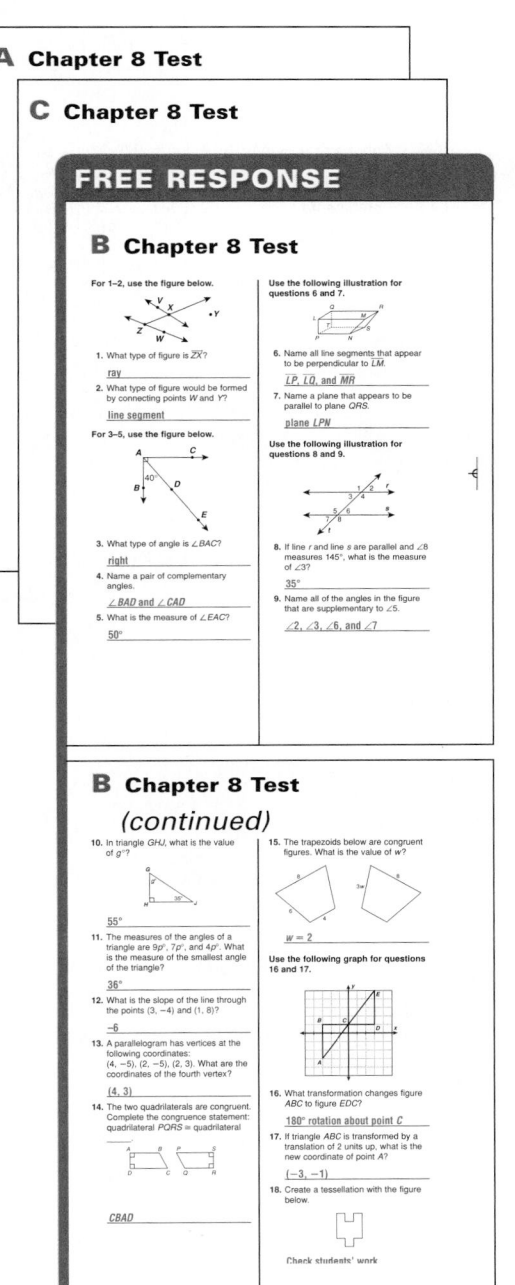

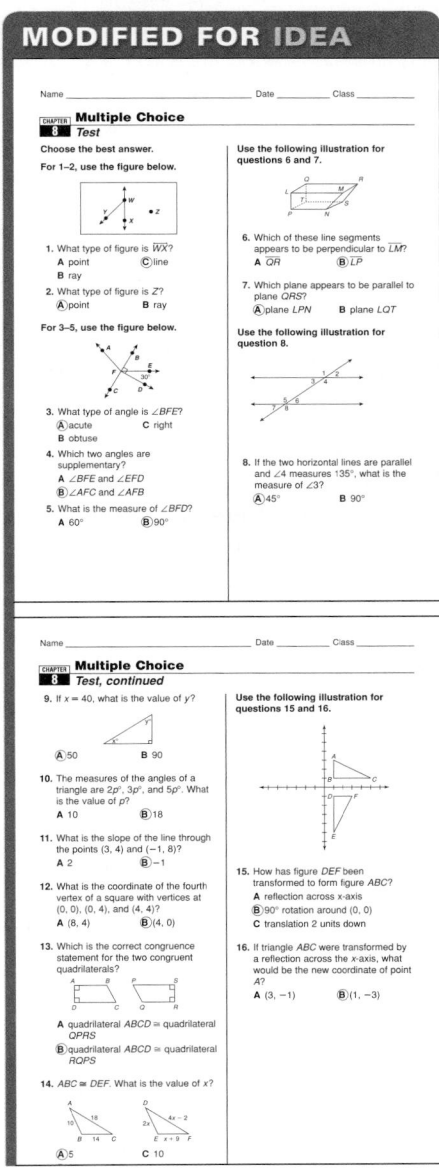

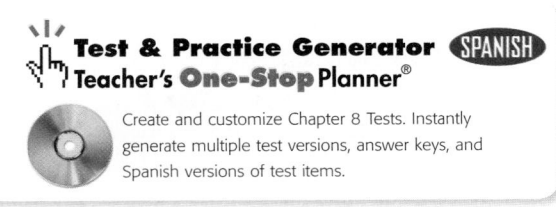

Test & Practice Generator SPANISH
Teacher's **One-Stop** Planner®

Create and customize Chapter 8 Tests. Instantly generate multiple test versions, answer keys, and Spanish versions of test items.

CHAPTER
8

CHAPTER
8

Foundations of Geometry

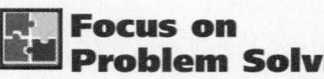

Focus on Problem Solving

On page 405, students focus on understanding problems by restating them in their own words.

CONCEPT CONNECTION On page 421, students use coordinate geometry, transformations, tessellations, and their knowledge of triangles to understand how geometric patterns can be woven into textiles.

CONCEPT CONNECTION

go.hrw.com
Chapter Project Online
KEYWORD: MT8CA Ch8

Math in *California*

The hexagonal columns of California's Devils Postpile were created by the cooling of lava approximately 100,000 years ago. In this chapter, students will learn about various two-dimensional figures and how they are represented in the real world.

Geometric figures can be represented by real-world objects, such as the hexagonal columns of Devils Postpile.

Devils Postpile National Monument, Mammoth Lakes

PROBLEM
SOLVING

Problem Solving Project

Understand, Plan, Solve, and Look Back

Have students:

• Complete The Ultimate Playground worksheet to analyze and create playground equipment using points, lines, planes, and angles.

• Make a chart listing playground equipment and the lines and angles that they see.

Science and Social Studies Connection

Project Resources

All project resources for teachers and students are provided online.

Materials:

• The Ultimate Playground worksheet

• construction materials (straws, toothpicks, chenille stems, tape, glue)

go.hrw.com
Project Teacher Support
KEYWORD: MT8CA PSProject8

ARE YOU READY?

✓ Vocabulary

Choose the best term from the list to complete each sentence.

1. In the __?__ (4, −3), 4 is the __?__, and −3 is the __?__. **ordered pair; x-coordinate; y-coordinate**

2. The __?__ and the __?__ divide the __?__ into four sections. **x-axis; y-axis; coordinate plane**

3. The point (0, 0) is called the __?__. **origin**

4. The point (0, −3) lies on the __?__, while the point (−2, 0) lies on the __?__. **y-axis; x-axis**

coordinate plane
ordered pair
origin
x-axis
x-coordinate
y-axis
y-coordinate

Complete these exercises to review skills you will need for this chapter.

✓ Ordered Pairs

Write the coordinates of the indicated points.

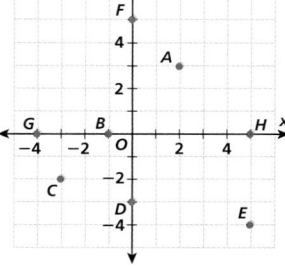

5. point A **(2, 3)**
6. point B **(−1, 0)**
7. point C **(−3, −2)**
8. point D **(0, −3)**
9. point E **(5, −4)**
10. point F **(0, 5)**
11. point G **(−4, 0)**
12. point H **(5, 0)**

✓ Similar Figures

Tell whether the figures in each pair appear to be similar.

13. 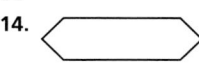 **yes**

14. 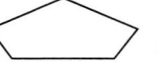 **no**

✓ Solve Equations

Solve each equation.

15. $2p = 18$ **p = 9**
16. $7 + h = 21$ **h = 14**
17. $\frac{x}{3} = 9$ **x = 27**
18. $y − 6 = 16$ **y = 22**
19. $4d + 1 = 13$ **d = 3**
20. $−2q − 3 = 3$ **q = −3**
21. $4(z − 1) = 16$ **z = 5**
22. $x + 3 + 4x = 23$ **x = 4**

Organizer

Objective: Assess students' understanding of prerequisite skills.

Prerequisite Skills

Ordered Pairs

Similar Figures

Solve Equations

Assessing Prior Knowledge

INTERVENTION

Diagnose and Prescribe

Use this page to determine whether intervention is necessary or whether enrichment is appropriate.

Resources

Are You Ready? Intervention and Enrichment Worksheets

Are You Ready? CD-ROM

Are You Ready? Online

my.hrw.com

ARE YOU READY?
Diagnose and Prescribe

 NO INTERVENE

 **YES ENRICH**

Are You Ready? Intervention, Chapter 8			
✓ **Prerequisite Skill**	✎ **Worksheets**	⚽ **CD-ROM**	🪐 **Online**
✓ Ordered Pairs	Skill 68	Activity 68	Diagnose and Prescribe Online
✓ Similar Figures	Skill 82	Activity 82	
✓ Solve Equations	Skills 58 and 60	Activities 58 and 60	

Are You Ready? Enrichment, Chapter 8
✎ **Worksheets**
💿 **CD-ROM**
🪐 **Online**

Organizer

Objective: Help students understand the new concepts they will learn in Chapter 8.

Academic Vocabulary Connections

Becoming familiar with the academic vocabulary on this student page will be helpful to students. Discussing some of the vocabulary terms in the chapter also may be helpful. Possible answers given.

1. The word *equilateral* contains the roots *equi*, which means "equal," and *lateral*, which means "of the side." What do you suppose an **equilateral triangle** is? An equilateral triangle has three sides of equal length.

2. The Greek prefix *poly* means "many," and the root *gon* means "angle." What do you suppose a **polygon** is? A polygon is a shape that has many angles.

3. Think of what **slope** means when you are talking about a hill. How do you think this applies to lines on a coordinate plane? The slope of a line represents the steepness—whether rise or fall—of the line.

The information below "unpacks" the standards. The Academic Vocabulary is highlighted and defined to help you understand the language of the standards. Refer to the lessons listed after each standard for help with the math terms and phrases. The Chapter Concept shows how the standard is applied in this chapter.

California Standard	Academic Vocabulary	Chapter Concept
MG3.1 Identify and construct basic elements of geometric figures (e.g., altitudes, midpoints, diagonals, angle bisectors, and perpendicular bisectors; central angles, radii, diameters, and chords of circles) **by using a compass and straightedge.** (Labs 8-1, 8-5)	**construct** make or draw using tools **elements** parts of	You learn parts of geometric figures such as points, lines, angles, and planes.
MG3.2 Understand and use coordinate graphs to plot simple figures, determine lengths and areas related to them, **and determine their image under translations and reflections.** (Lessons 8-5, 8-7; Lab 8-7)	**plot** draw on a graph **image** a picture	You draw geometric figures on a graph and then draw a picture of the figure after it is moved.
MG3.4 Demonstrate an understanding of conditions that indicate two geometrical figures are congruent and what congruence means about the relationship between the sides and angles of the two figures. (Lesson 8-6)	**indicate** show	You learn how to show that two figures are congruent.
MG3.6 Identify elements of three-dimensional geometric objects (e.g., diagonals of rectangular solids) and **describe how two or more objects are related in space** (e.g., skew lines, the possible ways three planes might **intersect.**) (Lesson 8-2)	**space** a three-dimensional region **intersect** meet or cross	You learn how geometric figures in a three-dimensional region may meet.

Standards AF3.3 and MG3.3 are also covered in this chapter. To see these standards unpacked, go to Chapter 4, p. 166 (MG3.3) and Chapter 7, p. 320 (AF3.3).

Looking Back

Previously, students

- located and named points on a coordinate plane.
- used critical attributes to define similarity.
- used coordinate planes to graph ordered pairs.

In This Chapter

Students will study

- graphing translations and reflections on a coordinate plane.
- using critical attributes to define congruency.
- finding the image of simple figures under translations and reflections on a coordinate plane.

Looking Forward

Students can use these skills

- to create tessellations.
- to find angle measures by using relationships within figures.
- to use coordinate planes to dilate simple figures.

Reading and Writing Math

California Standards
English-Language Arts, Reading 1.3

Writing Strategy: Use Your Own Words

Explaining a concept in your own words will help you better understand it. For example, learning to solve two-step inequalities might seem difficult if the textbook does not use the same words that you would use.

As you work through each lesson, do the following:

- Identify the important concepts.
- Use your own words to explain the concepts.
- Use examples to help clarify your thoughts.

What Miguel Reads

Solving a two-step inequality uses the same inverse operations as solving a two-step equation.

Multiplying or dividing an inequality by a negative number reverses the inequality symbol.

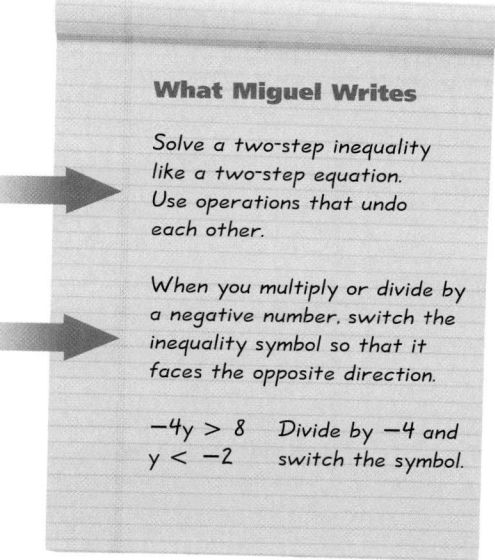

What Miguel Writes

Solve a two-step inequality like a two-step equation. Use operations that undo each other.

When you multiply or divide by a negative number, switch the inequality symbol so that it faces the opposite direction.

$-4y > 8$ Divide by -4 and
$y < -2$ switch the symbol.

Try This

Rewrite each statement in your own words.

1. Like terms can be grouped together because they have the same variable raised to the same power.

2. If an equation contains fractions, consider multiplying both sides of the equation by the least common denominator (LCD) to clear the fractions before you isolate the variable.

3. To solve multi-step equations with variables on both sides, first combine like terms and then clear fractions. Then add or subtract variable terms on both sides so that the variable occurs on only one side of the equation. Then use properties of equality to isolate the variable.

Reading and Writing Math

Organizer

Objective: Help students apply strategies to understand and retain key concepts.

 **Online Edition**

Resources

 Chapter 8 Resource File
Reading Strategies

Writing Strategy: Use Your Own Words

ENGLISH LANGUAGE LEARNERS

Discuss Students may understand a concept better if they can explain it in their own words.

Emphasize that students should practice using their own words to explain math concepts and problems aloud and in writing.

Extend As students work through Chapter 8, ask them to explain concepts, processes, and problems in their own words. Encourage them to use examples to further demonstrate their understanding.

Possible answers to *Try This*

1. Like terms are similar with the same variable to the same power.

2. Multiply an equation with fractions by the LCD to remove the fractions.

3. Combine like terms and clear fractions in a multi-step equation. Then isolate the variable by adding and subtracting terms and using the properties of equality to isolate the variable.

 **California Standards**

Reading 1.3 Clarify word meanings through the use of definition, example, restatement, or contrast.

Plane Geometry

One-Minute Section Planner

Lesson	Lab Resources	Materials
Lesson 8-1 Points, Lines, Planes, and Angles • Classify and name figures. **Preparation for MG3.1**	**Technology Lab 8-1** In *Chapter 8 Resource File*	**Optional** Straightedges (MK)
8-1 Hands-On Lab Construct Bisectors and Congruent Angles • Use a compass and a straightedge to bisect a line segment, bisect an angle, and construct congruent angles. **MG3.0, MG3.1**		**Required** Compasses, protractors (MK), straightedges (MK)
Lesson 8-2 Geometric Relationships • Describe how lines and planes are related in space. **MG3.6**		**Optional** Notebook or computer paper
Lesson 8-3 Angle Relationships • Identify parallel and perpendicular lines and the angles formed by a transversal. **Review of Grade 6** **MG2.1, MG2.2**	**Hands-On Lab 8-3** In *Chapter 8 Resource File*	**Optional** Protractors (MK), straightedges (MK)
Lesson 8-4 Triangles • Find unknown angles and line segment lengths in triangles. **MG3.0, MG3.3**	**Hands-On Lab 8-4** In *Chapter 8 Resource File*	**Optional** Push pins, rubber bands, triangle cutouts
8-4 Hands-On Lab Identify and Construct Altitudes • Use a compass and a straightedge to construct an altitude of a triangle. **MG3.1**		**Required** Compasses (MK), straightedges (MK)
Lesson 8-5 Coordinate Geometry • Identify polygons in the coordinate plane. **AF3.3, MG3.2**		**Optional** Graph paper
8-5 Hands-On Lab Angles in Polygons • Draw diagonals of a polygon to determine the sum of the interior angle measures. **MG3.1**		

MK = *Manipulatives Kit*

Notes

_____

_____

_____

_____

_____

_____

Math Background: Teaching the Standards

FOUNDATIONS OF GEOMETRY 🐻 MG3.1
Lesson 8-1

Points, lines, and planes are often called the building blocks of geometry because they are basic figures that are taken as *undefined terms*. Other figures can then be defined in terms of points, lines, and planes. For example, a line segment is defined to be the part of a line between two points. Notice how this definition uses both *line* and *point*. Figures that are defined in terms of points, lines, and planes can then be used to build definitions of more-complex figures.

CONSTRUCTIONS 🐻 MG3.1
Lessons 8-1 through 8-4

Constructions made with compass and straightedge date to antiquity. Although a compass is often thought of as a tool for making circles, its primary use in constructions is for marking equal distances. The straightedge is used to draw a line through two points or to extend an existing line segment. Unlike a ruler, the unmarked straightedge is never used for measuring distance.

Using these two seemingly primitive tools and working within the limits described above, one can construct virtually all of the fundamental figures of Euclidean geometry, including equilateral triangles, squares, and regular pentagons. Just as many origami figures are based on combinations of a few basic folds, compass-and-straightedge constructions depend on a handful of basic constructions that students should master. These constructions include bisecting a segment, bisecting an angle, and constructing a perpendicular to a line through a point not on the line.

Construction of elements of geometric figures can be considered special cases of the basic constructions. For example, constructing an altitude of a triangle is an application of constructing a perpendicular to a line through a point not on the line. Similarly, constructing the perpendicular bisector of a side of a triangle is a matter of bisecting the segment that forms that side of the triangle.

THREE-DIMENSIONAL SPACE 🐻 ⟵ MG3.6
Lesson 8-2

Many properties of two-dimensional figures are likely to seem familiar and intuitive to students. Understanding relationships among geometric figures in three-dimensional space can be a more formidable task. This increased difficulty is partially due to the challenges of visualizing objects in three dimensions and partially due to the greater complexity of three-dimensional space.

Students can develop the required skills by investigating specific combinations of figures, such as a line and a plane. In this case, students should recognize that there are three possible relationships, as suggested by the figure.

 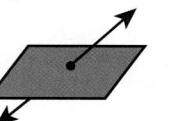 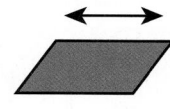

The line lies in the plane.   The line and plane intersect in a point.   The line and plane do not intersect.

THE TRIANGLE SUM THEOREM 🐻 ⟵ 6MG2.2
Lesson 8-4

The Triangle Sum Theorem states that the sum of the measures of the angles of a triangle is 180°. Although students can verify this result by using a number of hands-on techniques—such as tearing off the corners of a paper triangle and arranging the angles to form a straight line—these observations do not constitute a proof. The key ideas in the proof are as follows.

Given △*ABC*, we must show that m∠1 + m∠2 + m∠3 = 180°.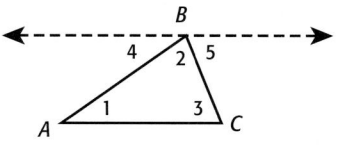

The first step is to construct the line through point *B* that is parallel to $\overline{AC}$. When parallel lines are intersected by a transversal, alternate interior angles are congruent, so ∠1 ≅ ∠4 and ∠3 ≅ ∠5. This means that m∠1 = m∠4 and m∠3 = m∠5. However, m∠4 + m∠2 + m∠5 = 180° because these three adjacent angles form a straight angle. Finally, substitution shows that m∠1 + m∠2 + m∠3 = 180°.

Objective: Students classify and name figures.

Technology Lab
In *Chapter 8 Resource File*

Online Edition
Tutorial Videos

Countdown to Mastery Week 15

Power Presentations
with PowerPoint®

Warm Up

Solve.

1. $x + 30 = 90$ $x = 60$
2. $103 + x = 180$ $x = 77$
3. $32 + x = 180$ $x = 148$
4. $90 = 61 + x$ $x = 29$
5. $x + 20 = 90$ $x = 70$

Also available on transparency

Math Fact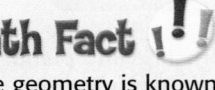

Plane geometry is known among mathematicians as Euclidean geometry. It is named for the Greek mathematician Euclid, who proposed five postulates that laid the foundations for geometry.

8-1 Points, Lines, Planes, and Angles

California Standards

Preparation for MG3.1 Identify and construct basic elements of geometric figures (e.g., altitudes, midpoints, diagonals, angle bisectors, and perpendicular bisectors; central angles, radii, diameters, and chords of circles) by using a compass and straightedge.

Vocabulary
point
line
plane
segment
ray
angle
acute angle
right angle
obtuse angle
straight angle
complementary angles
supplementary angles

Who uses this? Mapmakers use representations of points and lines to create maps. (See Exercises 28–32.)

Points, lines, and planes are the building blocks of geometry. Segments, rays, and angles are defined in terms of these basic figures.

A **point** names a location.	• A	point A
A **line** is perfectly straight and extends forever in both directions.		line ℓ, or $\overleftrightarrow{BC}$
A **plane** is a perfectly flat surface that extends forever in all directions.		plane P, or plane DEF
A **segment**, or line segment, is the part of a line between two points.		$\overline{GH}$
A **ray** is part of a line that starts at one point and extends forever in one direction.		$\overrightarrow{KJ}$

$\overleftrightarrow{BC}$ is read as "line *BC*." $\overline{GH}$ is read as "segment *GH*." $\overrightarrow{KJ}$ is read as "ray *KJ*."

EXAMPLE 1 **Naming Lines, Planes, Segments, and Rays**

Use the diagram to name each figure.

A a line
Possible answers:
$\overleftrightarrow{QS}$, $\overleftrightarrow{QR}$, or $\overleftrightarrow{RS}$
Any 2 points on the line can be used.

B a plane
Possible answers:
plane Z or plane QRT
Any 3 points in the plane that form a triangle can name a plane.

C four segments
Possible answers: $\overline{QR}$, $\overline{RS}$, $\overline{RT}$, $\overline{QS}$
Write the 2 points in any order, for example, $\overline{QR}$ or $\overline{RQ}$.

D five rays
$\overrightarrow{RQ}$, $\overrightarrow{RS}$, $\overrightarrow{RT}$, $\overrightarrow{SQ}$, $\overrightarrow{QS}$
Write the endpoint first.

Caution!
When naming a ray, always write the endpoint first.

---

1 Introduce

Alternate Opener

EXPLORATION

8-1 Points, Lines, Planes, and Angles

In each group, one picture is different from the others. Identify the picture that is different and explain why it is different.

1.

2.

3. Look at the picture for each geometry term and write a real-world example for each term.

Term	Picture	Example
Point	•	
Segment	•—•	
Ray	•—→	
Line	←—→	
Angle	∧	

Think and Discuss
4. **Explain** the difference between a *segment* and a *ray*.
5. **Explain** the difference between a *ray* and a *line*.

Motivate

On the board, draw a square, a triangle, and a rectangle. Ask the students to identify each figure. Explain to them that they are geometric figures comprised of points, line segments, and angles.

Explorations and answers are provided in *Alternate Openers: Explorations Transparencies*.

California Standards

Prep for Measurement and Geometry 3.1

An **angle** (∠) is formed by two rays, or sides, with a common endpoint called the *vertex*. You can name an angle several ways: by its vertex, by its vertex and a point on each ray, or by a number. When three points are used, the middle point must be the vertex.

Angles are usually measured in degrees (°). Since there are 360° in a circle, one degree is $\frac{1}{360}$ of a circle.

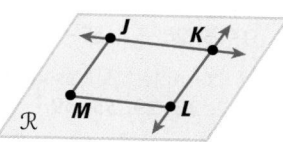

∠Y, ∠XYZ, ∠ZYX, or ∠1

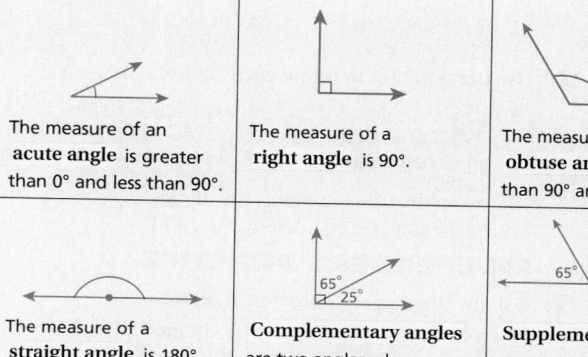

The measure of an **acute angle** is greater than 0° and less than 90°.	The measure of a **right angle** is 90°.	The measure of an **obtuse angle** is greater than 90° and less than 180°.
The measure of a **straight angle** is 180°.	**Complementary angles** are two angles whose measures add to 90°.	**Supplementary angles** are two angles whose measures add to 180°.

EXAMPLE 2 **Classifying Angles**

Reading Math

m∠AEC is read as "the measure of angle *AEC*."

Use the diagram to name each figure.

A a right angle
∠DEC

B two acute angles
∠AED, ∠CEB

C two obtuse angles
∠AEC, ∠DEB   m∠AEC = 150°; m∠DEB = 120°

D a pair of complementary angles
∠AED, ∠CEB   m∠AED + m∠CEB = 60° + 30° = 90°

E two pairs of supplementary angles
∠AED, ∠DEB   m∠AED + m∠DEB = 60° + 120° = 180°
∠AEC, ∠CEB   m∠AEC + m∠CEB = 150° + 30° = 180°

Possible answers to *Think and Discuss*

1. $\overrightarrow{XY}$ is a ray with endpoint *X* that passes through point *Y*; $\overleftrightarrow{XY}$ is a line that passes through points *X* and *Y*.

2. $\overleftrightarrow{JK}$ (or $\overleftrightarrow{KJ}$), $\overrightarrow{JK}$ (or $\overrightarrow{KJ}$), $\overline{JK}$, $\overline{KJ}$

Think and Discuss

1. **Explain** how $\overrightarrow{XY}$ is different from $\overleftrightarrow{XY}$.

2. **Name** all the possible lines, segments, and rays that include points *J* and *K*.

Example 1
Use the diagram to name each figure.

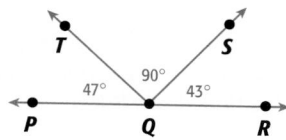

A. a line
$\overleftrightarrow{KL}$ or $\overleftrightarrow{JK}$

B. a plane
plane ℛ or plane *JKL*

C. four segments
$\overline{JK}$, $\overline{KL}$, $\overline{LM}$, $\overline{JM}$

D. four rays
$\overrightarrow{KJ}$, $\overrightarrow{KL}$, $\overrightarrow{JK}$, $\overrightarrow{LK}$

Example 2
Use the diagram to name each figure.

A. a right angle
∠TQS

B. two acute angles
∠TQP, ∠RQS

C. two obtuse angles
∠SQP, ∠RQT

D. a pair of complementary angles
∠TQP, ∠RQS

E. two pairs of supplementary angles
∠TQP, ∠TQR and ∠SQP, ∠SQR
Also available on transparency

2 Teach

Guided Instruction

In this lesson, students learn to classify and name figures. Discuss the concepts of points, lines, and planes as the building blocks of geometry (Teaching Transparency). Segments and rays are parts of lines, and angles consist of rays. Show students how to classify an angle by using the corner of a piece of paper to represent a right angle.

Teaching Tip

Language Support The meanings of *complement* and *supplement* are similar. *Complement* means "completes," and *supplement* means "fills up." Students may remember the difference as follows: "A complementary angle 'completes' a corner (right angle). A supplementary angle 'fills up' a straight line (angle)."

Universal Access
Through Modeling

Give each student a straightedge and have them draw the figure below as follows: Draw line *AC* through point *B*. Then draw ray *BE* perpendicular to line *AC* (using the corner of the straightedge). Draw ray *BD*. Draw line *DF* through point *B*. Then have them classify each angle and identify any special angle pairs.

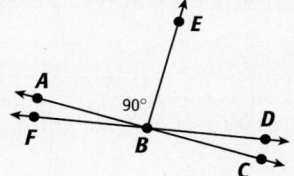

3 Close

ENGLISH LANGUAGE LEARNERS

Summarize

Review the vocabulary terms in the lesson. Ask volunteers to define each term and point out an example in the book. This will reinforce the vocabulary and encourage students to correctly name geometric figures. Discuss ways to remember the names of the different types of angles (e.g., an angle with a small measure is "a cute" little angle, and supplementary begins with *s* for *straight line*).

acute: ∠ABF, ∠DBC, ∠EBD; right: ∠ABE, ∠EBC; obtuse: ∠EBF, ∠FBC; complementary: ∠EBD and ∠DBC; supplementary: ∠ABE and ∠EBC, ∠FBE and ∠EBD

8-1 Exercises

California Standards Practice
Preparation for MG3.1

go.hrw.com
Homework Help Online
KEYWORD: MT8CA 8-1
Parent Resources Online
KEYWORD: MT8CA Parent

Assignment Guide

If you finished Example **1** assign:
Proficient 1–4, 10–13, 28–29, 35–39
Advanced 10–13, 28–32, 35–39

If you finished Example **2** assign:
Proficient 1–22, 28–29, 33–39
Advanced 10–39

Homework Quick Check
Quickly check key concepts.
Exercises: 10, 12, 14, 16, 18

Math Background

Points, lines, and planes are mathematical ideas rather than real objects. A point has no size, a line has no width, and a plane has no thickness. The drawings we use to represent points, lines, and planes are real objects; for example, they are composed of chalk dust or ink on paper. Such idealizations of actual objects are called *mathematical abstractions*.

GUIDED PRACTICE

See Example **1** — Use the diagram to name each figure.

1. a line $\overleftrightarrow{XY}$
2. a plane **plane** A or **plane** XYZ
3. three segments $\overline{XY}, \overline{YZ}, \overline{ZX}$
4. three rays $\overrightarrow{XY}, \overrightarrow{YZ}, \overrightarrow{YX}$

See Example **2** — Use the diagram to name each figure.

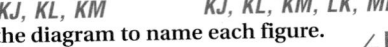

5. a right angle $\angle AEB$ or $\angle DEB$
6. two acute angles $\angle BEC, \angle CED$
7. an obtuse angle $\angle AEC$
8. a pair of complementary angles $\angle BEC$ and $\angle CED$
9. two pairs of supplementary angles $\angle AEB$ and $\angle BED$, $\angle AEC$ and $\angle CED$

INDEPENDENT PRACTICE

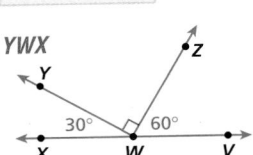

See Example **1** — Use the diagram to name each figure.

10. two lines $\overleftrightarrow{KL}, \overleftrightarrow{KM}$
11. a plane **plane** N or **plane** JKL
12. three segments $\overline{KJ}, \overline{KL}, \overline{KM}$
13. five rays $\overrightarrow{KJ}, \overrightarrow{KL}, \overrightarrow{KM}, \overrightarrow{LK}, \overrightarrow{MK}$

See Example **2** — Use the diagram to name each figure.

14. a right angle $\angle YWZ$
15. two acute angles $\angle VWZ, \angle YWX$
16. two obtuse angles $\angle VWY, \angle ZWX$
17. a pair of complementary angles $\angle VWZ, \angle YWX$
18. two pairs of supplementary angles $\angle VWZ$ and $\angle ZWX$, $\angle VWY$ and $\angle YWX$

PRACTICE AND PROBLEM SOLVING

Extra Practice
See page EP16.

Use the figure for Exercises 19–26. Write *true* or *false*. If a statement is false, rewrite it so it is true.

19. $\angle QUR$ is an obtuse angle.
    False; $\angle QUR$ is a right angle.
20. $\angle 4$ and $\angle 2$ are supplementary.
    true
21. $\angle 1$ and $\angle 6$ are supplementary.
    False; $\angle 1$ and $\angle 6$ are complementary.
22. $\angle 3$ and $\angle 1$ are complementary.
    true
23. If $m\angle 1 = 35°$, then $m\angle 6 = 40°$.
    False; if $m\angle 1 = 35°$, then $m\angle 6 = 55°$.
24. If $m\angle SUN = 150°$, then $m\angle SUR = 150°$.
    False; if $m\angle SUN = 150°$, then $m\angle SUR = 30°$.
25. If $m\angle 1 = x°$, then $m\angle PUQ = 180° - x°$.
    False; if $m\angle 1 = x°$, then $m\angle PUQ = 90° - x°$.
26. $m\angle 1 + m\angle 3 + m\angle 5 + m\angle 6 = 180°$.
    true
27. **Reasoning** Two complementary angles have a ratio of 1:2. What is the measure of each angle? 30°, 60°

California Standards

Standard	Exercises
NS2.1	35–38
MG1.2	39
Prep for MG3.1	1–34

REVIEW FOR MASTERY 8-1

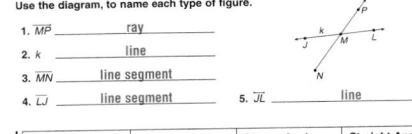

LESSON 8-1 Review for Mastery
Points, Lines, Planes, and Angles

Figure	Description	Diagram	Notation Write	Read
Line	an infinite collection of points with no beginning and no end		$\overleftrightarrow{AB}$ or $\overleftrightarrow{BA}$ or ℓ	line AB, line BA, line ℓ
Line Segment	part of a line, with two endpoints		$\overline{AB}$ or $\overline{BA}$	line segment AB, line segment BA
Ray	part of a line, with one endpoint		$\overrightarrow{AB}$	ray AB

Use the diagram to name each type of figure.

1. $\overline{MP}$ _____ ray
2. k _____ line
3. $\overline{MN}$ _____ line segment
4. $\overline{LJ}$ _____ line segment
5. $\overline{JL}$ _____ line

Acute Angle	Right Angle	Obtuse Angle	Straight Angle
Measures between 0° and 90°.	Measures exactly 90°.	Measures between 90° and 180°.	Measures exactly 180°.

Use the diagram to name each type of angle.

6. $\angle BCD$ _____ right angle
7. $\angle BAD$ _____ acute angle
8. $\angle BDA$ _____ obtuse angle
9. $\angle CDA$ _____ straight angle
10. $\angle BDC$ _____ acute angle
11. $\angle ABC$ _____ acute angle

PRACTICE 8-1

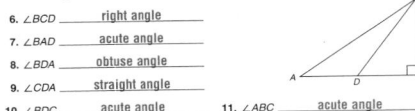

LESSON 8-1 Practice B
Points, Lines, Planes, and Angles

Use the diagram to name each figure.

1. four points
   R, S, T, W
2. a line
   $\overleftrightarrow{WT}$
3. a plane
   Possible answer: RST
4. three segments
   $\overline{RS}, \overline{ST}, \overline{TW},$ or $\overline{RW}$
5. four rays
   $\overrightarrow{AB}, \overrightarrow{AD}, \overrightarrow{DA}, \overrightarrow{DC}$

Use the diagram to name each figure.

6. a right angle
   $\angle NXP, \angle MXR, \angle MXN,$ or $\angle RXP$
7. two acute angles
   $\angle MXS$ and $\angle RXS$
8. two obtuse angles
   $\angle NXS$ and $\angle PXS$
9. a pair of complementary angles
   $\angle RXS$ and $\angle SXM$
10. three pairs of supplementary angles
    Possible answer: $\angle NXP$ and $\angle MXN, \angle RXM$ and $\angle MXN, \angle RXP$ and $\angle PXN$

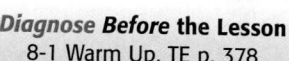
Mapmakers often include a *legend* on the maps they create. The legend explains what each symbol or location on the map represents.

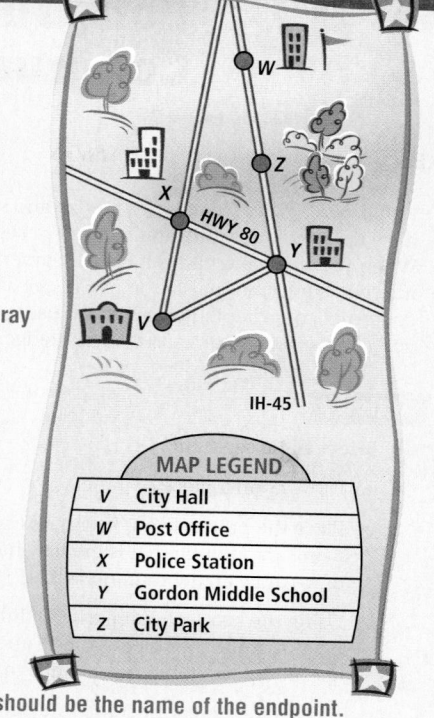

MAP LEGEND

V	City Hall
W	Post Office
X	Police Station
Y	Gordon Middle School
Z	City Park

28. Name the geometric figure suggested by each part of the map.

   a. City Hall and Gordon Middle School **points**

   b. Highway 80 **line**

   c. the section of the road from the park to the post office **line segment**

   d. the road from City Hall past the police station **ray**

29. A student rides her bike from Gordon Middle School to City Hall. She then rides to the city park, first passing through the intersection near the police station and then passing by the school. List the segments on the map that represent her route. $\overline{YV}, \overline{VX}, \overline{XY}, \overline{YZ}$

30. **Critical Thinking** Name a line segment, a ray, and a line that include the same two locations on the map, but do not include the city park. $\overline{XY}, \overrightarrow{XY}, \overleftrightarrow{XY}$

31. ✏ **Write About It** Explain why the road from City Hall that goes past the police station suggests a ray named $\overrightarrow{VX}$ rather than a ray named $\overrightarrow{XV}$. **The first letter in the name of a ray should be the name of the endpoint. *V* is the endpoint of the ray.**

32. ★ **Challenge** What are all the possible names for the line suggested by IH-45? $\overleftrightarrow{YZ}, \overleftrightarrow{YW}, \overleftrightarrow{ZY}, \overleftrightarrow{ZW},$ $\overleftrightarrow{WY}, \overleftrightarrow{WZ}$

![bear] **SPIRAL STANDARDS REVIEW** NS2.1, MG1.2, Prep for MG3.1

33. **Multiple Choice** When two angles are complementary, what is the sum of their measures?

   Ⓐ 90°   Ⓑ 180°   Ⓒ 270°   Ⓓ 360°

34. **Gridded Response** ∠1 and ∠3 are supplementary angles. If m∠1 = 63°, what is m∠3? **117°**

Simplify each expression. Write your answer in exponential form. (Lesson 4-3)

35. $m^3 \cdot m^2$ m^5 36. $w \cdot w^6$ w^7 37. $7^8 \cdot 7^3$ 7^{11} 38. $11^6 \cdot 11^9$ 11^{15}

39. Callie made a postcard that is 5 in. tall by 7 in. wide. A company would like to sell a poster based on the postcard. The poster will be 2 ft tall. How wide will the poster be? (Lesson 5-7) **2.8 ft**

Interdisciplinary  LINK

Science

Exercises 28–32 involve reading and interpreting a map. Students learn to work with maps in middle school social studies programs.

[Teaching Tip] **Multiple Choice** Students may need help remembering the difference between complementary and supplementary angles in **Exercise 33**.

✏ **Journal**

Have students find angles created by objects in the classroom, and then classify the angles as acute, right, or obtuse.

CHALLENGE 8-1

[LESSON] **Challenge**
8-1 *Let's Meet!*

Materials needed: paper strips, index cards, and scissors

1. Use a flat surface such as the top of your desk to represent a plane. Use strips of paper to represent lines. Move the lines around in the plane (**coplanar lines**) to determine the number of intersections that are possible. Summarize your results in a table.

Number of Coplanar Lines	Possible Number of Points of Intersection
2	0 or 1
3	0, 1, 2, or 3
4	0, 1, 3, 4, 5, or 6
5	0, 1, 4, 5, 6, 7, 8, 9, or 10

2. Slit one index card and connect two cards to model two intersecting planes.

   a. What is the intersection of two planes? **a line**

   b. Mark the diagram to illustrate the intersection of the two planes.

3. Using index cards to represent planes, determine the number of intersections that are possible. Summarize your results in a table.

Number of Planes	Possible Number of Lines of Intersection
2	0 or 1
3	0, 1, 2, or 3
4	0, 1, 3, 4, 5, or 6
5	0, 1, 4, 5, 6, 7, 8, 9, or 10

PROBLEM SOLVING 8-1

[LESSON] **Problem Solving**
8-1 *Points, Lines, Planes, and Angles*

Use the flag of the Bahamas to solve the problems.

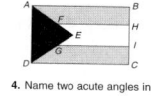

1. Name four points in the flag.
   Possible answers: *A, B, C, D*

2. Name four segments in the flag.
   Possible answers: $\overline{AB}, \overline{BH}, \overline{HI}, \overline{IC}$

3. Name a right angle in the flag.
   Possible answer: ∠ *DAB*

4. Name two acute angles in the flag.
   Possible answers: ∠*AED*, ∠ *DAE*

5. Name a pair of complementary angles in the flag.
   Possible answer: ∠*DAE*, ∠*EAB*

6. Name a pair of supplementary angles in the flag.
   Possible answer: ∠*DGI*, ∠*IGE*

The diagram illustrates a ray of light being reflected off a mirror. The angle of incidence is congruent to the angle of reflection. Choose the letter for the best answer.

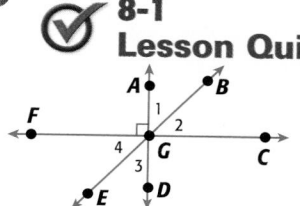

7. Name two rays in the diagram.
   A $\overrightarrow{AM}, \overrightarrow{MB}$ Ⓒ $\overrightarrow{MA}, \overrightarrow{MB}$
   B $\overrightarrow{MA}, \overrightarrow{BM}$ D $\overrightarrow{MA}, \overrightarrow{MB}$

8. Name a pair of complementary angles.
   Ⓕ ∠NMB, ∠BMD   H ∠CMA, ∠AMD
   G ∠AMN, ∠NMB   J ∠CMA, ∠DMB

9. Which angle is congruent to ∠2?
   A ∠1   Ⓒ ∠3
   B ∠4   D none

10. Find the measure of ∠4.
   F 65°   Ⓗ 25°
   G 35°   J 90°

11. Find the measure of ∠1.
   A 65°   Ⓒ 25°
   B 35°   D 90°

12. Find the measure of ∠3.
   F 90°   H 35°
   G 45°   Ⓙ 65°

Power Presentations
with PowerPoint®

✓ **8-1 Lesson Quiz**

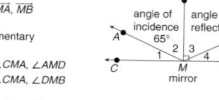

1. Name two lines in the figure.
   Possible answer: $\overleftrightarrow{AD}$ and $\overleftrightarrow{BE}$

2. Name a right angle in the figure.
   Possible answer: ∠*AGF*

3. Name a pair of complementary angles. Possible answer: ∠1 and ∠2

Also available on transparency

Organizer

Use with Lesson 8-1

Objective: Use a compass and a straightedge to bisect a line segment, bisect an angle, and construct congruent angles.

Materials: Compass, straight-edge, protractor

 Online Edition

 Countdown to Mastery Week 15

Teach
Discuss

Perform a few practice exercises with students to get accustomed to a straightedge and compass. Have students create straight lines and bisect them with angles and circles. Explain that near-exact drawings of most geometric figures can be constructed using only these tools.

Construct Bisectors and Congruent Angles

Use with Lesson 8-1

go.hrw.com
Lab Resources Online
KEYWORD: MT8CA Lab8

Congruent figures have the same size and shape. Congruent angles have the same measure, and congruent segments have the same length. When you *bisect* a figure, such as a segment or an angle, you divide it into two congruent parts. You can bisect segments and angles and construct congruent angles without using a protractor or ruler. Instead, you can use a compass and a straightedge.

California Standards

MG3.1 Identify and construct basic elements of geometric figures (e.g., altitudes, midpoints, diagonals, **angle bisectors, and perpendicular bisectors;** central angles, radii, diameters, and chords of circles) **by using a compass and straightedge.**

Activity

1 Bisect a line segment.

  a. Draw $\overline{JS}$ on a piece of paper.

  b. Place the point of your compass on endpoint J and, using an opening that is greater than half the length of $\overline{JS}$, draw an arc that intersects $\overline{JS}$.

  c. Using the same opening as you did in part **b**, place the point of your compass on endpoint S and draw an arc. This arc should intersect the first arc above and below $\overline{JS}$.

  d. Draw a line to connect the intersections of the arcs. Label the intersection of $\overline{JS}$ and the line point K.

Use a ruler to measure $\overline{JS}$, $\overline{JK}$, and $\overline{KS}$. What do you notice?

This bisector of $\overline{JS}$ is a *perpendicular bisector* because all of the angles formed measure 90°.

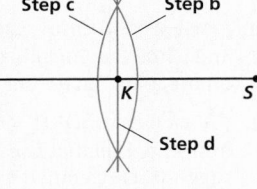

2 Bisect an angle.

  a. Draw an acute angle on a piece of paper. Label the vertex H.

  b. Place the point of your compass on H and draw an arc through both sides of the angle. Label points G and E where the arc crosses each side of the angle.

  c. Without changing your compass opening, draw intersecting arcs from point G and point E. Label the point of intersection D.

  d. Draw $\overrightarrow{HD}$.

Use your protractor to measure angles GHE, GHD, and DHE. What do you notice?

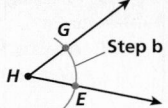

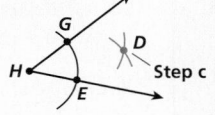

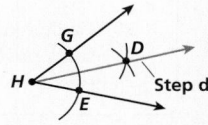

Close
Key Concept

You can use a compass and straightedge to bisect line segments and angles, and to construct congruent angles.

Assessment

1. Draw an angle and construct another angle that is congruent.

Check students' work.

2. Bisect the angle you constructed in problem 1.

Check students' work.

Answers to *Activity*

1. The lengths of $\overline{JK}$ and $\overline{KS}$ are the same, and they are both exactly half the length of $\overline{JS}$.

2. Angles GHD and DHE have the same measure, and they both have exactly half the measure of angle GHE.

California Standards

Measurement and Geometry 3.1
Also covered:
Measurement and Geometry
3.0 Students know the Pythagorean theorem and **deepen their understanding of plane** and solid **geometric shapes by constructing figures that meet given conditions** and by identifying attributes of figures.

3 Construct congruent angles.

a. Draw an angle on your paper. Label the vertex B.

b. To construct a congruent angle, begin by drawing a ray, and label its endpoint C.

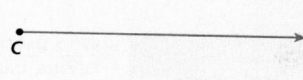

c. With your compass point on B, draw an arc that intersects both sides of your angle. Label the points of intersection A and M.

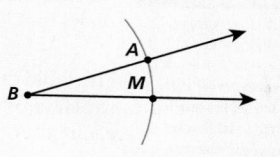

d. With the same compass opening, place the compass point on C and draw an arc through the ray. Label point D where the arc crosses the ray.

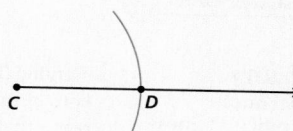

e. Set your compass opening to AM.

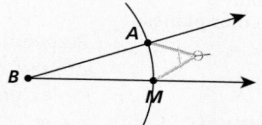

f. With the same compass opening, place your compass point on D, and draw another arc intersecting the first arc. Label the intersection F. Draw $\overrightarrow{CF}$.

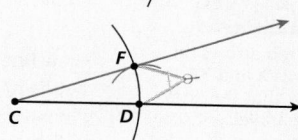

Use your protractor to measure $\angle ABM$ and $\angle FCD$. What do you notice?

Think and Discuss

1. How many bisectors would you use to divide an angle into four equal parts? **3 bisectors**

2. An 88° angle is bisected, and then each of the two angles formed are bisected. What is the measure of each of the smaller angles formed? **22°**

Try This

Use a compass and a straightedge to perform each construction.

1. Bisect a line segment.

2. Trace and then bisect angle GOB.

3. Construct an angle congruent to angle GOB.

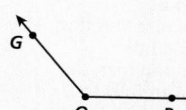

Answer to *Activity*

3. Angles ABM and FCD have the same measure.

Possible answers to *Try This*

1.

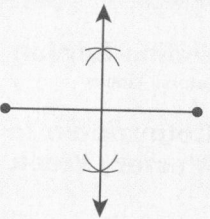

Check students' work.

2.

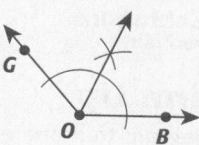

Check students' work.

3.

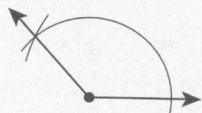

Check students' work.

Objective: Students describe how lines and planes are related in space.

Online Edition
Tutorial Videos

Countdown to Mastery Week 16

Power Presentations
with PowerPoint®

Warm Up

Use the diagram to name each figure.

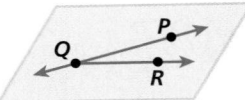

1. three points P, Q, R
2. a line $\overrightarrow{PQ}$
3. a plane   plane PQR
4. three rays $\overrightarrow{PQ}, \overrightarrow{QP}, \overrightarrow{QR}$
5. two segments $\overline{QP}, \overline{QR}$

Also available on transparency

Math Humor

Q: What do you call lines that are neither parallel nor intersecting, but that are good to eat?

A: Stew lines

8-2 **Geometric Relationships**

California Standards

◆━ **MG3.6** Identify elements of three-dimensional geometric objects (e.g., diagonals of rectangular solids) and **describe how two or more objects are related in space** (e.g., skew lines, the possible ways three planes might intersect).

Who uses this? Some artists, such as Sol LeWitt, base their designs on the different ways that lines and planes can intersect.

The table describes some ways in which two lines may be related to each other.

©2008 Sol LeWitt/Artists Rights Society (ARS), New York

Vocabulary
parallel lines
perpendicular lines
skew lines
parallel planes
perpendicular planes

Reading Math

The red arrows on lines WX and YZ show that the lines are parallel.

Parallel lines are lines in the same plane that never intersect.	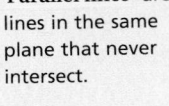	Line *WX* is parallel to line *YZ*. $\overleftrightarrow{WX} \parallel \overleftrightarrow{YZ}$
Perpendicular lines intersect to form 90° angles, or right angles.	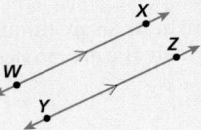	Line *RS* is perpendicular to line *TU*. $\overleftrightarrow{RS} \perp \overleftrightarrow{TU}$
Skew lines are lines that lie in different planes. They are neither parallel nor intersecting.		Line *AB* and line *ML* are skew lines. $\overleftrightarrow{AB}$ and $\overleftrightarrow{ML}$ are skew.

EXAMPLE 1 **Identifying Lines in Space**

Identify two lines that have the given relationship.

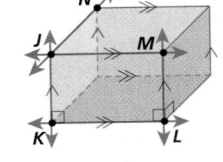

Caution!

Two lines may be perpendicular even though they do not appear to be perpendicular. Use the markings on the drawings and read the problem carefully to determine which lines are perpendicular.

A parallel lines
$\overleftrightarrow{JM} \parallel \overleftrightarrow{KL}$

The lines are in the same plane and do not intersect.

B perpendicular lines
$\overleftrightarrow{JK} \perp \overleftrightarrow{KL}$

The lines intersect to form 90° angles.

C skew lines
$\overleftrightarrow{JN}$ and $\overleftrightarrow{ML}$

The lines lie in different planes. They are neither parallel nor intersecting.

---

1 **Introduce**
Alternate Opener

EXPLORATION

8-2 **Geometric Relationships**

Tell whether the lines in each diagram appear to be *parallel, perpendicular,* or *skew* by putting a check mark in the appropriate box.

	Parallel Lines (never cross each other)	Perpendicular Lines (cross each other at 90° angles)	Skew Lines (do not cross and are not parallel)
1.			
2.			
3.			
4.			

Think and Discuss

5. **Discuss** a major difference between the lines in numbers 1–3 and the lines in number 4.

Motivate

Fold a sheet of paper in half in one direction, and then fold it in half in the other direction. Unfold the paper and ask students what they notice about the lines formed. They intersect. Ask students what type of angles are formed by the intersection. right angles Fold a second sheet of paper in half in one direction, and then fold it in half again in the same direction. Unfold the paper and ask students what they notice about these lines. They do not intersect. Tell students they will learn vocabulary for describing pairs of lines.

Explorations and answers are provided in *Alternate Openers: Explorations Transparencies.*

Like lines, planes may be parallel or perpendicular, but they cannot be skew.

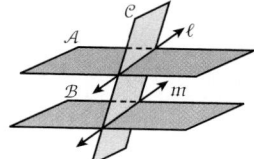

Parallel planes are planes that do not intersect.

Plane $\mathcal{M}$ is parallel to plane $\mathcal{N}$.

Plane $\mathcal{M} \parallel$ plane $\mathcal{N}$.

Perpendicular planes are planes that intersect to form right angles.

Plane $\mathcal{R}$ is perpendicular to plane $\mathcal{S}$.

Plane $\mathcal{R} \perp$ plane $\mathcal{S}$.

The intersections of planes may form parallel or perpendicular lines. In the figure, planes A and B are parallel. Plane C intersects planes A and B, forming a pair of parallel lines, ℓ and m.

EXAMPLE 2 Identifying Planes in Space

Identify two planes that appear to have the given relationship.

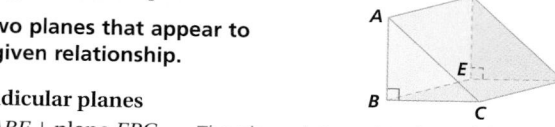

Remember!

A plane may be named by any three points in the plane that are not on the same line.

A perpendicular planes
   plane $ABE \perp$ plane EBC *The planes intersect to form right angles.*

B parallel planes
   plane $ABC \parallel$ plane DEF *The planes do not intersect.*

C neither perpendicular nor parallel
   plane ABE and plane DAC *The planes intersect, but they do not form right angles.*

Think and Discuss

1. **Give an example** of parallel lines, perpendicular lines, and skew lines found in your classroom.

2. **Determine** whether two lines must be parallel if they do not intersect. Explain.

3. **Explain** whether two lines can be both parallel and skew.

4. **Describe** a real-world example of parallel planes.

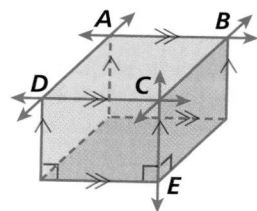
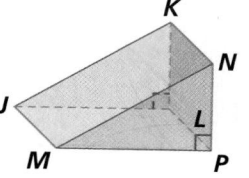

2 Teach

Guided Instruction

In this lesson, students learn to describe how lines and planes are related in space. As you present the material, ask students to point out classroom examples for each type of line relationship and plane relationship.

Teaching Tip **Visual** Understanding the concept of skew lines calls for thinking in three dimensions. You may wish to use yardsticks to show students a three-dimensional model of skew lines.

Universal Access
Through Graphic Organizers

Work with students to create a flowchart that shows how to describe a pair of lines.

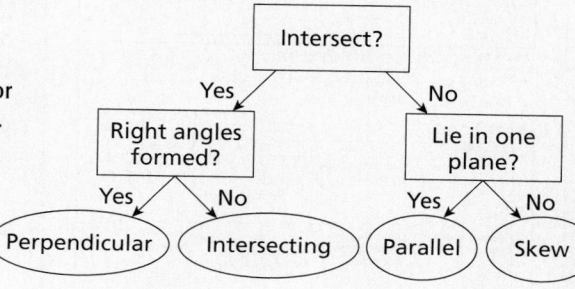

3 Close

Summarize

Ask students these questions to review the vocabulary in the lesson.

- What do you call lines that intersect to form 90° angles? perpendicular
- What do you call lines in the same plane that never intersect? parallel
- What do you call lines that do not lie in the same plane and never intersect? skew

Teaching Tip 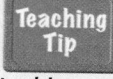 **Inclusion** Point out that two lines may intersect without forming 90° angles. In this case, the lines are neither parallel nor perpendicular.

go.hrw.com
Homework Help Online
KEYWORD: MT8CA 8-2
Parent Resources Online
KEYWORD: MT8CA Parent

Assignment Guide

If you finished Example **1** assign:
Proficient 1–3, 7–9, 13–16, 27,
29–33
Advanced 7–9, 16–20, 27, 29–33

If you finished Example **2** assign:
Proficient 1–16, 18–24 even, 27–33
Advanced 7–33

Homework Quick Check

Quickly check key concepts.
Exercises: 8, 10, 12, 16, 18

Answers

16, 23. See p. A7.

24. Perpendicular lines intersect but skew lines do not.

25. Similarities: neither parallel lines nor planes intersect; differences: parallel lines lie in one plane and parallel planes lie in different planes.

26. Yes; if line *r* does not intersect line *q*, then line *r* ∥ line *q*. This would mean line *r* ∥ line *p*, which contradicts the statement that line *r* intersects line *p*.

Math Background

Based on our experiences in everyday life, it seems reasonable to assume that parallel lines exist. This assumption is made explicit in Euclid's fifth postulate, now known as the Parallel Postulate. This postulate, set forth as a statement to be accepted without proof, offers the idea that through any point not on a given line, there exists exactly one line that can be drawn parallel to the given line.

In the nineteenth century, mathematicians came to realize that new geometries could be created that use alternative versions of the Parallel Postulate. These are known as non-Euclidean geometries.

California Standards

Standard	Exercises
AF2.2	29–32
AF4.2 ⚷	33
MG3.6 ⚷	1–28

1–3, 5–9, 11–12. Possible answers given.

GUIDED PRACTICE

See Example **1** Identify two lines that have the given relationship. $\overrightarrow{DG} \perp \overrightarrow{GH}$

1. perpendicular lines
2. skew lines $\overrightarrow{EF}$ and $\overrightarrow{GH}$
3. parallel lines $\overrightarrow{DG} \parallel \overrightarrow{EF}$

See Example **2** Identify two planes that appear to have the given relationship.

4. parallel planes plane *UVW* ∥ plane *XYZ*
5. perpendicular planes plane *UVY* ⊥ plane *WVY*
6. neither parallel nor perpendicular plane *UWZ* and plane *VWZ*

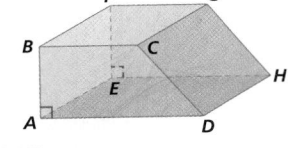

INDEPENDENT PRACTICE

See Example **1** Identify two lines that have the given relationship.

7. parallel lines $\overrightarrow{NP} \parallel \overrightarrow{RS}$
8. skew lines $\overrightarrow{NP}$ and $\overrightarrow{RQ}$
9. perpendicular lines $\overrightarrow{RS} \perp \overrightarrow{ST}$

See Example **2** Identify two planes that appear to have the given relationship.

10. parallel planes plane *BAD* ∥ plane *FEH*
11. perpendicular planes plane *BAE* ⊥ plane *EAD*
12. neither parallel nor perpendicular plane *EAD* and plane *CDH*

PRACTICE AND PROBLEM SOLVING

Extra Practice
See page EP16.

Describe each pair of lines as parallel, perpendicular, skew, or none of these.

13. none of these

14. parallel

15. skew

16. Capitol Street intersects 1st, 2nd, and 3rd Avenues, which are parallel to each other. West Street and East Street are perpendicular to 2nd Avenue.
  a. Draw a map showing the six streets.
  b. Suppose East and West Streets were perpendicular to Capitol Street rather than 2nd Avenue. Draw a map showing the streets.

REVIEW FOR MASTERY 8-2

PRACTICE 8-2

The lines in the figure intersect to form a rectangular box. Use the figure for Exercises 17–21.

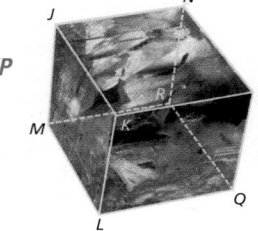

17. Name all the lines that are parallel to $\overleftrightarrow{AD}$. $\overleftrightarrow{BC}$, $\overleftrightarrow{FG}$, and $\overleftrightarrow{EH}$.

18. Name all the lines that are perpendicular to $\overleftrightarrow{FG}$. $\overleftrightarrow{BF}$, $\overleftrightarrow{EF}$, $\overleftrightarrow{CG}$, and $\overleftrightarrow{HG}$.

19. Name two lines that are skew lines. Possible answer: $\overleftrightarrow{AD}$ and $\overleftrightarrow{GH}$

20. Name all the lines that are not parallel to and do not intersect $\overleftrightarrow{DH}$. $\overleftrightarrow{AB}$, $\overleftrightarrow{EF}$, $\overleftrightarrow{BC}$, and $\overleftrightarrow{FG}$

21. Name all the planes that are perpendicular to plane *ABC*. plane *ABF*, plane *FBC*, plane *DAE*, and plane *DCG*

22. Science Calcite is one of the most common minerals on Earth. Name the pairs of planes that appear to be parallel in the calcite crystal at right. plane *JKL* || plane *NPQ*, plane *MJN* || plane *LKP*, and plane *MLQ* || plane *JKP*

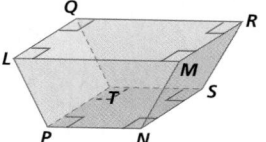

23. Reasoning Is it possible for three planes to intersect in a single straight line? If so, make a sketch. If not, explain why such an intersection is not possible. **Yes**

 24. What's the Error? A student identified a pair of lines in the classroom and claimed that they were both perpendicular and skew. Explain the error.

25. Write About It Explain the similarities and differences between parallel lines and parallel planes.

26. Challenge Lines *p*, *q*, and *r* are in a plane. Lines *p* and *q* are parallel, and line *r* intersects line *p*. Does line *r* intersect line *q*? Explain.

SPIRAL STANDARDS REVIEW
AF2.2, AF4.2, MG3.6

27. Multiple Choice Which of the following line segments appears to be skew to $\overline{MR}$?

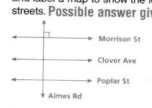

Ⓐ $\overline{LQ}$ Ⓒ $\overline{RQ}$
Ⓑ $\overline{QT}$ Ⓓ $\overline{SR}$

28. Multiple Choice Which plane appears to be parallel to plane *LPN*?

Ⓐ plane *MNS* Ⓑ plane *QLM* Ⓒ plane *TPN* Ⓓ plane *QTS*

Simplify. (Lesson 4-4)

29. $(6m^3)^2$ $36m^6$ **30.** $(-2a^3b^5)^4$ $16a^{12}b^{20}$ **31.** $(3x^4y)^3$ $27x^{12}y^3$ **32.** $(-2p^7q^2r^3)^3$ $-8p^{21}q^6r^9$

33. The table shows the number of Calories in melon slices of various weights. Determine whether the data set shows direct variation. (Lesson 7-9) **Yes**

Weight (oz)	3.5	7	10.5	14
Calories (Cal)	25	50	75	100

CHALLENGE 8-2

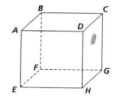
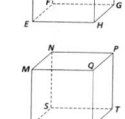
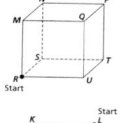
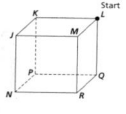
PROBLEM SOLVING 8-2

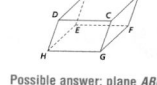
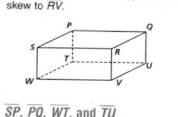
Teaching Tip **Multiple Choice** In Exercise 27, students can eliminate choices **C** and **D** because these segments contain point *R* and therefore intersect $\overline{MR}$.

Journal

Have students draw and label parallel, perpendicular, and skew lines and have them provide a brief explanation of each. Ask students to describe how they drew the skew lines on their paper.

✓ 8-2 Lesson Quiz

Identify two lines that have the given relationship.

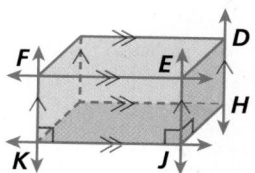

1. parallel lines $\overrightarrow{FK} || \overrightarrow{EJ}$
2. perpendicular lines $\overrightarrow{FK} \perp \overrightarrow{KJ}$
3. skew lines $\overrightarrow{FE}$ and $\overrightarrow{DH}$

Identify two planes that appear to have the given relationship.

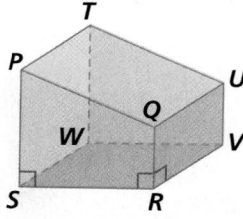

4. parallel planes plane *SPQ* || plane *WTU*
5. perpendicular planes plane *PSW* ⊥ plane *WSR*
6. neither perpendicular nor parallel plane *PQU* and plane *RQU*

Also available on transparency

Objective: Students identify parallel and perpendicular lines and the angles formed by a transversal.

Hands-On Lab
In *Chapter 8 Resource File*

Online Edition
Tutorial Videos, Interactivities

Countdown to Mastery Week 16

Power Presentations
with PowerPoint®

Warm Up

Complete each sentence.

1. Angles whose measures have a sum of 90° are __?__.
   complementary

2. A part of a line that starts at one point and extends forever in one direction is called a __?__.
   ray

3. Angles whose measures have a sum of 180° are __?__.
   supplementary

4. A part of a line between two points is called a __?__.
   segment

Also available on transparency

California Standards

Review of Grade 6
Measurement and Geometry ⊶ **2.2**

Also covered:

Measurement and Geometry
2.1 Identify angles as vertical, adjacent, complementary, or supplementary and provide descriptions of these terms.

 California Standards

Review of Grade 6
⊶ **MG2.2 Use the properties of** complementary and **supplementary angles** and the sum of the angles of a triangle **to solve problems involving an unknown angle.**
Also covered: **6MG2.1**

Who uses this? Submarine builders use parallel mirrors when making periscopes. (See Exercise 24.)

You can use what you know about complementary and supplementary angles to find missing angle measurements.

EXAMPLE 1 **Finding Angle Measures**

Use the diagram to find each angle measure.

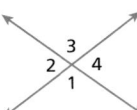

A If m∠2 = 75°, find m∠4.

$$m\angle 1 = 180° - 75°$$ ∠2 and ∠1 are supplementary.
$$= 105°$$
$$m\angle 4 = 180° - 105°$$ ∠1 and ∠4 are supplementary.
$$= 75°$$

So m∠2 = m∠4, or ∠2 ≅ ∠4.

Writing Math

Congruent angles have the same measure. The symbol for congruence is ≅, which is read as "is congruent to."

B If m∠3 = x°, find m∠1.

$$m\angle 4 = 180° - x°$$ ∠3 and ∠4 are supplementary.
$$m\angle 1 = 180° - m\angle 4$$ ∠1 and ∠4 are supplementary.
$$= 180° - (180° - x°)$$ Substitute 180° − x° for m∠4.
$$= 180° - 180° + x°$$ Distributive Property
$$= x°$$ Simplify.

So m∠1 = m∠3, or ∠1 ≅ ∠3.

The angles in Example 1 are examples of *adjacent angles* and *vertical angles*. These angles have special relationships because of their positions.

- **Adjacent angles** have a common vertex and a common side, but no common interior points. Angles 1 and 2 in the diagram above are adjacent angles.

- **Vertical angles** are the *nonadjacent* angles formed by two intersecting lines. Angles 1 and 3 are vertical angles. In Example 1, you found that vertical angles have the same measure, so vertical angles are congruent.

---

1 **Introduce**

Alternate Opener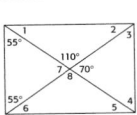

EXPLORATION

8-3 **Angle Relationships**

A flag is made by drawing two diagonals from corner to corner on a rectangular piece of cloth.

The diagonals on the flag form adjacent and vertical angles.

Adjacent angles have a common vertex and side, but no common interior points. **Vertical angles** are nonadjacent angles formed by two intersecting lines.

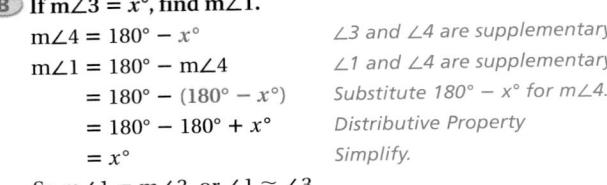

Find the measures of the numbered angles on the flag.

1. m∠1 = _____   2. m∠2 = _____
3. m∠3 = _____   4. m∠4 = _____
5. m∠5 = _____   6. m∠6 = _____
7. m∠7 = _____   8. m∠8 = _____

Think and Discuss

9. **Explain** how you found the measure of ∠1.
10. **Explain** how you found the measure of ∠7.
11. **Make** a conjecture about the measure of vertical angles. Then make a conjecture about the measure of adjacent angles.

Motivate

To introduce students to the concept of parallel and perpendicular lines, ask them to describe the lines that separate the panes in a window or the lines between tiles on a floor or wall. Ask a volunteer to draw a tic-tac-toe game on the board, and then ask students to describe the lines.

Explorations and answers are provided in *Alternate Openers: Explorations Transparencies.*

A **transversal** is a line that intersects two or more lines that lie in the same plane. Transversals to parallel lines form angle pairs with special properties.

Alternate interior angles

Alternate exterior angles

Corresponding angles

PROPERTIES OF TRANSVERSALS TO PARALLEL LINES

If two parallel lines are intersected by a transversal,
- corresponding angles are congruent,
- alternate interior angles are congruent,
- and alternate exterior angles are congruent.

If the transversal is perpendicular to the parallel lines, all of the angles formed are congruent 90° angles.

EXAMPLE **Finding Angle Measures of Parallel Lines Cut by Transversals**

In the figure, line *a* ‖ line *b*. Find the measure of each angle.

A ∠4

m∠4 = 74°   *Corresponding angles are congruent.*

B ∠3

m∠3 + 74° =	180°	*∠3 is supplementary to the 74° angle.*
− 74°	− 74°	*Subtract 74° from both sides.*
m∠3 =	106°	*Simplify.*

C ∠5

m∠5 = 106°   *∠3 and ∠5 are alternate interior angles, so they are congruent.*

Think and Discuss

1. Tell how many different angles would be formed by a transversal intersecting three parallel lines. How many different angle measures would there be?

2. Explain how a transversal could intersect two other lines so that corresponding angles are *not* congruent.

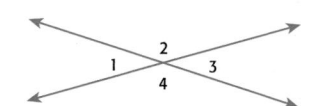
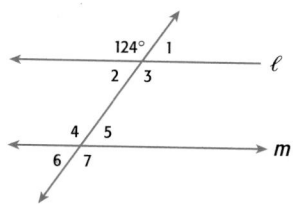

Possible answers to Think and Discuss

1. 12 angles; at most, two different angle measures (one, if the transversal is perpendicular)

2. when the two other lines are not parallel

② Teach

Guided Instruction

In this lesson, students learn to identify parallel and perpendicular lines and the angles formed by a transversal. Before reviewing **Example 1,** have students look at the diagram and try to identify which angles are congruent. Encourage students to use their knowledge of vertical angles. After students have measured the angles, encourage them to state a hypothesis about the angles formed by parallel lines and a transversal. Before presenting **Example 2,** review the definitions of complementary and supplementary angles. You may want to use a Teaching Transparency to introduce alternate interior, alternate exterior, and corresponding angles.

ENGLISH LANGUAGE LEARNERS

Universal Access
Through Auditory Cues

Have students write a set of instructions that describe how to create a pair of parallel lines cut by a transversal. Have students read their instructions aloud to a partner and have the partner follow the instructions to ensure that they are accurate.

Possible answer: Draw two intersecting lines. Measure one of the angles formed by the two intersecting lines. Draw a third line intersecting one of the original lines to form an angle congruent to the angle you measured. This line should be parallel to one of the original lines. Measure all angles in the diagram.

③ Close

Summarize

Show the following diagram. Note that line *a* ‖ line *b*. Ask students to find the measure of each numbered angle, and ask them to explain how they found each answer.

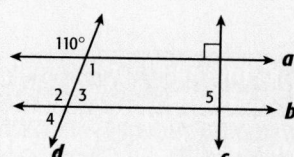

Possible answers: m∠1 and m∠2 = 110° because all obtuse angles formed by the transversal are congruent. m∠3 and m∠4 = 70° because all acute angles are supplementary to any obtuse angle. m∠5 = 90° because the transversal is perpendicular.

8-3 Angle Relationships   **389**

Assignment Guide

If you finished Example **1** assign:
Proficient 1–2, 7–8, 30–33
Advanced 7–8, 30–33

If you finished Example **2** assign:
Proficient 1–20, 24, 28–33
Advanced 7–33

Homework Quick Check

Quickly check key concepts.
Exercises: 8, 10, 12, 14, 16

Answers

20, 23. See p. A7.

21. Possible answer:

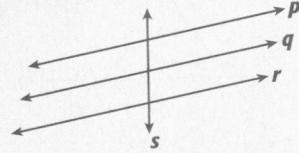

22. Possible answer:

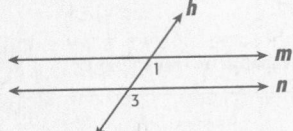

Math Background

There are various ways to prove that two lines are parallel. If two lines are cut by a transversal and any of the following is true, then those two lines are parallel:

- A pair of corresponding angles are congruent.
- A pair of alternate interior angles are congruent.
- A pair of alternate exterior angles are congruent.
- A pair of same-side interior angles are supplementary.
- The transversal is perpendicular to both lines.

California Standards

Standard	Exercises
6MG2.1	15
6MG2.2 🔑	1–2, 3, 7–8, 12, 17, 28–29
7AF3.1	32–33
7AF3.3 🔑	30–31

8-3 Exercises

🐻 **California Standards Practice**
Review of 6MG2.1 and
🔑 6MG2.2

🌐 **go.hrw.com**
Homework Help Online
KEYWORD: MT8CA 8-3
Parent Resources Online
KEYWORD: MT8CA Parent

GUIDED PRACTICE

See Example **1**   Use the diagram to find each angle measure.

1. If m∠3 = 105°, find m∠1. **105°**

2. If m∠2 = x°, find m∠4. **x°**

See Example **2**   In the figure, line *m* ∥ line *n*. Find the measure of each angle.

3. ∠1 **62°**   **4.** ∠4 **62°**

5. ∠6 **118°**   **6.** ∠7 **62°**

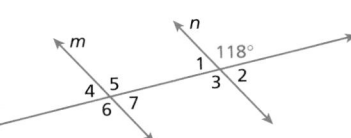
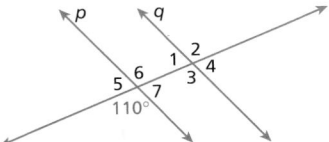

INDEPENDENT PRACTICE

See Example **1**   Use the diagram to find each angle measure.

7. If m∠2 = 126°, find m∠4. **126°**

8. If m∠1 = b°, find m∠3. **b°**

See Example **2**   In the figure, line *p* ∥ line *q*. Find the measure of each angle.

9. ∠1 **70°**

10. ∠4 **70°**

11. ∠6 **110°**

12. ∠7 **70°**

PRACTICE AND PROBLEM SOLVING

Extra Practice
See page EP16.

15. Possible answers: ∠1 and ∠2, ∠1 and ∠3, ∠3 and ∠4.

In the figure, line *t* ∥ line *s*.

13. Name all angles congruent to ∠1.
∠4, ∠5, and ∠8

14. Name all angles congruent to ∠2.
∠3, ∠6, and ∠7

15. Name three pairs of supplementary angles.

16. Which line is the transversal? **line *r***

17. If m∠4 is 51°, what is m∠2? **129°**

18. If m∠7 is 116°, what is m∠3? **116°**

19. If m∠5 is x°, what is m∠2? **180° − x°**

20. Reasoning Two parallel lines are cut by a transversal. Can you determine the measures of all the angles formed if given only one angle measure? Explain.

REVIEW FOR MASTERY 8-3

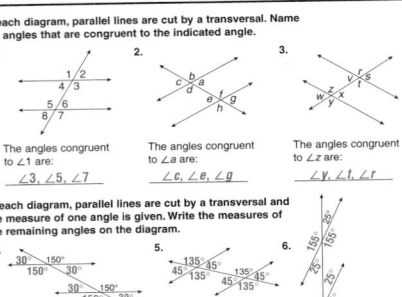

PRACTICE 8-3

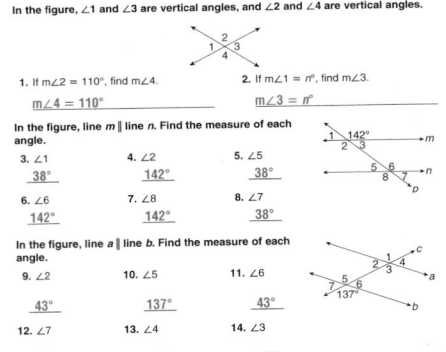

Draw a diagram to illustrate each of the following.

21. line $p \parallel$ line $q \parallel$ line r and line s is a transversal to lines p, q, and r

22. line $m \parallel$ line n and transversal h with congruent angles $\angle 1$ and $\angle 3$

23. line $h \parallel$ line j and transversal k with eight congruent angles

24. Science A periscope contains two parallel mirrors that face each other. With a periscope, a person in a submerged submarine can see above the surface of the water.

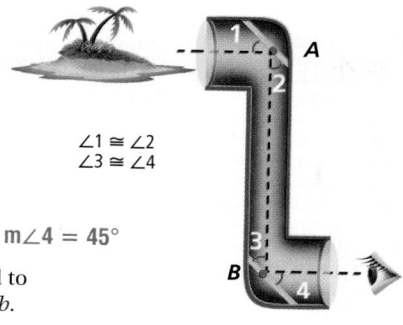

$\angle 1 \cong \angle 2$
$\angle 3 \cong \angle 4$

  a. Name the transversal in the diagram. $\overline{AB}$

  b. If m$\angle 1 = 45°$, find m$\angle 2$, m$\angle 3$, and m$\angle 4$. m$\angle 2 =$ m$\angle 3 =$ m$\angle 4 = 45°$

25. What's the Error? Line a is parallel to line b. Line c is perpendicular to line b. Line c forms a 60° angle with line a. Why is this figure impossible to draw?

26. Write About It Choose an example of abstract art or architecture with parallel lines. Explain how parallel lines, transversals, or perpendicular lines are used in the composition. **Check students' work.**

27. Challenge In the figure, $\angle 1$, $\angle 4$, $\angle 6$, and $\angle 7$ are all congruent, and $\angle 2$, $\angle 3$, $\angle 5$, and $\angle 8$ are all congruent. Does this mean that line s is parallel to line t? Explain.

SPIRAL STANDARDS REVIEW

Rev. of ➔ 6MG2.2, AF3.1, ➔ AF3.3

28. Multiple Choice Two parallel lines are intersected by a transversal. The measures of two corresponding angles that are formed are each 54°. What are the measures of each of the angles supplementary to the corresponding angles?

  Ⓐ 36°   Ⓑ 72°   Ⓒ 108°   Ⓓ 126°

29. Extended Response Suppose a transversal intersects two parallel lines. One angle that is formed is a right angle. What are the measures of the remaining angles? What is the relationship between the transversal and the parallel lines? **The measures of the remaining angles are 90°. The transversal is perpendicular to the parallel lines.**

Graph each linear function. (Lesson 7-3)

30. $y = -x + 1$

31. $y = 2x$

Create a table for each quadratic function, and use it to graph the function. (Lesson 7-4)

32. $y = -x^2 + 1$

33. $y = 2x^2 + x$

CHALLENGE 8-3

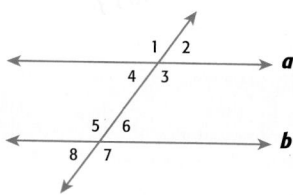

LESSON
8-3 **Challenge**
Pairing Off

When two parallel lines are cut by a transversal, eight angles are formed. Of these, four angles are between the parallel lines, **interior angles**.

1. In this diagram, name the four interior angles formed by the parallel lines and the transversal.

  $\angle 3$, $\angle 4$, $\angle 5$, $\angle 6$

2. Think of the interior angles in pairs. Name the two pairs of interior angles that are on opposite sides of the transversal.

  $\angle 3$ and $\angle 5$; $\angle 4$ and $\angle 6$

3. What is true about the measures of $\angle 3$ and $\angle 5$ in the diagram above? Use a protractor to verify your conjecture.

  $\angle 3 \cong \angle 5$

4. What is true about the measures of $\angle 4$ and $\angle 6$ in the diagram above? Use a protractor to verify your conjecture.

  $\angle 4 \cong \angle 6$

5. Interior angles that are on opposite sides of the transversal are called **alternate interior angles**.

Draw a conclusion about the measures of alternate interior angles formed by parallel lines and a transversal.

Alternate interior angles of parallel lines are equal in measure, or congruent.

Use your observation about the measures of alternate interior angles of parallel lines to find the measure of ∠x in each of these diagrams.

6. m$\angle x = $ __48°__

7. m$\angle x = 35° + 45° = 80°$

8. m$\angle x = 70° - 30° = 40°$

PROBLEM SOLVING 8-3

LESSON
8-3 **Problem Solving**
Angle Relationships

The figure shows the layout of parking spaces in a parking lot.
$AB \parallel CD \parallel EF$

1. Name all angles congruent to $\angle 1$.

  $\angle 3$, $\angle 5$, $\angle 7$, $\angle 9$

2. Name all angles congruent to $\angle 2$.

  $\angle 4$, $\angle 6$, $\angle 8$, $\angle 10$

3. Name a pair of supplementary angles.

  Possible answer: $\angle 1$, $\angle 2$

4. If m$\angle 1 = 75°$, find the measures of the other angles.

  m$\angle 3 =$ m$\angle 5 =$ m$\angle 7 =$ m$\angle 9$
  $= 75°$, m$\angle 2 =$ m$\angle 4 =$ m$\angle 6$
  $=$ m$\angle 8 =$ m$\angle 10 = 105°$

5. Name a pair of vertical angles.

  Possible answer: $\angle 2$, $\angle 8$

6. If m$\angle 1 = 90°$, then $\overline{GH}$ is perpendicular to

  Possible answers: $\overline{AB}$, $\overline{CD}$, $\overline{EF}$

The figure shows a board that will be cut along parallel segments GB and CF. $AD \parallel HE$. Choose the letter for the best answer.

7. Find the measure of $\angle 1$.

  A 45°   C 60°
  B 120°   D 90°

8. Find the measure of $\angle 2$.

  F 30°   Ⓗ 60°
  G 120°   J 90°

9. Find the measure of $\angle 3$.

  A 30°   C 60°
  B 120°   D 90°

10. Find the measure of $\angle 4$.

  F 45°   Ⓗ 60°
  G 120°   J 90°

11. Find the measure of $\angle 5$.

  A 30°   C 60°
  B 120°   D 90°

12. Find the measure of $\angle 6$.

  F 30°   Ⓗ 60°
  G 120°   J 90°

13. Find the measure of $\angle 7$.

  A 45°   C 60°
  B 120°   D 90°

FORMATIVE ASSESSMENT
and INTERVENTION

Diagnose Before the Lesson
8-3 Warm Up, TE p. 388

Monitor During the Lesson
8-3 Know-It Notebook
8-3 Questioning Strategies

Assess After the Lesson
8-3 Lesson Quiz, TE p. 391

Answers

25. Possible answer: If line c is perpendicular to line b, it must also be perpendicular to line a and therefore form a 90° angle with line a.

27, 30–33. See p. A7.

Teaching Tip **Multiple Choice** In **Exercise 28**, students may find it helpful to draw a diagram showing all the angles formed. Point out one of the supplementary angles in the diagram and remark that it is obtuse, eliminating choices **A** and **B**. Also, remind students that the measures of supplementary angles add up to 180°.

Journal

Have students think of two real-world examples of parallel lines. Have them write about how these examples are different from the mathematical concept of parallel lines.

Power Presentations with PowerPoint®

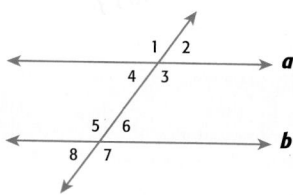

8-3 Lesson Quiz

In the figure, line $a \parallel$ line b.

1. Name all angles congruent to $\angle 3$.

  $\angle 1$, $\angle 5$, $\angle 7$

2. Name all angles supplementary to $\angle 6$. $\angle 1$, $\angle 3$, $\angle 5$, $\angle 7$

3. If m$\angle 1 = 105°$, what is m$\angle 3$? 105°

4. If m$\angle 5 = 120°$, what is m$\angle 2$? 60°

Also available on transparency

Objective: Students find unknown angles and line segment lengths in triangles.

Hands-On Lab
In *Chapter 8 Resource File*

Online Edition
Tutorial Videos, Interactivities

Countdown to Mastery Week 16

Power Presentations
with PowerPoint®

Warm Up

Solve each equation.

1. $62 + x + 37 = 180$ $x = 81$
2. $x + 90 + 11 = 180$ $x = 79$
3. $2x + 18 = 180$ $x = 81$
4. $180 = 3x + 72$ $x = 36$

Also available on transparency

Math Humor

The obtuse angle was always complaining about the heat, "I can't take this heat anymore. It must be over 90° in here!"

California Standards

Measurement and Geometry 🔑 **3.3**

Also covered:

Measurement and Geometry

3.0 Students know the Pythagorean theorem and deepen their understanding of plane and solid geometric shapes by constructing figures that meet given conditions and by identifying attributes of figures.

Rev. of Grade 6 Measurement and Geometry

🔑 **2.2 Use** properties of complementary and supplementary angles and **the sum of the angles of a triangle to solve problems involving an unknown angle.**

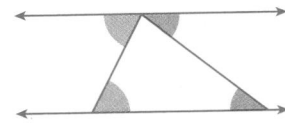
California Standards

🔑 **MG3.3 Know and understand the Pythagorean theorem** and its converse **and use it to find the length of the missing side of a right triangle and lengths of other line segments** and, in some situations, empirically verify the Pythagorean theorem by direct measurement.

Also covered: **Review of**
🔑 **6MG2.2**

Vocabulary
Triangle Sum Theorem
acute triangle
right triangle
obtuse triangle
equilateral triangle
isosceles triangle
scalene triangle
midpoint
altitude

Who uses this? Triangles are often used by designers to create unique flag designs. (See Exercise 22.)

If you tear off two corners of a triangle and place them next to the third corner, the three angles seem to form a straight angle. You can also show this in a drawing.

Draw a triangle and extend one side. Then draw a line parallel to the extended side, as shown below. The three angles in the triangle can be arranged to form a straight angle, or 180°.

Two sides of the triangle are transversals to the parallel lines. So both the blue angles and red angles are pairs of alternate interior angles.

TRIANGLE SUM THEOREM		
Words	**Numbers**	**Algebra**
The interior angle measures of a triangle add to 180°.	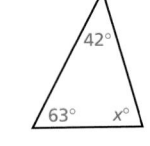 $43° + 58° + 79° = 180°$	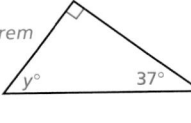 $r° + s° + t° = 180°$

An **acute triangle** has 3 acute angles. A **right triangle** has 1 right angle. An **obtuse triangle** has 1 obtuse angle.

EXAMPLE 1 Finding Angles in Acute, Right, or Obtuse Triangles

A Find *x* in the acute triangle.

$63° + 42° + x° = 180°$ *Triangle Sum Theorem*
$105 + x = 180$
$\underline{-105 \qquad -105}$ *Subtract 105 from both sides.*
$x = 75$

B Find *y* in the right triangle.

$37° + 90° + y° = 180°$ *Triangle Sum Theorem*
$127 + y = 180$
$\underline{-127 \qquad -127}$ *Subtract 127 from both sides.*
$y = 53$

---

1 Introduce

Alternate Opener

EXPLORATION

8-4 **Triangles**

The figure below shows two parallel lines *m* and *n*, and a triangle.

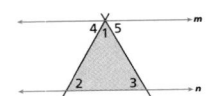

1. What is the sum of the measures of ∠4, ∠1, and ∠5?
2. Name an angle with the same measure as ∠4.
3. Name an angle with the same measure as ∠5.
4. What is the sum of the measures of ∠1, ∠2, and ∠3?

Think and Discuss

5. **Discuss** what would happen to the sum of the measures of ∠1, ∠2, and ∠3 if the triangle above were bigger.
6. **Explain** why each angle measure in an *equilateral triangle* is 60°. (In an equilateral triangle, the three sides are equal.)

Motivate

Use a rubber band to form triangles with different shapes. (Use a push pin and two pencils at a bulletin board, or use three pencils at the chalkboard with a student volunteer.) Show students that if one of the angles gets larger, another angle gets smaller. This fact supports the Triangle Sum Theorem, which states that the sum of the angle measures in any triangle is 180°.

Explorations and answers are provided in *Alternate Openers: Explorations Transparencies.*

An **equilateral triangle** has 3 congruent sides and 3 congruent angles. An **isosceles triangle** has at least 2 congruent sides and 2 congruent angles. A **scalene triangle** has no congruent sides and no congruent angles.

EXAMPLE 2 Finding Angles in Equilateral, Isosceles, or Scalene Triangles

A **Find the angle measures in the equilateral triangle.**

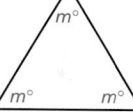

$3m° = 180°$	*Triangle Sum Theorem*
$\dfrac{3m}{3} = \dfrac{180}{3}$	*Divide both sides by 3.*
$m = 60$	

All three angles measure 60°.

B **Find the angle measures in the scalene triangle.**

$2p° + 3p° + 4p° = 180°$	*Triangle Sum Theorem*
$9p = 180$	*Simplify.*
$\dfrac{9p}{9} = \dfrac{180}{9}$	*Divide both sides by 9.*
$p = 20$	

The angle labeled $2p°$ measures $2(20°) = 40°$, the angle labeled $3p°$ measures $3(20°) = 60°$, and the angle labeled $4p°$ measures $4(20°) = 80°$.

EXAMPLE 3 Finding Angles in a Triangle That Meets Given Conditions

 Reasoning

The second angle in a triangle is twice as large as the first. The third angle is half as large as the second. Find the angle measures and draw a possible figure.

Let $x°$ = first angle measure. Then $2x°$ = second angle measure, and $\frac{1}{2}(2x)° = x°$ = third angle measure.

$x° + 2x° + x° = 180°$	*Triangle Sum Theorem*
$\dfrac{4x}{4} = \dfrac{180}{4}$	*Simplify, then divide both sides by 4.*
$x = 45$	

Two angles measure 45° and one angle measures 90°. The triangle has two congruent angles. The triangle is an isosceles right triangle.

The **midpoint** of a segment is the point that divides the segment into two congruent segments. An **altitude** of a triangle is a perpendicular segment from a vertex of the triangle to the line containing the opposite side.

altitude

Power Presentations with PowerPoint®

Additional Examples

Example 1
A. Find p in the acute triangle. **63**

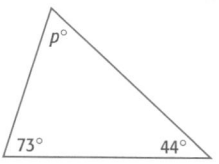

B. Find m in the obtuse triangle. **95**

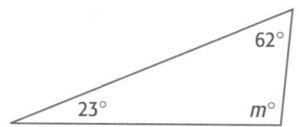

Example 2
A. Find the angle measures in the isosceles triangle. **59**

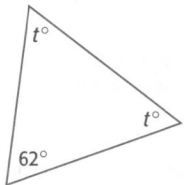

B. Find the angle measures in the scalene triangle. **36, 54, 90**

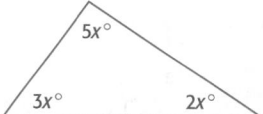

Example 3
The second angle in a triangle is six times as large as the first. The third angle is half as large as the second. Find the angle measures and draw a possible figure.

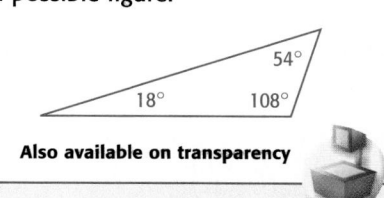

Also available on transparency

2 Teach

Guided Instruction

In this lesson, students learn to find unknown angles in triangles. The lesson is based on the Triangle Sum Theorem, one of the most important theorems in geometry (Teaching Transparency). Illustrate the Triangle Sum Theorem by tearing off two corners of a paper triangle and placing them next to the third corner to form a straight line, which measures 180°. Explain that a triangle can have at most one right angle or one obtuse angle because of the Triangle Sum Theorem.

Teaching Tip
Inclusion For **Example 2**, explain that in a triangle, angles opposite congruent sides are congruent.

Universal Access

For Advanced Learners/GATE

Show drawings of a square, a rectangle, and a parallelogram (Teaching Transparency).

Ask the students, "If a diagonal is drawn in each figure, what types of triangles will be created?"

square: isosceles right triangles

rectangle: scalene right triangles

parallelogram: scalene acute triangles

Additional Examples

Example 4

In the figure, T is the midpoint of $\overline{UV}$ and $\overline{ST}$ is perpendicular to $\overline{UV}$. Find the length of $\overline{ST}$.   **24 ft**

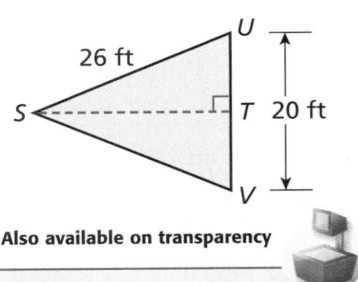

26 ft

S

U

T   20 ft

V

Also available on transparency

8-4 Exercises

Assignment Guide

If you finished Example **1** assign:
Proficient 1–3, 9–11, 27–34
Advanced 9–11, 17–19, 27–34

If you finished Example **2** assign:
Proficient 1–6, 9–14, 17–19, 22, 26–34
Advanced 9–14, 17–19, 20–34

If you finished Example **3** assign:
Proficient 1–7, 9–15, 17–19, 22, 26–34
Advanced 9–15, 17–19, 20–34

If you finished Example **4** assign:
Proficient 1–19, 22, 26–34
Advanced 9–34

Homework Quick Check

Quickly check key concepts.
Exercises: 10, 12, 14, 16, 18

California Standards

Standard	Exercises
6MG2.2	1–7, 9–15, 17–27
7NS2.4	28–31
7MG3.3	8, 16
7MG3.6	32–34

EXAMPLE 4 **Finding the Length of a Line Segment**

In the figure, M is the midpoint of $\overline{PQ}$ and $\overline{RM}$ is an altitude of $\triangle PQR$. Find the length of $\overline{RM}$.

R

20 m

P   M   Q

24 m

Step 1 Find the length of $\overline{MQ}$.

Reading Math

$\overline{MQ}$ is the name of a line segment.
MQ is the length of the segment.

$$MQ = \tfrac{1}{2}PQ \qquad \text{M is the midpoint of } \overline{PQ}.$$

$$= \tfrac{1}{2}(24) = 12$$

Step 2 Use the Pythagorean Theorem and $\triangle RMQ$. Let $RM = a$ and $MQ = b$.

$$
\begin{aligned}
a^2 + b^2 &= c^2 && \text{Pythagorean Theorem}\\
a^2 + 12^2 &= 20^2 && \text{Substitute 12 for b and 20 for c.}\\
a^2 + 144 &= 400 && \text{Simplify the powers.}\\
-144 &\;\; -144 && \text{Subtract 144 from each side.}\\
\hline
a^2 &= 256 \\
a &= 16 && \text{Find the square root.}
\end{aligned}
$$

The length of $\overline{RM}$ is 16 m, or RM is 16 m.

Answers to Think and Discuss

1. A right triangle cannot be equilateral because $90° + 90° + 90° = 270°$. A right triangle can be isosceles (as in Example 3) or scalene (e.g., 90°, 60°, and 30°).

2. No; Either would make the sum of the three angles in the triangle greater than 180°.

Think and Discuss

1. Explain whether a right triangle can be equilateral. Can it be isosceles? scalene?

2. Explain whether a triangle can have 2 right angles. Can it have 2 obtuse angles?

8-4 Exercises

California Standards Practice
Review of 6MG2.2; MG3.3

go.hrw.com
Homework Help Online
KEYWORD: MT8CA 8-4
Parent Resources Online
KEYWORD: MT8CA Parent

GUIDED PRACTICE

See Example **1**
1. Find q in the acute triangle.
$q = 77$
2. Find r in the right triangle.
$r = 59$
3. Find s in the obtuse triangle.
$s = 120$

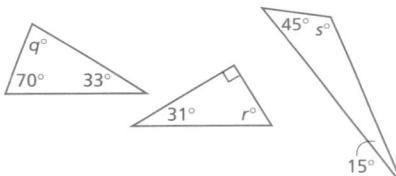

$q°$
70°   33°

45° $s°$
31° $r°$
15°

3 Close

Summarize

Review the vocabulary terms. Show the following triangles and ask students to write the equations that are needed to solve for x and r. Remind students to check their work by making sure their answers add up to 180°.

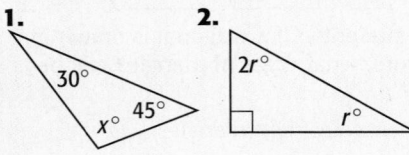

1.
30°
$x°$ 45°

2.
$2r°$
$r°$

Possible answers:

1. $x° + 30° + 45° = 180°$

2. $r° + 2r° + 90° = 180°$

4. Find the angle measures in the equilateral triangle. *a* = 60

5. Find the angle measures in the isosceles triangle. *c* = 56

6. *d* = 18, 4*d* = 72, 5*d* = 90

6. Find the angle measures in the scalene triangle.

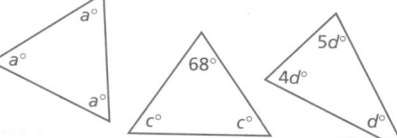

See Example 3

7. The second angle in a triangle is half as large as the first. The third angle is three times as large as the second. Find the angle measures and draw a possible figure. 60°, 30°, 90°

See Example 4

8. In the figure, $\overline{DB}$ is a diagonal of rectangle *ABCD*. Find the length of $\overline{AB}$. 48 ft

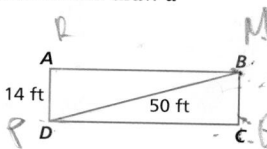

14 ft

50 ft

INDEPENDENT PRACTICE

See Example 1

9. Find *r* in the acute triangle. *r* = 86

10. Find *s* in the right triangle. *s* = 58

11. Find *t* in the obtuse triangle. *t* = 115

See Example 2

12. Find the angle measures in the equilateral triangle. *w* = 60

13. Find the angle measures in the isosceles triangle. *m* = 72

14. Find the angle measures in the scalene triangle. 2*g* = 20, 7*g* = 70, 9*g* = 90

See Example 3

15. The second angle in a triangle is five times as large as the first. The third angle is two-thirds as large as the first. Find the angle measures and draw a possible figure. 27°, 135°, 18°

See Example 4

16. In the figure, *K* is the midpoint of $\overline{JL}$ and $\overline{KM}$ is perpendicular to $\overline{JL}$. Find the length of $\overline{JM}$. 15 in.

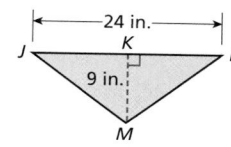

24 in.

9 in.

PRACTICE AND PROBLEM SOLVING

Extra Practice
See page EP16.

For more on classifying triangles, see page SB16.

Find the value of each variable. Classify the triangle by its sides and angles.

17.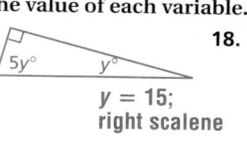

y = 15; right scalene

18.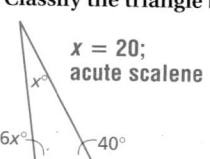

x = 20; acute scalene

19.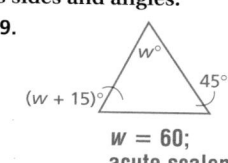

w = 60; acute scalene

Math Background

In many traditional geometry courses, the Triangle Sum Theorem is proved as outlined below.

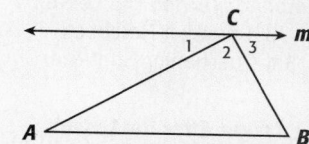

Consider the line *m* through point *C* parallel to $\overline{AB}$. m∠*A* = m∠1 because they are alternate interior angles, and m∠*B* = m∠3 for the same reason. m∠1 + m∠2 + m∠3 = 180° because *m* is a straight line. Substituting m∠*A* for m∠1 and m∠*B* for m∠3, we get m∠*A* + m∠2 + m∠*B* = 180°.

Answers

7.

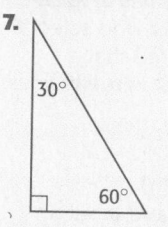

30°

60°

15.

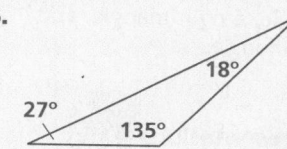

18°

27°

135°

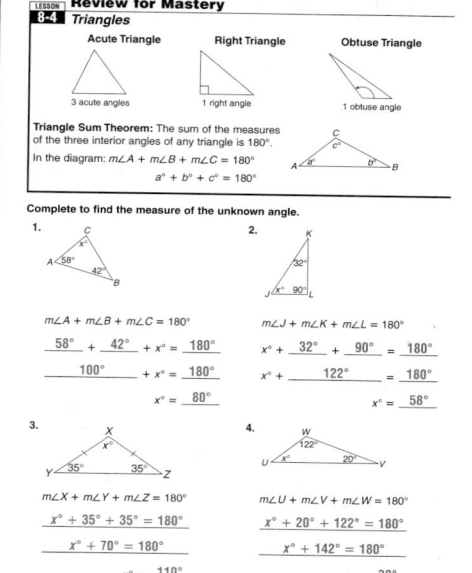
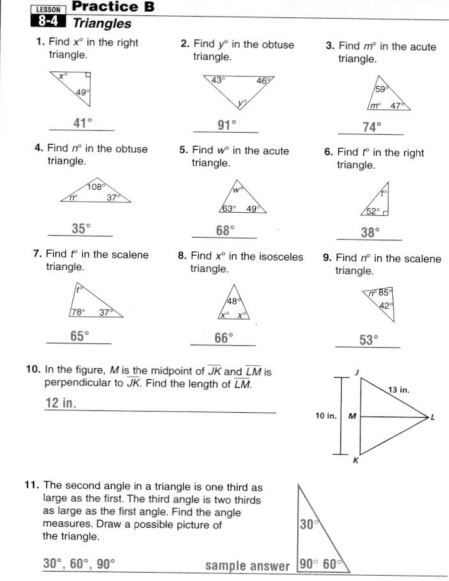

Answers
24. See p. A8.

Teaching Tip

Multiple Choice Remind students of the various types of triangles. In **Exercise 26,** the triangle has at least two congruent sides. Students who select **C** may not have remembered that a scalene triangle has no congruent sides.

 Journal

Ask students to sketch and label an acute triangle, a right triangle, and an obtuse triangle.

Power Presentations
with PowerPoint®

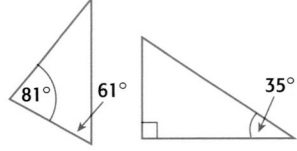

8-4
Lesson Quiz

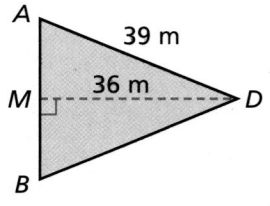

1. Find the missing angle measure in the acute triangle shown. **38°**

2. Find the missing angle measure in the right triangle shown. **55°**

3. Find the missing angle measure in an acute triangle with angle measures of **67°** and **63°**. **50°**

4. Find the missing angle measure in an obtuse triangle with angle measures of **10°** and **15°**. **155°**

5. In the figure, *M* is the midpoint of $\overline{AB}$ and $\overline{MD}$ is perpendicular to $\overline{AB}$. Find the length of $\overline{AB}$. **30 m**

Also available on transparency

---

20. Possible answer: No, if two angles measure 40°, the third angle would have to be 100°. It would be an obtuse triangle, not an acute triangle.

20. **Reasoning** Can an acute isosceles triangle have two angles that measure 40°? Explain.

21. Triangle *LMN* is an obtuse triangle and m∠*L* = 25°. ∠*M* is the obtuse angle. What is the largest m∠*N* can be to the nearest whole degree? **64°**

22. **Social Studies** American Samoa is a territory of the United States made up of a group of islands in the Pacific Ocean, about halfway between Hawaii and New Zealand. The flag of American Samoa is shown.

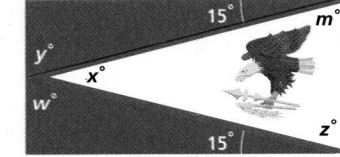

  a. Find the measure of each variable in the blue triangles. **w = 75; y = 75**

  b. Use your answers to part **a** to find *m*, *x*, and *z*. **m = 75; x = 30; z = 75**

  c. Classify the triangles in the flag by their sides and angles. **The blue triangles are right scalene. The white triangle is acute isosceles.**

23. **Choose a Strategy** Which of the following sets of angle measures can be used to create an isosceles triangle?

   (A) 45°, 45°, 95°   (B) 49°, 51°, 80°   (C) 27°, 27°, 126°   (D) 35°, 55°, 100°

24. **Write About It** Explain how to cut a square or an equilateral triangle in half to form two identical triangles. What are the angle measures in the resulting triangles in each case?

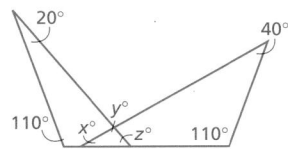

25. **Challenge** Find *x*, *y*, and *z* in the figure shown. **x = 30, y = 100, z = 50**

SPIRAL STANDARDS REVIEW   Rev. of 6MG2.2; NS2.4, MG3.6

26. **Multiple Choice** Which type of triangle can be constructed with a 50° angle between two 8-inch sides?

   (A) Equilateral   (B) Isosceles   (C) Scalene   (D) Obtuse

27. **Short Response** Two angles of a triangle are 45° and 30°. What is the measure of the third angle? Is the triangle acute, right, or obtuse? **105°, obtuse**

Each square root is between two integers. Name the integers. (Lesson 4-7)   **17 and 18**

28. $\sqrt{42}$ **6 and 7**   29. $\sqrt{71}$ **8 and 9**   30. $\sqrt{35}$ **5 and 6**   31. $\sqrt{296}$

Identify two lines that have the given relationship. (Lesson 8-2)

32. skew lines $\overleftrightarrow{AB}$ and $\overleftrightarrow{DE}$

33. parallel lines $\overleftrightarrow{AB} \parallel \overleftrightarrow{CD}$

34. perpendicular lines $\overleftrightarrow{AB} \perp \overleftrightarrow{BC}$

CHALLENGE 8-4

LESSON 8-4 Challenge
Change a This into a That

A **geometric dissection** involves cutting a figure into pieces that can then be rearranged to form another figure.

Trace each figure. Cut up the figure you have traced and rearrange the numbered pieces to form the indicated figure. Sketch your solution.

1. Rearrange the pieces of the equilateral triangle to form a square.

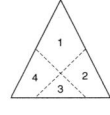 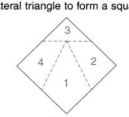

2. Rearrange the pieces of the star to form an equilateral triangle.

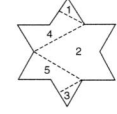 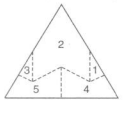

3. Rearrange the pieces of the cross to form an equilateral triangle.

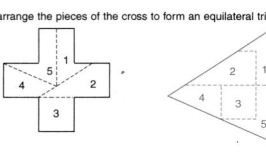

PROBLEM SOLVING 8-4

LESSON 8-4 Problem Solving
Triangles

The American flag must be folded according to certain rules that result in the flag being folded into the shape of a triangle. The figure shows a frame designed to hold an American flag.

1. Is the triangle acute, right, or obtuse?
   right

2. Is the triangle equilateral, isosceles, or scalene?
   isosceles

3. Find *x°*.
   x = 45°

4. Find *y°*.
   y = 45°

The figure shows a map of three streets. Choose the letter for the best answer.

5. Find *x°*.
   A 22°   C 30°
   (B) 128°   D 68°

6. Find *w°*.
   F 22°   (H) 30°
   G 128°   J 52°

7. Find *y°*.
   A 22°
   B 30°
   (C) 128°
   D 143°

8. Find *z°*.
   (F) 22°
   G 30°
   H 128°
   J 143°

9. Which word best describes the triangle formed by the streets?
   A acute
   B right
   (C) obtuse
   D equilateral

10. Which word best describes the triangle formed by the streets?
   F equilateral
   G isosceles
   (H) scalene
   J acute

Identify and Construct Altitudes

Use with Lesson 8-4

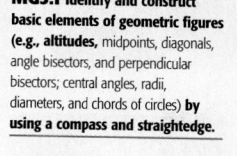
California Standards

MG3.1 Identify and construct basic elements of geometric figures (e.g., **altitudes**, midpoints, diagonals, angle bisectors, and perpendicular bisectors; central angles, radii, diameters, and chords of circles) **by using a compass and straightedge.**

go.hrw.com
Lab Resources Online
KEYWORD: MT8CA Lab8

Recall that an *altitude* of a triangle is a perpendicular segment from a vertex of the triangle to the line containing the opposite side. An altitude can be inside, outside, or on the triangle. You can use a compass and straightedge to construct an altitude of a triangle.

Activity

Follow these steps to construct the altitude from *P* to $\overline{QR}$ of △*PQR*.

a. Use your straightedge to extend $\overline{QR}$.

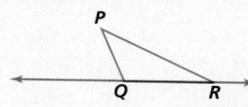

b. Place the point of your compass at *P*. Draw an arc that intersects $\overrightarrow{QR}$ at points *X* and *Y*.

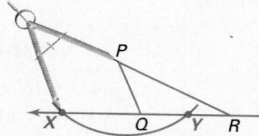

c. Draw arcs from points *X* and *Y* using the same compass opening. Label the intersection of the arcs point *Z*.

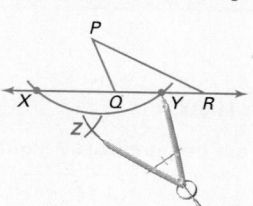

d. Place your straightedge so that it passes through points *P* and *Z*. Draw a segment from *P* to $\overrightarrow{QR}$. This is the required altitude.

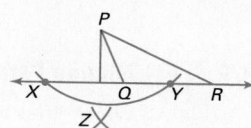

Think and Discuss

Use a protractor to make sure the altitude forms a 90° angle with $\overrightarrow{QR}$.

1. How could you check that the altitude is perpendicular to $\overrightarrow{QR}$?

2. How many different altitudes can you construct for any given triangle?   3

Try This

Copy each triangle. Then construct the altitude from *A* to $\overline{BC}$.

1.
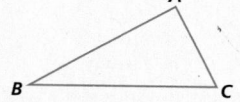

2.
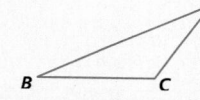

3.
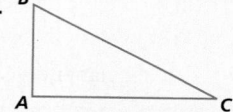

Answers to *Try This*

1.
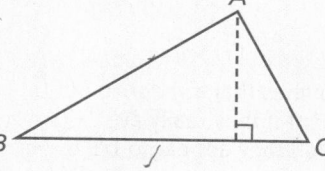

2.
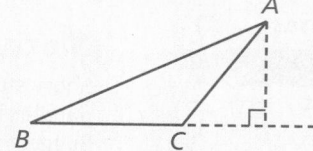

3.
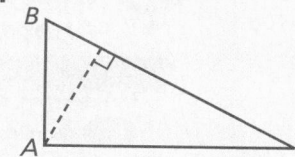

Teach
Discuss

The altitude of a triangle is a line segment from one vertex of a triangle to the opposite side so that the segment is perpendicular to that side. In an acute triangle, all of the altitudes are within the triangle. In an obtuse triangle, two altitudes are outside the triangle. In a right triangle, two altitudes are on the triangle.

Close
Key Concept

You can use a compass and straightedge to construct altitudes of triangles.

Assessment

Draw a triangle and construct the altitudes from each vertex to the opposite side. Check students' work.

California Standards

Measurement and Geometry 3.1

Objective: Students identify polygons in the coordinate plane.

 Online Edition
Tutorial Videos

Countdown to Mastery Weeks 16 and 17

Power Presentations
with PowerPoint®

Warm Up

Complete each statement.

1. Two lines in a plane that never meet are called ____?____ lines.   parallel

2. ____?____ lines intersect at right angles.   perpendicular

3. The symbol ∥ means that lines are ____?____.   parallel

4. When a transversal intersects two ____?____ lines, all of the acute angles are congruent.   parallel

Also available on transparency

Math Humor

What kind of geometric figure is like a runaway parrot? A polygon

---

8-5 Coordinate Geometry

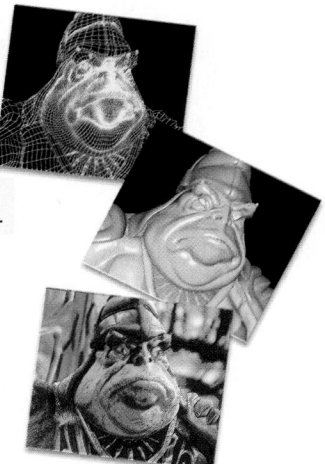

 California Standards

MG3.2 Understand and use coordinate graphs to plot simple figures, determine lengths and areas related to them, and determine their image under translations and reflections.
Also covered: **AF3.3**

Vocabulary
polygon
quadrilateral
trapezoid
parallelogram
rectangle
rhombus
square

Who uses this? Graphic designers use coordinate geometry to create movie images.

In computer graphics, a coordinate system is used to create images, from simple geometric figures to realistic figures used in movies.

Properties of the coordinate plane can be used to find information about figures in the plane, such as whether lines in the plane are parallel.

Slopes of Parallel and Perpendicular Lines
• Any two nonvertical lines with equal slopes are parallel. Any two vertical lines are parallel.
• Any two nonvertical lines whose slopes have a product of −1 are perpendicular. Vertical and horizontal lines are perpendicular.

EXAMPLE 1 **Finding Perpendicular and Parallel Lines**

Which lines are parallel? Which lines are perpendicular? Explain.

Step 1 Find the slope of each line.

slope of $\overleftrightarrow{PQ} = \frac{3}{2}$

slope of $\overleftrightarrow{RS} = \frac{4}{3}$

slope of $\overleftrightarrow{AB} = \frac{3}{2}$

slope of $\overleftrightarrow{PA} = \frac{-2}{2}$ or -1

slope of $\overleftrightarrow{GH} = \frac{-3}{4}$

slope of $\overleftrightarrow{XY} = \frac{-7}{8}$

Helpful Hint

If a line has slope $\frac{a}{b}$, then a line perpendicular to it has slope $-\frac{b}{a}$.

Step 2 Compare the slopes.

$\overleftrightarrow{PQ} \parallel \overleftrightarrow{AB}$ *The slopes are equal:* $\frac{3}{2} = \frac{3}{2}$.

$\overleftrightarrow{RS} \perp \overleftrightarrow{GH}$ *The slopes have a product of −1:* $\frac{4}{3} \cdot \frac{-3}{4} = -1$.

---

1 **Introduce**

Alternate Opener

EXPLORATION

8-5 Coordinate Geometry

Quadrilaterals are figures with four sides. Use the coordinate grid to draw each of the following quadrilaterals. Label vertices with A, B, C, and D.

	Quadrilateral	Graph
1.	Square A (3, 2), B (3, 8), C (−3, 8), D (−3, 2)	
2.	Rectangle A (7, −1.5), B (7, −7), C (−5, −7), D (−5, −1.5)	

Think and Discuss

3. **Describe** the relationship between the number of sides and the number of vertices of quadrilaterals.
4. **Discuss** whether the relationship you described in Problem 3 is also true for other polygons.

Motivate

Show students two lines that *appear* to be parallel, and ask them if they really are. Suggest that although they appear to be parallel, the appearance is not proof. Explain that by plotting the lines on a coordinate plane, you can find a measure of the "steepness" of each line, called *slope*. Slope can be used to determine if the two lines are truly parallel.

Explorations and answers are provided in *Alternate Openers: Explorations Transparencies*.

California Standards

Measurement and Geometry 3.2
Also covered:
Algebra and Functions
🔑 **3.3 Graph linear functions,** noting that the vertical change (change in *y*-value) per unit of horizontal change (change in *x*-value) is always the same and know that the ratio ("rise over run") is called the slope of a graph.

A **polygon** is a closed plane figure formed by three or more line segments called sides. Each side meets exactly two other sides, one on each end, in a common endpoint. **Quadrilaterals** are polygons with four sides and four angles. Quadrilaterals with certain properties are given additional names.

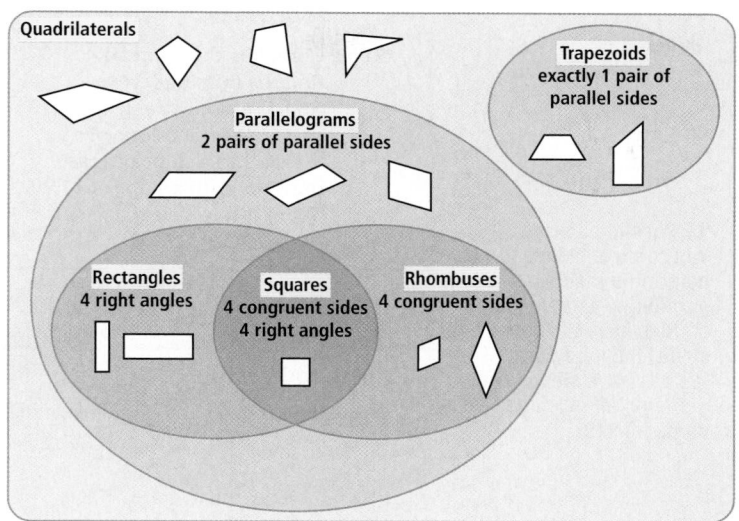

 **EXAMPLE 2** **Using Coordinates to Classify Quadrilaterals**

Reasoning

Graph the quadrilaterals with the given vertices. Give all of the names that apply to each quadrilateral.

Ⓐ $J(1, 2), K(4, 2),$
$L(4, -1), M(1, -1)$

Ⓑ $P(-1, 2), Q(2, 1),$
$R(-1, -2), S(-3, 0)$

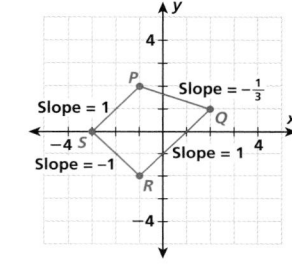

2 pairs of parallel sides
4 right angles
parallelogram, rectangle, rhombus, square

1 pair of parallel sides
trapezoid

For more on classifying quadrilaterals, see page SB16.

Example 1

Which lines are parallel? Which lines are perpendicular? Explain.

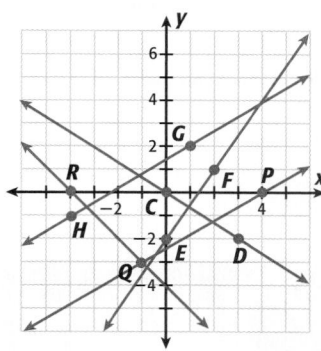

$\overleftrightarrow{GH} \parallel \overleftrightarrow{PQ}$ because the two lines have the same slope, $\overleftrightarrow{EF} \perp \overleftrightarrow{CD}$ because the product of the slopes of the two lines equals -1

Example 2

Graph the quadrilateral with the given vertices. Give all of the names that apply to the quadrilateral.

$A(3, -2), B(2, -1), C(4, 3), D(5, 2)$

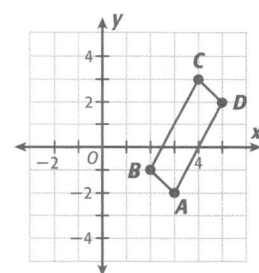

parallelogram

Also available on transparency

② Teach

Guided Instruction

In this lesson, students learn to identify polygons on the coordinate plane. To begin, you may want to review plotting points and lines on a coordinate plane. Show students how to find the slope of a line by using rise and run (Teaching Transparency). Explain that slope indicates how steep a line is and whether it slants up to the right (positive slope) or down to the right (negative slope). Discuss how to use slope to determine whether a pair of lines are parallel or perpendicular. Then show students how to apply these concepts to classify quadrilaterals.

Universal Access
Through Cooperative Learning

Have students work in pairs. Ask each student to create a quadrilateral *ABCD* on a coordinate plane that satisfies all of the following conditions:

$\overline{AB} \parallel \overline{CD}, \overline{AB} \perp \overline{CB},$ and $\overline{AD}$ not $\parallel \overline{CB}.$

Have partners exchange papers and write the slope of each segment on the diagram. Then have them classify the quadrilateral and decide whether it satisfies the conditions. Finally, have the partners return papers to each other for comparison and discussion.

Possible answers: slopes of zero, undefined, zero, and $\frac{2}{3}$; trapezoid; yes

8-5 Exercises

Answers

2. In each case, the product of the slopes of the two lines equals −1.

EXAMPLE 3 **Finding the Coordinates of a Missing Vertex**

Find the coordinates of the missing vertex of square *ABCD* with *A*(4, 0), *B*(0, 4), and *C*(−4, 0).

Step 1 Graph and connect the given points.

Step 2 Complete the figure to find the missing vertex. $\overline{AB}$ has a slope of −1, so draw $\overline{CD}$ with a slope of −1. $\overline{BC}$ has a slope of 1, so draw $\overline{AD}$ with a slope of 1. The rays intersect at (0, −4).

The coordinates of *D* are (0, −4).

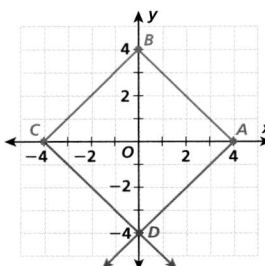

Think and Discuss

1. **Explain** how you can use slopes to classify a quadrilateral.

1. Possible answer: You can use slopes to determine if sides are parallel or perpendicular. If sides have the same slope, they are parallel. If sides have slopes with a product of −1, they are perpendicular.

8-5 Exercises

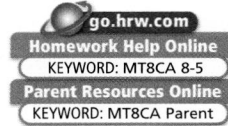

GUIDED PRACTICE $\overrightarrow{AN} \parallel \overrightarrow{CD}$; the slopes are the same.

See Example **1**
1. Which lines are parallel? Explain.

2. Which lines are perpendicular? Explain.
$\overrightarrow{MN} \perp \overrightarrow{AN}$, $\overrightarrow{MN} \perp \overrightarrow{CD}$, and $\overrightarrow{AD} \perp \overrightarrow{BE}$

See Example **2**
Graph the quadrilaterals with the given vertices. Give all of the names that apply to each quadrilateral.

3. *D*(−3, −2), *E*(−3, 3), *F*(2, 3), *G*(2, −2)

4. *R*(−4, −1), *S*(−2, 2), *T*(4, 2), *V*(5, −1)

See Example **3**
Find the coordinates of the missing vertex.

5. rhombus *ABCD* with *A*(2, 3), *B*(3, 1), and *D*(1, 1) *C*(2, −1)

6. square *JKLM* with *J*(−3, 1), *K*(0, 1), and *L*(0, −2) *M*(−3, −2)

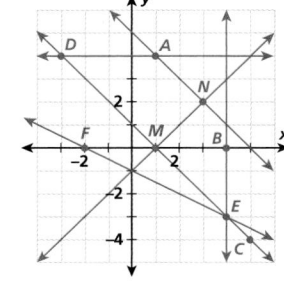

---

3. parallelogram, rhombus, rectangle, square

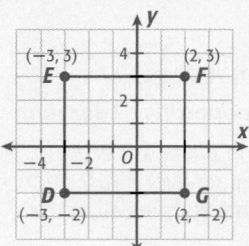

4. trapezoid

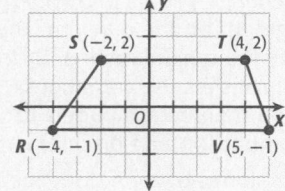

---

3 Close

Summarize

Discuss with students how slope can be used to determine whether lines in a coordinate plane are parallel or perpendicular. Discuss the slopes of horizontal and vertical lines. Remind students that they can use this information to classify quadrilaterals.

·Possible answers: If two lines have the same slope, they are parallel. If the product of the slopes of two lines equals −1, the lines are perpendicular. Also, if one line is horizontal and another is vertical, the lines are perpendicular. Horizontal lines have a slope of zero. Vertical lines have undefined slope.

See Example 1

7. Which lines are parallel? Explain. $\overrightarrow{CD} \parallel \overrightarrow{AB}$; the slopes are the same.

8. Which lines are perpendicular? Explain.
$\overrightarrow{HG} \perp \overrightarrow{CH}$, $\overrightarrow{FE} \perp \overrightarrow{CD}$, and $\overrightarrow{FE} \perp \overrightarrow{AB}$

See Example 2
Graph the quadrilaterals with the given vertices. Give all of the names that apply to each quadrilateral.

9. $D(-4, 3)$, $E(4, 3)$, $F(4, -5)$, $G(-4, -5)$

10. $W(-2, 1)$, $X(-2, -2)$, $Y(4, 1)$, $Z(0, 2)$

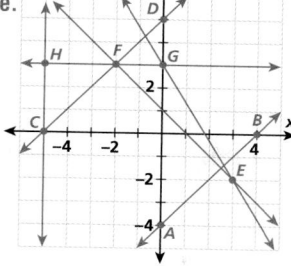

See Example 3
Find the coordinates of the missing vertex.

11. rectangle $ABCD$ with $A(-3, 3)$, $B(4, 3)$, and $D(-3, -1)$ $C(4, -1)$

12. trapezoid $JKLM$ with $J(-1, 5)$, $K(2, 3)$, and $L(2, 1)$ Possible answer: $M(-1, -1)$

8. In each case, the product of the slopes of the two lines equals -1.

PRACTICE AND PROBLEM SOLVING

Extra Practice
See page EP17.

Draw the line through the given points and find its slope.

13. $A(1, 0)$, $B(2, 3)$ **3**

14. $C(-3, 0)$, $D(-3, -4)$ **undefined**

15. $G(4, -2)$, $H(-1, -2)$ **0**

16. $E(-2, 1)$, $F(3, -2)$ $-\dfrac{3}{5}$

17. A line passes through the coordinates $P(1, 3)$ and $Q(-2, -3)$. Identify the slope of $\overrightarrow{PQ}$. Then name two coordinates and the slope of a line perpendicular to $\overrightarrow{PQ}$. **2; Possible answer: $(0, 0)$, $(-2, 1)$; $-\dfrac{1}{2}$**

18. On a coordinate grid draw a line m with slope 0 and a line n with slope -1. Then draw three lines through the intersection of lines m and n that have slopes between 0 and -1.

19. On a coordinate grid draw a line s with slope 0 and a line t with slope 1. Then draw three lines through the intersection of lines s and t that have slopes between 0 and 1.

Tell if each statement is true or false. If it is false, explain.

20. The slope of a line through the origin is always defined. **False; possible answer: the slope of the y-axis is undefined.**

21. Opposite sides of a rhombus have the same slope. **true**

22. All of the adjacent sides of quadrilaterals have slopes with a product of -1.

23. All parallelograms have two pairs of lines with the same slope and adjacent sides that have slopes with a product of -1.

24. A trapezoid has two pairs of sides that have the same slope.

25. The slope of a horizontal line is always 0. **true**

26. Reasoning Triangle LMN has vertices at $L(-2, 2)$, $M(0, 0)$, and $N(-5, -1)$. What kind of triangle is it? Explain.

REVIEW FOR MASTERY 8-5

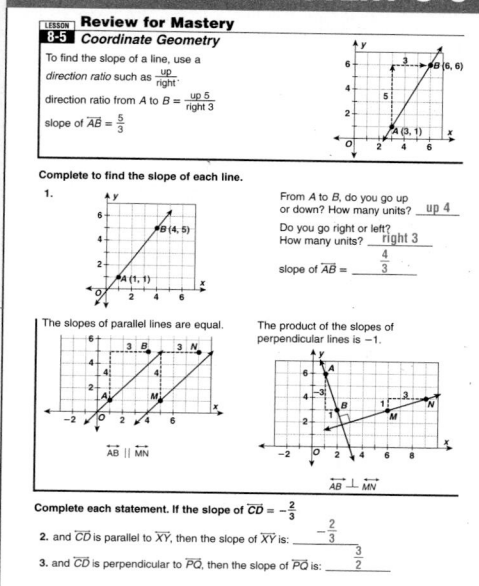

PRACTICE 8-5

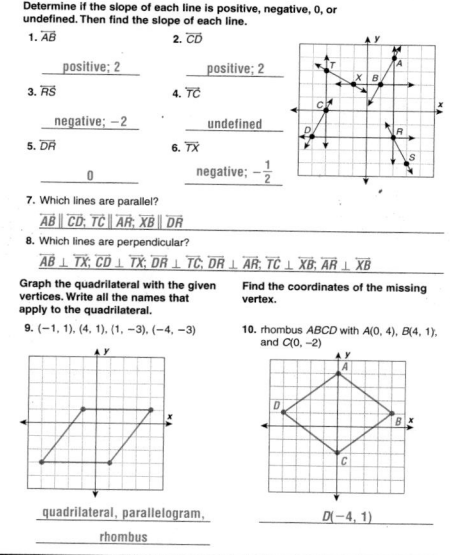

Answers

9. parallelogram, rhombus, rectangle, square

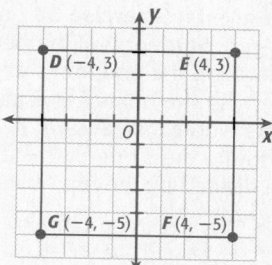

10. trapezoid

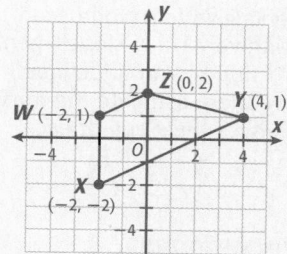

13.

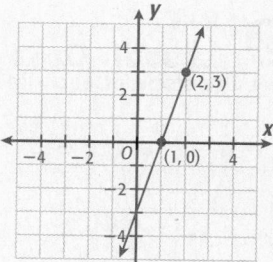

14.

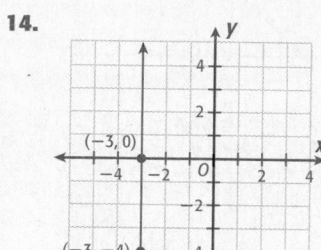

15–16, 18–19, 22–24, 26. See p. A8.

Answers

27–28, 33–35. See p. A8.

Teaching Tip **Multiple Choice** Have students plot the vertices given in **Exercise 36** on a coordinate grid. Students will be better able to determine the endpoints of the hypotenuse with the help of a visual aid. Students who chose answer **A** incorrectly found the slope by calculating the run divided by the rise, instead of rise over run.

Journal

Have students give real-world examples of things with very steep slopes, gentle slopes, zero slopes, and undefined slopes. Have them estimate the mathematical value for the slope of each example.

Power Presentations
with PowerPoint®

8-5 Lesson Quiz
Determine the slope of each line.

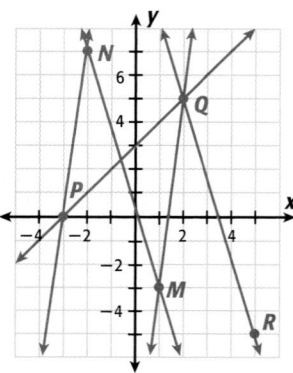

1. $\overleftrightarrow{PQ}$ 1
2. $\overleftrightarrow{MN}$ $-\frac{10}{3}$
3. $\overleftrightarrow{MQ}$ 8
4. $\overleftrightarrow{NP}$ 7
5. Which pairs of lines are parallel?
$\overleftrightarrow{MN}, \overleftrightarrow{RQ}$

Also available on transparency

---

27. $\overleftrightarrow{AB} \parallel \overleftrightarrow{CD}$ and the slope of $\overleftrightarrow{AB}$ is undefined. What can you tell about the slope of $\overleftrightarrow{CD}$? Explain.

28. Reasoning Square *ABCD* has vertices at (1, 2) and (1, −2). Find the possible coordinates of the two missing vertices to create the square with the least area. Justify your solution.

Identify and name each figure.

29. This figure has two sides with undefined slopes.   **D; rectangle**

30. This figure has a side with a slope of −1.
C; square

31. This figure has a side with a slope of 3.
B; right triangle

32. This figure has a side with a slope of $\frac{1}{3}$.
A; quadrilateral

 33. What's the Question? Points *P*(3, 7), *Q*(5, 2), *R*(3, −3), and *S*(1, 2) form the vertices of a polygon. The answer is that the segments are not perpendicular. What is the question?

 34. Write About It Explain how using different points on a line to find the slope affects the answer.

35. Challenge Use a square in a coordinate plane to explain why a line with slope 1 makes a 45° angle with the *x*-axis.

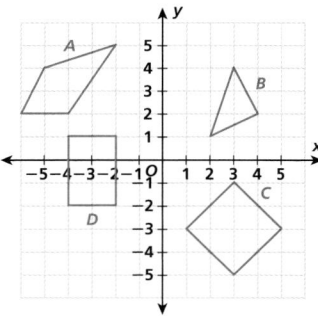

SPIRAL STANDARDS REVIEW
NS1.3, ⟵ AF3.3, ⟵ AF4.2

36. Multiple Choice A right triangle has vertices at (0, 0), (0,4), and (10, 4). What is the slope of the hypotenuse?

Ⓐ 2.5   Ⓑ 2   Ⓒ 1.8   Ⓓ 0.4

37. Gridded Response Find the slope of the line that crosses through the points *A*(2, 4) and *B*(−1, 5). $-\frac{1}{3}$

Find each number. (Lesson 6-4)

38. 60% of what number is 12? **20**

39. 112 is 80% of what number? **140**

40. 30 is 2% of what number? **1500**

41. 90% of what number is 18? **20**

Determine whether the data sets show direct variation. (Lesson 7-9)

42.

Amount of Chicken per Serving					
Amount (lb)	1	2	3	4	5
Servings	2	4	6	8	10

Yes

CHALLENGE 8-5

LESSON 8-5 Challenge
Are They Lined Up?

You can find the slope of a line by using the coordinates of two points on the line.

slope = $\frac{\text{difference of } y\text{-values}}{\text{difference of } x\text{-values}}$

Be sure to take the differences in the same order.

To find the slope of $\overleftrightarrow{AB}$ with *A*(−2, 5) and *B*(6, 7):

slope of $\overleftrightarrow{AB} = \frac{7-5}{6-(-2)} = \frac{2}{8} = \frac{1}{4}$, or

slope of $\overleftrightarrow{AB} = \frac{5-7}{-2-6} = \frac{-2}{-8} = \frac{1}{4}$

Find the slope of the line joining each pair of points. Verify your result on a graph.

1. (5, 5) and (2, 1) $\frac{4}{3}$

2. (4, 1) and (6, −2) $-\frac{3}{2}$

3. Find the value of *k* so that the line joining points (−4, 0) and (*k*, 4) is parallel to the line graphed in Exercise 1.
k = −1

4. Find the value of *k* so that the line joining points (0, *k*) and (−4, 3) is parallel to the line graphed in Exercise 2.
k = −3

5. Find the value of *k* so that the line joining points (*k*, −2) and (−1, 1) is perpendicular to the line graphed in Exercise 1.
k = 3

6. Find the value of *k* so that the line joining points (−1, 0) and (2, *k*) is perpendicular to the line graphed in Exercise 2.
k = 2

PROBLEM SOLVING 8-5

LESSON 8-5 Problem Solving
Coordinate Geometry

Write the correct answer.

1. Delia uses a coordinate plane to design jewelry. She designs an earring that is a quadrilateral with vertices (4, 1), (2, 4), (−1, 3), and (−2, −3). Give all the names that apply to the quadrilateral.
trapezoid

2. A graphic designer creates a logo by plotting the points (−1, 2), (3, 2), (2, −1) and (−2, −1). Then he connects the points to form a quadrilateral. Give all the names that apply to the quadrilateral.
parallelogram

3. Four towns form a square. On a map, three of the towns have coordinates (−2, 1), (−4, −1), and (−2, −3). What are the coordinates of the fourth town?
(0, −1)

4. Jeff is preparing a scavenger hunt. The clues are located around town at four places that form a rectangle. Three of the clues are located at (−1, 3), (−1, −2), and (3, −2). What are the coordinates of the location of the fourth clue?
(3, 3)

The figure shows a map of several roads. (Note: "Rte" is the abbreviation for "Route" and "Hwy" is the abbreviation for "Highway.") Use the figure for questions 5–7. Select the best answer.

5. Which of the following roads are parallel?
A Hwy 250 and Hwy 360
Ⓑ Hwy 360 and Hwy 470
C Rte 1 and Rte 5
D Rte 5 and Rte 9

6. Which of the following roads are perpendicular?
F Hwy 250 and Rte 5
G Hwy 360 and Rte 9
H Rte 1 and Hwy 470
Ⓙ Rte 5 and Hwy 360

7. Rte 1, Rte 9, Hwy 360, and Hwy 470 form a quadrilateral. Which of these names can be used to describe the quadrilateral?
Ⓐ parallelogram   C square
B rectangle   D trapezoid

Angles in Polygons

California Standards

MG3.1 Identify and construct basic elements of geometric figures (e.g., altitudes, midpoints, **diagonals,** angle bisectors, and perpendicular bisectors; central angles, radii, diameters, and chords of circles) by using a compass and straightedge.

go.hrw.com
Lab Resources Online
KEYWORD: MT8CA Lab8

A *diagonal* of a polygon is a segment that connects any two nonconsecutive vertices of the polygon. By drawing all possible diagonals from one vertex, you can find the sum of the interior angle measures of a polygon.

Activity

Pentagon *ABCDE* has been divided into three triangular regions by drawing all possible diagonals from one vertex.

1. Find each of the following:

   $m\angle 1 + m\angle 2 + m\angle 3 =$ ___?___ **180°**

   $m\angle 4 + m\angle 5 + m\angle 6 =$ ___?___ **180°**

   $m\angle 7 + m\angle 8 + m\angle 9 =$ ___?___ **180°**

2. Add the three expressions.

   $m\angle 1 + m\angle 2 + m\angle 3 + m\angle 4 + m\angle 5 + m\angle 6 + m\angle 7 + m\angle 8 + m\angle 9 =$ ___?___ **540°**

3. Determine the sum of the interior angle measures of pentagon *ABCDE* (that is, $m\angle EAB + m\angle B + m\angle BCD + m\angle CDE + m\angle E =$ ___?___). **540°**

4. Complete the table. Use sketches to illustrate your answers.

Polygon	Number of sides	Number of triangular regions	Sum of angle measures
triangle	3	1	180°
quadrilateral	4	2	360°
pentagon	5	3	540°
hexagon	6	4	720°
n-gon	*n*	*n* − 2	180(*n* − 2)

Think and Discuss

The Triangle Sum Theorem states that the sum of the measures of the interior angles of a triangle is 180°.

1. What information did you use to find the sums in Step 1?

2. Write a formula for the sum of the interior angle measures of an *n*-gon. 180(*n* − 2)

Try This

Find the sum of the measures of the angles of each polygon.

1. an octagon **1080°**

2. a decagon (10 sides) **1440°**

3. a nonagon (9 sides) **1260°**

Organizer

Use with Lesson 8-5

Objective: Draw diagonals of a polygon to determine the sum of the interior angle measures.

PREMIER **Online Edition**

Countdown to Mastery Week 17

Teach
Discuss

A diagonal of a polygon is a line segment from one vertex to another non-consecutive vertex. By drawing all of the diagonals from one vertex, you can divide a polygon into triangular regions.

Close
Key Concept

By drawing all of the diagonals from one vertex, you can determine the sum of the interior angle measures of a polygon.

Assessment

The sum of the measures of the interior angles of a polygon is 2340°. Determine the number of sides in this polygon. 15

California Standards

Measurement and Geometry 3.1

Organizer

Objective: Assess students' mastery of concepts and skills in Lessons 8-1 through 8-5.

Resources

 Assessment Resources
Section 8A Quiz

 Test & Practice Generator
 One-Stop Planner®

INTERVENTION ◀◆▶

Resources

 Ready to Go On?
Intervention and
Enrichment Worksheets

💿 **Ready to Go On? CD-ROM**

🪐 **Ready to Go On? Online**

my.hrw.com

Answers

13–14. See p. A8.

Quiz for Lessons 8-1 Through 8-5

1. ∠ABD and ∠DBE,
   ∠EBF and ∠FBC

2. ∠ABD and ∠DBC,
   ∠ABE and ∠EBC,
   ∠ABF and ∠FBC

8-1 Points, Lines, Planes, and Angles

Use the diagram to name each figure.

1. two pairs of complementary angles
2. three pairs of supplementary angles
3. two right angles ∠ABE, ∠EBC

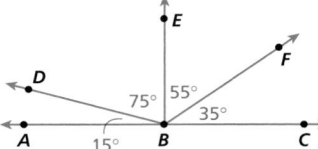

8-2 Geometric Relationships

4–6. Possible answers given.
Identify two figures that have the given relationship.

4. skew lines $\overleftrightarrow{EF}$ and $\overleftrightarrow{AD}$
5. parallel planes plane ABC ∥ plane HGF
6. perpendicular planes plane ABC ⊥ plane CDE

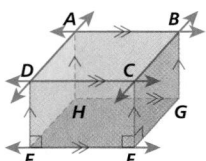

8-3 Angle Relationships

In the figure, line m ∥ line n. Find the measure of each angle.

7. ∠1 55°   8. ∠2 125°   9. ∠3 125°

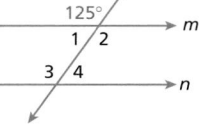

8-4 Triangles

Find x in each triangle.

10. 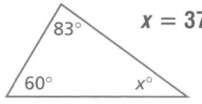 $x = 37$ 11.   $x = 53$

12. $\overline{PR}$ is a diagonal of rectangle PQRS. PQ is 28 ft and PR is 35 ft. Find the length of $\overline{QR}$.   21 ft

8-5 Coordinate Geometry

Graph the quadrilaterals with the given vertices. Give all of the names that apply to each quadrilateral.

13. $A(-2, 1)$, $B(3, 2)$, $C(2, 0)$, $D(-3, -1)$
    parallelogram
Find the coordinates of the missing vertex.

14. $P(-3, 4)$, $Q(2, 4)$, $R(2, -1)$, $S(-3, -1)$
    parallelogram, rhombus, rectangle, square

15. square ABCD with $A(-1, 1)$, $B(2, 1)$, and $C(2, -2)$ $D(-1, -2)$

16. parallelogram PQRS with $P(3, 3)$, $Q(4, 2)$, and $R(2, -2)$ $S(1, -1)$

READY TO GO ON?
Diagnose and Prescribe

NO INTERVENE			**YES** ENRICH

Ready to Go On? Intervention	**READY TO GO ON?** Intervention, Section 8A			READY TO GO ON? Enrichment, Section 8A
	Worksheets	CD-ROM	Online	
✓ Lesson 8-1 Prep for MG3.1	8-1 Intervention	Activity 8-1		Worksheets
✓ Lesson 8-2 MG3.6	8-2 Intervention	Activity 8-2	Diagnose and Prescribe Online	CD-ROM
✓ Lesson 8-3 6MG2.1, 6MG2.2	8-3 Intervention	Activity 8-3		Online
✓ Lesson 8-4 MG3.3	8-4 Intervention	Activity 8-4		
✓ Lesson 8-5 AF3.3, MG3.2	8-5 Intervention	Activity 8-5		

Focus on Problem Solving

California Standards

MR1.1 Analyze problems by identifying relationships, **distinguishing relevant from irrelevant information**, identifying missing information, **sequencing and prioritizing information**, and observing patterns.
Also covered: **MG3.0**

Understand the Problem

- **Restate the problem in your own words**

If you write a problem in your own words, you may understand it better. Before writing a problem in your own words, you may need to read it over several times—perhaps aloud, so you can hear yourself say the words.

Once you have written the problem in your own words, you may want to make sure you included all of the necessary information to solve the problem.

Write each problem in your own words. Check to make sure you have included all of the information needed to solve the problem.

1 In the figure, ∠1 and ∠2 are complementary, and ∠1 and ∠5 are supplementary. If m∠1 = 60°, find m∠3 + m∠4.

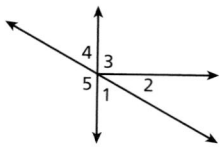

2 In triangle *ABC*, m∠A = 35° and m∠B = 55°. Is triangle *ABC* a right triangle?

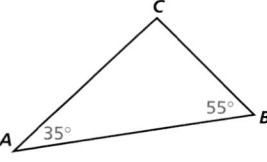

3 The second angle in a quadrilateral is eight times as large as the first angle. The third angle is half as large as the second. The fourth angle is as large as the first angle and the second angle combined. Find the approximate angle measures in the quadrilateral.

4 Parallel lines *m* and *n* are intersected by a transversal, line *p*. The acute angles formed by line *m* and line *p* measure 45°. Find the measure of the obtuse angles formed by the intersection of line *n* and line *p*.

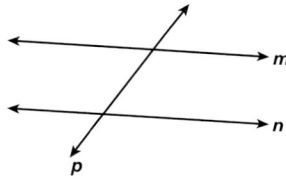

Answers

1. 150°

2. Triangle *ABC* is a right triangle.

3. ≈ 16.4°, ≈ 131.2°, ≈ 65.6°, and ≈ 147.6°

4. 135°

Possible answers to Discuss:

1. m∠1 and m∠2 add up to 90°.
   m∠1 and m∠5 add up to 180°.
   If m∠1 = 60°, find m∠3 + m∠4.

2. Find out if m∠C = 90° when m∠A = 35° and m∠B = 55°

3. First angle = x; second angle = 8x; third angle = 4x; fourth angle = 9x; the angles add up to 360°; find the measure of each angle.

4. Find the supplement of 45°.

California Standards

Mathematical Reasoning 1.1
Also covered:
Measurement and Geometry
3.0 Students know the Pythagorean theorem and **deepen their understanding of plane** and solid **geometric shapes** by constructing figures that meet given conditions and **by identifying attributes of figures.**

Congruence and Transformations

 **One-Minute Section Planner**

Lesson	Lab Resources	Materials
Lesson 8-6 Congruent Polygons ● Use properties of congruent figures to solve problems. 🐻 **MG3.0**, 🔑 **MG3.4**	**Hands-On Lab 8-6** In *Chapter 8 Resource File*	**Optional** Triangle cutouts, protractors (MK), rulers (MK), scissors
Lesson 8-7 Transformations ● Recognize, describe, and show transformations. 🐻 **MG3.2**	**Hands-On Lab 8-7** **Technology Lab 8-7** In *Chapter 8 Resource File*	**Optional** Cutout figures
8-7 Hands-On Lab Combine Transformations ● Use pattern blocks and a coordinate plane to explore compound transformations. 🐻 **MG3.2**		**Required** Pattern blocks (MK), graph paper
Lesson 8-8 Tessellations ● Create tessellations. 🐻 **Extension of MG3.2**		**Optional** Pictures, artwork, or fabric with tessellating designs, pattern blocks (MK), protractors (MK)

MK = *Manipulatives Kit*

Notes

Math Background: Teaching the Standards

Professional Development

CONGRUENT FIGURES 🐻 🔑 MG3.4
Lesson 8-6

Loosely speaking, two figures are congruent if they have exactly the same size and shape. Providing a more precise definition of congruence depends on first defining congruence for two of the most basic geometric figures—line segments and angles.

- Two line segments are congruent if they have the same length.

- Two angles are congruent if they have the same measure.

These definitions can be used to build a definition of congruence for polygons. Two polygons are congruent if their sides and angles can be paired so that all of the corresponding pairs of sides and angles are congruent. Note that this definition may be used in two directions. That is, if we know that corresponding sides and angles are congruent, we can conclude that the polygons are congruent. Conversely, if we know that two polygons are congruent, we can conclude that the corresponding sides and angles are congruent. This last observation is often useful in finding an unknown side length or angle measure in a pair of congruent polygons.

In future geometry courses, students will learn special conditions that guarantee that two polygons are congruent. For example, to demonstrate that two triangles are congruent, it is not necessary to verify that all three pairs of sides are congruent and that all three pairs of angles are congruent. There are numerous shortcuts by which to demonstrate congruence. One such shortcut is the Side-Side-Side Congruence Postulate, which states that two triangles are congruent if the three sides of one triangle are congruent to the three sides of the other triangle. That is, if the sides are congruent, the angles must also be congruent.

It is worth noting that congruence can be considered to be a special case of similarity. If two polygons are similar, then corresponding angles are congruent and corresponding sides have lengths that form equal ratios. When this ratio is 1, the polygons are congruent. To put this another way, similar figures are congruent when the scale factor is 1.

TRANSFORMATIONS 🐻 MG3.2
Lesson 8-7

In Lesson 8-7, students are introduced to three basic transformations: translations, reflections, and rotations. These transformations are closely connected to the concept of congruence. In particular, the image of any figure under a translation, reflection, or rotation is congruent to the original figure (called the pre-image). Transformations that preserve the size and shape of figures are known as *isometries*.

Congruence can also be defined in terms of transformations. That is, two figures are congruent if one figure can be transformed into the other through a series of translations, reflections, and rotations. This matches our intuitive notion of congruence: given two congruent paper triangles, one triangle may be made to fit exactly on top of the other by sliding, flipping, and turning the paper.

It is instructive to examine transformations on a coordinate plane. For example, when a point (a, b) is reflected across the x-axis, the image is the point $(a, -b)$. When (a, b) is reflected across the y-axis, the image is $(-a, b)$. The image of (a, b) under a 180° rotation about the origin is $(-a, -b)$. Notice that when (a, b) is reflected across the x-axis and the image is reflected across the y-axis, we have $(a, b) \rightarrow (a, -b) \rightarrow (-a, -b)$, so that the final image is the same as the image of (a, b) under a 180° rotation. In other words, successive reflections across the two axes are equivalent to a single 180° rotation about the origin.

Also of note is that composing two nonidentity reflections will give a rotation of twice the angle between the two lines of reflection.

Hands-On Lab
In *Chapter 8 Resource File*

 Online Edition
Tutorial Videos

 Countdown to Mastery Week 17

Power Presentations
with PowerPoint®

Warm Up
Find the measure of the indicated angle.

1. the fourth angle in a quadrilateral containing angles of 100°, 130°, and 75° **55°**

2. the third angle of a right triangle with an angle of 60° **30°**

3. the supplement of a 35° angle **145°**

Also available on transparency

Math Humor

Why were the two angles in the congruent triangles writing letters to each other? They were corresponding angles.

8-6 Congruent Polygons

Vocabulary
correspondence
congruent

Who uses this?
Biologists use congruence to compare DNA profiles.

Below are the DNA profiles of two pairs of twins. Twins A and B are identical twins. Twins C and D are fraternal twins.

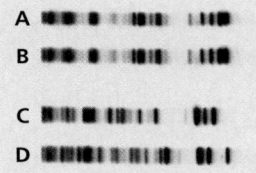

A **correspondence** is a way of matching up two sets of objects. The bands of DNA in each pair match up, or *correspond*. In the DNA of the identical twins, the corresponding bands are the same.

Congruent figures have the same size and shape. If two polygons are congruent, all of their corresponding sides and angles are congruent.

CONGRUENT TRIANGLES			
Diagram	Statement	Corresponding Angles	Corresponding Sides
A △ B D E F C	△ABC ≅ △DEF	∠A ≅ ∠D ∠B ≅ ∠E ∠C ≅ ∠F	$\overline{AB} \cong \overline{DE}$ $\overline{BC} \cong \overline{EF}$ $\overline{AC} \cong \overline{DF}$

To write a *congruence statement*, the vertices in the second polygon have to be written in order of correspondence with the first polygon.

EXAMPLE 1 **Writing Congruence Statements**

Write a congruence statement for the pair of congruent polygons.

A

Helpful Hint
Marks on the sides of a figure can be used to show congruence.
$\overline{KM} \cong \overline{RS}$ (1 mark)
$\overline{KL} \cong \overline{RQ}$ (2 marks)
$\overline{ML} \cong \overline{SQ}$ (3 marks)

∠K corresponds to ∠R.   ∠K ≅ ∠R
∠L corresponds to ∠Q.   ∠L ≅ ∠Q
∠M corresponds to ∠S.   ∠M ≅ ∠S

The congruence statement is triangle *KLM* ≅ triangle *RQS*.

---

① Introduce

Alternate Opener

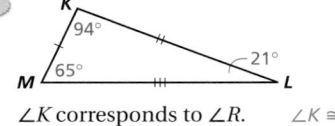

EXPLORATION

8-6 Congruent Polygons

Congruent figures have the same size and shape.

Determine whether the figures in each pair are congruent.

1.
2.
3.
4.

Think and Discuss
5. Explain how you decided whether the figures in Problems 1–4 were congruent or not.
6. Find two examples of objects that are congruent. What makes the two objects congruent?

Motivate

Show the students two triangles that are congruent. Ask them what they notice about the triangles. Help students respond with answers such as "they have the same size and shape," "the sides are the same length," and "the angles have the same measure." Alternately place one triangle on top of the other to show that each completely covers the other.

Explorations and answers are provided in *Alternate Openers: Explorations Transparencies.*

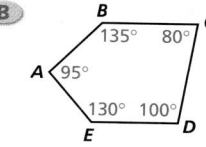
Helpful Hint

The vertices in a polygon are written in order around the polygon starting at any vertex.

Write a congruence statement for the pair of congruent polygons.

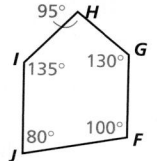

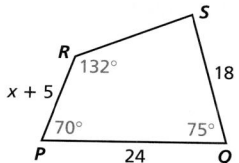

∠*A* corresponds to ∠*H*.   ∠*A* ≅ ∠*H*
∠*B* corresponds to ∠*I*.   ∠*B* ≅ ∠*I*
∠*C* corresponds to ∠*J*.   ∠*C* ≅ ∠*J*
∠*D* corresponds to ∠*F*.   ∠*D* ≅ ∠*F*
∠*E* corresponds to ∠*G*.   ∠*E* ≅ ∠*G*

The congruence statement is pentagon *ABCDE* ≅ pentagon *HIJFG*.

EXAMPLE 2 **Using Congruence Relationships to Find Unknown Values**

In the figure, quadrilateral *PQSR* ≅ quadrilateral *WTUV*.

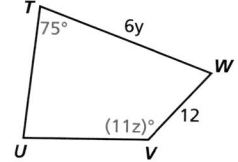

Answers to Think and Discuss

1. They have the same size and shape.

2. Name one of the polygons by listing its vertices in either clockwise or counter-clockwise order. Write the congruence symbol (≅), then name the other polygon by listing its vertices in corresponding order.

A Find **x**.

$x + 5 = 12$ $\overline{PR} \cong \overline{WV}$
$\underline{\quad -5 = -5}$ Subtract 5 from
$x \quad = \quad 7$ both sides.

B Find **y**.

$6y = 24$ $\overline{WT} \cong \overline{PQ}$
$\dfrac{6y}{6} = \dfrac{24}{6}$ Divide both sides by 6.
$y = 4$

C Find **z**.

$132 = 11z$ $\angle R \cong \angle V$
$\dfrac{132}{11} = \dfrac{11z}{11}$ Divide both sides by 11.
$12 = z$

Think and Discuss

1. **Explain** what it means for two polygons to be congruent.

2. **Tell** how to write a congruence statement for two polygons.

Additional Examples

Example 1

Write a congruence statement for each pair of congruent polygons.

A.

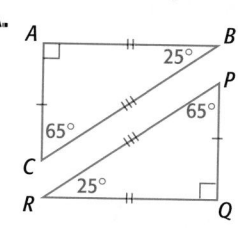

triangle *ABC* ≅ triangle *QRP*

B.

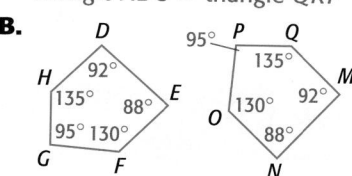

pentagon *DEFGH* ≅ pentagon *MNOPQ*

Example 2

In the figure, quadrilateral *VWXY* ≅ quadrilateral *JKLM*.

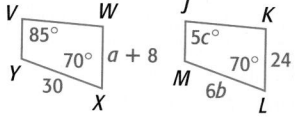

A. Find *a*. 16   **B.** Find *b*. 5

C. Find *c*. 17

Also available on transparency

---

2 Teach

Guided Instruction

In this lesson, students learn to use properties of congruent figures to solve problems. Begin by showing students how to write a congruence statement for a pair of congruent polygons. Make sure students understand the concepts of corresponding angles and corresponding sides. Discuss with students how to use a congruence statement to find an unknown measure of a side or angle and then to solve for a variable.

Teaching Tip **Communicating Math** Students can use a congruence statement to identify a pair of corresponding sides or angles. For example, if △*ABC* ≅ △*DEF*, then side *AC* ≅ side *DF*.

Universal Access
Through Concrete Manipulatives

Have students work in pairs. Have each student draw a polygon and hand it to their partner. The partner is responsible for drawing a polygon that appears to be congruent to the polygon they were given. Give each student a protractor, a ruler, and a pair of scissors. Students should measure and label all sides and all angles and then determine which pairs are congruent. You may want to set some rules for what is considered congruent (e.g., angle measures within 1° or side lengths within 1 mm). They can then cut out the polygons to check their work.

3 Close

Summarize

Remind students that when polygons are congruent, they have the same size and shape. Make sure students understand the importance of identifying corresponding parts of congruent figures. Show the students a pair of congruent polygons and name one of them. Ask the students to name the other polygon in the correct order and to name congruent parts.

Possible answers: triangles *ABC* and *XYZ*;
∠*A* ≅ ∠*X*; ∠*B* ≅ ∠*Y*; ∠*C* ≅ ∠*Z*;
$\overline{AB} \cong \overline{XY}$; $\overline{BC} \cong \overline{YZ}$; $\overline{AC} \cong \overline{XZ}$

8-6 Exercises

California Standards Practice

go.hrw.com
Homework Help Online
KEYWORD: MT8CA 8-6
Parent Resources Online
KEYWORD: MT8CA Parent

MG3.4

Assignment Guide

If you finished Example **1** assign:
Proficient 1, 2, 6, 7, 21–24
Advanced 6, 7, 16, 21–24

If you finished Example **2** assign:
Proficient 1–14, 19–24
Advanced 6–24

Homework Quick Check

Quickly check key concepts.
Exercises: 6, 8, 12

Math Background

The use of congruent figures is a dominant aspect in geometric patterns and designs. Fabric and wallpaper designs in particular make use of congruent figures by repeating a given figure throughout the material. A repeating pattern of congruent figures that completely covers a surface is a *tessellation* (Lesson 8-8). Sometimes the figures are rotated or reflected throughout the design. Rotations and reflections are types of *transformations* (Lesson 8-7).

GUIDED PRACTICE

See Example **1** Write a congruence statement for each pair of congruent polygons.

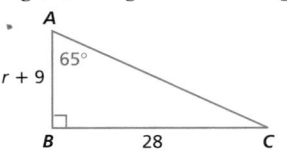
1.

triangle *ABC* ≅ triangle *FED*

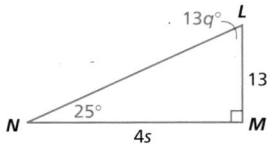
2.

quadrilateral *LMNO* ≅ quadrilateral *STQR*

See Example **2** In the figure, triangle *ABC* ≅ triangle *LMN*.

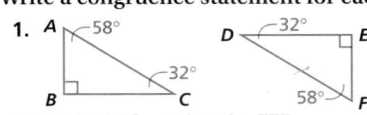

3. Find *q*. *q* = 5   **4.** Find *r*. *r* = 4   **5.** Find *s*. *s* = 7

INDEPENDENT PRACTICE

See Example **1** Write a congruence statement for each pair of congruent polygons.

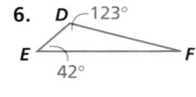
6.

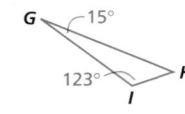

triangle *DEF* ≅ triangle *IHG*

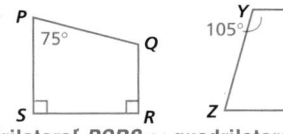
7.

quadrilateral *PQRS* ≅ quadrilateral *ZYXW*

See Example **2** In the figure, quadrilateral *ABCD* ≅ quadrilateral *LMNO*.

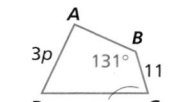 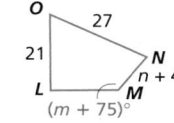

8. Find *m*. *m* = 56   **9.** Find *n*. *n* = 7   **10.** Find *p*. *p* = 7

PRACTICE AND PROBLEM SOLVING

Extra Practice
See page EP17.

Find the value of each variable.

m = 14, *n* = 32, *p* = 64

11. pentagon *ABCDE* ≅ pentagon *PQRST*   *x* = 19, *y* = 27, *z* = 18.1

12. hexagon *ABCDEF* ≅ hexagon *LMNOPQ*

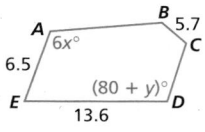 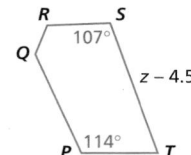 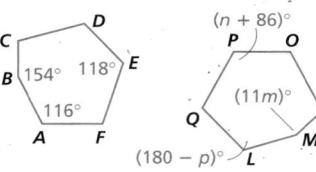

California Standards

Standard	Exercises
AF3.3	22
MG3.2	23–24
MG3.4	1–21

REVIEW FOR MASTERY 8-6

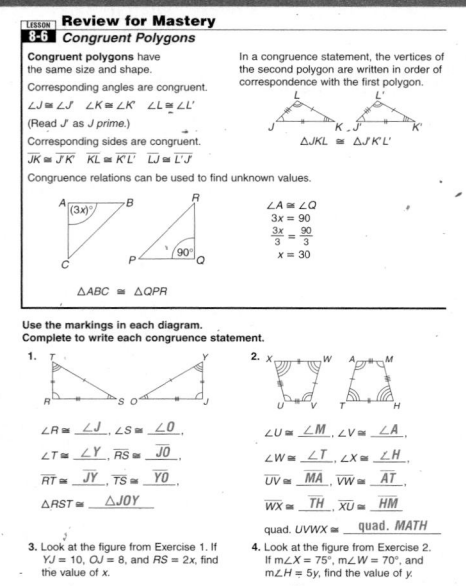

PRACTICE 8-6

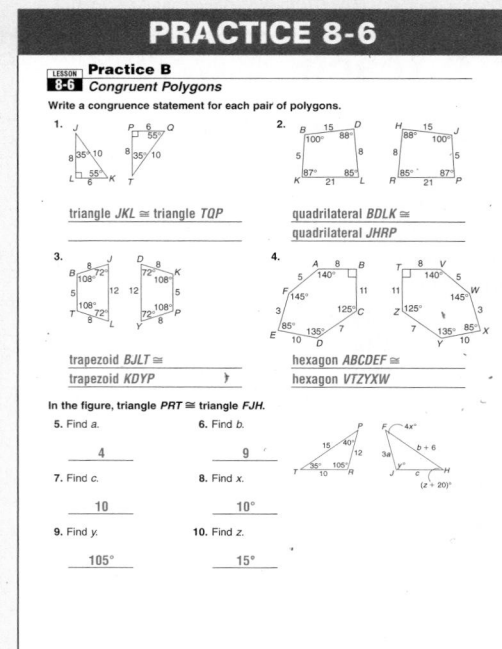

16. Possible answer: Write a congruence statement for the pair of triangles. Answer: triangle $ABC \cong$ triangle FED

Find the value of each variable.

13. quadrilateral $ABCD \cong$ quadrilateral $EFGH$

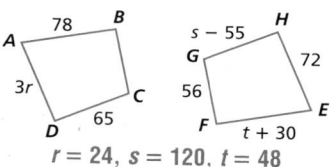

$r = 24$, $s = 120$, $t = 48$

14. heptagon $ABCDEFG \cong$ heptagon $JKLMNOP$

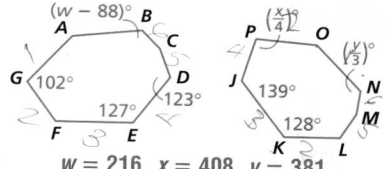

$w = 216$, $x = 408$, $y = 381$

17. Possible answer: By matching the angles and known measures, you can work back and forth to calculate unknown angles.

15. Right triangle $PQR \cong$ right triangle STU. $m\angle P = 28°$ and $m\angle U = 90°$. Find $m\angle Q$. **62°**

16. Write a Problem Write and solve a problem about the right triangles shown.

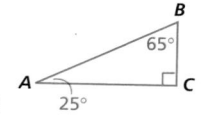 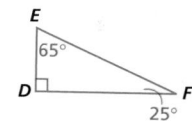

17. Write About It How can knowing that two polygons are congruent help you find angle measures of the polygons?

18. Challenge Triangle $ABC \cong$ triangle LMN and $\overline{AE} \parallel \overline{BD}$. Find $m\angle ACD$.
$m\angle ACD = 100°$

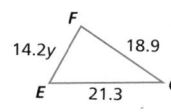 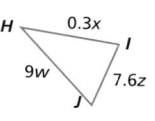

SPIRAL STANDARDS REVIEW ⬥ AF3.3, MG3.2, ⬥ MG3.4

19. Multiple Choice Triangle $EFG \cong$ triangle JIH. Find the value of x.

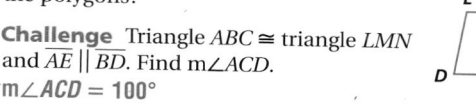 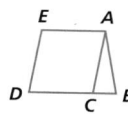 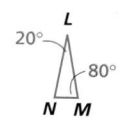

   Ⓐ $x = 5.67$ Ⓑ $x = 30$ Ⓒ $x = 63$ Ⓓ $x = 71$

20. Multiple Choice Triangle $ABC \cong$ triangle JKL. $m\angle A = 30°$ and $m\angle B = 50°$. Find $m\angle K$.

   Ⓐ 30°   Ⓑ 50°   Ⓒ 80°   Ⓓ 100°

21. Gridded Response Quadrilateral $ABCD \cong$ quadrilateral $WXYZ$. The length of $\overline{AB} = 21$ and the length of $\overline{WX} = 7m$. Find m. **3**

22. A function has an output value of 1 when the input value is 2; it has an ouput value of 2 when the input value is 4; and it has output value of -1 when the input value is 2. Is this a linear function? (Lesson 7-3) **no**

Find the coordinates of the missing vertex. (Lesson 8-5)

23. square $PQRS$ with $Q(-2, 1)$, $R(-2, -1)$, and $S(-4, -1)$ $P(-4, 1)$

24. rectangle $LMNO$ with $L(1, 3)$, $M(3, 3)$, and $N(3, -2)$ $O(1, -2)$

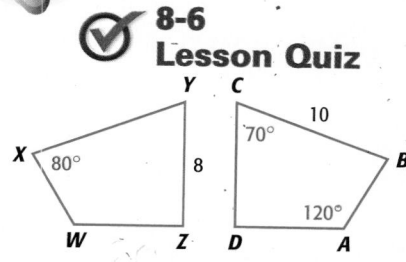

CHALLENGE 8-6

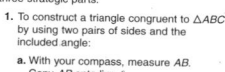
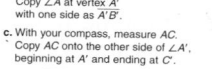
PROBLEM SOLVING 8-6

Hands-On Lab
In *Chapter 8 Resource File*

Technology Lab
In *Chapter 8 Resource File*

Online Edition
Tutorial Videos

Countdown to Mastery Week 17

Power Presentations
with PowerPoint®

Warm Up

1. Subtract 3 from the *x*-coordinate and 2 from the *y*-coordinate in (7, −4). (4, −6)

2. Multiply each coordinate by 3 in (4, 9). (12, 27)

3. Subtract 4 from the *x*-coordinate and add 3 to the *y*-coordinate in (−2, −1). (−6, 2)

Also available on transparency

Math Humor

What did the triangle say when it looked in the mirror? Wow, what a transformation!

California Standards

Measurement and Geometry 3.2

8-7 Transformations

California Standards

MG3.2 Understand and use coordinate graphs to plot simple figures, determine lengths and areas related to them, **and determine their image under translations and reflections.**

Vocabulary
transformation
image
translation
reflection
rotation

Who uses this? Professional ice skaters perform transformations during their routines.

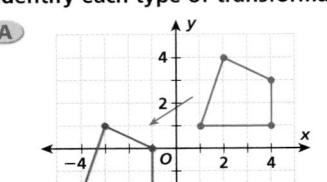

In the photograph, Michelle Kwan is performing a *layback spin*. She is holding her body in one position while she rotates. This is an example of a *transformation*.

In mathematics, a **transformation** changes the position or orientation of a figure. The resulting figure is the **image** of the original. Images resulting from the transformations described below are congruent to the original figures.

Translation	Reflection	Rotation
A **translation** slides a figure along a line without turning it.	A **reflection** flips a figure across a line to create a mirror image.	A **rotation** turns a figure around a point, called the center of rotation.

EXAMPLE 1 Identifying Types of Transformations

Identify each type of transformation.

Helpful Hint

The point that a figure rotates around may be on the figure or away from the figure.

A

The figure slides along a straight line.
It is a translation.

B

The figure flips across the x-axis.
It is a reflection.

---

1 Introduce

Alternate Opener

EXPLORATION

8-7 Transformations

1. Draw arrows from all the vertices (corners) of each original figure (blue) to the corresponding vertices of its *image* (red).

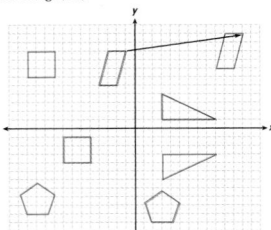

Think and Discuss

2. Explain whether the transformations in Problem 1 are congruent, which means that the image is the same shape and size as the original figure.

3. Compare the transformation of the triangle with the transformations of the other figures. How is it different? Find a name for this transformation.

Motivate

To introduce students to transformations, ask them to describe the movements of pieces in checkers, chess, or a similar game. After students describe the moves, have them explain how the moves affect the sizes and shapes of the pieces. Point out that the pieces do not change despite the moves in the game.

You may want to have students describe other ways to move shapes without changing their sizes or shapes, such as flipping them over or rotating them.

Explorations and answers are provided in *Alternate Openers: Explorations Transparencies.*

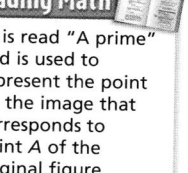
EXAMPLE 2 **Graphing Translations on a Coordinate Plane**

Graph the translation of △*ABC* 6 units right and 4 units down.

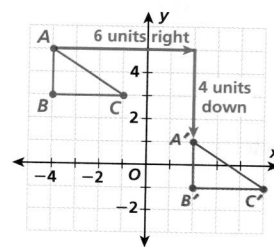

Each vertex is moved 6 units right and 4 units down.

EXAMPLE 3 **Graphing Reflections on a Coordinate Plane**

Graph the reflection of each figure across the indicated axis. Write the coordinates of the vertices of the image.

A *x*-axis

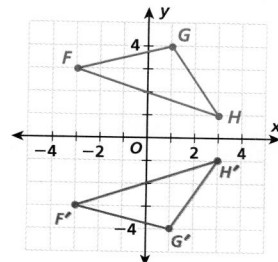

The x-coordinates of the corresponding vertices are the same, and the y-coordinates of the corresponding vertices are opposites.

The coordinates of the vertices of triangle *F'G'H'* are *F'*(−3, −3), *G'*(1, −4), and *H'*(3, −1).

B *y*-axis

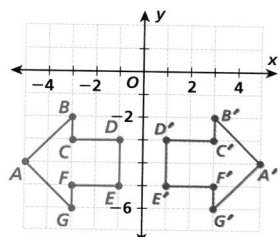

The y-coordinates of the corresponding vertices are the same, and the x-coordinates of the corresponding vertices are opposites.

The coordinates of the vertices of figure *A'B'C'D'E'F'G'* are *A'*(5, −4), *B'*(3, −2), *C'*(3, −3), *D'*(1, −3), *E'*(1, −5), *F'*(3, −5), and *G'*(3, −6).

2 Teach

Guided Instruction

In this lesson, students learn to recognize, describe, and show transformations. To help students understand the different types of transformations, continue to relate each type to real-world situations, such as sliding down a slide, looking in a mirror, and turning around. You may want to use the Teaching Transparency.

Universal Access
Through Concrete Manipulatives

Use cutout figures to illustrate types of transformations from the examples in the lesson. This will help emphasize that the sizes and shapes of the figures do not change under the transformations in this lesson. For **Example 4,** rotate the cutout figures on the coordinate plane.

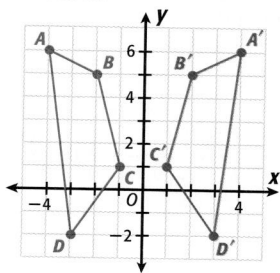
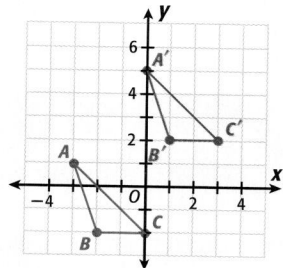
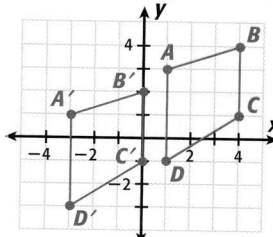
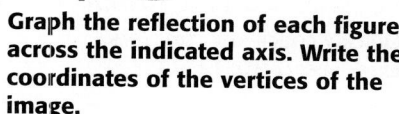
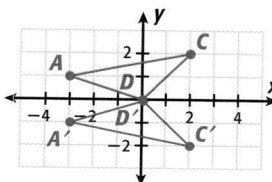
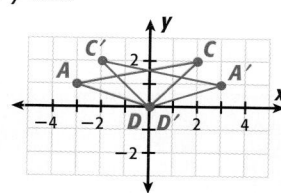

Example 4

Triangle *ABC* has vertices *A*(1,0), *B*(3,3), *C*(5,0). Rotate △*ABC* 180° about the vertex *A*.

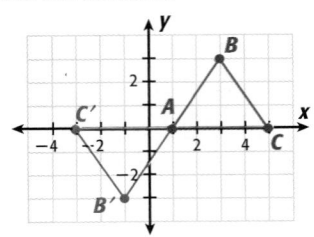

Also available on transparency

EXAMPLE 4 Graphing Rotations on a Coordinate Plane

Triangle *JKL* has vertices *J*(−3, 1), *K*(−3, −2), and *L*(1, −2). Rotate △*JKL* 90° counterclockwise about the vertex *J*.

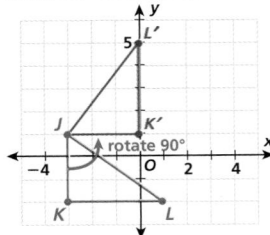

Notice that the corresponding sides, $\overline{JK}$ and $\overline{JK}'$, make a 90° angle.

Also notice that vertex K is 3 units below vertex J, and vertex K' is 3 units to the right of vertex J.

Possible answers to *Think and Discuss*

1. sliding a desk, without turning it, from one row to another

2. The x-coordinate remains the same, while the y-coordinate changes sign.

Think and Discuss

1. **Describe** a classroom situation that illustrates a translation.

2. **Tell** what happens to the x-coordinate and the y-coordinate after a point is reflected across the x-axis.

8-7 Exercises

8-7 Exercises

California Standards Practice
MG3.2

go.hrw.com
Homework Help Online
KEYWORD: MT8CA 8-7
Parent Resources Online
KEYWORD: MT8CA Parent

GUIDED PRACTICE

See Example 1 — Identify each type of transformation.

1.
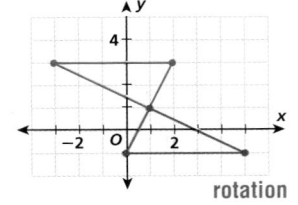
rotation

2.
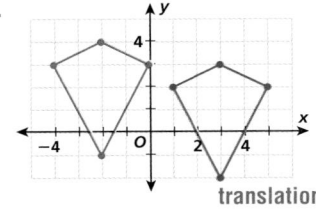
translation

See Example 2 — Graph each translation.

3. 2 units left and 3 units up
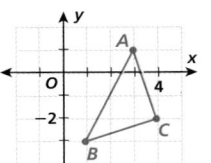

4. 3 units right and 4 units down
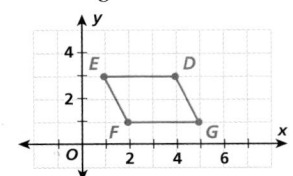

---

3 Close

Summarize

Ask students to describe each of the transformations introduced in this lesson and explain how to do each one.

Possible answers: A translation is a slide along a straight line with no turns. A rotation is a turn around a fixed point, and a reflection is a flip across a line of reflection.

Answers

3.
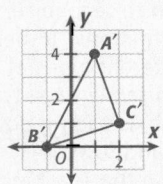

4.
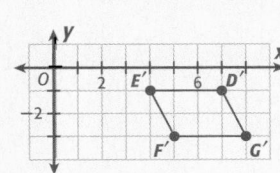

See Example **3** Graph the reflection of each figure across the indicated axis. Write the coordinates of the vertices of the image.

5. x-axis

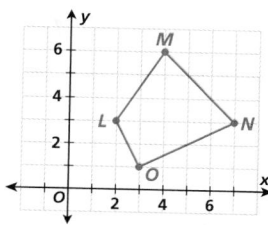

6. y-axis

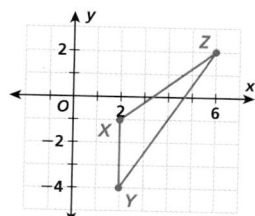

See Example **4** **7.** Triangle LMN has vertices L(0, 1), M(−3, 0), and N(−2, 4). Rotate △LMN 180° about the vertex L.

INDEPENDENT PRACTICE

See Example **1** Identify each type of transformation.

8.

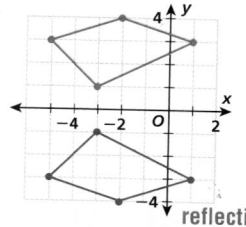

reflection

9. translation

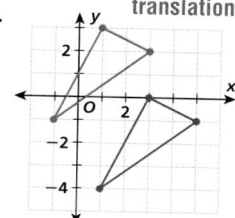

See Example **2** Graph each translation.

10. 5 units right and 1 unit down

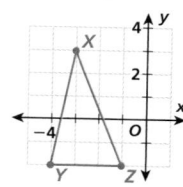

11. 4 units left and 3 units up

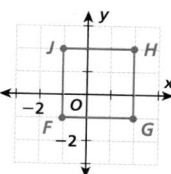

See Example **3** Graph the reflection of each figure across the indicated axis. Write the coordinates of the vertices of the image.

12. y-axis

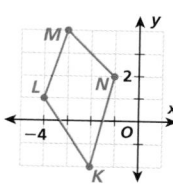

13. x-axis

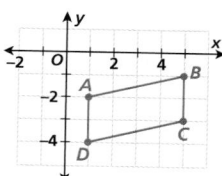

See Example **4** **14.** Triangle MNL has vertices M(0, 4), N(3, 3), and L(0, 0). Rotate △MNL 90° counterclockwise about the vertex L.

REVIEW FOR MASTERY 8-7

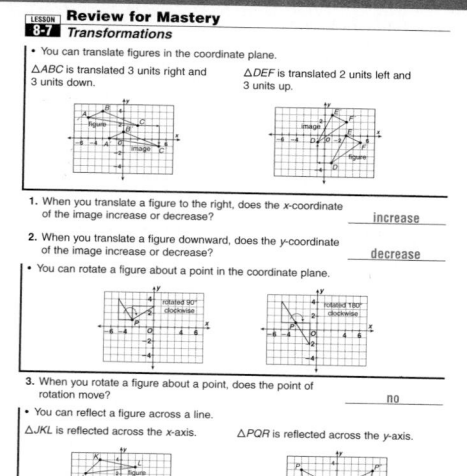

PRACTICE 8-7

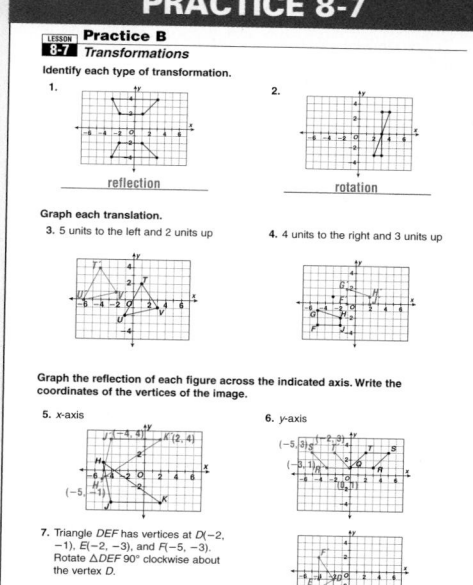

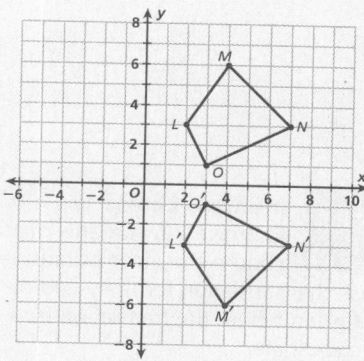
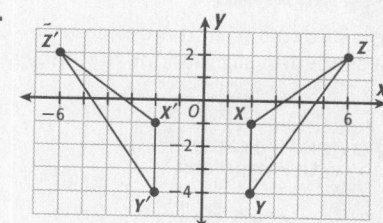
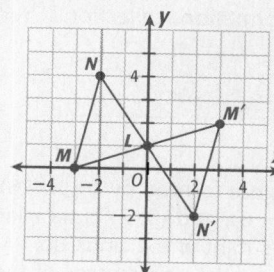
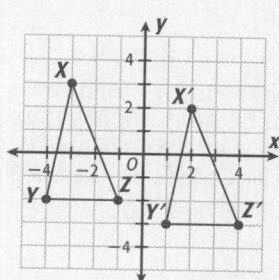

Answers

15–18, 25–27, 29. See pp. A8–9.

Teaching Tip **Multiple Choice** In **Exercise 28,** students may choose the incorrect answer because the translation for the *y*-coordinate is given before the translation for the *x*-coordinate.

 Journal

Ask students to find a design and describe transformations that they see.

Power Presentations
with PowerPoint®

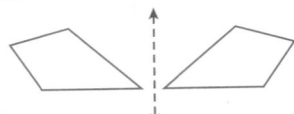

8-7 Lesson Quiz

1. Identify the type of transformation. reflection

2. The figure formed by (−5, −6), (−1, −6), and (3, 2) is translated 6 units right and 2 units up. What are the coordinates of the new figure?

(1, −4), (5, −4), (9, 4)

3. Graph the triangle with vertices A(−1, 0), B(−3, 0), C(−1, 4). Rotate △ABC 90° counterclockwise around vertex A and reflect the resulting image across the y-axis.

3. See p. A9.

Also available on transparency

PRACTICE AND PROBLEM SOLVING

Extra Practice
See page EP17.

Draw the image of the parallelogram *ABCD* with vertices (−3, 0), (−4, 3), (1, 4), and (2, 1) after each transformation.

15. translation 1 unit up

16. reflection across the *x*-axis

Draw the image of the quadrilateral *ABCD* with vertices (1, 1), (2, 4), (4, 5), and (5, 3) after each transformation.

17. translation 5 units down

18. reflection across the *y*-axis

Give the coordinates of each point after a reflection across the given axis.

19. (−3, 2); *x*-axis (−3, −2) **20.** (1, 4); *x*-axis (1, −4) **21.** (*m, n*); *y*-axis (−*m, n*)

22. (−2, 4); *y*-axis (2, 4) **23.** (5, −2); *y*-axis (−5, −2) **24.** (*m, n*); *x*-axis (*m, −n*)

25. Write a Problem Write a problem involving transformations on a coordinate grid that result in a pattern.

26. Write About It Explain how each type of transformation performed on the arrow would affect the direction the arrow is pointing.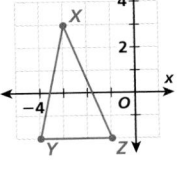

27. Challenge A triangle has vertices (2, 5), (3, 7), and (7, 5). After a reflection and a translation, the coordinates of the image are (7, −2), (8, −4), and (12, −2). Describe the transformations.

SPIRAL STANDARDS REVIEW ⬅ AF3.3, MG3.2, ⬅ MG3.4

28. Multiple Choice In the figure shown, what will be the coordinates of point X after a translation 2 units down and 3 units right?

Ⓐ (0, 1) Ⓑ (1, 0) Ⓒ (−1, 0) Ⓓ (0, −1)

29. Short Response Triangle *ABC* has vertices *A*(−3, 1), *B*(0, 1), and *C*(0, 6). Rotate △*ABC* 90° clockwise around vertex *B*. Draw △*ABC* and its image. *A'*(0, 4), *B'*(0, 1), *C'*(5, 1)

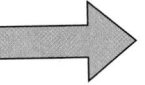

Determine whether the rates of change are constant or variable. (Lesson 7-6)

30.

x	−1	0	2	5	9
y	1	3	5	7	9

variable

31.

x	−2	0	2	4	6
y	1	0	−1	−2	−3

constant

Determine the missing measure in each set of congruent polygons. (Lesson 8-6)

32. 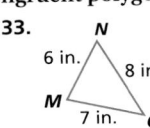 3 m **33.**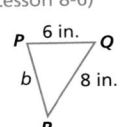

CHALLENGE 8-7

LESSON 8-7 Challenge
Follow That Transformation

You alone know the location of the secret treasure. You want to draw a map to direct your friend to the treasure, but you must do so in code. Use transformations to make the code.

First, draw a triangle on the coordinate plane below.

Next, list in order 5 transformations that must be done to the original figure. The treasure is located in the image of the last transformed triangle.

Then exchange your map with another student. Follow the directions and draw a triangle to show the location of the treasure. **Possible answer given.**

1. reflect across
   x-axis

2. rotate 180°
   about point (2, −3)

3. translate 4 units left
   and 10 units up

4. reflect across
   y-axis

5. translate 7 units left
   and 6 units down

PROBLEM SOLVING 8-7

LESSON 8-7 Problem Solving
Transformations

Write the correct answer.

Clock 1   Clock 2

1. If you reflect the hands of clock 1 across a line from 12 to 6, what time will it show?

11:00

2. If you rotate the hour hand on clock 2 by 90° clockwise, what time will it be?

6:00

3. The hands on clock 1 show 7:00 after a transformation of one hand. What was the transformation?

180° rotation of the hour hand

4. The hands on clock 2 show 9:00 after a transformation. Name 2 different transformations that could produce this change.

reflection across a line from 12 to 6, or rotating the hour hand 180°

Choose the letter for the best answer.

5. What transformation of triangle 1 created triangle 2?
A translation 3 units right and 1 unit down
Ⓑ translation 8 units right and 1 unit down
C rotation of 180° about the origin
D reflection across the y-axis

6. If you rotate triangle 2 90° clockwise about vertex D, what will be the coordinates of the new triangle?
Ⓕ D'(3, 1), E'(7, 1), F'(3, −3)
G D'(3, 1), E'(3, −3), F'(7, 1)
H D'(3, 1), E'(−4, 1), F'(−3, 3)
J D'(3, 1), E'(−3, 3), F'(−7, 1)

7. If you reflect triangle 1 across the x-axis, what will be the coordinates of the new triangle?
A A'(5, 2), B'(5, 6), C'(1, 2)
B A'(−5, 0), B'(−5, −4), C'(−1, 0)
C A'(5, −2), B'(5, −6), C'(1, −2)
Ⓓ A'(−5, −2), B'(−5, −6), C'(−1, −2)

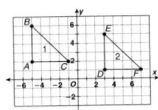

Combine Transformations

Use with Lesson 8-7

California Standards

MG3.2 Understand and use coordinate graphs to plot simple figures, determine lengths and areas related to them, **and determine their image under translations and reflections.**

You can use a coordinate plane when transforming a geometric figure.

go.hrw.com
Lab Resources Online
KEYWORD: MT8CA Lab8

Activity

Follow the steps below to transform a figure.

a. Place a rhombus on a coordinate plane. Trace the rhombus, and label the vertices.

b. Rotate the figure 90° clockwise about the origin.

c. Reflect the resulting figure across the *x*-axis. Draw the image and label the vertices.

d. Now place a rhombus in the same position as the original figure. Reflect the figure across the line *y* = *x*.

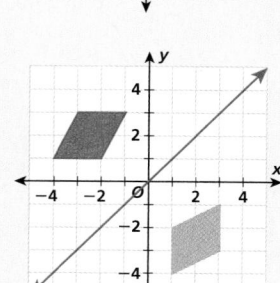

Think and Discuss

1. What do you notice about the images that result from the two transformations in parts **b** and **c** above and the image that results from the single transformation in part **d** above?
The two images are the same.

Try This

1. Place a pattern block on a coordinate plane. Trace the block and label the vertices. Perform two different transformations on the figure. Draw the image and label the vertices. Explain what single transformation of the original figure would result in the same image. **Check students' work.**

Describe two different ways to transform each figure from position A to position B.

2.

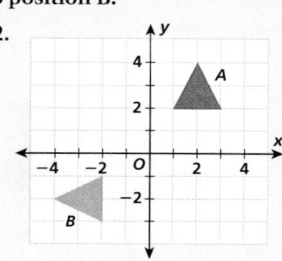

2. Possible answer:
1) Rotate the figure 90° clockwise about the origin. Reflect the resulting figure across the *y*-axis.
2) Reflect the figure across the line *y* = −*x*.

3.

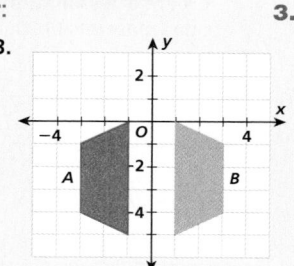

3. Possible answer:
1) Rotate the figure 180° clockwise about the origin. Reflect the resulting figure across the *x*-axis.
2) Reflect the figure across the *y*-axis.

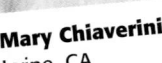

Objective: Use pattern blocks and a coordinate plane to explore compound transformations.
Materials: Pattern blocks, coordinate plane

 Online Edition

 Countdown to Mastery Week 18

Teach
Discuss

Before beginning the lab, have students practice placing pattern blocks on the coordinate plane. Ask them to place a rhombus so that one of the vertices is at (−3, −1). Then ask them to name the other two vertices.

Close
Key Concept

You can use a coordinate plane when transforming a geometric figure.

Assessment

1. Place a triangle on a coordinate plane. Trace it and label the vertices. Reflect the figure across the *y*-axis. Then rotate the figure 90° clockwise about the origin. Draw the new image and label the vertices. Check students' work.

California Standards

Measurement and Geometry 3.2

Objective: Students create tessellations.

 Online Edition
Tutorial Videos

Countdown to Mastery Week 18

Power Presentations
with PowerPoint®

Warm Up

Identify each quadrilateral.

1. quadrilateral with 4 right angles
rectangle

2. quadrilateral with 2 pairs of parallel sides   parallelogram

3. quadrilateral with 4 congruent sides and no right angles
rhombus

Also available on transparency

Math Fact

Even though regular pentagons cannot tessellate a plane (see **Think and Discuss 1**), there are irregular pentagons that can tessellate a plane.

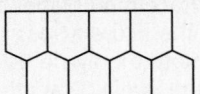

California Standards

Extension of MG3.2 Understand and use coordinate graphs to plot simple figures, determine lengths and areas related to them, **and determine their image under translations and reflections.**

Vocabulary
tessellation
regular tessellation

Why learn this? Tessellations are often used in art and architecture. (See Exercises 14–16.)

A repeating pattern of plane figures that completely covers a plane with no gaps or overlaps is a **tessellation**.

In a **regular tessellation**, a regular polygon is repeated to fill a plane. Since the angle measures at each vertex of a regular tessellation must add to 360°, only three regular tessellations exist.

Alcazar Palace in Seville, Spain

Equilateral triangles

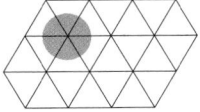

$6 \cdot 60° = 360°$

Squares

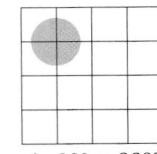

$4 \cdot 90° = 360°$

Regular hexagons

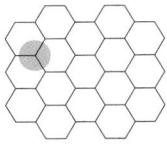

$3 \cdot 120° = 360°$

It is also possible to tessellate with polygons that are not regular. Since the angle measures of a triangle add to 180°, six triangles meeting at each vertex will tessellate. The angle measures of a quadrilateral add to 360°, so four quadrilaterals meeting at a vertex will tessellate.

EXAMPLE 1 **Creating a Tessellation**

Create a tessellation with quadrilateral *ABCD*.

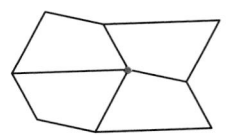

There must be a copy of each angle of quadrilateral ABCD at every vertex.

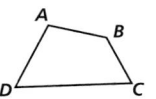

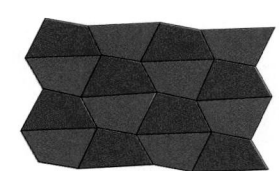

1 **Introduce**

Alternate Opener

EXPLORATION

8-8 **Tessellations**

Tile floors come in many different designs. For each figure, determine whether or not it could be used as a floor tile. Draw a model to show a possible tiling pattern.

	Figure	Model
1.		
2.		
3.		
4.		

Think and Discuss
5. Draw a figure that cannot be used as a tile for a floor.
6. Describe the common characteristics that make some of the figures above suitable for floor tiles.

Motivate

Show the students an image of the inside of a beehive (Teaching Transparency). Explain that when the bees construct their homes, they don't want the "rooms" to overlap, and they don't want any space between the "rooms." Bees are able to do this by building "rooms" out of hexagons. The inside of a beehive is an example of a tessellation.

Explorations and answers are provided in *Alternate Openers: Explorations Transparencies.*

California Standards

Ext. of Measurement and Geometry 3.2

EXAMPLE 2 Creating a Tessellation by Transforming a Polygon

Use rotations to create a variation of the tessellation in Example 1.

Step 1: Find the midpoint of a side.

Step 2: Make a new edge for half of the side.

Step 3: Rotate the new edge around the midpoint to form the edge of the other half of the side.

Step 4: Repeat with the other sides.

Step 5: Use the figure to make a tessellation.

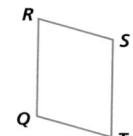

Think and Discuss

1. **Explain** why a regular pentagon cannot be used to create a regular tessellation.

2. **Describe** the transformations used to make the tessellation from the modified figure in Example 2.

3. **Explain** why modifying the sides of a tessellating polygon as shown in Example 2 will always yield another tessellating figure.

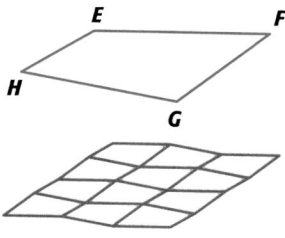
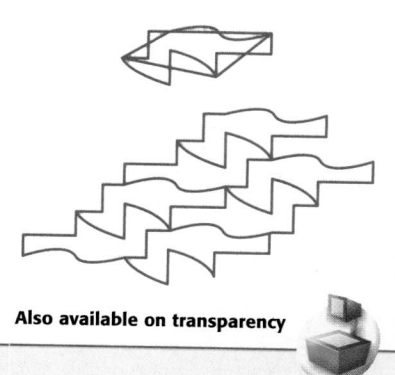

8-8 Exercises

California Standards Practice
Extension of MG3.2

go.hrw.com
Homework Help Online
KEYWORD: MT8CA 8-8
Parent Resources Online
KEYWORD: MT8CA Parent

GUIDED PRACTICE

See Example 1
1. Create a tessellation with quadrilateral *QRST*.

See Example 2
2. Use rotations to create a variation of the tessellation in Exercise 1.

---

2 Teach

Guided Instruction

In this lesson, students learn to predict and verify patterns involving tessellations. Begin by showing the students tessellating designs such as a picture of a honeycomb, a reproduction of an artwork by M. C. Escher, or a piece of clothing or fabric. Emphasize that in any tessellation, there are no gaps or overlaps. Show students the three regular tessellations (Teaching Transparency). Explain that for a regular polygon to tessellate, the measure of an interior angle must be a factor of 360°.

Universal Access
Through Modeling

Have students work in small groups. Give each group a set of pattern blocks (in Manipulatives Kit) containing equilateral triangles, regular hexagons, squares, rhombuses, trapezoids, and parallelograms. Ask each group to create as many different tessellations as they can with the pattern blocks and to draw each tessellation they find on a sheet of paper. If you want to provide an additional challenge, ask students to use a protractor to show that the sum of the measures of the angles around each vertex is 360°.

3 Close

Summarize

Review the requirements for a design to be a tessellation. The design must be a repeating pattern of plane figures that completely covers a plane with no gaps or overlaps.

Remind students that tessellations are found in nature, art, and manufactured structures. The lesson focused mainly on tessellations formed by polygons, but there are many tessellations formed by figures other than polygons.

Assignment Guide

If you finished Example **1** assign:
Proficient 1, 3, 5–10, 17–24
Advanced 3, 8–13, 17–24

If you finished Example **2** assign:
Proficient 1–10, 14, 17–24
Advanced 3, 4, 8–24

Homework Quick Check

Quickly check key concepts.
Exercises: 3, 4, 10

Answers

3.

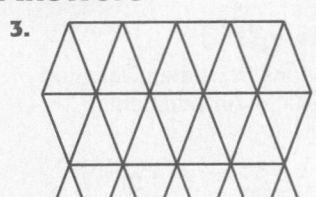

4.

5.

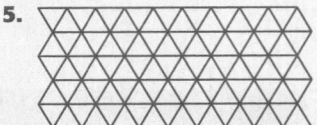

6–10, 13. See p. A9.

Math Background

Allowing students to learn mathematics through its application in art is a powerful motivator for some students. Other students, however, find the creative side of this work quite challenging. Computer programs can help these students create designs that tessellate. These programs allow a student to experiment with various designs and to see many more possibilities than would be practical with paper and pencil.

It might be useful to investigate the work of M. C. Escher, the artist most often associated with tessellations.

California Standards

Standard	Exercises
NS1.1	19–21
AF3.1	22–24
Ext. of MG3.2	1–18

INDEPENDENT PRACTICE

See Example **1**
3. Create a tessellation with triangle *PQR*.

See Example **2**
4. Use rotations to create a variation of the tessellation in Exercise 3.

PRACTICE AND PROBLEM SOLVING

Extra Practice
See page EP17.

Use each shape to create a tessellation.

5.    **6.** 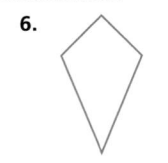   **7.**

8.    **9.**   **10.**

11. A piece is removed from one side of a rectangle and translated to the opposite side. Will this shape tessellate? **Yes, the shape will tessellate.**

12. A piece is removed from one side of a trapezoid and translated to the opposite side. Will this shape tessellate? **Yes, the shape will tessellate.**

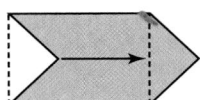

13. In a *semiregular tessellation,* two or more regular polygons are repeated to fill the plane and the vertices are all identical. Use each arrangement of regular polygons to create a semiregular tessellation.

a. 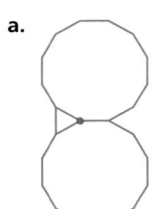   **b.** 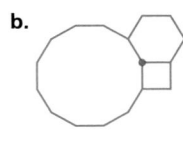   **c.**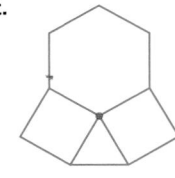

REVIEW FOR MASTERY 8-8

LESSON 8-8 Review for Mastery
Tessellations

A **tessellation** is a repeating pattern of shapes that completely covers a plane with no gaps or overlaps.

Not all plane shapes can be used to make a tessellation.

To make a tessellation of a figure, fit copies of the shape together. Remember, there can be no overlaps or gaps when you fit the shapes together.

You can make a tessellation using this hexagon.

You cannot make a tessellation using this pentagon.

The figures fit together with no gaps or overlaps.

The figures do not all fit together. There is a gap.

gap→

Can you make a tessellation using each shape? Write yes or no.

1. _____ yes

2. _____ no

Fit triangles shaped like this together to make a tessellation.

3.

_____ Sample answer:

PRACTICE 8-8

LESSON 8-8 Practice B
Tessellations

1. Create a tessellation with quadrilateral *ABCD*.

sample answer:

2. Use rotations to create a variation of the tessellation in Exercise 1.

sample answer:

3. Create a tessellation with hexagon *ABCDEF*.

sample answer:

4. Use rotations to create a variation of the tessellation in Exercise 3.

sample answer:

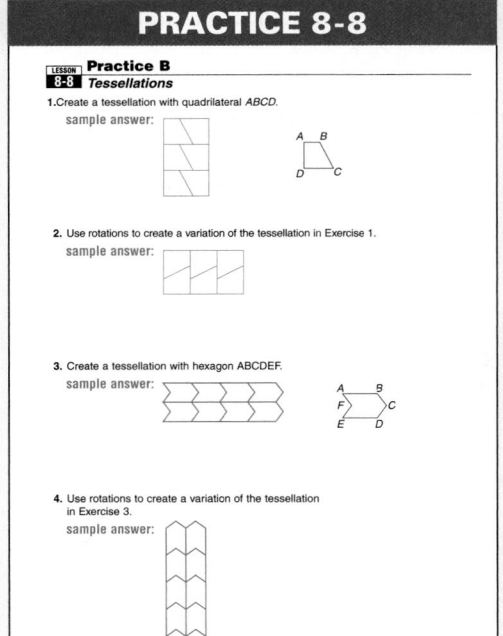

M. C. Escher created works of art by repeating interlocking shapes. He used both regular and nonregular tessellations. He often used what he called *metamorphoses*, in which shapes change into other shapes. Escher used his reptile pattern in many hexagonal tessellations. One of the most famous is entitled simply *Reptiles*.

14. The steps below show the method Escher used to make a bird out of a triangle. Use the bird to create a tessellation.

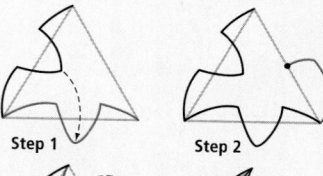

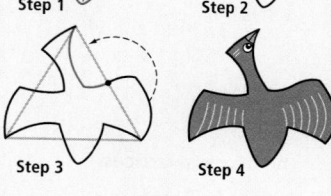

Step 1   Step 2
Step 3   Step 4

go.hrw.com
Web Extra!
KEYWORD: MT8CA Escher

15. Reasoning What regular polygon do you think Escher used to begin *Reptiles*? **hexagon**

16. ⭐ **Challenge** Create an Escher-like tessellation of your own design. **Check students' work.**

SPIRAL STANDARDS REVIEW   NS1.1, AF3.1, Ext. of MG3.2

17. Multiple Choice Which of the following shapes will NOT form a regular tessellation?

Ⓐ    Ⓑ    Ⓒ 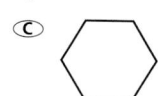   Ⓓ

18. Short Response Which set of polygons will create a tessellation? Explain.
Possible answer: A set of right triangles can tessellate to form a large rectangle or parallelogram.
Write each number in scientific notation. (Lesson 4-5)

19. 3,400,000,000 3.4×10^9 **20.** 0.00000045 4.5×10^{-7} **21.** 28,000 2.8×10^4

Create a table for each cubic function, and use it to graph the function. (Lesson 7-5)
22. $y = \frac{1}{3}x^3$ **23.** $y = -x^3 + 1$ **24.** $y = x^3 - 5$

CHALLENGE 8-8

PROBLEM SOLVING 8-8

Answers
14.

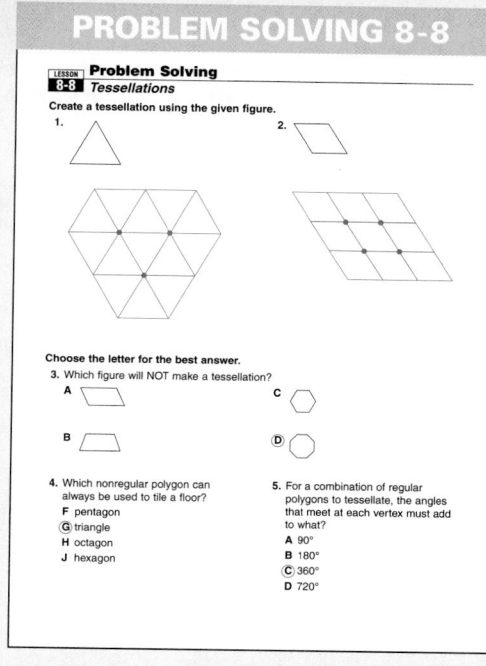

22–24. See p. A9.

✒ **Journal**
Have each student choose a favorite tessellation from the examples shown in class today. Ask students to write about their choices.

Power Presentations
with PowerPoint®

✓ **8-8**
Lesson Quiz
1. Explain why a regular tessellation with regular octagons is impossible. Each angle measure in a regular octagon is 135° and 135 is not a factor of 360.

2. Can a semiregular tessellation be formed using a regular 12-sided polygon and a regular hexagon? Explain. No; a regular 12-sided polygon has angles that measure 150° and a regular hexagon has angles that measure 120°. No combinations of 120° and 150° add to 360°.

Also available on transparency

SECTION 8B

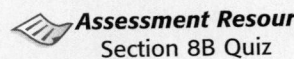

Organizer

Objective: Assess students' mastery of concepts and skills in Lessons 8-6 through 8-8.

Resources

 Assessment Resources
Section 8B Quiz

 Test & Practice Generator
One-Stop Planner®

INTERVENTION ◄►

Resources

 **Ready to Go On?**
Intervention and Enrichment **Worksheets**

⊙ **Ready to Go On? CD-ROM**

🪐 **Ready to Go On? Online**

my.hrw.com

Answers

4–7. See p. A9.

CHAPTER

8

SECTION 8B

Quiz for Lessons 8-6 Through 8-8

☑ **8-6** **Congruent Polygons**

In the figure, triangle $ABC \cong$ triangle LMN.

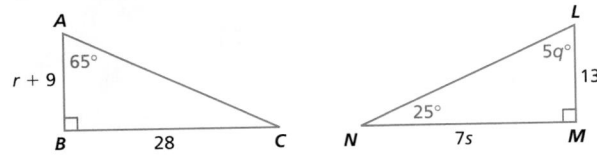

1. Find q. **13**   **2.** Find r. **4**   **3.** Find s. **4**

☑ **8-7** **Transformations**

Graph each transformation. Give the coordinates of the image's vertices.

4. Translate triangle *RST* 5 units down.

5. Reflect the figure across the *x*-axis.

6. Rotate triangle *JKL* 90° clockwise about vertex *L*.

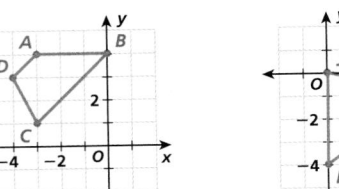

☑ **8-8** **Tessellations**

Copy the given figure and use it to create a tessellation.

7.

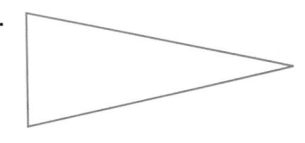

8.

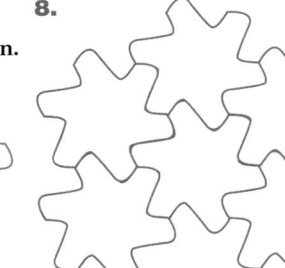

READY TO GO ON?
Diagnose and Prescribe

Ready to Go On? Intervention, Section 8B			
Ready to Go On? Intervention	🖋 **Worksheets**	⊙ **CD-ROM**	🪐 **Online**
☑ Lesson 8-6 🐻 ↞ MG3.4	8-6 Intervention	Activity 8-6	Diagnose and Prescribe Online
☑ Lesson 8-7 🐻 MG3.2	8-7 Intervention	Activity 8-7	
☑ Lesson 8-8 🐻 Ext. of MG3.2	8-8 Intervention	Activity 8-8	

READY TO GO ON?
Enrichment, **Section 8B**

🖋 **Worksheets**

⊙ **CD-ROM**

🪐 **Online**

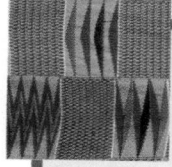

Cloth Creations The Asante people of Ghana are known for weaving Kente cloth, a colorful textile based on repeating geometric patterns. Susan is using a coordinate plane to design her own Kente cloth pattern.

1. Susan starts with triangle *ABC* as shown. Explain how she can use slopes to make sure the triangle is a right triangle.

2. To begin the pattern, Susan uses transformations to make a row of triangles that are all congruent to triangle *ABC*. Describe the transformations she should use to make these triangles.

3. Next, she extends the pattern by making additional rows of triangles. The first triangle in Row 2 is shown. Complete the table by writing the coordinates of the top vertex of each triangle in the pattern.

4. What patterns do you notice in the table?

5. Susan's Kente cloth pattern is a tessellation of what types of figures?

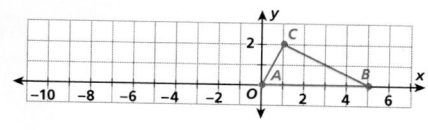

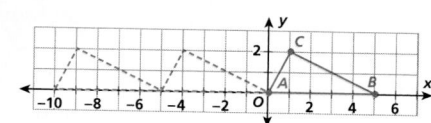

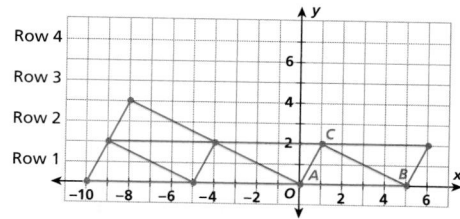

Row	Top Vertex of Triangles in Row			
Row 1	(−9, 2)	(−4, 2)	(1, 2)	(6, 2)
Row 2	(−8, 4)	(−3, 4)	(2, 4)	(7, 4)
Row 3	(−7, 6)	(−2, 6)	(3, 6)	(8, 6)
Row 4	(−6, 8)	(−1, 8)	(4, 8)	(9, 8)

Problem	Text reference
1	Lesson 8-5
2	Lesson 8-7
3	Lesson 8-7
4	Lesson 8-5
5	Lesson 8-8

Answers

1. Slope of $\overline{AC}$ = 2; slope of $\overline{CB} = -\frac{1}{2}$. The product of the slopes is −1, so the sides of the triangle are perpendicular. Therefore, the triangle is a right triangle.

2. Translate triangle *ABC* along the *x*-axis: 5 units to the right, 5 units to the left, and 10 units to the left.

4. Possible answer: To go from one row to the next, the *y*-coordinate increases by 2. The *x*-coordinates repeat every 5 rows.

5. Triangles, parallelograms, rectangles, and trapezoids

INTERVENTION ⬅➡

Scaffolding Questions

1. What is true about the two sides of a triangle that make up the right angle?
   The sides are perpendicular.

2. Is the row of three triangles shown at the right a tessellation? Explain your answer.
   No. A tessellation completely covers a plane. These three triangles do not.

3. What does the top vertex of each triangle in Row 2 have in common? They all have the same *y*-coordinate.

4. Let the *x*-coordinate of the top vertex of the first triangle in Row 1 be represented by the variable *x*. Write an expression that would represent the *x*-coordinate of the top vertex of the first triangle in Row 2.
   x + 1

5. Is the tessellation in Susan's cloth pattern a regular tessellation? Why or why not?
   The pattern is not a regular tessellation because the polygon used is not a regular polygon.

Extension

1. The first row of triangles in Susan's pattern begins along the *x*-axis. What pattern in the coordinates of the vertices would you notice if the first row of triangles began along the *y*-axis? The *x*-coordinates of the vertices in each row would be the same. The *y*-coordinates of the vertices would differ by 1 unit from one row to the next.

California Standards

Measurement and Geometry
3.2 Understand and use coordinate graphs to plot simple figures, determine lengths and areas related to them, **and determine their image under translations and reflections.**

Game Time

Organizer

Objective: Participate in games to practice and apply skills learned in Chapter 8.

 Online Edition

Resources

📖 **Chapter 8 Resource File**
Puzzles, Twisters & Teasers

Coloring Tessellations

Purpose: To extend the study of tessellations to a coloring problem

Discuss Ask students to explain the rule for coloring the tessellations. No two figures that share an edge can be colored with the same color. Explain why the tessellation of hexagons requires 3 colors. Choose any hexagon and color it with color 1. Color 1 cannot be used to color any of the surrounding hexagons because the surrounding hexagons all share an edge with the center hexagon. So you must color the 6 surrounding hexagons in order with colors 2, 3, 2, 3, 2, and 3.

Extend Give students a map of the United States. Ask them to color the map with as few colors as possible, using a different color for each state so that no states that share a border are the same color. The map can be colored with 4 colors.

Polygon Rummy

Purpose: To practice using the properties of polygons in a card game

Discuss Ask: Is there any set of 3 cards for which there is no polygon that has the properties on all 3 cards? Give an example. yes; triangle, quadrilateral, all angles obtuse What figure satisfies all the properties "pentagon," "all sides congruent," and "all angles congruent"? regular pentagon

Extend Ask students to name the cards that describe a square and those that describe a regular hexagon. Which figure meets the requirements of more cards? 8 cards describe a square; 6 cards describe a regular hexagon; square.

Game Time

Coloring Tessellations

Two of the three regular tessellations—triangles and squares—can be colored with two colors so that no two polygons that share an edge are the same color. The third—hexagons—requires three colors.

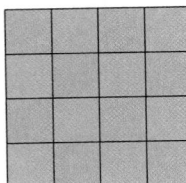 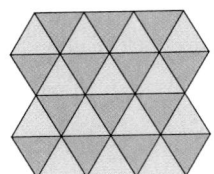 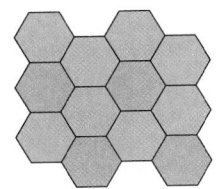

1. Determine if each semiregular tessellation can be colored with two colors. If not, tell the minimum number of colors needed.

 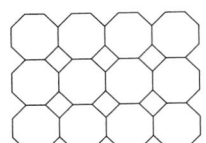 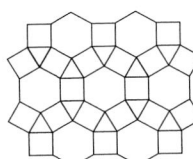

yes   no (3)   yes

2. Try to write a rule about which tessellations can be colored with two colors. A tessellation can be colored with two colors if each figure is bordered only by figures that do not border each other.

Polygon Rummy

The object of this game is to create geometric figures. Each card in the deck shows a property of a geometric figure. To create a figure, you must draw a polygon that matches at least three cards in your hand. For example, if you have the cards "quadrilateral," "a pair of parallel sides," and "a right angle," you could draw a rectangle.

A complete set of rules and playing cards is available online.

go.hrw.com
Game Time Extra
KEYWORD: MT8CA Games

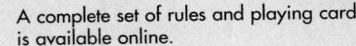

Materials
- 3 sheets of white paper
- CD or CD-ROM
- scissors
- tape
- markers
- empty CD case

It's in the Bag!

PROJECT Project CD Geometry

Make your own CD to record important facts about plane geometry.

❶ Fold a sheet of paper in half. Place a CD on top of the paper so that it touches the folded edge. Trace around the CD. **Figure A**

❷ Cut out the CD shape, being careful to leave the folded edge attached. This will create two paper CDs that are joined together. Cut a hole in the center of each paper CD. **Figure B**

❸ Repeat steps 1 and 2 with the other two sheets of paper.

❹ Tape the ends of the paper CDs together to make a string of six CDs. **Figure C**

❺ Accordion fold the CDs to make a booklet. Write the number and name of the chapter on the top CD. Store the CD booklet in an empty CD case.

Taking Note of the Math

Use the blank pages in the CD booklet to take notes on the chapter. Be sure to include definitions and sample problems that will help you review essential concepts about plane geometry.

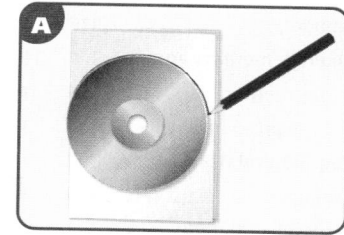
A

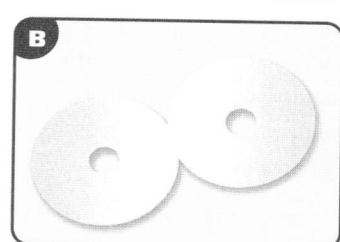
B

C

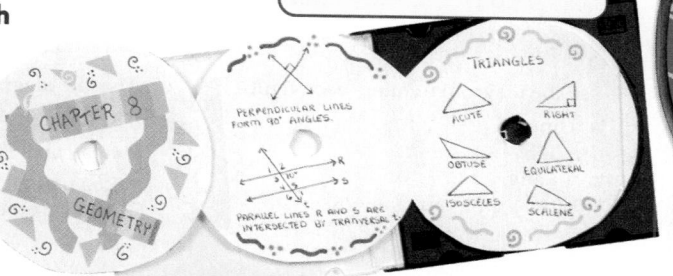

Tips from the Bag Ladies!

We always get lots of CD-ROMs in the mail from Internet service providers. We never throw those CDs away. This project is just one of the many uses we've found for them!

Students can make two booklets and store them in a double CD case. You can also have students make a square booklet that slides into the cover of the CD case. Note that regular cases or "slim" cases will work equally well for this project.

Organizer

Objective: Help students organize and review key concepts and skills presented in Chapter 8.

Online Edition
Multilingual Glossary

Resources

PuzzlePro®
One-Stop Planner®

Multilingual Glossary Online
go.hrw.com
KEYWORD: MT8CA Glossary

Lesson Tutorial Videos
CD-ROM

Test & Practice Generator
One-Stop Planner®

Answers

1. parallel lines; perpendicular lines
2. rectangle; square; rhombus; square
3. $\overrightarrow{KM}$
4. ∠LKM
5. ∠LKM and ∠JKM

Vocabulary

Complete the sentences below with vocabulary words from the list above.

1. Lines in the same plane that never meet are called ___?___.
   Lines that intersect at 90° angles are called ___?___.

2. A quadrilateral with 4 congruent angles is a(n) ___?___ or a(n) ___?___.
   A quadrilateral with 4 congruent sides is a(n) ___?___ or a(n) ___?___.

8-1 Points, Lines, Planes, and Angles (pp. 378–381) Prep for MG3.1

EXAMPLE

Use the diagram to name each figure.

- a line
  Possible answer: $\overleftrightarrow{AD}$
- a plane
  Possible answer: plane ADE

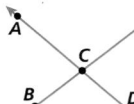

EXERCISES

Use the diagram to name each figure.

3. a ray
4. an acute angle
5. a pair of supplementary angles

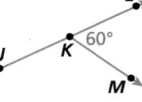

8-2 Geometric Relationships (pp. 384–387)

 MG3.6

EXAMPLE

■ Identify two planes that appear to be parallel.

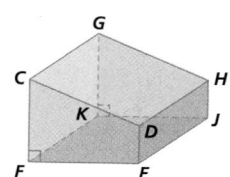

plane GCF ‖ plane HDE   The planes do not intersect.

EXERCISES

Identify two lines or planes that appear to have the given relationship.

6. skew lines
7. perpendicular planes
8. parallel planes

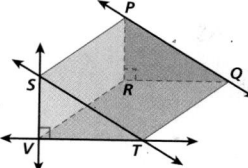

8-3 Angle Relationships (pp. 388–391)

 Rev. of 6MG2.2

EXAMPLE

Line j ‖ line k. Find each angle measure.

■ m∠1
  m∠1 = 143°

■ m∠2
  m∠2 + 143° =   180°
       − 143°   − 143°
  ─────────────────────
  m∠2   =   37°

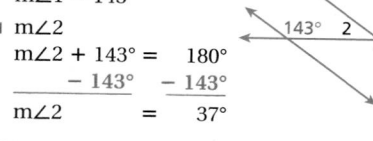

EXERCISES

Line p ‖ line q. Find each angle measure.

9. m∠1
10. m∠2
11. m∠3
12. m∠4
13. m∠5

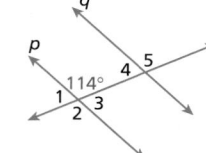

8-4 Triangles (pp. 392–396)

 MG3.3

EXAMPLE

■ Find n.

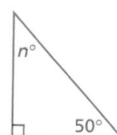

n° + 50° + 90° =   180°
     n + 140   =   180
       − 140   − 140
  ─────────────────────
       n   =   40

EXERCISES

14. Find m.

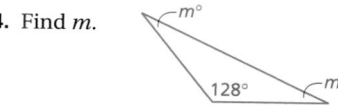

15. In the figure, D is the midpoint of $\overline{AC}$ and $\overline{DB}$ is perpendicular to $\overline{AC}$. Find the length of $\overline{AB}$.

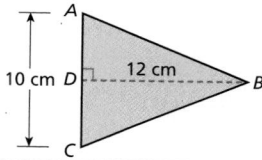

Answers

6. $\overrightarrow{PQ}$ and $\overrightarrow{SV}$
7. plane SVR ⊥ plane RVT
8. plane PQR ‖ plane STV
9. 66°
10. 114°
11. 66°
12. 66°
13. 114°
14. m = 26
15. 13 cm

Answers

16.

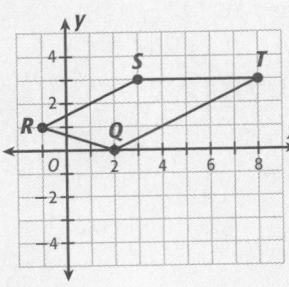

trapezoid

17.

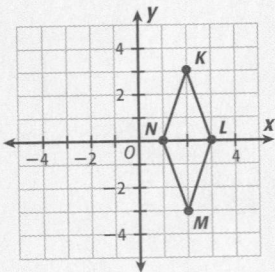

parallelogram, rhombus

18.

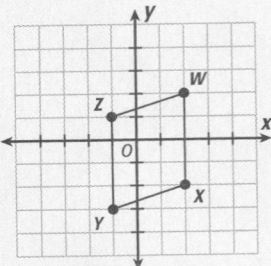

parallelogram

19. $x = 19$

20. $t = 2.4$

21. $q = 7$

22.

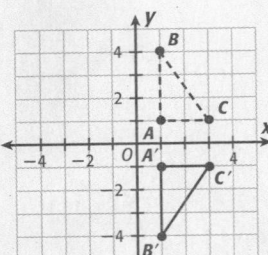

23.

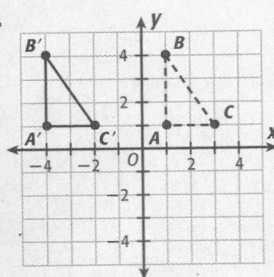

24.

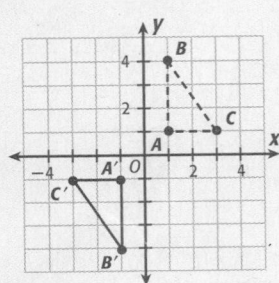

8-5 Coordinate Geometry (pp. 398–402)

MG3.2, ← AF3.3

EXAMPLE

■ Graph the quadrilateral with the given vertices. Give all the names that apply.
$D(-2, 1), E(2, 3), F(3, 1), G(-1, -1)$

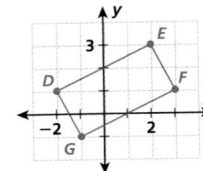

$\overline{DE} \parallel \overline{FG}$
$\overline{EF} \parallel \overline{GD}$
$\overline{DE} \perp \overline{EF}$
parallelogram, rectangle

EXERCISES

Graph the quadrilaterals with the given vertices. Give all the names that apply.

16. $Q(2, 0), R(-1, 1), S(3, 3), T(8, 3)$

17. $K(2, 3), L(3, 0), M(2, -3), N(1, 0)$

18. $W(2, 2), X(2, -2), Y(-1, -3), Z(-1, 1)$

8-6 Congruent Polygons (pp. 406–409)

← MG3.4

EXAMPLE

■ Triangle $ABC \cong$ triangle FDE. Find x.

$$x - 4 = 4$$
$$\underline{+4 \quad +4}$$
$$x \quad = \quad 8$$

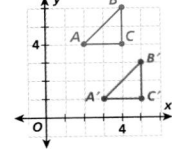

EXERCISES

Triangle $JQZ \cong$ triangle VTZ.

19. Find x.

20. Find t.

21. Find q.

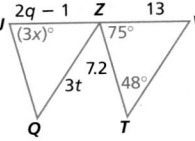

8-7 Transformations (pp. 410–414)

MG3.2

EXAMPLE

■ Graph the translation.
Translate $\triangle ABC$ 1 unit right and 3 units down.

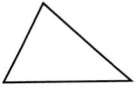

EXERCISES

Draw the image of a triangle ABC with vertices $(1, 1)$, $(1, 4)$, and $(3, 1)$ after each transformation.

22. reflection across the x-axis

23. translation 5 units left

24. 180° rotation around $(0, 0)$

8-8 Tessellations (pp. 416–419)

Ext. of MG3.2

EXAMPLE

■ Create a tessellation with the figure.

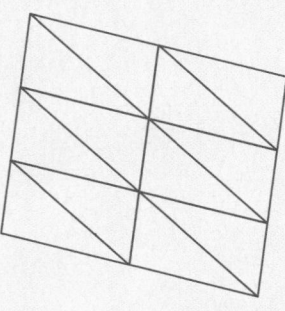

EXERCISES

Create a tessellation with each figure.

25. 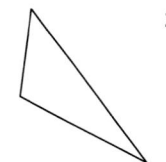 **26.**

---

25. Possible answer:

26. Possible answer:

In the figure, line *m* ‖ line *n*.   Possible answer: ∠1 and ∠2
1. Name two pairs of supplementary angles.
2. Find m∠1.   **135°** 3. Find m∠2.   **45°**
4. Find m∠3.   **45°**   5. Find m∠4.   **135°**

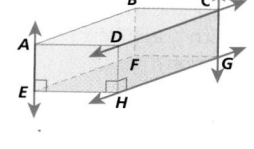

Identify two lines or planes that appear to have the given relationship.
6. skew lines $\overline{AE}$ and $\overline{DC}$
7. parallel planes **plane ADH ‖ plane BCG**
8. perpendicular planes **plane ADH ⊥ plane DCG**
9. Two angles in a triangle have measures of 44° and 57°. What is the measure of the third angle? **79°**
10. What are the measures of the congruent angles in an isosceles triangle if the measure of the third angle is 102°? **39°**
11. In the figure, *E* is the midpoint of $\overline{FG}$ and $\overline{DE}$ is perpendicular to $\overline{FG}$. Find the length of $\overline{DE}$. **15 cm**

 25 cm 40 cm

Give all of the names that apply to each figure.
12. 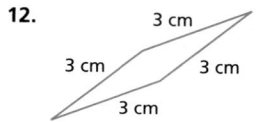 3 cm   **polygon, quadrilateral, parallelogram, rhombus**
13. 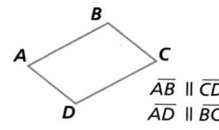   **polygon, quadrilateral, parallelogram**
$\overline{AB}$ ‖ $\overline{CD}$
$\overline{AD}$ ‖ $\overline{BC}$

Graph the quadrilateral with the given vertices. Give all of the names that apply to each quadrilateral.
14. *A*(3,4), *B*(8,4), *C*(5,0), *D*(0,0)
15. *K*(−4,0), *L*(−2,5), *M*(2,5), *N*(4,0)

In the figure, quadrilateral ABCD ≅ quadrilateral LMNO.
16. Find *m*. **86**
17. Find *n*. **5**
18. Find *p*. **7**

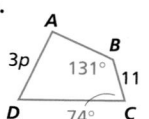 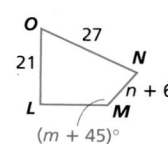

Pentagon ABCDE has vertices A(1, −2), B(3, −1), C(7, −2), D(6, −4), and E(2, −5). Find the coordinates of the image of each point after each transformation.
19. clockwise rotation 90° around the origin, point *E*   **(−5, −2)**
20. reflection across the *x*-axis, point *C*   **(7, 2)**
21. translation 6 units up, point *B*   **(3, 5)**
22. reflection across the *y*-axis, point *A*   **(−1, −2)**

CHAPTER TEST CHAPTER 8

Organizer

Objective: Assess students' mastery of concepts and skills in Chapter 8.

PREMIER **Online Edition**

Resources

Assessment Resources
Chapter 8 Tests
• Free Response (Levels A, B, C)
• Multiple Choice (Levels A, B, C)
• Performance Assessment

IDEA Works! CD-ROM
Modified Chapter 8 Test

Test & Practice Generator
One-Stop Planner®

Answers
14. rhombus; parallelogram
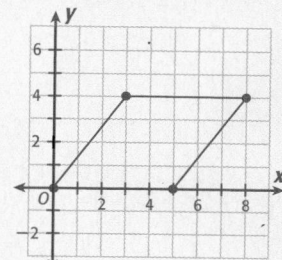

15. trapezoid
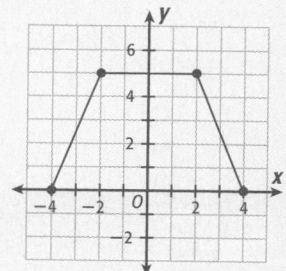

California Standards	
Standard	**Items**
Rev. of 6MG2.2	9–10
Prep for MG3.1	1
MG3.2	14–15, 20–23
MG3.3	11
MG3.4	16–18
MG3.6	6–8
Ext. of MG3.6	2–5

Chapter 8 Test **427**

CHAPTER
8
MASTERING THE STANDARDS

CHAPTER
8
MASTERING THE STANDARDS

go.hrw.com
Standards Practice Online
KEYWORD: MT8CA Practice

Organizer

Objective: Provide review and practice for Chapters 1–8.

Online Edition

Resources

Assessment Resources
Chapter 8 Cumulative Test

Focus on California Standards Benchmark Tests and Intervention

California Standards Practice CD-ROM

go.hrw.com
KEYWORD: MT8CA Practice

California Standards

Standard	Items
NS1.3	2, 5
NS1.4	3
NS1.7	9, 13
NS2.5	8
AF1.1	4
AF1.2	8, 11
AF1.5	1
AF3.3	6, 10, 12, 17
AF4.2	7, 14
MG3.2	16
MG3.6	15

Cumulative Assessment, Chapters 1–8

Multiple Choice

1. A bird flies from the ground to the top of a tree, sits there and sings for a while, flies down to the top of a picnic table to eat crumbs, and then flies back to the top of the tree to sing some more. Which graph best represents this situation?

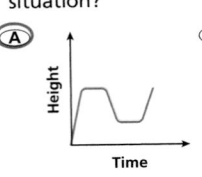
Ⓐ

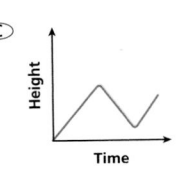
Ⓒ

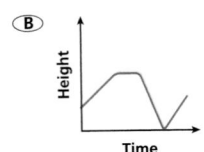
Ⓑ

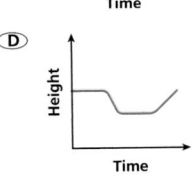
Ⓓ

2. There are 36 poodles entered in a dog show with a total of 144 entries. What percent of the dogs are poodles?
   - Ⓐ 10%
   - Ⓑ 25%
   - Ⓒ 75%
   - Ⓓ 400%

3. Which of the following is NOT a rational number?
   - Ⓐ $-\sqrt{196}$
   - Ⓑ $-5.8\overline{3}$
   - Ⓒ $-\sqrt{10}$
   - Ⓓ $-\frac{2}{3}$

4. Which statement describes the inequality $x < -1$?
   - Ⓐ A number is more than −1.
   - Ⓑ A number is at least −1.
   - Ⓒ A number is less than −1.
   - Ⓓ A number is at most −1.

5. An animal shelter needs to find homes for 40 dogs and 60 cats. If 15% of the dogs are female and 25% of the cats are female, what percent of the animals are female?
   - Ⓐ 21%
   - Ⓒ 40%
   - Ⓑ 22%
   - Ⓓ 42%

6. The line graph shows the activity of a savings account. What does the slope represent?

Savings Account Activity

   - Ⓐ The number of months it takes to save $4500
   - Ⓑ The initial amount in the account
   - Ⓒ The amount saved every 7 months
   - Ⓓ The amount saved every 2 months

7. Which equation represents a direct variation between x and y?
   - Ⓐ $y = x + 2$
   - Ⓒ $y = 2 - x$
   - Ⓑ $y = \frac{2}{x}$
   - Ⓓ $y = 2x$

8. Find the value of $|a| - b^2$ when $a = -3$ and $b = -5$.
   - Ⓐ −28
   - Ⓒ −7
   - Ⓑ −22
   - Ⓓ 4

Teaching Tip

Multiple Choice Remind students who did not choose answer **C** in item **3** that rational numbers include any number that can be expressed as a fraction, including negative numbers or numbers with repeating decimals. Some students may need to review commonly used perfect squares.

Point out to students that answers **A, B,** and **C** in item **7** can be eliminated because none contain the point (0, 0).

Answers

16. a.
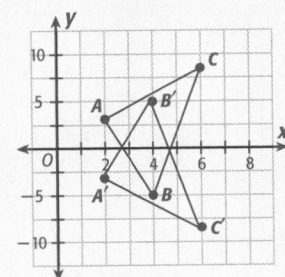

b. $A'(2, -3)$, $B'(4, 5)$, $C'(6, -8)$

17. See 4-Point Response work sample.

9. George earns a weekly salary of $575 plus a 6% commission on sales. How much would he make in a week if he sold $7500 worth of merchandise?

Ⓐ $450   Ⓒ $2300

Ⓑ $1025   Ⓓ $2750

 Use logic to eliminate answer choices that are incorrect. This will help you make an educated guess if you are having trouble with the question.

Gridded Response

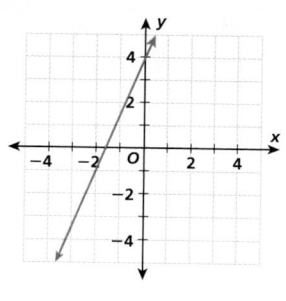

10. What is the slope of the line graphed? $\frac{5}{2}$

11. What is the output value for the function $y = x^3 + 2x$ when the input value is 4?   **72**

12. What is the value of x when the slope of the line connecting the points $(-1, 4)$ and $(x, 1)$ is $-\frac{3}{4}$?   **3**

13. Bob is buying a $35 sweater that is discounted 20%. What is the total price of the sweater when 5% sales tax is added?   **29.40**

14. Marilyn wants to save $240. She has saved $60 in the past 4 weeks. If she continues to save at the same rate, how many more weeks will it take her to save $240?   **12**

Short Response

15. Identify two lines that have the given relationship.

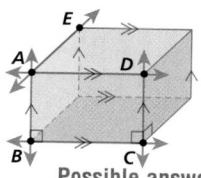

a. parallel lines   Possible answer: $\overleftrightarrow{AB} \parallel \overleftrightarrow{DC}$

b. perpendicular lines

c. skew lines   Possible answer: $\overleftrightarrow{BC} \perp \overleftrightarrow{CD}$

Possible answer: $\overleftrightarrow{AE}$ and $\overleftrightarrow{DC}$

16. Triangle ABC, with vertices $A(2, 3)$, $B(4, -5)$, and $C(6, 8)$, is reflected across the x-axis to form triangle $A'B'C'$.

a. On a coordinate grid, draw and label triangle ABC and triangle $A'B'C'$.

b. Give the coordinates of the vertices for new triangle $A'B'C'$.

Extended Response

17. Paul Revere had to travel 3.5 miles to Charlestown from Boston by boat. Assume that from Charlestown to Lexington he was able to ride a horse that traveled at a rate of $\frac{1}{8}$ mile per minute. His total distance traveled, y, is the sum of the distance to Charlestown and the distance from Charlestown to Lexington.

a. Write a linear equation that could be used to find the distance, y, Paul Revere traveled in x minutes.

b. What does the slope of the line represent?

c. Find the output value when the input value is 0 and tell what this point represents in Paul Revere's ride.

d. Graph your equation from part **a** on a coordinate plane.

Short Response Rubric
Items 15–16

2 Points = The student's answer is an accurate and complete execution of the task or tasks.

1 Point = The student's answer contains attributes of an appropriate response but is flawed.

0 Points = The student's answer contains no attributes of an appropriate response.

Extended Response Rubric
Item 17

4 Points = The student demonstrates a thorough understanding of all concepts and shows all work correctly.

3 Points = The student demonstrates a basic understanding of all concepts, but the work shows some flaws reflecting inattentive execution of mathematical procedures or some misunderstanding of the underlying mathematics.

2 Points = The student demonstrates only a partial understanding of the concepts or procedures embodied in the tasks. The approach may be correct, but the work shows a misunderstanding of one or more important concepts.

1 Point = The student demonstrates a very limited understanding of the concepts or procedures embodied in the tasks. The response may show some understanding but exhibits many flaws or is incomplete.

0 Points = The student provides no response at all or a completely incorrect or uninterpretable response.

Student Work Samples for Item 17

4-Point Response

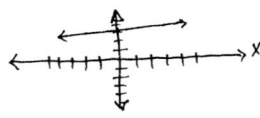

y = sum of distance
x = minutes traveled by horse

a. y = 1/8 X + 3.5

b. rate of travel

c. 3.5; distance traveled

The student applied the variables correctly, wrote a correct equation, and correctly interpreted the slope and y-intercept.

3-Point Response

a. x: miles traveled by boat
y: distance

y = 3.5 + $\frac{1}{8}$ x

b. slope: rate of travel by horse

c. y-int: distance by boat

d.

The student wrote the correct equation, made an adequate graph, but shows an incorrect understanding of the slope and y-intercept.

2-Point Response

a. y = 3.5 + 1/8

b. rate

c. distance

d.

The student needs a more detailed explanation for parts **b** and **c**, and their graph needs more detail. The equation in part **a** is missing the x-variable.

CHAPTER 9

Two-Dimensional Geometry

	Grade-level Standard
◀	Review
▶	Beyond the Standards
A	Assessment
O	Optional

Pacing Guide

Calendar Planner
Teacher's **One-Stop** Planner®

Lesson/Lab	California Standards	Time	Advanced Students	Benchmark* Students	Strategic** Students
9-1 Perimeter and Area of Parallelograms	MG2.1, MG2.2, MG2.4, MG3.2	100 min	✔	✔	✔
9-2 Perimeter and Area of Triangles and Trapezoids	MG2.1, MG3.2	50 min	✔	✔	✔
Ready to Go On?		25 min	A	A	A
Focus on Problem Solving		25 min	A	A	O
9-3 Circles	MG3.1	50 min	✔	✔	✔
9-4 Circumference and Area	MG2.1, MG3.2	50 min	✔	✔	✔
9-5 Area of Composite Figures	MG2.2	50 min	✔	✔	✔
9-6 Area of Irregular Figures	MG2.2	50 min	✔	✔	✔
Ready to Go On?		25 min	A	A	A
Concept Connection		25 min	A	A	O
Study Guide: Review		50 min	✔	✔	✔
Chapter Test		50 min	A	A	A

* **Benchmark students** are achieving at or near grade level.

** **Strategic students** may be a year or more below grade level and may require additional time for intervention.

Countdown to Mastery, Weeks ⑱, ⑲

ONGOING ASSESSMENT and INTERVENTION

DIAGNOSE	PRESCRIBE

Assess Prior Knowledge

Before Chapter 9

Diagnose readiness for the chapter.

Are You Ready? SE p. 431

Prescribe intervention.

Are You Ready? Intervention Skills 16, 51, 55, 58

Formative Assessment

Before Every Lesson

Diagnose readiness for the lesson.

Warm Up TE, every lesson

Prescribe intervention.

Skills Bank SE pp. SB2–SB24
Review for Mastery CRF, Chapters 1–9

During Every Lesson

Diagnose understanding of lesson concepts.

Questioning Strategies Chapter 9
Think and Discuss SE, every lesson
Write About It SE, lesson exercises
Journal TE, lesson exercises

Prescribe intervention.

Reading Strategies CRF, every lesson
Success for ELL Chapter 9
Lesson Tutorial Videos Chapter 9

After Every Lesson

Diagnose mastery of lesson concepts.

Lesson Quiz TE, every lesson
Ready to Go On? SE pp. 444, 462
Test and Practice Generator

Prescribe intervention.

Review for Mastery CRF, every lesson
Problem Solving CRF, every lesson
Ready to Go On? Intervention Chapter 9
Homework Help Online

Before Chapter 9 Testing

Diagnose mastery of concepts in the chapter.

Ready to Go On? SE pp. 444, 462
Focus on Problem Solving SE p. 445
Concept Connection SE p. 463
Section Quizzes AR pp. 165–166
Test and Practice Generator

Prescribe intervention.

Ready to Go On? Intervention Chapter 9
Scaffolding Questions TE p. 463

Before Assessment of California Standards

Diagnose mastery of California standards.

Focus on California Standards: Benchmark Tests
Mastering the Standards SE pp. 472–473
California Standards Practice CD-ROM

Prescribe intervention.

Focus on California Standards: Intervention

Summative Assessment

After Chapter 9

Check mastery of chapter concepts.

Multiple-Choice Tests (Forms A, B, C)
Free-Response Tests (Forms A, B, C)
Performance Assessment AR pp. 167–180
Test and Practice Generator

Prescribe intervention.

Review for Mastery CRF, every lesson
Lesson Tutorial Videos Chapter 9

KEY: **SE** = *Student Edition* **TE** = *Teacher's Edition* **CRF** = *Chapter Resource File* **AR** = *Assessment Resources*  Available on CD-ROM  Available online

Supporting the Teacher

Chapter 9 Resource File

Family Involvement
pp. 1–4, 21–24

Practice A, B, C
pp. 5–7, 13–15, 25–27, 33–35, 41–43, 49–51

Review for Mastery
pp. 8, 16, 28, 36, 44, 52

Challenge
pp. 9, 17, 29, 37, 45, 53

Problem Solving
pp. 10, 18, 30, 38, 46, 54

Reading Strategies ELL
pp. 11, 19, 31, 39, 47, 55

Puzzles, Twisters, and Teasers
pp. 12, 20, 32, 40, 48, 56

Hands-On Lab
pp. 57–60, 63–70

Technology Lab
pp. 61–62

Workbooks

Homework and Practice Workbook SPANISH
Teacher's Guide .... pp. 66–71

Know-It Notebook SPANISH
Teacher's Guide .... Chapter 9

Review for Mastery Workbook SPANISH
Teacher's Guide .... pp. 66–71

Focus on California Standards: Intervention Workbook SPANISH
Teacher's Guide

Teacher Tools

Power Presentations
Complete PowerPoint® presentations for Chapter 9 lessons

Lesson Tutorial Videos SPANISH
Holt authors Ed Burger and Freddie Renfro present tutorials to support the Chapter 9 lessons.

Teacher's One-Stop Planner SPANISH
Easy access to all Chapter 9 resources and assessments, as well as software for lesson planning, test generation, and puzzle creation

IDEA Works!
Key Chapter 9 resources and assessments modified to address special learning needs

Questioning Strategies .... Chapter 9
Solutions Key .... Chapter 9
Interactive Answers and Solutions

TechKeys   *Lab Resources*

Project Teacher Support   *Parent Resources*

Transparencies

Lesson Transparencies, Volume 2 .... Chapter 9
• Teacher Tools
• Warm Ups
• Teaching Transparencies
• Lesson Quizzes

Know-It Notebook .... Chapter 9
• Vocabulary   • Chapter Review
• Additional Examples   • Big Ideas

Alternate Openers: Explorations .... pp. 66–71
Countdown to Mastery .... pp. 35–38

Technology Highlights for the Teacher

 Power Presentations

Dynamic presentations to engage students. Complete PowerPoint® presentations for every lesson in Chapter 9.

2-1 Solving One-Step Equations

Isolate a variable by using inverse operations which "undo" operations on the variable.

An equation is like a balanced scale. To keep the balance, perform the same operation on both sides.

Inverse Operations	
Operation	**Inverse Operation**
Addition	Subtraction
Subtraction	Addition

 One-Stop Planner SPANISH

Easy access to Chapter 9 resources and assessments. Includes lesson-planning, test-generation, and puzzle-creation software.

Premier Online Edition SPANISH

Includes Tutorial Videos, Lesson Activities, Lesson Quizzes, Homework Help, Chapter Project and more.

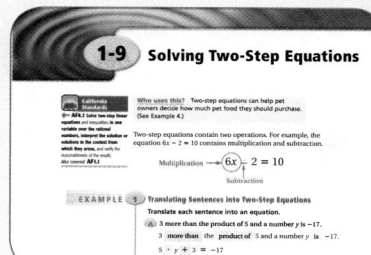

KEY: **SE** = *Student Edition*   **TE** = *Teacher's Edition*   ELL English Language Learners   SPANISH Spanish available   Available on CD-ROM    Available online

CHAPTER
9

Universal Access

Teaching tips to help all students appear throughout the chapter. A few that target specific students are included in the lists below.

Strategic Students

Practice A	CRF, every lesson
Review for Mastery	CRF, every lesson
Reading Strategies	CRF, every lesson
Academic Vocabulary Connections	TE p. 432
Reading Math	TE p. 455
Ready to Go On? Intervention	Chapter 9
Questioning Strategies	Chapter 9
Know-It Notebook SPANISH	Chapter 9
Homework Help Online 🪐	
Lesson Tutorial Videos 🪐 💿 SPANISH	
Online Interactivities 🪐 SPANISH	

Special Needs Students

Practice A	CRF, every lesson
Review for Mastery	CRF, every lesson
Reading Strategies	CRF, every lesson
Academic Vocabulary Connections	TE p. 432
Inclusion	TE pp. 445, 447, 459
IDEA Works! Modified Resources	Chapter 9
Ready to Go On? Intervention	Chapter 9
Know-It Notebook SPANISH	Chapter 9
Lesson Tutorial Videos 🪐 💿 SPANISH	
Online Interactivities 🪐 SPANISH	

English Learners

ENGLISH
LANGUAGE
LEARNERS

Reading Strategies	CRF, every lesson
Vocabulary Review	SE p. 466
Academic Vocabulary Connections	TE p. 432
English Language Learners	TE pp. 451, 455
Language Support	TE p. 450
Success for English Language Learners	Chapter 9
Know-It Notebook SPANISH	Chapter 9
Multilingual Glossary 🪐	
Lesson Tutorial Videos 🪐 💿 SPANISH	

Benchmark Students

Practice B	CRF, every lesson
Problem Solving	CRF, every lesson
Academic Vocabulary Connections	TE p. 432
Ready to Go On? Intervention	Chapter 9
Questioning Strategies	Chapter 9
Know-It Notebook SPANISH	Chapter 9
Homework Help Online 🪐	
Online Interactivities 🪐 SPANISH	

Advanced Students

Practice C	CRF, every lesson
Challenge	CRF, every lesson
Reading and Writing Math **EXTENSION**	TE p. 433
Concept Connection **EXTENSION**	TE p. 463
Ready to Go On? Enrichment	Chapter 9

Technology Highlights for Universal Access

💿 Lesson Tutorial Videos SPANISH

Starring Holt authors Ed Burger and Freddie Renfro! Live tutorials to support every lesson in Chapter 9.

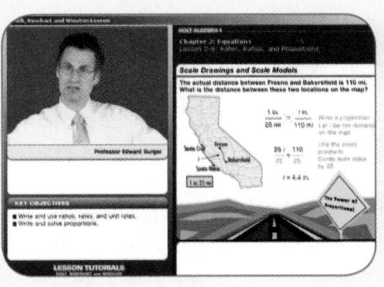

🪐 Multilingual Glossary

Searchable glossary includes definitions in English, Spanish, Vietnamese, Chinese, Hmong, Korean, and other languages.

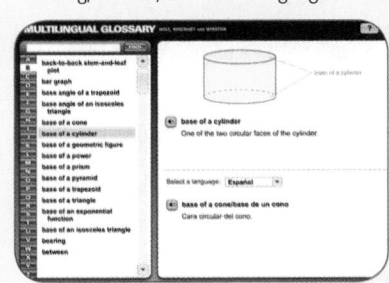

🪐 Online Interactivities SPANISH

Interactive tutorials provide visually engaging alternative opportunities to learn concepts and master skills.

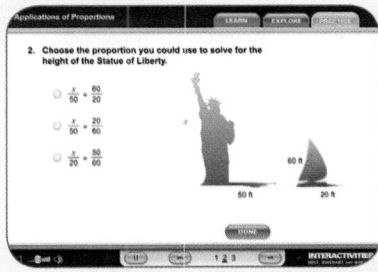

KEY: **SE** = *Student Edition* **TE** = *Teacher's Edition* **CRF** = *Chapter Resource File* SPANISH *Spanish available* 💿 *Available on CD-ROM* 🪐 *Available online*

Ongoing Assessment

Assessing Prior Knowledge

Determine whether students have the prerequisite concepts and skills for success in Chapter 9.

Are You Ready? SPANISH 🌐 💿 .... SE p. 431

Warm Up ✋ 💿 .... TE, every lesson

Chapter and Standards Assessment

Provide review and practice for Chapter 9 and standards mastery.

Concept Connection .... SE p. 463

Study Guide: Review .... SE pp. 466–468

Strategies for Success .... SE pp. 470–471

Mastering the Standards .... SE pp. 472–473

Countdown to Mastery Transparencies ✋ 💿 .....pp. 35–38

Focus on California Standards: Benchmark Tests 🌐 💿

Focus on California Standards: Intervention Workbook SPANISH

California Standards Practice **CD-ROM** 💿 SPANISH

IDEA Works! Modified Worksheets and Tests

Alternative Assessment

Assess students' understanding of Chapter 9 concepts and combined problem-solving skills.

Performance Assessment .... AR pp. 179–180

Portfolio Assessment .... AR p. xxxvi

Chapter 9 Project 🌐

Daily Assessment

Provide formative assessment for each day of Chapter 9.

Think and Discuss .... SE, every lesson

Write About It .... SE, lesson exercises

Journal .... TE, lesson exercises

Lesson Quiz ✋ 💿 .... TE, every lesson

Questioning Strategies .... Chapter 9

IDEA Works! Modified Lesson Quizzes .... Chapter 9

Weekly Assessment

Provide formative assessment for each week of Chapter 9.

Focus on Problem Solving .... SE p. 445

Concept Connection .... SE p. 463

Ready to Go On? SPANISH 🌐 💿 .... SE pp. 444, 462

Cumulative Assessment .... SE pp. 472–473

Test and Practice Generator SPANISH 💿 ...*One-Stop Planner*

Formal Assessment

Provide summative assessment of Chapter 9 mastery.

Section Quizzes .... AR pp. 165–166

Chapter 9 Test SPANISH .... SE p. 469

Chapter Test (Levels A, B, C) .... AR pp. 167–178
  • Multiple-Choice • Free-Response

Cumulative Test .... AR pp. 181–184

Test and Practice Generator SPANISH 💿 ...*One-Stop Planner*

IDEA Works! Modified Tests .... Chapter 9

Technology Highlights for the Teacher

🌐 **Are You Ready?** SPANISH

Automatically assess readiness and prescribe intervention for Chapter 9 prerequisite skills.

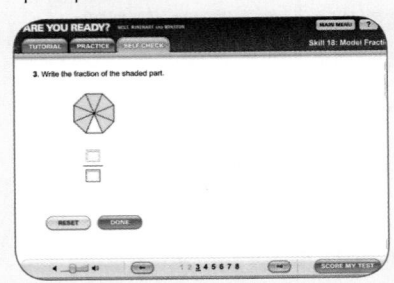

🌐 **Ready to Go On?** SPANISH

Automatically assess understanding of and prescribe intervention for Sections 9A and 9B.

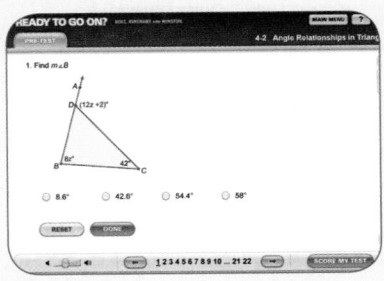

🌐 💿 **Focus on California Standards: Benchmark Tests and Intervention** SPANISH

Automatically assess proficiency with California Grade 7 Standards and provide intervention.

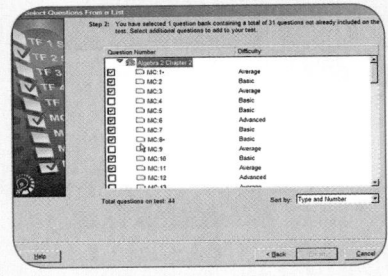

 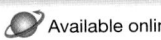

KEY: **SE** = *Student Edition* **TE** = *Teacher's Edition* **AR** = *Assessment Resources* SPANISH Spanish available 💿 Available on CD-ROM 🌐 Available online

Formal Assessment

Three levels (A, B, C) of multiple-choice and free-response chapter tests are available in the *Assessment Resources.*

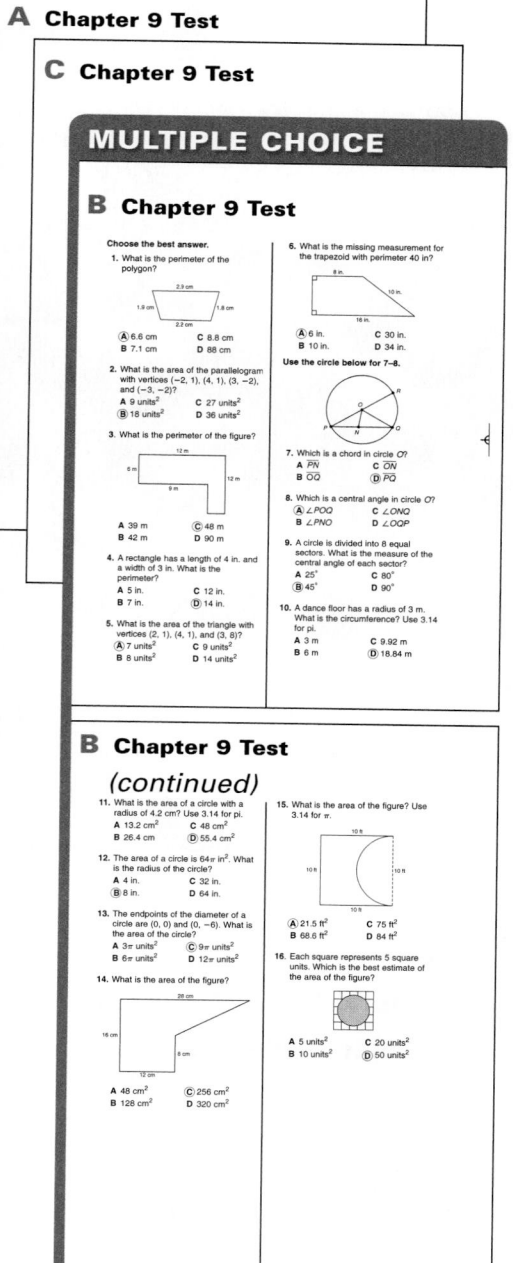

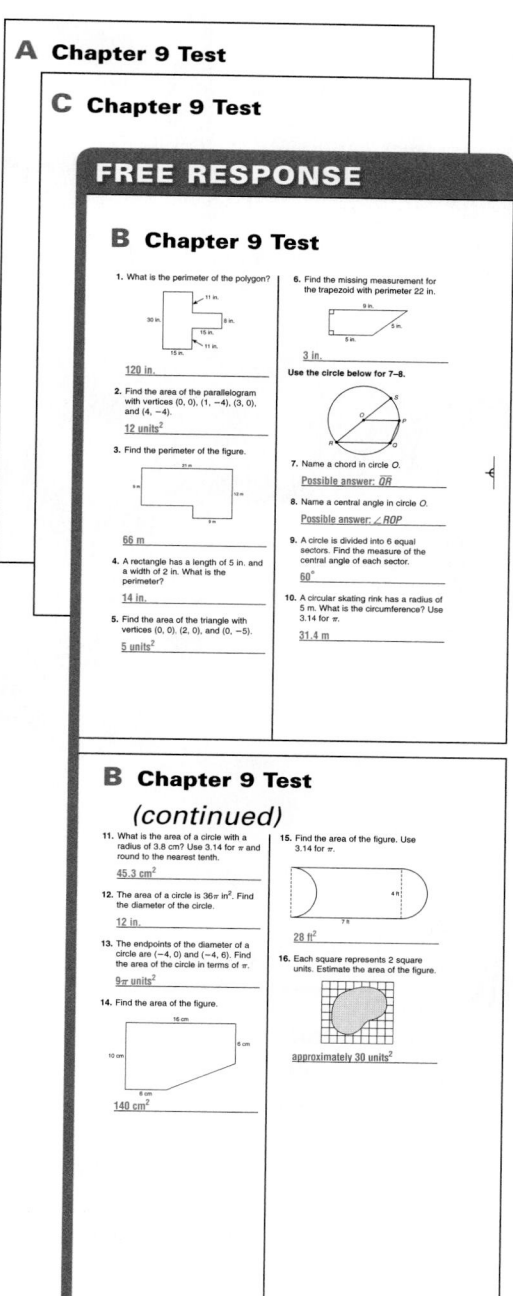

Modified tests and worksheets found in *IDEA Works!*

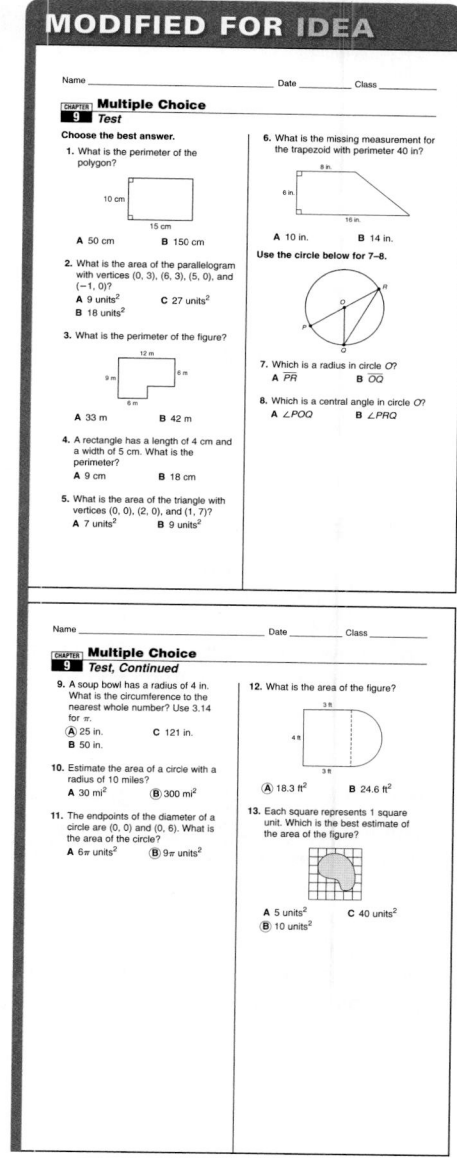

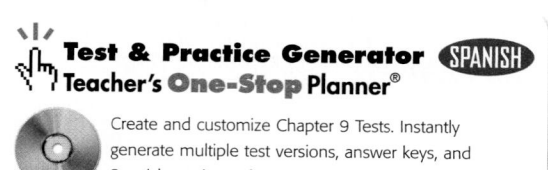

Test & Practice Generator SPANISH
Teacher's One-Stop Planner®

Create and customize Chapter 9 Tests. Instantly generate multiple test versions, answer keys, and Spanish versions of test items.

Focus on Problem Solving

On page 445, students focus on finding the solution that answers the question.

CONCEPT CONNECTION On page 463, students use perimeter and area formulas to calculate data about a family farm.

Two-Dimensional Geometry

9A   Perimeter and Area
9-1   Perimeter and Area of Parallelograms
9-2   Perimeter and Area of Triangles and Trapezoids

9B   Circles
9-3   Circles
9-4   Circumference and Area
9-5   Area of Composite Figures
9-6   Area of Irregular Figures

CONCEPT CONNECTION

go.hrw.com
Chapter Project Online
KEYWORD: MT8CA Ch9

Finding the circumference of a circle can help you determine the distance you travel while on a Ferris wheel.

Pacific Wheel,
Santa Monica

Math in *California*

Located on the Santa Monica Pier, the Pacific Wheel is the world's first solar-powered Ferris wheel. When the sun is shining, solar panels on the wheel's loading area produce enough electricity to keep the wheel in motion. On cloudy days, the wheel relies on conventional energy sources.

The Pacific Wheel lifts riders more than 130 feet above the Pacific Ocean, while turning at a rate of 2.5 revolutions per minute. Students will investigate properties of circular objects, such as the Pacific Wheel, in Lessons 9-3 and 9-4.

Problem Solving Project

Understand, Plan, Solve, and Look Back

Have students:

- Complete the Landscape Architect's Cost Estimate worksheet

- Design several new planted areas, exchange the dimensions with classmates, and calculate the total cost for covering these new areas with wood chips.

- Research different types of ground covers and the costs associated which each. How do the costs vary?

- Describe other situations in which areas may affect costs.

Social Studies Connection

Project Resources
All project resources for teachers and students are provided online.

Materials:

- Landscape Architect's Cost Estimate worksheet

go.hrw.com
Project Teacher Support
KEYWORD: MT8CA PSProject9

ARE YOU READY?

☑ Vocabulary

Choose the best term from the list to complete each sentence.

1. Lines that intersect to form right angles are __?__. **perpendicular lines**

2. To evaluate an algebraic expression, __?__ a given number for the variable. **substitute**

3. The __?__ of a circle is one-half the __?__ of the circle. **radius; diameter**

4. The __?__ can be used to find the length of any side of a right triangle. **Pythagorean Theorem**

5. To round 7.836 to the nearest tenth, look at the digit in the __?__ place. **hundredths**

Pythagorean
Theorem

diameter

perpendicular
lines

parallel lines

radius

substitute

tenths

hundredths

Complete these exercises to review skills you will need for this chapter.

☑ Round Decimals

Round each decimal to the underlined place.

6. 12.4̲5 **12**   7. 46.0̲92 **46.1**   8. 35.6̲666 **35.67**   9. 21.9̲91 **22.0**

10. 23.70̲9 **23.71** 11. 1̲3.93 **14**   12. 5.06̲49 **5.06**   13. 19.7̲5 **19.8**

☑ Order of Operations

Evaluate each expression.

14. $7^2 + 4^2$ **65**   15. $7 + \frac{1}{2}(8)(6)$ **31**   16. $30(15) - 4(2^2)$ **434**

17. $8^2 \div (4 \cdot 4)$ **4**   18. $\frac{17 - 9}{8} \cdot 13$ **13**   19. $6^2 \div (11 - 7)$ **9**

☑ Simplify Algebraic Expressions

Simplify each algebraic expression.

20. $2y + 9x - y + 9x$ **$y + 18x$**   21. $14z - 8 + 6z + 2$ **$20z - 6$**   22. $z - 8 - 6x + 2x + 6$ **$-4x + z - 2$**

☑ Solve One-Step Equations

Solve.

23. $p + 36 = 48$ **12**   24. $120 = 72 + x$ **48**   25. $12a = 72$ **6**

26. $\frac{1}{2}x = 3\frac{1}{2}$ **7**   27. $1.57 = 3.14x$ **$\frac{1}{2}$**   28. $56 = \frac{1}{4}h$ **224**

Organizer

Objective: Assess students' understanding of prerequisite skills.

Prerequisite Skills

Round Decimals

Order of Operations

Simplify Algebraic Expressions

Solve One-Step Equations

Assessing Prior Knowledge

INTERVENTION

Diagnose and Prescribe

Use this page to determine whether intervention is necessary or whether enrichment is appropriate.

Resources

 Are You Ready? Intervention and Enrichment Worksheets

 Are You Ready? CD-ROM

 Are You Ready? Online

my.hrw.com

ARE YOU READY?

Diagnose and Prescribe

NO INTERVENE

YES ENRICH

☑ Prerequisite Skill	📎 Worksheets	💿 CD-ROM	🪐 Online
☑ Round Decimals	Skill 16	Activity 16	
☑ Order of Operations	Skill 51	Activity 51	Diagnose and Prescribe Online
☑ Simplify Algebraic Expressions	Skill 55	Activity 55	
☑ Solve One-Step Equations	Skill 58	Activity 58	

ARE YOU READY? Intervention, Chapter 9

**ARE YOU READY?
Enrichment, Chapter 9**
📎 Worksheets
💿 CD-ROM
🪐 Online

Organizer

Objective: Help students understand the new concepts they will learn in Chapter 9.

Academic Vocabulary Connections

Becoming familiar with the academic vocabulary on this student page will be helpful to students. Discussing some of the vocabulary terms in the chapter also may be helpful. Possible answers given.

1. The word **circumference** contains the prefix *circum-*, which means "around." What do you suppose the circumference of a circle is? The circumference of a circle is the distance around the circle.

2. The Greek prefix *peri-* means "around," and the root *meter* means "means of measuring." What do you suppose **perimeter** means? Perimeter is the distance around the outside of a figure.

3. The Greek prefix *dia-* means "across." What do you suppose the **diameter** of a circle is? The diameter of a circle is the distance across the circle.

CHAPTER 9 Unpacking the Standards

The information below "unpacks" the standards. The Academic Vocabulary is highlighted and defined to help you understand the language of the standards. Refer to the lessons listed after each standard for help with the math terms and phrases. The Chapter Concept shows how the standard is applied in this chapter.

California Standard	Academic Vocabulary	Chapter Concept
MG2.1 Use formulas **routinely** for finding the perimeter and area of basic **two-dimensional** figures and the surface area and volume of basic three-dimensional figures, **including rectangles, parallelograms, trapezoids, squares, triangles, circles,** prisms, and cylinders. (Lessons 9-1, 9-2, and 9-4)	**routine** habit **two-dimensional** has length and width, but not height	You learn formulas for the perimeter and area of figures that have length and width. **Example:** Rectangle: Perimeter: $2\ell + 2w$ Area: ℓw Circle: Circumference: $2\pi r$ Area: πr^2
MG2.2 Estimate and compute the area of more **complex** or irregular **two-** and three-**dimensional figures by breaking the figures down into more basic geometric objects.** (Lessons 9-1, 9-5, and 9-6)	**complex** multi-part **breaking** dividing into parts	You divide geometric figures into familiar shapes such as rectangles, triangles, and parts of circles. **Example:**
MG3.1 Identify and construct **basic elements of geometric figures** (e.g., altitudes, midpoints, diagonals, angle bisectors, and perpendicular bisectors; **central angles, radii, diameters, and chords of circles**) by using a compass and straightedge. (Lesson 9-3)	**elements** parts of	You learn the names and properties of parts of circles.
MG3.2 Understand and use coordinate graphs to **plot** simple figures, **determine** lengths and areas related to **them,** and determine their image under translations and reflections. (Lessons 9-1 and 9-2)	**plot** draw on a graph **determine** find out	You draw figures on a graph to find out measurements from the graph.

Standard MG2.4 is also covered in this chapter. To see MG2.4 unpacked, go to Chapter 10, p. 476.

Looking Back

Previously, students

- used formulas to find the perimeter and area of basic figures.
- used circumference to find the radius and diameter of circles.
- found the perimeter and area of basic two-dimensional figures.

In This Chapter

Students will study

- using coordinate planes to plot basic figures and find their perimeter and area.
- finding the circumference of circles to a specified degree of accuracy.
- finding the perimeter and area of composite figures.

Looking Forward

Students can use these skills

- to construct two-dimensional patterns for three dimensional objects.
- to solve problems about rate, distance and circular objects.
- to find the perimeter and area of irregular figures.

Study Strategy: Concept Map

Concept maps are visual tools for organizing information. A concept map shows how key concepts are related and can help you summarize and analyze information in lessons or chapters.

Create a Concept Map

1. Give your concept map a title.

2. Identify the main idea of your concept map.

3. List the key concepts.

4. Link the concepts to show the relationships between the concepts and the main idea.

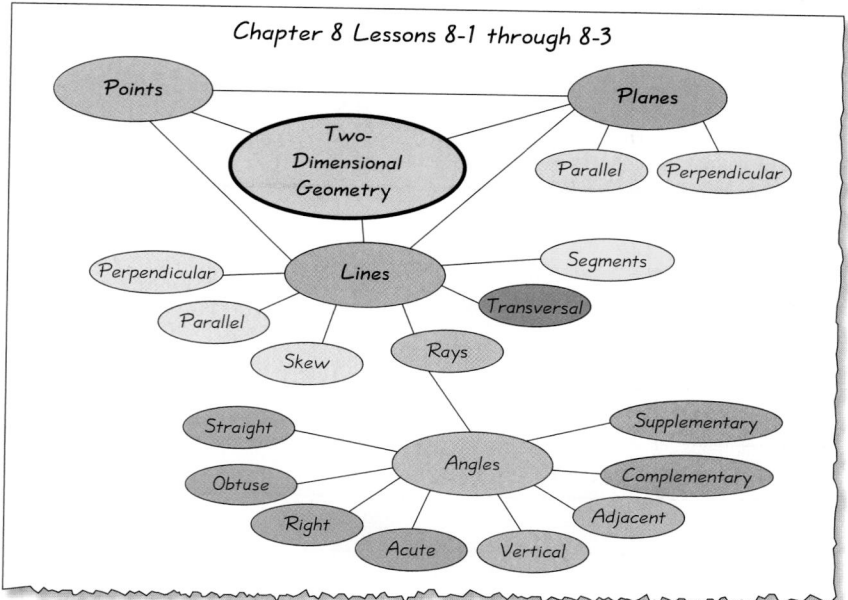

Chapter 8 Lessons 8-1 through 8-3

Try This

1. Complete the concept map above to include Lessons 8-4 and 8-5.

2. Create your own concept map for the concept of transformations.

Organizer

Objective: Help students apply strategies to understand and retain key concepts.

PREMIER Online Edition

Resources

 Chapter 9 Resource File
Reading Strategies

Study Strategy: Concept Map

ENGLISH LANGUAGE LEARNERS

Discuss Students will retain information longer when they organize it in a way that makes sense to them. A concept map is especially helpful to visual learners. Be sure students realize that there is more than one way to organize information within a concept map.

Extend As students work through Chapter 9, ask them to make a concept map of any lessons they found particularly difficult. Encourage them to exchange their maps with others. This may give them added insight into particular concepts covered in the chapter.

Possible answers to *Try This*

1.

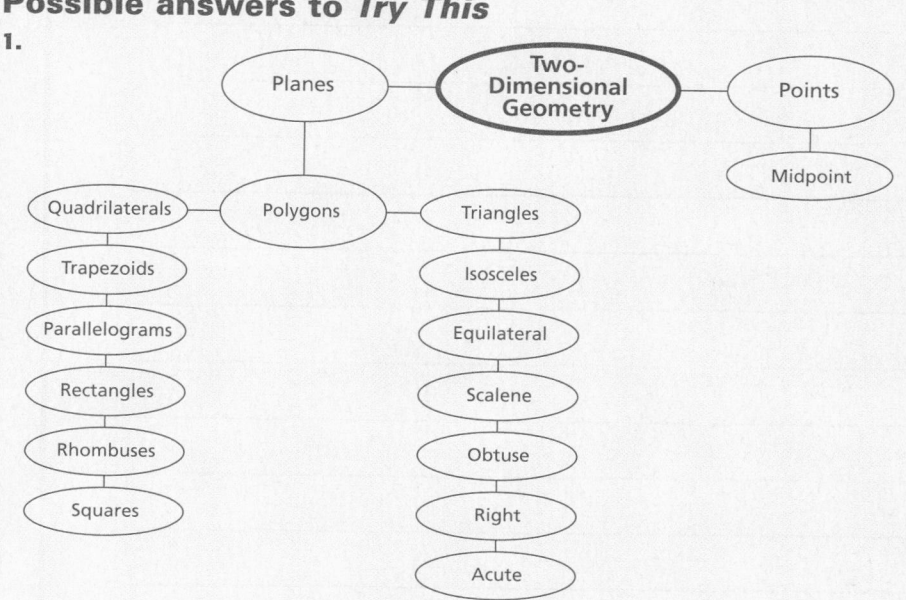

2.

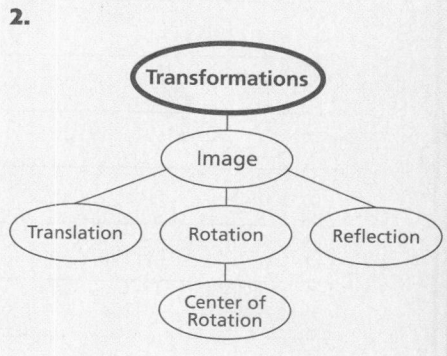

Perimeter and Area

One-Minute Section Planner

Lesson	Lab Resources	Materials
Lesson 9-1 Perimeter and Area of Parallelograms • Find the perimeter and area of parallelograms. 🐻 **MG2.0, MG2.1, MG2.2, MG2.4, MG3.2**	**Hands-On Lab 9-1** In *Chapter 9 Resource File*	**Required** Graph paper
Lesson 9-2 Perimeter and Area of Triangles and Trapezoids • Find the perimeter and area of triangles and trapezoids. 🐻 **MG2.1, MG3.2**	**Hands-On Lab 9-2** **Technology Lab 9-2** In *Chapter 9 Resource File*	**Optional** Cutout figures, scissors, graph paper

MK = *Manipulatives Kit*

Notes

_____

_____

_____

_____

_____

_____

_____

_____

_____

_____

_____

_____

_____

_____

_____

_____

Math Background: Teaching the Standards

UNDERSTANDING AREA 🐻 MG2.0, MG2.1

Lessons 9-1, 9-2

To define area, begin with the unit square. A *unit square* is a square whose sides have length 1 unit. For example, the figure shows a unit square with sides of length 1 cm.

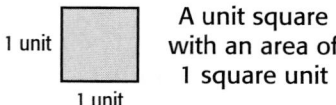

1 unit — 1 unit
A unit square with an area of 1 square unit

The area of a unit square is defined to be one square unit. Just as a one-centimeter segment may be used as a standard for measuring length, a unit square may be used as a standard for measuring area. In particular, the *area* of a plane figure is the number of non-overlapping unit squares needed to cover the figure.

It is easy to see that a rectangle with sides of length 2 cm and 3 cm may be covered by exactly 6 of the unit squares shown above. More generally, the area of a rectangle is the length of its base times its height, or $A = bh$.

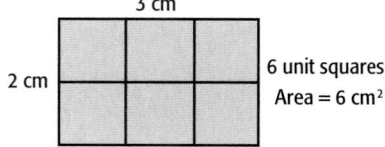

3 cm
2 cm
6 unit squares
Area = 6 cm²

This familiar formula for the area of a rectangle is the starting point for developing all other area formulas. The arguments that are used to develop other area formulas depend upon the Area Addition Postulate, which states that the area of a region is equal to the sum of the areas of its nonoverlapping parts. This postulate justifies the process of calculating areas by "cutting up" and rearranging figures.

For example, a parallelogram with base b and height h may be divided into a right triangle and a trapezoid. These two figures may be placed together to form a rectangle whose area is bh. Thus, the area of the parallelogram is also bh.

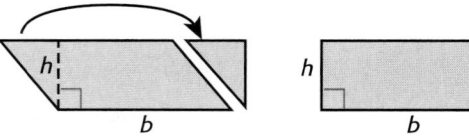

h — b — h — b

Any triangle with base b and height h may be placed next to a congruent copy of the triangle to form a parallelogram of area bh. Therefore, the area of the triangle is half that of the parallelogram, or $\frac{1}{2}bh$.

Similarly, given a trapezoid with height h and bases b_1 and b_2, you can use a congruent copy of the trapezoid to form a parallelogram as shown below. The area of the parallelogram is its base, $b_1 + b_2$, times its height, h. The area of the trapezoid is half that of the parallelogram, or $\frac{1}{2}h(b_1 + b_2)$.

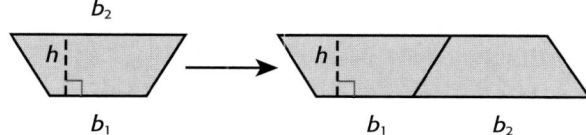

b_2
h
b_1
h
b_1 — b_2

PERIMETER AND AREA 🐻 MG2.0, MG2.1

Lessons 9-1, 9-2

Fractals offer an interesting perspective on the connection between perimeter and area. For example, the figures shown below illustrate the steps in creating a fractal called a Koch snowflake. It is constructed by first drawing an equilateral triangle. Then triangles with sides one-third the length of the original sides are added to the middle of each side. This step is subsequently repeated over and over.

 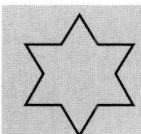 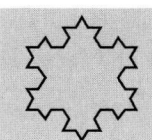 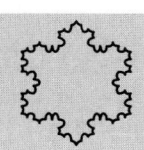

The area and perimeter of each figure are greater than the area and perimeter of the one before it. However, the area of any figure is never greater than the area of the shaded square that contains it. In fact, using calculus, it is possible to show that the areas converge to $\frac{8}{5}$ times the area of the original triangle. It is also possible to show that the perimeters increase without bound. In other words, the Koch snowflake is a figure with a finite area but an infinite perimeter!

Objective: Students find the perimeter and area of parallelograms.

 Hands-On Lab
In *Chapter 9 Resource File*

 Online Edition
Tutorial Videos

 Countdown to Mastery Week 18

Power Presentations
with PowerPoint®

Warm Up

Graph the line segment for each set of ordered pairs. Then find the length of the line segment.

1. (−7, 0), (0, 0)   7 units

2. (0, 3), (0, 6)   3 units

3. (−4, −2), (1, −2)   5 units

4. (−5, 4), (−5, −2)   6 units

Also available on transparency

 **Math Humor**

Teacher: If you measured the perimeter of Antarctica, what would the result be, in feet?
Student: Frostbite

 California Standards

Measurement and Geometry 2.1
Also covered:
Measurement and Geometry
2.0 Students compute the perimeter, area, and volume of common geometric objects and use the results to find measures of less common objects. They know how perimeter, area, and volume are affected by changes of scale.
2.2 Estimate and **compute the area of more complex** or irregular **two- and three-dimensional figures by breaking the figures down into more basic geometric objects.**
2.4 Relate the changes in measurement with a change of scale to the units used (e.g., **square inches, cubic feet**) and to conversions between units (1 square foot = 144 square inches or [1 ft.²] = [144 in.²]; 1 cubic inch is approximately 16.38 cubic centimeters or [1 in.³] = [16.38 cm³]).
3.2 Understand and use coordinate graphs to plot simple figures, determine lengths and areas related to them, and determine their image under translations and reflections.

 9-1 **Perimeter and Area of Parallelograms**

 **California Standards**

MG2.1 Use formulas routinely for finding the perimeter and area of basic two-dimensional figures and the surface area and volume of basic three-dimensional figures, **including rectangles, parallelograms,** trapezoids, **squares,** triangles, circles, prisms, and cylinders. *Also covered:* **MG2.2, MG2.4, MG3.2**

Vocabulary
perimeter
area
base
height
composite figure

Why learn this? You can use formulas to find the perimeter and area of objects such as quilts. (See Exercise 24.)

Perimeter is the distance around a polygon. To find the perimeter of any polygon, you add the lengths of its sides.

Since opposite sides of a parallelogram are equal in length, you can find a formula for the perimeter of a parallelogram.

$$P = w + \ell + w + \ell$$
$$= w + w + \ell + \ell$$
$$= 2w + 2\ell$$

PERIMETER OF A PARALLELOGRAM		
Words	**Formula**	**Numbers**
The perimeter P of a parallelogram is the sum of twice its width w and twice its length ℓ.	$P = 2w + 2\ell$	$P = 2(3) + 2(5) = 16$

EXAMPLE 1 **Finding the Perimeter of Parallelograms**

Find the perimeter of each figure.

A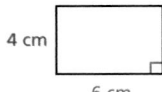
4 cm
6 cm

$P = 2w + 2\ell$ *Perimeter of a parallelogram*
$= 2(4) + 2(6)$ *Substitute 4 for w and 6 for ℓ.*
$= 8 + 12 = 20$ cm

B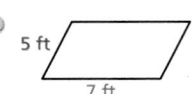
5 ft
7 ft

$P = 2w + 2\ell$ *Perimeter of a parallelogram*
$= 2(7) + 2(5)$ *Substitute 7 for w and 5 for ℓ.*
$= 14 + 10 = 24$ ft

---

1 **Introduce**
Alternate Opener

 **EXPLORATION**

9-1 **Perimeter and Area of Parallelograms**

Recall that the area of a rectangle is the product of its length times its width, or the product of its base times its height, *bh*. You can use this fact to develop the formula for the area of a parallelogram.

1. Draw a parallelogram on a sheet of graph paper. Label the base and height as shown.
2. Cut out the parallelogram.
3. Now cut a right triangle off the end of the parallelogram as shown.
4. Arrange the two pieces to form a rectangle.
5. What are the base and height of the rectangle you made? What is the rectangle's area?
6. How is the area of the parallelogram related to the area of the rectangle?

Think and Discuss

7. **Explain** how to write a formula for the area of a parallelogram with base *b* and height *h*.
8. **Describe** how you can use your formula to find the area of this parallelogram.
4 cm
6 cm

Motivate

Ask students how many measurements it would take to find the length of a wall in the classroom. one Explain that length is a *one-dimensional* measure because it requires only one measurement. Then ask them how many measurements it would take to find the size (area) of the floor. two Explain that area is *two-dimensional* because it requires two different measurements.

Explorations and answers are provided in *Alternate Openers: Explorations Transparencies.*

The **area** of a plane figure is the number of unit squares needed to cover the figure. While perimeter is expressed in linear units, such as inches (in.) or meters (m), area is expressed in square units, such as square feet (ft^2).

The **base** of a parallelogram is the length of one side. The **height** is the perpendicular distance from the base to the opposite side.

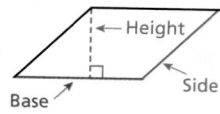

You can cut a parallelogram and shift the cut piece to form a rectangle whose base and height are the same as those of the original parallelogram. The same number of unit squares are needed to cover the two figures. So a parallelogram and a rectangle that have the same base and height have the same area.

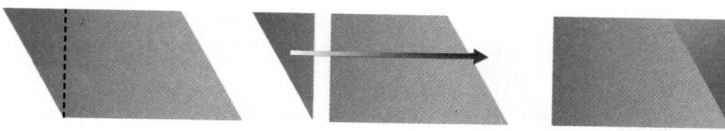

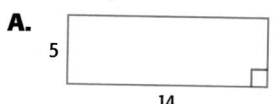

Additional Examples

Example 1

Find the perimeter of each figure.

A.

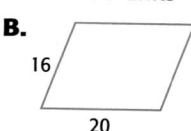
5
14

$P = 38$ units

B.

16
20

$P = 72$ units

Example 2

Graph and find the area of the figure with the given vertices.

A. $(-1, -2), (2, -2), (2, 3), (-1, 3)$

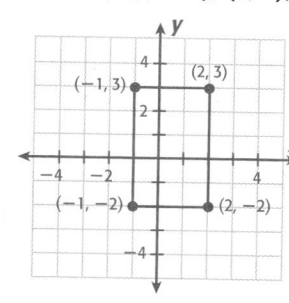

$(-1, 3)$ $(2, 3)$

$(-1, -2)$ $(2, -2)$

$A = 15$ units^2

Also available on transparency

Helpful Hint

Since the base and height of a rectangle are the same as its length and width, the formula for the area of a rectangle can also be written as $A = \ell w$.

AREA OF RECTANGLES AND PARALLELOGRAMS		
Words	**Formula**	**Numbers**
The area A of a rectangle or parallelogram is the base length b times the height h.	$A = bh$	5, 3 — $5 \cdot 3 = 15$ units^2 — **Rectangle** · 5, 3 — $5 \cdot 3 = 15$ units^2 — **Parallelogram**

EXAMPLE 2 **Using a Graph to Find Area**

Graph and find the area of each figure with the given vertices.

A $(-3, -2), (3, -2), (3, 1), (-3, 1)$

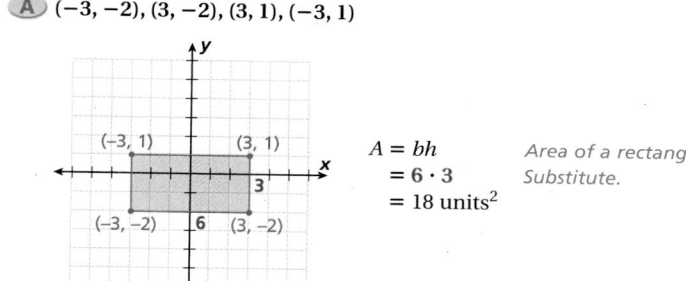

$(-3, 1)$ $(3, 1)$

$(-3, -2)$ 6 $(3, -2)$

$A = bh$ *Area of a rectangle*
$= 6 \cdot 3$ *Substitute.*
$= 18$ units^2

---

2 Teach

Guided Instruction

In this lesson, students learn to find perimeter and area of parallelograms. Explain to students that *perimeter* is the distance around the outside of a figure. Explain that the perimeter of a polygon can be found by adding up all of its side lengths, or for some special figures, by using a formula. Emphasize that perimeter is measured in linear units. Explain that area is a measure of the space inside a two-dimensional figure. Show students how the area of a rectangle can be found by counting the number of unit squares in the figure (Teaching Transparency). For this reason, area is measured in square units.

Universal Access

Through Multiple Representations

Have students use graph paper to find as many different rectangles as possible that have a perimeter of 16 units and then calculate the area of each. Then have them find as many different rectangles as possible that have an area of 24 units^2 and calculate the perimeter of each. Finally, have them describe any patterns they notice in tables.

Length	Width	Area	Perimeter
4	4	16 units^2	16 units
5	3	15 units^2	16 units
6	2	12 units^2	16 units
7	1	7 units^2	16 units

Length	Width	Perimeter	Area
6	4	20 units	24 units^2
8	3	22 units	24 units^2
12	2	28 units	24 units^2
24	1	50 units	24 units^2

Example 2

Graph and find the area of the figure with the given vertices.

B. (0, 0), (5, 0), (6, 4), (1, 4)

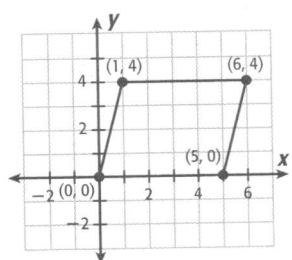

$A = 20$ units^2

Example 3

Find the perimeter and area of the figure.

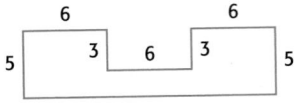

$P = 52$ units; $A = 72$ units^2

Answers to Think and Discuss

1. Possible answer: The area of the rectangle with base $2b$ and height $2h$ is four times the area of the rectangle with base b and height h.

2. Because the side lengths of a square are equal, both the base and the height can be represented by the same variable, s. Substituting s into both formulas for b and h gives $A = s^2$ and $P = 4s$.

Caution!

The height of a parallelogram is not the length of its slanted side. The height of a figure is always perpendicular to the base.

Graph and find the area of each figure with the given vertices.

B $(-4, -4)$, $(1, -4)$, $(3, 0)$, $(-2, 0)$

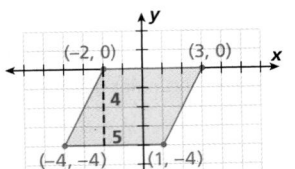

$A = bh$ *Area of a parallelogram*
$= 5 \cdot 4$ *Substitute.*
$= 20$ units^2

A **composite figure** is made up of basic geometric shapes such as rectangles, triangles, trapezoids, and circles. To find the area of a composite figure, find the areas of the geometric shapes and then add the areas.

EXAMPLE 3   **Finding Area and Perimeter of a Composite Figure**

Find the perimeter and area of the figure.

Reasoning

The length of the side that is not labeled is the same as the length of the opposite side, 2 m.

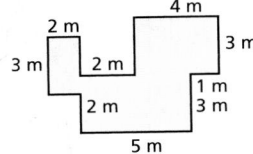

$P = 3 + 2 + 2 + 2 + 3 + 4 + 3 + 1 + 3$
    $+ 5 + 2 + 2$
$= 32$ m

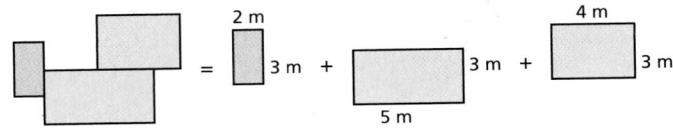

$A = (2 \cdot 3) + (5 \cdot 3) + (4 \cdot 3)$ *Add the areas.*
$= 6 + 15 + 12$
$= 33$ m^2

Think and Discuss

1. **Compare** the area of a rectangle with base b and height h with the area of a rectangle with base $2b$ and height $2h$.

2. **Express** the formulas for the area and perimeter of a square using s for the length of a side.

---

3 Close

Summarize

Review the important differences between perimeter and area. Remind students that perimeter is the distance around a figure and is measured in linear units. Remind them that area is the space inside a figure and is measured in square units. Show students some concrete examples, such as a photograph. Ask students which measure would help you find how much wood you would need to frame the photograph. perimeter Then ask which would tell you how much glass you would need. area As a challenge, you may want to ask them to estimate both measures.

California Standards Practice
MG1.3, MG2.1, MG2.2, MG2.4, MG3.2

go.hrw.com
Homework Help Online
KEYWORD: MT8CA 9-1
Parent Resources Online
KEYWORD: MT8CA Parent

GUIDED PRACTICE

See Example **1** Find the perimeter of each figure.

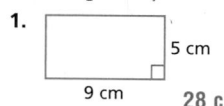

1.
5 cm
9 cm
28 cm

2.
8 in.
10 in.
36 in.

3.
1.5x ft
4.6x ft
12.2x ft

See Example **2** Graph and find the area of each figure with the given vertices.

4. $(-4, 3), (0, 3), (4, -1), (0, -1)$
16 units²

5. $(-2, -3), (-2, 0), (4, 0), (4, -3)$
18 units²

6. $(-6, -1), (-5, 2), (2, 2), (1, -1)$
21 units²

7. $(-2, 3), (0, 3), (0, -4), (-2, -4)$
14 units²

See Example **3** **8.** Find the perimeter and area of the figure.
36 m; 29 m²

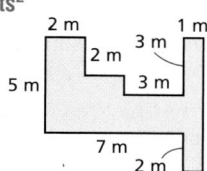
2 m 3 m 1 m
2 m
5 m 3 m
7 m
2 m

INDEPENDENT PRACTICE

See Example **1** Find the perimeter of each figure.

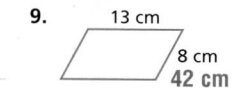

9.
13 cm
8 cm
42 cm

10.
0.9 in.
3.0 in.
7.8 in.

11.
5x m
8x m
26x m

See Example **2** Graph and find the area of each figure with the given vertices.

12. $(-1, -1), (-1, -6), (2, -6), (2, -1)$
15 units²

13. $(0, 3), (6, 3), (3, -1), (-3, -1)$
24 units²

14. $(-1, -2), (-1, 4), (1, 5), (1, -1)$
12 units²

15. $(3, -2), (6, -2), (6, 2), (3, 2)$
12 units²

See Example **3** **16.** Find the perimeter and area of the figure.
46 yd; 84 yd²

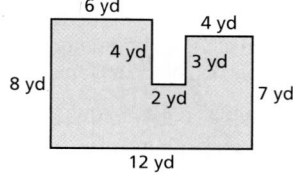
6 yd
4 yd 4 yd
8 yd 3 yd
2 yd 7 yd
12 yd

PRACTICE AND PROBLEM SOLVING

Extra Practice
See page EP18.

Find the perimeter and area of each figure.

17.
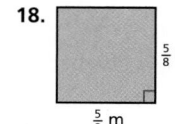
4.5 ft
12 ft
33 ft; 54 ft²

18.
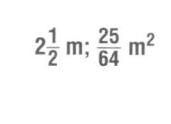
$\frac{5}{8}$ m
$\frac{5}{8}$ m
$2\frac{1}{2}$ m; $\frac{25}{64}$ m²

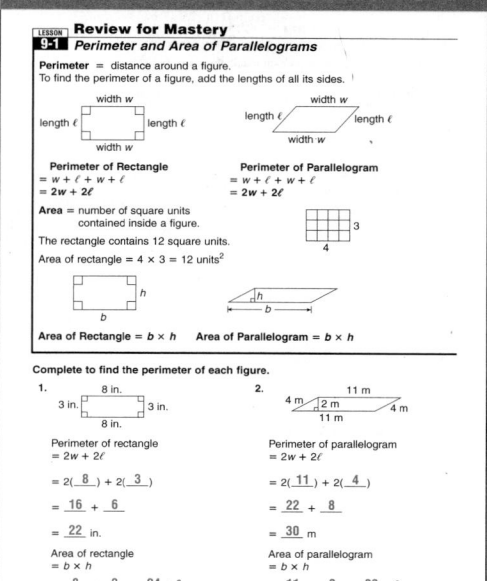

9-1 **Exercises**

Assignment Guide

If you finished Example **1** assign:
Proficient 1–3, 9–11, 21, 29–37
Advanced 9–11, 21, 29–37

If you finished Example **2** assign:
Proficient 1–7, 9–15, 17, 18, 21, 23, 27–37
Advanced 9–15, 17, 18, 21–24, 27–37

If you finished Example **3** assign:
Proficient 1–20, 21, 23, 27–37
Advanced 9–37

Homework Quick Check

Quickly check key concepts.
Exercises: 10, 14, 16

4.
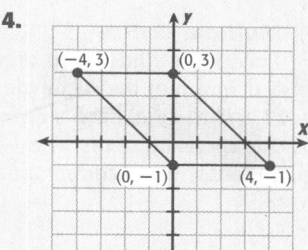
$(-4, 3)$ $(0, 3)$
$(0, -1)$ $(4, -1)$

Answers

5–7, 12–15. See pp. A9–10.

Math Background

The concepts in this lesson are important for more advanced studies in geometry. Students should begin to develop an understanding of dimensions and appropriate units. An object that has one directional measure (e.g., length) is one-dimensional, and its length is measured in linear units. Similarly, an object with two different directional measures (e.g., length and width) is two-dimensional, and its area is measured in square units. It is also important that students be able to apply basic formulas, such as those presented in this lesson.

California Standards

Standard	Exercises
NS1.4 🔑	33–37
AF4.1 🔑	29–32
MG1.3 🔑	22
MG2.1	1–3, 9–11, 17–18, 21–22, 24, 26–27
MG2.2	8, 16, 23
MG3.2	4–7, 12–15, 28

Answers

25. Possible answer: The figures have the same area, but the figure with the cutout has a greater perimeter because it has additional sides.

28. See p. A10.

 **Multiple Choice**
Teaching Tip Encourage students to draw a diagram of the rectangle in **Exercise 27** and to label each side with its possible measurements. This will help students identify the incorrect area answer choice.

 Journal

Ask students to write about a real-world situation in which they would need to find the perimeter and area of an object. Have them estimate the measures of the object they have chosen. Examples might include framing a picture or decorating a wall or floor.

 Power Presentations
with PowerPoint®

9-1 Lesson Quiz

1. Find the perimeter of the figure.
44 ft

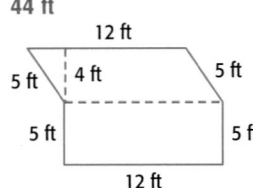

2. Find the area of the figure.
108 ft²

Graph and find the area of each figure with the given vertices.

Complete answers on p. A10.

3. (−4, 2), (6, 2), (6, −3), (−4, −3)
50 units²

4. (4, −2), (−2, −2), (−3, 5), (3, 5)
42 units²

Also available on transparency

Find the perimeter and area of each figure.

19.
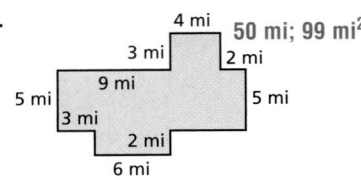
18 ft; 10.5 ft²

20.
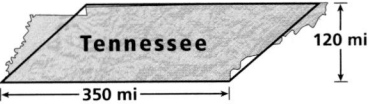
50 mi; 99 mi²

Multi-Step A rectangular ice-skating rink measures 50 ft by 75 ft.

21. It costs $13.50 per foot to install sheets of clear protective plastic around the rink. How much does it cost to enclose the rink with plastic sheets? **$3375**

22. A machine can clear 750 ft² of ice per minute. How long will it take the machine to clear the entire rink? **5 min**

23. Social Studies The state of Tennessee is shaped approximately like a parallelogram. Estimate the area of the state. **≈42,000 mi²**

Tennessee 120 mi — 350 mi —

24. Community The NAMES Project Foundation's AIDS Memorial Quilt contains 44,000 rectangular panels that each measure 3 ft by 6 ft. What is the area of the whole quilt? **792,000 ft²**

 25. Write About It A rectangle and an identical rectangle with a smaller rectangle cut from the bottom and placed on top are shown. Do the two figures have the same area? Do they have the same perimeter? Explain.

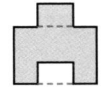

 26. Challenge A ruler is 30 cm long by 5 cm wide. How many rulers this size can be cut from a 544 cm² rectangular piece of wood with base length 32 cm? **3 rulers**

SPIRAL STANDARDS REVIEW ◄═ NS1.4, ◄═ AF4.1, MG2.1, MG3.2

27. Multiple Choice The lengths of the sides of a rectangle are whole numbers. If the rectangle's perimeter is 24 units, which of the following could NOT be the area of the rectangle?

Ⓐ 27 square units   Ⓑ 24 square units   Ⓒ 20 square units   Ⓓ 11 square units

28. Short Response Graph the figure with vertices (2, 5), (−3, 5), (−5, 1), and (0, 1). Find the area of the figure. Explain how you found the area.

Solve. Check your answer. (Lesson 2-8)

29. $5x + 2 = -18$
$x = -4$

30. $\frac{b}{-6} + 12 = 5$
$b = 42$

31. $\frac{a + 4}{11} = -3$
$a = -37$

32. $\frac{1}{3}x - \frac{1}{4} = \frac{5}{12}$
$x = 2$

State whether each number is rational, irrational, or not a real number. (Lesson 4-8)

33. -14
rational

34. $\sqrt{13}$
irrational

35. $\frac{127}{46,191}$
rational

36. $\sqrt{-\frac{5}{6}}$
not real

37. $\frac{21}{0}$
not real

CHALLENGE 9-1

Challenge
9-1 *Color Me Least!*

The basic rule for coloring a map is that no two regions that share a boundary can be the same color. However, two regions that meet at only a single point may have the same color.

In 1852, while coloring a map of England, Francis Guthrie noticed that no more than 4 colors were necessary. He conjectured that any map could be colored with no more than four colors.

What came to be known as the **Four Color Map Problem** was considered by mathematicians and school children alike for many years. No satisfactory proof was found until 1976, when K. Appel and W. Haken of the University of Illinois devised a computer program that took 1200 hours to run.

1. a. In this map of 5 distinct regions, can regions C and D have the same color? Explain.
No; they share a border.

b. Can regions C and E have the same color? Explain.
Yes; only one point in common.

c. What is the least number of colors required for this map? __3__
Use numbers to show your answer on the map. **Possible answer.**

2. Here is a map of 10 neighboring states. So far, as colored, only 3 colors are needed to distinguish among 9 of the 10.
Color 1: New Mexico, Nevada, and Wyoming
Color 2: Oregon, Arizona, and Montana
Color 3: Idaho, Colorado, and California
How can you color the state of Utah?
Utah needs a 4th color.

3. Use numbers to color these maps with the least number of colors possible. **Possible answer:**

PROBLEM SOLVING 9-1

Problem Solving
9-1 *Perimeter and Area of Parallelograms*

Use the following for Exercises 1–2. A quilt for a twin bed is 68 in. by 90 in.

1. What is the area of the backing applied to the quilt?
6120 in²

2. A ruffle is sewn to the edge of the quilt. How many feet of ruffle are needed to go all the way around the edge of the quilt?
26 $\frac{1}{3}$ ft

Use the following for Exercises 3–4. Jaime is building a rectangular dog run that is 12 ft by 8 ft.

3. If the run is cemented, how many square feet will be covered by cement?
96 ft²

4. How much fencing will be required to enclose the dog run?
40 ft

Use the following for Exercises 5–6. Jackie is painting the walls in a room. Two walls are 12 ft by 8 ft, and two walls are 10 ft by 8 ft. Choose the letter for the best answer.

5. What is the area of the walls to be painted?
Ⓐ 352 ft²   C 704 ft²
B 176 ft²   D 400 ft²

6. If a can of paint covers 300 square feet, how many cans of paint should Jackie buy?
F 1   H 3
Ⓖ 2   J 4

Use the following for Exercises 7–8. One kind of pool cover is a tarp that stretches over the area of the pool and is tied down on the edge of the pool. The cover extends 6 inches beyond the edge of the pool. Choose the letter for the best answer.

7. A rectangular pool is 20 ft by 10 ft. What is the area of the tarp that will cover the pool?
A 200 ft²   C 60 ft²
Ⓑ 231 ft²   D 215.25 ft²

8. If the tarp costs $2.50 per square foot, how much will the tarp cost?
F $500.00   H $150.00
G $538.13   Ⓙ $577.50

Perimeter and Area of Triangles and Trapezoids

 California Standards

MG2.1 Use formulas routinely for finding the perimeter and area of basic two-dimensional figures and the surface area and volume of basic three-dimensional figures, **including** rectangles, parallelograms, **trapezoids**, squares, **triangles**, circles, prisms, and cylinders.
Also covered: **MG3.2**

Who uses this? Aerospace engineers use triangles and trapezoids when designing aircraft. (See Exercises 28–34.)

Many polygons do not have a formula for perimeter because they do not have side lengths that are equal. To find the perimeter of these polygons you add the lengths of the sides. If you know the perimeter and the lengths of all but one side, you can solve for the missing side length.

 EXAMPLE 1 **Using Perimeter**

Find the missing measurement when the perimeter is 92 cm.

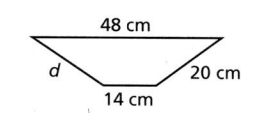

$$P = 48 + 14 + 20 + d$$
$$92 = 82 + d \quad \text{Substitute 92 for } P.$$
$$\underline{-82 \quad -82} \quad \text{Subtract 82 from}$$
$$10 = d \quad \text{both sides.}$$
$$d = 10 \text{ cm}$$

 EXAMPLE 2 *Multi-Step Application*

A farmer wants to fence a field that is in the shape of a right triangle. He knows that the two shorter sides of the field are 20 yards and 35 yards long. How long will the fence be to the nearest hundredth of a yard?

Step 1: Find the length of the third side.

$$a^2 + b^2 = c^2 \qquad \text{Use the Pythagorean Theorem.}$$
$$20^2 + 35^2 = c^2 \qquad \text{Substitute 20 for } a \text{ and 35 for } b.$$
$$400 + 1225 = c^2$$
$$1625 = c^2$$
$$40.31 \approx c \qquad \sqrt{1625} = \sqrt{c^2}$$

Step 2: Find the perimeter of the field.

$$P = a + b + c$$
$$= 20 + 35 + 40.31 \qquad \text{Add all sides.}$$
$$= 95.31$$

The fence will be about 95.31 yards long.

Organizer 9-2

Objective: Students find the perimeter and area of triangles and trapezoids.

 Hands-On Lab
In *Chapter 9 Resource File*

 Technology Lab
In *Chapter 9 Resource File*

 Online Edition
Tutorial Videos, Interactivities

 Countdown to Mastery Week 18

Power Presentations with PowerPoint®

Warm Up

A rectangle has side lengths of 12 ft and 20 ft.
1. Find the perimeter.   64 ft
2. Find the area.   240 ft²

Also available on transparency

Math Humor

Photographer: What are you doing in my darkroom?

Math Student: I'm waiting for my formula to develop!

---

1 Introduce

Alternate Opener

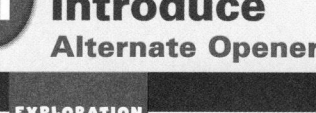

EXPLORATION

9-2 Perimeter and Area of Triangles and Trapezoids

You can use what you know about the area of a parallelogram to develop the formula for the area of a triangle.

1. Fold a sheet of paper in half.
2. Draw a triangle on the folded paper. Label the base, *b*, and height, *h*, as shown.
3. Cut out the triangle through both layers of paper. This will create a pair of congruent triangles.
4. Arrange the two triangles to form a parallelogram.
5. What are the base and height of the parallelogram you made? What is the parallelogram's area?
6. How is the area of one of the triangles related to the area of the parallelogram?

Think and Discuss

7. **Explain** how to write a formula for the area of a triangle with base *b* and height *h*.
8. **Describe** how you can use your formula to find the area of this triangle.

Motivate

Have students cut a parallelogram along a diagonal to form a pair of congruent triangles. Ask students how the area of each triangle compares to the area of the parallelogram. Help them see that each triangle is half of the original figure. Then have students place two congruent trapezoids side by side to form a parallelogram. Explain that the area of one of the trapezoids is half the area of the parallelogram.

Explorations and answers are provided in *Alternate Openers: Explorations Transparencies.*

 **California Standards**

Measurement and Geometry 2.1
Also covered:
Measurement and Geometry 3.2 Understand and use coordinate graphs to plot simple figures, determine lengths and areas related to them, and determine their image under translations and reflections.

Example 1

Find the missing measurement when the perimeter is 71 in.

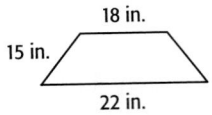

18 in.

15 in.

22 in.

16 in.

Example 2

A homeowner wants to plant a border of shrubs around her yard that is in the shape of a right triangle. She knows that the length of the shortest side of the yard is 12 feet and the length of the longest side is 20 feet. How long will the border be?   48 ft

Example 3

Graph and find the area of the figure with the given vertices.

A. (−2, 2), (4, 2), (0, 5)

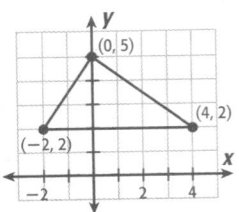

(0, 5)

(4, 2)

(−2, 2)

$A = 9$ units²

Also available on transparency

A triangle or a trapezoid can be thought of as half of a parallelogram. Therefore, the formulas for the area of a triangle or a trapezoid have $\frac{1}{2}$ as a factor.

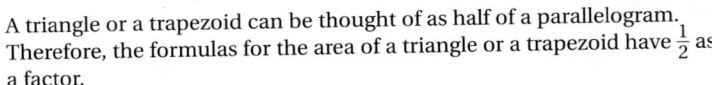

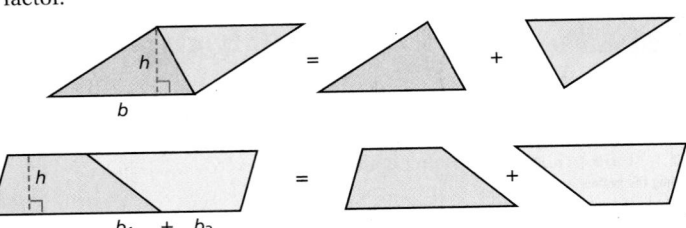

Reading Math

In the term b_1, the number 1 is called a *subscript*. It is read as "b one" or "b sub-one."

AREA OF TRIANGLES AND TRAPEZOIDS

Words	Formula	Numbers
Triangle: The area A of a triangle is one-half of the base length b times the height h.	$A = \frac{1}{2}bh$	4 8 $A = \frac{1}{2}(8)(4)$ $= 16$ units²
Trapezoid: The area of a trapezoid is one-half the height h times the sum of the base lengths b_1 and b_2.	$A = \frac{1}{2}h(b_1 + b_2)$	3 2 7 $A = \frac{1}{2}(2)(3 + 7)$ $= 10$ units²

EXAMPLE 3 **Finding the Area of Triangles and Trapezoids**

Graph and find the area of each figure with the given vertices.

A (−2, 2), (6, 2), (3, 7)

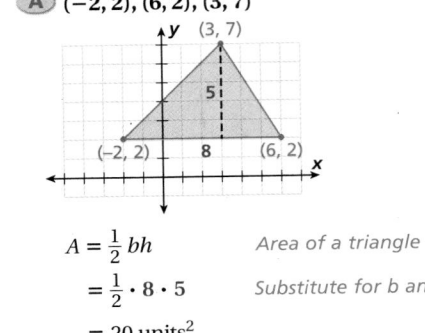

(3, 7)

5

(−2, 2)   8   (6, 2)

$A = \frac{1}{2} bh$ *Area of a triangle*

$= \frac{1}{2} \cdot 8 \cdot 5$ *Substitute for b and h.*

$= 20$ units²

---

2 Teach

Guided Instruction

In this lesson, students learn to find the area of triangles and trapezoids. Remind students that the perimeter of any polygon can be found by adding up all its side lengths. Review the formula for the area of a parallelogram. Use the diagrams in the lesson to show how a triangle or trapezoid can be thought of as half of a parallelogram (Teaching Transparency). Finally, introduce the formulas for area of triangles and trapezoids (Teaching Transparency). Point out that to find the area of a trapezoid, students must find the sum of the lengths of its bases.

Universal Access

Through Critical Thinking

Have students plot the geometric figure with vertices (3, 5), (2, 4), (4, 4), (5, 2), and (−1, 2) on a coordinate grid. Then have them divide the shape into any combination of rectangles, trapezoids, and triangles to find the area of the figure.   9 units²

Graph and find the area of each figure with the given vertices.

B (3, 0), (−1, 0), (−1, 2), (1, 2)

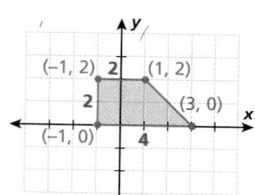

$A = \frac{1}{2}h(b_1 + b_2)$ Area of a trapezoid

$= \frac{1}{2} \cdot 2(4 + 2)$ Substitute for h, b_1, and b_2.

$= 6$ units^2

Think and Discuss

1. Describe what happens to the area of a triangle when the base is doubled and the height remains the same.

2. Describe what happens to the area of a trapezoid when the length of both bases are doubled and the height remains the same.

Answers to
Think and Discuss

1. The area doubles.

2. The area doubles.

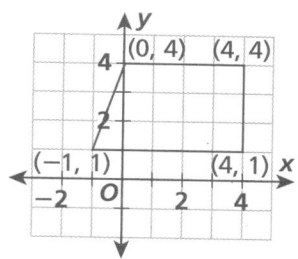

9-2 Exercises

California
Standards Practice
MG2.1, MG3.2, ← MG3.3

go.hrw.com
Homework Help Online
KEYWORD: MT8CA 9-2
Parent Resources Online
KEYWORD: MT8CA Parent

GUIDED PRACTICE

See Example 1 **Find the missing measurement for each figure with the given perimeter.**

1. perimeter = 34.5 units   2. perimeter = 84 units   3. perimeter = 18 units

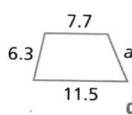
9 units

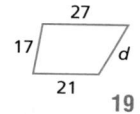
19 units

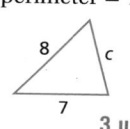
3 units

See Example 2 **4.** Jolene is putting trim around the edge of a triangle head scarf. The scarf forms a right triangle with legs that measure 15 inches each. Find how much trim Jolene needs to the nearest tenth of an inch. **51.2 in.**

See Example 3 **Graph and find the area of each figure with the given vertices.**

5. (−4, −2), (0, 5), (2, −2) **21 units^2**
6. (−2, 0), (4, 2), (−2, 4), (4, 0) **18 units^2**
7. (−5, −4), (0, −4), (−3, 2) **15 units^2**
8. (0, −1), (−7, −1), (−5, 4), (−2, 4) **25 units^2**

---

3 Close

Summarize

Show students a trapezoid that is divided into a rectangle and two triangles, such as the one below.

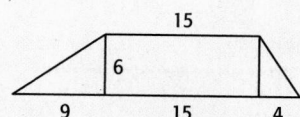

Have volunteers find the area of the trapezoid and of each individual section. Show them that the area of the trapezoid is equal to the sum of the areas of the sections.

trapezoid: 129 units^2; large triangle: 27 units^2; rectangle: 90 units^2; small triangle: 12 units^2; 27 + 90 + 12 = 129 units^2

Answers

5.

6.

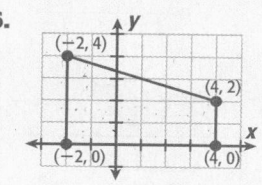

7–8. See p. A10.

Answers

13.

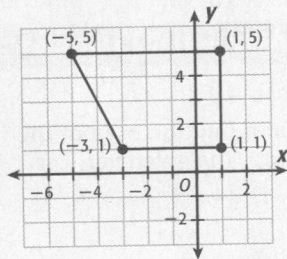

14.

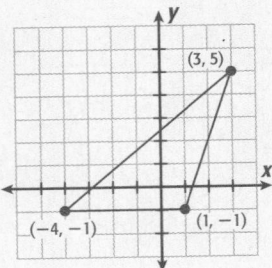

15.

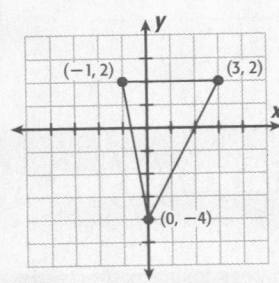

16. See p. A10.

Math Background

The formula for the area of a trapezoid is explained in the lesson by forming a parallelogram with two congruent trapezoids. An alternate method is to use a diagonal of a trapezoid to form two triangles.

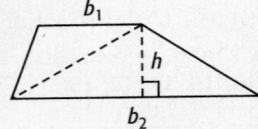

The area of the trapezoid is the sum of the areas of two triangles that share the same height:

$$A = \frac{1}{2}b_1h + \frac{1}{2}b_2h = \frac{1}{2}h(b_1 + b_2)$$

California Standards

Standard	Exercises
MG2.1	1–4, 9–12, 17–40
MG3.2	5–8, 13–16, 42–43
MG3.3	30, 41

INDEPENDENT PRACTICE

See Example ① **Find the missing measurement for each figure with the given perimeter.**

9. perimeter = 27 units

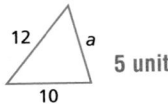

12
a
5 units
10

10. perimeter = 34 units

c
5
13
16 units

11. perimeter = 71 units

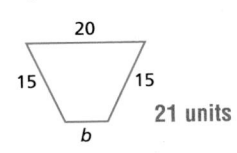

20
15   15
21 units
b

See Example ② **12.** Miguel is making a stained glass window. He cuts a 12 cm square along the diagonal to create two right triangles. Find the perimeter of each triangle to the nearest tenth of a centimeter. **41.0 cm**

See Example ③ **Graph and find the area of each figure with the given vertices.**

13. (1, 5), (1, 1), (−3, 1), (−5, 5) **20 units²** **14.** (−4, −1), (3, 5), (1, −1) **15 units²**

15. (−1, 2), (0, −4), (3, 2) **12 units²** **16.** (−4, 3), (2, 1), (2, −3), (−4, −5) **36 units²**

PRACTICE AND PROBLEM SOLVING

Extra Practice
See page EP18.

Find the area of each figure.

17.

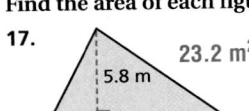

5.8 m
8 m
23.2 m²

18.

4.5 ft
3 ft
7.5 ft
18 ft²

19.

11 cm
6 cm
33 cm²

20.

16 in.
12 in.
21 in.
222 in²

21.

8 m
9.25 m
37 m²

22.

15 cm
8 cm
7 cm
88 cm²

Find the area of each figure with the given dimensions.

23. triangle: b = 10, h = 12 **60 units²**

24. trapezoid: $b_1 = 8$, $b_2 = 14$, h = 7 **77 units²**

25. triangle: b = 5x, h = 10 **25x units²**

26. trapezoid: $b_1 = 4.5$, $b_2 = 8$, h = 6.7 **41.875 units²**

27. The perimeter of a triangle is 37.4 ft. Two of its sides measure 16.4 ft and 11.9 ft, respectively. What is the length of its third side? **9.1 ft**

28. Reasoning The areas and heights of a triangle and a rectangle are the same. How do the lengths of their bases compare? **Possible answer: The base of the triangle is twice as long as the base of the rectangle.**

31. When the dimensions are multiplied by 4 the area will be 4^2 times as great and the perimeter will be 4 times as great.

29. The area of a triangle is 126 mm². Its height is 21 mm. What is the length of its base in centimeters? (*Hint:* 1 cm = 10 mm) **1.2 cm**

30. Multi-Step A right triangle has one leg that is 13 cm long. The hypotenuse is 27 cm long. Find the area of the triangle to the nearest tenth. **153.8 cm²**

31. Write About It What happens to the area and the perimeter of a rectangle when the length and width are multiplied by 4?

REVIEW FOR MASTERY 9-2

9-2 Review for Mastery
Perimeter and Area of Triangles and Trapezoids

To find the perimeter of a figure, add the lengths of all its sides.

Complete to find the perimeter of the figure.

1.
12 in.
8 in.   9 in.
6 in.

Perimeter of trapezoid
= _6_ + _9_ + _12_ + _8_
= _35_ in.

Area of Triangle = ½bh
The area of a triangle is one-half the product of a base length b and the height h drawn to that base.

Complete to find the area of the triangle.

2. Area of triangle
= ½bh
= ½ × _20_ × _4_
= ½ × _80_ = _40_ in²

4 in.
20 in.

Area of Trapezoid = ½h(b_1 + b_2)
The area of a trapezoid is one-half the height h times the sum of the base lengths b_1 and b_2.

Complete to find the area of the trapezoid.

3.
5 cm
8 cm
11 cm

Area of trapezoid
= ½h(b_1 + b_2)
= ½ × _8_ × (_5_ + _11_)
= _4_ × (_16_) = _64_ cm²

PRACTICE 9-2

9-2 Practice B
Perimeter and Area of Triangles and Trapezoids

Find the missing measurement for each figure with the given perimeter.

1. P = 22.8 cm
3.9 cm
5.6 cm   5.6 cm
?
2. P = 11c + 5 mi
(2c) mi
(2c + 1) mi
(4c + 2) mi
3c + 2 mi

3. P = 54 units
14
22
18 units

4. P = 34 units
11.6
8.3   ?
6.2
7.9 units

Graph and find the area of each figure with the given vertices.

5. (−1, 3), (4, 3), (4, −4), (−4, −4)

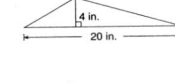

45.5 units²

6. (−1, 2), (−4, −2), (4, −2)

16 units²

7. The two shortest sides of a pennant shaped like a right triangle measure 10 inches and 24 inches. Hank wants to put colored tape around the edge of the pennant. How many inches of tape does he need?

60 in.

To fly, a plane must overcome gravity and achieve *lift*, the force that allows a flying object to have upward motion. The shape and size of a plane's wings affect the amount of lift that is created. The wings of high-speed airplanes are thin and usually angled back to give the plane more lift.

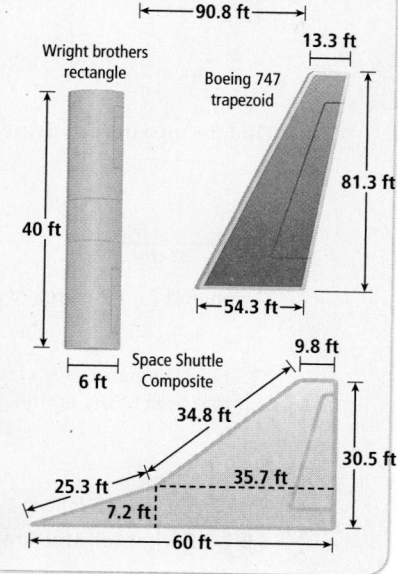

F-18 trapezoid 6 ft
15.8 ft 13 ft
15 ft

Concorde triangle 100 ft
42.5 ft
90.8 ft

Wright brothers rectangle
40 ft
6 ft
Space Shuttle Composite

Boeing 747 trapezoid
13.3 ft
81.3 ft
54.3 ft

9.8 ft
34.8 ft
30.5 ft
25.3 ft 35.7 ft
7.2 ft
60 ft

32. Find the area of a Concorde wing to the nearest tenth of a square foot. **1929.5 ft²**

33. Find the total perimeter of the two wings of a Concorde to the nearest tenth of a foot. **466.6 ft**

34. What is the area of a Boeing 747 wing to the nearest tenth of a square foot? **2747.9 ft²**

35. What is the perimeter of an F-18 wing to the nearest tenth of a foot? **49.8 ft**

36. What is the total area of the two wings of an F-18? **273 ft²**

37. Find the area and perimeter of the wing of a space shuttle rounded to the nearest tenth. **874.6 ft²; 160.4 ft**

38. ⭐ Challenge The wing of the Wright brothers' plane is about half the length of a Boeing 747 wing. Compare the area of the Wright brothers' wing with the area of a Boeing 747 wing. Is the area of the Wright brothers' wing half the area of the 747 wing? Explain.

 go.hrw.com
Web Extra!
KEYWORD: MT8CA Lift

39. **Multiple Choice** Find the area of a trapezoid with the dimensions $b_1 = 4$ cm, $b_2 = 6$ cm, and $h = 4.6$ cm.

Ⓐ 16.1 cm²   Ⓑ 18.4 cm²   Ⓒ 23 cm²   Ⓓ 46 cm²

40. **Gridded Response** The perimeter of a triangle is 24.9 feet. The length of one side is 9.6 feet. Another side is 8.2 feet. Find the length, in feet, of the third side. **7.1**

41. Triangle Park has a trail that follows the path of a right triangle. One leg of the trail is 2.1 miles, and the other leg is 3.0 miles. What is the distance of the third side of the trail to the nearest tenth of a mile? (Lesson 4-9) **3.7 mi**

Find the area of the quadrilateral with the given vertices. (Lesson 9-1)

42. (0, 0), (0, 9), (5, 9), (5, 0) **45 units²**   43. (−3, 1), (4, 1), (6, 3), (−1, 3) **14 units²**

ONGOING ASSESSMENT and INTERVENTION ⬅➡

Diagnose Before the Lesson
9-2 Warm Up, TE p. 439

Monitor During the Lesson
9-2 Know-It Notebook
9-2 Questioning Strategies

Assess After the Lesson
9-2 Lesson Quiz, TE p. 443

Interdisciplinary

Science

Exercises 32–38 involve using diagrams to solve problems about the perimeters and areas of wings.

Answers

38. Possible answer: No; the area of the Boeing 747 wing is more than 11 times the area of the Wright brothers' wing.

Teaching Tip **Multiple Choice** For **Exercise 39,** students who answered **D** did not divide the height by 2 before multiplying it by the sum of the bases. Remind students that the formula for the area of a trapezoid includes a factor of $\frac{1}{2}$.

Journal

Have students write about why it is not always possible to find areas by counting the square units inside a figure.

Power Presentations with PowerPoint®

CHALLENGE 9-2

LESSON 9-2 **Challenge**
Fence Me In!

You can find the area of a triangle in the coordinate plane that has no horizontal or vertical side.

Consider △ABC with vertices A(−3, 2), B(8, −3), and C(5, 6).

By drawing horizontal and vertical lines, △ABC is enclosed in rectangle PQBR.

Write the coordinates of the remaining vertices of the rectangle.

1. P (−3, 6)
   Q (8, 6)
   R (−3, −3)

Count boxes or subtract coordinates to find the indicated dimensions. Then find the indicated areas.

2. For rectangle PQBR:
   base RB = 11 units   height RP = 9 units   area = 99 units²

3. For right triangle APC:
   base PC = 8 units   height AP = 4 units   area = 16 units²

4. For right triangle CQB:
   base CQ = 3 units   height BQ = 9 units   area = 13.5 units²

5. For right triangle ARB:
   base RB = 11 units   height AR = 5 units   area = 27.5 units²

6. Explain how to combine the areas of the rectangle and the three right triangles to find the area of △ABC. Then find the area of △ABC.
   △ABC = rectangle PQBR − (△APC + △CQB + △ARB)
   △ABC = 99 − (16 + 13.5 + 27.5) = 42 units²

PROBLEM SOLVING 9-2

LESSON 9-2 **Problem Solving**
Perimeter and Area of Triangles and Trapezoids

Write the correct answer.

1. Find the area of the material required to cover the kite pictured below.
   5 ft²

2. Find the area of the material required to cover the kite pictured below.
   9 ft²

3. Find the approximate area of the state of Nevada.
   310 mi 210 mi 495 mi
   109,275 mi²

4. Find the area of the hexagonal gazebo floor.
   3.5 m 2.5 m 8.5 m
   30 m²

Choose the letter for the best answer.

5. Find the amount of flooring needed to cover the stage pictured below.
   20 ft 15 ft 30 ft
   A 4500 ft²
   B 750 ft²
   C 525 ft²
   Ⓓ 375 ft²

6. Find the combined area of the congruent triangular gables.
   5 ft 3 ft
   F 7.5 ft²
   Ⓖ 15 ft²
   J 60 ft²
   H 30 ft²

9-2 Lesson Quiz
Use the figure to find the following measurements.

4 cm
10 cm
15 cm
10 cm   8 cm
16 cm   9 cm

1. the perimeter of the triangle **36 cm**
2. the perimeter of the trapezoid **44 cm**
3. the perimeter of the combined figure **64 cm**
4. the area of the triangle **54 cm²**
5. the area of the trapezoid **104 cm²**

Also available on transparency

Organizer

Objective: Assess students' mastery of concepts and skills in Lessons 9-1 and 9-2.

Resources

 Assessment Resources
Section 9A Quiz

 Test & Practice Generator
One-Stop Planner®

INTERVENTION ⬅️ ➡️

Resources

 Ready to Go On? Intervention and Enrichment Worksheets

💿 **Ready to Go On? CD-ROM**

🪐 **Ready to Go On? Online**

my.hrw.com

Answers

5–6, 13–14. See p. A10.

Quiz for Lessons 9-1 Through 9-2

✓ **9-1** **Perimeter and Area of Parallelograms**

Find the perimeter of each figure.

1. 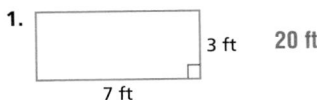 3 ft / 7 ft **20 ft**

2. 6.6 cm / 3.5 cm **20.2 cm**

Find the area of each figure.

3. 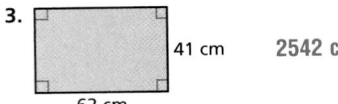 41 cm / 62 cm **2542 cm²**

4. $2\frac{1}{4}$ ft / $5\frac{1}{3}$ ft **12 ft²**

Graph and find the area of each figure with the given vertices. **18 units²**

5. $(-4, 4)$, $(2, 4)$, $(2, -3)$, $(-4, -3)$ **42 units²** **6.** $(-2, 3)$, $(-2, -1)$, $(2, -1)$, $(2, 4)$

7. Find the perimeter and area of the figure. 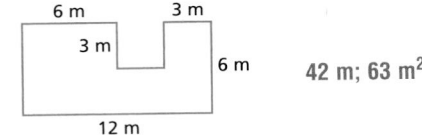 6 m / 3 m / 3 m / 6 m / 12 m **42 m; 63 m²**

✓ **9-2** **Perimeter and Area of Triangles and Trapezoids**

Find the perimeter of each figure.

8. 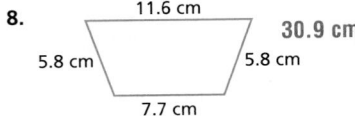 11.6 cm / 5.8 cm / 5.8 cm / 7.7 cm **30.9 cm**

9. 12 in. / 10 in. / 16 in. **38 in.**

Find the area of each figure.

10. 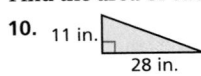 11 in. / 28 in. **154 in²**

11. 8 cm / 5 cm / 4 cm **30 cm²**

12. A garden is shaped like a right triangle with legs measuring 10 ft and 12 ft. Find the perimeter of the garden to the nearest tenth of a foot. **37.6 ft**

Graph and find the area of each figure with the given vertices.

13. $(-6, -2)$, $(4, -2)$, $(-3, 3)$ **25 units²** **14.** $(-4, 0)$, $(0, 0)$, $(3, 3)$ **6 units²**

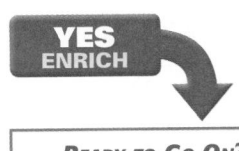
READY TO GO ON?
Diagnose and Prescribe

	READY TO GO ON? Intervention, Section 9A		
Ready to Go On? Intervention	📝 **Worksheets**	💿 **CD-ROM**	🪐 **Online**
✓ Lesson 9-1 🐾 MG2.1, MG2.2, MG3.2	9-1 Intervention	Activity 9-1	Diagnose and Prescribe Online
✓ Lesson 9-2 🐾 MG2.1, MG3.2	9-2 Intervention	Activity 9-2	

NO **INTERVENE**

YES **ENRICH**

READY TO GO ON? Enrichment, Section 9A
📝 **Worksheets**
💿 **CD-ROM**
🪐 **Online**

Focus on Problem Solving

California Standards

MR3.1 Evaluate the reasonableness of the solution in the context of the original situation.
Also covered: **MG2.1**

Look Back

• **Does your solution answer the question?**

When you think you have solved a problem, think again. Your answer may not really be the solution to the problem. For example, you may solve an equation to find the value of a variable, but to find the answer to the problem, the value of the variable may need to be substituted into an expression.

Write and solve an equation for each problem. Check to see whether the value of the variable is the answer to the question. If not, give the answer to the question.

1 Triangle *ABC* is an isosceles triangle. Find its perimeter.

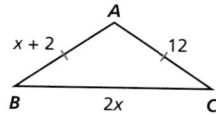

2 Find the measure of the smallest angle in triangle *DEF*.

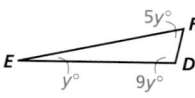

3 Find the measure of the largest angle in triangle *DEF*.

4 Find the area of right triangle *GHI*.

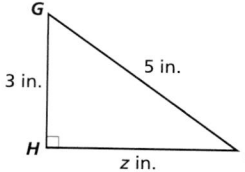

5 A *pediment* is a triangular space filled with statuary on the front of a building. The approximate measurements of an isosceles triangular pediment are shown below. Find the area of the pediment.

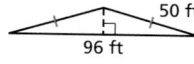

Answers

1. $x + 2 = 12$; $x = 10$; $12 + 20 + 12 = 44$
2. $15y = 180$; $y = 12°$
3. $9y = 9(12) = 108°$
4. $3^2 + z^2 = 5^2$; $z = 4$; $\frac{1}{2}(4)(3) = 6 \text{ in}^2$
5. $48^2 + h^2 = 50^2$; $h = 14$; $\frac{1}{2}(96)(14) = 672 \text{ ft}^2$

3. measure of largest angle; Value of 9y; no, but the value of the variable is needed to find the answer.

4. area; Pythagorean Theorem; length of the base (*z* in.) and height (3 in.); triangle area formula; no, but the value of the variable is needed to find the answer.

5. area; Length of half the base; value of *h*; length of base; triangle area formula; no, but the value of the variable is needed to find the answer.

Inclusion Remind students that tick marks are used to show that two sides of a geometric figure are congruent. In **Problems 1** and **5**, tick marks show the congruent sides in an isosceles triangle.

Focus on Problem Solving

Organizer

Objective: Focus on finding the solution that answers the question.

 Online Edition

Resources

 Chapter 9 Resource File
Reading Strategies

Problem Solving Process

This page focuses on the fourth step of the problem-solving process:
Look Back

Discuss

Each problem requires that the student solve for a variable. Have students discuss what they need to know in order to find the given measurement and tell whether the value of the variable is the solution to the problem.

Possible answers:

1. perimeter; Lengths of all three sides of the triangle (12, 2*x*, and *x* + 2); triangle perimeter formula; no, but the value of the variable is needed to find the answer.

2. measure of smallest angle; Triangle angle sum property; value of *y*; yes, the value of the variable is the answer since the smallest angle measures *y*°.

California Standards

Mathematical Reasoning 3.1
Also covered:
Measurement and Geometry
2.1 Use formulas routinely for finding the perimeter and area of basic two-dimensional figures and the surface area and volume of basic three-dimensional figures, **including** rectangles, parallelograms, trapezoids, squares, **triangles,** circles, prisms, and cylinders.

Circles

One-Minute Section Planner

Lesson	Lab Resources	Materials
Lesson 9-3 Circles • Identify parts of a circle and find central angle measures. **MG3.0, MG3.1**	**Hands-On Lab 9-3** In *Chapter 9 Resource File*	**Optional** Paper circles, scissors, analog clock
Lesson 9-4 Circumference and Area • Find the circumference and area of circles. **MG2.1, MG3.2**	**Hands-On Lab 9-4** In *Chapter 9 Resource File*	**Optional** Calculators, cans, tape measures
Lesson 9-5 Area of Composite Figures • Find the area of composite figures. **MG2.0, MG2.2**		**Optional** Set of tangrams
Lesson 9-6 Area of Irregular Figures • Estimate the area of irregular figures. **MG2.0, MG2.2**		**Optional** Map of U.S., graph paper

MK = *Manipulatives Kit*

Notes

_____

_____

_____

_____

_____

_____

_____

_____

_____

_____

_____

_____

Math Background: Teaching the Standards

CIRCLES MG2.0, MG2.1

Lessons 9-3, 9-4

The ratio of the circumference to the diameter of any circle is a constant. This essential property of circles has been known since ancient times. Egyptian, Babylonian, and Greek geometers all recognized that this constant ratio is a little greater than 3, with the Babylonians settling on the approximation $3\frac{1}{8}$ or 3.125. In 1706, the mathematician William Jones was the first to represent the constant by the Greek letter pi (π).

Today we know that pi is an irrational number. That is, its decimal representation neither terminates nor repeats. Over 1 trillion digits of pi have been computed. The first 20 digits to the right of the decimal point are shown below.

$$3.14159265358979323846\ldots$$

For most practical purposes, 3.14 is a satisfactory approximation of the value of pi, as is the fraction $\frac{22}{7}$.

The value of pi may be visualized by imagining a circle of diameter 1 sitting at the origin of a number line. As the circle rolls to the right, the point at the bottom of the circle that was originally touching the number line will next touch the number line at π.

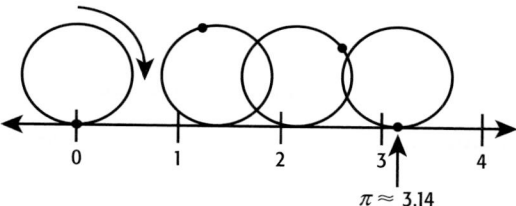

$\pi \approx 3.14$

CIRCUMFERENCE MG2.0, MG2.1

Lesson 9-4

For any circle, the ratio of the circumference C to the diameter d is π. Therefore $\frac{C}{d} = \pi$ and $C = \pi d$. Since the diameter is twice the radius r, the relationship may also be written in the familiar form $C = 2\pi r$.

Just as mathematicians have long sought to develop approximations for the constant π, so have they developed a variety of techniques for approximating the circumference of a circle. One well-known technique goes as follows. Given a circle of radius r,

inscribe a regular hexagon inside the circle by drawing radii at 60° intervals and connecting the adjacent points where the radii intersect the circle. It is easy to show that each triangle is equilateral, so each side of the hexagon has length r. Thus, the perimeter of the hexagon is $6r$. Clearly, the circumference of the circle is greater than the perimeter of the hexagon, so $C > 6r$. Substituting $2\pi r$ for C, we see that $2\pi r > 6r$, and by simplifying, $\pi > 3$.

It is interesting to note that the mathematician Archimedes used a similar technique involving 96-sided polygons to determine that π is between $\frac{223}{71}$ and $\frac{22}{7}$.

AREA OF A CIRCLE MG2.0, MG2.1

Lesson 9-4

The formula for the area of a circle is based on what we know about the circumference of a circle. To develop the formula, begin with a circle of radius r and divide the circle into equal sectors as shown below. Then rearrange the sectors to form a shape that is close to a parallelogram.

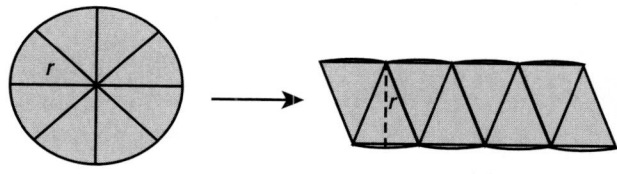

πr

The figure shows that the area of the circle is approximated by the area of the parallelogram. Notice that the base of the parallelogram is close to half the circumference of the circle, or πr. The height of the parallelogram is close to the radius r of one of the sectors. Thus, the area of the parallelogram is approximately $\pi r \cdot r = \pi r^2$. As you divide the circle into more sectors, the rearranged sectors more closely match the shape of a parallelogram. This idea of ever-finer approximations is an important technique in calculus, and one that may be used to give a more rigorous proof that the area of a circle of radius r is given by $A = \pi r^2$.

9-3 Organizer

Objective: Students identify parts of a circle and find central angle measures.

Hands-On Lab
In *Chapter 9 Resource File*

Online Edition
Tutorial Videos

Countdown to Mastery Week 19

Power Presentations with PowerPoint®

Warm Up

1. Two angles are supplementary. One angle measures 61°. Find the measure of the other angle. 119°
2. Two angles are complementary. One angle measures 19°. Find the measure of the other angle. 71°
3. Two angles are supplementary and congruent. Find the measure of each angle. 90°

Also available on transparency

Math Humor

A man tied a package using a diameter because it was the longest chord he could find.

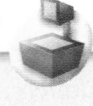

California Standards

Measurement and Geometry 3.1
Also covered:
Measurement and Geometry
3.0 Students know the Pythagorean theorem and **deepen their understanding of plane** and solid **geometric shapes** by constructing figures that meet given conditions and **by identifying attributes of figures.**

9-3 Circles

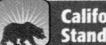

California Standards

MG3.1 Identify and construct **basic elements of geometric figures (e.g.,** altitudes, midpoints, diagonals, angle bisectors, and perpendicular bisectors; **central angles, radii, diameters, and chords of circles)** by using a compass and straightedge.

Vocabulary
circle
center of a circle
arc
radius
diameter
chord
central angle
sector

Why learn this? Vehicles with wheels—from ancient chariots to modern bicycles and cars—rely on the concept of a circle.

A **circle** is the set of all points in a plane that are the same distance from a given point, called the **center of a circle**. This distance is called the *radius* of the circle.

A circle is named by its center. For example, if point A is the center of a circle, then the name of the circle is circle A. There are special names for the different parts of a circle.

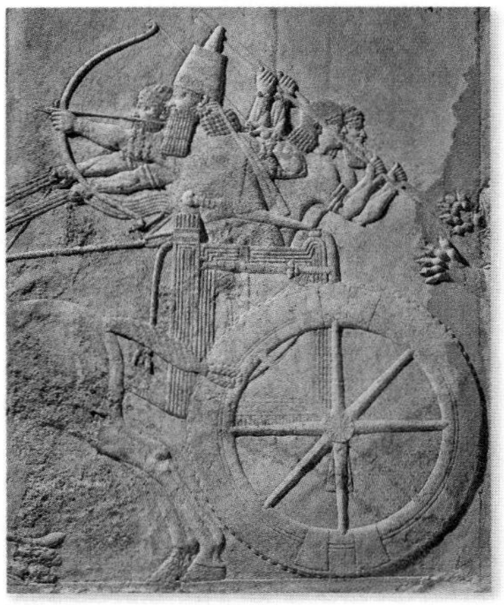

This relief sculpture was made around 645 B.C.E., and shows King Ashurbanipal of Nineveh riding on his chariot.

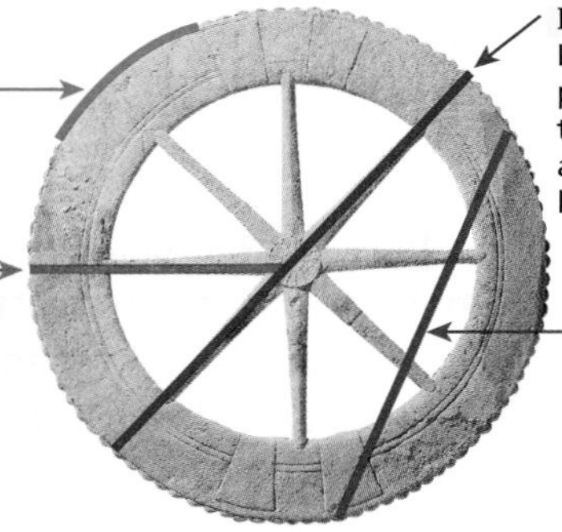
Arc
Part of a circle named by its endpoints
Radius
Line segment whose endpoints are the center of a circle and any point on the circle
Diameter
Line segment that passes through the center of a circle, and whose endpoints lie on the circle
Chord
Line segment whose endpoints are any two points on a circle

EXAMPLE 1 Identifying Parts of Circles

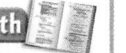

Reading Math
Radii is the plural form of *radius.*

Name the parts of circle *P*.

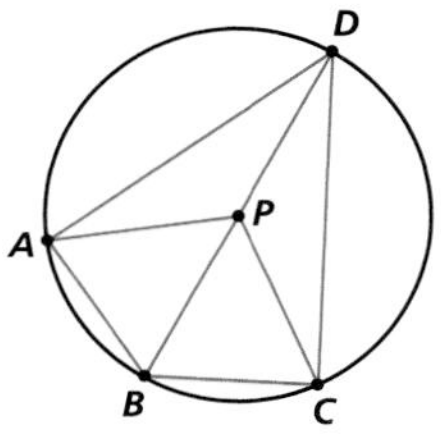
D
A
P
B
C

A radii
$\overline{PA}, \overline{PB}, \overline{PC}, \overline{PD}$

B diameter
$\overline{BD}$

C chords
$\overline{AD}, \overline{DC}, \overline{AB}, \overline{BC}, \overline{BD}$

1 Introduce

Alternate Opener

EXPLORATION

9-3 Circles

According to the August 2000 U.S. Census Bureau Population Survey, there are 48,721,000 school-age children in the U.S.

Use the percents in the circle graph, the number of school-age children (48,721,000), and the number of degrees in a circle (360°) to complete the table.

Access to Computers Among School-Age Children

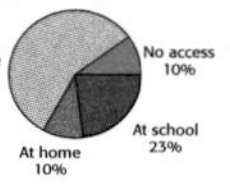
At school & at home 57%
No access 10%
At school 23%
At home 10%

	Access	Percent	Portion of Graph (degrees)	Number of Children
	None	10%	$0.10 \cdot 360° = 36°$	$0.10 \cdot 48{,}721{,}000 = 4{,}872{,}100$
1.	School	23%		
2.	Home	10%		
3.	School and home	57%		

Think and Discuss

4. **Explain** which percent should be eliminated and which should be increased if the goal is to provide access to computers.
5. **Discuss** other applications of a circle.

Motivate

Have students cut out a circle from paper. Have each student fold the circle in half. Then have each student open the circle and fold it in half again, but not in the same place. Have students repeat the folding activity several times. Then discuss the following questions:

1. How many different fold center lines can a circle have? infinitely many
2. What single point do all of the fold lines have in common? the center

Explorations and answers are provided in *Alternate Openers: Explorations Transparencies.*

A **central angle** of a circle is an angle formed by two radii. A **sector** of a circle is the part of the circle enclosed by two radii and an arc connecting them.

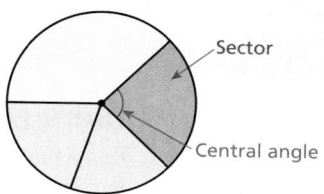

The sum of the measures of all of the nonoverlapping central angles in a circle is 360°. We say that there are 360° in a circle.

EXAMPLE 2 PROBLEM SOLVING APPLICATION

The circle graph shows the results of a survey to determine how people feel about keeping the penny in circulation. Find the central angle measure of the sector that shows the percent of people who are against keeping the penny.

Keep the Penny?
Uncertain 3%
Against 32%
For 65%

Source: USA Today, 2001

 Reasoning

1 Understand the Problem

List the **important information:**
- The percent of people who are against keeping the penny is 32%.

2 Make a Plan

The central angle measure of the sector that represents those people against keeping the penny is 32% of the angle measure of the whole circle. The angle measure of a circle is 360°. Since the sector is 32% of the circle graph, the central angle measure is 32% of 360°.

32% of 360° = 0.32 · 360°

3 Solve

0.32 · 360° = 115.2°   *Multiply.*
The central angle of the sector measures 115.2°.

4 Look Back

The 32% sector is about one-third of the graph, and 120° is one-third of 360°. Since 115.2° is close to 120°, the answer is reasonable.

Possible answers to *Think and Discuss*

1. A diameter is a chord because both of its endpoints lie on the circle. A radius has only one endpoint on the circle.

2.

Think and Discuss

1. **Explain** why a diameter is a chord but a radius is not.
2. **Draw** a circle with a central angle of 90°.

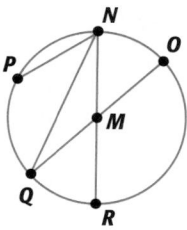
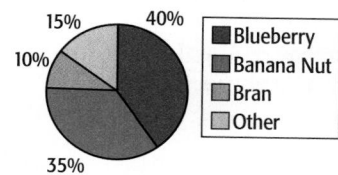
 **Teaching Tip**   **Language Support** In **Example 2,** the phrase *in circulation* means "in use as money."

---

2 Teach

Guided Instruction

In this lesson, students learn to identify and name different parts of a circle. As students identify the different parts of a circle, encourage them to discuss the characteristics of each part. You may want to use the Teaching Transparency. Point out that a diameter divides a circle in half. A diameter is a straight line and, therefore, has a straight angle of 180°, which is one-half of 360°. So the diameter forms a central angle of a circle.

Teaching Tip   **Inclusion** Before beginning **Example 2,** review the method of changing a percent to a decimal by moving the decimal point two places to the left.

Universal Access
Through Concrete Manipulatives

Use an analog clock to show central angles of sectors. Point out that there are 12 hours located equally around 360°. Therefore, at one o'clock the hands form a sector with a central angle measure of 30°, at two o'clock they form a sector with a central angle measure of 60°, and so on.

3 Close

Summarize

Have students identify one major difference between each pair of parts of a circle:

1. radius and diameter
2. central angle and sector
3. arc and chord

Possible answers:

1. radius, a segment from the center to a point on the circle; diameter, connecting two points on a circle
2. central angle, formed by two radii; sector, region enclosed by two radii
3. arc, a section of the circle; chord, a line connecting two points on a circle

9-3 Exercises

 California Standards Practice MG3.1

 go.hrw.com
Homework Help Online
KEYWORD: MT8CA 9-3
Parent Resources Online
KEYWORD: MT8CA Parent

Assignment Guide

If you finished **Example 1** assign:
Proficient 1–3, 5–7, 9, 20, 22–26
Advanced 5–7, 9, 20, 22–26

If you finished **Example 2** assign:
Proficient 1–14, 20–26
Advanced 5–10, 15–26

Homework Quick Check
Quickly check key concepts.
Exercises: 6, 8, 10

Math Background

Students probably have heard of magic squares, but they might not have heard of magic circles. Magic circles are intersecting circles, where the sum of all of the numbers at the intersections of each circle is the same constant. The circle below shows 3 magic circles with a magic constant of 14.

$5 + 6 + 2 + 1 = 14$
$5 + 3 + 2 + 4 = 14$
$1 + 3 + 6 + 4 = 14$

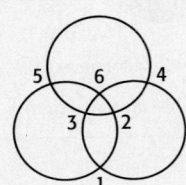

California Standards

Standard	Exercises
NS1.3	22–25
AF4.2 🔑	26
MG3.1	1–21

GUIDED PRACTICE

See Example 1 — **Name the parts of circle O.**
1. radii $\overline{OQ}, \overline{OR}, \overline{OS}, \overline{OT}$
2. diameter $\overline{RT}$
3. chords $\overline{RT}, \overline{RS}, \overline{ST}, \overline{TQ}$

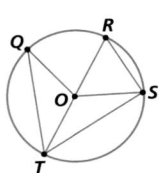

See Example 2 — 4. The circle graph shows the results of a survey in which the following question was asked: "If you had to describe your office environment as a type of television show, which would it be?" Find the central angle measure of the sector that shows the percent of people who described their workplace as a courtroom drama. **36°**

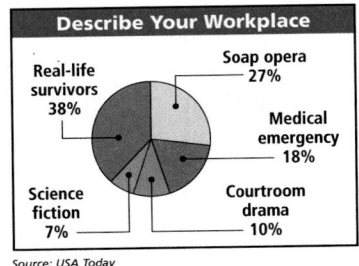
Describe Your Workplace
Real-life survivors 38%
Soap opera 27%
Medical emergency 18%
Science fiction 7%
Courtroom drama 10%
Source: USA Today

INDEPENDENT PRACTICE

See Example 1 — **Name the parts of circle C.**
5. radii $\overline{CA}, \overline{CB}, \overline{CD}, \overline{CE}, \overline{CF}$
6. diameters $\overline{AE}, \overline{BF}$
7. chords $\overline{GB}, \overline{BF}, \overline{DE}, \overline{FE}, \overline{AE}$

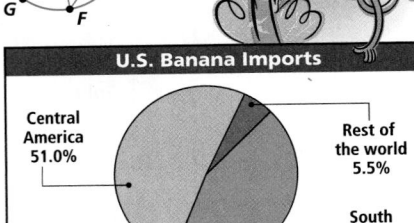

See Example 2 — 8. The circle graph shows the areas from which the United States imports bananas. Find the central angle measure of the sector that shows the percent of banana imports from South America. **156.6°**

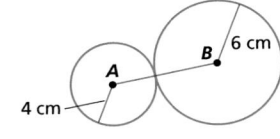
U.S. Banana Imports
Central America 51.0%
Rest of the world 5.5%
South America 43.5%
Source: US Bureau of the Census Trade Data

PRACTICE AND PROBLEM SOLVING

Extra Practice
See page EP18.

9. What is the distance between the centers of the circles at right? **10 cm**

10. A circle is divided into five equal sectors. Find the measure of the central angle of each sector. **72°**

4 cm — A — B — 6 cm

REVIEW FOR MASTERY 9-3

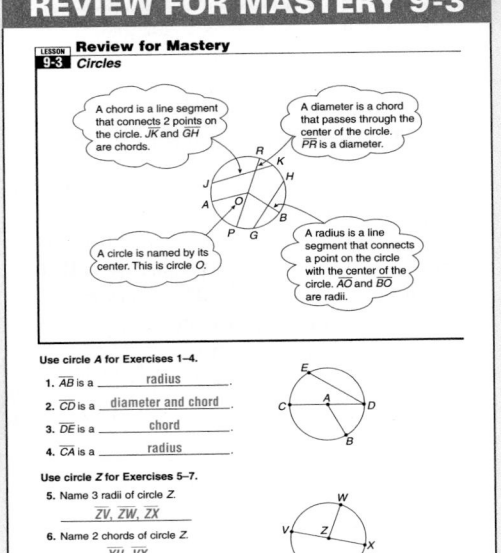

PRACTICE 9-3

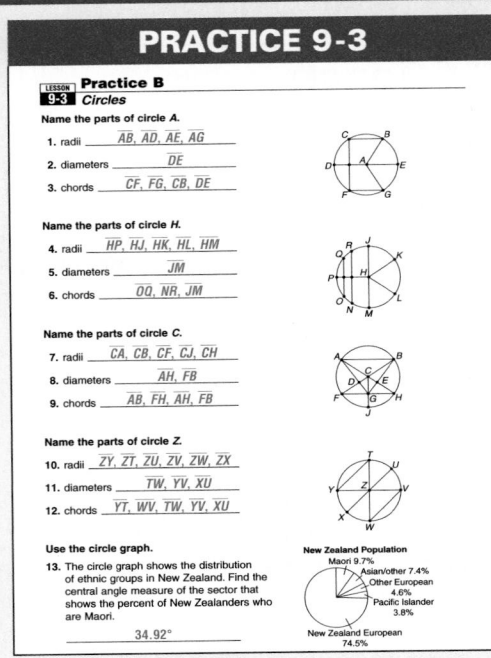

Find the central angle measure of the sector of a circle that represents the given percent of a whole.

11. 28% 100.8°   12. 15% 54°   13. 70% 252°   14. 43% 154.8°

Music Citizens of the United States were asked to choose a national song and a national anthem. The circle graph shows the results of the survey. Use the graphs for Exercises 15 and 16.

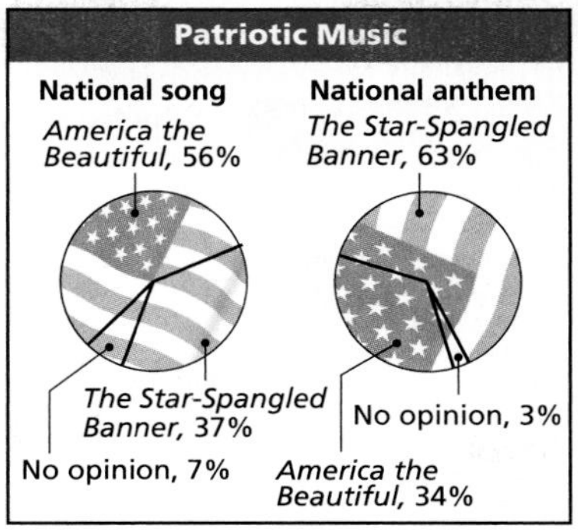

15. Find the central angle measure of the sector that shows the percent of people who prefer *The Star-Spangled Banner* as the national song.   133.2°

16. Find the central angle measure of the sector that shows the percent of people who prefer *America the Beautiful* as the national anthem.   122.4°

Patriotic Music

National song
America the Beautiful, 56%
The Star-Spangled Banner, 37%
No opinion, 7%

National anthem
The Star-Spangled Banner, 63%
No opinion, 3%
America the Beautiful, 34%

 17. **Write a Problem** Find a circle graph in your science or social studies textbook. Use the graph to write a problem that can be solved by finding the central angle measure of one of the sectors of the circle.

18. **Write About It** Compare central angles of a circle with sectors of a circle.

19. **Challenge** Find the angle measure between the minute and hour hands on the clock at right.   120°

SPIRAL STANDARDS REVIEW   NS1.3, ← AF4.2, MG3.1

Use the figure for Exercises 20 and 21.

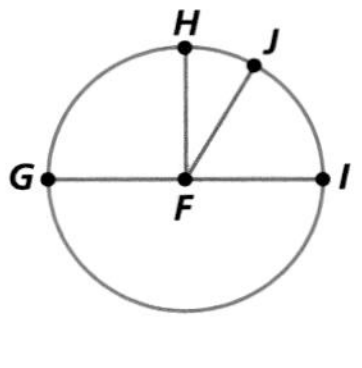

20. **Multiple Choice** Which statement is NOT true about the figure?

Ⓐ $\overline{GI}$ is a diameter of the circle.

Ⓑ $\overline{GI}$ is a chord of the circle.

Ⓒ ∠GIJ is a central angle of the circle.

Ⓓ ∠GFH and ∠HFI are supplementary angles.

21. **Gridded Response** The diameter of the circle is perpendicular to chord *HF*. What is the measure of ∠HFI in degrees?   90

Estimate. (Lesson 6-2) **Possible answers:**

22. 28% of 150 45   23. 21% of 90 18   24. 2% of 55 1   25. 53% of 72 35

26. The Parikh family is driving at a constant speed on the highway so their distance varies directly with their speed. They traveled 17.5 miles in 15 minutes. How far did they travel in 90 minutes? (Lesson 7-9) **105 mi**

Answers

17. Possible answer: A circle graph shows a population distribution of males and females. What is the measure of the central angle of the sector that shows the population distribution of females?

18. Possible answer: A central angle is an angle formed by two radii. A sector is the region inside the circle formed by a central angle and an arc.

Teaching Tip **Multiple Choice** Students that chose **B** for **Exercise 20** probably forgot that the diameter of a circle is also a chord of that circle. Remind students that a chord is any line segment that connects two points on a circle. Point out that this includes the diameter, but not the radius.

Journal

Have students find a circle graph in a textbook or a newspaper. Ask them to write about the graph and describe the central angles.

CHALLENGE 9-3

Challenge
Arc Length

An *arc* is a portion of the circumference of a circle. On the circle below, arc *QR* corresponds to the part of the circumference whose endpoints are the radii forming central angle *QCR*.

A *minor arc* is less than 180° and is named by its endpoints. Arc *QR* is a minor arc. A *major arc* is greater than 180° and is named by its endpoints and one other point that lies on the arc. Arc *QSR* is a major arc.

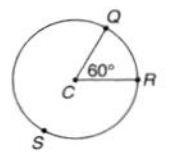

The degree measure of a minor arc is the measure of its central angle. The degree measure of a major arc is 360° minus the degree measure of the minor arc.

For circle *C* above, the measure of arc *QR* is 60°, and the measure of arc *QSR* is 360° − 60°, or 300°.

Find the degree measure of each arc.

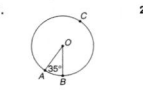 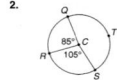 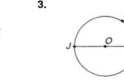

1.   arc BCA **325°**   2.   arc QRS **190°**   3.   arc JKL **180°**

 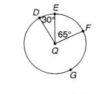 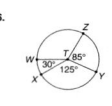

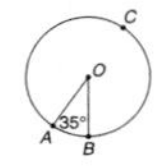

4.   arc BC **105°**   5.   arc DGF **265°**   6.   arc WZ **120°**

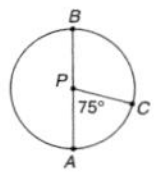

PROBLEM SOLVING 9-3

Problem Solving
Circles

Write the correct answer.

The circle graph shows the results of a survey in which people were asked to name their hobbies.

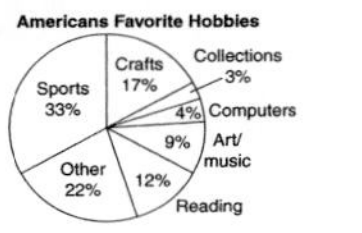

1. If 1,000 people were surveyed, how many said that collecting things is their favorite hobby?

   30 people

Americans' Favorite Hobbies
Sports 33%, Crafts 17%, Collections 3%, Computers 4%, Art/music 9%, Reading 12%, Other 22%

2. Find the central angle measure of the sector that shows the percent of people who named sports as their favorite hobby.

   118.8°

3. Find the central angle measure of the sector that shows the percent of people who named reading as their favorite hobby.

   43.2°

4. Find the central angle measure of the sector that shows the percent of people who like to do crafts as their favorite hobby.

   61.2°

Choose the letter for the best answer.

The circle graph shows the age breakdown of people who most enjoy snowboarding.

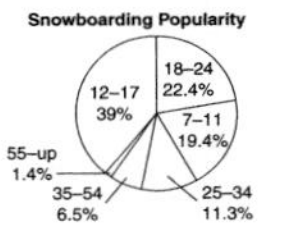

5. What is the central angle measure that shows the percent of 35–54-year-olds?
   A 5.1°   Ⓒ 23.4°
   B 6.5°   D 40.7°

Snowboarding Popularity
12–17 39%, 18–24 22.4%, 7–11 19.4%, 25–34 11.3%, 55–up 1.4%, 35–54 6.5%

6. With which age group is snowboarding least popular?
   F 7–11 years   H 25–34 years
   G 12–17 years   Ⓙ 55–up

7. With which age group is snowboarding most popular?
   A 7–11 years   C 18–24 years
   Ⓑ 12–17 years   D 25–34 years

8. What is the central angle measure that shows the percent of 12–17-year-olds?
   F 39°   H 108°
   Ⓖ 140.4°   J 180°

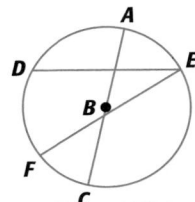

✓ **9-3 Lesson Quiz**
Name the parts of circle *B*.

1. radii $\overline{BA}$, $\overline{BC}$

2. diameter(s) $\overline{AC}$

3. chord(s) $\overline{DE}$, $\overline{FE}$, $\overline{AC}$

4. A pie is cut into 8 equal sectors. Find the measure of the central angle of one slice of pie. 45°

Also available on transparency

Objective: Students find the circumference and area of circles.

 Hands-On Lab
In *Chapter 9 Resource File*

 Online Edition
Tutorial Videos

Countdown to Mastery Week 19

Power Presentations
with PowerPoint®

Warm Up

1. Find the length of the hypotenuse of a right triangle that has legs 3 in. and 4 in. long. **5 in.**

2. The hypotenuse of a right triangle measures 17 in., and one leg measures 8 in. How long is the other leg? **15 in.**

3. To the nearest centimeter, what is the height of an equilateral triangle with sides 9 cm long? **8 cm**

Also available on transparency

Math Humor

The circle had a radius of 4. So what did the hungry circumference do?
Ate pi.

 **California Standards**

Measurement and Geometry 2.1
Also covered:
Measurement and Geometry
3.2 Understand and use coordinate graphs to plot simple figures, determine lengths and areas related to them, and determine their image under translations and reflections.

 **9-4** **Circumference and Area**

 California Standards

MG2.1 Use formulas routinely for finding the perimeter and area of basic two-dimensional figures and the surface area and volume of basic three-dimensional figures, **including** rectangles, parallelograms, trapezoids, squares, triangles, **circles**, prisms, and cylinders.
Also covered: **MG3.2**

Vocabulary
circumference

Remember!
Pi (π) is an irrational number that is often approximated by the rational numbers 3.14 and $\frac{22}{7}$.

Why learn this? You can use the circumference of a circle to determine how far a wheel travels during several revolutions. (See Exercise 6.)

The **circumference** of a circle is the distance around the circle.

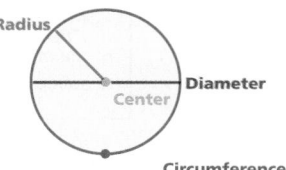

The diameter d is twice the radius r.
$$d = 2r$$

The ratio of the circumference to the diameter $\frac{C}{d}$ of any circle is the same for all circles. This ratio is called pi, or π. You can use this relationship to find a formula for circumference.

$$\frac{C}{d} = \pi$$ *The ratio equals pi.*

$$(d)\frac{C}{d} = \pi(d)$$ *Multiply both sides by d.*

$$C = \pi d$$

$$C = \pi 2r \text{ or } 2\pi r$$ *Since d = 2r, substitute 2r for d.*

CIRCUMFERENCE OF A CIRCLE		
Words	**Formula**	**Numbers**
The circumference C of a circle is π times the diameter d, or 2π times the radius r.	$C = \pi d$ or $C = 2\pi r$	$C = \pi(6)$ $= 2\pi(3)$ ≈ 18.8 units

EXAMPLE 1 **Finding the Circumference of a Circle**

Find the circumference of each circle, both in terms of π and to the nearest tenth. Use 3.14 for π.

A circle with radius 4 cm
$$C = 2\pi r$$
$$= 2\pi(4)$$
$$= 8\pi \text{ cm} \approx 25.1 \text{ cm}$$

B circle with diameter 4.5 in.
$$C = \pi d$$
$$= \pi(4.5)$$
$$= 4.5\pi \text{ in.} \approx 14.1 \text{ in.}$$

---

1 **Introduce**

Alternate Opener

EXPLORATION

9-4 **Circumference and Area**

First estimate the area of each circle by counting squares. Then square each circle's radius. Then compare each estimated area with the square of the radius by computing $\frac{A}{r^2}$.

		Radius	Estimated Area	r^2	$\frac{A}{r^2}$
1.		$r = 1$			
2.		$r = 2$			
3.		$r = 3$			
4.		$r = 4$			

Think and Discuss
5. Discuss how you can make a generalization about how to estimate the area of a circle if you know the radius.

Motivate

Ask students if they like pie. Ask them to describe the shape of a pie. circle Then explain that this will help them remember an important number called *pi*. Tell them pi is a special number that they will use to solve problems involving circles.

 **Teaching Tip** **Language Support** While *pi* and *pie* sound the same and both can be related to circles, *pi* is the sixteenth letter of the Greek alphabet. Pi is represented by the symbol π.

Explorations and answers are provided in *Alternate Openers: Explorations Transparencies.*

AREA OF A CIRCLE		
Words	**Formula**	**Numbers**
The area A of a circle is π times the square of the radius r.	$A = \pi r^2$	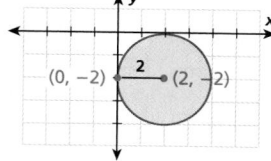 $A = \pi(3^2)$ $= 9\pi$ $\approx 28.3 \text{ units}^2$

EXAMPLE **2** **Finding the Area of a Circle**

Find the area of each circle, both in terms of π and to the nearest tenth. Use 3.14 for π.

A circle with radius 5 cm

$A = \pi r^2 = \pi(5^2)$
$= 25\pi \text{ cm}^2 \approx 78.5 \text{ cm}^2$

B circle with diameter 5.6 in.

$A = \pi r^2 = \pi(2.8^2)$ $\frac{d}{2} = 2.8$
$= 7.84\pi \text{ in}^2 \approx 24.6 \text{ in}^2$

EXAMPLE **3** **Finding Area and Circumference on a Coordinate Plane**

Graph the circle with center $(2, -2)$ that passes through $(0, -2)$. Find the area and circumference, both in terms of π and to the nearest tenth. Use 3.14 for π.

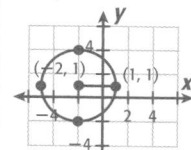

$A = \pi r^2$
$= \pi(2^2)$
$= 4\pi \text{ units}^2$
$\approx 12.6 \text{ units}^2$

$C = \pi d$
$= \pi(4)$
$= 4\pi \text{ units}$
$\approx 12.6 \text{ units}$

EXAMPLE **4** **Science Application**

The 20-G Centrifuge at NASA's Ames Research Center is used to study the effects of hypergravity. A subject is placed in a cab at the end of the rotating arm, which is 29 feet from the center of the centrifuge. If the subject remains in the centrifuge for 12 revolutions, how far does the subject travel? Use $\frac{22}{7}$ for π.

$C = 2\pi r = 2\pi(29) = \pi(58) \approx \frac{22}{7}\left(\frac{58}{1}\right) = \frac{1276}{7}$ *Find the circumference.*

$\frac{1276}{7} \cdot 12 = \frac{15,312}{7} \approx 2187.4 \text{ ft}$ *Multiply by the number of revolutions.*

Answers to *Think and Discuss:*

1. First divide the diameter by 2 to get the radius, and then substitute the radius into the formula for the area of a circle.

Think and Discuss

1. Explain how to find the area of a circle given the diameter.

2 Teach

Guided Instruction

In this lesson, students learn to find the area and circumference of circles. Review the diagram of the circular wheel and the vocabulary terms in Lesson 9-3. Point out the important relationship between radius and diameter ($d = 2r$). Explain that circumference, a measure of the distance around the outside of a circle, is like perimeter. Show them how to find circumference using the formula (Teaching Transparency). Explain that a formula is used to find circumference because unlike the perimeter of a polygon, it is not easy to measure. Then show students how to find the area of a circle. Point out that the radius must be squared when finding area.

Universal Access

Through Concrete Manipulatives

Provide each pair or group of students with cans of various sizes and a tape measure. Have students measure the diameter and circumference of the top of each can and enter the data in a table like the one shown.

Can	C	d	$\frac{C}{d}$

After the measurements are complete, have students use calculators to divide the circumference by the diameter for each circle and enter these results in the last column. Results should be close to π.

3 Close

Summarize

ENGLISH LANGUAGE LEARNERS

Review the vocabulary terms and the formulas from the lesson. Stress the importance of the difference between radius and diameter. Remind students that pi is the value of the circumference of a circle divided by its diameter. Show them that they can see that the equations $\pi = \frac{C}{d}$ and $C = \pi d$ are equivalent based on their knowledge of solving algebraic equations.

9-4 Exercises

9-4 Exercises

California Standards Practice
MG2.1, MG3.2

go.hrw.com
Homework Help Online
KEYWORD: MT8CA 9-4
Parent Resources Online
KEYWORD: MT8CA Parent

Assignment Guide

If you finished Example **1** assign:
Proficient 1, 2, 7, 8, 31–38
Advanced 7, 8, 16–18, 31–38

If you finished Example **2** assign:
Proficient 1–4, 7–10, 13–15, 22–25, 31–38
Advanced 7–10, 16–21, 25–27, 31–38

If you finished Example **3** assign:
Proficient 1–5, 7–11, 13–15, 22–25, 30–38
Advanced 7–11, 16–21, 25–38

If you finished Example **4** assign:
Proficient 1–15, 22–25, 30–38
Advanced 7–12, 16–21, 25–38

Homework Quick Check

Quickly check key concepts.
Exercises: 8, 10, 12

Answers

5.

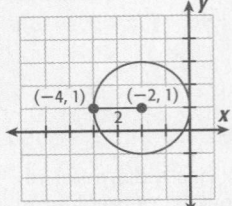

11.

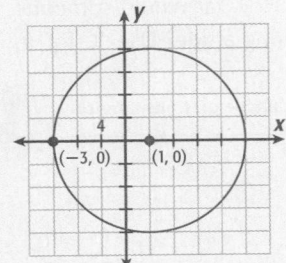

Math Background

Although π is often approximated as 3.14, it is actually an irrational number with an infinite number of nonrepeating decimal digits. From 2000 to 1600 B.C.E., the Babylonians approximated π as 3. Modern computers have calculated π to more than 68 billion decimal places.

California Standards

Standard	Exercises
NS2.1	33–36
MG2.1	1–4, 6–10, 12–29, 31–32
MG3.2	5, 11, 30, 37–38

GUIDED PRACTICE

See Example **1** Find the circumference of each circle, both in terms of π and to the nearest tenth. Use 3.14 for π.

1. circle with diameter 6 cm
   6π cm; 18.8 cm

2. circle with radius 3.2 in.
   6.4π in.; 20.1 in.

See Example **2** Find the area of each circle, both in terms of π and to the nearest tenth. Use 3.14 for π.

3. circle with radius 4.1 ft
   16.8π ft²; 52.8 ft²

4. circle with diameter 15 cm
   56.25π cm²; 176.6 cm²

See Example **3** 5. Graph a circle with center (−2, 1) that passes through (−4, 1). Find the area and circumference, both in terms of π and to the nearest tenth. Use 3.14 for π. $A = 4\pi$ units²; 12.6 units² $C = 4\pi$ units; 12.6 units

See Example **4** 6. A wheel has a diameter of 3.5 ft. Approximately how far does it travel if it makes 20 complete revolutions? Use $\frac{22}{7}$ for π.   220 ft

INDEPENDENT PRACTICE

See Example **1** Find the circumference of each circle, both in terms of π and to the nearest tenth. Use 3.14 for π.

7. circle with radius 9 in.
   18π in.; 56.5 in.

8. circle with diameter 6.3 m
   6.3π m; 19.8 m

See Example **2** Find the area of each circle, both in terms of π and to the nearest tenth. Use 3.14 for π.

9. circle with diameter 32 cm
   256π cm²; 803.8 cm²

10. circle with radius 2.5 yd
   6.3π yd²; 19.6 yd²

See Example **3** 11. Graph a circle with center (1, 0) that passes through (−3, 0). Find the area and circumference, both in terms of π and to the nearest tenth. Use 3.14 for π.
   $A = 16\pi$ units²; 50.2 units² $C = 8\pi$ units; 25.1 units

See Example **4** 12. If the diameter of a wheel is 5 ft, about how many miles does the wheel travel if it makes 134 revolutions? Use $\frac{22}{7}$ for π. (*Hint:* 1 mi = 5280 ft.)   0.4 mi

PRACTICE AND PROBLEM SOLVING

Extra Practice
See page EP19.

Find the circumference and area of each circle to the nearest tenth. Use 3.14 for π.

13.
1.7 m
$C \approx 10.7$ m;
$A \approx 9.1$ m²

14.
14 ft
$C \approx 44.0$ ft;
$A \approx 153.9$ ft²

15.
9 in.
$C \approx 56.5$ in.;
$A \approx 254.3$ in²

Reasoning Find the radius of each circle with the given measurement.

16. $C = 26\pi$ in.   13 in.

17. $C = 12.8\pi$ cm   6.4 cm

18. $C = 15\pi$ ft   7.5 ft

19. $A = 36\pi$ cm²   6 cm

20. $A = 289\pi$ in²   17 in.

21. $A = 136.89\pi$ m²   11.7 m

REVIEW FOR MASTERY 9-4

CHAPTER
9-4 *Circumference and Area*

A **radius** connects the **center** of a **circle** to any point on the circle.

A **diameter** passes through the center and connects two points on the circle.
diameter d = twice radius r
$d = 2r$

Circumference is the distance around a circle.
(The symbol ≈ means *is approximately equal to*.)

Circumference C = 3(diameter d)   Circumference C = 6(radius r)
$C = \pi d$ $C = 2\pi r$

For a circle with diameter = 8 in.   For a circle with radius = 8 in.
$C = \pi d$ $C = 2\pi r$
$C = \pi(8)$ $C = 2\pi(8)$
$C = 8\pi$ in. $C = 16\pi$ in.
$\pi \approx 3.14$ $C \approx 8(3.14) \approx 25.12$ in. $\pi \approx 3.14$ $C \approx 16(3.14) \approx 50.24$ in.

Find the circumference of each circle, exactly in terms of π and approximately when π = 3.14.

1. diameter = 15 ft
   $C = \pi d$
   $C = \pi(\underline{15}) = \underline{15\pi}$ ft
   $C \approx 3.14(\underline{15}) \approx \underline{47.1}$ ft

2. radius = 4 m
   $C = 2\pi r$
   $C = 2\pi(\underline{4}) = \underline{8\pi}$ m
   $C = \underline{8}$ (3.14) $\approx \underline{25.12}$ m

Area A = 3(the square of radius r)
$A = \pi r^2$
For a circle with radius = 5 in.: $A = \pi r^2 = \pi(5^2) = 25\pi$ in²
$A \approx 25(3.14) \approx 78.5$ in²

Find the area of each circle, exactly in terms of π and approximately when π = 3.14.

3. radius = 9 ft
   $A = \pi r^2$
   $A = \pi(\underline{9^2}) = \underline{81\pi}$ ft²
   $A \approx \underline{81}$ (3.14) $\approx \underline{254.34}$ ft²

4. diameter = 10 m, radius = $\underline{5}$ m
   $A = \pi r^2$
   $A = \pi(\underline{5^2}) = \underline{25\pi}$ m²
   $A \approx \underline{25}$ (3.14) $\approx \underline{78.5}$ m²

PRACTICE 9-4

LESSON
9-4 *Circumference and Area*

Practice B

Find the circumference of each circle, both in terms of π and to the nearest tenth. Use 3.14 for π.

1. circle with radius 10 in.
   20π in. or 62.8 in.

2. circle with diameter 13 cm
   13π cm or 40.8 cm

3. circle with diameter 18 m
   18π m or 56.5 m

4. circle with radius 15 ft
   30π ft or 94.2 ft

5. circle with radius 11.5 in.
   23π in. or 72.2 in.

6. circle with diameter 16.4 cm
   16.4π cm or 51.5 cm

Find the area of each circle, both in terms of π and to the nearest tenth. Use 3.14 for π.

7. circle with radius 9 in.
   81π in² or 254.3 in²

8. circle with diameter 14 cm
   49π cm² or 153.9 cm²

9. circle with radius 20 ft
   400π ft² or 1256 ft²

10. circle with diameter 17 m
   72.3π m² or 226.9 m²

11. circle with diameter 15.4 m
   59.3π m² or 186.2 m²

12. circle with radius 22 yd
   484π yd² or 1519.8 yd²

13. Graph a circle with center (0, 0) that passes through (0, −3). Find the area and circumference, both in terms of π and to the nearest tenth. Use 3.14 for π.
   $A = 9\pi$ units² or 28.3 units²;
   $C = 6\pi$ units or 18.8 units

14. A wheel has a radius of $2\frac{1}{3}$ feet. About how far does it makes 60 complete revolutions? Use $\frac{22}{7}$ for π.
   880 ft

Find the area of each circle. Use $\frac{22}{7}$ for π.

22.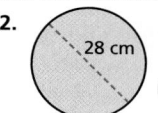
28 cm
616 cm²

23.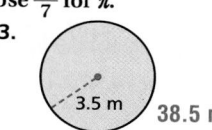
3.5 m
38.5 m²

24.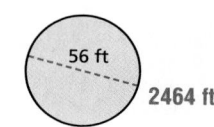
56 ft
2464 ft²

25.
$C = 30\pi$ ft
≈ 94.2 ft;
$A = 225\pi$ ft²
≈ 706.5 ft²

25. Sports The radius of a face-off circle on an NHL hockey rink is 15 ft. Find the circumference and area of a face-off circle to the nearest tenth. Use 3.14 for π.

26. Entertainment The Pacific Wheel, in Santa Monica, California, is the world's only solar-powered Ferris wheel. Its circumference is about 267 ft. Find the diameter of the Pacific Wheel to the nearest foot. Use 3.14 for π. **85 ft**

27. Food A restaurant serves small silver dollar pancakes and regular-size pancakes.
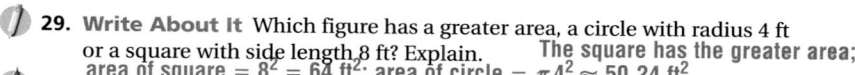
3.5 in.
6 in.

  a. What is the area of a silver dollar pancake to the nearest tenth? **9.6 in²**

  b. What is the area of a regular pancake to the nearest tenth? **28.3 in²**

  c. If 6 silver dollar pancakes are the same price as 3 regular pancakes, which is a better deal? **three regular pancakes**

 **28. What's the Error?** The area of a circle is 121π cm². A student says the diameter of the circle is 11 in. What is the student's error?

29. Write About It Which figure has a greater area, a circle with radius 4 ft or a square with side length 8 ft? Explain. **The square has the greater area; area of square = $8^2 = 64$ ft²; area of circle = $\pi 4^2 \approx 50.24$ ft².**

30. Challenge Graph the circle with center (1, 2) that passes through the point (4, 6). Find its area and circumference, both in terms of π and to the nearest tenth. **$A = 25\pi$ units² ≈ 78.5 units²; $C = 10\pi$ units ≈ 31.4 units**

SPIRAL STANDARDS REVIEW   NS2.1, MG2.1, MG3.2

31. Multiple Choice A circular flower bed has radius 22 inches. What is the circumference of the bed to the nearest tenth of an inch?

Ⓐ 69.1 inches   Ⓑ 103.7 inches   Ⓒ 138.2 inches   Ⓓ 1519.8 inches

32. Gridded Response The first Ferris wheel was constructed for the 1893 Chicago World's Fair. It had a diameter of 250 feet. Find the circumference of the Ferris wheel to the nearest foot. Use 3.14 for π. **785**

Simplify each expression. Write your answer in exponential form. (Lesson 4-3)

33. $m^{-3} \cdot m^7$ m^4 **34.** $4^{10} \cdot 4^{-15}$ 4^{-5} **35.** $\frac{8^2}{8^{-5}}$ 8^7 **36.** $\frac{r^{-1}}{r^{-4}}$ r^3

Graph and find the area of each figure with the given vertices. (Lesson 9-2)

37. (1, 0), (10, 0), (1, −6)   **27 units²**   **38.** (5, 5), (2, 1), (11, 1), (8, 5)   **24 units²**

CHALLENGE 9-4

Challenge
9-4 Circles

Work in $\triangle PQR$ at the bottom of this page.

1. Use a ruler to find the midpoints of the three sides of the triangle. Label these midpoints M_1, M_2, M_3.

2. An **altitude** of a triangle is a segment drawn from a vertex perpendicular to the opposite side. Draw the altitude to each side of the triangle. Use F_1, F_2, F_3 to label the foot of each altitude (where the altitude meets the side of the triangle at right angles).

3. The point at which the altitudes meet is the **orthocenter** of the triangle. Label the orthocenter O. Locate the midpoints of $\overline{OP}$, $\overline{OQ}$, $\overline{OR}$, the segments that connect orthocenter O to each vertex. Labels these midpoints D_1, D_2, D_3.

4. If you have been accurate in your measurements, the nine points – M_1, M_2, M_3, F_1, F_2, F_3, D_1, D_2, D_3 – lie on a circle. Draw the **nine-point circle** for $\triangle PQR$.

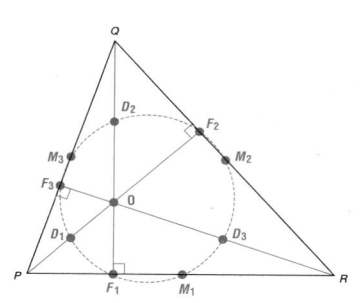

PROBLEM SOLVING 9-4

Problem Solving
9-4 Circumference and Area

Round to the nearest tenth. Use 3.14 for π. Write the correct answer.

1. The world's tallest Ferris wheel is in Osaka, Japan, and stands 369 feet tall. Its wheel has a diameter of 328 feet. Find the circumference of the Ferris wheel.
1029.9 ft

2. A dog is on a 15-foot chain that is anchored to the ground. How much area can the dog cover while he is on the chain?
706.5 ft²

3. A small pizza has a diameter of 10 inches, and a medium has a diameter of 12 inches. How much more pizza do you get with the medium pizza?
34.5 in²

4. How much more crust do you get with a medium pizza with a diameter of 12 inches than a small pizza with a 10 inch diameter?
6.3 in.

Round to the nearest tenth. Use 3.14 for π. Choose the letter for the best answer.

5. The wrestling mat for college NCAA competition has a wrestling circle with a diameter of 32 feet, while a high school mat has a diameter of 28 feet. How much more area is there in a college wrestling mat than a high school mat?
A 12.6 ft²
B 188.4 ft²
C 234.8 ft²
D 753.6 ft²

6. Many tire manufacturers guarantee their tires for 50,000 miles. If a tire has a 16-inch radius, how many revolutions of the tire are guaranteed? There are 63,360 inches in a mile. Round to the nearest revolution.
F 630.6 revolutions
G 3125 revolutions
H 31,528,662 revolutions
J 500,000,000 revolutions

7. In men's Olympic discus throwing competition, an athlete throws a discus with a diameter of 8.625 inches. What is the circumference of the discus?
A 13.5 in.
B 27.1 in.
C 58.4 in.
D 233.6 in.

8. An athlete in a discus competition throws from a circle that is approximately 8.2 feet in diameter. What is the area of the discus throwing circle?
F 52.8 ft²
G 25.7 ft²
H 12.9 ft²
J 211.1 ft²

FORMATIVE ASSESSMENT
and **INTERVENTION** ⟸ ⟹

Diagnose Before the Lesson
9-4 Warm Up, TE p. 450

Monitor During the Lesson
9-4 Know-It Notebook
9-4 Questioning Strategies

Assess After the Lesson
9-4 Lesson Quiz, TE p. 453

Answers

28. Possible answer: The student confused diameter with radius. The radius of the circle is 11 in.

30.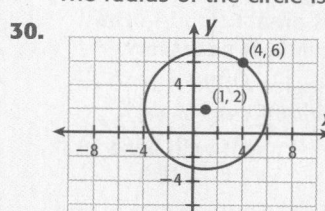

37–38. See p. A10.

Teaching Tip   **Multiple Choice** Students who chose **A** for **Exercise 31** did not correctly apply the circumference formula. Remind students that to find the circumference of a circle when given the radius, they must multiply the product of the radius and π by 2.

Journal
Ask students to write about any ideas they have for remembering the vocabulary terms and formulas from the lesson.

Power Presentations
with PowerPoint®

9-4
Lesson Quiz
Find the circumference of each circle, both in terms of π and to the nearest tenth. Use 3.14 for π.

1. radius 5.6 m   **11.2π m; 35.2 m**

2. diameter 113 mm   **113π mm; 354.8 mm**

Find the area of each circle, both in terms of π and to the nearest tenth. Use 3.14 for π.

3. radius 3 in.   **9π in²; 28.3 in²**

4. diameter 1 ft   **0.25π ft²; 0.8 ft²**

Also available on transparency

Objective: Students find the area of composite figures.

 Online Edition
Tutorial Videos

Countdown to Mastery Week 19

Power Presentations
with PowerPoint®

Warm Up

Find each area. Round to the nearest tenth, if necessary.

1. a rectangle with length 10 cm and width 4 cm   40 cm²

2. a parallelogram with base 18 ft and height 12 ft   216 ft²

3. a triangle with base 16 cm and height 8 cm   64 cm²

4. a circle with radius 5 in.   78.5 in²

Also available on transparency

Math Humor

Q: How do you find areas in an English class?

A: Use composition figures.

California Standards

Measurement and Geometry 2.2

Also covered:

Measurement and Geometry

2.0 Students compute the perimeter, area, and volume **of common geometric objects and use the results to find measures of less common objects.** They know how perimeter, area, and volume are affected by changes of scale.

9-5 **Area of Composite Figures**

 California Standards

MG2.2 Estimate and **compute the area of more complex** or irregular **two-** and three-**dimensional figures by breaking the figures down into more basic geometric objects.**

Who uses this? Landscape architects calculate the area of composite figures when they design patios. (See Example 3.)

To determine how many bricks are needed for a patio, you must first find the area of the patio. The patio may be made up of two or more simple shapes.

In Lesson 9-1, you saw composite figures made up of parallelograms. Composite figures can also be made by combining other shapes.

EXAMPLE **1** **Finding the Area of Composite Figures by Adding**

Find the shaded area. Round to the nearest tenth, if necessary.

A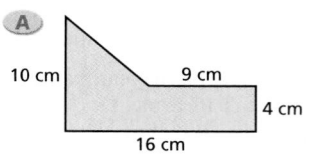

Divide the figure into a triangle and a rectangle.

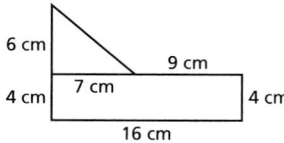

area of triangle:
$A = \frac{1}{2}bh = \frac{1}{2}(7)(6) = 21$ cm²

area of rectangle:
$A = bh = 16(4) = 64$ cm²

Add the area of the triangle and the area of the rectangle.

total area:
$A = 21 + 64 = 85$ cm²

B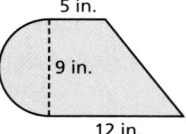

Divide the figure into a semicircle and a trapezoid.

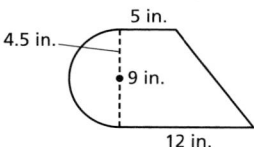

area of semicircle:
$A = \frac{1}{2}\pi r^2 = \frac{1}{2}\pi(4.5)^2$
$\approx \frac{1}{2}(3.14)(20.25) \approx 31.8$ in²

area of trapezoid:
$A = \frac{1}{2}h(b_1 + b_2) = \frac{1}{2}(9)(5 + 12)$
$= \frac{1}{2}(9)(17) = 76.5$ in²

Add the area of the semicircle and the area of the trapezoid.

total area:
$A = 31.8 + 76.5 = 108.3$ in²

---

1 **Introduce**
Alternate Opener

EXPLORATION

9-5 **Area of Composite Figures**

Phil and Louise are planning to sod their backyard. Sod is sold in square yards. They sketched their yard on a piece of graph paper, where the side length of each square represents 1 yard.

1. a. Divide the figure into several simpler figures.
  b. Name each figure from part **a.**
  c. Find the area in square yards of each figure.
  d. Add the areas in part **c.**

Think and Discuss
2. Discuss the strategies you used for finding area.
3. Explain how you could use squares to help you find the areas of irregular shapes.

Motivate

Draw a figure on the board like the one shown here. Ask students how they might find the area of the figure. If students suggest dividing the figure into familiar shapes, ask them whether there is more than one way to do this. Then tell students they will be learning how to divide up figures to find areas.

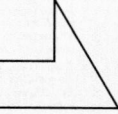

Explorations and answers are provided in *Alternate Openers: Explorations Transparencies.*

You can sometimes find the area of a composite figure by subtracting.

EXAMPLE 2 Finding the Area of Composite Figures by Subtracting

Find the shaded area.

Subtract the area of the triangle from the area of the rectangle.

area of rectangle:
$A = bh = 14(6) = 84 \text{ m}^2$

area of triangle:
$A = \frac{1}{2}bh = \frac{1}{2}(5)(4) = 10 \text{ m}^2$

shaded area:
$A = 84 - 10 = 74 \text{ m}^2$

EXAMPLE 3 Landscaping Application

 Reasoning

An architect is planning a brick patio for a restaurant as shown in the figure. What is the area of the patio? Round to the nearest tenth.

To find the area, divide the composite figure into a trapezoid, a rectangle, and a semicircle.

area of trapezoid:
$A = \frac{1}{2}h(b_1 + b_2) = \frac{1}{2}(8)(24 + 30)$
$= \frac{1}{2}(8)(54) = 216 \text{ ft}^2$

area of rectangle:
$A = bh = 12(8) = 96 \text{ ft}^2$

area of semicircle:
$A = \frac{1}{2}\pi r^2 = \frac{1}{2}\pi(6)^2 \approx \frac{1}{2}(3.14)(36) \approx 56.5 \text{ ft}^2$

area of patio:
$A = 216 + 96 + 56.5 = 368.5 \text{ ft}^2$

The area of the patio is approximately 368.5 ft².

Answers to _Think and Discuss_

1. Draw a vertical line to create a trapezoid and a rectangle.

2. Draw a diagonal to create two triangles.

Think and Discuss

1. **Describe** a different way to divide the figure in Example 1A.

2. **Explain** how you can find the area of a trapezoid using composite figures.

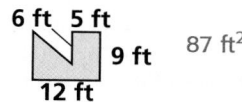
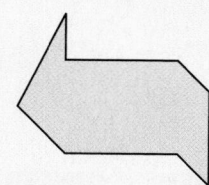
2 Teach

Guided Instruction

In this lesson, students learn to find the area of composite figures. Remind students that they have seen composite figures made up of rectangles in Lesson 9-1. Point out that the figures in this lesson may be made up of triangles, trapezoids, semicircles, or other shapes.

Teaching Tip **Reading Math** Tell students that the word composite comes from a Latin word meaning "to put together." Composite figures are made by putting together simple shapes. **ENGLISH LANGUAGE LEARNERS**

Universal Access

Through Concrete Manipulatives

Divide the class into groups and give each group a set of tangrams. Tell students that the small triangles each have an area of 1 square unit; the medium triangle, the square, and the parallelogram each have an area of 2 square units; and the large triangles each have an area of 4 square units. Have students use the pieces to create composite figures and then have them calculate the area of each figure.

3 Close

Summarize

Have students describe how they would divide the following figure in order to find its area.

Possible answer: Divide the figure with two vertical lines to create a triangle, a rectangle, and a parallelogram.

9-5 Exercises

California Standards Practice
MG2.2

go.hrw.com
Homework Help Online
KEYWORD: MT8CA 9-5
Parent Resources Online
KEYWORD: MT8CA Parent

Assignment Guide

If you finished Example **1** assign:
Proficient 1, 2, 6, 7, 20–25
Advanced 6, 7, 14, 15, 20–25

If you finished Example **2** assign:
Proficient 1–4, 6–9, 18, 20–25
Advanced 6–9, 14–18, 20–25

If you finished Example **3** assign:
Proficient 1–13, 18–25
Advanced 6–25

Homework Quick Check
Quickly check key concepts.
Exercises: 6, 8, 10, 12

Math Background

Finding the area of a figure by dividing it into simpler shapes is the fundamental idea behind many area formulas. For example, any trapezoid can be divided into two triangles by drawing one of the diagonals of the trapezoid. Knowing the formula for the area of a triangle therefore yields a formula for the area of a trapezoid. In a similar way, the formula for the area of a circle is based on dividing the circle into many sectors that are nearly triangular in shape. This method of dividing the circle into simpler shapes that approximate its area is one of the essential underpinnings of calculus.

GUIDED PRACTICE

See Example **1** Find the shaded area. Round to the nearest tenth, if necessary.

1. 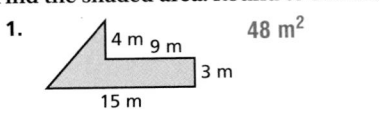 48 m²

2. 245.5 in²
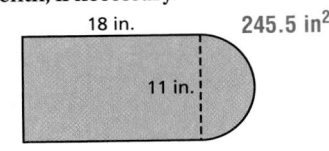

See Example **2**

3. 109.5 cm²
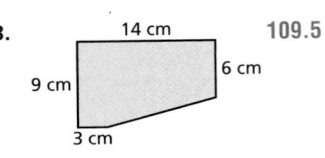

4. 8.4 ft²
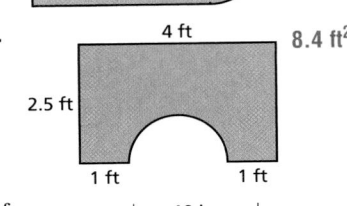

See Example **3**

5. **Hobbies** Catherine makes hearts out of fabric by sewing two semicircles onto a triangle as shown. How much fabric is needed to make each heart? **59.6 in²**

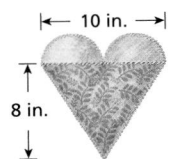

INDEPENDENT PRACTICE

See Example **1** Find the shaded area. Round to the nearest tenth, if necessary.

6. 53.5 in²
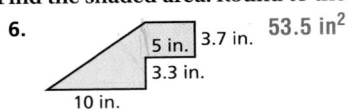

7. 88.1 ft²
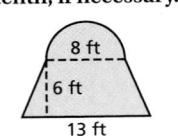

See Example **2**

8. 33.9 m²

9. 54 cm²
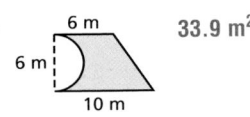

See Example **3**

10. Derrick takes a rectangular piece of paper and cuts four congruent triangles from the corners as shown. Find the area of the remaining piece of paper. **68 in²**

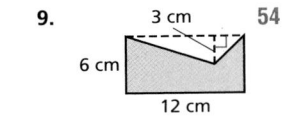

PRACTICE AND PROBLEM SOLVING

Extra Practice
See page EP19.

11. A carpenter cuts out a circle from a square piece of wood as shown. What is the area of the remaining piece of wood? Round to the nearest tenth. **23.4 in²**

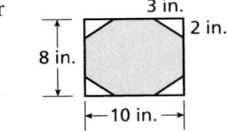

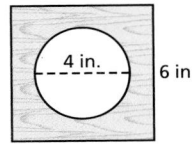

REVIEW FOR MASTERY 9-5

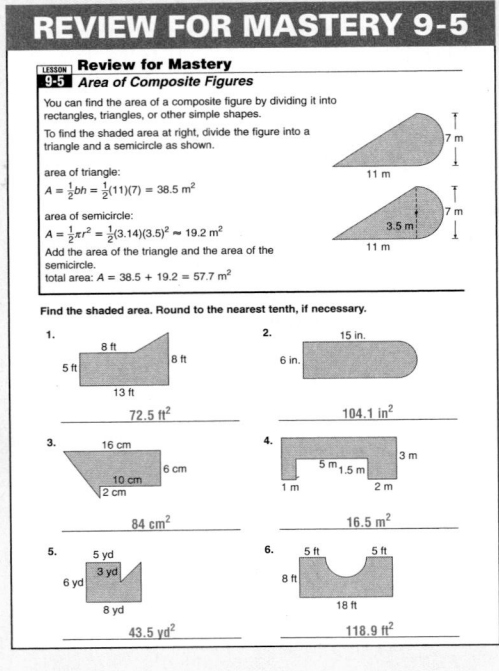

PRACTICE 9-5

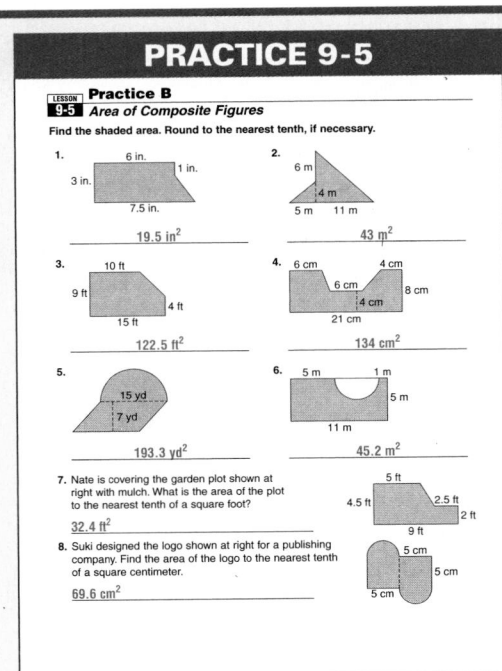

California Standards	
Standard	**Exercises**
AF4.2	20–22
MG2.1	23–25
MG2.2	1–19

15. Possible answer: $A = 8 \cdot 10 + \frac{1}{2} \cdot 6 \cdot 5 = 80 + 15 = 95 \text{ m}^2$

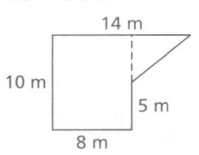

14 m / 10 m / 5 m / 8 m

16. (1) Find the area of the larger outer rectangle and subtract the area of the square. (2) Draw a vertical line to divide the figure into two rectangles. Both methods give an area of 206 m².

12. Multi-Step The Wilson family is putting new wall-to-wall carpet in their living room. The figure shows the dimensions of the room. Carpeting costs $12 per square yard. How much will it cost to carpet the room? **$264**

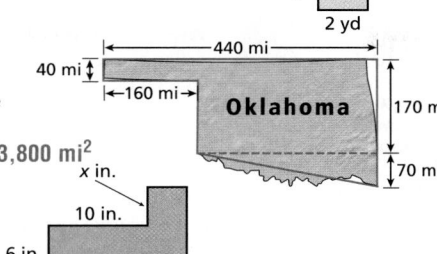

6 yd / 2 yd / 2 yd / 6 yd / 2 yd / 2 yd

13. Social Studies The shape of Oklahoma can be approximated by the figure shown in red on the map. Use the figure to find the approximate area of the state. **63,800 mi²**

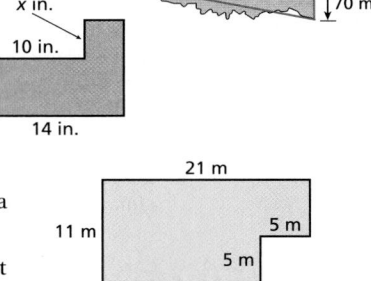

440 mi / 40 mi / 160 mi / **Oklahoma** / 170 mi / 70 mi

14. Reasoning The purple figure has an area of 100 in². What is the value of x? **4 in.**

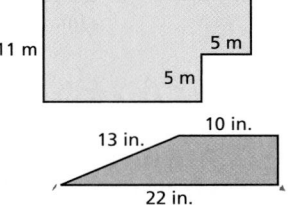

x in. / 10 in. / 6 in. / 14 in.

15. Write a Problem Draw a figure that can be divided into a rectangle and a triangle. Label the lengths of the sides. Explain how you can find the area of the figure. Then find the area.

21 m / 11 m / 5 m / 5 m

16. Write About It Describe two different ways to find the area of the yellow figure. Do both methods give the same result?

13 in. / 10 in. / 22 in.

17. Challenge Find the area of the blue figure. **80 in²**

SPIRAL STANDARDS REVIEW ⚷ AF4.2, MG2.1, MG2.2

18. Multiple Choice A right triangle is removed from a rectangle as shown. Find the area of the shaded figure.

Ⓐ 52 cm² Ⓑ 56 cm² Ⓒ 64 cm² Ⓓ 72 cm²

8 cm / 2 cm / 5 cm / 12 cm

19. Multiple Choice The figure shows a plan for a flower bed. Which of the following is the best estimate for the area of the flower bed?

Ⓐ 40 ft² Ⓑ 46 ft² Ⓒ 52 ft² Ⓓ 88 ft²

10 ft / 4 ft

Find each equation of direct variation, given that y varies directly with x. (Lesson 7-9)

20. y is 18 when x is 6 $y = 3x$ **21.** y is 35 when x is 7 $y = 5x$ **22.** y is 12 when x is 9 $y = \frac{4}{3}x$

Find the circumference of each circle, both in terms of π and to the nearest tenth. Use 3.14 for π. (Lesson 9-4)

23. circle with radius 5 in. **24.** circle with radius 3.7 m **25.** circle with diameter 8.2 cm
10π in.; 31.4 in. 7.4π m; 23.2 m 8.2π cm; 25.7 cm

CHALLENGE 9-5

LESSON 9-5 Challenge
Composites Meet Coordinates

You can use what you know about composite figures to find the area of composite figures on a coordinate plane. Find the area of each shaded figure. Express your answer in terms of square units and round to the nearest tenth, if necessary.

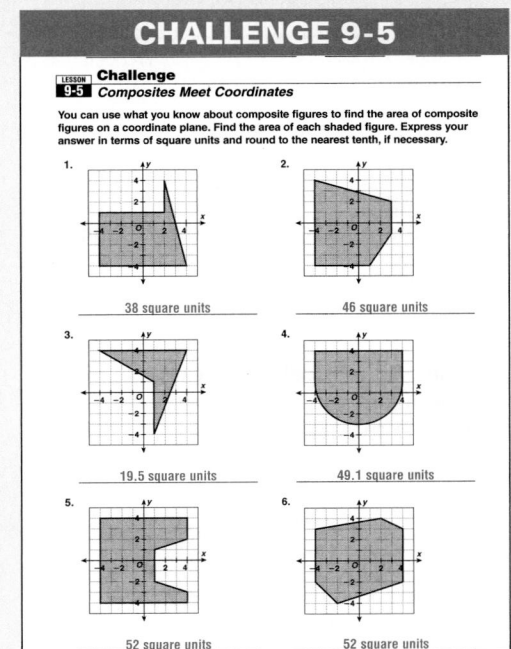

1. 38 square units 2. 46 square units
3. 19.5 square units 4. 49.1 square units
5. 52 square units 6. 52 square units

PROBLEM SOLVING 9-5

LESSON 9-5 Problem Solving
Area of Composite Figures

Write the correct answer.

1. Tamiko is covering this flower bed with wildflower seeds. What is the area of the flower bed? **39.5 ft²**

2. A partition for an office cubicle has the dimensions shown. What is the area of the partition? **68 ft²**

3. For an art project, Lee cuts out a piece of fabric in the shape shown below. What is the area of the fabric to the nearest tenth of a square centimeter? **236.9 cm²**

4. Kyle drills five holes in the rectangular piece of wood shown below. Each hole has a diameter of 1 cm. What is the area of the remaining piece of wood to the nearest tenth of a square centimeter? **28.1 cm²**

The figure shows the floor plan for the first floor of a house. Use the figure for Exercises 5–7. Select the best answer.

5. What is the area of the dining room?
A 100 ft² Ⓒ 250 ft²
B 200 ft² D 300 ft²

6. Which is the best estimate for the area of the living room?
F 200 ft² Ⓗ 357 ft²
G 239 ft² J 514 ft²

7. Which of these is closest to the total area of the first floor of the house?
A 600 ft² C 940 ft²
Ⓑ 860 ft² D 1020 ft²

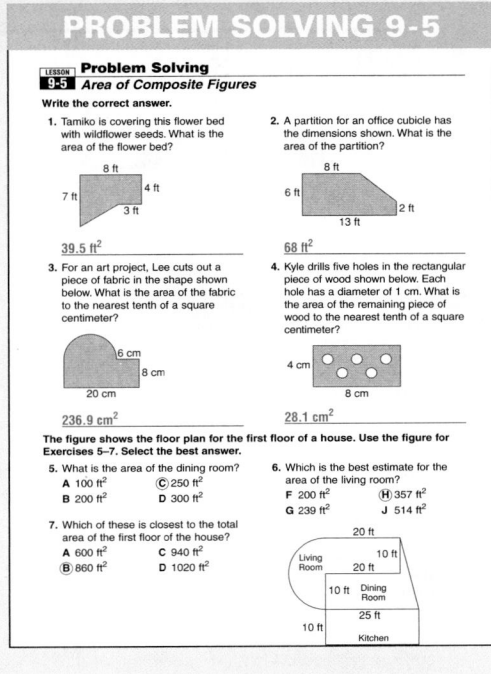

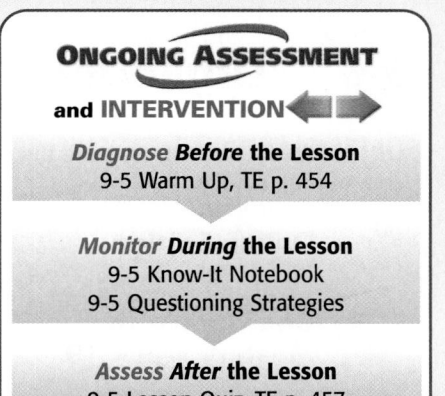
✓ **9-5**
Lesson Quiz
Find the shaded area of each figure. Round to the nearest tenth, if necessary.

1.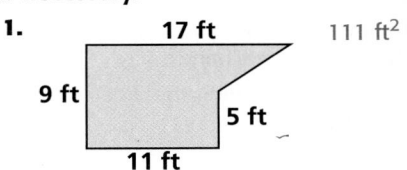
17 ft / 9 ft / 5 ft / 11 ft **111 ft²**

2.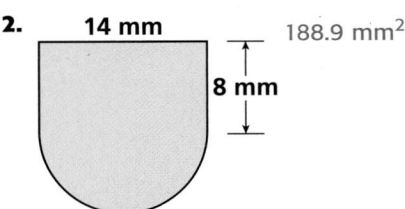
14 mm / 8 mm **188.9 mm²**

3.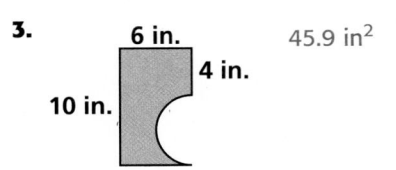
6 in. / 4 in. / 10 in. **45.9 in²**

4. The figure gives the dimensions of a backdrop for a school play. Find the area of the backdrop. **97 ft²**

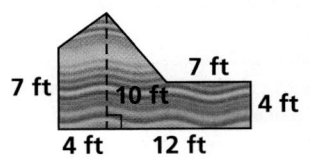
7 ft / 10 ft / 7 ft / 4 ft / 4 ft / 12 ft

Also available on transparency

9-5 Area of Composite Figures   **457**

Power Presentations
with PowerPoint®

Warm Up

Find the area of each figure. Round to the nearest tenth, if necessary.

1. a trapezoid with bases 10 cm and 12 cm and height 5 cm
   55 cm²

2. a parallelogram with base 9 in. and height 8 in.   **72 in²**

3. a semicircle with radius 5 m
   39.3 m²

4. a semicircle with diameter 8 cm
   25.1 cm²

Also available on transparency

Math Humor

Teacher: Why are you covering that shape with your hand?

Student: I'm finding the area using composite fingers.

9-6 Area of Irregular Figures

Who uses this? Landowners use estimation to find the area of irregularly shaped pieces of property.

When colonists settled the land that would become the United States, ownership boundaries were sometimes determined by landmarks such as rivers, trees, and hills. As a result, pieces of property were often shaped like irregular figures.

One method of estimating the area of an irregular figure is to count the number of squares the figure covers.

EXAMPLE **Finding Area by Counting**

Find the area of each figure.

A

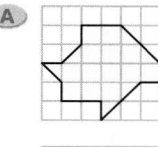

Count the full squares: 13
Count the half-full squares: 6
Add the number of full squares plus half the number of half-full squares:
$13 + \frac{1}{2}(6) = 13 + 3 = 16.$

The area is 16 square units.

Helpful Hint

For shapes such as the one in Example 1B, you can only estimate the area.

B

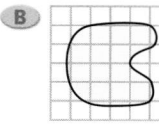

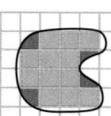

Count the full and almost-full squares: 12
Count the squares that are about half full: 4
Add the number of full squares plus half the number of half-full squares:
$12 + \frac{1}{2}(4) = 12 + 2 = 14.$

The area is approximately 14 square units.

---

1 Introduce

Alternate Opener

EXPLORATION

9-6 Area of Irregular Figures

The figure shows an aerial view of an oilspill. You can use a grid to estimate the area of the spill. In the grid, each square represents one square mile.

1. How many whole or almost-whole squares are contained within the boundary of the spill?

2. How many half or almost-half squares are contained within the boundary of the spill?

3. What is the total area of the whole or almost-whole squares?

4. What is the total area of the half or almost-half squares?

5. What is the approximate area of the spill?

Think and Discuss

6. **Explain** how you found the total area of the whole or almost-whole squares.

7. **Explain** how you found the total area of the half or almost-half squares.

Motivate

Ask students to imagine that you spilled a glass of water and that it made a puddle on the classroom floor. Have students brainstorm ways they could estimate the area of the puddle. Possible answers: count the number of floor tiles that the puddle covers; approximate the puddle with a circle. Tell students that a puddle is an example of an irregular figure and that they will learn how to estimate the area of such figures.

Explorations and answers are provided in *Alternate Openers: Explorations Transparencies.*

You can sometimes use composite figures to estimate the area of an irregular shape. To do this, first draw a composite figure that is close to the irregular shape. Then separate the composite figure into basic geometric shapes.

EXAMPLE **2** **Estimating Area Using Composite Figures**

Use a composite figure to estimate the shaded area.

A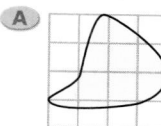

Draw a composite figure that approximates the irregular shape. Divide the composite figure into simple shapes.

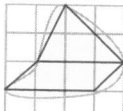

area of triangle:
$A = \frac{1}{2}bh = \frac{1}{2}(3)(2) = 3$ square units

area of parallelogram:
$A = bh = 3(1) = 3$ square units

area of composite figure:
$A = 3 + 3 = 6$ square units

The shaded area is approximately 6 square units.

B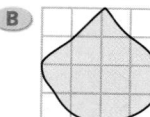

Draw a composite figure that approximates the irregular shape. Divide the composite figure into simple shapes.

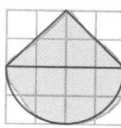

area of triangle:
$A = \frac{1}{2}bh = \frac{1}{2}(4)(2) = 4$ square units

area of semicircle:
$A = \frac{1}{2}\pi r^2 = \frac{1}{2}\pi(2)^2 \approx \frac{1}{2}(3.14)(4) = 6.28$ square units

area of composite figure:
$A = 4 + 6.28 = 10.28$ square units

The shaded area is approximately 10.3 square units.

Answers to *Think and Discuss*

1. It is an underestimate because the composite figure fits inside the irregular figure.

2. The figure contains 8 full or almost-full squares and 6 half-full squares, so the area is approximately $8 + \frac{1}{2}(6) = 11$ square units.

Think and Discuss

1. **Explain** whether the estimate in Example 2A is an overestimate (greater than the exact answer) or an underestimate (less than the exact answer).

2. **Describe** how you could count squares in Example 2B to check whether the estimate is reasonable.

 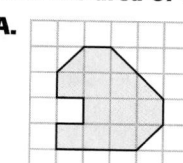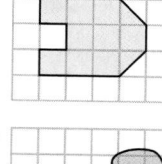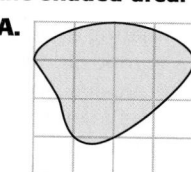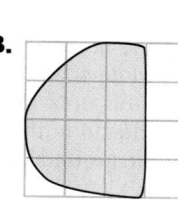
---

2 Teach

Guided Instruction

In this lesson, students learn to estimate the area of irregular figures. Tell students that one square of a grid has an area of one square unit. Ask students how many square units are covered by the figure in **Example 1A.** Then present the examples to show students two different ways to estimate the area of an irregular figure.

 **Inclusion** As students estimate an area by counting squares, encourage them to check their answer by counting the squares in a different order.

 **Universal Access**
Through Curriculum Integration

Social Studies Have students choose several states from a map of the United States and trace the states' outlines on graph paper. Then have students decide how to approximate the shape of each state with a composite figure. As an extension, have students use the scale of the map and their composite figures to estimate the area of each state.

 **Inclusion** Remind students that if a figure is shown on a grid and there is no information about the size of the grid's squares, they should express the area using square units.

3 Close

Summarize

Have students describe two different ways they could estimate the area of the figure shown below.

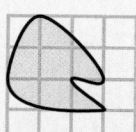

Possible answer: Count full squares and half squares, or approximate the figure with a triangle and a parallelogram. Either way, the area is about 5 square units.

9-6 Exercises

California Standards Practice
NS1.3, MG2.2

go.hrw.com
Homework Help Online
KEYWORD: MT8CA 9-6
Parent Resources Online
KEYWORD: MT8CA Parent

Assignment Guide

If you finished Example **1** assign:
Proficient 1–3, 7–9, 18–24
Advanced 7–9, 14–16, 18–24

If you finished Example **2** assign:
Proficient 1–14, 18–24
Advanced 7–24

Homework Quick Check

Quickly check key concepts.
Exercises: 8, 10, 12, 14

GUIDED PRACTICE

See Example **1** Find the area of each figure. 2–6. Possible answers given.

1. 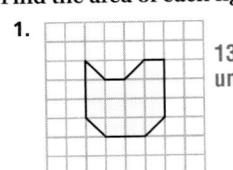 13 square units

2. 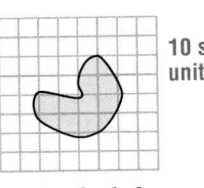 10 square units

3. 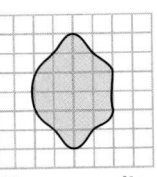 16 square units

See Example **2** Use a composite figure to estimate the shaded area.

4. 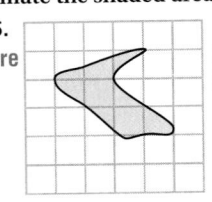 7 square units

5. 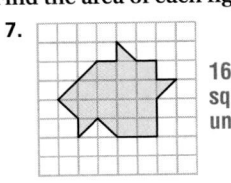 5 square units

6. 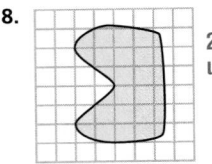 7.9 square units

INDEPENDENT PRACTICE

See Example **1** Find the area of each figure. 8–12. Possible answers given.

7. 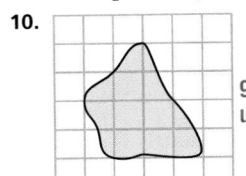 16.5 square units

8. 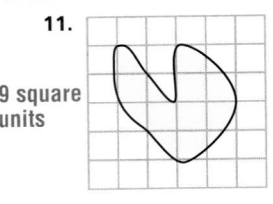 22 square units

9. 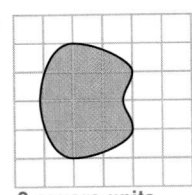 13 square units

See Example **2** Use a composite figure to estimate the shaded area.

10. 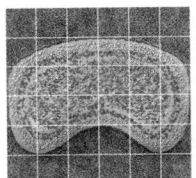 9 square units

11. 10.3 square units

12. 9 square units

PRACTICE AND PROBLEM SOLVING

Extra Practice
See page EP19.

13. **Reasoning** The figure shows an area of a garden that is to be covered with wood chips. It costs $2.50 to cover one square yard with wood chips. The gardener budgets $40 for the wood chips. Will this be enough? Why or why not?

□ = 1 yd²

No; the area to be covered is about 18 yd², and $2.50 · 18 = $45.

Math Background

The method of approximating an irregular shape with a composite figure is an important idea in calculus. For example, calculus students learn to approximate the area between the graph of a function and the *x*-axis by dividing the region into many narrow trapezoids and adding the areas of the trapezoids. Although middle school students may not study this until much later, the methods introduced in this lesson establish the basic groundwork.

REVIEW FOR MASTERY 9-6

Review for Mastery
9-6 *Area of Irregular Figures*

You can estimate the area of an irregular figure by counting the number of squares the figure covers.

To find the shaded area at right, count the full squares and then count the half-full squares.

Number of full squares: 10
Number of half-full squares: 4

Add the number of full squares plus half the number of half-full squares.

total area: $A = 10 + \frac{1}{2}(4) = 10 + 2 = 12$ square units

Full square
Half-full square

Find the area of each figure.

1. 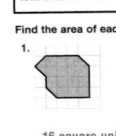 12 square units

2. 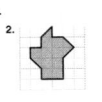 12.5 square units

3. 14 square units

4. 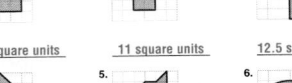 12 square units

5. 12.5 square units

6. 14 square units

7. 11.5 square units

8. 9 square units

9. 15 square units

PRACTICE 9-6

Practice B
9-6 *Area of Irregular Figures*

Find the area of each figure.

1. 14.5 square units

2. 12 square units

3. 13 square units

4. 14 square units

5. 12 square units

6. 16.5 square units

Use a composite figure to estimate the shaded area.

7. 6 square units

8. 7 square units

9. 8 square units

The figure shows an irregular area that is part of Elena's garden. She wants to cover the area with pebbles.

10. Estimate the area that is to be covered with pebbles.

13.5 ft²

11. It costs $3 per square foot to cover an area of the garden with pebbles. How much should Elena plan to spend on the pebbles? Explain.

□ = 1 ft²

$40.50, because the cost is $3 × 13.5

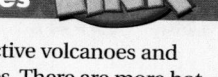 **Social Studies LINK**

Iceland has many active volcanoes and frequent earthquakes. There are more hot springs in Iceland than in any other country.

Sightseers watch the eruption of Geyser Namafjall in the Myvatn Region of North Iceland.

Use the map for Exercises 14–17.

14. Choose a Strategy One square on the map represents 1700 km². Which of the following is a reasonable estimate for the area of Iceland?

Ⓐ Less than 65,00 km²

Ⓑ Between 90,000 and 105,000 km²

Ⓒ Between 120,000 and 135,000 km²

Ⓓ Greater than 150,000 km²

15. Estimation About 10% of the area of Iceland is covered by glaciers. Estimate the area covered by glaciers. **Possible answer: between 9000 and 10,500 km²**

16. Write About It The map has a total of 80 squares, and each square represents 1700 km². Explain why the area of Iceland cannot be greater than 136,000 km².

17. ★ Challenge The white area on the map near the bottom right is a glacier. Show how you can use a composite figure to estimate the area of this glacier.

go.hrw.com
Web Extra!
KEYWORD: MT8CA Iceland

SPIRAL STANDARDS REVIEW ⟵ NS1.4, MG1.2, MG2.2

18. Multiple Choice Each square of the grid represents 1 ft². Which of the following is the best estimate for the area of the shaded figure?

Ⓐ 9 ft²   Ⓑ 11 ft²   Ⓒ 15 ft²   Ⓓ 25 ft²

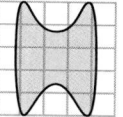

19. Multiple Choice Which figure has an area closest to 10 square units?

Ⓐ 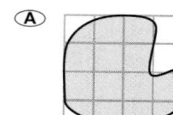   Ⓑ 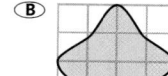   Ⓒ 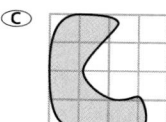   Ⓓ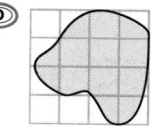

State whether each number is rational, irrational, or not a real number. (Lesson 4-8)

20. $\sqrt{15}$ irrational   **21.** $-\sqrt{64}$ rational   **22.** $\sqrt{\frac{1}{2}}$ irrational   **23.** $\sqrt{\frac{9}{25}}$ rational

24. A model of a sculpture uses the scale 1 in : 0.75 ft. If the model is 16 in. tall, how tall is the actual sculpture? (Lesson 5-7) **12 ft**

CHALLENGE 9-6

LESSON 9-6 Challenge
Figure It Out!

Complete the outline of each figure so that the figure has the given area.
Possible answers are shown.

1. 12.5 square units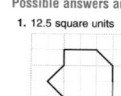
2. 13 square units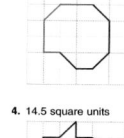
3. 13 square units
4. 14.5 square units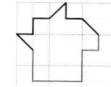
5. 12.5 square units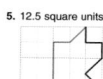
6. 11 square units

PROBLEM SOLVING 9-6

LESSON 9-6 Problem Solving
Area of Irregular Figures

Write the correct answer.

1. Brian is using tiles to cover the shaded area shown below. Each square of the grid is one square foot. What is the area that he must cover with tiles?

11 ft²

2. Alison is using a stencil to paint this design around her bedroom walls. Each square of the grid is one square inch. What is the area of the design?

12 in²

3. The grid shows a map of Anderson Lake. Each square of the grid is one square kilometer. What is the approximate area of Anderson Lake?

8.5 km²

4. José traced a leaf on centimeter grid paper as shown below. What is the approximate area of the leaf? Explain.

18 cm²; divide the shape into two triangles with base 6 and height 3

The figure shows a map of a state park that is divided into three areas. Use the map for Exercises 5–7. Select the best answer.

5. Which is the best estimate for the area of Glenn Forest?
   A 19 mi²   C 22.5 mi²
   Ⓑ 20.5 mi²   D 28 mi²

6. Which is the closest to the area of Jackson Woods?
   F 18.5 mi²   H 20.5 mi²
   Ⓖ 19.5 mi²   J 21.5 mi²

7. Which is the best description for the total area of the park?
   A Less than 40 mi²
   B Between 40 mi² and 45 mi²
   C Between 45 mi² and 50 mi²
   Ⓓ Greater than 50 mi²

Jackson Woods / Glenn Forest / Mount Orange   □ = 1 mi²

FORMATIVE ASSESSMENT
and INTERVENTION ◀⬧▶

Diagnose *Before* the Lesson
9-6 Warm Up, TE p. 458

Monitor *During* the Lesson
9-6 Know-It Notebook
9-6 Questioning Strategies

Assess *After* the Lesson
9-6 Lesson Quiz, TE p. 461

Answers

16–17. See p. A10.

Teaching Tip **Multiple Choice** For **Exercise 18,** students can eliminate choice **D.** The figure is shown on a 5-by-5 grid, so the area of the figure must be less than 25 ft².

Journal

Have students draw their own irregular figure on a piece of graph paper. Then have them describe two different methods of estimating the area of the figure.

Power Presentations
with PowerPoint®

 **9-6**
Lesson Quiz
Find the area of each figure.

1.
8 square units

2.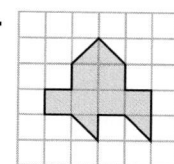
approximately 12 square units

Use a composite figure to estimate the shaded area.

3.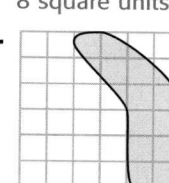
approximately $4\frac{1}{2}$ square units

4.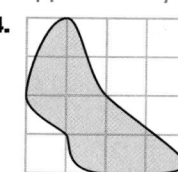
approximately 6 square units

Also available on transparency

Organizer

Objective: Assess students' mastery of concepts and skills in Lessons 9-3 through 9-6.

Resources

 Assessment Resources
Section 9B Quiz

 Test & Practice Generator
One-Stop Planner®

INTERVENTION ◄═══►

Resources

 Ready to Go On? Intervention and Enrichment Worksheets

💿 **Ready to Go On? CD-ROM**

🪐 **Ready to Go On? Online**

my.hrw.com

Answers

8.

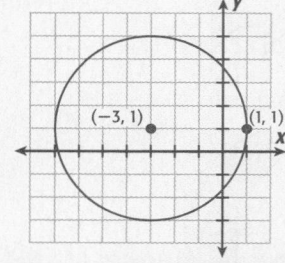

Quiz for Lessons 9-3 Through 9-6

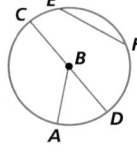

✅ **9-3 Circles**

Name the parts of circle B.

1. radii $\overline{BC}$, $\overline{BD}$, $\overline{BA}$
2. diameter $\overline{CD}$
3. chords $\overline{EF}$, $\overline{CD}$

4. A circle is divided into 6 equal sectors. Find the measure of the central angle of each sector. **60°**

✅ **9-4 Circumference and Area**

Find the area and circumference of each circle, both in terms of π and to the nearest tenth. Use 3.14 for π.

5. radius = 19 cm
6. diameter = 4.3 ft
7. radius = $7\frac{1}{2}$ ft

8. Graph a circle with center $(-3, 1)$ that passes through $(1, 1)$. Find the area and circumference, both in terms of π and to the nearest tenth. Use 3.14 for π. $A = 16\pi$ units$^2 \approx 50.2$ units^2; $C = 8\pi$ units ≈ 25.1 units

✅ **9-5 Area of Composite Figures**

Find the shaded area. Round to the nearest tenth, if necessary.

9. 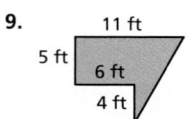 52.5 ft^2
10. 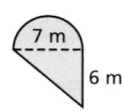 40.2 m^2
11.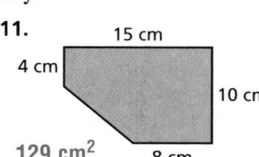
129 cm^2

12. Kendra is putting new linoleum on her kitchen floor. The figure shows the area of the floor that is to be covered. How many square feet of linoleum will Kendra need? 112.5 ft^2

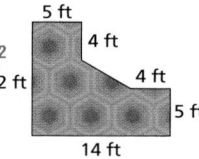

5. $A = 361\pi$ cm$^2 \approx 1133.5$ cm^2; $C = 38\pi$ cm ≈ 119.3 units
6. $A = 4.6\pi$ ft$^2 \approx 14.5$ ft^2; $C = 4.3\pi$ ft ≈ 13.5 units
7. $A = 56.3\pi$ ft$^2 \approx 176.8$ ft^2; $C = 15\pi$ ft ≈ 47.1 ft

✅ **9-6 Area of Irregular Figures**

Estimate each shaded area. 14–15. Possible answers given.

13. 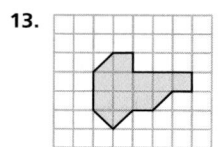 11 square units
14. 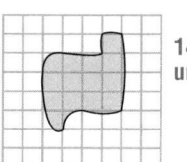 14 square units
15. 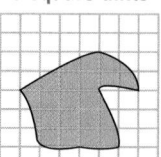 18 square units

---

READY TO GO ON?
Diagnose and Prescribe

NO INTERVENE

YES ENRICH

READY TO GO ON? Intervention, Section 9B			
Ready to Go On? Intervention	🖊 **Worksheets**	💿 **CD-ROM**	🪐 **Online**
✅ Lesson 9-3 🐻 **MG3.1**	9-3 Intervention	Activity 9-3	
✅ Lesson 9-4 🐻 **MG2.1, MG3.2**	9-4 Intervention	Activity 9-4	Diagnose and Prescribe Online
✅ Lesson 9-5 🐻 **MG2.2**	9-5 Intervention	Activity 9-5	
✅ Lesson 9-6 🐻 **MG2.2**	9-6 Intervention	Activity 9-6	

READY TO GO ON? Enrichment, Section 9B

🖊 Worksheets
💿 CD-ROM
🪐 Online

Home on the Range Many rural areas in the United States are configured in sections. A section is one square mile, which is equal to 640 acres. A family owns the 4-section farm shown in the diagram. They are preparing information about the farm for their tax return.

1. What is the area in square miles for each of the five crops on the farm?

2. What is the area in acres for each of the crops?

3. A road goes around the perimeter of the field that is planted with barley. What is the length of the road to the nearest tenth of a mile? Explain how you made your calculation.

4. The farm includes a circular reservoir. What is the area of the surface of the reservoir to the nearest tenth of a square mile? Use 3.14 for π.

5. How many acres of unused land are there in the square plot that surrounds the reservoir?

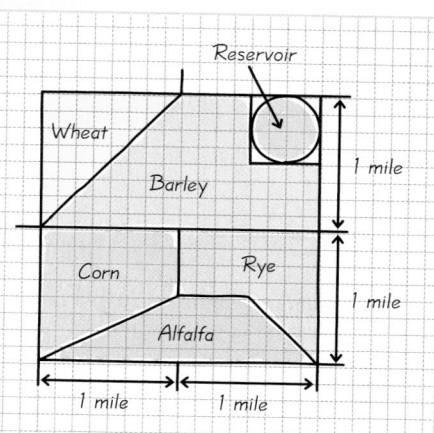

INTERVENTION

Scaffolding Questions

1. **How can you divide up the barley field into familiar shapes?** Possible answer: a triangle, a square, and a rectangle **What shape is the corn field?** Trapezoid **What are the lengths of the bases of this trapezoid?** 1 mi and $\frac{1}{2}$ mi

2. **What should you do to convert the areas into acres?** Multiply the number of square miles by 640

3. **How can you find the length of the diagonal portion of the road?** Pythagorean Theorem

4. **What is the diameter of the reservoir?** $\frac{1}{2}$ mi **What is the radius of the reservoir?** $\frac{1}{4}$ mi **What formula can you use to find the reservoir's area?** $A = \pi r^2$

5. **How many acres are in the square plot including the reservoir? Why?** 160; it is $\frac{1}{4}$ of a section **What is the area of the reservoir in acres?** 128 acres **How can you find the area of the unused land?** Subtract: $160 - 128 = 32$ acres

Extension

Which road is longer, the road surrounding the rye field or the road surrounding the alfalfa field? How much longer? Alfalfa; 0.6 mi

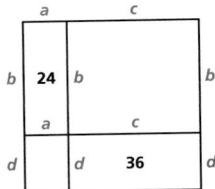
Organizer

Objective: Apply solving geometric problems to create puzzles.

 Online Edition

Resources

Chapter 9 Resource File
Puzzles, Twisters & Teasers

Shape Up

Purpose: To apply solving geometric problems to create fun puzzles

Discuss Ask students to explain how they found the area of the whole square.

Possible answer: I found the factors of 24 and 36. I used 8 and 3 for 24 and 9 and 4 for 36, since 8 + 4 = 9 + 3. The length of each side of the square is 12, so the area of the square is 144.

Suggest that students make the table below to find the maximum number of times that 6 circles can intersect.

Number of Circles	Number of Intersections
2	2
3	6
4	12
5	20
6	30

Extend Challenge students to solve the following problem: A rectangle of length 8 cm and width 6 cm is inscribed in a circle. What is the area of the regions between the rectangle and the circle? Explain how you got your answer.

Possible answer: By the Pythagorean Theorem, the diagonal of the rectangle, which is also the diameter of the circle, is 10. The area of the circle is 78.5 cm². The area of the rectangle is 48 cm². The area of the regions between the circle and the rectangle is 78.5 − 48 = 30.5 cm².

Circles and Squares

Purpose: To play a game with circles and squares

Discuss Have students discuss the strategies they used to play the game.

Extend Have students create their own sequences and play the game with a partner.

Shape Up

Rectangles

The square below has been divided into four rectangles. The areas of two of the rectangles are given. If the length of each of the segments in the diagram is an integer, what is the area of the original square?

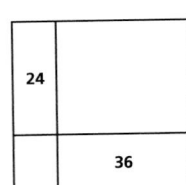

$a = 3$;
$b = 8$;
$c = 9$;
$d = 4$;
$A = 144$ units²

(*Hint:* Remember $a + c = b + d$.)

Use different lengths and a different answer to create your own version of this puzzle. **Check students' work.**

Circles

What is the maximum number of times that six circles of the same size can intersect? To find the answer, start by drawing two circles that are the same size. What is the greatest number of times they can intersect? Add another circle, and another, and so on. **30; 2; Check students' work.**

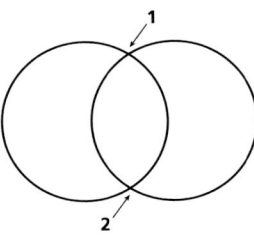

Circles and Squares

Two players start with a sequence of circles and squares. Before beginning the game, each player chooses whether to be a "circle" or a "square." The goal of the game is to have the final remaining shape be the shape you chose to be. Shapes are removed from the sequence according to the following rules: On each move, a player selects two shapes. If the shapes are identical, they are replaced with one square. If the shapes are different, they are replaced with one circle.

A complete copy of the rules and game pieces are available online.

go.hrw.com
Game Time Extra
KEYWORD: MT8CA Games

Materials
• Magnetic strip
• construction paper
• glue
• scissors
• 6 paint chip samples
• small metal box

PROJECT **Perfectly Packaged Perimeters**

This metal box stores magnetic vocabulary tiles and small squares that you can use to create a variety of shapes.

Directions

❶ Glue construction paper onto the magnetic strip.

❷ Write vocabulary words from this chapter on the magnetic strip. Then cut the words apart to form magnetic vocabulary tiles. **Figure A**

❸ Cut the paint chips into smaller squares, each approximately $1\frac{1}{4}$ inches by $1\frac{1}{4}$ inches.

❹ Glue a small piece of construction paper onto the lid of the metal box. Label it with the number and title of the chapter. **Figure B**

❺ Store the vocabulary tiles and the small squares in the metal box.

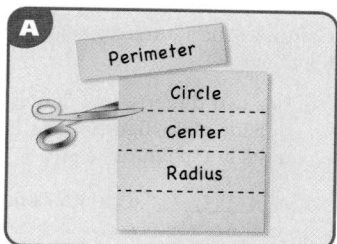
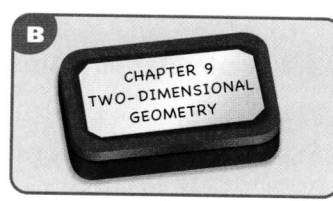

Putting the Math into Action

Place the vocabulary tiles on the outside of the box or on another metal surface to review key terms from the chapter. Arrange the small squares to form shapes with various perimeters. What is the greatest perimeter you can make?

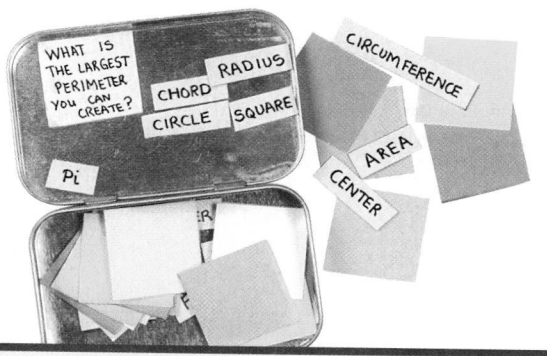

Tips from the Bag Ladies!

Flexible magnetic strips are available in rolls at hardware and home-improvement stores. If paint chips are not available, you can have students cut out 1-inch squares from card stock, empty cereal boxes, or pieces of recycled cardboard.

We sometimes have students make activity cards by writing problems and challenges on the backs of business cards. The cards are just the right size to store in the metal box along with everything else.

Organizer

Objective: Make a box that stores magnetic vocabulary tiles and small squares that can be used to create a variety of shapes.

Materials: magnetic strip, construction paper, glue, scissors, 6 paint chip samples, small metal box

Online Edition

Using the Page

Preparing the Materials
Several days before you begin the project, ask students to save any small metal containers that are used to package mints, teas, and other foods.

Making the Project
Remind students to write their vocabulary words on the magnetic strip before cutting it apart into rectangular tiles. This will ensure that the words fit on the magnetic tiles.

Extending the Project
Have pairs of students pool the squares that they made from the paint chips. Challenge the teams to arrange all of their squares into the shapes with the greatest possible perimeter and the least possible perimeter.

Organizer

Objective: Help students organize and review key concepts and skills presented in Chapter 9.

 Online Edition
Multilingual Glossary

Resources

 PuzzlePro®
One-Stop Planner®

 Multilingual Glossary Online

go.hrw.com
[KEYWORD: MT8CA Glossary]

 Lesson Tutorial Videos
CD-ROM

 Test & Practice Generator
One-Stop Planner®

Answers

1. perimeter; area
2. chord
3. 12 in.; $7\frac{2}{9}$ in^2
4. 80 m; 198 m^2
5. $11\frac{1}{2}$ ft; $5\frac{5}{8}$ ft^2
6. 20 yd; 11 yd^2

Vocabulary

Complete the sentences below with vocabulary words from the list above.

1. In a two-dimensional figure, ___?___ is the distance around the outside of the figure, while ___?___ is the number of square units in the figure.

2. A(n) ___?___ of a circle is a line segment whose endpoints are on the circle.

9-1 Perimeter and Area of Parallelograms (pp. 434–438)

 MG2.1, MG2.2, MG2.4, MG3.2

EXAMPLE

■ Find the perimeter and area of the rectangle.

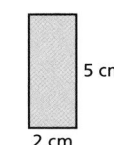

5 cm

2 cm

$P = 2l + 2w$
$\quad = 2(5) + 2(2)$
$\quad = 10 + 4$
$\quad = 14$ cm

$A = bh$
$\quad = 5(2)$
$\quad = 10$ cm^2

EXERCISES

Find the perimeter and area of each figure.

3.
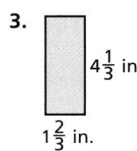
$4\frac{1}{3}$ in.
$1\frac{2}{3}$ in.

4.
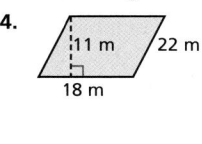
11 m 22 m
18 m

5.
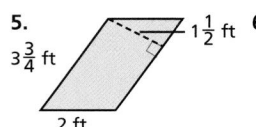
$3\frac{3}{4}$ ft $1\frac{1}{2}$ ft
2 ft

6.
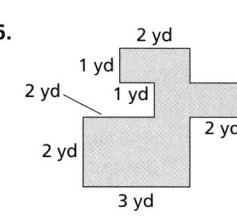
2 yd
1 yd
2 yd 1 yd
2 yd
2 yd
3 yd

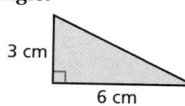

9-2 Perimeter and Area of Triangles and Trapezoids (pp. 439–443)

MG2.1, MG3.2

EXAMPLE

■ Find the area and perimeter of the right triangle.

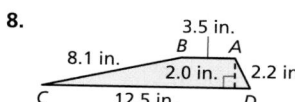
3 cm

6 cm

$A = \frac{1}{2}bh = \frac{1}{2}(6)(3) = 9 \text{ cm}^2$

$P = 6 + 3 + c$
$6^2 + 3^2 = c^2$
$6.71 \approx c$
$P = 6 + 3 + 6.71 = 15.71 \text{ cm}$

EXERCISES

Find the area and perimeter of each figure.

7.

6.1 cm   3 cm   2.1 cm
6 cm

8.
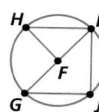
3.5 in.
B   A
8.1 in.   2.0 in.   2.2 in.
C   12.5 in.   D

9. A right triangle has legs that measure 9 feet and 12 feet. Find the perimeter of the triangle.

9-3 Circles (pp. 446–449)

MG3.1

EXAMPLE

Name the parts of circle D.
■ radii
$\overline{DB}, \overline{DC}, \overline{DE}$
■ diameter
$\overline{EB}$
■ chords
$\overline{AB}, \overline{EB}, \overline{EF}$

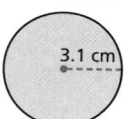
A   B
D   C
E   F

EXERCISES

Name the parts of circle F.

10. radii

11. diameter

12. chords

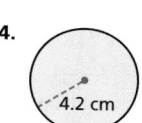
H   I
F
G   J

9-4 Circumference and Area (pp. 450–453)

MG2.1, MG3.2

EXAMPLE

■ Find the area and circumference of the circle both in terms of π and to the nearest tenth. Use 3.14 for π.

3.1 cm

$A = \pi r^2$
$= \pi(3.1)^2$
$= 9.61\pi \approx 30.2 \text{ cm}^2$

$C = 2\pi r$
$= 2\pi(3.1)$
$= 6.2\pi \approx 19.5 \text{ cm}$

EXERCISES

Find the area and circumference of each circle, both in terms of π and to the nearest tenth. Use 3.14 for π.

13.

12 in.

14.
4.2 cm

15.
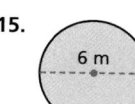
6 m

16.
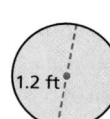
1.2 ft

Answers

7. 9 cm^2; 14.2 cm

8. 16 in^2; 26.3 in.

9. 36 ft

10. $\overline{HF}, \overline{FI}, \overline{FG}$

11. $\overline{GI}$

12. $\overline{HI}, \overline{GI}, \overline{GJ}, \overline{JI}$

13. $A = 144\pi \approx 452.2 \text{ in}^2$;
$C = 24\pi \approx 75.4 \text{ in.}$

14. $A = 17.64\pi \approx 55.4 \text{ cm}^2$;
$C = 8.4\pi \approx 26.4 \text{ cm}$

15. $A = 9\pi \approx 28.3 \text{ m}^2$;
$C = 6\pi \approx 18.8 \text{ m}$

16. $A = 0.36\pi \approx 1.1 \text{ ft}^2$;
$C = 1.2\pi \approx 3.8 \text{ ft}$

Answers

17. 57 m²
18. 40.57 ft²
19. 73.5 cm²
20. 14 square units
21. 15 square units
22. 12 square units
23. 10 square units

9-5 Area of Composite Figures (pp. 454–457)

EXAMPLE

■ Find the shaded area.

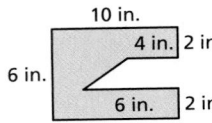

area of rectangle:
$A = bh = 10(6) = 60 \text{ in}^2$

area of trapezoid:
$A = \frac{1}{2}h(b_1 + b_2) = \frac{1}{2}(2)(4 + 6) = 10 \text{ in}^2$

total area:
$A = (60 - 10) = 50 \text{ in}^2$

EXERCISES

Find the shaded area. Round to the nearest tenth, if necessary.

17.

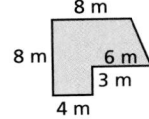

18.

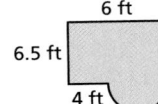

19.

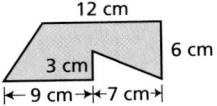

9-6 Area of Irregular Figures (pp. 458–461)

EXAMPLE

■ Estimate the shaded area.

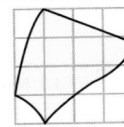

Draw a composite figure.

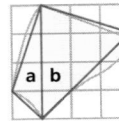

area of triangle **a**:
$A = \frac{1}{2}bh = \frac{1}{2}(4)(1) = 2 \text{ square units}$

area of triangle **b**:
$A = \frac{1}{2}bh = \frac{1}{2}(4)(3) = 6 \text{ square units}$

area of composite figure:
$A = 2 + 6 = 8 \text{ square units}$

EXERCISES

Estimate each shaded area.

20.

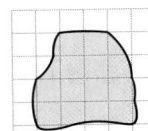

21.

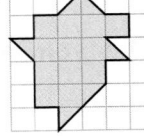

22.

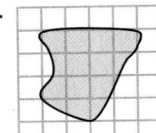

23.

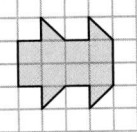

Find the perimeter of each figure.

1.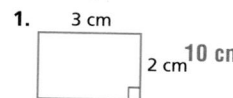
3 cm
2 cm 10 cm

2.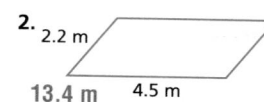
2.2 m
13.4 m   4.5 m

3.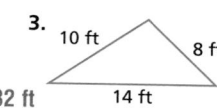
10 ft   8 ft
32 ft   14 ft

Find the area of each figure.

4.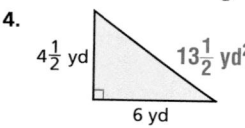
$4\frac{1}{2}$ yd $13\frac{1}{2}$ yd^2
6 yd

5.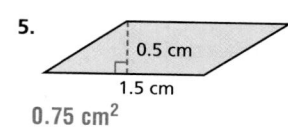
0.5 cm
1.5 cm
0.75 cm^2

6.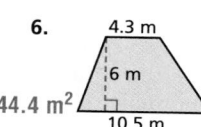
4.3 m
6 m
44.4 m^2 10.5 m

Graph and find the area of each figure with the given vertices.

7. $(-3, 2), (-3, -2), (5, -2), (5, 2)$ **32 units^2** **8.** $(2, 4), (7, 4), (5, 0), (0, 0)$ **20 units^2**

9. $(-5, 0), (0, 0), (4, 4)$ **10 units^2** **10.** $(0, 4), (3, 6), (3, -3), (0, -3)$ **24 units^2**

Name the parts of circle E.

11. radii $\overline{AE}, \overline{EC}, \overline{BE}$

12. chords $\overline{AD}, \overline{AC}$

13. diameter $\overline{AC}$

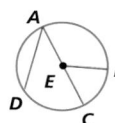

Find the area and circumference of each circle, both in terms of π and to the nearest tenth. Use 3.14 for π.

14. radius = 15 cm

15. diameter = 6.5 ft

16. radius = 2.2 m

Find the shaded area. Round to the nearest tenth, if necessary.

17.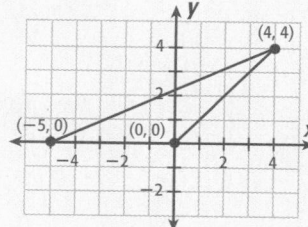
←8.2 in.→
6 in.
63.3 in^2

18.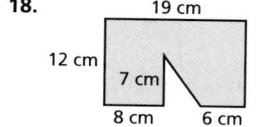
19 cm
12 cm
7 cm
8 cm   6 cm
210.5 cm^2

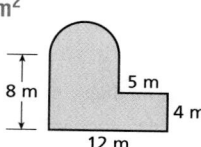
8 m   5 m
4 m
12 m

19. The figure shows the floorplan of the main gallery of an art museum. What is the area of the gallery floor? **95.2 m^2**

Estimate each shaded area. **21–22. Possible answers given.**

20.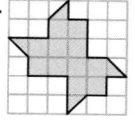
13 square units

21.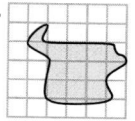
11 square units

22.
19 square units

9.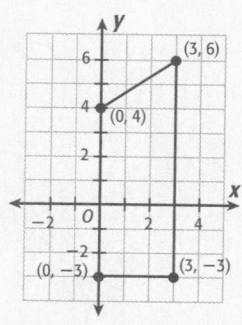
(4, 4)
(−5, 0)   (0, 0)

10.
(3, 6)
(0, 4)
(0, −3)   (3, −3)

14. $A = 225\pi \approx 706.5$ cm^2;
$C = 30\pi \approx 94.2$ cm

15. $A = 10.6\pi \approx 33.3$ ft^2;
$C = 6.5\pi \approx 20.4$ ft

16. $A = 4.75\pi \approx 15.2$ m^2;
$C = 4.4\pi \approx 13.8$ m

CHAPTER TEST

CHAPTER 9

Organizer

Objective: Assess students' mastery of concepts and skills in Chapter 9.

 **Online Edition**

Resources

Assessment Resources

Chapter 9 Tests
• Free Response
  (Levels A, B, C)
• Multiple Choice
  (Levels A, B, C)
• Performance Assessment

IDEA Works! CD-ROM
Modified Chapter 9 Test

Test & Practice Generator
One-Stop Planner®

Answers

7.
(−3, 2)   (5, 2)
(−3, −2)   (5, −2)

8.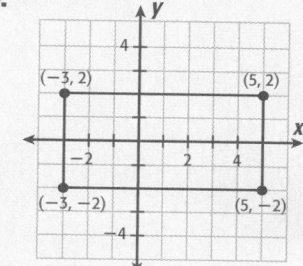
(2, 4)   (7, 4)
(0, 0)   (5, 0)

California Standards

Standard	Items
MG2.1	1–6, 14–16
MG2.2	17–22
MG3.1	11–13
MG3.2	7–10

Organizer

Objective: Provide opportunities to learn and practice common test-taking strategies.

 Online Edition

 This Strategies for Success **Teaching Tip** focuses on test items with graphics that may inadvertently mislead students. Advise students that diagrams are not always drawn to scale. They should not rely on the appearance of a drawing to answer the question. Students may need to look at how the drawing is labeled and determine if they need to redraw the diagram to better depict the scenario.

Any Type: Using a Graphic

Look carefully at any drawings that are given with a test item. Keep in mind that figures are not always drawn to scale and can be misleading.

EXAMPLE 1

Multiple Choice The two circles shown have radii of 10 cm and 15 cm. What is the approximate difference between the areas of the two circles?

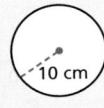 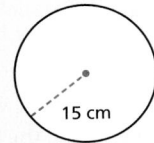

Ⓐ 31.4 cm²   Ⓑ 94.2 cm²   Ⓒ 392.5 cm²   Ⓓ 706.5 cm²

First, find the area of each circle.

area of smaller circle:
$$A = \pi r^2$$
$$= \pi(10)^2$$ *Use the formula for the area of a circle.*
$$= 100\pi$$

area of larger circle:
$$A = \pi r^2$$
$$= \pi(15)^2$$
$$= 225\pi$$

Next, subtract the area of the smaller circle from the area of the larger circle.

$$225\pi - 100\pi = 125\pi$$
$$\approx 125(3) \approx 375$$ *Use 3 as an approximation for π.*

The difference between the areas is about 375 cm², so the correct answer must be choice C.

EXAMPLE 2

Short Response An ice rink has an area of 3750 ft² and length of 75 ft. What is the perimeter of the ice rink? Explain your reasoning and show your work.

Draw a diagram to help you visualize the problem.

3750 ft²   *h*

75 ft

$$A = bh$$ *You know the area and base. You need to find the height.*
$$3750 = 75h$$
$$50 = h$$

$$P = 2(b + h)$$ *Use the formula for perimeter.*
$$= 2(75 + 50)$$ *Substitute the known values.*
$$= 2(125) = 250$$

The perimeter of the ice rink is 250 ft.

Find the perimeter of each figure.

1.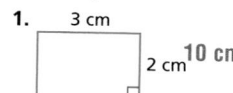
3 cm
2 cm 10 cm

2.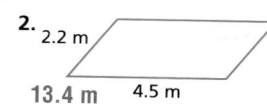
2.2 m
13.4 m   4.5 m

3.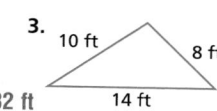
10 ft   8 ft
32 ft   14 ft

Find the area of each figure.

4.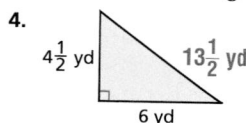
$4\frac{1}{2}$ yd $13\frac{1}{2}$ yd^2
6 yd

5.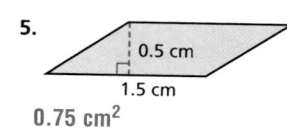
0.5 cm
1.5 cm
0.75 cm^2

6.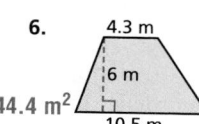
4.3 m
6 m
44.4 m^2 10.5 m

Graph and find the area of each figure with the given vertices.

7. $(-3, 2), (-3, -2), (5, -2), (5, 2)$ **32 units^2**   **8.** $(2, 4), (7, 4), (5, 0), (0, 0)$ **20 units^2**

9. $(-5, 0), (0, 0), (4, 4)$ **10 units^2**   **10.** $(0, 4), (3, 6), (3, -3), (0, -3)$ **24 units^2**

Name the parts of circle E.

11. radii $\overline{AE}, \overline{EC}, \overline{BE}$

12. chords $\overline{AD}, \overline{AC}$

13. diameter $\overline{AC}$

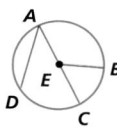

Find the area and circumference of each circle, both in terms of π and to the nearest tenth. Use 3.14 for π.

14. radius = 15 cm

15. diameter = 6.5 ft

16. radius = 2.2 m

Find the shaded area. Round to the nearest tenth, if necessary.

17.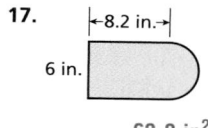
8.2 in.
6 in.
63.3 in^2

18.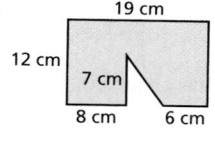
19 cm
12 cm
7 cm   **210.5 cm^2**
8 cm   6 cm

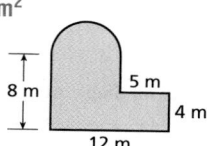
8 m   5 m
4 m
12 m

19. The figure shows the floorplan of the main gallery of an art museum. What is the area of the gallery floor? **95.2 m^2**

Estimate each shaded area. **21–22. Possible answers given.**

20.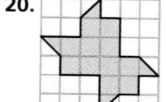
13 square units

21.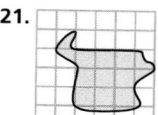
11 square units

22.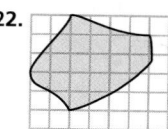
19 square units

9.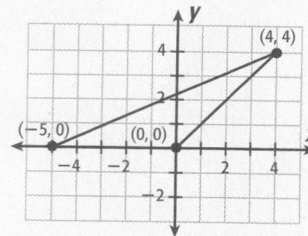

10.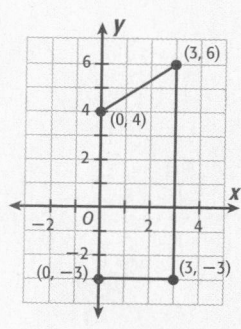

Organizer

Objective: Assess students' mastery of concepts and skills in Chapter 9.

 **Online Edition**

Resources

📜 **Assessment Resources**

   Chapter 9 Tests
   • Free Response
     (Levels A, B, C)
   • Multiple Choice
     (Levels A, B, C)
   • Performance Assessment

💿 **IDEA Works! CD-ROM**
   Modified Chapter 9 Test

🖐 **Test & Practice Generator**
   One-Stop Planner®

Answers

7.

8.

14. $A = 225\pi \approx 706.5$ cm^2;
     $C = 30\pi \approx 94.2$ cm

15. $A = 10.6\pi \approx 33.3$ ft^2;
     $C = 6.5\pi \approx 20.4$ ft

16. $A = 4.75\pi \approx 15.2$ m^2;
     $C = 4.4\pi \approx 13.8$ m

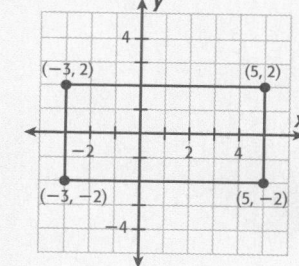

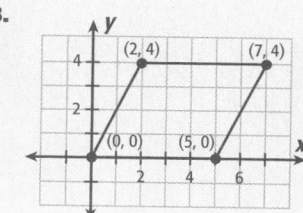

Standard	Items
MG2.1	1–6, 14–16
MG2.2	17–22
MG3.1	11–13
MG3.2	7–10

California Standards

Organizer

Objective: Provide opportunities to learn and practice common test-taking strategies.

Online Edition

Teaching Tip This Strategies for Success focuses on test items with graphics that may inadvertently mislead students. Advise students that diagrams are not always drawn to scale. They should not rely on the appearance of a drawing to answer the question. Students may need to look at how the drawing is labeled and determine if they need to redraw the diagram to better depict the scenario.

Any Type: Using a Graphic

Look carefully at any drawings that are given with a test item. Keep in mind that figures are not always drawn to scale and can be misleading.

EXAMPLE 1

Multiple Choice The two circles shown have radii of 10 cm and 15 cm. What is the approximate difference between the areas of the two circles?

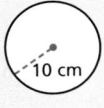
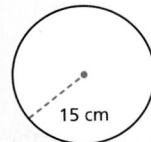

Ⓐ 31.4 cm²   Ⓑ 94.2 cm²   Ⓒ 392.5 cm²   Ⓓ 706.5 cm²

First, find the area of each circle.

area of smaller circle:
$$A = \pi r^2$$ *Use the formula for*
$$= \pi(10)^2$$ *the area of a circle.*
$$= 100\pi$$

area of larger circle:
$$A = \pi r^2$$
$$= \pi(15)^2$$
$$= 225\pi$$

Next, subtract the area of the smaller circle from the area of the larger circle.

$$225\pi - 100\pi = 125\pi$$
$$\approx 125(3) \approx 375$$ *Use 3 as an approximation for π.*

The difference between the areas is about 375 cm², so the correct answer must be choice C.

EXAMPLE 2

Short Response An ice rink has an area of 3750 ft² and length of 75 ft. What is the perimeter of the ice rink? Explain your reasoning and show your work.

Draw a diagram to help you visualize the problem.

3750 ft² h 75 ft

$$A = bh$$ *You know the area and base. You*
$$3750 = 75h$$ *need to find the height.*
$$50 = h$$

$$P = 2(b + h)$$ *Use the formula for perimeter.*
$$= 2(75 + 50)$$ *Substitute the known values.*
$$= 2(125) = 250$$

The perimeter of the ice rink is 250 ft.

Draw a diagram if one is not provided to help you visualize the problem.

Read each test problem and answer the questions that follow.

Item A
Short Response A restaurant sells a 12-inch (diameter) small pizza, a 14-inch medium pizza, and a 16-inch large pizza. How much more pizza do you get for a large pizza than a small pizza? Explain your reasoning and show your work.

1. Draw a diagram to help you visualize the problem.

2. Use information from your diagram to solve the problem.

Item B
Multiple Choice A middle school has 1000 students. According to the circle graph, how many students are in track?

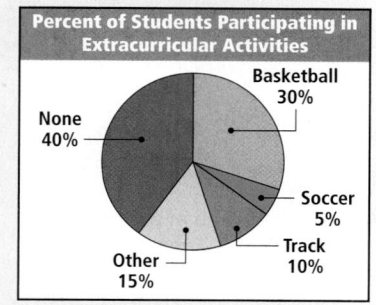

Percent of Students Participating in Extracurricular Activities
- Basketball 30%
- None 40%
- Soccer 5%
- Track 10%
- Other 15%

Ⓐ 400 students   Ⓒ 100 students
Ⓑ 300 students   Ⓓ 30 students

3. What percent of the students are in track? How do you know?

4. How do you find the number of students who are in track?

Item C
Extended Response When a rectangle is divided into thirds, three squares are formed, each with a perimeter of 9.6 cm. What is the perimeter of the original rectangle?

5. Draw a diagram to help you visualize the problem.

6. What information from your diagram do you need to solve the problem?

7. If your answer is a decimal, what do you need to remember to do on the grid?

8. Show how you would grid your response.

Item D
Multiple Choice The radius of the circle below is 50 millimeters. What is the approximate area of the shaded region?

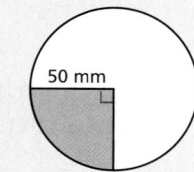

50 mm

Ⓐ 225 mm²   Ⓒ 1965 mm²
Ⓑ 625 mm²   Ⓓ 2500 mm²

9. What variables are used to represent radius and area?

10. What formula should you use to solve this problem? Explain your reasoning.

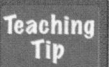 **Teaching Tip** Let students know that just because a test item may not include a diagram, that it may still be beneficial for them to make a quick sketch. Show students the importance of labeling their sketch with the information provided in the test item.

Answers

1. Possible answer: Students should draw three circles to represent the different pizzas. Each pizza should be labeled with its diameter in inches.

2. Possible answer: Find the difference between the area of the large pizza and the area of the small pizza.

   You get 87.92 in² more.

   $A = \pi r^2$

Small 12 in.	Large 16 in.
$A = \pi 6^2$	$A = \pi 8^2$
$A = 36\pi$	$A = 64\pi$
$A = 113.04$	$A = 200.96$

3. 10%; The label on the circle graph for the red section gives the percent.

4. Change 10% to a decimal and multiply by the total number of students in the school. $0.1 \times 1000 = 100$

5.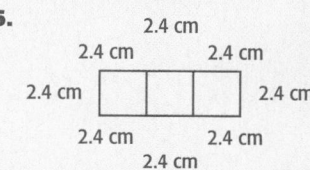

   2.4 cm

6. the length of each side of a square

7. Shade the decimal point in the grid.

8.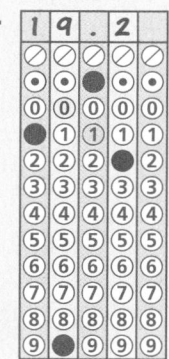

9. radius = r; area = A

10. Possible answer: Area of a circle $(A) = \pi r^2$; I can estimate the area of the circle using πr^2 and then find $\frac{1}{4}$ of the area.

CHAPTER
9

MASTERING THE STANDARDS

go.hrw.com
Standards Practice Online
KEYWORD: MT8CA Practice

Organizer

Objective: Provide review and practice for Chapters 1–9.

 Online Edition

Resources

 Assessment Resources
Chapter 9 Cumulative Test

 Focus on California Standards Benchmark Tests and Intervention

 California Standards Practice CD-ROM

go.hrw.com
KEYWORD: MT8CA Practice

Cumulative Assessment, Chapters 1–9
Multiple Choice

1. Which addition equation represents the number line diagram below?

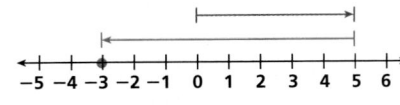

   (A) $5 + (-8)$ (C) $-5 + 8$
   (B) $5 + 8$ (D) $-5 + (-8)$

2. A semicircle is removed from a rectangle as shown in the figure. Find the area of the shaded figure to the nearest tenth.

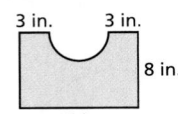

   (A) 39.5 in^2 (C) 81.9 in^2
   (B) 67.7 in^2 (D) 110.1 in^2

3. If $\frac{g^8}{g^5} = g^x$ and $g^{-3} \cdot g^4 = g^y$, what is the value of $x + y$?

   (A) -4 (C) 6
   (B) 4   (D) 14

4. Eduardo invests his savings at 3% simple interest for 5 years and earns $150 in interest. How much money did Eduardo invest?

   (A) $10   (C) $1000
   (B) $22.50   (D) $2250

5. Which word does NOT describe the number $\sqrt{16}$?

   (A) rational   (C) whole
   (B) integer   (D) irrational

6. For which positive radius, r, is the circumference of a circle the same as the area of a circle?

   (A) $r = 1$ (C) $r = 3$
   (B) $r = 2$ (D) $r = 4$

7. Which is an equation of the line shown in the graph?

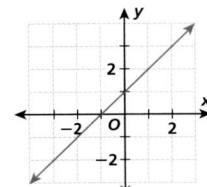

   (A) $y = x - 1$ (C) $y = 2x + 1$
   (B) $y = x + 1$ (D) $y = x + 2$

8. Armen rollerblades at a rate of 12 km/h. What is Armen's rate in meters per second?

   (A) 200 m/s   (C) $\frac{1}{3}$ m/s
   (B) $3\frac{1}{3}$ m/s   (D) $\frac{3}{10}$ m/s

9. What is the solution to the equation $\frac{2}{3}x + \frac{1}{6} = 1$?

   (A) $x = \frac{5}{9}$ (C) $x = 1\frac{1}{4}$
   (B) $x = \frac{4}{5}$ (D) $x = 3\frac{2}{3}$

 California Standards

Standard	Items
NS1.2	1
NS1.3	18
NS1.4	5
NS1.7	4
AF1.1	18
AF2.2	3
AF3.3	7, 14
AF4.1	9, 11
MG1.1	8
MG1.3	17
MG2.1	6, 10, 15
MG2.2	2, 16
MG3.2	13
MG3.3	12

Teaching Tip **Multiple Choice For item 3,** remind students to add the exponents when multiplying numbers or variables with the same base and to subtract the exponents when dividing numbers or variables with the same base.

Students who chose answer **A** for **item 9** did not use the reciprocal when dividing by the coefficient $\frac{2}{3}$.

Answers

15–16. See p. A10.

17. Possible answer:
$C = 2\pi r$
$C \approx 2 \cdot 3.14 \cdot 37$
$C \approx 232.36$ in.
The point travels 232.36 inches in one revolution. The propeller makes 2500 revolutions in one minute.
$232.36 \cdot 2500 = 580{,}900$ in.
The point travels 580,900 inches, or about 9.2 miles, in one minute.
There are 60 minutes in an hour, so
$9.2 \cdot 60 = 552$ miles.
The point travels about 552 miles in one hour.

18. See 4-Point Response work sample.

10. Suzanne plans to install a fence around the perimeter of her land. How much fencing does she need?

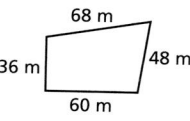

Ⓐ 212 m   Ⓒ 2448 m

Ⓑ 368 m   Ⓓ 2800 m

When a variable is used more than one time in an expression or an equation, it always has the same value.

11. The Cougars, the Wildcats, and the Broncos won a total of 18 games during the football season. The Cougars won 8 games. The Broncos won $\frac{2}{3}$ as many games as the Wildcats. How many games did the Wildcats win?

Ⓐ 2 games   Ⓒ 6 games

Ⓑ 4 games   Ⓓ 8 games

Gridded Response

12. In the figure, K is the midpoint of $\overline{JL}$, and $\overline{KM}$ is perpendicular to $\overline{JL}$. Find the length of $\overline{KM}$, in inches. **6**

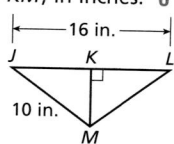

13. What is the y-coordinate of the point $(-3, 6)$ that has been translated down 4 units? **2**

14. What is the slope of the line below? $\frac{2}{3}$

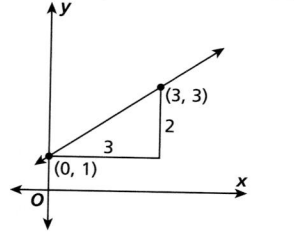

Short Response

15. Draw a rectangle with base length 7 cm and height 4 cm. Then draw a rectangle with base length 14 cm and height 1 cm. Which rectangle has the larger area? Which rectangle has the larger perimeter? Show your work.

16. Each square of the grid represents 1 cm². What is the best estimate for the area of the shaded figure? Explain how you determined your answer.

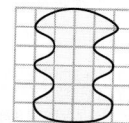

17. An airplane propeller is 37 inches from its tip to the center axis of its rotation. Suppose the propeller spins at a rate of 2500 revolutions per minute. How far will a point on the tip of the propeller travel in one minute? How far will the point on the tip travel in one hour? Show your work.

Extended Response

18. You are designing a house to fit on a rectangular lot that has 90 feet of lake frontage and is 162 feet deep. The building codes require that the house not be built closer than 10 feet to the lot boundary lines.

a. Write an inequality and solve it to find how long the front of the house facing the lake can be.

b. If you want the house to cover no more than 20% of the lot, what would be the maximum square footage of the house?

c. If you want to spend a maximum of $100,000 building the house, to the nearest whole dollar, what would be the maximum you could spend per square foot for a 1988-square-foot house?

Student Work Samples for Item 18

4-Point Response

a. $x =$ length of front of house
$x < 90 - 2(10)$
$x < 70$

b. $A =$ area, $l =$ length of lot, $w =$ width of lot
$A = lw = (162)(90) = 14,580$
$(0.20) = 20\%$
$(0.20)(14,580) = 2916 \text{ ft}^2$

c. $\frac{100,000}{1988} > \frac{1988x}{1988}$ if $x = \text{cost}/\text{ft}^2$
$50.3 > x$
cost must be less than \$50/ft²

The student wrote the correct inequality and found both the maximum square footage and maximum amount per square foot given the conditions.

3-Point Response

a. let $l =$ length of front of house
$l < 70$

b. let $A =$ area, $l =$ length of lot, $w =$ width of lot
$(.20)(14,580) = 2916 \text{ ft}^2$

c. $100,000 > 1988x$ if $x = \text{cost}/\text{ft}^2$
cost must be less than \$50/ft²

The student wrote and solved the correct inequality. However, the explanations are insufficient.

2-Point Response

a. $x = 90$

b. $20 \cdot 90 \cdot 162$
$= 291,600$

c. $x(100,000) > \left(\frac{1988}{x}\right)x$
$100,000x > 1988$

The student exhibits a very limited understanding of the concepts involved. Very little work is shown. Explanations are lacking.

CHAPTER
10

Three-Dimensional Geometry

	Grade-level Standard
✔	Grade-level Standard
◄	Review
►	Beyond the Standards
A	Assessment
O	Optional

Pacing Guide

🖐 **Calendar Planner**
Teacher's **One-Stop** Planner®

	Lesson/Lab	🐻 California Standards	⏱ Time	Advanced Students	Benchmark* Students	Strategic** Students
LAB	Explore Three-Dimensional Figures	Prep for **MG2.1**	25 min	◄	◄	◄
10-1	Three-Dimensional Figures	Prep for **MG2.1**	50 min	O	O	◄
LAB	Explore Volume of Prisms	**AF3.2, MG2.3**	25 min	✔	✔	✔
10-2	Volume of Prisms and Cylinders	**MG2.1, MG2.4**	75 min	✔	✔	✔
10-3	Volume of Pyramids and Cones	Ext. of **MG2.1**	50 min	►	O	O
Ready to Go On?			25 min	A	A	A
Focus on Problem Solving			25 min	A	A	O
LAB	Nets of Prisms and Cylinders	**MG3.5**	25 min	✔	✔	✔
10-4	Surface Area of Prisms and Cylinders	**MG2.1, MG2.2, MG2.3**	75 min	✔	✔	✔
LAB	Nets of Cones	**MG3.5**	25 min	✔	✔	✔
10-5	Surface Area of Pyramids and Cones	Ext. of **MG2.1**	50 min	►	O	O
10-6	Spheres	Ext. of **MG2.1**	50 min	►	O	O
10-7	Scaling Three-Dimensional Figures	**MG2.3**	50 min	✔	✔	✔
Ready to Go On?			25 min	A	A	A
Concept Connection			25 min	A	A	O
Study Guide: Review			50 min	✔	✔	✔
Chapter Test			50 min	A	A	A

* **Benchmark students** are achieving at or near grade level.

** **Strategic students** may be a year or more below grade level
and may require additional time for intervention.

Countdown to Mastery, Weeks ㉒, ㉑, ㉒

ONGOING ASSESSMENT and INTERVENTION

DIAGNOSE	PRESCRIBE

Assess Prior Knowledge

Before Chapter 10

Diagnose readiness for the chapter.
Are You Ready? SE p. 475

Prescribe intervention.
Are You Ready? Intervention Skills 11, 40, 44, 45

Formative Assessment

Before Every Lesson

Diagnose readiness for the lesson.
Warm Up TE, every lesson

Prescribe intervention.
Skills Bank SE pp. SB2–SB24
Review for Mastery CRF, Chapters 1–10

During Every Lesson

Diagnose understanding of lesson concepts.
Questioning Strategies Chapter 10
Think and Discuss SE, every lesson
Write About It SE, lesson exercises
Journal TE, lesson exercises

Prescribe intervention.
Reading Strategies CRF, every lesson
Success for ELL Chapter 10
Lesson Tutorial Videos Chapter 10

After Every Lesson

Diagnose mastery of lesson concepts.
Lesson Quiz TE, every lesson
Ready to Go On? SE pp. 494, 516
Test and Practice Generator

Prescribe intervention.
Review for Mastery CRF, every lesson
Problem Solving CRF, every lesson
Ready to Go On? Intervention Chapter 10
Homework Help Online

Before Chapter 10 Testing

Diagnose mastery of concepts in the chapter.
Ready to Go On? SE pp. 494, 516
Focus on Problem Solving SE p. 495
Concept Connection SE p. 517
Section Quizzes AR pp. 185–186
Test and Practice Generator

Prescribe intervention.
Ready to Go On? Intervention Chapter 10
Scaffolding Questions TE p. 517

Before Assessment of California Standards

Diagnose mastery of California standards.
Focus on California Standards: Benchmark Tests
Mastering the Standards SE pp. 524–525
California Standards Practice CD-ROM

Prescribe intervention.
Focus on California Standards: Intervention

Summative Assessment

After Chapter 10

Check mastery of chapter concepts.
Multiple-Choice Tests (Forms A, B, C)
Free-Response Tests (Forms A, B, C)
Performance Assessment AR pp. 187–200
Test and Practice Generator

Prescribe intervention.
Review for Mastery CRF, every lesson
Lesson Tutorial Videos Chapter 10

KEY: **SE** = *Student Edition* **TE** = *Teacher's Edition* **CRF** = *Chapter Resource File* **AR** = *Assessment Resources*  *Available on CD-ROM* 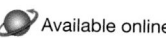 *Available online*

Supporting the Teacher

Chapter 10 Resource File

Family Involvement
pp. 1–2, 29–30

Practice A, B, C
pp. 5–7, 13–15, 21–23, 33–35, 41–43, 49–51, 57–59

Review for Mastery
pp. 8, 16, 24, 36, 44, 52, 60

Challenge
pp. 9, 17, 25, 37, 45, 53, 61, 69, 77

Problem Solving
pp. 10, 18, 26, 38, 46, 54, 62, 70, 78

Reading Strategies ELL
pp. 11, 19, 27, 39, 47, 55, 63, 71, 79

Puzzles, Twisters, and Teasers
pp. 12, 20, 28, 40, 48, 56, 64, 72, 80

Hands-On Lab
pp. 68–69, 70–71, 72–73, 75–76, 77–78, 81–82, 83–84, 85–86, 87, 88–89, 92–93

Technology Lab
pp. 67, 74, 79–80, 90–91

Workbooks

Homework and Practice Workbook SPANISH
Teacher's Guide .... pp. 72–78

Know-It Notebook SPANISH
Teacher's Guide .... Chapter 10

Review for Mastery Workbook SPANISH
Teacher's Guide .... pp. 72–78

Focus on California Standards: Intervention Workbook SPANISH
Teacher's Guide

Teacher Tools

Power Presentations
Complete PowerPoint® presentations for Chapter 10 lessons

Lesson Tutorial Videos SPANISH
Holt authors Ed Burger and Freddie Renfro present tutorials to support the Chapter 10 lessons.

Teacher's One-Stop Planner SPANISH
Easy access to all Chapter 10 resources and assessments, as well as software for lesson planning, test generation, and puzzle creation

IDEA Works!
Key Chapter 10 resources and assessments modified to address special learning needs

Questioning Strategies .... Chapter 10

Solutions Key .... Chapter 10

Interactive Answers and Solutions

TechKeys   **Lab Resources**

Project Teacher Support   **Parent Resources**

Transparencies

Lesson Transparencies, Volume 2 .... Chapter 10
• Teacher Tools
• Warm Ups
• Teaching Transparencies
• Lesson Quizzes

Know-It Notebook .... Chapter 10
• Vocabulary   • Chapter Review
• Additional Examples   • Big Ideas

Alternate Openers: Explorations .... pp. 72–78

Countdown to Mastery .... pp. 38–43

Technology Highlights for the Teacher

 Power Presentations
Dynamic presentations to engage students. Complete PowerPoint® presentations for every lesson in Chapter 10.

 One-Stop Planner SPANISH
Easy access to Chapter 10 resources and assessments. Includes lesson-planning, test-generation, and puzzle-creation software.

Premier Online Edition SPANISH
Includes Tutorial Videos, Lesson Activities, Lesson Quizzes, Homework Help, Chapter Project and more.

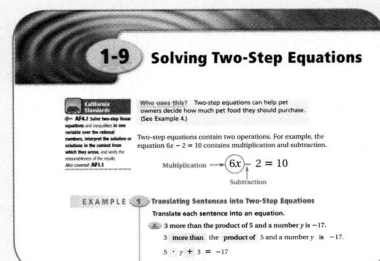

KEY: **SE** = *Student Edition*   **TE** = *Teacher's Edition*   English Language Learners   Spanish available   Available on CD-ROM    Available online

Universal Access

Teaching tips to help all students appear throughout the chapter. A few that target specific students are included in the lists below.

Strategic Students

Practice A .... CRF, every lesson
Review for Mastery .... CRF, every lesson
Reading Strategies .... CRF, every lesson
Academic Vocabulary Connections ....TE p. 476
Modeling ....TE pp. 486, 491
Ready to Go On? Intervention .... Chapter 10
Questioning Strategies .... Chapter 10
Know-It Notebook SPANISH .... Chapter 10
Homework Help Online 🪐
Lesson Tutorial Videos 🪐 💿 SPANISH
Online Interactivities 🪐 SPANISH

Special Needs Students

Practice A .... CRF, every lesson
Review for Mastery .... CRF, every lesson
Reading Strategies .... CRF, every lesson
Academic Vocabulary Connections ....TE p. 476
Inclusion ....TE p. 499
IDEA Works! Modified Resources .... Chapter 10
Ready to Go On? Intervention .... Chapter 10
Know-It Notebook SPANISH .... Chapter 10
Lesson Tutorial Videos 🪐 💿 SPANISH
Online Interactivities 🪐 SPANISH

English Learners

Reading Strategies .... CRF, every lesson
Vocabulary Review .... SE p. 520
Academic Vocabulary Connections ....TE p. 476
English Language Learners ....TE pp. 499, 505
Language Support ....TE p. 505
Success for English Language Learners .... Chapter 10
Know-It Notebook SPANISH .... Chapter 10
Multilingual Glossary 🪐
Lesson Tutorial Videos 🪐 💿 SPANISH

Benchmark Students

Practice B .... CRF, every lesson
Problem Solving .... CRF, every lesson
Academic Vocabulary Connections ....TE p. 476
Ready to Go On? Intervention .... Chapter 10
Questioning Strategies .... Chapter 10
Know-It Notebook SPANISH .... Chapter 10
Homework Help Online 🪐
Online Interactivities 🪐 SPANISH

Advanced Students

Practice C .... CRF, every lesson
Challenge .... CRF, every lesson
Reading and Writing Math **EXTENSION** ....TE p. 477
Concept Connection **EXTENSION** ....TE p. 517
Ready to Go On? Enrichment .... Chapter 10

Technology Highlights for Universal Access

💿 Lesson Tutorial Videos SPANISH

Starring Holt authors Ed Burger and Freddie Renfro! Live tutorials to support every lesson in Chapter 10.

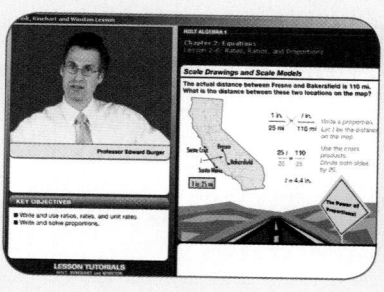

🪐 Multilingual Glossary

Searchable glossary includes definitions in English, Spanish, Vietnamese, Chinese, Hmong, Korean, and other languages.

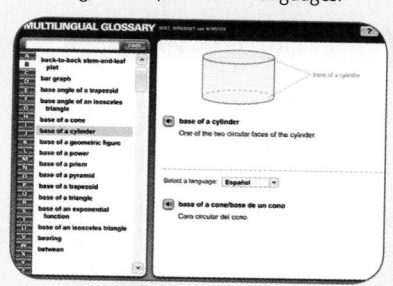

🪐 Online Interactivities SPANISH

Interactive tutorials provide visually engaging alternative opportunities to learn concepts and master skills.

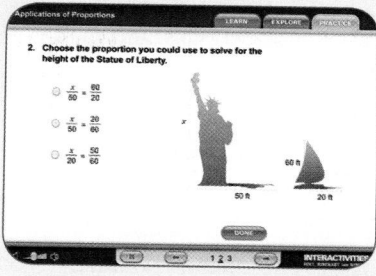

KEY: **SE** = *Student Edition*   **TE** = *Teacher's Edition*   **CRF** = *Chapter Resource File*   SPANISH Spanish available   💿 Available on CD-ROM   🪐 Available online

Ongoing Assessment

Assessing Prior Knowledge

Determine whether students have the prerequisite concepts and skills for success in Chapter 10.

Are You Ready? SPANISH .... SE p. 475
Warm Up .... TE, every lesson

Chapter and Standards Assessment

Provide review and practice for Chapter 10 and standards mastery.

Concept Connection .... SE p. 517
Study Guide: Review .... SE pp. 520–522
Mastering the Standards .... SE pp. 524–525
Countdown to Mastery Transparencies ..... pp. 38–43
Focus on California Standards: Benchmark Tests
Focus on California Standards: Intervention Workbook SPANISH
California Standards Practice CD-ROM SPANISH
IDEA Works! Modified Worksheets and Tests

Alternative Assessment

Assess students' understanding of Chapter 10 concepts and combined problem-solving skills.

Performance Assessment .... AR pp. 199–200
Portfolio Assessment .... AR p. xxxvi
Chapter 10 Project

Daily Assessment

Provide formative assessment for each day of Chapter 10.

Think and Discuss .... SE, every lesson
Write About It .... SE, lesson exercises
Journal .... TE, lesson exercises
Lesson Quiz .... TE, every lesson
Questioning Strategies .... Chapter 10
IDEA Works! Modified Lesson Quizzes .... Chapter 10

Weekly Assessment

Provide formative assessment for each week of Chapter 10.

Focus on Problem Solving .... SE p. 495
Concept Connection .... SE p. 517
Ready to Go On? SPANISH .... SE pp. 494, 516
Cumulative Assessment .... SE pp. 524–525
Test and Practice Generator SPANISH ...One-Stop Planner

Formal Assessment

Provide summative assessment of Chapter 10 mastery.

Section Quizzes .... AR pp. 185–186
Chapter 10 Test SPANISH .... SE p. 523
Chapter Test (Levels A, B, C) .... AR pp. 187–198
 • Multiple-Choice • Free-Response
Cumulative Test .... AR pp. 524–525
Test and Practice Generator SPANISH ...One-Stop Planner
IDEA Works! Modified Tests .... Chapter 10

Technology Highlights for the Teacher

Are You Ready? SPANISH

Automatically assess readiness and prescribe intervention for Chapter 10 prerequisite skills.

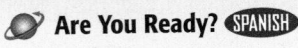
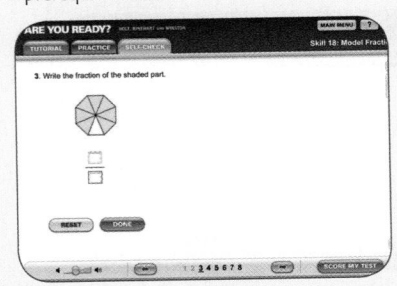

Ready to Go On? SPANISH

Automatically assess understanding of and prescribe intervention for Sections 10A and 10B.

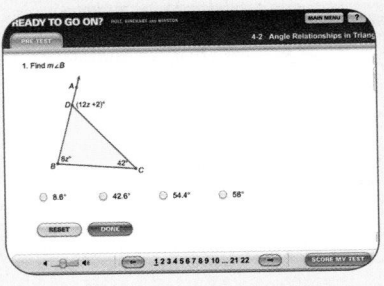

Focus on California Standards: Benchmark Tests and Intervention SPANISH

Automatically assess proficiency with California Grade 7 Standards and provide intervention.

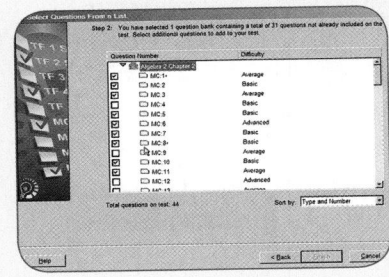

KEY: **SE** = Student Edition **TE** = Teacher's Edition **AR** = Assessment Resources SPANISH Spanish available 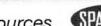 Available on CD-ROM 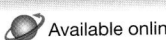 Available online

Formal Assessment

Three levels (A, B, C) of multiple-choice and free-response chapter tests are available in the *Assessment Resources*.

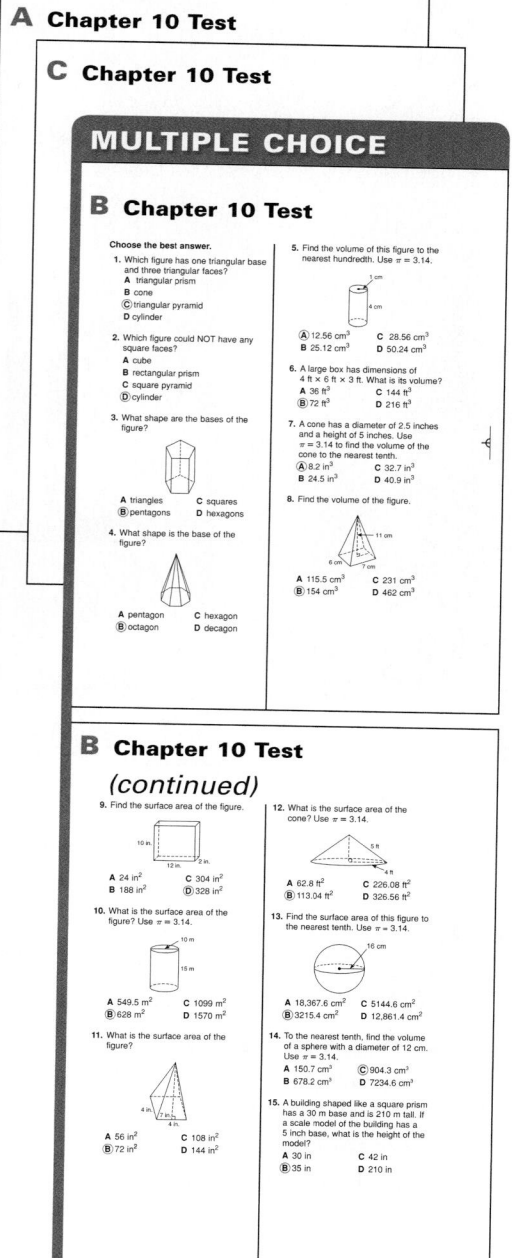

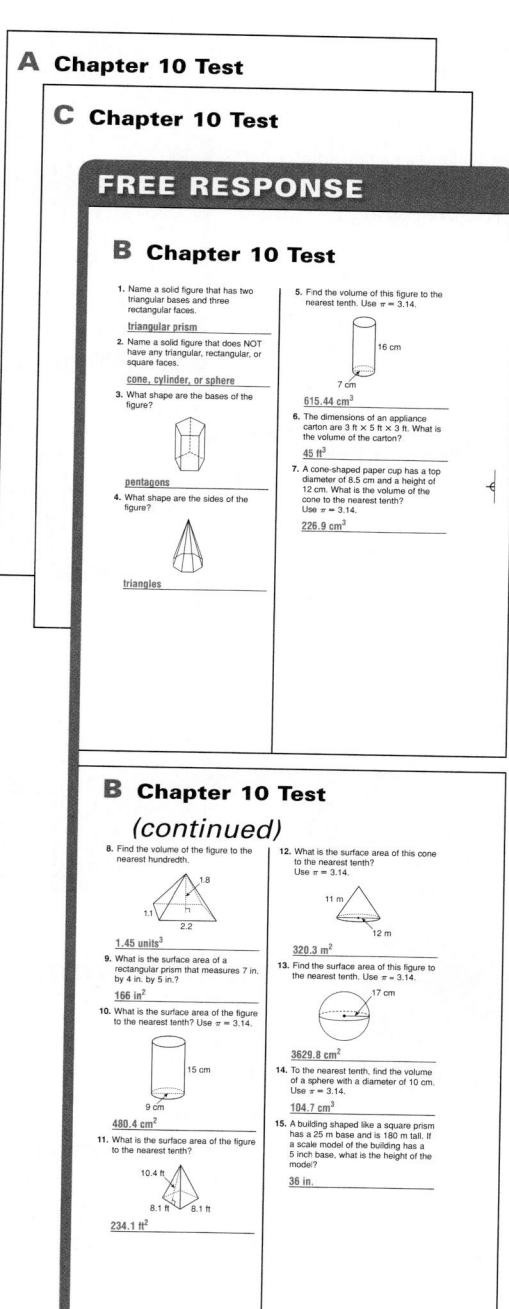

Modified tests and worksheets found in *IDEA Works!*

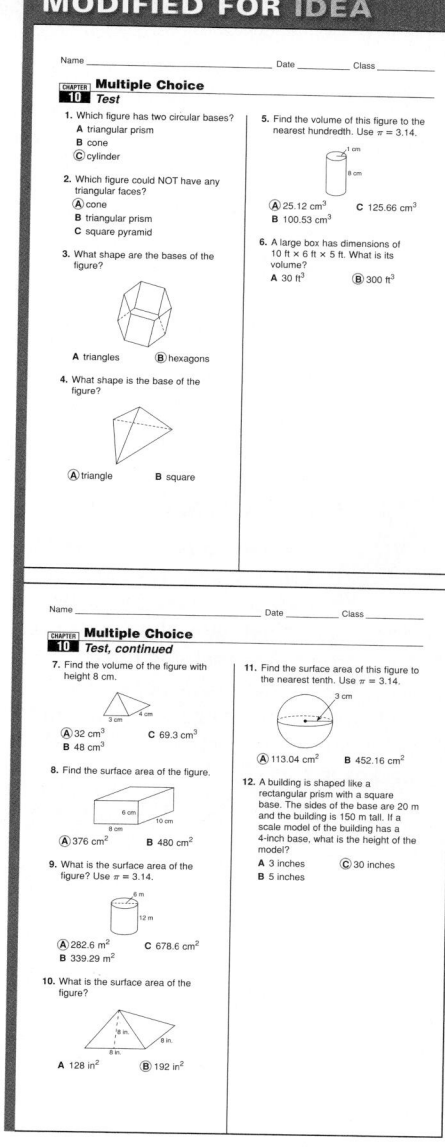

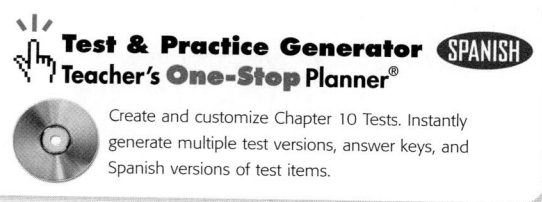

Test & Practice Generator SPANISH
Teacher's One-Stop Planner®

Create and customize Chapter 10 Tests. Instantly generate multiple test versions, answer keys, and Spanish versions of test items.

CHAPTER 10

Focus on Problem Solving

On page 495, students focus on prioritizing and sequencing information when solving real-world problems.

CONCEPT CONNECTION On page 517, students apply properties of three-dimensional figures to draw conclusions about boxing and shipping gifts for a fundraiser.

Math in *California*

Pershing Square, a park in Los Angeles, has been redesigned several times since its original dedication in 1866. The current plan features three-dimensional figures designed by architect Ricardo Legoretta. Students will learn about three-dimensional figures in this chapter.

CHAPTER 10

Three-Dimensional Geometry

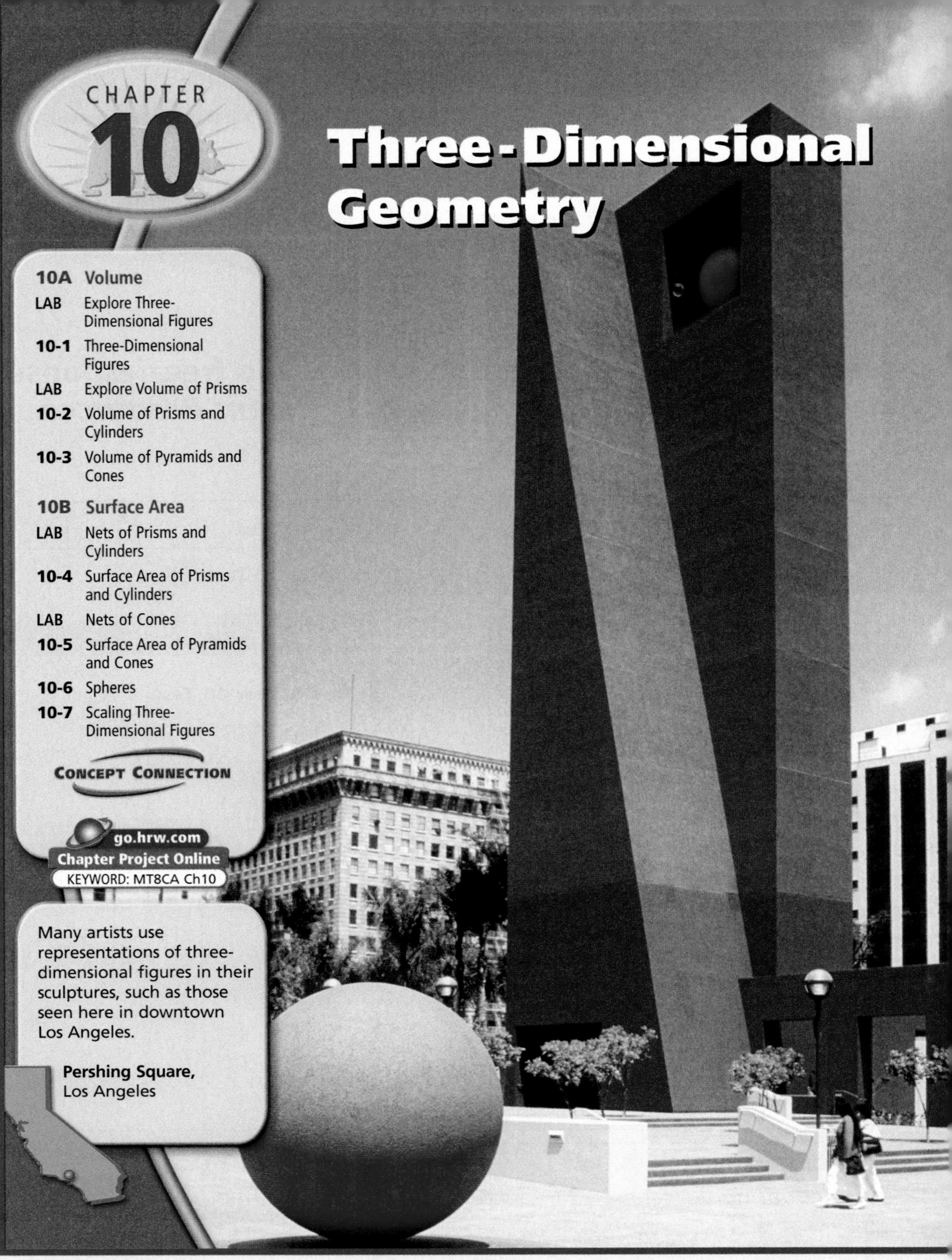

10A Volume
LAB   Explore Three-Dimensional Figures
10-1 Three-Dimensional Figures
LAB   Explore Volume of Prisms
10-2 Volume of Prisms and Cylinders
10-3 Volume of Pyramids and Cones

10B Surface Area
LAB   Nets of Prisms and Cylinders
10-4 Surface Area of Prisms and Cylinders
LAB   Nets of Cones
10-5 Surface Area of Pyramids and Cones
10-6 Spheres
10-7 Scaling Three-Dimensional Figures

CONCEPT CONNECTION

go.hrw.com
Chapter Project Online
KEYWORD: MT8CA Ch10

Many artists use representations of three-dimensional figures in their sculptures, such as those seen here in downtown Los Angeles.

Pershing Square,
Los Angeles

Problem Solving Project

Understand, Plan, Solve, and Look Back

Have students:

• Complete the Mystery Solids worksheet to become familiar with the characteristics of geometric solids.

• Play a game by taking turns showing parts of a three-dimensional object on the overhead and having classmates see how much of the object must be revealed before they can identify the object.

• Do research to discover information on laparoscopic surgery. Interview people who have had laparoscopic surgery or a surgeon who performs the surgery.

Life Science Connection

Project Resources
All project resources for teachers and students are provided online.

Materials:
• The Mystery Solids worksheet
• geometrical and common-item mystery solids
• overhead projector

go.hrw.com
Project Teacher Support
KEYWORD: MT8CA PSProject10

Vocabulary

Choose the best term from the list to complete each sentence.

1. A(n) __?__ is a number written as a ratio that represents a part of a whole.   **fraction**

2. A(n) __?__ is another way of writing a fraction.   **decimal**

3. To multiply 7 by the fraction $\frac{2}{3}$, multiply 7 by the __?__ of the fraction and then divide the result by the __?__ of the fraction.   **numerator; denominator**

decimal
denominator
fraction
numerator
perfect square
whole number

Complete these exercises to review skills you will need for this chapter.

Find the Square of a Number

Evaluate.

4. 16^2 **256**   5. 9^2 **81**   6. $(4.1)^2$ **16.81**   7. $(0.5)^2$ **0.25**

8. $\left(\frac{1}{4}\right)^2$ $\frac{1}{16}$ 9. $\left(\frac{2}{5}\right)^2$ $\frac{4}{25}$ 10. $\left(\frac{1}{2}\right)^2$ $\frac{1}{4}$ 11. $\left(\frac{2}{3}\right)^2$ $\frac{4}{9}$

Multiply Fractions

Multiply.

12. $\frac{1}{2} \times \frac{8}{9}$ $\frac{4}{9}$ 13. $\frac{1}{2} \times \frac{2}{3}$ $\frac{1}{3}$ 14. $\frac{1}{3} \times \frac{9}{11}$ $\frac{3}{11}$ 15. $\frac{1}{3} \times \frac{6}{7}$ $\frac{2}{7}$

16. $\frac{2}{5} \times \frac{5}{4}$ $\frac{1}{2}$ 17. $\frac{1}{5} \times \frac{4}{3}$ $\frac{4}{15}$ 18. $\frac{2}{3} \times \frac{6}{11}$ $\frac{4}{11}$ 19. $\frac{3}{4} \times \frac{5}{6}$ $\frac{5}{8}$

Decimal Operations

Multiply. Write each answer to the nearest tenth.

20. 3.14×2.5 **7.9**   21. 3.14×1.25 **3.9**   22. 3.14×3.5 **11.0**   23. 3.14×1.75 **5.5**

Multiply with Fractions and Decimals

Multiply. Write each answer to the nearest tenth.

24. 3.14×7 **22.0**   25. 3.14×10 **31.4**

26. 3.14×20 **62.8**   27. 3.14×15 **47.1**

28. $\frac{22}{7} \times 14$ **44.0**   29. $\frac{22}{7} \times 21$ **66.0**

30. $1\frac{1}{3} \times 15$ **20.0**   31. $1\frac{1}{3} \times 36$ **48.0**

Prerequisite Skills

Find the Square of a Number

Multiply Fractions

Decimal Operations

Multiply with Fractions and Decimals

Assessing Prior Knowledge
INTERVENTION

Diagnose and Prescribe

Use this page to determine whether intervention is necessary or whether enrichment is appropriate.

Resources

 Are You Ready? Intervention and Enrichment Worksheets

 Are You Ready? CD-ROM

Are You Ready? Online

my.hrw.com

ARE YOU READY?
Diagnose and Prescribe

	ARE YOU READY? Intervention, Chapter 10		
Prerequisite Skill	**Worksheets**	**CD-ROM**	**Online**
Find the Square of a Number	Skill 11	Activity 11	
Multiply Fractions	Skill 44	Activity 44	Diagnose and Prescribe Online
Decimal Operations	Skill 40	Activity 40	
Multiply with Fractions and Decimals	Skill 45	Activity 45	

NO INTERVENE

YES ENRICH

ARE YOU READY? Enrichment, Chapter 10
Worksheets
CD-ROM
Online

Organizer

Objective: Help students understand the new concepts they will learn in Chapter 10.

Academic Vocabulary Connections

Becoming familiar with the academic vocabulary on this student page will be helpful to students. Discussing some of the vocabulary terms in the chapter also may be helpful.
Possible answers given.

1. The word *edge* comes from the Latin word *acer,* meaning "sharp." How does the Latin root help you define an **edge** of a three-dimensional figure? The edge of a three-dimensional figure is where one of the sides of the figure comes to a sharp end.

2. The word *vertex* can mean "peak" or "highest point." What part of a cone or pyramid is the **vertex**? The vertex of a cone or pyramid is the highest point, or peak, of the figure.

3. The word *prism* comes from the Greek word *priein,* meaning "to saw." How might you describe a **prism** in terms of something sawn or cut off? A prism is a transparent solid object with flat faces and ends that have been "sawed" off.

CHAPTER 10 Unpacking the Standards

The information below "unpacks" the standards. The Academic Vocabulary is highlighted and defined to help you understand the language of the standards. Refer to the lessons listed after each standard for help with the math terms and phrases. The Chapter Concept shows how the standard is applied in this chapter.

California Standard	Academic Vocabulary	Chapter Concept
AF3.2 Plot the values from the volumes of three-dimensional shapes for various values of the edge lengths (e.g., cubes with varying edge lengths or a triangle prism with a **fixed** height and an equilateral triangle base of varying lengths). (Lab 10-2)	**e.g.** abbreviation that stands for the Latin phrase *exempli gratia,* which means "for example" **fixed** in this case, set or unchanging	You analyze the relationship between length and volume in three-dimensional figures.
MG2.3 Compute the length of the perimeter, the surface area of the faces, and the volume of a three-dimensional object built from rectangular solids. Understand that when the lengths of all **dimensions** are multiplied by a scale factor, the surface area is multiplied by the square of the scale factor and the volume is multiplied by the cube of the scale factor. (Lab 10-2; Lessons 10-4, 10-7)	**compute** determine by using mathematical operations such as addition and multiplication **dimensions** measurement in length, width, or thickness	You find the surface area and volume of similar three-dimensional figures.
MG2.4 Relate the changes in measurement with a change of scale to the units used (e.g., square inches, cubic feet) and to conversions between units (1 square foot = 144 square inches or [1 ft.^{2}] = [144 in.^{2}]; 1 cubic inch is **approximately** 16.38 cubic centimeters or [1 in.^{3}] = [16.38 cm^3]). (Lesson 10-2)	**relate** to show a connection between **approximately** estimated to be	You understand the measurements used in describing the area and volume of objects. ***Example:*** Area is measured in square units, such as square inches (in^2) and square meters (m^2). Volume is measured in cubic units, such as cubic inches (in^3) and cubic meters (m^3).
MG3.5 Construct two-dimensional patterns for three-dimensional models, such as cylinders, prisms, and cones. (Labs 10-4, 10-5)	**construct** to build or draw	You make nets for cylinders, prisms, and cones.

Standards MG2.1 and MG2.2 are also covered in this chapter. To see these standards unpacked, go to Chapter 9, p. 432.

Looking Back

Previously, students

- found the circumference and area of circles.
- learned how to find the area of basic two-dimensional geometric figures.
- used formulas to find the volume of rectangular prisms, triangular prisms, and cylinders.

In This Chapter

Students will study

- finding the surface area and volume of cylinders.
- making nets of prisms, cylinders, and cones to find their surface area.
- using scale factors to find surface area and volume of similar rectangular solids.

Looking Forward

Students can use these skills

- to find the surface area and volume of spheres.
- to memorize formulas for finding the surface area of prisms and cylinders.
- to determine how changes in dimensions affect attributes of common solid objects.

Reading and Writing Math

Writing Strategy: Draw Three-Dimensional Figures

When you encounter a three-dimensional figure such as a cylinder, cone, sphere, prism, or pyramid, it may help you to make a quick sketch so that you can visualize its shape.

Use these tips to help you draw quick sketches of three-dimensional figures.

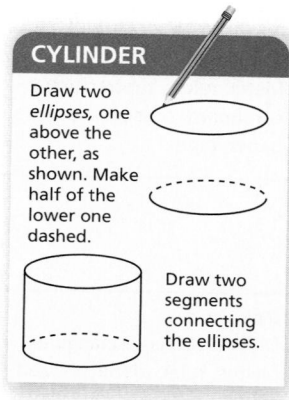

CYLINDER

Draw two *ellipses*, one above the other, as shown. Make half of the lower one dashed.

Draw two segments connecting the ellipses.

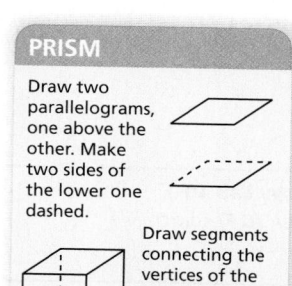

PRISM

Draw two parallelograms, one above the other. Make two sides of the lower one dashed.

Draw segments connecting the vertices of the parallelograms. Use a dashed segment for the hidden edge.

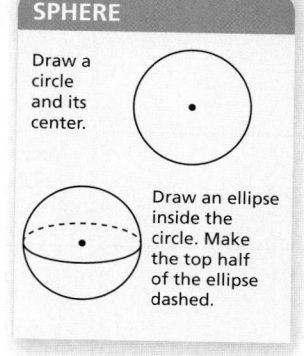

SPHERE

Draw a circle and its center.

Draw an ellipse inside the circle. Make the top half of the ellipse dashed.

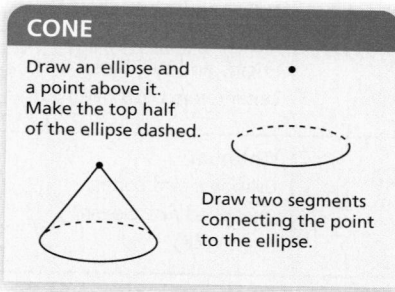

CONE

Draw an ellipse and a point above it. Make the top half of the ellipse dashed.

Draw two segments connecting the point to the ellipse.

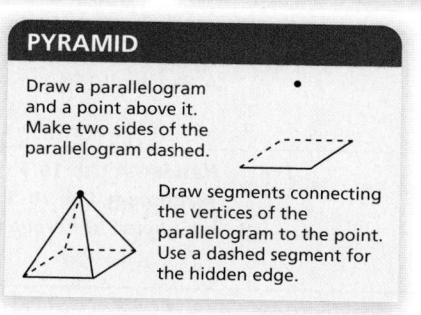

PYRAMID

Draw a parallelogram and a point above it. Make two sides of the parallelogram dashed.

Draw segments connecting the vertices of the parallelogram to the point. Use a dashed segment for the hidden edge.

Try This

1. Explain and show how to draw a *cube*, which is a prism with equal length, width, and height.

2. Draw a prism, starting with two hexagons. (*Hint:* Draw the hexagons as if you were viewing them at an angle.)

3. Draw a pyramid, starting with a triangle and a point above the triangle.

 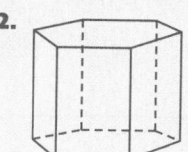

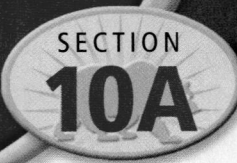

SECTION
10A

Volume

 **One-Minute Section Planner**

Lesson	Lab Resources	Materials
10-1 Hands-On Lab Explore Three-Dimensional Figures • Use models to explore properties of prisms and cylinders. 🐻 **Prep for MG2.1**		**Required** Metric rulers, protractors, cardboard, scissors, heavy paper, tape
Lesson 10-1 Three-Dimensional Figures • Identify various three-dimensional figures. 🐻 **Prep for MG2.1**	**Technology Lab 10-1** In *Chapter 10 Resource File*	
10-2 Hands-On Lab Explore Volume of Prisms • Use empty cartons to explore the volume of prisms. 🐻 **AF3.0, AF3.2, MG2.3**		**Required** Different-sized rectangular prisms, ruler, identical-sized cubes
Lesson 10-2 Volume of Prisms and Cylinders • Find the volume of prisms and cylinders. 🐻 **MG2.0, MG2.1, MG2.4**	**Hands-On Lab 10-2** In *Chapter 10 Resource File*	**Optional** Prisms and cylinders, centimeter cubes (MK)
Lesson 10-3 Volume of Pyramids and Cones • Find the volume of pyramids and cones. 🐻 **Ext. of MG2.1**	**Hands-On Lab 10-3** **Technology Lab 10-3** In *Chapter 10 Resource File*	**Optional** Cylinders and cones, uncooked rice, beans, rulers (MK)

MK = *Manipulatives Kit*

Notes

_____

_____

_____

_____

_____

_____

_____

_____

_____

_____

Math Background: Teaching the Standards

VOLUME 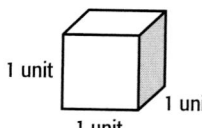 MG2.0, MG2.1, MG2.3

Lessons 10-2, 10-3

In the same way that the area of a plane figure is the number of nonoverlapping unit squares needed to cover the figure, the volume of a three-dimensional figure is the number of nonoverlapping unit cubes needed to fill the figure. As shown below, a unit cube is a cube whose length, width, and height are all one unit.

1 unit

A unit cube with a volume of 1 cubic unit

The volume of a unit cube is one cubic unit. Thus, a three-dimensional figure that can be filled by exactly 12 unit cubes has a volume of 12 cubic units. In the case of a rectangular prism, the number of unit cubes contained in the figure may be counted by multiplying the length times the width times the height, or, more generally, by multiplying the area of the base times the height.

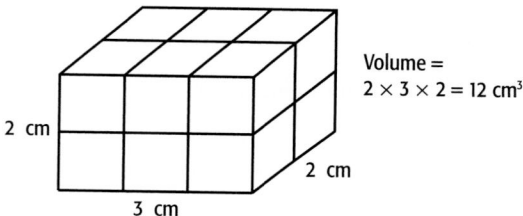

Volume = 2 × 3 × 2 = 12 cm³

2 cm

2 cm

3 cm

DEVELOPING VOLUME FORMULAS

MG2.0, MG2.1

Lessons 10-2, 10-3

The formula for the volume of a rectangular prism ($V = Bh$) is the starting point for developing the volume formulas for other three-dimensional figures. Another important ingredient in developing volume formulas is Cavalieri's Principle. This principle says that if two three-dimensional figures have the same height and the same cross-sectional area at every level, then they have the same volume.

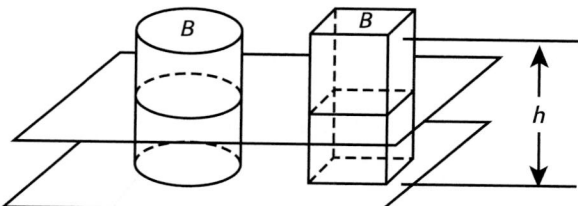

To find the volume of a cylinder with height h and base area B, construct a rectangular prism of height h so that each rectangular cross-section has area B. As shown in the figure, the prism and cylinder can be positioned so that the area of any cross-section of the cylinder created by a plane parallel to the base has the same area as the corresponding cross-section of the prism. By Cavalieri's Principle, the volume of the cylinder is equal to that of the prism. That is, $V = Bh$. For a cylinder with a circular base, this formula may be written as $V = \pi r^2 h$.

Students should recognize that a right cylinder with a circular base can be visualized as the three-dimensional figure that is traced when a solid circular disc is swept through space in a direction perpendicular to the base.

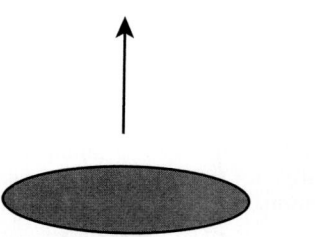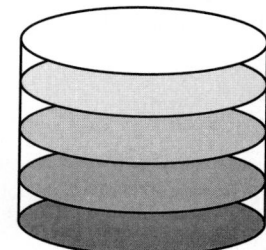

A *generalized cylinder* can be created by removing the restrictions that the base be a circle and that the base be swept through space in a direction perpendicular to the base.

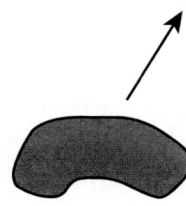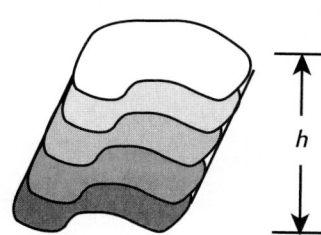

Cavalieri's Principle may be used to show that the volume of a generalized cylinder is still given by Bh, where B is the area of the two-dimensional region that forms the base and h is the perpendicular distance between the top and bottom bases of the cylinder.

A rigorous development of the formula for the volume of a pyramid or cone is more complex. However, the argument for both three-dimensional figures depends upon Cavalieri's Principle, and the result for both figures is the same: the volume of a pyramid or cone with base area B and height h is $\frac{1}{3}Bh$.

Objective: Use models to explore properties of prisms and cylinders.

Materials: Metric rulers, protractors, cardboard, scissors, heavy paper, tape

 Online Edition

 Countdown to Mastery Week 19

Teach
Discuss

Explain that a flat surface of a three-dimensional figure is called a *face*. Prisms have faces that are polygons. Prisms are named for the shape of their bases. Thus, a prism with triangular bases is called a *triangular prism*. The faces of a prism that are not bases are rectangles. Cylinders have two circular faces that are connected by a curved surface.

Close
Key Concept

Prisms and cylinders have two congruent parallel bases. The bases of prisms are polygons, and the bases of cylinders are circles.

Assessment

A prism has two congruent parallel bases that are trapezoids. Describe the shape and number of the other surfaces of the prism.

4 rectangles

Hands-On LAB 10-1

Explore Three-Dimensional Figures
Use with Lesson 10-1

go.hrw.com
Lab Resources Online
KEYWORD: MT8CA Lab10

A *prism* is a three-dimensional figure with two parallel and congruent polygons called the *bases*. The remaining edges join corresponding vertices of the bases so that the remaining surfaces are rectangles. You can use this definition to make models of prisms.

California Standards

Preparation for MG2.1 Use formulas routinely for finding the perimeter and area of basic two-dimensional figures and **the surface area and the volume of basic three-dimensional figures, including** rectangles, parallelograms, trapezoids, squares, triangles, circles, **prisms, and cylinders.**

Activity 1

❶ Use a ruler and protractor to draw two squares with side lengths of 3 centimeters on cardboard. Then cut out the squares.

❷ From heavy paper, cut out a rectangle that measures 12 centimeters by 6 centimeters. Fold the paper into fourths as shown.

❸ Fold the rectangle into an open-ended box, and tape together the 6-centimeter edges. Form a prism by taping the edges of the squares to the open ends of the box.

❹ Use a ruler and protractor to draw two equilateral triangles with side lengths of 4 centimeters on cardboard. Then cut out the triangles. (*Hint:* Each angle of an equilateral triangle measures 60°.)

❺ From heavy paper, cut out a rectangle that measures 12 centimeters by 6 centimeters. Fold the paper into thirds as shown.

❻ Tape together the 6-centimeter edges. Form a prism by taping the edges of the triangles to the open ends of the folded paper.

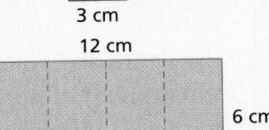
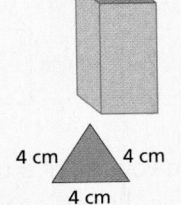
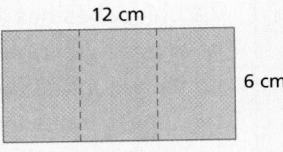
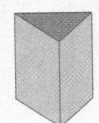

Think and Discuss

1. What shape are the bases of each prism that you modeled?
   square; triangular
2. What shape are the other surfaces of each prism?   rectangular

3. How is the second prism that you modeled different from the first prism? How are the prisms alike?

Activity 1
Answers to Think and Discuss

3. Possible answer: The bases of the prisms are different shapes. The second prism has one fewer rectangular surface than the first prism. Both prisms have two congruent, parallel bases. The remaining surfaces of both prisms are rectangles.

Try This

Tell whether each figure below is a prism. Explain your answer.

1.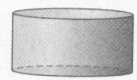

2.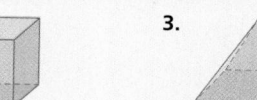

3.

A *cylinder* is a three-dimensional figure with two parallel congruent circular bases. The third surface of a cylinder consists of all parallel circles of the same radius whose centers lie on the line segment joining the centers of the bases. You can use this definition to model a cylinder.

Activity 2

❶ Use a compass to draw at least 10 circles with a radius of 3 centimeters each on cardboard. Then cut out the circles.

❷ Poke a hole through the center of each circle.

❸ Unbend a paper clip part way to form a right angle. Then push the paper clip through the center of each circle to model a cylinder. Use the paper clip to keep the stack of cardboard circles aligned.

Think and Discuss

1. Describe the bases of your cylinder.   They are circles.

2. How is your model of a cylinder different from your models of prisms? How are they the same?   Possible answer: The bases of the prisms are polygons, and the bases of the cylinder are circles. The prisms have rectangular faces. The cylinder does not. Both the prisms and cylinder are three-dimensional figures with two parallel and congruent bases.

Try This

Tell whether each figure below is a cylinder. Explain your answer.

1.    No; the figure does not have two parallel congruent circular bases.

2. 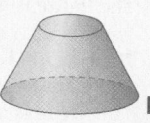   No; the bases of the figure are not congruent circles.

3.

Activity 1

Answers to *Try This*

1. No; possible answer: the bases of this figure are not polygons.

2. Yes; possible answer: the figure has two congruent parallel bases that are squares. The remaining edges of the figure join corresponding vertices of the bases so that the remaining faces are squares.

3. No; possible answer: this figure does not have two parallel bases.

Activity 2

Answers to *Try This*

3. Yes; possible answer: the figure has two parallel congruent circular bases. The third surface consists of all parallel congruent circles whose centers lie on the segment joining the centers of the bases.

Objective: Students identify various three-dimensional figures.

 Technology Lab
In *Chapter 10 Resource File*

 Online Edition
Tutorial Videos, Interactivities

 Countdown to Mastery Week 20

Power Presentations
with PowerPoint®

Warm Up

Identify each two-dimensional figure described.

1. four sides that are all congruent
   rhombus
2. six sides hexagon
3. four sides with parallel opposite sides parallelogram
4. four right angles and four congruent sides square

Also available on transparency

Math Humor

Teacher: What 3-D figure can cure strep throat?
Student: A penicillinder

California Standards

Preparation for MG2.1 Use formulas routinely for finding the perimeter and area of basic two-dimensional figures and **the surface area and volume of basic three-dimensional figures, including** rectangles, parallelograms, trapezoids, squares, triangles, circles, **prisms, and cylinders.**

Vocabulary
face
edge
polyhedron
vertex
base
prism
pyramid
cylinder
cone

Why learn this? You can name and describe three-dimensional shapes used in historical structures. (See Exercises 19–22.)

Three-dimensional figures have three dimensions: length, width, and height. A flat surface of a three-dimensional figure is a **face**. An **edge** is where two faces meet.

A **polyhedron** is a three-dimensional figure whose faces are all polygons. A **vertex** of a polyhedron is a point where three or more edges meet. The face that is used to name a polyhedron is called a **base**.

Prisms	Pyramids
• Two parallel congruent bases that are polygons • Remaining faces are parallelograms	• One base that is a polygon • Remaining faces are triangles

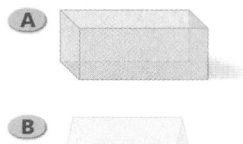

EXAMPLE 1 Naming Prisms and Pyramids

Describe the bases and faces of each figure. Then name the figure.

A
There are two rectangular bases.
There are four other rectangular faces.
The figure is a rectangular prism.

Helpful Hint

The bottom face of a prism is not always one of its bases. For example, the bottom face of the triangular prism in Example 1B is not one of its triangular bases.

B
There are two triangular bases.
There are three rectangular faces.
The figure is a triangular prism.

C
There is one hexagonal base.
There are six triangular faces.
The figure is a hexagonal pyramid.

1 Introduce
Alternate Opener

EXPLORATION

10-1 Three-Dimensional Figures

The figures below represent three-dimensional objects.

Prism   Pyramid   Cylinder   Cone

Write the name of the base (the shaded face) of each three-dimensional object shown above.

	Figure	Name of Base
1.	Prism	
2.	Pyramid	
3.	Cylinder	
4.	Cone	

Give a real-world example of each figure.

	Figure	Real-World Example
5.	Prism	
6.	Pyramid	
7.	Cylinder	
8.	Cone	

Think and Discuss

9. **Explain** what the third dimension of a three-dimensional figure is, given that the base is a two-dimensional figure.

Motivate

Review polygons by having students name types of polygons and give the number of sides for each. (See Skills Bank p. SB16.) To introduce three-dimensional figures, ask students to describe as many different kinds of three-dimensional figures as they can find in the classroom. For each three-dimensional figure, have students name the shapes of the sides and bases.

Explorations and answers are provided in *Alternate Openers: Explorations Transparencies.*

Other three-dimensional figures include *cylinders* and *cones*. These figures are not polyhedrons because they are not made of faces that are all polygons.

Cylinder	Cone
• Two parallel congruent bases that are circles • Bases connected by a curved surface	• One base that is a circle • Curved surface that comes to a point
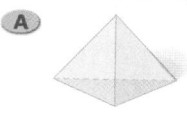 2 bases	Vertex  1 base

You can use properties to classify three-dimensional figures.

EXAMPLE 2 **Classifying Three-Dimensional Figures**

Classify each figure as a polyhedron or not a polyhedron. Then name the figure.

A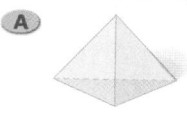
The faces are all polygons, so the figure is a polyhedron.
There is one triangular base.
The figure is a triangular pyramid.

B
The faces are not all polygons, so the figure is not a polyhedron.
There are two circular bases.
The figure is a cylinder.

C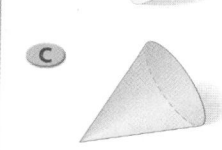
The faces are not all polygons, so the figure is not a polyhedron.
There is one circular base.
The figure is a cone.

Think and Discuss

1. **Explain** how to identify a prism or a pyramid.

2. **Compare and contrast** cylinders and prisms. How are they alike? How are they different?

3. **Compare and contrast** pyramids and cones. How are they alike? How are they different?

Example 1

Describe the bases and faces of each figure. Then name the figure.

A. 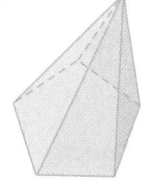 pentagonal pyramid

B.  C.

Example 2

Classify each figure as a polyhedron or not a polyhedron. Then name the figure.

A. 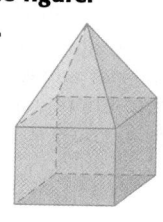 B.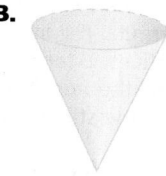

C. 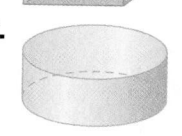 not a polyhedron, cylinder

Complete answers 1–2. See p. A10.

Also available on transparency

Possible answers to *Think and Discuss*

1. Prisms and pyramids are polyhedrons, so all of their faces are polygons. A prism has two parallel, congruent bases, and a pyramid has one base.

2. Both have two parallel, congruent bases. The bases of cylinders are circles, and the bases of prisms are polygons. The bases of cylinders are connected by a curved surface, and the bases of prisms are connected by polygonal faces.

3. Both have one base. The base of a pyramid is a polygon, and the base of a cone is a circle.

2 Teach

Guided Instruction

In this lesson, students learn to identify various three-dimensional figures. Prisms and pyramids are named according to the shapes of their bases (Teaching Transparency). However, cylinders and cones have basically only one shape and only one name. The cube and the tetrahedron are both examples of regular polyhedrons because all the faces of each figure are congruent.

 **Teaching Tip** **Reasoning** Point out that in a rectangular prism, any of the pairs of parallel faces can be considered to be bases, but in other types of prisms, the bases must be the pair of non-rectangular sides.

 Universal Access
Through Graphic Organizers

Have students make a web that can be used to classify solid figures. Use these words in the web: *solid figures, prisms, cones, polyhedrons, pyramids,* and *cylinders.*

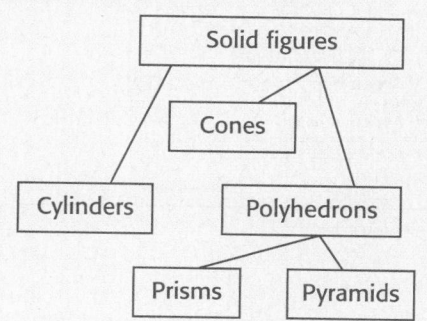

3 Close

Summarize

Have students write brief descriptions of each of the three-dimensional figures in this lesson.

Possible answers: A prism is a polyhedron with two parallel congruent faces and other faces that are parallelograms.
A pyramid is a polyhedron with a vertex and base at opposite ends and faces that are triangles.
A cylinder has two parallel congruent circular bases that are connected by a curved surface.
A cone has a circular base, a vertex, and a curved face.

Assignment Guide

If you finished Example **1** assign:
Proficient 1–3, 7–9, 13–18, 23–29
Advanced 7–9, 13–29

If you finished Example **2** assign:
Proficient 1–18, 23–29
Advanced 7–29

Homework Quick Check

Quickly check key concepts.
Exercises: 8, 10, 12, 14, 16

Math Background

The vertices, edges, and faces of the polyhedrons discussed in this lesson satisfy a relationship known as Euler's formula. If V stands for the number of vertices, E for the number of edges, and F for the number of faces, then Euler's formula states that $V - E + F = 2$.

10-1 Exercises

California Standards Practice
Preparation for MG2.1

go.hrw.com
Homework Help Online
KEYWORD: MT8CA 10-1
Parent Resources Online
KEYWORD: MT8CA Parent

GUIDED PRACTICE

See Example 1 Describe the bases and faces of each figure. Then name the figure.

1.  pentagon; triangles; pentagonal pyramid

2. octagons; rectangles; octagonal prism

3. triangles; rectangles; triangular prism

See Example 2 Classify each figure as a polyhedron or not a polyhedron. Then name the figure.

4. not a polyhedron; cone

5. polyhedron; hexagonal pyramid

6. not a polyhedron; cylinder

INDEPENDENT PRACTICE

See Example 1 Describe the bases and faces of each figure. Then name the figure.

7. triangle; triangles; triangular pyramid

8. rectangles; rectangles; rectangular prism

9. hexagon; triangles; hexagonal pyramid

See Example 2 Classify each figure as a polyhedron or not a polyhedron. Then name the figure.

10. polyhedron; octagonal prism

11. not a polyhedron; cylinder

12. polyhedron; triangular pyramid

PRACTICE AND PROBLEM SOLVING

 **Extra Practice**
See page EP20.

Identify the three-dimensional figure described.

13. two parallel, congruent square bases and four other polygonal faces   square prism

14. two parallel, congruent circular bases and one curved surface   cylinder

15. one triangular base and three other triangular faces   triangular pyramid

16. one circular base and one curved surface   cone

Name two examples of the three-dimensional figure described.

17. two parallel, congruent bases   Possible answer: cylinder, rectangular prism

18. one base   Possible answer: cone, rectangular pyramid

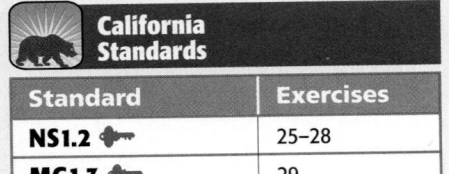

REVIEW FOR MASTERY 10-1

Review for Mastery
10-1 Three-Dimensional Figures

A **polyhedron** is a three-dimensional figure whose faces are polygons. There are two types of polyhedrons.

Prisms   Pyramids

A **prism** has 2 bases that are congruent and parallel polygons. The other faces are parallelograms or rectangles.

A **pyramid** has one base that is a polygon. Its faces are triangles that meet at one vertex.

Prisms and pyramids are named by their bases.

1. Look at the figure at the right.
   Its base is a ____square____.
   Its faces are ____triangles____.
   It is called a square pyramid.

2. Look at the figure at the right.
   It has 2 congruent and parallel bases that are ____pentagons____.
   Its faces are ____rectangles____.
   It is called a pentagonal prism.

If a three-dimensional figure has a face that is curved, it is not a polyhedron.

not a polyhedron

Is each figure a polyhedron?

3. yes   4. no   5. yes

PRACTICE 10-1

Practice B
10-1 Three-Dimensional Figures

Describe the base or bases of each figure. Then name the figure.

1. square, square pyramid

2. triangle, triangular pyramid

3. pentagon, pentagonal prism

4. rectangle, rectangular prism

5. hexagon, hexagonal pyramid

6. octagon, octagonal prism

Classify each figure as a polyhedron or not a polyhedron. Then name the figure.

7. polyhedron; hexagonal prism

8. not a polyhedron; cylinder

9. polyhedron; rectangular pyramid

10. polyhedron; triangular prism

11. not a polyhedron; cone

12. polyhedron; pentagonal pyramid

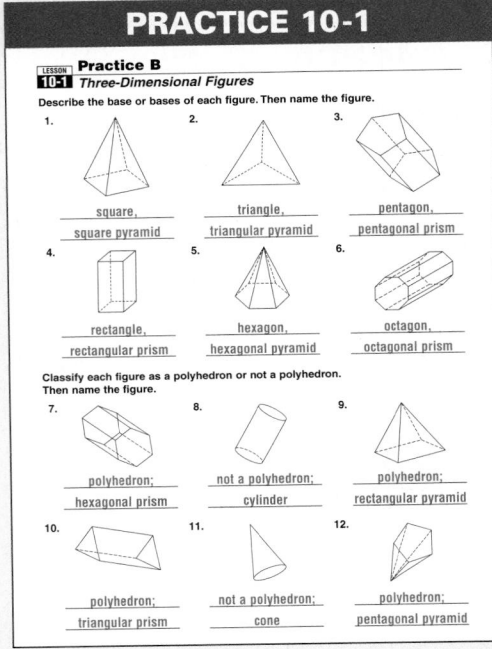

19. The structures in the photo at right are tombs of ancient Egyptian kings. No one knows exactly when the tombs were built, but some archaeologists think the first one might have been built around 2780 B.C.E. Name the shape of the ancient Egyptian structures. **rectangular pyramid**

20. The Parthenon was built around 440 B.C.E. by the ancient Greeks. Its purpose was to house a statue of Athena, the Greek goddess of wisdom. Describe the three-dimensional shapes you see in the structure.
Possible answer: cylinders, rectangular prism

21. The Leaning Tower of Pisa began to lean as it was being built. To keep the tower from falling over, the upper sections (floors) were built slightly off center so that the tower would curve away from the way it was leaning. What shape is each section of the tower? **cylinder**

22. ⭐ **Challenge** The stainless steel structure at right, called the Unisphere, became the symbol of the New York World's Fair of 1964–1965. A sphere is a three-dimensional figure with a surface made up of all the points that are the same distance from a given point. Explain why the structure is not a sphere.
Possible answer: The Unisphere is not a true sphere because it has gaps in its surface.

2600 B.C.E.
Ancient Egyptian structures at Giza

440 B.C.E.
Parthenon

1173
Leaning Tower of Pisa

1964
Unisphere

go.hrw.com
Web Extra!
KEYWORD: MT8CA Structures

SPIRAL STANDARDS REVIEW 🐾 NS1.2, 🐾 MG1.3

23. Multiple Choice Which figure has six rectangular faces?

Ⓐ Rectangular prism   Ⓒ Triangular pyramid

Ⓑ Triangular prism   Ⓓ Rectangular pyramid

24. Multiple Choice Which figure does NOT have two congruent bases?

Ⓐ Cube   Ⓑ Pyramid   Ⓒ Prism   Ⓓ Cylinder

Add. Write each answer in simplest form. (Lesson 2-3)

25. $\frac{2}{5} + \frac{3}{8}$ $\frac{31}{40}$

26. $\frac{1}{16} + \frac{4}{9}$ $\frac{73}{144}$

27. $\frac{7}{9} + \frac{11}{12}$ $1\frac{25}{36}$

28. $\frac{1}{10} + \frac{1}{16}$ $\frac{13}{80}$

29. A store sells two sizes of detergent: 300 ounces for $21.63 and 100 ounces for $6.99. Which size detergent has the lowest price per ounce? (Lesson 5-2)
100 oz for $6.99

CHALLENGE 10-1

LESSON 10-1 Challenge
Platonic Solids

A three-dimensional figure in which all the faces are polygons is called a *polyhedron*. A polyhedron whose faces are all congruent regular polygons is called a *regular polyhedron*. Regular polyhedrons are called *Platonic solids*.

Below are patterns for four Platonic solids. Copy each pattern. You may enlarge the pattern if you like. Then cut out the pattern and fold it to build a model of the solid. Use your models to answer the questions.

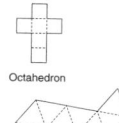
Hexahedron

Tetrahedron

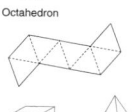
Octahedron

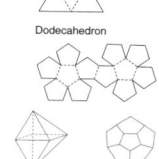
Dodecahedron

1. How many faces does a hexahedron have? What is another name for a hexahedron?
6 faces; square prism or cube

2. How many faces does a tetrahedron have? What is another name for a tetrahedron?
4 faces; triangular pyramid

3. How many faces does an octahedron have?
8 faces

4. How many faces does a dodecahedron have?
12 faces

PROBLEM SOLVING 10-1

LESSON 10-1 Problem Solving
Three-Dimensional Figures

Write the correct answer.

1. The picture above shows the top of the Chrysler Building in New York City. It was completed in 1930. Does the top of the tower most resemble a prism or a pyramid? Explain.
pyramid; The top of the tower is a vertex, and the sides are triangular.

2. The picture above shows the rooftop of Himeji Castle, completed in 1614 in Donjon, Himeji City, Japan. Do the rooftops resemble pyramids or prisms? Explain.
a prism; It has triangular bases and parallelograms form the other faces.

3. An architect designed a structure for the top of a building. The structure has a vertex, one circular base, and a curved surface. What three-dimensional figure is it?
a cone

4. On a farm, grain is stored in a silo. This is a very tall structure with a circular base and top and a curved surface. What three-dimensional figure does it resemble?
a cylinder

Choose the letter of the correct answer.

5. James put two blocks together to build the figure shown. Identify the two figures he used.

A two pyramids
Ⓑ a pyramid and a prism
C a pyramid and a cone
D two prisms

6. Jaime constructs a figure that has one rectangular base and four triangular faces. What is the figure?

F a cone
G a triangular pyramid
Ⓗ a rectangular pyramid
J a rectangular prism

7. The shape of a log is most like which figure?
Ⓐ cylinder   C prism
B pyramid   D cone

Interdisciplinary LINK

History

Exercises 19–22 involve applying students' knowledge of geometric shapes to their understanding of the architecture of historical structures.

Teaching Tip **Multiple Choice** In **Exercise 23**, remind students that a pyramid has triangular faces and only one possible rectangular face, its base. Therefore, students can quickly eliminate **C** and **D**. Drawing a sketch may be helpful.

Journal

Have students look in magazines or on the Internet to find buildings that are constructed from the figures shown in this lesson and describe them.

Power Presentations
with PowerPoint®

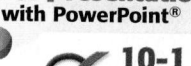
10-1 Lesson Quiz

Describe the bases and faces of each figure. Then name the figure.

1.
square pyramid

2.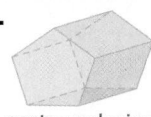
pentagonal prism

Classify each figure as a polyhedron or not a polyhedron. Then name the figure.

3.
polyhedron, rectangular prism

4.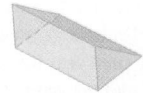
polyhedron, triangular prism

Complete answers 1–2. See p. A10.

Also available on transparency

Organizer

Use with Lesson 10-2

Objective: Use empty cartons to explore the volume of prisms.

Materials: Different-sized rectangular prisms, ruler, identical-sized cubes

 Online Edition

 Countdown to Mastery Week 20

Teach

Discuss

Discuss with students how to use a ruler to precisely measure the dimensions of each figure. Explain that there is more than one way to find the volume of a three-dimensional figure.

Close

Key Concept

You can find the volume of a rectangular prism by counting the number of cubes that it takes to fill the prism.

Assessment

1. How could you find the volume of an irregular solid?

   Possible answer: Fill the solid with water, then measure the volume of water used with a measuring cup.

Activity 1

Possible answers to *Think and Discuss*

1. The volume of each rectangular prism is the product of the area of the base and the height.

2. You can find the volume of any rectangular prism by multiplying the area of the base times the height of the figure.

 **Explore Volume of Prisms**

Use with Lesson 10-2

You can use models to explore the volume of rectangular prisms.

Activity 1

Use five different-sized rectangular prisms, such as empty cartons.   **Check students' work.**

   a. Cover the bottom of each prism with cubes to find the area of the prism's base. Record the information in a table.

   b. Fill the prism with cubes. Find the height. Then count the cubes to find the prism's volume. Record the information in a table.

Object	
Area of Base	
Height	
Volume	

Think and Discuss

1. What do you notice about the relationship between the area of the base, the height, and the volume of the rectangular prisms?

2. Make a conjecture about how to find the volume of any rectangular prism.

Activity 2

Consider several prisms with square bases of various side lengths and a fixed height of 5 units.

   a. Find the area of each square base. Record the information in a table.

   b. Use your conjecture from Activity 1 to find the volume of each prism. Record your answers in a table.

   c. Make a graph by plotting the volume of each prism as a function of the side length of the base.

Height	Side Length	Area of Base	Volume
5	1	1 unit^2	5 units^3
5	2	4 units^2	20 units^3
5	3	9 units^2	45 units^3
5	4	16 units^2	80 units^3
5	5	25 units^2	125 units^3

Think and Discuss

1. Think about the functions you studied in Chapter 7. Which type of function best matches the graph? **quadratic**

Try This

1. Consider cubes with edge lengths of 1 unit, 2 units, 3 units, 4 units, and 5 units. Make a graph by plotting the volume of each cube as a function of the edge length. Which type of function best matches the graph? **cubic**

Activity 2

Answers

c.

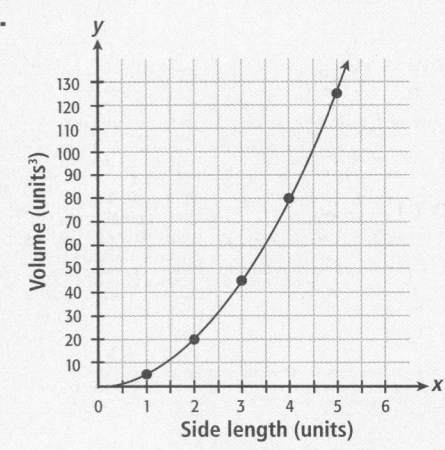

Answers to *Try This*

1.

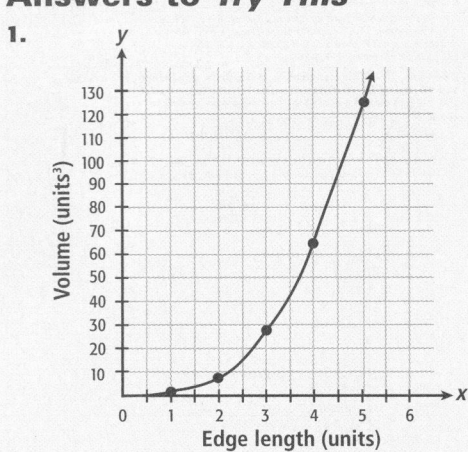

Volume of Prisms and Cylinders

California Standards

MG2.1 Use formulas routinely for finding the perimeter and area of basic two-dimensional figures and the surface area and **volume of basic three-dimensional figures, including** rectangles, parallelograms, trapezoids, squares, triangles, circles, **prisms, and cylinders.**
Also covered: **MG2.4**

Vocabulary
volume

Why learn this? You can use a formula to find the approximate volume of a drum. (See Example 3.)

In Lesson 9-1, you saw that the *area* of a two-dimensional figure is the number of unit squares needed to cover the figure. Similarly, any three-dimensional figure can be filled completely with congruent cubes and parts of cubes. The **volume** of a three-dimensional figure is the number of cubes it can hold. Each cube represents a unit of measure called a cubic unit.

The circumference of this Taiko drum is about half that of the largest drum ever made.

Triangular prism 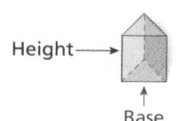   **Rectangular prism** 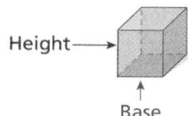   **Cylinder**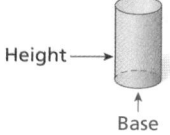

VOLUME OF PRISMS AND CYLINDERS		
Words	**Formula**	**Numbers**
Prism: The volume V of a prism is the area of the base B times the height h.	$V = Bh$	$B = 5(2)$ $= 10$ units^2 $V = (10)(3)$ $= 30$ units^3
Cylinder: The volume of a cylinder is the area of the base B times the height h.	$V = Bh$ $= (\pi r^2)h$	$B = \pi(2^2)$ $= 4\pi$ units^2 $V = (4\pi)(6) = 24\pi$ ≈ 75.4 units^3

EXAMPLE **Finding the Volume of Prisms and Cylinders**

Find the volume of the figure to the nearest tenth.

A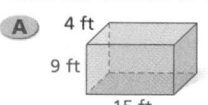

$B = 15 \cdot 4 = 60$ ft^2 *The base is a rectangle.*
$V = Bh$ *Volume of a prism*
$\quad = 60 \cdot 9$ *Substitute for B and h.*
$\quad = 540$ ft^3 *Multiply.*

Organizer 10-2

Objective: Students find the volume of prisms and cylinders.

 Hands-On Lab
In *Chapter 10 Resource File*

 Online Edition
Tutorial Videos, Interactivities

 Countdown to Mastery Week 20

Power Presentations
with PowerPoint®

Warm Up

Find the area of each figure described. Use 3.14 for π.

1. a triangle with a base of 6 feet and a height of 3 feet   9 ft^2

2. a circle with radius 5 in.   78.5 in^2

Also available on transparency

Math Humor

What happens to mathematicians who commit a crime? They go to prism!

---

1 Introduce

Alternate Opener

EXPLORATION

10-2 **Volume of Prisms and Cylinders**

A box of sugar cubes contains 126 cubes. The box below is called a *rectangular prism* because its base is a rectangle.

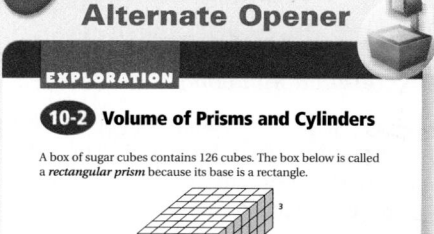

1. Sketch two different models that show how the same number of cubes (126) might be stacked in boxes with different dimensions. Label the dimensions of each box.

2. Use the formula *volume = length · width · height* to calculate the volume of each box you sketched in number 1.

Think and Discuss

3. **Explain** how you can determine the volume of a box if you know the dimensions.

4. **Explain** why the formula *volume = length · width · height* is equivalent to the formula *volume = area of base · height* when working with rectangular prisms.

Motivate

Show students prisms and cylinders of different shapes and sizes. Include prisms other than rectangular prisms. Point out that all of the solids you show have at least two congruent surfaces, which are called *bases*. Explain that to find the volume of one of these solids, you would multiply the area of the base by the height.

Explorations and answers are provided in *Alternate Openers: Explorations Transparencies.*

 **California Standards**

Measurement and Geometry 2.1
Also covered:
Measurement and Geometry
2.0 Students compute the perimeter, area, and **volume of common geometric objects and use the results to find measures of less common objects.** They know how perimeter, area, and volume are affected by changes of scale.

2.4 Relate the changes in measurement with a change of scale to the units used (e.g., square inches, cubic feet) and to conversions between units (1 square foot = 144 square inches or [1 ft.^{2}] = [144 in.^{2}]; 1 cubic inch is approximately 16.38 cubic centimeters or [1 in.^{3}] = [16.38 cm^3]).

Example 1

Find the volume of each figure to the nearest tenth. Use 3.14 for π.

A.

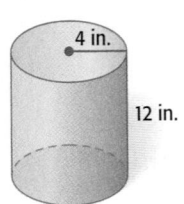

4 ft
4 ft
12 ft

192 ft³

B.

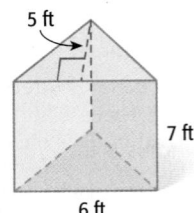

4 in.
12 in.

$192\pi \approx 602.9$ in³

C.

5 ft
7 ft
6 ft

105 ft³

Example 2

A. A juice box measures 3 in. by 2 in. by 4 in. Explain whether tripling only the length, width, or height of the box would triple the amount of juice the box holds. The original box has a volume of 24 in³. You could triple the volume to 72 in³ by tripling any one of the dimensions. So tripling only the length, width, or height would triple the amount of juice the box holds.

Find the volume of each figure to the nearest tenth. Use 3.14 for π.

B

15 m   6 m

$B = \pi(6^2) = 36\pi$ m²	*The base is a circle.*
$V = Bh$	*Volume of a cylinder*
$= 36\pi \cdot 15$	*Substitute for B and h.*
$= 540\pi \approx 1695.6$ m³	*Multiply.*

C

4 ft
7 ft
11 ft

$B = \frac{1}{2} \cdot 4 \cdot 7 = 14$ ft²	*The base is a triangle.*
$V = Bh$	*Volume of a prism*
$= 14 \cdot 11$	*Substitute for B and h.*
$= 154$ ft³	*Multiply.*

Reading Math

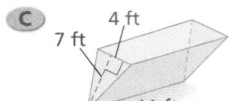

Any unit of measurement with an exponent of 3 is a cubic unit. For example, m³ means "cubic meter" and ft³ means "cubic feet."

The formula for volume of a rectangular prism can be written as $V = \ell wh$, where ℓ is the length, w is the width, and h is the height.

EXAMPLE 2 **Exploring the Effects of Changing Dimensions**

 **Reasoning**

A A cereal box measures 6 in. by 2 in. by 9 in. Explain whether doubling only the length, width, or height of the box would double the amount of cereal the box holds.

Original Dimensions	Double Only the Length	Double Only the Width	Double Only the Height
$V = \ell wh$	$V = (2\ell)wh$	$V = \ell(2w)h$	$V = \ell w(2h)$
$= 6 \cdot 2 \cdot 9$	$= 12 \cdot 2 \cdot 9$	$= 6 \cdot 4 \cdot 9$	$= 6 \cdot 2 \cdot 18$
$= 108$ in³	$= 216$ in³	$= 216$ in³	$= 216$ in³

The original box has a volume of 108 in³. You could double the volume to 216 in³ by doubling any one of the dimensions. So doubling only the length, width, or height would double the amount of cereal the box holds.

B A can of corn has a radius of 2.5 in. and a height of 4 in. Explain whether doubling only the height of the can would have the same effect on the volume as doubling the radius.

Original Dimensions	Double Only the Height	Double Only the Radius
$V = \pi r^2 h$	$V = \pi r^2(2h)$	$V = \pi(2r)^2 h$
$= 2.5^2\pi \cdot 4$	$= 2.5^2\pi \cdot 8$	$= 5^2\pi \cdot 4$
$= 25\pi$ in³	$= 50\pi$ in³	$= 100\pi$ in³

By doubling only the height, you would double the volume. By doubling only the radius, you would increase the volume four times the original.

---

2 Teach

Guided Instruction

In this lesson, students learn to find the volume of prisms and cylinders. Point out that the congruent bases of a prism are polygons (such as rectangles and triangles) and that the bases of a cylinder are circles (Teaching Transparency). Review the area formulas for these figures. Explain that the volume of any prism or cylinder is found by multiplying the area of its base by its height. Explain that because these figures are three-dimensional, volume is measured in cubic units.

 Universal Access

Through Modeling

Have students build a variety of prisms using centimeter cubes. Ask students to count the cubes to find the height, area of the base, and volume of each prism and to record the data in a table as shown.

Area of base	Height	Volume

Ask students to find a relationship between the area of the base, the height, and the volume. Possible answer: The volume is the product of the area of the base and the height, or $V = Bh$.

EXAMPLE 3 *Music Application*

The Asano Taiko Company of Japan built the world's largest drum in 2000. The drum's diameter is 4.8 meters, and its height is 4.95 meters. Estimate the volume of the drum.

$d = 4.8 \approx 5$, $h = 4.95 \approx 5$ *Use compatible numbers.*

$r = \dfrac{d}{2} = \dfrac{5}{2} = 2.5$

$V = (\pi r^2)h$ *Volume of a cylinder*

     $= (3.14)(2.5)^2 \cdot 5$ *Use 3.14 for π.*

     $= (3.14)(6.25)(5)$

     $= 19.625 \cdot 5$

     $= 98.125 \approx 98$

The volume of the drum is approximately 98 m^3.

To find the volume of a composite three-dimensional figure, find the volume of each part and add the volumes together.

EXAMPLE 4 **Reasoning**   **Finding the Volume of Composite Figures**

Find the volume of the figure.

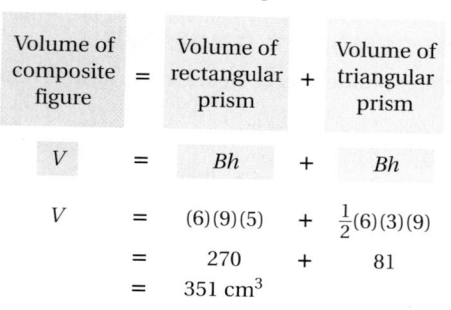

Volume of composite figure	=	Volume of rectangular prism	+	Volume of triangular prism
V	=	Bh	+	Bh
V	=	$(6)(9)(5)$	+	$\frac{1}{2}(6)(3)(9)$
	=	270	+	81
	=	351 cm^3		

The volume of the figure is 351 cm^3.

Think and Discuss

1. **Use models** to show that two rectangular prisms can have different heights but the same volume.

2. **Apply** your results from Example 2 to make a conjecture about changing dimensions in a triangular prism.

3. **Use a model** to describe what happens to the volume of a cylinder when the diameter of the base is tripled.

---

3 Close

Summarize

Review the definitions of *prism* and *cylinder*. Review the formula for finding the volume of each. Discuss the differences between area and volume. You may want to show some examples of two-dimensional and three-dimensional figures and ask students which measure applies to each one. As a challenge, you may want them to estimate the value of each measure.

Possible answer: Area applies to two-dimensional figures and is measured in square units. Volume applies to three-dimensional figures and is measured in cubic units.

Power Presentations
with PowerPoint®

Additional Examples

Example 2

B. A juice can has a radius of 2 in. and a height of 5 in. Explain whether tripling only the height of the can would have the same effect on the volume as tripling the radius. Tripling only the height triples the volume; tripling only the radius increases the volume to 9 times the original volume.

Example 3

A drum company advertises a snare drum that is 4 inches high and 12 inches in diameter. Estimate the volume of the drum. 452 in^3

Example 4

Find the volume of the barn.

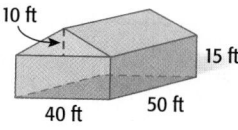

40,000 ft^3

Also available on transparency

Possible answers to Think and Discuss

1. A prism with a 2 × 3 unit base and a height of 2 units has the same volume (12 units^3) as a prism with a 6 × 2 unit base and a height of 1 unit.

2. If you double one dimension of a triangular prism, the prism's volume doubles. If you double two dimensions, the volume becomes 4 times the original volume. If you double three dimensions, the volume becomes 8 times the original volume.

3. The volume will increase by a factor of 3^2, or 9.

10-2 Exercises

California Standards Practice
NS1.1, MG2.1, MG2.4

go.hrw.com
Homework Help Online
KEYWORD: MT8CA 10-2
Parent Resources Online
KEYWORD: MT8CA Parent

Assignment Guide

If you finished Example 1 assign:
Proficient 1–3, 7–9, 21–25
Advanced 7–9, 15–18, 21–25

If you finished Example 2 assign:
Proficient 1–4, 7–10, 20–25
Advanced 7–10, 15–18, 20–25

If you finished Example 3 assign:
Proficient 1–5, 7–11, 13–14, 20–25
Advanced 7–11, 14–18, 20–25

If you finished Example 4 assign:
Proficient 1–15, 20–25
Advanced 7–25

Homework Quick Check

Quickly check key concepts.
Exercises: 8, 10, 12, 14

Answers

13b. Possible answer: If you double any dimension, you will double the volume of the box. So 20.4 in. by 4.2 in. by 19.9 in. is one example.

Math Background

The volume formula, $V = Bh$, applies to *right* cylinders and prisms, as studied in the lesson, and also to *oblique* cylinders and prisms, in which the axis is not perpendicular to the base.

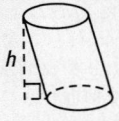
Oblique cylinder

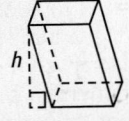
Oblique prism

California Standards

Standard	Exercises
NS1.1	15
MG2.1	1–21, 25
MG2.4	18
MG3.2	22–24

GUIDED PRACTICE

See Example 1 Find the volume of each figure to the nearest tenth. Use 3.14 for π.

1. 463.1 cm³
6.3 cm, 21 cm, 7 cm

2. 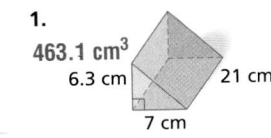 3 in., 4 in., 8 in. 96.0 in³

3. 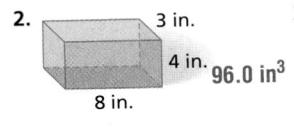 ←16 m→, 5 m 1256.0 m³

See Example 2 **4.** A can of juice has a radius 3 in. and a height 6 in. Explain whether tripling only the radius would triple the volume of the can.

See Example 3 **5.** Grain is stored in cylindrical structures called *silos*. Estimate the volume of a silo with diameter 11.1 feet and height 20 feet. ≈ 1500 ft³

25 ft, 20 ft, 10 ft, 18 ft, 15 ft

See Example 4 **6.** Find the volume of the barn at right. 4725 ft³

4. No; the volume of the can is 54π in³. Tripling the radius gives a volume of 486π in³, which is 9 times the original.

INDEPENDENT PRACTICE

See Example 1 Find the volume of each figure to the nearest tenth. Use 3.14 for π.

7. 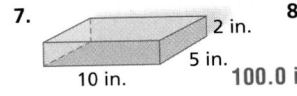 2 in., 5 in., 10 in. 100.0 in³

8. 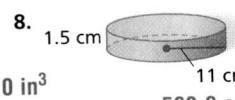 1.5 cm, 11 cm 569.9 cm³

9. 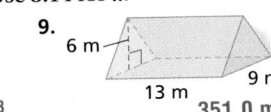 6 m, 13 m, 9 m 351.0 m³

See Example 2 **10.** A jewelry box measures 7 in. by 5 in. by 8 in. Explain whether increasing only the height 4 times, from 8 in. to 32 in., would increase the volume 4 times.

See Example 3 **11.** A toy box is 5.1 cm by 3.2 cm by 4.2 cm. Estimate the volume of the toy box.

See Example 4 **12.** Find the volume of the treehouse at right. 168 ft³

2 ft, 4 ft, 6 ft, 6 ft

10. Yes; the volume of the box is 280 in³. Increasing the height by 4 times gives a volume of 1120 in³, which is 4 times the original.

11. ≈ 60 cm³

PRACTICE AND PROBLEM SOLVING

Extra Practice
See page EP20.

13. While Karim was at camp, his father sent him a care package. The box measured 10.2 in. by 19.9 in. by 4.2 in.

a. Estimate the volume of the box. 800 in³

b. What might be the measurements of a box with twice its volume?

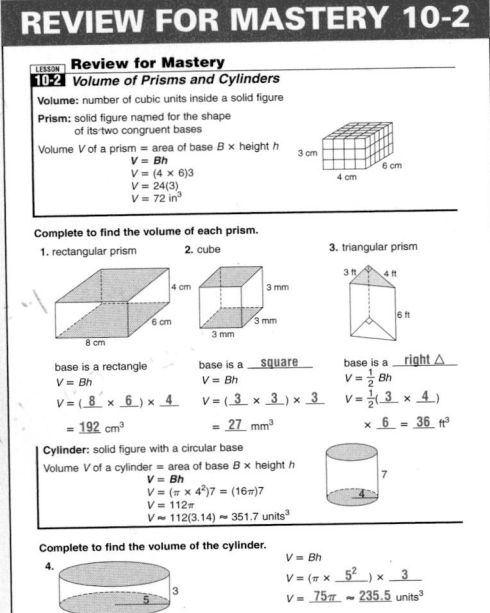
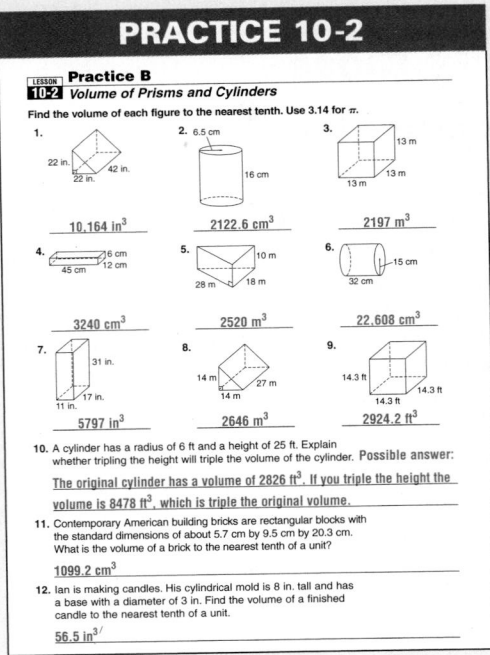

Life Science

Through the 52 large windows of the Giant Ocean Tank, visitors can see 3000 corals and sponges as well as large sharks, sea turtles, barracudas, moray eels, and hundreds of tropical fishes.

14. Social Studies The tablet held by the Statue of Liberty is approximately a rectangular prism with volume 1,107,096 in³. Estimate the thickness of the tablet. **about 20.5 in.**

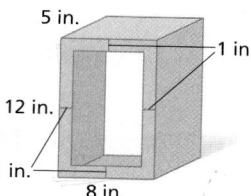

15. Life Science The cylindrical Giant Ocean Tank at the New England Aquarium in Boston has a volume of 200,000 gallons.

a. One gallon of water equals 231 cubic inches. How many cubic inches of water are in the Giant Ocean Tank? Write your answer in scientific notation. **4.62×10^7 in³**

b. Use your answer from part **a** as the volume. The tank is 24 ft deep. Find the radius in feet of the Giant Ocean Tank. **about 18.8 ft**

16. Reasoning As many as 60,000 bees can live in 3 cubic feet of space. There are about 360,000 bees in a rectangular observation beehive that is 2 ft long by 3 ft high. What is the smallest possible width of the observation hive? **3 ft**

17. What's the Error? A student read this statement in a book: "The volume of a triangular prism with height 15 in. and base area 20 in. is 300 in³." Correct the error in the statement.

18. Write About It Explain why 1 cubic yard is the same as 27 cubic feet.

19. Challenge A 5-inch section of a hollow brick measures 12 inches tall and 8 inches wide on the outside. The brick is 1 inch thick. Find the volume of the brick, not the hollow interior. **180 in³**

5 in. 1 in. 12 in. 1 in. 8 in.

SPIRAL STANDARDS REVIEW

MG2.1, MG3.2

20. Multiple Choice Cylinder A has a radius of 6 cm and a height of 14 cm. Cylinder B has a radius that is half as long as cylinder A's radius. If cylinder B has a height of 14 cm, what is the volume of cylinder B? Use 3.14 for π.

(A) 393.5 cm³　　(B) 395.6 cm³　　(C) 422.3 cm³　　(D) 791.3 cm³

21. Multiple Choice A tractor trailer has dimensions of 13 feet by 53 feet by 8 feet. What is the volume of the trailer?

(A) 424 ft³　　(B) 689 ft³　　(C) 2756 ft³　　(D) 5512 ft³

Give the coordinates of each point after a reflection across the given axis. (Lesson 8-7)

22. (−3, 4); y-axis **(3, 4)**　　**23.** (5, 9); x-axis **(5, −9)**　　**24.** (6, −3); y-axis **(−6, −3)**

25. Find the width of a rectangle with perimeter 14 inches and length 3 inches. What is the area of the rectangle? (Lesson 9-1) **4 in.; 12 in²**

CHALLENGE 10-2

Challenge
10-2 Looking Askance

So far, you have considered prisms in which the outside edges are perpendicular to the plane of the base.

Now, you will consider prisms in which the outside edges are not perpendicular to the plane of the base.

Right Prism　　Oblique Prism

1. Explain why these two prisms have the same volume.
Areas of bases are equal; heights are equal.

A prism can have any polygon as its base. Consider an oblique prism with a base that is a parallelogram.

To find the volume of this prism, first look at parallelogram JKLM which is the base of the prism.

2. How long is JK, the base of parallelogram JKLM?
JK = ____ **9 units**

3. Find MQ, the height of parallelogram JKLM. Explain your method.
MQ = ____ **4 units; Pythagorean Theorem**

4. What is the area of the base of the prism?
B = ____ **9 × 4 = 36 units²**

5. Find KR, the height of the prism. Explain your method.
KR = ____ **12 units; Pythagorean Theorem**

6. Find the volume of the prism.
V = ____ **36 × 12 = 432 units³**

PROBLEM SOLVING 10-2

Problem Solving
10-2 Volume of Prisms and Cylinders

Round to the nearest tenth. Write the correct answer.

1. A contractor pours a sidewalk that is 4 inches deep, 1 yard wide, and 20 yards long. How many cubic yards of concrete will be needed? (Hint: 36 inches = 1 yard.)
2.2 yd³

2. A refrigerator has inside measurements of 50 cm by 118 cm by 44 cm. What is the capacity of the refrigerator?
259,600 cm³

A rectangular box is 2 inches high, 3.5 inches wide and 4 inches long. A cylindrical box is 3.5 inches high and has a diameter of 3.2 inches. Use 3.14 for π. Round to the nearest tenth.

3. Which box has a larger volume?
Cylinder

4. How much bigger is the larger box?
0.1 in³

Use 3.14 for π. Choose the letter for the best answer.

5. A child's wading pool has a diameter of 5 feet and a height of 1 foot. How much water would it take to fill the pool? Round to the nearest gallon. (Hint: 1 cubic foot of water is approximately 7.5 gallons.)
A 79 gallons
B 589 gallons
C 59 gallons
(D) 147 gallons

6. How many cubic feet of air are in a room that is 15 feet long, 10 feet wide and 8 feet high?
F 33 ft³
(G) 1200 ft³
H 1500 ft³
J 3768 ft³

7. How many gallons of water will the water trough hold? Round to the nearest gallon. (Hint: 1 cubic foot of water is approximately 7.5 gallons.)
A 19 gallons　C 141 gallons
(B) 71 gallons　D 565 gallons

8. A can has diameter of 9.8 cm and is 13.2 cm tall. What is the capacity of the can? Round to the nearest tenth.
F 203.1 cm³
(G) 995.2 cm³
H 3980.7 cm³
J 959.2 cm³

FORMATIVE ASSESSMENT
and INTERVENTION

Diagnose Before the Lesson
10-2 Warm Up, TE p. 485

Monitor During the Lesson
10-2 Know-It Notebook
10-2 Questioning Strategies

Assess After the Lesson
10-2 Lesson Quiz, TE p. 489

Answers

17. Possible answer: The base area should be in square inches.

18. Possible answer: Since there are 3 feet in every yard, a 1-yard cube would be the same as a 3-foot cube. The volume of a 3-foot cube is 27 cubic feet.

Teaching Tip **Multiple Choice** Be sure that students realize that the basic shape of a tractor trailer is a rectangular prism. For **Exercise 21,** that means they can find the volume of the tractor trailer by multiplying together the three dimensions given in the problem.

Journal

Have students describe the steps they would take to measure and calculate the volume of the classroom in cubic feet.

Power Presentations
with PowerPoint®

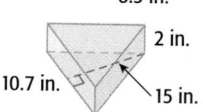

10-2 Lesson Quiz

Find the volume of each figure to the nearest tenth. Use 3.14 for π.

10 in. 12 in. 8.5 in.
12 in. 3 in.
2 in. 10.7 in. 15 in.

1. the cylinder **942 in³**
2. the rectangular prism **306 in³**
3. the triangular prism **160.5 in³**
4. Explain whether doubling only the radius of the cylinder above will double the volume. **No; the volume would be quadrupled because you have to use the square of the radius to find the volume.**

Also available on transparency

Hands-On Lab
In *Chapter 10 Resource File*

Technology Lab
In *Chapter 10 Resource File*

Online Edition
Tutorial Videos

Countdown to Mastery Week 20

Power Presentations
with PowerPoint®

Warm Up

1. Find the volume of a rectangular prism that is 4 in. tall, 16 in. wide, and 48 in. deep. **3072 in³**

2. A cylinder has a height of 4.2 m and a diameter of 0.6 m. To the nearest tenth of a cubic meter, what is the volume of the cylinder? Use 3.14 for π. **1.2 m³**

3. A triangular prism's base is an equilateral triangle. The sides of the triangle are 4 ft, and the height of the prism is 8 ft. To the nearest cubic foot, what is the volume of the prism? **55.4 ft³**

Also available on transparency

California Standards

Ext. of Measurement and Geometry 2.1

10-3 Volume of Pyramids and Cones

California Standards

Extension of MG2.1 Use formulas routinely for finding the perimeter and area of basic two-dimensional figures and the surface area and **volume of basic three-dimensional figures,** including rectangles, parallelograms, trapezoids, squares, triangles, circles, prisms, and cylinders.

Why learn this? You can use a formula to find the approximate volume of the Great Pyramid of Giza. (See Example 3.)

The height of a pyramid or cone is measured from the vertex to the base along a line perpendicular to the base.

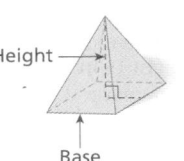

Rectangular pyramid — Height, Base

Triangular pyramid — Height, Base

Cone — Height, Base

VOLUME OF PYRAMIDS AND CONES		
Words	**Formula**	**Numbers**
Pyramid: The volume V of a pyramid is one-third of the area of the base B times the height h.	$V = \frac{1}{3}Bh$	$B = 3(3)$ $= 9$ units² $V = \frac{1}{3}(9)(4)$ $= 12$ units³
Cone: The volume of a cone is one-third of the area of the circular base B times the height h.	$V = \frac{1}{3}Bh$ or $V = \frac{1}{3}\pi r^2 h$	$B = \pi(2^2)$ $= 4\pi$ units² $V = \frac{1}{3}(4\pi)(3)$ $= 4\pi$ ≈ 12.6 units³

EXAMPLE 1 Finding the Volume of Pyramids and Cones

Find the volume of the figure.

A

9 cm, 9 cm, 4 cm

$B = \frac{1}{2}(4 \cdot 9) = 18$ cm²

$V = \frac{1}{3} \cdot 18 \cdot 9$ $V = \frac{1}{3}Bh$

$= 54$ cm³

---

1 Introduce
Alternate Opener

EXPLORATION

10-3 Volume of Pyramids and Cones

The *volume of a pyramid* is one-third the volume of a prism with the same height and a congruent base.

$V = 2 \cdot 2 \cdot 6 = 24$ ft³ $V = \frac{1}{3} \cdot 24 = 8$ ft³

Use the example above as a guide to find the volume of each prism and the volume of each pyramid.

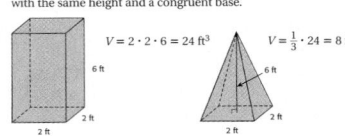
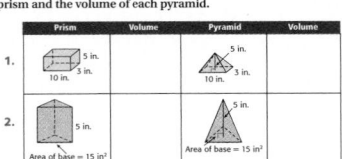

Think and Discuss
3. **Explain** the relationship between the volume of a prism and the volume of a pyramid that has the same height and a congruent base.

Motivate

Show students an empty cylinder and an empty cone that have congruent circular bases and equal heights. Have students guess how many cones it will take to fill the cylinder. Fill the cone and pour it into the cylinder. (You can use water or uncooked rice or beans.) Repeat until the cylinder is full. Students will see that the volume of the cylinder is three times the volume of the cone.

Explorations and answers are provided in *Alternate Openers: Explorations Transparencies.*

Find the volume of each figure. Use 3.14 for π.

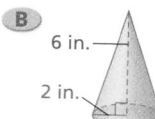

B

6 in.

2 in.

$B = \pi(2^2) = 4\pi \text{ in}^2$

$V = \frac{1}{3} \cdot 4\pi \cdot 6$ $V = \frac{1}{3}Bh$

$= 8\pi$ *Use 3.14 for π.*

$\approx 25 \text{ in}^3$

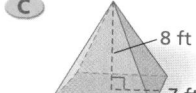

C

8 ft

7 ft

9 ft

$B = 9 \cdot 7 = 63 \text{ ft}^2$

$V = \frac{1}{3} \cdot 63 \cdot 8$ $V = \frac{1}{3}Bh$

$= 168 \text{ ft}^3$

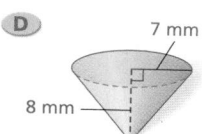

D

7 mm

8 mm

$B = \pi(7^2) = 49\pi \text{ mm}^2$

$V = \frac{1}{3} \cdot 49\pi \cdot 8$ $V = \frac{1}{3}Bh$

$= \frac{392}{3}\pi$ *Use 3.14 for π.*

$\approx 410.3 \text{ mm}^3$

EXAMPLE 2 *Social Studies Application*

The Great Pyramid of Giza is a square pyramid. Its height is 481 ft, and its base has side lengths of 756 ft. Find the volume of the pyramid.

Step 1: Find the area of the base.

$B = 756^2$ `The base is a square.`

$= 571,536 \text{ ft}^2$ *Multiply.*

Step 2: Find the volume.

$V = \frac{1}{3}Bh$ *Write the formula.*

$= \frac{1}{3} \cdot 571,536 \cdot 481$ *Substitute for B and h.*

$= 91,636,272 \text{ ft}^3$ *Multiply*

The volume of the pyramid is $91,636,272 \text{ ft}^3$.

Possible answers to *Think and Discuss*

1. You can double the height of the pyramid. You can double either dimension of the rectangular base. (In fact; you can multiply one dimension by *a*, the second by *b*, and the third by *c*, as long as *abc* = 2. For example, *a* = 3, *b* = 2, and *c* = $\frac{1}{3}$.)

2. The volume of the pyramid is one-third the volume of the cube. The volume of the cube is 1 × 1 × 1 = 1 in³. The volume of the square pyramid is $\frac{1}{3}$ × (1 × 1)(1) = $\frac{1}{3}$ in³.

Think and Discuss

1. **Describe** two or more ways that you can change the dimensions of a rectangular pyramid to double its volume.

2. **Use a model** to compare the volume of a cube with 1 in. sides with a pyramid that is 1 in. high and has a 1 in. square base.

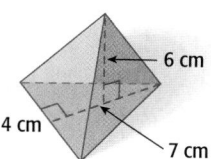
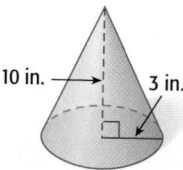

Teaching Tip
Communicating Math Be sure that students understand that the height of a pyramid or a cone as used in the volume formula is the *vertical* height.

---

2 Teach

Guided Instruction

In this lesson, students learn to find the volume of pyramids and cones. Remind students how they found the volumes of prisms and cylinders. Illustrate that the volume of a pyramid is $\frac{1}{3}$ the volume of a prism with an equal height and a congruent base (Teaching Transparency). Show that the volume of a cone is $\frac{1}{3}$ the volume of a cylinder with an equal height and a congruent base.

Teaching Tip
Critical Thinking Explain to students that the activity in Motivate is not a mathematical proof of the volume formula. The formula will, however, be proven in future math classes.

Universal Access
Through Modeling

Give each group of students a model of a pyramid and a cone, as well as a ruler (nets are provided in Teaching Tools). Have students find the approximate volume of the pyramid and the cone by taking the appropriate measurements. Have students compare the volume of the pyramid and the cone.

3 Close

Summarize

Remind students that the volumes of pyramids and cones are related to the volumes of prisms and cylinders. Show them the table below to emphasize the connection.

Prisms	Pyramids
$V = Bh$	$V = \frac{1}{3}Bh$
Cylinders	**Cones**
$V = Bh$ or $V = \pi r^2 h$	$V = \frac{1}{3}Bh$ or $V = \frac{1}{3}\pi r^2 h$

10-3 Exercises

California Standards Practice
Extension of MG2.1, MG2.4

go.hrw.com
Homework Help Online
KEYWORD: MT8CA 10-3
Parent Resources Online
KEYWORD: MT8CA Parent

Assignment Guide

If you finished Example **1** assign:
Proficient 1–6, 8–13, 28–32
Advanced 8–13, 15–19, 28–32

If you finished Example **2** assign:
Proficient 1–20, 26–32
Advanced 8–32

Homework Quick Check

Quickly check key concepts.
Exercises: 8, 10, 16, 18

Math Background

A polyhedron is any three-dimensional figure whose surfaces are all polygons. A regular polyhedron is one whose faces are all congruent regular polygons and whose polyhedral angles are all congruent. There are only five different regular polyhedrons: A tetrahedron has 4 triangular faces, a hexahedron has 6 square faces, an octahedron has 8 triangular faces, a dodecahedron has 12 pentagonal faces, and an icosahedron has 20 triangular faces. A tetrahedron is a triangular pyramid. A hexahedron is a cube. An octahedron can be formed by joining two square pyramids at their bases.

GUIDED PRACTICE

See Example **1**   Find the volume of each figure to the nearest tenth. Use 3.14 for π.

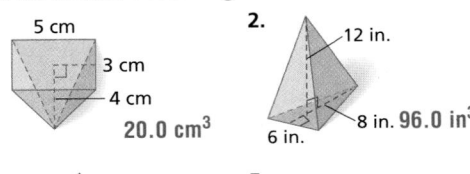

1. 5 cm, 3 cm, 4 cm   **20.0 cm³**

2. 12 in., 6 in., 8 in.   **96.0 in³**

3. 9.3 ft, 3.2 ft   **99.7 ft³**

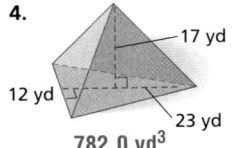

4. 17 yd, 12 yd, 23 yd   **782.0 yd³**

5. 2.4 cm, 1.9 cm   **9.1 cm³**

6. 13, 27, 27   **3159.0 units³**

See Example **2**   **7.** The Transamerica Pyramid in San Francisco has a base area of 22,000 ft² and a height of 853 ft. Find the volume of the building to the nearest thousand.   **6,255,000 ft³**

INDEPENDENT PRACTICE

See Example **1**   Find the volume of each figure to the nearest tenth. Use 3.14 for π.

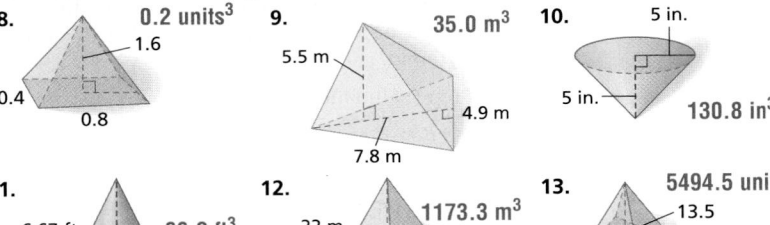

8. 1.6, 0.4, 0.8   **0.2 units³**

9. 5.5 m, 4.9 m, 7.8 m   **35.0 m³**

10. 5 in., 5 in.   **130.8 in³**

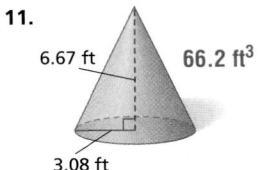

11. 6.67 ft, 3.08 ft   **66.2 ft³**

12. 22 m, 20 m, 16 m   **1173.3 m³**

13. 13.5, 33, 37   **5494.5 units³**

See Example **2**   **14.** A cone-shaped building has a diameter of 50 m and a height of 20 m. What is the volume of the building to the nearest hundredth?   **13,083.33 m³**

PRACTICE AND PROBLEM SOLVING

Extra Practice
See page EP20.

Find the missing measure to the nearest tenth. Use 3.14 for π.

15. cone:
radius = 4 in.
height = ▩ **6.0 in.**
volume = 100.5 in³

16. cylinder:
radius = ▩ **3.0 m**
height = 2.5 m
volume = 70.65 m³

17. triangular pyramid:
base height = ▩ **11.0 ft**
base width = 8 ft
height = 6 ft
volume = 88 ft³

REVIEW FOR MASTERY 10-3

Review for Mastery
10-3 *Volume of Pyramids and Cones*

Pyramid: solid figure named for the shape of its base, which is a polygon; all other faces are triangles

Cone: solid figure with a circular base

This rectangular pyramid and prism have congruent bases and congruent heights.

This cone and cylinder have congruent bases and congruent heights.

Volume of Pyramid = $\frac{1}{3}$ Volume of Prism

Volume of Cone = $\frac{1}{3}$ Volume of Cylinder

$V = \frac{1}{3} Bh$

$V = \frac{1}{3} Bh$

Complete to find the volume of each figure.

1. $h = 10$ in., $r = 3$ in.

2. rectangular pyramid   5 in., 6 in., 8 in.

radius r of base = __3__ in.

$V = \frac{1}{3} Bh$
$V = \frac{1}{3} (\pi r^2) h$
$V = \frac{1}{3} (\pi \times \underline{3^2}) \times \underline{10}$
$V = \frac{1}{3} (\underline{9\pi}) \times \underline{10}$
$V = \frac{\underline{3\pi} \times \underline{10}}{}$
$V = \underline{30\pi}$
$V \approx \underline{30} \times 3.14$
$V \approx \underline{94.2}$ in³

base is a ___rectangle___

$V = \frac{1}{3} Bh$
$V = \frac{1}{3}$ (area of rectangle) $\times h$
$V = \frac{1}{3} (\underline{8} \times \underline{6}) \times \underline{5}$
$V = \frac{1}{3} (\underline{48}) \times \underline{5}$
$V = \underline{80}$ in³

PRACTICE 10-3

Practice B
10-3 *Volume of Pyramids and Cones*

Find the volume of each figure to the nearest tenth. Use 3.14 for π.

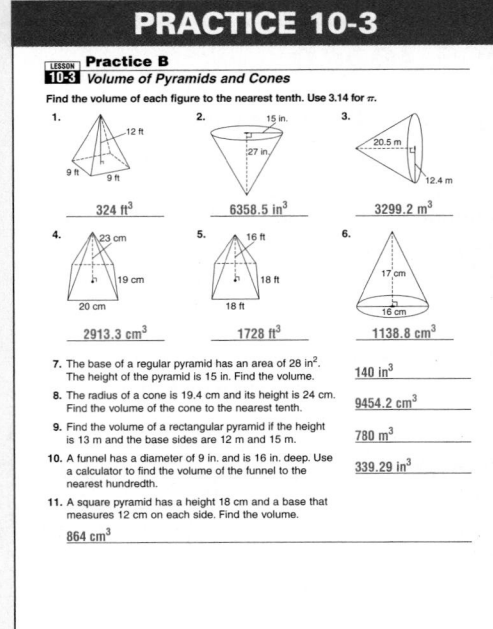

1. 12 ft, 9 ft, 9 ft   **324 ft³**

2. 15 in., 27 in.   **6358.5 in³**

3. 20.5 m, 12.4 m   **3299.2 m³**

4. 23 cm, 19 cm, 20 cm   **2913.3 cm³**

5. 16 ft, 18 ft, 18 ft   **1728 ft³**

6. 17 cm, 16 cm   **1138.8 cm³**

7. The base of a regular pyramid has an area of 28 in². The height of the pyramid is 15 in. Find the volume.   **140 in³**

8. The radius of a cone is 19.4 cm and its height is 24 cm. Find the volume of the cone to the nearest tenth.   **9454.2 cm³**

9. Find the volume of a rectangular pyramid if the height is 13 cm and the base sides are 12 cm and 15 cm.   **780 cm³**

10. A funnel has a diameter of 9 in. and is 16 in. deep. Use a calculator to find the volume of the funnel to the nearest hundredth.   **339.29 in³**

11. A square pyramid has a height 18 cm and a base that measures 12 cm on each side. Find the volume.   **864 cm³**

California Standards

Standard	Exercises
AF4.1 🔑	28–31
Ext. of MG2.1	1–27, 32
MG2.4	20, 21

Find the volume of each figure to the nearest tenth. Use 3.14 for π.

18. 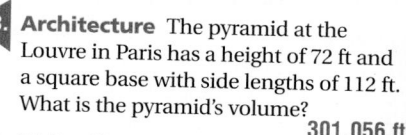 **98.1 in³**

19.  **736.0 cm³**

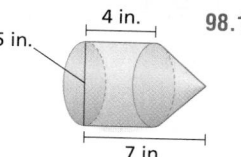

Architecture

I. M. Pei, designer of the Louvre Pyramid, has designed more than 50 buildings around the world and has won many major awards.

go.hrw.com
Web Extra!
KEYWORD: MT8CA Pei

20. Architecture The Pyramid of the Sun, in Teotihuacán, Mexico, is about 65 m tall and has a square base with side lengths of 225 m.

   a. What is the volume in cubic meters of the pyramid? **1,096,875 m³**

   b. How many cubic meters are in a cubic kilometer? **1,000,000,000 m³**

   c. What is the volume in cubic kilometers of the pyramid to the nearest thousandth? **0.001 km³**

21. Estimation Approximate the volume in cubic inches of an orange traffic cone with height 2 feet and diameter 10 inches by using 3 in place of π. **600 in³**

22. What's the Error? A student says that the formula for the volume of a cylinder is the same as the formula for the volume of a pyramid, $\frac{1}{3}Bh$. What error did the student make?

23. Architecture The pyramid at the Louvre in Paris has a height of 72 ft and a square base with side lengths of 112 ft. What is the pyramid's volume? **301,056 ft³**

24. Write About It How would a cone's volume be affected if you doubled the height? the radius? Use a model to help explain your answer.

25. Challenge The diameter of a cone is x cm, the height is 18 cm, and the volume is 96π cm³. Find the value of x. **8**

SPIRAL STANDARDS REVIEW
AF4.1, MG2.1

26. Multiple Choice A pyramid has a rectangular base measuring 12 cm by 9 cm. Its height is 15 cm. What is the volume of the pyramid?

  Ⓐ 540 cm³   Ⓑ 405 cm³   Ⓒ 315 cm³   Ⓓ 270 cm³

27. Multiple Choice A cone has diameter 12 cm and height 9 cm. Using 3.14 for π, find the volume of the cone to the nearest tenth.

  Ⓐ 1356.5 cm³   Ⓑ 339.1 cm³   Ⓒ 118.3 cm³   Ⓓ 56.5 cm³

Solve. (Lesson 2-8)

28. $3x + 5 = 17$ **29.** $\frac{1}{2}x + 1\frac{1}{2} = 9$ **30.** $2.6 - x = 8.9$ **31.** $3.1 + 5.2x = -43.7$
    $x = 4$ $x = 15$ $x = -6.3$ $x = -9$

32. Find the area of a circle with diameter 15 ft. (Lesson 9-4) 56.25π ft², or 176.6 ft²

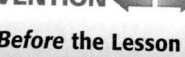

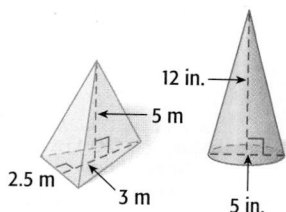

Organizer

Objective: Assess students' mastery of concepts and skills in Lessons 10-1 through 10-3.

Resources

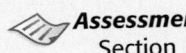
Assessment Resources
Section 10A Quiz

Test & Practice Generator
One-Stop Planner®

INTERVENTION ◄═══►

Resources

Ready to Go On?
Intervention and
Enrichment Worksheets

Ready to Go On? CD-ROM

Ready to Go On? Online

my.hrw.com

Quiz for Lessons 10-1 Through 10-3

☑ **10-1** **Three-Dimensional Figures**

Classify each figure as a polyhedron or not a polyhedron. Then name the figure.

1.  not a polyhedron; cone

2. polyhedron; hexagonal pyramid

3. polyhedron; triangular pyramid

☑ **10-2** **Volume of Prisms and Cylinders**

Find the volume of each figure to the nearest tenth. Use 3.14 for π.

4. 5 cm, 6 cm, 7 cm   **210.0 cm³**

5. 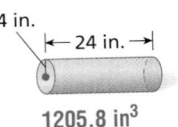 4 in. ← 24 in. →   **1205.8 in³**

6. 2 ft, 8 ft, 12 ft   **96.0 ft³**

7. A can is shaped like a cylinder. It is 5.2 cm wide and 2.3 cm tall. Find its volume to the nearest tenth. Use 3.14 for π.   **48.8 cm³**

8. Find the volume of the composite figure at right.
   336 cm³

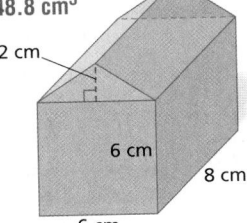
2 cm
6 cm
8 cm
6 cm

☑ **10-3** **Volume of Pyramids and Cones**

Find the volume of each figure to the nearest tenth. Use 3.14 for π.

9. **45.0 ft³** 9 ft, 3 ft, 5 ft

10.  9 m, 4 m   **37.7 m³**

11. 7 cm, 6 cm, 5 cm   **35.0 cm³**

12. A cone has a radius of 2.5 cm and a height of 14 cm. What is the volume of the cone to the nearest hundredth? Use 3.14 for π.   **91.58 cm³**

READY TO GO ON?
Diagnose and Prescribe

NO INTERVENE

READY TO GO ON? Intervention, Section 10A			
Ready to Go On? Intervention	**Worksheets**	💿 **CD-ROM**	🪐 **Online**
☑ Lesson 10-1 🐘 Prep for MG2.1	10-1 Intervention	Activity 10-1	Diagnose and Prescribe Online
☑ Lesson 10-2 🐘 MG2.1, MG2.4	10-2 Intervention	Activity 10-2	
☑ Lesson 10-3 🐘 Ext. of MG2.1	10-3 Intervention	Activity 10-3	

YES ENRICH

READY TO GO ON? Enrichment, Section 10A
 **Worksheets**
💿 **CD-ROM**
🪐 **Online**

Focus on Problem Solving

California Standards

MR1.1 Analyze problems by identifying relationships, distinguishing relevant from irrelevant information, identifying missing information, **sequencing and prioritizing information,** and observing patterns.
Also covered: **MG1.1**

Make a Plan

• **Prioritize and sequence information**

Some problems contain a lot of information. Read the entire problem carefully to be sure you understand all of the facts. You may need to read it over several times—perhaps aloud so that you can hear yourself say the words.

Then decide which information is most important (prioritize). Is there any information that is absolutely necessary to solve the problem? This information is most important.

Finally, put the information in order (sequence). Use comparison words like *before, after, longer, shorter,* and so on to help you. Write down the sequence before you try to solve the problem.

Read each problem below, and then answer the questions that follow.

① Five friends are standing in line for the opening of a movie. They are in line according to their time of arrival. Tiffany arrived 3 minutes after Cedric. Roy took his place in line at 8:01 P.M. He was 1 minute behind Celeste and 7 minutes ahead of Tiffany. The first person arrived at 8:00 P.M. Blanca showed up 6 minutes after the first person's arrival.

a. Whose arrival information helped you determine each arrival time?

b. Can you determine the order without the time?

c. List the friends' order from the earliest to arrive to the last to arrive.

② There are four children in the Putman family. Isabelle is half the age of Maxwell. Joe is 2 years older than Isabelle. Maxwell is 14. Hazel is twice Joe's age and 4 years older than Maxwell. What are the ages of the children?

a. Whose age must you figure out first before you can find Joe's age?

b. What are two ways to figure out Hazel's age?

c. List the Putman children from oldest to youngest.

Answers

1. a. Roy

b. Yes

c. Celeste, Roy, Cedric, Blanca, Tiffany

2. a. Isabelle or Hazel

b. Multiply Joe's age by 2 or add 4 years to Maxwell's age.

c. Hazel, Maxwell, Joe, Isabelle

 Focus on Problem Solving

Organizer

Objective: Focus on prioritizing and sequencing information.

 Online Edition

Resources

Chapter 10 Resource File
Reading Strategies

Problem Solving Process

This page focuses on the second step of the problem-solving process:
Make a Plan

Discuss

Discuss which sentences contain the most important information. Ask students to examine the differences between these sentences and the rest of the information given in the problems.

Possible answers

1. The third, fourth, fifth, and seventh sentences all contain vital data needed to determine the time and order of arrivals. The sixth sentence is not necessary at all because it can be determined using information from the fourth and fifth sentences.

2. The second, third, fourth and fifth sentences contain all the information needed to solve the problem. However, the information that Hazel is 4 years older than Maxwell from the fifth sentence is unnecessary because the order of their ages can be determined using the information already given.

 California Standards

Mathematical Reasoning 1.1
Also covered:
Measurement and Geometry
1.1 Compare weights, capacities, geometric measures, **times,** and temperatures within and between measurement systems (e.g., miles per hour and feet per second, cubic inches to cubic centimeters).

Surface Area

One-Minute Section Planner

Lesson	Lab Resources	Materials
10-4 Hands-On Lab Nets of Prisms and Cylinders • Use models and nets to explore the surface area of prisms and cylinders. 🐻 **MG3.0, MG3.5**		**Required** Rectangular and triangular prisms, grid paper
Lesson 10-4 Surface Area of Prisms and Cylinders • Find the surface area of prisms and cylinders. 🐻 **MG2.1, MG2.2, MG2.3**	**Hands-On Lab 10-4** **Technology Lab 10-4** In *Chapter 10 Resource File*	**Optional** Boxes
10-5 Hands-On Lab Nets of Cones • Use nets to explore the surface area of cones. 🐻 **MG3.5**		**Required** Cone-shaped paper cups, grid paper, scissors
Lesson 10-5 Surface Area of Pyramids and Cones • Find the surface area of pyramids and cones. 🐻 **Ext. of MG2.1**	**Hands-On Lab 10-5** In *Chapter 10 Resource File*	**Optional** Rulers (MK), pyramid and cone nets, paper cones
Lesson 10-6 Spheres • Find the volume and surface area of spheres. 🐻 **Ext. of MG2.1**	**Hands-On Lab 10-6** **Technology Lab 10-6** In *Chapter 10 Resource File*	**Optional** Sphere models (balls, beads, etc.)
Lesson 10-7 Scaling Three-Dimensional Figures • Find the volume and surface area of similar three-dimensional figures. 🐻 **MG2.0, MG2.3**		**Optional** Centimeter cubes (MK), graph paper

MK = *Manipulatives Kit*

Notes

_____

_____

_____

_____

_____

_____

_____

_____

_____

_____

Math Background:
Teaching the Standards

SURFACE AREA AND NETS 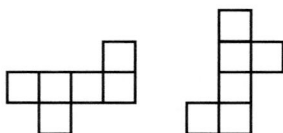 MG2.1, MG3.5

Lessons 10-4, 10-5

A *net* is a diagram of the surfaces of a three-dimensional figure that may be cut out and folded to form the three-dimensional figure. Nets provide students with valuable experiences in visualization as well as with opportunities to study the connection between two-dimensional figures and three-dimensional figures.

When they create or identify nets, students are often confronted with situations in which they need to decide if two nets are identical. Two nets are considered to be identical if one may be transformed into the other through a series of translations, reflections, and/or rotations. Two nets for a cube are shown below. The nets are identical because the net on the left may be transformed into the one on the right through a reflection and a rotation.

Nets for three-dimensional figures are generally not unique. For example, there are 11 distinct nets that can be folded to form a cube. These are shown below.

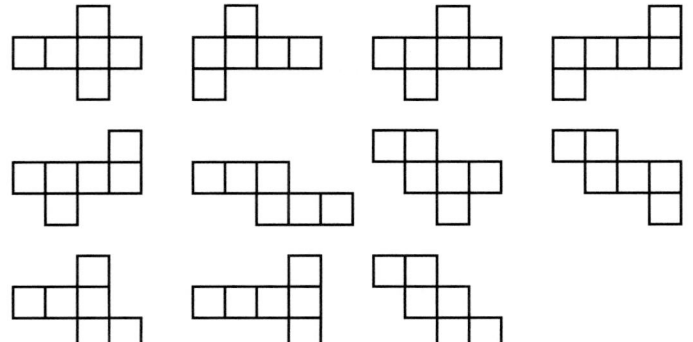

A regular dodecahedron, which is a three-dimensional solid that has 12 pentagonal faces, has more than 43,000 distinct nets!

SURFACE AREA FORMULAS 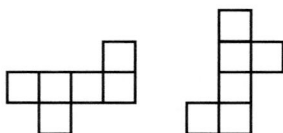 MG2.1

Lessons 10-4, 10-5

Nets are useful in developing surface area formulas because they turn a three-dimensional problem into a two-dimensional problem. For example, any right prism consists of two congruent bases and a set of rectangular lateral faces. A net for any right prism can be drawn as shown below.

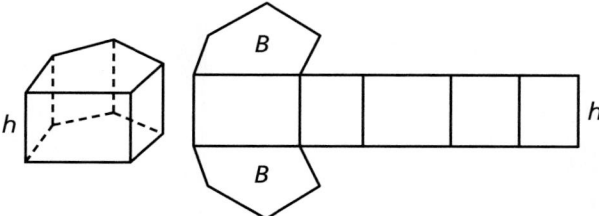

The net makes it clear that the prism's surface area is the area of the two bases (2*B*) plus the area of the long rectangle formed by the lateral faces. The height of this rectangle is *h*, and the base of the rectangle is equal to the perimeter *P* of the base of the prism. Thus, the formula for the surface area *S* of the prism is $S = Ph + 2B$.

A right cylinder with circular bases can be seen as a *limiting case* of a right prism whose bases are regular *n*-gons. As *n* gets larger and larger, the prism approaches the shape of a cylinder. This idea can be used as the basis of a proof to show that for a right cylinder of radius *r* and height *h*, the perimeter in the above formula may be replaced by the circumference of the base, $2\pi r$, and the area of the base may be replaced by πr^2, yielding the formula $S = 2\pi rh + 2\pi r^2$.

SCALING MG2.3

Lesson 10-8

As students work with three-dimensional figures, it is essential for them to understand the effect of multiplying all dimensions of a figure by a positive scale factor *k*. The surface area is multiplied by k^2, and the volume is multiplied by k^3. This relationship has important implications in physical science and life science. For example, it explains why giant monsters such as King Kong cannot exist. If a creature had dimensions 10 times those of a normal gorilla, the creature's volume (and weight) would be 10^3, or 1000 times those of a normal gorilla. However, the amount of weight that could be supported by the creature's legs would depend on the cross-sectional area of the legs, and this area increases by a factor of only 10^2, or 100. In other words, the legs would not be strong enough to support the greatly increased volume.

Objective: Use models and nets to explore the surface area of prisms and cylinders.

Materials: Rectangular and triangular prisms, grid paper

 Online Edition

 Countdown to Mastery Week 21

Teach

Discuss

Show students how the net of a figure actually forms that solid figure when it is assembled.

Close

Key Concept

You can find the surface area of prisms and cylinders by finding the total area of the net of the figure.

Assessment

1. Name other solid figures that you could find their surface area by using the method shown in this lab.
   Possible answers: pyramids and cones

Hands-On

LAB
10-4

Nets of Prisms and Cylinders

Use with Lesson 10-4

 **go.hrw.com**
Lab Resources Online
KEYWORD: MT8CA Lab10

 **California Standards**

MG3.5 Construct two-dimensional patterns for three-dimensional models, such as cylinders, prisms, and cones.

A *net* is an arrangement of two-dimensional figures that can be folded to form a three-dimensional figure. You can explore the surface area of prisms and cylinders using nets.

Activity 1   Check students' work.

1. Find four different-sized rectangular and triangular prisms. Follow these steps to make a net for each prism.

   a. Trace around each face of the prism on grid paper.

   b. Label the bases A and B. Continue labeling the lateral faces.

   c. Copy the tables shown. Fill in the information for each prism.

Rectangular Prism	
Face	Area
Base A	
Base B	
Lateral face C	
Lateral face D	
Lateral face E	
Lateral face F	
Total Surface Area	

Triangular Prism	
Face	Area
Base A	
Base B	
Lateral face C	
Lateral face D	
Lateral face E	
Total Surface Area	

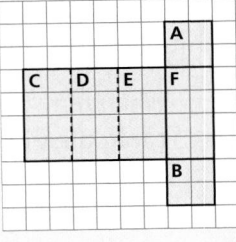

2. For each prism from ❶, find the perimeter of a base. Then multiply the perimeter of the base by the prism's height. Finally, find the total area of the lateral faces.

Think and Discuss

1. In ❷, how did the product of the base's perimeter and the prism's height compare with the sum of the areas of the lateral faces?   They are equal.

2. Write a rule for finding the surface area of any prism.   2(area of base) + (perimeter)(height)

Try This

1. Use your rule from Think and Discuss 2 to find the surface area of two new prisms. Check your rule by following the steps in ❶. Revise your rule as needed.
   Check students' work.

 **California Standards**

Measurement and Geometry 3.5

Also covered:

Measurement and Geometry

3.0 Students know the Pythagorean theorem and deepen their understanding of plane and solid geometric shapes by constructing figures that meet given conditions and by identifying attributes of figures.

Check students' work.

1 Find four different-sized cylinders. Follow these steps to make a net for each cylinder.

  a. Trace around the top of the cylinder on grid paper.

  b. Lay the cylinder on the grid paper so that it touches the circle, and mark its height. Then roll the cylinder one complete revolution, marking where the cylinder begins and ends. Draw a rectangle that has the same height as the cylinder and a width equal to one revolution of the cylinder.

  c. Trace the bottom of the cylinder so that it touches the bottom of the rectangle.

  d. Find the approximate area of each piece by counting squares.

  e. Add the areas to find the total surface area of the cylinder.

  f. Copy the table shown. Record the information in the table.

Cylinder		
Face	Area by Counting Squares	Area by Using Formula
Circular base A		
Circular base B		
Lateral face C		
Total Surface Area		

2 Follow these steps for each cylinder from **1**.

  a. Tape your pieces together to make a cylinder.

  b. Use area formulas to find the area of each base and the lateral face.

  c. Add the areas to find the total surface area of your net.

  d. Record the information in the table.

Think and Discuss

1. How did the area found by counting squares compare with the area found by using a formula?

2. How does the circumference of the base compare with the length of the lateral face?   They are the same.

3. Make a rule for finding the surface area of any cylinder.
    2(area of base) + circumference × height, or $2\pi r^2 + 2\pi rh$

Try This

1. Use your rule from Think and Discuss 3 to find the surface area of a new cylinder. Check your rule by following the steps in the activity. Revise your rule as needed.   Check students' work.

Answers to Think and Discuss

1. Possible answer: The area found by counting squares is slightly different due to estimating the area of the bases.

Donald R. Price
Rowland Heights, CA

Teacher to Teacher

I have an activity that I call *Rolling Rectangles*. I give each student and myself an 8.5" by 11" piece of paper. We each make a cylinder out of our piece of paper by touching the longer edges together. We then unfold the long cylinder and use the same piece of paper to make another cylinder, this time by touching the shorter sides together. I ask students which cylinder would hold more, and almost always the students will say that the cylinders would hold the same amount. Students believe this because the same piece of paper is used to make both cylinders. This activity entices students to learn the formula for volume in order to find out which cylinder holds more. (The shorter cylinder has greater volume.)

Objective: Students find the surface area of prisms and cylinders.

 Hands-On Lab
In *Chapter 10 Resource File*

 Technology Lab
In *Chapter 10 Resource File*

 Online Edition
Tutorial Videos, Interactivities

 Countdown to Mastery Week 21

Power Presentations
with PowerPoint®

Warm Up

1. A triangular pyramid has a base area of 1.2 m² and a height of 7.5 m. What is the volume of the pyramid?　　　3 m^3

2. A cone has a radius of 4 cm and a height of 10 cm. What is the volume of the cone to the nearest cubic centimeter? Use 3.14 for π.　　　167 cm^3

Also available on transparency

Math Humor

Teacher: How do you catch a 3-D figure?
Student: With a net

California Standards

Measurement and Geometry 2.1
Also covered:
Measurement and Geometry
2.2 Estimate and **compute the area of more complex** or irregular two- and **three-dimensional figures by breaking the figures down into more basic geometric objects.**
2.3 Compute the length of the perimeter, **the surface area of the faces,** and the volume of a three-dimensional object **built from rectangular solids.** Understand that when the lengths of all dimensions are multiplied by a scale factor, the surface area is multiplied by the square of the scale factor and the volume is multiplied by the cube of the scale factor.

10-4 Surface Area of Prisms and Cylinders

California Standards

MG2.1 Use formulas routinely for finding the perimeter and area of basic two-dimensional figures and **the surface area** and volume **of basic three-dimensional figures, including** rectangles, parallelograms, trapezoids, squares, triangles, circles, **prisms, and cylinders.**
Also covered: **MG2.2, MG2.3**

Why learn this? You can estimate the amount of reflective material you need to create an anamorphic image. (See Example 4.)

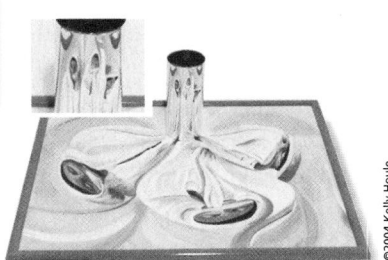
©2004 Kelly Houle

The **surface area** of a three-dimensional figure is the sum of the areas of all of its surfaces. You can use centimeter cubes to explore the surface area of prisms.

EXAMPLE 1 Finding Surface Area of Figures Built of Cubes

Find the surface area of each figure. The figure is made up of congruent cubes.

Vocabulary
surface area
lateral face
lateral area
lateral surface

A
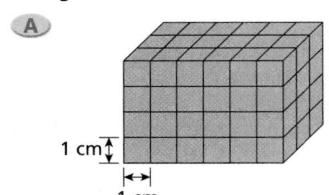

Draw each view of the figure.

Top　Front　Left
Bottom　Back　Right

Find the area of each view.
$18 + 24 + 12 + 18 + 24 + 12 = 108$　　*Add the areas.*
The surface area is 108 cm².

B
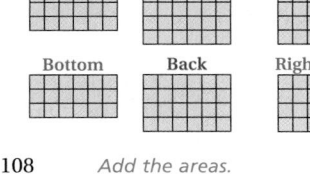

Draw each view of the figure.

Top　Front　Left
Bottom　Back　Right

Find the area of each view.
$8 + 10 + 8 + 8 + 10 + 8 = 52$　　*Add the areas.*
The surface area is 52 cm².

The **lateral faces** of a prism are parallelograms that connect the bases.
The **lateral area** of a prism is the sum of the areas of the lateral faces.

---

1 Introduce
Alternate Opener

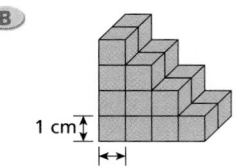

EXPLORATION

10-4 Surface Area of Prisms and Cylinders

The figure below is called a **net.** A net is a flat two-dimensional shape that can be folded to form a three-dimensional figure.

1. Suppose that you fold the net into a figure. What three-dimensional figure would be formed?
2. Find the area of each of the six faces of the three-dimensional figure.
3. Add the areas of the six faces. The total area is called the **surface area.**

Think and Discuss
4. **Explain** how you can find the surface area of a box.
5. **Describe** the net of a cylinder, such as a juice can.

Motivate

Show students an empty cereal box. Point out that if they find the volume, they will find the amount of cereal the box can hold. Rip the seams so the box will lie flat. Tell the students that now they will find the surface area of shapes like the box. The surface area determines how much cardboard is needed to make the box.

Explorations and answers are provided in
Alternate Openers: Explorations Transparencies.

SURFACE AREA OF PRISMS

Words	Formula	Numbers
The surface area S of a prism is twice the base area B plus the lateral area L. The lateral area is the base perimeter P times the height h.	$S = 2B + L$ or $S = 2B + Ph$	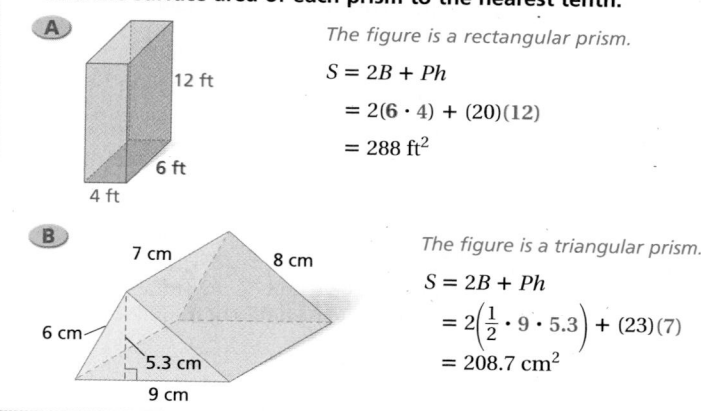 $S = 2(3 \cdot 2) + (10)(5) = 62 \text{ units}^2$

EXAMPLE 2 **Finding Surface Area of Prisms**

Find the surface area of each prism to the nearest tenth.

A

12 ft, 6 ft, 4 ft

The figure is a rectangular prism.

$S = 2B + Ph$
$= 2(6 \cdot 4) + (20)(12)$
$= 288 \text{ ft}^2$

B

7 cm, 8 cm, 6 cm, 5.3 cm, 9 cm

The figure is a triangular prism.

$S = 2B + Ph$
$= 2\left(\dfrac{1}{2} \cdot 9 \cdot 5.3\right) + (23)(7)$
$= 208.7 \text{ cm}^2$

The **lateral surface** of a cylinder is the curved surface that connects the bases.

SURFACE AREA OF CYLINDERS

Words	Formula	Numbers
The surface area S of a cylinder is twice the base area B plus the lateral area L. The lateral area is the base circumference $2\pi r$ times the height h.	$S = 2B + L$ or $S = 2\pi r^2 + 2\pi rh$	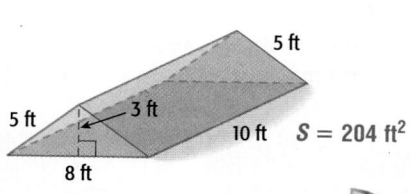 $S = 2\pi(5^2) + 2\pi(5)(6) \approx 345.4 \text{ units}^2$

 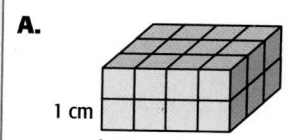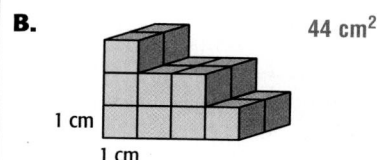

Teaching Tip **Inclusion** Remind students that lateral area and surface area are measured in square units even though the figures are three-dimensional. Help them visualize this by showing them a three-dimensional figure and its net. The surface area of the figure is equal to the area of the net.

---

2 Teach

Guided Instruction

In this lesson, students learn to find the surface area of prisms and cylinders. Have students open samples of prisms and cylinders so they can see the two-dimensional surfaces that form the three-dimensional figures (Teaching Transparency). Explain that the surface area is the sum of all the areas of these two-dimensional surfaces.

 **Teaching Tip** **Reading Math** Remind students that the word *lateral* means "of or relating to the side." Think of the word *quadrilateral*, which means "four sides," or a *lateral* pass in football, which is thrown sideways.

ENGLISH LANGUAGE LEARNERS

Universal Access
Through Cognitive Strategies

Discuss with students descriptions of real-world examples of area and volume, such as the amount of soup in a can, the amount of paper needed to make a label around a can, or the amount of wallpaper needed to cover the walls of a room. Have students identify the measure that applies to each situation and the appropriate formula.

Possible answers: volume of a cylinder: $V = Bh$; lateral surface area of a cylinder: $L = 2\pi rh$; area of lateral faces of a prism: $L = Ph$

3 Close

Summarize

Point out that the formulas for surface area of prisms and cylinders are based on area formulas for rectangles and circles. Discuss the difference between surface area and volume.

Possible answer: Surface area is the sum of the areas of all surfaces of a figure and is measured in square units. Volume is the space that a figure occupies and is measured in cubic units.

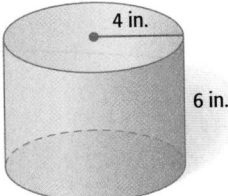

10-4 Exercises

EXAMPLE 3 Finding Surface Area of Cylinders

Find the surface area of the cylinder to the nearest tenth. Use 3.14 for π.

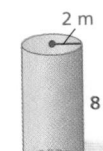

2 m

8 m

$S = 2\pi r^2 + 2\pi rh$ *Surface area of a cylinder*
$= 2\pi(2^2) + 2\pi(2)(8)$ *Substitute for r and h.*
$= 40\pi \text{ m}^2$
$\approx 125.6 \text{ m}^2$

EXAMPLE 4 Art Application

An anamorphic image is a distorted picture that becomes recognizable when reflected onto a cylindrical mirror. A cylinder is 49 mm in diameter and 107 mm tall. Estimate the amount of reflective material you would need to cover the cylinder.

The cylinder's diameter is about 50 mm, and its height is about 100 mm.

$L = 2\pi rh$ *Only the lateral surface needs to be covered.*
$= 2\pi(25)(100)$ *diameter ≈ 50 mm, so r ≈ 25 mm*
$\approx 15,700 \text{ mm}^2$

Possible answer to
Think and Discuss

1. The drinking glass only has one base, but a cylinder has two bases. So the surface area of the glass would be $\pi r^2 + 2\pi rh$ instead of $2\pi r^2 + 2\pi rh$.

Think and Discuss

1. Explain how finding the surface area of a cylindrical drinking glass would be different from finding the surface area of a cylinder.

10-4 Exercises

GUIDED PRACTICE

See Example **1** Find the surface area of each figure. The figure is made up of congruent cubes.

1.
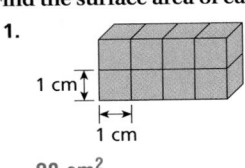
1 cm
1 cm
28 cm²

2.
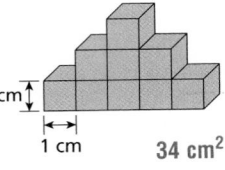
1 cm
1 cm
34 cm²

3.
52 cm²
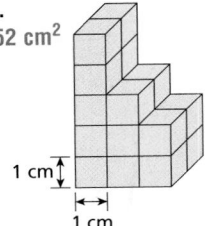
1 cm
1 cm

See Example 2 Find the surface area of each prism to the nearest tenth.

4. 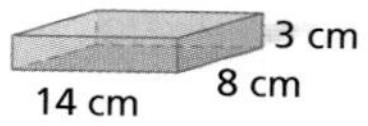 3 cm, 14 cm, 8 cm
356.0 cm²

5. 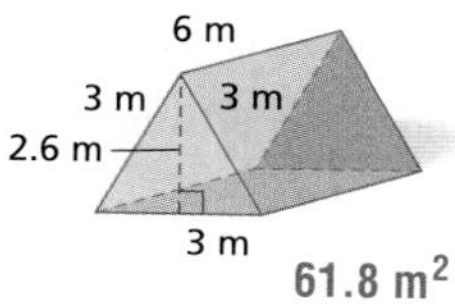 6 m, 3 m, 3 m, 2.6 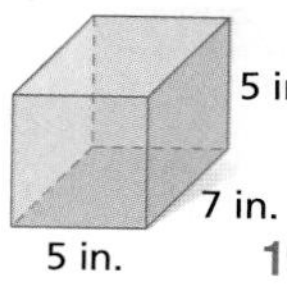 m, 3 m
61.8 m²

6. 5 in., 7 in., 5 in.
190.0 in²

See Example 3 Find the surface area of each cylinder to the nearest tenth. Use 3.14 for π.

7. 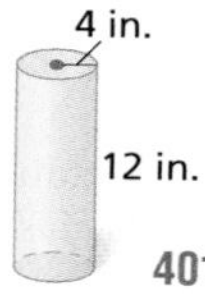 4 in., 12 in.
401.9 in²

8. 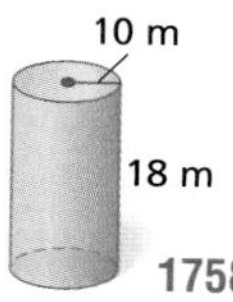 10 m, 18 m
1758.4 m²

9. 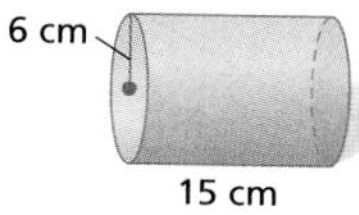 6 cm, 15 cm
791.3 cm²

See Example 4 **10.** Tilly is covering the lateral surface area of a can with colored paper. The can is 8 in. tall and has a radius of 2 in. Estimate the amount of paper she needs.
$\approx$ **96 in²**

INDEPENDENT PRACTICE

See Example 1 Find the surface area of each figure. The figure is made up of congruent cubes.

11. 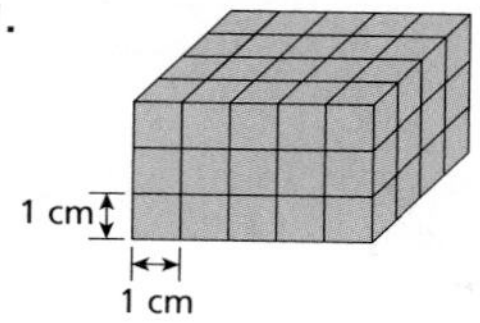 1 cm, 1 cm
94 cm²

12. 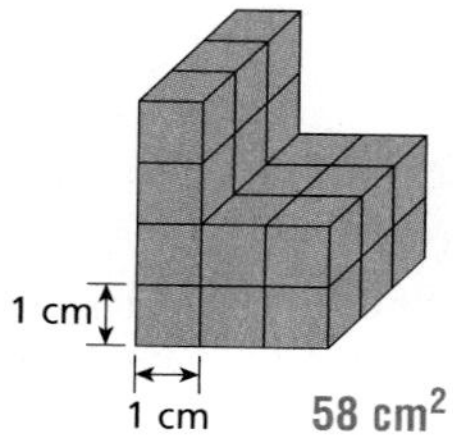 1 cm, 1 cm
58 cm²

13. 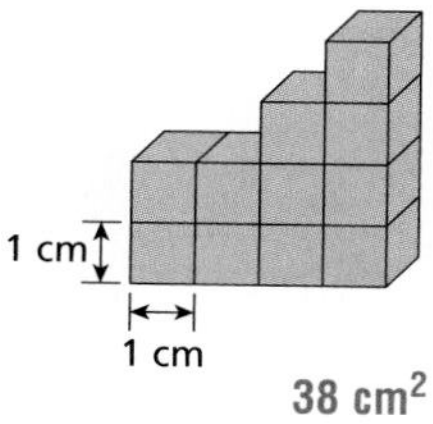 1 cm, 1 cm
38 cm²

See Example 2 Find the surface area of each prism to the nearest tenth.

14. 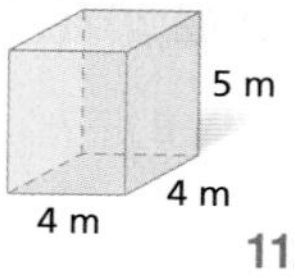 5 m, 4 m, 4 m
112.0 m²

15. 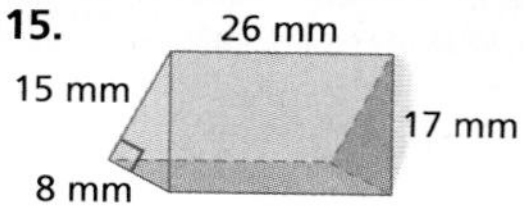 26 mm, 15 mm, 17 mm, 8 mm
1160.0 mm²

16. 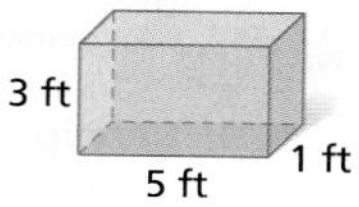 3 ft, 5 ft, 1 ft
46.0 ft²

See Example 3 Find the surface area of each cylinder to the nearest tenth. Use 3.14 for π.

17. 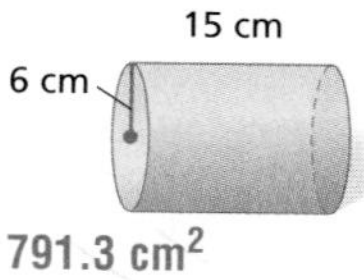 15 cm, 6 cm
791.3 cm²

18. 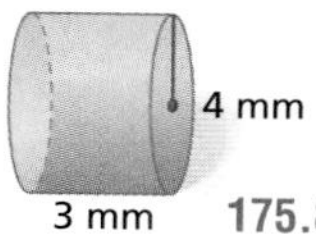 4 mm, 3 mm
175.8 mm²

19. 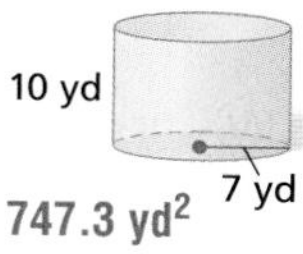 10 yd, 7 yd
747.3 yd²

See Example 4 **20.** Frank is wrapping a present. The box measures 6.2 cm by 9.9 cm by 5.1 cm. Estimate the amount of wrapping paper, not counting overlap, that Frank needs.
$\approx$ **280 cm²**

COMMON ERROR ALERT

When calculating the surface area of a cylinder, students may leave out the 2 in $2\pi rh$ or $2\pi r^2$. Use a diagram or model to show them that the 2 in $2\pi rh$ comes from the formula for the circumference of a circle, $C = 2\pi r$, while the 2 in the term $2\pi r^2$ comes from the fact that there are two circular bases.

Math Background

Research has found that children who play with blocks and other building toys have a better-developed spatial sense than those who do not. Even older students can benefit from hands-on activities in their study of three-dimensional figures. Many students in high school geometry classes are at a disadvantage that can be partially attributed to a lack of hands-on experience in prior grades. Students should, however, be familiar with basic concepts and have a clear understanding of the objectives of hands-on activities.

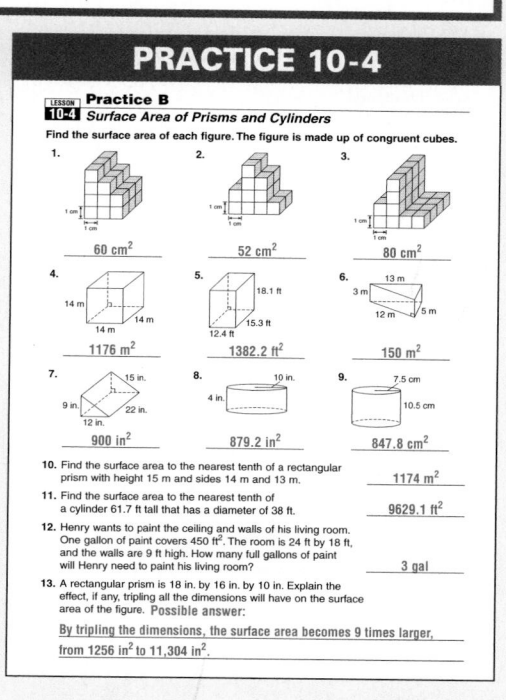

REVIEW FOR MASTERY 10-4

Review for Mastery
10-4 Surface Area of Prisms and Cylinders

Find the number of tiles needed to cover the faces of the prism. Unfold the prism to get a better look at its six faces.

An unfolded cylinder results in two circles and a lateral surface drawn as a rectangle. The base of the rectangle equals the circumference of the circular base. The height of the rectangle equals the height of the cylinder.

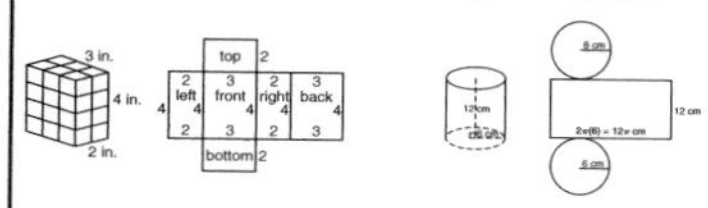

S = Surface Area of a Prism
S = area of bases + area of lateral faces
S = 2B + perimeter of the base × height of prism
S = 2B + Ph
S = 2(3 × 2) + (3 + 2 + 3 + 2) × 4
S = 12 + (10) × 4
S = 12 + 40
S = 52 in²

S = Surface Area of a Cylinder
S = area of 2 circular bases + area of lateral surface (rectangle)
S = 2(πr^2) + circumference × height
S = 2πr^2 + 2π × h
S = 2πr^2 + 2πrh
S = 2$\pi(6^2)$ + 2$\pi(6)(12)$
S = 72π + 144π = 216π cm²
S = 216(3.14)
S ≈ 678.24 cm²

1. Complete to find the surface area of the prism.
S = 2B + Ph
S = 2(5×7) + ($5 + 7 + 5 + 7$) × 3
S = 2(35) + (24) × 3
S = 70 + 72 = 142 in²

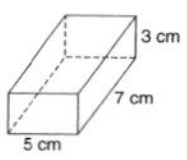

2. Complete to find the surface area of the cylinder.
S = 2πr^2 + 2πrh
S = 2π(12^2) + 2π × 12 × 8
S = 288 π + 192 π
S = 480 π
S ≈ 480 (3.14)

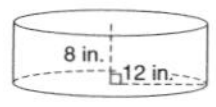

PRACTICE 10-4

Practice B
10-4 Surface Area of Prisms and Cylinders

Find the surface area of each figure. The figure is made up of congruent cubes.

1. 1 cm, 1 cm, 1 cm
60 cm²

2. 1 cm, 1 cm, 1 cm
52 cm²

3. 1 cm, 1 cm, 1 cm
80 cm²

4. 14 m, 14 m, 14 m
1176 m²

5. 18.1 ft, 15.3 ft, 12.4 ft
1382.2 ft²

6. 13 m, 3 m, 12 m, 5 m
150 m²

7. 15 in., 9 in., 12 in.
900 in²

8. 10 in., 4 in., 22 in.
879.2 in²

9. 7.5 cm, 10.5 cm
847.8 cm²

10. Find the surface area to the nearest tenth of a rectangular prism with height 15 m and sides 14 m and 13 m.
1174 m²

11. Find the surface area to the nearest tenth of a cylinder 61.7 ft tall that has a diameter of 38 ft.
9629.1 ft²

12. Henry wants to paint the ceiling and walls of his living room. One gallon of paint covers 450 ft². The room is 24 ft by 18 ft, and the walls are 9 ft high. How many full gallons of paint will Henry need to paint his living room?
3 gal

13. A rectangular prism is 18 in. by 16 in. by 10 in. Explain the effect, if any, tripling all the dimensions will have on the surface area of the figure. Possible answer:
By tripling the dimensions, the surface area becomes 9 times larger, from 1256 in² to 11,304 in².

Teaching Tip **Multiple Choice** Students who chose answer **A** for **Exercise 30** did not square the radius when finding the area of the cylinder's base. Remind students to write down the formula before calculating the answer.

Journal

Have students consider the question, "Is it possible for two rectangular prisms to have the same volume and different surface areas?" Have them answer the question and include examples to support their answers.

Power Presentations
with PowerPoint®

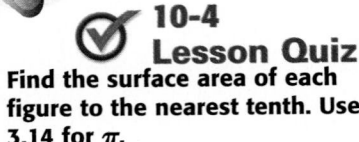

10-4 Lesson Quiz

Find the surface area of each figure to the nearest tenth. Use 3.14 for π.

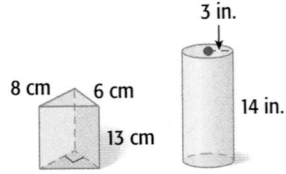

1. the triangular prism 360 cm^2

2. the cylinder 320.3 in^2

3. All outer surfaces of a box are covered with gold foil, except the bottom. The box measures 6 in. long, 4 in. wide, and 3 in. high. How much gold foil was used? 84 in^2

Also available on transparency

PRACTICE AND PROBLEM SOLVING

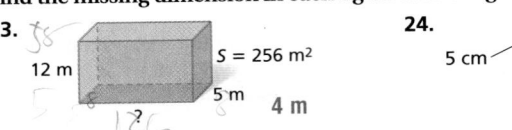

Extra Practice
See page EP21.

Find the surface area of each figure to the nearest tenth. Use 3.14 for π.

21. cylinder: $d = 30$ mm, $h = 49$ mm $1920\pi \approx 6028.8 \text{ mm}^2$

22. rectangular prism: $5\frac{1}{4}$ in. by 8 in. by 12 in. 402.0 in^2

Find the missing dimension in each figure with the given surface area.

23. 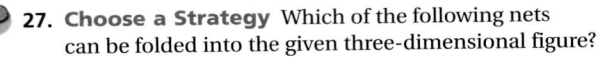 $S = 256 \text{ m}^2$ 12 m 5 m 4 m

24. 5 cm ? $S = 120\pi \text{ cm}^2$ 21.5 cm

25. Multi-Step Jesse makes 12 in. by 6 in. by 8 in. rectangular glass aquariums. Glass costs \$0.08 per square inch. How much will glass for one aquarium cost?   \$34.56

26. Reasoning A cylinder has diameter 10 in. and height 4 in. Explain whether doubling only the height would have the same effect on the surface area as doubling only the radius. What happens if you double both dimensions?

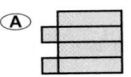 **27. Choose a Strategy** Which of the following nets can be folded into the given three-dimensional figure?

Ⓐ 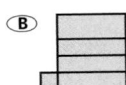   Ⓑ   Ⓒ 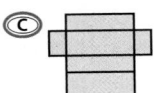   Ⓓ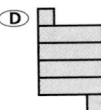

 28. Write About It Explain how you would find the side lengths of a cube with a surface area of 512 ft^2.

29. Challenge The rectangular wood block shown has a hole with diameter 4 cm drilled through its center. What is the total surface area of the block? $426 + 12\pi \approx 463.7 \text{ cm}^2$

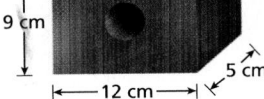 9 cm 12 cm 5 cm

---

SPIRAL STANDARDS REVIEW   NS1.2, MG2.1

30. Multiple Choice Find the surface area of a cylinder with radius 5 feet and height 3 feet. Use 3.14 for π.

Ⓐ 125.6 ft^2 Ⓑ 150.72 ft^2 Ⓒ 172.7 ft^2 Ⓓ 251.2 ft^2

31. Gridded Response A rectangular prism has dimensions 2 meters by 4 meters by 18 meters. Find the surface area, in square meters, of the prism.   232

Add or subtract. (Lesson 2-3)

32. $-0.4 + 0.7$ 0.3

33. $1.35 - 5.6$ -4.25

34. $-0.01 - 0.25$ -0.26

35. $-0.65 + (-1.12)$ -1.77

Find the area of each figure with the given dimensions. (Lesson 9-2)

36. triangle: $b = 3\frac{1}{2}$, $h = 5$ 8.75 square units

37. triangle: $b = 17$, $h = 13$ 110.5 square units

38. trapezoid: $b_1 = 3.4$, $b_2 = 6.6$, $h = 1.8$ 9 square units

---

CHALLENGE 10-4

LESSON 10-4 Challenge
Eight Snips

A **cube** is a prism with six congruent square faces and eight vertices.

By cutting off the corners of the cube $\frac{1}{3}$ of the way into each edge, a **truncated cube** is created.

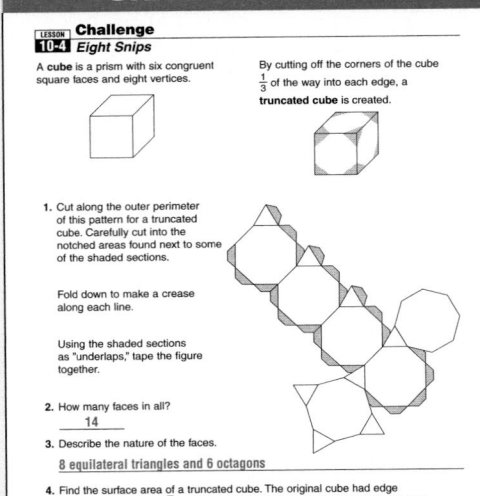

1. Cut along the outer perimeter of this pattern for a truncated cube. Carefully cut into the notched areas found next to some of the shaded sections.

Fold down to make a crease along each line.

Using the shaded sections as "underlaps," tape the figure together.

2. How many faces in all?   14

3. Describe the nature of the faces.
   8 equilateral triangles and 6 octagons

4. Find the surface area of a truncated cube. The original cube had edge length = 24 in. Use $\sqrt{3} \approx 1.73$. Answer to the nearest tenth of a square inch.
   3130.88 in²

PROBLEM SOLVING 10-4

LESSON 10-4 Problem Solving
Surface Area of Prisms and Cylinders

An important factor in designing packaging for a product is the amount of material required to make the package. Consider the three figures described in the table below. Use 3.14 for π. Round to the nearest tenth. Write the correct answer.

1. Find the surface area of each package given in the table.

2. Which package has the lowest materials cost? Assume all of the packages are made from the same material.
   cylinder

Package	Dimensions	Volume	Surface Area
Prism	Base: 2" × 16" Height = 2"	64 in³	136 in²
Prism	Base: 4" × 4" Height = 4"	64 in³	96 in²
Cylinder	Radius = 2" Height = 5.1"	64.06 in³	89.2 in²

Use 3.14 for π. Round to the nearest hundredth.

3. How much cardboard material is required to make a cylindrical oatmeal container that has a diameter of 12.5 cm and a height of 24 cm, assuming there is no overlap? The container will have a plastic lid.
   1064.66 cm²

4. What is the surface area of a rectangular prism that is 5 feet by 6 feet by 10 feet?
   280 ft²

Use 3.14 for π. Round to the nearest tenth. Choose the letter for the best answer.

5. How much metal is required to make the trough pictured below?
   2 ft 6 ft
   Ⓐ 22.0 ft²   C 44.0 ft²
   B 34.0 ft²   D 56.7 ft²

6. A can of vegetables has a diameter of 9.8 cm and is 13.2 cm tall. How much paper is required to make the label, assuming there is no overlap? Round to the nearest tenth.
   F 203.1 cm²
   Ⓖ 406.2 cm²
   H 557.0 cm²
   J 812.4 cm²

Hands-On LAB 10-5

Nets of Cones

Use with Lesson 10-5

go.hrw.com
Lab Resources Online
KEYWORD: MT8CA Lab10

California Standards

MG3.5 Construct two-dimensional patterns for three-dimensional models, such as cylinders, prisms, and **cones**.

REMEMBER

• A net is an arrangement of two-dimensional figures that can fold to form a three-dimensional figure.

You can estimate the surface area of cones using models and nets.

Activity

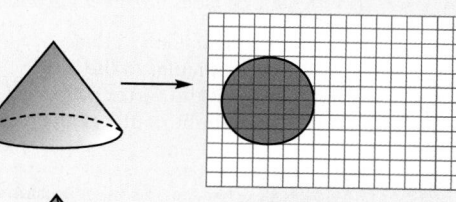

❶ Turn a cone-shaped paper cup upside down and trace the bottom onto grid paper. This represents the base of a cone.

❷ Use scissors to cut a straight line from the edge of the cup to the vertex. Then flatten the shape made by the cut cup.

❸ Trace the flattened cup onto the grid paper so that the curved edge touches the edge of the circle you drew for the base. This is a net for a cone.

❹ Estimate the surface area of the cone by adding the number of whole and almost-whole squares covered by the shapes and half the number of half-squares covered by the shapes.

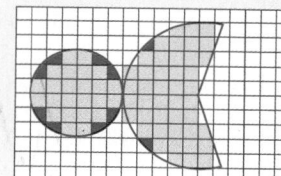

Number of whole and almost-whole squares: 68
Number of half-squares: 10

$$68 + \frac{1}{2}(10) = 73$$

The surface area of the cone is about 73 square units.

Think and Discuss

1. The flattened shape made by cutting the cup is a portion of another shape. What shape do you think that is? Explain. **a circle; the original shape was the base of a cone, which is a circle.**

Try This

1. Find another cone-shaped object, such as a party hat, and repeat the steps in the Activity. Estimate the surface area of a cone the size of the object. **Check students' work.**

Hands-On LAB

Organizer

Use with Lesson 10-5

Objective: Use nets to explore the surface area of cones.

Materials: Grid paper, scissors, paper cones

Online Edition

Countdown to Mastery Week 21

Teach
Discuss

Explain that the flattened shape made by the cut cup is called the *lateral surface* of a cone. By tracing the base and lateral surface on grid paper, you can estimate the surface area of a cone.

Close
Key Concept

The surface area of a cone is the sum of the area of the base and the area of the lateral surface.

Assessment

Have students make cone shapes out of paper and estimate the surface area of the cone modeled by his or her cone shape. **Check students' work.**

California Standards

Measurement and Geometry 3.5

Hands-On Lab
In *Chapter 10 Resource File*

 Online Edition
Tutorial Videos

Countdown to Mastery Week 21

 **Power Presentations**
with PowerPoint®

Warm Up

1. A rectangular prism is 0.6 m by 0.4 m by 1.0 m. What is the surface area?   **2.48 m²**

2. A cylindrical can has a diameter of 14 cm and a height of 20 cm. What is the surface area to the nearest tenth? Use 3.14 for π.
1186.9 cm²

Also available on transparency

 **Math Humor**

Pharaoh: I want the burial chamber to be built in the center of my tomb.

Architect: You mean in the *pyramiddle*?

 **Teaching Tip**
Communicating Math
Emphasize the difference between the height of a pyramid or cone and the slant height. The height is used to find volume, and the slant height is used to find lateral area.

 **California Standards**

Ext. of Measurement and Geometry 2.1

10-5 **Surface Area of Pyramids and Cones**

 California Standards

Extension of MG2.1 Use formulas routinely for finding the perimeter and area of basic two-dimensional figures and **the surface area** and volume **of basic three-dimensional figures, including** rectangles, parallelograms, trapezoids, squares, triangles, circles, prisms, and cylinders.

Vocabulary
slant height
regular pyramid
right cone

Why learn this? You can use a formula to find the lateral surface area of an ant lion's pit. (See Example 3.)

The **slant height** of a pyramid or cone is measured along its lateral surface.

The base of a **regular pyramid** is a regular polygon, and the lateral faces are all congruent.

In a **right cone**, a line perpendicular to the base through the vertex passes through the center of the base.

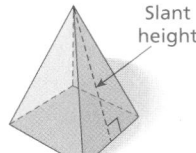 Slant height
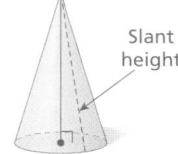 Slant height

Regular pyramid   **Right cone**

SURFACE AREA OF PYRAMIDS AND CONES

Words	Formula	Numbers
Pyramid: The surface area S of a regular pyramid is the base area B plus the lateral area L. The lateral area is one-half the base perimeter P times the slant height ℓ.	$S = B + L$ or $S = B + \frac{1}{2}P\ell$	  $S = (12 \cdot 12) + \frac{1}{2}(48)(8) = 336$ units²
Cone: The surface area S of a right cone is the base area B plus the lateral area L. The lateral area is one-half the base circumference $2\pi r$ times the slant height ℓ.	$S = B + L$ or $S = \pi r^2 + \pi r \ell$	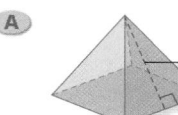 $S = \pi(2^2) + \pi(2)(5) = 14\pi \approx 43.98$ units²

EXAMPLE 1 **Finding Surface Area**

Find the surface area of the figure to the nearest tenth.

A

$$S = B + \frac{1}{2}P\ell$$
$$= (2.5 \cdot 2.5) + \frac{1}{2}(10)(3)$$
$$= 21.25 \text{ in}^2$$

---

1 **Introduce**
Alternate Opener

EXPLORATION

10-5 **Surface Area of Pyramids and Cones**

Look at how the figures are built to answer each question.

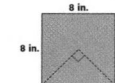

8 in.
8 in.

1. What is the surface area of the pyramid without a base?

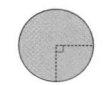

Area of circle = 16π in²

2. What is the surface area of the cone without a base?

Think and Discuss

3. **Explain** what you would need to do to find the surface area of the pyramid and cone including the base.

Motivate

Show students a cone-shaped paper cup. Ask students for the word that describes how much the cone holds. **volume** Ask students for the term that describes the amount of paper. **lateral surface area** Tell students that they will find surface area of cones and pyramids.

Explorations and answers are provided in *Alternate Openers: Explorations Transparencies.*

Find the surface area of the figure to the nearest tenth. Use 3.14 for π.

B

7 m   4 m

$S = \pi r^2 + \pi r \ell$
$= \pi(4)^2 + \pi(4)(7)$
$= 16\pi + 28\pi$
$= 44\pi \approx 138.2 \text{ m}^2$

EXAMPLE 2   **Exploring the Effects of Changing Dimensions**

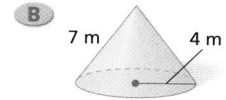

Answers to *Think and Discuss*

1. Possible answer: Both formulas require adding the base area to the product of one-half the distance around the base and the slant height.

A cone has diameter 6 in. and slant height 4 in. Explain whether doubling only the slant height would have the same effect on the surface area as doubling only the radius. Use 3.14 for π.

Original Dimensions	Double the Slant Height	Double the Radius
$S = \pi r^2 + \pi r \ell$	$S = \pi r^2 + \pi r(2\ell)$	$S = \pi(2r)^2 + \pi(2r)\ell$
$= \pi(3)^2 + \pi(3)(4)$	$= \pi(3)^2 + \pi(3)(8)$	$= \pi(6)^2 + \pi(6)(4)$
$= 21\pi \text{ in}^2 \approx 66.0 \text{ in}^2$	$= 33\pi \text{ in}^2 \approx 103.6 \text{ in}^2$	$= 60\pi \text{ in}^2 \approx 188.4 \text{ in}^2$

They would not have the same effect. Doubling the radius would increase the surface area more than doubling the slant height.

EXAMPLE 3   **Life Science Application**

Life Science

Ant lions are the larvae of an insect similar to a dragonfly. They dig cone-shaped pits in the sand to trap ants and other crawling insects.

An ant lion pit is an inverted cone with the dimensions shown. What is the lateral surface area of the pit?

The slant height, radius, and depth of the pit form a right triangle.

$a^2 + b^2 = \ell^2$ *Pythagorean Theorem*
$(2.5)^2 + 2^2 = \ell^2$
$10.25 = \ell^2$
$\sqrt{10.25} = \sqrt{\ell^2}$
$\ell \approx 3.2$
$L = \pi r \ell$ *Lateral surface area*
$= \pi(2.5)(3.2) \approx 25.1 \text{ cm}^2$

2.5 cm

2 cm ℓ

Think and Discuss

1. Compare the formula for surface area of a pyramid to the formula for surface area of a cone.

2. Explain how you would find the slant height of a square pyramid with base edge length 6 cm and height 4 cm.

Power Presentations
with PowerPoint®

Additional Examples

Example 1

Find the surface area of the figure to the nearest tenth.

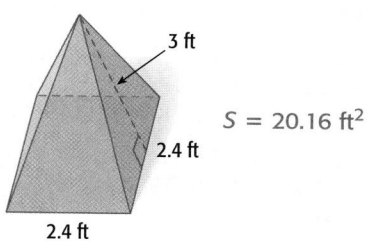

3 ft

$S = 20.16 \text{ ft}^2$

2.4 ft

2.4 ft

Example 2

A cone has diameter 8 in. and slant height 3 in. Explain whether tripling only the slant height would have the same effect on the surface area as tripling only the radius. Use 3.14 for π.

They would not have the same effect. Tripling the radius would increase the surface area more than tripling the slant height.

Example 3

The upper portion of an hourglass is approximately an inverted cone with the given dimensions. What is the lateral surface area of the upper portion of the hourglass?

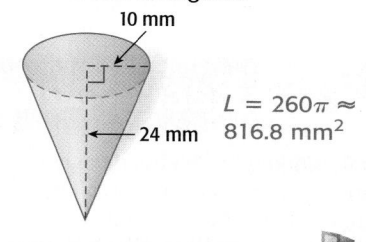

10 mm

$L = 260\pi \approx$
816.8 mm^2

24 mm

Also available on transparency

---

② Teach

Guided Instruction

In this lesson, students learn to find the surface area of pyramids and cones. Show students nets for a pyramid and a cone. Remind students that they found the total surface area of prisms and cylinders by adding the lateral area and *two* base areas. Note that for pyramids and cones, students will add the lateral area and *one* base area. You may want to display the Teaching Transparency.

Teaching Tip   **Language Support** Students may not be familiar with the word *inverted*. *Invert* means "to turn upside down." The *inverted* cone in **Example 3** is "upside-down" on its tip rather than its base.

Universal Access

Through Modeling

Create a few models of pyramids and cones. (Nets are provided in Teaching Tools.) Give students a list of the surface areas. Ask students to use estimation to match the surface areas and the models. Then allow the students to use rulers to measure one of the models and calculate its surface area. Based on this result, allow students to revise their estimates. Then ask students to measure the remaining models, calculate the surface areas, and compare the actual surface areas with their estimates.

③ Close

Summarize

Suggest to students that being able to visualize how a three-dimensional figure can be formed from a two-dimensional figure will help them understand surface area. Draw the two-dimensional patterns for a prism, a cylinder, a pyramid, and a cone, but do not label them. Ask students to identify each.

Answer to *Think and Discuss*

2. Possible answer: make a right triangle with its hypotenuse as the slant height of the pyramid, one leg as the height (4), and the other leg as half the base (3). Use the Pythagorean Theorem to find that the slant height is 5.

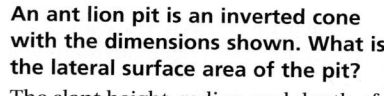

10-5 Surface Area of Pyramids and Cones   **505**

California Standards Practice
Extension of MG2.1, MG2.4

go.hrw.com
Homework Help Online
KEYWORD: MT8CA 10-5
Parent Resources Online
KEYWORD: MT8CA Parent

Assignment Guide

If you finished Example **1** assign:
Proficient 1–3, 6–8, 11, 12, 19–26
Advanced 6–8, 11, 12, 17, 19–26

If you finished Example **2** assign:
Proficient 1–4, 6–9, 11, 12, 19–26
Advanced 6–9, 11, 12, 17, 19–26

If you finished Example **3** assign:
Proficient 1–14, 19–26
Advanced 6–26

Homework Quick Check

Quickly check key concepts.
Exercises: 6, 9, 10, 12

Answers

4. No; doubling the dimensions results in a surface area that is 4 times the original. The cone has a surface area of 282.6 in². Doubling the dimensions results in a surface area of 1120.4 in².

9. No; doubling the dimensions results in a surface area that is 4 times the original. The pyramid has a surface area of 264 yd². Doubling the dimensions results in a surface area of 1056 yd².

Math Background

When working problems involving irrational numbers, such as *pi* and some square roots, different methods of rounding can result in different answers. For example, the answer to Exercise 14 is ≈ 527,237 ft² if calculated on a calculator and rounded at the last step. However, the answer is 526,800 ft² if the values are rounded to the nearest square foot at each step. Unless otherwise indicated, given answers have been calculated on a calculator and rounded at the last step.

Teaching Tip **Geometry** Caution students that to find the base area *B* of a regular triangular pyramid they must use the Pythagorean Theorem to find the height of the triangular base.

California Standards

Standard	Exercises
NS1.2 🔑	21–24
Ext. of MG2.1	1–20, 25–26
MG2.4	14

GUIDED PRACTICE

See Example **1** Find the surface area of each figure to the nearest tenth. Use 3.14 for π.

1. 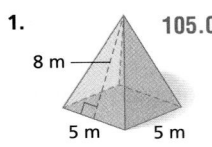 105.0 m²
8 m
5 m   5 m

2. 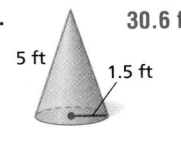 30.6 ft²
5 ft
1.5 ft

3. 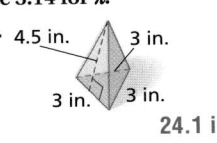 4.5 in.   3 in.
3 in.   3 in.
24.1 in²

See Example **2** **4.** A cone has diameter 12 in. and slant height 9 in. Explain whether doubling both dimensions would double the surface area.

See Example **3** **5.** The rooms at the Wigwam Village Motel in Cave City, Kentucky, are cones about 20 ft high and have a diameter of about 20 ft. Estimate the lateral surface area of a room.   ≈ 702.5 ft²

INDEPENDENT PRACTICE

See Example **1** Find the surface area of each figure to the nearest tenth. Use 3.14 for π.

6. 5.5 in.   4 in.
4 in.   4 in.   39.9 in²

7. 6 mm
4 mm   125.6 mm²

8. 9 m   144.0 m²
6 m   6 m

See Example **2** **9.** A regular square pyramid has a base with 12 yd sides and slant height 5 yd. Explain whether doubling both dimensions would double the surface area.

See Example **3** **10.** In the late 1400s, Leonardo da Vinci designed a parachute shaped like a pyramid. His design called for a tent-like structure made of linen, measuring 21 feet on each side and 12 feet high. Estimate how much material would be needed to make the parachute.   ≈ 669.7 ft²

PRACTICE AND PROBLEM SOLVING

Extra Practice
See page EP21.

Find the surface area of each figure with the given dimensions. Use 3.14 for π.

11. regular triangular pyramid:
base area = 0.06 km²
base perimeter = 0.8 km
slant height = 0.3 km   **0.18 km²**

12. cone:
radius = 5 mi
slant height = 13 mi
90π ≈ 282.6 mi²

REVIEW FOR MASTERY 10-5

LESSON 10-5 Review for Mastery
Surface Area of Pyramids and Cones

A regular pyramid has a base that is a regular polygon, and lateral faces that are congruent triangles. When a square pyramid is unfolded, there are 5 faces: a square and 4 congruent triangles.

An unfolded cone results in a circle and a lateral surface drawn as a sector of a circle. The slant height of the cone is the radius of the circle sector.

Slant height
6 cm
5 cm   5 cm

5 cm   5 cm
11 cm
11 cm

S = Surface Area of a Pyramid
S = sum of the areas of the pyramid's faces
S = area of base + area of lateral faces
S = area of square + 4(area of triangle)
$S = B + \frac{1}{2}$ perimeter *P* of base × slant height ℓ of prism
$S = B + \frac{1}{2}P\ell$
$S = (5 \times 5) + \frac{1}{2} \times (5 \times 4) \times 6$
$S = 25 + 60$
$S = 85 \text{ cm}^2$

S = Surface Area of a Cone
S = area of circular base + area of lateral surface (circle sector)
$S = \pi r^2 + \frac{1}{2} (2\pi r) \times \ell$
$S = \pi r^2 + \pi r\ell$
$S = \pi(5^2) + \pi(5)(11)$
$S = 25\pi + 55\pi = 80\pi \text{ cm}^2$
$S = 80(3.14) \approx 251.2 \text{ cm}^2$

1. Complete to find the surface area of the square pyramid.
$S = B + \frac{1}{2}P\ell$
$S = \underline{(9 \times 9)} + \frac{1}{2} \times \underline{36} \times \underline{12}$
$S = \underline{81} + \underline{216}$
$S = \underline{297} \text{ ft}^2$

12 ft
9 ft   9 ft

2. Complete to find the surface area of the cone.
$S = \pi r^2 + \pi r\ell$
$S = \pi(\underline{4^2}) + \pi \times \underline{4} \times \underline{7}$
$S = \underline{16} \pi + \underline{28} \pi = \underline{44} \pi$
$S \approx \underline{44} (3.14)$
$S \approx \underline{138.16} \text{ in}^2$

7 in.
4 in.

PRACTICE 10-5

LESSON 10-5 Practice B
Surface Area of Pyramids and Cones

Find the surface area of each figure to the nearest tenth. Use 3.14 for π.

1. 12 ft
15 ft
1017.4 ft²

2. 24 ft
18 ft   18 ft
1188 ft²

3. 15 cm
12 cm
9 cm
423 cm²

4. 13.5 in.
13 in.
1081.7 in²

5. 16 cm
13 cm
11 cm
527 cm²

6. 22.5 in.
19.6 in.   19.6 in.
1266.2 in²

7. 18 m
22 m
2260.8 m²

8. 15 ft
17.9 ft   16.2 ft
801.5 ft²

9. 15.8 m   17.6 m
1657.0 m²

10. Find the surface area of a regular square pyramid with a slant height of 17 m and a base perimeter of 44 m.   495 m²

11. Find the length of the slant height of a square pyramid if one side of the base is 15 ft and the surface area is 765 ft².   18 ft

12. Find the length of the slant height of a cone with a radius of 15 cm and a surface area of 1884 cm².   25 cm

13. A cone has a diameter of 12 ft and a slant height of 20 ft. Explain whether tripling both dimensions would triple the surface area. Possible answer:
The surface area of the first cone is 489.84 ft². The surface area of the cone with the new dimensions is 4408.56 ft². It increases the surface area by a factor of 9.

16. Possible answer: What is the lateral area of the cone? Solution: $\pi(2)(11) = 69.08$ in^2

17. Possible answer: Create a right triangle using the slant height as the hypotenuse, the radius of the base as one leg, and the height as the other leg. Then use the Pythagorean Theorem to find the slant height.

13. Science When the Moon is between the Sun and Earth, it casts a conical shadow called the *umbra*. If the shadow is 2140 mi in diameter and 260,955 mi along the edge, what is the lateral area of the umbra? Give your answer in terms of π.
$\approx 279{,}221{,}850\pi$

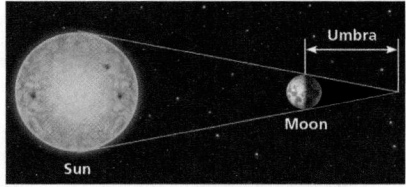

14. Social Studies The Pyramid Arena in Memphis, Tennessee, is 321 feet tall and has a square base with side length 200 yards. What is the lateral area of the pyramid in feet? $\approx 527{,}237$ ft^2

15. The table shows the dimensions of three square pyramids.

a. Complete the table. ≈ 481; ≈ 277

b. Which pyramid has the least lateral area? What is its lateral area? Menkaure; $\approx 191{,}684$ ft^2

c. Which pyramid has the greatest volume? What is its volume? Khufu; 91,636,272 ft^3

Dimensions of Giza Pyramids (ft)			
Pyramid	Height	Slant Height	Side of Base
Khufu		612	756
Khafre	471	588	704
Menkaure	216		346

 16. Write a Problem A cone has a diameter of 4 in. and a slant height of 11 in. Write and solve a problem about the cone.

 17. Write About It The height and base dimensions of a cone are known. Explain how to find the slant height.

 18. Challenge The oldest pyramid is said to be the Step Pyramid of King Zoser, built around 2650 B.C. in Saqqara, Egypt. The base is a rectangle that measures 358 ft by 411 ft, and the height of the pyramid is 204 ft. Find the lateral area of the pyramid.
$\approx 215{,}208$ ft^2; answers may vary due to rounding.

SPIRAL STANDARDS REVIEW
NS1.2, MG2.1

19. Multiple Choice Find the surface area of a triangular pyramid with base area 12 square meters, base perimeter 24 meters, and slant height 8 meters.

Ⓐ 72 m^2　　Ⓑ 108 m^2　　Ⓒ 204 m^2　　Ⓓ 2304 m^2

20. Gridded Response What is the lateral surface area of a cone with diameter 12 centimeters and slant height 6 centimeters? Use 3.14 for π.
113.04 cm^2

Simplify. (Lesson 1-6)

21. $-4(6+8)$　-56　　**22.** $3(-5-4)$　-27　　**23.** $-2(4)-9$　-17　　**24.** $-6(8-9)$　6

Find the volume of each rectangular prism. (Lesson 10-2)

25. length 5 ft, width 3 ft, height 8 ft　120 ft^3　　**26.** length 2.5 m, width 3.5 m, height 7 m
61.25 m^3

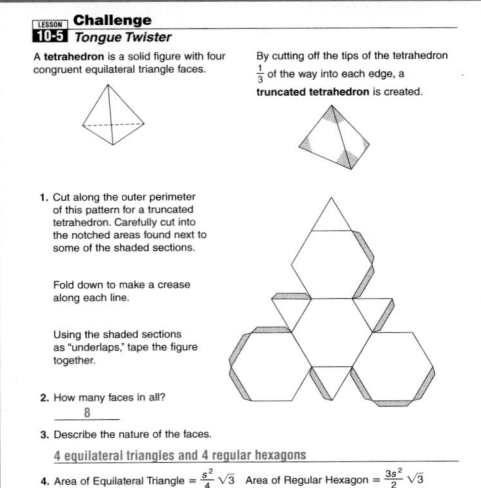

Teaching Tip　**Multiple Choice For Exercise 19,** remind students to use one-half the base perimeter when calculating the surface area of a triangular pyramid. Students who chose answer **C** used the entire base perimeter in their calculations.

 Journal

Students have learned how to find the surface area of prisms, cylinders, pyramids, and cones. Ask students to write about whether any one of the four figures has a surface area that is easier to find than the others. Have students explain their answers.

Power Presentations with PowerPoint®

10-5 Lesson Quiz

Find the surface area of each figure to the nearest tenth. Use 3.14 for π.

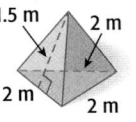
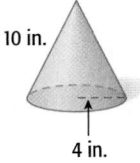

1. the triangular pyramid　6.2 m^2

2. the cone　175.8 in^2

3. Tell whether doubling the dimensions of the cone will double the surface area. It will more than double the surface area because you square the radius to find the area of the base.

Also available on transparency

Hands-On Lab
In *Chapter 10 Resource File*

 Technology Lab
In *Chapter 10 Resource File*

 Online Edition
Tutorial Videos

 Countdown to Mastery Week 22

Power Presentations with PowerPoint®

Warm Up

1. Find the surface area of a square pyramid whose base is 3 m on a side and whose slant height is 5 m. **39 m²**

2. Find the surface area of a cone whose base has a radius of 10 in. and whose slant height is 14 in. Use 3.14 for π. **753.6 in²**

Also available on transparency

Math Fact

Latitude and longitude "lines" on a globe are actually circles.

California Standards

Ext. of Measurement and Geometry 2.1

10-6 Spheres

California Standards

Extension of MG2.1 Use formulas routinely for finding the perimeter and area of basic two-dimensional figures and the surface area and volume **of basic three-dimensional figures,** including rectangles, parallelograms, trapezoids, squares, triangles, circles, prisms, and cylinders.

Vocabulary
sphere
hemisphere

Why learn this? You can find the surface area of Earth.

A **sphere** is the set of points in three dimensions that are a fixed distance from a given point, the center. Earth is not a perfect *sphere*, but it has been molded by gravitational forces into an approximately spherical shape.

A plane that intersects a sphere through its center divides the sphere into two halves, or **hemispheres**. The edge of a hemisphere is a *great circle*.

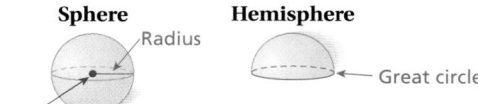

The volume of a hemisphere is exactly halfway between the volume of a cone and the volume of a cylinder with the same radius r and height equal to r.

VOLUME OF A SPHERE		
Words	**Formula**	**Numbers**
The volume V of a sphere is $\frac{4}{3}\pi$ times the cube of the radius r.	$V = \frac{4}{3}\pi r^3$	$V = \frac{4}{3}\pi(3^3)$ $= \frac{108}{3}\pi$ $= 36\pi$ ≈ 113.1 units^3

EXAMPLE 1 Finding the Volume of a Sphere

Helpful Hint

Answers given in terms of π represent exact values, and answers rounded to a given place value are estimates.

Find the volume of a sphere with radius 9 ft, both in terms of π and to the nearest tenth. Use 3.14 for π.

$V = \frac{4}{3}\pi r^3$ *Volume of a sphere*

$= \frac{4}{3}\pi(9)^3$ *Substitute 9 for r.*

$= 972\pi \text{ ft}^3 \approx 3052.1 \text{ ft}^3$

---

1 Introduce

Alternate Opener

EXPLORATION

10-6 Spheres

A basketball is an example of a sphere. The radius of a basketball is about 4.5 inches. A *hemisphere* is half a sphere.

To find the volume of a basketball, imagine the ball is sliced into two halves. Then find the volume of one half and multiply times 2.

The volume of a hemisphere is exactly halfway between the volume of a cone and the volume of a cylinder that both have the same radius r as the hemisphere and a height equal to r.

Use a calculator to find the volume of the following spheres.

	Volume of Cylinder Sitting on Top Half of Sphere	Volume of Cone = $\frac{1}{3}$ · Volume of Cylinder	Volume of Hemisphere = Halfway Between Vol. of Cylinder and Vol. of Cone	Volume of Sphere = Volume of Hemisphere · 2
1.	63.62 in³	$\frac{1}{3}$ · 63.62 = 21.21 in³	$\frac{63.62 + 21.21}{2}$ = 42.42 in³	42.42 · 2 = 84.84 in³
2.	70 in³			
3.	27 in³			
4.	123 in³			

Think and Discuss

5. **Describe** how you could find the volume of the solid at right. The height of the dome is the same as the height of the cylinder, which is equal to the radius of the base.

Motivate

Ask students to name some sports or games that involve a ball. Ask them if they know the mathematical name for the shape of a ball. **sphere** Tell students that they will learn to find the volume and surface area of spheres.

Explorations and answers are provided in *Alternate Openers: Explorations Transparencies.*

The surface area of a sphere is four times the area of a great circle.

SURFACE AREA OF A SPHERE		
Words	**Formula**	**Numbers**
The surface area S of a sphere is 4π times the square of the radius r.	$S = 4\pi r^2$	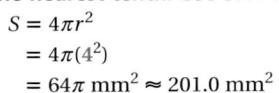 $S = 4\pi(2^2)$ $= 16\pi$ $\approx 50.3 \text{ units}^2$

E X A M P L E 2 Finding Surface Area of a Sphere

 4 mm

Find the surface area, both in terms of π and to the nearest tenth. Use 3.14 for π.

$S = 4\pi r^2$
$\quad = 4\pi(4^2)$ *Surface area of a sphere*
$\quad = 64\pi \text{ mm}^2 \approx 201.0 \text{ mm}^2$ *Substitute 4 for r.*

E X A M P L E 3 Comparing Volumes and Surface Areas

 Reasoning

Compare the volume and surface area of a sphere with radius 42 cm with that of a rectangular prism measuring $56 \times 63 \times 88$ cm.

Sphere:

$V = \frac{4}{3}\pi r^3 = \frac{4}{3}\pi(42)^3$

$\quad \approx \left(\frac{4}{3}\right)\left(\frac{22}{7}\right)(74,088)$

$\quad \approx 310,464 \text{ cm}^3$

$S = 4\pi r^2 = 4\pi(42)^2$

$\quad = 7056\pi$

$\quad \approx 7056\left(\frac{22}{7}\right) \approx 22,176 \text{ cm}^2$

Rectangular prism:

$V = \ell wh$

$\quad = (56)(63)(88)$

$\quad = 310,464 \text{ cm}^3$

$S = 2\ell w + 2\ell h + 2wh$

$\quad = 2(56)(63) + 2(56)(88) + 2(63)(88)$

$\quad = 28,000 \text{ cm}^2$

The sphere and the prism have approximately the same volume, but the prism has a larger surface area.

Possible answers to *Think and Discuss*

1. The area of one great circle would cover $\frac{1}{4}$ of its corresponding sphere because the surface area of a sphere is 4 times the area of one of its great circles.

2. The hemispherical bowl has a volume of $\frac{2}{3}\pi r^3$. The cylindrical glass has a volume of πr^3. The conical cup has a volume of $\frac{1}{3}\pi r^3$. The cylindrical glass has the greatest volume, so it would hold the most water.

Think and Discuss

1. **Compare** the area of a *great circle* with the surface area of a sphere.

2. **Explain** which would hold the most water: a bowl in the shape of a hemisphere with radius r, a cylindrical glass with radius r and height r, or a conical drinking cup with radius r and height r.

Additional Examples

Example 1

Find the volume of a sphere with radius 12 cm, both in terms of π and to the nearest tenth. Use 3.14 for π.

$V = 2304\pi \approx 7234.6 \text{ cm}^3$

Example 2

Find the surface area, both in terms of π and to the nearest tenth. Use 3.14 for π.

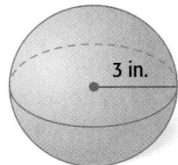 3 in.

$S = 36\pi \approx 113.0 \text{ in}^2$

Example 3

Compare the volume and surface area of a sphere with radius 42 cm with that of a rectangular prism measuring 44 cm by 84 cm by 84 cm.

The sphere and the prism have approximately the same volume, but the prism has a larger surface area.

Also available on transparency

 **Teaching Tip**

Communicating Math
Remind students that answers given in terms of π represent exact values and that answers rounded to a given place value are estimates.

---

② Teach

Guided Instruction

In this lesson, students learn to find the volume and surface area of spheres. Explain that the volume of a hemisphere is the average of the volumes of a cone and a cylinder that each have radius and height equal to the radius of the hemisphere. Share with students that this fact leads to the formula for the volume of a sphere (Teaching Transparency). Explain that the surface area of a sphere is four times the area of one of its great circles. Discuss the conclusion of **Example 3:** A sphere and a prism that contain the same quantity when filled do not necessarily have the same surface area.

Universal Access
Through Concrete Manipulatives

Have students gather five spheres of different sizes (balls, beads, etc.), measure their diameters, and calculate their volumes and surface areas. Have them record their data in a table like the one below.

Object	Volume	Surface Area

You may want to have students compare findings to see if they used some of the same objects and came up with similar results.

③ Close

Summarize

Remind students that both the volume formula and the surface area formula for spheres involve the radius. Ask students if there seems to be a relationship between the exponent on the radius and the units used for each formula.

Possible answer: Yes; because the radius is cubed in the volume formula, the answer is expressed in cubic units. Because the radius is squared in the surface area formula, the answer is expressed in square units.

Assignment Guide

If you finished Example ① assign:
Proficient 1–4, 10–13, 25, 30–36
Advanced 10–13, 24, 25, 30–36

If you finished Example ② assign:
Proficient 1–8, 10–17, 19–22, 25, 26, 28–36
Advanced 10–17, 19–22, 24–36

If you finished Example ③ assign:
Proficient 1–22, 25, 26, 28–36
Advanced 10–36

Homework Quick Check
Quickly check key concepts.
Exercises: 10, 16, 18, 26

Answers

23. Possible answer: Because the volume of a hemisphere is exactly halfway between the volume of a cone and the volume of a cylinder with the same radius and height, it can be shown that the volume of a sphere is exactly halfway between the volume of a cylinder with the same diameter and height and two cones with the same diameter and half the height.

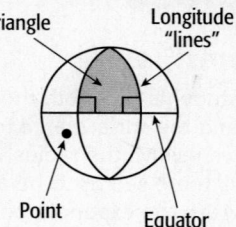

Math Background

Traditional (Euclidean) geometry is based on points, straight lines, and flat planes. In spherical geometry, a point has the traditional meaning, but flat planes are replaced by spherical surfaces, and straight lines are replaced by great circles of the sphere. There are no parallel lines, and there are "triangles" with two right angles.

Triangle
Longitude "lines"
Point
Equator

California Standards

Standard	Exercises
NS2.4	30–34
Ext. of MG2.1	1–29, 35–36

10-6 Exercises

 California Standards Practice
Extension of MG2.1

 go.hrw.com
Homework Help Online
KEYWORD: MT8CA 10-6
Parent Resources Online
KEYWORD: MT8CA Parent

GUIDED PRACTICE

See Example ① Find the volume of each sphere, both in terms of π and to the nearest tenth. Use 3.14 for π.

1. $r = 3$ cm 36π cm³; 113.0 cm³
2. $r = 12$ ft 2304π ft³; 7234.6 ft³
3. $d = 3.4$ m 6.6π m³; 20.7 m³
4. $d = 10$ mi 166.7π mi³; 523.3 mi³

See Example ② Find the surface area of each sphere, both in terms of π and to the nearest tenth. Use 3.14 for π.

5. 1 in. 4π in²; 12.6 in²
6. 7.7 mm 237.2π mm²; 744.7 mm²
7. 8 cm 256π cm²; 803.8 cm²
8. 17 yd 289π yd²; 907.5 yd²

See Example ③
9. Compare the volume and surface area of a sphere with radius 4 in. with that of a cube with sides measuring 6.45 in. The volume of the sphere and the cube are about equal (≈268 in³). The surface area of the sphere is about 201 in², and the surface area of the cube is about 250 in².

INDEPENDENT PRACTICE

See Example ① Find the volume of each sphere, both in terms of π and to the nearest tenth. Use 3.14 for π.

10. $r = 14$ ft
11. $r = 5.7$ cm
12. $d = 26$ mm
13. $d = 2$ in. 1.3π in³; 4.2 in³

See Example ② Find the surface area of each sphere, both in terms of π and to the nearest tenth. Use 3.14 for π.

14. 4 ft 64π ft²; 201 ft²
15. 7.2 m 207.4π m²; 651.2 m²
16. 7 km 49π km²; 153.9 km²
17. 20 cm 400π cm²; 1256 cm²

See Example ③
18. Compare the volume and surface area of a sphere with diameter 5 ft with that of a cylinder with height 2 ft and a base with radius 3 ft.

10. 3658π ft³; 11,488.3 ft³
11. 246.9π cm³; 775.3 cm³
12. 2929.3π mm³; 9198.1 mm³

PRACTICE AND PROBLEM SOLVING

Extra Practice
See page EP21.

Find the missing measurements of each sphere, both in terms of π and to the nearest hundredth. Use 3.14 for π.

18. The volume of the sphere is 20.8π ft³, and its surface area is 25π ft². The volume of the cylinder is 18π ft³, and its surface area is 30π ft².

19. radius = 6.5 in.
volume = ▓
surface area = 169π in² 366.17π in³; 1149.76 in³

20. radius = 11.2 m
volume = 1873.24π m³
surface area = ▓ 501.76π m²; 1575.53 m²

21. diameter = 6.8 yd
volume = ▓
surface area = ▓ $V = 52.41\pi \approx$ 164.55 yd³; $S = 46.24\pi \approx$ 145.19 yd²

22. radius = ▓
diameter = 22 in.
surface area = ▓ 11 in.; 484$\pi \approx$ 1519.76 in²

23. **Reasoning** Use models of a sphere, a cylinder, and two cones. The sphere and cylinder have the same diameter and height. The cones have the same diameter and half the height of the sphere. Describe the relationship between the volumes of these shapes.

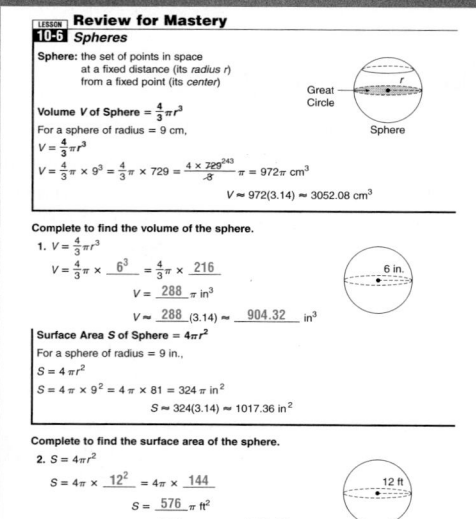
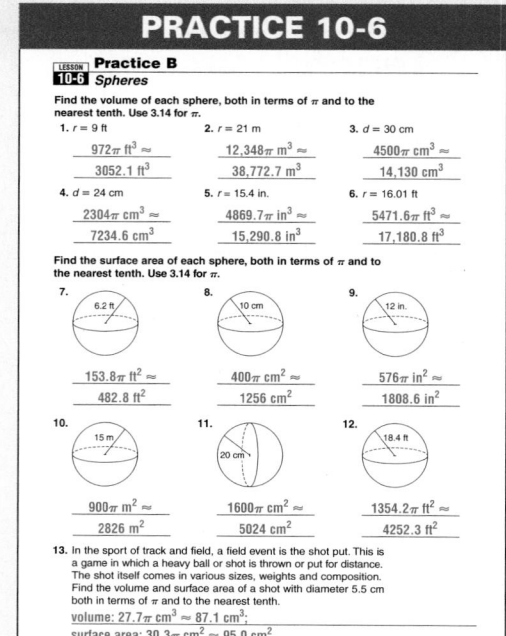

Eggs come in many different shapes. The eggs of birds that live on cliffs are often extremely pointed to keep the eggs from rolling. Other birds, such as great horned owls, have eggs that are nearly spherical. Turtles and crocodiles also have nearly spherical eggs, and the eggs of many dinosaurs were spherical.

24. To lay their eggs, green turtles travel hundreds of miles to the beach where they were born. The eggs are buried on the beach in a hole about 40 cm deep. The eggs are approximately spherical, with an average diameter of 4.5 cm, and each turtle lays an average of 113 eggs at a time. Estimate the total volume of eggs laid by a green turtle at one time. $\approx$ **5392 cm³**

25. Fossilized embryos of dinosaurs called titanosaurid sauropods have recently been found in spherical eggs in Patagonia. The eggs were 15 cm in diameter, and the adult dinosaurs were more than 12 m in length. Find the volume of an egg. $\approx$ **1767.15 cm³**

26. Hummingbirds lay eggs that are nearly spherical and about 1 cm in diameter. Find the surface area of an egg. $\approx$ **3.14 cm²**

27. ⭐ **Challenge** A spherical-shaped ostrich egg has about the same volume as a sphere with a diameter of 5 inches. If the shell is about $\frac{1}{12}$ inch thick, estimate the volume of just the shell, not including the interior of the egg. $\approx$ **6.33 in³**

SPIRAL STANDARDS REVIEW
NS2.4, MG2.1

28. Multiple Choice The surface area of a sphere is 50.24 square centimeters. Find the length of the diameter. Use 3.14 for π.

   Ⓐ 1 cm   Ⓑ 2 cm   Ⓒ 2.5 cm   Ⓓ 4 cm

29. Gridded Response Find the surface area, in square feet, of a sphere with radius 3 feet. Use 3.14 for π. **113.04**

Simplify. (Lesson 4-6)

30. $\sqrt{144}$ **12**   **31.** $\sqrt{64}$ **8**   **32.** $\sqrt{169}$ **13**   **33.** $\sqrt{225}$ **15**   **34.** $\sqrt{1}$ **1**

Find the surface area of each figure. Use 3.14 for π. (Lesson 10-5)

35. a square pyramid with base 13 m by 13 m and slant height 7.5 m **364 m²**

36. a cone with a diameter 90 cm and slant height 125 cm **24,021 cm²**

Interdisciplinary LINK

Life Science

Exercises 24–27 involve using formulas to find the surface area and volume of eggs. Bird, reptile, and insect eggs are studied in middle school science programs, such as *Holt California Life Science*.

Teaching Tip   **Multiple Choice** Remind students that for **Exercise 28,** they must solve the equation $S = 4\pi r^2$ for r, then double the value of r to find the diameter of the sphere. Students who chose answer choice **B** found the radius.

✒ Journal

Remind students that scientific notation is a way to express very large or very small numbers (Lesson 4-5). Ask them to write about some spherical or hemispherical objects with volumes or surface areas that could be expressed in scientific notation. Examples might include the moon or a plant cell.

CHALLENGE 10-6

Challenge
10-6 *Useful and Intriguing*

A **geodesic dome** is a structure made of a complex network of triangles that form a roughly spherical surface. The dome gets its efficiency from the characteristics of a sphere.

The first contemporary geodesic dome (1922) is attributed to the German Walter Bauersfeld. The great-circle principle used in his dome has been used in Asia for centuries to weave fish traps and baskets. In the 1940's, the American Buckminster Fuller used the dome to design efficient houses.

The classic geodesic dome takes its form from the **icosahedron**, a regular solid with 20 equilateral triangles as faces, 30 congruent edges, and 12 vertices.

Consider an icosahedron with edge $s = 12$ ft.

1. Find the surface area with the formula Area of Equilateral Triangle $= \frac{s^2}{4}\sqrt{3}$. Use $\sqrt{3} \approx 1.73$ to answer to the nearest tenth of a square foot.
$20\left(\frac{12^2}{4}\sqrt{3}\right) = 720\sqrt{3} \approx 720(1.73) \approx 1245.6$ ft²

2. Find the volume with the formula Volume of Icosahedron $= \frac{5}{12}(3 + \sqrt{5})s^2$. Use $\sqrt{5} \approx 2.24$ to answer to the nearest tenth of a cubic foot.
$\frac{5}{12}(3 + \sqrt{5})12^2 = 60(3 + \sqrt{5}) \approx 60(3 + 2.24) \approx 314.4$ ft³

3. Find an approximate value for the radius r of the sphere that has approximately the same volume as the icosahedron.
$\frac{4}{3}\pi r^3 \approx 314.4 \rightarrow \frac{4}{3}(3.14)r^3 \approx 314.4 \rightarrow 4.19r^3 \approx 314.4 \rightarrow r^3 \approx$
$\frac{75}{?} \rightarrow r \approx 4.2$

4. Using your value of r, find the surface area of that sphere.
$4(3.14)(4.2^2) \approx 221.6$ ft³

5. Use your results to make an observation about why a sphere is more efficient than an icosahedron. Possible answer:
For a given volume, a sphere exposes less surface area than an icosahedron.

PROBLEM SOLVING 10-6

Problem Solving
10-6 *Spheres*

Early golf balls were smooth spheres. Later it was discovered that golf balls flew better when they were dimpled. On January 1, 1932, the United States Golf Association set standards for the weight and size of a golf ball. The minimum diameter of a regulation golf ball is 1.680 inches. Use 3.14 for π. Round to the nearest hundredth.

1. Find the volume of a smooth golf ball with the minimum diameter allowed by the United States Golf Association.
2.48 in³

2. Find the surface area of a smooth golf ball with the minimum diameter allowed by the United States Golf Association.
8.86 in²

3. Would the dimples on a golf ball increase or decrease the volume of the ball?
decrease

4. Would the dimples on a golf ball increase or decrease the surface area of the ball?
increase

Use 3.14 for π. Use the following information for Exercises 5–6. A track and field expert recommends changes to the size of a shot put. One recommendation is that a shot put should have a diameter between 90 and 110 mm. Choose the letter for the best answer.

5. Find the surface area of a shot put with a diameter of 90 mm.
Ⓐ 25,434 mm²
B 101,736 mm²
C 381,520 mm²
D 3,052,080 mm²

6. Find the surface area of a shot put with diameter 110 mm.
F 9,499 mm²
Ⓖ 22,834 mm²
Ⓗ 37,994 mm²
J 151,976 mm²

7. Find the volume of the earth if the average diameter of the earth is 7926 miles.
A 2.0 × 10⁸ mi³
Ⓑ 2.6 × 10¹¹ mi³
C 7.9 × 10⁹ mi³
D 2.1 × 10¹² mi³

8. An ice cream cone has a diameter of 4.2 cm and a height of 11.5 cm. One spherical scoop of ice cream is put on the cone that has a diameter of 5.6 cm. If the ice cream were to melt in the cone, how much of it would overflow the cone? Round to the nearest tenth.
F 0 cm³
G 12.3 cm³
Ⓗ 38.8 cm³
J 54.3 cm³

Power Presentations
with PowerPoint®

✓ 10-6 Lesson Quiz

Find the volume of each sphere, both in terms of π and to the nearest tenth. Use 3.14 for π.

1. $r = 4$ ft   85.3π ft³, 267.8 ft³

2. $d = 6$ m   36π m³, 113.0 m³

Find the surface area of each sphere, both in terms of π and to the nearest tenth. Use 3.14 for π.

3. $r = 22$ in.   1936π in², 6079.0 in²

4. $d = 1.5$ mi   2.25π mi², 7.1 mi²

5. A basketball has a circumference of 29 in. To the nearest cubic inch, what is its volume? 412 in³

Also available on transparency

Online Edition
Tutorial Videos

Countdown to Mastery Week 22

Power Presentations
with PowerPoint®

Warm Up
Find the surface area of each rectangular prism.

1. length 14 cm, width 7 cm, height 7 cm 490 cm²

2. length 30 in., width 6 in., height 21 in. 1872 in²

3. length 3 mm, width 6 mm, height 4 mm 108 mm²

4. length 37 in., width 9 in., height 18 in. 2322 in²

Also available on transparency

Math Humor

When the student was caught climbing the statues in the city park, she explained that she was just doing her math homework—she was *scaling three-dimensional figures*.

California Standards

Measurement and Geometry 2.3
Also covered:

Measurement and Geometry
2.0 Students compute the perimeter, area, and volume of common geometric objects and use the results to find measures of less common objects.
They know how perimeter, area, and volume are affected by changes of scale.

 10-7 **Scaling Three-Dimensional Figures**

California Standards

MG2.3 Compute the length of the perimeter, **the surface area of the faces, and the volume of a three-dimensional object built from rectangular solids. Understand that when the lengths of all dimensions are multiplied by a scale factor, the surface area is multiplied by the square of the scale factor and the volume is multiplied by the cube of the scale factor.**

Who uses this? Companies use scaling when creating boxes for packaging products.

A packaging company offers a supply of cube boxes with measurements shown. What is the volume and surface area of each of these boxes?

 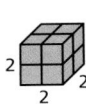 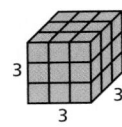

Edge Length	1 ft	2 ft	3 ft
Volume	$1 \times 1 \times 1 = 1\ \text{ft}^3$	$2 \times 2 \times 2 = 8\ \text{ft}^3$	$3 \times 3 \times 3 = 27\ \text{ft}^3$
Surface Area	$6 \cdot 1 \times 1 = 6\ \text{ft}^2$	$6 \cdot 2 \times 2 = 24\ \text{ft}^2$	$6 \cdot 3 \times 3 = 54\ \text{ft}^2$

Corresponding edge lengths of any two cubes are in proportion to each other because the cubes are similar. However, volumes and surface areas do not have the same scale factor as edge lengths.

Each edge of the 2 ft cube is 2 times as long as each edge of the 1 ft cube. However, the cube's volume, or *capacity*, is $2^3 = 8$ times as large, and its surface area is $2^2 = 4$ times as large as the 1 ft cube's.

EXAMPLE 1 **Scaling Models That Are Cubes**

A 6 cm cube is built from small cubes, each 2 cm on an edge. Compare the following values.

A the edge lengths of the large and small cubes

$$\frac{6\ \text{cm cube}}{2\ \text{cm cube}} \rightarrow \frac{6\ \text{cm}}{2\ \text{cm}} = 3 \qquad \textit{Ratio of corresponding edges}$$

The edge length of the large cube is 3 times that of the small cube.

B the surface areas of the two cubes

$$\frac{6\ \text{cm cube}}{2\ \text{cm cube}} \rightarrow \frac{216\ \text{cm}^2}{24\ \text{cm}^2} = 9 \qquad \textit{Ratio of corresponding areas}$$

The surface area of the large cube is $3^2 = 9$ times that of the small cube.

C the volumes of the two cubes

$$\frac{6\ \text{cm cube}}{2\ \text{cm cube}} \rightarrow \frac{216\ \text{cm}^3}{8\ \text{cm}^3} = 27 \qquad \textit{Ratio of corresponding volumes}$$

The volume of the large cube is $3^3 = 27$ times that of the small cube.

---

1 Introduce
Alternate Opener

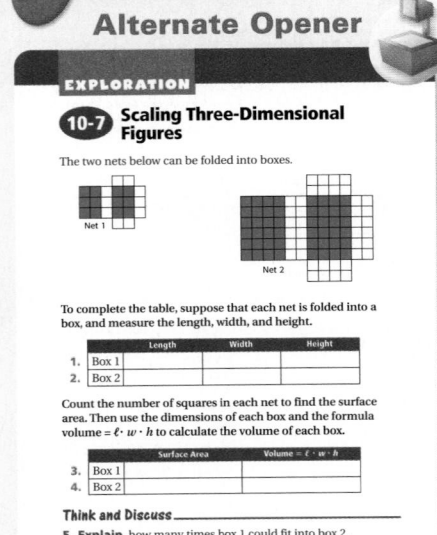

EXPLORATION

10-7 Scaling Three-Dimensional Figures

The two nets below can be folded into boxes.

Net 1
Net 2

To complete the table, suppose that each net is folded into a box, and measure the length, width, and height.

	Length	Width	Height
1. Box 1			
2. Box 2			

Count the number of squares in each net to find the surface area. Then use the dimensions of each box and the formula volume = $\ell \cdot w \cdot h$ to calculate the volume of each box.

	Surface Area	Volume = $\ell \cdot w \cdot h$
3. Box 1		
4. Box 2		

Think and Discuss

5. **Explain** how many times box 1 could fit into box 2.
6. **Predict** how many times box 2 would fit into box 2 if each dimension of box 2 were multiplied by 3.

Motivate

Provide students with graph paper. Tell them to draw squares with side lengths of 1, 3, 6, and 12 units. Have students find the area of each of the squares. 1, 9, 36, and 144 units² Then tell students to compare the areas of pairs of squares. Point out that all the squares are similar. Encourage students to compare the areas of the squares with the scale factors of the squares. For example, the square with side length 3 is similar to the square with side length 12. The scale factor is 4. The area of the larger square is 16 times more than the area of the smaller square.

Explorations and answers are provided in *Alternate Openers: Explorations Transparencies*.

The previous example suggests that the following ratios are true for similar three-dimensional figures.

Reading Math

Three-dimensional figures are sometimes referred to as *solids*.

RATIOS OF SIMILAR SOLIDS

- If two three-dimensional figures are similar by a scale of k, then the surface areas of the figures have a ratio of k^2.
- If two three-dimensional figures are similar by a scale of k, then the volumes of the figures have a ratio of k^3.

 EXAMPLE 2 Finding Surface Area and Volume of Similar Solids

A The surface area of a box is 27 in². What is the surface area of a similar box that is larger by a scale factor of 5?

$$S = 27 \cdot 5^2 \qquad \text{Multiply by the square of the scale factor.}$$
$$= 27 \cdot 25 \qquad \text{Simplify the power.}$$
$$= 675 \text{ in}^2 \qquad \text{Multiply.}$$

B The volume of a bucket is 6237 in³. What is the volume of a similar bucket that is smaller by a scale factor of $\frac{1}{3}$?

$$V = 6237 \cdot \left(\frac{1}{3}\right)^3 \qquad \text{Multiply by the cube of the scale factor.}$$
$$= 6237 \cdot \frac{1}{27} \qquad \text{Simplify the power.}$$
$$= 231 \text{ in}^3 \qquad \text{Multiply.}$$

EXAMPLE 3 *Business Application*

A machine fills a cube box that has edge lengths of 1 ft with shampoo samples in 3 seconds. How long does it take the machine to fill at the same rate a cube box that has edge lengths of 4 ft?

$$V = 4 \text{ ft} \cdot 4 \text{ ft} \cdot 4 \text{ ft} = 64 \text{ ft}^3 \qquad \text{Find the volume of the larger box.}$$
$$\frac{3}{1 \text{ ft}^3} = \frac{x}{64 \text{ ft}^3} \qquad \text{Set up a proportion and solve.}$$
$$3 \cdot 64 = x \qquad \text{Cross multiply.}$$
$$192 = x \qquad \text{Calculate the fill time.}$$

It takes 192 seconds to fill the larger box.

Possible answers to Think and Discuss

1. The volume of the model is $\frac{1}{8}$ the volume of the original object.

2. Possible answer: Multiply each of the dimensions of the prism by the square root of 2.

Think and Discuss

1. **Describe** how the volume of a model compares to the original object if the scale factor of the model is 1:2.

2. **Explain** one possible way to double the surface area of a rectangular prism.

Power Presentations
with PowerPoint®

Additional Examples

Example 1

A 3 cm cube is built from small cubes, each 1 cm on an edge. Compare the following values.

A. the edge lengths of the two cubes

The length of the edges of the larger cube is 3 times the length of the edges of the smaller cube.

B. the surface areas of the two cubes

The surface area of the larger cube is 9 times that of the smaller cube.

C. the volumes of the two cubes

The volume of the larger cube is 27 times that of the smaller cube.

Example 2

A. The surface area of a box is 1300 in². What is the surface area of a similar box that is smaller by a scale factor of $\frac{1}{2}$? 325 in²

B. The volume of a child's swimming pool is 28 ft³. What is the volume of a similar pool that is larger by a scale factor of 4? 1792 ft³

Example 3

It takes 30 seconds for a pump to fill a cubic container whose edge measures 1 ft. How long does it take for the pump to fill a cubic container whose edge measures 2 ft? 240 s, or 4 min

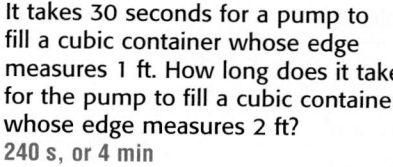

Also available on transparency

2 Teach

Guided Instruction

In this lesson, students learn to make scale models of three-dimensional, or solid, figures. Review with students how to find the volume and surface area of a 1 ft cube, a 2 ft cube, and a 3 ft cube. Share with students that capacity is the same as volume. In **Example 1,** compare the ratios of corresponding edges, surface areas, and volumes for a 2 ft cube and a 6 ft cube. Point out that the ratio of surface areas is the *square* of the ratio of corresponding edges, and the ratio of volumes is the *cube* of the ratio of corresponding edges. Also in this lesson students learn to find volume and surface area of similar three-dimensional figures. Emphasize that the method does not depend on the shape of the figures but on the similarity of the figures.

Universal Access
Through Concrete Manipulatives

Have students work in pairs. Provide each pair with a set of 8 to 125 centimeter cubes (provided in the Manipulatives Kit). Ask students to build larger cubes from the centimeter cubes. For each larger cube, students should find the length of the edge, the surface area (by counting the visible square centimeters on the faces of the cube), and the volume (by counting the number of centimeter cubes needed to build the larger cube). Have them record their data and compare with another group's data.

3 Close

Summarize

Show students models or drawings of a 1 in. cube and a 1 ft cube. Ask students to find the surface area of each figure in square inches and the volume of each figure in cubic inches. Have them also identify the scale factor if the small cube is a model of the larger cube.

surface areas: 6 in² and 864 in²; volumes: 1 in³ and 1728 in³; scale factor: $\frac{1}{12}$

California Standards Practice
MG2.3, MG2.4

go.hrw.com
Homework Help Online
KEYWORD: MT8CA 10-7
Parent Resources Online
KEYWORD: MT8CA Parent

Assignment Guide

If you finished Example **1** assign:
Proficient 1–3, 7–9, 13–15, 23, 26–35
Advanced 7–9, 13–19, 23, 25–35

If you finished Example **2** assign:
Proficient 1–5, 7–11, 13–15, 23–24, 26–35
Advanced 7–11, 13–20, 22–35

If you finished Example **3** assign:
Proficient 1–15, 23–24, 26–35
Advanced 7–35

Homework Quick Check

Quickly check key concepts.
Exercises: 8, 10, 12, 14

Math Background

Capacity and volume are both measures of the amount of space inside a three-dimensional object. Capacity is normally used to indicate the amount a container will hold. The tables show some common units.

Volume

U. S. Customary	Metric
$1728 \text{ in}^3 = 1 \text{ ft}^3$	$1000 \text{ mm}^3 = 1 \text{ cm}^3$
$27 \text{ ft}^3 = 1 \text{ yd}^3$	$1{,}000{,}000 \text{ cm}^3 = 1 \text{ m}^3$

Capacity

U. S. Customary	Metric
$32 \text{ oz} = 1 \text{ qt}$	$1000 \text{ mL} = 1 \text{ L}$
$4 \text{ qt} = 1 \text{ gal}$	$1000 \text{ L} = 1 \text{ kL}$

GUIDED PRACTICE

See Example **1** An 8 in. cube is built from small cubes, each 2 in. on an edge. Compare the following values.

1. the edge lengths of the large and small cubes **4:1**

2. the surface areas of the two cubes **16:1**

3. the volumes of the two cubes **64:1**

See Example **2** 4. The surface area of a box is 10.4 cm^2. What is the surface area of a similar box that is larger by a scale factor of 3? **93.6 cm²**

5. The volume of a cylinder is about 523 cm^3. What is the volume, to the nearest tenth, of a similar cylinder that is smaller by a scale factor of $\frac{1}{4}$? **8.2 cm³**

See Example **3** 6. A 3 ft by 1 ft by 1 ft fish tank in the shape of a rectangular prism drains in 3 min. How long would it take a 7 ft by 4 ft by 4 ft fish tank to drain at the same rate? **112 min**

INDEPENDENT PRACTICE

See Example **1** A 6 m cube is built from small cubes, each 3 m on an edge. Compare the following values.

7. the edge lengths of the large and small cubes **2:1**

8. the surface areas of the two cubes **4:1**

9. the volumes of the two cubes **8:1**

See Example **2** 10. The surface area of a car frame is about 200 ft^2. What is the surface area, to the nearest tenth, of a model of the car that is smaller by a scale factor of $\frac{1}{12}$? **1.4 ft²**

11. The volume of an ice chest is 2160 in^3. What is the volume of a similar ice chest that is larger by a scale factor of 2.5? **33,750 in³**

See Example **3** 12. An aboveground pool 5 ft tall with a diameter of 40 ft is filled with water in 50 minutes. How long will it take to fill an aboveground pool that is 6 ft tall with a diameter of 36 ft? **48.6 min**

PRACTICE AND PROBLEM SOLVING

Extra Practice
See page EP21.

For each cube, a reduced scale model is built using a scale factor of $\frac{1}{2}$. Find the length of the model and the number of 1 cm cubes used to build it.

13. a 2 cm cube
1 cm; 1 cube

14. a 6 cm cube
3 cm; 27 cubes

15. an 18 cm cube
9 cm; 729 cubes

16. a 4 cm cube
2 cm; 8 cubes

17. a 14 cm cube
7 cm; 343 cubes

18. a 16 cm cube
8 cm; 512 cubes

19. What is the volume in cubic centimeters of a 1 m cube? **1,000,000 cm³**

20. **Art** A sand castle requires 3 pounds of sand. How much sand would be required to double all the dimensions of the sand castle? **24 lb**

California Standards

Standard	Exercises
AF4.0 🔑	28–31
MG2.1	32–35
MG2.3	1–27
MG2.4	19, 21

REVIEW FOR MASTERY 10-7

Review for Mastery
10-7 *Scaling Three-Dimensional Figures*

Any two cubes are similar. The sides of this larger cube are 3 times as long as the sides of this smaller cube.

$$\frac{\text{side of larger cube}}{\text{side of smaller cube}} = \frac{9 \text{ in.}}{3 \text{ in.}} = \frac{3}{1} = 3$$

The scale factor is 3.

The ratio of the surface areas S of two cubes is the square of the scale factor.

$$\frac{S \text{ larger}}{S \text{ smaller}} = \frac{6(\text{area one face})}{6(\text{area one face})} = \frac{6(9 \times 9)}{6(3 \times 3)} = \left(\frac{3}{1}\right)^2 = 9$$

The ratio of the surface areas of the two cubes is 9.

The ratio of the volumes V of two cubes is the cube of the scale factor.

$$\frac{V \text{ larger}}{V \text{ smaller}} = \frac{\ell \times w \times h}{\ell \times w \times h} = \frac{9 \times 9 \times 9}{3 \times 3 \times 3} = \left(\frac{3}{1}\right)^3 = 27$$

The ratio of the volumes of the two cubes is 27.

Find the scale factor for each pair of cubes. Then find the ratio of the surface areas.

1. side of smaller cube = 16 in.   scale factor = $\frac{1}{4}$
side of larger cube = 64 in.   ratio of surface areas
$\frac{\text{smaller}}{\text{larger}} = \frac{16 \text{ in.}}{64 \text{ in.}} = \frac{1}{4}$ $= (\text{scale factor})^2 = \left(\frac{1}{4}\right)^2 = \frac{1}{16}$

Find the scale factor for each pair of cubes. Then find the ratio of the volumes.

2. side of larger cube = 100 in.   3. side of smaller cube = 6 m
side of smaller cube = 25 in.   side of larger cube = 36 m
$\frac{\text{larger}}{\text{smaller}} = \frac{100 \text{ in.}}{25 \text{ in.}} = \frac{4}{1} = 4$ $\frac{\text{smaller}}{\text{larger}} = \frac{6 \text{ m}}{36 \text{ m}} = \frac{1}{6}$
scale factor = 4   scale factor = $\frac{1}{6}$
ratio of volumes   ratio of volumes
$= (\text{scale factor})^3 = (4)^3 = 64$ $= (\text{scale factor})^3 = \left(\frac{1}{6}\right)^3 = \frac{1}{216}$

PRACTICE 10-7

Practice B
10-7 *Scaling Three-Dimensional Figures*

A 10 in. cube is built from small cubes, each 2 in. on a side. Compare the following values.

1. The side lengths of the two cubes
The sides of the 10 in. cube are 5 times as long as the sides of the 2 in. cube.

2. The surface area of the two cubes
The surface area of the 10 in. cube is 25 times that of the 2 in. cube.

3. The volumes of the two cubes
The volume of the 10 in. cube is 125 times that of the 2 in. cube.

A 9 cm cube is built from small cubes, each 3 cm on a side. Compare the following values.

4. The side lengths of the two cubes
The sides of the 9 cm cube are 3 times as long as the sides of the 3 cm cube.

5. The surface area of the two cubes
The surface area of the 9 cm cube is 9 times that of the 3 cm cube.

6. The volumes of the two cubes
The volume of the 9 cm cube is 27 times that of the 3 cm cube.

7. The surface area of a bucket is 6176 cm². What is the surface area of a similar bucket that is smaller by a scale of $\frac{1}{4}$?
386 cm²

8. The volume of a cone is 316 in³. What is the volume of a similar cone that is larger by a scale of 3?
8532 in³

9. It takes a machine 40 seconds to fill a cubic box with sides measuring 10 in. How long will it take the same machine to fill a cubic box with sides measuring 15 in.?
135 seconds

21. A kitchen sink measures 21 in. by 16 in. by 8 in. It takes 4 minutes 30 seconds to fill with water. A smaller kitchen sink takes 4 min 12 seconds to fill with water.

  a. What is the volume of the smaller kitchen sink? **2508.8 in³**

  b. About how many gallons of water does the smaller kitchen sink hold?
  (*Hint:* 1 gal = 231 in³) **about 10.9 gal**

22. **Recreation** If it took 100,000 Lego® blocks to build a cylindrical monument with a 5 m diameter, about how many Legos would be needed to build a monument with an 8 m diameter and the same height? **256,000**

23. Reasoning If you double the length of each edge of a cube, are the surface area and volume of the cube also doubled? Explain.

24. Choose a Strategy Six 1 cm cubes are used to build a solid. How many cubes are used to build a scale model of the solid with a scale factor of 2 to 1? Describe the tools and techniques you used.

  (A) 12 cubes   (B) 24 cubes   (C) 48 cubes   (D) 144 cubes

25. Write About It If the scale factor of a model is $\frac{1}{5}$, what is the relationship between the volume of the original object and the volume of the model?

26. Challenge To double the volume of a rectangular prism, what number is multiplied by each of the prism's linear dimensions? Give your answer to the nearest hundredth. **the cube root of 2, or about 1.26**

25. Possible answer: The volume of the original object is 125 times the volume of the model.

Legoland, in Billund, Denmark, contains Lego models of the Taj Mahal, Mount Rushmore, other monuments, and visitors, too.

 SPIRAL STANDARDS REVIEW   ← **AF4.0, MG2.1, MG2.3**

27. Multiple Choice A 9-inch cube is built from small cubes, each 1 inch on an edge. What is the ratio of the volume of the larger cube to the volume of the smaller cube?

  (A) 1:9   (B) 9:1   (C) 81:1   (D) 729:1

28. Extended Response A 5-inch cube is built from small cubes, each 1 inch on an edge. Compare the edge lengths, surface areas, and volumes of the large and the small cubes. **ratio of edge lengths 5:1, ratio of surface area 25:1, ratio of volume 125:1**

Solve. (Lesson 1-9)

29. $3 + 4x = 35$ **30.** $-y - 6 = 8$ **31.** $21 = 5w + 11$ **32.** $-24 = 10b - 4$
    $x = 8$ $y = -14$ $w = 2$ $b = -2$

Find the surface area of each sphere to the nearest tenth. Use 3.14 for π.
(Lesson 10-6)

33. radius 5 mm   **34.** radius 12.2 ft   **35.** diameter 4 in.   **36.** diameter 20 cm
    314 mm²   **1869.4 ft²**   **50.2 in²**   **1256 cm²**

Organizer

Objective: Assess students' mastery of concepts and skills in Lessons 10-4 through 10-7.

Resources

 Assessment Resources
Section 10B Quiz

 Test & Practice Generator
 One-Stop Planner®

INTERVENTION ←⬌→

Resources

Ready to Go On?
Intervention and
Enrichment Worksheets

Ready to Go On? CD-ROM

Ready to Go On? Online

my.hrw.com

Quiz for Lessons 10-4 Through 10-7

✓ 10-4 Surface Area of Prisms and Cylinders

Find the surface area of each figure to the nearest tenth. Use 3.14 for π.

1.

9 cm
12 cm   5 cm

426.0 cm²

2.

4 m
5 m

282.6 m²

3.

5 in.
3 in.   2 in.

49.0 in²

✓ 10-5 Surface Area of Pyramids and Cones

Find the surface area of each figure to the nearest tenth. Use 3.14 for π.

4.   105.6 ft²

10 ft   6 ft
6 ft   6 ft

5.   201.0 cm²

12 cm
4 cm

6.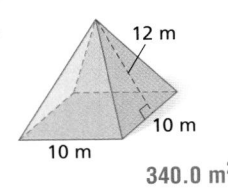

12 m
10 m
10 m

340.0 m²

✓ 10-6 Spheres

Find the volume and surface area of each sphere to the nearest tenth.
Use 3.14 for π.

7.

6.6 mm

1203.6 mm³; 547.1 mm²

8.

9 cm

3052.1 cm³; 1017.4 cm²

9.

15 yd

1766.3 yd³; 706.5 yd²

✓ 10-7 Scaling Three-Dimensional Figures

10. The surface area of a cylinder is 109 cm². What is the surface area of a similar cylinder that is smaller by a scale factor of $\frac{1}{3}$? $12\frac{1}{9}$ cm²

11. The volume of a cube is 35 ft³. What is the volume of a similar cube that is larger by a scale factor of 9?   25,515 ft³

READY TO GO ON?

Diagnose and Prescribe

NO INTERVENE

YES ENRICH

	READY TO GO ON? Intervention, Section 10B		
Ready to Go On? Intervention	 **Worksheets**	**CD-ROM**	**Online**
✓ Lesson 10-4 MG2.1, MG2.2, MG2.3	10-4 Intervention	Activity 10-4	
✓ Lesson 10-5 Ext. of MG2.1	10-5 Intervention	Activity 10-5	Diagnose and Prescribe Online
✓ Lesson 10-6 Ext. of MG2.1	10-6 Intervention	Activity 10-6	
✓ Lesson 10-7 MG2.3	10-7 Intervention	Activity 10-7	

READY TO GO ON?
Enrichment, Section 10B

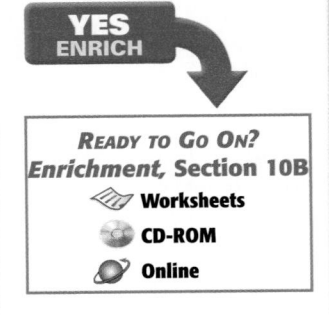 **Worksheets**

CD-ROM

Online

CONCEPT CONNECTION

It's a Wrap! Kim and Miguel are raising money for their school track team by running a gift-wrapping service at the mall. Customers can also have their gifts boxed for shipping. Kim and Miguel have rolls of gift wrap, shipping boxes, cardboard, and packing peanuts.

1. A customer wants to wrap and ship a gift that is in the shape of a rectangular prism. The dimensions of the gift are 10 in. by 15 in. by 4 in. How many square inches of wrapping paper are needed to wrap the gift? **500 in²**

2. Kim chooses a shipping box that is 18 in. by 12 in. by 6 in. After the gift is placed inside the box, she will fill the empty space with packing peanuts. How many cubic inches of packing peanuts will Kim need? Explain.

3. Another customer wants to ship a large cone-shaped art piece made out of recycled glass. The figure shows the dimensions of the conic art. Miguel decides to use poster board to make a cylindrical container that is just large enough to hold the art. How much poster board will he need? **785 in²**

4. Once the conic art is placed in the cylindrical container, how many cubic inches of packing peanuts will be needed to fill the empty space? **1046.7 in³**

20 in.

5 in.

2. 696 in³; the volume of the gift box is (10 in.)(15 in.)(4 in.) = 600 in³ and the volume of the shipping box is (18 in.)(12 in.)(6 in.) = 1296 in³. The volume of the empty space is 1296 in³ − 600 in³ = 696 in³

INTERVENTION

Scaffolding Questions

1. How do you find the surface area of a rectangular prism? Add the areas of the faces What formula can you use? $S = 2lw + 2lh + 2wh$ Does it matter which dimensions you choose to call the length, width, and height? No

2. What is the volume of the gift? 600 in³ What is the volume of the shipping box? 1296 in³ What operation should you use to solve the problem? Subtraction

3. What will be the radius of the cylindrical container? 5 in. What will be the height? 20 in. What formula can you use to find the amount of material needed to make the cylinder? $S = 2\pi r^2 + 2\pi rh$

4. What is the volume of the cylindrical container? 1570 in³ What is the volume of the cone? 523.3 in³ What operation should you use to solve the problem? Subtraction

Extension

1. A customer wants to wrap a soccer ball that has a radius of 4.5 inches. Kim decides to wrap the ball in decorative foil. How much foil is needed? 254.3 in²

2. How many cubic inches of packing peanuts are needed to fill the empty space when the soccer ball is placed in a box that measures 10 in. by 10 in. by 10 in.? 618.5 in³

Organizer

Objective: Assess students' ability to apply concepts and skills in Chapter 10 in a real-world format.

 **Online Edition**

Problem	Text reference
1	Lesson 10-4
2	Lesson 10-2
3	Lesson 10-4
4	Lessons 10-2, 10-3

California Standards

Measurement and Geometry
2.1 Use formulas routinely for finding the perimeter and area of basic two-dimensional figures and **the surface area and volume of basic three-dimensional figures, including** rectangles, parallelograms, trapezoids, squares, triangles, circles, **prisms, and cylinders.**

Game Time

Organizer

Objective: Participate in games to practice and apply skills learned in Chapter 10.

 Online Edition

Resources

 Chapter 10 Resource File
Puzzles, Twisters & Teasers

Planes in Space

Purpose: To apply knowledge of three-dimensional figures to visualizing solids of revolution

Discuss Ask students to describe the technique used to create the figures in the examples.
Possible answer: Begin with a two-dimensional figure (circle, polygon, etc.). Rotate the figure around a line, or translate it along a line to form a three-dimensional figure. What kind of figure is formed when the figure below is rotated around the line shown? cup shape shown below

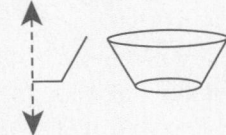

Extend Challenge students to identify objects in the real world that can be described as having been generated by rotating a two-dimensional figure around a line. Have them sketch the figures and lines.
Possible answer:

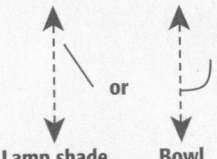

Lamp shade   Bowl

Game Time

Planes in Space

Some three-dimensional figures can be generated by plane figures.

Experiment with a circle first. Move the circle around. See if you recognize any three-dimensional shapes.

If you rotate a circle around a diameter, you get a sphere.

If you translate a circle up along a line perpendicular to the plane that the circle is in, you get a cylinder.

If you rotate a circle around a line outside the circle but in the same plane as the circle, you get a donut shape called a *torus*.

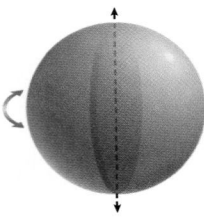 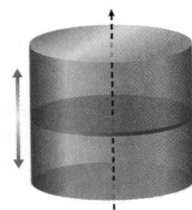 

Draw or describe the three-dimensional figure generated by each plane figure.

① a square translated along a line perpendicular to the plane it is in   rectangular prism
② a rectangle rotated around one of its edges   cylinder
③ a right triangle rotated around one of its legs   cone

Magic Cubes

Four magic cubes are used in this fun puzzle. A complete set of rules and nets for making the cubes can be found online. Each side of the four cubes has the number 1, 2, 3, or 4 written on it. The object of the game is to stack the cubes so that the numbers along each side of the stack add up to 10. No number can be repeated along any side of the stack.

go.hrw.com
Game Time Extra
KEYWORD: MT8CA Games

Magic Cubes

Purpose: To practice finding sums in a game format

Discuss When a student gets a sum of 10 on each side of the stack, have him or her demonstrate for the class how the winning solution was obtained.

Extend Have students do this puzzle by using magic cubes that have the numbers 3, 4, 5, and 6 written on the sides of the cubes. Ask students to identify the target sum for these cubes.   18

Materials
- white paper
- scissors
- decorative paper
- stapler
- hole punch
- twine or yarn
- cardboard tube
- glue
- markers

It's in the Bag!

PROJECT · The Tube Journal

Use this journal to take notes on perimeter, area, and volume. Then roll up the journal and store it in a tube for safekeeping!

Directions

❶ Start with several sheets of paper that measure $8\frac{1}{2}$ inches by 11 inches. Cut an inch off the end of each sheet so they measure $8\frac{1}{2}$ inches by 10 inches.

❷ Stack the sheets and fold them in half lengthwise to form a journal that is approximately $4\frac{1}{4}$ inches by 10 inches. Cover the outside of the journal with decorative paper, trim it as needed, and staple everything together along the edge. **Figure A**

❸ Punch a hole through the journal in the top left corner. Tie a 6-inch piece of twine or yarn through the hole. **Figure B**

❹ Use glue to cover a cardboard tube with decorative paper. Then write the name and number of the chapter on the tube.

Taking Note of the Math

Use your journal to take notes on perimeter, area, and volume. Then roll up the journal and store it in the cardboard tube. Be sure the twine hangs out of the tube so that the journal can be pulled out easily.

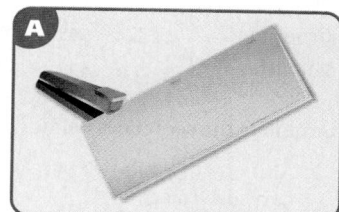

A

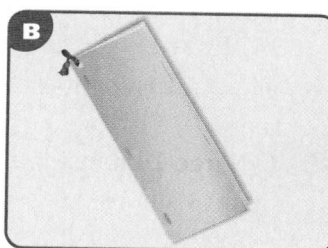

B

Organizer

Objective: Make a journal in which to take notes on surface area and volume.

Materials: white paper, scissors, decorative paper, stapler, hole punch, twine or yarn, cardboard tube, glue, markers

 Online Edition

Using the Page

Preparing the Materials

Students should use at least three sheets of paper to make their journals. When the sheets are folded, they will have a 12-page journal.

Making the Project

After students have trimmed the sheets that will form the journal, suggest that they check to be sure the sheets will fit inside the cardboard tube when they are rolled up. If the sheets are still too long, have students cut off another inch or two.

Extending the Project

Have students look through magazines to find photographs of real-world examples of the two- and three-dimensional figures in the chapter. Students can cut out the pictures and add them to the appropriate pages of the journal.

Tips from the Bag Ladies!

Cardboard tubes from rolls of paper towels work best for this project, but students can use any type of cardboard tube. Long tubes from gift wrap can be cut into three tubes that are just the right size. Students can also tape together two small tubes from bathroom tissue to make a single tube that is the correct length.

To make the journals even more useful, consider having students tie a small pen or pencil to the end of the twine.

Organizer

Objective: Help students organize and review key concepts and skills presented in Chapter 10.

 Online Edition
Multilingual Glossary

Resources

 **PuzzlePro®**
One-Stop Planner®

 Multilingual Glossary Online

go.hrw.com
KEYWORD: MT8CA Glossary

Lesson Tutorial Videos
CD-ROM

Test & Practice Generator
One-Stop Planner®

Answers

1. cylinder
2. surface area
3. cone
4. cylinder
5. rectangular pyramid
6. 364 cm³
7. 24 mm³

Vocabulary

base 480	lateral face 498	slant height 504
cone 481	lateral surface 499	sphere 508
cylinder 481	polyhedron 480	surface area 498
edge 480	prism 480	vertex 480
face 480	pyramid 480	volume 485
hemisphere 508	regular pyramid 504	
lateral area 498	right cone 504	

Complete the sentences below with vocabulary words from the list above.

1. A(n) ___?___ has two parallel, congruent circular bases connected by a curved surface.

2. The sum of the areas of the surfaces of a three-dimensional figure is called the ___?___.

3. A(n) ___?___ has one circular base and a curved surface.

10-1 **Three-Dimensional Figures** (pp. 480–483)   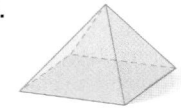 Prep for MG2.1

EXAMPLE

■ Name the figure.

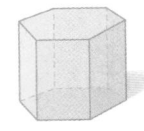

There are two bases that are hexagons.

The figure is a hexagonal prism.

EXERCISES

Name each figure.

4. **5.**

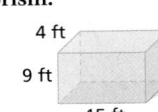

10-2 **Volume of Prisms and Cylinders** (pp. 485–489)    MG2.1, MG2.4

EXAMPLE

■ Find the volume of the prism.

$V = Bh$
$V = (15 \cdot 4) \cdot 9$
$V = 540$
The volume is 540 ft³.

EXERCISES

Find the volume of each prism.

6. **7.**

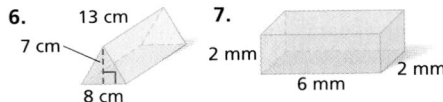

EXAMPLE

■ Find the volume of the cylinder to the nearest tenth. Use 3.14 for π.

$V = \pi r^2 h$
$V \approx 3.14 \cdot 3^2 \cdot 4$
$V \approx 113.04$
The volume is about 113.0 cm^3.

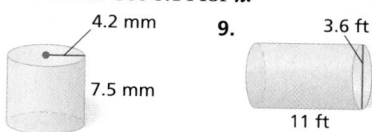

EXERCISES

Find the volume of each cylinder to the nearest tenth. Use 3.14 for π.

8.

9.

10-3 Volume of Pyramids and Cones (pp. 490–493)

Ext. of MG2.1

EXAMPLES

■ Find the volume of the pyramid.

$V = \frac{1}{3} Bh$
$V = \frac{1}{3} \cdot (5 \cdot 6) \cdot 7$
$V = 70$
The volume is 70 m^3.

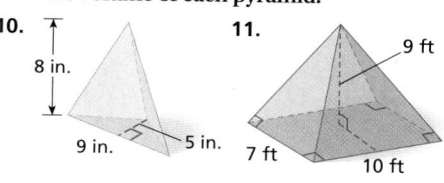

■ Find the volume of the cone to the nearest tenth. Use 3.14 for π.

$V = \frac{1}{3} \pi r^2 h$
$V \approx \frac{1}{3} \cdot 3.14 \cdot 4^2 \cdot 9$
$V \approx 150.72$
The volume is about 150.7 ft^3.

EXERCISES

Find the volume of each pyramid.

10.

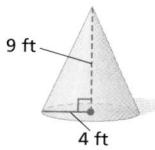

11.

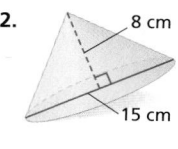

Find the volume of each cone to the nearest tenth. Use 3.14 for π.

12.

13.

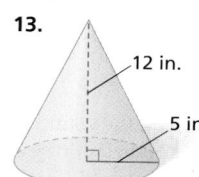

10-4 Surface Area of Prisms and Cylinders (pp. 498–502)

MG2.1, MG2.2, MG2.3

EXAMPLE

■ Find the surface area of the prism.

$S = 2B + Ph$
$\quad = 2(6) + (10)(4)$
$\quad = 52 \text{ in}^2$

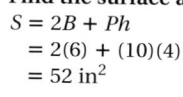

EXERCISES

Find the surface area of each prism.

14.

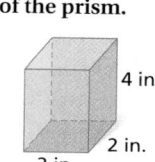

15.

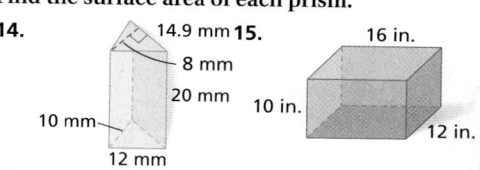

Answers

8. 415.4 mm^3
9. 111.9 ft^3
10. 60 in^3
11. 210 ft^3
12. 471 cm^3
13. 314 m^3
14. 857.2 mm^2
15. 944 in^2

EXAMPLE

■ Find the surface area of the cylinder. Use 3.14 for π.

$$S = 2\pi r^2 + 2\pi rh$$
$$= 2\pi(3)^2 + 2\pi(3)(7)$$
$$= 18\pi + 42\pi$$
$$= 60\pi$$
$$\approx 188.4 \text{ m}^2$$

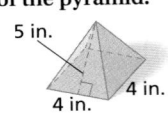

EXERCISES

Find the surface area of each cylinder. Use 3.14 for π.

16. **17.**

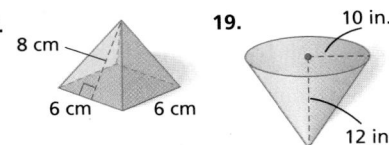

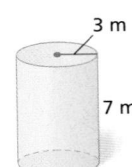 **10-5** **Surface Area of Pyramids and Cones** (pp. 504–507) 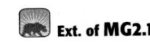 **Ext. of MG2.1**

EXAMPLE

■ Find the surface area of the pyramid.

$$S = B + \frac{1}{2}P\ell$$
$$= 16 + \frac{1}{2}(16)(5)$$
$$= 56 \text{ in}^2$$

EXERCISES

Find the surface area of each figure. Use 3.14 for π.

18. **19.**

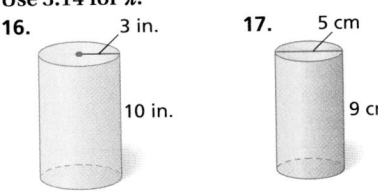 **10-6** **Spheres** (pp. 508–511)  **Ext. of MG2.1**

EXAMPLE

■ Find the volume of a sphere with radius 12 cm. Use 3.14 for π.

$$V = \frac{4}{3}\pi r^3 = \frac{4}{3}\pi(12^3)$$
$$= 2304\pi \text{ cm}^3 \approx 7234.6 \text{ cm}^3$$

EXERCISES

Find the volume of each sphere, both in terms of π and to the nearest tenth. Use 3.14 for π.

20. r = 6 in. **21.** d = 36 m

10-7 **Scaling Three-Dimensional Figures** (pp. 512–515)  **MG2.3**

EXAMPLE

■ A 4 in. cube is built from small cubes, each 2 in. on an edge. Compare the volumes of the large cube and the small cube.

$$\frac{\text{vol. of large cube}}{\text{vol. of small cube}} = \frac{4^3 \text{ in}^3}{2^3 \text{ in}^3} = \frac{64 \text{ in}^3}{8 \text{ in}^3} = 8$$

The volume of the large cube is 8 times that of the small cube.

EXERCISES

A 9 ft cube is built from small cubes, each 3 ft on an edge. Compare the indicated measures of the large cube and the small cube.

22. edge lengths

23. surface areas

24. volumes

Classify each figure as a polyhedron or not a polyhedron. Then name the figure.

1.

polyhedron; rectangular prism

2.

not a polyhedron; cylinder

3.

polyhedron; hexagonal pyramid

Find the volume of each figure to the nearest tenth. Use 3.14 for π.

4.

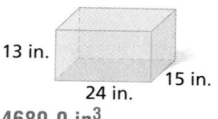

13 in.
15 in.
24 in.

4680.0 in³

5.

7 m
8.4 m

1292.4 m³

6.

3.9 mm
6.7 mm   4.2 mm

54.9 mm³

7.

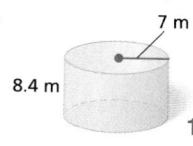

12 ft
13 ft   18 ft

936.0 ft³

8.

15 cm
5.6 cm

492.4 cm³

9.

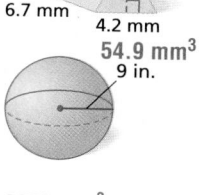

9 in.

3052.1 in³

10. Find the surface area of the figure at right.

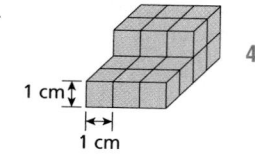

48 cm²

1 cm
1 cm

Find the surface area of each figure to the nearest tenth. Use 3.14 for π.

11.

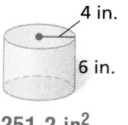

4 in.
6 in.

251.2 in²

12.

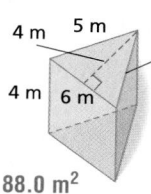

4 m   5 m
5 m
4 m   6 m

88.0 m²

13.

279.0 in²

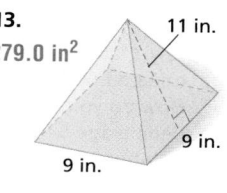

11 in.
9 in.
9 in.

14. a cone with diameter 6 cm and slant height 8 cm   103.6 cm²

15. a sphere with radius 3 ft   113.0 ft²

16. The surface area of a rectangular prism is 45 ft². What is the surface area of a similar prism that is larger by a scale factor of 3?   405 ft²

17. The volume of a flowerpot is 7.5 cm³. What is the volume, to the nearest hundredth, of a similar flowerpot that is smaller by a scale factor of $\frac{1}{2}$?   0.94 cm³

Organizer

Objective: Assess students' mastery of concepts and skills in Chapter 10.

PREMIER **Online Edition**

Resources

Assessment Resources

Chapter 10 Tests
• Free Response
  (Levels A, B, C)
• Multiple Choice
  (Levels A, B, C)
• Performance Assessment

IDEA Works! CD-ROM
Modified Chapter 10 Test

Test & Practice Generator
One-Stop Planner®

California Standards	
Standard	**Items**
Prep for MG2.1	1–3
MG2.1	4–6, 10–11
Ext. of MG2.1	7–9, 12–15
MG2.2	10
MG2.3	16–17

Organizer

Objective: Provide review and practice for Chapters 1–10.

 Online Edition

Resources

 Assessment Resources
Chapter 10 Cumulative Test

 Focus on California Standards Benchmark Tests and Intervention

 California Standards Practice CD-ROM

go.hrw.com
KEYWORD: MT8CA Practice

CHAPTER
10

MASTERING THE
STANDARDS

go.hrw.com
Standards Practice Online
KEYWORD: MT8CA Practice

Cumulative Assessment, Chapters 1–10

Multiple Choice

1. What is the ratio of gold to silver in the chart below?

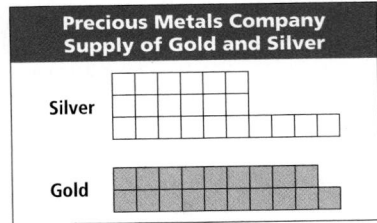

Precious Metals Company
Supply of Gold and Silver

Silver

Gold

Ⓐ $\frac{19}{22}$ Ⓒ $\frac{22}{19}$

Ⓑ $\frac{13}{19}$ Ⓓ $\frac{19}{11}$

2. The regular price of a bracelet is $96. Serena buys the bracelet on sale at 20% off. How much money does Serena save?

Ⓐ $1.92   Ⓒ $19.20

Ⓑ $9.60   Ⓓ $76.80

3. Nationally, there were 217.8 million people age 18 and over and 53.3 million children ages 5 to 17 as of July 1, 2003, according to estimates released by the U.S. Census Bureau. How do you write the number of people age 5 and older in scientific notation?

Ⓐ 2.711×10^2

Ⓑ 2.711×10^6

Ⓒ 2.711×10^7

Ⓓ 2.711×10^8

4. Which situation describes the graph?

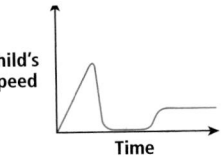

Child's speed

Time

Ⓐ Linda sits on her bike.
Linda runs to see the neighbor's dog.
Linda sits and pets the dog.

Ⓑ Jim climbs on the jungle gym.
Jim slides down the pole.
Jim lies in the sand and rests.

Ⓒ Carlos runs to answer the phone.
Carlos sits and talks on the phone.
Carlos walks into another room.

Ⓓ Juan walks to his friend's house.
Juan knocks on the door.
Juan leaves his friend's house.

5. Which expression is **NOT** equivalent to $4 \cdot 4 \cdot 4 \cdot 4 \cdot 4$?

Ⓐ $\frac{1}{4^{-5}}$ Ⓒ $4^2 \cdot 4^3$

Ⓑ 20   Ⓓ 1024

6. A trapezoid has two bases, b_1 and b_2, and height, h. For which values of b_1, b_2, and h is the area of a trapezoid equal to 32 in.?

Ⓐ $b_1 = 9$ in., $b_2 = 7$ in., $h = 2$ in.

Ⓑ $b_1 = 5$ in., $b_2 = 3$ in., $h = 4$ in.

Ⓒ $b_1 = 2$ in., $b_2 = 8$ in., $h = 4$ in.

Ⓓ $b_1 = 9$ in., $b_2 = 7$ in., $h = 4$ in.

California Standards	
Standard	**Items**
NS1.1	3
NS1.3	1
NS1.6	6
NS2.1	5
AF1.2	12
AF1.5	4
AF2.1	5, 8
AF3.3 🔑	14
MG2.0	9, 10, 15, 17
MG2.1	6, 7, 11, 15, 16, 17
MG3.2	14
MG3.3 🔑	13

Teaching Tip **Multiple Choice** For **item 5**, be sure students realize that $4 \cdot 4 \cdot 4 \cdot 4 \cdot 4$ is equivalent to 4^5 and not 4×5.

Students who missed **item 6** may need to review the formula for the area of a trapezoid. Also, emphasize following the order of operations when using a formula to evaluate.

Answers

14. Slope of $\overline{AD}$ and $\overline{BC}$ is 5; slope of $\overline{AB}$ and $\overline{CD}$ is $\frac{1}{3}$; parallelogram; $\overline{AD}$ and $\overline{BC}$ are parallel, and $\overline{AB}$ and $\overline{CD}$ are parallel.

15.

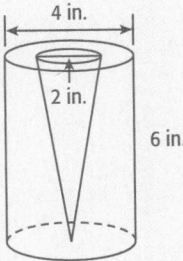

4 in.

2 in.

6 in.

69.11 in³ of water left in the cylinder

17. See 4-Point Response work sample.

7. The area of a circle is 49π. What is the diameter of the circle?

(A) 7 units   (C) 21 units

(B) 14 units   (D) 49 units

8. If the value of a^5 is positive, then which is true?

(A) a is positive.

(B) a is negative.

(C) a^5 is odd.

(D) a^5 is even.

 **HOT TIP!** When problems involve objects, you can draw a diagram to make the problem easier to understand. You can use the diagram to look for relationships among the given data to solve the problem.

Gridded Response

9. A cone-shaped cup has a height of 3 in. and a volume of 9 in³. What is the length of the diameter of the cone? Round your answer to the nearest hundredth of an inch. **3.39**

10. Shaunda measures the diameter of a ball as 12 in. How many cubic inches of air does this ball hold? Round your answer to the nearest tenth. **904.8**

11. An $8\frac{1}{2} \times 11$ in. photograph is being cropped to fit into a special frame. One-fourth of an inch will be cropped from all sides of the photo. What is the area, in square inches, of the photograph that will be seen in the frame? **84**

12. Find the value of $\frac{2a}{a^3}$ if $4 - a = 6$. $\frac{1}{2}$ **or 0.5**

13. What is the length, in centimeters, of the diagonal of a square with side lengths 8 cm? Round your answer to the nearest hundredth. **11.31**

Short Response

14. Plot the points $A(-5, -4)$, $B(1, -2)$, $C(2, 3)$, and $D(-4, 1)$. Use line segments to connect the points in order. Then find the slope of each line segment. What special kind of quadrilateral is *ABCD*? Explain.

15. A cylinder with height 6 in. and diameter 4 in. is filled with water. A cone with height 6 in. and diameter 2 in. is placed inside the cylinder, vertex down, with its base even with the top of the cylinder. Draw a diagram to illustrate the situation described. Then determine how much water is left in the cylinder. Show your work.

16. Rory made a pentagon by cutting two triangles from a square as shown.

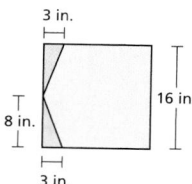

3 in.

16 in.

8 in.

3 in.

What is the area of the pentagon? Show your work. **232 in²**

Extended Response

17. The surface of a *geodesic dome* is approximately spherical.

a. A pattern for a geodesic dome that approximates a hemisphere uses 30 triangles with base 8 ft and height 5.63 ft and 75 triangles with base 8 ft and height 7.13 ft. Find the surface area of the dome.

b. The base of the dome is approximately a circle with diameter 41 ft. Use a hemisphere with this diameter to estimate the surface area of the dome.

c. Compare your answer from part **a** with your estimate from part **b**. Explain the difference.

Student Work Samples for Item 17

4-Point Response

a. area of triangles = surface area
$30 \cdot \frac{1}{2}(8) \cdot 5.63 = 675.6$
$+ \ 75 \cdot \frac{1}{2}(8) \cdot 7.13 = \underline{2139}$
               2814.6 ft^2

b. hemisphere surface area = $2\pi r^2$
$r = \frac{1}{2}(41) = 20.5$
$2\pi r^2 = 840.5\pi \approx 2640.5 \text{ ft}^2$

c. $\begin{array}{r} 2814.6 \\ -2640.5 \\ \hline 174.1 \end{array}$ The surface area of the dome is 174.1 ft² greater. A sphere is smooth and the dome is not.

The student accurately found the surface areas and gave a plausible reason for their differences.

3-Point Response

a. area of triangles equals S.A.
$30 \cdot 0.5 \cdot 8 \cdot 5.63 \approx 676 \text{ ft}^2$
$75 \cdot 0.5 \cdot 8 \cdot 7.13 = 2139 \text{ ft}^2$
$\Rightarrow 676 + 2139 = 2815 \text{ ft}^2$

b. surface area of hemisphere = $2\pi r^2$
$r = 0.5 \cdot 41 \approx 20 \text{ ft}$
$2\pi r^2 = 2 \cdot \pi \cdot 20^2 \approx 2512 \text{ ft}^2$

c. $2815 - 2512 = 303 \text{ ft}^2$
The S.A. of the dome is about 303 ft² larger.

The student correctly applies formulas and concepts in parts **a, b,** and **c** but applies a rounding strategy that yields numerical values that are far from correct.

2-Point Response

a. $30 \times 8 \times 5.63 = 1351.2$
$75 \times 8 \times 7.13 = \underline{4278}$
     Surface Area 5629.2

b. $4\pi r^2$ Surface Area
$= 4\pi \left(\frac{d}{2}\right)^2$
$= 4\pi \times (20.5)^2 = 1681\pi = 5281.0$

c. The hemisphere is slightly smaller.

The student left key information out of a formula and calculated correctly but did not give a plausible reason for differences.

CHAPTER 11

Data, Statistics, and Probability

Pacing Guide

Calendar Planner
Teacher's **One-Stop** Planner®

	Grade-level Standard
◄	Review
►	Beyond the Standards
A	Assessment
O	Optional

Lesson/Lab	California Standards	Time	Advanced Students	Benchmark* Students	Strategic** Students
LAB Use a Spreadsheet to Make Graphs	SDAP1.0	25 min	✔	✔	✔
11-1 Line Plots and Stem-and-Leaf Plots	SDAP1.1	50 min	✔	✔	✔
11-2 Mean, Median, Mode, and Range	⚷ SDAP1.3	50 min	✔	✔	✔
11-3 Box-and-Whisker Plots	SDAP1.1, ⚷ SDAP1.3	75 min	✔	✔	✔
LAB Make a Box-and-Whisker Plot	SDAP1.1, ⚷ SDAP1.3	25 min	O	✔	✔
11-4 Scatter Plots	SDAP1.2	50 min	✔	✔	✔
LAB Make a Scatter Plot	SDAP1.0, SDAP1.2	25 min	O	O	✔
Ready to Go On?		25 min	A	A	A
Focus on Problem Solving		25 min	A	A	O
11-5 Probability	Review of ⚷ 6SDAP3.3	50 min	O	O	◄
11-6 Experimental Probability	Review of 6SDAP3.2, ⚷ 6SDAP3.3	50 min	O	◄	◄
11-7 Theoretical Probability	Review of ⚷ 6SDAP3.1, ⚷ 6SDAP3.3, 6SDAP3.4	50 min	O	◄	◄
11-8 Independent and Dependent Events	Review of ⚷ 6SDAP3.3, 6SDAP3.4, ⚷ 6SDAP3.5	50 min	O	◄	◄
Ready to Go On?		25 min	A	A	A
Concept Connection		25 min	A	A	O
Study Guide: Review		50 min	✔	✔	✔
Chapter Test		50 min	A	A	A

* **Benchmark students** are achieving at or near grade level.

** **Strategic students** may be a year or more below grade level and may require additional time for intervention.

Countdown to Mastery, Weeks 22, 23, 24

ONGOING ASSESSMENT and INTERVENTION

DIAGNOSE	PRESCRIBE

Assess Prior Knowledge

Before Chapter 11

Diagnose readiness for the chapter.
Are You Ready? SE p. 527

Prescribe intervention.
Are You Ready? Intervention Skills 1, 16, 17, 94

Formative Assessment

Before Every Lesson

Diagnose readiness for the lesson.
Warm Up TE, every lesson

Prescribe intervention.
Skills Bank SE pp. SB2–SB24
Review for Mastery CRF, Chapters 1–11

During Every Lesson

Diagnose understanding of lesson concepts.
Questioning Strategies Chapter 11
Think and Discuss SE, every lesson
Write About It SE, lesson exercises
Journal TE, lesson exercises

Prescribe intervention.
Reading Strategies CRF, every lesson
Success for ELL Chapter 11
Lesson Tutorial Videos Chapter 11

After Every Lesson

Diagnose mastery of lesson concepts.
Lesson Quiz TE, every lesson
Ready to Go On? SE pp. 554, 574
Test and Practice Generator

Prescribe intervention.
Review for Mastery CRF, every lesson
Problem Solving CRF, every lesson
Ready to Go On? Intervention Chapter 11
Homework Help Online

Before Chapter 11 Testing

Diagnose mastery of concepts in the chapter.
Ready to Go On? SE pp. 554, 574
Focus on Problem Solving SE p. 555
Concept Connection SE p. 575
Section Quizzes AR pp. 205–206
Test and Practice Generator

Prescribe intervention.
Ready to Go On? Intervention Chapter 11
Scaffolding Questions TE p. 575

Before Assessment of California Standards

Diagnose mastery of California standards.
Focus on California Standards: Benchmark Tests
Mastering the Standards SE pp. 584–585
California Standards Practice CD-ROM

Prescribe intervention.
Focus on California Standards: Intervention

Summative Assessment

After Chapter 11

Check mastery of chapter concepts.
Multiple-Choice Tests (Forms A, B, C)
Free-Response Tests (Forms A, B, C)
Performance Assessment AR pp. 207–220
Test and Practice Generator

Prescribe intervention.
Review for Mastery CRF, every lesson
Lesson Tutorial Videos Chapter 11

KEY: **SE** = *Student Edition*   **TE** = *Teacher's Edition*   **CRF** = *Chapter Resource File*   **AR** = *Assessment Resources*   Available on CD-ROM    Available online

CHAPTER 11

Supporting the Teacher

Chapter 11 Resource File

Family Involvement
pp. 1–2, 37–38

Practice A, B, C
pp. 5–7, 13–15, 21–23, 29–31, 41–43, 49–51, 57–59, 65–67

Review for Mastery
pp. 8, 16, 24, 32, 44, 52, 60, 68

Challenge
pp. 9, 17, 25, 33, 45, 53, 61, 69

Problem Solving
pp. 10, 18, 26, 34, 46, 54, 62, 70

Reading Strategies ELL
pp. 11, 19, 27, 35, 47, 55, 63, 71

Puzzles, Twisters, and Teasers
pp. 12, 20, 28, 36, 48, 56, 64, 72

Hands-On Lab
pp. 86–87, 88–89, 90–91, 92–93

Technology Lab
pp. 73–74, 75–76, 77–78, 79–81, 82–83, 84–85

Workbooks

Homework and Practice Workbook SPANISH
Teacher's Guide .... pp. 79–86

Know-It Notebook SPANISH
Teacher's Guide .... Chapter 11

Review for Mastery Workbook SPANISH
Teacher's Guide .... pp. 79–86

Focus on California Standards: Intervention Workbook SPANISH
Teacher's Guide

Teacher Tools

Power Presentations
Complete PowerPoint® presentations for Chapter 11 lessons

Lesson Tutorial Videos SPANISH
Holt authors Ed Burger and Freddie Renfro present tutorials to support the Chapter 11 lessons.

Teacher's One-Stop Planner SPANISH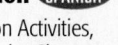
Easy access to all Chapter 11 resources and assessments, as well as software for lesson planning, test generation, and puzzle creation

IDEA Works!
Key Chapter 11 resources and assessments modified to address special learning needs

Questioning Strategies .... Chapter 11

Solutions Key .... Chapter 11

Interactive Answers and Solutions

TechKeys   **Lab Resources**

Project Teacher Support   **Parent Resources**

Transparencies

Lesson Transparencies, Volume 2 .... Chapter 11
• Teacher Tools
• Warm Ups
• Teaching Transparencies
• Lesson Quizzes

Know-It Notebook .... Chapter 11
• Vocabulary   • Chapter Review
• Additional Examples   • Big Ideas

Alternate Openers: Explorations .... pp. 79–86

Countdown to Mastery .... pp. 43–48

Technology Highlights for the Teacher

Power Presentations
Dynamic presentations to engage students. Complete PowerPoint® presentations for every lesson in Chapter 11.

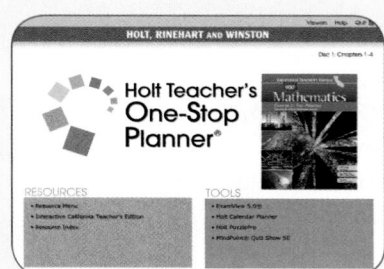

One-Stop Planner SPANISH
Easy access to Chapter 11 resources and assessments. Includes lesson-planning, test-generation, and puzzle-creation software.

Premier Online Edition SPANISH
Includes Tutorial Videos, Lesson Activities, Lesson Quizzes, Homework Help, Chapter Project and more.

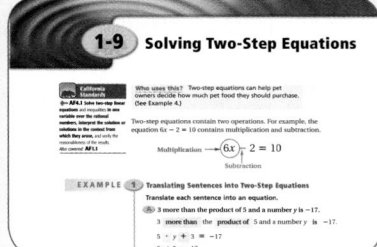

KEY: **SE** = *Student Edition*   **TE** = *Teacher's Edition*   English Language Learners   Spanish available   Available on CD-ROM    Available online

Universal Access

Teaching tips to help all students appear throughout the chapter. A few that target specific students are included in the lists below.

ENGLISH
LANGUAGE
LEARNERS

Strategic Students

Practice A	CRF, every lesson
Review for Mastery	CRF, every lesson
Reading Strategies	CRF, every lesson
Academic Vocabulary Connections	TE p. 528
Modeling	TE p. 533
Ready to Go On? Intervention	Chapter 11
Questioning Strategies	Chapter 11
Know-It Notebook SPANISH	Chapter 11
Homework Help Online	
Lesson Tutorial Videos SPANISH	
Online Interactivities SPANISH	

Special Needs Students

Practice A	CRF, every lesson
Review for Mastery	CRF, every lesson
Reading Strategies	CRF, every lesson
Academic Vocabulary Connections	TE p. 528
Inclusion	TE pp. 539, 570
IDEA Works! Modified Resources	Chapter 11
Ready to Go On? Intervention	Chapter 11
Know-It Notebook SPANISH	Chapter 11
Lesson Tutorial Videos SPANISH	
Online Interactivities SPANISH	

English Learners

Reading Strategies	CRF, every lesson
Vocabulary Review	SE p. 46
Academic Vocabulary Connections	TE p. 528
English Language Learners	TE pp. 529, 566
Language Support	TE pp. 529, 566
Success for English Language Learners	Chapter 11
Know-It Notebook SPANISH	Chapter 11
Multilingual Glossary	
Lesson Tutorial Videos SPANISH	

Benchmark Students

Practice B	CRF, every lesson
Problem Solving	CRF, every lesson
Academic Vocabulary Connections	TE p. 528
Ready to Go On? Intervention	Chapter 11
Questioning Strategies	Chapter 11
Know-It Notebook SPANISH	Chapter 11
Homework Help Online	
Online Interactivities SPANISH	

Advanced Students

Practice C	CRF, every lesson
Challenge	CRF, every lesson
Reading and Writing Math EXTENSION	TE p. 529
Concept Connection EXTENSION	TE p. 575
Ready to Go On? Enrichment	Chapter 11

Technology Highlights for Universal Access

 **Lesson Tutorial Videos** SPANISH

Starring Holt authors Ed Burger and Freddie Renfro! Live tutorials to support every lesson in Chapter 11.

 Multilingual Glossary

Searchable glossary includes definitions in English, Spanish, Vietnamese, Chinese, Hmong, Korean, and other languages.

 Online Interactivities SPANISH

Interactive tutorials provide visually engaging alternative opportunities to learn concepts and master skills.

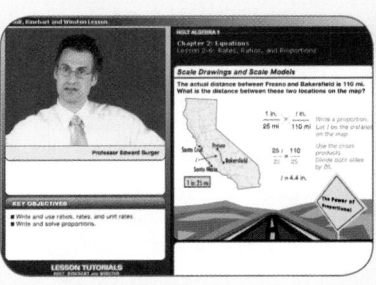
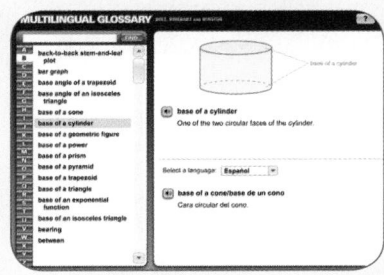
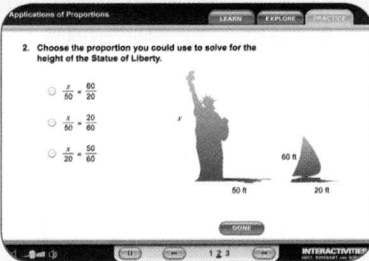

KEY: **SE** = *Student Edition*   **TE** = *Teacher's Edition*   **CRF** = *Chapter Resource File*   SPANISH Spanish available   Available on CD-ROM   Available online

CHAPTER 11

Ongoing Assessment

Assessing Prior Knowledge

Determine whether students have the prerequisite concepts and skills for success in Chapter 11.

Are You Ready? SPANISH .... SE p. 527
Warm Up .... TE, every lesson

Chapter and Standards Assessment

Provide review and practice for Chapter 11 and standards mastery.

Concept Connection .... SE p. 575
Study Guide: Review .... SE pp. 578–580
Strategies for Success .... SE pp. 582–583
Mastering the Standards .... SE pp. 584–585
Countdown to Mastery Transparencies .....pp. 43–48
Focus on California Standards: Benchmark Tests
Focus on California Standards: Intervention Workbook SPANISH
California Standards Practice CD-ROM SPANISH
IDEA Works! Modified Worksheets and Tests

Alternative Assessment

Assess students' understanding of Chapter 11 concepts and combined problem-solving skills.

Performance Assessment ....AR pp. 219–220
Portfolio Assessment ....AR p. xxxvi
Chapter 11 Project

Daily Assessment

Provide formative assessment for each day of Chapter 11.

Think and Discuss ....SE, every lesson
Write About It ....SE, lesson exercises
Journal ....TE, lesson exercises
Lesson Quiz ....TE, every lesson
Questioning Strategies .... Chapter 11
IDEA Works! Modified Lesson Quizzes .... Chapter 11

Weekly Assessment

Provide formative assessment for each week of Chapter 11.

Focus on Problem Solving .... SE p. 555
Concept Connection .... SE p. 575
Ready to Go On? SPANISH .... SE pp. 554, 574
Cumulative Assessment .... SE pp. 584–585
Test and Practice Generator SPANISH ...One-Stop Planner

Formal Assessment

Provide summative assessment of Chapter 11 mastery.

Section Quizzes ....AR pp. 205–206
Chapter 11 Test SPANISH .... SE p. 581
Chapter Test (Levels A, B, C) ....AR pp. 207–208
                    • Multiple-Choice • Free-Response
Cumulative Test ....AR pp. 221–224
Test and Practice Generator SPANISH ...One-Stop Planner
IDEA Works! Modified Tests................. Chapter 11

Technology Highlights for the Teacher

Are You Ready? SPANISH

Automatically assess readiness and prescribe intervention for Chapter 11 prerequisite skills.

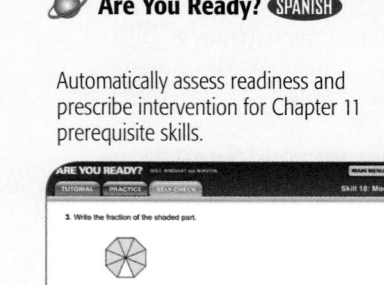

Ready to Go On? SPANISH

Automatically assess understanding of and prescribe intervention for Sections 11A and 11B.

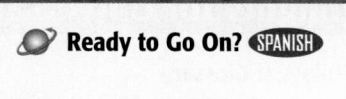
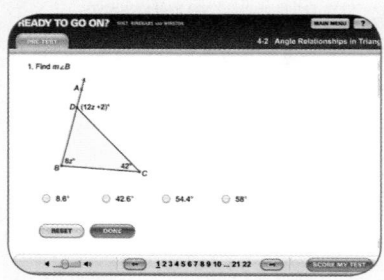

Focus on California Standards: Benchmark Tests and Intervention SPANISH

Automatically assess proficiency with California Grade 7 Standards and provide intervention.

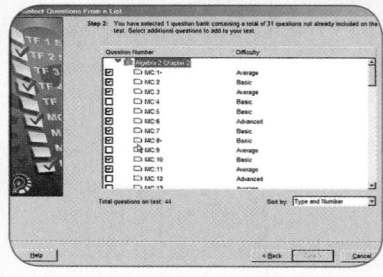

KEY: **SE** = *Student Edition* **TE** = *Teacher's Edition* **AR** = *Assessment Resources* SPANISH Spanish available Available on CD-ROM Available online

Formal Assessment

Three levels (A, B, C) of multiple-choice and free-response chapter tests are available in the *Assessment Resources.*

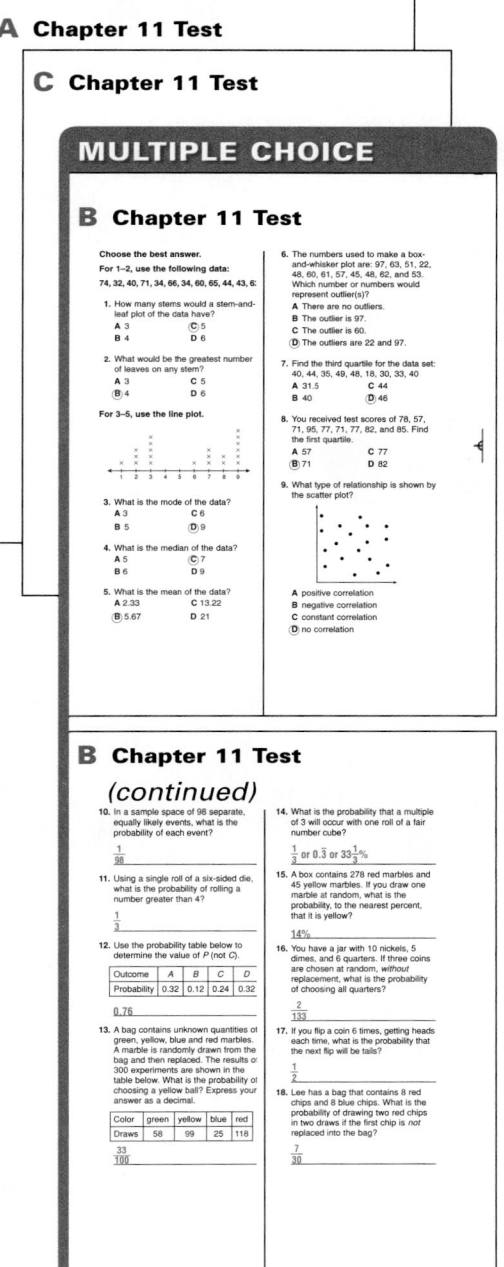

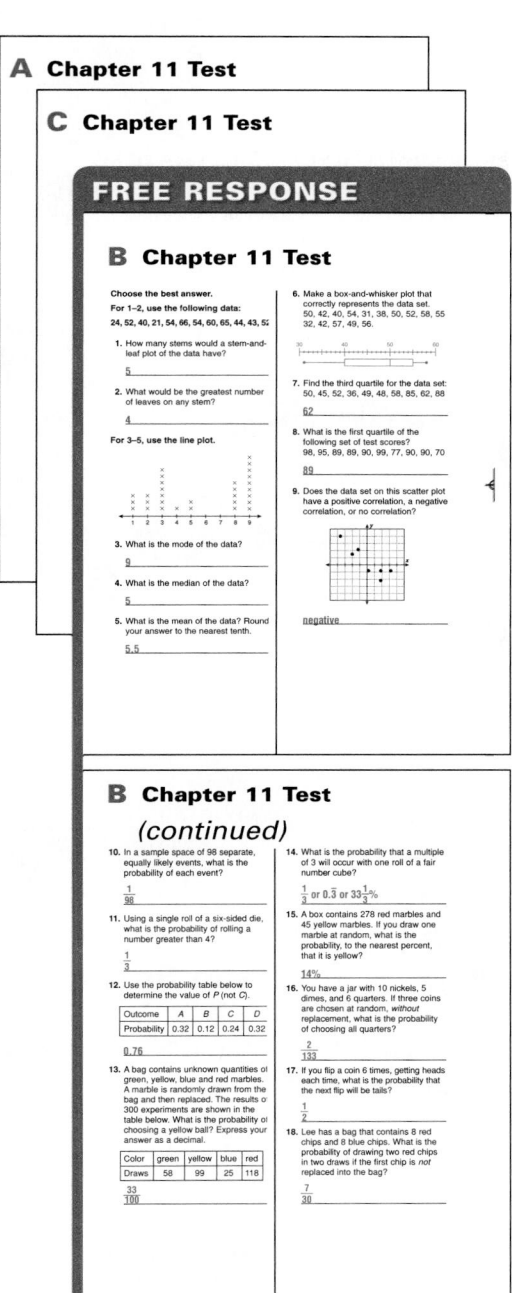

Modified tests and worksheets found in IDEA Works!

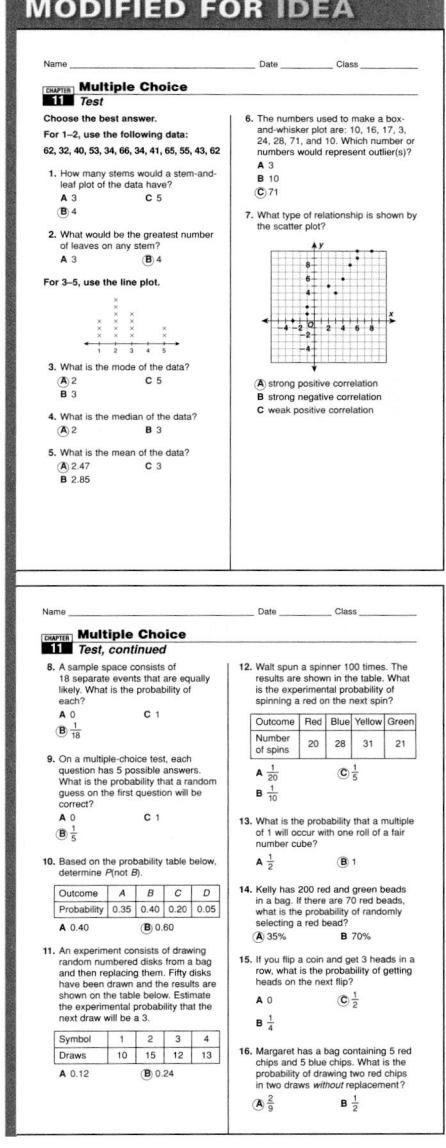

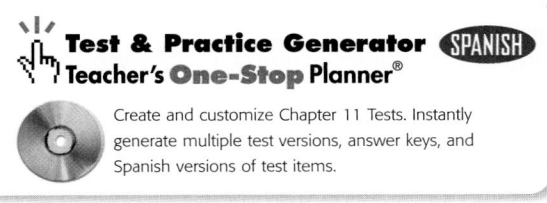

Test & Practice Generator SPANISH
Teacher's One-Stop Planner®

Create and customize Chapter 11 Tests. Instantly generate multiple test versions, answer keys, and Spanish versions of test items.

Focus on Problem Solving

On page 555, students focus on identifying too much or too little information.

CONCEPT CONNECTION On page 575, students use measures of central tendency, line plots, stem-and-leaf plots, and scatter plots to analyze and organize bowling scores.

Math in *California*

The Northern Elephant Seal is a large mammal that lives in the Eastern Pacific Ocean, including off the shores of California. To track wildlife populations, scientists may use scatter plots and trend lines. Students will study these topics in Lesson 11-4 of this chapter.

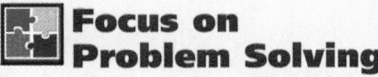

Data, Statistics, and Probability

11A Collecting, Describing, and Displaying Data
LAB Use a Spreadsheet to Make Graphs
11-1 Line Plots and Stem-and-Leaf Plots
11-2 Mean, Median, Mode, and Range
11-3 Box-and-Whisker Plots
LAB Make a Box-and-Whisker Plot
11-4 Scatter Plots
LAB Make a Scatter Plot
11B Probability
11-5 Probability
11-6 Experimental Probability
11-7 Theoretical Probability
11-8 Independent and Dependent Events

CONCEPT CONNECTION

go.hrw.com
Chapter Project Online
KEYWORD: MT8CA Ch11

Scientists can use data to make predictions about populations of animals, such as these elephant seals which were once hunted nearly to extinction.

Problem Solving Project

Understand, Plan, Solve, and Look Back

Have students:

- Complete the Making Quality Products worksheet to practice organizing data to describe results.

- Select a company and create a graph. Have them compare their company to the companies of other students.

- Discuss the role of quality assurance in companies. Why do they think this work is important?

- Research companies that have gotten into trouble because of their errors. What did they do to correct their problem?

Social Studies Connection

Project Resources

All project resources for teachers and students are provided online.

Materials:
- Making Quality Products worksheet

go.hrw.com
Project Teacher Support
KEYWORD: MT8CA PSProject11

ARE YOU READY?

✓ Vocabulary

Choose the best term from the list to complete each sentence.

1. A __?__ is a uniform measure where equal distances are marked to represent equal amounts. **scale**

2. __?__ is the process of approximating to a given __?__. **Rounding; place value**

3. Ordered pairs of numbers are graphed on a __?__. **coordinate grid**

coordinate grid

number line

period

place value

rounding

scale

Complete these exercises to review skills you will need for this chapter.

✓ Round Decimals

Round each number to the indicated place value.

4. 34.7826; nearest tenth **34.8**

5. 137.5842; nearest whole number **138**

6. 287.2872; nearest thousandth **287.287**

7. 362.6238; nearest hundred **400**

✓ Compare and Order Decimals

Order each sequence of numbers from greatest to least.

8. 3.005, 3.05, 0.35, 3.5 **3.5; 3.05; 3.005; 0.35**

9. 0.048, 0.408, 0.0408, 0.48 **0.48; 0.408; 0.048; 0.0408**

10. 5.01, 5.1, 5.011, 5.11 **5.11; 5.1; 5.011; 5.01**

11. 1.007, 0.017, 1.7, 0.107 **1.7; 1.007; 0.107; 0.017**

✓ Place Value of Whole Numbers

Write each number in standard form.

12. 1.3 million **1,300,000**

13. 7.59 million **7,590,000**

14. 4.6 billion **4,600,000,000**

15. 2.83 billion **2,830,000,000**

✓ Read Bar Graphs

Use the table for problems 16–18.

16. Which activity experienced the greatest change in participation from 2000 to 2001? **basketball**

17. Which activity experienced the greatest positive change in participation from 2000 to 2001? **soccer**

18. Which activity experienced the least change in participation from 2000 to 2001? **softball**

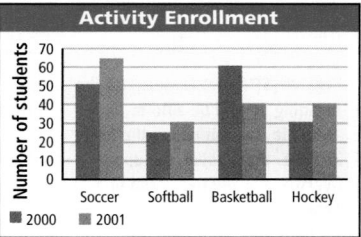

Activity Enrollment

■ 2000 ■ 2001

ARE YOU READY?
Organizer

Objective: Assess students' understanding of prerequisite skills.

Prerequisite Skills

Round Decimals

Compare and Order Decimals

Place Value of Whole Numbers

Read Bar Graphs

Assessing Prior Knowledge
INTERVENTION ◀━ ━▶

Diagnose and Prescribe

Use this page to determine whether intervention is necessary or whether enrichment is appropriate.

Resources

Are You Ready?
Intervention and
Enrichment Worksheets

Are You Ready? CD-ROM

Are You Ready? Online

my.hrw.com

NO INTERVENE

ARE YOU READY?
Diagnose and Prescribe

YES ENRICH

✓ Prerequisite Skill	✓ Worksheets	CD-ROM	Online
ARE YOU READY? Intervention, Chapter 11			
✓ Round Decimals	Skill 16	Activity 16	
✓ Compare and Order Decimals	Skill 17	Activity 17	Diagnose and Prescribe Online
✓ Place Value of Whole Numbers	Skill 1	Activity 1	
✓ Read Bar Graphs	Skill 94	Activity 94	

ARE YOU READY?
Enrichment, Chapter 11
Worksheets
CD-ROM
Online

Organizer

Objective: Help students understand the new concepts they will learn in Chapter 11.

Academic Vocabulary Connections

Becoming familiar with the academic vocabulary on this student page will be helpful to students. Discussing some of the vocabulary terms in the chapter also may be helpful.
Possible answers given.

1. The word *median* is derived from the Latin word *medius,* meaning "middle." What might the **median** value in a set of data be? The median is the middle value of a set of data.

2. The word *dependent* means "determined by another." What do you think **dependent events** are? Dependent events are events that are determined by other events.

3. The prefix *in-* often means "not." What do you think **independent events** are? Independent events are events that are not determined by other events.

The information below "unpacks" the standards. The Academic Vocabulary is highlighted and defined to help you understand the language of the standards. Refer to the lessons listed after each standard for help with the math terms and phrases. The Chapter Concept shows how the standard is applied in this chapter.

California Standard	Academic Vocabulary	Chapter Concept
SDAP1.0 Students collect, organize, and represent data sets that have one or more variables and identify relationships among variables within a data set by hand and through the use of an electronic spreadsheet software program. (Labs 11-1, 11-4)	**represent** show or describe **relationships** connections	You discover how data sets relate to one another.
SDAP1.1 Know various forms of display for data sets, including a stem-and-leaf plot or box-and-whisker plot; use the forms to display a single set of data or to compare two sets of data. (Lessons 11-1, 11-3; Lab 11-3)	**various** different from each other **to display** to show **compare** determine how items are the same or different	You learn different ways to display data in graphs.
SDAP1.2 Represent two numerical variables on a scatterplot and informally describe how the data points are distributed and any apparent relationship that exists between the two variables (e.g., between time spent on homework and grade level). (Lesson 11-4; Lab 11-4)	**informal** casual **apparent** visible; easily seen	You describe how two data sets relate to each other by graphing them on a coordinate plane.
SDAP1.3 Understand the meaning of, and be able to compute, the minimum, the lower quartile, the median, the upper quartile, and the maximum of a data set. (Lessons 11-2, 11-3; Lab 11-3)	**compute** determine by using mathematical operations such as addition and subtraction	You learn how to find different values that describe a data set. These values will be used to make box-and-whisker plots.

Looking Back

Previously, students

- described a set of data using mean, median, mode, and range.
- represented all possible outcomes for compound events in tables, lists, and tree diagrams.
- found the probability of independent events.

In This Chapter

Students will study

- selecting the appropriate measure of central tendency to describe data.
- expressing the theoretical probabilities of each outcome for compound events.
- finding the probabilities of independent and dependent events.

Looking Forward

Students can use these skills

- to determine how including or excluding outliers affects computations.
- to use combinations and permutations to compute probabilities.
- to determine if events are dependent or independent.

Reading Strategy: Interpret Graphics

Knowing how to interpret figures, diagrams, charts, and graphs will help you gather the information you need to solve the problem.

What You See
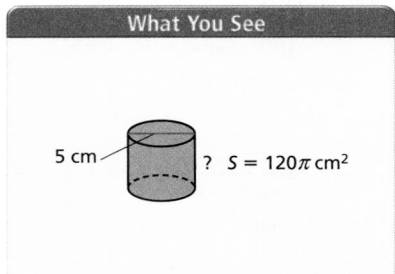 5 cm   ? $S = 120\pi \text{ cm}^2$

How to Interpret
✔ **Read all labels.** Diameter = 5 cm Surface Area = 120π cm^2 The height of the cylinder is unknown. ✘ **Do not assume anything.** The height of the cylinder appears to be about the same as the diameter, but you can't know this without calculating the height.

What You See

How to Interpret
✔ **Read the title.** "Loan Options" ✔ **Read each axis label.** Horizontal Indicates the amounts of the loans measured in dollars Vertical Indicates the loan options ✔ **Determine what information is represented.** The amounts of principal and interest for two loans are shown.

Look up each exercise in the text and answer the corresponding questions.

1. Lesson 1-6 Exercise 40: What is the title of the graph? How deep is the deepest trench?

2. Lesson 2-3 Exercises 38 and 39: What does each number in the graph represent? What source provided the most energy?

3. Lesson 10-5 Exercise 2: What is the slant height of the cone? What is the radius of the base of the cone?

Organizer

Objective: Help students apply strategies to understand and retain key concepts.

 **Online Edition**

Resources

Chapter 11 Resource File
Reading Strategies

ENGLISH
LANGUAGE
LEARNERS

Reading Strategy:
Interpret Graphics

Discuss Encourage students to take time to carefully examine any graphic included in a problem. Suggest they list the information provided in the graphic, the information they are being asked to solve, and any formulas or relationships they know might be helpful.

Extend Students will need to be able to interpret graphic information in subjects other than math. Ask them to bring in an example of a graphic containing information that they ran across in another subject, newspaper, or magazine. Discuss these graphics with the class.

Possible answers to
Try This

1. Depths of Ocean Trenches; −35,840 feet

2. Each number represents the amount, in quadrillion Btu, of renewable energy used by the United States; hydroelectric

3. 5 ft; 1.5 ft

SECTION 11A

Collecting, Describing, and Displaying Data

One-Minute Section Planner

Lesson	Lab Resources	Materials
11-1 Technology Lab Use a Spreadsheet to Make Graphs • Use a spreadsheet to make circle graphs, line graphs, and bar graphs. 🐻 **SDAP1.0**		**Required** Spreadsheet software
Lesson 11-1 Line Plots and Stem-and-Leaf Plots • Organize and interpret data in line plots and stem-and-leaf plots. 🐻 **SDAP1.0, SDAP1.1**	**Technology Lab 11-1** In *Chapter 11 Resource File*	**Optional** Tape measures (MK)
Lesson 11-2 Mean, Median, Mode, and Range • Find the mean, median, mode, and range of a data set and identify the most useful measure for describing a data set. 🐻 🔑 **SDAP1.3**	**Technology Lab 11-2** In *Chapter 11 Resource File*	
Lesson 11-3 Box-and-Whisker Plots • Display and analyze data in box-and-whisker plots. 🐻 **SDAP1.1, 🔑 SDAP1.3**		**Optional** Note cards
11-3 Technology Lab Make a Box-and-Whisker Plot • Use a graphing calculator to make a box-and-whisker plot. 🐻 **SDAP1.1, 🔑 SDAP1.3**		**Required** Graphing calculators
Lesson 11-4 Scatter Plots • Create and interpret scatter plots. 🐻 **SDAP1.0, SDAP1.2**	**Hands-On Lab 11-4** **Technology Lab 11-4** In *Chapter 11 Resource File*	**Optional** Science books
11-4 Technology Lab Make a Scatter Plot • Use a graphing calculator to display relationships between data sets in a scatter plot. 🐻 **SDAP1.0, SDAP1.2**		**Required** Graphing calculators

MK = *Manipulatives Kit*

Notes

_____

_____

_____

_____

_____

_____

_____

Math Background: Teaching the Standards

UNDERSTANDING DATA 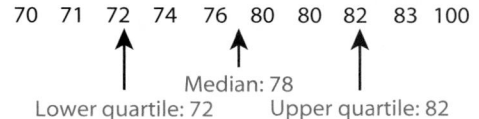 SDAP1.1, SDAP1.3

Lessons 11-1 through 11-3

Statistics is the branch of mathematics that is concerned with collecting, analyzing, and presenting data. The subfield known as *descriptive statistics* focuses on numerical or graphical ways to summarize sets of data. *Inferential statistics* is used to seek patterns in the data that can then be used to make predictions about the larger population.

Among the tools of descriptive statistics are the familiar measures of central tendency—mean, median, and mode—that summarize an entire data set with a single number. Other forms of measurement and display, such as box-and-whisker plots, provide more information than the measures of central tendency while still offering a convenient "snapshot" of the data set.

Although the study of statistics dates to the eighteenth century, many methods of displaying data are of relatively recent vintage. The American statistician John Tukey introduced the box-and-whisker plot (also called a box plot) and the stem-and-leaf plot in his 1977 book *Exploratory Data Analysis.* Both types of displays provide a wealth of information yet are easy to create, so it is not surprising that they quickly became standard statistical tools.

A box-and-whisker plot is based on the idea of a quartile (from the Latin word *quartilis*, meaning one-"fourth"). In general, a *quartile* is a set of three values that divide a data set into four equal parts, with each part containing one-fourth of the data set. The second quartile, or *median*, divides the data set in half. The *lower quartile* (or first quartile) is the median of the lower half of the data set, and the *upper quartile* (or third quartile) is the median of the upper half of the data set. Note that the quartiles may or may not be values in the data set.

A box-and-whisker plot shows how data are distributed by depicting the quartiles on a number line. Vertical segments show the three quartiles, and a rectangle groups the data between the lower and upper quartiles. The whiskers extend from the minimum data value to the lower quartile and from the upper quartile to the maximum value.

As an example, consider this set of test scores: {71, 74, 83, 80, 70, 80, 100, 82, 76, 72}. Listing the scores in ascending order makes it easy to identify the quartiles.

70 71 72 74 76 80 80 82 83 100

Lower quartile: 72   Median: 78   Upper quartile: 82

Turning this into a box-and-whisker plot offers a valuable perspective on the data. The "box" shows that much of the data are clustered between 72 and 82, while the long "whisker" on the right side of the plot shows that 100 is an outlier.

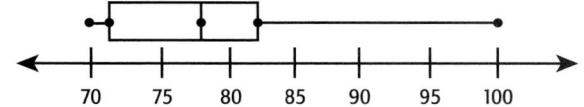

SCATTER PLOTS SDAP1.2

Lesson 11-4

A scatter plot is a graph that shows *bivariate data*; that is, data for which there are two variables, such as height and weight, for each observation. Each point on the scatter plot represents one data pair. Students are often tempted to connect points on a graph. It is essential that students understand that a scatterplot shows all of the collected data and that, in general, it is meaningless to draw a jagged path connecting the points.

Note that data in a scatter plot may be highly correlated (in other words, there may be a strong relationship between the two variables), but the points on the scatter plot may not be well-represented by a straight line. For example, if there is a quadratic relationship between the two variables, the data points can be approximated by a parabola. But for many scatter plots, drawing a line of best fit offers a straightforward way to predict data values that may not be displayed on the graph.

Organizer
Use with Lesson 11-1

Objective: Use a spreadsheet to make circle graphs, line graphs, and bar graphs.

Materials: Spreadsheet

Online Edition

Countdown to Mastery Week 22

Teach
Discuss

Have students discuss how to create circle graphs, line graphs, and bar graphs without the use of a computer.

Close
Key Concept

You can use a spreadsheet to construct circle, line, and bar graphs.

Assessment

1. What other type of graph can you construct using a spreadsheet?

   Possible answer: scatter plot

Technology
LAB
11-1

Use a Spreadsheet to Make Graphs

Use with Lesson 11-1

go.hrw.com
Lab Resources Online
KEYWORD: MT8CA Lab11

A spreadsheet allows you to model and compare different situations easily.

California Standards

SDAP1.0 Students collect, organize, and represent data sets **that have one** or more **variables** and identify relationships among variables within a data set by hand and **through the use of an electronic spreadsheet software program.**

Activity

1. Suppose a farmer has 22 pigs, 2 cows, 4 goats, 3 sheep, and 6 chickens. You can use a spreadsheet to make a circle graph of the data.

	A	B	C	D	E	F	G
1							
2		pig	cow	goat	sheep	chicken	
3		22	2	4	3	6	
4							

In row 2, enter the type of animal.

In row 3, enter the number of each type of animal.

Select the data by clicking in cell B2 and dragging over to cell F3.

Chart Wizard icon

Click the Chart Wizard icon in the top toolbar.

Click "Pie" under Chart Type in the Chart Wizard window. (*Pie chart* is another name for a circle graph.)

Click the top left circle graph under the Chart Sub-Type.

Click "Next" until the Finish button appears. Click "Finish."

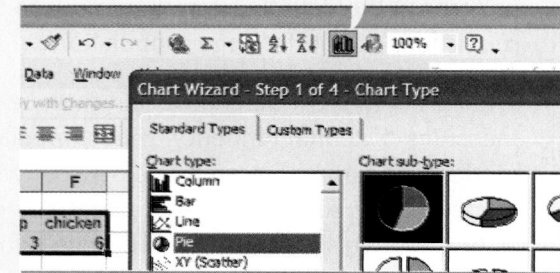

Now change the number of pigs to 12 and the number of goats to 11. Notice how the circle graph changes to reflect the new data.

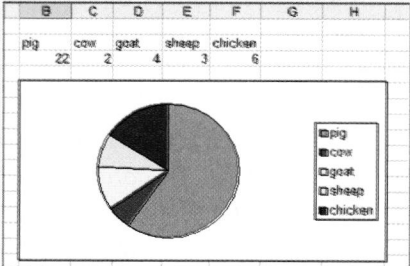

California Standards

Statistics, Data Analysis, and Probability 1.0

2 Use the spreadsheet to draw a line graph of the data.

Right click on the graph and select "Chart Type . . ."

Click "Line" and make sure that the top left graph is selected.

Click "OK."

Now change the number of animals. Notice how the line graph changes to reflect the new data.

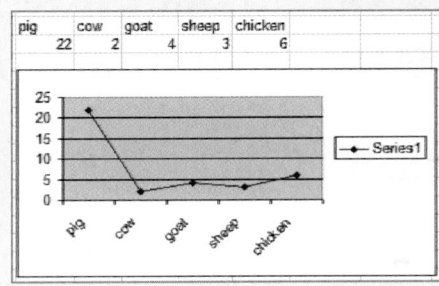

3 Use the spreadsheet to make a bar graph of the data.

Right click on the graph and select "Chart Type . . ."

Click "Column" and make sure that the top left graph is selected.

Click "OK."

Now change the number of animals. Notice how the line graph changes to reflect the new data.

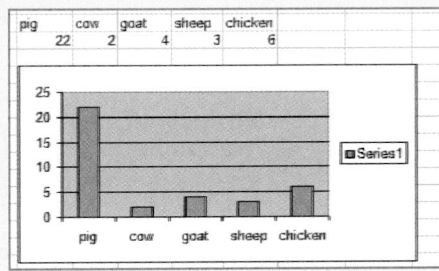

Think and Discuss

1. Compare the three types of graphs. When might you prefer using one type over the others? Which is the best representation of the animal data? Explain.

2. Explain the value of spreadsheets for modeling different situations.

3. Describe a situation when you would want to use a spreadsheet to make a circle graph.

Try This

1. Take a walk in your neighborhood, and record the color of the first 30 cars you see. Use a spreadsheet to make a circle graph, a line graph, and a bar graph of your data. Which represents the data best? Explain. **Check students' work.**

2. Now record the color of the next 30 cars you see. Modify your data from Try This 1. How did each graph change? **Check students' work.**

Possible answers to *Think and Discuss*

1. A circle graph is best to compare percentages of a whole. A line graph is best to show how data change over time. A bar graph is best to compare data from different groups. A bar graph is the best representation of the animal data because you can compare the different categories easily.

2. Spreadsheets allow you to create data displays quickly, without having to draw the displays yourself.

3. A spreadsheet could be used to keep track of the money you spend each week and then to create a circle graph to display how you spend your money in a way that's easy to understand.

11-1 Line Plots and Stem-and-Leaf Plots

Why learn this? You can use a line plot to organize and display fitness data.

A seventh-grade class participated in a month-long fitness challenge. Students in the class recorded the number of miles that they ran, walked, or biked during the first week.

Organizing raw data such as these can help you see patterns and trends. One way to organize data is to use a *line plot*. A **line plot** uses a number line and **X**'s to show how often a value occurs in a data set. A line plot can help you see how the data are distributed.

Vocabulary
line plot
stem-and-leaf plot
back-to-back stem-and-leaf plot

EXAMPLE 1 **Organizing Data in Line Plots**

Use a line plot to organize the data for the seventh-grade fitness challenge.

Number of Miles Run, Walked, or Biked									
7	5	6	5	5	10	9	9	9	3
3	10	1	0	8	6	8	2	3	1
5	0	4	6	4	8	9	3	4	4

Step 1: Find the least and greatest values in the data set. Then draw a number line that includes these values.
least value: 0
greatest value: 10

Step 2: Place an **X** above the number on the number line that corresponds to the number of miles each student ran, walked, or biked.

Miles Run, Walked, or Biked

```
                X  X  X                    X
                X  X  X  X        X  X     X
       X  X     X  X  X  X  X     X  X  X  X
    X  X  X  X  X  X  X  X  X  X  X  X  X  X
   +--+--+--+--+--+--+--+--+--+--+--+
   0  1  2  3  4  5  6  7  8  9  10
```

There are 30 numbers in the data set and 30 X's above the number line.

A **stem-and-leaf plot** uses the digits of each number in a data set to group the individual numbers, usually in increasing or decreasing order. Each *leaf* on the plot represents the right-hand digit in a data value, and each *stem* represents the remaining left-hand digits. The key shows the values of the data on the plot.

Stems	Leaves
2	4 7 9
3	0 6

Key: 2|7 means 27

EXAMPLE 2 **Organizing and Interpreting Data in a Stem-and-Leaf Plot**

The table shows the number of minutes students spent doing their Spanish homework. Make a stem-and-leaf plot of the data. Then find the number of students who studied longer than 45 minutes.

Minutes Spent Doing Homework

38	48	45	32	29	48
32	45	36	22	21	64
35	45	47	26	43	29

Step 1: Order the data from least to greatest. Since the data values range from 21 to 64, use tens digits for the stems and ones digits for the leaves.

Step 2: List the stems from least to greatest on the plot.

Step 3: List the leaves for each stem from least to greatest.

Step 4: Add a key, and title the graph.

Helpful Hint

To represent 5 minutes in the stem-and-leaf plot in Example 2, you would use 0 as the stem and 5 as the leaf.

Minutes Spent Doing Homework

The stems are the tens digits.

Stems	Leaves
2	1 2 6 9 9
3	2 2 5 6 8
4	3 5 5 5 7 8 8
5	
6	4

The stem 5 has no leaves, so there are no data values in the 50's.

Key: 3|2 means 32

The leaves are the ones digits.

The entries in the second row represent the data values 32, 32, 35, 36, and 38.

One student studied for **47** minutes, 2 students studied for **48** minutes, and 1 student studied for **64** minutes. A total of 4 students studied longer than 45 minutes.

A **back-to-back stem-and-leaf plot** can be used to compare two sets of data. The stems are in the center, and the leaves for one set of data are to the right of the stems. The leaves for the other set of data are to the left of the stems.

Example 1

Use a line plot to organize the math exam scores.

Student Test Scores

100	95	75	80
60	100	60	75
90	85	80	100
50	90	65	80

50 55 60 65 70 75 80 85 90 95 100

Example 2

The data shows the number of years coached by the top 15 coaches in all-time NFL coaching victories. Make a stem-and-leaf plot of the data. Then find the number of coaches who coached fewer than 25 years.

33, 40, 29, 33, 23, 22, 20, 21, 18, 23, 17, 15, 15, 12, 17

Number of Years Coached

Stems	Leaves
1	2 5 5 7 7 8
2	0 1 2 3 3 9
3	3 3
4	0

Key: 2|1 means 21

11 coaches

Also available on transparency

2 Teach

Guided Instruction

In this lesson, students learn to organize data in line plots and stem-and-leaf plots. Stem-and-leaf plots are effective for organizing a data set in which all of the values represent the same characteristic. Show students how to order the data first. Then they can determine the stems and the leaves, create a key, and draw the plot. You may want to have students create a stem-and-leaf plot from data that include 3-digit values (e.g., 104, 95, 87, 98, 108, and 100).

Universal Access
Through Modeling

Create groups of four or five students. Have them use the tape measures provided in the Manipulatives Kit to measure one another's height in inches and record the data. Then have each group create a stem-and-leaf plot to display the data. You may also want to combine the data and create a stem-and-leaf plot for the whole class.

Example 3

Use the given data to make a back-to-back stem-and-leaf plot.

U.S. Representatives for Selected States, 1950 and 2000					
	IL	MA	MI	NY	PA
1950	25	14	18	43	31
2000	19	10	15	29	19

```
1950  |   | 2000
  4 8 | 1 | 0 5 9 9
    5 | 2 | 9
    1 | 3 | Key: |2|9 means 29
    3 | 4 |     8|1| means 18
```

Also available on transparency

11-1 Exercises

EXAMPLE 3 Organizing Data in Back-to-Back Stem-and-Leaf Plots

Use the given data to make a back-to-back stem-and-leaf plot.

Super Bowl Scores, 1995–2005											
	1995	1996	1997	1998	1999	2000	2001	2002	2003	2004	2005
Winning	49	27	35	31	34	23	34	20	48	32	24
Losing	26	17	21	24	19	16	7	17	21	29	21

Super Bowl Scores, 1995–2005
```
      Losses  |   | Wins
           7  | 0 |
       9 7 7 6 | 1 |
   9 6 4 1 1 1 | 2 | 0 3 4 7
              | 3 | 1 2 4 4 5    Key: |3|1 means 31 points
              | 4 | 8 9                1|2| means 21 points
```

Possible answers to *Think and Discuss*

1. The leaf side will show the ones digits, and the stem side will show all remaining digits: 0|4; 8|9.

2. The number of leaves; the number of stems can be less than or equal to the number of data values.

Think and Discuss

1. **Describe** how the numbers 4 and 89 can be shown on a stem-and-leaf plot.

2. **Tell** which number is always the same as the number of data values in a stem-and-leaf plot: the number of stems or the number of leaves. Explain.

11-1 Exercises

GUIDED PRACTICE

Use the table for Exercises 1 and 2.

Number of Electoral Votes for Select States (2004)											
CA	55	GA	15	IN	11	MI	17	NY	31	PA	21
NJ	15	IL	21	KY	8	NC	15	OH	20	TX	34

See Example **1**
1. Make a line plot of the data. For the states shown, what was the most common number of electoral votes in 2004? **15**

See Example **2**
2. Make a stem-and-leaf plot of the data. How many of the states had more than 30 electoral votes in 2004? **3**

3 Close

Summarize

Remind students that line plots and stem-and-leaf plots are good ways to organize data and make the data easy to understand. Ask students to give an example of a situation that could be represented by each type of display.

Possible answer: A line plot could represent the number of hours that students watch TV in one week. A stem-and-leaf plot could show the number of people attending school functions.

3. Use the data below to make a back-to-back stem-and-leaf plot.

Political Divisions of the U.S. Senate

Congress	89th	90th	91st	92nd	93rd	94th	95th	96th	97th	98th
Democrats	68	64	57	54	56	61	61	58	46	46
Republicans	32	36	43	44	42	37	38	41	53	54

INDEPENDENT PRACTICE

The table shows the ages of the first 18 U.S. presidents when they took office. Use the table for Exercises 4 and 5.

President	Age	President	Age	President	Age
Washington	57	Jackson	61	Fillmore	50
Adams	61	Van Buren	54	Pierce	48
Jefferson	57	Harrison	68	Buchanan	65
Madison	57	Tyler	51	Lincoln	52
Monroe	58	Polk	49	Johnson	56
Adams	57	Taylor	64	Grant	46

4. Make a line plot of the data. What was the most common age at which the presidents took office? **57**

5. Make a stem-and-leaf plot of the data. How many of the presidents were in their 40's when they took office? **3**

6. Use the data below to make a back-to-back stem-and-leaf plot.

Miles per Gallon Ratings of a Car Company's Models

Model	A	B	C	D	E	F	G	H	I	J
City Miles	11	17	28	19	18	15	18	22	14	20
Highway Miles	15	24	36	28	26	20	23	25	17	29

PRACTICE AND PROBLEM SOLVING

Extra Practice
See page EP22.

Use the stem-and-leaf plot for Exercises 7–9.

7. What is the least data value?
What is the greatest data value? **4; 31**

8. Which data value occurs most often? **18**

9. **Reasoning** Which of the following is most likely the source of the data in the stem-and-leaf plot?

(A) Shoe sizes of 12 middle school students

(B) Number of hours 12 adults exercised in one month

(C) Number of boxes of cereal per household at one time

(D) Monthly temperatures in degrees Fahrenheit in Chicago, Illinois

Stems	Leaves
0	4 6 6 9
1	2 5 8 8 8
2	0 3
3	1

Key: 1|2 means 12

Answers

1.

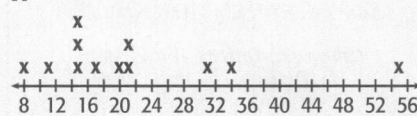

2.

Stems	Leaves
0	8
1	1, 5, 5, 5, 7
2	0, 1, 1
3	1, 4
4	
5	5

Key: 3|1 = 31

3.

Democrats		Republicans
	3	2 6 7 8
6 6	4	1 2 3 4
8 7 6 4	5	3 4
8 4 1 1	6	

Key: |4|1 means 41
6|4| means 46

4.

Ages of American Presidents

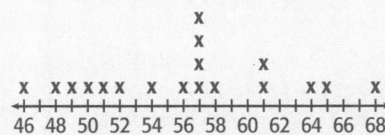

5. Ages of American Presidents

Stems	Leaves
4	6 8 9
5	0 1 2 4 6 7 7 7 7 8
6	1 1 4 5 8

6.

City		Highway
9 8 8 7 5 4 1	1	5 7
8 2 0	2	0 3 4 5 6 8 9
	3	6

Key: 7|1| means 17
|2|3 means 23

California Standards

Standard	Exercises
NS1.5	20–23
MG2.1	24, 25
SDAP1.1	1–19

Left Sidebar

FORMATIVE ASSESSMENT and INTERVENTION

Diagnose Before the Lesson
11-1 Warm Up, TE p. 532

Monitor During the Lesson
11-1 Know-It Notebook
11-1 Questioning Strategies

Assess After the Lesson
11-1 Lesson Quiz, TE p. 536

Answers

14a.

Bowling Scores

Marty		Bill
7 3 1	12	4 8 9
7 4	13	0 8 9
9 3	14	1 5 9
	15	
8 7 2	16	0

Key: |14|1 means 141
3|14|means 143

17, 19. See p. A11.

Teaching Tip **Multiple Choice** Remind students that in a stem-and-leaf plot, the leaf represents the right-hand digit. With that in mind, one-digit numbers have 0 as the stem. Because, for **Exercise 18,** there are single-digit numbers as well as those with 1, 2, and 3 in the tens place in the data, there will be 4 stems in the stem-and-leaf plot.

Journal

Ask students to write why a back-to-back stem-and-leaf plot is a good way to show the data in **Example 3.**

Power Presentations with PowerPoint®

11-1 Lesson Quiz

The data shows the ages of some hospital nurses.

33, 35, 23, 39, 23, 24, 34, 21, 57, 45, 57, 60, 45, 24, 31, 42, 61, 45, 35, 38

1. Make a line plot of the data. What age occurs most often? **45**

2. Make a stem-and-leaf plot of the data. How many nurses are over the age of 45? **4**

Answers 1–2. See p. A11.

Also available on transparency

Main Content

The stem-and-leaf plot shows the scores for a recent math test. Use the plot for Exercises 10–13.

Math Test Scores

Boys		Girls
1 5	6	9
6 8 8 9	7	1 5 5 5
1 1 1 5 9	8	2 2 8
1 8 9	9	1 2 2 7 9

Key: 5|6| means 65
|7|1 means 71

10. What was the highest score received? **99**

11. What was the lowest score received? **61**

12. Did more boys or girls take the test? **boys**

13. How many students took the test? **27**

14. Marty's and Bill's bowling scores are given below.
Marty: 137, 149, 167, 134, 121, 127, 143, 123, 168, 162
Bill: 129, 138, 141, 124, 139, 160, 149, 145, 128, 130

  a. Make a back-to-back stem-and-leaf plot to compare the data.

  b. Whose scores were higher overall? Explain. **Marty's**

15. What's the Error? Two students made stem-and-leaf plots for the following data: 530, 545, 550, 555, 570. Which plot is incorrect? Explain.

A; there is no stem for 56.

A

Stem	Leaves
53	0
54	5
55	0 5
57	0

Key: 52|5 means 525

B

Stem	Leaves
53	0
54	5
55	0 5
56	
57	0

Key: 52|5 means 525

16. Write About It Explain why it is important for a stem-and-leaf plot to have a key. **Possible answer: Without a key, you would not know how to read each value.**

17. Challenge Make a line plot and a stem-and-leaf plot for the following data: 9.9, 8.2, 10, 8.5, 9.3, 8, 10, 9.7, 8.4, 8.8, 9.3, 10.

SPIRAL STANDARDS REVIEW

← NS1.5, MG2.1, SDAP1.1

18. Multiple Choice How many stems would a stem-and-leaf plot of the data in the table have?

20	30	9	25	28
8	11	12	7	18
33	26	10	9	2

  Ⓐ 1   Ⓒ 3
  Ⓑ 2   Ⓓ 4

19. Extended Response Make a stem-and-leaf plot and a line plot of the data in the table. Which data display best shows the distribution of data? Explain.

Write each decimal as a fraction in simplest form. (Lesson 2-1)

20. 0.32 $\frac{8}{25}$ **21.** 0.025 $\frac{1}{40}$ **22.** 0.06 $\frac{3}{50}$ **23.** 0.9 $\frac{9}{10}$

Find the area of each figure with the given dimensions. (Lesson 9-2)

24. trapezoid: $b_1 = 3$, $b_2 = 5$, $h = 8$ **32 units^2**
25. triangle: $b = 16$, $h = 9$ **72 units^2**

CHALLENGE 11-1

LESSON 11-1 Challenge
Read From the Middle Out

In a double stem-and-leaf plot, the stem is in the middle and the leaves are on both sides. You read from the middle to the left for the left data and the middle to the right for the right data.

The double stem-and-leaf plot compares the average monthly temperatures in Bloomington, Indiana, and Richmond, Virginia, in degrees Fahrenheit.

Average Monthly Temperatures (°F)

Bloomington		Richmond
Leaves	Stems	Leaves
7	2	
3 1	3	8
5 2	4	0 0 8 9
6 3	5	7 9
7 3	6	6
6 4 2	7	0 4 7 8

Key: 7 | 2 | means 27°F
Key: | 3 | 8 means 38°F

Use the double stem-and-leaf plot above to answer the questions. **Possible answers are given.**

1. What is the greatest average monthly temperature in Bloomington? in Richmond?

76°F; 78°F

2. Which city had the lowest monthly temperature?

Bloomington

3. Which city has more months with monthly temperatures below 30°F?

Bloomington

4. Which city has more variation in temperatures? Explain.

Bloomington; It has more low temperatures.

5. What average temperature did Richmond have twice?

40°F

6. How many months was the average monthly temperature above 68° in Richmond?

4 months

7. What was the lowest average monthly temperature in Bloomington?

27°F

8. Compare the highest average monthly temperature in Bloomington to the highest average monthly temperature in Richmond.

Richmond's highest average temperature was 2° higher than Bloomington's.

PROBLEM SOLVING 11-1

LESSON 11-1 Problem Solving
Line Plots and Stem-and-Leaf Plots

Write the correct answer.

The table shows the time in minutes that Naima talked on the phone during the last 3 weeks.

Phone Time (min)

	Mon	Tues	Wed	Thurs	Fri	Sat	Sun
Week 1	12	15	25	45	52	30	31
Week 2	22	25	46	51	10	19	33
Week 3	44	21	30	20	10	24	52

1. If Naima makes a stem-and-leaf plot of the data, which stem has the most leaves? What are they?

stem 2; leaves 0, 1, 2, 4, 5, 5

2. Naima made a line plot of the data. Which numbers had more than one X above them?

10, 25, 30, 52

The stem-and-leaf plot that shows the total number of medals won by different countries in the 2000 Summer Olympics. Choose the letter for the best answer.

3. List all the data values in the stem-and-leaf plot.

A 2, 4, 5, 6, 7, 8, 9
B 23, 25, 26, 28, 28, 29, 34, 38, 40, 57, 58, 59, 60, 70, 88, 97
C 23, 25, 26, 28, 29, 34, 38, 57, 58, 59, 88, 97
Ⓓ 23, 25, 26, 28, 28, 29, 34, 38, 57, 58, 59, 88, 97

2000 Olympic Medals

2	3 5 6 8 8 9
3	4 8
4	
5	7 8 9
6	
7	
8	8
9	7

4. What is the least number of medals won by a country represented in the stem-and-leaf plot?

F 3
G 4
Ⓗ 23
J 97

5. What is the greatest number of medals won by a country represented in the stem-and-leaf plot?

A 9
B 70
C 79
Ⓓ 97

11-2 Mean, Median, Mode, and Range

California Standards

⬅ **SDAP1.3 Understand the meaning of, and be able to compute,** the minimum, the lower quartile, **the median,** the upper quartile, and the maximum **of a data set.**

Vocabulary
mean
median
mode
range
outlier

Why learn this? You can use the mean to determine the average number of hours that people exercise in one week. (See Example 2.)

The *mean, median, mode,* and *range* are commonly used to describe a set of numerical data.

- The **mean** is the sum of the data values divided by the number of data items.

- The **median** is the middle value of an odd number of data items arranged in order. For an even number of data items, the median is the mean of the two middle values.

- The **mode** is the value or values that occur most often. When all of the data values occur the same number of times, there is no mode.

- The **range** is the difference between the greatest and least values in the set.

EXAMPLE 1 Finding the Mean, Median, Mode, and Range of a Data Set

Find the mean, median, mode, and range of the data set.

2, 1, 8, 0, 2, 4, 3, 4

Helpful Hint

The mean is sometimes called the *average*.

mean:

$2 + 1 + 8 + 0 + 2 + 4 + 3 + 4 = 24$ *Add the values.*

$\frac{24}{8} = 3$ *Divide the sum by the number of items.*

The mean is 3.

median:

0, 1, 2, 2, 3, 4, 4, 8   *Arrange the values in order.*

$\frac{2 + 3}{2} = 2.5$ *There are two middle values, so find the mean of these values.*

The median is 2.5.

mode:

0, 1, 2, 2, 3, 4, 4, 8   *The values 2 and 4 occur twice.*

The modes are 2 and 4.

range:

$8 - 0 = 8$ *Subtract the least value from the greatest value.*

The range is 8.

Organizer 11-2

Objective: Students find the mean, median, mode, and range of a data set and identify the most useful measure for describing a data set.

 Technology Lab
In *Chapter 11 Resource File*

 Online Edition
Tutorial Videos, Interactivities

 Countdown to Mastery Week 23

Power Presentations
with PowerPoint®

Warm Up

Order the numbers from least to greatest.

1. 7, 4, 15, 9, 5, 2
2, 4, 5, 7, 9, 15

2. 70, 21, 36, 54, 22
21, 22, 36, 54, 70

Divide.

3. 820 ÷ 4   205

4. 650 ÷ 10   65

5. 1125 ÷ 25   45

6. 2275 ÷ 7   325

Also available on transparency

---

1 Introduce

Alternate Opener

EXPLORATION

11-2 Mean, Median, Mode, and Range

1. Students in a class completed a survey in which they were asked what their heights in inches are. Their responses are shown below.

49	53	60	55	48
72	65	66	58	68
75	65	64	57	59
61	67	64	58	62
63	59	61	55	65

a. Write the numbers in order from least to greatest.

b. What number appears most often?

c. What number is in the middle of the data set?

d. Add the numbers and divide the total by 25 to find the mean.

Think and Discuss

2. **Discuss** which number from Problems 1b, 1c, and 1d best represents the entire set of numbers. Why?

3. **Describe** a set of numbers arranged from least to greatest in which the middle number is not close to the value of the mean.

Motivate

Pose the following situation:

Seth is hired for a job that pays $6 per hour at a place where the average wage is $8 per hour. He discovers that most of the employees earn $6 per hour too.

Ask students why they think the average wage is $8 per hour. Explain to students that if the manager and supervisor each earn $16 per hour and eight others earn $6 per hour, the average (mean) is $8 per hour.

Explorations and answers are provided in *Alternate Openers: Explorations Transparencies.*

 **California Standards**

Statistics, Data Analysis, and Probability
⬅ **1.3**

Students might choose one of the two center numbers in an even number of values as the median. Remind students that in this case, the median is the average of the two middle values.

Power Presentations
with PowerPoint®

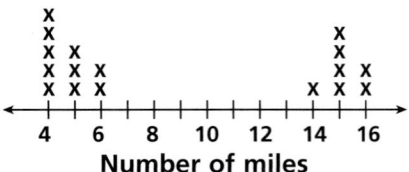

Additional Examples

Example 1

Find the mean, median, mode, and range of the data set.

4, 7, 8, 2, 1, 2, 4, 2

mean: 3.75; median: 3; mode: 2; range: 7

Example 2

The line plot shows the number of miles each of the 17 members of the cross-country team ran in a week. Find the mean and median of the data. Which measure best describes the typical number of miles ran? Justify your answer.

```
 x                          x
 x                          x
 x  x                       x  x  x
 x  x  x                    x  x  x
 x  x  x                 x  x  x
+--+--+--+--+--+--+--+--+--+--+--+--+--
 4     6     8    10    12    14    16
```
Number of miles

mean, 9; median, 6; the mean best describes the typical number of miles ran because the data are clustered fairly evenly about two areas.

Also available on transparency

The mean and median are *measures of central tendency* used to represent the "middle" of a data set. To decide which measure is most appropriate for describing a set of data, think about what each measure tells you about the data. The measure that you choose may depend on how the information in the data set is being used.

EXAMPLE 2 **Choosing the Best Measure to Describe a Set of Data**

⚬⚬ **Reasoning**

The line plot shows the number of hours 15 people exercised in one week. Find the mean and median of the data. Which measure best describes the typical amount of time a person exercised? Justify your answer.

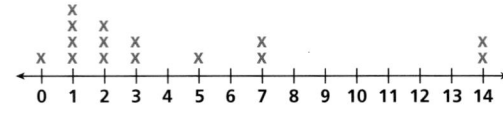

```
       x
       x  x
       x  x  x        x
 x  x  x  x     x     x              x
                                    x
+--+--+--+--+--+--+--+--+--+--+--+--+--+--+--+--
 0  1  2  3  4  5  6  7  8  9 10 11 12 13 14
```
Number of hours

mean:

$$\frac{0 + 1 + 1 + 1 + 1 + 2 + 2 + 2 + 3 + 3 + 5 + 7 + 7 + 14 + 14}{15} = \frac{63}{15} = 4.2$$

The mean is 4.2.

The mean is greater than most of the data values, so it is not the best choice to describe the typical amount of time exercised.

median:

0, 1, 1, 1, 1, 2, 2, 2, 3, 3, 5, 7, 7, 14, 14

The median is 2.

Since the majority of the data is clustered around the data value 2, the median is a more useful description of the typical amount of time exercised.

Helpful Hint

One way to help identify an outlier is by making a line plot.

In the data set in Example 2, the value 14 is much greater than the other values in the set. A value such as this that is very different from the other values in the set is called an **outlier**.

Outliers can greatly affect the mean of a data set. For this reason, the mean may not be the best measure to describe a set of data with an outlier.

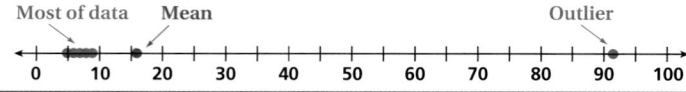

```
Most of data   Mean                              Outlier
+--+--●●●●●--+--●--+--+--+--+--+--+--+--+--+--●--+--+--
 0    10     20    30    40    50    60    70    80   90   100
```

---

2 Teach

Guided Instruction

In this lesson, students learn to find the mean, median, mode, and range of a data set. Focus on the type of information each measure provides and the type of situation in which each is most useful. The mean is a good measure to use to describe data that are close in value. The median more accurately describes data with an outlier. The mode is a good measure to use when you have categorical data; for example, if each student records his or her favorite color, the color (a category) listed most often is the mode of the data.

Universal Access

Through Curriculum Integration

Language Arts Have students research the local daily high and low temperatures for the previous 10 days. Then have students write a paragraph that summarizes the temperature data they collected by incorporating measures of central tendency. Have students share and compare their paragraphs.

EXAMPLE 3 · Exploring the Effects of Outliers

The table shows the number of art pieces created by students in a glass-blowing workshop. Identify the outlier in the data set. Then determine how the outlier affects the mean, median, and mode of the data.

Name	Number of Pieces
Suzanne	5
Glen	1
Charissa	3
Eileen	4
Hermann	14
Tom	2

The number of art pieces created by Hermann is much greater than the other values in the set. The outlier is 14.

Without the Outlier

mean:

$$\frac{5 + 1 + 3 + 4 + 2}{5} = 3$$

The mean is 3.

With the Outlier

mean:

$$\frac{5 + 1 + 3 + 4 + 14 + 2}{6} \approx 4.8$$

The mean is about 4.8.

The outlier increases the mean of the data by about 1.8.

median:
1, 2, 3, 4, 5

The median is 3.

median:
1, 2, 3, 4, 5, 14

$$\frac{3 + 4}{2} = 3.5$$

The median is 3.5.

The outlier increases the median of the data by 0.5.

mode:
No value occurs most often. There is no mode.

mode:
No value occurs most often. There is no mode.

The outlier does not change the mode of the data.

The mean is most affected by the outlier.

> **Caution!**
> Since all the data values occur the same number of times, the set has no mode.

Think and Discuss

1. **Describe** a situation in which the mean would best describe a data set.
2. **Give an example** of a data set in which the mean, median, and mode have the same value.
3. **Explain** how an outlier affects the mean, median, and mode of a data set.

Power Presentations
with PowerPoint®

Additional Examples

Example 3

The data show Sara's scores for the last 5 math tests: 88, 90, 55, 94, and 89. Identify the outlier in the data set. Then determine how the outlier affects the mean, median, and mode of the data.

The outlier is 55. Without the outlier, the mean is 90.25 and the median is 89.5. With the outlier, the mean is 83.2 and the median is 89. Adding the outlier decreases the mean by 7.05 and the median by 0.5. There is no mode with or without the outlier.

Also available on transparency

> **Teaching Tip**
> **Inclusion** Discuss how an outlier can skew the information about a set of data when you are finding the mean. Point out that the description of the data can be misleading when using the mean with the outlier as in **Example 3.**

Answers to Think and Discuss

1. Possible answer: A mean can be used when determining grades from several scored assignments.
2. Possible answer: {1, 1, 2, 2, 2, 3, 3}
3. An outlier usually has the most affect on the mean. The median may not be affected as much because it is the data value in the middle position. The mode will not be affected at all.

3 Close

Summarize

Display the following data on the board: 12, 14, 22, 24, 15, 12, 20

Ask volunteers to describe how to find one of the measures discussed in this lesson without naming it. Have students identify the measure described.

Possible answers: Mean: If I add the numbers and divide by 7, I get 17. Mode: The data value that appears most often is 12. Range: The difference between the highest and lowest value is 12. Median: The middle value is 15.

11-2 Exercises

California Standards Practice
SDAP1.3

go.hrw.com
Homework Help Online
KEYWORD: MT8CA 11-2
Parent Resources Online
KEYWORD: MT8CA Parent

Assignment Guide

If you finished Example **1** assign:
Proficient 1, 2, 5–7, 16, 20–23
Advanced 5–8, 16, 17, 20–23

If you finished Example **2** assign:
Proficient 1–3, 5–7, 9, 15, 16, 20–23
Advanced 5–9, 12, 14–17, 19–23

If you finished Example **3** assign:
Proficient 1–13, 15, 16, 20–23
Advanced 5–23

Homework Quick Check

Quickly check key concepts.
Exercises: 6, 10, 15, 16

Math Background

Karl Pearson (1857–1936), a British geneticist, coined the term *mode* in 1895 in "Skew Variation in Homogeneous Material." Pearson was known for using statistical methods to analyze and describe biological data. He used the term *mode* to distinguish the information he was describing from the mean and median. He stated, "I have found it convenient to use the term *mode* for the abscissa corresponding to the ordinate of maximum frequency. Thus the 'mean,' the 'mode,' and the 'median' have all distinct characters."

Answers

3. Mean: 352.5; median: 350; mean or median; the mean and median have close to the same value.

9. Mean = 6.2; median = 6.5; the measures are so close, either value could describe the number of letters.

10. 5; including the outlier decreased the mean and the median by 1.5. The mode did not change.

11. 151; adding the outlier increased the mean by 10 and the median by 7.5. The mode did not change because there was no mode.

California Standards

Standard	Exercises
NS1.7 🔑	22
SDAP1.1	23
SDAP1.3 🔑	1–11, 13–18, 21

GUIDED PRACTICE

See Example **1** Find the mean, median, mode, and range of each data set.

1. 5, 30, 35, 20, 5, 25, 20
20; 20; 5 and 20; 30

2. 44, 68, 48, 61, 59, 48, 63, 49
55; 54; 48; 24

See Example **2** **3.** The line plot shows cooking temperatures required by different recipes. Find the mean and median of the data. Which measure best describes the typical cooking temperature? Justify your answer.

Cooking Temperatures

150°F 200°F 250°F 300°F 350°F 400°F 450°F

See Example **3** **4.** The table shows the number of glasses of water consumed in one day. Identify the outlier in the data set. Then determine how the outlier affects the mean, median, and mode of the data.

Water Consumption							
Name	Randy	Lori	Anita	Jana	Sonya	Victor	Mark	Jorge
Glasses	4	12	3	1	4	7	5	4

12; including the outlier increased the mean by 1. The median and the mode did not change.

INDEPENDENT PRACTICE

See Example **1** Find the mean, median, mode, and range of each data set.

5. 92, 88, 65, 68, 76, 90, 84, 88, 93, 89
83.3; 88; 88; 28

6. 23, 43, 5, 3, 4, 14, 24, 15, 15, 13
15.9; 14.5; 15; 40

7. 2.0, 4.4, 6.2, 3.2, 4.4, 6.2, 3.7
4.3; 4.4; 4.4 and 6.2; 4.2

8. 13.1, 7.5, 3.9, 4.8, 17.1, 14.6, 8.3, 3.9
9.15; 7.9; 3.9; 13.2

See Example **2** **9.** The line plot shows the number of letters in the spellings of the 12 months. Find the mean and median of the data. Which measure best describes the typical number of letters? Justify your answer.

Number of Letters

0 1 2 3 4 5 6 7 8 9 10 11 12

See Example **3** Identify the outlier in each data set. Then determine how the outlier affects the mean, median, and mode of the data.

10. 13, 18, 20, 5, 15, 20, 13, 20

11. 45, 48, 63, 85, 151, 47, 88, 44, 68

PRACTICE AND PROBLEM SOLVING

Extra Practice
See page EP22.

12. Health Based on the data from three annual checkups, Jon's mean height is 62 in. At the first two checkups Jon's height was 58 in. and 61 in. What was his height at the third checkup? 67 in.

REVIEW FOR MASTERY 11-2

Review for Mastery
11-2 Mean, Median, Mode, and Range

You can use mean, median, mode, and range to describe a data set.
Find the mean, median, mode, and range of each of 8, 3, 5, 4, 1, and 3.
List in order: 1, 3, 3, 4, 5, 8

Find the **mean**. The mean is the sum of the values divided by the number of values in the data set.
$1 + 3 + 3 + 4 + 5 + 8 = 24$
$24 \div 6 = 4$
mean = 4

Find the **range**. Find the difference between the least and greatest values.
$8 - 1 = 7$
range = 7

Find the **median**. The median is the middle value.
median = 3.5

Find the **mode**. The mode is the value that occurs most often. Sometimes there is no mode.
mode = 3

Find the range, mean, median, and mode of each data set.

1. 6, 5, 3, 6, 8
5; 5.6; 6; 6

2. 12, 15, 17, 9, 17
8; 14; 15; 17

An **outlier** is a value that is much greater than or much less than the other values in a data set.

How does the outlier affect the mean, median, and mode of the data?
Write the data in order and identify the outlier.
7, 9, 30, 9, 5, 6 ⟶ 5, 6, 7, 9, 9, 30 ⟵ outlier

	With the Outlier	Without the Outlier
Find the mean.	$7 + 9 + 30 + 9 + 5 + 6 = 66$ $66 \div 6 = 11$ The mean is 11.	$7 + 9 + 9 + 5 + 6 = 36$ $36 \div 5 = 7.2$ The mean is 7.2.
Find the median.	5, 6, 7, 9, 9, 30 $7 + 9 = 16$ $16 \div 2 = 8$ The median is 8.	5, 6, 7, 9, 9 The median is 7.
	The mode is 9.	The mode is 9.

Use the data set to answer the questions.
4, 6, 3, 6, 25, 3, 2

3. Is there an outlier? If so, what is it? Yes; 25

4. How does the outlier affect the mean and the median?
It increases the mean by 3 and the median by 0.5.

PRACTICE 11-2

Practice B
11-2 Mean, Median, Mode, and Range

Find the mean, median, mode, and range of each data set.

1. 46, 35, 23, 37, 29, 53, 43
38; 37; no mode; 30

2. 72, 56, 47, 69, 75, 48, 56, 57
60; 56.5; 56; 28

3. 19, 11, 80, 19, 27, 19, 10, 25, 15
25; 19; 19; 70

4. 7, 8, 20, 6, 9, 11, 10, 8, 9, 8
9.6; 8.5; 8, 14

5. The line plot shows the number of hours 15 students said they spent on homework in one week. Does the mean or median best describe the data? Justify your answer.

0 2 4 6 8 10 12 14 16 18 20 22 24

The median best describes data set because it is closest to the numbers of hours reported by most of the students.

Identify the outlier in each data set. Then determine how the outlier affects the mean, median, and mode of the data.

6. 14, 16, 13, 15, 5, 16, 12
Outlier, 5; It decreased the mean by 1.3 and the median by 0.5. It did not affect the mode.

7. 48, 46, 52, 92, 57, 58, 52, 61, 56
Outlier, 92; It increased the mean by 4.25 and the median by 2. It did not affect the mode.

A **box-and-whisker plot** shows the distribution of data. The middle half of the data is represented by a "box" with a vertical line at the median. The lower fourth of the data and upper fourth of the data are represented by "whiskers" that extend to the **minimum** (least) and **maximum** (greatest) values.

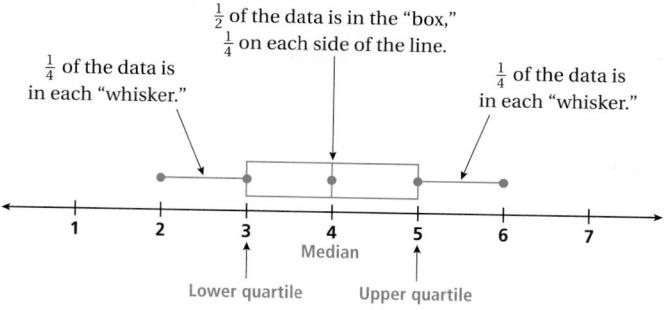

$\frac{1}{4}$ of the data is in each "whisker."

$\frac{1}{2}$ of the data is in the "box," $\frac{1}{4}$ on each side of the line.

$\frac{1}{4}$ of the data is in each "whisker."

Median

Lower quartile   Upper quartile

EXAMPLE **2**   **Making a Box-and-Whisker Plot**

Use the given data to make a box-and-whisker plot.

23 16 51 23 56 22 63 51 22 15 19 42 44 50 38 31 47

Step 1:   Order the data from least to greatest. Then find the minimum, lower quartile, median, upper quartile, and maximum.

15, 16, 19, 22, 22, 23, 23, 31, 38, 42, 44, 47, 50, 51, 51, 56, 63

minimum: 15

lower quartile: $\frac{22 + 22}{2} = 22$

median: 38

upper quartile: $\frac{50 + 51}{2} = 50.5$

maximum: 63

Step 2:   Draw a number line, and plot a point above each value from Step 1.

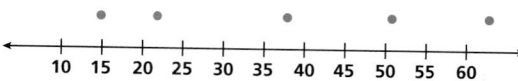

Step 3:   Draw the box and whiskers.

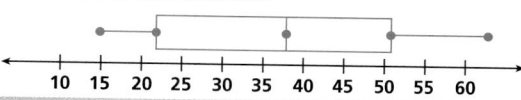

Power Presentations with PowerPoint®

Additional Examples

Example 1

Find the lower and upper quartiles for each data set.

A. 15, 83, 75, 12, 19, 74, 21

lower quartile: 15;
upper quartile: 75

B. 75, 61, 88, 79, 79, 99, 63, 77

lower quartile: 69;
upper quartile: 83.5

Example 2

Use the given data to make a box-and-whisker plot.

21, 25, 15, 13, 17, 19, 19, 21

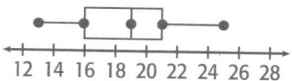

12 14 16 18 20 22 24 26 28

Also available on transparency

② Teach

Guided Instruction

In this lesson, students learn to display and analyze data in box-and-whisker plots (Teaching Transparency). Illustrate how to divide the data into four parts, first by writing the numbers on cards and dividing them into groups, and then by using the median of the entire set and the medians of the top and bottom halves. Point out that the data values at the ends of the whiskers are the least and greatest values in the set. Ask students to describe the significance of the numbers at each end and the numbers in the middle of the box.

 Universal Access
Through Cognitive Strategies

Provide each student with his or her quiz or homework scores so far in the class, or show students a set of example quiz scores. Have students make a box-and-whisker plot of the scores, and then ask what insight the shape of the plot reveals about the students' performance. Point out that boxes with long ranges suggest inconsistent performance, while boxes with small ranges represent consistent performances. Also, explain that low outliers could represent a particular math topic the student has trouble understanding.

Additional Examples

Example 3

These box-and-whisker plots compare the ages of the first ten U.S. presidents with the ages of the last ten presidents (through George W. Bush) when they took office.

Age of First Ten Presidents at Inauguration

51 57 61   68

Age of Last Ten Presidents at Inauguration

43   52 55.5 62   69

40   50   60   70

A. Compare the medians and ranges.

The median for the first ten presidents is slightly greater.

The range for the last ten presidents is greater.

B. Compare the ranges of the middle half of the data for each.

The range of the middle half of the data is greater for the last ten presidents.

Also available on transparency

11-3 Exercises

Assignment Guide

If you finished Example **1** assign:
Proficient 1, 2, 7, 8, 13–16, 29–35
Advanced 7, 8, 13–16, 29–35

If you finished Example **2** assign:
Proficient 1–4, 7–10, 13–19, 27–35
Advanced 7–10, 14–20, 22, 25–35

If you finished Example **3** assign:
Proficient 1–19, 21, 27–35
Advanced 7–12, 15–35

Homework Quick Check

Quickly check key concepts.
Exercises: 8, 10, 12, 21

EXAMPLE 3 Comparing Data Sets Using Box-and-Whisker Plots

The number of touchdown passes that Brett Favre and Dan Marino threw during each of the first 14 years of their careers is shown in the box-and-whisker plots.

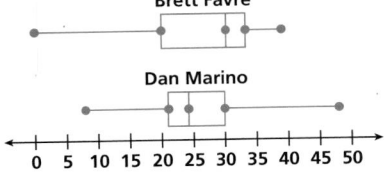

Brett Favre

Dan Marino

0 5 10 15 20 25 30 35 40 45 50

A Compare the medians and ranges.

Brett Favre's median is greater than Dan Marino's.
Dan Marino's range is greater than Brett Favre's.

B Compare the ranges of the middle half of the data for each.

The range of the middle of each data set is the length of the "box." So, the range of the middle half of the data is greater for Brett Favre.

Possible answers to *Think and Discuss*

1. When the data is ordered, it is easier to find the smallest value, lower quartile, median, upper quartile, and largest value, all of which are needed to make a box-and-whisker plot.

2. The box contains about the same number of data values as the two whiskers combined.

Think and Discuss

1. **Explain** why the data must first be ordered from least to greatest before making a box-and-whisker plot.

2. **Compare** the number of data values in the box with the number of data values in the whiskers.

11-3 Exercises

California Standards Practice
SDAP1.1, SDAP1.3

go.hrw.com
Homework Help Online
KEYWORD: MT8CA 11-3
Parent Resources Online
KEYWORD: MT8CA Parent

GUIDED PRACTICE

See Example **1** Find the lower and upper quartiles for each data set.

1. 52, 75, 55, 30, 70, 56, 66   **52; 70**   2. 4, 1, 3, 0, 6, 3, 5, 4, 3, 2, 6, 2   **2; 4.5**

See Example **2** Use the given data to make a box-and-whisker plot.

3. 32, 47, 42, 33, 23, 59, 29, 19, 34   4. 41, 11, 26, 58, 54, 32, 38, 56, 21

See Example **3** Use the box-and-whisker plots to compare the data sets.

5. Compare the medians and ranges.

6. Compare the ranges of the middle half of the data for each set.

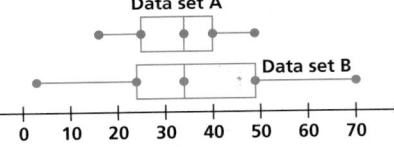

Data set A

Data set B

0   10   20   30   40   50   60   70

---

3 Close

Summarize

Show students an example of a box-and-whisker plot, and ask them to point out the location of the least value, the lower quartile, the median, the upper quartile, and the greatest value. Ask them which part of the plot represents the range. Have students describe the change to the plot when a very large outlier is added to the data set.

Possible answers: The least and greatest values are the ends of the line. The lower and upper quartiles are the ends of the box. The median is the line in the middle of the box. The range is the length of the line. An outlier would make the line extend far beyond the box to the right.

Answers

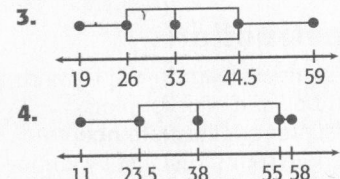

3.

19   26   33   44.5   59

4.

11   23.5   38   55 58

5. The medians are equal, but data set B has a much greater range.

6. The range of the middle half of the data is greater for data set B.

INDEPENDENT PRACTICE

See Example 1   Find the lower and upper quartiles for each data set.

7. 48, 72, 43, 42, 69, 50, 56, 48, 52
    45.5; 62.5

8. 18, 17, 13, 7, 6, 25, 55, 3, 6 **6; 21.5**

See Example 2   Use the given data to make a box-and-whisker plot.

9. 50, 68, 85, 54, 80, 75, 68

10. 7, 4, 5.7, 1.4, 6.8, 6.3, 11, 3.2

See Example 3   Use the box-and-whisker plots to compare the data sets.

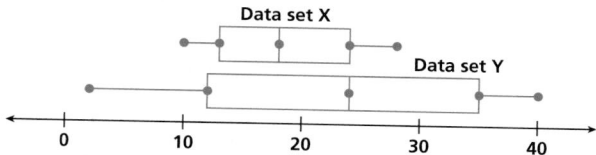

11. Compare the medians and ranges.

12. Compare the ranges of the middle half of the data for each set.

11. Data set Y has a greater median. Data set Y has a greater range.

12. Data set Y has a greater range of the middle half of the data.

PRACTICE AND PROBLEM SOLVING

Extra Practice
See page EP22.

Find the lower and upper quartiles for each data set.

13. 88, 78, 85, 74, 66, 82, 68 **68; 85**

14. 9, 2, 8, 6, 1, 7, 3, 11 **2.5; 8.5**

15. 46, 53, 67, 29, 35, 54, 49, 61, 35
    35; 57.5

16. 3.5, 3.4, 3.7, 3.5, 3.4, 3.3, 3.4, 3.4
    3.4; 3.5

Use the given data to make a box-and-whisker plot.

17. 87, 79, 95, 99, 67, 71, 83, 91

18. 16, 3, 9.3, 11.3, 14, 7, 7, 4.2, 4.5

19. 0, 2, 5, 2, 1, 3, 5, 2, 4, 3, 5, 4

20. 6.4, 8.0, 6.5, 3.0, 5.4, 2.2, 5.3

21. Science Hurricanes and tropical storms form in all seven ocean basins. Use a box-and-whisker plot to compare the number of tropical storms in every ocean basin per year with the number of hurricanes in every ocean basin per year.

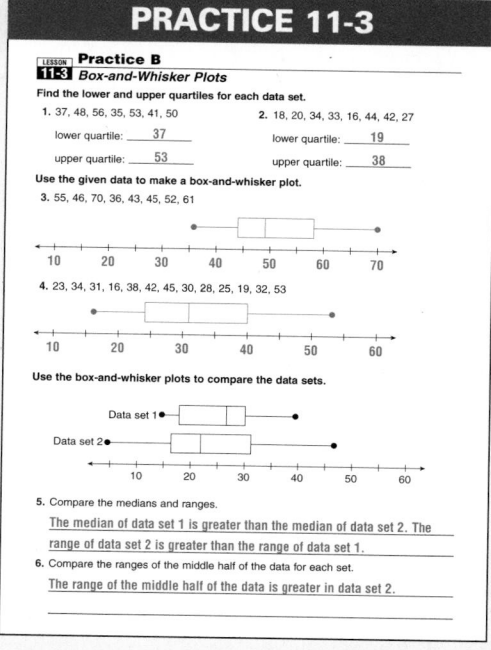

Number of Storms Per Year

Ocean Basin	Tropical Storms	Hurricanes
NW Pacific	26	16
NE Pacific	17	9
SW Pacific	9	4
Atlantic	10	5
N Indian	5	3
SW Indian	10	4
SE Indian	7	3

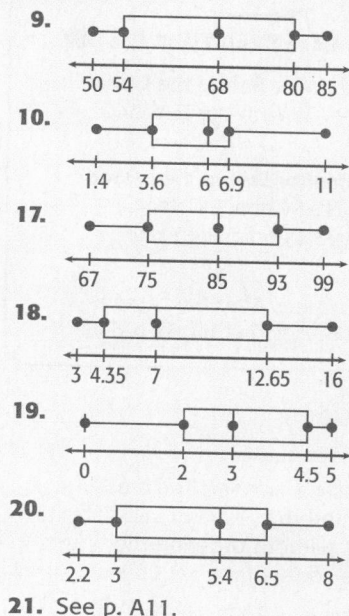

9.

10.

17.

18.

19.

20.

21. See p. A11.

Math Background

A box-and-whisker plot shows the variability of a data set, or how the data set is distributed. One important measure of this is the interquartile range (IQR). The IQR is the difference between the upper quartile and the lower quartile. The IQR is represented on the plot by the length of the box. If a whisker appears very long compared to the length of the box, then there may be one or more outliers on that whisker. Outliers can be mathematically identified as follows: Subtract 1.5 times the IQR from the first quartile. Any value less than that difference is an outlier. Add 1.5 times the IQR to the third quartile. Any value greater than that sum is an outlier.

REVIEW FOR MASTERY 11-3

LESSON 11-3 Review for Mastery
Box-and-Whisker Plots

Quartiles divide a data set into four equal parts.

1 1 3 3 3 ④ 4 6 6 6 6 ⑥ 7 7 7 7 ⑧ 9 9 9 9 9

The **lower quartile** is the median of the lower half.

The **median** divides the data into two halves.

The **upper quartile** is the median of the upper half.

For each data set, circle and label the median *M*. Circle and label the lower quartile. Circle and label the upper quartile.

1. 3 ③ 3 ④ 5 ⑥ 7
   lower   *M*   upper

2. 3 3 ③ 4 4 ⑤ 6 7 ⑨ 10 10
   lower   *M*   upper

A **box-and-whisker** plot displays the quartile values as well as the minimum and maximum of a data set. The sides of the box are the lower and upper quartiles; the median is inside the box. The whiskers connect the box to the minimum and maximum.

This plot displays the values for the data set at the top of this page.

minimum = 1
lower quartile = 4
median = 6
upper quartile = 8
maximum = 9

Complete to make a box-and-whisker plot for the data set 45, 47, 47, 48, 48, 49, 53.

3. First, calculate three significant values for the data set.

median = __48__   lower quartile = __47__   upper quartile = __49__

PRACTICE 11-3

LESSON 11-3 Practice B
Box-and-Whisker Plots

Find the lower and upper quartiles for each data set.

1. 37, 48, 56, 35, 53, 41, 50

lower quartile: __37__

upper quartile: __53__

2. 18, 20, 34, 33, 16, 44, 42, 27

lower quartile: __19__

upper quartile: __38__

Use the given data to make a box-and-whisker plot.

3. 55, 46, 70, 36, 43, 45, 52, 61

4. 23, 34, 31, 16, 38, 42, 45, 30, 28, 25, 19, 32, 53

Use the box-and-whisker plots to compare the data sets.

5. Compare the medians and ranges.

The median of data set 1 is greater than the median of data set 2. The range of data set 2 is greater than the range of data set 1.

6. Compare the ranges of the middle half of the data for each set.

The range of the middle half of the data is greater in data set 2.

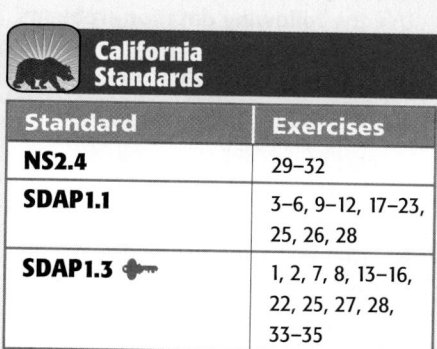

Standard	Exercises
NS2.4	29–32
SDAP1.1	3–6, 9–12, 17–23, 25, 26, 28
SDAP1.3	1, 2, 7, 8, 13–16, 22, 25, 27, 28, 33–35

Answers

23, 28. See p. A11.

24. Possible answer: The student subtracted the first and last data values without ordering them first. The correct range is 65 − 25 = 40.

25. Possible answer: Box-and-whisker plots show how the data are spread out from the median. They also show the range and quartiles.

Teaching Tip **Multiple Choice** Students may not recall that the lower quartile on a box-and-whisker plot is on the leftmost side of the box. Students who chose **C** or **D** for **Exercise 27** may need to review the five points used to construct box-and-whisker plots.

 Journal

Refer students to **Example 3** in the lesson. Ask students to write about whether they think Brett Favre or Dan Marino was the better touchdown passer and why.

Power Presentations
with PowerPoint®

Find the lower and upper quartiles for each data set.

1. 48, 52, 68, 32, 53, 47, 51

lower = 47; upper = 53

2. 3, 18, 11, 2, 7, 5, 9, 6, 13, 1, 17, 8, 0

lower = 2.5; upper = 12

Use the following data for problems 3 and 4.

91, 87, 98, 93, 89, 78, 94

3. Make a box-and-whisker plot.

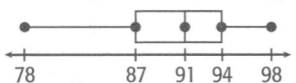

4. What is the median and range of the data? 91; 20

Also available on transparency

---

22. Match each set of data with a box-and-whisker plot.

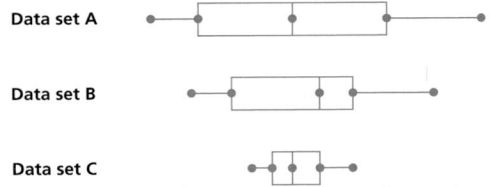

Data set A

Data set B

Data set C

| 0 | 10 | 20 | 30 | 40 | 50 |

a. range: 49
lower quartile: 11
upper quartile: 39.5
Data set A

b. range: 15
lower quartile: 23
upper quartile: 29.5
Data set C

c. range: 36
lower quartile: 18
upper quartile: 35
Data set B

23. **Reasoning** Make a box-and-whisker plot of the following data: 18, 16, 21, 10, 15, 25, 13, 22, 25, 13, 15, 10. Add 50 to the list of data, and make a new box-and-whisker plot. How did the addition of an outlier affect the box-and-whisker plot?

 24. **What's the Error?** A student wrote that the data set 33, 28, 29, 56, 27, 43, 33, 25, 40, 65 has a range of 32. What's the error?

 25. **Write About It** What do box-and-whisker plots tell you about data that measures of central tendency do not?

 26. **Challenge** What would an exceptionally short box with extremely long whiskers tell you about a data set? **Possible answer: The minimum and maximum values are outliers.**

 **SPIRAL STANDARDS REVIEW** NS2.4, SDAP1.1, ◆ SDAP1.3

27. **Multiple Choice** Find the lower quartile for the data set shown in the box-and-whisker plot.

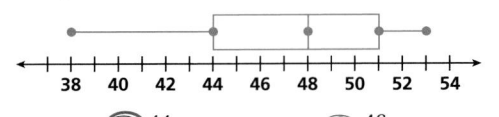

| 38 | 40 | 42 | 44 | 46 | 48 | 50 | 52 | 54 |

Ⓐ 38 Ⓑ 44 Ⓒ 46 Ⓓ 48

28. **Extended Response** Ken recorded his golf scores during a three week period. His scores were: 85, 76, 83, 99, 83, 74, 75, 81, and 87. Find the range, median, and lower and upper quartiles. Make a box-and-whisker plot of the data. **Range: 25; median: 83; lower quartile: 75.5; upper quartile: 86**

Find the two square roots of each number. (Lesson 4-6)

29. 16 4 and −4   **30.** 81 9 and −9   **31.** 100 10 and −10   **32.** 1 1 and −1

Find the mean, median, and mode of each data set to the nearest tenth. (Lesson 11-2)

33. 3, 5, 5, 6, 9, 3, 5, 2, 5   **34.** 17, 15, 14, 16, 18, 13   **35.** 100, 75, 48, 75, 48, 63, 45
≈ 4.8; 5; 5   15.5; 15.5; no mode   ≈ 64.9; 63; 48 and 75

CHALLENGE 11-3

LESSON 11-3 **Challenge**
What's Normal?

Standard deviation (symbol σ, *sigma*) is a measure of variability that tells how far data are spread out from the mean of a data set.

In many situations, such as scores on the SAT or other standardized tests, the data cluster around the mean in such a way that if they are graphed to show the frequency of measures, the graph appears as a **bell-shaped curve**, also called the **normal curve**.

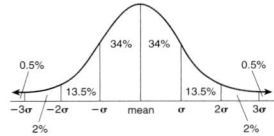

0.5%	13.5%	34%	34%	13.5%	0.5%
−3σ	−2σ	−σ	mean	σ	2σ	3σ
2%						2%

If the mean math score for males on the 2001 SAT I was 533 and the standard deviation was 115, determine the scores achieved by about 68% of the male participants.

According to the normal curve, 68% of scores fall between − σ and σ.
mean − σ = 533 − 115 = 418   mean + σ = 533 + 115 = 648
So, the scores for about 68% of the males fell between 418 and 648.

Assume a normal distribution for each situation.

1. A survey of 16-year-olds showed that they watched an average (mean) of 9.4 hours of TV per week, with a standard deviation of 1.2 hours. Determine how many hours of TV were watched by about:

a. 68% of the participants.   between 8.2 and 10.6 hours

b. 95% of the participants.   between 7 and 11.8 hours

2. On a certain standardized test, the mean score was 50 and the standard deviation 3. About what percent of the participants scored:

a. between 50 and 56?   47.5%

b. 44 and 47?   13.5%

PROBLEM SOLVING 11-3

LESSON 11-3 **Problem Solving**
Box-and-Whisker Plots

Write the correct answer.

1. Find the median of the data.

14.5 points

2. Find the lower and upper quartiles of the data.

lower = 10, upper = 23

3. Make a box-and-whisker plot of the data.

| 0 | 10 | 20 | 30 | 40 |

Super Bowl Point Differences

Year	Point Difference
2001	27
2000	7
1999	15
1998	7
1997	14
1996	10
1995	23
1994	17
1993	35
1992	13

The box-and-whisker plots compare the highest recorded Fahrenheit temperatures on the seven continents with the lowest recorded temperatures. Choose the letter for the best answer.

4. Which statement is true?
  A The median of the high temperatures is less than the median of the low temperatures.
  B The range of low temperatures is greater than the range of high temperatures.
  C The range of the middle half of the data is greater for the high temperatures.
  D The median of the high temperatures is 49°F.

5. What is the median of the high temperatures?
  F 128°F   **H** −67°F
  G 120°F   **J** −90°F

6. What is the range of the low temperatures?
  A 77°F   **C** 120°F
  B 79°F   **D** 129°F

---

546 Chapter 11 Data, Statistics, and Probability

Technology LAB 11-3

Make a Box-and-Whisker Plot

Use with Lesson 11-3

go.hrw.com
Lab Resources Online
KEYWORD: MT8CA Lab11

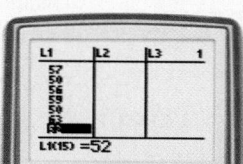
California Standards

SDAP1.1 Know various forms of display for data sets, including a stem-and-leaf plot or box-and-whisker plot; use the forms to display a single set of data or to compare two sets of data.
Also covered: **SDAP1.3**

The data below are the heights in inches of the 15 girls in Mrs. Lopez's 8th-grade class.

57, 62, 68, 52, 53, 56, 58, 56, 57, 50, 56, 59, 50, 63, 52

Activity

Graph the heights of the 15 girls in Mrs. Lopez's class on a box-and-whisker plot.

Press **STAT** **Edit** to enter the values into List 1 (**L1**). If necessary, press the up arrow and then **CLEAR** **ENTER** to clear old data. Enter the data from the class into **L1**. Press **ENTER** after each value.

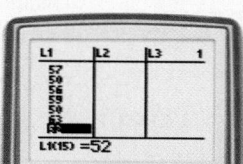

Use the **STAT PLOT** editor to obtain the plot setup menu. Press **2nd** **Y=** **ENTER**. Use the arrow keys and **ENTER** to select **On** and then the fifth type. **Xlist** should be **L1**, and **Freq** should be 1, as shown. Press **ZOOM** **9:ZoomStat**.

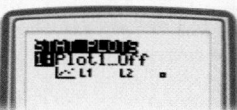

Use the **TRACE** key and the ◄ and ► keys to see all five summary statistical values (minimum: **MinX**, first (or lower) quartile: **Q1**, median: **MED**, third (or upper) quartile: **Q3**, and maximum: **MaxX**). The minimum value in the data set is 50 in., the first quartile is 52 in., the median is 56 in., the third quartile is 59 in., and the maximum is 68 in.

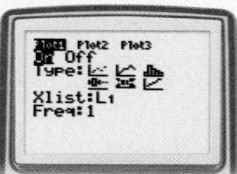

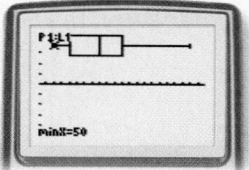

Think and Discuss

1. Explain how the box-and-whisker plot gives information that is hard to see by just looking at the numbers.

Try This

1. The data below shows the number of hours slept one night for each of the 11 boys from Mrs. Lopez's 8th-grade class.

   7.5, 6.5, 5, 6, 8, 7.25, 6.5, 7, 7, 8, 6.75

   Make a box-and-whisker plot of this data. What are the minimum, first quartile, median, third quartile, and maximum values of the data set?

   minimum: 5;
   first quartile: 6.5;
   median: 7;
   third quartile: 7.5;
   maximum: 8

Answers to *Think and Discuss*

1. Possible answer: The box-and-whisker plot makes it easy to see the minimum and maximum values, the position of the quartiles, and the median.

Answers to *Try This*

1.
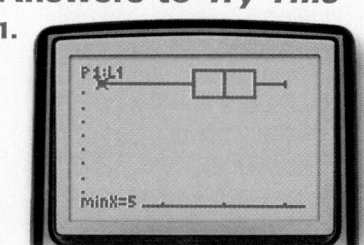

Answers to *Assessment*

1.
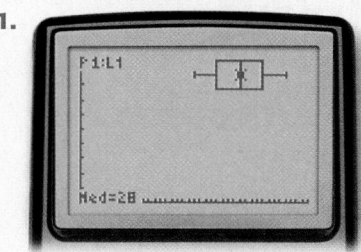

minimum: 20
first quartile: 24
median: 28
third quartile: 32
maximum: 36

Technology LAB **Organizer**
Use with Lesson 11-3

Objective: Using a graphing calculator to make a box-and-whisker plot.

Materials: Graphing calculator

 Online Edition
Statistics Calculator, TechKeys

 Countdown to Mastery Week 23

Teach
Discuss

Graphing calculators are a powerful tool that can help students analyze and display data. Ensure students understand the significance of each keystroke so they are not blindly following steps.

Close
Key Concept

You can use a graphing calculator to produce graphic displays of data, such as box-and-whisker plots.

Assessment

1. Make a box-and-whisker plot from the following data:

   30, 27, 29, 24, 20, 36, 32, 24, 21, 35

What are the minimum, first quartile, median, third quartile, and maximum values of the data set?

California Standards

Statistics, Data Analysis, and Probability 1.1
Also covered:
Statistics, Data Analysis, and Probability
1.3 Understand the meaning of, and be able to compute, **the minimum, the lower quartile, the median, the upper quartile, and the maximum of a data set.**

Objective: Students create and interpret scatter plots.

 Hands-On Lab
In *Chapter 11 Resource File*

 Technology Lab
In *Chapter 11 Resource File*

 Online Edition
Tutorial Videos

 Countdown to Mastery Week 23

Power Presentations
with PowerPoint®

Warm Up
Graph each point on the same coordinate plane.

1. *A*(5, 20) **2.** *B*(20, 15)

3. *C*(10, 40) **4.** *D*(30, 35)

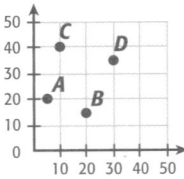

Also available on transparency

Math Humor

When too many pieces of data are clustered together, I guess you can call it a graphic jam.

California Standards

Statistics, Data Analysis, and Probability 1.2
Also covered:

Statistics, Data Analysis, and Probability 1.0 Students collect, organize, and represent data sets that have one or more variables and identify relationships among variables within a data set by hand and through the use of an electronic spreadsheet software program.

 11-4 **Scatter Plots**

California Standards

SDAP1.2 Represent two numerical variables on a scatterplot and informally describe how the data points are distributed and any apparent relationship that exists between the two variables (e.g., between time spent on homework and grade level).

Who uses this? Health care professionals can use scatter plots to help them analyze the benefits of physical activity.

A **scatter plot** is a graph with points plotted to show a possible relationship between two sets of data.

Vocabulary
scatter plot
correlation
positive correlation
negative correlation
no correlation
line of best fit

EXAMPLE 1 **Making a Scatter Plot of a Data Set**

A teacher surveyed her students about the amount of physical activity they get each week. She then had their body mass index (BMI) measured. Use her data to make a scatter plot.

Student	Active Hours per Week	BMI	Student	Active Hours per Week	BMI
A	10	16	F	8	18
B	3	25	G	7	21
C	6	24	H	2	28
D	8	20	I	19	9
E	10	16	J	14	12

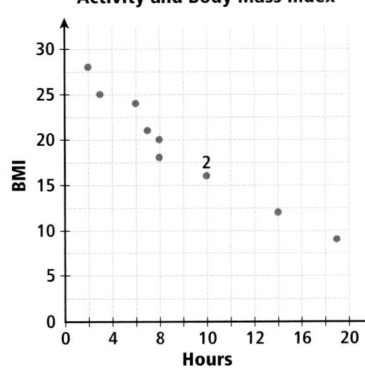

Activity and Body Mass Index

Use the table to make ordered pairs for the scatter plot.

The points are (10, 16), (3, 25), (6, 24), (8, 20), (10, 16), (8, 18), (7, 21), (2, 28), (19, 9), and (14, 12). The **2** at (10, 16) indicates that the point occurs twice.

 **1** **Introduce**
Alternate Opener

EXPLORATION

11-4 **Scatter Plots**

1. The table shows the numbers of pages in some paperback books and the books' prices. Plot the data on the graph provided.

Pages	Price ($)
300	2.25
200	1.75
130	1.65
450	3.00
180	1.75
75	1.25
250	2.50

2. The table shows the number of hours some people spent outside and spent watching TV in one day. Plot the data on the graph provided.

TV hours	Outside hours
2.0	1.5
0.5	3.5
1.5	1.5
1.0	2.5
2.5	0.5
1.5	2.0
2.0	0.5

Think and Discuss

3. **Explain** what the shape of a graph tells you about the data being displayed.

Motivate

Discuss cause and effect with the students. Ask them to provide examples of cause-and-effect relationships. Some possible examples follow: The more I practice baseball, the more hits I will get. The more I study, the higher my grades will be. Explain that the term *correlation* describes a relationship between two data sets, but point out that correlation is not the same thing as cause and effect.

Explorations and answers are provided in *Alternate Openers: Explorations Transparencies.*

A **correlation** describes a relationship between two data sets. The correlation can help you analyze trends and make predictions. There are three types of correlations between data.

Positive Correlation

The values in both data sets increase at the same time.

Negative Correlation

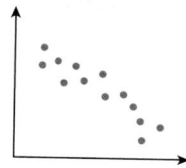

The values in one data set increase as the values in the other set decrease.

No Correlation

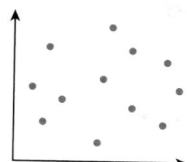

There is no relationship between the data sets.

EXAMPLE 2 Determining Relationships Between Two Sets of Data

Write *positive correlation, negative correlation,* or *no correlation* to describe each relationship. Explain.

A Rectangle Dimensions

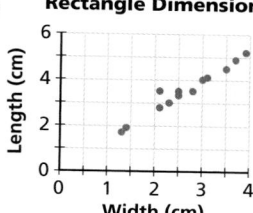

The graph shows that as width increases, length increases.

The graph shows a positive correlation between the data sets.

B Automobile Fuel Economy

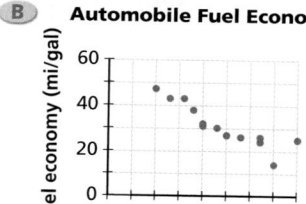

The graph shows that as an automobile's engine size increases, fuel economy decreases.

The graph shows a negative correlation between the data sets.

A **line of best fit**, or trend line, is a straight line that approximates the relationship between the data on a scatter plot. It can help show the correlation between the data more clearly. You can also use a line of best fit when making predictions based on data.

Example 1

Use the given data to make a scatter plot of the weight and height of each member of a basketball team.

Height (in.)	71	68	70	73	74
Weight (lb)	170	160	175	180	190

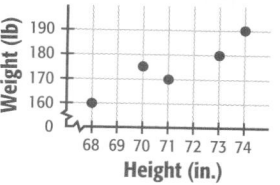

Example 2

Write *positive correlation, negative correlation,* or *no correlation* to describe the relationship. Explain.

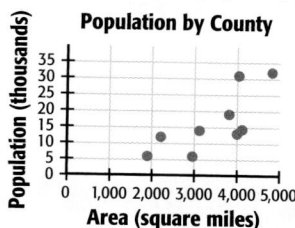

Population increases with area; positive correlation.

Also available on transparency

Teaching Tip
Visual Remind students that to plot the points on a scatter plot, move *across* to the first number of the data pair and *up* to the second number of the data pair.

---

② Teach

Guided Instruction

In this lesson, students learn to create and interpret scatter plots. Review the data in **Example 1.** Make certain that students understand that BMI is a number that shows weight adjusted for height. Explain that this study shows a negative correlation. You may want to display the Teaching Transparency while you discuss correlation. Emphasize the difference between correlation and a cause-and-effect relationship.

Universal Access
Through Curriculum Integration

Science Scientists often display data on a scatter plot because a scatter plot allows them to determine if there is a trend in the data collected. Ask students to identify statements or ideas in their science books that represent the three types of correlations. Have them exchange statements and identify each other's statements as having positive, negative, or no correlation.

Possible answers: positive correlation: the size of an animal and its weight; no correlation: the size of an animal and the number of legs it has; negative correlation: the size of an animal and the number of offspring produced

Additional Examples

Example 3

Use the data to predict how much a worker will earn in tips in 10 hours.

Hours	4	8	3	2	11
Tips ($)	12	20	7	7	26

approximately $24

Also available on transparency

Answers

1.

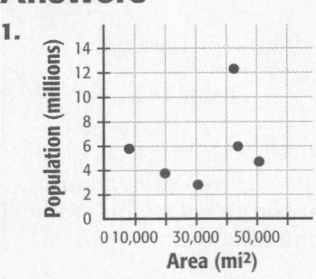

EXAMPLE 3 Using a Scatter Plot to Make Predictions

Reasoning

Possible answers to *Think and Discuss*

1. Negative correlation; the more frequently students are absent, the more work they would probably miss, and the poorer their grades would be.

2. Negative correlation: number of days spent practicing a jump in skating and the number of times you fall per practice session; positive correlation: time spent studying for a test and the final test grade.

Use the data to predict the exam grade for a student who studies 10 hours per week.

Hours Studied	5	9	3	12	1
Exam Grade	80	95	75	98	70

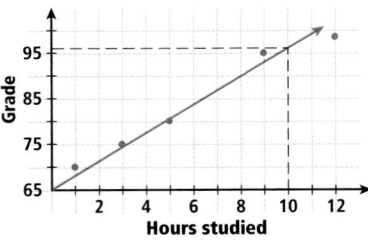

Hours Studied and Exam Grade

Draw a line that has about the same number of points above and below it. Your line may or may not go through data points.

Find the point on the line whose x-value is 10. The corresponding y-value is 96.

According to the graph, a student who studies 10 hours per week should earn a score of about 96.

Think and Discuss

1. **Describe** the type of correlation you would expect between the number of absences in a class and the grades in the class.

2. **Give an example** of a relationship between two sets of data that you would expect to show a negative correlation. Then give an example that you would expect to show a positive correlation.

11-4 Exercises

Assignment Guide

If you finished Example **1** assign:
Proficient 1, 5, 6, 19–21
Advanced 5, 6, 19–21

If you finished Example **2** assign:
Proficient 1–3, 5–8, 10–13, 17–21
Advanced 5–8, 10–14, 16–21

If you finished Example **3** assign:
Proficient 1–13, 17–21
Advanced 5–21

Homework Quick Check

Quickly check key concepts.
Exercises: 5, 6, 8, 12

California Standards Practice
SDAP1.2

go.hrw.com
Homework Help Online
KEYWORD: MT8CA 11-4
Parent Resources Online
KEYWORD: MT8CA Parent

11-4 Exercises

GUIDED PRACTICE

See Example **1**

1. Use the given data to make a scatter plot.

Country	Area (mi²)	Population
Guatemala	42,467	12,335,580
Honduras	43,715	5,997,327
El Salvador	8,206	5,839,079
Nicaragua	50,503	4,717,132
Costa Rica	19,929	3,674,490
Panama	30,498	2,778,526

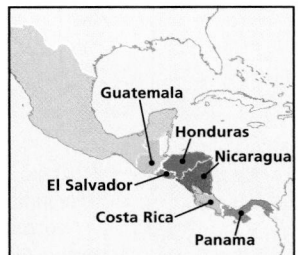

---

3 Close

Summarize

Review the vocabulary words from the lesson. Then have students explain the differences among positive correlation, negative correlation, and no correlation. Ask students to give examples of each.

Possible answers: Positive means both data sets increase or decrease together (e.g., size of a soda bottle and its price). Negative means one increases and the other decreases (e.g., speed of a runner and the time it takes to run a lap). No correlation means there is no discernable pattern between the two (e.g., size of a soda bottle and its flavor).

California Standards

Standard	Exercises
MG2.1	19, 20
MG2.3	21
SDAP1.2	1–18

Write *positive correlation*, *negative correlation*, or *no correlation* to describe each relationship. Explain.

2.

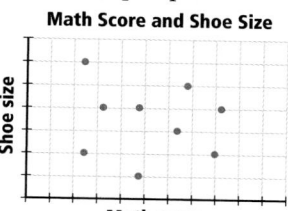

Math Score and Shoe Size

Shoe size | Math score

no correlation

3.

Work Experience

Years of work | Age

positive correlation

See Example ③ **4.** Use the data to predict the wind chill at 35 mi/h.

Apparent Temperature Due to Wind at 15°F					
Wind Speed (mi/h)	10	20	30	40	50	60
Wind Chill (°F)	2.7	−2.3	−5.5	−7.9	−9.8	−11.4

approximately −6.7°F

INDEPENDENT PRACTICE

See Example ① Use the given data to make a scatter plot.

5.

Car Brand	Cost ($1000)	Fuel Economy (mi/gal)
A	25	19
B	19	31
C	34	15
D	28	23
E	22	33

6.

Name	Length (ft)	Weight (tons)
Triceratops	30	6
Tyrannosaurus	39	7
Euhelopus	50	25
Brachiosaurus	82	50
Supersaurus	100	55

See Example ② Write *positive correlation*, *negative correlation*, or *no correlation* to describe each relationship. Explain.

7.

Sales

Weekly sales | Advertising cost

positive correlation

8.

Car's Mileage and Value

Value ($) | Mileage (thousands)

negative correlation

See Example ③ **9.** Use the data to predict the apparent temperature at 70% humidity.

73°F

Temperature Due to Humidity at a Room Temperature of 72°F						
Humidity (%)	0	20	40	60	80	100
Apparent Temperature (°F)	64	67	70	72	74	76

Math Background

A scatter plot shows a relationship between two sets of data. As in the graph of a line, points are plotted using *x*- and *y*-coordinates. Unlike the graph of a line, the points are not automatically connected.

Sometimes a line of best fit can be drawn through a scatter plot to show a linear trend in the data. If there is a positive correlation between the data sets, a line of best fit will have a positive slope. If there is a negative correlation between the data sets, a line of best fit will have a negative slope. If there is no correlation between the data sets, there is no line of best fit.

Answers

5.

Miles peer gallon | Price ($1000)

6.

Dinosaur Sizes

Weight (tons) | Length (ft)

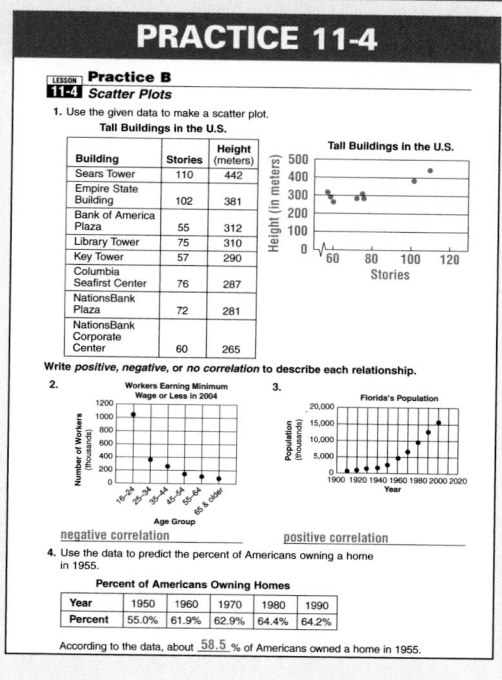

REVIEW FOR MASTERY 11-4

Review for Mastery
11-4 *Scatter Plots*

Two sets of data can be graphed as points in a **scatter plot**. If there is a relationship between the data sets, a **line of best fit** can be drawn.

Positive correlation: both sets of data increase together.

Negative correlation: values of one set increase while values of the other set decrease.

No correlation: points neither increase nor decrease together.

Make a scatter plot. Include a line of best fit if there is a correlation. Describe the correlation.

1.

Time (hours)	1	2	2.5	6
Distance (miles)	50	150	175	270

The values for time are: increasing
distance are: __increasing__
So, there is a __positive__ correlation.

2.

Number of Workers	6	4	2	1
Number of Days	1	2	5	7

The values for
the number of workers are: __decreasing__
the number of days are: __increasing__
So, there is a __negative__ correlation.

PRACTICE 11-4

Practice B
11-4 *Scatter Plots*

1. Use the given data to make a scatter plot.

Tall Buildings in the U.S.

Building	Stories	Height (meters)
Sears Tower	110	442
Empire State Building	102	381
Bank of America Plaza	55	312
Library Tower	75	310
Key Tower	57	290
Columbia Seafirst Center	76	287
NationsBank Plaza	72	281
NationsBank Corporate Center	60	265

Tall Buildings in the U.S.

Write *positive*, *negative*, or *no correlation* to describe each relationship.

2. Workers Earning Minimum Wage or Less in 2004

negative correlation

3. Florida's Population

positive correlation

4. Use the data to predict the percent of Americans owning a home in 1955.

Percent of Americans Owning Homes

Year	1950	1960	1970	1980	1990
Percent	55.0%	61.9%	62.9%	64.4%	64.2%

According to the data, about __58.5__% of Americans owned a home in 1955.

FORMATIVE ASSESSMENT
and INTERVENTION ◄══►

Diagnose *Before* the Lesson
11-4 Warm Up, TE p. 548

Monitor *During* the Lesson
11-4 Know-It Notebook
11-4 Questioning Strategies

Assess *After* the Lesson
11-4 Lesson Quiz, TE p. 552

Answers
14. See p. A11.

Teaching Tip **Short Response** If students are experiencing difficulty with **Exercise 18,** suggest that they think of several number pairs that fit the situation and imagine them in a scatter plot.

Journal
Have students consider the question "Will more people or fewer people buy an item if the price goes up?" Have them explain the relationship and describe the correlation.

Power Presentations
with PowerPoint®

11-4 ✓ Lesson Quiz
1. Use the given data to make a scatter plot.

Grading Period	1	2	3	4
Number of A's	5	6	8	10

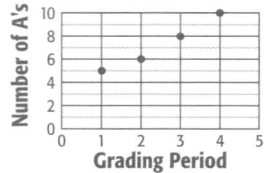

Identify the correlation that you would expect to see between each pair of data sets.

2. the minimum wage and the year
positive correlation

3. amount of precipitation and the day of the week no correlation

4. the number of germs on your hands and the number of times you wash your hands in a day
negative correlation

Also available on transparency

PRACTICE AND PROBLEM SOLVING

Extra Practice
See page EP22.

Identify the correlation that you would expect to see between each pair of data sets. Explain.

10. the number of hours of daylight and the amount of rainfall in a day
No correlation; there is no relationship.

11. the number of hours a plane is in flight and the number of miles flown
Positive correlation; as the length of the flight increases, the number of miles flown increases.

12. the number of students in a district and the number of buses in the district
Positive correlation; as the number of students increases, the number of buses increases.

13. the number of knots tied in a rope and the length of the rope
Negative correlation; as the number of knots increases, the length of the rope decreases.

14. Life Science The table shows pollen levels measured in grains per cubic meter. Use the data to make a scatter plot. Then describe the relationship between the data sets.

Pollen Levels		
Day	Weed Pollen	Grass Pollen
1	350	16
2	51	1
3	49	9
4	309	3
5	488	29
6	30	3
7	65	12

15. Write About It Conduct a survey of your classmates to find their age in months and their shoe size. Predict whether there will be a positive correlation, a negative correlation, or no correlation. Then graph the data in a scatter plot. What is the relationship between the two data sets? Was your prediction correct?
Check students' work.

16. Challenge A location's elevation is negatively correlated to its average temperature and positively correlated to the amount of snow the location receives. What type of correlation would you expect to see between temperature and the amount of snowfall? Explain.
Negative correlation; the lower the temperature, the more snow the location receives.

SPIRAL STANDARDS REVIEW   MG2.1, MG2.3, SDAP1.2

17. Multiple Choice The scatter plot shows the amount of money spent on advertising and the amount earned in sales. Which statement is best supported by the scatter plot?

(A) Weekly sales increase as advertising costs increase.

(B) Weekly sales decrease as advertising costs increase.

(C) Weekly sales remain constant as advertising costs increase.

(D) There is no relationship between the amount spent on advertising and the amount earned in sales.

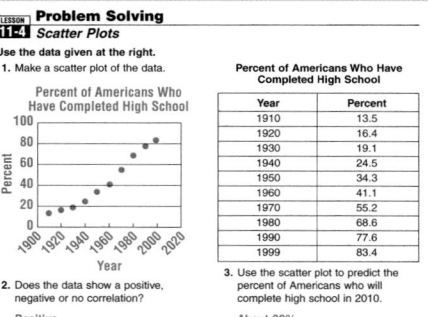

18. Short Response What type of correlation would you expect to see between a person's height and his or her birthday? Explain.
No correlation; there are people of all heights, and there are birthdays in each month of the year.

Find the area of each circle to the nearest tenth. Use 3.14 for π. (Lesson 9-4)

19. circle with diameter 10 cm 78.5 cm² **20.** circle with radius 5.2 yd 84.9 yd²

21. A 9 cm cube is built from 1 cm cubes. Compare the ratio of the length of an edge of the large cube to the length of an edge of a small cube. (Lesson 10-7) 9 to 1

CHALLENGE 11-4

LESSON Challenge
11-4 This Fits Nicely!

When two sets of data show a correlation, you can draw a **line of best fit** that approximates a trend.

Here are some data relating the gestation periods of selected animals to their average life spans. The data are separated into 3 equal sets.

	Set I			Set II			Set III	
Gestation (days)	31	61	68	105	151	167	285	330	365
Longevity (years)	13	12	4	5	8	20	15	20	12

1. Determine the **median-median point** for each set of points by getting the median value for the gestation values and the median value for the longevity values.

The median-median point for
Set I is: (61, 12)   Set II is: (151, 8)   Set III is: (330, 15)

2. Make a scatter plot for the given data. Describe the correlation. __positive__

3. Using an X for each, plot the three median-median points on your graph.
Using a ruler, draw a dotted line through the median-median points for Sets I and III. See graph
Keeping the ruler at the level of the dotted line, estimate the vertical distance between the dotted line and the median-median point for Set II. Then slide the ruler down about one-third this distance. Draw a solid line parallel to the dotted line. This solid line is called the median-median line and it is a line of best fit for the given data. See graph

---

PROBLEM SOLVING 11-4

LESSON Problem Solving
11-4 Scatter Plots

Use the data given at the right.

1. Make a scatter plot of the data.

Percent of Americans Who Have Completed High School

Year	Percent
1910	13.5
1920	16.4
1930	19.1
1940	24.5
1950	34.3
1960	41.1
1970	55.2
1980	68.6
1990	77.6
1999	83.4

2. Does the data show a positive, negative or no correlation?
__Positive__

3. Use the scatter plot to predict the percent of Americans who will complete high school in 2010.
__About 90%__

Choose the letter for the best answer.

4. What kind of correlation would you expect to find between a city's annual snowfall amount and the size of its population?
A positive correlation
B negative correlation
C no correlation
D impossible to say

5. What kind of correlation would you expect to find between a movie's length and the number of times it can be shown in a day?
F positive correlation
G negative correlation
H no correlation
J impossible to say

6. What kind of correlation would you expect to find between an animal's mass and the number of calories it consumes in a day?
A positive correlation
B negative correlation
C no correlation
D impossible to say

7. What kind of correlation would you expect to find between a person's height and his or her income?
F positive correlation
G negative correlation
H no correlation
J impossible to say

Technology LAB 11-4

Make a Scatter Plot

 go.hrw.com
Lab Resources Online
KEYWORD: MT8CA Lab11

Use with Lesson 11-4

 California Standards

SDAP1.2 Represent two numerical variables on a scatterplot and informally describe how the data points are distributed and any apparent relationship that exists between the two variables (e.g., between time spent on homework and grade level).
Also covered: **SDAP1.0**

You can use a graphing calculator to display relationships between data sets in a scatter plot.

Activity

The table shows heights and weights of students in Mr. Devany's class. Use a graphing calculator to create a scatter plot of the data.

To enter the data, press **STAT** **ENTER** to select "1:Edit"

In L1, enter the heights. In L2, enter the weights.

To see a scatter plot of the data, press **2nd** **Y=** **ENTER** to select **STAT PLOT** "STAT PLOTS 1:"

Scroll and press **ENTER** to select "On" and the scatter plot icon. Scroll to "Xlist=" and press **2nd** 1.

Scroll to "Ylist=" and press **2nd** 2. Finally, scroll to "Mark:" and choose the box.

To view the scatter plot, press **ZOOM** 9. Press **TRACE** and the arrow keys to read the histogram.

Height (in.)	Weight (lb)
41	92
43	111
46	105
50	120
51	110
55	107
60	125
62	125
62	125
66	152
69	175
70	210

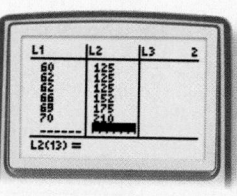

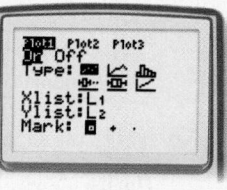

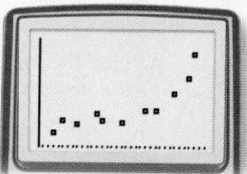

Think and Discuss

1. Describe the relationship between height and weight that is shown in the scatter plot. The plot shows a positive correlation; as height increases, weight increases.

2. Suppose you added a third category: boy or girl. How could the height, weight, and gender data be displayed?
Possible answer: The heights and weights of boys could be displayed using one symbol, and the heights and weights of girls could be displayed using another symbol.

Try This

Use a graphing calculator to create a scatter plot of the data.

1.

x	41	43	46	50	51	55	60	62	66	69	70
y	92	111	105	120	110	107	125	142	152	175	210

Answer to *Try This*

1.

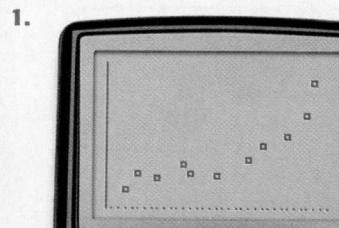

Technology LAB

Organizer
Use with Lesson 11-4

Objective: Use a graphing calculator to display relationships between data sets in a scatter plot.
Materials: Graphing calculator

PREMIER **Online Edition**
Statistics Calculator, TechKeys

Countdown to Mastery Week 24

Teach
Discuss

Ask students to compare using a pencil and coordinate grid to using a graphing calculator to make a scatter plot. Discuss the benefits of each method and whether one type is easier to interpret than the other.

Close
Key Concept

You can use a graphing calculator to display relationships between data sets in a scatter plot.

Assessment

1. Does the scatter plot you created in the activity have a negative or positive correlation? positive

2. Have students collect data found in a newspaper, magazine, or another textbook and display the data in a scatter plot using a graphing calculator. Check students' work.

 California Standards

Statistics, Data Analysis, and Probability 1.2
Also covered:
Statistics, Data Analysis, and Probability 1.0 Students collect, organize, and represent data sets that have one or more variables and identify relationships among variables within a data set by hand and through the use of an electronic spreadsheet software program.

Organizer

Objective: Assess students' mastery of concepts and skills in Lessons 11-1 through 11-4.

Resources

 Assessment Resources
Section 11A Quiz

 Test & Practice Generator
One-Stop Planner®

INTERVENTION ◄══►

Resources

 Ready to Go On?
Intervention and
Enrichment **Worksheets**

💿 **Ready to Go On? CD-ROM**

🪐 **Ready to Go On? Online**

my.hrw.com

Answers

1–3, 6–8. See p. A11.

Quiz for Lessons 11-1 Through 11-4

11-1 Line Plots and Stem-and-Leaf Plots

1. Use a line plot to organize the data of the ages of people playing bridge.

72	78	76	75	79	70	74	80	72	78
71	69	70	72	68	70	69	75	75	74

2. The list below shows the top speeds of various land animals. Make a stem-and-leaf plot of the data.

42 55 62 48 65 51 47 59 67 61 49 54 55 52 44

3. Use the given data to make a back-to-back stem-and-leaf plot.

Greatest Number of Home Runs by a Player, 2000–2004					
	2000	**2001**	**2002**	**2003**	**2004**
American League	47	52	57	47	43
National League	50	73	49	47	48

11-2 Mean, Median, Mode, and Range

The list shows the life spans in years of vampire bats in captivity.

18 22 5 21 19 21 17 3 19 20 29 18 17

4. Find the mean, median, mode, and range of the data set. Round your answers to the nearest tenth of a year. 17.6; 19; 17, 18, 19, and 21; 26

5. Which measure, mean or median, best describes the typical life span of a vampire bat in captivity? Justify your answer. Median; the outliers affect the mean, so the median is best.

11-3 Box-and-Whisker Plots

Use the given data to make a box-and-whisker plot.

6. 43, 36, 25, 22, 34, 40, 18, 32, 43   **7.** 21, 51, 36, 38, 45, 52, 28, 16, 41

11-4 Scatter Plots

8. Use the given data of the estimated U.S. population to make a scatter plot.

Year	1998	1999	2000	2001	2002	2003	2004
Population (in millions)	270.2	272.7	282.2	285.1	287.9	290.8	293.7

Identify the correlation you would expect to see between each pair of data sets. Explain.

9. a person's date of birth and eye color   No correlation; there is no relationship.

10. the number of miles on a used car and the value of the car
Negative correlation; as the number of miles increases, the value of the car decreases.

READY TO GO ON?

Diagnose and Prescribe

NO
INTERVENE

YES
ENRICH

READY TO GO ON? **Intervention, Section 11A**			
Ready to Go On? Intervention	🖎 **Worksheets**	💿 **CD-ROM**	🪐 **Online**
✓ Lesson 11-1 **SDAP1.1**	11-1 Intervention	Activity 11-1	Diagnose and Prescribe Online
✓ Lesson 11-2 🗝 **SDAP1.3**	11-2 Intervention	Activity 11-2	
✓ Lesson 11-3 **SDAP1.1**, 🗝 **SDAP1.3**	11-3 Intervention	Activity 11-3	
✓ Lesson 11-4 **SDAP1.2**	11-4 Intervention	Activity 11-4	

READY TO GO ON?
Enrichment, **Section 11A**
🖎 **Worksheets**
💿 **CD-ROM**
🪐 **Online**

Focus on Problem Solving

California Standards

MR1.1 Analyze problems by identifying relationships, **distinguishing relevant from irrelevant information, identifying missing information,** sequencing and prioritizing information, and observing patterns.
Also covered: **NS1.2**

Plan

Make a Plan

• **Identify too much/too little information**

When you read a problem, you must decide if the problem has too much or too little information. If the problem has too much information, you must decide what information to use to solve the problem. If the problem has too little information, then you should determine what additional information you need to solve the problem.

Read the problems below and decide if there is too much or too little information in each problem. If there is too much information, tell what information you would use to solve the problem. If there is too little information, tell what additional information you would need to solve the problem.

1 On Monday, 20 students took an exam. There were 10 students who scored above 85 and 10 students who scored below 85. What was the average score?

2 The average elevation in California is about 2900 ft above sea level. The highest point, Mt. Whitney, has an elevation of 14,494 ft above sea level. The lowest point, Death Valley, has an elevation of 282 ft below sea level. What is the range of elevations in California?

3 Use the table to find the median number of marriages per year in the United States for the years between 1940 and 2000.

4 Aishya is cross-training for a marathon. She ran for 50 minutes on Monday, 70 minutes on Wednesday, and 45 minutes on Friday. On Tuesday and Thursday, she lifted weights at the gym for 45 minutes each day. She swam for 45 minutes over the weekend. What was the average amount of time per day Aishya spent running last week?

5 Mrs. Wong wants to put a fence around her vegetable garden. One side of her garden measures 8 ft. Another side measures 5 ft. What length of fencing does Mrs. Wong need to enclose her garden?

Number of Marriages in the United States							
Year	1940	1950	1960	1970	1980	1990	2000
Number (thousands)	1596	1667	1523	2159	2390	2443	2329

Source: National Center for Health Statistics

Answers

1. too little information

2. 14,776 ft

3. too little information

4. 23.6 min/day

5. too little information

Focus on Problem Solving

Organizer

Objective: Focus on identifying too much or too little information.

 Online Edition

Resources

 Chapter 11 Resource File
Reading Strategies

Problem Solving Process

This page focuses on the second step of the problem-solving process: **Make a Plan**

Discuss

Have students identify whether the problem gives too little, too much, or just the right amount of information. Then ask them to explain what information is needed.

Possible answers:

1. too little information; need to know each individual score

2. too much information; use the lowest elevation and the highest elevation

3. too little information; need the number of marriages each year from 1940 to 2000

4. too much information; use the number of minutes spent running each day

5. too little information; need to know the shape of the garden; need the lengths of all of the garden's sides

California Standards

Mathematical Reasoning 1.1
Also covered:
Number Sense
1.2 Add, subtract, multiply, and divide rational numbers (integers, fractions, and terminating decimals) and take positive rational numbers to whole-number powers.

Probability

One-Minute Section Planner

Lesson	Lab Resources	Materials
Lesson 11-5 Probability • Find the probability of an event by using the definition of probability. 🖼 **Review of Grade 6** 🗝 **SDAP3.3**	**Hands-On Lab 11-5** In *Chapter 11 Resource File*	
Lesson 11-6 Experimental Probability • Estimate probability using experimental methods. 🖼 **Review of Grade 6** **SDAP3.2,** 🗝 **SDAP3.3**		**Optional** Number cubes (MK), coins (MK)
Lesson 11-7 Theoretical Probability • Estimate probability using theoretical methods. 🖼 **Review of Grade 6** 🗝 **SDAP3.1,** 🗝 **SDAP3.3, SDAP3.4**		**Optional** Index cards, deck of cards, bags
Lesson 11-8 Independent and Dependent Events • Find the probabilities of independent and dependent events. 🖼 **Review of Grade 6** 🗝 **SDAP3.3, SDAP3.4,** 🗝 **SDAP3.5**	**Hands-On Lab 11-8** In *Chapter 11 Resource File*	**Optional** Two-color counters (MK)

MK = *Manipulatives Kit*

Notes

_____

_____

_____

_____

_____

_____

_____

_____

_____

_____

_____

_____

Math Background:
Teaching the Standards

PROBABILITY  Rev. of 6SDAP3.3

Lessons 11-5 through 11-8

The birth of modern probability theory can be traced to a famous letter. In 1654, the Chevalier de Mere, a French nobleman, wrote to the renowned philosopher and mathematician Blaise Pascal to seek Pascal's advice about a gambling situation. The Chevalier de Mere sometimes bet his friends that he could roll a 6 in four rolls of a die. His experience told him that this tended to be a winning proposition, but he asked Pascal to provide a mathematical explanation.

This situation provides a good illustration of experimental probability versus theoretical probability. The Chevalier de Mere might have recorded his results and found that he won 52 times out of a total of 100 bets. In this case, the *experimental probability* of winning is 0.52 or 52%. In general, the experimental probability of an event is the ratio of the number of times an event occurs to the total number of trials.

Pascal calculated the probability of winning the bet using *theoretical probability*. The theoretical probability of an event is the ratio of the number of ways the event can occur to the total number of possible outcomes. For the Chevalier de Mere's situation, this ratio works out to be $\frac{671}{1296}$, or approximately 0.5177, confirming the chevalier's experience that the chances of winning the bet were slightly in his favor.

REPRESENTING PROBABILITIES

Rev. of 6SDAP3.3

Lesson 11-5

A probability may be expressed as a ratio, a decimal, or a percent. In some situations, one representation may be more enlightening than another. For instance, the probability of rolling a 3 on a number cube is $\frac{1}{6}$, or $16.66\overline{6}\%$. The ratio makes it easy to see that rolling a 3 is one out of six possible outcomes. When comparing two or more probabilities, it may be most useful to express the probabilities as decimals or percents. Regardless of how probabilities are expressed, students should understand that a probability is always a real number between 0 and 1, inclusive, or a percent between 0% and 100%, inclusive.

CALCULATING PROBABILITIES

Rev. of 6SDAP3.3, 6SDAP3.4, 6SDAP3.5

Lessons 11-5 through 11-8

Given an event E, the *complement* of the event (sometimes written $\sim E$) is the set of all outcomes that are not included in the event. An event and its complement are disjoint (that is, they have no events in common), and together E and $\sim E$ form the entire sample space. Therefore, $P(E) + P(\sim E) = 1$, and consequently $P(E) = 1 - P(\sim E)$. This last fact is often useful in calculating probabilities of events that contain many outcomes. In such cases it may be easier to calculate the probability of the complement of the event and then subtract this value from 1.

Two events are *independent events* if the occurrence of one event does not affect the probability of the other. For independent events, $P(A \text{ and } B) = P(A) \cdot P(B)$. A specific example illustrates why the probabilities are multiplied. Consider the following independent events.

> Event A: Spinning a 1 or 2 on a spinner with five congruent sectors labeled 1 through 5
>
> Event B: Rolling a 1, 2, or 3 on a number cube

Clearly, $P(A) = \frac{2}{5}$ and $P(B) = \frac{3}{6}$. To find $P(A \text{ and } B)$, notice that the sample space, shown below, consists of $5 \times 6 = 30$ outcomes. The event "A and B," shown by the green rectangle, consists of $2 \times 3 = 6$ outcomes. Thus, $P(A \text{ and } B) = \frac{2 \times 3}{5 \times 6} = \frac{2}{5} \times \frac{3}{6} = P(A) \cdot P(B)$.

		Event B				
	1	**2**	**3**	**4**	**5**	**6**
1	1, 1	1, 2	1, 3	1, 4	1, 5	1, 6
2	2, 1	2, 2	2, 3	2, 4	2, 5	2, 6
3	3, 1	3, 2	3, 3	3, 4	3, 5	3, 6
4	4, 1	4, 2	4, 3	4, 4	4, 5	4, 6
5	5, 1	5, 2	5, 3	5, 4	5, 5	5, 6

Event A labels rows 1 through 5.

Two events are *dependent events* if the occurrence of one event affects the probability of the other event. In this case, $P(A \text{ and } B) = P(A) \cdot P(B \text{ after } A)$, where $P(B \text{ after } A)$ means the probability of event B given that event A has already occurred.

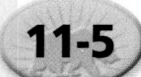

Hands-On Lab
In *Chapter 11 Resource File*

Online Edition
Tutorial Videos

Countdown to Mastery Week 24

Power Presentations
with PowerPoint®

Warm Up

Write each fraction in simplest form.

1. $\frac{16}{20}$ $\frac{4}{5}$ 2. $\frac{12}{36}$ $\frac{1}{3}$

3. $\frac{8}{64}$ $\frac{1}{8}$ 4. $\frac{39}{195}$ $\frac{1}{5}$

Also available on transparency

Math Humor

Did you hear about the man who wore half a raincoat to work? The weather report said there was a 50% chance of rain.

11-5 Probability

California Standards

Review of Grade 6

SDAP3.3 Represent probabilities as ratios, proportions, decimals between 0 and 1, and percentages between 0 and 100 and verify that the probabilities computed are reasonable; know that if *P* is the probability of an event, 1-*P* is the probability of an event not occurring.

Vocabulary
experiment
trial
outcome
sample space
event
probability

 **Who uses this?** Newscasters use probability when reporting the weather. (See Example 1.)

An **experiment** is an activity in which results are observed. Each observation is called a **trial**, and each result is called an **outcome**. The **sample space** is the set of all possible outcomes of an experiment.

Experiment	Sample Space
Flipping a coin	Heads, tails
Rolling a number cube	1, 2, 3, 4, 5, 6

An **event** is any set of one or more outcomes. The **probability** of an event is a number from 0 (or 0%) to 1 (or 100%) that tells you how likely the event is to happen. You can write probability as a fraction, a decimal, or a percent.

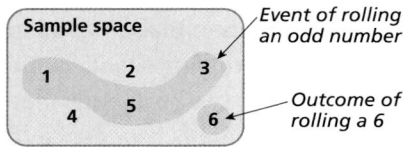

- A probability of 0 means the event is impossible, or can never happen.
- A probability of 1 means the event is certain, or will always happen.
- The probabilities of all the outcomes in the sample space add up to 1.

Never happens		Happens about half the time		Always happens
0	$\frac{1}{4}$	$\frac{1}{2}$	$\frac{3}{4}$	1
0	0.25	0.5	0.75	1
0%	25%	50%	75%	100%

EXAMPLE 1   **Finding Probabilities of Outcomes in a Sample Space**

Give the probability for each outcome.

Writing Math
The probability of an event can be written as *P*(event).

A The weather forecast shows a 30% chance of snow.

$P(\text{snow}) = 30\% = 0.3$

$P(\text{no snow}) = 1 - 0.3 = 0.7$, or 70%

Outcome	Snow	No snow
Probability		

---

1 Introduce
Alternate Opener

EXPLORATION

11-5 Probability

A plastic container contains 10 marbles: 4 red, 3 yellow, 2 green, and 1 blue. An experiment consists of shaking the container and then drawing a number of marbles.

1. If you draw one marble, which color is it most likely to be?
2. If you draw one marble, which color is it least likely to be?
3. If you draw two marbles at the same time, which colors might you draw two of?
4. If you repeatedly draw one marble and return it to the container before the next draw, which color do you think you would draw most often?

Think and Discuss

5. **Discuss** real-world situations in which probability is used.
6. **Explain,** using the marble experiment, why the probability of drawing a blue marble is $\frac{1}{10}$. (*Hint:* Compare the number of blue marbles to the total number of marbles.)

California Standards

Review of Grade 6

Statistics, Data Analysis, and Probability
3.3

Motivate

Ask students to count the number of students in the room. Ask them if you put all of their names in a hat and pulled one out, how likely it would be for each one to be chosen. Ask how likely it would be for the name of someone from the first row to be chosen. Explain that *probability* is a branch of mathematics that predicts the likelihood of events like these.

Explorations and answers are provided in *Alternate Openers: Explorations Transparencies.*

Give the probability for each outcome.

B

Outcome	Red	Yellow	Blue
Probability			

$P(\text{red}) = \frac{1}{2}$ *One-half of the spinner is red, so $\frac{1}{2}$ is a reasonable estimate.*

$P(\text{yellow}) = \frac{1}{4}$ *One-fourth of the spinner is yellow, so $\frac{1}{4}$ is a reasonable estimate.*

$P(\text{blue}) = \frac{1}{4}$ *One-fourth of the spinner is blue, so $\frac{1}{4}$ is a reasonable estimate.*

Check The probabilities of all the outcomes must add to 1.

$\frac{1}{2} + \frac{1}{4} + \frac{1}{4} = 1$ ✔

To find the probability of an event, add the probabilities of all the outcomes included in the event.

EXAMPLE 2 **Finding Probabilities of Events**

A quiz contains 3 multiple-choice questions and 2 true-false questions. Suppose you guess randomly on every question. The table below gives the probability of each score.

Score	0	1	2	3	4	5
Probability	0.105	0.316	0.352	0.180	0.043	0.004

A What is the probability of guessing 4 or more correct?

The event "4 or more correct" consists of the outcomes 4 and 5.
$P(\text{four or more correct}) = 0.043 + 0.004$
$= 0.047, \text{ or } 4.7\%$

B What is the probability of guessing fewer than 3 correct?

The event "fewer than 3 correct" consists of the outcomes 0, 1, and 2.
$P(\text{fewer than 3 correct}) = 0.105 + 0.316 + 0.352$
$= 0.773, \text{ or } 77.3\%$

Possible answers to *Think and Discuss*

1. usually: 0.8; sometimes: 0.4; always: 1 (only acceptable answer); never: 0 (only acceptable answer)

2. An outcome is any possible result of a *single* trial. An event consists of one or *more* outcomes.

Think and Discuss

1. **Give** a probability for each of the following: usually, sometimes, always, never. Compare your values with the rest of your class.

2. **Explain** the difference between an outcome and an event.

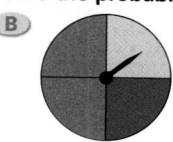
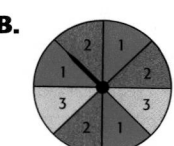

2 Teach

Guided Instruction

In this lesson, students learn to find the probability of an event by using the definition of probability. Discuss the new vocabulary. Explain that if an event has a probability of 0, that event *can never* happen (e.g., rolling a 7 on a number cube), and if an event has a probability of 1, that event *will certainly* happen (e.g., rolling a number less than 10 on a number cube). All other possible events have a probability greater than 0 and less than 1 (Teaching Transparency). Emphasize that the sum of the probabilities of all the possible outcomes in the sample space equals 1.

Universal Access
Through Cognitive Strategies

Have students write the complete sample space for the experiments described in some of the exercises in this lesson. An example is given below.

1. Choose two coins from a jar that contains a penny, a nickel, and a dime. penny and nickel, penny and dime, nickel and dime

3 Close

Summarize

Tell students that Jim is ready to roll a number cube numbered 1 through 6. Ask students to complete each statement with a vocabulary word.

1. Jim rolling the number cube is a(n) __?__.

2. Rolling a 4 is a possible __?__.

3. Rolling a number less than 3 is an example of a(n) __?__.

4. The probability that Jim will roll a 9 is __?__.

5. The probability that Jim will roll a number less than 7 is __?__.

1. experiment; 2. outcome or event;

3. event; 4. zero; 5. one

Assignment Guide

If you finished Example **1** assign:
Proficient 1, 4, 11–13, 16, 20–29
Advanced 4, 16–29

If you finished Example **2** assign:
Proficient 1–13, 16, 20–29
Advanced 4–10, 14–29

Homework Quick Check

Quickly check key concepts.
Exercises: 4, 6, 8, 10

Math Background

Probability plays an important role in many aspects of daily life. Predictions about the weather, results of elections, and winners of sporting events are based on probabilities. When an insurance company determines a rate to charge for a policy, it uses probability theory. When doctors choose a method of treatment for an injury and when people decide which investments to make, they often use probability theory.

California Standards Practice
Review of Grade 6
← SDAP3.3

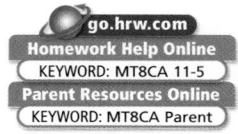

go.hrw.com
Homework Help Online
KEYWORD: MT8CA 11-5
Parent Resources Online
KEYWORD: MT8CA Parent

GUIDED PRACTICE

See Example **1**

1. The weather forecast calls for a 60% chance of rain. Give the probability for each outcome. **0.6, or 60%; 0.4, or 40%**

Outcome	Rain	No rain
Probability		

See Example **2**

A game consists of randomly selecting 4 colored ducks from a pond and counting the number of green ducks. The table gives the probability of each outcome.

Number of Green Ducks	0	1	2	3	4
Probability	0.043	0.248	0.418	0.248	0.043

2. What is the probability of selecting at most 1 green duck? **0.291, or 29.1%**

3. What is the probability of selecting more than 1 green duck? **0.709, or 70.9%**

INDEPENDENT PRACTICE

See Example **1**

4. Give the probability for each outcome. $\frac{1}{3}, \frac{1}{3}, \frac{1}{6}, \frac{1}{6}$

Outcome	Red	Blue	Yellow	Green
Probability				

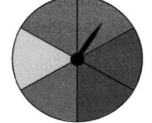

See Example **2**

Customers at Pizza Palace can order up to 5 toppings on a pizza. The table gives the probabilities for the number of toppings ordered on a pizza.

Number of Toppings	0	1	2	3	4	5
Probability	0.205	0.305	0.210	0.155	0.123	0.002

5. What is the probability that at least 2 toppings are ordered? **0.49, or 49%**

6. What is the probability that fewer than 3 toppings are ordered? **0.72, or 72%**

PRACTICE AND PROBLEM SOLVING

Extra Practice
See page EP23.

Use the table to find the probability of each event.

Outcome	A	B	C	D	E
Probability	0.306	0	0.216	0.115	0.363

7. A, C, or E occurring **0.885**

8. B or D occurring **0.115**

9. A, B, D, or E occurring **0.784**

10. A not occurring **0.694**

REVIEW FOR MASTERY 11-5

LESSON 11-5 Review for Mastery
Probability

The **probability** that something will happen is how often you can expect that **event** to occur. This depends upon how many outcomes are possible, the **sample space**.

In the spinner shown, the circle is divided into four equal parts. There are 4 possible outcomes.

So, in a single spin:

$P(A) = P(B) = P(C) = P(D) = 25\% = \frac{1}{4}$

Complete to give the probability for each event.

	1. A fair coin is tossed.	**2.** A number cube is rolled.
List all the possible outcomes.	heads, tails	1, 2, 3, 4, 5, 6
How many outcomes in sample space?	2	6
Find the probability of the event shown.	$P(\text{heads}) = \frac{1}{2}$	$P(5) = \frac{1}{6}$

• A probability of 0 means the event is **impossible**, or can never happen. On the spinner above, $P(F) = 0$.
• A probability of 1 means the event is **certain**, or has to happen. In one roll of a number cube, $P(\text{a whole number from 1 through 6}) = 1$.

Give the probability for each event.

3. selecting a rectangle from the set of squares

$P(\text{rectangle}) = 1$

4. selecting a negative number from the set of whole numbers

$P(\text{negative number}) = 0$

• The sum of the probabilities of all the possible outcomes in a sample space is 1. If the probability of *snow* is 30%, then the probability of *no snow* is 70%.

$P(\text{snow}) + P(\text{no snow}) = 1$

5. If the probability of selecting a senior for a committee is 60%, then the probability of not selecting a senior is:

40%

6. If the probability of choosing a red ball from a certain box is 0.35, then the probability of not choosing a red ball is:

0.65

PRACTICE 11-5

LESSON 11-5 Practice B
Probability

These are the results of the last math test. The teacher determines that anyone with a grade of more than 70 passed the test. Give the probability for the indicated grade.

Grade	65	70	80	90	100
# of Students	5	3	12	10	2

1. $P(70)$ $\frac{3}{32}$

2. $P(100)$ $\frac{1}{16}$

3. $P(80)$ $\frac{3}{8}$

4. $P(\text{passing})$ $\frac{3}{4}$

5. $P(\text{grade} > 80)$ $\frac{3}{8}$

6. $P(60)$ 0

7. $P(\text{failing})$ $\frac{1}{4}$

8. $P(\text{grade} \leq 80)$ $\frac{5}{8}$

A bowling game consists of rolling a ball and knocking up to 5 pins down. The number of pins knocked down are then counted. The table gives the probability of each outcome.

Number of Pins Down	0	1	2	3	4	5
Probability	0.175	0.189	0.264	0.205	0.132	0.035

9. What is the probability of knocking down all 5 pins?
0.035, or 3.5%

10. What is the probability of knocking down no pins?
0.175, or 17.5%

11. What is the probability of knocking down at most 2 pins?
0.628, or 62.8%

12. What is the probability of knocking down at least 2 pins?
0.636, or 63.6%

13. What is the probability of knocking down more than 3 pins?
0.167, or 16.7%

California Standards

Standard	Exercises
6SDAP3.3 🔑	1–21
7NS2.1	22–25
7AF3.3 🔑	26–29

11. sample space: blue, green, red, yellow; outcome shown: yellow

12. sample space: HH, HT, TH, TT; outcome shown: HT

13. sample space: 1, 2, 3, 4, 5, 6; outcome shown: 4

Identify the sample space and the outcome shown for each experiment.

11. spinning a spinner

12. tossing two coins

13. rolling a number cube

14. Reasoning You are told there are 4 possible events that may occur. Event A has a 25% chance of occurring, event B has a probability of $\frac{1}{5}$, and events C and D have an equal likelihood of occurring. What steps would you take in order to find the probabilities of events C and D?

15. Consumer Math A cereal company puts "prizes" in some of its boxes to attract shoppers. There is a 0.005 probability of getting two tickets to a movie theater, $\frac{1}{8}$ probability of finding a watch, 12.5% probability of getting an action figure, and 0.2 probability of getting a sticker. What is the probability of not getting any prize? **0.545**

16. Give an example of an event that has 0 probability of occurring.

 17. What's the Error? Two people are playing a game. One of them says, "Either I will win or you will. The sample space contains two outcomes, so we each have a probability of one-half." What is the error?

 18. Write About It Suppose an event has a probability of p. What can you say about the value of p? What is the probability that the event will not occur? Explain.

 19. Challenge List all possible events in the sample space with outcomes A, B, and C.

SPIRAL STANDARDS REVIEW ← 6SDAP3.3, 7NS2.1, ← 7AF3.3

20. Multiple Choice The local weather forecaster said there is a 60% chance of rain tomorrow. What is the probability that it will NOT rain tomorrow?

Ⓐ 0.6　　　Ⓑ 0.4　　　Ⓒ 60　　　Ⓓ 40

21. Gridded Response A sports announcer states that a runner has an 84% chance of winning a race. Give the probability, as a fraction in lowest terms, that the runner will NOT win the race. $\frac{4}{25}$

Simplify the powers of 10. (Lesson 4-2)

22. 10^{-4} **0.0001**　　　**23.** 10^{-1} **0.1**　　　**24.** 10^{-5} **0.00001**　　　**25.** 10^{-7} **0.0000001**

Find the slope of the line through the given points. (Lesson 7-7)

26. $R(8, 4)$, $S(10, 1)$ $-\frac{3}{2}$　**27.** $G(4, -3)$, $H(5, 2)$ **5**　**28.** $A(-2, 5)$, $B(-2, 4)$ **undefined**　**29.** $J(3, 2)$, $K(-1, 2)$ **0**

CHALLENGE 11-5

LESSON 11-5 Challenge
Why We Look Like Our Parents

Each parent carries two genes with respect to a specific trait and each passes one of these genes on to an offspring who then also has two genes for that trait.

In pea plants, a tall gene is dominant over a short gene. So, if a pea plant has at least one tall gene, the plant is tall. If T represents *tall* and t represents *short*, one way to represent the gene makeup with respect to height of a tall pea plant would be Tt.

1. What is another way to represent the gene makeup with respect to height of a tall pea plant? **TT**

An early 20th-century English geneticist, Reginald Punnett, invented a method to display the gene makeup of parents and their offspring.

2. The **Punnett square** at the right shows the gene makeup of one tall parent plant as the labels for the columns. Insert your result from Question 1 for the other tall parent plant as the row labels.

3. a. The label for each column has been inserted in each box of its column, as the first gene of the offspring plant. Insert your labels for each row as the second gene of each offspring plant.

b. According to the two genes now in each of the boxes for the new offspring plants, tell if the new plant will be tall or short.

c. What is the probability that an offspring of these tall parent plants will be tall? $\frac{4}{4}$ or 1 or 100%

4. Suppose the gene makeup for both tall parent pea plants is Tt.

a. Complete a Punnett square to display the gene makeup of these tall parent pea plants.

b. What is the probability that an offspring of these tall parent plants will be tall? $\frac{3}{4}$ or 75%

PROBLEM SOLVING 11-5

LESSON 11-5 Problem Solving
Probability

Write the correct answer.

1. To get people to buy more of their product, a company advertises that in selected boxes of their popsicles is a super hero trading card. There is a $\frac{1}{4}$ chance of getting a trading card in a box. What is the probability that there will not be a trading card in the box of popsicles that you buy? $\frac{3}{4}$

2. The probability of winning a lucky wheel television game show in which 6 preselected numbers are spun on a wheel numbered 1–49 is $\frac{1}{13,983,816}$ or 0.000007151%. What is the probability that you will not win the game show? $\frac{13,983,815}{13,983,816}$

Based on world statistics, the probability of identical twins is 0.004, while the probability of fraternal twins is 0.023.

3. What is the probability that a person chosen at random from the world will be a twin? **0.027, or 2.7%**

4. What is the probability that a person chosen at random from the world will not be a twin? **0.973, or 97.3%**

Use the table below that shows the probability of multiple births by country. Choose the letter for the best answer.

5. In which country is it most likely to have multiple births?
A Japan　　C Sweden
Ⓑ United States　D Switzerland

6. In which country is it least likely to have multiple births?
Ⓕ Japan　　H Sweden
G United States　J Switzerland

7. In which two countries are multiple births equally likely?
A United Kingdom, Canada
B Canada, Switzerland
Ⓒ Sweden, United Kingdom
D Japan, United States

Probability of Multiple Births

Country	Probability
Canada	0.012
Japan	0.008
United Kingdom	0.014
United States	0.029
Sweden	0.014
Switzerland	0.013

FORMATIVE ASSESSMENT and **INTERVENTION** ← →

Diagnose Before the Lesson
11-5 Warm Up, TE p. 556

Monitor During the Lesson
11-5 Know-It Notebook
11-5 Questioning Strategies

Assess After the Lesson
11-5 Lesson Quiz, TE p. 559

Answers

14. Possible answer: Find the probabilities of A and B in decimal form, and then subtract their sum from 1. Divide the difference by 2.

16. Possible answer: rolling an 8 on a number cube labeled 1 to 6

17. Possible answer: The probabilities must have a sum of 1, but they do not have to be equal. For example, one could be 0.4 and the other could be 0.6.

18–19. See p. A11.

Teaching Tip
Multiple Choice Students frequently confuse percent chance with probability. Point out that both **Exercise 20** and **21** ask for a probability, even though a percent chance is given in the problem statement. Remind students that a percent chance is a percent between 0% and 100% and a probability is a number between 0 and 1.

 Journal
Ask students to identify some examples of probability in their everyday lives. Examples may include weather forecasts, sports, or board games.

Power Presentations with PowerPoint®

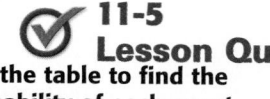

✓ **11-5 Lesson Quiz**
Use the table to find the probability of each event.

Outcome	Probability
1	0.024
2	0.327
3	0.126
4	0.341
5	0.182

1. 1 or 2 occurring　**0.351**

2. 3 not occurring　**0.874**

3. 2, 3, or 4 occurring　**0.794**

Also available on transparency

Objective: Students estimate probability using experimental methods.

 Online Edition
Tutorial Videos, Interactivities

Countdown to Mastery Week 24

Power Presentations
with PowerPoint®

Warm Up
Use the table to find the probability of each event.

Outcome	Probability
A	0.34
B	0.154
C	0.258
D	0.196
E	0.052

1. A or B occurring   0.494

2. C not occurring   0.742

3. A, D, or E occurring   0.588

Also available on transparency

 **California Standards**

Review of Grade 6
Statistics, Data Analysis, and Probability 3.2
Also covered:
Statistics, Data Analysis, and Probability
3.3 Represent probabilities as ratios, proportions, **decimals between 0 and 1, and percentages between 0 and 100** and verify that the probabilities computed are reasonable; know that if *P* is the probability of an event, 1-*P* is the probability of an event not occurring.

 **11-6** **Experimental Probability**

 California Standards

Review of Grade 6
SDAP3.2 Use data to estimate the probability of future events (e.g., batting averages or number of accidents per mile driven).
Also covered: **6SDAP3.3**

Vocabulary
experimental probability

Who uses this? Insurance companies estimate the probability of accidents by studying accident rates for different types of vehicles. (See Example 2.)

In **experimental probability**, the likelihood of an event is estimated by repeating an experiment many times and observing the number of times the event happens. That number is divided by the total number of trials. The more times the experiment is repeated, the more accurate the estimate is likely to be.

> ### EXPERIMENTAL PROBABILITY
> $$\text{probability} \approx \frac{\text{number of times the event occurs}}{\text{total number of trials}}$$

EXAMPLE **1** **Estimating the Probability of an Event**

A After 1000 spins of the spinner, the following information was recorded. Estimate the probability of the spinner landing on red.

Outcome	Blue	Red	Yellow
Spins	448	267	285

$$\text{probability} \approx \frac{\text{number of spins that landed on red}}{\text{total number of spins}} = \frac{267}{1000} = 0.267$$

The probability of landing on red is about 0.267, or 26.7%.

B A marble is randomly drawn out of a bag and then replaced. The table shows the results after 100 draws. Estimate the probability of drawing a yellow marble.

Outcome	Green	Red	Yellow	Blue	White
Draws	12	35	21	18	14

$$\text{probability} \approx \frac{\text{number of yellow marbles drawn}}{\text{total number of draws}} = \frac{21}{100} = 0.21$$

The probability of drawing a yellow marble is about 0.21, or 21%.

---

 1 **Introduce**
Alternate Opener

EXPLORATION

11-6 **Experimental Probability**

Use a plastic lid to make a spinner such as the one below. Color $\frac{1}{2}$ of the lid red, $\frac{1}{4}$ yellow, and the other $\frac{1}{4}$ green. Use a paper clip to secure the spinner to the center.

1. Spin the spinner 20 times, and record the results in the table.

Color	Number of Spins
Red	
Yellow	
Green	

a. Write a ratio to compare the number of spins for each color to 20, the total number of spins.
b. Add the three ratios in a. What is this sum equal to?

Think and Discuss
2. **Discuss** which color had the largest ratio in Problem 1a.
3. **Explain** whether the sum in Problem 1b is what you expected.

Motivate

Flip a coin two times and note the results. Ask students to predict how many heads and how many tails you would get if you flipped the coin 100 times. Tell students that if you actually performed the experiment, the results would provide a way to estimate the probability of getting heads or of getting tails on a flip of a coin.

Explorations and answers are provided in *Alternate Openers: Explorations Transparencies.*

C A researcher has been observing the types of vehicles passing through an intersection. Of the last 50 cars, 29 were sedans, 9 were trucks, and 12 were SUVs. Estimate the probability that the next vehicle through the intersection will be an SUV.

Outcome	Sedan	Truck	SUV
Observations	29	9	12

$$\text{probability} \approx \frac{\text{number of SUVs}}{\text{total number of vehicles}} = \frac{12}{50} = 0.24 = 24\%$$

The probability that the next vehicle through the intersection will be an SUV is about 0.24, or 24%.

EXAMPLE 2 *Safety Application*

Use the table to compare the probability of being involved in a fatal traffic crash in an SUV with being in a fatal traffic crash in a mid-size car.

Traffic Crashes in Ohio, 2004		
Vehicle Class	Number of Fatal Crashes	Total Number of Crashes
Sub-compact cars	23	7,962
Compact cars	266	110,598
Mid-size cars	464	200,433
Full-size cars	161	76,570
Minivan	97	45,043
SUVs	172	75,593

Source: Ohio Department of Public Safety

$$\text{probability} \approx \frac{\text{number of fatal crashes}}{\text{total number of crashes}}$$

$$\text{probability of SUV} \approx \frac{172}{75,593} \approx 0.0023$$

$$\text{probability of mid-size car} \approx \frac{464}{200,433} \approx 0.0023$$

In 2004, an accident involving an SUV was just as likely to be fatal as an accident involving a mid-size car.

Think and Discuss

1. **Compare** the probability in Example 1A of the spinner landing on red to what you think the probability should be.

2. **Give** a possible number of marbles of each color in the bag in Example 1B. Explain your reasoning.

Possible answers to Think and Discuss

1. The red section appears to be about 25% of the spinner, so the probability should be close to 25%. That estimate is close to the experimental probability of 26.7%.

2. 24 green, 70 red, 42 yellow, 36 blue, and 28 white; The number of marbles of each color in the jar can be estimated using the probabilities that resulted from the experiment. For example, choose a total number of marbles, say 200, and take 12% of that number to find the number of green marbles.

---

2 Teach

Guided Instruction

In this lesson, students learn to estimate probability using experimental methods. Explain that *experimental probability* is a ratio that compares the number of times a particular event occurs to the total number of trials. Point out that experimental probability is based on actual results, so the experimental probability for an event may differ from one experiment to the next. However, as the number of trials in each experiment increases, the difference in the probabilities is likely to decrease.

Universal Access
Through Concrete Manipulatives

Have students work in pairs. Give each pair of students one number cube. Have one student toss the number cube 15 times while the other student records the number of times each of the outcomes, 1 through 6, occurs. Then have them switch roles and repeat the experiment. Finally, have them compare the results of the two experiments. Discuss the different results with students. If time permits, you may want to add up all of the data to find the cumulative experimental probability.

3 Close

Summarize

Remind students that experimental probability is based on actual results, so the experimental probability for an event from one experiment may be different than the experimental probability for the same event from a different experiment. Discuss with students why experimental probability is more reliable with a greater number of trials.

Possible answer: Sometimes you can have runs of outcomes (like getting four tails in a row on coin flips) that make the experimental probability seem much different than it usually is.

go.hrw.com
Homework Help Online
KEYWORD: MT8CA 11-6
Parent Resources Online
KEYWORD: MT8CA Parent

Assignment Guide

If you finished Example ① assign:
Proficient 1, 2, 5, 6, 9–13, 18–23
Advanced 5, 6, 9–13, 18–23

If you finished Example ② assign:
Proficient 1–16, 18–23
Advanced 5–23

Homework Quick Check

Quickly check key concepts.
Exercises: 6, 8, 10, 14

Math Background

Students will probably be familiar with the idea that the probability of getting heads on a flip of a coin is 50/50, which means 50% or $\frac{1}{2}$. Explain that such a probability is called a *theoretical probability* (Lesson 11-7). *Experimental probability* is a ratio that uses *actual results* of an experiment. We expect the experimental probability to get closer to the theoretical probability as the number of trials increases. Experimental probability has numerous real-world applications, including insurance, sports, and weather forecasts.

GUIDED PRACTICE

See Example ①

1. A game spinner was spun 500 times. The spinner landed on A 170 times, B 244 times, and C 86 times. Estimate the probability that the spinner will land on A. ≈ **0.34, or 34%**

2. A coin was randomly drawn from a bag and then replaced. After 300 draws, it was found that 45 pennies, 76 nickels, 92 dimes, and 87 quarters had been drawn. Estimate the probability of drawing a quarter. ≈ **0.29, or 29%**

See Example ②

3. Use the table to compare the probability that a student walks to school to the probability that a student bikes to school.
≈ **0.136; ≈ 0.113; more likely to walk**

4. Use the table to compare the probability that a student takes the bus to school to the probability that a student rides in a car to school. ≈ **0.34; ≈ 0.41; more likely to ride in a car**

Mode of Transportation	Number of Students
Bus	265
Car	313
Walk	105
Bike	87

INDEPENDENT PRACTICE

See Example ①

5. A researcher polled 260 students at a university and found that 83 of them owned a laptop computer. Estimate the probability that a randomly selected college student owns a laptop computer. ≈ **0.319, or 31.9%**

6. A soccer player made 12 out of her last 58 shots on goal. Estimate the probability that she will make her next shot on goal. ≈ **0.207, or 20.7%**

See Example ②

7. Stefan polled 113 students about the number of siblings they have. Use the table to compare the probability that a student has one sibling to the probability that a student has two siblings.
≈ **0.398; ≈ 0.239; more likely to have one sibling**

8. Use the table to compare the probability that a student has no siblings to the probability that a student has three siblings.
≈ **0.12; ≈ 0.13; more likely to have 3 siblings**

Number of Siblings	Number of Students
0	14
1	45
2	27
3	15
4+	12

PRACTICE AND PROBLEM SOLVING

Extra Practice
See page EP23.

Use the table for Exercises 9–13.
Estimate the probability of each event.

9. The batter hits a single. **0.25**

10. The batter hits a double. **0.15**

11. The batter hits a triple. **0.025**

12. The batter hits a home run. **0.1**

13. The batter makes an out. **0.35**

Result	Number
Single	20
Double	12
Triple	2
Home run	8
Walk	10
Out	28
Total	80

REVIEW FOR MASTERY 11-6

Review for Mastery
11-6 *Experimental Probability*

A machine is filling boxes of apples by choosing 50 apples at random from a selection of six types of apples. An inspector records the results for one filled box in the table below.

Type	Pink Lady	Red Delicious	Granny Smith	Golden Delicious	Fuji	MacIntosh
Number	8	12	6	4	15	5

The inspector then expands the table to find the experimental probability.

$$\text{probability} = \frac{\text{number of type of apple}}{\text{total number of apples}}$$

Type	Pink Lady	Red Delicious	Granny Smith	Golden Delicious	Fuji	MacIntosh
Experimental Probability (ratio)	$\frac{8}{50}$, or $\frac{4}{25}$	$\frac{12}{50}$, or $\frac{6}{25}$	$\frac{6}{50}$, or $\frac{3}{25}$	$\frac{4}{50}$, or $\frac{2}{25}$	$\frac{15}{50}$, or $\frac{3}{10}$	$\frac{5}{50}$, or $\frac{1}{10}$
Experimental Probability (percent)	16%	24%	12%	8%	30%	10%

Find each sum for the apple experiment.

1. The sum of the experimental probability ratios.
probability = $\frac{8}{50} + \frac{12}{50} + \frac{6}{50} + \frac{4}{50} + \frac{15}{50} + \frac{5}{50} = \frac{50}{50}$ or **1**

2. The sum of the experimental probability percents.
probability = 16% + 24% + 12% + 8% + 30% + 10% = **100**% or **1**

Complete the table to find the experimental probability.

3. Five types of seed are inserted at random in a pre-seeded strip ready for planting.

Type	Marigold	Impatiens	Snapdragon	Daisy	Petunia
Number	40	100	80	60	120
Experimental Probability (ratio)	$\frac{40}{400}$, or $\frac{1}{10}$	$\frac{100}{400}$, or $\frac{1}{4}$	$\frac{80}{400}$, or $\frac{1}{5}$	$\frac{60}{400}$, or $\frac{3}{20}$	$\frac{120}{400}$, or $\frac{3}{10}$
Experimental Probability (percent)	10%	25%	20%	15%	30%

PRACTICE 11-6

Practice B
11-6 *Experimental Probability*

1. A number cube was thrown 150 times. The results are shown in the table below. Estimate the probability for each outcome.

Outcome	1	2	3	4	5	6
Frequency	33	21	15	36	27	18
Probability	22%	14%	10%	24%	18%	12%

A movie theater sells popcorn in small, medium, large and jumbo sizes. The customers of the first show purchase 4 small, 20 medium, 40 large, and 16 jumbo containers of popcorn. Estimate the probability of the purchase of each of the different size containers of popcorn.

2. P(small container)
$\frac{1}{20}$ or 5%

3. P(medium container)
$\frac{1}{4}$ or 25%

4. P(large container)
$\frac{1}{2}$ or 50%

5. P(jumbo container)
$\frac{1}{5}$ or 20%

Janessa polled 154 students about their favorite winter sport.

Outcome	Frequency
Skiing	46
Sledding	21
Snowboarding	64
Ice Skating	14
Other	9

6. Use the table to compare the probability that a student chose snowboarding to the probability that a student chose skiing.
≈0.415; ≈0.299; more likely

7. Use the table to compare the probability that a student chose ice skating to the probability that a student chose sledding.
≈0.091; ≈0.136; less likely

8. The class president made 75 copies of the flyer advertising the school play. It was found that 8 of the copies were defective. Estimate the probability that a flyer will be printed properly. ≈0.893

California Standards

Standard	Exercises
6SDAP3.2	1–19
6SDAP3.3 🔑	1–8
7NS1.2 🔑	20–22
7SDAP1.2	23

The strength of an earthquake is measured on the Richter scale. A *major* earthquake measures between 7 and 7.9 on the Richter scale, and a *great* earthquake measures 8 or higher. The table shows the number of major and great earthquakes per year during a 20-year period.

14. Estimate the probability that there will be more than 15 major earthquakes in Year 21. **0.2**

15. Estimate the probability that there will be fewer than 12 major earthquakes in Year 21. **0.3**

16. Estimate the probability that there will be no great earthquakes in Year 21. **0.4**

17. ⭐ **Challenge** Estimate the probability that there will be more than one major earthquake in the next month.
Possible answer: 0.7

go.hrw.com
Web Extra!
KEYWORD: MT8CA Quake

Number of Earthquakes

Year	Major	Great	Year	Major	Great
1	13	1	11	22	3
2	5	1	12	14	1
3	11	0	13	16	0
4	8	0	14	11	1
5	6	1	15	18	0
6	12	0	16	14	1
7	11	0	17	15	1
8	23	0	18	13	0
9	15	1	19	14	1
10	13	2	20	14	2

SPIRAL STANDARDS REVIEW
6SDAP3.2, ← 7NS1.2, 7SDAP1.2

18. Multiple Choice A spinner was spun 220 times. The outcome was red 58 times. Estimate the probability of the spinner landing on red.

(A) about 0.126   (B) about 0.225   (C) about 0.264   (D) about 0.32

19. Short Response A researcher observed students buying lunch in a cafeteria. Of the last 50 students, 22 bought an apple, 17 bought a banana, and 11 bought a pear. If 150 more students buy lunch, estimate the number of students who will buy a banana. Explain. **51; The probability is $\frac{17}{50}$. Solve the proportion $\frac{17}{50} = \frac{x}{150}$; $x = 51$**

Evaluate each expression for the given value of the variable. (Lesson 2-3)

20. $45.6 + x$ for $x = -11.1$ **34.5**   **21.** $17.9 - b$ for $b = 22.3$ **−4.4**   **22.** $r + (-4.9)$ for $r = 31.8$ **26.9**

23. What type of correlation would you expect to see between the number of jackets purchased at a department store and the outside temperature? Explain. (Lesson 11-4)
Negative correlation; as the temperature decreases, the number of jackets purchased increases.

CHALLENGE 11-6

LESSON 11-6 Challenge
Tossing and Spinning

The more times you repeat an experiment, the closer the experimental probability and the theoretical probability become.

Toss a penny 200 times.

	Heads	Tails

1. Record your results in the table. **Results will vary.**

2. What is the theoretical probability of:
getting heads? $\frac{1}{2}$ getting tails? $\frac{1}{2}$

3. What is your experimental probability of:
getting heads? **near $\frac{1}{2}$**   getting tails? **near $\frac{1}{2}$**

4. How close are your experimental probabilities to the theoretical probabilities?
Possible answer: very close

Spin a penny 200 times.

	Heads	Tails

5. Record your results in the table. **Results will vary.**

6. What is your experimental probability of:
getting heads? $\frac{1}{2}$ getting tails? $\frac{1}{2}$

7. Compare your experimental probabilities for tossing the penny and spinning the penny. Are they close? Explain.
Answers will vary.

Roll a number cube 200 times. **Results will vary.**

1	2	3	4	5	6

8. Record your results in the table.

9. What is the theoretical probability of:
getting a 1? $\frac{1}{6}$ a 2? $\frac{1}{6}$ a 3? $\frac{1}{6}$ a 4? $\frac{1}{6}$ a 5? $\frac{1}{6}$ a 6? $\frac{1}{6}$

10. What is your experimental probability of getting:
a 1? **vary** a 2? **vary** a 3? **vary** a 4? **vary** a 5? **vary** a 6? **vary**

11. How close are your experimental probabilities to the theoretical probabilities?
Possible answer: very close

PROBLEM SOLVING 11-6

LESSON 11-6 Problem Solving
Experimental Probability

Use the table below. Round to the nearest percent. Write the correct answer.

1. Estimate the probability of sunshine in Buffalo, NY.
48%

2. Estimate the probability of sunshine in Fort Wayne, IN.
59%

3. Estimate the probability of sunshine in Miami, FL.
70%

4. Estimate the probability that it will not be sunny in Raleigh, NC.
42%

5. Estimate the probability that it will not be sunny in Miami, FL.
30%

6. Estimate the probability of sunshine in Richmond, VA.
63%

Average Number of Days of Sunshine Per Year for Selected Cities

City	Number of Days
Buffalo, NY	175
Fort Wayne, IN	215
Miami, FL	256
Raleigh, NC	212
Richmond, VA	230

Use the table below that shows the number of deaths and injuries caused by lightning strikes. Choose the letter for the best answer.

7. Estimate the probability of being injured by a lightning strike in New York.
A 0.0000007%   (C) 0.00007%
B 0.0000002%   D 0.000002%

8. Estimate the probability of being killed by lightning in North Carolina.
F 0.0000006%   H 0.00002%
(G) 0.000006%   J 0.000002%

9. Estimate the probability of being struck by lightning in Florida.
A 0.00006%
(B) 0.00026%
C 0.0000026%
D 0.0006%

States with Most Lightning Deaths

State	Average deaths per year	Average injuries per year	Population
Florida	9.6	32.7	15,982,378
North Carolina	4.6	12.9	8,049,313
Texas	4.6	9.3	20,851,820
New York	3.6	12.5	18,976,457
Tennessee	3.4	9.7	5,689,283

10. In which two states do you have the highest probability of being struck by lightning?
F Florida, North Carolina
(G) Florida, Tennessee
H Texas, New York
J North Carolina, Tennessee

FORMATIVE ASSESSMENT
and **INTERVENTION**

Diagnose Before the Lesson
11-6 Warm Up, TE p. 560

Monitor During the Lesson
11-6 Know-It Notebook
11-6 Questioning Strategies

Assess After the Lesson
11-6 Lesson Quiz, TE p. 563

Interdisciplinary LINK

Science

Exercises 14–17 involve calculating probabilities using data about earthquakes. Students study earthquakes in middle school science programs.

Teaching Tip **Short Response** If students have trouble making a plan for **Exercise 19,** ask them to estimate how many students will buy a banana if only 50 more students come to lunch . . . 17 100 more students . . . 17 × 2 = 34 150 more students . . . 17 × 3 = 51 Then, show them how to set up a proportion to solve the problem more rapidly.

Journal

Ask students to write how the data in **Example 2** helps explain why insurance rates differ for different age groups.

Power Presentations
with PowerPoint®

11-6 Lesson Quiz

1. Of 425, 234 seniors were enrolled in a math course. Estimate the probability that a randomly selected senior is enrolled in a math course. **0.55, or 55%**

2. Mason made a hit 34 out of his last 125 times at bat. Estimate the probability that he will make a hit his next time at bat. **0.27, or 27%**

3. Christina polled 176 students about their favorite yogurt flavor. 63 students' favorite flavor is vanilla and 40 students' favorite flavor is strawberry. Compare the probability of a student's liking vanilla to a student's liking strawberry. **about 36% to about 23%**

Also available on transparency

Objective: Students estimate probability using theoretical methods.

 Online Edition
Tutorial Videos, Interactivities

Countdown to Mastery Week 24

Power Presentations
with PowerPoint®

Warm Up

1. If you roll a number cube, what are the possible outcomes?
   1, 2, 3, 4, 5, or 6

2. Add $\frac{1}{12} + \frac{1}{6}$. $\frac{1}{4}$

3. Add $\frac{1}{2} + \frac{2}{36}$. $\frac{5}{9}$

Also available on transparency

Math Humor

If you want to win the flip of a coin, call, "Heads, I win. Tails, you lose."

California Standards

Review of Grade 6
 **SDAP3.1 Represent all possible outcomes for compound events in an organized way** (e.g., tables, grids, tree diagrams) **and express the theoretical probability of each outcome.**
Also covered: **6SDAP3.3, 6SDAP3.4**

Vocabulary
theoretical probability
equally likely
fair
mutually exclusive
disjoint events

Why learn this? Theoretical probability can be used to determine the likelihood of specific outcomes in board games. (See Example 4.)

Theoretical probability is used to estimate probabilities by making certain assumptions about an experiment. Suppose a sample space has 5 outcomes that are **equally likely**—that is, they all have the same probability x. The probabilities must add to 1.

$$x + x + x + x + x = 1$$
$$5x = 1$$
$$x = \frac{1}{5}$$

The probability of any one outcome is $\frac{1}{5}$.

THEORETICAL PROBABILITY FOR EQUALLY LIKELY OUTCOMES

Suppose there are n equally likely outcomes in the sample space of an experiment.
- The probability of each outcome is $\frac{1}{n}$.
- The probability of an event is $\dfrac{\text{number of outcomes in the event}}{n}$.

A coin, die, or other object is called **fair** if all outcomes are equally likely.

EXAMPLE 1 **Calculating Theoretical Probability**

An experiment consists of rolling a fair number cube. Find the probability of each event.

A $P(5)$
The number cube is fair, so all 6 outcomes in the sample space are equally likely: 1, 2, 3, 4, 5, and 6.
$$P(5) = \frac{\text{number of ways to roll a 5}}{6} = \frac{1}{6}$$

B $P(\text{even number})$
There are 3 possible even numbers: 2, 4, and 6.
$$P(\text{even number}) = \frac{\text{number of possible even numbers}}{6} = \frac{3}{6} = \frac{1}{2}$$

California Standards

Review of Grade 6
Statistics, Data Analysis, and Probability
 **3.1**

Also covered:
Statistics, Data Analysis, and Probability
 **3.3 Represent probabilities as ratios,** proportions, **decimals between 0 and 1, and percentages between 0 and 100** and verify that the probabilities computed are reasonable; know that if P is the probability of an event, $1-P$ is the probability of an event not occurring.
3.4 Understand that the probability of either of two disjoint events occurring is the sum of the two individual probabilities and that the probability of one event following another, in independent trials, is the product of the two probabilities.

1 Introduce
Alternate Opener

EXPLORATION

11-7 Theoretical Probability

The *theoretical probability* of an event tells you the probability of the event without your having to conduct an experiment.

For example, the experiment of rolling two dice and adding the two numbers that each die shows does not have to be conducted to know the possible sums of numbers.

1. Use the number of times each sum occurs to complete the table.

Sum	2	3	4	5	6	7	8	9	10	11	12
Outcomes	1	2									
Theoretical Probability	$\frac{1}{36}$	$\frac{2}{36}$									

Think and Discuss
2. **Explain** which sum is most likely to occur.

Motivate

Show the students five index cards, numbered 1, 2, 3, 3, and 3. Put the five cards in a bag, and ask the students which number they think you will most likely pull out. Now show three cards numbered 1, 2, and 3. Put the three cards in a bag, and ask the students which number they think you will most likely pull out.

Explorations and answers are provided in *Alternate Openers: Explorations Transparencies*.

Suppose you roll two fair number cubes. Are all outcomes equally likely? If you look at the total shown on the number cubes, all outcomes are not equally likely. For example, there is only one way to get a total of 2, 1 + 1, but a total of 5 can be 1 + 4, 2 + 3, 3 + 2, or 4 + 1.

EXAMPLE 2 Calculating Probability for Two Fair Number Cubes

An experiment consists of rolling two fair number cubes. Find the probability of each event.

A $P(\text{total shown} = 1)$

First find the sample space that has all outcomes equally likely.

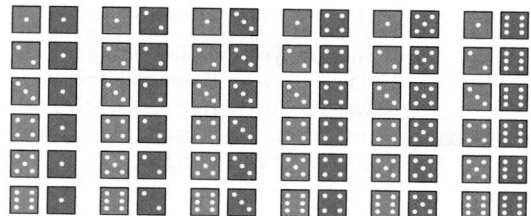

There are 36 possible outcomes in the sample space.
Then find the number of outcomes in the event "total shown = 1."
There is no way to get a total of 1.
$P(\text{total shown} = 1) = \frac{0}{36} = 0$

B $P(\text{at least one 6})$

There are 11 outcomes in the event rolling "at least one 6."
$P(\text{at least one 6}) = \frac{11}{36}$

EXAMPLE 3 Altering Probability

A bag contains 5 blue chips and 8 green chips. How many yellow chips should be added to the bag so that the probability of drawing a green chip is $\frac{2}{5}$?

Adding chips will increase the number of possible outcomes.

$\frac{8}{13 + x} = \frac{2}{5}$ *Set up a proportion. Let x be the number of yellow chips.*

$2(13 + x) = 8(5)$ *Find the cross products.*

$26 + 2x = 40$ *Multiply.*

$\underline{-26 \qquad -26}$ *Subtract 26 from both sides.*

$\frac{2x}{2} = \frac{14}{2}$ *Divide both sides by 2.*

$x = 7$

Seven yellow chips should be added to the bag.

2 Teach

Guided Instruction

In this lesson, students learn to calculate probability using theoretical methods. Remind the students that an experimental probability ratio compares the number of times an event *actually* occurs to the total number of *actual trials.* In theoretical probability, there are no actual trials or actual results. If you can identify all possible outcomes and assume that all those possible outcomes are *equally likely,* you can create a theoretical probability ratio (Teaching Transparency).

Universal Access
Through Cooperative Learning

Provide each group of students with a deck of playing cards. Have each group write five probability problems for another group to solve. Examples include finding the probability of drawing an eight, a diamond, or a red jack. After each group has written five questions, have them exchange lists with another group. Students can then solve the problems by identifying the outcomes that make each event occur. You may want each group to return the solved problems to the original group for review.

Two events are **mutually exclusive**, or **disjoint events**, if they cannot both occur in the same trial of an experiment. For example, rolling a 5 and an even number on a number cube are mutually exclusive events because they cannot both happen at the same time.

PROBABILITY OF MUTUALLY EXCLUSIVE EVENTS

Suppose A and B are two mutually exclusive events.

• $P(\text{both } A \text{ and } B \text{ will occur}) = 0$
• $P(\text{either } A \text{ or } B \text{ will occur}) = P(A) + P(B)$

 E X A M P L E 4 **Finding the Probability of Mutually Exclusive Events**

Suppose you are playing a game and have just rolled doubles two times in a row. If you roll doubles again, you will lose a turn. You will also lose a turn if you roll a total of 3 because you are 3 spaces away from the "Lose a Turn" square. What is the probability that you will lose a turn?

Writing Math

You can write the outcome of a 1 on one cube and a 1 on a second cube as the ordered pair (1, 1).

It is impossible to roll doubles and a total of 3 at the same time, so the events are mutually exclusive. Add the probabilities of the events to find the probability of losing a turn on the next roll.

The event "doubles" consists of six outcomes—(1, 1), (2, 2), (3, 3), (4, 4), (5, 5), and (6, 6).

$P(\text{doubles}) = \frac{6}{36}$

The event "total shown = 3" consists of two outcomes—(1, 2) and (2, 1).

$P(\text{total shown} = 3) = \frac{2}{36}$

$P(\text{losing a turn}) = P(\text{doubles}) + P(\text{total shown} = 3)$

$$= \frac{6}{36} + \frac{2}{36}$$

$$= \frac{8}{36}$$

The probability that you will lose a turn is $\frac{8}{36} = \frac{2}{9}$, or about 22.2%.

3. You pull a tile from a bag with 5 red, 5 blue, 5 green, and 5 white tiles.

Think and Discuss

1. **Describe** a sample space for tossing two coins that has all outcomes equally likely.

2. **Give an example** of an experiment in which it would not be reasonable to assume that all outcomes are equally likely.

3. **Give an example** of a fair experiment.

③ Close

ENGLISH LANGUAGE LEARNERS

California
Standards Practice
Review of Grade 6
SDAP3.1, SDAP3.3

go.hrw.com
Homework Help Online
KEYWORD: MT8CA 11-7
Parent Resources Online
KEYWORD: MT8CA Parent

11-7 **Exercises**

GUIDED PRACTICE

See Example 1 — An experiment consists of rolling a fair number cube. Find the probability of each event.

1. P(odd number) $\frac{1}{2}$

2. P(2 or 4) $\frac{1}{3}$

See Example 2 — An experiment consists of rolling two fair number cubes. Find the probability of each event.

3. P(total shown = 10) $\frac{1}{12}$

4. P(rolling two 2's) $\frac{1}{36}$

5. P(rolling two odd numbers) $\frac{1}{4}$

6. P(total shown > 8) $\frac{5}{18}$

See Example 3 — **7.** What color should you shade the blank region so that the probability of the spinner landing on that color is about $\frac{1}{2}$? **red**

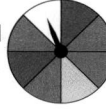

See Example 4 — **8.** Suppose you are playing a game in which two fair dice are rolled. To make the first move, you need to roll doubles or a sum of 3 or 11. What is the probability that you will be able to make the first move? $\frac{5}{18}$

INDEPENDENT PRACTICE

See Example 1 — An experiment consists of rolling a fair number cube. Find the probability of each event.

9. $P(9)$ **0**

10. P(not 6) $\frac{5}{6}$

11. $P(< 5)$ $\frac{2}{3}$

12. $P(> 3)$ $\frac{1}{2}$

See Example 2 — An experiment consists of rolling two fair number cubes. Find the probability of each event.

13. P(total shown = 3) $\frac{1}{18}$

14. P(at least one even number) $\frac{3}{4}$

15. P(total shown > 0) **1**

16. P(total shown < 9) $\frac{13}{18}$

See Example 3 — **17.** A bag contains 20 pennies, 25 nickels, and 15 quarters. How many dimes should be added so that the probability of drawing a quarter is $\frac{1}{6}$? **30**

See Example 4 — **18.** Suppose you are playing a game in which two fair dice are rolled. You need 9 to land on the finish by an exact count or 3 to land on a "roll again" space. What is the probability of landing on the finish or rolling again? $\frac{1}{6}$

PRACTICE AND PROBLEM SOLVING

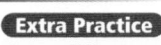
Extra Practice
See page EP23.

Three fair coins are tossed: a penny, a dime, and a quarter. Find the sample space with all outcomes equally likely. Then find each probability.

19. P(TTH) $\frac{1}{8}$

20. P(THH) $\frac{1}{8}$

21. P(dime heads) $\frac{1}{2}$

22. P(exactly 2 tails) $\frac{3}{8}$

23. P(0 tails) $\frac{1}{8}$

24. P(at most 1 tail) $\frac{1}{2}$

Assignment Guide

If you finished Example **1** assign:
Proficient 1, 2, 9–12, 28–32
Advanced 9–12, 28–32

If you finished Example **2** assign:
Proficient 1–6, 9–16, 19–24, 28–32
Advanced 9–16, 19–24, 28–32

If you finished Example **3** assign:
Proficient 1–7, 9–17, 19–24, 28–32
Advanced 9–17, 19–24, 28–32

If you finished Example **4** assign:
Proficient 1–25, 28–32
Advanced 9–32

Homework Quick Check

Quickly check key concepts.
Exercises: 10, 12, 14, 16, 18

Answers

19–24. See p. A11.

Math Background

In probability study, the words *outcome* and *event* have very precise meanings. An outcome is a particular result of one trial of an experiment. An event is either a single outcome or a set of outcomes. Suppose an experiment is to roll two fair number cubes, and we are interested in the probabilities of the sums that could occur. We call rolling a sum of 5 an event, and it consists of the following possible outcomes: (1, 4), (2, 3), (3, 2), and (4, 1).

REVIEW FOR MASTERY 11-7

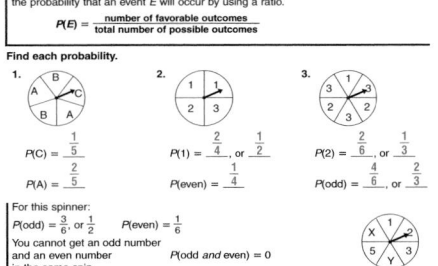

PRACTICE 11-7

LESSON 11-7 Practice B
Theoretical Probability

An experiment consists of rolling one fair number cube. Find the probability of each event.

1. $P(3)$ $\frac{1}{6}$

2. $P(7)$ 0

3. P(1 or 4) $\frac{1}{3}$

4. P(not 5) $\frac{5}{6}$

5. $P(< 5)$ $\frac{2}{3}$

6. $P(> 4)$ $\frac{1}{3}$

7. P(2 or odd) $\frac{2}{3}$

8. $P(\le 3)$ $\frac{1}{2}$

An experiment consists of rolling two fair number cubes. Find the probability of each event.

9. P(total shown = 3) $\frac{1}{18}$

10. P(total shown = 7) $\frac{1}{6}$

11. P(total shown = 9) $\frac{1}{9}$

12. P(total shown = 2) $\frac{1}{36}$

13. P(total shown = 4) $\frac{1}{12}$

14. P(total shown = 13) 0

15. P(total shown > 8) $\frac{5}{18}$

16. P(total shown ≤ 12) 1

17. P(total shown < 7) $\frac{5}{12}$

18. A bag contains 9 pennies, 8 nickels, and 5 dimes. How many quarters should be added to the bag so the probability of drawing a dime is $\frac{1}{6}$? **8 quarters**

19. In a game two fair number cubes are rolled. To make the first move, you need to roll a total of 6, 7, or 8. What is the probability that you will be able to make the first move? $\frac{4}{9}$

California Standards

Standard	Exercises
6SDAP3.1	1–7, 9–17, 19–24
6SDAP3.3	1–29
6SDAP3.4	8, 18
7AF1.1	30
7SDAP1.3	31, 32

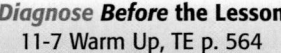
Interdisciplinary

Life Science

Exercises 25–27 involve using a Punnett square to determine probabilities of genetic traits. Students study Punnett squares and genetic combinations in middle school life science programs, such as *Holt California Life Science*.

Answers

27. See p. A11.

 **Gridded Response** If students answer $\frac{1}{6}$ for **Exercise 29,** they may have calculated the probability of rolling a 2 instead of rolling a 2 or higher. Suggest that they carefully write out all of the different successful events before they calculate the probability.

 **Journal**

Ask students to write about how probability has affected a game they have played.

Power Presentations
with PowerPoint®

 11-7
Lesson Quiz
An experiment consists of rolling a fair number cube. Find each probability.

1. P(rolling an odd number) $\frac{1}{2}$

2. P(rolling a prime number) $\frac{1}{2}$

An experiment consists of rolling two fair number cubes. Find each probability.

3. P(rolling two 3's) $\frac{1}{36}$

4. P(total shown > 10) $\frac{1}{12}$

Also available on transparency

Life Science

What color are your eyes? Can you roll your tongue? These traits are determined by the genes you inherited from your parents. A *Punnett square* shows all possible gene combinations for two parents whose genes are known.

To make a Punnett square, draw a two-by-two grid. Write the genes of one parent above the top row and the other parent along the side. Then fill in the grid as shown.

	B	b
b	Bb	bb
b	Bb	bb

25. In the Punnett square above, one parent has the gene combination *Bb*, which represents one gene for brown eyes and one gene for blue eyes. The other parent has the gene combination *bb*, which represents two genes for blue eyes. If all outcomes in the Punnett square are equally likely, what is the probability of a child with the gene combination *bb*? $\frac{1}{2}$

26. Make a Punnett square for two parents who both have the gene combination *Bb*.

  a. If all outcomes in the Punnett square are equally likely, what is the probability of a child with the gene combination *BB*? $\frac{1}{4}$

  b. The gene combinations *BB* and *Bb* will result in brown eyes, and the gene combination *bb* will result in blue eyes. What is the probability that the couple will have a child with brown eyes? $\frac{3}{4}$

27. **Challenge** The combinations *Tt* and *TT* represent the ability to roll your tongue, while *tt* means you cannot roll your tongue. Draw a Punnett square that results in a probability of $\frac{1}{2}$ that the child can roll his or her tongue. Explain whether the parents can roll their tongues.

SPIRAL STANDARDS REVIEW ← 6SDAP3.3, 7AF1.1, ← 7SDAP1.3

28. Multiple Choice A bag has 3 red marbles and 6 blue marbles in it. What is the probability of drawing a red marble?

  Ⓐ 1   Ⓑ $\frac{2}{3}$ Ⓒ $\frac{1}{3}$ Ⓓ $\frac{1}{2}$

29. Gridded Response On a fair number cube, what is the probability, written as a fraction, of rolling a 2 or higher? $\frac{5}{6}$

30. The temperature in an oven is increasing at a rate of 50°F per minute, so the temperature in the oven is 50 times the number of minutes. Write a linear function that describes the temperature in the oven over time. (Lesson 7-3) $y = 50x$

Find the upper and lower quartiles and the median for each data set. (Lesson 11-3)

31. 42, 65, 45, 20, 60, 46, 56   60; 42; 46   **32.** 51, 21, 36, 68, 64, 42, 48, 66, 31   65; 33.5; 48

CHALLENGE 11-7

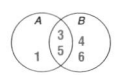 **Challenge**
11-7 *Picture This*

Venn diagrams can be used to illustrate and solve problem situations involving probability.

Consider a cube numbered 1–6.

Let *Event A* = rolling an even number on the cube.
  favorable outcomes = 2, 4, 6

Let *Event B* = rolling a number less than 5 on the cube.
  favorable outcomes = 1, 2, 3, 4

Note that the numbers 2 and 4 are in both events and, thus, lie in the intersection of the two circles that represent *Events A* and *B*.

So, to determine the probability of getting an even number that is also less than 5, the favorable outcomes are in the intersection of the circles.

$P(A \text{ and } B) = \frac{\text{number of favorable outcomes}}{\text{total number of possible outcomes}} = \frac{2}{6}$, or $\frac{1}{3}$

Then, to determine the probability of getting an even number *or* a number that is less than 5, count the elements in the intersection only once.

$P(A \text{ or } B) = \frac{\text{number of favorable outcomes}}{\text{total number of possible outcomes}} = \frac{5}{6}$

Draw a Venn diagram to solve each problem.
A cube numbered 1–6 is rolled once.

1. Find the probability of getting an odd number that is greater than 2.

  Event A = a number that is __odd__

  Event B = a number that is __>2__

2. Find the probability of getting an even number or a number less than 3.

  Event A = a number that is __even__

  Event B = a number that is __<3__

$P(A \text{ and } B) = \frac{2}{6}, \text{ or } \frac{1}{3}$ $P(A \text{ or } B) = \frac{4}{6}, \text{ or } \frac{2}{3}$

PROBLEM SOLVING 11-7

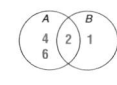 **Problem Solving**
11-7 *Theoretical Probability*

A company that sells frozen pizzas is running a promotional special. Out of the next 100,000 boxes of pizza produced, randomly chosen boxes will be prize winners. There will be one grand prize winner who will receive $100,000. Five hundred first prize winners will get $1000, and 3,000 second prize winners will get a free pizza. Write the correct answer in fraction and percent form.

1. What is the probability that the box of pizza you just bought will be a grand prize winner?
  $\frac{1}{100,000}$; 0.001%

2. What is the probability that the box of pizza you just bought will be a first prize winner?
  $\frac{1}{200}$; 0.5%

3. What is the probability that the box of pizza you just bought will be a second prize winner?
  $\frac{3}{100}$; 3%

4. What is the probability that you will win anything with the box of pizza you just bought?
  $\frac{3,501}{100,000}$; 3.501%

Researchers at the National Institutes of Health are recommending that instead of screening all people for certain diseases, they can use a Punnett square to identify the people who are most likely to have the disease. By only screening these people, the cost of screening will be less. Fill in the Punnett square below and use them to choose the letter for the best answer.

	D	d
D	DD	Dd
d	Dd	dd

5. What is the probability of DD?
  A 0%   C 50%
  Ⓑ 25%   D 75%

6. What is the probability of Dd?
  F 25%   H 75%
  Ⓖ 50%   J 100%

7. What is the probability of dd?
  A 0%   C 50%
  Ⓑ 25%   D 75%

8. DD or Dd indicates that the patient will have the disease. What is the probability that the patient will have the disease?
  F 25%   Ⓗ 75%
  G 50%   J 100%

EXAMPLE 3 Finding the Probability of Dependent Events

A jar contains 16 quarters and 10 nickels.

A If 2 coins are chosen at random, what is the probability of getting 2 quarters?

Because the first coin is not replaced, the sample space is different for the second coin, so the events are dependent. Find the probability that the first coin chosen is a quarter.

$$P(\text{quarter}) = \frac{16}{26} = \frac{8}{13}$$

If the first coin chosen is a quarter, then there would be 15 quarters and a total of 25 coins left in the jar. Find the probability that the second coin chosen is a quarter.

$$P(\text{quarter}) = \frac{15}{25} = \frac{3}{5}$$

$$\frac{8}{13} \cdot \frac{3}{5} = \frac{24}{65} \qquad \textit{Multiply.}$$

The probability of getting two quarters is $\frac{24}{65}$.

B If 2 coins are chosen at random, what is the probability of getting 2 coins that are the same?

There are two possibilities: 2 quarters or 2 nickels. The probability of getting 2 quarters was calculated in Example 3A. Now find the probability of getting 2 nickels.

$$P(\text{nickel}) = \frac{10}{26} = \frac{5}{13} \qquad \textit{Find the probability that the first coin chosen is a nickel.}$$

If the first coin chosen is a nickel, there are now only 9 nickels and 25 total coins in the jar.

$$P(\text{nickel}) = \frac{9}{25} \qquad \textit{Find the probability that the second coin chosen is a nickel.}$$

$$\frac{5}{13} \cdot \frac{9}{25} = \frac{9}{65} \qquad \textit{Multiply.}$$

The events of 2 quarters and 2 nickels are mutually exclusive, so you can add their probabilities.

$$\frac{24}{65} + \frac{9}{65} = \frac{33}{65} \qquad \textit{P(quarters) + P(nickels)}$$

The probability of getting 2 coins the same is $\frac{33}{65}$.

Remember!
Two mutually exclusive events cannot both happen at the same time.

Think and Discuss

1. Give an example of a pair of independent events and a pair of dependent events.

2. Tell how you could make the events in Example 1B independent events.

COMMON ERROR ALERT

Some students may have trouble deciding when to add probabilities and when to multiply them. Emphasize that when outcomes are separated by the word *or,* their probabilities are usually added (e.g., rolling a 4 *or* a 5 on a number cube). When outcomes are separated by *and,* their probabilities are usually multiplied (e.g., drawing a red marble *and* a blue marble out of a bag).

Power Presentations
with PowerPoint®

Additional Examples

Example 3

The letters in the word *dependent* are placed in a box.

A. If two letters are chosen at random, without replacing the first letter, what is the probability that they will both be consonants? $\frac{5}{12}$

B. If two letters are chosen at random, without replacing the first letter, what is the probability that they will both be consonants or both be vowels? $\frac{1}{2}$

Also available on transparency

Possible answers to Think and Discuss

1. independent: rolling a pair of 3's on two number cubes; dependent: choosing the letter *Q* and the letter *U* in the game Scrabble®

2. Replace the first card in the deck before drawing the second card.

 Close

Summarize

Discuss the difference between dependent and independent events. Have students identify each of the following as dependent or independent events:

1. a football team winning two games in a row *independent*

2. drawing the names of two brothers out of a hat *dependent*

3. drawing a red and then a green piece of candy from the same bag *dependent*

4. rolling a pair of 6's on two number cubes and flipping two coins on heads *independent*

11-8 Exercises

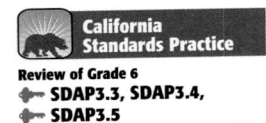

California Standards Practice

Review of Grade 6
SDAP3.3, SDAP3.4, SDAP3.5

go.hrw.com
Homework Help Online
KEYWORD: MT8CA 11-8

Parent Resources Online
KEYWORD: MT8CA Parent

Assignment Guide

If you finished Example **1** assign:
Proficient 1, 2, 6, 7, 23–25
Advanced 6, 7, 23–25

If you finished Example **2** assign:
Proficient 1–3, 6–9, 13, 15, 20–25
Advanced 6–9, 13–15, 20–25

If you finished Example **3** assign:
Proficient 1–13, 15, 16, 20–25
Advanced 6–25

Homework Quick Check

Quickly check key concepts.
Exercises: 6, 8, 10, 16

Math Background

Some students may want to know how to calculate probabilities for games. A simple example is finding the probability that two cards drawn from a standard deck of 52 cards will match. Drawing a pair of matching cards consists of two dependent events. Drawing a pair of aces is equivalent to drawing an ace and then drawing another ace from the remaining 51 cards.

$$P(\text{ace, ace}) = \frac{4}{52} \cdot \frac{3}{51} = \frac{1}{221}$$

There are 13 cards in each suit, and the probability of drawing a pair of any of those 13 cards is calculated the same way, so $P(\text{any pair}) = \frac{1}{221} \cdot 13 = \frac{1}{17}$, or about 6%.

GUIDED PRACTICE

See Example **1** **Determine if the events are dependent or independent.**

1. drawing a red and a blue marble at the same time from a bag containing 6 red and 4 blue marbles   **dependent**

2. drawing a heart from a deck of cards and a coin landing on tails   **independent**

See Example **2** **Each spinner is divided into 8 equal sectors. An experiment consists of spinning each spinner one time.**

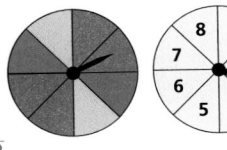

3. Find the probability that the first spinner lands on yellow and the second spinner lands on 8. $\frac{1}{32}$

See Example **3** **A sock drawer contains 10 white socks, 6 black socks, and 8 blue socks.**

4. If 2 socks are chosen at random, without replacing the first sock, what is the probability of getting a pair of white socks? $\frac{15}{92}$

5. If 3 socks are chosen at random, without replacing the first sock, what is the probability of getting first a black sock, then a white sock, and then a blue sock? $\frac{10}{253}$

INDEPENDENT PRACTICE

See Example **1** **Determine if the events are dependent or independent.**

6. drawing the name Roberto from a hat without replacing the name and then drawing the name Paulo from the hat   **dependent**

7. rolling 2 fair number cubes and getting both a 1 and a 6   **independent**

See Example **2** **An experiment consists of tossing 2 fair coins, a penny and a nickel.**

8. Find the probability of heads on the penny and tails on the nickel. $\frac{1}{4}$

9. Find the probability that both coins will land the same way. $\frac{1}{2}$

See Example **3** **A box contains 4 berry, 3 cinnamon, 4 apple, and 5 oat granola bars.**

10. If Dawn randomly selects 2 bars, without replacing the first bar, what is the probability that they will both be cinnamon? $\frac{1}{40}$

11. If two bars are selected randomly, without replacing the first bar, what is the probability that they will be the same kind? $\frac{5}{24}$

PRACTICE AND PROBLEM SOLVING

Extra Practice
See page EP23.

A box contains 6 red marbles, 4 blue marbles, and 8 yellow marbles.

12. Find $P(\text{yellow then red})$ if a marble is selected and then a second marble is selected without replacing the first marble. $\frac{8}{51}$

13. Find $P(\text{yellow then red})$ if a marble is selected and replaced and then a second marble is selected. $\frac{4}{27}$

California Standards

Standard	Exercises
6SDAP3.3 🔑	3–5, 8–17, 19–22
6SDAP3.4	3–5, 8–17, 19–22
6SDAP3.5 🔑	1–19, 21, 22
7MG2.1	25
7SDAP1.3 🔑	23, 24

REVIEW FOR MASTERY 11-8

Review for Mastery
11-8 Independent and Dependent Events

Carlos is to draw 2 straws at random from a box of straws that contains 4 red, 4 white, and 4 striped straws.

$P(\text{1st straw is striped}) = \frac{4}{12}$ ← number of striped straws
   ← total number of straws

If Carlos *returns* the 1st straw to the box before drawing the 2nd straw, the probability that the 2nd straw is striped remains the same.

$P(\text{2nd straw is striped})$

$= \frac{4}{12}$ ← same number of striped straws
   ← same total number of straws

When the 1st straw is returned before the 2nd draw, the 2nd draw occurs as though the 1st draw never happened. **independent events.**

$P(\text{striped and striped}) = \frac{4}{12} \times \frac{4}{12}$
$= \frac{1}{3} \times \frac{1}{3} = \frac{1}{9}$

If Carlos *does not return* the first straw to the box before drawing the second straw, the probability that the second straw is striped changes.

$P(\text{2nd straw is striped})$

$= \frac{3}{11}$ ← one striped straw has been taken
   ← one less straw in total number

When the 1st straw is not returned before the 2nd draw, the number of straws remaining is changed. **dependent events.**

$P(\text{striped and striped}) = \frac{4}{12} \times \frac{3}{11}$
$= \frac{1}{3} \times \frac{3}{11} = \frac{1}{11}$

Describe the events as independent or dependent.

1. Josh tosses a coin and spins a spinner.   **independent**

2. Ana draws a colored toothpick from a jar. Without replacing it, she draws a second toothpick.   **dependent**

3. Sue draws a card from a deck of cards and replaces it. Then she draws a second card from the deck.   **independent**

Each situation begins with a box of marbles that contains 2 red, 3 blue, 4 green, and 3 yellow marbles. Complete to find each probability.

4. A 1st marble is drawn and replaced. Then a 2nd marble is drawn.
$P(\text{red and blue}) = \frac{2}{12} \times \frac{3}{12} = \frac{1}{24}$

5. A 1st marble is drawn and not replaced. A 2nd marble is drawn.
$P(\text{red and blue}) = \frac{2}{12} \times \frac{3}{11} = \frac{1}{22}$

6. A 1st marble is drawn and replaced. Then a 2nd marble is drawn.
$P(\text{red and red}) = \frac{2}{12} \times \frac{2}{12} = \frac{1}{36}$

7. A 1st marble is drawn and not replaced. A 2nd marble is drawn.
$P(\text{red and red}) = \frac{2}{12} \times \frac{1}{11} = \frac{1}{66}$

PRACTICE 11-8

Practice B
11-8 Independent and Dependent Events

Determine if the events are dependent or independent.

1. choosing a tie and shirt from the closet   **independent**

2. choosing a month and tossing a coin   **independent**

3. rolling two fair number cubes once, then rolling them again if you received the same number on both number cubes on the first roll   **dependent**

An experiment consists of rolling a fair number cube and tossing a fair coin.

4. Find the probability of getting a 5 on the number cube and tails on the dime. $\frac{1}{12}$

5. Find the probability of getting an even number on the number cube and heads on the dime. $\frac{1}{4}$

6. Find the probability of getting a 2 or 3 on the number cube and heads on the dime. $\frac{1}{6}$

A box contains 3 red marbles, 6 blue marbles, and 1 white marble. The marbles are selected at random, one at a time, and are not replaced. Find the probability.

7. $P(\text{blue and red})$
$\frac{1}{5} = 0.2$

8. $P(\text{white and blue})$
$\frac{1}{15} \approx 0.066$

9. $P(\text{red and white})$
$\frac{1}{30} \approx 0.033$

10. $P(\text{red and white and blue})$
$\frac{1}{40} = 0.025$

11. $P(\text{red and red and blue})$
$\frac{1}{20} = 0.05$

12. $P(\text{red and blue and blue})$
$\frac{1}{8} = 0.125$

13. $P(\text{red and red and red})$
$\frac{1}{120} = 0.00833$

14. $P(\text{white and blue and blue})$
$\frac{1}{24} = 0.041\overline{6}$

15. $P(\text{white and red and white})$
0

14. You roll a fair number cube twice. What is the probability of rolling two 3's if the first roll is a 5? Explain. **Possible answer: The probability of rolling two 3's is 0 if the first roll is a 5 because it will be impossible to get two 3's.**

$\frac{1}{32} = 0.03125$ 15. **School** On a quiz, there are 5 true-false questions. A student guesses on all 5 questions. What is the probability that the student gets all 5 questions right?

16. **Games** The table shows the number of letter tiles available at the start of a word-making game. There are 100 tiles: 42 vowels and 58 consonants. To begin play, each player draws a tile. The player with the tile closest to the beginning of the alphabet goes first.

Letter Distribution		
A-9	B-3	C-2
D-4	E-12	F-2
G-2	H-2	I-9
J-1	K-2	L-4
M-2	N-6	O-7
P-2	Q-1	R-6
S-5	T-6	U-5
V-2	W-2	X-1
Y-2	Z-1	

    a. If you draw first, what is the probability that you will select an A? $\frac{9}{100} = 0.09$

    b. If you draw first and do not replace the tile, what is the probability that you will select an E and your opponent will select an I? $\frac{3}{275} \approx 0.01$

    c. If you draw first and do not replace the tile, what is the probability that you will select an E and your opponent will win the first turn? $\frac{6}{275} \approx 0.02$

17. **Write a Problem** Write a problem about the probability of an event in a board game, and then solve the problem. **Check students' work.**

18. **Write About It** In an experiment, two cards are drawn from a deck. How is the probability different if the first card is replaced before the second card is drawn than if the first card is not replaced?

19. **Challenge** Suppose you deal yourself 7 cards from a standard 52-card deck. What is the probability that you will deal all red cards? ≈ 0.0049

SPIRAL STANDARDS REVIEW
↞ SDAP1.3

20. **Multiple Choice** If A and B are independent events such that $P(A) = 0.14$ and $P(B) = 0.28$, what is the probability that both A and B will occur?

    Ⓐ 0.0392   Ⓑ 0.0784   Ⓒ 0.24   Ⓓ 0.42

21. **Multiple Choice** A number cube is rolled twice. What is the probability of getting a 2 on both rolls?

    Ⓐ $\frac{1}{3}$ Ⓑ $\frac{1}{4}$ Ⓒ $\frac{1}{9}$ Ⓓ $\frac{1}{36}$

22. **Gridded Response** A bag contains 8 red marbles and 2 blue marbles. What is the probability, written as a fraction, of choosing a red marble and then choosing a blue marble without replacing the first marble? $\frac{8}{45}$

Find the lower and upper quartiles for each data set. (Lesson 11-3)

23. 19, 24, 13, 18, 21, 8, 11 **11; 21**   24. 56, 71, 84, 66, 52, 11, 80 **52; 80**

25. Find the volume, in cubic feet, of a sphere with radius 2 feet. Use 3.14 for π. (Lesson 10-6) **33.49 cubic feet**

Answers

18. Possible answer: If the first card is replaced, then the number of cards to choose from is the same for each draw. If the card is not replaced, there will be one fewer card to choose from when the second card is drawn.

Teaching Tip **Multiple Choice** For **Exercise 20,** students who answered **D** attempted to calculate the probability of *both* events by *adding* the probabilities of each event. Remind students that the probability of both events occurring is found by multiplying the given probabilities.

 Journal

Ask students to write in their own words the difference between dependent events and independent events.

Power Presentations with PowerPoint®

11-8 Lesson Quiz

Determine if each event is dependent or independent.

1. drawing a red ball from a bucket and then drawing a green ball without replacing the first **dependent**

2. spinning a 7 on a spinner three times in a row **independent**

3. A bucket contains 5 yellow and 7 red balls. If 2 balls are selected randomly without replacement, what is the probability that they will both be yellow? $\frac{5}{33}$

Also available on transparency

Organizer

Objective: Assess students' mastery of concepts and skills in Lessons 11-5 through 11-8.

Resources

 Assessment Resources
Section 11B Quiz

 Test & Practice Generator
One-Stop Planner®

INTERVENTION

Resources

 Ready to Go On?
Intervention and
Enrichment Worksheets

💿 **Ready to Go On? CD-ROM**

🪐 **Ready to Go On? Online**

my.hrw.com

Quiz for Lessons 11-5 Through 11-8

✓ **11-5** Probability

Use the table to find the probability of each event.

Outcome	A	B	C	D
Probability	0.3	0.1	0.4	0.2

1. $P(C)$ **0.4**
2. $P(\text{not } B)$ **0.9**
3. $P(A \text{ or } D)$ **0.5**
4. $P(A, B, \text{ or } C)$ **0.8**

✓ **11-6** Experimental Probability

A colored chip is randomly drawn from a box and then replaced. The table shows the results after 400 draws.

Outcome	Red	Green	Blue	Yellow
Draws	76	172	84	68

5. Estimate the probability of drawing a red chip. **0.19**
6. Estimate the probability of drawing a green chip. **0.43**
7. Use the table to compare the probability of drawing a blue chip to the probability of drawing a yellow chip. **0.21; 0.17; more likely to draw blue**

✓ **11-7** Theoretical Probability

An experiment consists of rolling two fair number cubes. Find the probability of each event.

8. $P(\text{total shown} = 7)$ $\frac{1}{6}$
9. $P(\text{two 5's})$ $\frac{1}{36}$
10. $P(\text{two even numbers})$ $\frac{1}{4}$

✓ **11-8** Independent and Dependent Events

11. An experiment consists of tossing 2 fair coins, a penny and a nickel. Find the probability of tails on the penny and heads on the nickel. $\frac{1}{4}$
12. A jar contains 5 red marbles, 2 blue marbles, 4 yellow marbles, and 4 green marbles. If two marbles are chosen at random, what is the probability that they will be the same color? $\frac{23}{105}$

READY TO GO ON?
Diagnose and Prescribe

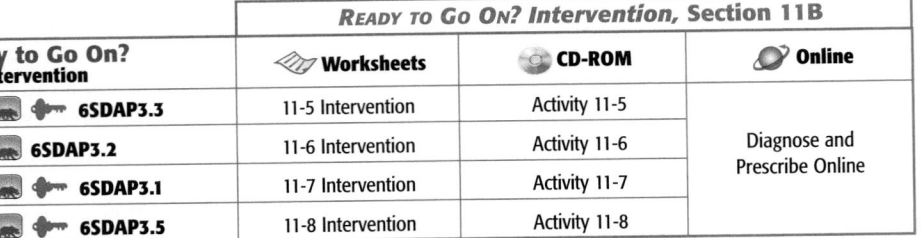

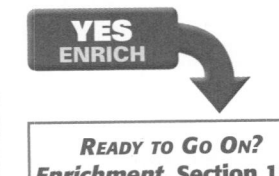

	READY TO GO ON? Intervention, Section 11B		
Ready to Go On? Intervention	🗞 **Worksheets**	💿 **CD-ROM**	🪐 **Online**
✓ Lesson 11-5 🐻 🔑 6SDAP3.3	11-5 Intervention	Activity 11-5	Diagnose and Prescribe Online
✓ Lesson 11-6 🐻 6SDAP3.2	11-6 Intervention	Activity 11-6	
✓ Lesson 11-7 🐻 🔑 6SDAP3.1	11-7 Intervention	Activity 11-7	
✓ Lesson 11-8 🐻 🔑 6SDAP3.5	11-8 Intervention	Activity 11-8	

NO INTERVENE

YES ENRICH

READY TO GO ON?
Enrichment, Section 11B
🗞 **Worksheets**
💿 **CD-ROM**
🪐 **Online**

CONCEPT CONNECTION

Bowled Over A group of middle school students forms a bowling club. The table shows the number of years each student has been bowling and the scores from the group's first trip to the bowling alley.

1. The club's president prepares a newsletter describing the "typical" student in the club. Choose either the mean, median, or mode to describe the typical number of years that the club members have been bowling. Then choose a measure to describe their typical score. Justify your choices.

2. Make a line plot of the number of years bowling.

3. Make a stem-and-leaf plot of the scores. What can you say about the scores based on the stem-and-leaf plot?

4. Make a scatter plot of the data.

5. A new student joins the club. She has been bowling for 5 years. Use your scatter plot to predict her score the next time the group goes bowling. **120**

Student	Years Bowling	Score
Jessica	3	90
Brian	3	100
Chandra	2	81
Roberto	7	128
Lee	1	84
Flora	3	92
Mike	4	102
Hisako	3	90
Isabel	6	135
Warren	1	65
Kendall	2	90
Mei	1	77

INTERVENTION

Scaffolding Questions

1. What are the measures of central tendency that can be used to describe data? mean, median, mode, and range

2. What information can be easily determined from the line plot of the number of years spent bowling? Possible answer: the least and greatest number of years spent bowling; how often a value occurs, such as the number of students and the number of years each spent bowling; how the data is distributed, such as most students have bowled less than 4 years.

3. Can you use a back-to-back stem-and-leaf plot to display this data? no Why or why not? A back-to-back stem-and-leaf plot is used to compare two sets of data. This question asks to display one data set, the bowling scores.

4. What information should go along the x-axis? the number of years bowling What information should go along the y-axis? the scores

5. What must you do to make a prediction from data displayed in a scatter plot? Draw a line of best fit and extend it to include the data point you're interested in.

Extension

1. Which type of graph would you use if you wanted to show how Roberto's score changed with the number of years he bowled? a line graph

2. Describe the type of data from the bowling club that could be displayed in a circle graph. Possible answer: the number of hours that members bowled each week

CONCEPT CONNECTION
CHAPTER 11

Organizer

Objective: Assess students' ability to apply concepts and skills in Chapter 11 in a real-world format.

 Online Edition

Problem	Text reference
1	Lesson 11-2
2	Lesson 11-1
3	Lesson 11-1
4	Lesson 11-4
5	Lesson 11-4

Answers

1. Possible answers: The mean, median, and mode are all 3; the median, 90, since there are high scores that may be outliers.

2.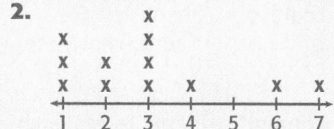
Number of years bowling

3. Possible answer: Scores cluster around 90; the scores of 128 and 135 are outliers.

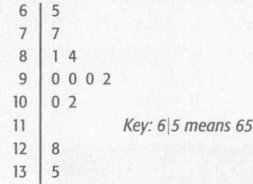

4.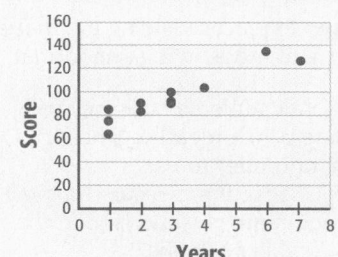

Game Time

Organizer

Objective: Participate in games to practice and apply skills learned in Chapter 11.

 Online Edition

Resources

Chapter 11 Resource File
Puzzles, Twisters & Teasers

Buffon's Needle

Purpose: To perform an experiment to re-create the first problem of geometric probability

Discuss Ask each student to check whether Buffon's formula holds for his or her experiment. Then combine the results of all the students and ask whether the combined results appear to be more accurate than the individual results.
Possible answer: The combined results are more accurate because they are the results of an experiment with more trials.

Extend Encourage students to research other methods of estimating the value of π.
Possible answer: Measure the diameter of a circular object. Wrap a piece of string around the object to find its circumference. Measure the length of the string. Compare the length of the string to the diameter.

Math in the Middle

Purpose: To practice finding the mean, median, and mode in a game format

Discuss Ask students how they will determine which measure (mean, median, or mode) to use. Possible answer: Choose the measure that will allow your game piece to land in the most favorable position.

Extend Have students play the game again, using 8 number cubes instead of 5. Have students round the mean and the median to the nearest whole number.

Game Time

Buffon's Needle

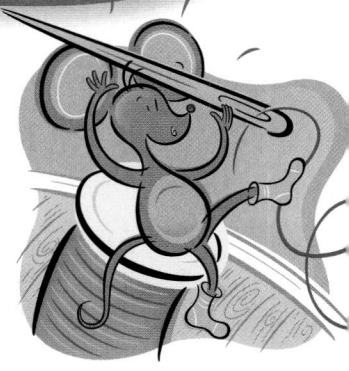

If you drop a needle of a given length onto a wooden floor with evenly spaced cracks, what is the probability that it will land across a crack?

Comte de Buffon (1707–1788) posed this geometric probability problem. To answer his question, Buffon developed a formula using ℓ to represent the length of the needle and d to represent the distance between the cracks.

$$\text{probability} = \frac{2\ell}{\pi d}$$

To re-create this experiment, you need a paper clip and several evenly spaced lines drawn on a piece of paper. Make sure that the distance between the lines is greater than the length of the paper clip. Toss the paper clip onto the piece of paper at least a dozen times. Divide the number of times the paper clip lands across a line by the number of times you toss the paper clip. Compare this quotient to the probability given by the formula.

The other interesting result of Buffon's discovery is that you can use the probability of the needle toss to estimate *pi*.

$$\pi = \frac{2\ell}{\text{probability} \cdot d}$$

Toss the paper clip 20 times to find the experimental probability. Use this probability in the formula above, and compare the result to 3.14.

Math in the Middle

This game can be played by two or more players. On your turn, roll 5 number cubes. The number of spaces you move is your choice of the mean, rounded to the nearest whole number; the median; or the mode, if it exists. The winner is the first player to land on the *Finish* square by exact count.

A complete set of rules and a game board are available online.

go.hrw.com
Game Time Extra
KEYWORD: MT8CA Games

Materials
- 7 large sticky notes
- glue
- markers

It's in the Bag!

PROJECT **Probability Post-Up**

Fold sticky notes into an accordion booklet. Then use the booklet to record notes about probability.

Directions

1. Make a chain of seven overlapping sticky notes by placing the sticky portion of one note on the bottom portion of the previous note. **Figure A**

2. Glue the notes together to make sure they stay attached.

3. Fold the notes in such a way that they look like an accordion. The folds should occur at the bottom edge of each note in the chain. **Figure B**

4. Write the name and number of the chapter on the first sticky note.

Taking Note of the Math

Use the sticky-note booklet to record key information from the chapter. Be sure to include definitions, examples of probability experiments, and anything else that will help you review the material in the chapter.

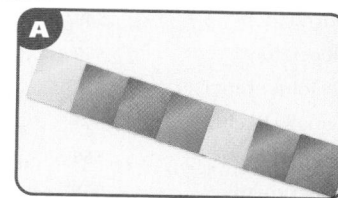
A

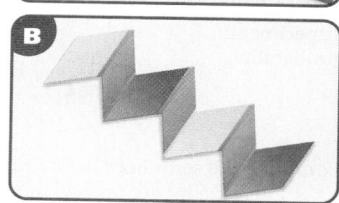
B

Tips from the Bag Ladies!

It's nice to use sticky notes of several different colors in each booklet so that the individual pages really stand out.

Health-care professionals often get pads of sticky notes from pharmaceutical companies. Check with physicians or pharmacists in your area. They may be able to donate pads of sticky notes to your class.

Organizer

Objective: Make a sticky-note booklet in which to record notes on probability.

Materials: 7 large sticky notes, glue, markers

PREMIER **Online Edition**

Using the Page

Preparing the Materials
Four-inch square sticky notes work especially well for this project. A pad of sticky notes typically contains 90 or 100 notes, which is enough for 12 to 14 students.

Making the Project
When students accordion-fold the booklet, they should fold back the first sticky note so that it forms a cover for the booklet.

Extending the Project
Students can make longer booklets by adding additional sticky notes. Have students use the extra space to draw sample outcomes of probability experiments involving coins, spinners, or number cubes.

Organizer

Objective: Help students organize and review key concepts and skills presented in Chapter 11.

 Online Edition
Multilingual Glossary

Resources

 PuzzlePro®
 One-Stop Planner®

 Multilingual Glossary Online

go.hrw.com
KEYWORD: MT8CA Glossary

 Lesson Tutorial Videos
CD-ROM

 Test & Practice Generator
One-Stop Planner®

Answers

1. median; mode
2. probability
3. line of best fit; scatter plot; correlation
4.

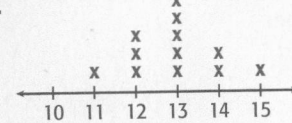

Vocabulary

Complete the sentences below with vocabulary words from the list above.

1. The ___?___ of a data set is the middle value, while the ___?___ is the value that occurs most often.

2. The ___?___ of an event tells you how likely the event is to happen.

3. The ___?___ is the line that comes closest to all the points on a(n) ___?___. ___?___ describes the type of relationship between two data sets.

11-1 Line Plots and Stem-and-Leaf Plots (pp. 532–536)

 SDAP1.1

EXAMPLE

■ Use a line plot to organize the data.

7 10 6 9 7 4 8 9
3 8 2 10 5 9 7

```
                    x
                x   x   x
        x x x x x x x x x
      +-+-+-+-+-+-+-+-+-+-+-+
      0 1 2 3 4 5 6 7 8 9 10
```

EXERCISE

Use a line plot to organize the data.

4.

Ages of People at a Skate Park					
12	13	13	14	12	11
14	15	13	13	12	13

11-2 Mean, Median, Mode, and Range (pp. 537–541)

 SDAP1.3

EXAMPLE

■ Find the mean, median, mode, and range of the data set 3, 7, 10, 2, and 3.

Mean: $3 + 7 + 10 + 2 + 3 = 25$ $\frac{25}{5} = 5$

Median: 2, 3, 3, 7, 10

Mode: 3

Range: $10 - 2 = 8$

EXERCISES

Find the mean, median, mode, and range of each data set.

5. 324, 233, 324, 399, 233, 299

6. 48, 39, 27, 52, 45, 47, 49, 37

11-3 Box-and-Whisker Plots (pp. 542–546)

 SDAP1.1, ← SDAP1.3

EXAMPLE

■ Use the given data to make a box-and-whisker plot.

7, 10, 14, 16, 17, 17, 18, 20, 20

7 (10 14) 16) (17) (17 (18 20) 20)

minimum: 7

lower quartile: $\frac{10 + 14}{2} = 12$

median: 17

upper quartile: $\frac{18 + 20}{2} = 19$

maximum: 20

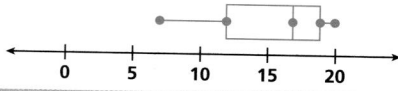

EXERCISES

Use the given data to make a box-and-whisker plot.

7. 56, 56, 56, 59, 63, 68, 68, 73, 73, 73

8. 87, 87, 80, 72, 85, 82, 53, 65, 65

9. 80, 80, 80, 82, 85, 87, 87, 90, 90, 90

11-4 Scatter Plots (pp. 548–552)

SDAP1.2

EXAMPLE

■ Identify the correlation you would expect to see between the age of a battery in a flashlight and the intensity of the flashlight beam. Explain.

Negative correlation; as the age of the battery increases, the intensity of the flashlight beam decreases.

EXERCISES

Identify the correlation you would expect to see between each pair of data sets. Explain.

10. the number of miles on a car's odometer and the size of the gas tank

11. height from which an object is dropped and time the object takes to hit the ground

---

Answers

5. 302; 311.5; 233 and 324; 166

6. 43; 46; none; 25

7.

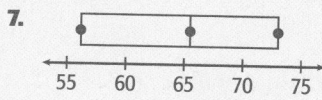

8.

9.

10. No correlation; there is no relationship.

11. Positive correlation; as the height increases, the length of time increases.

11-5 Probability (pp. 556–559)

🐻 ← 6SDAP3.3

EXAMPLE

- Of the garbage collected in a city, it is expected that about $\frac{1}{5}$ of the garbage will be recycled. Give the probability for each outcome.

Outcome	Recycled	Not Recycled
Probability	▪	▪

$P(\text{recycled}) = \frac{1}{5} = 0.2 = 20\%$

$P(\text{not recycled}) = 1 - \frac{1}{5} = \frac{4}{5} = 0.8 = 80\%$

EXERCISES

Give the probability for each outcome.

12. About 85% of the people attending a band's CD signing have already heard the CD.

Outcome	Heard	Not Heard
Probability	▪	▪

11-6 Experimental Probability (pp. 560–563)

🐻 6SDAP3.2, ← 6SDAP3.3

EXAMPLE

- The table shows the results of spinning a spinner 72 times. Estimate the probability of the spinner landing on red.

Outcome	White	Red	Blue	Black
Spins	18	28	12	14

$\text{probability} \approx \frac{28}{72} = \frac{7}{18} \approx 0.389 = 38.9\%$

EXERCISES

13. The table shows the result of rolling a number cube 80 times. Estimate the probability of rolling a 4.

Outcome	1	2	3	4	5	6
Rolls	13	15	10	12	5	25

11-7 Theoretical Probability (pp. 564–568)

🐻 ← 6SDAP3.1, ← 6SDAP3.3, 6SDAP3.4

EXAMPLE

- A fair number cube is rolled once. Find the probability of getting a 4.

$P(4) = \frac{1}{6}$

EXERCISES

14. A marble is drawn at random from a box that contains 8 red, 15 blue, and 7 white marbles. What is the probability of getting a red marble?

11-8 Independent and Dependent Events (pp. 569–573)

🐻 ← 6SDAP3.3, 6SDAP3.4, ← 6SDAP3.5

EXAMPLE

- Two marbles are drawn from a jar containing 5 blue marbles and 4 green. What is $P(\text{blue, green})$ if the first marble is not replaced?

	P(blue)	P(green)	P(blue, green)
Not replaced	$\frac{5}{9}$	$\frac{4}{8}$	$\frac{20}{72} \approx 0.28$

EXERCISES

15. A fair number cube is rolled four times. What is the probability of getting a 6 all four times?

16. Two cards are drawn at random from a deck that has 26 red and 26 black cards. What is the probability that the first card is red and the second card is black?

Use the data set 12, 18, 12, 22, 28, 23, 32, 10, 29, and 36 for problems 1–4.

1. Make a line plot of the data.

1.

2. Make a stem-and-leaf plot of the data.

3. Find the mean, median, mode, and range of the data set. **22.2; 22.5; 12; 26**

4. How would the outlier 57 affect the mean of the data set? **It would increase the mean.**

Find the lower and upper quartiles for each data set.

5. 62, 63, 62, 64, 68, 62, 62   **62; 64**

6. 104, 68, 90, 96, 101, 106, 95, 88   **89; 102.5**

Use the given data to make a box-and-whisker plot.

7. 62, 60, 77, 66, 92, 87, 62, 60, 64

8. 2.2, 6.8, 6.4, 8, 6.5, 4.2, 6.5, 5, 8

9. Use the given data to make a scatter plot. Write *positive correlation*, *negative correlation*, or *no correlation* to describe the relationship. Explain.

Food	Pizza	Hamburger	Taco	Hot Dog	Caesar Salad	Taco Salad
Fat (g)	11	13	14	12	4	21
Calories	374	310	220	270	90	410

10. Identify the correlation that you would expect to see between the speed of a car and the time required to travel a certain distance. Explain.

Use the table to find the probability of each event.

11. $P(D)$ **0.5**

12. $P(\text{not } A)$ **0.8**

13. $P(B \text{ or } C)$ **0.3**

Outcome	A	B	C	D
Probability	0.2	0.2	0.1	0.5

A coin is randomly drawn from a box and then replaced. The table shows the results.

14. Estimate the probability of each outcome. **0.26; 0.35; 0.19; 0.2**

15. Estimate $P(\text{penny or nickel})$. **0.61**

16. Estimate $P(\text{not dime})$. **0.81**

Outcome	Penny	Nickel	Dime	Quarter
Probability	26	35	19	20

An experiment consists of rolling two fair number cubes. Find the probability of each event.

17. $P(\text{total shown} = 3)$ $\frac{1}{18}$

18. $P(\text{rolling two 6's})$ $\frac{1}{36}$

19. $P(\text{total} < 2)$ 0

20. A jar contains 6 red tiles, 2 blue, 3 yellow, and 5 green. If two tiles are chosen at random, what is the probability that they both will be green? $\frac{1}{12}$

Organizer

Objective: Assess students' mastery of concepts and skills in Chapter 11.

Resources

 Assessment Resources

Chapter 11 Tests
- Free Response
  (Levels A, B, C)
- Multiple Choice
  (Levels A, B, C)
- Performance Assessment

IDEA Works! CD-ROM
Modified Chapter 11 Test

Test & Practice Generator
One-Stop Planner®

Answers

2.

Stem	Leaves
1	0 2 2 8
2	2 3 8 9
3	2 6

Key: 3|2 means 32

7.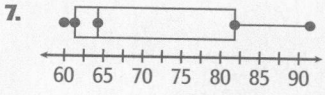

8.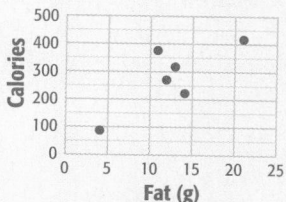

9. Possible answer: positive correlation; as the amount of fat increases, the number of calories increases.

10. Negative correlation; as the speed of the car increases, the time required to travel decreases.

Organizer

Objective: Provide opportunities to learn and practice common test-taking strategies.

 **Online Edition**

Teaching Tip **Multiple Choice** The Strategies for Success focuses on reading each option thoroughly before making a choice. Students should be reminded to eliminate each choice that is false. Sometimes they will be left with only one response that is possibly correct. Once they have eliminated the false responses, they should compare the responses that are left in order to find the correct one.

Read each problem aloud and then each option. Review with students how to find probability. Students may also need to review how to solve multi-step equations and two-step inequalities.

Multiple Choice:
Answering Context-Based Test Items

For some test items, you cannot answer just by reading the problem statement. You will need to read each option carefully to determine the correct response. Review each option and eliminate those that are false.

EXAMPLE 1

Multiple Choice Which statement is true for the given spinner?

(A) The probability of spinning green is $\frac{1}{3}$.

(B) The probability of spinning blue is $\frac{1}{6}$.

(C) The probability of spinning white is the same as the probability of spinning green.

(D) The probability of spinning green is the same as the probability of spinning yellow or white.

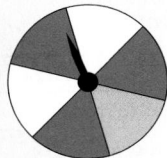

Read each option carefully. Eliminate options that are false.

Option A: Find the probability of spinning green.

$$P(\text{green}) = \frac{3}{6}, \text{ or } \frac{1}{2}$$

Option A is false.

Option B: Find the probability of spinning blue.

$$P(\text{blue}) = \frac{0}{6}, \text{ or } 0$$

Option B is false.

Option C: Find the probabilities and compare.

$$P(\text{white}) = \frac{2}{6}, \text{ or } \frac{1}{3} \qquad P(\text{green}) = \frac{3}{6}, \text{ or } \frac{1}{2}$$

$\frac{1}{3} \neq \frac{1}{2}$, so $P(\text{white}) \neq P(\text{green})$

Option C is false.

Option D: Find the probabilities and compare.

$$P(\text{green}) = \frac{3}{6}, \text{ or } \frac{1}{2} \qquad P(\text{white or yellow}) = \frac{2}{6} + \frac{1}{6} = \frac{3}{6}, \text{ or } \frac{1}{2}$$

$\frac{1}{2} = \frac{1}{2}$, $P(\text{green}) = P(\text{white or yellow})$

Option D is true. It is the correct response.

Be sure to review all of the answer options carefully before you make your choice.

Read each test item and answer the questions that follow.

Item A
Which equation has a solution of $x = 3$?

Ⓐ $-6 = 3(x - 1)$

Ⓑ $-12 = \frac{3}{2}(-2x - 2)$

Ⓒ $2(x - 6) = 3$

Ⓓ $-2(x - 6) = 3$

1. What property do you have to use to solve each equation?

2. What two methods could you use to determine if $x = 3$ is a solution of one of the equations?

3. Which is the correct option? Explain.

Item B
An experiment consists of rolling a fair number cube labeled 1 to 6. Which statement is true?

Ⓐ $P(\text{odd}) = P(\text{even})$

Ⓑ $P(\text{multiple of 3}) > P(\text{multiple of 2})$

Ⓒ $P(7) = 1$

Ⓓ $P(\text{less than 4}) = P(\text{greater than 5})$

4. What does *multiple* mean? What are multiples of 3? What are multiples of 2?

5. How many numbers are less than 4 on the number cube? How many numbers are greater than 5?

6. Which is the correct option? Explain.

Item C
Which inequality has 0 as a part of its solution set?

Ⓐ $-3y < -6$

Ⓒ $4 - 9y < 13$

Ⓑ $8a + 3 > 7$

Ⓓ $-\frac{5t}{6} > 5$

7. What must you remember to do if you multiply or divide both sides of an inequality by a negative number?

8. Which is the correct option? Explain.

Item D
A poll was taken at Jefferson Middle School. Which statement is true for the given data?

Favorite Type of Movie	Number of Students
Drama	25
Comedy	40
Science fiction	28
Action	32

Ⓐ The probability that a student at Jefferson Middle School does *not* like dramas best is $\frac{4}{5}$.

Ⓑ The probability that a student likes comedies best is $\frac{17}{25}$.

Ⓒ Out of a population of 1200 students, you can predict that 280 students will like science fiction movies best.

Ⓓ The probability that a student likes action movies best is $\frac{8}{31}$.

9. How can you find the probability of an event not occurring?

10. How can you use probability to make a prediction?

11. Which is the correct option? Explain.

Answers

1. You have to use the Distributive Property in each equation in order to solve for x.

2. Method 1: You could solve each equation and find which one has 3 as a solution.

Method 2: You could substitute 3 for x into each equation and see which equation is true.

3. Option B is correct:
$$-12 = \frac{3}{2}(-2x - 2)$$
$$-12 = -3x - 3$$
$$-9 = -3x$$
$$3 = x$$

or

$$-12 = \frac{3}{2}(-2(3) - 2)$$
$$-12 = \frac{3}{2}(-6 - 2)$$
$$-12 = \frac{3}{2}(-8)$$
$$-12 = -12$$

4. The product of any number and a whole number is a multiple of that number. The multiples of 3 include 3, 6, 9, 12, 15, ... The multiples of 2 include 2, 4, 6, 8, 10, ...

5. There are 3 numbers less than 4: 1, 2, and 3. There is 1 number greater than 5: 6.

6. The correct response is A. There are 3 possible outcomes for odd: 1, 3, and 5. There are 3 possible outcomes for even: 2, 4, and 6.
$$P(\text{odd}) = \frac{3}{6}, \text{ or } \frac{1}{2}$$
$$P(\text{even}) = \frac{3}{6}, \text{ or } \frac{1}{2}$$
$$P(\text{odd}) = P(\text{even})$$

7. If you multiply or divide both sides of an inequality by a negative number, you must reverse the inequality symbol.

8. The correct response is C.

$4 - 9y < 13$

$\dfrac{-4 \qquad -4}{-9y < 9}$ Subtract 4 from both sides.

$\dfrac{-9y}{-9} > \dfrac{9}{-9}$ Divide each side by -9; change $<$ to $>$.

$y > -1$

$0 > -1$, so it is part of the solution set.

9. To find the probability of an event not occurring, find the probability of the event occurring and subtract it from 1.

10. Write the known probability as one ratio. Write another ratio of the number of favorable outcomes to the total number of possible outcomes. Then write a proportion by having the two ratios equal each other. Solve the proportion.

11. The correct response is A. Find the total number of students who voted:
$25 + 40 + 28 + 32 = 125$. Estimate the probability of voting for drama.

$P \approx \dfrac{\text{number of students who voted for drama}}{\text{total number of students who voted}}$

$\approx \dfrac{25}{125}, \text{ or } \dfrac{1}{5}$

Subtract this probability from 1 to estimate the probability of not voting for drama.

$1 - \dfrac{1}{5} = \dfrac{4}{5}$

$P(\text{not voting for drama}) = \dfrac{4}{5}$

California Standards

🔑 **AF4.1**

CHAPTER
11

MASTERING THE STANDARDS

Organizer

Objective: Provide review and practice for Chapters 1–11.

 Online Edition

Resources

 Assessment Resources
Chapter 11 Cumulative Test

 Focus on California Standards Benchmark Tests and Intervention

 California Standards Practice CD-ROM

go.hrw.com
KEYWORD: MT8CA Practice

Cumulative Assessment, Chapters 1–11
Multiple Choice

1. In a box containing marbles, 78 are blue, 24 are orange, and the rest are green. If the probability of selecting a green marble is $\frac{2}{5}$, how many green marbles are in the box?
   - (A) 30
   - (B) 68
   - (C) 102
   - (D) 150

2. A 6-inch model is made to represent a 30-foot plane. What is the scale?
   - (A) 1 in. = 5 ft
   - (B) 5 in. = 1 ft
   - (C) 6 in. = 5 ft
   - (D) 30 in. = 5 ft

3. A soup company is producing a cylindrical can to package its new soup. The radius of the cylinder is 1.5 in., and the volume of the cylinder has to be 14 in^3. What must the height of the can be, rounded to the nearest whole inch?
   - (A) 1 in.
   - (B) 2 in.
   - (C) 3 in.
   - (D) 4 in.

4. What is the value of $(-2 - 4)^3 + 3^0$?
   - (A) −215
   - (B) −8
   - (C) 217
   - (D) 219

5. About what percent of 75 is 55?
   - (A) 25%
   - (B) 66%
   - (C) 75%
   - (D) 135%

6. Which does NOT describe $\frac{\sqrt{25}}{-5}$?
   - (A) real
   - (B) rational
   - (C) integer
   - (D) irrational

7. The figure formed by the vertices $(-2, 5)$, $(2, 5)$, $(4, -1)$, and $(0, -1)$ can be best described by which type of quadrilateral?
   - (A) square
   - (B) rectangle
   - (C) parallelogram
   - (D) trapezoid

8. How many vertices are in the prism below?

   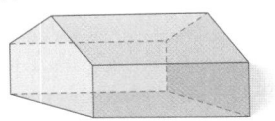

   - (A) 7
   - (B) 8
   - (C) 10
   - (D) 12

9. A triangular reflecting pool has an area of 350 ft^2. If the height of the triangle is 25 ft, what is the length of the hypotenuse to the nearest tenth?

   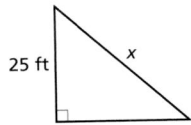

   25 ft   x

   - (A) 28.7 ft
   - (B) 37.5 ft
   - (C) 38.9 ft
   - (D) 42.3 ft

10. Which is a solution to the equation $-10 + 5x = -25$?
    - (A) $x = -15$
    - (B) $x = -7$
    - (C) $x = -3$
    - (D) $x = -1$

California Standards

Standard	Items
Rev. of 6SDAP3.2	1
Rev. of 6SDAP3.4	14
Rev. of 6SDAP3.5 🔑	14
NS1.3	5
NS1.4 🔑	6
NS1.7 🔑	12
AF2.1	4
AF3.0	15
AF3.4 🔑	18
AF4.1 🔑	10, 16, 17
MG1.2	2
MG2.1	3, 9, 11
MG3.2	7
MG3.3 🔑	9
MG3.4 🔑	13
MG3.6 🔑	8
SDAP1.2	19

Teaching Tip
Multiple Choice Probability word problems such as **item 1** are often too abstract for students to remember an effective solution strategy. Remind them that proportions are often used in these situations. Show them how to set up a proportion, such as $\frac{2}{5} = \frac{x}{102 + x}$, which uses the variable x for the unknown amount of green marbles. Remind them how to solve proportions using cross products. Try to keep students from using trial and error, except as a last resort.

Answers

17a. Let $x =$ the smallest number.
$x + (2x - 8) = 58$

b. $x + (2x - 8) = 58$
$3x - 8 = 58$
$3x = 66$
$x = 22$
The numbers are 22 and 36.

18a. Input values: $-6 \leq x \leq 6$
Output values: $3 \leq y \leq 8$

19. See 4-Point Response work sample.

11. If the diameter of the dartboard is 10 in., what is the area of the 50-point portion, to the nearest tenth of a square inch?

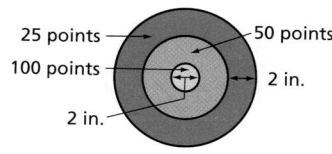

25 points · 50 points
100 points · 2 in.
2 in.

Ⓐ 3.1 in^2 Ⓒ 9.4 in^2
Ⓑ 6.3 in^2 Ⓓ 25.1 in^2

Read a graph or diagram as closely as you do the actual question. These visual aids contain important information.

Gridded Response

12. Emma buys a refrigerator on sale for $665. This is a 30% discount. What is the original price, in dollars, of the refrigerator? **950**

13. If triangle $JQZ \cong$ triangle VTZ, what is the value of r? **8.5**

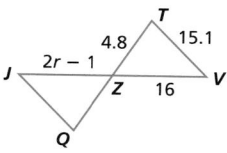

14. What is the probability of rolling an even number on a number cube and tossing heads on a coin? $\frac{1}{4}$, or **0.25**

15. The function $y = -16t^2 + 180$ models the distance an object falls when it is dropped from the top of a building 180 ft tall in t seconds. How many feet does the stone fall after 2 seconds? **116**

16. What is the value of x for the equation $7 = \frac{2}{3}x - 3$? **15**

Short Response

17. Two numbers have a sum of 58. Twice the first number is 8 more than the second number.
  a. Write an equation that can be used to find the two numbers.
  b. What are the two numbers? Show your work.

18. A function is graphed below.

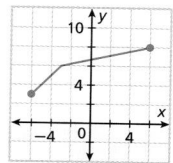

  a. Write an inequality expressing the input values and an inequality expressing the output values.
  b. Determine whether the rate of change is constant or variable. **variable**

Extended Response

19. Twenty students in a gym class kept a record of their jogging. The results are shown in the scatter plot.

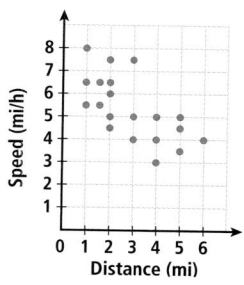

  a. Describe the correlation of the data in the scatter plot.
  b. Find the average speeds of joggers who run 1, 2, 3, 4, and 5 miles.
  c. Explain the relationship between your answer from part **a** and your answers from part **b**.

Student Work Samples for Item 19

4-Point Response

a. There is a weak negative correlation.
b. $\frac{5.5 + 6.5 + 8}{3} \approx 6.7$
$\frac{4.5 + 5 + 6 + 6.5 + 7.5}{5} = 5.9$
$\frac{4 + 5 + 7.5}{3} = 5.5$
$\frac{3 + 4 + 5}{3} = 4$
$\frac{3.5 + 4.5 + 5}{3} \approx 4.3$
c. A negative correlation is shown on the graph, and the averages decreased as the number of miles increased.

The student understood differences in types of correlations, correctly identified the weak negative correlation, found average speeds, and understood relationships.

3-Point Response

a. A weak negative correlation
b. $\frac{5.5 + 6.5 + 8}{3} \approx 6.7$
$\frac{4.5 + 5 + 6 + 6.5 + 7.5}{5} = 5.9$
$\frac{4 + 5 + 7.5}{3} = 5.5$
$\frac{3 + 4 + 5}{3} = 4$
$\frac{3.5 + 4.5 + 5}{3} \approx 4.3$
c. There is a correlation among the average speeds.

The student answers correctly, but does not give a thorough enough explanation for why the averages reflect a negative correlation.

2-Point Response

a. There is a weak negative correlation
b. $5.5 + 6.5 + 8 + 4.5 + 5 + 6 + 6.5 + 7.5 + 4 + 5 + 3.5 + 4.5 + 5 + 4$
$= 95$
$95 \div 18 \approx 5.28$
c. As the number of joggers went from 1 to 6, the average was 5.28.

The student correctly identified the weak negative correlation, but used wrong data and showed limited understanding of relationships.

CHAPTER 12

Preview of Algebra 1 **Polynomials**

✔	Grade-level Standard
◀	Review
▶	Beyond the Standards
A	Assessment
O	Optional

Pacing Guide

☀ **Calendar Planner**
Teacher's **One-Stop** Planner®

Lesson/Lab	🐻 California Standards	🕐 Time	Advanced Students	Benchmark* Students	Strategic** Students
12-1　Polynomials	Prep for 🔑 1A10.0; 7AF1.2	50 min	▶	▶	O
LAB　Model Polynomials	Prep for 🔑 1A10.0	25 min	O	▶	O
12-2　Simplifying Polynomials	Prep for 🔑 1A10.0; 🔑 7AF1.3	50 min	▶	▶	O
Ready to Go On?		25 min	A	A	O
Focus on Problem Solving		25 min	A	A	O
LAB　Model Polynomial Addition	🔑 1A10.0	25 min	▶	▶	O
12-3　Adding Polynomials	🔑 1A10.0; 🔑 7AF1.3	50 min	▶	▶	O
LAB　Model Polynomial Subtraction	🔑 1A10.0	25 min	O	▶	O
12-4　Subtracting Polynomials	🔑 1A10.0; 🔑 7AF1.3	50 min	▶	▶	O
12-5　Multiplying Polynomials by Monomials	🔑 1A10.0; 7AF1.2, 🔑 7AF1.3, 7AF2.2	50 min	▶	▶	O
LAB　Multiply Polynomials	🔑 1A10.0	25 min	▶	▶	O
12-6　Multiplying Binomials	🔑 1A10.0	50 min	▶	▶	O
Ready to Go On?		25 min	A	A	O
Concept Connection		25 min	A	A	O
Study Guide: Review		50 min	▶	▶	O
Chapter Test		50 min	A	A	O

* **Benchmark students** are achieving at or near grade level.

** **Strategic students** may be a year or more below grade level
　 and may require additional time for intervention.

ONGOING ASSESSMENT and INTERVENTION

DIAGNOSE	PRESCRIBE

Assess Prior Knowledge

Before Chapter 12

Diagnose readiness for the chapter.
Are You Ready? SE p. 587

Prescribe intervention.
Are You Ready? Intervention Skills 47, 54, 55, 85

Formative Assessment

Before Every Lesson

Diagnose readiness for the lesson.
Warm Up TE, every lesson

Prescribe intervention.
Skills Bank SE pp. SB2–SB24
Review for Mastery CRF, Chapters 1–12

During Every Lesson

Diagnose understanding of lesson concepts.
Questioning Strategies Chapter 12
Think and Discuss SE, every lesson
Write About It SE, lesson exercises
Journal TE, lesson exercises

Prescribe intervention.
Reading Strategies CRF, every lesson
Success for ELL Chapter 12
Lesson Tutorial Videos Chapter 12

After Every Lesson

Diagnose mastery of lesson concepts.
Lesson Quiz TE, every lesson
Ready to Go On? SE pp. 600, 622
Test and Practice Generator

Prescribe intervention.
Review for Mastery CRF, every lesson
Problem Solving CRF, every lesson
Ready to Go On? Intervention Chapter 12
Homework Help Online

Before Chapter 12 Testing

Diagnose mastery of concepts in the chapter.
Ready to Go On? SE pp. 600, 622
Focus on Problem Solving SE p. 601
Concept Connection SE p. 623
Section Quizzes AR pp. 225–226
Test and Practice Generator

Prescribe intervention.
Ready to Go On? Intervention Chapter 12
Scaffolding Questions TE p. 623

Before Assessment of California Standards

Diagnose mastery of California standards.
Focus on California Standards: Benchmark Tests
Mastering the Standards SE pp. 630–631
California Standards Practice CD-ROM

Prescribe intervention.
Focus on California Standards: Intervention

Summative Assessment

After Chapter 12

Check mastery of chapter concepts.
Multiple-Choice Tests (Forms A, B, C)
Free-Response Tests (Forms A, B, C)
Performance Assessment AR pp. 227–240
Test and Practice Generator

Prescribe intervention.
Review for Mastery CRF, every lesson
Lesson Tutorial Videos Chapter 12

KEY: **SE** = Student Edition **TE** = Teacher's Edition **CRF** = Chapter Resource File **AR** = Assessment Resources Available on CD-ROM Available online

CHAPTER 12

Supporting the Teacher

Chapter 12 Resource File

Family Involvement
pp. 1–2, 21–22

Practice A, B, C
pp. 5–7, 13–15, 25–27, 33–35, 41–43, 49–51

Review for Mastery
pp. 8, 16, 28, 36, 44, 52

Challenge
pp. 9, 17, 29, 37, 45, 53

Problem Solving
pp. 10, 18, 30, 38, 46, 54

Reading Strategies ELL
pp. 11, 19, 31, 39, 47, 55

Puzzles, Twisters, and Teasers
pp. 12, 20, 32, 40, 48, 56

Hands-On Lab
p. 57

Workbooks

Homework and Practice Workbook SPANISH
Teacher's Guide.................................pp. 87–92

Know-It Notebook SPANISH
Teacher's Guide................................. Chapter 12

Review for Mastery Workbook SPANISH
Teacher's Guide.................................pp. 87–92

Focus on California Standards: Intervention Workbook SPANISH
Teacher's Guide

Teacher Tools

Power Presentations
Complete PowerPoint® presentations for Chapter 12 lessons

Lesson Tutorial Videos SPANISH
Holt authors Ed Burger and Freddie Renfro present tutorials to support the Chapter 12 lessons.

Teacher's One-Stop Planner SPANISH
Easy access to all Chapter 12 resources and assessments, as well as software for lesson planning, test generation, and puzzle creation

IDEA Works!
Key Chapter 12 resources and assessments modified to address special learning needs

Questioning Strategies...............................Chapter 12

Solutions Key..Chapter 12

Interactive Answers and Solutions

TechKeys Lab Resources

Project Teacher Support Parent Resources

Transparencies

Lesson Transparencies, Volume 2...........................Chapter 12
• Teacher Tools
• Warm Ups
• Teaching Transparencies
• Lesson Quizzes

Know-It Notebook...Chapter 12
• Vocabulary
• Additional Examples
• Chapter Review
• Big Ideas

Alternate Openers: Explorations.............................pp. 87–92

Technology Highlights for the Teacher

 Power Presentations

Dynamic presentations to engage students. Complete PowerPoint® presentations for every lesson in Chapter 12.

One-Stop Planner SPANISH

Easy access to Chapter 12 resources and assessments. Includes lesson-planning, test-generation, and puzzle-creation software.

Premier Online Edition SPANISH

Includes Tutorial Videos, Lesson Activities, Lesson Quizzes, Homework Help, Chapter Project and more.

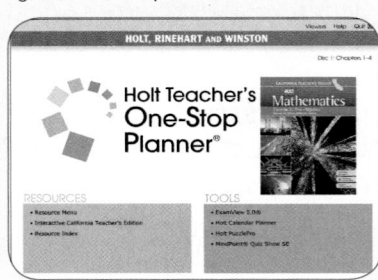

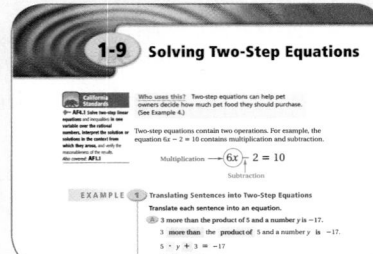

KEY: **SE** = *Student Edition* **TE** = *Teacher's Edition* **ELL** English Language Learners **SPANISH** Spanish available  Available on CD-ROM  Available online

Universal Access

Teaching tips to help all students appear throughout the chapter. A few that target specific students are included in the lists below.

ENGLISH
LANGUAGE
LEARNERS

Strategic Students

Practice A	CRF, every lesson
Review for Mastery	CRF, every lesson
Reading Strategies	CRF, every lesson
Academic Vocabulary Connections	TE p. 588
Modeling	TE p. 619
Ready to Go On? Intervention	Chapter 12
Questioning Strategies	Chapter 12
Know-It Notebook SPANISH	Chapter 12
Homework Help Online	
Lesson Tutorial Videos SPANISH	
Online Interactivities SPANISH	

Special Needs Students

Practice A	CRF, every lesson
Review for Mastery	CRF, every lesson
Reading Strategies	CRF, every lesson
Academic Vocabulary Connections	TE p. 588
Inclusion	TE pp. 604, 609
IDEA Works! Modified Resources	Chapter 12
Ready to Go On? Intervention	Chapter 12
Know-It Notebook SPANISH	Chapter 12
Lesson Tutorial Videos SPANISH	
Online Interactivities SPANISH	

English Learners

Reading Strategies	CRF, every lesson
Vocabulary Review	SE p. 46
Academic Vocabulary Connections	TE p. 588
English Language Learners	TE p. 597
Language Support	TE p. 591
Success for English Language Learners	Chapter 12
Know-It Notebook SPANISH	Chapter 12
Multilingual Glossary	
Lesson Tutorial Videos SPANISH	

Benchmark Students

Practice B	CRF, every lesson
Problem Solving	CRF, every lesson
Academic Vocabulary Connections	TE p. 588
Ready to Go On? Intervention	Chapter 12
Questioning Strategies	Chapter 12
Know-It Notebook SPANISH	Chapter 12
Homework Help Online	
Online Interactivities SPANISH	

Advanced Students

Practice C	CRF, every lesson
Challenge	CRF, every lesson
Reading and Writing Math EXTENSION	TE p. 589
Concept Connection EXTENSION	TE p. 623
Advanced Learners/GATE	TE p. 591
Ready to Go On? Enrichment	Chapter 12

Technology Highlights for Universal Access

 Lesson Tutorial Videos SPANISH

Starring Holt authors Ed Burger and Freddie Renfro! Live tutorials to support every lesson in Chapter 12.

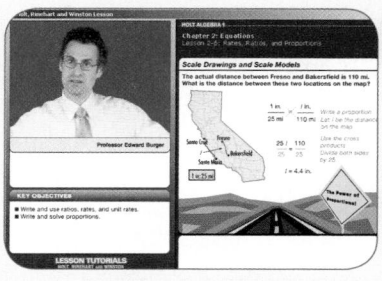

 **Multilingual Glossary**

Searchable glossary includes definitions in English, Spanish, Vietnamese, Chinese, Hmong, Korean, and other languages.

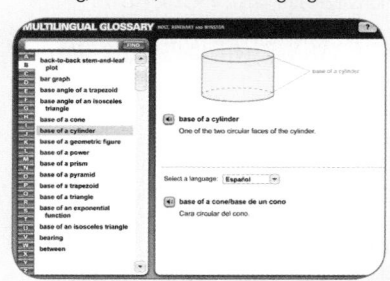

Online Interactivities SPANISH

Interactive tutorials provide visually engaging alternative opportunities to learn concepts and master skills.

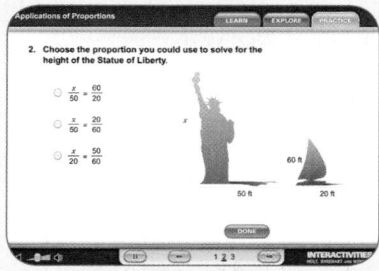

KEY: **SE** = *Student Edition*   **TE** = *Teacher's Edition*   **CRF** = *Chapter Resource File*   SPANISH Spanish available   Available on CD-ROM   Available online

586D

CHAPTER 12

Ongoing Assessment

Assessing Prior Knowledge

Determine whether students have the prerequisite concepts and skills for success in Chapter 12.

Are You Ready? SPANISH .... SE p. 587
Warm Up .... TE, every lesson

Chapter and Standards Assessment

Provide review and practice for Chapter 12 and standards mastery.

Concept Connection .... SE p. 623
Study Guide: Review .... SE pp. 626–628
Mastering the Standards .... SE pp. 630–631
Focus on California Standards: Benchmark Tests
Focus on California Standards: Intervention Workbook SPANISH
California Standards Practice CD-ROM SPANISH
IDEA Works! Modified Worksheets and Tests

Alternative Assessment

Assess students' understanding of Chapter 12 concepts and combined problem-solving skills.

Performance Assessment .... AR pp. 239–240
Portfolio Assessment .... AR p. xxxvi
Chapter 12 Project

Daily Assessment

Provide formative assessment for each day of Chapter 12.

Think and Discuss .... SE, every lesson
Write About It .... SE, lesson exercises
Journal .... TE, lesson exercises
Lesson Quiz .... TE, every lesson
Questioning Strategies .... Chapter 12
IDEA Works! Modified Lesson Quizzes .... Chapter 12

Weekly Assessment

Provide formative assessment for each week of Chapter 12.

Focus on Problem Solving .... SE p. 601
Concept Connection .... SE p. 623
Ready to Go On? SPANISH .... SE pp. 600, 622
Cumulative Assessment .... SE pp. 630–631
Test and Practice Generator SPANISH ...One-Stop Planner

Formal Assessment

Provide summative assessment of Chapter 12 mastery.

Section Quizzes .... AR pp. 225–226
Chapter 12 Test SPANISH .... SE p. 629
Chapter Test (Levels A, B, C) .... AR pp. 227–238
                    • Multiple-Choice • Free-Response
Cumulative Test .... AR pp. 241–244
Test and Practice Generator SPANISH ...One-Stop Planner
IDEA Works! Modified Tests .... Chapter 12

Technology Highlights for the Teacher

 **Are You Ready?** SPANISH

Automatically assess readiness and prescribe intervention for Chapter 12 prerequisite skills.

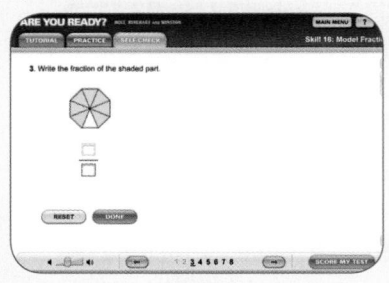

 **Ready to Go On?** SPANISH

Automatically assess understanding of and prescribe intervention for Sections 12A and 12B.

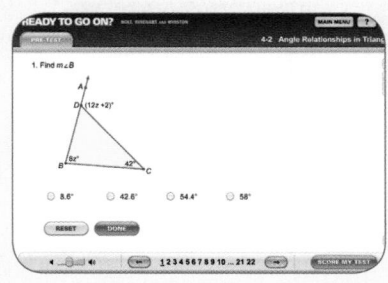

 Focus on California Standards: Benchmark Tests and Intervention SPANISH

Automatically assess proficiency with California Grade 7 Standards and provide intervention.

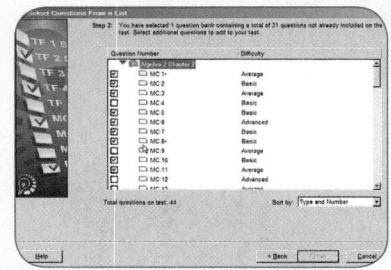

KEY: **SE** = *Student Edition* **TE** = *Teacher's Edition* **AR** = *Assessment Resources* SPANISH Spanish available   Available on CD-ROM   Available online

CHAPTER
12

Formal Assessment

Three levels (A, B, C) of multiple-choice and free-response chapter tests are available in the *Assessment Resources.*

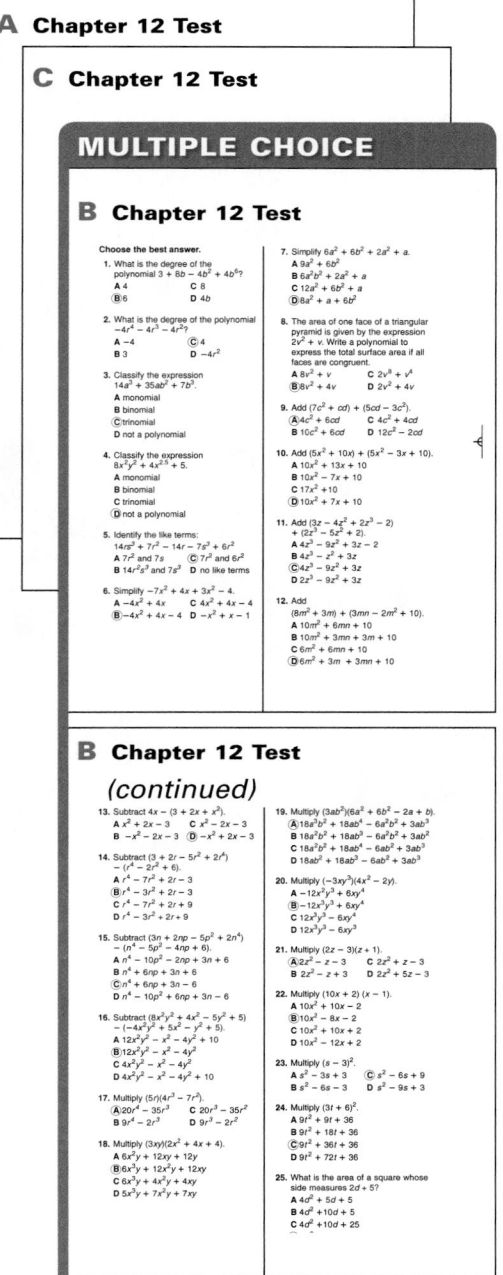

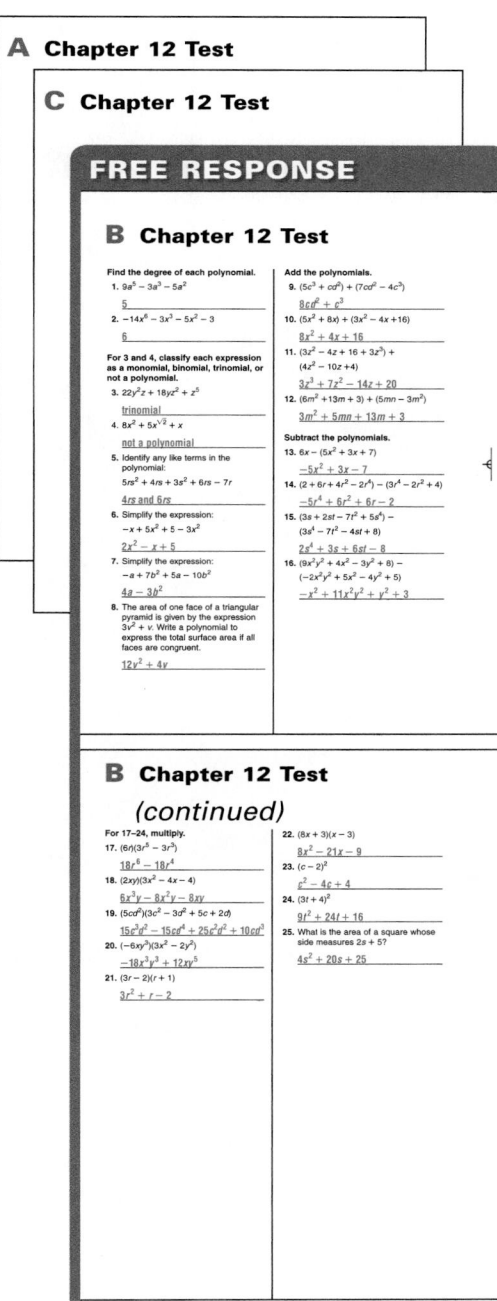

Modified tests and worksheets found in *IDEA Works!*

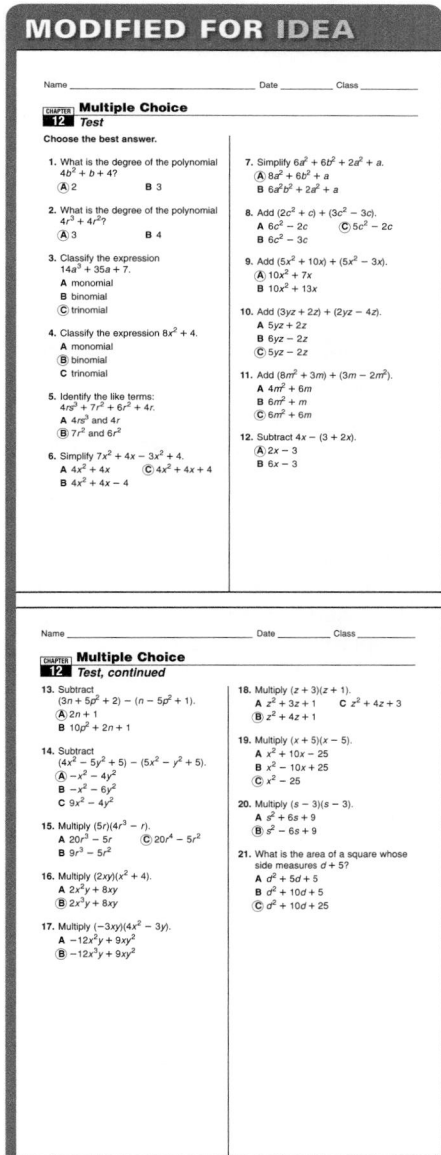

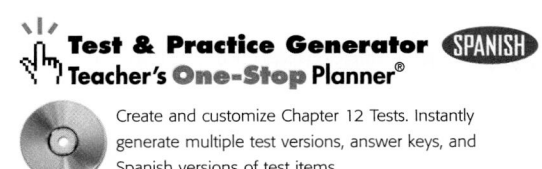

Test & Practice Generator SPANISH
Teacher's One-Stop Planner®

Create and customize Chapter 12 Tests. Instantly generate multiple test versions, answer keys, and Spanish versions of test items.

CHAPTER
12

Preview of Algebra 1
Polynomials

go.hrw.com
Chapter Project Online
KEYWORD: MT8CA Ch12

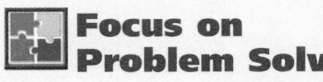
Focus on Problem Solving

On page 601, students focus on estimating to check that the answers to real-world problems are reasonable.

CONCEPT CONNECTION On page 623, students use polynomials to find dimensions for a kitchen remodeling project.

Math in *California*

Aerial fireworks are popular for celebrations throughout the world. Pyrotechnicians use mathematical methods with charts, graphs, and computer programs to plan their displays, choreograph them to music, and determine whether some shells, which contain the chemicals that produce the light displays, will exceed the safe zone for a particular site. In this chapter, students will learn how polynomials can be used in this process.

Polynomials can be used to calculate the height of fireworks.

Walt Disney Concert Hall, Los Angeles

Problem Solving Project

Understand, Plan, Solve, and Look Back

Have students:

- Complete the What Did We Make? worksheet to learn more about algebra and polynomials.

- Write this statement as an algebraic equation: Total cost equals fixed costs plus variable costs times the number of units. Does this equation contain any polynomials? Why or why not?

- Explain which variables affect the fixed costs of a company.

- Explain which aspects are affected by the number of CDs that are produced at one time.

Social Studies Connection

Project Resources
All project resources for teachers and students are provided online.

Materials:
- What Did We Make? worksheet

go.hrw.com
Project Teacher Support
KEYWORD: MT8CA PSProject12

ARE YOU READY?

✓ Vocabulary

Choose the best term from the list to complete each sentence.

1. __?__ have the same variables raised to the same powers.

2. In the expression $4x^2$, 4 is the __?__. coefficient

3. $5 + (4 + 3) = (5 + 4) + 3$ by the __?__. Associative Property

4. $3 \cdot 2 + 3 \cdot 4 = 3(2 + 4)$ by the __?__. Distributive Property

Associative Property

coefficient

Distributive Property

like terms

Commutative Property

Complete these exercises to review skills you will need for this chapter.

✓ Integer Operations

Add or subtract.

5. $12 - 4$ 8

6. $8 - 10$ -2

7. $14 - (-4)$ 18

8. $-9 - 5$ -14

9. $-9 - (-5)$ -4

10. $9 - (-5)$ 14

11. $-17 + 8$ -9

12. $-12 + (-19)$ -31

13. $23 + (-5)$ 18

✓ Evaluate Expressions

Evaluate the expression for the given value of the variable.

14. $-(x + y) - z$ for $x = 8, y = -3, z = -4$ -1

15. $-7ab + 5$ for $a = -3, b = 4$ 89

16. $2(n + 3)^2$ for $n = -1$ 8

17. $6(t - 4)^2$ for $t = -2$ 216

✓ Simplify Algebraic Expressions

Simplify each algebraic expression.

18. $8 + 4x - x - 9$ $3x - 1$

19. $9b + a + 11 - 3a - 12$ $-2a + 9b - 1$

20. $-n + 10m - 9n + 4$ $10m - 10n + 4$

✓ Area of Squares, Rectangles, and Triangles

Find the area of each figure.

21.
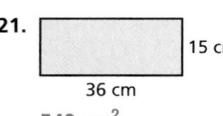
15 cm
36 cm
$540\ cm^2$

22.
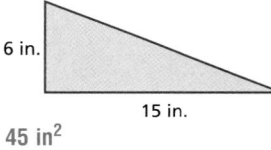
6 in.
15 in.
$45\ in^2$

23.
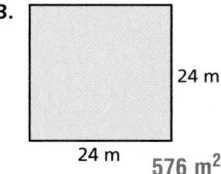
24 m
24 m
$576\ m^2$

ARE YOU READY?

Organizer

Objective: Assess students' understanding of prerequisite skills.

Prerequisite Skills

Integer Operations

Evaluate Expressions

Simplify Algebraic Expressions

Area of Squares, Rectangles, and Triangles

Assessing Prior Knowledge
INTERVENTION

Diagnose and Prescribe

Use this page to determine whether intervention is necessary or whether enrichment is appropriate.

Resources

 Are You Ready? Intervention and Enrichment Worksheets

 Are You Ready? CD-ROM

 Are You Ready? Online

my.hrw.com

ARE YOU READY?
Diagnose and Prescribe

NO INTERVENE

YES ENRICH

ARE YOU READY? Intervention, Chapter 12			
✓ Prerequisite Skill	Worksheets	CD-ROM	Online
✓ Integer Operations	Skill 47	Activity 47	
✓ Evaluate Expressions	Skill 54	Activity 54	Diagnose and Prescribe Online
✓ Simplify Algebraic Expressions	Skill 55	Activity 55	
✓ Area of Squares, Rectangles, and Triangles	Skill 85	Activity 85	

ARE YOU READY? Enrichment, Chapter 12
 Worksheets
CD-ROM
Online

Organizer

Objective: Help students understand the new concepts they will learn in Chapter 12.

Academic Vocabulary Connections

Becoming familiar with the academic vocabulary on this student page will be helpful to students. Discussing some of the vocabulary terms in the chapter also may be helpful.
Possible answers given.

1. The root of the words *monomial, binomial,* and *trinomial* is *-nomial,* which means "term." This root's prefix—such as *bi-* or *tri-*—tells you how many terms are in an algebraic expression. How many terms do you think there are in a **monomial**? in a **binomial**? in a **trinomial**? A monomial has one term, a binomial has two terms, and a trinomial has three terms.

2. The prefix *poly-* means "many." Knowing what you do about how the word *polygon* relates to the words *pentagon, hexagon,* and *octagon,* how do you think the word **polynomial** relates to the words *monomial, binomial,* and *trinomial*? Monomials, binomials, and trinomials are all examples of polynomials.

The information below "unpacks" the standards. The Academic Vocabulary is highlighted and defined to help you understand the language of the standards. Refer to the lessons listed after each standard for help with the math terms and phrases. The Chapter Concept shows how the standard is applied in this chapter.

California Standard	Academic Vocabulary	Chapter Concept
Preview of Algebra 1 ⟵ 10.0 **Students add, subtract, multiply,** and divide **monomials and polynomials. Students solve multistep problems, including word problems, by using these techniques.** (Lessons 12-3, 12-4, 12-5, 12-6; Labs 12-3, 12-4, 12-6)	**multistep** more than one step **technique** a way of doing something	You use your knowledge of exponents to add, subtract, and multiply polynomials, and you use polynomials to solve problems. ***Example:*** You simplify expressions such as $3x^2 - 2x + 5x^2 - 1$ and $x(3x^4 - 5x^3 - x^2)$.

Standards AF1.2 and AF1.3 are also covered in this chapter. To see these standards unpacked, go to Chapter 1, p. 4 (AF1.2) and Chapter 3, p. 114 (AF1.3).

Looking Back

Previously, students

- classified figures by their characteristics.
- simplified numerical expressions.
- added, subtracted, and multiplied rational numbers.

In This Chapter

Students will study

- classifying polynomials by the number of terms and finding the degree of a polynomial.
- simplifying polynomial expressions by combining like terms.
- adding, subtracting, and multiplying monomials and binomials.

Looking Forward

Students can use these skills

- to determine the number of solutions in quadratic equations.
- to simplify fractions with polynomials in the numerator and denominator.
- to solve quadratic equations.

Reading and Writing Math

Study Strategy: Study for a Final Exam

A cumulative final exam will cover material you have learned over the course of the year. You must be prepared if you want to be successful. It may help you to make a study timeline like the one below.

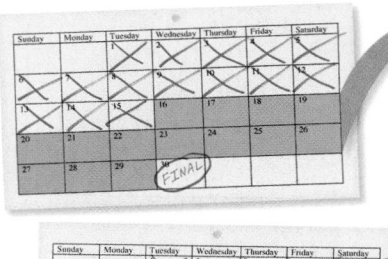

2 weeks before the final:

- Look at previous exams and homework to determine areas I need to focus on; rework problems that were incorrect or incomplete.
- Make a list of all formulas I need to know for the final.
- Create a practice exam using problems from the book that are similar to problems from each exam.

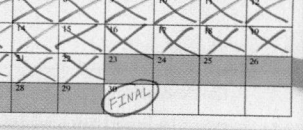

1 week before the final:

- Take the practice exam and check it. For each problem I miss, find two or three similar problems and work those.
- Work with a friend in the class to quiz each other on formulas from my list.

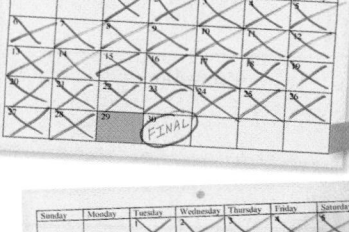

1 day before the final:

- Make sure I have pencils and scratch paper.

Try This

Complete the following to help you prepare for your cumulative test.

1. Create a timeline that you will use to study for your final exam.

Organizer

Objective: Help students apply strategies to understand and retain key concepts.

 Online Edition

Resources

✎ **Chapter 12 Resource File**
Reading Strategies

Study Strategy: Study for a Final Exam

Discuss Explain to students that a final exam is a cumulative test of the knowledge from a course, and is different from a chapter test. Give examples of topics that may be covered on a final exam. Suggest that students take more time to study for the final exam, since it covers more material than a chapter test. Discourage cramming for any test.

Extend Ask students to use the strategy presented here to create a timeline they can use to study for the Chapter 12 Chapter Test.

Possible answers to *Try This*

1. **2 weeks before the final:**
    1. Look at previous tests.
    2. Make sure I remember how to solve all the problems.
    3. Rework problems I missed.
    4. Make flash cards of all the formulas I will need to know.
    5. Create a practice exam.

   1 week before the final:
    1. Take the practice exam.
    2. Review the lessons that covered topics I missed on the exam.
    3. Have someone quiz me using my formula flash cards.

   1 day before the final:
    1. Get a good night's sleep.
    2. Make sure I have pencils and scratch paper.

Introduction to Polynomials

 **One-Minute Section Planner**

Lesson	Lab Resources	Materials
Lesson 12-1 Polynomials • Classify polynomials by degree and by the number of terms. **Preview of Algebra 1** Prep for ☞ 10.0; 7AF1.2		
12-1 Hands-On Lab Model Polynomials • Use algebra tiles to model polynomials. **Preview of Algebra 1** Prep for ☞ 10.0; ☞ 7AF1.3		**Required** Algebra tiles (MK)
Lesson 12-2 Simplifying Polynomials • Simplify polynomials. **Preview of Algebra 1** Prep for ☞ 10.0; ☞ 7AF1.3		**Optional** Algebra tiles (MK), coins (MK), index cards

MK = *Manipulatives Kit*

Notes

_____
_____
_____
_____
_____
_____
_____
_____
_____
_____
_____
_____
_____
_____

Math Background: Teaching the Standards

POLYNOMIALS 🐻 Prev. of 🔑 1A10.0

Lesson 12-1

Monomials were introduced in Chapter 4. Recall that a monomial is an algebraic expression that is either a number, a variable, or a product of numbers and variables with exponents that are whole numbers. The expressions $6x^7$, $-5a^2b^3$, $\sqrt{2n}$, and 14 are all monomials. The expressions $\sqrt{2n}$ and x^{-2} are not monomials.

Monomials are the basic units from which polynomials are built. A *polynomial* is simply a sum of monomials. For example, the polynomial $7x^5 - 2x - 5$ may be written as $7x^5 + (-2x) + (-5)$. Thus, it is the sum of the monomials $7x^5$, $-2x$, and -5. Note that polynomials, like monomials, may contain more than one variable, as in the polynomial $-2x^3y + xz^2$.

There are several similarities between polynomials and counting numbers. Because our number system is based on 10, any counting number can be written in expanded form in terms of powers of 10. Consider the expanded form of 792.

$$792 = 7 \cdot 100 + 9 \cdot 10 + 2 \cdot 1$$
$$= 7 \cdot 10^2 + 9 \cdot 10^1 + 2 \cdot 10^0$$

Now replace each of the 10's in the expanded form of the number with a variable, such as x.

$$7 \cdot 10^2 \quad + 9 \cdot 10^1 \quad + 2 \cdot 10^0$$
$$\downarrow \qquad\qquad \downarrow \qquad\qquad \downarrow$$
$$7 \cdot x^2 \quad + 9 \cdot x^1 \quad + 2 \cdot x^0$$

The resulting expression is a polynomial, which may be written in the more familiar form $7x^2 + 9x + 2$. For counting numbers, the only permissible multipliers of the powers of 10 are the digits 0 through 9, inclusive. For polynomials, any real number can be a multiplier of the variables that are raised to powers.

The goal of this analogy is not to suggest that there is a one-to-one correspondence between counting numbers and polynomials, but to demonstrate that diverse mathematical concepts sometimes share underlying structures. As such, it makes sense to pose

some of the same questions about polynomials that one might pose about counting numbers. For example, how do we add, subtract, and multiply polynomials? These questions are addressed in Section B of this chapter.

SIMPLIFYING POLYNOMIALS

🐻 Prev. of 🔑 1A10.0

Lesson 12-2

The monomials that make up a polynomial are the polynomial's terms. *Like terms* have the same variables raised to the same powers. A polynomial may be simplified by adding or subtracting like terms.

In the polynomial $2x^2 + 4x + 5x^2 + 6x + 1$, the terms $2x^2$ and $5x^2$ are like terms, as are $4x$ and $6x$. Combining the like terms shows that the polynomial simplifies to $7x^2 + 10x + 1$. Below is a closer look at this simplification process.

First, to say that $2x^2 + 4x + 5x^2 + 6x + 1$ simplifies to $7x^2 + 10x + 1$ means that the two expressions are equivalent. That is, for every value of the variable x, both expressions have the same value.

Also, it is important to note that many of the properties of rational numbers that were introduced in Lesson 3-1 have been applied here. For example, the first step in combining like terms is rewriting the polynomial so that its like terms are next to each other.

$$2x^2 + 4x + 5x^2 + 6x + 1 = 2x^2 + 5x^2 + 4x + 6x + 1$$

Switching the order of $4x$ and $5x^2$ is justified by the Commutative and Associative Properties of Addition. The Associative Property of Addition justifies grouping the addends as follows.

$$(2x^2 + 5x^2) + (4x + 6x) + 1$$

Finally, the Distributive Property is used to add the coefficients of the like terms.

$$2x^2 + 5x^2 = (2 + 5)x^2 = 7x^2$$
$$4x + 6x = (4 + 6)x = 10x$$

At this level, students should not be expected to justify every step of their work in such detail, but they should begin to recognize that the properties that they studied in Chapter 3 can help make sense of the algebraic manipulations in later chapters.

Objective: Students classify polynomials by degree and by the number of terms.

PREMIER **Online Edition**
Tutorial Videos

Power Presentations
with PowerPoint®

Warm Up

Identify the base and exponent of each power.

1. 3^4 3; 4   **2.** 2^a 2; a   **3.** x^5 x; 5

Determine whether each number is a whole number.

4. 0 yes   **5.** −3 no   **6.** 5 yes

Also available on transparency

Math Fact

There are different mathematical meanings of the word *degree*. It is used as a unit of measure for temperature, as a unit of measure for angles, and as a means to classify polynomials.

California Standards

Preview of Algebra 1
Prep for 10.0
Also covered:
Grade 7 Algebra and Functions
1.2 Use the correct order of operations to evaluate algebraic expressions such as $3(2x + 5)^2$.

 # 12-1 Polynomials

California Standards

Preview of Algebra 1
Preparation for 10.0
Students add, subtract, multiply, and divide **monomials** and **polynomials**. Students solve multistep problems, including word problems, by using these techniques.
Also covered: **7AF1.2**

Why learn this? You can use polynomials to find the height of a firework when it explodes. (See Example 4.)

Recall that a *monomial* is a number, variable, or a product of numbers and variables with exponents that are whole numbers.

Monomials	$2n$, x^3, $4a^4b^3$, 7
Not monomials	$p^{2.4}$, 2^x, $\sqrt{x}$, $\frac{5}{g^2}$

Vocabulary
polynomial
bionomial
trinomial
degree of a polynomial

EXAMPLE 1 — Identifying Monomials

Determine whether each expression is a monomial.

A $\frac{1}{3}x^4y^7$
monomial
4 and 7 are whole numbers.

B $10xy^{0.3}$
not a monomial
0.3 is not a whole number.

A **polynomial** is one monomial or the sum or difference of monomials. A simplified polynomial can be classified by the number of monomials, or terms, that it contains. A monomial has 1 term, a **binomial** has 2 terms, and a **trinomial** has 3 terms.

EXAMPLE 2 — Classifying Polynomials by the Number of Terms

Classify each expression as a monomial, a binomial, a trinomial, or not a polynomial.

A $35.55h + 19.55g$
binomial   *Polynomial with 2 terms*

B $-2x^3y$
monomial   *Polynomial with 1 term*

C $6x^2 - 4xy + \frac{2}{x}$
not a polynomial   *$\frac{2}{x}$ can be written as $2x^{-1}$, where the exponent is not a whole number.*

D $7mn + 4m - 5n$
trinomial   *Polynomial with 3 terms*

---

1 Introduce
Alternate Opener

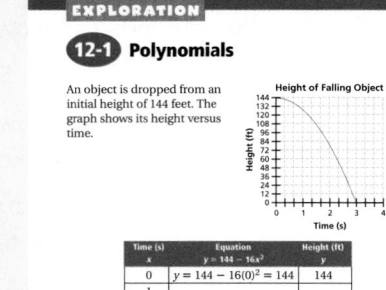

EXPLORATION

12-1 Polynomials

An object is dropped from an initial height of 144 feet. The graph shows its height versus time.

Height of Falling Object

Time (s) x	Equation y = 144 − 16x²	Height (ft) y
0	y = 144 − 16(0)² = 144	144
1		
2		
3		

1. What does the point (0, 144) represent?
2. When does the object reach the ground?
3. You can use the equation $y = 144 - 16x^2$ to model the object's fall. Complete the table and label the points on the graph.

Think and Discuss
4. **Explain** why the graph of a falling object is not a straight line.

Motivate

ENGLISH LANGUAGE LEARNERS

Give students a group of words like *monolingual, bilingual,* and *trilingual.* Discuss the meaning of each word and its prefix. able to speak one, two, or three languages, respectively Then introduce the new vocabulary terms *monomial, binomial,* and *trinomial.* Ask students to think about the meaning of each word.

Explorations and answers are provided in *Alternate Openers: Explorations Transparencies.*

The *degree of a term* is the sum of the exponents of the variables in the term. The **degree of a polynomial** is the same as the degree of the term with the greatest degree. A polynomial can be classified by its degree.

$$\underbrace{4x^2}_{\text{Degree 2}} + \underbrace{2x^5}_{\text{Degree 5}} + \underbrace{xy}_{\text{Degree 2}} + \underbrace{5}_{\text{Degree 0}}$$
$$\underbrace{\qquad\qquad\qquad\qquad\qquad\qquad}_{\text{Degree 5}}$$

E X A M P L E 3 **Classifying Polynomials by Their Degrees**

Find the degree of each polynomial.

Ⓐ $6x^2 + 3x + 4$

$$\underset{\text{Degree 2}}{6x^2} + \underset{\text{Degree 1}}{3x} + \underset{\text{Degree 0}}{4}$$

The greatest degree is 2, so the degree of $6x^2 + 3x + 4$ is 2.

Ⓑ $6 + 3m^2 + 4m^5$

$$\underset{\text{Degree 0}}{6} + \underset{\text{Degree 2}}{3m^2} + \underset{\text{Degree 5}}{4m^5}$$

The greatest degree is 5, so the degree of $6 + 3m^2 + 4m^5$ is 5.

To evaluate a polynomial, substitute the given number for each variable.

E X A M P L E 4 *Physics Application*

The height in feet of a firework launched straight up into the air from *s* feet off the ground at velocity *v* after *t* seconds is given by the polynomial $-16t^2 + vt + s$. Find the height of a firework launched from a 10 ft platform at 200 ft/s after 5 seconds.

Helpful Hint

A polynomial is an algebraic expression. For help with evaluating algebraic expressions, see Lesson 1-1.

$-16t^2 + vt + s$	*Write the polynomial expression for height.*
$-16(5)^2 + 200(5) + 10$	*Substitute 5 for t, 200 for v, and 10 for s.*
$-400 + 1000 + 10$	*Simplify.*
610	

The firework is 610 feet high 5 seconds after launching.

Think and Discuss

1. **Describe** two ways you can classify a polynomial. Give a polynomial with three terms, and classify it two ways.
2. **Explain** why $-5x^2 - 3$ is a polynomial but $-5x^{-2} - 3$ is not.

Possible answers to Think and Discuss

1. You can classify a polynomial by the number of terms and by the degree. The polynomial $5x^3 + 3x + 1$ is a trinomial with a degree of 3.

2. $-5x^2 - 3$ is a difference of monomials; The exponent of $-5x^{-2} - 3$ is not a whole number.

---

2 Teach

Guided Instruction

In this lesson, students learn to classify polynomials by degree and the number of terms. After discussing the meanings of *monomial, binomial,* and *trinomial,* review **Examples 1** and **2**. Give examples of expressions that are not polynomials, such as $(3x^2 + 2\sqrt{x})$ and $(4x^3 + 5x^{-2})$. Explain why these are not polynomials. Explain that the degree of a monomial with one variable is the exponent of the variable. Point out that the degree of a constant is zero.

Teaching Tip **Language Support** Remind students that *velocity* and *speed* have similar meanings. Both words refer to the rate of change of position (feet, meters, miles, etc.) relative to time (seconds, minutes, hours, etc.).

Universal Access
For Advanced Learners/GATE

Give each student some related polynomials, such as $3xy$ and $3 + x - y$. Have students classify each polynomial by its number of terms. Then have them identify the operations (+, −, or ×) used in each polynomial. Finally, have students draw a conclusion about how operations are related to types of polynomials.

3 Close

Summarize

Remind students that a polynomial is a monomial or the sum or difference of monomials. A binomial has two monomial terms, and a trinomial has three monomial terms. The degree of a monomial with one variable is the exponent of the variable. The degree of a polynomial is the degree of the monomial with the greatest degree.

12-1 Exercises

California
Standards Practice
Preparation for Algebra 1 ➡ 10.0;
7AF1.2

go.hrw.com
Homework Help Online
KEYWORD: MT8CA 12-1
Parent Resources Online
KEYWORD: MT8CA Parent

Assignment Guide

If you finished Example **1** assign:
Proficient 1–4, 13–18, 52–58
Advanced 13–18, 48, 52–58

If you finished Example **2** assign:
Proficient 1–8, 13–24, 52–58
Advanced 13–24, 48, 52–58

If you finished Example **3** assign:
Proficient 1–11, 13–30, 33–44,
51–58
Advanced 13–30, 33–44, 46–48,
51–58

If you finished Example **4** assign:
Proficient 1–45, 50–58
Advanced 13–58

Homework Quick Check

Quickly check key concepts.
Exercises: 16, 20, 26, 31, 37

Math Background

The lesson addresses degree only for polynomials containing one variable. The degree of a monomial is the sum of the exponents of each variable. For example, $5x^2yz^4$ has a degree of 7, because $2 + 1 + 4 = 7$.

The degree of a polynomial is the greatest degree of its terms. For example, $3ab^5 + a^2b^2$ has a degree of 6, because the degree of $3ab^5$ is 6, and the degree of a^2b^2 is 4.

GUIDED PRACTICE

See Example **1** Determine whether each expression is a monomial.

1. $-2x^2y$ yes **2.** $\frac{4}{3x}$ no **3.** $\sqrt{3x}$ no **4.** 9 yes

See Example **2** Classify each expression as a monomial, a binomial, a trinomial, or not a polynomial.

5. $\frac{3}{4}x + y$ binomial **6.** $5r - 3r^2 + 6$ trinomial **7.** $\frac{3}{x^2} + 2x$ not a polynomial **8.** 2 monomial

See Example **3** Find the degree of each polynomial.

9. $-7m^5 + 3m^8$ 8 **10.** $x^4 - 4$ 4 **11.** 52 0

See Example **4** **12.** The trinomial $-16t^2 + 24t + 72$ describes the height in feet of a ball thrown straight up from a 72 ft platform with a velocity of 24 ft/s after t seconds. What is the ball's height after 2 seconds? 56 feet

INDEPENDENT PRACTICE

See Example **1** Determine whether each expression is a monomial.

13. $5.2x^3$ yes **14.** $-3x^{-4}$ no **15.** $\frac{5y^4}{6x}$ no

16. $\frac{4}{7}x^4y^2$ yes **17.** 210 yes **18.** 3^x no

See Example **2** Classify each expression as a monomial, a binomial, a trinomial, or not a polynomial.

19. $-9m^2n^6$ monomial **20.** $6g^{\frac{1}{3}}h^2$ not a polynomial **21.** $4x^3 + 2x^5 + 3$ trinomial

22. $-a + 3$ binomial **23.** $2\sqrt{x}$ not a polynomial **24.** $5v^3s$ monomial

See Example **3** Find the degree of each polynomial.

25. $2x^2 - 7x + 1$ 2 **26.** $-3m^2 + 4m^3 - 2$ 3 **27.** $-2 + 3x + 4x^4$ 4

28. $6p^4 + 7p^2$ 4 **29.** $n + 2$ 1 **30.** $3y^8$ 8

See Example **4** **31.** The volume of a box with height x, length $x + 2$, and width $3x - 5$ is given by the trinomial $3x^3 + x^2 - 10x$. What is the volume of the box if its height is 2 inches? 8 in^3

PRACTICE AND PROBLEM SOLVING

Extra Practice
See page EP24.

32. **Transportation** The distance in feet required for a car traveling at r mi/h to come to a stop can be approximated by the binomial $\frac{r^2}{20} + r$. About how many feet will be required for a car to stop if it is traveling at 70 mi/h? about 315 ft

REVIEW FOR MASTERY 12-1

Review for Mastery
12-1 *Polynomials*

Expressions such as $2x$ and $4y^2$ are called **monomials**. A monomial has only one term. Monomials do not have fractional exponents, negative exponents, variable exponents, roots of variables, or variables in a denominator.

Determine whether each expression is a monomial.

1. $3x - 5$ no **2.** $-9a^4$ yes **3.** $21m^{0.5}$ no **4.** $7m^3n^2$ yes

A monomial or a sum or difference of monomials is called a **polynomial**. Polynomials can be classified by the number of terms. A monomial has 1 term, a **binomial** has 2 terms, and a **trinomial** has 3 terms.

Classify each expression as a monomial, a binomial, a trinomial, or not a polynomial.

5. $7y + 3x^2 + 5$ trinomial **6.** $6y + \sqrt{x}$ not a polynomial

7. m^2n monomial **8.** $-6a + 2b^4$ binomial

The degree of a polynomial is the degree of the term with the greatest degree. The **degree** of a term is the greatest value of a variable's exponent.

terms
$3x^5 + 5x^3 + 6$
5th degree 3rd degree 0 degree
The above polynomial is a 5th degree trinomial.

Find the degree of each polynomial.

9. $5x + 3x^3 + 2x^2$ 3 **10.** $-3m^4 + m^2 + 2$ 4 **11.** $4y + 2y^3 + y^5$ 5 **12.** $7a^2 + 8a$ 2

PRACTICE 12-1

Practice B
12-1 *Polynomials*

Determine whether each expression is a monomial.

1. $-135x^5$ yes **2.** $2.4x^3y^{19}$ yes **3.** $\frac{2p^2}{q^3}$ no

4. $3r^{\frac{1}{2}}$ no **5.** $43a^2b^{6.1}$ no **6.** $\frac{7}{9}x^2yz^5$ yes

Classify each expression as a monomial, a binomial, a trinomial, or not a polynomial.

7. $-8.9xy + \frac{6}{y^5}$ not a polynomial **8.** $\frac{9}{8}ab^8c^2d$ monomial **9.** $x^9 + x + 1$ trinomial

10. $-7pq^{-2}r^4$ not a polynomial **11.** $5n^{15} - 9n + \frac{1}{3}$ trinomial **12.** $r^8 - 5.5r^{75}$ binomial

Find the degree of each polynomial.

13. $7 - 14x$ 1 **14.** $5a + a^2 + \frac{6}{7}a^3$ 3 **15.** $7w - 16u + 3v$ 1

16. $9p - 9q - 9p^3 - 9q^2$ 3 **17.** $z^9 + 10y^8 - x$ 9 **18.** $100,050 + \frac{4}{5}k - k^4$ 4

19. The volume of a box with height x, length $x - 1$, and width $2x + 2$ is given by the binomial $2x^3 - 2x$. What is the volume of the box if its height is 4 feet? 120 ft^3

20. The trinomial $-16t^2 + 32t + 32$ describes the height in feet of a ball thrown upward after t seconds. What is the height of the ball $\frac{5}{8}$ seconds after it was thrown? 45.75 feet

Classify each expression as a monomial, a binomial, a trinomial, or not a polynomial. If it is a polynomial, give its degree.

33. $4x^3$ monomial; 3   **34.** $7x^{0.7} + 3x$ **35.** $-\dfrac{5}{6}x + \dfrac{3}{5}x^2$ binomial; 2   **36.** $7y^2 - 6y$
    not a polynomial   binomial; 2

37. $2f^3 + 5f^5 - f$ **38.** $3 - \dfrac{2}{x}$ **39.** $6x + 4\sqrt{x}$ **40.** $6x^{-4}$
    trinomial; 5   not a polynomial   not a polynomial   not a polynomial

41. $3b^2 - 9b - 8b^3$ **42.** $4 + 5x$ **43.** $2x^{\frac{1}{2}} - 3x^4 + 5$ **44.** 5   monomial; 0
    trinomial; 3   binomial; 1   not a polynomial

45. Transportation Gas mileage at speed s in miles per hour can be estimated using the given polynomials. Evaluate the polynomials to complete the table.

	Gas Mileage (mi/gal)		
	40 mi/h	50 mi/h	60 mi/h
Compact $-0.025s^2 + 2.45s - 30$	28	30	27
Midsize $-0.015s^2 + 1.45s - 13$	21	22	20
Van $-0.03s^2 + 2.9s - 53$	15	17	13

46. Possible answer: I looked for the polynomial with the greatest degree.

46. Reasoning Without evaluating, tell which of the following binomials has the greatest value when $x = 10$. Explain what method you used.

   Ⓐ $3x^5 + 8$ Ⓑ $3x^8 + 8$ Ⓒ $3x^2 + 8$ Ⓓ $3x^6 + 8$

47. What's the Error? A student says that the degree of the polynomial $4b^5 - 7b^9 + 6b$ is 5. What is the error?

48. Write About It Give some examples of words that start with *mono-*, *bi-*, *tri-*, and *poly-*, and relate the meaning of each to polynomials.

49. Challenge The base of a triangle is described by the binomial $x + 2$, and its height is described by the trinomial $2x^2 + 3x - 7$. What is the area of the triangle if $x = 5$?   203 units²

SPIRAL STANDARDS REVIEW

NS1.1, NS2.4, AF1.2

50. Multiple Choice The height in feet of a soccer ball kicked straight up into the air from s feet off the ground at velocity v after t seconds is given by the trinomial $-16t^2 + vt + s$. What is the height of the soccer ball kicked from 2 feet off the ground at 90 ft/s after 3 seconds?

   Ⓐ 3 ft   Ⓑ 15 ft   Ⓒ 90 ft   Ⓓ 128 ft

51. Gridded Response What is the degree of the polynomial $6 + 7k^4 - 8k^9$?   9

Write each number in scientific notation. (Lesson 4-5)

52. 4,080,000 4.08×10^6 **53.** 0.000035 3.5×10^{-5} **54.** 5,910,000,000 5.91×10^9

Find the two square roots of each number. (Lesson 4-6)

55. 49 ± 7 **56.** 9 ± 3 **57.** 81 ± 9 **58.** 169 ± 13

Hands-On LAB
Organizer
Use with Lesson 12-1

Objective: Use algebra tiles to model polynomials.
Materials: Algebra tiles

Online Edition
Algebra Tiles

Teach
Discuss
Be sure students understand what each algebra tile represents.

Close
Key Concept
You can use algebra tiles to represent monomials and polynomials.

Assessment
1. Represent the polynomial $2x + 1$ with algebra tiles.

2. Write the polynomial modeled by the tiles below.

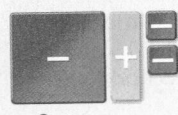

$-x^2 + x - 2$

Hands-On LAB 12-1
Model Polynomials
Use with Lesson 12-1

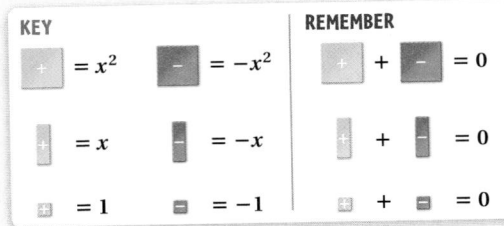

KEY | **REMEMBER**

California Standards
Preview of Algebra 1
Preparation for ➤ **10.0** Students add, subtract, multiply, and divide monomials and polynomials. Students solve multistep problems, including word problems, by using these techniques.

You can use algebra tiles to model polynomials. To model the polynomial $4x^2 + x - 3$, you need four x^2-tiles, one x-tile, and three -1-tiles.

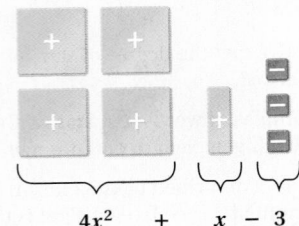

$$4x^2 + x - 3$$

Activity 1
1. Use algebra tiles to model the polynomial $2x^2 + 4x + 6$.

   All signs are positive, so use all yellow tiles.

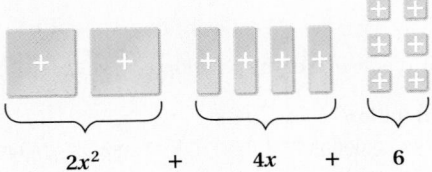

$$2x^2 + 4x + 6$$

Teacher to Teacher

As students progress from the concrete to the abstract, it is important for them to be able to visualize abstract concepts such as polynomials. I like to have students create large models of polynomials that can be displayed in the classroom. Students work in pairs to create the models on poster board. After the posters are displayed, each team can identify the different polynomials that are modeled. The students enjoy moving around and seeing other students' work.

Miguel Carrizales
San Antonio, Texas

2 Use algebra tiles to model the polynomial $-x^2 + 6x - 4$.

Modeling $-x^2 + 6x - 4$ is similar to modeling $2x^2 + 4x + 6$. Remember to use red tiles for negative values.

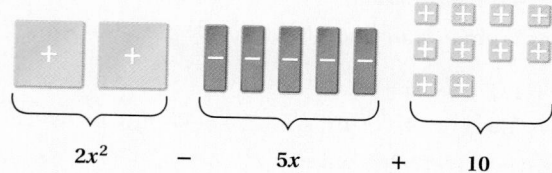

$-x^2$ $+$ $6x$ $-$ 4

Think and Discuss

1. How do you know when to use red tiles?   Possible answer: Red tiles represent terms that have negative coefficients.

Try This

Use algebra tiles to model each polynomial.

1. $2x^2 + 3x - 5$ **2.** $-4x^2 + 5x - 1$ **3.** $5x^2 - x + 9$

Activity 2

1 Write the polynomial modeled by the algebra tiles below.

$2x^2$ $-$ $5x$ $+$ 10

The polynomial modeled by the tiles is $2x^2 - 5x + 10$.

Think and Discuss

1. How do you know the coefficient of the x^2-term in Activity 2?   There are two large, square, yellow tiles, so the coefficient is 2.

Try This

Write a polynomial modeled by each group of algebra tiles.

1.

$2x^2 - 2x$

2.

$x^2 - 2x + 1$

3.

$-2x^2 + 3x - 2$

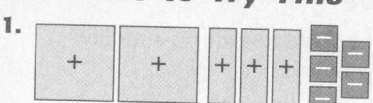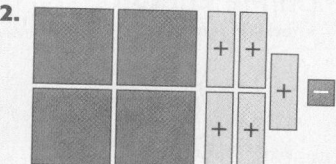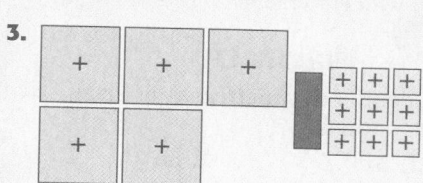

Objective: Students simplify polynomials.

Online Edition
Tutorial Videos

Power Presentations
with PowerPoint®

Warm Up

Identify the coefficient of each monomial.

1. $3x^4$ 3   **2.** ab 1
3. $\dfrac{x}{2}$ $\dfrac{1}{2}$ **4.** $-cb^3$ -1

Use the Distributive Property to simplify each expression.

5. $9(6+7)$ 117   **6.** $4(10-2)$ 32

Also available on transparency

Math Humor

How do you know when your parrot is a mathematician? It says, "Polly wants a nomial."

California Standards

Preview of Algebra 1
Preparation for ➤ 10.0
Students add, subtract, multiply, and divide **monomials and polynomials. Students solve multistep problems, including word problems, by using these techniques.**
Also covered: ➤ **7AF1.3**

Why learn this? You can simplify polynomials to determine the amount of lumber that can be harvested from a tree. (See Example 4.)

You can simplify a polynomial by adding or subtracting like terms.

Like terms   *The variables have the same powers.*

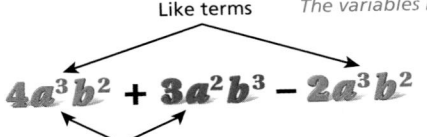

Not like terms   *The variables have different powers.*

EXAMPLE 1 Identifying Like Terms

Identify the like terms in each polynomial.

Ⓐ $2a + 4a^2 - 3 + 5a - 6a^2$
$(2a) + \boxed{4a^2} - 3 + (5a) - \boxed{6a^2}$ *Identify like terms.*
Like terms: $2a$ and $5a$; $4a^2$ and $-6a^2$

Ⓑ $-4x^5y^3 + 12x^5y^3 - 4x^3 - 6x^5y^3$
$(-4x^5y^3) + (12x^5y^3) - 4x^3 - (6x^5y^3)$ *Identify like terms.*
Like terms: $-4x^5y^3$, $12x^5y^3$, and $-6x^5y^3$

Ⓒ $5m^2 - 3mn + 4m$
$5m^2 - 3mn + 4m$ *Identify like terms.*
There are no like terms.

To simplify a polynomial, combine like terms. First arrange the terms from highest degree to lowest degree by using the Commutative Property.

EXAMPLE 2 Simplifying Polynomials by Combining Like Terms

Simplify.

Remember!
When you rearrange terms, move the operation symbol in front of each term with that term.

Ⓐ $x^2 + 5x^4 - 6 + 7x^2 + 3x^4 - 4x^2$
$\boxed{x^2} + (5x^4) - 6 + \boxed{7x^2} + (3x^4) - \boxed{4x^2}$ *Identify like terms.*
$(5x^4) + (3x^4) + \boxed{x^2} + \boxed{7x^2} - \boxed{4x^2} - 6$ *Commutative Property*
$8x^4 + 4x^2 - 6$ *Combine coefficients:*
          $5 + 3 = 8$ and $1 + 7 - 4 = 4$.

---

1 Introduce

Alternate Opener

EXPLORATION

12-2 **Simplifying Polynomials**

You can use algebra tiles to model polynomials. The polynomial $2x^2 + 2x + 2 + x^2 - x - 3$ is modeled below.

1. Use tiles to show that $2x^2 + 2x + 2 + x^2 - x - 3 = 3x^2 + x - 1$.

Use algebra tiles to simplify each expression.

2. $4x^2 - 2x - 5 - 3x^2 + x - 4$
3. $3x^2 - x + 1 - x^2 - x + 3$

Think and Discuss
4. **Explain** how you can use tiles to simplify polynomials.
5. **Explain** why you cannot simplify the polynomial $3x^2 + 4x - 9$.

Motivate

Show students a small pile of various coins. You may want to use the play money provided in the Manipulatives Kit. Ask students how they would sort the money. Group like coins together. Explain that like terms in polynomials can be grouped in the same way. You may want to remind students that they have worked with like terms before.

California Standards

Preview of Algebra 1
Prep for ➤ 10.0
Also covered:
Grade 7 Algebra and Functions
➤ **1.3** Simplify numerical expressions by applying properties of rational numbers (e.g., identity, inverse, distributive, associative, **commutative**) and justify the process used.

Explorations and answers are provided in *Alternate Openers: Explorations Transparencies.*

Simplify.

B $-5a^2b + 12ab^2 - 4a^2b - ab^2 + 3ab$

⟨$-5a^2b$⟩ + 12ab² − ⟨4a²b⟩ − ab² + 3ab   *Identify like terms.*

⟨$-5a^2b$⟩ − ⟨4a²b⟩ + 12ab² − ab² + 3ab   *Commutative Property*

$-9a^2b + 11ab^2 + 3ab$ *Combine coefficients:*
                                       $-5 - 4 = -9$ and $12 - 1 = 11$.

You may need to use the Distributive Property to simplify a polynomial.

EXAMPLE 3   **Simplifying Polynomials by Using the Distributive Property**

Simplify.

A $4(3x^2 + 5x)$

$4(3x^2 + 5x)$ *Distributive Property*

$4(3x^2) + 4(5x)$

$12x^2 + 20x$ *No like terms*

B $2(4ab^2 - 5b) + 3ab^2 + 6$

$2(4ab^2 - 5b) + 3ab^2 + 6$ *Distributive Property*

$2(4ab^2) - 2(5b) + 3ab^2 + 6$

⟨$8ab^2$⟩ − 10b + ⟨3ab²⟩ + 6   *Identify like terms.*

$11ab^2 - 10b + 6$ *Combine coefficients.*

EXAMPLE 4   *Business Application*

A *board foot* is equal to the volume of a 1 ft by 1 ft by 1 in. piece of lumber. The amount of lumber that can be harvested from a tree with diameter *d* in. is approximately $20 + 0.005(d^3 - 30d^2 + 300d - 1000)$ board feet. Use the Distributive Property to write an equivalent expression.

$20 + 0.005(d^3 - 30d^2 + 300d - 1000) = 20 + 0.005d^3 - 0.15d^2 + 1.5d - 5$
$= 15 + 0.005d^3 - 0.15d^2 + 1.5d$

Possible answers to *Think and Discuss*

1. The terms are either numbers or terms with the same variables raised to the same powers, and they are separated by plus or minus signs.

2. $8(3x + 2) = 24x + 16$; $8x + 3x = 11x$

Think and Discuss

1. Tell how you know when you can combine like terms.

2. Give an example of an expression that you could simplify by using the Distributive Property. Then give an expression that you could simplify by combining like terms.

2 Teach

Guided Instruction

In this lesson, students learn to simplify polynomials. First, be sure that students know how to identify like terms. You may want to use the Teaching Transparency. Explain that like terms are either constants or terms with the same variables raised to the same powers. After students are able to identify like terms, discuss how to simplify polynomials by combining like terms. Then discuss how to use the Distributive Property to simplify expressions.

Universal Access

Through Concrete Manipulatives

Have students work in groups. Each group should write one of the following monomials on an index card:

$3x^2$, 3, $\frac{1}{2}x^4$, x, $-5x$, $-2x^3$, $5x^2$, 0, x^3, $\frac{1}{2}x^4$

Have each group find the other group whose card contains a like term; then, have them combine all of the like terms into one term.

3 and 0, $-5x$ and x, $3x^2$ and $5x^2$, $-2x^3$ and x^3, $\frac{1}{2}x^4$ and $\frac{1}{2}x^4$ Then you may want to have the class write all of the terms as one polynomial.

$x^4 - x^3 + 8x^2 - 4x + 3$

3 Close

ENGLISH
LANGUAGE
LEARNERS

Summarize

Ask students to define *like terms*. Remind them that like terms can be combined by addition or subtraction. Make sure students understand how to apply the Distributive Property to polynomials.

Possible answer: Like terms are terms that have the same variable(s) raised to the same powers. Constants are also considered like terms.

12-2 Exercises

California Standards Practice
Preparation for Algebra 1 ➤ 10.0;
➤ 7AF1.3

go.hrw.com
Homework Help Online
KEYWORD: MT8CA 12-2
Parent Resources Online
KEYWORD: MT8CA Parent

Assignment Guide

If you finished Example **1** assign:
Proficient 1, 2, 9, 10, 30–34,
Advanced 9, 10, 30–34

If you finished Example **2** assign:
Proficient 1–4, 9–12, 17, 18, 29–34
Advanced 9–12, 17, 18, 28–34

If you finished Example **3** assign:
Proficient 1–7, 9–15, 17–22, 29–34
Advanced 9–15, 19–24, 28–34

If you finished Example **4** assign:
Proficient 1–22, 25, 26, 29–34
Advanced 9–34

Homework Quick Check

Quickly check key concepts.
Exercises: 10, 12, 14, 16

Math Background

In the lesson, **Example 3** addresses using the Distributive Property to simplify expressions. The process of combining like terms used in **Example 2** is also an application of the Distributive Property (e.g., $3x + 2x = (3 + 2)x = 5x$).

The Distributive Property may be used several times in the simplification of a polynomial. For example:

$4(3x + 2z) + 5x - 6z$
$\quad 12x + 8z + 5x - 6z$
$\quad 12x + 5x + 8z - 6z$
$\quad (12 + 5)x + (8 - 6)z$
$\qquad 17x + 2z$

GUIDED PRACTICE

See Example **1**   Identify the like terms in each polynomial.

1. $-3b^2 + 5b + 4b^2 - b + 6$ $-3b^2$ and $4b^2$, $5b$ and $-b$

2. $7mn - 5m^2n^2 + 8m^2n + 4m^2n^2$ $-5m^2n^2$ and $4m^2n^2$

See Example **2**   Simplify.

3. $2x^2 - 3x + 5x^2 + 7x - 5$ $7x^2 + 4x - 5$

4. $6 - 3b + 2b^4 - 7b^2 + 9 + 4b - 3b^2$ $2b^4 - 10b^2 + b + 15$

See Example **3**   5. $4(3x - 8)$ $12x - 32$ 6. $7(2x^2 + 4x)$ $14x^2 + 28x$ 7. $5(3a^2 - 5a) + 2a^2 + 4a$ $17a^2 - 21a$

See Example **4**   8. The level of nitric oxide emissions, in parts per million, from a car engine is approximated by the polynomial $-40,000 + 5x(800 - x^2)$, where x is the air-fuel ratio. Use the Distributive Property to write an equivalent expression. $-40,000 + 4000x - 5x^3$

INDEPENDENT PRACTICE

See Example **1**   Identify the like terms in each polynomial.

9. $-t + 4t^2 - 5t^2 + 5t - 2$ $-t$ and $5t$, $4t^2$ and $-5t^2$

10. $8rs - 3r^2s^2 + 5r^2s^2 + 2rs - 5$ $8rs$ and $2rs$, $-3r^2s^2$ and $5r^2s^2$

See Example **2**   Simplify.

11. $2p - 3p^2 + 5p + 12p^2$ $9p^2 + 7p$

12. $3fg + f^2g - fg^2 - 3fg + 4f^2g + 6fg^2$ $5f^2g + 5fg^2$

See Example **3**   13. $5(x^2 - 5x) + 4x^2 - 7x$ 14. $2(b - 3) + 5b - 3b^2$ 15. $\frac{1}{2}(6y^3 - 8) + 3y^3$
     $9x^2 - 32x$ $-3b^2 + 7b - 6$ $6y^3 - 4$

See Example **4**   16. The concentration of a certain medication in an average person's bloodstream h hours after injection can be estimated using the expression $6(0.03h - 0.002h^2 - 0.01h^3)$. Use the Distributive Property to write an equivalent expression. $0.18h - 0.012h^2 - 0.06h^3$

PRACTICE AND PROBLEM SOLVING

Extra Practice
See page EP24.

Simplify.

17. $2s^2 - 3s + 10s^2 + 5s - 3$ $12s^2 + 2s - 3$

18. $5gh^2 + 4g^2h + 2g^2h - g^2h$ $5gh^2 + 5g^2h$

19. $2(x^2 - 5x + 4) - 3x + 7$ $2x^2 - 13x + 15$

20. $5(x - x^5 + x^3) - 3x$ $-5x^5 + 5x^3 + 2x$

21. $4(2m - 3m^2) + 7(3m^2 - 4m)$ $9m^2 - 20m$

22. $6b^4 + 2b^2 + 3(b^2 - 6)$ $6b^4 + 5b^2 - 18$

23. $5mn - 3m^3n^2 + 3(m^3n^2 + 4mn)$ $17mn$

24. $3(4x + y) + 2(3x - 2y)$ $18x - y$

25. **Life Science** The rate of flow in cm/s of blood in an artery at d cm from the center is given by the polynomial $1000(0.04 - d^2)$. Use the Distributive Property to write an equivalent expression. $40 - 1000d^2$

Abstract artists often use geometric shapes, such as cubes, prisms, pyramids, and spheres, to create sculptures.

26. Suppose the volume of a sculpture is approximately $s^3 + 0.52s^3 + 0.18s^3 + 0.33s^3$ cm³ and the surface area is approximately $6s^2 + 3.14s^2 + 7.62s^2 + 3.24s^2$ cm².

   a. Simplify the polynomial expression for the volume of the sculpture, and find the volume of the sculpture for $s = 5$. **$2.03s^3$; 253.75 cm³**

   b. Simplify the polynomial expression for the surface area of the sculpture, and find the surface area of the sculpture for $s = 5$. **$20s^2$; 500 cm²**

Balanced/Unbalanced O by Fletcher Benton

27. A sculpture features a large ring with an outer lateral surface area of about $44xy$ in², an inner lateral surface area of about $38xy$ in², and 2 bases, each with an area of about $41y$ in². Write and simplify a polynomial that expresses the surface area of the ring. **$82xy + 82y$ in²**

28. ⭐ **Challenge** The volume of the ring on the sculpture from Exercise 27 is $49\pi xy^2 - 36\pi xy^2$ in³. Simplify the polynomial, and find the volume for $x = 12$ and $y = 7.5$. Give your answer both in terms of π and to the nearest tenth. **$13\pi xy^2$; $8775\pi \approx 27{,}567.5$ in³**

Pyramid Balancing Cube and Sphere, artist unknown

go.hrw.com
Web Extra!
KEYWORD: MT8CA Art

SPIRAL STANDARDS REVIEW

NS1.3, AF3.1

29. **Multiple Choice** Simplify the expression $4x^2 + 8x^3 - 9x^2 + 2x$.

   (A) $8x^3 - 5x^4 + 2x$ (B) $8x^3 + 13x^2 + 2x$ (C) $8x^3 - 5x^2 + 2x$ (D) $5x^3$

30. **Short Response** Identify the like terms in the polynomial $3x^4 + 5x^2 - x^4 + 4x^2$. Then simplify the polynomial. **The like terms are: "$3x^4$ and $-x^4$" and "$5x^2$ and $4x^2$"; $2x^4 + 9x^2$**

Find each percent to the nearest tenth. (Lesson 6-3)

31. What percent of 82 is 42? **51.2%**

32. What percent of 195 is 126? **64.6%**

Create a table for each quadratic function, and use it to graph the function. (Lesson 7-4)

33. $y = -x^2 + 1$

34. $y = x^2 + 2x - 1$

Interdisciplinary LINK

Art

Exercises 26–28 involve applying polynomial concepts to finding the volume and surface area of sculptures. Knowing these measurements can help artists determine the amount of materials they need to complete a project.

Answers

33–34. See p. A11.

Teaching Tip **Multiple Choice** Students who chose answer **D** in **Exercise 29** mistakenly combined the coefficients of unlike terms. Recommend that students review the definition of like terms.

Journal

Explain that you want to evaluate $3x^2 + 5x + 2x^2 - 4x$ for $x = 3$. Ask students to explain whether you should evaluate or simplify the polynomial first. Have them justify their opinions.

CHALLENGE 12-2

LESSON 12-2 Challenge
Coming To Terms

For each polynomial, use the simplified polynomial to find the missing term.

	Polynomial	Simplified Polynomial	Missing Term
1.	$7x^2 - 4x + \_ + 3x - 5$	$5x^2 - x - 5$	$-2x^2$
2.	$6(9x + \_)$	$54x + 18$	3
3.	$12 + 2m + 3m^4 - 8m^2 + 5 + \_ - 7m^2$	$3m^4 - 15m^2 + 6m + 17$	$4m$
4.	$\_(2b^2 - 9b) + 4b^2 + 11b$	$14b^2 - 34b$	5
5.	$7(x^3 + 3x) - 5x^3 + \_$	$2x^3 + 11x$	$-10x$
6.	$4ab + \_ + 3a^2b^2 + 2ab - 8$	$2a^2b^2 + 6ab - 8$	$-a^2b^2$
7.	$\_ + 7 + 10w^2 - 4w^2 + 5w - 2$	$6w^2 + 4w + 5$	$-w$
8.	$2(t - 7) + \_ - 2t^2$	$-2t^2 + 14t - 14$	$12t$
9.	$3hk - h^2k + hk^2 + 4hk + \_ + 3hk^2$	$4hk^2 - 3h^2k + 7hk$	$-2h^2k$
10.	$4y^3 + 6y - 7y^2 + 2y^3 + \_$	$6y^3 - 6y^2 + 6y$	y^2
11.	$\_ - n^3 - \frac{1}{4}n^4 + \frac{2}{3}n^3 - \frac{1}{3}n^3$	$\frac{1}{4}n^4 - \frac{5}{6}n^3$	$\frac{1}{2}n^4$
12.	$3(12v^3 + \_ + 2v^3) + v^3$	$46v^3$	v^3
13.	$1.5pq^3 + 0.7p^2q + \_ + 2.4p^2q$	$1.5pq^3 + 3.1p^2q - 3.8pq$	$-3.8pq$
14.	$-9(\_ + 8w) + 4(-2w^2 + 18w)$	w^2	$-w^2$

PROBLEM SOLVING 12-2

LESSON 12-2 Problem Solving
Simplifying Polynomials

Write the correct answer.

1. The area of a trapezoid can be found using the expression $\frac{h}{2}(b_1 + b_2)$ where h is height, b_1 is the length of base$_1$, and b_2 is the length of base$_2$. Use the Distributive Property to write an equivalent expression.

   $\frac{hb_1}{2} + \frac{hb_2}{2}$

2. The sum of the measures of the interior angles of a polygon with n sides is $180(n - 2)$ degrees. Use the Distributive Property to write an equivalent expression, and use the expression to find the sum of the measures of the interior angles of an octagon.

   $180n - 360$; 1,080 degrees

3. The volume of a box of height h is $2h^4 + h^3 + h^2 + h^2 + h$ cubic inches. Simplify the polynomial and then find the volume if the height of the box is 3 inches.

   $2h^4 + h^3 + 2h^2 + h$;
   210 cubic inches

4. The height, in feet, of a rocket launched upward with an initial velocity of 64 feet per second after t seconds is given by $16(4t - t^2)$. Write an equivalent expression for the rocket's height after t seconds. What is the height of the rocket after 4 seconds?

   $64t - 16t^2$; 0 ft

Circle the letter of the correct answer.

5. The surface area of a square pyramid with base b and slant height l is given by the expression $b(b + 2l)$. What is the surface area of a square pyramid with base 3 inches and slant height 5 inches?

   A 13 square inches
   B 19 square inches
   C 39 square inches
   D 55 square inches

6. The volume of a box with a width of $3x$, a height of $4x - 2$, and a length of $3x + 5$ can be found using the expression $3x(12x^2 + 14x - 10)$. Which is this expression, simplified by using the Distributive Property?

   F $36x^2 + 42x - 30$
   G $15x^3 + 17x^2 - 7x$
   H $36x^3 + 14x - 10$
   J $36x^3 + 42x^2 - 30x$

✓ 12-2 Lesson Quiz

Identify the like terms in each polynomial.

1. $2x^2 - 3z + 5x^2 + z + 8z^2$
   $2x^2$ and $5x^2$, z and $-3z$

2. $2ab^2 + 4a^2b - 5ab^2 - 4 + a^2b$
   $2ab^2$ and $-5ab^2$, $4a^2b$ and a^2b

Simplify.

3. $5(3x^2 + 2)$ $15x^2 + 10$

4. $-2k^2 + 10 + 8k^2 + 8k - 2$
   $6k^2 + 8k + 8$

5. $3(2mn^2 + 3n) + 6mn^2$
   $12mn^2 + 9n$

Also available on transparency

Organizer

Objective: Assess students' mastery of concepts and skills in Lessons 12-1 through 12-2.

Resources

 Assessment Resources
Section 12A Quiz

 Test & Practice Generator
One-Stop Planner®

INTERVENTION ◄───►

Resources

 Ready to Go On?
Intervention and
Enrichment Worksheets

Ready to Go On? CD-ROM

Ready to Go On? Online

my.hrw.com

 **READY TO GO ON?**

SECTION 12A

Quiz for Lessons 12-1 Through 12-2

12-1 **Polynomials**

Determine whether each expression is a monomial.

1. $\frac{1}{5x^2}$ no   **2.** $\frac{1}{3}x^2 - x^3$ no   **3.** $7c^2d^8$ yes

Classify each expression as a monomial, a binomial, a trinomial, or not a polynomial.

4. $\frac{1}{x} + x^2$ not a polynomial   **5.** $a^3 + 2a - 17$ trinomial   **6.** $y + 2$ binomial

Find the degree of each polynomial.

7. $u^6 + 7$ 6   **8.** $3c^2 + c^5 + c + 1$ 5   **9.** 43   0

10. The depth, in feet below the ocean surface, of a submerging exploration submarine after y minutes can be approximated by the polynomial $0.001y^4 - 0.12y^3 + 3.6y^2$. Estimate the depth after 45 minutes.   456 ft

12-2 **Simplifying Polynomials**

Identify the like terms in each polynomial. $-z^2$ and $4z^2$, $7z$ and $-z$
11. $-5x^2y^2 + 4xy + x^2y^2$ $-5x^2y^2$ and x^2y^2 **12.** $-z^2 + 7z + 4z^2 - z + 9$
13. $t + 8 - 2t - 6$ t and $-2t$, -6 and 8   **14.** $8ab + 3ac + 5bc - 4ac + 6ab$
                                                         $8ab$ and $6ab$, $3ac$ and $-4ac$
Simplify. $13y^2 - 3y - 5$
15. $6 + 3b^5 - 2b^3 + 7 - 5b^3$ $3b^5 - 7b^3 + 13$ **16.** $6y^2 + y + 7y^2 - 4y - 5$
17. $6(x^2 - 7x) + 2x^2 + 7x$ $8x^2 - 35x$ **18.** $y + 5 - 5y - 4(5y + 2)$
                                                              $-24y - 3$

19. The area of one face of a cube is given by the expression $3s^2 + 5s$. Write a polynomial to represent the total surface area of the cube. $18s^2 + 30s$

20. The area of each lateral face of a regular square pyramid is given by the expression $\frac{1}{2}b^2 + 2b$. Write a polynomial to represent the lateral surface area of the pyramid. $2b^2 + 8b$

READY TO GO ON?
Diagnose and Prescribe

NO **INTERVENE**

READY TO GO ON? Intervention, Section 12A			
Ready to Go On? **Intervention**	**Worksheets**	**CD-ROM**	**Online**
✓ Lesson 12-1 Prep for 1A10.0	12-1 Intervention	Activity 12-1	Diagnose and Prescribe Online
✓ Lesson 12-2 Prep for 1A10.0	12-2 Intervention	Activity 12-2	

YES **ENRICH**

READY TO GO ON?
Enrichment, Section 12A
 **Worksheets**
CD-ROM
Online

Focus on Problem Solving

California Standards

MR2.1 Use estimation to verify the reasonableness of calculated results.
Also covered: **NS1.7**

 Focus on Problem Solving

Organizer

Objective: Focus on estimating to check that your answer is reasonable.

 Online Edition

 Look Back

- **Estimate to check that your answer is reasonable**

Before you solve a word problem, you can often read through the problem and make an estimate of the correct answer. Make sure your answer is reasonable for the situation in the problem. After you have solved the problem, compare your answer with the original estimate. If your answer is not close to your estimate, check your work again.

Resources

 **Chapter 12 Resource File**
Reading Strategies

Problem Solving Process

This page focuses on the last step of the problem-solving process:
Look Back

Each problem below has an incorrect answer given. Explain why the answer is not reasonable, and give your own estimate of the correct answer.

1 The perimeter of rectangle *ABCD* is 48 cm. What is the value of *x*?

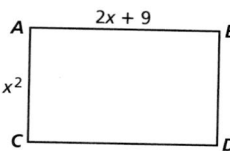

Answer: x = −5

2 A patio layer can use $4x + 6y$ ft of accent edging to divide a patio into three sections measuring *x* ft long by *y* ft wide. If each section must be at least 15 ft long and have an area of at least 165 ft^2, what is the minimum amount of edging needed for the patio?

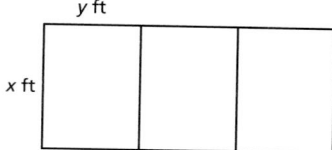

Answer: 52 ft

3 A baseball is thrown straight up from a height of 3 ft at 30 mi/h. The height of the baseball in feet after *t* seconds is $-16t^2 + 44t + 3$. How long will it take the baseball to reach its maximum height?

Answer: 5 minutes

4 Jacob deposited $2000 in a savings account that earns 6% simple interest. How much money will he have in the account after 7 years?

Answer: $1925

Discuss

Have students discuss why the answer given for each problem is unreasonable. Then have them explain how to estimate a more reasonable answer.

Possible answers:

1. Distance cannot be a negative number, so the length $2x + 9$ must be positive. Because of the two x^2 terms that are part of the perimeter, the value of *x* must be less than 5. A more reasonable estimate would be 3.

2. If the length *x* is at least 15 ft, then $4x$ is at least 60 ft. So, 52 ft of fencing is not nearly enough. If the length is 15 ft and the area is at least 165 ft^2, the width must be at least 11 ft. So, a reasonable estimate of the amount of fencing needed is about $4(15) + 6(11) = 126$.

Answers

1. 3 cm
2. 126 ft
3. 1.375 s
4. $2840

3. It's impossible for a person to throw a baseball that continues to go up for 5 minutes. A more realistic answer would be 1 or 2 seconds.

4. The amount in the account after 7 years cannot be less than the original deposit. The amount of interest earned in 1 year is 6% of $2000, which is $120. Earning about $100 each year for 7 years gives interest of about $700 and a total balance of about $2700.

 California Standards

Mathematical Reasoning 2.1
Also covered:

Grade 7 Number Sense
1.7 Solve problems that involve discounts, markups, commissions, and profit and **compute simple** and compound **interest.**

Polynomial Operations

 **One-Minute Section Planner**

Lesson	Lab Resources	Materials
12-3 Hands-On Lab Model Polynomial Addition Use algebra tiles to model polynomial addition. 🐻 **Preview of Algebra 1** 🔑 **1A10.0**		**Required** Algebra tiles (MK)
Lesson 12-3 Adding Polynomials ● Add polynomials. 🐻 **Preview of Algebra 1** 🔑 **1A10.0;** 🔑 **7AF1.3**		**Optional** Algebra tiles (MK), graphing calculators
12-4 Hands-On Lab Model Polynomial Subtraction Use algebra tiles to model polynomial subtraction. 🐻 **Preview of Algebra 1** 🔑 **1A10.0**		**Required** Algebra tiles (MK)
Lesson 12-4 Subtracting Polynomials ● Subtract polynomials. 🐻 **Preview of Algebra 1** 🔑 **1A10.0;** 🔑 **7AF1.3**		**Optional** Algebra tiles (MK)
Lesson 12-5 Multiplying Polynomials by Monomials ● Multiply polynomials by monomials. 🐻 **Preview of Algebra 1** 🔑 **1A10.0;** **7AF1.2,** 🔑 **7AF1.3, 7AF2.2**		**Optional** Algebra tiles (MK), index cards
12-6 Hands-On Lab Multiply Binomials Use algebra tiles to model multiplying binomials. 🐻 **Preview of Algebra 1** 🔑 **1A10.0**		**Required** Algebra tiles (MK)
Lesson 12-6 Multiplying Binomials ● Multiply binomials. 🐻 **Preview of Algebra 1** 🔑 **1A10.0**	**Technology Lab 12-6** In *Chapter 12 Resource File*	**Optional** Algebra tiles (MK), graphing calculators

MK = *Manipulatives Kit*

Notes

_____

_____

_____

_____

_____

_____

_____

Math Background: Teaching the Standards

Professional Development

OPERATIONS WITH POLYNOMIALS

 **Prev. of** ⟜ **1A10.0**

Lessons 12-3 through 12-6

Fluency with polynomial operations is an important stepping stone for further work in algebra. In future mathematics courses students will be called upon to solve quadratic equations by factoring trinomials, to solve systems of equations by elimination, and to solve rational equations by multiplying both sides of the equation by a polynomial. Understanding how to add, subtract, and multiply polynomials is a basic prerequisite for all of these skills.

ADDING POLYNOMIALS  **Prev. of** ⟜ **1A10.0**

Lesson 12-3

Polynomials may be added horizontally or vertically. The horizontal format emphasizes the fact that polynomial addition is essentially a matter of combining like terms, which was introduced in Lesson 12-2. The vertical format has the advantage of resembling the familiar algorithm for whole-number addition.

To further explore the connection between polynomial addition and whole-number addition, consider the sum $521 + 76$. Note the expanded form on the right.

$$
\begin{array}{rcl}
521 & \to & 5 \cdot 10^2 + 2 \cdot 10^1 + 1 \cdot 10^0 \\
+\ 76 & \to\ + & 7 \cdot 10^1 + 6 \cdot 10^0 \\
\hline
597 & \to & 5 \cdot 10^2 + 9 \cdot 10^1 + 7 \cdot 10^0
\end{array}
$$

The expanded form shows how the terms are arranged according to place value. In this format, the addition is carried out by adding the multipliers of the powers of 10 in each column.

Similarly, when adding polynomials, the terms are arranged so that corresponding powers of the variable are aligned. Then the coefficients may be added in each column.

$$
\begin{array}{r}
5x^2 + 2x + 1 \\
+ 7x + 6 \\
\hline
5x^2 + 9x + 7
\end{array}
$$

SUBTRACTING POLYNOMIALS

 Prev. of ⟜ **1A10.0**

Lesson 12-4

To subtract one polynomial from another, add the opposite of the second polynomial to the first. The main difficulty here is in finding the opposite of a polynomial, since students sometimes have trouble distributing the minus sign. For example, the subtraction problem $(3x^2 - 2x - 1) - (x^2 - 3x + 1)$ requires finding the opposite of $x^2 - 3x + 1$. To do so, multiply by -1 using the Distributive Property.

$$
\begin{aligned}
(-1)(x^2 - 3x + 1) &= (-1)(x^2) + (-1)(-3x) + (-1)(+1) \\
&= -x^2 + 3x - 1
\end{aligned}
$$

Thus, the subtraction problem is converted to the addition problem $(3x^2 - 2x - 1) + (-x^2 + 3x - 1)$.

MULTIPLYING POLYNOMIALS

 **Prev. of** ⟜ **1A10.0**

Lessons 12-5, 12-6

Multiplying polynomials depends greatly on multiplying monomials, which students learned in Chapter 4. Multiplying a polynomial by a monomial is a matter of using the multiplying monomials skill along with the Distributive Property, as shown below.

$$
\begin{aligned}
6x^3(2x^2 + 5) &= (6x^3)(2x^2) + (6x^3)(5) \\
&= 12x^5 + 30x^3
\end{aligned}
$$

When multiplying a binomial by a binomial, the Distributive Property is used repeatedly, as in the following product.

$$
\begin{aligned}
(2x + 5)(3x + 1) &= (2x)(3x + 1) + 5(3x + 1) \\
&= 6x^2 + 2x + 15x + 5 \\
&= 6x^2 + (2 + 15)x + 5 \\
&= 6x^2 + 17x + 5
\end{aligned}
$$

Students may benefit from seeing the same product calculated in a vertical format that parallels the one used for whole-number multiplication.

$$
\begin{array}{r}
3x + 1 \\
\times\ 2x + 5 \\
\hline
15x + 5 \quad \leftarrow 5(3x + 1) \\
6x^2 + 2x \quad \leftarrow 2x(3x + 1) \\
\hline
6x^2 + 17x + 5
\end{array}
$$

Notice the similarities in the two methods. As shown in the vertical format, the expressions in the intermediate rows come from the products $5(3x + 1)$ and $2x(3x + 1)$, which are precisely the two intermediate products that are calculated in the horizontal format.

602B

Hands-On LAB

Organizer
Use with Lesson 12-3

Objective: Use algebra tiles to model polynomial addition.
Materials: Algebra tiles

Online Edition
Algebra Tiles

Teach
Discuss
Remind students what a zero pair means. Ask them to give examples of zero pairs.

Close
Key Concept
You can use algebra tiles to model polynomial addition.

Assessment
Use algebra tiles to find each sum.

1. $(x^2 + 3x - 1) + (x^2 - x + 1)$
 $2x^2 + 2x$

2. $(3y^2 - 2y) + (2y^2 + 2y + 4)$
 $5y^2 + 4$

Hands-On LAB 12-3

Model Polynomial Addition
Use with Lesson 12-3

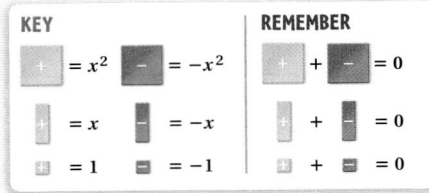

go.hrw.com
Lab Resources Online
KEYWORD: MT8CA Lab12

California Standards

Preview of Algebra 1
🔑 **10.0 Students add,** subtract, multiply, and divide monomials and **polynomials.** Students solve multistep problems, including word problems, by using these techniques.

You can use algebra tiles to model polynomial addition.

Activity

1 Use algebra tiles to find $(2x^2 - 2x + 3) + (x^2 + x - 5)$.

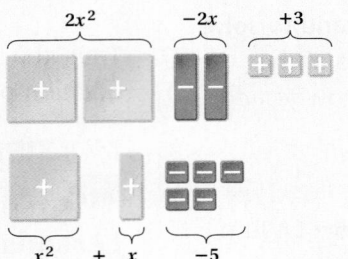

Use tiles to represent all terms from both expressions.

Remove any zero pairs.

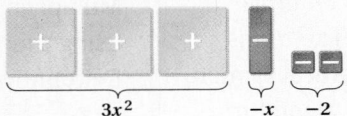

The remaining tiles represent the sum $3x^2 - x - 2$.

Think and Discuss

1. Explain what happens when you add the x-terms in $(-2x + 5) + (2x - 4)$.
Possible answer: $-2x + 2x$ represents a zero pair, so the sum of the x-terms is 0.

Try This

Use algebra tiles to find each sum.

1. $(3m^2 + 2m + 6) + (4m^2 + m + 3)$ $7m^2 + 3m + 9$ **2.** $(-5b^2 + 4b - 1) + (b - 1)$ $-5b^2 + 5b - 2$

12-3 Adding Polynomials

California Standards

Preview of Algebra 1

🔑 **10.0** Students add, subtract, multiply, and divide monomials and **polynomials. Students solve multistep problems, including word problems, by using these techniques.**

Also covered: 🔑 **7AF1.3**

Why learn this? You can add polynomials to find the amount of material needed to mat and frame a picture. (See Example 3.)

Adding polynomials is similar to simplifying polynomials. One way to add polynomials is to write them horizontally. First write the polynomials as one polynomial, and then use the Commutative Property to combine like terms.

 E X A M P L E **1** **Adding Polynomials Horizontally**

Add.

Ⓐ $(6x^2 - 3x + 4) + (7x - 6)$

$6x^2 - 3x + 4 + 7x - 6$ *Write as one polynomial.*

$6x^2 - 3x + 7x + 4 - 6$ *Commutative Property*

$6x^2 + 4x - 2$ *Combine like terms.*

Ⓑ $(-4cd^2 - 3cd + 6) + (7cd - 6cd^2 - 6)$

$-4cd^2 - 3cd + 6 + 7cd - 6cd^2 - 6$ *Write as one polynomial.*

$-4cd^2 - 6cd^2 - 3cd + 7cd + 6 - 6$ *Commutative Property*

$-10cd^2 + 4cd$ *Combine like terms.*

Ⓒ $(ab^2 + 4a) + (3ab^2 + 4a - 3) + (a + 5)$

$ab^2 + 4a + 3ab^2 + 4a - 3 + a + 5$ *Write as one polynomial.*

$ab^2 + 3ab^2 + 4a + 4a + a - 3 + 5$ *Commutative Property*

$4ab^2 + 9a + 2$ *Combine like terms.*

You can also add polynomials in a vertical format. Write the second polynomial below the first one. Be sure to line up the like terms. If the terms are rearranged, remember to keep the correct sign with each term.

Organizer 12-3

Objective: Students add polynomials.

🪐 **Online Edition**
Tutorial Videos

Power Presentations with PowerPoint®

Warm Up

Combine like terms.

1. $9x + 4x$	$13x$
2. $-3y + 7y$	$4y$
3. $7n + (-8n) + 12n$	$11n$

Find the perimeter of each rectangle.

4. a 10 ft by 12 ft rectangle	44 ft
5. a 5 m by 8 m rectangle	26 m

Simplify.

6. $3(2x^2 - x) + x^2 + 1$
$7x^2 - 3x + 1$

Also available on transparency

Math Humor

Why wasn't the monomial re-elected? She could have only one term.

---

① Introduce

Alternate Opener

EXPLORATION

12-3 Adding Polynomials

You can use algebra tiles to model addition of polynomials. The addition problem $(2x^2 + 2x - 2) + (x^2 - 4x - 3)$ is modeled below.

$2x^2 + 2x - 2$ $x^2 - 4x - 3$

1. Use tiles to show that
$(2x^2 + 2x - 2) + (x^2 - 4x - 3) = 3x^2 - 2x - 5$.

You can use a graphing calculator to check. Enter the left side of the equation in **Y1** and the right side in **Y2**, and compare tables.

Use algebra tiles to add each pair of polynomials. Check your answers with a graphing calculator.

2. $(x^2 + 7x) + (3x^2 - 7x - 5)$

3. $(-3x^2 - x - 1) + (4x^2 - 3x - 2)$

Think and Discuss

4. **Explain** how you can use tiles to add polynomials.

Motivate

Ask students to imagine that two students collected coins to donate to a local charity. Louis collected 3 rolls of quarters, 3 rolls of dimes, and 2 rolls of nickels. Lisa collected 2 rolls of quarters, 4 rolls of dimes, and 3 rolls of nickels. Ask students how they could determine the total amount of money collected. Possible answer: Add the number of each type of roll together, and multiply by the value of each roll. Point out that this example models addition of polynomials.

Explorations and answers are provided in *Alternate Openers: Explorations Transparencies.*

California Standards

Preview of Algebra 1

🔑 **10.0**

Also covered:

Grade 7 Algebra and Functions

🔑 **1.3** Simplify numerical expressions by applying properties of rational numbers (e.g., identity, inverse, distributive, associative, **commutative**) and justify the process used.

Example 1

Add.

A. $(5x^3 + x^2 + 2) + (4x^3 + 6x^2)$
$9x^3 + 7x^2 + 2$

B. $(6x^3 + 8y^2 + 5xy) + (4xy - 2y^2)$
$6x^3 + 6y^2 + 9xy$

C. $(3x^2y - 5x) + (4x + 7) + 6x^2y$
$9x^2y - x + 7$

Example 2

Add.

A. $(4x^2 + 2x + 11) + (2x^2 + 6x + 9)$
$6x^2 + 8x + 20$

B. $(3mn^2 - 6m + 6n) + (5mn^2 + 2m - n)$
$8mn^2 - 4m + 5n$

C. $(-x^2y^2 + 5x^2) + (-2y^2 + 2) + (x^2 + 8)$
$-x^2y^2 + 6x^2 - 2y^2 + 10$

Example 3

Rachel wants to frame two photographs. The first photograph has dimensions b inches and h inches, and each dimension of the other photograph is twice the corresponding dimension of the first. She needs enough wood for the frames to cover both perimeters, and the width of the wood is $1\frac{1}{2}$ inches. Find an expression for the length of wood she needs to frame both photographs. $6b + 6h + 24$ in.

EXAMPLE 2 Adding Polynomials Vertically

Add.

A $(5a^2 + 4a + 2) + (4a^2 + 3a + 1)$

$5a^2 + 4a + 2$
$\underline{+ 4a^2 + 3a + 1}$ *Place like terms in columns.*
$9a^2 + 7a + 3$ *Combine like terms.*

B $(2xy^2 + 3x - 4y) + (8xy^2 - 2x + 3)$

$2xy^2 + 3x - 4y$
$\underline{+8xy^2 - 2x + 3}$ *Place like terms in columns.*
$10xy^2 + x - 4y + 3$ *Combine like terms.*

C $(4a^2b^2 + 3a^2 - 6ab) + (-4ab + a^2 - 5) + (3 + 7ab)$

$4a^2b^2 + 3a^2 - 6ab$
$a^2 - 4ab - 5$
$\underline{+ 7ab + 3}$ *Place like terms in columns.*
$4a^2b^2 + 4a^2 - 3ab - 2$ *Combine like terms.*

EXAMPLE 3 **Art Application**

Reasoning

Mina is putting a mat of width m and a frame of width f around an 11-inch by 14-inch picture. Find an expression for the amount of framing material she needs.

The amount of material Mina needs equals the perimeter of the outside of the frame. Draw a diagram to help you determine the outer dimensions of the frame.

Width $= 14 + m + m + f + f$ Length $= 11 + m + m + f + f$
$= 14 + 2m + 2f$ $= 11 + 2m + 2f$

$P = 2(11 + 2m + 2f) + 2(14 + 2m + 2f)$ $P = 2w + 2\ell$
$ = 22 + 4m + 4f + 28 + 4m + 4f$ *Simplify.*
$ = 50 + 8m + 8f$ *Combine like terms.*

She will need $50 + 8m + 8f$ inches of framing material.

Possible answers to Think and Discuss

1. To add horizontally, you first write like terms side by side. To add vertically, you first line up like terms in columns.

2. To do both you use the Commutative Property and combine like terms.

Think and Discuss

1. **Compare** adding $(5x^2 + 2x) + (3x^2 - 2x)$ vertically with adding it horizontally.

2. **Explain** how adding polynomials is similar to simplifying polynomials.

---

2 Teach

Guided Instruction

In this lesson, students learn to add polynomials. Explain that adding polynomials is very similar to the process of simplifying polynomials studied in the previous lesson. Show students the horizontal and vertical methods of adding polynomials.

Teaching Tip **Inclusion** Encourage students to be sure to keep the correct sign with each term as they move or reorder the terms in a problem.

Universal Access
Through Concrete Manipulatives

Give each student or group of students a set of algebra tiles (provided in the Manipulatives Kit). Have students use the algebra tiles to add polynomials, such as $(2x^2 + 3x + 1)$ and $(x^2 - 2x - 3)$. $3x^2 + x - 2$ Remind students that a pair of tiles having the same shape but different colors equals zero and can be removed from the expression.

3 Close

Summarize

Remind students that they need to identify like terms and combine them to add polynomials. Ask them how many terms they will end up with if they add two trinomials.

Possible answer: It will depend on the number of like terms in the trinomials. If each trinomial is already simplified, the number of terms in the sum will be between 3 and 6.

California Standards Practice
Preview of Algebra 1 ⚷ **10.0;**
🔑 **7AF1.3**

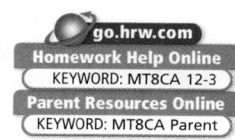
go.hrw.com
Homework Help Online
KEYWORD: MT8CA 12-3
Parent Resources Online
KEYWORD: MT8CA Parent

12-3 **Exercises**

GUIDED PRACTICE

See Example **1** **Add.**

1. $(5x^3 + 6x - 1) + (-3x + 7)$ $5x^3 + 3x + 6$

2. $(22x - 6) + (14x - 3)$ $36x - 9$

3. $(r^2s + 3rs) + (4r^2s - 8rs) + (6r^2s + 14rs)$ $11r^2s + 9rs$

See Example **2** **4.** $(4b^2 - 5b + 10) + (6b^2 + 7b - 8)$ $10b^2 + 2b + 2$

5. $(9ab^2 - 5ab + 6a^2b) + (8ab - 12a^2b + 6) + (6ab^2 + 5a^2b - 14)$ $15ab^2 + 3ab - a^2b - 8$

6. $(h^4j - hj^3 + hj - 6) + (5hj^3 + 5) + (6h^4j - 7hj)$ $7h^4j + 4hj^3 - 6hj - 1$

See Example **3** **7.** Colette is putting a mat of width $3w$ and a frame of width w around a 16-inch by 48-inch poster. Find an expression for the amount of frame material she needs. **128 + 32w in.**

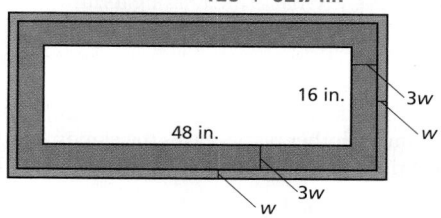
16 in.
48 in.
3w
w
3w
w

INDEPENDENT PRACTICE

See Example **1** **Add.**

8. $(5x^2y - 4xy + 3) + (7xy - 3x^2y)$ $2x^2y + 3xy + 3$

9. $(5g - 9) + (7g^2 - 4g + 8)$ $7g^2 + g - 1$

10. $(6bc - 2b^2c^2 + 8bc^2) + (6bc - 3bc^2)$ $12bc - 2b^2c^2 + 5bc^2$

11. $(9h^4 + 5h - 4h^6) + (h^6 - 6h + 3h^4)$ $-3h^6 + 12h^4 - h$

12. $(4pq - 5p^2q + 9pq^2) + (6p^2q - 11pq^2) + (2pq^2 - 7pq + 6p^2q)$ $-3pq + 7p^2q$

See Example **2** **13.** $(8t^2 + 4t + 3) + (5t^2 - 8t + 9)$ $13t^2 - 4t + 12$

14. $(5b^3c^2 - 3b^2c + 2bc) + (8b^3c^2 - 3bc + 14) + (b^2c - 5bc - 9)$ $13b^3c^2 - 2b^2c - 6bc + 5$

15. $(w^2 - 3w + 5) + (-2w - 3w^2 - 1) + (w^2 + w - 6)$ $-w^2 - 4w - 2$

See Example **3** **16.** Each side of an equilateral triangle has length $w + 3$. Each side of a square has length $4w - 2$. Write an expression for the sum of the perimeter of the equilateral triangle and the perimeter of the square. $19w + 1$

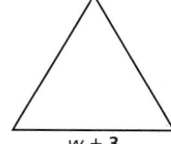
$w + 3$

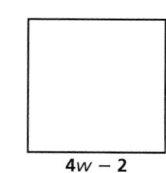
$4w - 2$

Assignment Guide

If you finished Example **1** assign:
Proficient 1–3, 8–12, 17, 18, 25, 28–34
Advanced 8–12, 17, 18, 22, 23, 25, 26, 28–34

If you finished Example **2** assign:
Proficient 1–6, 8–15, 17, 18, 25, 28–34
Advanced 8–15, 17, 18, 22, 23, 25, 26, 28–34

If you finished Example **3** assign:
Proficient 1–21, 25, 27–34
Advanced 8–34

Homework Quick Check

Quickly check key concepts.
Exercises: 10, 12, 14, 16

Math Background

Adding polynomials vertically demonstrates the same principle as using place value to add numbers. Consider the examples below.

$$
\begin{array}{r}
3x^2 + 4x + 1 \\
+\ \ x^2 + 5x + 6 \\
\hline
4x^2 + 9x + 7
\end{array}
$$

$$
\begin{array}{r}
341 \longrightarrow 3(10^2) + 4(10) + 1 \\
+\ 156 \longrightarrow 1(10^2) + 5(10) + 6 \\
\hline
4(10^2) + 9(10) + 7
\end{array}
$$

REVIEW FOR MASTERY 12-3

LESSON 12-3 Review for Mastery
Adding Polynomials

Adding polynomials is like simplifying polynomials. You can regroup the terms and then combine like terms. Or you can place the polynomials in columns and then combine like terms.

Find an expression for the perimeter of the triangle below.

$2a + 1$
$3a - 2$
$a^2 + 2$

To find an expression for the perimeter, add the polynomials.

$(2a + 1) + (3a - 2) + (a^2 + 2)$

like terms   like terms

Place like terms in columns and combine them.

$$
\begin{array}{r}
2a + 1 \\
3a - 2 \\
+\ a^2\ \ \ \ + 2 \\
\hline
a^2 + 5a + 1
\end{array}
$$

So, an expression for the perimeter of the triangle is $a^2 + 5a + 1$.

Add.

1. $(3x^2 + 3xy^3 + 5y + 2) + (4xy^3 - 3y)$

$$
\begin{array}{r}
3x^2 + 3xy^3 + 5y + 2 \\
+\ \ \ \ \ \ \ 4xy^3\ \ \ \ - 3y \\
\hline
3x^2 + 7xy^3 + 2y + 2
\end{array}
$$

2. $(4a^2b - 3a^2 + 3b) + (6a^2b + 4ab - 2b)$

$$
\begin{array}{r}
4a^2b - 3a^2\ \ \ \ \ \ \ \ \ + 3b \\
+\ 6a^2b\ \ \ \ \ \ \ + 4ab - 2b \\
\hline
10a^2b - 3a^2 + 4ab + b
\end{array}
$$

3. $(4mn + 5n^3 + 3n) + (3m^2 + 5n)$

$4mn + 3m^2 + 5n^3 + 8n$

4. $(-5r^3 + 2r + 7) + (2r^3 + 4r^2 - 6r + 1)$

$-3r^3 + 4r^2 - 4r + 8$

PRACTICE 12-3

LESSON 12-3 Practice B
Adding Polynomials

Add.

1. $(a^2 + a + 3) + (15a^2 + 2a + 9)$

$16a^2 + 3a + 12$

2. $(5x + 2x^2) + (3x - 2x^2)$

$8x$

3. $(mn - 10 + mn^2) + (5 + 3mn - 4mn^2)$

$-3mn^2 + 4mn - 5$

4. $(7y^2z + 9 + yz^2) + (y^2z - 2yz^2)$

$8y^2z - yz^2 + 9$

5. $(s^3 + 3s - 3) + (2s^3 + 9s - 2) + (s - s^3)$

$2s^3 + 13s - 5$

6. $(6wv - 4w^2v + 7wv^2) + (5w^2v - 7wv^2) + (wv^2 - 5wv + 6w^2v)$

$7w^2v + wv^2 + wv$

7. $(6b^2c^2 - 4b^2c + 3bc) + (9b^2c^2 - 4bc + 12) + (2b^2c - 3bc - 8)$

$15b^2c^2 - 2b^2c - 4bc + 4$

8. $(7e^2 + 3e + 2) + (9 - 6e + 4e^2) + (9e + 2 - 6e^2) + (4e^2 - 7e + 8)$

$9e^2 - e + 21$

9. $(f^4g - fg^3 + 2fg - 4) + (3fg^3 + 3) + (4f^4g - 5fg) + (3 - 12fg^3 + f^4g)$

$6f^4g - 10fg^3 - 3fg + 2$

10. Six blocks of height $4h + 4$ each and 3 blocks of height $8 - 2h$ each are stacked on top of each other to form one big tower. Find an expression for the overall height of the tower.

$18h + 48$

Answers

21. Possible answer: Add the expression representing the distance from the airport to the first plane to the expression representing the distance from the airport to the second plane. The planes are $4x^2 - 48x + 500$ miles apart after 2 hours.

Teaching Tip   **Multiple Choice** For **Exercise 27,** students who chose answer **A** found only half the combined perimeter. They may want to review the formula for finding the perimeter of a rectangle.

  Journal

Show students the following polynomial addition problem:
$(2x^2 + 3x + 4) + (3x^2 + 5x + 3)$.
Have them compare this problem to the addition problem $234 + 353$.

Power Presentations
with PowerPoint®

PRACTICE AND PROBLEM SOLVING

Business

According to the Toy Industry Association, $24.6 billion was spent on toys worldwide in 2000.

go.hrw.com
Web Extra!
KEYWORD: MT8CA Toys

25. Possible answer: First identify like terms. Then add like terms by adding their coefficients.

Add.

17. $(3w^2y + 3wy^2 - 4wy) + (5wy - 2wy^2 + 7w^2y) + (wy^2 - 5wy - 3w^2y)$
$7w^2y + 2wy^2 - 4wy$

18. $(2p^2t - 3pt + 5) + (p^2t + 2pt^2 - 3pt) + (1 - 5pt^2 + p^2t)$
$4p^2t - 6pt + 6 - 3pt^2$

19. **Geometry** Write and simplify an expression for the combined volumes of a sphere with volume $\frac{4}{3}\pi r^3$, a cube with volume r^3, and a prism with volume $r^3 + 4r^2 + 5r + 2$. Use 3.14 for π. $\approx 6.19r^3 + 4r^2 + 5r + 2$

20. **Business** The cost of producing n toys at a factory is given by the polynomial $0.5n^2 + 3n + 12$. The cost of packaging is $0.25n^2 + 5n + 4$. Write and simplify an expression for the total cost of producing and packaging n toys.
$0.75n^2 + 8n + 16$

21. **Reasoning** Two airplanes depart from the same airport, traveling in opposite directions. After 2 hours, one airplane is $x^2 + 2x + 400$ miles from the airport, and the other airplane is $3x^2 - 50x + 100$ miles from the airport. How could you determine the distance between the two planes? Explain.

22. Write two polynomials whose sum is $3m^2 + 4m + 6$.
Possible answer: $(2m^2 + 2m + 3) + (m^2 + 2m + 3)$

23. **Choose a Strategy** What is the missing term?
$(-6x^2 + 4x - 3) + (3x^2 + \blacksquare - 5) = -3x^2 - 6x - 8$

(A) $2x$ (B) $-2x$ (C) $-10x$ (D) $10x$

24. **Write a Problem** A plane leaves an airport heading north at $x + 3$ mi/h. At the same time, another plane leaves the same airport, heading south at $x + 4$ mi/h. Write a problem using the speeds of both planes.
Possible answer: How far apart will the planes be after 3 hours? Answer: $6x + 21$ mi

25. **Write About It** Explain how to add polynomials.

26. **Challenge** What polynomial would have to be added to $6x^2 - 4x + 5$ so that the sum is $3x^2 + 4x - 7$?
$-3x^2 + 8x - 12$

 SPIRAL STANDARDS REVIEW   NS1.5, MG1.2

27. **Multiple Choice** Debbie is putting a deck of width $5w$ around her 20 foot by 80 foot pool. Which is the expression for the perimeter of the pool and deck combined?

(A) $100 + 10w$ (B) $150 + 15w$ (C) $200 + 40w$ (D) $250 + 25w$

28. **Gridded Response** What is the sum of $(-10x^3 + 4x^4 - 3x^5 - 10)$, $(9x^3 - 8x^4 + 20x^5 + 15)$, and $(x^3 + 4x^4 - 17x^5 + 2)$? 7

Find the fraction equivalent of each decimal. (Lesson 2-1)

29. 1.1 $\frac{11}{10}$ or $1\frac{1}{10}$ **30.** 0.08 $\frac{2}{25}$ **31.** 0.24 $\frac{6}{25}$ **32.** 4.05 $\frac{81}{20}$ or $4\frac{1}{20}$

Using the scale 1 in. = 6 ft, find the height or length of each object. (Lesson 5-7)

33. a 14 in. tall model of an office building   84 ft

34. a 2.5 in. long model of a train   15 ft

12-3 Lesson Quiz

Add.

1. $(2m^2 - 3m + 7) + (7m^2 - 1)$
$9m^2 - 3m + 6$

2. $(yz^2 + 5yz + 7) + (2yz^2 - yz)$
$3yz^2 + 4yz + 7$

3. $(2xy^2 + 2x - 6) + (5xy^2 + 3y + 8)$
$7xy^2 + 2x + 3y + 2$

4. $(3np^3 + 4n) + (5np^3 - n - 6) + (2n - 3)$
$8np^3 + 5n - 9$

5. The base of an isosceles triangle has length $x + 4$. The two legs of the triangle have lengths $3x + y$. Write an expression for the perimeter of the triangle.
$7x + 2y + 4$

Also available on transparency

CHALLENGE 12-3

Challenge
12-3 Perimeters

Write a polynomial for the perimeter of each figure. Simplify each polynomial.

1.
$x + 3$
$x + 7$
Perimeter: $4x + 20$

2.
$x^2 + 1$
$x + 4$
x
$x + 6$
Perimeter: $x^2 + 3x + 11$

3.
$2x^2 + 3$
Perimeter: $4x^2 + 6x + 24$
$3x + 9$

4.
$x^2 + 3$
$x^2 + x + 2$
x^2
Perimeter: $3x^2 + x + 5$

5.
x
$2x$
$2x$
Perimeter: $16x$

6.
$2x + 1.4$
$3x$
$3x$
$2x + 1.4$
Perimeter: $10x + 2.8$

PROBLEM SOLVING 12-3

Problem Solving
12-3 Adding Polynomials

Write the correct answer.

1. What is the perimeter of the quadrilateral?
$3x + 1$
$4x - 4$
$x^2 - 3$
$x^2 + 2x - 1$
$2x^2 + 9x - 7$

2. Jasmine purchased two rugs. One rug covers an area of $x^2 + 8x + 15$ and the other rug covers an area of $x^2 + 3x$. Write and simplify an expression for the combined area of the two rugs.
$2x^2 + 11x + 15$

3. Anita's school photo is 12 inches long and 8 inches wide. She will surround the photo with a mat of width w. She will surround the mat with a frame that is twice the width of the mat. Find an expression for the perimeter of the framed photo.
$24w + 40$

4. The volume of a right cylinder is given by $\pi r^2 h$. The volume of a right cone is given by $\frac{1}{3}\pi r^2 h$. Write and simplify an expression for the total volume of a right cylinder and right cone combined, if the cylinder and cone have the same radius and height. Use 3.14 for π.
about $4.19r^2 h$

Choose the letter of the correct answer.

5. Each side of a square has length $4s - 2$. Which is an expression for the perimeter of the square?
A $8s - 2$
(B) $16s - 8$
C $8s - 4$
D $16s - 4$

6. The side lengths of a certain triangle can be expressed using the following binomials: $x + 3$, $2x + 2$, and $3x - 2$. Which is an expression for the perimeter of the triangle?
F $2x + 5$
G $2x - 1$
H $3x + 5$
(J) $6x + 3$

7. What polynomial can be added to $2x^2 + 3x + 1$ to get $2x^2 + 8x$?
A $5x$
B $5x + 1$
C $5x^2 - 1$
(D) $5x - 1$

8. Which of the following sums is NOT a binomial when simplified?
(F) $(b^2 + 5b + 1) + (b^2 + 5b + 1)$
G $(b^2 + 5b + 1) + (b^2 + 5b - 1)$
H $(b^2 + 5b + 1) + (b^2 - 5b + 1)$
J $(b^2 + 5b + 1) + (-b^2 + 5b + 1)$

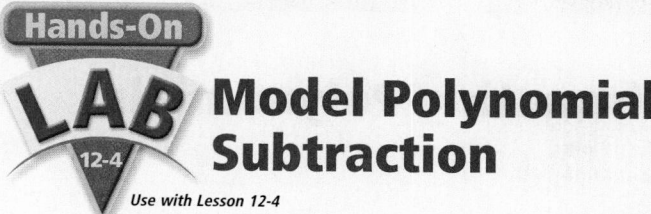

go.hrw.com
Lab Resources Online
KEYWORD: MT8CA Lab12

KEY

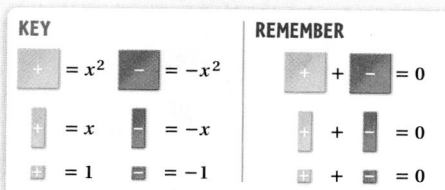

REMEMBER

California Standards

Preview of Algebra 1
🔑 **10.0 Students** add, **subtract,** multiply, and divide monomials and **polynomials.** Students solve multistep problems, including word problems, by using these techniques.

You can use algebra tiles to model polynomial subtraction.

Activity

① Use algebra tiles to find $(2x^2 - 2x + 3) - (x^2 + x - 3)$.

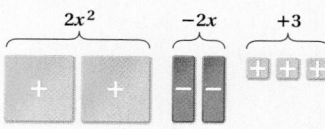

$2x^2$ $-2x$ $+3$

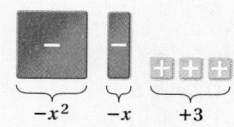

$-x^2$ $-x$ $+3$

Remember, subtracting is the same as adding the opposite. Use the opposite of each term in $x^2 + x - 3$.

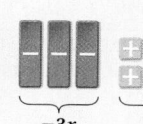

Remove any zero pairs.

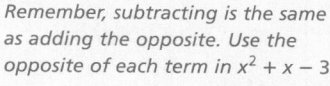

x^2 $-3x$ $+6$

The remaining tiles represent the difference $x^2 - 3x + 6$.

Think and Discuss

1. Why do you have to add the opposite when subtracting?
   Subtraction is the same as addition of the opposite.

Try This

Use algebra tiles to find each difference.

1. $(6m^2 + 2m) - (4m^2)$ $2m^2 + 2m$

2. $(-5b^2 - 9) - (b - 9)$ $-5b^2 - b$

Objective: Use algebra tiles to model polynomial subtraction.
Materials: Algebra tiles

Online Edition
Algebra Tiles

Teach
Discuss

Review the rules for subtracting integers. Remind students that only like terms can be combined.

Close
Key Concept

You can use algebra tiles to model polynomial subtraction.

Assessment

Use algebra tiles to find each difference.

1. $(6y^2 + 3y + 1) - (y^2 + y - 1)$
   $5y^2 + 2y + 2$
2. $(-4x^2 - 4) - (-x^2 + 2x)$
   $-3x^2 - 2x - 4$

California Standards
Preview of Algebra 1
🔑 **10.0**

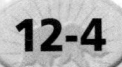

Objective: Students subtract polynomials.

 Online Edition
Tutorial Videos

Power Presentations
with PowerPoint®

Warm Up
Write the opposite of each integer.

1. 10 −10   **2.** −7 7

Subtract.

3. 19 − (−12)   **4.** −16 − 21
31   −37

Add.

5. $(3x^2 + 7) + (x^2 − 3x)$
$4x^2 − 3x + 7$

6. $(2m^2 − 3m) + (−5m^2 + 2)$
$−3m^2 − 3m + 2$

Also available on transparency

 **Math Humor**

Why was the expression $\frac{0}{3x^5}$ always cold? It was 5 degrees below zero.

California Standards

Preview of Algebra 1
 10.0

Also covered:

Grade 7 Algebra and Functions
1.3 Simplify numerical expressions by applying properties of rational numbers (e.g., identity, inverse, **distributive**, associative, **commutative**) and justify the process used.

12-4 Subtracting Polynomials

California Standards

Preview of Algebra 1
10.0 Students add, **subtract,** multiply, and divide monomials and **polynomials. Students solve multistep problems, including word problems, by using these techniques.**
Also covered: **7AF1.3**

Who uses this? Manufacturers can subtract polynomials to estimate the cost of making a product and the revenue from sales. (See Example 4.)

Recall that to subtract an integer, you add its opposite. To subtract a polynomial, you first need to find its opposite.

EXAMPLE **1** **Finding the Opposite of a Polynomial**

Find the opposite of each polynomial.

A $8x^3y^6z$
$−(8x^3y^6z)$ *The opposite of a positive term*
$−8x^3y^6z$ *is a negative term.*

B $12x^2 − 5x$
$−(12x^2 − 5x)$
$−12x^2 + 5x$ *Distributive Property*

C $−3ab^2 − 4ab + 3$
$−(−3ab^2 − 4ab + 3)$
$3ab^2 + 4ab − 3$ *Distributive Property*

To subtract a polynomial, add its opposite.

EXAMPLE **2** **Subtracting Polynomials Horizontally**

Subtract.

A $(n^3 − n + 5n^2) − (7n − 4n^2 + 9)$
$(n^3 − n + 5n^2) + (−7n + 4n^2 − 9)$ *Add the opposite.*
$n^3 + 5n^2 + 4n^2 − n − 7n − 9$ *Commutative Property*
$n^3 + 9n^2 − 8n − 9$ *Combine like terms.*

B $(−2cd^2 + cd + 4) − (−7cd^2 + 2 − 5cd)$
$(−2cd^2 + cd + 4) + (7cd^2 − 2 + 5cd)$ *Add the opposite.*
$−2cd^2 + 7cd^2 + cd + 5cd + 4 − 2$ *Commutative Property*
$5cd^2 + 6cd + 2$ *Combine like terms.*

---

1 Introduce

Alternate Opener

EXPLORATION

12-4 Subtracting Polynomials

You can use algebra tiles to find the opposite of a polynomial. To do this, replace each tile with its opposite.

The opposite of
$x^2 + 3x − 2$
is
$−x^2 − 3x + 2$.

Use algebra tiles to find the opposite of each polynomial.

1. $4x^2 − 2x − 5$
2. $−x^2 − 7x + 3$
3. $2x^2 + 3x − 3$

Think and Discuss

4. **Explain** how you can use tiles to find opposites.
5. **Discuss** how opposites of polynomials might be useful if you were subtracting polynomials.

Motivate

Ask students what steps they would take to solve the subtraction problem 8 − (−8). Possible answer: Change subtraction to addition of the opposite. Remind students that they have learned this concept before (Lesson 1-5). Explain that the same principle applies to subtraction of polynomials.

Explorations and answers are provided in *Alternate Openers: Explorations Transparencies.*

You can also subtract polynomials in a vertical format. Write the second polynomial below the first one, lining up the like terms.

EXAMPLE 3  **Subtracting Polynomials Vertically**

Subtract.

A $(x^3 + 4x + 1) - (6x^3 + 3x + 5)$

$$
\begin{array}{ll}
(x^3 + 4x + 1) & x^3 + 4x + 1 \\
- (6x^3 + 3x + 5) \longrightarrow & + -6x^3 - 3x - 5 \quad \text{Add the opposite.} \\
\hline
& -5x^3 + \ x - 4
\end{array}
$$

B $(4m^2n - 3mn - 4m) - (-8m^2n - 6mn + 3)$

$$
\begin{array}{ll}
(4m^2n - 3mn - 4m) & 4m^2n - 3mn - 4m \\
- (-8m^2n - 6mn + 3) \longrightarrow & + \ 8m^2n + 6mn \qquad - 3 \quad \text{Add the} \\
\hline
& 12m^2n + 3mn - 4m - 3 \quad \text{opposite.}
\end{array}
$$

C $(4x^2y^2 + xy - 6x) - (7x + 5xy - 6)$

$$
\begin{array}{ll}
(4x^2y^2 + \ xy - 6x) & 4x^2y^2 + \ xy - \ 6x \\
- (7x \ + 5xy - 6) \longrightarrow & + \qquad\quad - 5xy - \ 7x + 6 \quad \text{Rearrange terms} \\
\hline
& 4x^2y^2 - 4xy - 13x + 6 \quad \text{as needed.}
\end{array}
$$

EXAMPLE 4 *Business Application*

Suppose the cost in dollars of producing x model kits is given by the polynomial $3x + 400{,}000$ and the revenue generated from sales is given by the polynomial $-0.00004x^2 + 20x$. Find a polynomial expression for the profit from making and selling x model kits, and evaluate the expression for $x = 200{,}000$.

$$
\begin{array}{ll}
-0.00004x^2 + 20x - (3x + 400{,}000) & \textit{revenue} - \textit{cost} \\
-0.00004x^2 + 20x + (-3x - 400{,}00) & \textit{Add the opposite.} \\
-0.00004x^2 + 20x - 3x - 400{,}000 & \textit{Commutative Property} \\
-0.00004x^2 + 17x - 400{,}000 & \textit{Combine like terms.}
\end{array}
$$

The profit is given by the polynomial $-0.00004x^2 + 17x - 400{,}000$. For $x = 200{,}000$,

$$-0.00004(200{,}000)^2 + 17(200{,}000) - 400{,}000 = 1{,}400{,}000.$$

The profit is \$1,400,000, or \$1.4 million.

Think and Discuss

1. **Explain** how to find the opposite of a polynomial.

2. **Compare** subtracting polynomials with adding polynomials.

---

2 Teach

Guided Instruction

In this lesson, students learn to subtract polynomials. First review how to find and express the opposite of a polynomial. Emphasize the importance of distributing the opposite sign to every term in the polynomial that is being subtracted. Students can do this operation horizontally or vertically.

 **Inclusion** Discuss how distributing a negative sign results in changing the sign of every term of a polynomial.

 **Universal Access**
Through Concrete Manipulatives

Group students in pairs, and provide each pair with a set of algebra tiles (provided in the Manipulatives Kit). Have one student in each group create a polynomial, and have the other create its opposite. Then have them exchange roles and repeat the activity.

3 Close

Summarize

Remind students that to subtract a polynomial, they must add its opposite. Remind them that the opposite of a polynomial contains the opposite of every monomial in the polynomial.

Possible answers to Think and Discuss

1. Change the sign of every term in the polynomial to its opposite.

2. To subtract a polynomial, you first change the polynomial that is being subtracted to its opposite, and then you add.

Assignment Guide

If you finished Example **1** assign:
Proficient 1–6, 14–19, 36, 38–44
Advanced 14–19, 33, 36, 38–44

If you finished Example **2** assign:
Proficient 1–9, 14–22, 27, 28, 34, 36, 38–44
Advanced 14–22, 27–29, 33–36, 38–44

If you finished Example **3** assign:
Proficient 1–12, 14–25, 27–29, 34, 36, 38–44
Advanced 14–25, 27–29, 33–36, 38–44

If you finished Example **4** assign:
Proficient 1–29, 32, 34, 36–44
Advanced 14–44

Homework Quick Check

Quickly check key concepts.
Exercises: 18, 22, 24, 26

Math Background

The concept of distributing a minus sign through a polynomial can be difficult to grasp. It may be useful to insert a coefficient of 1 in front of the parentheses before distributing. The example below shows one method of finding the opposite of $4x^2 - 2x + 7$.

$$-(4x^2 - 2x + 7)$$
$$-1(4x^2 - 2x + 7)$$
$$(-1)(4x^2) + (-1)(-2x) + (-1)(7)$$
$$-4x^2 + 2x - 7$$

California Standards Practice
Preview of Algebra 1 → 10.0; → 7AF1.3

go.hrw.com
Homework Help Online
KEYWORD: MT8CA 12-4
Parent Resources Online
KEYWORD: MT8CA Parent

GUIDED PRACTICE

See Example **1** Find the opposite of each polynomial.

1. $4x^2y \quad -4x^2y$

2. $-5x + 4xy^5 \quad 5x - 4xy^5$

3. $3x^2 - 8x + 5 \quad -3x^2 + 8x - 5$

4. $-5y^2 - 2y + 4 \quad 5y^2 + 2y - 4$

5. $-8x^3 + 5x - 6 \quad 8x^3 - 5x + 6$

6. $6xy^2 + 4y + 2 \quad -6xy^2 - 4y - 2$

See Example **2** Subtract.

7. $(2b^3 + 5b^2 - 8) - (4b^3 + b - 12) \quad -2b^3 + 5b^2 - b + 4$

8. $7b - (4b^2 + 3b - 12) \quad -4b^2 + 4b + 12$

9. $(4m^2n - 7mn + 3mn^2) - (-5mn - 4m^2n) \quad 8m^2n + 3mn^2 - 2mn$

See Example **3** **10.** $(8x^2 - 4x + 1) - (5x^2 + 2x + 3) \quad 3x^2 - 6x - 2$

11. $(-2x^2y - xy + 3x - 4) - (4xy - 7x + 4) \quad -2x^2y - 5xy + 10x - 8$

12. $(-5ab^2 + 4ab - 3a^2b) - (7 - 5ab + 3ab^2 + 4a^2b) \quad -8ab^2 - 7a^2b + 9ab - 7$

See Example **4** **13.** The volume of a rectangular prism, in cubic inches, is given by the expression $x^3 + 3x^2 + 5x + 7$. The volume of a smaller rectangular prism is given by the expression $5x^3 - 6x^2 - 7x - 14$. How much greater is the volume of the larger rectangular prism? Evaluate the expression for $x = 3$.
$-4x^3 + 9x^2 + 12x + 21$ in^3; 30 in^3

INDEPENDENT PRACTICE

26. $t^3 - 3t^2 - 3t + 100$

See Example **1** Find the opposite of each polynomial.

14. $-4rn^2 \quad 4rn^2$

15. $3v - 5v^2 \quad -3v + 5v^2$

16. $4m^2 - 6m + 2 \quad -4m^2 + 6m - 2$

17. $4xy^2 + 2xy \quad -4xy^2 - 2xy$

18. $-8n^6 + 5n^3 - n \quad 8n^6 - 5n^3 + n$

19. $-9b^2 - 2b - 9 \quad 9b^2 + 2b + 9$

See Example **2** Subtract.

20. $(6w^2 + 3w + 6) - (3w^2 + 4w - 5) \quad 3w^2 - w + 11$

21. $(14a + a^2) - (8 + a^2 + 9a) \quad 5a - 8$

22. $(7r^2s^2 - 5rs^2 + 6r^2s + 7rs) - (3rs^2 - 3r^2s + 8rs) \quad 7r^2s^2 - 8rs^2 + 9r^2s - rs$

See Example **3** **23.** $(4x^2 + 6x - 1) - (3x^2 + 9x - 5) \quad x^2 - 3x + 4$

24. $(3a^2b^2 - 4ab - 2a - 4) - (4a^2b^2 + 5a - 3b + 6) \quad -a^2b^2 - 4ab - 7a + 3b - 10$

25. $(4pt^2 - 6p^3 + 5p^2t^2) - (5p^2 - 6pt^2 + 7p^2t^2) \quad -6p^3 - 5p^2 - 2p^2t^2 + 10pt^2$

See Example **4** **26.** The current in an electrical circuit at t seconds is $4t^3 - 5t^2 + 2t + 200$ amperes. The current in another electrical circuit is $3t^3 - 2t^2 + 5t + 100$ amperes. Write an expression to show the difference in the two currents.

REVIEW FOR MASTERY 12-4

LESSON **12-4** Review for Mastery
Subtracting Polynomials

When subtracting polynomials, you can distribute a factor of -1.

Subtract. $(5x^2 + 7x + 3) - (4x^2 + 3x - 5)$.

Rewrite the expression. $(5x^2 + 7x + 3) + (-1)(4x^2 + 3x - 5)$.

Apply the Distributive Property.

$-1(4x^2 + 3x - 5) = (-1 \cdot 4x^2) + (-1 \cdot 3x) + (-1 \cdot -5) = -4x^2 - 3x + 5$

Distributing the -1 changes the sign of each term.
$(5x^2 + 7x + 3) + (-4x^2 - 3x + 5)$

Use the Commutative Property to rearrange the polynomial and combine like terms.

$5x^2 - 4x^2 + 7x - 3x + 3 + 5 = x^2 + 4x + 8$

Subtract.

1. $(3b^3 + 4b^2 + 6) - (b^3 - 5b - 3)$

$3b^3 + 4b^2 + 6 + -1(b^3 - 5b - 3)$ Rewrite the expression.
$3b^3 + 4b^2 + 6 + (-b^3 + 5b + 3)$ Apply the Distributive Property.
$3b^3 + 4b^2 + 6 - b^3 + 5b + 3$ Remove the parentheses.
$\underline{2b^3 + 4b^2 + 5b + 9}$

2. $(3m^2n^2 - 4m^2n + m^2) - (m^2n^2 + 5m^2n - 5)$
$\underline{2m^2n^2 - 9m^2n + m^2 + 5}$

3. $(2x^3y^2 + x^2y - 4) - (x^2y - 8x + 3)$
$\underline{2x^3y^2 + 8x - 7}$

4. $(6y^2 + 3xy - 9x^2) - (-4y^2 + 8xy + x^2)$
$\underline{10y^2 - 5xy - 10x^2}$

PRACTICE 12-4

LESSON **12-4** Practice B
Subtracting Polynomials

Find the opposite of each polynomial.

1. $18xy^3$

$\underline{-18xy^3}$

2. $-9a + 4$

$\underline{9a - 4}$

3. $6d^2 - 2d - 8$

$\underline{-6d^2 + 2d + 8}$

Subtract.

4. $(4n^3 - 4n + 4n^2) - (6n + 3n^2 - 8)$

$\underline{4n^3 + n^2 - 10n + 8}$

5. $(-2h^4 + 3h - 4) - (2h - 3h^4 + 2)$

$\underline{h^4 + h - 6}$

6. $(6m + 2m^2 - 7) - (-6m^2 - m - 7)$

$\underline{8m^2 + 7m}$

7. $(17x^2 - x + 3) - (14x^2 + 3x + 5)$

$\underline{3x^2 - 4x - 2}$

8. $w + 7 - (3w^4 + 5w^3 - 7w^2 + 2w - 10)$

$\underline{-3w^4 - 5w^3 + 7w^2 - w + 17}$

9. $(9r^3s - 3rs + 4rs^3 + 5r^2s^2) - (2rs^2 - 2r^2s^2 + 6rs + 7r^3s - 9)$

$\underline{2r^3s + 7r^2s^2 + 4rs^3 - 2rs^2 - 9rs + 9}$

10. $(3qr^2 - 2 + 14q^2r^2 - 9qr) - (-10qr + 11 - 5qr^2 + 6q^2r^2)$

$\underline{8q^2r^2 + 8qr^2 + qr - 13}$

11. The volume of a rectangular prism, in cubic meters, is given by the expression $x^3 + 7x^2 + 14x + 8$. The volume of a smaller rectangular prism is given by the expression $x^3 + 5x^2 + 6x$. How much greater is the volume of the larger rectangular prism?

$\underline{2x^2 + 8x + 8 \text{ cubic meters}}$

12. Sarah has a table with an area, in square inches, given by the expression of $y^2 + 30y + 200$. She has a tablecloth with an area, in square inches, given by the expression of $y^2 + 18y + 80$. She wants the tablecloth to cover the top of the table. What expression represents the number of square inches of additional fabric she needs to cover the top of the table?

$\underline{12y + 120 \text{ more square inches of fabric}}$

Extra Practice
See page EP25.

Subtract.

27. $(6a + 3b - 5ab) - (6a + 5b - 7ab)$ $-2b + 2ab$

28. $(4pq^2 - 6p^2q + 3pq) - (7pq^2 + 7p^2q - 3pq)$ $-3pq^2 - 13p^2q + 6pq$

29. $(9y^2 - 5x^2y + x^2) - (3y^2 + 7x^2y - 4x^2)$
    $6y^2 - 12x^2y + 5x^2$

30. The area of the rectangle is $2a^2 - 4a + 5$ cm^2. The area of the square is $a^2 - 2a - 6$ cm^2. What is the area of the shaded region?
    $a^2 - 2a + 11$ cm^2

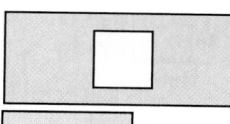

31. The area of the square is $4x^2 - 2x - 6$ in^2. The area of the triangle is $2x^2 + 4x - 5$ in^2. What is the area of the shaded region?
    $2x^2 - 6x - 1$ in^2

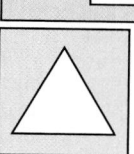

34.
Possible answer:
Find the opposite of $5x^3 - 3x - 6$, and add it to $4x^3 + 7x + 1$. The result is $-x^3 + 10x + 7$.

32. **Business** The price in dollars of one share of stock after y years is modeled by the expression $3y^3 - 6y + 4.25$. The price of one share of another stock is modeled by $3y^3 + 24y + 25.5$. What expression shows the difference in price of the two stocks after y years? $30y + 21.25$ dollars

33. **Choose a Strategy** Which polynomial has the greatest value when $x = 6$?
    Ⓐ $x^2 - 3x + 8$
    Ⓑ $2x^4 + 7x + 14$
    Ⓒ $-x^3 - 30x - 200$
    Ⓓ $x^5 - 100x^4 + 10$

34. **Write About It** Explain how to subtract the polynomial $5x^3 - 3x - 6$ from $4x^3 + 7x + 1$.

35. **Challenge** Find the values of a, b, c, and d that make the equation true.
    $(2t^3 - at^2 - 4bt - 6) - (ct^3 + 4t^2 + 7t + 1) = 4t^3 - 5t^2 - 15t + d$
    $a = 1; b = 2; c = -2; d = -7$

SPIRAL STANDARDS REVIEW

AF1.2, ➡ AF1.3, AF2.2

36. **Multiple Choice** What is the opposite of the polynomial $-4a^2b - 3ab^2 + 5ab$?
    Ⓐ $4a^2b + 3ab^2 + 5ab$
    Ⓑ $4a^2b - 3ab^2 + 5ab$
    Ⓒ $-4a^2b - 3ab^2 - 5ab$
    Ⓓ $4a^2b + 3ab^2 - 5ab$

37. **Extended Response** A square has an area of $x^2 + 10x + 25$. A triangle inside the square has an area of $x^2 - 4$. Create an expression for the area of the square minus the area of the triangle. Evaluate the expression for $x = 8$.
    $10x + 29; 109$

Multiply. (Lesson 4-4)

38. $(3x)(6x)$ $18x^2$

39. $(9m^3)(7m^2)$ $63m^5$

40. $(8ab^4)(-5a^4)$
    $-40a^5b^4$

41. $(-4r^4s)(2r^6s^9)$
    $-8r^{10}s^{10}$

Simplify. (Lesson 12-2)

42. $x^3y^2 - 2x^2y - 4x^3y^2$ $-3x^3y^2 - 2x^2y$

43. $4(zy^3 - 2zy) + 3zy - 5zy^3$ $-zy^3 - 5zy$

44. $6(3x^2 - 6x - 1)$ $18x^2 - 36x - 6$

CHALLENGE 12-4

Challenge
12-4 **Grade a Polynomial Quiz**
Check the student's quiz shown below. If an answer is wrong, write the correct answer.

Name: _Poly Nomial_   Date: _October 5, 2003_

DIRECTIONS: Find each sum. Show all your work.

1. $(2 - 3x + x^2) + (-5 + 7x - 3x^2 + x^3)$
    $x^2 - 3x + 2$
    $+ x^3 - 3x^2 + 7x - 5$
    $x^3 - 2x^2 + 10x - 3$
    $x^3 - 2x^2 + 4x - 3$

2. $(-5b^3 + 6b^2 - 1) + (4b^3 + 3b^2 + 2)$
    $-5b^3 + 6b^2 - 1$
    $+ 4b^3 + 3b^2 + 2$
    $-b^3 + 9b^2 + 1$
    Correct

3. $(3m^3 - 4m^2 - 7 + m) + (7m^2 + 4m + 3)$
    $3m^3 - 4m^2 + m - 7$
    $+ 7m^2 - 4m + 3$
    $3m^3 + 3m^2 - 3m - 4$
    Correct

4. $(-8t + 6t^3 - 1 + 4t^2) + (t^3 - 6t^2 + t - 1)$
    $6t^3 + 4t^2 - 8t - 1$
    $+ t^3 - 6t^2 + t - 1$
    $7t^3 - 2t^2 + 7t - 2$
    $7t^3 - 2t^2 - 7t^2 - 2$

DIRECTIONS: Find each difference. Show all your work.

5. $(7 + p - 5p^3 + 2p^2) - (-5p^3 + 3p - 7)$
    $-5p^3 + 2p^2 + p + 7$
    $-5p^3 + 3p - 7$
    $-10p^3 + 2p^2 + 4p$
    $2p^2 - 2p + 14$

6. $(-a^3 + 3a^2 - 4 + 2a) - (3a^3 + a^2 + 2)$
    $-a^3 + 3a^2 + 2a - 4$
    $-3a^3 - a^2 - 2$
    $-4a^3 + 2a^2 + 2a - 6$
    Correct

7. $(-4h^4 + h^2 - 9h + h^3) - (4h^2 - 3h^4 - 9h)$
    $4h^4 + h^3 + h^2 - 9h$
    $-3h^4 + 4h^2 - 9h$
    $h^4 + h^3 + 5h^2 - 18h$
    $-h^4 + h^3 - 3h^2$

8. $(-8k + 3k^3 - 6 + k^2) - (5k^3 - k^2 + k^4 - 8)$
    $3k^3 + k^2 - 8k - 6$
    $-5k^3 + k^2 - k - 8$
    $-3k^3 + 2k^2 - 9k - 14$
    $-k^4 - 2k^3 + 2k^2 - 8k + 2$

PROBLEM SOLVING 12-4

Problem Solving
12-4 **Subtracting Polynomials**
Write the correct answer.

1. Molly made a frame for a painting. She cut a rectangle with an area of $x^2 + 3x$ square inches from a piece of wood that had an area of $2x^2 + 9x + 10$ square inches. Write an expression for the area of the remaining frame.
    $x^2 + 6x + 10$

2. The volume of a rectangular prism, in cubic inches, is given by the expression $2t^3 + 7t^2 + 3t$. The volume of a smaller rectangular prism is given by the expression $t^3 + 2t^2 + t$. How much greater is the volume of the larger rectangular prism?
    $t^3 + 5t^2 + 2t$

3. The area of a square piece of cardboard is $4y^2 - 16y + 16$ square feet. A piece of the cardboard with an area of $2y^2 + 2y - 12$ square feet is cut out. Write an expression to show the area of the cardboard that is left.
    $2y^2 - 18y + 28$

4. A container is filled with $3a^3 + 10a^2 - 8a$ gallons of water. Then $2a^3 - 3a^2 - 3a + 2$ gallons of water are poured out. How much water is left in the container?
    $a^3 + 13a^2 - 5a - 2$ gallons

Circle the letter of the correct answer.

5. The perimeter of a rectangle is $4x^2 + 2x - 2$ meters. Its length is $x^2 + x - 2$ meters. What is the width of the rectangle?
    A $3x^2 + x + 2$ meters
    B $2x^2 + 2$ meters
    Ⓒ $x^2 + 1$ meters
    D $\frac{3}{2}x - \frac{1}{2}x + 1$ meters

6. On a map, points A, B, and C lie in a straight line. Point A is $x^2 + 2xy + 5y$ miles from Point B. Point C is $3x^2 - 5xy + 2y$ miles from Point A. How far is Point B from Point C?
    $x^2 + 2xy + 5y$ miles

    A────────B────────C
         $3x^2 - 5xy + 2y$ miles

    F $-2x^2 + 7 + 3y$ miles
    G $4x^2 - 3xy + 7y$ miles
    H $-4x^2 + 3xy - 7y$ miles
    Ⓙ $2x^2 - 7xy - 3y$ miles

Teaching Tip **Multiple Choice For Exercise 36,** remind students that the opposite of a positive number is a negative number and the opposite of a negative number is a positive number. Also, remind them that when finding the opposite of a polynomial, they must find the opposite of each term, not just the first term.

 Journal

Ask students to consider whether the difference of two polynomials can be zero. Ask them to explain their answer and give an example.

Power Presentations
with PowerPoint®

 12-4
Lesson Quiz

Find the opposite of each polynomial.

1. $3a^2b^2c^3$
   $-3a^2b^2c^3$

2. $-3m^3 + 2m^2n$
   $3m^3 - 2m^2n$

Subtract.

3. $(3z^2 - 7z + 6) - (2z^2 + z - 12)$
   $z^2 - 8z + 18$

4. $-18h^3 - (4h^3 + h^2 - 12h + 2)$
   $-22h^3 - h^2 + 12h - 2$

5. $(3b^2c + 5bc^2 - 8b^2) - (4b^2c + 2bc^2 - c^2)$
   $-b^2c + 3bc^2 - 8b^2 + c^2$

Also available on transparency

Objective: Students multiply polynomials by monomials.

PREMIER **Online Edition**
Tutorial Videos

Power Presentations
with PowerPoint®

Warm Up

Multiply. Write each product as one power.

1. $x \cdot x$ x^2 **2.** $6^2 \cdot 6^3$ 6^5

3. $k^2 \cdot k^8$ k^{10} **4.** $19^5 \cdot 19^2$ 19^7

5. $m \cdot m^5$ m^6 **6.** $26^6 \cdot 26^5$ 26^{11}

7. Find the volume of a rectangular prism that measures 5 cm by 2 cm by 6 cm. **60 cm³**

Also available on transparency

Math Humor

Why did the binomial get mad when the mathematician added the term $4x^3$? It didn't like being given the third degree.

California Standards

Preview of Algebra 1
🔑 **10.0**

Also covered:

Grade 7 Algebra and Functions

1.2 Use the correct order of operations to evaluate algebraic expressions such as $3(2x + 5)^2$.

🔑 **1.3** Simplify numerical expressions by applying properties of rational numbers (e.g., identity, inverse, **distributive**, associative, **commutative**) and justify the process used.

2.2 Multiply and divide monomials; extend the process of taking powers and extracting roots **to monomials** when the latter results in a monomial with an integer exponent.

 **12-5** **Multiplying Polynomials by Monomials**

California Standards

Preview of Algebra 1
🔑 **10.0** Students add, subtract, **multiply**, and divide **monomials and polynomials. Students solve multistep problems, including word problems, by using these techniques.**
Also covered: **7AF1.2,**
🔑 **7AF1.3, 7AF2.2**

Why learn this? You can multiply polynomials and monomials to determine the dimensions of a planter box. (See Example 3.)

Remember that when you multiply two powers with the same bases, you add the exponents. To multiply two monomials, multiply the coefficients and add the exponents of the variables that are the same.

$$(5m^2n^3)(6m^3n^6) = 5 \cdot 6 \cdot m^{2+3}n^{3+6} = 30m^5n^9$$

EXAMPLE 1 **Multiplying Monomials**

Multiply.

A $(4r^3s^4)(6r^5s^6)$

$4 \cdot 6 \cdot r^{3+5} \cdot s^{4+6}$ *Multiply coefficients. Add exponents that*
$24r^8s^{10}$ *have the same base.*

B $(9x^2y)(-2x^3yz^6)$

$9 \cdot -2 \cdot x^{2+3} \cdot y^{1+1} \cdot z^6$ *Multiply coefficients. Add exponents that*
$-18x^5y^2z^6$ *have the same base.*

To multiply a polynomial by a monomial, use the Distributive Property. Multiply every term of the polynomial by the monomial.

EXAMPLE 2 **Multiplying a Polynomial by a Monomial**

Multiply.

A $\frac{1}{4}x(y + z)$

$\frac{1}{4}x(y + z)$ *Multiply each term in the parentheses by $\frac{1}{4}x$.*
$\frac{1}{4}xy + \frac{1}{4}xz$

Helpful Hint

When multiplying a polynomial by a negative monomial, be sure to distribute the negative sign.

B $-5a^2b(3a^4b^3 + 6a^2b^3)$

$-5a^2b(3a^4b^3 + 6a^2b^3)$ *Multiply each term in the parentheses*
$-15a^6b^4 - 30a^4b^4$ *by $-5a^2b$.*

---

1 **Introduce**
Alternate Opener

EXPLORATION

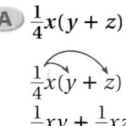 **12-5** **Multiplying Polynomials by Monomials**

You can use algebra tiles to model multiplication. The model shows that $2(-3) = -6$.

Find each product.

1. $2(2x - 3)$ **2.** $x(2x - 3)$

Use algebra tiles to model and find each product.

3. $2(3x + 2)$ **4.** $2x(3x - 1)$

Think and Discuss

5. Explain how area applies to modeling multiplication.
6. Write the factors and product modeled by the tiles shown.

Motivate

Ask students to add the following polynomials:

$$2x^2 + 3x - 6$$
$$2x^2 + 3x - 6$$
$$2x^2 + 3x - 6$$
$$\underline{+\ 2x^2 + 3x - 6}$$

The sum is $8x^2 + 12x - 24$. Ask students whether they can tell you another way to find the answer. Multiply $4(2x^2 + 3x - 6)$.

Explorations and answers are provided in *Alternate Openers: Explorations Transparencies.*

Multiply.

C $5rs^2(r^2s^4 + 3rs^3 - 4rst)$

$5rs^2(r^2s^4 + 3rs^3 - 4rst)$
$5r^3s^6 + 15r^2s^5 - 20r^2s^3t$

Multiply each term in the parentheses by $5rs^2$.

EXAMPLE **3** **PROBLEM SOLVING APPLICATION**

Chrystelle is making a planter box with a square base. She wants the height of the box to be 3 inches more than the side length of the base. If she wants the volume of the box to be 6804 in³, what should the side length of the base be?

 Reasoning

1 **Understand the Problem**

If the side length of the base is s, then the height is $s + 3$. The volume is $s \cdot s \cdot (s + 3) = s^2(s + 3)$. The **answer** will be a value of s that makes the volume of the box equal to 6804 in³.

2 **Make a Plan**

You can make a table of values for the polynomial to try to find the value of s. Use the Distributive Property to write the expression $s^2(s + 3)$ another way. Use substitution to complete the table.

3 **Solve**

$s^2(s + 3) = s^3 + 3s^2$ *Distributive Property*

s	15	16	17	18
$s^3 + 3s^2$	$15^3 + 3(15)^2$ $= 4050$	$16^3 + 3(16)^2$ $= 4864$	$17^3 + 3(17)^2$ $= 5780$	$18^3 + 3(18)^2$ $= 6804$

The side length of the base should be 18 inches.

4 **Look Back**

If the side length of the base were 18 inches and the height were 3 inches more, or 21 inches, then the volume would be $18 \cdot 18 \cdot 21 = 6804$ in³. The answer is reasonable.

Think and Discuss

1. **Compare** multiplying two monomials with multiplying a polynomial by a monomial.

Power Presentations with PowerPoint®

Additional Examples

Example **1**

Multiply.

A. $(2x^3y^2)(6x^5y^3)$ ⟶ $12x^8y^5$

B. $(9a^5b^7)(-2a^4b^3)$ ⟶ $-18a^9b^{10}$

Example **2**

Multiply.

A. $3m(5m^2 + 2m)$
$15m^3 + 6m^2$

B. $-6x^2y^3(5xy^4 + 3x^4)$
$-30x^3y^7 - 18x^6y^3$

C. $-5y^3(y^2 + 6y - 8)$
$-5y^5 - 30y^4 + 40y^3$

Example **3**

The length of a picture in a frame is 8 in. less than three times its width. Find the length and the width if the area is 60 in². $\ell = 10$ in.; $w = 6$ in.

Also available on transparency

Possible answers to Think and Discuss

1. To multiply two monomials, multiply the coefficients and add exponents of powers with the same bases. To multiply a polynomial by a monomial, apply the Distributive Property and multiply the resulting monomials.

---

2 **Teach**

Guided Instruction

In this lesson, students learn to multiply polynomials by monomials. Review the rules for multiplying powers (Lesson 4-3). Show students how to multiply monomials by multiplying coefficients and adding the exponents of powers with the same bases. Then show them how to use the Distributive Property to multiply a polynomial by a monomial.

 **Inclusion** Remind students to pay attention to the sign of each term when they multiply.

 Universal Access
Through Cooperative Learning

Divide students into groups of three and have them each write a monomial on an index card. Have two students in each group add their expressions to create a binomial. (If they happen to have like terms, they can create a monomial.) Then have the group multiply the binomial (or monomial) by the remaining monomial. Repeat with each of the other two pairs in each group.

3 **Close**

Summarize

Remind students that the Distributive Property can be used to multiply a polynomial by a monomial. Explain that the Distributive Property works for numbers, expressions, and polynomials. Ask students how many terms result from multiplying a polynomial by a monomial.

Possible answer: The number of terms in the resulting polynomial is the same as in the original polynomial.

12-5 Exercises

Assignment Guide

If you finished Example **1** assign:
Proficient 1–6, 12–17, 25–27, 44–48
Advanced 12–17, 25–27, 44–48

If you finished Example **2** assign:
Proficient 1–10, 12–23, 25–34, 44–48
Advanced 12–23, 25–36, 40, 44–48

If you finished Example **3** assign:
Proficient 1–34, 37, 42–48
Advanced 12–24, 29–48

Homework Quick Check

Quickly check key concepts.
Exercises: 12, 16, 20, 24

Math Background

Factoring the greatest common divisor from a polynomial is an important algebraic skill that is essentially the opposite of multiplying a polynomial by a monomial. Understanding how to multiply polynomials is a prerequisite for factoring. When you factor the GCD from a polynomial, you divide out the greatest monomial divisor that is common to all terms. Then you write the new expression as a monomial times a polynomial. For example, the greatest common divisor of the polynomial $4x^4 + 6x^3 + 8x^2$ is $2x^2$. Factoring the polynomial yields $2x^2(2x^2 + 3x + 4)$.

GUIDED PRACTICE

See Example **1** Multiply.

6. $130g^{10}h^5$

1. $(-5s^2t^2)(3st^3)$ $-15s^3t^5$
2. $(x^2y^3)(6x^4y^3)$ $6x^6y^6$
3. $(5h^2j^4)(-7h^4j^6)$ $-35h^6j^{10}$

4. $6m(4m^5)$ $24m^6$
5. $7p^3r(5pr^4)$ $35p^4r^5$
6. $13g^5h^3(10g^5h^2)$

See Example **2**
7. $2h(3m - 4h)$ $6hm - 8h^2$
8. $4ab(a^2b - ab^2)$ $4a^3b^2 - 4a^2b^3$

9. $-3x(x^2 - 5x + 10)$ $-3x^3 + 15x^2 - 30x$
10. $6c^2d(3cd^3 - 5c^3d^2 + 4cd)$ $18c^3d^4 - 30c^5d^3 + 24c^3d^2$

See Example **3**
11. The formula for the area of a trapezoid is $A = \frac{1}{2}h(b_1 + b_2)$, where h is the trapezoid's height and b_1 and b_2 are the lengths of its bases. Use the Distributive Property to simplify the expression. Then use the expression to find the area of a trapezoid with height 12 in. and base lengths 9 in. and 7 in.
$A = \frac{1}{2}b_1h + \frac{1}{2}b_2h$; 96 in^2

INDEPENDENT PRACTICE

See Example **1** Multiply.

21. $-6c^4d^3 + 12c^2d^3$

12. $(6x^2y^5)(-3xy^4)$ $-18x^3y^9$
13. $(-gh^3)(-2g^2h^5)$ $2g^3h^8$
14. $(4a^2b)(2b^3)$ $8a^2b^4$

15. $(-s^4t^3)(2st)$ $-2s^5t^4$
16. $12x^9y^7\left(\frac{1}{2}x^3y\right)$ $6x^{12}y^8$
17. $2.5j^3(3h^5j^7)$ $7.5h^5j^{10}$

See Example **2**
18. $(3m^3n^4)(1 - 5mn^5)$ $3m^3n^4 - 15m^4n^9$
19. $3z(5z^2 - 4z)$ $15z^3 - 12z^2$

20. $-3h^2(6h + 3h^3)$ $-18h^3 - 9h^5$
21. $-3cd(2c^3d^2 - 4cd^2)$

22. $-2b(4b^4 - 7b + 10)$ $-8b^5 + 14b^2 - 20b$
23. $-3s^2t^2(4s^2t + 5st - 2s^2t^2)$ $-12s^4t^3 - 15s^3t^3 + 6s^4t^4$

See Example **3**
24. A rectangle has a base of length $3x^2y$ and a height of $2x^3 - 4xy - 3$. Write and simplify an expression for the area of the rectangle. Then find the area of the rectangle if $x = 2$ and $y = 1$.
$6x^5y - 12x^3y^2 - 9x^2y$; 60 units^2

PRACTICE AND PROBLEM SOLVING

Extra Practice
See page EP25.

Multiply.

25. $(-3b^2)(8b^4)$ $-24b^6$
26. $(4m^2n)(2mn^4)$ $8m^3n^5$

27. $(-2a^2b^2)(-3ab^4)$ $6a^3b^6$
28. $7g(g - 5)$ $7g^2 - 35g$

29. $-3m^2(m^3 - 5m)$ $-3m^5 + 15m^3$
30. $2ab(3a^2b + 3ab^2)$ $6a^3b^2 + 6a^2b^3$

31. $x^4(x - x^3y^5)$ $x^5 - x^7y^5$
32. $m(x + 3)$ $mx + 3m$

33. $f^2g^2(3 + f - g^3)$ $3f^2g^2 + f^3g^2 - f^2g^5$
34. $x^2(x^2 - 4x + 9)$ $x^4 - 4x^3 + 9x^2$

35. $(4m^2p^4)(5m^2p^4 - 3mp^3 + 6m^2p)$ $20m^4p^8 - 12m^3p^7 + 24m^4p^5$
36. $-3wz(5w^4z^2 + 4wz^2 - 6w^2z^2)$ $-15w^5z^3 - 12w^2z^3 + 18w^3z^3$

37. Felix is building a cylindrical-shaped storage container. The height of the container is $x^3 - y^3$. Write and simplify an expression for the volume using the formula $V = \pi r^2h$. Then find the volume with $r = 1\frac{1}{2}$ feet, $x = 3$, and $y = -1$. $V = \pi r^2 x^3 - \pi r^2 y^3$; 63π

REVIEW FOR MASTERY 12-5

LESSON 12-5 Review for Mastery
Multiplying Polynomials by Monomials

To multiply a monomial by a monomial, follow the steps used in the example below.

$(7x^2y^3)(3xy^4)$

1. Multiply the coefficients.
$(7)(3) = 21$

2. Multiply the variables.
To multiply two powers with the same base, you keep the base and **add** the exponents.
$(x^2)(x) = (x^2)(x^1) = x^3$ $(y^3)(y^4) = y^7$

Remember: If a variable has no exponent, the exponent is 1.
$x = x^1$

3. Write the monomial product.
$21x^3y^7$

Multiply.

1. $(3x^2)(4x^3y^2)$ 2. $(6a^3b)(2a^3b^4)$ 3. $(2m^4n^2)(-5m^2n^2)$
   $12x^5y^2$ $12a^6b^5$ $-10m^6n^4$

To multiply a polynomial by a monomial, multiply each term of the polynomial by the monomial.

   $4a^2 + 2ab + 6b^2$
$\times$ $3a^3$
$12a^5 + 6a^4b + 18a^3b^2$

Multiply.

4. $3r^2s^3 - 2r^2 + 10$ 5. $5x^5 + x^2 - 3x$
$\times$ $2s$ $\times$ $4x^3$
$6r^2s^4 - 4r^2s + 20s$ $20x^8 + 4x^5 - 12x^4$

6. $m^2n - 3mn^2 - 8n^3$
$\times$ $-3mn$
$-3m^3n^2 + 9m^2n^3 + 24mn^4$

PRACTICE 12-5

LESSON 12-5 Practice B
Multiplying Polynomials by Monomials

Multiply.

1. $(x^2)(-3x^2y^3)$ 2. $(-9pr^4)(p^2r^2)$
   $-3x^4y^3$ $-9p^3r^6$

3. $(2st^9)(-st^2)$ 4. $(3efg^2)(-3e^2f^2g)$
   $-2s^2t^{11}$ $-9e^3f^3g^3$

5. $2q(4q^2 - 2)$ 6. $-x(x^2 + 2)$
   $8q^3 - 4q$ $-x^3 - 2x$

7. $5m(-3m^2 + 2m)$ 8. $6x(-x^5 + 2x^3 + x)$
   $-15m^3 + 10m^2$ $-6x^6 + 12x^4 + 6x^2$

9. $-4st(st - 12t - 2s)$ 10. $-9ab(a^2 + 2ab - b^2)$
   $-4s^2t^2 + 48st^2 + 8s^2t$ $-9a^3b - 18a^2b^2 + 9ab^3$

11. $-7v^2w^2(vw^2 + 2vw + 1)$ 12. $8p^4(p^2 - 8p + 17)$
   $-7v^3w^4 - 14v^3w^3 - 7v^2w^2$ $8p^6 - 64p^5 + 136p^4$

13. $4x(-x^2 - 2xy + 3)$ 14. $7x^2(3x^2y + 7x^2 - 2x)$
   $-4x^3 - 8x^2y + 12x$ $21x^4y + 49x^4 - 14x^3$

15. $-4t^3r^2(3t^2r - t^5r - 6t^2r^2)$ 16. $h^2k(2hk^2 - hk + 7k)$
   $-12t^5r^3 + 4t^8r^3 + 24t^5r^4$ $2h^3k^3 - h^3k^2 + 7h^2k^2$

17. A triangle has a base of $4x^2$ and a height of $6x + 3$. Write and simplify an expression for the area of the triangle.
   $12x^3 + 6x^2$

38. Health The table gives some formulas for finding the target heart rate for a person of age a exercising at p percent of his or her maximum heart rate.

Target Heart Rate	Male	Female
Nonathletic	$p(220 - a)$	$p(226 - a)$
Fit	$\frac{1}{2}p(410 - a)$	$\frac{1}{2}p(422 - a)$

   a. Use the Distributive Property to simplify each expression.

   b. Use your answer from part **a** to write an expression for the difference between the target heart rate for a fit male and for a fit female. Both people are age a and are exercising at p percent of their maximum heart rates. $-6p$

 39. What's the Question? A square prism has a base area of x^2 and a height of $3x + 4$. If the answer is $3x^3 + 4x^2$, what is the question? If the answer is $14x^2 + 16x$, what is the question? **Possible answers: What is the volume of the prism? What is the surface area of the prism?**

 40. Write About It If a polynomial is multiplied by a monomial, what can you say about the number of terms in the answer? What can you say about the degree of the answer?

40. The number of terms in the answer is the same as the number of terms in the polynomial. The degree of the answer is the degree of the polynomial plus the degree of the monomial.

 41. Challenge On a multiple-choice test, if the probability of guessing each question correctly is p, then the probability of guessing two or more correctly out of four is $6p^2(1 - 2p - p^2) + 4p^3(1 - p) + p^4$. Simplify the expression. Then write an expression for the probability of guessing fewer than two out of four correctly. $6p^2 - 8p^3 - 9p^4$; $1 - 6p^2 + 8p^3 + 9p^4$

 SPIRAL STANDARDS REVIEW   AF1.3, MG2.1

42. Multiple Choice The width of a rectangle is 13 feet less than twice its length. Which of the following shows an expression for the area of the rectangle?

   Ⓐ $2\ell^2 - 13\ell$ Ⓑ $2\ell^2 - 13$ Ⓒ $2\ell - 13\ell$ Ⓓ $6\ell - 26$

43. Short Response A triangle has base $10cd^2$ and height $3c^2d^2 - 4cd^2$. Write and simplify an expression for the area of the triangle. Then evaluate the expression for $c = 2$ and $d = 3$. $15c^3d^4 - 20c^2d^4$; 3,240 square units

Combine like terms. (Lesson 3-2)

44. $8x + 3y + x + 7$ $9x + 3y + 7$ **45.** $4m - n + 7 - 2n - 5$ **46.** $9a - 11 + 6b - 10a - 7b$
                                               $4m - 3n + 2$ $-a - b - 11$

Find the surface area of each figure. Use 3.14 for π. (Lesson 10-4)

47. a rectangular prism with base 4 in. by 3 in. and height 2.5 in.   59 in^2

48. a cylinder with radius 10 cm and height 7 cm   1067.6 cm^2

CHALLENGE 12-5

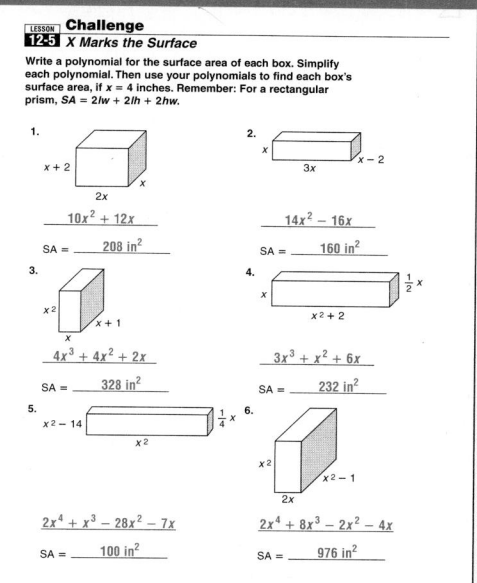

PROBLEM SOLVING 12-5

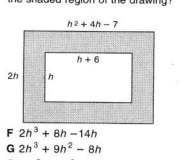

Answers

38. a.

	Male	Female
Nonathletic	$220p - pa$	$226p - pa$
Fit	$205p - \frac{1}{2}pa$	$211p - \frac{1}{2}pa$

Teaching Tip   **Multiple Choice** For **Exercise 42,** if students select **B** or **C,** they did not use the Distributive Property correctly. If they select **D,** they multiplied the width by 2 instead of by ℓ.

 **Journal**

Ask students to explain how multiplying 321 by 3 is similar to multiplying a polynomial by a monomial.

Power Presentations with PowerPoint®

✓ **12-5 Lesson Quiz**

Multiply.

1. $(3a^2b)(2ab^2)$ $6a^3b^3$

2. $(4x^2y^2z)(-5xy^3z^2)$ $-20x^3y^5z^3$

3. $3n(2n^3 - 3n)$ $6n^4 - 9n^2$

4. $-5p^2(3q - 6p)$ $-15p^2q + 30p^3$

5. $-2xy(2x^2 + 2y^2 - 2)$
                 $-4x^3y - 4xy^3 + 4xy$

6. The width of a garden is 5 feet less than 2 times its length. Find the garden's length and width if its area is 63 ft^2. $\ell = 7$ ft, $w = 9$ ft

Also available on transparency

Objective: Use algebra tiles to model multiplying binomials.

Materials: Algebra tiles

Online Edition
Algebra Tiles

Teach

Discuss

Discuss with students what each algebra tile represents and how to model the product of two binomials.

Close

Key Concept

You can use algebra tiles to model multiplying binomials.

Assessment

Use algebra tiles to model each product.

1. $(x + 2)(x - 4)$

2. $(2x - 1)(x + 3)$

Hands-On LAB 12-6

Multiply Binomials

Use with Lesson 12-6

go.hrw.com
Lab Resources Online
KEYWORD: MT8CA Lab12

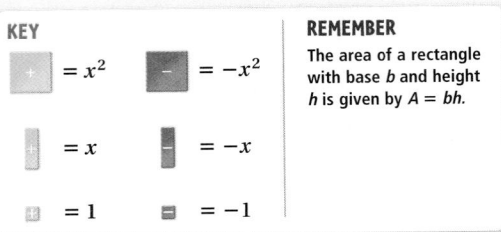

KEY

$\boxed{+} = x^2$ $\boxed{-} = -x^2$

$\boxed{+} = x$ $\boxed{-} = -x$

$\boxed{+} = 1$ $\boxed{-} = -1$

REMEMBER
The area of a rectangle with base b and height h is given by $A = bh$.

California Standards

Preview of Algebra 1
🔑 **10.0 Students** add, subtract, **multiply**, and divide monomials and **polynomials**. Students solve multistep problems, including word problems, by using these techniques.

You can use algebra tiles to find the product of two binomials.

Activity 1

1 To model $(x + 3)(2x + 1)$ with algebra tiles, make a rectangle with base $x + 3$ and height $2x + 1$.

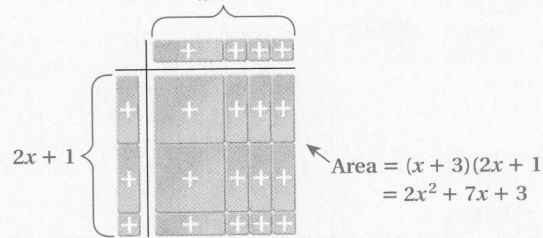

Area $= (x + 3)(2x + 1)$
$= 2x^2 + 7x + 3$

2 Use algebra tiles to find $(x - 2)(-x + 1)$.

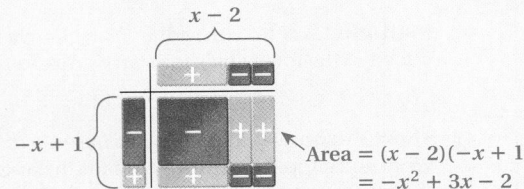

Area $= (x - 2)(-x + 1)$
$= -x^2 + 3x - 2$

Think and Discuss

1. Explain how to determine the signs of each term in the product when you are multiplying $(x - 3)(x - 2)$.

2. How can you use algebra tiles to find $(x + 3)(x - 3)$?

The product of two negatives or two positives is positive, so the x^2 and constant terms are positive. The product of a positive and a negative is negative, so the x-terms are negative.

Possible Answers to *Think and Discuss*

2. Make a rectangle with base $x + 3$ and height $x - 3$. The product has one yellow x^2-tile, 3 red x-tiles, 3 yellow x-tiles, and 9 red unit tiles. The 3 red and 3 yellow x-tiles form 3 zero pairs. The product is $x^2 - 9$.

2.

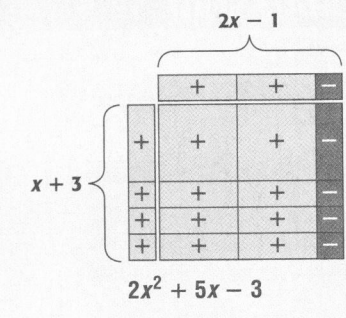

$2x^2 + 5x - 3$

Answers to Assessment

1.

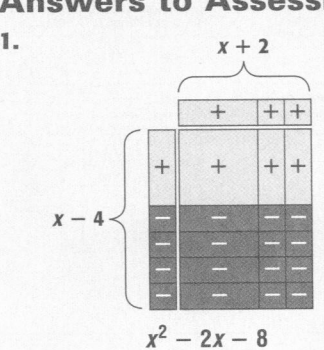

$x^2 - 2x - 8$

Use algebra tiles to find each product.

1. $(x + 4)(x - 4)$ **2.** $(x - 3)(x + 2)$ **3.** $(x - 5)(-x + 3)$

Activity 2

Write two binomials whose product is modeled by the algebra tiles below, and then write the product as a polynomial expression.

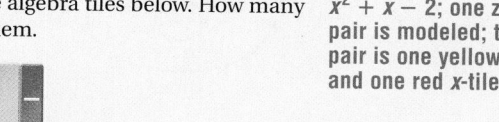

The base of the rectangle is $x - 5$ and the height is $x - 2$, so the binomial product is $(x - 5)(x - 2)$.

The model shows one x^2-tile, seven $-x$-tiles, and ten 1-tiles, so the polynomial expression is $x^2 - 7x + 10$.

Think and Discuss

1. Write an expression modeled by the algebra tiles below. How many zero pairs are modeled? Describe them.

$x^2 + x - 2$; one zero pair is modeled; the pair is one yellow x-tile and one red x-tile.

Try This

Write two binomials whose product is modeled by each set of algebra tiles below, and then write the product as a polynomial expression.

1.

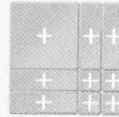

$(x + 2)(x + 2)$;
$x^2 + 4x + 4$

2.

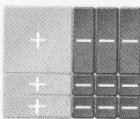

$(x + 2)(x - 3)$;
$x^2 - x - 6$

3.

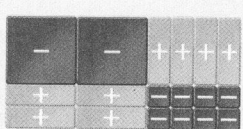

$(-2x + 4)(x - 2)$;
$-2x^2 + 8x - 8$

Activity 1

Answers to Try This

1.

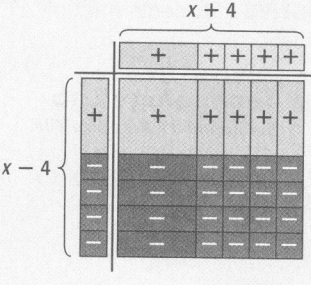

$(x + 4)(x - 4) = x^2 - 16$

2.

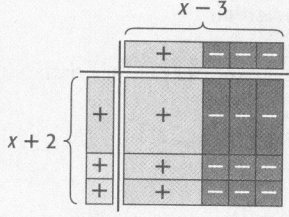

$(x - 3)(x + 2) = x^2 - x - 6$

3.

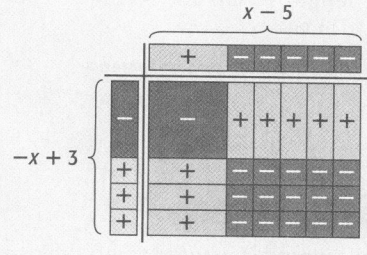

$(x - 5)(-x + 3) =$
$-x^2 + 8x - 15$

Power Presentations
with PowerPoint®

Warm Up

Multiply.

1. $x(x + 2)$ $x^2 + 2x$
2. $-3(p - 4)$ $-3p + 12$
3. $2x(3x - 7)$ $6x^2 - 14x$
4. Find the area of a rectangle with length 16 cm and width 21 cm.
   336 cm^2

Also available on transparency

Math Humor

Two binomials wanted to go their separate ways. What did they say when they were multiplied together? "Drats! Foiled again!"

12-6 Multiplying Binomials

California Standards

Preview of Algebra 1
🔑 **10.0** Students add, subtract, **multiply**, and divide monomials and polynomials. Students solve multistep problems, including word problems, by using these techniques.

Vocabulary
FOIL

Why learn this? You can multiply binomials to determine the area of a walkway around a cactus garden. (See Example 2.)

You can use the Distributive Property to multiply two binomials.

$$(x + y)(x + z) = x(x + z) + y(x + z)$$
$$= x^2 + xz + yx + yz$$

The product can be simplified using the FOIL method: multiply the First terms, the Outer terms, the Inner terms, and the Last terms of the binomials.

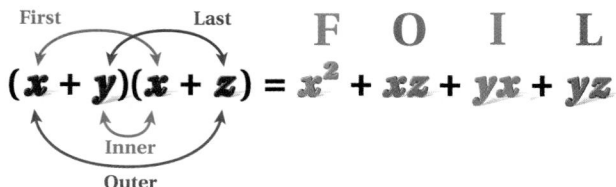

First   Last

$$(\boldsymbol{x} + \boldsymbol{y})(\boldsymbol{x} + \boldsymbol{z}) = \boldsymbol{x}^2 + \boldsymbol{xz} + \boldsymbol{yx} + \boldsymbol{yz}$$

Inner

Outer

EXAMPLE 1   Multiplying Two Binomials

Multiply.

Helpful Hint

When you multiply two binomials, you will get four products. Then combine like terms.

A $(p + 2)(3 - q)$

$(p + 2)(3 - q)$ *FOIL*

$3p - pq + 6 - 2q$

B $(m + n)(p + q)$

$(m + n)(p + q)$

$mp + mq + np + nq$

C $(x + 2)(x + 5)$

$(x + 2)(x + 5)$ *FOIL*

$x^2 + 5x + 2x + 10$
$x^2 + 7x + 10$ *Combine like terms.*

D $(3m + n)(m - 2n)$

$(3m + n)(m - 2n)$

$3m^2 - 6mn + mn - 2n^2$
$3m^2 - 5mn - 2n^2$

---

1 Introduce

Alternate Opener

EXPLORATION

12-6 Multiplying Binomials

You can use algebra tiles to model multiplication of binomials. The model shows the product of $(x + 2)(x + 4)$.

1. Use the model to find the product of $(x + 2)(x + 4)$.

Use a graphing calculator to check your answer. Enter $(x + 2)(x + 4)$ for **Y1** and your answer for **Y2**, and compare tables.

Use algebra tiles to model and find each product. Check your answers with a graphing calculator.

2. $(x + 2)(x + 1)$ 3. $(x + 2)(x + 3)$

Think and Discuss

4. Write the factors and product modeled by the tiles shown.

Motivate

Ask students to multiply 42 by 25. 1050 Show them that the numbers can also be multiplied by using the Distributive Property as shown below.

$$(42)(25)$$
$$(40 + 2)(20 + 5)$$
$$(40)(20 + 5) + (2)(20 + 5)$$
$$(40)(20) + (40)(5) + (2)(20) + (2)(5)$$
$$800 + 200 + 40 + 10$$
$$1050$$

Explorations and answers are provided in *Alternate Openers: Explorations Transparencies.*

California Standards

Preview of Algebra 1
🔑 **10.0**

EXAMPLE 2 Landscaping Application

Find the area of a bark walkway of width x ft around a 12 ft by 5 ft cactus garden.

$$
\begin{aligned}
\text{Area of Walkway} &= \text{Total Area} - \text{Area of Flower Bed}\\
&= (5 + 2x)(12 + 2x) - (5)(12)\\
&= 60 + 10x + 24x + 4x^2 - 60\\
&= 34x + 4x^2
\end{aligned}
$$

The walkway area is $4x^2 + 34x$ ft^2.

Binomial products of the form $(a + b)^2$, $(a - b)^2$, and $(a + b)(a - b)$ are often called *special products*.

EXAMPLE 3 Special Products of Binomials

Multiply.

A $(x - 3)^2$

$(x - 3)(x - 3)$

$x^2 - 3x - 3x + 3^2$

$x^2 - 6x + 9$

B $(a + b)^2$

$(a + b)(a + b)$

$a^2 + ab + ab + b^2$

$a^2 + 2ab + b^2$

C $(n + 3)(n - 3)$

$(n + 3)(n - 3)$

$n^2 - 3n + 3n - 3^2$

$n^2 - 9$ $-3n + 3n = 0$

Special Products of Binomials

$(a + b)^2 = a^2 + ab + ab + b^2 = a^2 + 2ab + b^2$

$(a - b)^2 = a^2 - ab - ab + b^2 = a^2 - 2ab + b^2$

$(a + b)(a - b) = a^2 - ab + ab - b^2 = a^2 - b^2$

Possible answers to Think and Discuss

1. 4 terms:
$(a + b)(c + d) = ac + ad + bc + bd;$

3 terms:
$(x + 1)(x + 2) = x^2 + 3x + 2;$

2 terms:
$(x + 1)(x - 1) = x^2 - 1$

Think and Discuss

1. **Give an example** of a product of two binomials that has 4 terms, one that has 3 terms, and one that has 2 terms.

Power Presentations with PowerPoint®

Additional Examples

Example 1

Multiply.

A. $(n - 2)(m - 8)$
$nm - 8n - 2m + 16$

B. $(x + 3)(x + z)$
$x^2 + xz + 3x + 3z$

C. $(a + 3)(a + 5)$
$a^2 + 8a + 15$

D. $(x - 4y)(x + 7y)$
$x^2 + 3xy - 28y^2$

Example 2

An 8 in. by 10 in. photo has a wooden frame that extends x in. beyond each side. Represent the area of the frame in terms of x. $36x + 4x^2$ in^2

Example 3

Multiply.

A. $(x + 6)^2$ $x^2 + 12x + 36$

B. $(n - m)^2$ $n^2 - 2nm + m^2$

C. $(x - 7)(x + 7)$ $x^2 - 49$

Also available on transparency

---

2 Teach

Guided Instruction

In this lesson, students learn to multiply binomials. Explain that the Distributive Property is used to multiply binomials. Demonstrate how the mnemonic device FOIL can help students remember the necessary steps (Teaching Transparency). As you work the examples, take care to show the four products separately before simplifying. Introduce students to the special binomial products: $(a + b)^2$, $(a - b)^2$, and $(a + b)(a - b)$. Encourage students to write the perfect square binomials as the product of two binomials before they multiply.

Universal Access
Through Modeling

Show students a rectangle that has side lengths $(x + 4)$ and $(x + 2)$ and is divided into four smaller rectangles. Have students write expressions for the areas of the smaller rectangles and add them to find an expression for the area of the largest rectangle. Then have them find the area of the largest rectangle by using the FOIL method. Finally, have them compare their results. You may want to have students work in pairs or small groups. Since the areas of the small rectangles are x^2, $4x$, $2x$, and 8, the area of the largest rectangle is $x^2 + 4x + 2x + 8 = x^2 + 6x + 8$. By FOIL, the area of the largest rectangle is $(x + 4)(x + 2) = x^2 + 6x + 8$. The results are the same.

3 Close

Summarize

Remind students that the FOIL method is an application of the Distributive Property. Ask students to explain why the expressions in **Example 3** are called *special products*.

Possible answer: The expressions in **Examples 3A** and **3B** are binomials raised to the second power (perfect square binomials). The expression in **Example 3C** is a binomial multiplied by a similar binomial with a different sign in the middle.

Assignment Guide

If you finished Example **1** assign:
Proficient 1–6, 12–20, 29–31, 45–53
Advanced 12–20, 33–35, 39, 45–53

If you finished Example **2** assign:
Proficient 1–7, 12–21, 29–31, 41, 45–53
Advanced 12–21, 33–35, 39, 41–53

If you finished Example **3** assign:
Proficient 1–33, 36, 38, 40, 41, 45–53
Advanced 12–53

Homework Quick Check

Quickly check key concepts.
Exercises: 16, 20, 21, 24, 26

Math Background

To multiply binomials vertically, you can use a method similar to the traditional method of multiplying two-digit numbers. For example, the product of $(x + 2)(x + 3)$ may be found as shown below.

$$\begin{array}{r} x + 2 \\ \times \quad x + 3 \\ \hline 3x + 6 \\ x^2 + 2x \quad\quad \\ \hline x^2 + 5x + 6 \end{array}$$

This method can also be useful when you are multiplying polynomials with more than two terms.

California Standards Practice
Preview of Algebra 1 ← 10.0

go.hrw.com
Homework Help Online
KEYWORD: MT8CA 12-6
Parent Resources Online
KEYWORD: MT8CA Parent

GUIDED PRACTICE

See Example **1** Multiply.

1. $(x - 5)(y + 4)$
$xy + 4x - 5y - 20$

2. $(x - 3)(x + 7)$
$x^2 + 4x - 21$

3. $(3m - 5)(4m + 9)$
$12m^2 + 7m - 45$

4. $(h + 2)(3h + 4)$
$3h^2 + 10h + 8$

5. $(m - 2)(m - 7)$
$m^2 - 9m + 14$

6. $(b + 3c)(4b + c)$
$4b^2 + 13bc + 3c^2$

See Example **2**
7. A courtyard is 20 ft by 30 ft. There is a walkway of width x all the way around the courtyard. Find the area of the walkway. $4x^2 + 100x$ ft^2

See Example **3** Multiply.

8. $(x + 2)^2$
$x^2 + 4x + 4$

9. $(b - 3)(b + 3)$
$b^2 - 9$

10. $(x - 4)^2$
$x^2 - 8x + 16$

11. $(3x + 5)^2$
$9x^2 + 30x + 25$

INDEPENDENT PRACTICE

See Example **1** Multiply.

12. $(x + 4)(x - 3)$
$x^2 + x - 12$

13. $(v - 1)(v + 5)$
$v^2 + 4v - 5$

14. $(w + 6)(w + 2)$
$w^2 + 8w + 12$

15. $(3x - 5)(x + 6)$
$3x^2 + 13x - 30$

16. $(4m - 1)(3m + 2)$
$12m^2 + 5m - 2$

17. $(3b - c)(4b + 5c)$
$12b^2 + 11bc - 5c^2$

18. $(3t - 1)(t + 1)$
$3t^2 + 2t - 1$

19. $(3r + s)(4r - 5s)$
$12r^2 - 11rs - 5s^2$

20. $(5n - 3b)(n + 2b)$
$5n^2 + 7bn - 6b^2$

See Example **2**
21. Construction The Gonzalez family is having a pool to swim laps built in their backyard. The pool will be 25 yards long by 5 yards wide. There will be a cement deck of width x yards around the pool. Find the total area of the pool and the deck. $4x^2 + 60x + 125$ yd^2

See Example **3** Multiply.

22. $(x - 5)^2$
$x^2 - 10x + 25$

23. $(b + 3)^2$
$b^2 + 6b + 9$

24. $(x - 4)(x + 4)$
$x^2 - 16$

25. $(2x + 3)(2x - 3)$
$4x^2 - 9$

26. $(4x - 1)^2$
$16x^2 - 8x + 1$

27. $(a + 7)^2$
$a^2 + 14a + 49$

PRACTICE AND PROBLEM SOLVING

Extra Practice
See page EP25.

Multiply.

28. $(m - 6)(m + 6)$
$m^2 - 36$

29. $(b - 5)(b + 12)$
$b^2 + 7b - 60$

30. $(q + 6)(q + 5)$
$q^2 + 11q + 30$

31. $(t - 9)(t - 4)$
$t^2 - 13t + 36$

32. $(g + 3)(g - 3)$
$g^2 - 9$

33. $(3b + 7)(b - 4)$
$3b^2 - 5b - 28$

34. $(3t - 1)(6t + 7)$
$18t^2 + 15t - 7$

35. $(4m - n)(m + 3n)$
$4m^2 + 11mn - 3n^2$

36. $(3a + 6b)^2$
$9a^2 + 36ab + 36b^2$

37. $(r + 5)(r - 5)$
$r^2 - 25$

38. $(5q - 2)^2$
$25q^2 - 20q + 4$

39. $(3r - 2s)(5r - 4s)$
$15r^2 - 22rs + 8s^2$

40.
$300 - 70x + 4x^2$ in^2
A metalworker makes a box from a 15 in. by 20 in. piece of tin by cutting a square with side length x out of each corner and folding up the sides. Write and simplify an expression for the area of the base of the box.

REVIEW FOR MASTERY 12-6

LESSON 12-6 Review for Mastery
Multiplying Binomials

To multiply a binomial by a binomial, multiply each term of the first binomial by each term of the second binomial.

$(a + b)(c + d) = ac + ad + bc + bd$

You can remember the product as FOIL: First terms, Outer terms, Inner terms, and Last terms.

$(5x + 3)(3x - 2)$

Multiply the First terms.	$(5x)(3x) = 15x^2$
Multiply the Outside terms.	$(5x)(-2) = -10x$
Multiply the Inside terms.	$(3)(3x) = 9x$
Multiply the Last terms.	$(3)(-2) = -6$
Add the products.	$15x^2 - 10x + 9x - 6$
Combine like terms.	$15x^2 - x - 6$

You can also multiply binomials vertically.

Align the binomials.	$5x + 3$
Multiply each term of one	$\times\ 3x - 2$
binomial by each term of the	$-10x - 6$
other binomial.	$15x^2 + 9x$
Combine like terms.	$15x^2 - x - 6$

Multiply.

1. $(4x + 3)(2x + 5)$
$8x^2 + 26x + 15$

2. $(7t - 4)(2t + 3)$
$14t^2 + 13t - 12$

3. $(3 + 5b)(2b - 3b^2)$
$6b + b^2 - 15b^3$

4. $(x - 1)(x + 5)$
$x^2 + 4x - 5$

5. $(6m - 3n)(2m + 3n)$
$12m^2 + 12mn - 9n^2$

6. $(c + 7)(c + 1)$
$c^2 + 8c + 7$

7. $6n - 3$
$\times\ 3n + 3$
$18n^2 + 9n - 9$

8. $2y + 4$
$\times\ y + 6$
$2y^2 + 16y + 24$

PRACTICE 12-6

LESSON 12-6 Practice B
Multiplying Binomials

Multiply.

1. $(z + 1)(z + 2)$
$z^2 + 3z + 2$

2. $(1 - y)(2 - y)$
$2 - 3y + y^2$

3. $(2x + 1)(2x + 4)$
$4x^2 + 10x + 4$

4. $(w + 1)(w - 3)$
$w^2 - 2w - 3$

5. $(3v + 1)(v - 1)$
$3v^2 - 2v - 1$

6. $(t + 2)(2t - 2)$
$2t^2 + 2t - 4$

7. $(-3g + 4)(2g - 1)$
$-6g^2 + 11g - 4$

8. $(3c + d)(c - 2d)$
$3c^2 - 5cd - 2d^2$

9. $(2a + b)(a + 2b)$
$2a^2 + 5ab + 2b^2$

10. A box is formed from a 1 in. by 18 in. piece of cardboard by cutting a square with side length m inches out of each corner and folding up the sides. Write and simplify an expression for the area of the base of the box.
$18 - 38m + 4m^2$ in.^{2}

11. A table is placed in a 14 ft × 14 ft room so that there is an equal amount of space of width s feet all the way around the table. Write and simplify an expression for the area of the table.
$252 - 64s + 4s^2$ ft^2

12. A circular swimming pool with a radius of 14 ft is surrounded by a deck with width y feet. Write and simplify an expression for the total area of the pool and the deck. Use $\frac{22}{7}$ for pi.
$616 + 88y + \frac{22}{7}y^2$ ft^2

Multiply.

13. $(r - 2)^2$
$r^2 - 4r + 4$

14. $(2 + q)^2$
$4 + 4q + q^2$

15. $(p + 4)(p - 4)$
$p^2 - 16$

16. $(3n - 3)(3n + 3)$
$9n^2 - 9$

17. $(a + b)(a - b)$
$a^2 - b^2$

18. $(4e - f)^2$
$16e^2 - 8ef + f^2$

19. $(2y + z)^2$
$4y^2 + 4yz + z^2$

20. $(9p - 2)(-2 + 9p)$
$81p^2 - 36p + 4$

21. $(m - 1)^2$
$m^2 - 2m + 1$

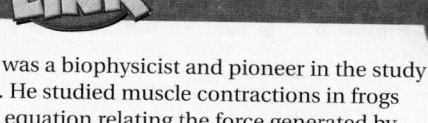
A. V. Hill (1886–1977) was a biophysicist and pioneer in the study of how muscles work. He studied muscle contractions in frogs and came up with an equation relating the force generated by a muscle to the speed at which the muscle contracts. Hill expressed this relationship as

$$(P + a)(V + b) = c,$$

where P is the force generated by the muscle, a is the force needed to make the muscle contract, V is the speed at which the muscle contracts, b is the smallest contraction rate of the muscle, and c is a constant.

41. Use the FOIL method to simplify Hill's equation.
$PV + bP + aV + ab = c$

42. Suppose the force a needed to make the muscle contract is approximately $\frac{1}{4}$ the maximum force the muscle can generate. Use Hill's equation to write an equation for a muscle generating the maximum possible force M. Simplify the equation.

43.  **Write About It** In Hill's equation, what happens to V as P increases? What happens to P as V increases? (*Hint:* You can substitute the value of 1 for a, b, and c to help you see the relationship between P and V.)

44. ★ **Challenge** Solve Hill's equation for P. Assume that no variables equal 0.
$P = \dfrac{c}{V + b} - a$

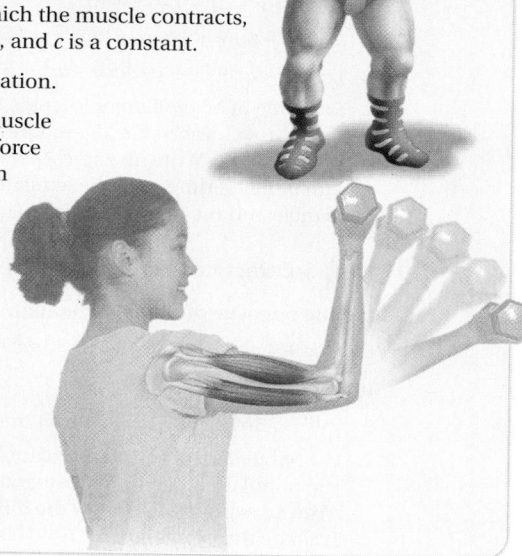

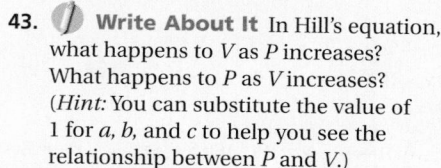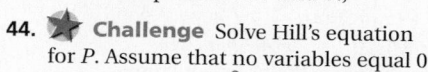

SPIRAL STANDARDS REVIEW

AF1.3, AF4.1

45. **Multiple Choice** Which polynomial shows the result of using the FOIL method to find $(x - 2)(x + 6)$?

Ⓐ $x^2 - 12$ Ⓑ $x^2 + 6x - 2x - 12$ Ⓒ $2x - 2x - 12$ Ⓓ $x^2 + 4$

46. **Gridded Response** Multiply $3a - 2b$ and $5a + 8b$. What is the coefficient of ab?   **14**

Solve. (Lesson 2-8)

47. $5x - 33.6 = 91.9$ **25.1**

48. $14 - 1.2j = 16.4$ **−2**

49. $4.4 = -0.6y - 6.82$ **−18.7**

50. $-3.7 = 26.2x + 9.4$ **−0.5**

Simplify. (Lesson 12-2)

51. $-4(m^2 - 3m + 6)$
$-4m^2 + 12m - 24$

52. $3(a^2b - 4a + 3ab) - 2ab$
$3a^2b - 12a + 7ab$

53. $x^2y + 4(xy^2 - 3x^2y + 4xy)$
$-11x^2y + 4xy^2 + 16xy$

FORMATIVE ASSESSMENT
and **INTERVENTION**

Diagnose Before the Lesson
12-6 Warm Up, TE p. 618

Monitor During the Lesson
12-6 Know-It Notebook
12-6 Questioning Strategies

Assess After the Lesson
12-6 Lesson Quiz, TE p. 621

Interdisciplinary

Life Science

Exercises 41–44 relate polynomial concepts to muscle contraction. Muscles and their contractions are studied in middle school life science programs, such as *Holt California Life Science*.

Answers

42. $(M + \frac{1}{4}M)(V + b) = c$;
$\frac{5}{4}MV + \frac{5}{4}Mb = c$

43. Possible answer: As P increases, V decreases, and as V increases, P decreases.

Teaching Tip   **Multiple Choice** Students who chose answer **A** did not multiply the inner terms of the binomials in **Exercise 45.** If students chose the wrong answer, they should review the FOIL method.

 **Journal**
Ask students to explain the FOIL method of multiplication.

Power Presentations with PowerPoint®

✓ **12-6 Lesson Quiz**

Multiply.

1. $(x + 5)(x + 2)$ $x^2 + 7x + 10$

2. $(c - 4)(c - 2)$ $c^2 - 6c + 8$

3. $(2y + 2)(y - 3)$ $2y^2 - 4y - 6$

4. $(2m + 2)(3n + 2)$
$6mn + 4m + 6n + 4$

5. $(a - 1)^2$ 6. $(b + 3)(b - 3)$
$a^2 - 2a + 1$ $b^2 - 9$

7. Find the area of a cement walkway of width w yd that is around a 20 yd by 30 yd pool.
$4w^2 + 100w$ yd^2

Also available on transparency

CHALLENGE 12-6

LESSON 12-6 Challenge
Multiplication Tables

You can use a table to multiply binomials. Label each column with a term from one of the binomials, and label each row with a term from the other binomial of the coefficients. Then multiply the same as in a multiplication table (column × row). Finish by combining like terms in the product.

Example: $(x + 3)(x - 2)$

	x	3
x	x^2	$3x$
-2	$-2x$	-6

$x^2 + 3x - 2x - 6 = x^2 + x - 6$

Use the given tables to find each product.

1. $(x - 4)(x - 5)$

	x	-4
x	x^2	$-4x$
-5	$-5x$	20

$x^2 - 9x + 20$

2. $(3m + 5)^2$

	$3m$	5
$3m$	$9m^2$	$15m$
5	$15m$	25

$9m^2 + 30m + 25$

3. $(2h + 1)(h - 4)$

	$2h$	1
h	$2h^2$	h
-4	$-8h$	-4

$2h^2 - 7h - 4$

4. $(7p - q)(p + 6q)$

	$7p$	$-q$
p	$7p^2$	$-pq$
$6q$	$42pq$	$-6q^2$

$7p^2 + 41pq - 6q^2$

5. $(3a + 4b)^2$

	$3a$	$4b$
$3a$	$9a^2$	$12ab$
$4b$	$12ab$	$16b^2$

$9a^2 + 24ab + 16b^2$

6. $(5w - 10)(2w - v)$

	$5w$	-10
$2w$	$10w^2$	$-20w$
$-v$	$-5wv$	$10v$

$10w^2 - 5wv - 20w + 10v$

PROBLEM SOLVING 12-6

LESSON 12-6 Problem Solving
Multiplying Binomials

Write and simplify an expression for the area of each polygon.

	Polygon	Dimensions	Area
1.	rectangle	length: $(n + 5)$; width: $(n - 4)$	$n^2 + n - 20$
2.	rectangle	length: $(3y + 3)$; width: $(2y - 1)$	$6y^2 + 3y - 3$
3.	triangle	base: $(2b - 5)$; height: $(b^2 + 2)$	$b^3 - \frac{5}{2}b^2 + 2b - 5$
4.	square	side length: $(m + 13)$	$m^2 + 26m + 169$
5.	square	side length: $(2g - 4)$	$4g^2 - 16g + 16$
6.	circle	radius: $(3c + 2)$	$(9c^2 + 12c + 4)\pi$

Choose the letter of the correct answer.

7. A photo is 8 inches by 11 inches. A frame of width x inches is placed around the photo. Which expression shows the total area of the frame and photo?
A $x^2 + 19x + 88$
Ⓑ $4x^2 + 38x + 88$
C $8x + 38$
D $4x + 19$

8. Three consecutive odd integers are represented by the expressions, x, $(x + 2)$ and $(x + 4)$. Which expression gives the product of the three odd integers?
F $x^3 + 8$
Ⓖ $x^3 + 6x^2 + 8x$
H $x^3 + 6x^2 + 8$
J $x^3 + 2x^2 + 8x$

9. A square garden has a side length of $(b - 4)$ yards. Which expression shows the area of the garden?
A $2b - 8$
B $b^2 + 16$
C $b^2 - 8b - 16$
Ⓓ $b^2 - 8b + 16$

10. Which expression gives the product of $(3m + 4)$ and $(9m - 2)$?
Ⓕ $27m^2 + 30m - 8$
G $27m^2 + 42m - 8$
H $27m^2 + 42m + 8$
J $27m^2 + 30m + 8$

READY TO GO ON?

Organizer

Objective: Assess students' mastery of concepts and skills in Lessons 12-3 through 12-6.

Resources

 Assessment Resources
Section 12B Quiz

 Test & Practice Generator
One-Stop Planner®

INTERVENTION ⬅➡

Resources

 Ready to Go On?
Intervention and
Enrichment Worksheets

💿 **Ready to Go On?** CD-ROM

🪐 **Ready to Go On?** Online

my.hrw.com

READY TO GO ON?

Quiz for Lessons 12-3 Through 12-6

✓ **12-3** Adding Polynomials

Add.

3. $15b^3c^2 - 2b^2c - 7bc + 4$

$8x^3 + 4x + 3$

$42x - 12$

1. $(8x^3 + 6x - 3) + (-2x + 6)$ **2.** $(30x - 7) + (12x - 5)$

3. $(7b^3c^2 - 6b^2c + 3bc) + (8b^3c^2 - 5bc + 13) + (4b^2c - 5bc - 9)$

4. $(2w^2 - 4w + 6) + (-3w - 4w^2 - 5) + (w^2 - 4)$ $-w^2 - 7w - 3$

5. Each side of an equilateral triangle has length $w + 2$. Each side of a square has length $3w - 4$. Write an expression for the sum of the perimeter of the equilateral triangle and the perimeter of the square.
$15w - 10$

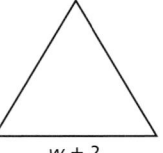 

$w + 2$ $3w - 4$

✓ **12-4** Subtracting Polynomials

Find the opposite of each polynomial. $-2m^2 + 6m - 3$

6. $-3x + 4xy^3$ $3x - 4xy^3$ **7.** $2m^2 - 6m + 3$ **8.** $5v - 7v^2$ $-5v + 7v^2$

Subtract. $7b^2 - 6b + 8$

$a^2 + 5a - 9$

$3x^2 - x$

9. $10b^2 - (3b^2 + 6b - 8)$ **10.** $(13a + a^2) - (9 + a + 7a)$ **11.** $(6x^2 + 6x) - (3x^2 + 7x)$

12. The population of a bacteria colony after h hours is $4h^3 - 5h^2 + 2h + 200$. The population of another bacteria colony is $3h^3 - 2h^2 + 5h + 200$. Write an expression to show the difference between the two populations. Evaluate the expression for $h = 1000$. $h^3 - 3h^2 - 3h$; 996,997,000 bacteria

✓ **12-5** Multiplying Polynomials by Monomials

Multiply.

13. $(4x^3y^3)(-3xy^6)$ $-12x^4y^9$ **14.** $(3hj^5)(-6h^4j^5)$ $-18h^5j^{10}$ **15.** $-4s^2t^2(4s^2t + 3st - s^2t^2)$

16. A triangle has a base of length $2x^2y$ and a height of $x^3 - xy - 2$. Write and simplify an expression for the area of the triangle. Then find the area of the triangle if $x = 2$ and $y = 1$. $x^5y - x^3y^2 - 2x^2y$; 16

15. $-16s^4t^3 - 12s^3t^3 + 4s^4t^4$

✓ **12-6** Multiplying Binomials

Multiply. $x^2 + 4x - 12$

$6m^2 + 16m - 32$

$n^2 - 8n + 15$

17. $(x - 2)(x + 6)$ **18.** $(3m - 4)(2m + 8)$ **19.** $(n - 5)(n - 3)$

20. $(x - 6)^2$ $x^2 - 12x + 36$ **21.** $(x - 5)(x + 5)$ $x^2 - 25$ **22.** $(3x + 2)(3x - 2)$

23. A rug is placed in a 10 ft × 20 ft room so that there is an uncovered strip $9x^2 - 4$
of width x all the way around the rug. Find the area of the rug.
$4x^2 - 60x + 200$ in^2

READY TO GO ON?

Diagnose and Prescribe

 **NO**
INTERVENE

 **YES**
ENRICH

READY TO GO ON? Intervention, Section 12B			
Ready to Go On? Intervention	Worksheets	CD-ROM	Online
✓ Lesson 12-3 🐻 Preview of 🔑 1A10.0	12-3 Intervention	Activity 12-3	
✓ Lesson 12-4 🐻 Preview of 🔑 1A10.0	12-4 Intervention	Activity 12-4	Diagnose and Prescribe Online
✓ Lesson 12-5 🐻 Preview of 🔑 1A10.0	12-5 Intervention	Activity 12-5	
✓ Lesson 12-6 🐻 Preview of 🔑 1A10.0	12-6 Intervention	Activity 12-6	

READY TO GO ON?
Enrichment, Section 12B

 **Worksheets**

 **CD-ROM**

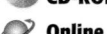 **Online**

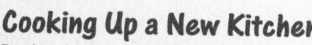

Cooking Up a New Kitchen

Javier is a contractor who remodels kitchens. He drew the figure to help calculate the dimensions of a countertop surrounding a sink that is x inches long and y inches wide.

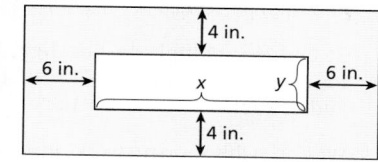

1. Write a polynomial that Javier can use to find the perimeter of the outer edge of the countertop. $2x + 2y + 40$

2. Someone orders a countertop for a sink that is 18 inches long and 12 inches wide. Javier puts tape around the outer edge of the countertop to protect it while it is being moved. Use the polynomial to determine how many inches of tape are needed. **100 in.**

3. Write a polynomial that Javier can use to find the area of the countertop for any size sink. $8x + 12y + 96$

4. The marble for the countertop costs $1.25 per square inch. Write a polynomial that gives the cost of the countertop. $10x + 15y + 120$

5. Find the cost of the countertop for the 18-inch by 12-inch sink. Explain your answer.

INTERVENTION

Scaffolding Questions

1. What is the formula used to find the perimeter of a rectangle? $2(l + w)$

2. How long is the countertop? **30 in.**
How wide is the countertop? **20 in.**

3. Does the area of the countertop also include the area of the sink? **No**

4. What are the units for the area of the countertop? in^2

5. Why can't you find the cost of the countertop by multiplying $1.25(6 + 6 + 4 + 4)$?
Possible answer: Because that expression does not take into account the length and width of the sink.

Extension

1. What if someone wanted a sink half the size of the 18-inch by 12-inch sink Javier is installing. Can you still use the same polynomial you found in **item 3** to calculate the area of the countertop? Explain.

Possible answer: You can use the polynomial from **item 3** to find the area of the countertop for any size sink, because the length and width of the sink are represented by variables that can change.

Organizer

Objective: Participate in games to practice and apply skills learned in Chapter 12.

 Online Edition

Resources

Chapter 12 Resource File
Puzzles, Twisters & Teasers

Short Cuts

Purpose: To apply the skill of multiplying binomials to developing a multiplication trick

Discuss Ask students to explain how the trick works. What general expression can you write to represent a two-digit number that ends in 5? $10n + 5$, where n is the digit in the tens place What is the square of the expression? $100n^2 + 100n + 25$ or $100n(n + 1) + 25$ How does the square of the expression model a numerical answer? The expression $100n(n + 1)$ provides the hundreds (and thousands) place of the answer; the 25 provides the tens and ones places.

Extend Challenge students to create a trick for multiplying two-digit numbers with a first digit of 2, and then with first digits of 3, 4, and 5. Ask them to look for a pattern.

$(20 + n)(20 + b) =$
$400 + 20(n + b) + nb$

$(30 + n)(30 + b) =$
$900 + 30(n + b) + nb$

$(40 + n)(40 + b) =$
$1600 + 40(n + b) + nb$

$(50 + n)(50 + b) =$
$2500 + 50(n + b) + nb$

Rolling for Tiles

Purpose: To practice operations with monomials in a game format

Discuss When a student models an expression that can be added, subtracted, multiplied, or divided to equal a polynomial on the game board, have him or her demonstrate the operation for the class.

Extend Have students create new polynomial expressions for the game board. Use the new expressions to play again.

Short Cuts

You can use properties of algebra to explain many arithmetic shortcuts. For example, to square a two-digit number that ends in 5, multiply the first digit by one more than the first digit, and then place a 25 at the end.

To find 35^2, multiply the first digit, 3, by one more than the first digit, 4. You get $3 \cdot 4 = 12$. Place a 25 at the end, and you get 1225. So $35^2 = 1225$.

Why does this shortcut work? You can use FOIL to multiply 35 by itself:

$$35^2 = 35 \cdot 35 = (30 + 5)(30 + 5) = 900 + 150 + 150 + 25$$
$$= 900 + 300 + 25$$
$$= 1200 + 25 \qquad 1200 = 30 \cdot 40$$
$$= 1225$$

First use the shortcut to find each square. Then use FOIL to multiply the number by itself.

1. 15^2 **225** 2. 45^2 **2025** 3. 85^2 **7225** 4. 65^2 **4225** 5. 25^2 **625**

6. Can you explain why the shortcut works?

Use FOIL to multiply each pair of numbers.

7. $11 \cdot 14$ **154** 8. $12 \cdot 16$ **192** 9. $13 \cdot 15$ **195** 10. $14 \cdot 17$ **238** 11. $18 \cdot 19$ **342**

12. Write a shortcut for multiplying two-digit numbers with a first digit of 1.

Rolling for Tiles

For this game, you will need a number cube, a set of algebra tiles, and a game board. Roll the number cube, and draw an algebra tile:

$1 = \square, 2 = \blacksquare, 3 = $ ▯ $, 4 = $ ▮ $, 5 = $ ▨ $, 6 = $ ▩ .

The goal is to model expressions that can be added, subtracted, multiplied, or divided to equal the polynomials on the game board.

A complete set of rules and a game board are available online.

go.hrw.com
Homework Help Online
KEYWORD: MT8CA Games

Answers

6. Possible answer: The shortcut is an application of the FOIL method. The expression $(10n + 5)^2$ is equal to $100n^2 + 100n + 25$, or $100n(n + 1) + 25$. The 25 provides the tens and ones places, and $n(n + 1)$ provides the hundreds (and thousands) place(s).

12. Possible answer: The general product can be represented by $(10 + a)(10 + b)$. Applying FOIL yields $100 + 10(a + b) + ab$. So the shortcut is to add 100, 10 times the sum of the last 2 digits, and the product of the last 2 digits together.

Materials
- 3 sheets of decorative paper
- ruler
- compass
- scissors
- glue
- markers

It's in the Bag!

PROJECT   Polynomial Petals

Pick a petal and find a fact about polynomials!

Directions

❶ Draw a 5-inch square on a sheet of decorative paper. Use a compass to make a semicircle on each side of the square. Cut out the shape. **Figure A**

❷ Draw a $3\frac{1}{2}$-inch square on another sheet of decorative paper. Use a compass to make a semicircle on each side of the square. Cut out the shape.

❸ Draw a $2\frac{1}{2}$-inch square on the last sheet of decorative paper. Use a compass to make a semicircle on each side of the square. Cut out the shape.

❹ Glue the medium square onto the center of the large square so that the squares are at a 45° angle to each other. **Figure B**

❺ Glue the small square onto the center of the medium square in the same way.

Taking Note of the Math

Write examples of different types of polynomials on the petals. Then use the remaining petals to take notes on the key concepts from the chapter. When you're done, fold up the petals.

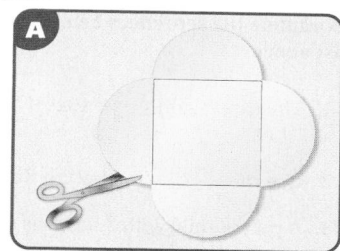

A

B

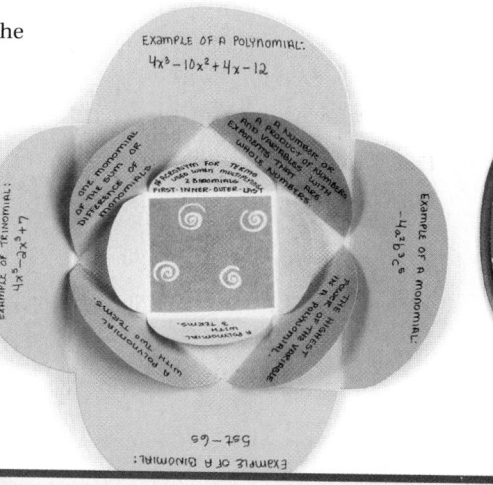

It's in the Bag!

Organizer

Objective: Make a "petal" notebook on which to record notes about polynomials.

Materials: 3 sheets of decorative paper, ruler, compass, scissors, glue, markers

Using the Page

Preparing the materials
You can do this project with any type of decorative paper (construction paper, wallpaper samples, gift wrap, etc.) or you can use card stock.

Making the Project
Encourage students to draw the squares carefully. If students make the squares accurately, they will fit together perfectly in the last steps of the project.

Extending the Project
Have students write on the petals in a question-and-answer format. The top of each petal should contain a question about polynomials. The underside of the petal should contain the answer. Students can then quiz each other by exchanging their projects.

Tips from the Bag Ladies!

Scrapbook paper works really well for this project because it is decorated on both sides, but ordinary construction paper is also fine.

If students make the squares slightly smaller, they can store the project in an empty CD case. In fact, it's an interesting challenge to have students calculate the appropriate sizes for the squares so that one fits correctly on top of the next and the finished product fits in a CD case.

Organizer

Objective: Help students organize and review key concepts and skills presented in Chapter 12.

 Online Edition
Multilingual Glossary

Resources

 PuzzlePro®
One-Stop Planner®

 Multilingual Glossary Online
go.hrw.com
[KEYWORD: MT8CA Glossary]

 Lesson Tutorial Videos
CD-ROM

Test & Practice Generator
One-Stop Planner®

Answers

1. polynomial; degree
2. FOIL; binomials
3. binomial; trinomial
4. trinomial
5. not a polynomial
6. not a polynomial
7. monomial
8. not a polynomial
9. binomial
10. 8
11. 4
12. 3
13. 5
14. 6

Vocabulary

binomial 590

degree of a polynomial 591

FOIL 618

polynomial 590

trinomial 590

Complete the sentences below with vocabulary words from the list above.

1. The expression $4x^3 - 10x^2 + 4x - 12$ is an example of a ___?___ whose ___?___ is 3.

2. Use the ___?___ method to find the product of two ___?___.

3. A polynomial with 2 terms is called a ___?___. A polynomial with 3 terms is called a ___?___.

 **12-1 Polynomials** (pp. 590–593)

Preview of ◄━ 1A10.0; 7AF1.2

EXAMPLE

Classify each expression as a monomial, a binomial, a trinomial, or not a polynomial.

■ $4x^5 - 2x^3 + 7$
trinomial

■ $4xy - \frac{3}{x^4} + 7x^2y^4$
not a polynomial

Find the degree of each polynomial.

■ $x^3 - 2x + 1$
degree 3

■ $n + 3n^4 + 16n^2$
degree 4

EXERCISES

Classify each expression as a monomial, a binomial, a trinomial, or not a polynomial.

4. $-5t^2 + 7t - 8$

5. $r^{-4} + 3r^{-2} + 5$

6. $12g + 7g^3 - \frac{5}{g^2}$

7. $-4a^2b^3c^5$

8. $\sqrt{x} - 2\sqrt{xy}$

9. $6st - 7s$

Find the degree of each polynomial.

10. $-3x^5 - 6x^8 + 5x$

11. $x^4 - 4x^2 + 3x - 1$

12. $14 + 8r^2 - 9r^3$

13. $\frac{1}{3}m^3 - \frac{1}{6}m^5 + \frac{7}{9}m^2$

14. $-3x^6 + 5x^5 - 9x$

12-2 Simplifying Polynomials (pp. 596–599)

Preview of ⬅ 1A10.0; ⬅ 7AF1.3

EXAMPLE

Simplify.

■ $5x^2 - 2x + 4 - 5x - 3 + 4x^2$

$\boxed{5x^2} - \boxed{2x} + \boxed{4} - \boxed{5x} - \boxed{3} + \boxed{4x^2}$

$9x^2 - 7x + 1$

■ $4(2x - 7) - 5x + 4$

$\boxed{8x} - \boxed{28} - \boxed{5x} + \boxed{4}$

$3x - 24$

EXERCISES

Simplify.

15. $4t^2 - 6t + 3t - 4t^2 + 7t^2 + 1$

16. $4gh - 5g^2h + 7gh - 4g^2h$

17. $4(5mn - 3m)$

18. $4(2a^2 - 4b) + 6b$

19. $5(4st^2 - 6t) + 16st^2 + 7t$

12-3 Adding Polynomials (pp. 603–606)

Preview of ⬅ 1A10.0; ⬅ 7AF1.3

EXAMPLE

Add.

■ $(3x^2 - 2x) + (5x^2 + 3x + 2)$

$\boxed{3x^2} - \boxed{2x} + \boxed{5x^2} + \boxed{3x} + 2$ *Identify like terms.*

$8x^2 + x + 2$ *Combine like terms.*

■ $(8t^3 + 4t + 6) + (4t^2 - 7t - 2)$

$\begin{array}{r} 8t^3 \qquad\quad + 4t + 6 \\ + \qquad 4t^2 - 7t - 2 \\ \hline 8t^3 + 4t^2 - 3t + 4 \end{array}$

Place like terms in columns.

Combine like terms.

EXERCISES

Add.

20. $(4x^2 + 3x - 7) + (2x^2 - 5x + 12)$

21. $(5x^4 - 3x^2 + 4x - 2) + (4x^2 - 5x + 9)$

22. $(5h + 5) + (2h^2 + 3) + (3h - 1)$

23. $(3xy^2 - 5x^2y - 4xy) + (3x^2y + 6xy - xy^2)$

24. $(4n^2 + 6) + (3n^2 - 2) + (8 + 6n^2)$

12-4 Subtracting Polynomials (pp. 608–611)

Preview of ⬅ 1A10.0; ⬅ 7AF1.3

EXAMPLE

■ Subtract.

$(6x^2 - 4x + 5) - (7x^2 - 8x + 2)$

$6x^2 - 4x + 5 + (-7x^2 + 8x - 2)$ *Add the opposite.*

$6x^2 - 4x + 5 - 7x^2 + 8x - 2$ *Associative Property*

$-x^2 + 4x + 3$ *Combine like terms.*

EXERCISES

Subtract.

25. $(x^2 - 4) - (4 - 5x^2)$

26. $(w^2 - 4w + 6) - (2w^2 + 8w - 8)$

27. $(3x^2 + 8x - 9) - (7x^2 - 8x + 5)$

28. $(4ab^2 - 5ab + 7a^2b) - (3a^2b + 6ab)$

29. $(3p^3q^2 - 4p^2q^2) - (2pq^2 + 4p^3q^2)$

Answers

15. $7t^2 - 3t + 1$

16. $11gh - 9g^2h$

17. $20mn - 12m$

18. $8a^2 - 10b$

19. $36st^2 - 23t$

20. $6x^2 - 2x + 5$

21. $5x^4 + x^2 - x + 7$

22. $2h^2 + 8h + 7$

23. $2xy^2 - 2x^2y + 2xy$

24. $13n^2 + 12$

25. $6x^2 - 8$

26. $-w^2 - 12w + 14$

27. $-4x^2 + 16x - 14$

28. $4ab^2 - 11ab + 4a^2b$

29. $-p^3q^2 - 4p^2q^2 - 2pq^2$

Answers

30. $-12s^2t^4 + 4s^2t^3 + 32st^3$

31. $12a^4b^3 + 30a^3b^3 - 36a^3b + 24a^2b^2$

32. $2m^3 - 16m^2 + 2m$

33. $10g^3h^3 - 15gh^5 + 20gh - 30h^2$

34. $2j^5k^3 - \frac{3}{2}j^4k^4 + j^6k^5$

35. $18x^7y^{14} - 15x^6y^{12} + 12x^3y^7 - 24x^3y^6$

36. $p^2 - 8p + 12$

37. $b^2 + 10b + 24$

38. $3r^2 + 11r - 4$

39. $3a^2 - 11ab - 20b^2$

40. $m^2 - 14m + 49$

41. $9t^2 - 36$

42. $6b^2 - 2bt - 28t^2$

43. $-3x^2 - 2x + 40$

44. $y^2 - 22y + 121$

12-5 Multiplying Polynomials by Monomials (pp. 612–615)

Preview of 1A10.0; 7AF1.2, 7AF1.3, 7AF2.2

EXAMPLE

Multiply.

■ $(3x^2y^3)(2xy^2)$

$(3x^2y^3)(2xy^2)$

$3 \cdot 2 \cdot x^{2+1}y^{3+2}$

$6x^3y^5$

Multiply the coefficients and add the exponents.

■ $(-2ab^2)(4a^2b^2 - 3ab + 6a - 8)$

$(-2ab^2)(4a^2b^2 - 3ab + 6a - 8)$

$-8a^3b^4 + 6a^2b^3 - 12a^2b^2 + 16ab^2$

EXERCISES

Multiply.

30. $(4st^3)(s - 3st + 8)$

31. $-6a^2b(-2a^2b^2 - 5ab^2 + 6a - 4b)$

32. $2m(m^2 - 8m + 1)$

33. $-5h(3gh^4 - 2g^3h^2 + 6h - 4g)$

34. $\frac{1}{2}j^3k^2(4j^2k - 3jk^2 + 2j^3k^3)$

35. $3x^2y^5(-5x^4y^7 + 6x^5y^9 - 8xy + 4xy^2)$

12-6 Multiplying Binomials (pp. 618–621)

Preview of 1A10.0

EXAMPLE

Multiply.

■ $(r + 8)(r - 6)$

$(r + 8)(r - 6)$ *FOIL*

$r^2 - 6r + 8r - 48$ *Combine like terms.*

$r^2 + 2r - 48$

■ $(b + 6)^2$

$(b + 6)(b + 6)$ *FOIL*

$b^2 + 6b + 6b + 36$ *Combine like terms.*

$b^2 + 12b + 36$

EXERCISES

Multiply.

36. $(p - 6)(p - 2)$

37. $(b + 4)(b + 6)$

38. $(3r - 1)(r + 4)$

39. $(3a + 4b)(a - 5b)$

40. $(m - 7)^2$

41. $(3t - 6)(3t + 6)$

42. $(3b - 7t)(2b + 4t)$

43. $(10 - 3x)(4 + x)$

44. $(y - 11)^2$

 CHAPTER TEST  CHAPTER 12

Classify each expression as a monomial, a binomial, a trinomial, or not a polynomial.

1. $t^2 + 2t^{0.5} - 4$ **not a polynomial**   2. $-\frac{1}{2}a^3b^6$ **monomial**   3. $4m^4 - 5m + 8$ **trinomial**

Find the degree of each polynomial.

4. $6 - 9b + 2m^4$ **4**   5. 54 **0**   6. $4 + y$ **1**

7. The volume of a cube with side length $x + 2$ is given by the polynomial $x^3 + 6x^2 + 12x + 8$. What is the volume of the cube if $x = 3$? **125**

Simplify.   10. $-4x^2y + 3xy^2$ 11. $27b^2 - 37b$

8. $2a - 4b - 5b + 6a - 2b$ **$8a - 11b$**   9. $3(x^2 - 6x + 10)$ **$3x^2 - 18x + 30$**

10. $-2x^2y + 3xy^2 - 4x^2y + 2x^2y$ 11. $6(4b^2 - 7b) + 3b^2 + 5b$

12. The area of one face of a cube is given by the expression $2s^2 + 9s$. Write a polynomial to represent the total surface area of the cube. **$12s^2 + 54s$**

Add.   15. $5bc - b^2c^2 + 4bc^2$ 16. $-h^6 + 6h^5 + 5h^4 + 3h^3 - 2h$

13. $(4x^2 + 2x - 1) + (-2x + 5)$ **$4x^2 + 4$**   14. $(12x - 5) + (9x - 5)$ **$21x - 10$**

15. $(3bc - b^2c^2 + 5bc^2) + (2bc - bc^2)$ 16. $(6h^5 + 3h^3 - 2h^6) + (h^6 - 2h + 5h^4)$

17. $(b^3c^2 - 8b^2c + 5bc) + (6b^3c^2 - 4bc + 3) + (b^2c - 3bc - 11)$ **$7b^3c^2 - 7b^2c - 2bc - 8$**

18. Harold is placing a mat of width $w + 4$ around a 16 in. by 20 in. portrait. Write an expression for the perimeter of the outer edge of the mat. **$8w + 104$**

19. $-3mn + mn^2$ 20. $4a - 6$

Subtract.   21. $10a^2b - 7a^2b^2 + 6ab^2$ 22. $j^4 - 5j^3 + 9j^2 + 2j - 1$

19. $(4m^2n - 5mn + mn^2) - (-2mn + 4m^2n)$ 20. $(12a + a^2) - (6 + a^2 + 8a)$

21. $(3a^2b - 5a^2b^2 + 6ab^2) - (2a^2b^2 - 7a^2b)$ 22. $(j^4 + 7j^2 - 4j) - (5j^3 - 2j^2 - 6j + 1)$

23. A circle whose area is $2x^2 + 3x - 4$ is cut from a rectangular piece of plywood with area $4x^2 + 3x - 1$ and discarded. Write an expression for the area of the remaining plywood. Evaluate the expression for $x = 4$ in.   **$2x^2 + 3$; 35 in^2**

27. $a^4 - 4a^2 + 5a$ 29. $3a^4b^2 - 6a^4b + 24a^4$

Multiply.   28. $6m^6n^8 - 15m^5n^6$ 30. $x^2 + 14x + 24$

24. $(3x)(5x^4)$ **$15x^5$**   25. $(4x^2y)(-5xy^3)$ **$-20x^3y^4$**   26. $(2a^2b^4)(5a^4b^5)$ **$10a^6b^9$**

27. $a(a^3 - 4a + 5)$ 28. $3m^3n^4(2m^3n^4 - 5m^2n^2)$ 29. $3a^3(ab^2 - 2ab + 8a)$

30. $(x + 2)(x + 12)$ 31. $(x + 2)(x - 4)$ **$x^2 - 2x - 8$**   32. $(a - 3)(a - 7)$ **$a^2 - 10a + 21$**

33. A student forms a box from a 10 in. by 15 in. piece of cardboard by cutting a square with side length x out of each corner and folding up the sides. Write and simplify an expression for the area of the base of the box. **$4x^2 - 50x + 150$**

Organizer

Objective: Provide review and practice for Chapters 1–12.

 Online Edition

Resources

 Assessment Resources
Chapter 12 Cumulative Test

 Focus on California Standards Benchmark Tests and Intervention

 California Standards Practice CD-ROM

go.hrw.com
KEYWORD: MT8CA Practice

Cumulative Assessment, Chapters 1–12
Multiple Choice

1. Jerome walked on a treadmill for 45 minutes at a speed of 4.2 miles per hour. How far did Jerome walk?

Ⓐ 1.89 miles   Ⓒ 3.15 miles
Ⓑ 2.1 miles   Ⓓ 5.6 miles

2. Which line has a slope of −3?

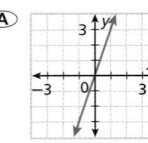
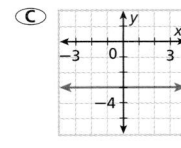
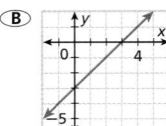
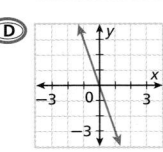

3. How much water can the cone-shaped cup hold? Use 3.14 for π.

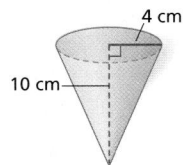

Ⓐ 41.9 cm³   Ⓒ 167.47 cm³
Ⓑ 502.4 cm³   Ⓓ 1507.2 cm³

4. Twenty-two percent of the sales of a general store are due to snack sales. If the store sold $1350 worth of goods, how much of the total was due to snack sales?

Ⓐ $167   Ⓒ $1053
Ⓑ $297   Ⓓ $2970

5. If rectangle MNQP is similar to rectangle ABDC, then what is the area of rectangle ABDC?

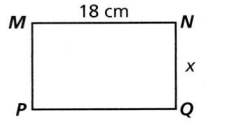
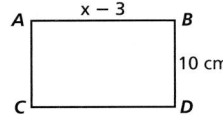

Ⓐ 44 cm²   Ⓒ 120 cm²
Ⓑ 66 cm²   Ⓓ 270 cm²

6. Which statement is modeled by $3f + 2 > -16$?

Ⓐ Two added to 3 times f is at least −16.
Ⓑ Three times the sum of f and 2 is at most −16.
Ⓒ The sum of 2 and 3 times f is more than −16.
Ⓓ The product of 3f and 2 is no more than −16.

7. If the area of a circle is 49π and the circumference of the circle is 14π, what is the diameter of the circle?

Ⓐ 7 units   Ⓒ 21 units
Ⓑ 14 units   Ⓓ 49 units

8. Nationally, there were 217.8 million people age 18 and over and 53.3 million children ages 5 to 17 as of July 1, 2003, according to the U.S. Census Bureau. How do you write the number of people age 5 and older in scientific notation?

Ⓐ 2.711×10^2 Ⓒ 2.711×10^7
Ⓑ 2.711×10^6 Ⓓ 2.711×10^8

Teaching Tip

Multiple Choice In item 1, point out to students that because Jerome's rate is 4.2 mi/h and he walked less than an hour, **D** is not possible, even if he walked for 1 hour.

If students did not select **D** in **item 2,** remind them that lines with negative slopes will always slant down to the right.

Answers

14. a. area of the triangle = $x^2 + 2x$;
area of the square = $9x^2 + 24x + 16$
b. area of gray region = $8x^2 + 22x + 16$

15. $2x^2 + 11x + 15$

16. See 4-Point Response work sample.

California Standards	
Standard	**Items**
NS1.1	8
NS1.3	4, 9
NS1.7 ⚷	11
AF1.1	6
AF1.2	14
AF3.3 ⚷	2
MG1.3 ⚷	1
MG2.0	3
MG2.1	7
MG2.2	10, 14
MG3.3 ⚷	12
1A10.0 ⚷	5, 13–16

9. There are 36 flowers in a bouquet. Two-thirds of the flowers are roses. One-fourth of the roses are red. What percent of the bouquet is made up of red roses?

Ⓐ 9%   Ⓒ 25%
Ⓑ $16\frac{2}{3}$%   Ⓓ $66\frac{2}{3}$%

 HOT TIP! If a problem involves decimals, you may be able to eliminate answer choices that do not have the correct number of places after the decimal point.

Gridded Response

10. The floor in the entrance way of Kendra's house is square and measures 6.5 feet on each side. Colored tiles have been set in the center of the floor in a square measuring 4 feet on each side. The remaining floor consists of white tiles.

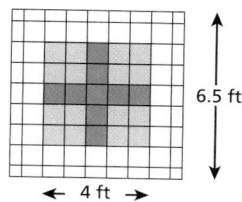

6.5 ft

← 4 ft →

How many square feet of the entrance way floor consists of white tiles? **26.25**

11. Rosalind purchased a sewing machine discounted 20%. The original selling price of the machine was $340. What was the sale price in dollars? **272**

12. What is the length, in centimeters, of the diagonal of a square with side length 8 cm? Round your answer to the nearest hundredth. **11.31**

13. The length of a rectangle is 2 units greater than the width. The area of the rectangle is 24 square units. What is its width? **4**

Short Response

14. A quilt is made by connecting squares like the one below.

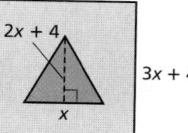

$2x + 4$

$3x + 4$

x

a. Write an expression for the area of the triangle and an expression for the area of the square.

b. Write an expression for the area of the gray region.

15. Draw a model for the product of the two binomials $(x + 3)$ and $(2x + 5)$ with the following tiles. Use the model to determine the product.

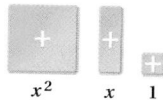

x^2 x 1

Extended Response

16. A cake pan is made by cutting four squares from a 18 cm by 24 cm piece of tin and folding the sides as shown.

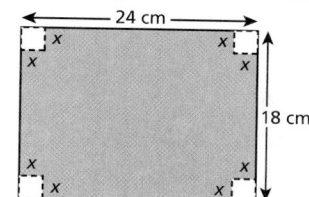

← 24 cm →

x x

x x

18 cm

x x

x x

a. Write an expression for the length, width, and height of the cake pan in terms of x.

b. Multiply the expressions from part **a** to find a polynomial that gives the volume of the cake pan.

c. Evaluate the polynomial for $x = 1$, $x = 2$, $x = 3$, and $x = 4$. Which value of x gives the cake pan with the largest volume? Give the dimensions and the volume of the largest cake pan.

Short Response Rubric
Items 14–15

2 Points = The student's answer is an accurate and complete execution of the task or tasks.

1 Point = The student's answer contains attributes of an appropriate response but is flawed.

0 Points = The student's answer contains no attributes of an appropriate response.

Extended Response Rubric
Item 16

4 Points = The student demonstrates a thorough understanding of all concepts and shows all work correctly.

3 Points = The student demonstrates a basic understanding of all concepts, but the work shows some flaws reflecting inattentive execution of mathematical procedures or some misunderstanding of the underlying mathematics.

2 Points = The student demonstrates only a partial understanding of the concepts or procedures embodied in the tasks. The approach may be correct, but the work shows a misunderstanding of one or more important concepts.

1 Point = The student demonstrates a very limited understanding of the concepts or procedures embodied in the tasks. The response may show some understanding but exhibits many flaws or is incomplete.

0 Points = The student provides no response at all or a completely incorrect or uninterpretable response.

Student Work Samples for Item 16

4-Point Response

17.a. length = 24-2x
     width = 18-2x
     height = x
b. V = (24-2x)(18-2x)(x)
     = x(432-48x-36x+4x²)
     = 432x - 84x² + 4x³
c. when x=1, V=352
   when x=2, V=560
   when x=3, V=648
   when x=4, V=640
When x=3, the cake pan has the largest volume. Height=3cm, Width=12cm, Length=18cm, Volume=648 cm³

The student correctly created the expressions, multiplied them together, and identified the dimensions of the box that maximized the volume.

3-Point Response

a. length = 24-2x
   width = 18-2x
   height = x
b. V = (24-2x)(18-2x)·x
     = x(432-48x-36x+4x²)
     = 4x³-84x²+432
c. When x=1, V=352
   x=2, V=128
   x=3, V=-216
   x=4, V=-656
When x=1, the cake pan has the largest volume (h=1 cm, l=22cm, w=16 cm, V=352 cm³)

The student understood the concepts, but neglected to distribute x to one of the terms in part **b.** This error results in incorrect responses to part **c.**

2-Point Response

17. a. $\ell = 24-x$
        $w = 18-x$
        $h = x$
b. volume = (24-x)(18-x)(x)
   volume = (432-24x-18x-x²)x
   volume = 432x-42x²-x³
c. x=1, 389   x=2, 688
   x=3, 891   x=4, 992
Volume is largest when x=4.
ℓ=20 w=14 h=4 V=992

The student correctly applied the proper method at each step, but created two expressions incorrectly. The student also incorrectly multiplied in part **b.**

Student Handbook

Extra Practice

LESSON 1-1

Evaluate each expression for the given value(s) of the variable(s).

1. $3 + x$ for $x = 5$ 8
2. $6m - 2$ for $m = 3$ 16
3. $2(p + 3)$ for $p = 8$ 22
4. $4x + y$ for $x = 1, y = 3$ 7
5. $2y - x$ for $x = 3, y = 6$ 9
6. $5x + 1.5y$ for $x = 2, y = 4$ 16

LESSON 1-2

Write an algebraic expression for each word phrase.

7. seven less than a number b $b - 7$
8. eight more than the product of 7 and a $7a + 8$
9. a quotient of 8 and a number $8 \div m$
10. five times the sum of c and 18 $5(c + 18)$

Write a word phrase for each algebraic expression.

11. $9 + \frac{x}{5}$ 9 plus the quotient of x and 5
12. $19x - 14$ 14 less than the product of 19 and x
13. $\frac{1}{3}(x + 1)$ $\frac{1}{3}$ of the sum of x and 1
14. $\frac{4}{x} - 100$ 100 less than the quotient of 4 and x
15. Write a word problem that can be evaluated by the algebraic expression $x - 122$, and then evaluate the expression for $x = 225$. Possible answer: There are 122 students on a field trip. If x students went to school this morning, how many students did not go on the field trip? $225 - 122 = 103$

LESSON 1-3

16. In a miniature golf game the scores of four brothers relative to par are Jesse 3, Jack −2, James −5, and Jarod 1. Use <, >, or = to compare Jack's and Jarod's scores. Then list the brothers in order from the lowest score to the highest.
$-2 < 1$; James, Jack, Jarod, Jesse

Write the integers in order from least to greatest.

17. −4, 6, −2 −4, −2, 6
18. 1, −16, 9 −16, 1, 9
19. −14, −2, −19 −19, −14, −2

Simplify each expression.

20. $|9| + |-4|$ 13
21. $|-3| + |-19|$ 22
22. $|52 - 12|$ 40
23. $|5 + 7| - |8 - 6|$ 10
24. $|-4| - |1 + 3|$ 0
25. $|13 - 9| + |-15|$ 19

LESSON 1-4

Add.

26. $-4 + 6$ 2
27. $3 + (-8)$ −5
28. $-6 + (-2)$ −8
29. $7 + (-11)$ −4

Evaluate each expression for the given value of the variable.

30. $x + 9$ for $x = -8$ 1
31. $x + 3$ for $x = -3$ 0
32. $x + 5$ for $x = -7$ −2

33. The middle school registrar is checking her records. Use the information in the table to find the net change in the number of students for this school for the week. 2 students

Day	Students Registering	Students Withdrawing
Monday	4	2
Tuesday	6	7
Wednesday	5	5
Thursday	1	4
Friday	4	0

LESSON 1-5

Subtract.

34. $-6 - 4$ −10
35. $8 - (-3)$ 11
36. $-6 - (-3)$ −3
37. $-5 - 8$ −13

Evaluate each expression for the given value of the variable.

38. $7 - x$ for $x = -4$ 11
39. $-8 - s$ for $s = -6$ −2
40. $-8 - b$ for $b = 12$ −20
41. $|3 + x|$ for $x = -2$ 1
42. $|-7 - b|$ for $b = 10$ 13
43. $|-5 - m| + |-6|$ for $m = 3$ 14
44. An elevator rises 351 feet above ground level and then drops 415 feet to the basement. What is the position of the elevator relative to ground level? −64 feet

LESSON 1-6

Multiply or divide.

45. $8(-6)$ −48
46. $\frac{-63}{7}$ −9
47. $-7(-3)$ 21
48. $\frac{52}{-4}$ −13

Simplify.

49. $8(4 - 5)$ −8
50. $-5(9) - 11$ −56
51. $-4(-16 + 4)$ 48
52. $3 + 7(10 - 14)$ −25

LESSON 1-7

Solve.

53. $4 + x = 13$ $x = 9$
54. $t - 3 = 8$ $t = 11$
55. $17 = m + 11$ $m = 6$
56. $5 + a = 7$ $a = 2$
57. $p - 5 = 23$ $p = 28$
58. $31 + y = 50$ $y = 19$
59. $18 + k = 34$ $k = 16$
60. $g - 16 = 23$ $g = 39$
61. Richard biked 39 miles on Saturday. This distance is 13 more miles than Trevor biked. How many miles did Trevor bike on Saturday? 26 miles

LESSON 1-8

Solve and check.

62. $\frac{a}{-4} = -2$ $a = 8$
63. $-49 = 7d$ $d = -7$
64. $\frac{c}{-2} = -8$ $c = 16$
65. $-57 = 3p$ $p = -19$
66. $-8b = 64$ $b = -8$
67. $144 = -9y$ $y = -16$
68. $\frac{x}{2} = -78$ $x = -156$
69. $19c = 152$ $c = 8$
70. Jessica hiked a total of 36 miles on her vacation. This distance is 4 times as far as she typically hikes. How many miles does Jessica typically hike? 9 miles

LESSON 1-9

Translate each sentence into an equation.

71. 8 less than the product of 5 and a number x is 53. $5x - 8 = 53$
72. 7 more than the quotient of a number t and 6 is 9. $\frac{t}{6} + 7 = 9$

Solve.

73. $3m + 5 = 23$ 6
74. $9 + \frac{x}{4} = 31$ 88
75. $-1 = 6y + 11$ −2
76. $-16 = -7 + \frac{m}{5}$ −45

LESSON 2-1

Write each fraction as a decimal.

1. $\frac{1}{8}$ 0.125
2. $\frac{7}{12}$ $0.58\overline{3}$
3. $-\frac{5}{3}$ $-1.\overline{6}$
4. $\frac{9}{20}$ 0.45

Write each decimal as a fraction in simplest form.

5. 0.4 $\frac{2}{5}$
6. 0.05 $\frac{1}{20}$
7. 0.125 $\frac{1}{8}$
8. 0.625 $\frac{5}{8}$

Write each repeating decimal as a fraction in simplest form.

9. $0.\overline{7}$ $\frac{7}{9}$
10. $0.\overline{25}$ $\frac{25}{99}$
11. $0.\overline{45}$ $\frac{5}{11}$
12. $0.\overline{009}$ $\frac{1}{111}$

LESSON 2-2

Compare. Write <, >, or =.

13. $\frac{6}{7} \blacksquare \frac{4}{5}$ >
14. $\frac{11}{15} \blacksquare \frac{9}{10}$ <
15. $\frac{1}{8} \blacksquare \frac{5}{6}$ <
16. $-\frac{4}{5} \blacksquare \frac{1}{8}$ <
17. $1\frac{5}{8} \blacksquare 1\frac{2}{3}$ <
18. $-2\frac{1}{8} \blacksquare -2\frac{1}{2}$ >
19. $\frac{12}{17} \blacksquare 0.75$ <
20. $5\frac{7}{8} \blacksquare 5.9$ <

21. In a sewing class, students were instructed to measure and cut cloth to a width of 3 yards. While checking four students' work, the teacher found that the four pieces of cloth were cut to the following measurements: 3.5 yards, 2.75 yards, $2\frac{11}{16}$ yards, and $3\frac{3}{8}$ yards. List these measurements from least to greatest. $2\frac{11}{16}$, 2.75, $3\frac{3}{8}$, 3.5

LESSON 2-3

22. Hannah and Elizabeth drove to Niagara Falls for vacation. Hannah drove $98\frac{3}{4}$ miles, and Elizabeth drove 106.44 miles. How far did they drive together? 205.19 miles

Add or subtract. Write each answer in simplest form.

23. $\frac{3}{4} - \frac{7}{4}$ −1
24. $\frac{19}{8} + \frac{11}{8}$ $\frac{15}{4}$, or $3\frac{3}{4}$
25. $\frac{5}{4} - \frac{15}{4}$ $-\frac{5}{2}$, or $-2\frac{1}{2}$
26. $-\frac{7}{4} + \frac{11}{4}$ 1
27. $\frac{9}{2} - \frac{15}{2}$ −3
28. $\frac{11}{2} + \frac{14}{2}$ $\frac{25}{2}$, or $12\frac{1}{2}$
29. $\frac{9}{4} - \frac{22}{4}$ $-\frac{13}{4}$, or $-3\frac{1}{4}$
30. $-\frac{21}{3} + \frac{16}{3}$ $-\frac{5}{3}$, or $-1\frac{2}{3}$

Evaluate each expression for the given value of the variable.

31. $32.9 + x$ for $x = -15.8$ 17.1
32. $21.3 + a$ for $a = -37.6$ −16.3
33. $-\frac{3}{5} + z$ for $z = 3\frac{1}{5}$ $\frac{13}{5}$, or $2\frac{3}{5}$

LESSON 2-4

Multiply. Write each answer in simplest form.

34. $-\frac{3}{4}\left(-\frac{5}{9}\right)$ $\frac{5}{12}$
35. $\frac{7}{12}\left(-\frac{3}{5}\right)$ $-\frac{7}{20}$
36. $-\frac{4}{5}\left(-\frac{9}{10}\right)$ $\frac{18}{25}$
37. $-\frac{3}{7}\left(\frac{13}{14}\right)$ $-\frac{39}{98}$
38. $-4.7(-8)$ 37.6
39. $-4.1(8.6)$ −35.26
40. $-0.06(5.2)$ −0.312
41. $-0.003(-2.6)$ 0.0078
42. Rosie ate $2\frac{1}{2}$ bananas on Saturday. On Sunday she ate $\frac{1}{2}$ as many bananas as she ate on Saturday. How many bananas did Rosie eat over the weekend? $3\frac{3}{4}$ bananas

---

LESSON 2-5

Divide. Write each answer in simplest form.

43. $2\frac{3}{4} \div \frac{1}{3}$ $\frac{33}{4}$, or $8\frac{1}{4}$
44. $5\frac{1}{5} \div \frac{1}{8}$ $\frac{208}{5}$, or $5\frac{33}{35}$
45. $3\frac{5}{9} \div \frac{3}{4}$ $\frac{128}{27}$, or $4\frac{20}{27}$
46. $3\frac{1}{8} + \frac{2}{5}$ $\frac{125}{16}$, or $7\frac{13}{16}$
47. $5.68 \div 0.2$ 28.4
48. $7.65 \div 0.05$ 153
49. $1.76 \div 0.8$ 2.2
50. $0.744 \div 8$ 0.093

Evaluate each expression for the given value of the variable.

51. $\frac{7.4}{x}$ for $x = 0.5$ 14.8
52. $\frac{11.88}{x}$ for $x = 0.08$ 148.5
53. $\frac{15.3}{x}$ for $x = -1.2$ −12.75
54. Yolanda is making bows that each take $21\frac{1}{2}$ inches of ribbon to make. She has 344 inches of ribbon. How many bows can she make? 16

LESSON 2-6

Add or subtract. Write each answer in simplest form.

55. $\frac{8}{9} + \frac{2}{7}$ $\frac{74}{63}$, or $1\frac{11}{63}$
56. $\frac{3}{8} - \frac{2}{3}$ $-\frac{7}{24}$
57. $\frac{2}{4} + \frac{1}{7}$ $\frac{17}{14}$
58. $\frac{5}{9} - \frac{4}{7}$ $-\frac{7}{18}$
59. $4\frac{1}{8} + \left(-2\frac{1}{7}\right)$ $\frac{72}{35}$, or $2\frac{2}{35}$
60. $3\frac{2}{3} + \left(-1\frac{7}{8}\right)$ $\frac{43}{24}$, or $1\frac{19}{24}$
61. $4\frac{1}{8} + \left(-1\frac{3}{5}\right)$ $\frac{101}{40}$, or $2\frac{21}{40}$
62. $8\frac{1}{7} + \left(-4\frac{1}{10}\right)$ $\frac{283}{70}$, or $4\frac{3}{70}$

Evaluate each expression for the given value of the variable.

63. $8\frac{1}{2} + x$ for $x = 4\frac{2}{9}$ $\frac{229}{18}$, or $12\frac{13}{18}$
64. $n - \frac{1}{9}$ for $n = -1\frac{7}{8}$ $-\frac{143}{72}$, or $-1\frac{71}{72}$
65. $1\frac{1}{8} + y$ for $y = -4\frac{4}{7}$ $-\frac{31}{56}$
66. A container has $10\frac{1}{2}$ gallons of milk. If the children at a preschool drink $7\frac{3}{4}$ gallons of milk, how many gallons are left in the container? $2\frac{3}{4}$ gallons

LESSON 2-7

Solve.

67. $x - 3.2 = 5.1$ $x = 8.3$
68. $-3.1p = 15.5$ $p = -5$
69. $\frac{a}{-2.3} = 7.9$ $a = -18.17$
70. $-4.3x = 34.4$ $x = -8$
71. $m - \frac{1}{3} = \frac{5}{8}$ $m = \frac{23}{24}$
72. $x - \frac{3}{7} = \frac{1}{9}$ $x = \frac{34}{63}$
73. $\frac{4}{5}w = \frac{2}{3}$ $w = \frac{5}{6}$
74. $\frac{9}{10}z = \frac{5}{8}$ $z = \frac{25}{36}$
75. Peter estimates that it will take him $9\frac{3}{4}$ hours to paint a room. If he gets two of his friends to help him and they work at the same rate as he does, how long will they take to paint the room? $3\frac{1}{4}$ hours

LESSON 2-8

76. A bill from the plumber was $383. The plumber charged $175 for parts and $52 per hour for labor. How long did the plumber work at this job? 4 hours

Solve.

77. $\frac{a}{2} - 3 = 8$ $a = 22$
78. $2.4 = -0.8x + 3.2$ $x = 1$
79. $0.9m - 1.6 = -5.2$ $m = -4$
80. $\frac{b}{5} + 2 = -3$ $b = -25$
81. $\frac{x - 4}{3} = 7$ $x = 25$
82. $-8.6 = 3.4k - 1.8$ $k = -2$
83. $6c + 1.2 = 4.2$ $c = 0.5$
84. $7 - 4d = 8$ $d = -0.25$
85. $\frac{y + 9}{3} = 2$ $y = -3$

Extra Practice ▪ Chapter 3

LESSON 3-1

Name the property that is illustrated in each equation.

1. $5 \cdot (6 \cdot x) = (5 \cdot 6) \cdot x$ Assoc. Prop. of Mult.

2. $8 + (-1) = (-1) + 8$ Comm. Prop. of Add.

3. $4 \cdot m = m \cdot 4$ Comm. Prop. of Mult.

Simplify each step. Justify each step.

4. $\frac{1}{5} \cdot 9 \cdot 35$ 63

5. $23 + 14 + 7$ 44

6. $\frac{2}{7} + 6 + \frac{5}{7}$ 7

Write each product using the Distributive Property. Then simplify.

7. $3(94)$ $3(90 + 4) = 282$

8. $8(47)$ $8(40 + 7) = 376$

9. $6(52)$ $6(50 + 2) = 312$

LESSON 3-2

Combine like terms.

10. $5x + 4x + 7x$ $16x$

11. $6x - 4x + 9 + 5x + 7$ $7x + 16$

12. $2x + 3 - 2x + 5$ 8

13. $7a - 2b + 6 + 4b - 5a$ $2a + 2b + 6$

14. $4s + 9r - 9$ $4s + 9r - 9$

15. $6m + 4n - 6m + n$ $5n$

Simplify.

16. $6(y + 4) - y$ $5y + 24$

17. $3(3b - 3) + 3b$ $12b - 9$

18. $4(x + 2) + 3x - 8$ $7x$

LESSON 3-3

Solve.

19. $4a - 5 + 2a + 9 = 28$ $a = 4$

20. $5 - 8b + 6 - 2b = 61$ $b = -5$

21. $4x - 6 - 8x - 9 = 21$ $x = -9$

22. $g - 9 + 4g + 6 = 12$ $g = 3$

23. $2 - 3f - 5 + 5f = 6$ $f = \frac{9}{2}$

24. $4r - 8 + 7 - 6r = -9$ $r = 4$

25. $\frac{4a}{5} - \frac{7}{5} = -\frac{3}{5}$ $a = 1$

26. $\frac{1}{3} - \frac{2b}{3} = \frac{2}{3}$ $b = -3$

27. $\frac{4z}{11} + \frac{3}{11} = -1$ $z = -\frac{14}{4}$ or $-\frac{7}{2}$

28. $\frac{2f}{4} + 4 = -\frac{24}{4}$ $f = 4$

29. $\frac{10c}{4} - \frac{2}{6} = \frac{56}{6}$ $c = 6$

30. $\frac{9x}{9} - \frac{45}{9} + \frac{36x}{6} = -\frac{126}{9}$ $x = -1$

31. A round-trip car ride took 12 hours. The first half of the trip took 7 hours at a rate of 45 miles per hour. What was the average rate of speed on the return trip? **63 miles per hour**

LESSON 3-4

Solve.

32. $4z - 2 = z + 1$ $z = 1$

33. $-4a - 4 = a + 11$ $a = -3$

34. $4p - 6 = 3 + 4p$ no solution

35. $6 + 5c = 3c - 4$ $c = -5$

36. $7d - 3 + 2d = 5d - 8 + 1$ $d = -1$

37. $3f - 4 - 5f = f + 4 + f$ $f = -2$

38. $5k - 4 - k = 3k - 6 + 2k$ $k = 2$

39. $\frac{w}{4} + \frac{5}{8} - \frac{2w}{8} = \frac{7}{8} - \frac{2w}{4}$ $w = 1$

40. $\frac{a}{3} - \frac{1}{6} + \frac{5a}{6} = \frac{9}{6} + \frac{2a}{3} + \frac{a}{3}$ $a = 10$

41. $\frac{2q}{3} + \frac{5}{9} - \frac{q}{6} = \frac{5q}{6} - \frac{18}{9}$ $q = 2$

42. A cafeteria charges a fixed price per ounce for the salad bar. A sandwich costs $3.10, and a large drink costs $1.75. If a 7-ounce salad and a drink cost the same as a 4-ounce salad and a sandwich, how much does the salad cost per ounce? **$0.45**

Extra Practice ▪ Chapter 3

LESSON 3-5

Write an inequality for each situation or statement.

43. The cafeteria could hold no more than 50 people. number of people ≤ 50

44. There were fewer than 20 boats in the marina. number of boats < 20

45. A number n decreased by 4 is more than 13. $n - 4 > 13$

46. A number x divided by 5 is at most 28. $\frac{x}{5} \le 28$

Graph each inequality. For 47–50, see p. A12.

47. $y < -2$

48. $f \ge 3$

49. $n \le -1.5$

50. $x > 4$

Write a compound inequality for each statement.

51. A number m is both less than 8.5 and greater than or equal to 0. $0 \le m < 8.5$

52. A number c is either greater than 1.5 or less than or equal to -1. $c > 1.5$, or $c \le -1$

LESSON 3-6

Solve and graph. For 53–60, see p. A12.

53. $x - 3.5 \ge 7x \ge 10.5$

54. $h - 5 \le 13$ $h \le 18$

55. $5 \ge q + 3\frac{1}{2}$ $q \le 1\frac{1}{2}$

56. $m + 1 > 0.25$ $m > -0.75$

57. $n + 4\frac{2}{3} < 5\frac{1}{3}$ $n < \frac{2}{3}$

58. $q - 0.5 \ge -1$ $q \ge -0.5$

59. $-30 < h - 23$ $h > -7$

60. $7 \le x + 6\frac{4}{5}$ $x \ge \frac{1}{5}$

LESSON 3-7

Solve and graph. For 61–68, see p. A12.

61. $5 \le \frac{v}{2}$ $10 \le v$, or $v \ge 10$

62. $-40 \ge 4q$ $-10 \ge q$, or $q \le -10$

63. $-9x > 72$ $x < -8$

64. $-2 \le -\frac{s}{3}$ $6 \ge s$, or $s \le 6$

65. $\frac{p}{3} > -6$ $p > -18$

66. $3 > \frac{w}{-5}$ $-15 < w$, or $w > -15$

67. $-f \le 4$ $f \ge -4$

68. $-5y > -55$ $y < 11$

69. Reese is running for student council president. In order for a student to be elected president, at least $\frac{1}{3}$ of the students must vote for him. If there are 432 students in a class, at least how many students must vote for Reese in order for him to be elected class president? **at least 144 students**

LESSON 3-8

Solve and graph. For 70–77, see p. A12.

70. $3a + 6 < 12$ $a < 2$

71. $-\frac{5}{3} \le 4x + 7$ $-3 \le x$, or $x \ge -3$

72. $2b + 8 > 16$ $b > 4$

73. $4z + 8 \le -4$ $z \le -3$

74. $\frac{x}{6} - \frac{1}{3} > -\frac{2}{3}$ $x > -2$

75. $\frac{1}{2}k + 8 \ge 9$ $k \ge 2$

76. $\frac{d}{3} + \frac{4}{5} < 2$ $d < \frac{12}{5}$

77. $\frac{2}{3} + \frac{p}{6} < \frac{7}{6}$ $p < 3$

78. Nikko wants to make flyers promoting a library book sale. The printer charges $40 plus $0.03 per flyer. How many flyers can Nikko make without spending more than the library's $54 budget? **466 flyers**

Extra Practice ▪ Chapter 4

LESSON 4-1

Write in exponential form.

1. $3 \cdot 3 \cdot 3 \cdot 3$ 3^4

2. $6a \cdot 6a \cdot 6a \cdot 6a \cdot 6a$ $(6a)^5$

3. $(-9) \cdot (-9)$ $(-9)^2$

4. b b^1

Simplify.

5. 2^5 32

6. 3^4 81

7. $(-6)^2$ 36

8. $(-3)^5$ -243

Evaluate each expression for the given values of the variables.

9. $s^4 + y(s + 3)$ for $s = 1$ and $y = -2$ -7

10. $10 + x^2 - \frac{x}{2}(y + 4)$ for $x = 3$ and $y = -2$ 16

LESSON 4-2

Simplify the powers of 10.

11. 10^{-1} 0.1

12. 10^{-2} 0.01

13. 10^{-3} 0.001

14. 10^{-4} 0.0001

Simplify.

15. $(-4)^{-2}$ $\frac{1}{16}$

16. 3^{-3} $\frac{1}{27}$

17. $(-5)^{-4}$ $\frac{1}{625}$

18. $\frac{3^2}{3^4} + (9 + 3)^0$ $1\frac{1}{9}$

19. $13 - (-3) + 19(1 + 2)^2$ 187

20. $4^5 \cdot 3^2 \cdot (-3)^{-3}$ $-\frac{1024}{3}$

LESSON 4-3

Simplify each expression. Write your answer in exponential form.

21. $2^4 \cdot 2^5$ 2^9

22. $w^7 \cdot w^7$ w^{14}

23. $\frac{4^9}{4^9}$ 4^0

24. $\frac{c^6}{c^2}$ c^4

25. $\frac{x^3}{y^3}$ $\left(\frac{x}{y}\right)^3$

26. $(3^0)^4$ 3^0

27. $(3^{-2})^3$ 3^{-6}

28. $(-a^3)^4$ a^{12}

LESSON 4-4

Multiply or divide. Assume that no denominator equals zero.

29. $(x^5)(4x^4)$ $4x^9$

30. $(7a^4b^2)(-3b^4)$ $-21a^4b^6$

31. $(8m^6n^3)(5mn^7)$ $40m^7n^{10}$

32. $\frac{22m^{10}}{2m^5}$ $11m^5$

33. $\frac{18x^8y^7}{12x^8y}$ $\frac{3}{2}y^6$

34. $\frac{45a^5b^9}{9a^2b^5}$ $5a^3b^4$

Simplify.

35. $(3y)^5$ $243y^5$

36. $(9p^3r)^2$ $81p^6r^2$

37. $(-4a^7b^4)^3$ $-64a^{21}b^{12}$

LESSON 4-5

Write each number in scientific notation.

38. 0.00384 3.84×10^{-3}

39. 1,450,000,000 1.450×10^9

40. 0.654 6.54×10^{-1}

Write each number in standard form.

41. 2.4×10^3 2,400

42. 3.62×10^5 362,000

43. 5.036×10^{-4} 0.0005036

44. 8.93×10^{-2} 0.0893

45. The population of the United States was approximately 2.9×10^8 people in July 2006. In the same month, the population of Canada was approximately 3.3×10^7 people. Which country had the greater population in July 2006? **United States**

Extra Practice ▪ Chapter 4

LESSON 4-6

Find the two square roots of each number.

46. 25 $5, -5$

47. 49 $7, -7$

48. 289 $17, -17$

49. 169 $13, -13$

50. The area of a square garden is 1,681 square feet. What are the dimensions of the garden? **41 feet × 41 feet**

Simplify each expression.

51. $\sqrt{400x^{20}}$ $20x^{10}$

52. $\sqrt{49y^6}$ $7|y^3|$

53. $\sqrt{m^{14}n^{12}}$ $|m^7|n^6$

54. $\sqrt{196a^{16}b^8}$ $14a^8b^4$

LESSON 4-7

Each square root is between two integers. Name the integers. Explain your answer. For 55–58, see p. A12.

55. $\sqrt{30}$

56. $\sqrt{61}$

57. $\sqrt{93}$

58. $-\sqrt{124}$

59. Each tile on Michelle's patio is 18 square inches. If her patio is square shaped and consists of 81 tiles, about how big is her patio? **38.2 inches × 38.2 inches**

Approximate each square root to the nearest hundredth.

60. $\sqrt{52}$ 7.20

61. $\sqrt{83}$ 9.11

62. $\sqrt{166}$ 12.88

63. $\sqrt{246}$ 15.68

LESSON 4-8

Write all classifications that apply to each number.

64. $\sqrt{5}$ irrational, real

65. -61.2 rational, real

66. $\frac{\sqrt{16}}{2}$ rational, real

67. -6 integer, rational, real

State if the number is rational, irrational, or not a real number.

68. $\sqrt{\frac{4}{25}}$ rational

69. $\sqrt{-9}$ not real

70. $\sqrt{17}$ irrational

71. $\frac{13}{0}$ not real

Find a real number between each pair of numbers. 72–74. Possible answers given.

72. $5\frac{1}{8}$ and $5\frac{5}{8}$ $5\frac{3}{8}$

73. $4\frac{1}{3}$ and $4\frac{2}{3}$ $4\frac{1}{2}$

74. $3\frac{5}{7}$ and $3\frac{6}{7}$ $5\frac{11}{14}$

LESSON 4-9

Use the Pythagorean Theorem to find each missing measure.

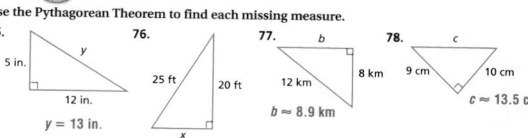

75. 5 in., 12 in. $y = 13$ in.

76. 25 ft, 20 ft $x = 15$ ft

77. 12 km, 8 km $b \approx 8.9$ km

78. 9 cm, 10 cm $c \approx 13.5$ cm

Tell whether the given side lengths form a right triangle.

79. 6, 8, 10 yes

80. 8, 11, 13 no

81. 7, 10, 12 no

82. 0.8, 1.5, 1.7 yes

Extra Practice

Extra Practice ▪ Chapter 5

LESSON 5-1

Write each ratio in simplest form.

1. 2 cups of milk to 8 eggs $\frac{1}{4}$ **2.** 36 inches to 2 feet $\frac{3}{2}$ **3.** 4 feet to 20 yards $\frac{1}{15}$

Simplify to tell whether the ratios are equivalent.

4. $\frac{5}{30}$ and $\frac{3}{18}$ yes   **5.** $\frac{12}{21}$ and $\frac{16}{28}$ yes   **6.** $\frac{15}{21}$ and $\frac{10}{16}$ no   **7.** $\frac{52}{64}$ and $\frac{91}{112}$ yes

LESSON 5-2

8. Nikko jogs 3 miles in 30 minutes. How many miles does she jog per hour? 6 miles

9. A penny has a mass of 2.5 g and a volume of approximately 0.442 cm³.
What is the approximate density of a penny? 5.66 g/cm³

Estimate the unit rate.   50 mg/oz

10. 384 mg of calcium for 8 oz of yogurt   **11.** $57.50 for 5 hours $12/h

12. Determine which brand of detergent
has the lower unit rate.
Bubbling detergent, at 2.3¢ per ounce

Detergent Brand	Size (oz)	Price ($)
Pizzazz	128	3.08
Spring Clean	64	1.60
Bubbling	196	4.51

LESSON 5-3

Tell whether the ratios are proportional.

13. $\frac{7}{8}$ and $\frac{3}{4}$ no   **14.** $\frac{3}{4}$ and $\frac{24}{32}$ yes   **15.** $\frac{32}{48}$ and $\frac{18}{27}$ yes   **16.** $\frac{12}{20}$ and $\frac{6}{12}$ no

17. Mark is making 35 sandwiches for a luncheon. He made the first 15 sandwiches in
45 minutes. If he continues to work at the same rate, how many more minutes will he
take to complete the job? 60 min

18. An 18-pound weight is positioned 6 inches from a fulcrum. At what distance from the
fulcrum must a 24-pound weight be positioned to keep the scale balanced? 4.5 in.

LESSON 5-4

19. A water fountain dispenses 8 cups of water per minute. Find this rate
in pints per minute. 4 pt/min

20. Jo's car uses 1664 quarts of gas per year. Find this rate in gallons per week. 8 gal/wk

21. Toby walked 352 feet in one minute. What is his rate in miles per hour? 4 mi/h

22. A three-toed sloth has a top speed of 0.22 feet per second. A giant tortoise
has a top speed of 2.992 inches per second. Convert both speeds to miles
per hour, and determine which animal is faster.
Sloth: 0.15 mi/h; tortoise: 0.17 mi/h; the tortoise is faster.

23. There are markers every 1000 feet along the side of a road. While cycling,
Ben passes marker number 6 at 3:35 P.M. and marker number 24 at 3:47 P.M.
Find Ben's average speed in feet per minute. Use dimensional analysis to
check the reasonableness of your answer.   1500 ft/min (≈17mi/h)

Extra Practice ▪ Chapter 5

LESSON 5-5

24. Which triangles are similar? triangles A and C

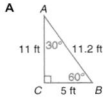
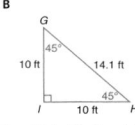
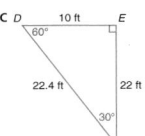

25. Khaled scans a photo that is 5 in. wide by 7 in. long into his computer. If
the length of the scanned photo is reduced to 3.5 in., how wide should the
scanned photo be for the two photos to be similar? 2.5 in.

26. Mutsuko drew an 8.5-inch-wide by 11-inch-tall picture that will be
turned into a 34-inch-wide poster. How tall will the similar poster be? 44 in.

27. A right triangle has legs that measure 3 cm and 4 cm. The shorter leg of a
similar right triangle measures 6 cm. What is the length of the other leg of
the similar triangle? 8 cm

LESSON 5-6

28. Brian casts a 9 ft shadow at the same time that Carrie casts an 8 ft
shadow. If Brian is 6 ft tall, how tall is Carrie? about 5.3 ft

29. A telephone pole casts an 80 ft shadow, and a child standing nearby
who is 3.5 ft tall casts a 6 ft shadow. How tall is the pole? about 46.7 ft

LESSON 5-7

Use the map to answer each question.

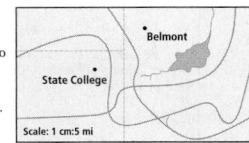

30. On the map, the distance from State College to
Belmont is 2 cm. What is the actual distance
between the two locations? 10 mi

31. Henderson City is 83 miles from State College.
How many centimeters apart should the two
locations be placed on the map? 16.6 cm

32. What is the scale of a drawing in which a building that is 95 ft tall is drawn 6 in. tall?
1 in:15.83 ft

33. A model of a skyscraper was made using a scale of 0.5 in:5 ft. If the
actual skyscraper is 570 feet tall, what is the height of the model? 4.75 ft or 57 in.

34. Julio uses a scale of $\frac{1}{8}$ inch = 1 foot when he paints landscapes. In one
painting, a giant sequoia tree is 34.375 inches tall. How tall is the actual tree? 275 ft

35. On a scale drawing of a house plan, the master bathroom is $1\frac{1}{2}$ inches
wide and $2\frac{5}{8}$ inches long. If the scale of the drawing is $\frac{3}{16}$ inches =
1 foot, what are the actual dimensions of the bathroom? 8 ft × 14 ft

---

Extra Practice ▪ Chapter 6

LESSON 6-1

Compare. Write <, >, or =.

1. $\frac{3}{5}$ ▓ 62%   **2.** $\frac{2}{3}$ ▓ $66\frac{2}{3}$ %   **3.** 24% ▓ 0.25   **4.** 1% ▓ 0.11
    <   =   <   <

Order the numbers from least to greatest.

5. 0.11, 11.5%, 10%, $\frac{1}{8}$ 10%, 0.11, 11.5%, $\frac{1}{8}$ **6.** $\frac{1}{5}$, 100%, $26\frac{2}{3}$ %, 0.3 $\frac{1}{5}$, $26\frac{2}{3}$ %, 0.3, 100%

7. $\frac{7}{6}$, 115%, 83, 83.3%   83, 83.3%, 115%, $\frac{7}{6}$ **8.** 67.5%, $\frac{7}{3}$, 160%, 2.2   67.5%, 160%, 2.2, $\frac{7}{3}$

9. A molecule of ammonia is made up of 3 atoms of hydrogen and 1 atom of
nitrogen. What percent of an ammonia molecule is made up of hydrogen
atoms? 75%

LESSON 6-2

Estimate.

10. 51% of 1019 510   **11.** 33% of 60 20   **12.** 60% of 79 48   **13.** $66\frac{2}{3}$ % of 211 140

14. Approximately 23% of each class walks to school. A student said that in
a class of 20 students, approximately 2 students walk to school.
Estimate to determine if the student's number is reasonable. Explain.
Possible answer: No, 23% is close to 25%, and
25% of 20 is 5. 5 is much more than 2.

LESSON 6-3

15. What percent of 364 is 92? about 25.3%   **16.** What percent of 48 is 5? about 10.4%

17. What percent of 164 is 444? about 270.7%   **18.** What percent of 50 is 4? 8%

19. Mt. McKinley in Alaska is 20,320 feet tall. The height of Mt. Everest is
about 143% of the height of Mt. McKinley. Estimate the height of Mt.
Everest. Round to the nearest thousand. about 29,000 ft

20. A restaurant bill for $64.45 was split among four people. Dona paid
25% of the bill. Sandy paid $\frac{1}{3}$ of the bill. Mara paid $14.25. Greta paid
the remainder of the bill. Who paid the most money? Greta

LESSON 6-4

21. 38 is 42% of what number? about 90.5   **22.** 46 is 74% of what number? about 62.2

23. 23 is 8% of what number? 287.5   **24.** 93 is 62% of what number? 150

25. 315 is 92% of what number? about 342.4   **26.** 52 is 120% of what number? about 43.3

27. A certain rock is a compound of several minerals. Tests show that the
sample contains 17.3 grams of quartz. If 27.5% of the rock is quartz,
find the mass in grams of the entire rock. about 62.9 grams

28. The Alabama River is 729 miles in length, or about 31% of the length of
the Mississippi River. Estimate the length of the Mississippi River.
Round to the nearest mile. 2352 miles

Extra Practice ▪ Chapter 6

LESSON 6-5

Find each percent of increase or decrease to the nearest percent.

29. from 10 to 17   **30.** from 38 to 65   **31.** from 91 to 44   **32.** from 3 to 25
70% increase   71% increase   52% decrease   733% increase
33. from 86 to 27   **34.** from 38 to 46   **35.** from 19 to 60   **36.** from 88 to 23
69% decrease   21% increase   216% increase   74% decrease

37. A stereo that sells for $895 is on sale for 20% off the regular price. What
is the discounted price of the stereo? $716

38. Mr. Schultz's hardware store marks up merchandise 28% over warehouse
cost. What is the selling price for a wrench that costs him $12.45? $15.94

LESSON 6-6

Find each sales tax to the nearest cent.

39. total sales: $12.89   **40.** total sales: $87.95   **41.** total sales: $119.99
sales tax rate: 8.25%   sales tax rate: 6.5%   sales tax rate: 7%
$1.06 $5.72 $8.40

Find the total sales.

42. commission: $127.92 $1599   **43.** commission: $32.45 $649
commission rate: 8%   commission rate: 5%

44. An electronics salesperson sold $15,486 worth of computers last
month. She makes 3% commission on all sales and earns a monthly
salary of $1200. What was her total pay last month? $1664.58

45. Jon bought a printer for $189 and a set of printer cartridges for $129. Sales
tax on these items was 6.5%. How much tax did Jon pay for those items? $20.67

46. In her shop, Stephanie earns 16% profit on all of the clothes she sells. If
total sales were $3920 this month, what was her profit? $627.20

LESSON 6-7

Find the simple interest and the total amount to the nearest cent.

47. $3000 at 5.5% per year for 2 years $330; $3330

48. $15,599 at 9% per year for 3 years $4211.73; $19,810.73

49. $32,000 at 3.6% per year for 5 years $5760; $37,760

50. $124,500 at 8% per year for 20 years $199,200; $323,700

51. Rebekah invested $15,000 in a mutual fund at a yearly rate of 8%. She
earned $7200 in simple interest. How long was the money invested? 6 years

52. Shu invested $6000 in a savings account for 4 years at a rate of 5%.
a. What would be the value of the investment if the account is
compounded semiannually? $7310.42
b. What would be the value of the investment if the account is
compounded quarterly? $7319.34

Extra Practice ▪ Chapter 7

LESSON (7-1)   For 1–3, see p. A12.

Identify the quadrant that contains each point. Plot each point on a coordinate plane.

1. $M(-1, 1)$ II   **2.** $N(4, 4)$ I   **3.** $Q(3, -1)$ IV

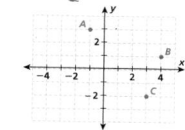

Give the coordinates of each point.

4. A $(-1, 3)$ **5.** B $(4, 1)$ **6.** C $(3, -2)$

LESSON (7-2)

Determine if each relationship represents a function.

7. 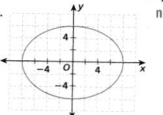   no

8.
x	y
-3	1
-1	1
-1	-2
0	-2
2	0
yes

9. 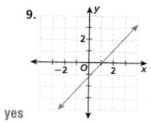   yes

LESSON (7-3)

Graph each linear function.   For 10–12, see p. A12.

10. $y = 2x + 2$ **11.** $y = x - 3$ **12.** $y = -x + 2$

13. The outside temperature is 52°F and is increasing at a rate of 6°F per hour. Write a linear function that describes the temperature over time. Then make a graph to show the temperature over the first 3 hours. $y = 6n + 52$; for graph, see p. A12.

LESSON (7-4)   For 14–16, see p. A12.

Create a table for each quadratic function, and use the table to graph the function.

14. $y = x^2 - 2$ **15.** $y = x^2 - x + 8$ **16.** $y = x^2 + x - 6$

LESSON (7-5)   For 17–19, see p. A12.

Create a table for each cubic function, and use the table to graph the function.

17. $y = x^3 - 1$ **18.** $y = 4x^3$ **19.** $y = -\frac{1}{4}x^3$

Tell whether each function is linear, quadratic, or cubic.

20. 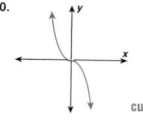   cubic

21. 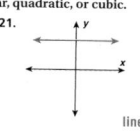   linear

22. 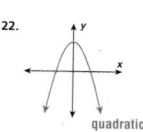   quadratic

EP14   *Extra Practice*

Extra Practice ▪ Chapter 7

LESSON (7-6)

Find the slope of each line.

23. 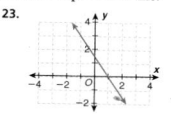 $-\frac{3}{2}$

24. 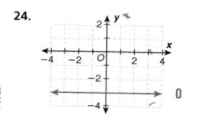   0

25. 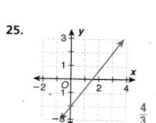 $\frac{4}{3}$

LESSON (7-7)   For 30, see p. A12.

Find the slope of the line that passes through each pair of points. $\frac{7}{2}$

26. $(3, 4)$ and $(-2, 2)$ $\frac{2}{5}$ **27.** $(6, 2)$ and $(-2, -6)$ **28.** $(3, 3)$ and $(1, -4)$ **29.** $(-2, 4)$ and $(1, 1)$ -1

30. The table shows how much money Andy and Margie made while working at the concession stand at a baseball game one weekend. Use the data to make a graph. Find the slope of the line, and explain what the slope means.

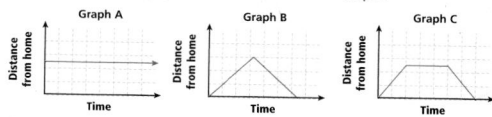

Time (h)	2	4	6	8
Money Earned ($)	15	30	45	60

slope: $\frac{15}{2}$, or 7.5; they earn $7.50 per hour

LESSON (7-8)   For 32, see p. A12.

31. Abby rode her bike to the park. She had a picnic there with friends and then rode home. Which graph best shows the situation?   Graph C

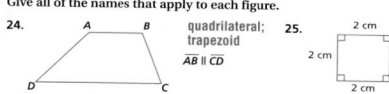

Graph A   Graph B   Graph C

32. Greg walked to a café for lunch. Then he walked across the street to a store before returning home. Sketch a graph to show Greg's distance compared to time.

LESSON (7-9)

33. Instructions for a chemical-concentrate swimming-pool cleaner state that 2 ounces of concentrate should be added to every $1\frac{1}{2}$ gallons of water used. How many ounces of concentrate should be added to 18 gallons of water?   24 ounces

34. The distance d that an object falls varies directly with the square of the time t of the fall. This relationship is expressed by the formula $d = k \cdot t^2$. An object falls 90 feet in 3 seconds. How far will the object fall in 15 seconds?   2250 ft

Extra Practice   EP15

Extra Practice ▪ Chapter 8

LESSON (8-1)   5–8. Possible answers given.

Use the diagram to name each figure.

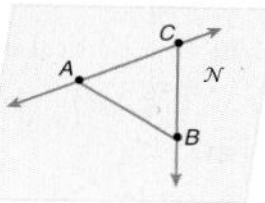

1. a line $\overline{AC}$ **2.** three rays $\overrightarrow{AC}, \overrightarrow{CB}, \overrightarrow{CA}$

3. a plane   plane N or plane ABC   **4.** three segments $\overline{AC}, \overline{CB}, \overline{BA}$

Use the diagram to name each figure.

5. a right angle $\angle AEB$ or $\angle DEB$

6. two acute angles $\angle BEC, \angle CED$

7. an obtuse angle $\angle AEC$

8. a pair of complementary angles $\angle BEC$ and $\angle CED$

LESSON (8-2)   9–11. Possible answers given.

Identify two lines that have the given relationship.

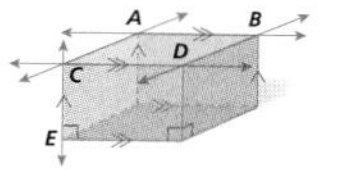

9. perpendicular lines $\overline{AC} \perp \overline{CE}$

10. skew lines $\overline{DB}$ and $\overline{CE}$

11. parallel lines $\overline{AB}$ and $\overline{CD}$

Identify two planes that appear to have the given relationship.

12. parallel planes   plane DEH || plane GFI

13. perpendicular planes   plane DEF ⊥ plane GFI

14. neither parallel nor perpendicular   plane HDG and plane HIF

LESSON (8-3)

Use the diagram to find each angle measure.

15. If $m\angle 1 = 107°$, find $m\angle 3$.   107°

16. If $m\angle 2 = 46°$, find $m\angle 4$.   46°

In the figure, line $d \parallel$ line f. Find the measure of each angle.

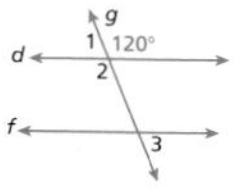

17. $\angle 1$ 60°   **18.** $\angle 2$ 120°   **19.** $\angle 3$ 60°

LESSON (8-4)

Find the missing angle measures in each triangle.

20. 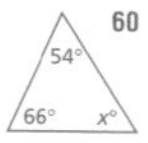   60

21. 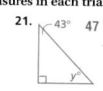   43°   47

22. 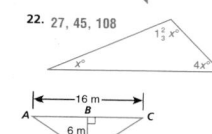   27, 45, 108

23. In the figure, B is the midpoint of $\overline{AC}$ and $\overline{BD}$ is perpendicular to $\overline{AC}$. Find the length of $\overline{AD}$.   10 m

EP16   *Extra Practice*

Extra Practice ▪ Chapter 8

LESSON (8-5)

Give all of the names that apply to each figure.

24. 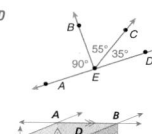   quadrilateral; trapezoid $\overline{AB} \parallel \overline{CD}$

25. 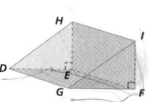   quadrilateral; parallelogram; rectangle; rhombus; square

Find the coordinates of the missing vertex. Then tell which lines are parallel and which lines are perpendicular.

26. rhombus $ABCD$ with $A(2, 3)$, $B(3, 0)$, and $D(1, 0)$ $C(2, -3)$, $\overline{AD} \parallel \overline{BC}$, $\overline{DC} \parallel \overline{AB}$

27. square $JKLM$ with $J(1, 1)$, $K(4, 1)$, and $L(4, -2)$ $M(1, -2)$; $\overline{JM} \parallel \overline{KL}$, $\overline{JK} \parallel \overline{ML}$, $\overline{JM} \perp \overline{JK}$, $\overline{KL} \perp \overline{LM}$, $\overline{LM} \perp \overline{MJ}$, $\overline{JK} \perp \overline{KL}$

28. rectangle $ABCD$ with $A(-4, 3)$, $B(-1, 3)$, and $D(-4, -1)$ $C(-1, -1)$; $\overline{AD} \parallel \overline{BC}$, $\overline{AB} \parallel \overline{DC}$, $\overline{AB} \perp \overline{BC}$, $\overline{BC} \perp \overline{CD}$, $\overline{CD} \perp \overline{DA}$, $\overline{DA} \perp \overline{AB}$

29. trapezoid $JKLM$ with $J(-2, 1)$, $K(2, 1)$, and $L(1, -1)$ Possible answer: $M(-2, -1)$, $\overline{JK} \parallel \overline{ML}$, $\overline{JK} \perp \overline{JM}$

LESSON (8-6)

In the figure, quadrilateral $ABCD \cong$ quadrilateral $KLMN$.

30. Find x. $x = 8$

31. Find y. $y = 4$

32. Find z. $z = 50$

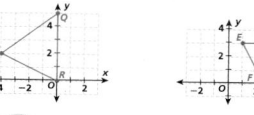

LESSON (8-7)

Graph each transformation.   For 33–35, see p. A13.

33. Rotate $\triangle PQR$ 90° counterclockwise about vertex R.

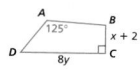

34. Reflect the figure across the y-axis.

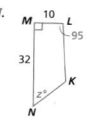

35. Translate $\triangle RST$ 3 units right and 3 units down.

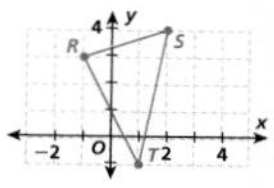

LESSON (8-8)

Create a tessellation with each figure.   For 36–37, see p. A13.

36. 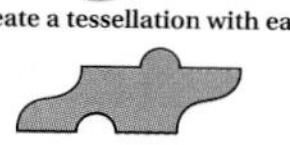 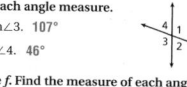   **37.**

Extra Practice   EP17

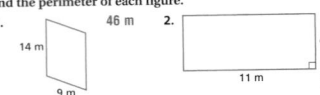

LESSON 9-1

Find the perimeter of each figure.

1. 46 m; 14 m, 9 m

2. 6 m; 11 m, 34 m

3. $13\frac{1}{3}$ in.; $3\frac{1}{3}$ in., $3\frac{1}{3}$ in.

Graph and find the area of each figure with the given vertices. For 4–5, see p. A13.

4. (−2, 1), (5, 1), (−2, 4), (5, 4) 21 units²

5. (1, 2), (2, −1), (5, 2), (6, −1) 12 units²

6. Find the perimeter and area of the figure. 52 units; 100 units²

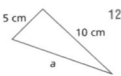

LESSON 9-2

Find the missing measurement for each figure with the given perimeter.

7. perimeter = 27 cm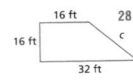

8. perimeter = 92 ft

9. perimeter = 16 units

Graph and find the area of each figure with the given vertices. For 10–11, see p. A13.

10. (−4, 3), (2, 3), (2, −1) 12 units²

11. (2, −1), (5, 3), (0, −1), (−3, 3) 20 units²

12. The sail of a toy sailboat forms a right triangle with legs that measure 5 inches each. Find the perimeter and area of the sail. about 17 in.; $12\frac{1}{2}$ in²

LESSON 9-3

Name the parts of circle *I*.

13. radii $\overline{IH}, \overline{IJ}, \overline{IK}, \overline{IM}$

14. diameters $\overline{JK}, \overline{HM}$

15. chords $\overline{LM}, \overline{JK}, \overline{HM}$

Find the central angle measure of the sector of a circle that represents the given percent of a whole.

16. 12% 43.2°

17. 40.5% 145.8°

18. 82% 295.2°

19. 50% 180°

LESSON 9-4

Find the circumference and area of each circle, both in terms of *π* and to the nearest hundredth. Use 3.14 for *π*.

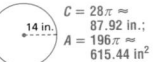 C = 14π ≈ 43.96 ft; A = 49π ≈ 153.86 ft²

20. 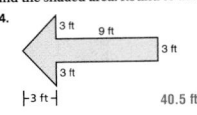 4 cm C = 8π ≈ 25.12 cm; A = 16π ≈ 50.24 cm²

21. 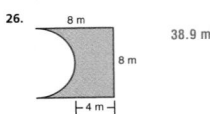 14 in. C = 28π ≈ 87.92 in.; A = 196π ≈ 615.44 in²

22. 14 ft

23. A wheel has a radius of 14 in. Approximately how far does a point on the wheel travel if it makes 15 complete revolutions? Use $\frac{22}{7}$ for *π*. 1320 in. or 110 ft

LESSON 9-5

Find the shaded area. Round to the nearest tenth, if necessary.

24. 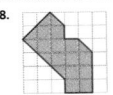 3 ft, 9 ft, 3 ft, 3 ft, 3 ft 40.5 ft²

25. 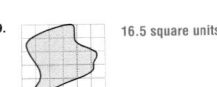 5 m, 13 m 84.6 m²

26. 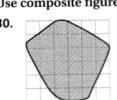 8 m, 8 m, 4 m 38.9 m²

27. 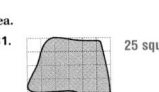 3 yd, 4 yd, 1 yd, 7 yd 22 yd²

LESSON 9-6 29–31. Possible answers given.

Find the area of each figure.

28. 15.5 square units

29. 16.5 square units

Use composite figures to estimate the shaded area.

30. 22 square units

31. 25 square units

LESSON 10-1

Describe the bases and faces of each figure. Then name the figure.

1. rectangle; triangles; rectangular pyramid

2. octagon; rectangles; octagonal prism

3.  hexagon; triangles; hexagonal pyramid

Classify each figure as a polyhedron or not a polyhedron. Then name the figure.

4. 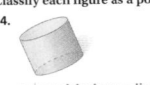 not a polyhedron; cylinder

5. not a polyhedron; cone

6.  polyhedron; rectangular prism

LESSON 10-2

Find the volume of each figure to the nearest tenth. Use 3.14 for *π*.

7. 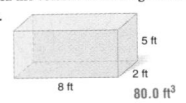 5 ft, 2 ft, 8 ft 80.0 ft³

8. 2 cm, 4 cm 50.2 cm³

9. 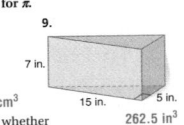 7 in., 15 in., 5 in. 262.5 in³

10. A can has a diameter of 3 in. and a height of 5 in. Explain whether doubling only the height of the can would have the same effect on the volume as doubling only the diameter. No; doubling the height would change the volume to $\pi(1.5)^2 \cdot 10 = 22.5\pi$ in³, but doubling the diameter would change the volume to $\pi(3)^2 \cdot 5 = 45\pi$ in³.

11. A shoe box is 6.8 in. by 5.9 in. by 16 in. Estimate the volume of the shoe box. 672 in³

12. Find the volume of the composite figure. 339 cubic units

LESSON 10-3

Find the volume of each figure to the nearest tenth. Use 3.14 for *π*.

13. 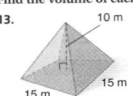 10 m, 15 m, 15 m 750 m³

14. 4.2 yd, 8 yd 147.7 yd³

15. 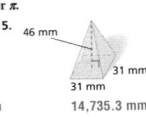 46 mm, 31 mm, 31 mm, 31 mm 14,735.3 mm³

16. A rectangular pyramid has a height of 15 ft and a base that measures 5 ft by 7.5 ft. Find the volume of the pyramid. 187.5 ft³

LESSON 10-4

Find the surface area of each prism to the nearest tenth.

17. 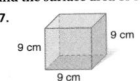 9 cm, 9 cm, 9 cm 486 cm²

18. 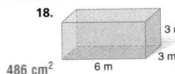 3 m, 6 m, 3 m 90 m²

19. 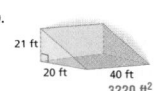 21 ft, 20 ft, 40 ft 3220 ft²

Find the surface area of each cylinder to the nearest tenth. Use 3.14 for *π*.

20. 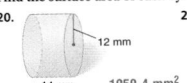 12 mm, 14 mm 1959.4 mm²

21. 6 m, 20 m 979.7 m²

22. 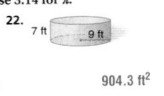 7 ft, 9 ft 904.3 ft²

LESSON 10-5

Find the surface area of each figure to the nearest tenth. Use 3.14 for *π*.

23. 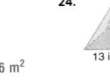 1 m, 1 m 7.6 m²

24. 15 in., 13 in., 13 in. 559.0 in²

25. 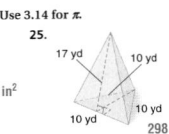 17 yd, 10 yd, 10 yd, 10 yd 298.3 yd²

Find the surface area of each figure with the given dimensions. Use 3.14 for *π*.

26. cone: diameter = 4 in. slant height = 3 in. 31.4 in²

27. regular square pyramid: base area = 64 ft² slant height = 8 ft 192 ft²

LESSON 10-6

Find the volume of each sphere, both in terms of *π* and to the nearest tenth. Use 3.14 for *π*.

28. r = 5 ft V ≈ 166.7π ≈ 523.3 ft³

29. d = 40 cm V ≈ 10,666.7π ≈ 33,493.3 cm³

Find the surface area of each sphere, both in terms of *π* and to the nearest tenth. Use 3.14 for *π*.

30. r = 3.8 mm 57.76π ≈ 181.4 mm²

31. d = 1.5 ft 2.25π ≈ 7.1 ft²

LESSON 10-7 For 32–34, see p. A13.

An 8 cm cube and a 5 cm cube are both part of a demonstration kit for architects. Compare the following values of the two cubes.

32. edge length

33. surface area

34. volume

LESSON 11-1 For 1–2, see p. A13.

1. Use a line plot to organize the data showing the number of miles that students cycled over a weekend. What number of miles did students cycle the most? **12 mi**

Number of Miles Cycled by Students
12 21 12 8 10 15 15 18 12 11 9 10 9 6 0 5 12 5 14 14 10 8 12 10 9

2. Use the given data to make a back-to-back stem-and-leaf plot.

World Series Win/Loss Records of Selected Teams (through 2001)							
Team	Yankees	Pirates	Giants	Tigers	Cardinals	Dodgers	Orioles
Wins	26	5	5	4	9	6	3
Losses	12	2	11	5	6	12	4

LESSON 11-2 For 5, see p. A13.

Find the mean, median, mode, and range of each data set.

3. 13, 8, 40, 19, 5, 8 **15.5; 10.5; 8; 35**
4. 21, 19, 23, 26, 15, 25, 25 **22; 23; 25; 11**

5. The table shows the number of points a player scored in ten games. Find the mean and median of the data. Which measure best describes the typical number of points scored in a game? Justify your answer.

Points a Player Scored in Ten Games										
Game	1	2	3	4	5	6	7	8	9	10
Points	36	34	28	50	30	30	31	47	55	29

LESSON 11-3

Find the lower and upper quartiles for each data set.

6. 27, 31, 26, 24, 33, 31, 24, 28, 31, 24, 22, 27, 31, 28, 26 **lower quartile: 24; upper quartile: 31**
7. 84, 79, 77, 72, 81, 82, 89, 94, 72, 80, 76, 80, 83, 86, 73 **lower quartile: 76; upper quartile: 84**

Use the given data to make a box-and-whisker plot. For 8–9, see p. A13.

8. 11, 4, 9, 17, 16, 12, 5, 16, 9, 11, 13
9. 57, 53, 52, 31, 48, 59, 64, 86, 56, 54, 55

LESSON 11-4 There is a positive correlation between the data sets; see p. A13 for graph.

10. The table shows the relationship between the number of years of post high school education and salary. Use the given data to make a scatter plot. Then describe the relationship between the data sets.

Number of Years of Post High School Education and Salary										
Years	1	1	3	4	4	4	5	5	6	6	8	8
Salary ($1000's)	18	20.5	28	35	51	43	58	52	64	58	75	73.5

LESSON 11-5

Refer to the spinner at right. Give the probability for each outcome.

11. not red $\frac{5}{8}$ 12. blue $\frac{3}{8}$ 13. not yellow $\frac{3}{4}$

A game consists of randomly selecting four colored marbles from a jar and counting the number of red marbles in the selection. The table gives the experimental probability of each outcome.

Number of Red Marbles	0	1	2	3	4
Probability	0.043	0.248	0.418	0.248	0.043

14. What is the probability of selecting 2 or more red marbles? **0.709, or 70.9%**
15. What is the probability of selecting at most 1 red marble? **0.291, or 29.1%**

LESSON 11-6

A utensil is drawn from a drawer and replaced. The table shows the results after 100 draws.

Outcomes	Draws
Spoon	33
Knife	36
Fork	31

16. Estimate the probability of drawing a spoon. **≈0.33, or 33%**
17. Estimate the probability of drawing a fork. **≈0.31, or 31%**

A sales assistant tracks the sales of a particular sweater. The table shows the data after 1000 sales.

Outcomes	Sales
White	361
Beige	207
Brown	189
Black	243

18. Use the table to compare the probability that the next customer will buy a brown sweater to the probability that the next customer will buy a beige sweater. **≈0.189; ≈ 0.207; more likely to buy a beige sweater**

LESSON 11-7

An experiment consists of rolling a fair number cube. There are six possible outcomes: 1, 2, 3, 4, 5, and 6. Find the probability of each event.

19. P(rolling an odd number) $\frac{1}{2}$
20. P(rolling a 2) $\frac{1}{6}$
21. P(rolling a number greater than 3) $\frac{1}{2}$
22. P(rolling a 7) 0

An experiment consists of rolling two fair number cubes. Find each probability.

23. P(rolling a total of 4) $\frac{1}{12}$
24. P(rolling a total less than 2) 0
25. P(rolling a total greater than 12) 0
26. P(rolling a total of 9) $\frac{1}{9}$

LESSON 11-8

27. An experiment consists of rolling a fair number cube three times. For each toss, all outcomes are equally likely. What is the probability of rolling a 2 three times in a row? $\frac{1}{216}$
28. A jar contains 3 blue marbles and 9 red marbles. What is the probability of drawing 2 red marbles at the same time? $\frac{6}{11}$

LESSON 12-1

Determine whether each expression is a monomial.

1. $\frac{1}{4}r^2st^5$ **yes**
2. $-6xy^3$ **yes**
3. 2^yx^4 **no**
4. $\frac{3m^3}{n^5}$ **no**

Classify each expression as a monomial, a binomial, a trinomial, or not a polynomial.

5. $-4x^3 + x^2 + \frac{1}{4}$ **trinomial**
6. $-9x^5y^2z^4$ **monomial**
7. $\frac{4}{5}m^4n^3 + m^3$ **binomial**
8. $h - 2h^{0.5} + 1$ **not a polynomial**
9. $xw^7 - 7wz$ **binomial**
10. $-\frac{3}{z^4}$ **not a polynomial**
11. $\frac{2}{3}a^4 + a^3 - 5$ **trinomial**
12. $13st^6$ **monomial**

Find the degree of each polynomial.

13. $3x^3 + 4x^5 + 8$ **5**
14. $b^2 - 9b^3 - b^4 - 8$ **4**
15. $z^2 + 5z^6 - 9z^3$ **6**
16. $4 - t$ **1**

17. The trinomial $-16t^2 + vt + 12$ describes the height in feet of a baseball thrown straight up from a 12-foot platform with a velocity of v ft/s after t seconds. What is the height of the ball after 3 seconds if $v = 55$ ft/s? **33 ft**

18. The trinomial $-4x^2 + 270x - 2000$ gives the net profit in dollars that a custom bicycle manufacturer earns by selling x bikes in a given month. What is the net profit for a month if $x = 15$ bicycles? **$1150**

LESSON 12-2

Identify the like terms in each polynomial.

19. $-s - 5r^2 + 7r - 9r^2 + 3s$ **−s and 3s, −5r² and −9r²**
20. $4x^2 - 9 - 7x + x^5 + 10$ **−9 and 10**
21. $5x^2y - 7x^2z + 7yz^2 - 3x^2y + xz^2$ **5x²y and −3x²y**
22. $-3mn + 3p^2 + 3p - 5p^2 + 3mn$ **−3mn and 3mn, 3p² and −5p²**
23. $8s^2 + 6 - 7s + 6s^4 - 13$ **6 and −13**
24. $25 + 15xy - 10x^2 + 3xy - 5y^2 - 5$ **25 and −5, 15xy and 3xy**

Simplify.

25. $5z^2 + 2z - z^2 + 11z - 9$ **4z² + 13z − 9**
26. $5 - 7(a^2 - 9) + 3a^2 - 7$ **−4a² + 61**
27. $-y^2z + 8xz - 6xy^2 + 10y^2z + xy^2$ **−5xy² + 8xz + 9y²z**
28. $5c^2 + 11cd - d^2 = 5(c^2 - d^2)$ **−2c(c + d)**
29. $5(a^2b^2 + 3ab) + 3(ab^2 - 5ab)$ **5a²b² + 3ab²**
30. $2s^2t^2 + st^2 + 5s^2t^2 - 7s^2t - 3st^2 + s^2t$ **7s²t² − 2st² − 6s²t**

31. A rectangle has a width of 12 cm and a length of $(2x^2 + 6)$ cm. The area is given by the expression $12(2x^2 + 6)$ cm². Use the Distributive Property to write an equivalent expression. **24x² + 72**

32. A parallelogram has a base of $(3x^2 - 4)$ in. and a height of 4 in. The area is given by the expression $4(3x^2 - 4)$ in². Use the Distributive Property to write an equivalent expression. **12x² − 16**

LESSON 12-3

Add.

33. $(2x^2y^3 - 7x^3y^2 + xy) + (x^2y^3 + 2x^3y^2 + 3xy)$ **−5x³y² + 3x²y³ + 4xy**
34. $(3a^2 + 4ab^2) + (a^2b + 2b^2) + (-a^2b - 7ab^2)$ **3a² − 3ab² + 2b²**
35. $(m^3 + 3m^2n^2 + 4) + (6m^2n^2 - 9)$ **m³ + 9m²n² − 5**
36. $(10r^3s^2 - 7r^2s + 4r) + (-4r^3s^2 + 3r)$ **6r³s² − 7r²s + 7r**

37. A rectangle has a width of $(x - 7)$ cm and a length of $(3x + 5)$ cm. An equilateral triangle has sides of length $x^2 - 2x + 3$. Write an expression for the sum of the perimeters of the rectangle and the triangle. **3x² + 2x + 5**

LESSON 12-4

Find the opposite of each polynomial.

38. $-6xy - 2y^3$ **6xy + 2y³**
39. $4a^3b + 7ab - 8$ **−4a³b − 7ab + 8**
40. $-2x^6 - 3x + x^3$ **2x⁶ + 3x − x³**
41. $7g^5 + gh^4$ **−7g⁵ − gh⁴**

Subtract.

42. $(5x^2 + 2xy - 3y^2) - (3x^2 + 2y^2 - 8)$ **2x² + 2xy − 5y² + 8**
43. $14a - (5a^3 - 3a + 6)$ **−5a³ + 17a − 6**
44. $(5r^2s^2 + 9r^2s + rs) - (-3r^2s - 7rs + 2r^2)$ **5r²s² + 12r²s + 8rs − 2r²**
45. $(12y^3 - 6xy + 1) - (8xy - 2x + 1)$ **12y³ − 14xy + 2x**

46. The area of the larger rectangle is $(10x^2 - 2x + 15)$ cm². The area of the smaller rectangle is $(5x^2 - 3x)$ cm². What is the area of the shaded region? **(5x² + x + 15) cm²**

LESSON 12-5

Multiply.

47. $(5xy^2)(7x^3y^2)$ **35x⁴y⁴**
48. $(2a^2bc^2)(-5a^3b^2)$ **−10a⁵b³c²**
49. $(6m^3n^4)(2mn)$ **12m⁴n⁵**
50. $6t(9s - 5t)$ **54st − 30t²**
51. $-p(2p^2 + pq - 5)$ **−2p³ − p²q + 5p**
52. $3xy^2(2x^3y^2 + 4x^2y - xy^6 - 11xy)$ **6x⁴y⁴ + 12x³y³ − 3x²y⁸ − 33x²y³**

53. A rectangle has a width of $3x^2y$ ft and a length of $(2x^2 + 4xy + 7)$ ft. Write and simplify an expression for the area of the rectangle. Then find the area of the rectangle if $x = 2$ and $y = 3$. **6x⁴y + 12x³y² + 21x²y; 1404 ft²**

LESSON 12-6

Multiply.

54. $(y + 5)(y - 3)$ **y² + 2y − 15**
55. $(s + 3)(s - 5)$ **s² − 2s − 15**
56. $(3m + 2)(4m - 3)$ **12m² − m − 6**
57. $(y + 1)^2$ **y² + 2y + 1**
58. $(d - 5)^2$ **d² − 10d + 25**
59. $(a + 9)(a - 9)$ **a² − 81**
60. $(x - 11)(x + 5)$ **x² − 6x − 55**
61. $(7b - 2)(7b + 2)$ **49b² − 4**
62. $(2m - n)(6m + 8n)$ **12m² + 10mn − 8n²**

Skills Bank

Skills Bank ..... Review Skills

Place Value to the Billions
🖥 ← 4NS1.1

A place-value chart can help you read and write numbers. The number 345,012,678,912.5784 (three hundred forty-five billion, twelve million, six hundred seventy-eight thousand, nine hundred twelve and five thousand seven hundred eighty-four ten-thousandths) is shown.

Billions	Millions	Thousands	Ones	Tenths	Hundredths	Thousandths	Ten-Thousandths
345,	012,	678,	912 .	5	7	8	4

EXAMPLE
Name the place value of the digit.

Ⓐ the 7 in the thousands column
7 ⟶ ten thousands place

Ⓑ the 0 in the millions column
0 ⟶ hundred millions place

Ⓒ the 5 in the billions column
5 ⟶ one billion, or billions, place

Ⓓ the 8 to the right of the decimal point
8 ⟶ thousandths

PRACTICE
Name the place value of the underlined digit.

1. 123,456,789,123.0594
2. 123,456,789,123.0594
3. 123,456,789,123.0594
4. 123,456,789,123.0594
5. 123,456,789,123.0594
6. 123,456,789,123.0594
1. hundred millions
2. ten billions
3. thousandths
4. ones
5. tenths
6. millions

Round Whole Numbers and Decimals
🖥 ← 4NS1.3, 5NS1.1

To round to a certain place, follow these steps.
1. Locate the digit in that place, and consider the next digit to the right.
2. If the digit to the right is 5 or greater, round up. Otherwise, round down.
3. Change each digit to the right of the rounding place to zero.

EXAMPLE
Ⓐ Round 125,439.378 to the nearest thousand.
125,439.378   Locate the digit.
The digit to the right, 4, is less than 5, so round down.
125,000.000 = 125,000

Ⓑ Round 125,439.378 to the nearest tenth.
125,439.378   Locate the digit.
The digit to the right, 7, is greater than 5, so round up.
125,439.400 = 125,439.4

PRACTICE
Round 259,345.278 to the place indicated.
1. hundred thousand   2. ten thousand
3. thousand
4. hundredth

1. 300,000
2. 260,000
3. 259,000
4. 259,345.28

SB2 *Skills Bank*

Compare and Order Whole Numbers
🖥 ← 4NS1.2

You can use place values to compare and order whole numbers.

EXAMPLE
Order the numbers from least to greatest: 42,810; 142,997; 42,729; 42,638.

Start at the left most place value.

There is one number with a digit in the greatest place. It is the greatest of the four numbers.

Compare the remaining three numbers. All values in the next two places, the ten thousands and thousands, are the same.

In the hundreds place, the values are different. Use this digit to order the remaining numbers.

42,638; 42,729; 42,810; 142,997

42,810
142,997
42,729
42,638

PRACTICE
Order the numbers in each set from least to greatest.
1. 2,564; 2,546; 2,465; 2,654
   2,465; 2,546; 2,564; 2,654
2. 6,237; 6,372; 6,273; 6,327
   6,237; 6,273; 6,327; 6,372
3. 132,957; 232,795; 32,975; 31,999
   31,999; 32,975; 132,957; 232,795
4. 9,614; 29,461; 129,164; 129,146
   9,614; 29,461; 129,146; 129,164

Compare and Order Decimals
🖥 ← 4NS1.2

You can also use place values to compare and order decimals.

EXAMPLE
Order the decimals from least to greatest: 14.35, 14.3, 14.05.

14.35   14.30 < 14.35   Compare two of the numbers at a time.
14.30   Write 14.3 as "14.30."

14.35   14.05 < 14.35   Start at the left and compare the digits.
14.05

14.30   14.05 < 14.30   Look for the first place the digits are different.
14.05
Graph the numbers on a number line.

14.05   14.30 14.35

14 14.1 14.2 14.3 14.4 14.5 14.6 14.7 14.8 14.9 15

The numbers are in order from left to right: 14.05, 14.3, and 14.35.

PRACTICE
Order the decimals in each set from least to greatest.
1. 9.5, 9.35, 9.65
   9.35, 9.5, 9.65
2. 4.18, 4.1, 4.09
   4.09, 4.1, 4.18
3. 1.56, 1.62, 1.5
   1.5, 1.56, 1.62
4. 6.7, 6.07, 6.23
   6.07, 6.23, 6.7

Skills Bank **SB3**

Divisibility Rules
🖥 4NS4.1

A number is divisible by another number if the division results in a remainder of 0. Some divisibility rules are shown below.

A number is divisible by . . .	Divisible	Not Divisible
2 if the last digit is an even number.	11,994	2175
3 if the sum of the digits is divisible by 3.	216	79
4 if the last two digits form a number divisible by 4.	1028	621
5 if the last digit is 0 or 5.	15,195	10,007
6 if the number is even and divisible by 3.	1332	44
8 if the last three digits form a number divisible by 8.	25,016	14,100
9 if the sum of the digits is divisible by 9.	144	33
10 if the last digit is 0.	2790	9325

PRACTICE
Determine whether each number is divisible by 2, 3, 4, 5, 6, 8, 9, or 10.
1. 56 2, 4, 8
2. 200 2, 4, 5, 8, 10
3. 75 3, 5
4. 324 2, 3, 4, 6, 9
5. 42 2, 3, 6
6. 812 2, 4
7. 784 2, 4, 8
8. 501 3
9. 2345 5
10. 555,555 3, 5
11. 3009 3
12. 2001 3

Factors and Multiples
🖥 4NS4.1

When two numbers are multiplied to form a third, the two numbers are said to be **factors** of the third number. **Multiples** of a number can be found by multiplying the number by 1, 2, 3, 4, and so on.

EXAMPLE
Ⓐ List all the factors of 48.
The possible factors are whole numbers from 1 to 48.
$1 \cdot 48 = 48$, $2 \cdot 24 = 48$, $3 \cdot 16 = 48$,
$4 \cdot 12 = 48$, and $6 \cdot 8 = 48$
The factors of 48 are
1, 2, 3, 4, 6, 8, 12, 16, 24, and 48.

Ⓑ Find the first five multiples of 3.
$3 \cdot 1 = 3$, $3 \cdot 2 = 6$, $3 \cdot 3 = 9$,
$3 \cdot 4 = 12$, and $3 \cdot 5 = 15$
The first five multiples of 3 are 3, 6, 9, 12, and 15.

PRACTICE
List all the factors of each number.
1. 8 1, 2, 4, 8
2. 20 1, 2, 4, 5, 10, 20
3. 9 1, 3, 9
4. 51 1, 3, 17, 51
5. 16 1, 2, 4, 8, 16
6. 27 1, 3, 9, 27
Find the first five multiples of each number.
7. 9 9, 18, 27, 36, 45
8. 10 10, 20, 30, 40, 50
9. 20 20, 40, 60, 80, 100
10. 15 15, 30, 45, 60, 75
11. 7 7, 14, 21, 28, 35
12. 18 18, 36, 54, 72, 90

SB4 *Skills Bank*

Prime and Composite Numbers
🖥 ← 4NS4.2

A **prime number** has exactly two factors, 1 and the number itself.

A **composite number** has more than two factors.

2   Factors: 1 and 2; prime
11   Factors: 1 and 11; prime
47   Factors: 1 and 47; prime

4   Factors: 1, 2, and 4; composite
12   Factors: 1, 2, 3, 4, 6, and 12; composite
63   Factors: 1, 3, 7, 9, 21, and 63; composite

EXAMPLE
Determine whether each number is prime or composite.

Ⓐ 17
Factors
1, 17 ⟶ prime

Ⓑ 16
Factors
1, 2, 4, 8, 16 ⟶ composite

Ⓒ 51
Factors
1, 3, 17, 51 ⟶ composite

PRACTICE
Determine whether each number is prime or composite.
1. 5 prime
2. 14 composite
3. 18 composite
4. 2 prime
5. 23 prime
6. 27 composite
7. 13 prime
8. 39 composite
9. 72 composite
10. 49 composite
11. 9 composite
12. 89 prime

Prime Factorization
🖥 ← 5NS1.4

A composite number can be expressed as a product of prime numbers. This is the **prime factorization** of the number. To find the prime factorization of a number, you can use a factor tree.

EXAMPLE
Find the prime factorization of 24.

24	24	24
2·12	3·8	4·6
2·3·4	3·2·4	2·2·2·3
2·3·2·2	3·2·2·2	

The prime factorization of 24 is $2 \times 2 \times 2 \times 3$, or $2^3 \times 3$.

PRACTICE
Find the prime factorization of each number.
1. 25 5×5, or 5^2
2. 16 $2 \times 2 \times 2 \times 2$, or 2^4
3. 56 $2 \times 2 \times 2 \times 7$, or $2^3 \times 7$
4. 18 $2 \times 3 \times 3$, or 2×3^2
5. 72 $2 \times 2 \times 2 \times 3 \times 3$, or $2^3 \times 3^2$
6. 40 $2 \times 2 \times 2 \times 5$, or $2^3 \times 5$

Skills Bank **SB5**

Greatest Common Divisor (GCD)

◆ 6NS2.4

The **greatest common divisor (GCD)** of two or more whole numbers is the greatest whole number that divides evenly into each number.

EXAMPLE

Find the greatest common divisor of 24 and 32.

Method 1: List all the factors of both numbers. Then find all the common factors.

24: 1, 2, 3, 4, 6, 8, 12, 24
32: 1, 2, 4, 8, 16, 32

The common factors are 1, 2, 4, and 8, so the GCD of 24 and 32 is 8.

Method 2: Find the prime factorization. Then find the common prime factors.

24: $2 \cdot 2 \cdot 2 \cdot 3$
32: $2 \cdot 2 \cdot 2 \cdot 2 \cdot 2$

The common prime factors are 2, 2, and 2. The GCD is the product of the factors, so the GCD of 24 and 32 is $2 \cdot 2 \cdot 2 = 8$.

PRACTICE

Find the GCD of each pair of numbers by either method.

1. 9, 15 3
2. 25, 75 25
3. 18, 30 6
4. 4, 10 2
5. 12, 17 1
6. 30, 96 6
7. 54, 72 18
8. 15, 20 5
9. 40, 60 20
10. 40, 50 10
11. 14, 21 7
12. 14, 28 14

Least Common Multiple (LCM)

◆ 6NS2.4

The **least common multiple (LCM)** of two or more numbers is the common multiple with the least value.

EXAMPLE

Find the least common multiple of 8 and 10.

Method 1: List multiples of both numbers. Then find the least value that is in both lists.

8: 8, 16, 24, 32, 40, 48, 56
10: 10, 20, 30, 40, 50, 60

The least value that is in both lists is 40, so the LCM of 8 and 10 is 40.

Method 2: Find the prime factorization. Then find the most occurrences of each factor.

8: $2 \cdot 2 \cdot 2$
10: $2 \cdot 5$

The LCM is the product of the factors, so the LCM of 8 and 10 is $2 \cdot 2 \cdot 2 \cdot 5 = 40$.

PRACTICE

Find the LCM of each pair of numbers by either method.

1. 2, 4 4
2. 3, 15 15
3. 10, 25 50
4. 10, 15 30
5. 3, 7 21
6. 18, 27 54
7. 12, 21 84
8. 9, 21 63
9. 24, 30 120
10. 9, 18 18
11. 16, 24 48
12. 8, 36 72

SB6 *Skills Bank*

Multiply and Divide by Powers of Ten

◆ 4NS3.2, ◆ 5NS2.2

When you *multiply* by powers of ten, move the decimal point one place to the right for each zero in the power of ten. When you *divide* by powers of ten, move the decimal point one place to the left for each zero in the power of ten.

EXAMPLE

Find each product or quotient.

A $0.37 \cdot 100$
$0.37 \cdot 100 = 0.\underset{\smile}{37}$
$= 37$

B $43 \cdot 1000$
$43 \cdot 1000 = 43.\underset{\smile}{000}$
$= 43,000$

C $0.24 \div 10$
$0.24 \div 10 = 0.\underset{\smile}{024}$
$= 0.024$

D $1467 \div 100$
$1467 \div 100 = 14\underset{\smile}{67}$
$= 14.67$

PRACTICE

Find each product or quotient.

1. $10 \cdot 8.53$ 85.3
2. $0.55 \cdot 10^4$ 5,500
3. $48.6 \cdot 1000$ 48,600
4. $2.487 \div 1000$ 0.002487
5. $6.03 \div 10^3$ 0.00603
6. $10^3 \cdot 12.1$ 12,100
7. $3.75 \cdot 10$ 37.5
8. $8.5 \div 10$ 0.85
9. $6420 \div 10^3$ 6.42
10. $1.9 \div 10$ 0.19

Dividing Whole Numbers

◆ 5NS2.2

Division is used to separate a quantity into equal groups. The number to be divided is the **dividend**, and the number you are dividing by is the **divisor**. The answer to a division problem is known as the **quotient**.

EXAMPLE

Divide 8208 by 72.

$$
\begin{array}{r}
114 \\
72\overline{)8208} \\
\underline{72}\!\downarrow \\
100 \\
\underline{72}\!\downarrow \\
288 \\
\underline{288} \\
0
\end{array}
$$

Write the dividend under the long division symbol.
Subtract.
Bring down the next digit.
Subtract.
Bring down the next digit.
Subtract.

PRACTICE

Divide.

1. $125\overline{)4125}$ 33
2. $158\overline{)20{,}698}$ 131
3. $268\overline{)4556}$ 17
4. $39\overline{)3471}$ 89
5. $99\overline{)4653}$ 47
6. $321\overline{)38{,}841}$ 121
7. $120\overline{)5040}$ 42
8. $108\overline{)10{,}476}$ 97
9. $741\overline{)107{,}445}$ 145

Skills Bank **SB7**

Plot Numbers on a Number Line

◆ 5NS1.5, ◆ 6NS1.1

You can order rational numbers by graphing them on a number line.

EXAMPLE

Put the numbers 0.25, $\frac{3}{4}$, 0.1, and $\frac{4}{5}$ on a number line. Then order the numbers from least to greatest.

$\frac{3}{4} = 0.75$
$\frac{4}{5} = 0.8$

The values increase from left to right: 0.1, 0.25, $\frac{3}{4}$, $\frac{4}{5}$.

PRACTICE

Plot each set of numbers on a number line. Then order the numbers from least to greatest.

1. 2.6, $2\frac{2}{5}$, $2\frac{1}{2}$ $2\frac{2}{5}$, $2\frac{1}{2}$, 2.6
2. 0.45, $\frac{3}{8}$, $\frac{4}{9}$ $\frac{3}{8}$, $\frac{4}{9}$, 0.45
3. 0.55, $\frac{2}{3}$, 0.6 0.55, 0.6, $\frac{2}{3}$
4. 5.25, $5\frac{1}{3}$, 5.05, 5.5 5.05, 5.25, $5\frac{1}{3}$, 5.5
5. 0.4, $\frac{1}{4}$, 0.42, $\frac{3}{5}$ $\frac{1}{4}$, 0.4, 0.42, $\frac{3}{5}$
6. $\frac{4}{9}$, 0.6, $\frac{6}{7}$ $\frac{4}{9}$, 0.6, $\frac{6}{7}$
7. 0.18, $\frac{1}{7}$, $\frac{1}{6}$, 0.12 0.12, $\frac{1}{7}$, $\frac{1}{6}$, 0.18
8. 0.3, $\frac{2}{7}$, 0.4, $\frac{3}{8}$ 0.3, $\frac{3}{8}$, $\frac{2}{7}$, 0.4
9. $\frac{7}{8}$, $\frac{6}{7}$, 0.65, $\frac{4}{7}$ $\frac{4}{7}$, 0.65, $\frac{5}{6}$, $\frac{7}{8}$

Simplest Form of Fractions

◆ 6NS2.4

A fraction is in simplest form when the greatest common divisor of its numerator and denominator is 1.

EXAMPLE

Simplify.

A $\frac{24}{30}$
24: 1, 2, 3, 4, 6, 8, 12, 24
30: 1, 2, 3, 5, 6, 10, 15, 30
Find the greatest common divisor of 24 and 30.

$\frac{24 \div 6}{30 \div 6} = \frac{4}{5}$ *Divide both the numerator and the denominator by 6.*

B $\frac{18}{28}$
18: 1, 2, 3, 6, 9, 18
28: 1, 2, 4, 7, 14, 28
Find the greatest common divisor of 18 and 28.

$\frac{18 \div 2}{28 \div 2} = \frac{9}{14}$ *Divide both the numerator and the denominator by 2.*

PRACTICE

Simplify.

1. $\frac{15}{20}$ $\frac{3}{4}$
2. $\frac{32}{40}$ $\frac{4}{5}$
3. $\frac{14}{35}$ $\frac{2}{5}$
4. $\frac{30}{75}$ $\frac{2}{5}$
5. $\frac{17}{51}$ $\frac{1}{3}$
6. $\frac{18}{42}$ $\frac{3}{7}$
7. $\frac{19}{38}$ $\frac{1}{2}$
8. $\frac{22}{121}$ $\frac{2}{11}$
9. $\frac{10}{32}$ $\frac{5}{16}$
10. $\frac{39}{91}$ $\frac{3}{7}$

SB8 *Skills Bank*

Mixed Numbers and Improper Fractions

◆ 6NS1.0

Mixed numbers can be written as fractions greater than 1, and fractions greater than 1 can be written as mixed numbers.

EXAMPLE

A Write $\frac{23}{5}$ as a mixed number.

$\frac{23}{5}$ *Divide the numerator by the denominator.*

$$
\begin{array}{r}
4 \\
5\overline{)23} \\
\underline{20} \\
3
\end{array}
\rightarrow 4\frac{3}{5}
$$
← *Write the remainder as the numerator of a fraction.*

B Write $6\frac{2}{7}$ as a fraction.

Multiply the denominator by the whole number.   *Add the product to the numerator.*

$6\frac{2}{7} \rightarrow 7 \cdot 6 = 42$ $42 + 2 = 44$

Write the sum over the denominator. $\rightarrow \frac{44}{7}$

PRACTICE

Write each mixed number as a fraction. Write each fraction as a mixed number.

1. $\frac{22}{5}$ $4\frac{2}{5}$
2. $9\frac{1}{7}$ $\frac{64}{7}$
3. $\frac{41}{8}$ $5\frac{1}{8}$
4. $5\frac{7}{9}$ $\frac{52}{9}$
5. $\frac{7}{3}$ $2\frac{1}{3}$
6. $4\frac{9}{11}$ $\frac{53}{11}$
7. $\frac{47}{16}$ $2\frac{15}{16}$
8. $3\frac{3}{8}$ $\frac{27}{8}$
9. $\frac{31}{9}$ $3\frac{4}{9}$
10. $8\frac{2}{3}$ $\frac{26}{3}$
11. $\frac{33}{5}$ $6\frac{3}{5}$
12. $12\frac{1}{9}$ $\frac{109}{9}$

Finding a Common Denominator

◆ 6NS2.4

You must often rewrite two or more fractions so that they have the same denominator, or a **common denominator**. One way to find a common denominator is to multiply the denominators. Or you can use the **least common denominator** (LCD), which is the LCM of the denominators.

EXAMPLE

Rewrite $\frac{3}{4}$ and $\frac{1}{6}$ so that they have a common denominator.

Method 1: Multiply the denominators: $4 \cdot 6 = 24$

$\frac{3}{4} = \frac{3 \cdot 6}{4 \cdot 6} = \frac{18}{24}$ $\frac{1}{6} = \frac{1 \cdot 4}{6 \cdot 4} = \frac{4}{24}$

For each fraction, multiply the denominator by a number to get the common denominator. Then multiply the numerator by the same number.

Method 2: Find the LCD. The LCM of the denominators, 4 and 6, is 12. So the LCD is **12**.

$\frac{3}{4} = \frac{3 \cdot 3}{4 \cdot 3} = \frac{9}{12}$ $\frac{1}{6} = \frac{1 \cdot 2}{6 \cdot 2} = \frac{2}{12}$

PRACTICE

1–5. Answers given use the LCD.

Rewrite each pair of fractions so that they have a common denominator.

1. $\frac{5}{6}$, $\frac{4}{9}$ $\frac{15}{18}$, $\frac{8}{18}$
2. $\frac{1}{6}$, $\frac{5}{8}$ $\frac{4}{24}$, $\frac{15}{24}$
3. $\frac{3}{10}$, $\frac{1}{8}$ $\frac{12}{40}$, $\frac{5}{40}$
4. $\frac{1}{4}$, $\frac{3}{14}$ $\frac{7}{28}$, $\frac{6}{28}$
5. $\frac{2}{5}$, $\frac{5}{12}$ $\frac{8}{36}$, $\frac{15}{36}$

Skills Bank **SB9**

Adding Fractions

🚌 ← 5NS2.3

To add fractions, first make sure they have a common denominator. Then add the numerators and keep the common denominator.

EXAMPLE

Add. Write your answer in simplest form.

Ⓐ $\frac{7}{8} + \frac{3}{8}$

$\frac{7}{8} + \frac{3}{8} = \frac{7+3}{8} = \frac{10}{8} = \frac{5}{4}$ *Add the numerators. Keep the denominator.*

Ⓑ $\frac{5}{6} + \frac{3}{5}$

Step 1 Find the LCD. The LCD is 30.

Step 2 Rewrite the fractions using the LCD: $\frac{5}{6} = \frac{5 \cdot 5}{6 \cdot 5} = \frac{25}{30}$ $\frac{3}{5} = \frac{3 \cdot 6}{5 \cdot 6} = \frac{18}{30}$

Step 3 Add: $\frac{25}{30} + \frac{18}{30} = \frac{43}{30}$ *Add the numerators. Keep the denominator.*

PRACTICE

Add. Write your answer in simplest form.

1. $\frac{3}{5} + \frac{1}{5}$ $\frac{4}{5}$ 2. $\frac{6}{7} + \frac{3}{7}$ $\frac{9}{7}$ 3. $\frac{3}{8} + \frac{1}{4}$ $\frac{5}{8}$ 4. $\frac{2}{3} + \frac{5}{9}$ $\frac{11}{9}$ 5. $\frac{3}{4} + \frac{2}{5}$ $\frac{23}{20}$

Subtracting Fractions

🚌 ← 5NS2.3

To subtract fractions, first make sure they have a common denominator. Then subtract the numerators and keep the common denominator.

EXAMPLE

Subtract. Write your answer in simplest form.

Ⓐ $\frac{7}{10} - \frac{3}{10}$

$\frac{7}{10} - \frac{3}{10} = \frac{7-3}{10} = \frac{4}{10} = \frac{2}{5}$ *Subtract the numerators. Keep the denominator.*

Ⓑ $\frac{3}{8} - \frac{1}{6}$

Step 1 Find the LCD. The LCD is 24.

Step 2 Rewrite the fractions using the LCD: $\frac{3}{8} = \frac{3 \cdot 3}{8 \cdot 3} = \frac{9}{24}$ $\frac{1}{6} = \frac{1 \cdot 4}{6 \cdot 4} = \frac{4}{24}$

Step 3 Subtract: $\frac{9}{24} - \frac{4}{24} = \frac{5}{24}$ *Subtract the numerators. Keep the denominator.*

PRACTICE

Subtract. Write your answer in simplest form.

1. $\frac{9}{7} - \frac{5}{7}$ $\frac{4}{7}$ 2. $\frac{8}{9} - \frac{5}{9}$ $\frac{1}{3}$ 3. $\frac{11}{12} - \frac{2}{3}$ $\frac{1}{4}$ 4. $\frac{8}{9} - \frac{4}{5}$ $\frac{4}{45}$ 5. $\frac{7}{10} - \frac{3}{8}$ $\frac{13}{40}$

Multiplying Fractions

🚌 ← 5NS2.4, 5NS2.5

To multiply fractions, you do *not* need a common denominator. Multiply the numerators, and then multiply the denominators.

EXAMPLE

Multiply $\frac{5}{7} \cdot \frac{2}{5}$. **Write your answer in simplest form.**

$\frac{5}{7} \cdot \frac{2}{5} = \frac{5 \cdot 2}{7 \cdot 5}$ *Multiply numerators and denominators.*

$= \frac{10}{35}$

$= \frac{2}{7}$ *Write in simplest form.*

PRACTICE

Multiply. Write your answer in simplest form.

1. $\frac{1}{2} \cdot \frac{4}{7}$ $\frac{2}{7}$ 2. $\frac{3}{8} \cdot \frac{4}{5}$ $\frac{3}{10}$ 3. $\frac{1}{5} \cdot \frac{3}{5}$ $\frac{3}{25}$ 4. $\frac{6}{14} \cdot \frac{7}{12}$ $\frac{1}{4}$ 5. $\frac{1}{3} \cdot \frac{3}{8}$ $\frac{1}{8}$

6. $\frac{2}{7} \cdot \frac{14}{4}$ 1 7. $\frac{3}{5} \cdot \frac{5}{7}$ $\frac{3}{7}$ 8. $\frac{6}{9} \cdot \frac{1}{2}$ $\frac{1}{3}$ 9. $\frac{5}{8} \cdot \frac{7}{10}$ $\frac{7}{16}$ 10. $\frac{10}{13} \cdot \frac{1}{5}$ $\frac{2}{13}$

Dividing Fractions

🚌 ← 5NS2.4, 5NS2.5

Two numbers are *reciprocals* if their product is 1. To find the reciprocal of a fraction, switch the numerator and denominator. Dividing by a fraction is the same as multiplying by its reciprocal. So, to divide fractions, multiply the first fraction by the reciprocal of the second fraction.

EXAMPLE

Divide $\frac{2}{5} \div \frac{3}{10}$. **Write your answer in simplest form.**

$\frac{2}{5} \div \frac{3}{10} = \frac{2}{5} \cdot \frac{10}{3}$ *Change the division to multiplication by the reciprocal.*

$= \frac{2 \cdot 10}{5 \cdot 3}$ *Multiply numerators and denominators.*

$= \frac{20}{15}$

$= \frac{4}{3}$ *Write in simplest form.*

PRACTICE

Divide. Write your answer in simplest form.

1. $\frac{3}{8} \div \frac{5}{6}$ $\frac{9}{20}$ 2. $\frac{5}{8} \div \frac{3}{4}$ $\frac{5}{6}$ 3. $\frac{7}{12} \div \frac{3}{4}$ $\frac{7}{9}$ 4. $\frac{2}{9} \div \frac{6}{7}$ $\frac{7}{27}$ 5. $\frac{3}{5} \div \frac{4}{5}$ $\frac{3}{4}$

6. $\frac{3}{12} \div \frac{3}{4}$ $\frac{1}{3}$ 7. $\frac{1}{6} \div \frac{2}{3}$ $\frac{1}{4}$ 8. $\frac{9}{11} \div \frac{3}{22}$ 6 9. $\frac{5}{6} \div \frac{5}{9}$ $\frac{3}{2}$ 10. $\frac{7}{8} \div \frac{3}{4}$ $\frac{7}{6}$

Adding Decimals

🚌 ← 5NS2.1

When adding decimals, first align the numbers at their decimal points. You may need to add zeros to one or more of the numbers so that they all have the same number of decimal places. Then add the same way you would with whole numbers.

EXAMPLE

Add 23.7 + 1.426.

```
  23.700      Align the numbers at their decimal points. Place two zeros after 23.7.
+  1.426
  25.126      Add and bring the decimal point straight down.
```

You can estimate the sum to check that your answer is reasonable: $24 + 1 = 25$ ✔

PRACTICE

Add.

1. $4.761 + 3.41$ 8.171 2. $14.2 + 16.9$ 31.1 3. $5.785 + 0.215$ 6 4. $32 + 1.75$ 33.75

Subtracting Decimals

🚌 ← 5NS2.1

When subtracting decimals, first align the numbers at their decimal points. You may need to add zeros to one or more of the numbers so that they all have the same number of decimal places. Then subtract the same way you would with whole numbers.

EXAMPLE

Subtract.

Ⓐ $42.543 - 6.7$

```
  42.543      Align the numbers at their decimal points.
-  6.700      Place two zeros after 6.7.
  35.843      Subtract and bring the decimal point straight down.
```

Estimate to check that your answer is reasonable: $43 - 7 = 36$ ✔

Ⓑ $5.0 - 0.003$

```
  5.000       Place two zeros after 5.0.
- 0.003       Align the numbers at their decimal points.
  4.997       Subtract and bring the decimal point straight down.
```

PRACTICE

Subtract.

1. $4.761 - 3.41$ 1.351 2. $30.79 - 28.18$ 2.61 3. $24.912 - 22.98$ 1.932 4. $20.11 - 8.284$ 11.826

Multiplying Decimals

🚌 ← 5NS2.1

When multiplying decimals, multiply as you would with whole numbers. The sum of the number of decimal places in the factors equals the number of decimal places in the product.

EXAMPLE

Find each product.

Ⓐ $81.2 \cdot 6.547$

```
    6.547  ← 3 decimal places
  × 81.2   ← 1 decimal place
    1 3094
    6 5470
  523 7600
  531.6164 ← 4 decimal places
```

Ⓑ $0.376 \cdot 0.12$

```
   0.376  ← 3 decimal places
 × 0.12   ← 2 decimal places
    752
   3760
 0.04512  ← 5 decimal places
```

PRACTICE

Find each product.

1. $0.97 \cdot 0.76$ 0.7372 2. $0.5 \cdot 3.761$ 1.8805 3. $42 \cdot 17.654$ 741.468 4. $7.005 \cdot 32.1$ 224.8605

5. $9.76 \cdot 16.254$ 158.63904 6. $296.5 \cdot 2.4$ 711.60 or 711.6 7. $7.7 \cdot 6.5$ 50.05 8. $8.92 \cdot 2.8$ 24.976

9. $3.65 \cdot 4.2$ 15.33 10. $0.002 \cdot 8.1$ 0.0162 11. $0.03 \cdot 0.204$ 0.00612 12. $98.6 \cdot 4.9$ 483.14

Dividing Decimals

🚌 ← 5NS2.1

When dividing with decimals, set up the division as you would with whole numbers. Pay attention to the decimal places, as shown below.

EXAMPLE

Find each quotient.

Ⓐ $89.6 \div 16$

```
      5.6
  16)89.6
      80
      96
      96
       0
```

Ⓑ $3.4 \div 4$

```
      0.85      Place decimal point.
  4)3.40    ← Insert zeros if necessary.
    3 2
      20
      20
       0
```

PRACTICE

Find each quotient.

1. $242.76 \div 68$ 3.57 2. $40.5 \div 18$ 2.25 3. $121.03 \div 98$ 1.235 4. $3.6 \div 4$ 0.9

5. $1.58 \div 5$ 0.316 6. $0.2835 \div 2.7$ 0.105 7. $8.1 \div 0.09$ 90 8. $0.42 \div 0.28$ 1.5

9. $480.48 \div 7.7$ 62.4 10. $36.9 \div 0.003$ $12,300$ 11. $0.784 \div 0.04$ 19.6 12. $15.12 \div 0.063$ 240

Skills Bank

Order of Operations

6AF1.3, 6AF1.4

When simplifying expressions, follow the order of operations.

1. Simplify within parentheses.
2. Simplify exponents.
3. Multiply and divide from left to right.
4. Add and subtract from left to right.

EXAMPLE

Simplify each expression.

A $3^2 \cdot (11 - 4)$

$3^2 \cdot (11 - 4)$

$3^2 \cdot 7$ *Simplify within parentheses.*

$9 \cdot 7$ *Simplify the exponent.*

63 *Multiply.*

B $\frac{-22 - 2^2}{5 - 3}$

$\frac{-22 - 2^2}{5 - 3}$

$\frac{(-22 - 2^2)}{(5 - 3)}$ *The fraction bar acts as a grouping symbol. Simplify the numerator and the denominator before dividing.*

$\frac{-22 - 4}{5 - 3}$ *Simplify the power in the numerator.*

$\frac{-26}{5 - 3}$ *Subtract to simplify the numerator.*

$\frac{-26}{2}$ *Subtract to simplify the denominator.*

-13 *Divide.*

PRACTICE

Simplify each expression.

1. $45 - 15 \div 3$ 40
2. $\frac{4^2}{5 - 3}$ 8
3. $35 \div (15 - 8)$ 5
4. $\frac{0 - 24}{6 + 2}$ -3
5. $24 \div 3 - 6 + 12$ 14
6. $6 \cdot 8 \div 2^2$ 12
7. $\frac{4 + 9 \cdot 4}{20 - 3 \cdot 4}$ 5
8. $3^2 - 10 \div 2 + 4 \cdot 2$ 12
9. $27 \div (3 + 6) + 6^2$ 39
10. $4 \div 2 + 8 \cdot 2^3 - 4$ 62
11. $\frac{2 + 3(6)}{2^2}$ 5
12. $8^2 \cdot 4 - 12 \cdot 13 + 5$ 105
13. $\frac{7^2}{4 + 2}$ 24.5
14. $37 - 21 \div 7$ 34
15. $9^2 - 32 \div 8$ 77
16. $10 \div 2 + 8 \cdot 2$ 21
17. $\frac{2^3 - 8}{2 - 1}$ 0
18. $4 \cdot 12 - 4 + 8 \div 2$ 48
19. $28 - 3^2 + 27 \div 3$ 28
20. $9 + (50 - 16) \div 2$ 26
21. $\frac{-18 - 6^2}{-9}$ 6

SB14   *Skills Bank*

Measurement

6AF2.1

The measurements for time are the same worldwide.

1 min = 60 s	1 wk = 7 days	1 leap yr = 366 days
1 h = 60 min	1 yr = 12 mo	
1 day = 24 h	1 yr = 365 days	

The **customary system** of measurement is used in the United States.

Length	Capacity	Weight
12 in. = 1 ft	8 oz = 1 c	16 oz = 1 lb
3 ft = 1 yd	2 c = 1 pt	2000 lb = 1 ton
5280 ft = 1 mi	2 pt = 1 qt	

The **metric system** is used elsewhere and in science worldwide.

Length	Capacity	Mass
1 mm = 0.001 m	1 mL = 0.001 L	1 mg = 0.001 g
1 cm = 0.01 m	1 kL = 1000 L	1 kg = 1000 g
1 km = 1000 m		

Use the table below to convert from metric to customary measurements.

Length	Capacity	Mass/Weight	Temperature
1 cm ≈ 0.394 in.	1 L ≈ 1.057 qt	1 g ≈ 0.0353 oz	
1 m ≈ 3.281 ft	1 L ≈ 0.264 gal	1 kg ≈ 2.205 lb	$F = \left(\frac{9}{5} \times C\right) + 32$
1 m ≈ 1.094 yd	1 L ≈ 4.227 c	1 kg ≈ 0.001 ton	
1 km ≈ 0.621 mi	1 mL ≈ 0.338 fl oz	1 metric T ≈ 1.102 ton	

Use the table below to convert from customary to metric measurements.

Length	Capacity	Weight/Mass	Temperature
1 in. ≈ 2.540 cm.	1 qt ≈ 0.946 L	1 oz ≈ 28.350 g	
1 ft ≈ 0.305 m	1 gal ≈ 3.785 L	1 lb ≈ 0.454 kg	$C = \frac{5}{9} \times (F - 32)$
1 yd ≈ 0.914 m	1 c ≈ 0.237 L	1 ton ≈ 907.185 kg	
1 mi ≈ 1.609 km	1 fl oz ≈ 29.574 mL	1 ton ≈ 0.907 metric ton	

EXAMPLE

A Write <, >, or =.

35 in. ▨ 1 yd
35 in. ▨ 3 ft   *1 yd = 3 ft*
35 in. < 36 in.   *3 ft = 36 in.*
35 in. < 1 yd

B Convert 32 km to mi.

1 km ≈ 0.621 mi
32 km ≈ 32 · 0.621 mi
32 km ≈ 19.872 mi

C Convert 25°C to °F.

$F = \left(\frac{9}{5} \times 25\right) + 32$
$F = 45 + 32$
$F = 77°F$

PRACTICE

Write <, >, or =.

1. 3 lb ▨ 40 oz   >
2. 200 cm ▨ 2 m   =
3. 6 c ▨ 2 qt   >

Convert.

4. 15 mi to km   24.135 km
5. 2 weeks to hours   336 hours
6. 32 fl oz to mL   946.368 mL
7. 95°F to °C   35°C
8. 14 tons to kg   12,700.59 kg

Skills Bank   **SB15**

Polygons

◆—3MG2.1

A **polygon** is a closed figure with three or more sides. The name of a polygon is determined by its number of sides.

If all the sides are the same length, and all the angles have the same measure, the polygon is a **regular polygon**. Sides and angles with the same measures are marked with the same symbol.

Number of Sides	Name	Number of Sides	Name
3	Triangle	8	Octagon
4	Quadrilateral	9	Nonagon
5	Pentagon	10	Decagon
6	Hexagon	12	Dodecagon
7	Heptagon	n	n-gon

EXAMPLE

Identify each polygon.

A

regular hexagon

The mark on each side indicates that the sides are all the same length. The arch inside each angle indicates that the angles all have the same measure.

B

pentagon

PRACTICE

Identify each polygon.

1. heptagon
2. regular octagon
3. quadrilateral

Geometric Patterns

3MG2.0

Patterns involving polygons may deal with size, color, position, or shape.

EXAMPLE

Predict the next term: △, ☐, ⬠, ...

hexagon   *Each term has one more side than the previous term. The next term will have six sides.*

PRACTICE

1. Predict the next term.

△, ◇, ◯, ... dodecagon

2. Describe the missing term.

☐, ⬠, ___, ◯, ... octagon

SB16   *Skills Bank*

Classify Triangles and Quadrilaterals

4MG3.7, 4MG3.8

A triangle can be classified according to its angle measurements or according to the number of congruent sides it has.

Classifying by Angles		Classifying by Sides	
Acute	Three acute angles	Scalene	No sides congruent
Right	One right angle	Isosceles	At least 2 sides congruent
Obtuse	One obtuse angle	Equilateral	All sides congruent

EXAMPLE 1

Classify each triangle according to its angles and sides.

A   acute isosceles

B   4 cm, 12 cm, 9 cm   obtuse scalene

C   acute equilateral

Quadrilaterals can also be classified according to their sides and angles.

Parallelograms	
Parallelogram 2 pairs of parallel, congruent sides	
Rectangle 4 right angles	
Rhombus 4 congruent sides	
Square 4 right angles and 4 congruent sides	

Other Quadrilaterals	
Trapezoid exactly 1 pair of parallel sides	
Isosceles Trapezoid congruent, nonparallel legs	
Kite 2 pairs of adjacent, congruent sides	

EXAMPLE 2

Tell whether the following statement is always, sometimes, or never true:
A square is a rectangle.

always   *A rectangle must have four right angles, and a square always has four right angles.*

PRACTICE

Classify each triangle according to its angles and sides.

1. 35°, 110°, 35°   obtuse isosceles
2.   right scalene
3. 2 in., 4 in., 4 in.   acute isosceles

Tell whether each statement is always, sometimes, or never true.

4. A rectangle is a square.   sometimes
5. A trapezoid is a parallelogram.   never

Name the quadrilaterals that always meet the given conditions. parallelogram, rectangle, rhombus, square, kite

6. All sides are congruent.   square, rhombus
7. Two pairs of sides are congruent.

Skills Bank   **SB17**

Bar Graphs

 5SDAP1.2

A **bar graph** displays data using vertical or horizontal bars that do not touch. Bar graphs are often a good way to display and compare data that can be organized into categories.

EXAMPLE 1

Use the bar graph to answer each question.

A Which language has the most native speakers?
The bar for Mandarin is the longest, so Mandarin has the most native speakers.

B About how many more people speak Mandarin than speak Hindi?
About 500 million more people speak Mandarin than speak Hindi.

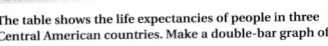

You can use a **double-bar graph** to compare two related sets of data.

EXAMPLE 2

The table shows the life expectancies of people in three Central American countries. Make a double-bar graph of the data.

Country	Male	Female
El Salvador	67	74
Honduras	63	66
Nicaragua	65	70

Step 1 Choose a scale and interval for the vertical axis.

Step 2 Draw a pair of bars for each country's data. Use different colors to show males and females.

Step 3 Label the axes and give the graph a title.

Step 4 Make a key to show what each bar represents.

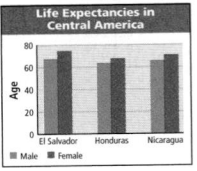

PRACTICE

The bar graph shows the average amount of fresh fruit consumed per person in the United States in 1997. Use the graph for Exercises 1–3.

1. Which fruit was eaten the least? **grapes**
2. About how many pounds of apples were eaten per person? **about 17.5 pounds**
3. About how many more pounds of bananas than pounds of oranges were eaten per person? **about 15 pounds**

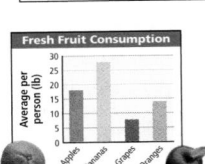

SB18 *Skills Bank*

Line Graphs

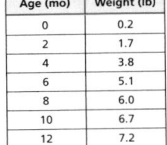 5SDAP1.2

You can use a *line graph* to show how data changes over a period of time. In a **line graph**, line segments are used to connect data points on a coordinate grid. The result is a visual record of change.

EXAMPLE

Make a line graph of the data in the table. Use the graph to determine during which 2-month period the kitten's weight increased the most.

Age (mo)	Weight (lb)
0	0.2
2	1.7
4	3.8
6	5.1
8	6.0
10	6.7
12	7.2

Step 1 Determine the scale and interval for each axis. Place units of time on the horizontal axis.

Step 2 Plot a point for each pair of values. Connect the points using line segments.

Step 3 Label the axes and give the graph a title.

The graph shows the steepest line segment between 2 and 4 months. This means the kitten's weight increased most between 2 and 4 months.

PRACTICE

1. The table shows average movie theater ticket prices in the United States. Make a line graph of the data. Use the graph to determine during which 5-year period the average ticket price increased the least. **1990–1995**

Year	1965	1970	1975	1980	1985	1990	1995	2000	2005
Price ($)	1.01	1.55	2.05	2.69	3.55	4.23	4.35	5.39	6.41

2. The table shows the number of teams in the National Basketball Association (NBA). Make a line graph of the data. Use the graph to determine during which 5-year period the number of NBA teams increased the most. **1965–1970**

Year	1965	1970	1975	1980	1985	1990	1995	2000	2005
Teams	9	14	18	22	23	27	27	29	30

Skills Bank **SB19**

Histograms

 5SDAP1.2

A **histogram** is a bar graph that shows the frequency of data within equal intervals. The bars must be of equal width and should touch, but not overlap.

EXAMPLE

The table shows survey results about the number of CDs students own. Make a histogram of the data.

1	III	5	卌 I	9	卌 I	13	卌 IIII	17	卌 IIII
2	II	6	III	10	卌 卌	14	卌 卌 I	18	卌 卌 I
3	卌	7	卌 III	11	卌 卌 I	15	卌 卌 I	19	II
4	卌 I	8	卌 II	12	卌 卌	16	卌 卌 I	20	卌 I

Number of CDs

Step 1 Make a frequency table of the data. Be sure to use a scale that includes all of the data values and separate the scale into equal intervals. Use these intervals on the horizontal axis of your histogram.

Number of CDs	Frequency
1–5	22
6–10	34
11–15	52
16–20	35

Step 2 Choose an appropriate scale and interval for the vertical axis. The greatest value on the scale should be at least as great as the greatest frequency.

Step 3 Draw a bar for each interval. The height of the bar is the frequency for that interval. Bars must touch but not overlap.

Step 4 Label the axes and give the graph a title.

PRACTICE
1–2. See p. A13.

1. The list below shows the ages of musicians in a local orchestra. Make a histogram of the data.

14, 35, 22, 18, 49, 38, 30, 27, 45, 19, 35, 46, 27, 21, 32, 30

2. The list below shows the results of a typing test in words per minute. Make a histogram of the data.

62, 55, 68, 47, 50, 41, 62, 39, 54, 70, 56, 47, 71, 55, 60, 42

SB20 *Skills Bank*

Circle Graphs

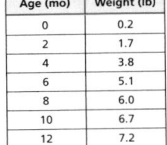 5SDAP1.2

A **circle graph** shows parts of a whole. The entire circle represents 100% of the data and each sector represents a percent of the total.

EXAMPLE

At Mazel Middle School, students were surveyed about their favorite types of TV programs. Use the given data to make a circle graph.

Type of Program	Number of Students
Science	25
Cooking	15
Sports	50
Sitcoms	150
Movies	60
Cartoons	200

Step 1 Find the total number of students surveyed.
25 + 15 + 50 + 150 + 60 + 200 = 500

Step 2 Find the percent of the total students who like each type of program.

Step 3 Find the angle measure of each sector of the graph. There are 360° in a circle, so multiply each percent by 360°.

Percent	Angle of Sector
$\frac{25}{500} = 5\%$	$0.05 \cdot 360° = 18°$
$\frac{15}{500} = 3\%$	$0.03 \cdot 360° = 10.8°$
$\frac{50}{500} = 10\%$	$0.1 \cdot 360° = 36°$
$\frac{150}{500} = 30\%$	$0.3 \cdot 360° = 108°$
$\frac{60}{500} = 12\%$	$0.12 \cdot 360° = 43.2°$
$\frac{200}{500} = 40\%$	$0.4 \cdot 360° = 144°$

Step 4 Use a compass to draw a large circle. Use a straightedge to draw a radius.

Step 5 Use a protractor to measure the angle of the first sector. Draw the angle.

Step 6 Use the protractor to measure and draw each of the other angles.

Step 7 Give the graph a title, and label each sector with its name and percent. Color the sectors.

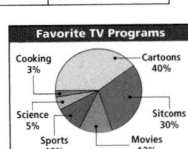

PRACTICE

1. Use the given data to make a circle graph.

Favorite Pets					
Type of Pet	Dog	Fish	Bird	Cat	Other
Number of People	225	150	112	198	65

1. See p. A13.

Skills Bank **SB21**

Sampling

⬛ ◆—6SDAP2.2

A **population** is a group that someone is gathering information about.

A **sample** is part of a population. For example, if 5 students are chosen to represent a class of 20 students, the 5 chosen students are a sample of the population of 20 students.

The sample is a **random sample** if every member of the population had an equal chance of being chosen.

EXAMPLE

Jamal telephoned people on a list of 100 names in the order in which they appeared. He surveyed the first 20 people who answered their phone. Explain whether the sample is random.

Names at the beginning of the list have a greater chance of being selected than those at the end of the list, so the sample is not random.

PRACTICE ▮

Explain whether each sample is random.

1. Rebecca surveyed every person in a theater who was sitting in a seat along the aisle.
   1. No; people not sitting in an aisle seat have no chance of being chosen.

2. Inez assigned 50 people a number from 1 to 50. Then she used a calculator to generate 10 random numbers from 1 to 50 and surveyed those with matching numbers.
   Yes; every person had a number that the calculator could have selected.

Bias

⬛ ◆—6SDAP2.4

Bias is error that favors part of a population and/or does not accurately represent the population. Bias can occur from using sampling methods that are not random or from asking confusing or leading questions.

EXAMPLE

Jenn went to a movie theater and asked people who exited if they agree that the theater should be torn down to build office space. Explain why the survey is biased.

People usually only go to movies if they enjoy them, so those exiting a movie theater would not want it torn down. People who do not use the theater did not have a chance to answer.

PRACTICE ▮

Explain why each survey is biased.

1. A surveyor asked, "Is it not true that you do not oppose the candidate's views?"
   1. Someone may not understand what his or her answer means because the question was worded in a confusing way.

2. Brendan asked everyone on his track team how they thought the money from the athletic department fund-raiser should be spent.
   The track team would want the money to benefit their own team, not others. Athletes on other teams did not have a chance to answer.

SB22 *Skills Bank*

Compound Events

⬛ ◆—6SDAP2.2

A **compound event** consists of two or more single events.

EXAMPLE

Marilyn randomly draws 1 of 6 cards, numbered from 1 to 6, from a box and then randomly selects 1 of 2 marbles, 1 red (R) and 1 blue (B), from a jar. Find the probability that the card will show an even number and that the marble will be red.

	1	2	3	4	5	6
R	1, R	2, R	3, R	4, R	5, R	6, R
B	1, B	2, B	3, B	4, B	5, B	6, B

Use a table to list all possible outcomes. Circle or highlight the outcomes with an even number and "red."

$P(\text{even, red}) = \frac{3 \text{ ways outcome can occur}}{12 \text{ equally likely outcomes}} = \frac{3}{12} = \frac{1}{4}$

In the Example, a table was used to list the possible outcomes. Another way to list outcomes of a compound event is to use a **tree diagram**.

Card Number   Marble

List all possible outcomes for the six cards: 1, 2, 3, 4, 5, 6.

Then, for each outcome of the six cards, list all possible outcomes for the marbles: red and blue for each card.

PRACTICE ▮

1. If you spin the spinner twice, what is the probability that it will land on blue on the first spin and on green on the second spin? $\frac{1}{16}$

2. What is the probability that the spinner will land on either red or yellow on the first spin and blue on the second spin? $\frac{1}{8}$

3. What is the probability that the spinner will land on the same color twice in a row? $\frac{1}{16}$

Skills Bank **SB23**

Inductive and Deductive Reasoning

⬛ 6AF2.0, 7MR2.4

Inductive reasoning involves examining a set of data to determine a pattern and then making a conjecture about the data. In **deductive reasoning**, you reach a conclusion by using logical reasoning based on given statements, properties, or premises that you assume to be true.

EXAMPLE

A Use inductive reasoning to determine the 30th number of the sequence.
   3, 5, 7, 9, 11, . . .
   Examine the pattern to determine the relationship between each term in the sequence and its value.

Term	1st	2nd	3rd	4th	5th
Value	3	5	7	9	11

$1 \cdot 2 + 1 = 2 + 1 = 3$ $4 \cdot 2 + 1 = 8 + 1 = 9$
$2 \cdot 2 + 1 = 4 + 1 = 5$ $5 \cdot 2 + 1 = 10 + 1 = 11$
$3 \cdot 2 + 1 = 6 + 1 = 7$

To obtain each value, multiply the term by 2 and add 1. So the 30th term is $30 \cdot 2 + 1 = 60 + 1 = 61$.

B Use deductive reasoning to make a conclusion from the given premises.
   Premise: Makayla needs at least an 89 on her exam to get a B for the quarter in math class.
   Premise: Makayla got a B for the quarter in math class.
   Conclusion: Makayla got at least an 89 on her exam.

PRACTICE ▮

Use inductive reasoning to determine the 100th number in each pattern.

1. $\frac{1}{2}$, 1, $1\frac{1}{2}$, 2, $2\frac{1}{2}$, . . .   **50**
2. 1, 4, 9, 16, 25, . . .   **10,000**
3. 4, 6, 8, 10, 12, . . .   **202**
4. 0, 3, 6, 9, 12, 15, . . .   **297**

Use deductive reasoning to make a conclusion from the given premises.

5. Premise: If it is raining, then there must be a cloud in the sky.
   Premise: It is raining.   *There is a cloud in the sky.*

6. Premise: A quadrilateral with four congruent sides and four right angles is a square.
   Premise: Quadrilateral *ABCD* has four right angles.
   Premise: Quadrilateral *ABCD* has four congruent sides.   *Quadrilateral ABCD is a square.*

7. Premise: Darnell is 3 years younger than half his father's age.
   Premise: Darnell's father is 40 years old.   *Darnell is 17 years old.*

SB24 *Skills Bank*

Selected Answers

Selected Answers

Chapter 1

1-1 Exercises
1. 15 **3.** 3 **5.** 18 **7.** 2 c **9.** $2\frac{1}{2}$ c **11.** 37 **13.** 57 **15.** 13 pt **17.** 10 pt **19.** 22 **21.** 10 **23.** 20 **25.** 16 **27.** 45 **29.** 138 **31.** 20.7 **33.** 36 **35.** 105 **37.** 11 **39.** 32 **41.** 21 **43.** 19 **45.** \$110 **47.** B **49.** yes **51.** A **53.** 15, 21, 61, 71 **55.** 49, 81 **57.** 202 **59.** 400 **61.** 200.2 **63.** 40

1-2 Exercises
1. $3p - 5$ **3.** $16 + \frac{d}{7}$ **5.** 18 plus the product of 43 and s **7.** 10 plus the quotient of y and 31 **9.** $5n$; \$75; \$125; \$175; \$225 **11.** $1 + \frac{5}{n}$ **13.** $78j - 45$ **15.** $14 + 59q$ **17.** 12 more than the product of 16 and g **19.** 51 less than the quotient of w and 182 **23.** $6y + 9$ **25.** $\frac{1}{3+g}$ **27.** $13y - 6$ **29.** $2\left(\frac{m}{35}\right)$ **31.** $8\left(\frac{2}{3} + x\right)$ **33.** 8 times the sum of m and 5 **35.** 17 times the quotient of 16 and w **37.** $\frac{1}{4}(x + 7)$ or $\frac{x+7}{4}$ **41.** C **43.** $9n$; \$9450 **45.** 24 **47.** 7

1-3 Exercises
1. $-4 < -2$ **3.** −17, −8, 6 **5.** −7, 0, 3 **7.** 15 **9.** 5 **11.** 21 **13.** 14 **15.** −6, −2, 5 **17.** −30, −27, −25 **19.** 9 **21.** 11 **23.** 5 **25.** 0 **27.** < **29.** = **31.** < **33.** > **35.** −16, −12, 24 **37.** −45, −25, 35 **39.** 50 **41.** 1 **43.** 72 **45.** 6 **47.** 9 **49.** 38 **51.** 16 **53.** Antarctica, Asia, North America, Europe, South America, Africa, Australia **57.** −7, −6, −5 **59.** A **61.** 9 **63.** 64 **65.** $7t + 8$

1-4 Exercises
1. 6 **3.** 2 **5.** −7 **7.** 6 **9.** 11 **11.** −10 **13.** −2 **15.** −5 **17.** 22 **19.** −16 **21.** 7 **23.** −32 **25.** 23 **27.** 9 **29.** $-3 + (-4) = -7$ **31.** −12 **33.** −17 **35.** −22 **37.** 43 **39.** 8 **41.** −30 **43.** −15 **45a.** \$1,146,137,000,000 **b.** −\$1,763,863,000,000 **c.** about −\$618,000,000,000 or −\$618 billion **49.** C **51.** 4 **53.** 12 **55.** 13

1-5 Exercises
1. −14 **3.** 12 **5.** 17 **7.** 18 **9.** −10 **11.** 17 **13.** 17 **15.** 10 **17.** $-6 - (-4) = -2$ **19.** 3 **21.** −56 **23.** −26 **25.** −20 **27.** −24 **29.** 13 **31.** ≈190 ft above the starting point **33.** Great Pyramid to Cleopatra; about 500 years **35.** Cleopatra takes the throne and Napoleon invades Egypt. **39.** 8 **41.** 3 **43.** −12

1-6 Exercises
1. −32 **3.** 84 **5.** 49 **7.** −24 **9.** gains \$15 **11.** 21 **13.** −84 **15.** 3 **17.** −140 **19.** −60 **21.** −39 **23.** +\$100 **25.** $\frac{15}{3}$, 5; $\frac{-6}{3}$, −2; $\frac{9}{3}$, 3; $\frac{-15}{3}$, −5 **27.** −12 **29.** −4 **31.** 8 **33.** 36 **35.** 11 **37.** −8 **39.** −6 **45.** D **47.** $j - 18$ **49.** $y - 22$ **51.** 9 **53.** −254

1-7 Exercises
1. 12 **3.** −14 **5.** −23 **7.** 39 **9.** 15,635 ft **11.** 32 **13.** 44 **15.** −74 **17.** 35 **19.** 5 **21.** 24 **23.** 3 **25.** 949 **27.** 110 **29.** −17 **31.** −138 **33.** −1784 **35.** $t - 600 = -173$; 427°C **37.** 40 **39.** 1 **41.** −59 **47.** B **49.** −14 **51.** −13 **53.** −56 **55.** −2

1-8 Exercises
1. −7 **3.** 2 **5.** −60 **7.** −6 **9.** 54 people **11.** −15 **13.** 7 **15.** 2 **17.** −4 **19.** 54 **21.** 96 **23.** −161 **25.** −252 **27.** −7 **29.** 2 **31.** 56 **33.** −72 **35.** 17 **37.** 207 **39.** −48 **41.** −15 **43.** $8n = 32$; $n = 4$ servings **45.** 16 h; \$160 **47.** $7 + n = 15$; $n = 8$ **49.** $12 = q - (-8)$; $q = 4$ **51.** 74 mi **53.** $\$195 = \$156 + m$; $m = \$39$ **57.** C **59.** −16 **61.** −12 **63.** $x = 9$ **65.** $x = -26$

1-9 Exercises
1. $9x + 6 = -12$ **3.** 2 **5.** −8 **7.** −5 **9.** 24 **11.** 42 **13.** 88 **15.** 18 DVDs **17.** $4z + 18 = -54$ **19.** 1 **23.** 5 **25.** −2 **27.** −9 **29.** −4 **31.** 40 **33.** 55 **35.** −30 **37.** 5 h **39.** Nine less than 4 times a number is 3; 3 **41.** −21 **43.** −3 **45.** 0 **47.** $\frac{x}{9} - 3 = 8$; $x = 99$ **49.** $5 - 3m = -4$; $m = 3$ **51.** $16m = 42{,}000$; $m = 2625$ miles per year **53.** $\frac{1}{6}m = 22$; m = 132 miles **55.** A **57.** 44 **59.** −30 **60.** −6 **61.** −72 **62.** −3 **63.** 147 **64.** −9

Chapter 1 Study Guide: Review

1. equation **2.** opposite **3.** absolute value **4.** 147 **5.** 152 **6.** 278 **7.** $2(k + 4)$ **8.** $4t + 5$ **9.** 10 less than the product of 5 and b **10.** 32 plus the product of 23 and s **11.** 12 less than the quotient of 10 and r **12.** 16 more than the quotient of y and 8 **13.** 1 **14.** 15 **15.** 34 **16.** 21 **17.** 14 **18.** −1 **19.** −2 **20.** −12 **21.** −3 **22.** 1 **23.** −24 **24.** 8 **25.** −8 **26.** −16 **27.** 17 **28.** 3 **29.** 15 **30.** −22 **31.** −4 **32.** 16 **33.** −5 **34.** −35 **35.** −18 **36.** 52 **37.** 25 **38.** 120 **39.** 2 **40.** $z = 23$ **41.** $t = 8$ **42.** $k = 15$ **43.** $x = -15$ **44.** 1300 lb **45.** 3300 mi^2 **46.** $g = -8$ **47.** $k = 9$ **48.** $p = -80$ **49.** $w = -48$ **50.** $y = -40$ **51.** $z = 192$ **52.** 705 mi **53.** 24 months **54.** $x = -6$ **55.** $y = 96$ **56.** $n = -49$ **57.** $x = 4$ **58.** $n = -24$ **59.** $y = -11$ **60.** 3 hours

Chapter 2

2-1 Exercises
1. 0.625 **3.** $0.41\overline{6}$ **5.** $0.\overline{1}$ **7.** 0.375 **9.** 0.35 **11.** $\frac{3}{4}$ **13.** $\frac{2}{5}$ **15.** $-2\frac{1}{5}$ **17.** $3\frac{21}{100}$ **19.** $\frac{9}{11}$ **21.** $\frac{115}{333}$ **23.** $\frac{73}{99}$ **25.** $\frac{58}{99}$ **27.** −0.375 **29.** −1.8 **31.** 1.6 **33.** −4.6 **35.** $1.\overline{3}$ **37.** $\frac{3}{5}$ **39.** $\frac{18}{25}$ **41.** $1\frac{377}{1000}$ **43.** $-1\frac{2}{5}$ **45.** $\frac{5}{33}$ **47.** $\frac{4}{11}$ **49.** $\frac{3}{11}$ **51.** $\frac{151}{333}$ **53.** yes **55.** no **57.** yes **59.** yes **61.** $3\frac{3}{8}$ **63a.** $\frac{4}{9}$; $\frac{1}{6}$; $\frac{1}{4}$; $\frac{7}{15}$; $\frac{9}{16}$; $\frac{12}{25}$; $\frac{5}{8}$; $\frac{3}{8}$ **b.** 3 × 3; 2 × 3; 2 × 2; 3 × 5; 2 × 2 × 2 × 2; 5 × 5; 2 × 2 × 2 **c.** $0.\overline{4}$, repeating; $0.1\overline{6}$, repeating; 0.25, terminating; $0.4\overline{6}$, repeating; 0.5625, terminating; 0.48, terminating; 0.625, terminating; 0.375, terminating **65.** GCD = 2; $\frac{21}{34}$ **69.** C **71.** 9.875 **73.** 28; 48 **75.** −20 **77.** 21 **79.** 180 **81.** −126

2-2 Exercises
1. < **3.** = **5.** > **7.** < **9.** $7\frac{5}{16}$ in., 7.5 in., $8\frac{1}{8}$ in., 8.25 in. **11.** > **13.** = **15.** > **17.** < **19.** > **21.** < **23.** = **25.** = **27.** < **29.** < **37a.** apricot, sulphur, large orange sulphur, white-angled sulphur, great white **b.** between the apricot sulphur and the large orange sulphur **41.** $|0.62|$, $\left|-\frac{2}{3}\right|$, $|-0.75|$, $\left|\frac{5}{6}\right|$ **43.** D **45.** 10 **47.** −47 **49.** 0.75 **51.** 2.5 **53.** 0.95

2-3 Exercises
1. 30.01 **3.** 24.125 **5.** 0.56 s **7.** $-1\frac{1}{5}$ **9.** $\frac{1}{5}$ **11.** $\frac{4}{9}$ **13.** 33.67 **15.** −12.902 **17.** 10.816 s **19.** $-\frac{14}{17}$ **21.** $-\frac{8}{33}$ **23.** $\frac{1}{3}$ **25.** 7.9375 **27.** $4\frac{69}{200}$ **29.** $\frac{1}{4}$ in. **31.** $-\frac{6}{11}$ **33.** $-2\frac{5}{9}$ **35.** −1 **37.** $-1\frac{1}{2}$ **39.** 0.186 quadrillion Btu **43.** D **45.** $\frac{11}{15}$ **47.** $b = 1$ **49.** $a = -5$ **51.** < **53.** =

2-4 Exercises
1. $\frac{5}{32}$ **3.** $5\frac{5}{8}$ **5.** $4\frac{1}{2}$ miles **7.** 0.162 **9.** −0.42 **11.** $-\frac{7}{36}$ **13.** $\frac{7}{24}$ **15.** $1\frac{1}{2}$ **17.** $\frac{21}{40}$ **19.** 27 boys **21.** −0.235 **23.** −4.125 **25.** −0.496 **27.** −0.368 **29.** $-8\frac{7}{11}$ **31.** $15\frac{5}{9}$ **33.** 1.82 **35.** −0.558 **37.** $2\frac{53}{54}$ **39.** $-\frac{55}{192}$ **41.** $\frac{3}{8}$ **43a.** $1\frac{1}{4}$ tsp **b.** $1\frac{1}{2}$ tsp **c.** 2 tsp **47.** A **49.** C **51.** > **53.** > **55.** $-\frac{5}{6}$ **57.** $-\frac{2}{9}$

2-5 Exercises
1. $\frac{2}{3}$ **3.** $-\frac{2}{7}$ **5.** $1\frac{11}{80}$ **7.** $1\frac{2}{5}$ **9.** 12.4 **11.** 15.3 **13.** $4.2\overline{3}$ **15.** 490 **17.** −19.4 **19.** 45 **21.** −18 **23.** $\frac{1}{6}$ serving **25.** $1\frac{9}{35}$ **27.** $1\frac{3}{5}$ **29.** $-\frac{8}{21}$ **31.** $2\frac{1}{28}$ **33.** 83 **35.** 9.7 **37.** 40.55 **39.** 13.6 **41.** 12 **43.** −11 **45.** 370 **47.** 11 glasses **49.** $3\frac{31}{48}$ in. **53.** about $\frac{1}{3}$ **55.** B **57.** 11 **59.** $\frac{13}{20}$ **61.** $\frac{723}{1000}$ **63.** $-\frac{4}{5}$

2-6 Exercises
1. $\frac{19}{21}$ **3.** $-4\frac{3}{10}$ **5.** $\frac{1}{40}$ **7.** $-8\frac{7}{12}$ **9.** $\frac{1}{2}$ **11.** $\frac{69}{130}$ **13.** 4 yd **15.** $1\frac{11}{72}$ **17.** $\frac{13}{14}$ **19.** $\frac{19}{21}$ **21.** $1\frac{1}{3}$ **23.** $-\frac{29}{126}$ **25.** $1\frac{4}{45}$ **27.** $\frac{39}{833}$ **29.** $\frac{11}{120}$ **31.** $1\frac{1}{8}$ miles **33.** $\frac{1}{12}$ **35.** $\frac{19}{42}$ **37.** $\frac{7}{34}$ **39.** $\frac{5}{8}$ in. **41.** $-\frac{145}{168}$ **43.** $\frac{67}{72}$ **45.** $-4\frac{1}{3}$ **47.** $2\frac{5}{8}$ cups **49a.** $16\frac{3}{8} - m$ **b.** $11\frac{1}{8}$ mi **c.** $27\frac{1}{2}$ mi **51.** $\frac{73}{100}$ meter **53.** $19\frac{19}{100}$ meters **55.** The company did not find a common denominator when adding $\frac{1}{2}$ and $\frac{1}{4}$. **57.** −28 **59.** $-1\frac{3}{11}$ **61.** $-\frac{5}{6}$

2-7 Exercises
1. $y = -82.3$ **3.** $m = -19.2$ **5.** $s = 97.146$ **7.** $x = -\frac{5}{9}$ **9.** $w = -\frac{7}{15}$ **11.** $y = -8$ **13.** 8 days **15.** $m = -7$ **17.** $k = -3.6$ **19.** $c = 3.12$ **21.** $d = \frac{6}{25}$ **23.** $x = -\frac{1}{24}$ **25.** $r = -\frac{5}{7}$ **27.** $d = 1\frac{1}{21}$ **29.** $2258\frac{4}{15}$ carats **31.** Cullinan III **33.** $z = \frac{1}{3}$ **35.** $j = -21.6$ **37.** $t = 7$ **39.** $d = -\frac{1}{2}$ **41.** $v = -30.25$ **43.** $y = -4.2$ **45.** $c = -\frac{1}{20}$ **47.** $y = 54.2$ **49.** $m = -1.4$ **53.** 60 carats **55.** $3v = 6\frac{1}{4}$; $2\frac{1}{12}$ minutes **56.** $p - 15$ **57.** $\frac{1}{2}(m + 19)$ **59.** $10\frac{5}{12}$ **61.** $2\frac{4}{45}$

2-8 Exercises
1. 7 hours **3.** $y = 11$ **5.** $x = 5$ **7.** $a = 22$ **9.** $y = \frac{2}{5}$ **11.** $m = 12\frac{3}{10}$ **13.** $r = 6\frac{3}{4}$ **15.** 2.02 **17.** 17.5 **19.** $\frac{1}{15}$ **21.** $\frac{1}{18}$ **23.** 10 **25.** 64 **27.** 1.3 **29.** $-\frac{11}{5}$ **31.** $\frac{n-7}{5} = 13$; 72 **35.** 110,000 **37.** 25 in. **39.** B **41.** $-\frac{5}{8}$ **43.** $\frac{1}{12}$ **45.** y = −4.4 **47.** $m = -25.6$

Chapter 2 Study Guide: Review

1. rational number **2.** terminating decimal **3.** reciprocal or multiplicative inverse **4.** $\frac{3}{5}$ **5.** $\frac{1}{4}$ **6.** $\frac{21}{40}$ **7.** $\frac{5}{11}$ **8.** $\frac{1}{3}$ **9.** $\frac{212}{999}$ **10.** 1.75 **11.** $0.\overline{26}$ **12.** $0.\overline{7}$ **13.** < **14.** = **15.** −0.9, $-\frac{2}{3}$, 0.25, $\frac{1}{2}$ **16.** −0.11, 0, 0.67, $\frac{9}{10}$ **17.** $-\frac{6}{13}$ **18.** $\frac{7}{5}$ **19.** $\frac{5}{9}$ **20.** $\frac{1}{6}$ **21.** $\frac{1}{11}$ **22.** $\frac{12}{13}$ **23.** $-1\frac{1}{5}$ **24.** $7\frac{3}{5}$ **25.** $\frac{8}{15}$ **26.** −4 **27.** $2\frac{1}{4}$ **28.** $3\frac{1}{4}$ **29.** 13 **30.** $-\frac{7}{18}$ **31.** 6 **32.** $\frac{3}{8}$ **33.** $\frac{2}{9}$ **34.** −16 **35.** $\frac{5}{4}$ **36.** 2 **37.** $1\frac{1}{6}$ **38.** $\frac{5}{18}$ **39.** $11\frac{3}{10}$ **40.** $4\frac{7}{20}$ **41.** $3\frac{17}{60}$ **42.** $-9\frac{11}{36}$ **43.** −21.8 **44.** −18 **45.** $-\frac{5}{8}$ **46.** 2 **47.** $\frac{95}{99}$ **48.** −2 **49.** 44.6 **50.** −6 **51.** \$108 **52.** $m = 10$ **53.** $y = -8$ **54.** $c = -16$ **55.** $r = -3$ **56.** $t = 16$ **57.** $w = 64$ **58.** $r = -42$ **59.** $h = -50$ **60.** $x = 52$ **61.** $d = -33$ **62.** $a = 67$ **63.** $c = 90$ **64.** 11

Chapter 3

3-1 Exercises
1. Comm. Prop. of Add. **3.** 39 **5.** 700 **7.** 130 **9.** 168 **11.** 54 **13.** 396 **15.** Comm. Prop. of Mult. **17.** 109 **19.** 1300 **21.** 24 **23.** 133 **25.** 132 **27.** 21 **29.** Distrib. Prop. **31.** Assoc. Prop. of Add. **33.** Comm. Prop. of Add. **35.** 40 **37.** 15 **39.** \$53 **43.** 8; Distrib. Prop. **45.** y; Assoc. Prop. of Add. **47.** $24 + 19 + 26 + 21 = 24 + 26 + 19 + 21$ (Comm. Prop. of Add.) $= (24 + 26) + (19 + 21)$ (Assoc. Prop. of Add.) $= 50 + 40 = 90$ in. **49.** The sentence should read, "You can use the Commutative Property of Addition..." **51.** $12 \cdot \left(\frac{1}{3} + \frac{1}{6} + \frac{1}{4}\right) = 12 \cdot \frac{1}{3} + 12 \cdot \frac{1}{6} + 12 \cdot \frac{1}{4}$ (Distrib. Prop.) $= 4 + 2 + 3$ (Mult.) $= (4 + 2) + 3$ (Assoc. Prop. of Add.) $= 6 + 3$ (Add) $= 9$ **53.** C **55.** $1\frac{2}{5}$ **57.** $-\frac{1}{25}$ **59.** $2\frac{1}{10}$ **61.** 28

3-2 Exercises
1. $5x$ **3.** $12f + 8$ **5.** $6p - 9$ **7.** $5x + 8y$ **9.** $9x + y$ **11.** $7g + 5h - 12$ **13.** $r + 12$ **15.** $2t + 56$ **17.** $10y + 17$ **19.** $13y$ **21.** $6a + 15$ **23.** $5x + 3$ **25.** $7z + b - 5$ **27.** $11x + 4y - 8$ **29.** $6d + 3e + 12$ **31.** $4y + 10$ **33.** $11x + 18$ **35.** $3x - 48$ **37.** $2(5x + x)$; $12x$ **39.** no; $6r - 12m - 5m - 15 + 5r + 7$, Distrib. Prop.; $6r + 5r - 12m - 5m - 15 + 7$, Comm. Prop.; $6r + 5r - 12m - 5m - 15 + 7$; $11r - 17m - 8$ **41.** $7d + 1$ **43.** $6r^2 + 11r$ **45.** $k + 13$ **47.** $49g + 53s + 44b$ **49.** $y^2 - 2(x + y^2)$; $-y^2 - 2x$ **53.** $4\frac{5}{6}x + 11\frac{1}{2}$ **55.** 16 **57.** $a = -80$ **59.** 2; Distrib. Prop. **61.** 5; Assoc. Prop. of Mult.

3-3 Exercises
1. $d = 3$ **3.** $e = 6$ **5.** $h = 7$ **7.** $x = -1$ **9.** $p = -1$ **11.** 6 hours **13.** $k = -10$ **15.** $w = 3$ **17.** $y = 5$ **19.** $h = 6$ **21.** $m = 2$ **23.** $x = -12$ **25.** $n = 2$ **27.** $b = -13$ **29.** $x = 17$ **31.** $y = -7$ **33.** \$11.80 per hour **35.** 31 and 32 **37.** 212°F **41.** C **43.** $n = -3$ **45.** $x = 121$ **47.** $6t + 3k - 15$

3-4 Exercises
1. $x = 1$ **3.** $x = 2$ **5.** $x = -20$ **7.** $x = 1$ **9.** $d = 5$ **11.** 250 min; \$8.75 **13.** $x = 1$ **15.** all real numbers **17.** $y = 6$ **19.** $x = 16.2$ **21.** $a = 13$ **23.** $y = 2$ **25.** $n = 5$ **27.** $x = 5$ **29.** 22, 23 **31.** $x - 25 = 10 - 4x$; $x = 7$ **33.** 350 units **35a.** 17 protons **b.** 11 **39.** C **41.** $x = 3$ **43.** $g = -12$ **45.** < **47.** <

3-5 Exercises
1. $p \le 60$ **3.** $m + 7 \ge 15$
5. 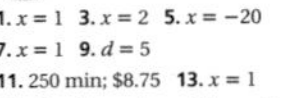

7. 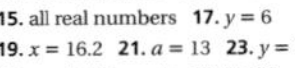

9. $s < -5$ or $s \ge 3$ **11.** $s < 10$ **13.** $x - 11 < 35$ **15.** $\frac{y}{7} \le 10$
17. 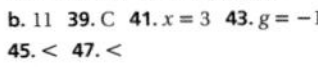

19. 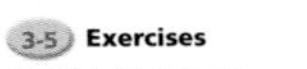

21. 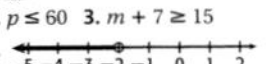

23. 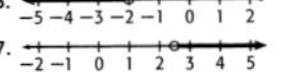

25. $c \ge \frac{1}{2}$ or $c \le -7$ **27.** $5w \ge 60$ **29.** $m - 2\frac{2}{5} \le 3\frac{1}{5}$ **31.** $x \le 9$ **33.** $x \ge 4$ **35.** $d \le 89{,}000$ **39.** B **41.** −25, −19, −12 **43.** −11, −9, −7, −5 **45.** $\frac{1}{11}$ **47.** $-1\frac{1}{3}$

3-6 Exercises
1. $x < -7$ **3.** $f < -24$ **5.** $k \ge 9.3$ **7.** $6\frac{1}{2} + x \le 16$; $x \le 9\frac{1}{2}$ **9.** $x \ge 56$ **11.** $x \ge 15$ **13.** $c < 3\frac{1}{3}$ **15.** $21.75 + x \ge 50$; $x \ge 28.25$ **17.** $z > 0$ **19.** $y \ge -1.8$ **21.** $k \le 1$ **23.** $\{x : x < -20\}$ **25.** $\{b : b > -3.5\}$ **27a.** $98{,}200 + s > 201{,}522$; $s > 103{,}322$ **29.** The solution is $x \le 4$. **33.** B **35.** $\frac{19}{28}$ **37.** $\frac{1}{15}$ **39.** $t + 2 < 8$

3-7 Exercises
1. $r > 18$ **3.** $120 \ge j$, or $j \le 120$ **5.** $-40 \ge a$, or $a \le -40$ **7.** $r > -63$ **9.** 104 sandwiches **11.** $75 < x$, or $x > 75$ **13.** $-77 \ge p$, or $p \le -77$ **15.** $h > 12$ **17.** $q \ge -4$ **19.** $6 > r$, or $r < 6$ **21.** $w \ge -3$ **23.** $t < 95$ **25.** $a < 120$ **33.** A **37.** 27 lb, 135 lb **39.** at least \$13.34 per week **41.** $-\frac{5}{33}$ **43.** $-8\frac{1}{3}$

3-8 Exercises
1. $k > 2$ **3.** $y < -8$ **5.** $y \ge 7$ **7.** $x < 3$ **9.** $h \le 1$ **11.** $d < -1$ **13.** at least 21 caps **15.** $x > 4$ **17.** $q \le 2$ **19.** $x \le -7$ **21.** $a \ge -3$ **23.** $k \ge 3$ **25.** $r < 3$ **27.** $p \le \frac{22}{3}$ **29.** $w > -1$ **31.** $a > \frac{1}{2}$ **33.** $q < 6$ **35.** $b < 2.7$ **37.** $f \le -2.7$ **39.** 7 **41.** at least 31 beads **43a.** \$158 **b.** 17 mo **47.** B **49.** Comm. Prop. of Mult. **51.** Comm. Prop. of Add. **53.** $7r - 60$

Chapter 3 Study Guide: Review

1. inequality **2.** Comm. Prop. **3.** terms **4.** Comm. Prop. of Add. **5.** Assoc. Prop. of Add. **6.** Dist. Prop. **7.** Assoc. Prop. of Add. **8.** $19m - 10$ **9.** $14w + 6$ **10.** $2x + 3y$ **11.** $2t^2 - 4t + 3t^3$ **12.** $y = -1$ **13.** $h = 2$ **14.** $t = -1$ **15.** $r = 3$ **16.** $z = 2$ **17.** $a = 12$ **18.** $s = 7$ **19.** $c = 24$ **20.** $x = \frac{1}{6}$ **21.** $y = \frac{2}{3}$ **22.** no solution **23.** $z = 5$ **24.** Let d = distance; $d \le 1$ mi **25.** Let c = cost; $c \ge 1500$ **26.** Let s = number of students; $s < 45$
27. 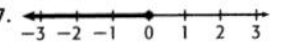

28. 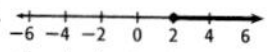

29. 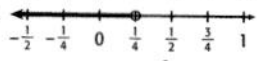

30. $r \geq 4$ 31. $n < -\frac{1}{2}$ 32. $x > 0.2$ 33. $y \leq -5$ 34. $n + 17.75 \leq 20$; $n \leq 2.25$ 35. $m \geq 18$ 36. $n \leq -3$ 37. $t > -16$ 38. $p < -3$ 39. $b \geq -27$ 40. $a > 8$ 41. $z > 1$ 42. $h \geq 6$ 43. $a < 24$ 44. $x \geq -6$ 45. $k > 3$ 46. $y > \frac{1}{8}$

Chapter 4

4-1 Exercises

1. 12^1 3. 2^2b^3 5. 64 7. $\frac{1}{8}$ 9. 4096 11. −5 13. −710 15. 5^6 17. 3^2d^2 19. $(-4)^2c^3$ 21. 256 23. $\frac{1}{32{,}768}$ 25. $\frac{1}{36}$ 27. 173 29. 1 31. −36 33. −1 35. −325 37. −1 39. −426 41. 2^{18} = 262,144 bacteria 43. $(3d)^2$ 45. $(7x)^4$ 47. ≈1728 cm³ 51. B 53. 625 55. −83 57. 55 59. 0.14 61. 0.375

4-2 Exercises

1. 0.01 3. 0.000001 5. $\frac{1}{64}$ 7. $\frac{1}{27}$ 9. $13\frac{1}{125}$ 11. $\frac{1}{8}$ 13. 0.1 15. 0.00000001 17. $-\frac{1}{4}$ 19. $\frac{1}{10{,}000}$, or 0.0001 21. $-1\frac{3}{4}$ 23. $11\frac{4}{81}$ 25. $\frac{1}{32}$ 27. $\frac{3}{4}$ 29. $\frac{4}{9}$ 31. 28 33. 13.02 35. $\frac{3}{4}$ 37. $11^{-4} = \frac{1}{11 \times 11 \times 11 \times 11} = \frac{1}{14{,}641}$ 39. $-6^{-3} = -\frac{1}{6 \times 6 \times 6} = -\frac{1}{216}$ 41. $\frac{3}{250{,}000}$ meter 45. 38,340 lb 47. $\frac{1}{480}$ 49. C 51. $8x + 21$ 53. $7x + 24y$ 55. 81 57. −125 59. −32

4-3 Exercises

1. 5^{15} 3. m^4 5. 6^2 7. $12^0 = 1$ 9. 3^{20} 11. 4^{-6} or $\frac{1}{4^6}$ 13. 10^{17} 15. r 17. $\left(\frac{1}{3}\right)^{-2}$ 19. y^{-3} 21. 5^4 23. $t^{13}r$ 25. $\frac{1}{4^3}$ 27. $6^0 = 1$ 29. $5^0 = 1$ 31. $\frac{1}{3^4}$ 33. $(-1)^9$ or −1

35. $\frac{1}{t^8}$ 37. 4^4 39. a^7 41. x^{10} 43. 7^{12} 45. cannot combine 47. $y^0 = 1$ 49. 26^2, or 676 51. 12^2; 12^1 53. 4 55. 0 57a. 10^{100} b. 10^{200} 61. B 63. 25 65. 22.8 67. $1\frac{1}{11}$ 69. $\frac{1}{9}$ 71. 1

4-4 Exercises

1. $56y^7$ 3. $-6a^5b^5$ 5. $4xy$ 7. $3n^3$ 9. $\frac{3}{2}ab^3$ 11. $6c^5$ 13. $125a^3$ 15. $216x^6y^{15}$ 17. $32m^{15}n^{10}$ 19. $-22z^{12}$ 21. $-2x^{10}$ 23. $6a^2b^5$ 25. $5x^2$ 27. $2q^3$ 29. $\frac{3}{2}xy^5$ 31. $256y^8$ 33. $256b^8$ 35. $32a^{15}b^{50}$ 37. $144m^4$ 39. $\frac{6}{5}a^3b^5$ 41. −9 43. $\frac{r}{3}$ 45. $16m^4n^5$ 47. $6x^3y^2$ 49a. The degree of a monomial is the sum of the exponents of the variables in the monomial. b. 8 53. D 55. $20y - 18$ 57. $21 + 21k$ 59. g^{11} 61. 7^1 or 7

4-5 Exercises

1. 15,000 3. 208,000 5. 5.7×10^{-5} 7. 6.98×10^6 9. 4170 11. 62,000,000 13. no 15. 80,000 17. 400,000 19. 5,500,000,000 21. 700,300 23. 6.5×10^6 25. 5.87×10^{-6} 27. 0.00067 29. 524,000,000 31. 140,000 33. 78 35. 0.000000053 37. 559,000 39. 7,113,000 41. 0.00029 43a. 1.5×10^{-4} g b. 1.5×10^{26} g 45. 367,000 47. 4 49. 340 51. 540,000,000 53. 9.8×10^8 feet per second 55. 8.58×10^{-3} 57. 5.9×10^6 59. 7.6×10^{-3} 61. 4.2×10^3 63. 6×10^{-10} 65. 7×10^6 67. 5.85×10^{-3}, 1.5×10^{-2}, 2.3×10^{-2}, 1.2×10^6, 5.5×10^6 71. C 73. number of students ≥ 35 75. 7^2 77. t^3

4-6 Exercises

1. ±2 3. ±11 5. 16 ft 7. $|y^3|$ 9. $7a^4$ 11. ±13 13. ±19 15. $|s^3|$ 17. $6x^4$ 19. ±6 21. ±15 23. ±21 25. ±24 29. 104 ft 31. $8x^8$

33. $4|y^7|$ 35. $a^2|b^3|$ 37. $13|p^{15}|q^{12}$ 39. $\pm\frac{9}{4}$ 41. $\pm\frac{1}{2}$ 43. 8 45. $\sqrt{x^2} = |x|$; $\sqrt{x^4} = x^2$; $\sqrt{x^6} = |x^3|$; $\sqrt{x^8} = x^4$; $\sqrt{x^{10}} = |x^5|$; $\sqrt{x^{12}} = x^6$ 49. C 51. $\frac{7}{20}$ 53. $-7\frac{9}{50}$ 55. 1.97×10^9 57. 3.14×10^{10} 59. 6×10^{-3}

4-7 Exercises

1. 6 and 7 3. 12 and 13 5. 15 and 16 7. 6.48 9. 12.49 11. 16.58 13. 5.8 15. 13.8 17. 7 and 8 19. 24 and 25 21. 20 and 21 23. 4.36 25. 11.09 27. 17.03 29. 9.6 31. 12.2 33. B 35. E 37. F 39. 89.6 in. 41. 40 ft 43. $\sqrt{25}$, $5\frac{2}{3}$, 7.15, $\frac{29}{4}$, 3^2 45. 151 km

47. 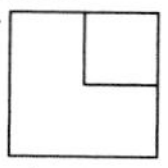

49a. about 610 mi/h b. about 7.8 h 51. B 53. 21 55. 18 57. ±8 59. ±36

4-8 Exercises

1. irrational, real 3. rational, real 5. rational 7. irrational 9. rational 11. rational 17. rational, real 19. integer, rational, real 21. rational 23. irrational 25. irrational 27. not real 31. whole, integer, rational, real 33. irrational, real 35. rational, real 37. rational, real 39. rational, real 41. integer, rational, real 43. $\frac{3}{0}$ is undefined so it is not a real number. $\frac{0}{3}$ is 0 so it is a rational number. 55. irrational 57. rational 59. irrational 63. C 65. C 67. Dist. Prop. 69. 32,768 71. 625

4-9 Exercises

1. 20 m 3. 24 cm 5. yes 7. yes 9. 15 ft 11. about 21.2 mi 13. no

15. 5 17. 13 19. 9 21. Yes. $6^2 + 8^2 = 10^2$ 23. 22.6 ft 25a. 110 m b. 155.6 m 27. 208.5 m 31. C 33. $x \geq -3$ 35. $x > -\frac{1}{4}$ 37. 5 and 6 39. 7 and 8

Chapter 4 Study Guide: Review

1. irrational number 2. scientific notation 3. Pythagorean theorem; legs; hypotenuse 4. real numbers 5. $(-3)^2$ 6. k^4 7. $(-9)^1$ 8. $6x^2$ 9. 625 10. −32 11. −1 12. 256 13. −3 14. 64 15. $\frac{1}{125}$ 16. $-\frac{1}{64}$ 17. $\frac{1}{11}$ 18. $\frac{1}{10{,}000}$ 19. 1 20. $-\frac{1}{36}$ 21. $\frac{1}{8}$ 22. 1 23. $\frac{1}{2}$ 24. 0 25. 4^7 26. 9^6 27. p^4 28. 15^3 29. 6^4 30. x^{10} 31. 8^3 32. 9^2 33. m^5 34. 3^7 35. 4^0, or 1 36. y^9 37. 4^{12} 38. $\frac{1}{x^{10}}$ 39. $(-10)^0 = 1$ 40. $-5m^{10}n^{10}$ 41. $-7x^3z^{11}$ 42. a^7b^2 43. $20r^6s^6$ 44. $9p$ 45. $-6t^2$ 46. $-2x^3y^2$ 47. $\frac{7}{6}m^9n^3$ 48. $16t^6$ 49. $49p^{10}q^{12}$ 50. $-216x^{12}y^3$ 51. $10{,}000m^8n^{20}$ 52. 8×10^{-9} 53. 7.3×10^7 54. 9.6×10^{-6} 55. 5.64×10^{10} 56. 1620 57. 0.00162 58. 910,000 59. 0.000091 60. -3.1×10^5, -1.7×10^{-4}, 2.3×10^{-5}, 4.9×10^4 61. 4 and −4 62. 30 and −30 63. 26 and −26 64. $7m^2$ 65. $2|a^3|$ 66. x^6 67. 9 and 10 68. 3 and 4 69. 11 and 12 70. 6 and 7 71. 16 and 17 72. 13 and 14 73. rational 74. irrational 75. rational 76. irrational 77. rational 78. not a real number 79. Possible answer: 3.5 80. 10 81. 10 82. no 83. yes 84. no

Chapter 5

5-1 Exercises

1. $\frac{2}{5}$ 3. $\frac{10}{7}$ 5. $\frac{15}{1}$ 7. $\frac{4}{11} \neq \frac{2}{11}$ 9. $\frac{7}{4} = \frac{7}{4}$ 11. yes 13. $\frac{25}{12}$ 15. $\frac{12}{1}$ 17. $\frac{2}{5}$ 19. $\frac{3}{5} = \frac{3}{5}$ 21. $\frac{1}{3} \neq \frac{1}{4}$ 23. no 25. $\frac{2}{4} = \frac{3}{6}$; $\frac{2}{5} = \frac{4}{10}$; $\frac{12}{3} = \frac{4}{1}$; $\frac{12}{8} = \frac{9}{6}$ 27. yes 29. no 31. yes 33. no 35. $\frac{39}{18}$ 39. C 41. yes 43. −5.44 45. 0.642 47. 1.2×10^7 49. 1.1×10^{-6}

5-2 Exercises

1. 3 mi 3. approximately 40 students per bus 5. approximately 500 Calories per serving 7. 38 oz box 9. 3.52 g/cm³ 11. approximately 2 cups per batch 13. approximately \$4 per lb 15. 16 oz package 17. 14 points per game 19. 16 beats per measure 21. approximately 50 beats per minute 23. approximately 4 apples per pound 25. \$3.75/lb; \$4.50/lb; $\frac{2}{3}$ lb 27. approximately \$110 per day 31. width: 20 in.; height: 15 in. 33. The bunch of 4 has the lower unit price. 35. $w = 1\frac{1}{3}$ 37. $t = -8.4$ 39. no 41. no

5-3 Exercises

1. yes 3. no 5. no 7. $5\frac{1}{3}$ in. 9. no 11. no 13. yes 15. 2.25 m 17. $\frac{8}{4}$, $\frac{24}{12}$ 19. $\frac{81}{39}$, $\frac{27}{13}$ 21. $\frac{0.5}{6}$, $\frac{1}{12}$ 23. \$144 25. 64 minutes 27. 12 computers 29. 14 molecules 31a. about 3:2 b. about 68 mm Hg 33. 154 and 56 35. 16 37. −33 39. 6-ounce can

5-4 Exercises

1. 0.694 km/s 3. 7.5 mi/h 5. 0.075 page/min 7. 1.8 km/h 9. 480 cereal boxes 11. 6 fish 13. ≈5.8 mi 15. ≈0.88 g 17. ≈28.75 tons 19. ≈10.3 m/s 21. ≈2.85 gal 23. C 27. B 29. 32 31. 2^{-2} 33. 10^{12} 35. 2^7 37. m^{13}

39. ≈\$0.175 per oz 41. \$249 per monitor

5-5 Exercises

1. triangle A and triangle B 3. 16.5 cm 5. ≈2.98 gal 7. similar 9. similar 11. yes 13. $x = 6$ ft 15. 18 in. 17. 15 ft 21. 31.5 cm² 23. 70 25. 3328 quarts

5-6 Exercises

1. 128 yd 3. 5.6 ft 5. 4 ft 7. 90 ft 9. 85 ft 11. 65 ft 15. C 17. $-\frac{1}{5}$ 19. $\frac{1}{6}$ 21. $\frac{1}{49}$ 23. $1\frac{1}{2}$

5-7 Exercises

1. 300 ft 3. 14 in. 5. 25 mi 7. 7.5 ft 9. $\frac{12}{1}$ 11. $\frac{1}{20}$ 13. 630 ft 15. 6.25 ft 17. ≈16 in. 19. ≈960 in²; ≈6.7 ft² 23. D 25. 5 and 6 27. 7 and 8 29. 6 and 7 31. \$0.17 per apple

Chapter 5 Study Guide: Review

1. ratio; proportion 2. rate; unit rate 3. similar; scale factor 4. $\frac{5}{4}$ 5. $\frac{27}{40}$ 6. $\frac{3}{4}$ 7. $\frac{2}{1}$ 8. yes 9. no 10. yes 11. no 12. 75 disks 13. unit prices are the same 14. 8-pack 15. $x = 15$ 16. $h = 6$ 17. $w = 21$ 18. $y = 29\frac{1}{3}$ 19. 72 min 20. 90,000 m/h 21. 4500 ft/min 22. $583\frac{1}{3}$ m/min 23. 0.8 mi/min (= 48 mi/h) 24. 12.5 in. 25. 3.125 in. 26. 18 ft 27. 6.2 ft 28. 43.75 miles 29. 3 in. 30. 46 mi 31. 57.5 mi 32. 153 mi

Chapter 6

6-1 Exercises

1. $\frac{1}{4}$ 3. 87.5% 5. > 7. = 9. 0.3, $33\frac{1}{3}$%, 36%, $\frac{3}{8}$ 11. $33\frac{1}{3}$% 13. $\frac{39}{100}$ 15. 125% 17. < 19. = 21. 0.04, $\frac{2}{5}$, 42%, 70% 23. 40%, 30%, 20%, 10% 25. 40%, 30%, 25%, 5% 33. B 35. < 37. = 39. $z \geq 5.5$

6-2 Exercises

1. 50 3. 30 5. 13 7. 16 11. 100 13. 6 15. 32 17. 9 21. B 23. B 25. C 27. 150 29. 40 31. 800 33. 30 35. 100 37. ≈ 300 cars 39. ≈ 475,000 41. ≈ 14 hours 43a. no b. yes c. ≈ 1 per mi²; ≈ 1000 per mi² 47. B 49. B 51. 9 53. −64 55. 125 57. 8 59. $\frac{23}{50}$ 61. 0.5 63. 0.525

6-3 Exercises

1. 49.5% 3. 75% 5. 23% 7. 1.6 mi 9. 400% 11. 1% 13. $29\frac{1}{6}$% 15. ≈ 54.0 ft above sea level 17. 24.4 19. 399 21. 500 23a. 10 b. 20 c. 40 29. 1.0% 31. Lena: \$11.87, Ana: \$12.36, Joseph: \$12.50, George: \$12.71 35. B 37. 1000 g/1 kg 39. 1 mi/5280 ft 41. 16 oz/1 lb 43. 100 45. 40

6-4 Exercises

1. 60 3. 166.7 5. ≈ 2.4 oz 7. 135 9. 1333.3 11. 400 cards 13a. 250 b. 125 c. 62.5 15a. 30 b. 20 c. 15 17. 657,000 19. 6.7% 21. 98,000 23. C 25. 5 and 6 27. 7 and 8 29. 11 and 12 31. 10 and 11 33. 14 and 15 35. 0.625 37. 0.71 39. −0.75 41. 1.23 43. 3.5

6-5 Exercises

1. 48% increase 3. 100% increase 5. \$9773.60 7. 22% increase 9. ≈ 8.6% 11. 33% decrease 13. 39% decrease 15. 24% decrease 17. \$500 19. 120 21. 50 23a. \$78 b. \$117 c. \$39 d. 80% 25. 24,900% 27. decrease; 13% 29. C 31. 25% 33. \$7.49; \$31.76 35. 50% 37. 311.75

6-6 Exercises

1. \$574 3. 11.6% 5. \$603.50 7. 3.1% 9. \$15.23 11. \$38.07

13. \$81,200 15. Deborah should choose the salary option that pays \$2100 plus 4% of sales. 17a. \$64,208 b. \$12,717 c. ≈ 17.8% d. ≈ 19.8% 19. \$695 21. x^2 23. $\frac{y^2}{x^2}$ 25. 50% decrease

6-7 Exercises

1. \$2234.38; \$9384.38 3. \$1430.24 5. about \$2971.89 7. 17 years 9. 5.5% 11. \$94.50, \$409.50 13. \$446.25, \$4696.25 15. \$9.26, \$626.26 17. 5 years 21. How long did Alice keep her money in the savings account? 25. B 27. 1 gal/4 qt 29. 95

Chapter 6 Study Guide: Review

1. percent 2. percent of change 3. commission 4. 0.4375 5. 43.75% 6. $1\frac{1}{8}$ 7. 112.5% 8. $\frac{7}{10}$ 9. 0.7 10. 30 11. 62 12. 3.3 13. 18 14. \$7.50 15. \$16.00 16. 33% 17. 4200 ft 18. 7930 mi 19. 5 lb 7 oz 20. 472,750% 21. 34.4% 22. \$21 23. \$16,830 24. \$3.55 25. \$2000 26. \$3171.88 27. \$400 28. 7% 29. 0.5 yr 30. \$1000 at 3.75% for 3 years; \$7.50 31. about \$574.44

Chapter 7

7-1 Exercises

1. II 3. III

5, 7. 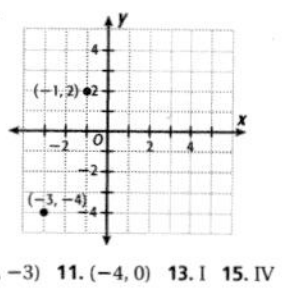

9. (6, −3) 11. (−4, 0) 13. I 15. IV

17, 19. 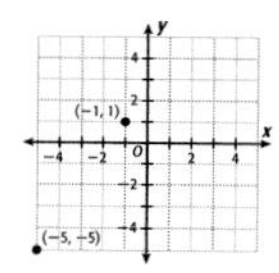

21. (−4, 4) 23. (−5, −4) 25. (5, 6)

27. 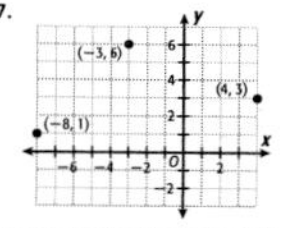

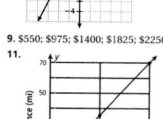

29. triangle; Quadrants I and II 31. III 33. (12, 7) 35. a. (−68°, 26°) b. (−80°, 26°) c. (−91°, 32°) 39. B 41. about \$22 per hour 43. about 16 students per teacher 45. 0.14, $\frac{1}{7}$, 15%, $\frac{1}{6}$

7-2 Exercises

5. yes 7. no 13. no 15. no 17. yes 19. a. yes b. input: {0, 20, 40, 60, 80, 100}; output: {0, 150, 300, 450, 600, 750} 21. a. \$0.20 b. any nonnegative number of hours ($x \geq 0$) c. 550 hours 25. All real numbers 27. D 29. −7 31. 6 33. 100 35. \$3

7-3 Exercises

1. 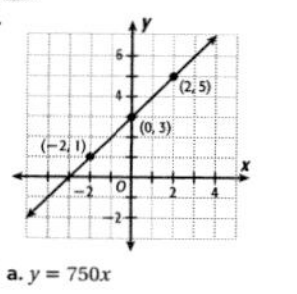

3. a. $y = 750x$

b. 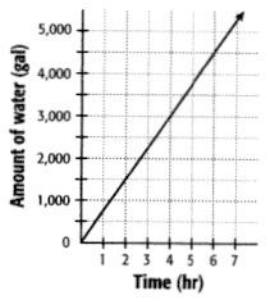
Amount of water (gal)
Time (hr)

5. 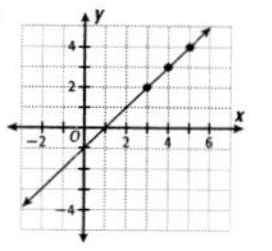

7. 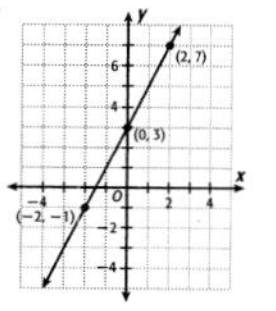

9. \$550; \$975; \$1400; \$1825; \$2250

11. 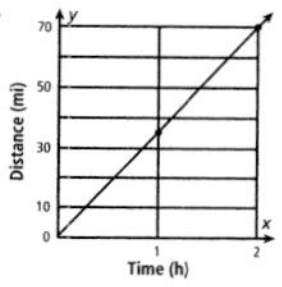
Distance (mi)
Time (h)

13. 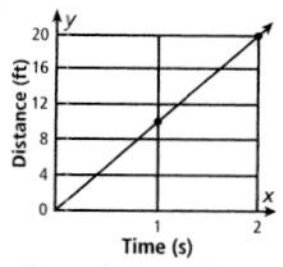
Distance (ft)
Time (s)

15. a. 5 ppm b. about 382 ppm 19. It is not linear.

21. Simon calculated the y-coordinates incorrectly. 23. 32.3 25. 2.3

7-4 Exercises

1. 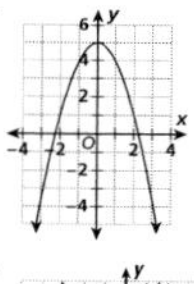

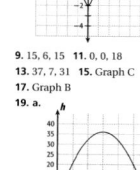

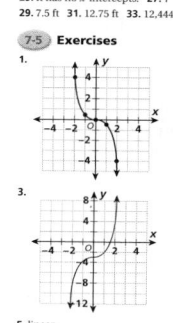

3. 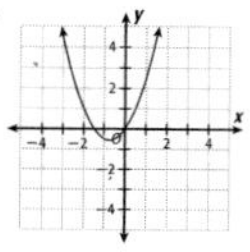

5. 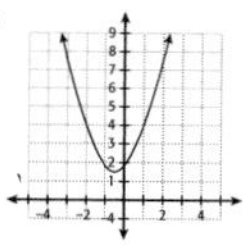

7. 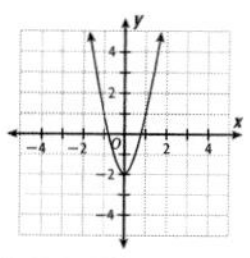

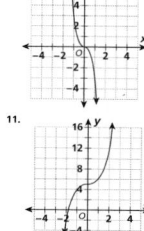

9. 15, 6, 15 11. 0, 0, 18 13. 37, 7, 31 15. Graph C 17. Graph B

19. a. 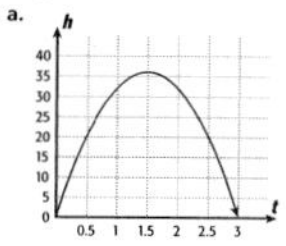

b. 3 s 21. a. \$4860, \$4940, \$5000, \$5040, \$5060 b. 7 23. B 25. It has no x-intercepts. 27. 7 29. 7.5 ft 31. 12.75 ft 33. 12,444.4

7-5 Exercises

1. 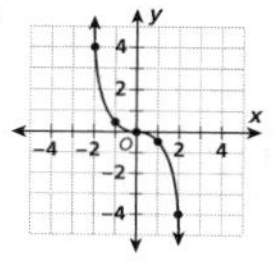

3. 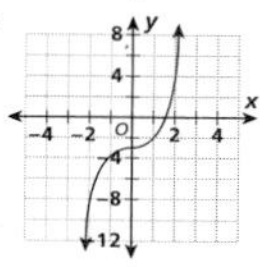

5. linear

7. 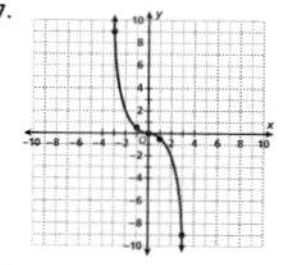

9. 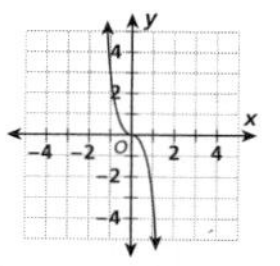

11. 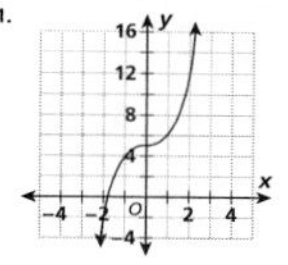

13. quadratic 15. quadratic

17.
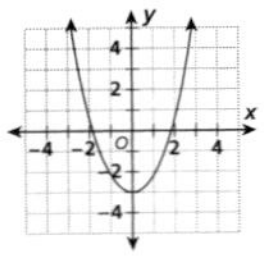

19.
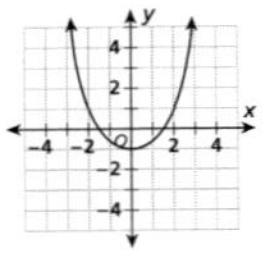

21.
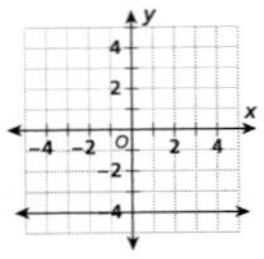

23. The sign determines whether the curve rises or falls from left to right.

25. a.
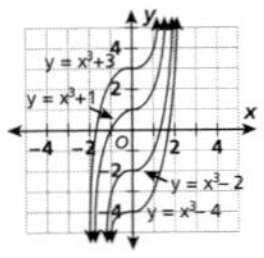

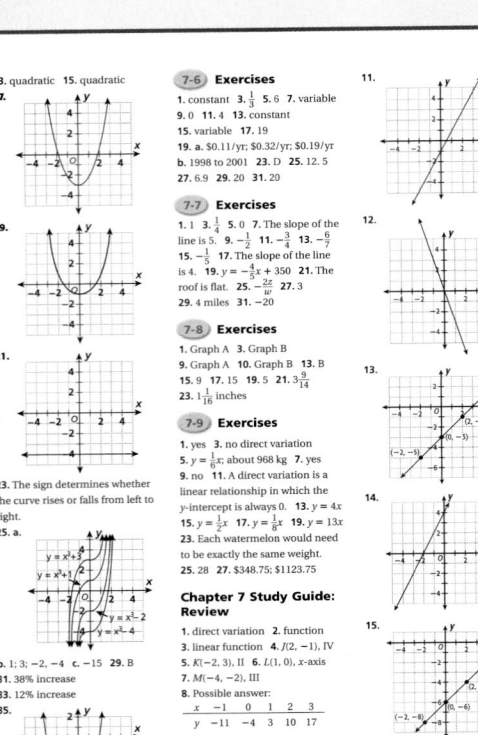

b. 1; 3; −2, −4 c. −15 29. B
31. 38% increase
33. 12% increase

35.
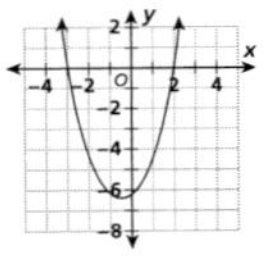

7-6 Exercises

1. constant 3. $\frac{1}{3}$ 5. 6 7. variable 9. 0 11. 4 13. constant 15. variable 17. 19 19. a. \$0.11/yr; \$0.32/yr; \$0.19/yr b. 1998 to 2001 23. D 25. 12. 5 27. 6.9 29. 20 31. 20

7-7 Exercises

1. 1 3. $\frac{1}{4}$ 5. 0 7. The slope of the line is 5. 9. $-\frac{1}{2}$ 11. $-\frac{3}{4}$ 13. $-\frac{6}{7}$ 15. $-\frac{1}{5}$ 17. The slope of the line is 4. 19. $y = -\frac{4}{5}x + 350$ 21. The roof is flat. 25. $-\frac{2z}{w}$ 27. 3 29. 4 miles 31. −20

7-8 Exercises

1. Graph A 3. Graph B 9. Graph A 10. Graph B 13. B 15. 9 17. 15 19. 5 21. $3\frac{9}{14}$ 23. $1\frac{1}{16}$ inches

7-9 Exercises

1. yes 3. no direct variation 5. $y = \frac{1}{6}x$; about 968 kg 7. yes 9. no 11. A direct variation is a linear relationship in which the y-intercept is always 0. 13. $y = 4x$ 15. $y = \frac{1}{2}x$ 17. $y = \frac{1}{8}x$ 19. $y = 13x$ 23. Each watermelon would need to be exactly the same weight. 25. 28 27. \$348.75; \$1123.75

Chapter 7 Study Guide: Review

1. direct variation 2. function 3. linear function 4. $J(2, -1)$, IV 5. $K(-2, 3)$, II 6. $L(1, 0)$, x-axis 7. $M(-4, -2)$, III

8. Possible answer:

x	−1	0	1	2	3
y	−11	−4	3	10	17

9. Possible answer:

x	−1	0	1	2	3
y	−2	0	−2	−8	−18

10. yes

11.
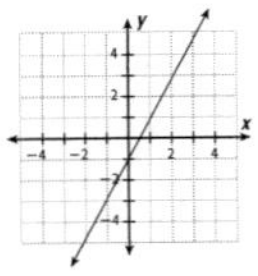

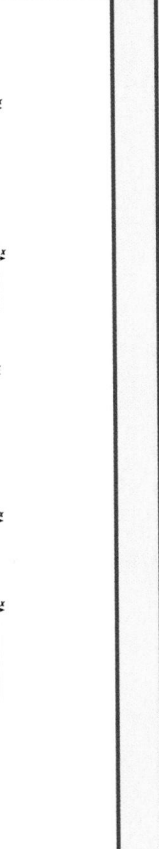

12.
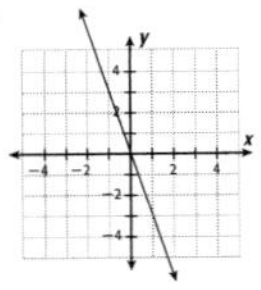

13.
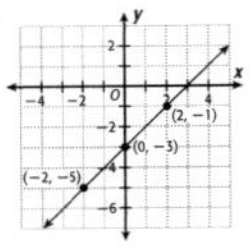

14.
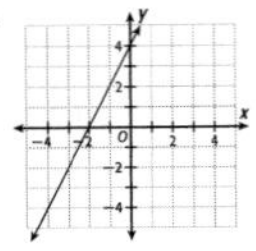

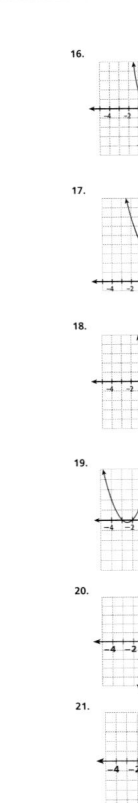

15.
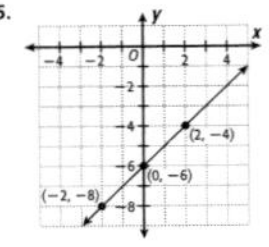

16.
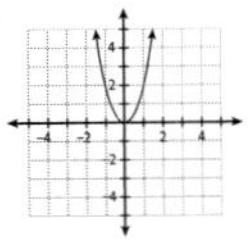

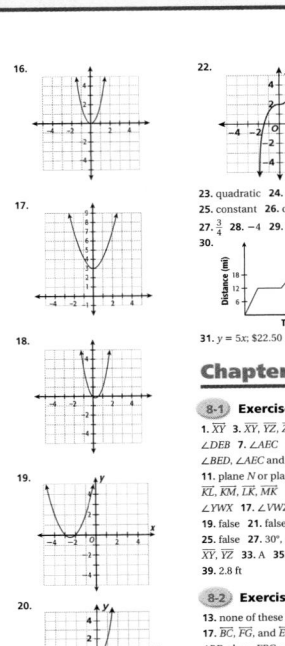

17.
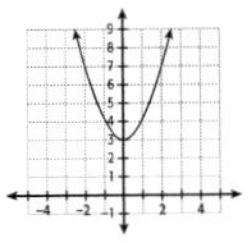

18.
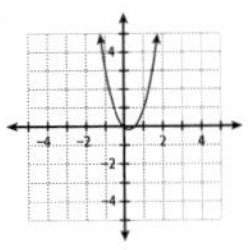

19.
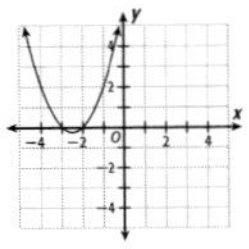

20.
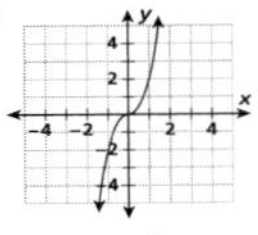

21.
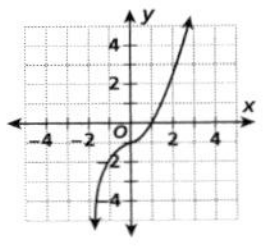

22.
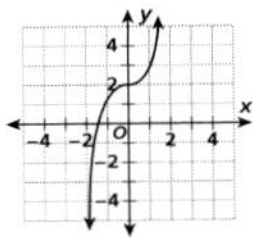

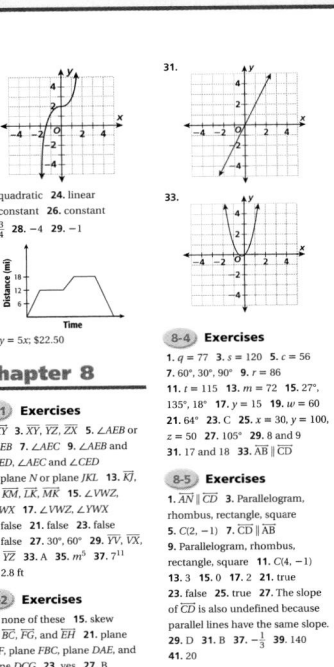

23. quadratic 24. linear 25. constant 26. constant 27. $\frac{3}{4}$ 28. −4 29. −1

30.
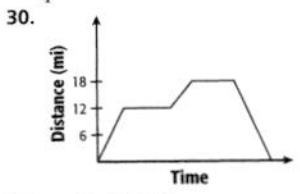

31. $y = 5x$; \$22.50

Chapter 8

8-1 Exercises

1. $\overleftrightarrow{XY}$ 3. $\overrightarrow{XY}$, $\overrightarrow{YZ}$, $\overrightarrow{ZX}$ 5. ∠AEB or ∠DEB 7. ∠AEC 9. ∠AEB and ∠BED, ∠AEC and ∠CED 11. plane N or plane JKL 13. $\overrightarrow{KJ}$, $\overrightarrow{KL}$, $\overrightarrow{KM}$, $\overrightarrow{LK}$, $\overrightarrow{MK}$ 15. ∠VWZ, ∠YWX 17. ∠VWZ, ∠YWX 19. false 21. false 23. false 25. false 27. 30°, 60° 29. $\overline{YV}$, $\overline{VX}$, $\overline{XY}$, $\overline{YZ}$ 33. A 35. m^5 37. 7^{11} 39. 2.8 ft

8-2 Exercises

13. none of these 15. skew 17. $\overline{BC}$, $\overline{FG}$, and $\overline{EH}$ 21. plane ABF, plane FBC, plane DAE, and plane DCG 23. yes 27. B 29. $36m^6$ 31. $27x^{12}y^3$ 33. yes

8-3 Exercises

1. 105° 3. 62° 5. 118° 7. 126° 9. 70° 11. 110° 13. ∠4, ∠5, and ∠8 17. 129° 19. 180° − x° 29. The measures of the remaining angles are 90°.

31.
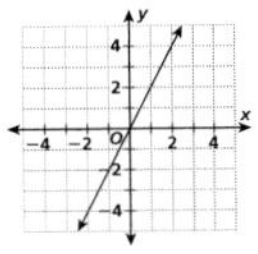

33.
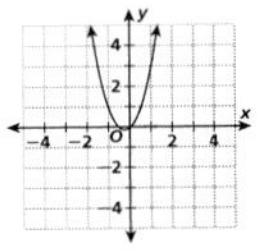

8-4 Exercises

1. $q = 77$ 3. $s = 120$ 5. $c = 56$ 7. 60°, 30°, 90° 9. $r = 86$ 11. $t = 115$ 13. $m = 72$ 15. 27°, 135°, 18° 17. $y = 15$ 19. $w = 60$ 21. 64° 23. C 25. $x = 30$, $y = 100$, $z = 50$ 27. 105° 29. 8 and 9 31. 17 and 18 33. $\overleftrightarrow{AB} \parallel \overleftrightarrow{CD}$

8-5 Exercises

1. $\overleftrightarrow{AN} \parallel \overleftrightarrow{CD}$ 3. Parallelogram, rhombus, rectangle, square 5. $C(2, -1)$ 7. $\overleftrightarrow{CD} \parallel \overleftrightarrow{AB}$ 9. Parallelogram, rhombus, rectangle, square 11. $C(4, -1)$ 13. 3 15. 0 17. 2 21. true 23. false 25. true 27. The slope of $\overleftrightarrow{CD}$ is also undefined because parallel lines have the same slope. 29. D 31. B 37. $-\frac{1}{3}$ 39. 140 41. 20

8-6 Exercises

1. triangle ABC ≅ triangle FED 3. $q = 5$ 5. $s = 7$ 7. quadrilateral PQRS ≅ quadrilateral ZYXW 9. $n = 7$ 11. $x = 19$, $y = 27$, $z = 18.1$ 13. $r = 24$, $s = 120$, $t = 48$ 15. 62° 19. C 21. 3 23. $P(-4, 1)$

8-7 Exercises

1. rotation

3.
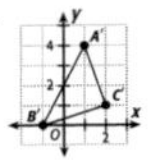

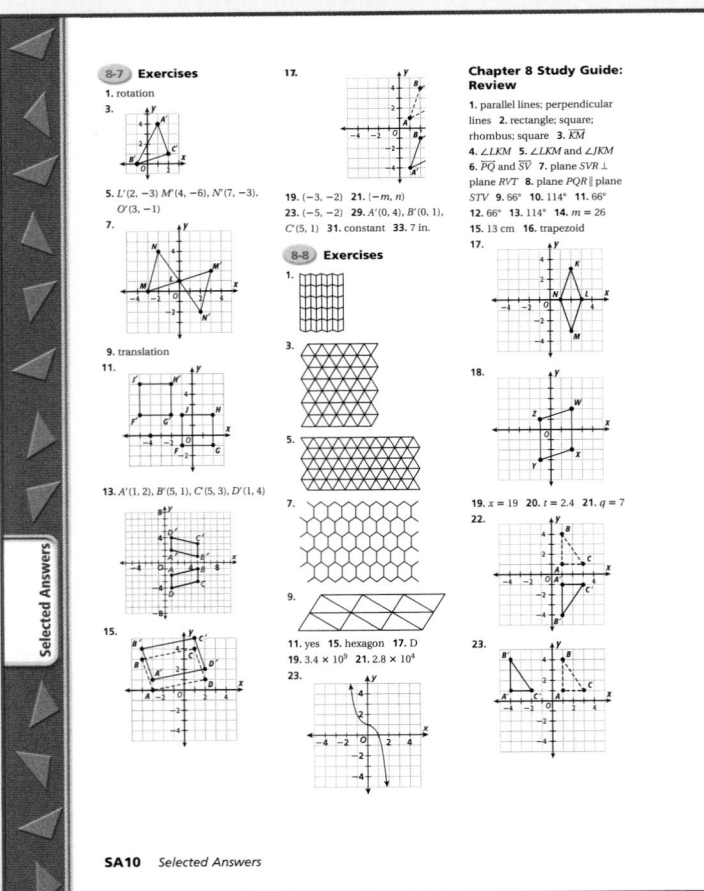

5. $L'(2, -3)$ $M'(4, -6)$, $N'(7, -3)$, $O'(3, -1)$

7.
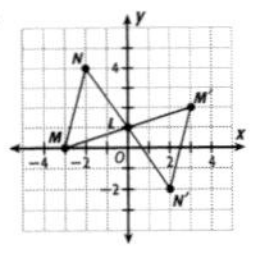

9. translation

11.
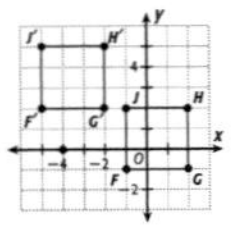

13. $A'(1, 2)$, $B'(5, 1)$, $C'(5, 3)$, $D'(1, 4)$
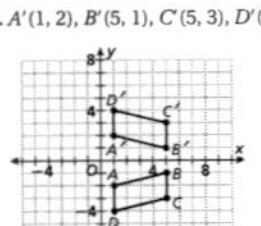

15.
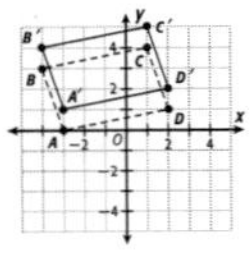

17.
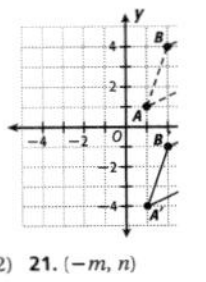

19. (−3, −2) 21. (−m, n) 23. (−5, −2) 29. $A'(0, 4)$, $B'(0, 1)$, $C'(5, 1)$ 31. constant 33. 7 in.

8-8 Exercises

1.
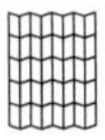

3.
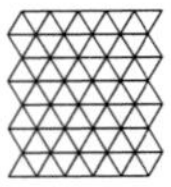

5.
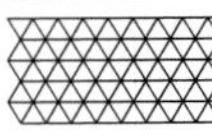

7.
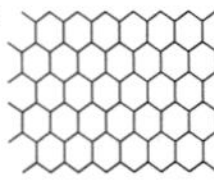

9.
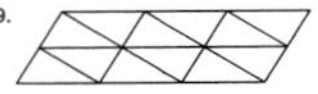

11. yes 15. hexagon 17. D 19. 3.4×10^9 21. 2.8×10^4

23.
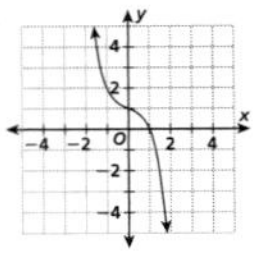

Chapter 8 Study Guide: Review

1. parallel lines; perpendicular lines 2. rectangle; square; rhombus; square 3. $\overrightarrow{KM}$ 4. ∠LKM 5. ∠LKM and ∠JKM 6. $\overrightarrow{PQ}$ and $\overrightarrow{SV}$ 7. plane SVR ⊥ plane RVT 8. plane PQR ∥ plane STV 9. 66° 10. 114° 11. 66° 12. 66° 13. 114° 14. $m = 26$ 15. 13 cm 16. trapezoid

17.
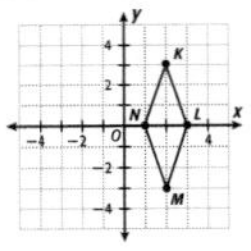

18.
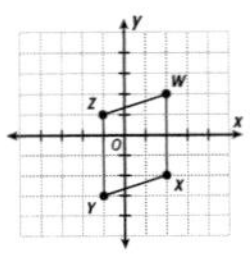

19. $x = 19$ 20. $t = 2.4$ 21. $q = 7$

22.
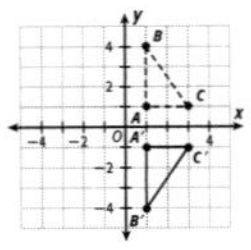

23.
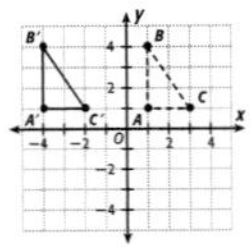

24.
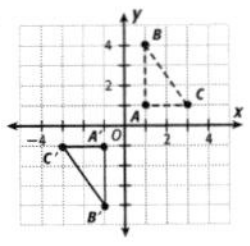

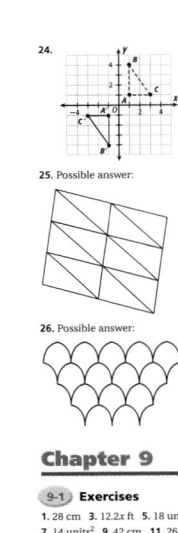

25. Possible answer:
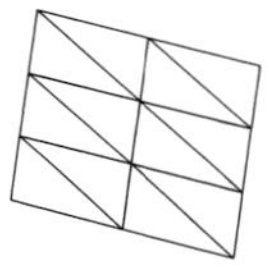

26. Possible answer:

Chapter 9

9-1 Exercises

1. 28 cm 3. 12.2x ft 5. 18 units² 7. 14 units² 9. 42 cm 11. 26x m 13. 24 units² 15. 12 units² 17. 33 ft; 54 ft² 19. 18 ft; 10.5 ft² 21. \$3375 23. ≈42,000 mi² 27. B 29. $x = -4$ 31. $a = -37$ 33. rational 35. rational 37. not a real number

9-2 Exercises

1. 9 units 3. 3 units 5. 21 units² 7. 15 units² 9. 5 units 11. 21 units 13. 20 units² 15. 12 units² 17. 23.2 m² 19. 33 cm² 21. 37 m² 23. 60 units² 25. 25x units²

27. 9.1 ft 29. 1.2 cm 31. When the dimensions are multiplied by 4, the area will be 4^2 times as great and the perimeter will be 4 times as great. 33. 466.6 ft 35. 49.8 ft 37. 874.6 ft²; 160.4 ft 39. C 41. 3.7 mi 43. 14 units²

9-3 Exercises

1. $\overline{OQ}$, $\overline{OR}$, $\overline{OS}$, $\overline{OT}$ 3. $\overline{RT}$, $\overline{RS}$, $\overline{ST}$, $\overline{TQ}$ 5. $\overline{CA}$, $\overline{CB}$, $\overline{CD}$, $\overline{CE}$, $\overline{CF}$ 7. $\overline{GB}$, $\overline{BF}$, $\overline{DE}$, $\overline{FE}$, $\overline{AE}$ 9. 10 cm 11. 100.8° 13. 252° 15. 133.2° 19. 120° 21. 90° 23. 18 25. 35

9-4 Exercises

1. 6π cm; 18.8 cm 3. 16.8π ft²; 52.8 ft² 5. $A = 4\pi$ units²; 12.6 units²; $C = 4\pi$ units; 12.6 units 7. 18π in.; 56.5 in. 9. 256π cm²; 803.8 cm² 11. $A = 16\pi$ units²; 50.2 units²; $C = 8\pi$ units; 25.1 units 13. $C \approx 10.7$ m; $A \approx 9.1$ m² 15. $C \approx 56.5$ in.; $A \approx 254.3$ in.² 17. 6.4 cm 19. 6 cm 21. 11.7 m 23. 38.5 m² 25. $C = 30\pi$ ft ≈ 94.2 ft; $A = 225\pi$ ft² ≈ 706.5 ft² 27.a. 9.6 in.² b. 28.3 in.² c. three regular pancakes 31. C 33. m^4 35. 8^7 37. 27 units²

9-5 Exercises

1. 48 m² 3. 109.5 cm² 5. 59.6 in² 7. 88.1 ft² 9. 54 cm² 11. 23.4 in² 13. 63,800 mi² 17. 80 in² 19. C 21. $y = 5x$ 23. 10π in.; 31.4 in. 25. 8.2π cm; 25.7 cm

9-6 Exercises

13. no 17. Approximate the area of the glacier with a trapezoid ($b_1 = 2$, $b_2 = 3$, $h = 1$) that has area $\frac{5}{2}$ and a triangle ($b = 3$, $h = 1$) that has area $\frac{3}{2}$. 19. D 21. rational 23. rational

Chapter 9 Study Guide: Review

1. perimeter, area 2. chord 3. about $7\frac{2}{9}$ in², 12 in. 4. 198 m², 80 m 5. $11\frac{1}{2}$ ft; $5\frac{5}{8}$ ft² 6. 20 yd; 11 yd² 7. 9 cm², 14.2 cm 8. 16 in², 26.3 in. 9. 36 ft 10. $\overline{HF}$, $\overline{FI}$, $\overline{FG}$ 11. $\overline{GI}$ 12. $\overline{HI}$, $\overline{GI}$, $\overline{GJ}$, $\overline{JI}$ 13. A = 144π ≈ 452.2 in²; C = 24π ≈ 75.4 in 14. A = 17.6π ≈ 55.4 cm²; C = 8.4π ≈ 26.4 cm 15. A = 9π ≈ 28.3 m²; C = 6π ≈ 18.8 m 16. A = 0.36π ≈ 1.1 ft²; C = 1.2π ≈ 3.8 ft 17. 57 m² 18. 40.57 ft² 19. 73.5 cm² 20. 14 units² 21. 15 units² 22. 12 units² 23. 10 units²

Chapter 10

10-1 Exercises

1. pentagon; triangles; pentagonal pyramid 3. triangles; rectangles; triangular prism 5. polyhedron; hexagonal pyramid 7. triangle; triangles; triangular pyramid 9. hexagon; triangles; hexagonal pyramid 11. not a polyhedron; cylinder 13. square prism 15. triangular pyramid 19. rectangular pyramid 21. cylinder 23. A 25. $\frac{31}{40}$ 27. $1\frac{25}{36}$ 29. 100 oz for \$6.99

10-2 Exercises

1. 463.1 cm³ 3. 1256 m³ 5. ≈1500 ft³ 7. 100 in³ 9. 351 m³ 11. ≈60 cm³ 13. a. 800 in³ 15. a. 4.62×10^7 in³ b. about 18.8 ft 19. 180 in³ 21. D 23. (5, −9) 25. 4 in.; 12 in²

10-3 Exercises

1. 20 cm³ 3. 99.7 ft³ 5. 9.1 cm³ 7. 6,255,000 ft³ 9. 35.0 m³ 11. 66.2 ft³ 13. 5494.5 units³ 15. 6 in 17. 11 ft 19. 736 cm³

Left page (SA12)

21. 600 in³ 23. 301,056 ft³ 25. 8
27. B 29. $x = 15$ 31. $x = -9$
33. 56.25π ft²; 176 ft²

10-4 Exercises
1. 28 cm² 3. 52 cm² 5. 61.8 m²
7. 401.9 in² 9. 791.3 cm²
11. 94 cm² 13. 38 cm²
15. 1160 mm² 17. 791.3 cm²
19. 747.3 yd² 21. $1920\pi \approx$
6028.8 mm² 23. 4 m 25. \$34.56
27. C 31. 232 33. -4.25
35. -1.77 37. 110.5 units²

10-5 Exercises
1. 105 m² 3. 24.1 in² 5. $\approx$ 702.5 ft²
7. 125.6 mm² 9. no 11. 0.18 km²
13. $279{,}221{,}850\pi$ mi²
15. a. $\approx$ 481; $\approx$ 277
b. Menkaure; $\approx$ 191,684 ft²
c. Khufu; 91,636,272 ft² 19. B
21. -56 23. -17 25. 120 ft²

10-6 Exercises
1. 36π cm³; 113.0 cm³ 3. 6.6π m³;
20.7 m³ 5. 4π in²; 12.6 in²
7. 256π cm²; 803.8 cm²
9. The volume of the sphere and
the cube are about equal
($\approx$ 268 in³). 11. 246.9π cm³;
775.3 cm³ 13. 1.3π in³; 4.2 in³
15. 207.4π m²; 651.2 m²
17. 400π cm²; 1256 cm²
19. 366.17π in³; 1149.76 in³
21. $V = 52.41\pi \approx 164.55$ yd³;
$S = 46.24\pi \approx 145.19$ yd²
25. $\approx$1767.15 cm³ 27. $\approx$6.33 in³
29. 113.04 31. 8 33. 15
35. 364 m²

10-7 Exercises
1. 4:1 3. 64:1 5. 8.2 cm³ 7. 2:1
9. 8:1 11. 33,750 in³ 13. 1 cm;
1 cube 15. 9 cm; 729 cubes
17. 7 cm; 343 cubes
19. 1,000,000 cm³ 21a. 2508.8 in³
b. about 10.9 gal 23. No; the
surface area increases by 4 times;
the volume increases by 8 times.

SA12 *Selected Answers*

27. D 29. $x = 8$ 31. $w = 2$
33. 314 mm² 35. 50.2 in²

Chapter 10 Study Guide: Review
1. cylinder 2. surface area
3. cone 4. cylinder
5. rectangular pyramid 6. 364 cm³
7. 24 mm³ 8. 415.4 mm³
9. 111.9 ft³ 10. 60 in³ 11. 210 ft³
12. 471 cm³ 13. 314 m³
14. 857.2 mm² 15. 944 in²
16. 244.92 in² 17. 180.6 cm²
18. 132 cm² 19. $\approx$804.9 in²
20. $288\pi \approx 904.32$ in³
21. $7776\pi \approx 24{,}416.6$ m³ 22. 3:1
23. 9:1 24. 27:1

Chapter 11

11-1 Exercises
1. 15
3.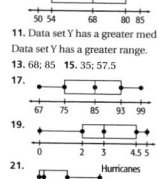

Democrats	Republicans
6	2 6 7 8
8 7 6 4	1 2 3 4
8 4 1 1	3 4
	6

Key: 4 | 1 means 41 / 6 | 4 means 46

5. 3 7. 4; 31 9. B 11. 61 13. 27
19. line plot 21. $\frac{1}{40}$ 23. $\frac{9}{10}$
25. 72 units²

11-2 Exercises
1. 20; 20; 5 and 20; 30
3. Mean: 352.5; median: 350
5. 83.3; 88; 88; 28 7. 4.3; 4.4; 4.4
and 6.2; 4.2 9. mean = 6.2;
median = 6.5 11. 151 13. 9; 8; 12
21. D
23.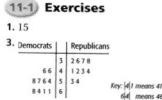

Stems	Leaves
4	3 5 8
5	1 7
6	0 2 2

11-3 Exercises
1. 52; 70
3.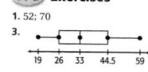
19 26 33 44.5 59

5. The medians are equal, but data set B has a much greater range.
7. 45.5; 62.5
9.
50 54 68 80 85
11. Data set Y has a greater median. Data set Y has a greater range.
13. 68; 85 15. 35; 57.5
17.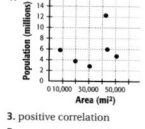
67 75 85 93 99
19.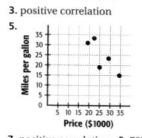
0 2 3 4.5
21.
Hurricanes
34 9 16
Tropical storms
5 7 10 17 26
27. B 29. 4 and -4
31. 10 and -10 33. $\approx$ 4.8; 5; 5
35. $\approx$ 64.9; 63; 48 and 75

11-4 Exercises
1.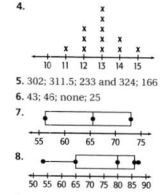
(Population (millions) vs Area (mi²))
3. positive correlation
5.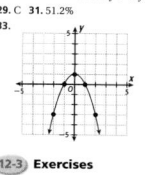
(Miles per gallon vs Price (\$1000))
7. positive correlation 9. 73°F
11. positive correlation
13. negative correlation 17. A
19. 78.5 cm² 21. 9 to 1

11-5 Exercises
1. 0.6, or 60%; 0.4, or 40%
3. 0.709, or 70.9% 5. 0.49, or 49%

Right page (SA13)

7. 0.885 9. 0.784 11. sample space: blue, green, red, yellow; outcome shown: yellow
13. sample space: 1, 2, 3, 4, 5, 6; outcome shown: 4 15. 0.545
21. $\frac{4}{25}$ 23. 0.1 25. 0.0000001
27. 5 29. 0

11-6 Exercises
1. 0.34, or 34% 3. ≈ 0.136;
≈ 0.113 5. ≈ 0.319, or 31.9%
7. ≈ 0.398; ≈ 0.239 9. 0.25
11. 0.025 13. 0.35 15. 0.3
19. 51 21. -4.4 23. negative correlation

11-7 Exercises
1. $\frac{1}{2}$ 3. $\frac{1}{12}$ 5. $\frac{1}{4}$ 7. red 9. 0
11. $\frac{2}{3}$ 13. $\frac{1}{18}$ 15. 1 17. 30 19. $\frac{1}{8}$
21. $\frac{1}{2}$ 23. $\frac{1}{6}$ 25. $\frac{1}{2}$ 29. $\frac{5}{6}$
31. 60; 42; 46

11-8 Exercises
1. dependent 3. $\frac{1}{32}$ 5. $\frac{10}{253}$
7. independent 9. $\frac{1}{5}$ 11. $\frac{9}{52}$
13. $\frac{4}{27}$ 15. $\frac{1}{32} = 0.03125$ 21. D
23. 11; 21 25. 33.49 cubic feet

Chapter 11 Study Guide: Review
1. median; mode 2. probability
3. line of best fit; scatter plot; correlation
4.
x
x x
x x x
x x x x x x
10 11 12 13 14 15
5. 302; 311.5; 233 and 324; 166
6. 43; 46; none; 25
7.
55 60 65 70 75
8.
50 55 60 65 70 75 80 85 90
9.
80 82 84 86 88 90 92 94
10. no correlation 11. positive

correlation 12. 0.85, or 85%;
0.15, or 15% 13. 0.15, or 15%
14. $\frac{4}{15}$ 15. $\frac{1}{1296}$ 16. $\frac{13}{51}$

Chapter 12

12-1 Exercises
1. yes 3. no 5. binomial 7. not a
polynomial 9. 8 11. 0 13. yes
15. no 17. yes 19. monomial
21. trinomial 23. not a
polynomial 25. 2 27. 4 29. 1
31. 8 in³ 33. monomial; 3
35. binomial; 2 37. trinomial; 5
39. not a polynomial
41. trinomial; 3 43. not a
polynomial 51. 9 53. 3.5×10^{-5}
55. ± 7 57. ± 9

12-2 Exercises
1. $-3b^2$ and $4b^2$, $5b$ and $-b$
3. $7x^2 + 4x - 5$ 5. $12x - 32$
7. $17a^2 - 21a$ 9. $-t$ and $5t$, $4r^2$
and $-5r^2$ 11. $9p^2 + 7p$
13. $9x^2 - 32x$ 15. $6y^3 - 4$
17. $12s^2 + 2s - 3$
19. $2x^2 - 13x + 15$
21. $9m^2 - 20m$ 23. $17mn$
25. $40 - 1000d^2$ 27. $82xy + 82y$ in²
29. C 31. 51.2%
33.
(graph)

12-3 Exercises
1. $5x^3 + 3x + 6$ 3. $11r^2s + 9rs$
5. $15ab^2 + 3ab - a^2b - 8$
7. $128 + 32w$ in. 9. $7g^2 + g - 1$
11. $-3h^5 + 12h^4 - h$
13. $13t^2 - 4t + 12$
15. $-w^2 - 4w - 2$
17. $7w^2y + 2wy^2 - 4wy$
19. $\approx 6.19r^3 + 4r^2 + 5r + 2$

27. C 29. $\frac{11}{10}$ or $1\frac{1}{10}$ 31. $\frac{6}{25}$
33. 84 ft

12-4 Exercises
1. $-4x^2y$ 3. $-3x^2 + 8x - 5$
5. $8x^3 - 5x + 6$
7. $-2b^3 + 5b^2 - b + 4$
9. $8m^2n + 3mn^2 - 2mn$
11. $-2x^2y - 5xy + 10x - 8$
13. $-4x^3 + 9x^2 + 12x + 21$ in³;
30 in³ 15. $-3v + 5v^2$
17. $-4xy^2 - 2xy$ 19. $9b^2 + 2b + 9$
21. $5a - 8$ 23. $x^2 - 3x + 4$
25. $-6p^3 - 5p^2 - 2p^2t^2 + 10pt^2$
27. $-2b + 2ab$
29. $6y^2 - 12x^2y + 5x^2$ 31. $2x^2 -$
$6x - 1$ in² 37. $10x + 29$; 109
39. $63m^5$ 41. $-8r^{10}s^{10}$
43. $-zy^3 - 5zy$

12-5 Exercises
1. $-15s^3t^5$ 3. $-35h^6j^{10}$ 5. $35p^4r^5$
7. $6hm - 8h^2$ 9. $-3x^3 + 15x^2 -$
$30x$ 11. $A = \frac{1}{2}b_1h + \frac{1}{2}b_2h$
13. $2g^3h^8$ 15. $-2s^5t^4$ 17. $7.5h^5j^{10}$
19. $15z^3 - 12z^2$
21. $-6c^4d^3 + 12c^2d^3$
23. $-12s^4t^3 - 15s^3t^3 + 6s^4t^4$
25. $-24b^7$ 27. $6a^3b^6$
29. $-3m^5 + 15m^3$ 31. $x^5 - x^7y^5$
33. $3f^6g^2 + f^3g^2 - f^2g^2$
35. $20m^4p^3 - 12m^3p^2 + 24m^4p^5$
37. $V = \pi r^2x^3 - \pi r^2y^3$; 63π
43. $15c^3d^4 - 20c^2d^4$
45. $4m - 3n + 2$ 47. 59 in²

12-6 Exercises
1. $xy + 4x - 5y - 20$
3. $12m^2 + 7m - 45$
5. $m^2 - 9m + 14$
7. $4x^2 + 100x$ ft² 9. $b^2 - 9$
11. $9x^2 + 30x + 25$
13. $v^2 + 4v - 5$
15. $3x^2 + 13x - 30$
17. $12b^2 + 11bc - 5c^2$
19. $12r^2 - 11rs - 5s^2$
21. $4x^2 + 60x + 125$ yd²
23. $b^2 + 6b + 9$ 25. $4x^2 - 9$
27. $a^2 + 14a + 49$ 29. $b^2 + 7b - 60$

Selected Answers SA13

Bottom page (SA14)

31. $t^2 - 13t + 36$ 33. $3b^2 - 5b - 28$
35. $4m^2 + 11mn - 3n^2$ 37. $r^2 - 25$
39. $15r^2 - 22rs + 8s^2$
41. $PV + bP + aV + ab = c$ 45. B
47. 25.1 49. -18.7
51. $-4m^2 + 12m - 24$
53. $-11x^2y + 4xy^3 + 16xy$

Chapter 12 Study Guide: Review
1. polynomial; degree 2. FOIL;
binomials 3. binomial; trinomial
4. trinomial 5. not a polynomial

6. not a polynomial 7. monomial
8. not a polynomial 9. binomial
10. 8 11. 4 12. 3 13. 5 14. 6
15. $7t^2 - 3t + 1$ 16. $11gh - 9g^2h$
17. $20mn - 12m$ 18. $8a^2 - 10b$
19. $36st^2 - 23t$ 20. $6x^2 - 2x + 5$
21. $5x^4 + x^2 - x + 7$ 22. $2h^2 +$
$8h + 7$ 23. $2xy^2 - 2x^2y + 2xy$
24. $13n^2 + 12$ 25. $6x^2 - 8$
26. $-w^2 - 12w + 14$ 27. $-4x^2 +$
$16x - 14$ 28. $4ab^2 - 11ab + 4a^2b$
29. $-p^3q^2 - 4p^3q^2 - 2pq^2$
30. $-12s^2t^4 + 4s^2t^3 + 32st^3$

31. $12a^4b^3 + 30a^3b^3 - 36a^3b +$
$24a^2b^2$ 32. $2m^3 - 16m^2 + 2m$
33. $10g^3h^3 - 15gh^5 + 20gh - 30h^2$
34. $2f^6k^3 - \frac{3}{2}f^3k^4 + f^6k^5$
35. $18x^2y^{14} - 15x^8y^{12} + 12x^3y^7 -$
$24x^3y^6$ 36. $p^2 - 8p + 12$ 37. $b^2 +$
$10b + 24$ 38. $3r^2 + 11r - 4$
39. $3a^2 - 11ab - 20b^2$
40. $m^2 - 14m + 49$ 41. $9r^2 - 36$
42. $6b^2 - 2bt - 28t^2$
43. $-3x^2 - 2x + 40$
44. $y^2 - 22y + 121$

SA14 *Selected Answers*

Notes

Additional Answers

Chapter 1

1-2 Exercises

5. 18 plus the product of 43 and s

6. 37 less than the quotient of 22 and r

7. 10 plus the quotient of y and 31

8. the product of 29 and b minus 93

10. Possible answer: Calvin has 450 less songs on his MP3 player than his friend Brian. How many songs does Calvin have on his MP3 player if Brian has 1325 songs? 875 songs

16. 142 minus the product of 19 and t

17. the product of 16 and g plus 12

18. 14 plus the quotient of 5 and d

19. 51 less than the quotient of w and 182

21. Possible answer: The total cost of a new radiator is $372 plus labor. How much is the total cost if the cost of labor is $137? $509

1-5 Exercises

36. Possible answer: The number of the year expressed in B.C.E. decreases as time goes forward. This is what happens with the negative part of the number line. As you move to the right and get closer to zero, the absolute value of the numbers decreases.

37. Possible answer: The calculations that involve an C.E. and B.C.E. year would be one less than originally calculated. But any calculations strictly in C.E. or B.C.E. would remain the same.

Chapter 2

2-1 Exercises

63b. 3×3; 2×3;
2×2; 3×5;
$2 \times 2 \times 2 \times 2$; 5×5;
$2 \times 2 \times 2$; $2 \times 2 \times 2$

c. $0.\overline{4}$; repeating
$0.1\overline{6}$; repeating
0.25; terminating
$0.4\overline{6}$; repeating
0.5625; terminating
0.48; terminating
0.625; terminating
0.375; terminating

d. Possible answer: If the prime factors of the denominators are 2's and 5's, the fraction is equivalent to a terminating decimal. If there are any other prime factors, the fraction is equivalent to a repeating decimal.

Chapter 3

3-1 Exercises

48. No; $8 \div 2 = 4$ and $2 \div 8 = \frac{1}{4}$, so $8 \div 2 \neq 2 \div 8$. Therefore, division is not commutative.

49. The sentence should read, "You can use the Commutative Property of Addition. . ."

50. The total number of cans is $5 \cdot 24$. By the Distrib. Prop., $5 \cdot 24 = 5(20 + 4) = 5 \cdot 20 + 5 \cdot 4 = 100 + 20 = 120$, so there are 120 cans.

51. $12 \cdot \left(\frac{1}{3} + \frac{1}{6} + \frac{1}{4}\right) = 12 \cdot \frac{1}{3} + 12 \cdot \frac{1}{6} + 12 \cdot \frac{1}{4}$ (Distrib. Prop.) $= 4 + 2 + 3$ (Mult.) $= (4 + 2) + 3$ (Assoc. Prop. of Add.) $= 6 + 3$ (Add) $= 9$

3-5 Exercises

7.
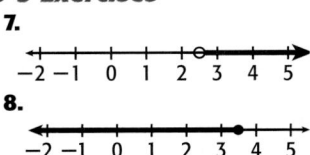

8.

16.

17.

18.

19.

20.

21.

22.

23.

3-6 Exercises

4. $z > 21$

5. $k \geq 9.3$

6. $x < 1\frac{2}{3}$

9. $x \geq 56$

10. $t > 5$

11. $x \geq 15$

12. $y \geq -1.32$

13. $c < 3\frac{1}{3}$

14. $a > 7$

17. $z > 0$

18. $x < 3\frac{2}{7}$

19. $y \geq -1.8$

20. $m \geq 6$

21. $k \leq 1$

22. $g < -24$

26. $x > 3$

27b. Possible answer: The answer shows that sales for the rest of the year must be greater than approximately $100,000. This is reasonable since the operating costs are about $200,000 and sales so far are about $100,000.

28. $65 + p \geq 189$ so $p \geq 124$, and $65 + p \leq 494$ so $p \leq 429$.

30. Possible answer: The water in an aquarium must be heated to no more than 75°. The current temperature is 40°. By how many degrees can the water be heated?

31. Possible answer: Choose a value in the solution set, substitute the value in the original inequality, and check that it results in a true inequality.

3-7 Exercises

10.

11.

12.

13.

14.

15.

16.

17.

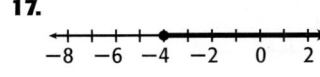

19.

1 2 3 4 5 6 7 8 9 10 11

20.

−86 −84 −82 −80 −78

21.

−4 −3 −2 −1 0 1 2 3 4

22.

−711 −709 −707 −705

23.

90 91 92 93 94 95 96 97 98 99

24.

31 32 33 34 35 36 37 38 39 40

25.

116 117 118 119 120 121 122

26.

7 8 9 10 11 12 13 14 15 16

3-8 Exercises

3.

−12 −10 −8 −6 −4

4. $x \le -2$

−5 −2 0

5.

2 3 4 5 6 7 8 9 10 11 12

6. $k > 5$

0 5 10

7. $x < 3$

0 3 5

8.

−4 −3 −2 −1 0 1 2 3 4 5

9. $h \le 1$

−5 0 1 5

10. $c > 2$

0 2 5

11.

−5 −4 −3 −2 −1 0 1 2 3 4

12.

−4 −3 −2 −1 0 1 2 3 4 5

14.

−2 −1 0 1 2 3 4 5 6 7 8

15.

−1 0 1 2 3 4 5 6 7 8 9

16.

−18 −16 −14 −12 −10 −8

17.

−3 −2 −1 0 1 2 3 4 5 6 7

18. $n < 3$

0 3 5

19.

−12 −10 −8 −6 −4 −2

20.

−12 −10 −8 −6 −4 −2

21. $a \ge -3$

−5 −3 0

22.

0 1 2

23. $k \ge 3$

0 3 5

24. $n \le -14$

−16 −14 −12

25. $r < 3$

0 3 5

27. $p \le \frac{22}{3}$

7 $7\frac{1}{3}$ 8

28. $n > -3$

−5 −3 0

29. $w > -1$

−5 −1 0

30. $x \le -4$

−8 −4 0

31. $a > \frac{1}{2}$

0 1 $\frac{1}{2}$ 2

32. $y \le -\frac{7}{2}$

−4 $-3\frac{1}{2}$ −2

33. $q < 6$

2 4 6 8

34. $m > \frac{5}{6}$

0 $\frac{1}{2}$ $\frac{5}{6}$ 1

35. $b < 2.7$

2 2.5 2.7 3

36. $k \ge -\frac{2}{3}$

−1 $-\frac{2}{3}$ 0

37. $f \le -27$

−30 −27 −25

38. $v \le \frac{3}{5}$

0 $\frac{3}{5}$ 1

44. Possible answer: Sergio paid $5.95 for the shipping on this last purchase, and his total was less than $49.45. Write and solve an inequality to describe the cost of the merchandise he bought. Answer: $x + \$5.95 < \$49.95$; $x < \$43.50$.

45. Possible answer: Method 1: Subtract x from both sides. Add 4 to both sides. Divide both sides by −4, and reverse the inequality symbol. Method 2: Add $3x$ to both sides, and divide both sides by 4.

48.

0 0.2

3B Ready To Go On?

5.

−2 −1 0 1

6.

−6 −5 −4 −3 −2 −1 0 1 2

9. $n < -\frac{4}{5}$

$-\frac{7}{5}$ $-\frac{6}{5}$ −1 $-\frac{4}{5}$ $-\frac{3}{5}$ $-\frac{2}{5}$ $-\frac{1}{5}$

10. $y > -7$

−11 −9 −7 −5 −3

11. $x \le 12$

8 9 10 11 12 13 14 15 16 17 18

12.

28 29 30 31 32 33 34 35 36

13.

−6 −5 −4 −3 −2 −1 0 1 2

14.

3 4 5 6 7 8 9 10 11 12 13

15.

−8 −6 −4 −2 0 2

16.

22 23 24 25 26 27 28 29 30

17.

−20 −18 −16 −14 −12

18.

−8 −6 −4 −2 0 2

19.

4 5 6 7 8 9 10 11 12

20.

−90 −89 −88 −87 −86 −85 −84 −83 −82

22.

−1 0 1 2 3 4 5 6 7 8

23.

16 17 18 19 20 21 22 23 24

24.

−2 −1 0 1 2 3 4 5 6

25.

−25 −23 −21 −19 −17

26.

−6 −5 −4 −3 −2 −1 0 1 2

27.

−14 −12 −10 −8 −6

Chapter 4

4-7 Exercises

1. 6 and 7; possible answer: 40 is between 36 and 49

2. 9 and 10; possible answer: 90 is between 81 and 100

3. 12 and 13; possible answer: 156 is between 144 and 169

4. 17 and 18; possible answer: 306 is between 289 and 324

17. 7 and 8; possible answer: 52 is between 49 and 56

18. 1 and 2; possible answer: 3 is between 1 and 4

19. 24 and 25; possible answer: 600 is between 576 and 625

20. 44 and 45; possible answer: 2000 is between 1936 and 2025

Chapter 5

5-1 Exercises

23. No; she needs $3\frac{1}{2}$ cups of pancake mix to make 14 servings.

24. No; February is the only month that is equivalent to 4 weeks (28 days). Other months have 30 or 31 days.

25. $\frac{2}{4} = \frac{3}{6}; \frac{2}{5} = \frac{4}{10}; \frac{12}{3} = \frac{4}{1};$ $\frac{12}{8} = \frac{9}{6};$

Possible answer: $\frac{3}{9} \ne \frac{2}{10}$

37. Possible answer: Multiply the numerator and denominator by the same number; divide the numerator and denominator by the same common factor.

38. $\frac{3}{9} = \frac{27}{81}; \frac{9}{3} = \frac{81}{27}; \frac{27}{81} = \frac{3}{9}; \frac{81}{27} = \frac{9}{3}; \frac{3}{27} = \frac{9}{81}; \frac{9}{81} = \frac{3}{27}; \frac{27}{3} = \frac{81}{9}; \frac{81}{9} = \frac{27}{3}$

5-5 Exercises

19. Possible answer: A scale drawing of a rectangular-shaped table is 9 cm wide and 12 cm long. If the table is 3 ft wide, how long is the table? Solution: $\frac{9}{3} = \frac{12}{x}$; 4 ft

20. False; Possible answer: Some, not all, similar figures are congruent. Similar figures have proportional measurements. If those measurements are also *equal,* then the figures are congruent.

Chapter 6

6-1 Exercises

27. Possible answer: finding scores for a test that has a total of 75 points possible

29. Possible answer: The student used 6% instead of 0.06%. Written as a ratio, 0.06% is $\frac{6}{10,000}$, or 6 out of every 10,000.

30. Possible answer: First write all the numbers in the same form: $\frac{1}{3} = 0.\overline{3} = 33.\overline{3}\%$ and 0.33 = 33%. Then compare and order the percents: 30%, 33%, 33.3%. Finally, write the numbers in their original form in the same order: 30%, 0.33, $\frac{1}{3}$.

31. Possible answer: Wyatt and Allyson both got the same answer because the proportions they used to find their answers were the same. For 13% of 38: $\frac{13}{100} = \frac{x}{38}$; for 38% of 13: $\frac{38}{100} = \frac{x}{13}$. In both cases, the cross products are 13(38) = 100x. This would work for any two numbers for the same reason.

6-7 Exercises

19. Possible answer: It is impossible to tell without knowing how long each kept money in her account. Sabrina may have had a lower interest rate but kept her money in the account longer.

20. a. A: $50,143.75, B: $46,505
b. A: 8.25%, B: 7.75%
c. A: $835.73, B: $968.85
d. $3638.75

21. How long did Alice keep her money in the savings account?

22. Possible answer: the 3-year loan would cost the borrower less ($675, compared with $720). The interest saved would be $45.

23. Possible answer: The payments are equal. For example, the interest on a $1000 loan for 5 years at 3% is 1000 · 0.03 · 5 = $150. The interest on the same loan with a monthly rate of 0.25% is 1000 · 0.0025 · 60 = $150.

Cumulative Assessment

18. The package that contains 1872 in² of paper; Possible answer: 1 ft² = 12² in², since 12 in. = 1 ft. $\frac{1872 \text{ in}^2}{144 \text{ in}^2}$ = 13 ft². 13 ft² is greater than 12 ft².

19. Possible answer: The discount was $48.80 × 0.2 = $9.76. The discounted price was $48.80 − $9.76 = $39.04. The total price plus sales tax was $39.04 × 1.0725 = $41.87. Each person paid $41.87 ÷ 4 = $10.4675, or about $10.47.

Chapter 7

7-1 Exercises

5–8.

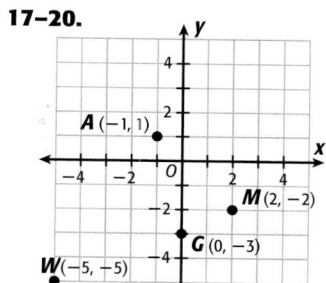

17–20.

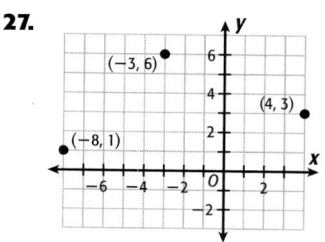

27.

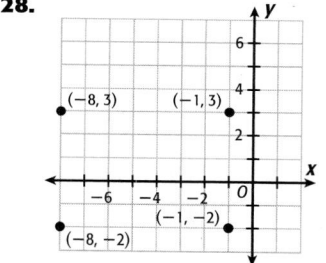

28.

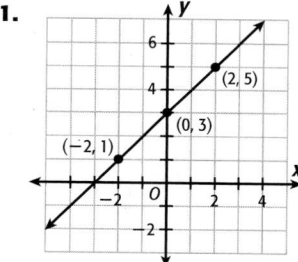

36. The student should have moved 12 units left from the origin and then 1 unit up.

37. Possible answer: If order is disregarded, a pair of coordinates could refer to either of two points in the same plane.

7-2 Exercises

1.

x	2x − 4	y
−2	2(−2) − 4	−8
0	2(0) − 4	−4
2	2(2) − 4	0

2.

x	3x + 4	y
−2	3(−2) + 4	−2
0	3(0) + 4	4
2	3(2) + 4	10

3.

x	4x²	y
−2	4(−2)²	16
0	4(0)²	0
2	4(2)²	16

4.

x	−x + 1	y
−2	−(−2) + 1	3
0	−(0) + 1	1
2	−(2) + 1	−1

8.

x	2x + 5	y
−2	2(−2) + 5	1
0	2(0) + 5	5
2	2(2) + 5	9

9.

x	3(x + 1)	y
−2	3(−2 + 1)	−3
0	3(0 + 1)	3
2	3(2 + 1)	9

10.

x	−3x²	y
−2	−3(−2)²	−12
0	−3(0)²	0
2	−3(2)²	−12

11.

x	2(1 − 2x)	y
−2	2(1 − 2(−2))	10
0	2(1 − 2(0))	2
2	2(1 − 2(2))	−6

7-3 Exercises

1.

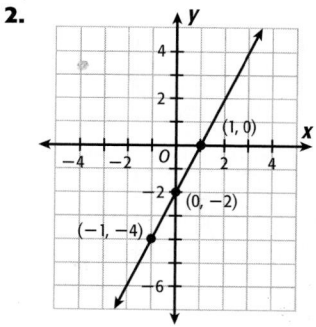

2.

3b. $y = 750x$

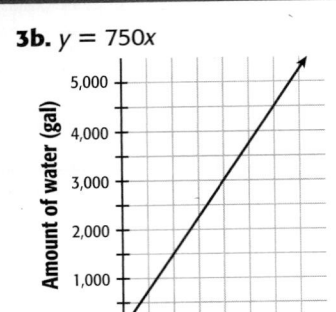

4.

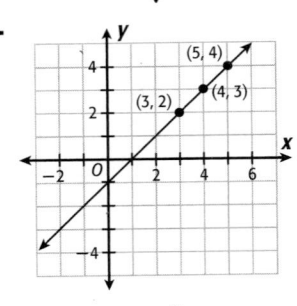

5.

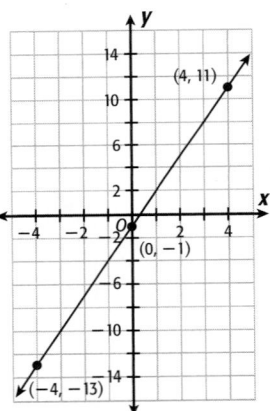

6.

7.

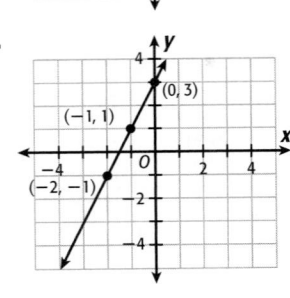

8b. $y = 3x + 40$

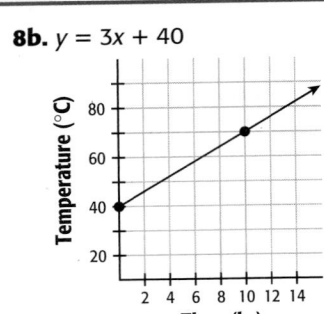

11.

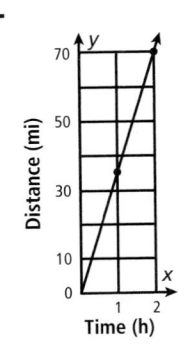

12.

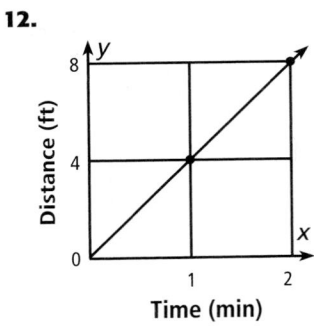

13.

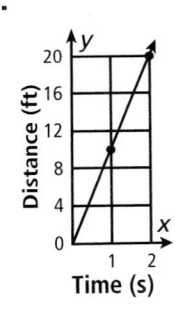

14. $x = 3$

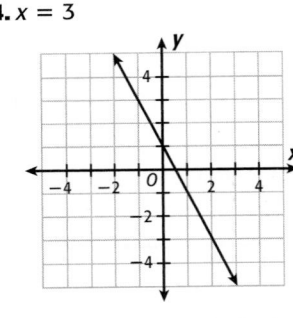

18. Possible answer: Find y for three values of x, graph the three points, and connect them with a straight line.

21. Simon graphed the y-coordinates incorrectly. He should have used the points $(0, 3)$, $(-1, 4)$, and $(1, 2)$.

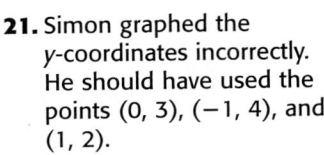

7-4 Exercises

1.

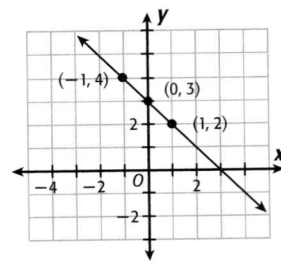

x	y
−3	−4
−2	1
−1	4
0	5
1	4
2	1
3	−4

2.

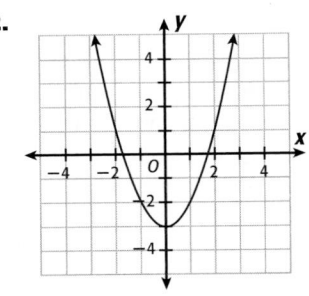

x	y
−3	6
−2	1
−1	−2
0	−3
1	−2
2	1
3	6

3.

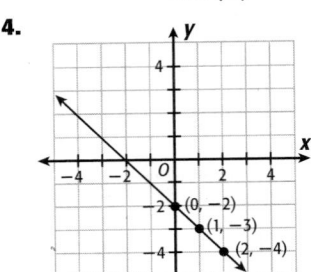

x	y
−3	4.5
−2	1
−1	−0.5
0	0
1	2.5
2	7
3	13.5

5.

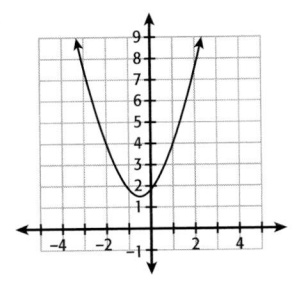

x	y
−3	8
−2	4
−1	2
0	2
1	4
2	8
3	14

6.

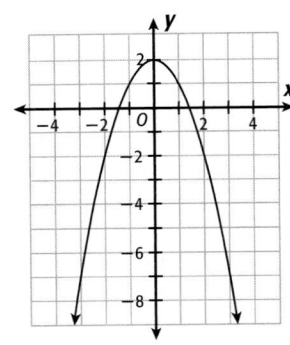

x	y
−3	−7
−2	−2
−1	1
0	2
1	1
2	−2
3	−7

7.

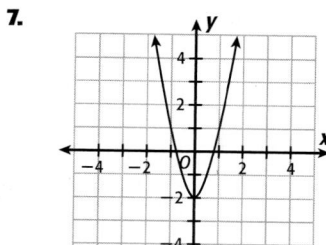

x	y
−3	25
−2	10
−1	1
0	−2
1	1
2	10
3	25

19a.

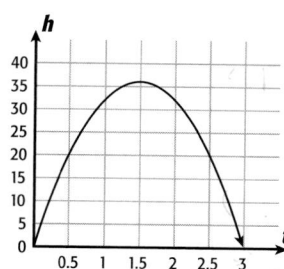

22. $h = 0$; The object reaches the ground 4 seconds after it was dropped; a feather; a feather would take longer to reach the ground because of air resistance, whereas a rock would probably reach the ground in less than 4 seconds.

24. Possible answer: The function $y = 2^x$ will grow more quickly as x gets larger. For example, when $x = 10$, 2^{10} is 1024, but 10^2 is only 100.

25.

x	−2	−1	0	1	2
y	−15	−6	−3	−6	−15

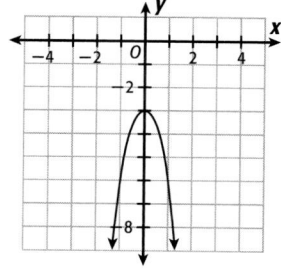

7-5 Exercises

1.

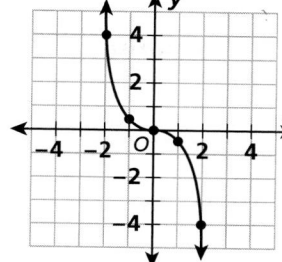

2.

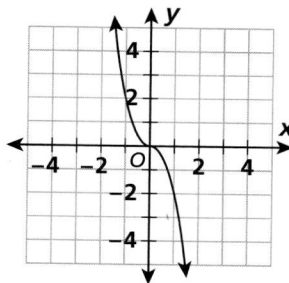

3.

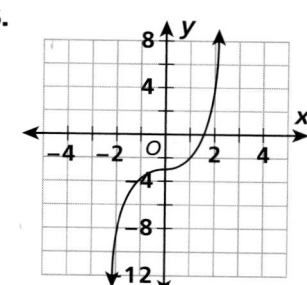

7.

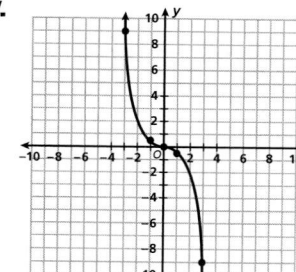

8.

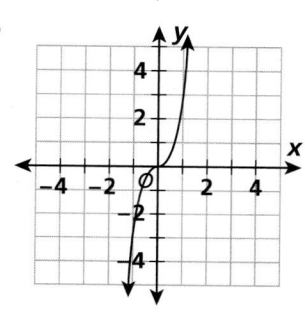

9.

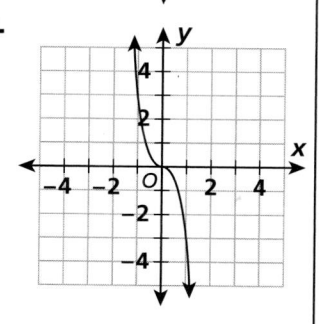

10.

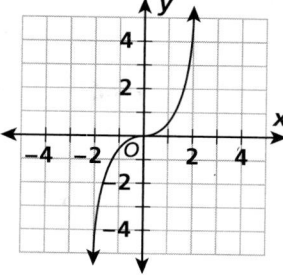

11.

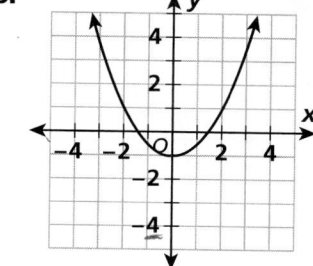

12.

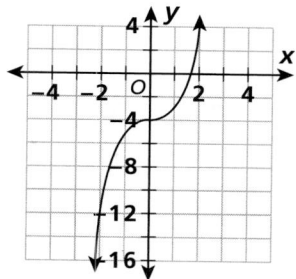

16.

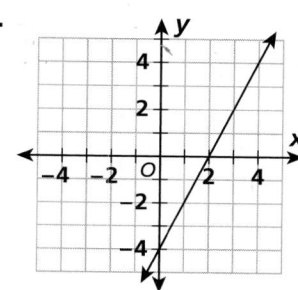

17.

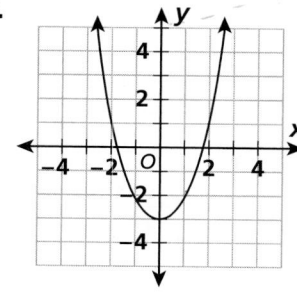

18.

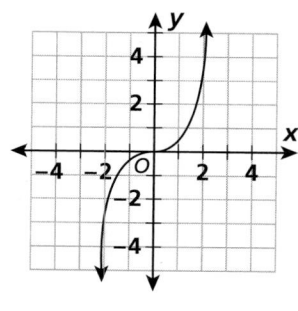

19.

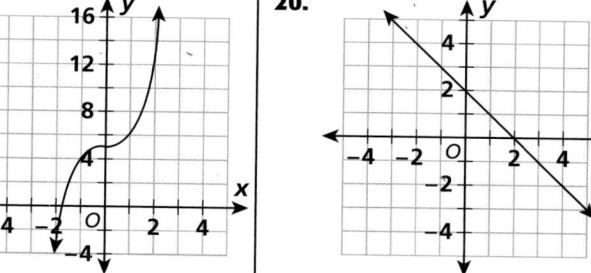

20.

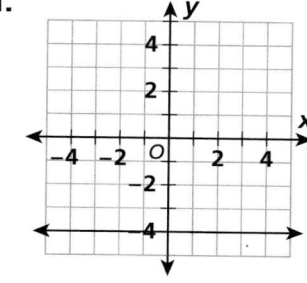

21.

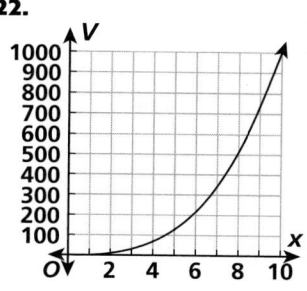

22.

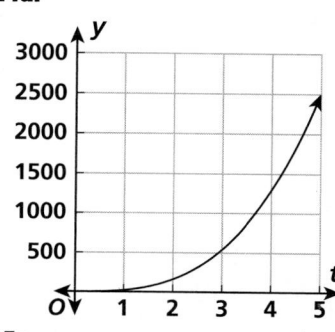

24a.

25a.

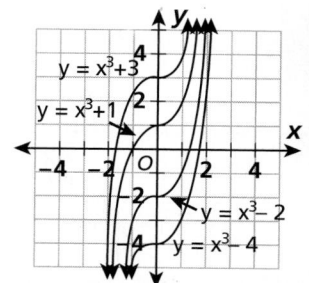

$y = x^3 + 3$
$y = x^3 + 1$
$y = x^3 - 2$
$y = x^3 - 4$

28.

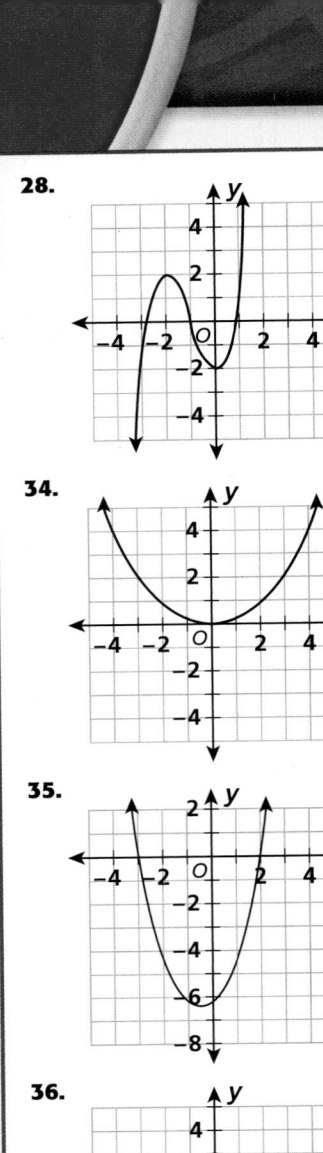

34.

35.

36.

7A Ready To Go On?

1–4.

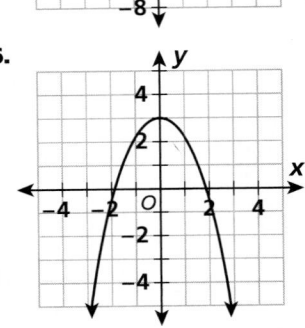

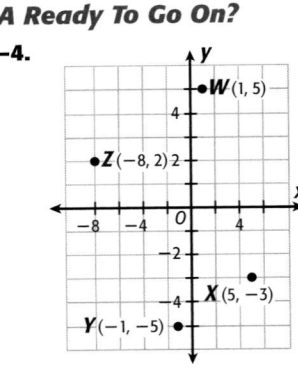

W(1, 5)

Z(−8, 2)

X(5, −3)

Y(−1, −5)

9.

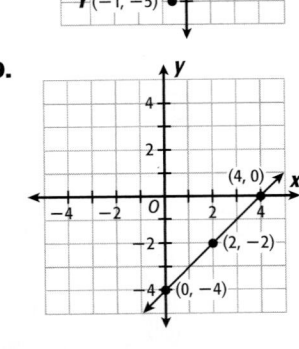

(4, 0)

(2, −2)

(0, −4)

10.

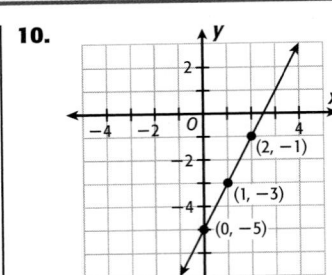

(2, −1)

(1, −3)

(0, −5)

11.

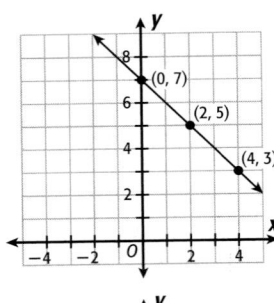

(0, 7)

(2, 5)

(4, 3)

12.

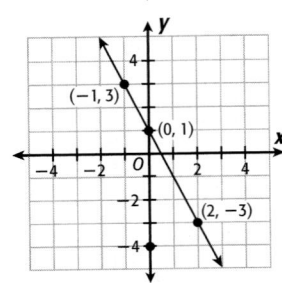

(−1, 3)

(0, 1)

(2, −3)

13.

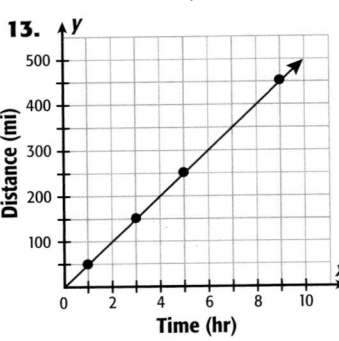

Distance (mi)

Time (hr)

14.

x	y
−3	13
−2	8
−1	5
0	4
1	5
2	8
3	13

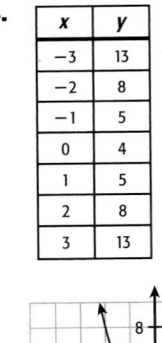

15.

x	y
−3	1.5
−2	−1
−1	−1.5
0	0
1	3.5
2	9
3	16.5

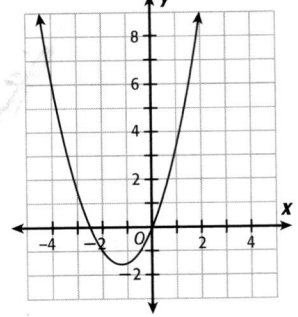

16.

x	y
−3	5
−2	1
−1	−1
1	1
2	5

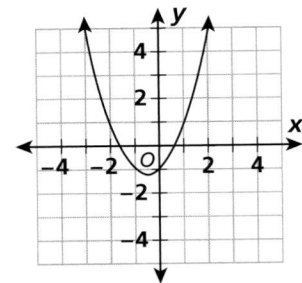

7-6 Exercises

21. The slope is positive if the line slants upward from left to right. The slope is negative if the line slants downward from left to right. The slope is 0 if the line is horizontal.

22.

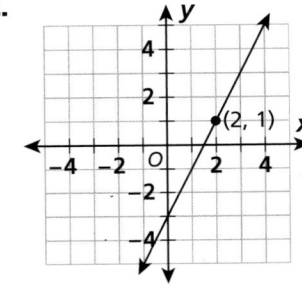

(2, 1)

7-7 Additional Examples

2.

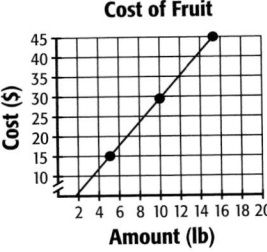

Cost of Fruit

Cost ($)

Amount (lb)

7-7 Exercises

7.

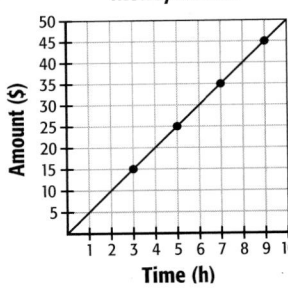

Money Earned

Amount ($)

Time (h)

17.

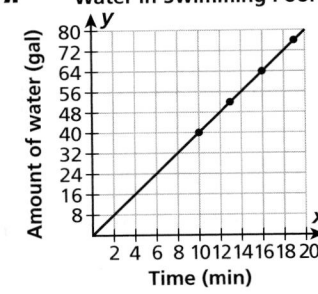

Water in Swimming Pool

Amount of water (gal)

Time (min)

19.

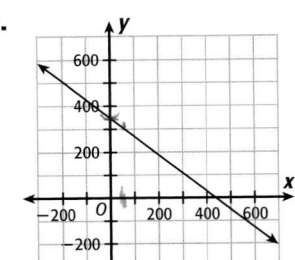

23. Possible answer: The formula for slope is $\frac{y_2 - y_1}{x_2 - x_1}$ so the y-values should be in the numerator instead of the x-values.

24. Possible answer: For the line $x = 3$, find the slope by using any two points on the line. Using the points $(3, 4)$ and $(3, 7)$, the slope is $\frac{7-4}{3-3} = \frac{3}{0}$, which is undefined.

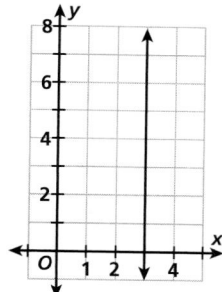

7-7 Lesson Quiz

3.

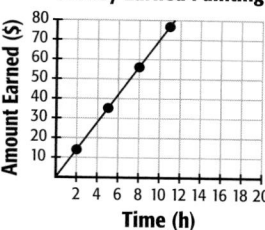

Money Earned Painting

The slope of the line is 7. This means that Susan earned 7 dollars for every hour she worked.

7-8 Exercises

12. Possible answer: The temperature gradually increases from its starting point, then increases more rapidly. Then the temperature fluctuates, possibly while the food is cooking and the oven door is opened and closed.

7-9 Exercises

22. Possible answer: The constant of variation represents the slope of the line graphed by a direct variation equation. The greater the constant, the steeper the slope of the line.

Chapter 7 Test

12.

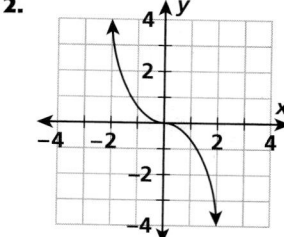

13.

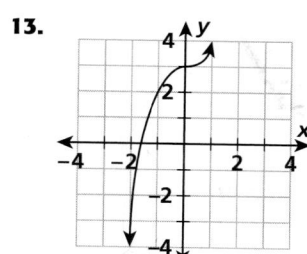

17.

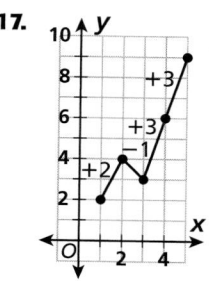

18.

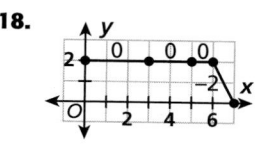

22.

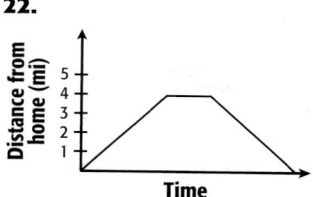

Time

23.

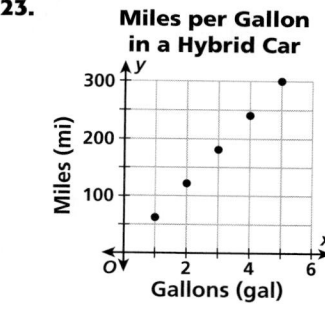

Miles per Gallon in a Hybrid Car

yes

Chapter 8

8-2 Exercises

16. a. Possible answer:

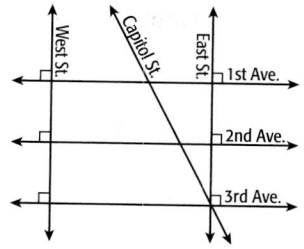

b. Possible answer:

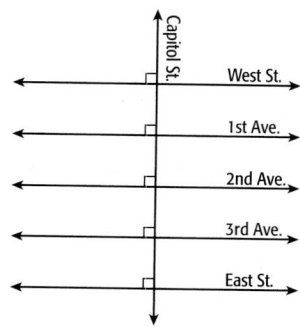

23.

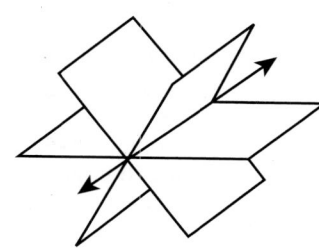

8-3 Exercises

20. Possible answer: Yes, vertical angles are congruent, corresponding angles are congruent, alternate interior angles are congruent, and alternate exterior angles are congruent. Therefore, if you are given one angle measure, you can find three other angles congruent to the original. All other angles will be supplementary to the first four angles you found.

23. Possible answer:

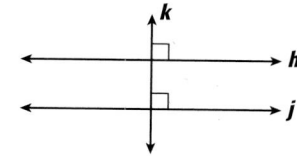

---

27. Possible answer: No, unless all of the angles are right angles. The acute angles between line s and line t will be two angles in an isosceles triangle.

30.

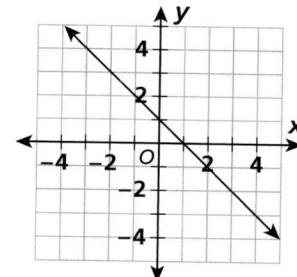

31.

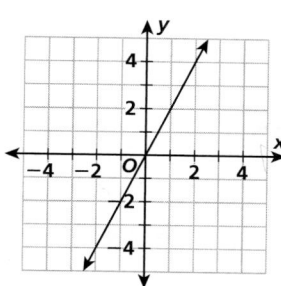

32.

x	y
-2	-3
-1	0
0	1
1	0
2	-3

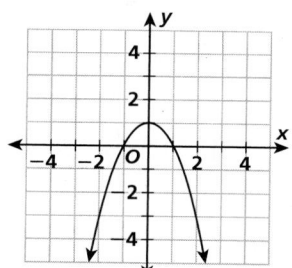

33.

x	y
-2	6
-1	1
0	0
1	3
2	10

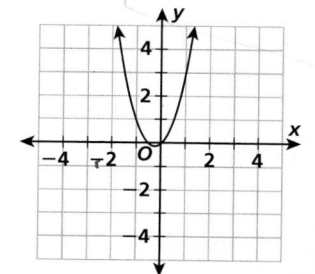

8-4 Exercises

24. Possible answer: Cut the square in half diagonally. The angle measures are 90°, 45°, and 45°. Cut the triangle from one vertex to the midpoint of the opposite side. The angles are 30°, 60°, and 90°.

8-5 Exercises

15.

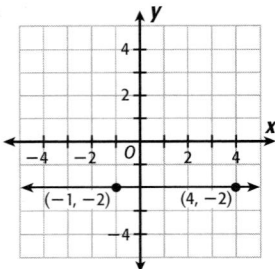

16.

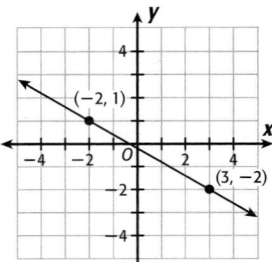

18. Possible answer:

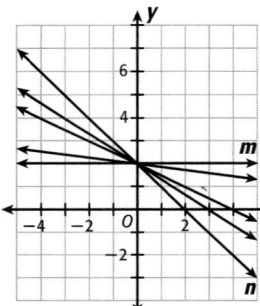

19. Possible answer:

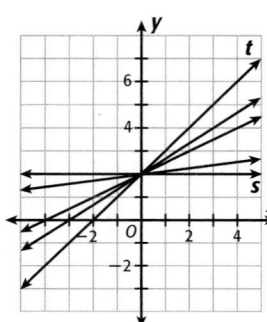

22. False: possible answer: all of the adjacent sides of a trapezoid are not perpendicular.

23. False; possible answer: a rhombus that is not a square does not have perpendicular adjacent sides.

24. False; possible answer: a trapezoid has only one pair of sides that have the same slope.

26. Possible answer: It is a right triangle because the slope of $\overline{LM} = -1$ and the slope of $\overline{LN} = 1$. The product of the slopes is -1, so the line segments are perpendicular and form a right angle.

27. The slope of $\overleftrightarrow{CD}$ is also undefined because parallel lines have the same slope.

28. Possible answer: The given vertices are the endpoints for the diagonal of the square. The missing vertices are $(-1, 0)$ and $(3, 0)$. This forms a square with an area of 8 square units.

33. Possible answer: Are the points the vertices of a square?

34. Possible answer: The slope of a line will have the same value, regardless of which two points on a line you use to determine the slope.

35. Possible answer: Draw a square with vertices $(0, 0)$, $(1, 0)$, $(1, 1)$, and $(0, 1)$. A line through the diagonal has a slope of 1 and cuts the square into two congruent right triangles that have angle measures 45°, 45°, and 90°.

8A Ready To Go On?

13.

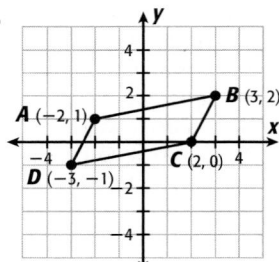

14.

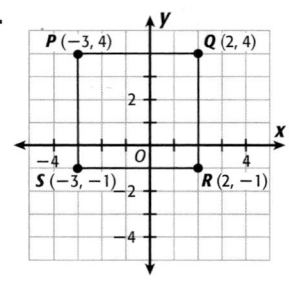

8-7 Exercises

11.

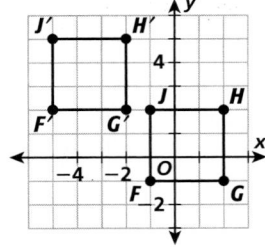

12.

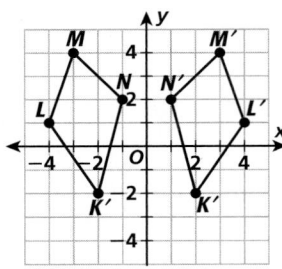

$K'(2, -2)$, $L'(4, 1)$, $N'(1, 2)$, $M'(3, 4)$

13.

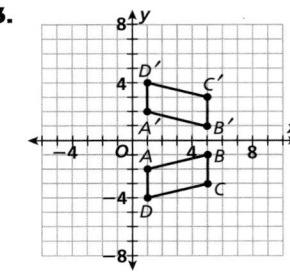

$A'(1, 2)$, $B'(5, 1)$, $C'(5, 3)$, $D'(1, 4)$

14.

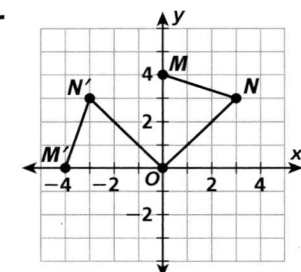

15.

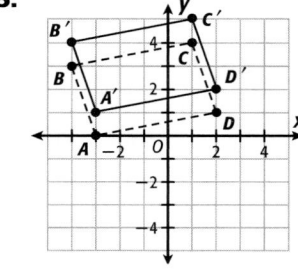

16.

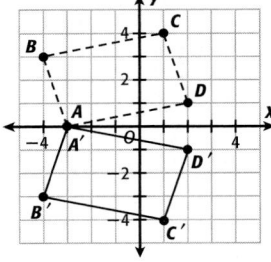

17.

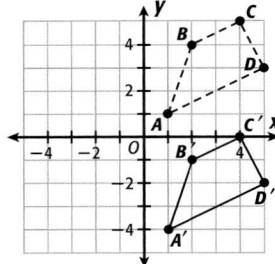

18.

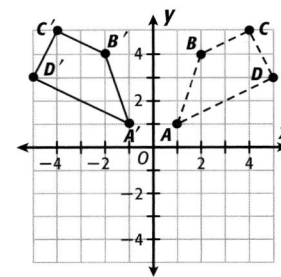

25. Possible answer: Draw a triangle. Translate it down 5 units and up 5 units. Translate all three figures left 5 units and right 5 units.

26. Possible answer: Any translation or a reflection across a horizontal line will not affect the direction. A reflection across a vertical line will reverse the direction. Rotations or reflections over other lines will change the direction by varying amounts.

27. Reflect across the x-axis; translate 5 units right and 3 units up.

29.

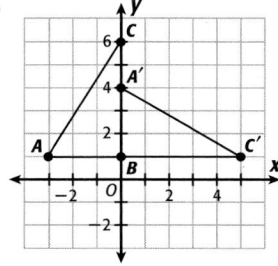

8-7 Lesson Quiz

3.
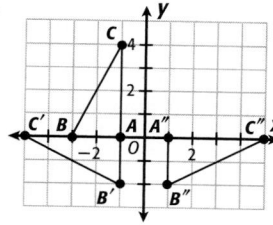

8-8 Exercises

1.
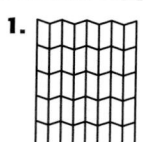

2. Possible answer:
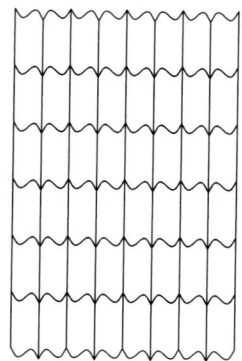

6.
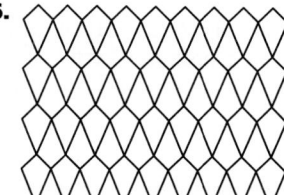

7.
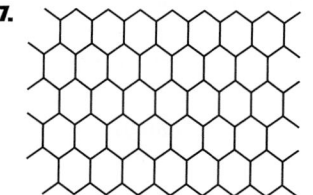

8.

9.
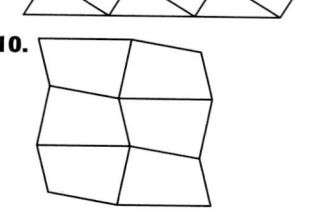

10.

13. a. Possible answer:
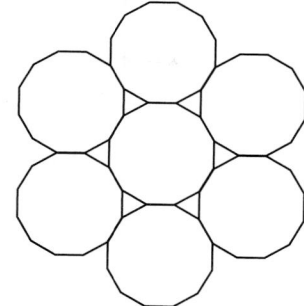

b. Possible answer:
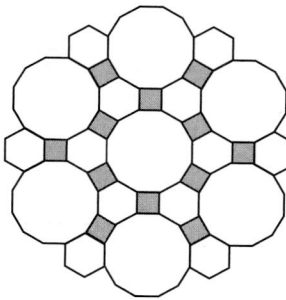

c. Possible answer:
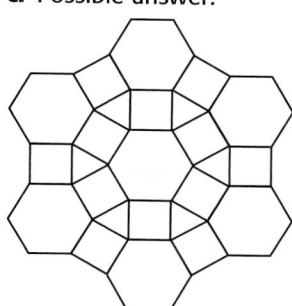

22.

x	y
−2	$-2\frac{2}{3}$
−1	$-\frac{1}{3}$
0	0
1	$\frac{1}{3}$
2	$2\frac{2}{3}$

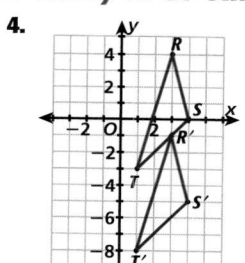

23.

x	y
−2	9
−1	2
0	1
1	0
2	−7

24.

x	y
−2	−13
−1	−6
0	−5
1	−4
2	3

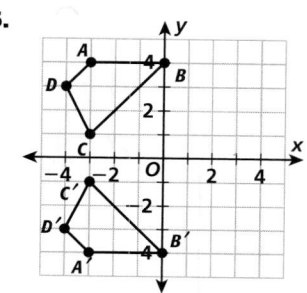

8B Ready To Go On?

4.
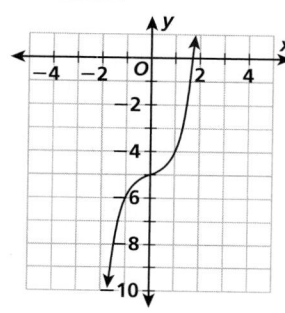

$R'(3, -1), S'(4, -5), T'(1, -8)$

5.

$A'(-3, -4), B'(0, -4),$
$C'(-3, -1), D'(-4, -3)$

6.
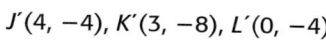
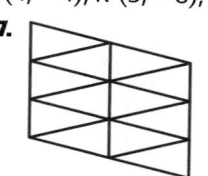

$J'(4, -4), K'(3, -8), L'(0, -4)$

7.

Chapter 9

9-1 Exercises

5.
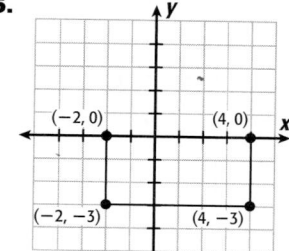

6.
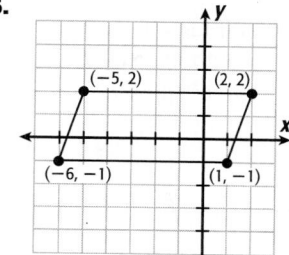

7.
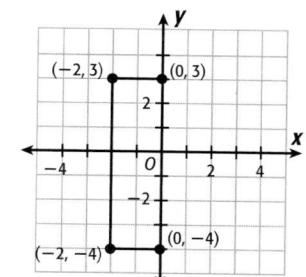

12.
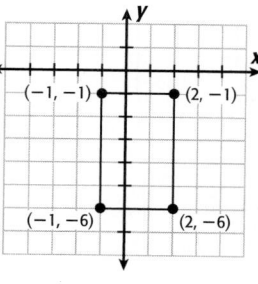

13.

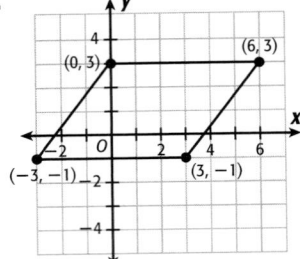

14.

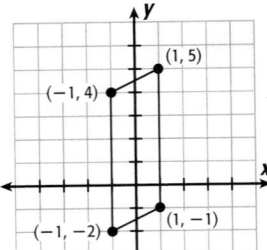

15.

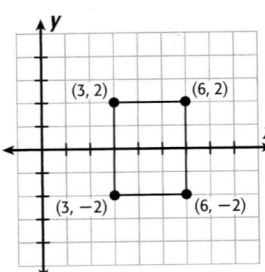

28. The area of the parallelogram is 20 square units.
The height of the parallelogram is 4 units, and the
length of the base of the
parallelogram is 5 units.
$4 \times 5 = 20$

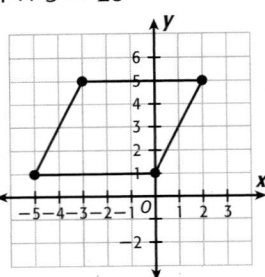

9-1 Lesson Quiz

3.

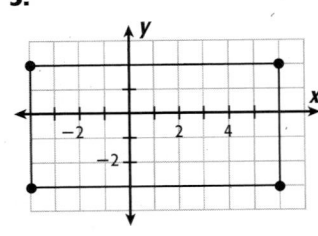

4.

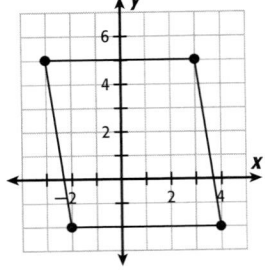

9-2 Exercises

7.

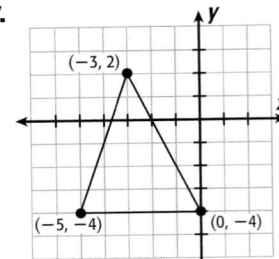

8.

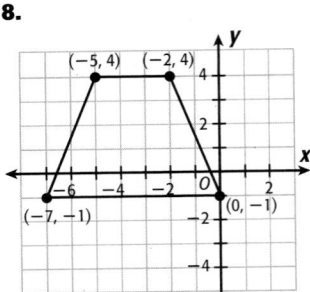

16.

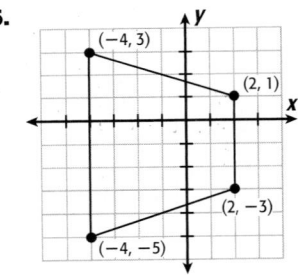

9A Ready To Go On?

5.

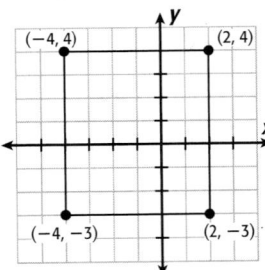

6.

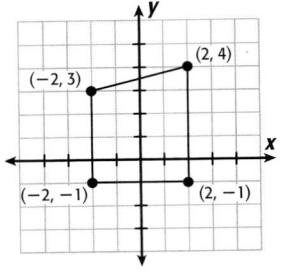

13.

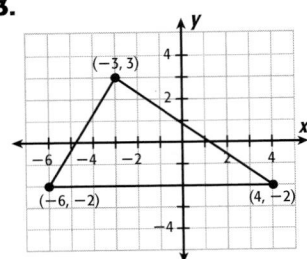

14.

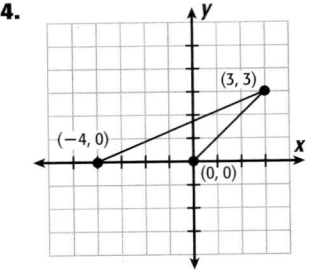

9-4 Exercises

37.

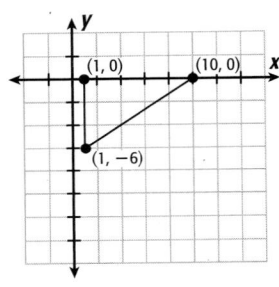

38.

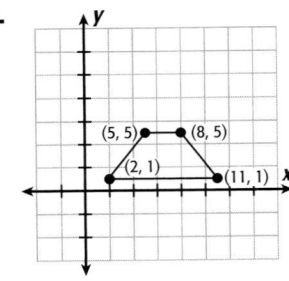

9-6 Exercises

16. The total area represented
by the squares is
$80 \times 1700 = 136,600$
km². Since Iceland fits
completely within the
80 squares, its area must
be less than 136,000 km².

17. Approximate the area of
the glacier with a trapezoid
($b_1 = 2$, $b_2 = 3$, $h = 1$)
that has area $\frac{5}{2}$ and a
triangle ($b = 3$, $h = 1$)
that has area $\frac{3}{2}$. The total
area of this composite
figure is $\frac{5}{2} + \frac{3}{2} = 4$
squares, or 6800 km².

Cumulative Assessment

15.

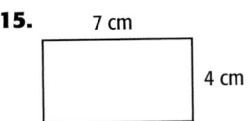

Rectangle with dimensions
7 cm × 4 cm has the larger
area; rectangle with dimensions 14 cm × 1 cm has
the larger perimeter

16. 18 cm²; count the full
squares and the half-full
squares. There are 12 full
squares and 12 half-full
squares.

Add the number of full
squares plus half the
number of half-full
squares:
$12 + \frac{1}{2}(12) = 12 + 6 = 18$
The area is 18 cm².

Chapter 10

10-1 Additional Examples

1. **A.** one pentagonal base,
five triangular faces;
pentagonal pyramid

B. one triangular base,
three triangular faces;
triangular pyramid

C. two hexagonal bases, six
rectangular faces; hexag-
onal prism

2. **A.** polyhedron, rectangular
pyramid and rectangular
prism

B. not a polyhedron, cone

10-1 Lesson Quiz

1. one square base, four triangular faces, square pyramid

2. one pentagonal base,
five rectangular faces,
pentagonal prism

10-3 Exercises

22. Possible answer: The student probably confused a cylinder with a cone. The volume formulas for a cylinder ($V = Bh$) and a pyramid ($V = \frac{1}{3}Bh$) are not the same. However, the volume formulas for a cone and a pyramid are the same ($V = \frac{1}{3}Bh$).

24. Possible answer: When the height of the cone is doubled, the volume is doubled. When the radius is doubled, the volume is increased by a factor of 4.

10-4 Exercises

26. No, they would not have the same effect. Doubling the height affects the lateral surface area only. The lateral surface area would double. Doubling the radius affects both the total area of the bases and the lateral surface area. The total area of the bases would quadruple and the lateral surface area would double. Doubling both the height and the radius would quadruple the total surface area of the cylinder.

28. Possible answer: Because a cube has 6 congruent square faces, divide 512 by 6 to find the surface area of each face. Take the square root of the area of one face to get the length of each side.

10-7 Exercises

23. No, doubling the length of each edge gives a surface area that is quadrupled and a volume that is increased by a factor of 8.

Chapter 11

11-1 Exercises

17.

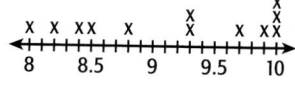

Stem	Leaves
8	0 2 4 5 8
9	3 3 7 9
10	0 0 0

Key: 8 | 0 means 8.0 or 8

19. Line plot; the range of the data is displayed on the line plot, so the distribution of data is more clear than on the stem-and-leaf plot.

Stems	Leaves
0	2 7 8 9 9
1	0 1 2 8
2	0 5 6 8
3	0 3

11-1 Lesson Quiz

1.

2.

Stems	Leaves
2	1, 3, 3, 4, 4
3	1, 3, 4, 5, 5, 8, 9
4	2, 5, 5, 5
5	7, 7
6	0, 1

Key: 4|2 means 42

11-2 Lesson Quiz

2. The outlier is 64. Without the outlier the mean is ≈85, the median is 83, and there is no mode. With the outlier the mean is ≈82, the median is 82, and there is no mode. Including the outlier decreases the mean by 3 and the median by 1. The mode did not change.

11-3 Exercises

21.

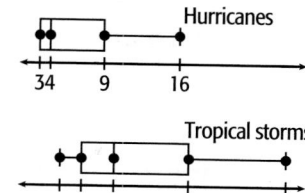

Possible answer: The median number of tropical storms is greater than the median number of hurricanes.

23.

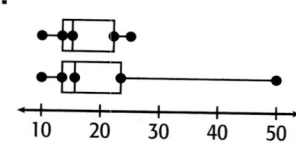

The introduction of an outlier created a disproportionately long whisker.

28.

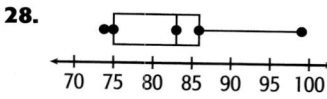

11-4 Exercises

14.

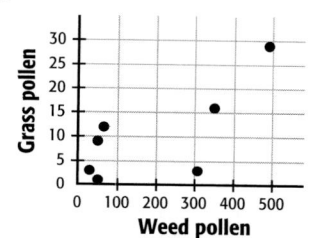

There is a positive correlation between the pollen levels.

11A Ready To Go On?

1.

2. Speeds of Various Land Animals

Stems	Leaves
4	2 4 7 8 9
5	1 2 4 5 5 9
6	1 2 5 7

Key: 4|2 means 42

3.

American League		National League
3, 7, 7	4	7, 8, 9
2, 7	5	0
	6	
	7	3

6.

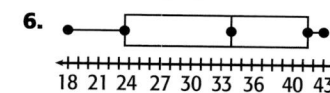

7.

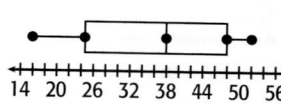

8.

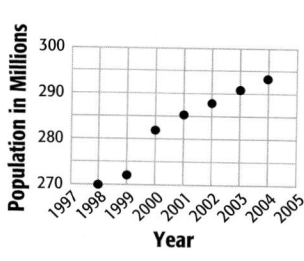

11-5 Exercises

18. Possible answer: The value of p is greater than or equal to 0 and less than or equal to 1. The probability that the event will not occur is $1 - p$, because the two probabilities must add to 1.

19. A, B, C, (A and B), (A and C), (B and C), and (A, B, and C)

11-7 Exercises

19–24.

Penny	Dime	Quarter	Outcome
H	H	H	HHH
H	H	T	HHT
H	T	H	HTH
H	T	T	HTT
T	H	H	THH
T	H	T	THT
T	T	H	TTH
T	T	T	TTT

27. Possible answer:

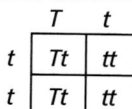

	T	t
t	Tt	tt
t	Tt	tt

One parent has a *Tt* combination and can roll his or her tongue, and the other has a *tt* combination and cannot roll his or her tongue.

Chapter 12

12-2 Exercises

33.

x	y
−2	−3
−1	0
0	1
1	0
2	−3

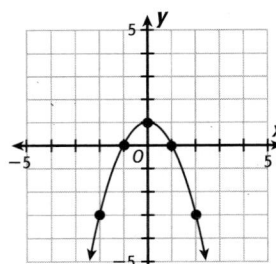

34.

x	y
−2	−1
−1	−3
0	−1
1	2
2	7

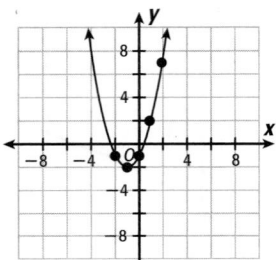

Extra Practice

Chapter 3

47.
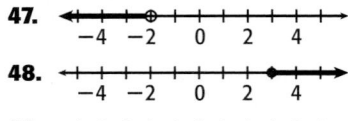

48.

49.

50.

53.

54.

55.

56.

57.

58.

59.
−11 −9 −7 −5 −3

60.
−1/5 0 1/5 2/5 3/5 4/5 1

61.
6 8 10 12 14

62.
−14 −12 −10 −8 −6

63.
−12 −10 −8 −6 −4

64.
1 2 3 4 5 6 7 8 9 10

65.
−26 −22 −18 −14 −10

66.
−35 −25 −15 −5 0 5

67.
−8 −6 −4 −2 0

68.
7 8 9 10 11 12 13 14 15

70.
−2 −1 0 1 2 3 4 5 6

71.
−7 −5 −3 −1 0 1

72.
0 1 2 3 4 5 6 7 8

73.
−7 −5 −3 −1 0 1

74.
−6 −4 −2 0 1 2

75.
−2 0 2 4 6

76.
8/5 9/5 2 11/5 12/5 13/5 14/5 3 16/5

77.
−1 0 1 2 3 4 5 6 7

Chapter 4

55. $\sqrt{30}$ is between 5 and 6 because 30 is between 25 and 36.

56. $\sqrt{61}$ is between 7 and 8 because 61 is between 49 and 64.

57. $\sqrt{93}$ is between 9 and 10 because 93 is between 81 and 100.

58. $-\sqrt{124}$ is between −11 and −12 because 124 is between 121 and 144.

Chapter 7

1–3.
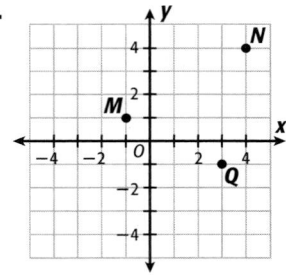

10.
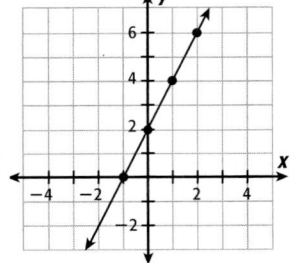

11.
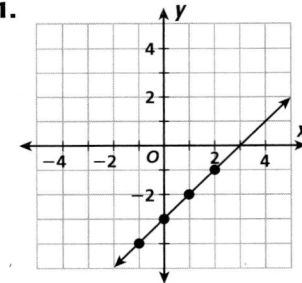

12.
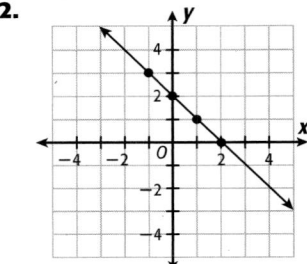

13.

14.

15.

16.

17.

18.
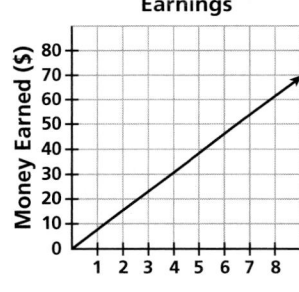

19.

30. **Concession Stand Earnings**
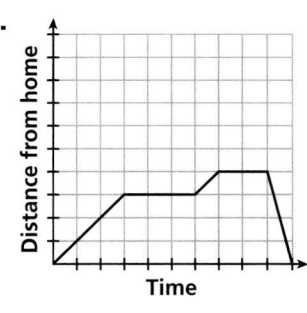

32.
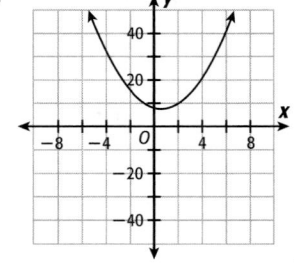

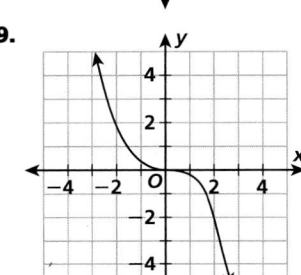

Chapter 8

33.
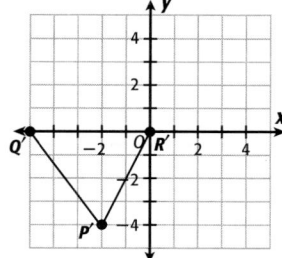

34.
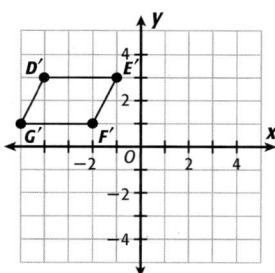

35.
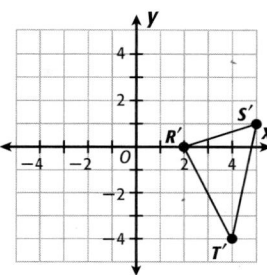

36.

37.
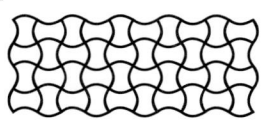

Chapter 9

4.
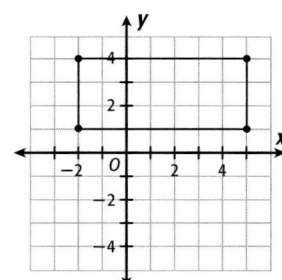

5.
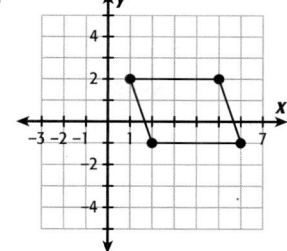

10.
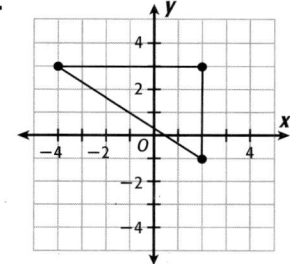

11.
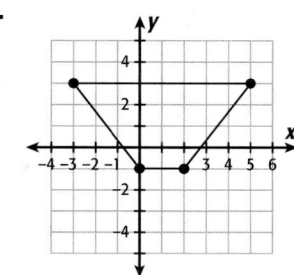

Chapter 10

32. 8 cm: 5 cm; the sides of the larger cube are $\frac{8}{5}$, or 1.6, times longer than those of the smaller cube.

33. 384 cm²: 150 cm²; the surface area of the larger cube is 2.56 times greater than the surface area of the smaller cube.

34. 512 cm³: 125 cm³; the volume of the larger cube is 4.096 times greater than the volume of the smaller cube.

Chapter 11

1.

```
                              x
                       x  x
                       xx  x
               x   xxx  x  xx
       x      xx  xxxxx  xx    x    x
      <+-+-+-+-+-+-+-+-+-+-+-+-+->
       0  2  4  6  8 10 12 14 16 18 20 22
```

2.

Losses		Wins
2 4 5 6	0	3 4 5 5 6 9
1 2 2	1	
	2	6

---

5. mean: 37; median: 32.5; The median best describes the data because the majority of the data clusters around the value 32.5.

8.
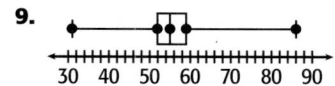

9.
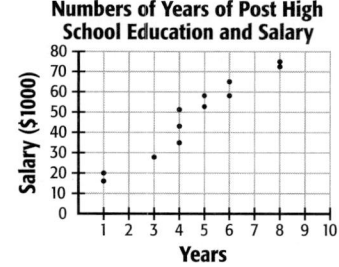

10.
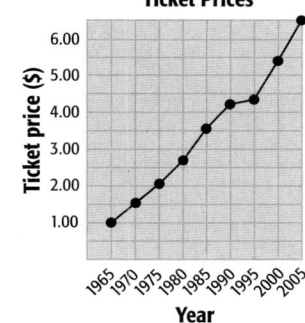

Numbers of Years of Post High School Education and Salary

Skills Bank

Line Graphs

1.
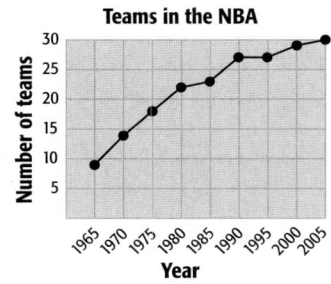

Average Movie Theater Ticket Prices

2.
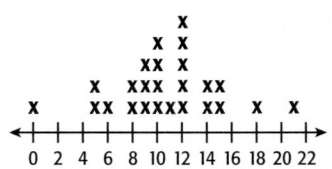

Teams in the NBA

Histograms

1.
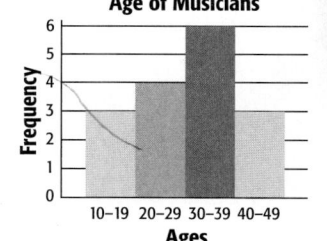

2.
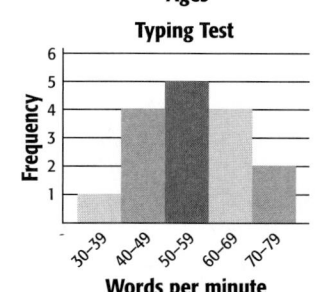

Circle Graphs

1.
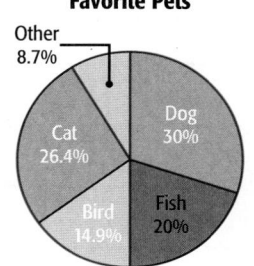

Favorite Pets

Notes

Glossary/Glosario

A

ENGLISH	SPANISH	EXAMPLES
absolute value The distance of a number from zero on a number line; shown by ||. (p. 15)	**valor absoluto** Distancia a la que está un número de 0 en una recta numérica. El símbolo del valor absoluto es ||.	$\|5\| = 5$ $\|-5\| = 5$
acute angle An angle that measures less than 90°. (p. 379)	**ángulo agudo** Ángulo que mide menos de 90°.	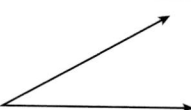
acute triangle A triangle with all angles measuring less than 90°. (p. 392)	**triángulo acutángulo** Triángulo en el que todos los ángulos miden menos de 90°.	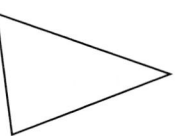
Addition Property of Equality The property that states that if you add the same number to both sides of an equation, the new equation will have the same solution. (p. 33)	**Propiedad de igualdad de la suma** Propiedad que establece que puedes sumar el mismo número a ambos lados de una ecuación y la nueva ecuación tendrá la misma solución.	$14 - 6 = 8$ $\underline{+\,6 \quad +\,6}$ $14 = 14$
Addition Property of Opposites The property that states that the sum of a number and its opposite equals zero. (p. 18)	**Propiedad de la suma de los opuestos** Propiedad que establece que la suma de un número y su opuesto es cero.	$12 + (-12) = 0$
additive inverse The opposite of a number. (p. 8)	**inverso aditivo** El opuesto de un número.	The additive inverse of 5 is −5.
adjacent angles Angles in the same plane that are side by side and have a common vertex and a common side. (p. 388)	**ángulos adyacentes** Ángulos en el mismo plano que comparten un vértice y un lado.	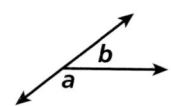
algebraic expression An expression that contains at least one variable. (p. 6)	**expresión algebraica** Expresión que contiene al menos una variable.	$x + 8$ $4(m - b)$
algebraic inequality An inequality that contains at least one variable. (p. 136)	**desigualdad algebraica** Desigualdad que contiene al menos una variable.	$x + 3 > 10$ $5a > b + 3$
alternate exterior angles A pair of angles on the outer sides of two lines cut by a transversal that are on opposite sides of the transversal. (p. 389)	**ángulos alternos externos** Par de ángulos en los lados externos de dos líneas intersecadas por una transversal, que están en lados opuestos de la transversal.	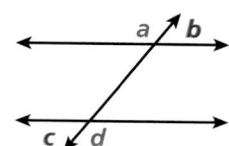 ∠a and ∠d are alternate exterior angles.

ENGLISH	SPANISH	EXAMPLES
alternate interior angles A pair of angles on the inner sides of two lines cut by a transversal that are on opposite sides of the transversal. (p. 389)	**ángulos alternos internos** Par de ángulos en los lados internos de dos líneas intersecadas por una transversal, que están en lados opuestos de la transversal.	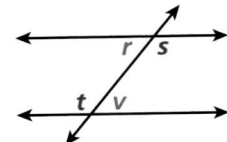 ∠r and ∠v are alternate interior angles.
altitude (of a triangle) A perpendicular segment from a vertex to the line containing the opposite side. (p. 393)	**altura (de un triángulo)** Segmento perpendicular que se extiende desde un vértice hasta la recta que forma el lado opuesto.	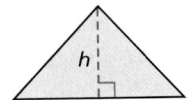
angle A figure formed by two rays with a common endpoint called the vertex. (p. 379)	**ángulo** Figura formada por dos rayos con un extremo común llamado vértice.	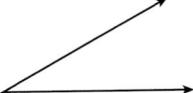
angle bisector A line, segment, or ray that divides an angle into two congruent angles. (p. 382)	**bisectriz de un ángulo** Línea, segmento o rayo que divide un ángulo en dos ángulos congruentes.	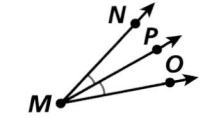
arc An unbroken part of a circle. (p. 446)	**arco** Parte continua de un círculo.	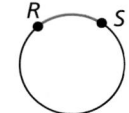
area The number of non-overlapping unit squares needed to cover a given surface. (p. 435)	**área** El número de unidades cuadradas que se necesitan para cubrir una superficie dada.	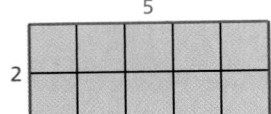 The area is 10 square units.
Associative Property of Addition The property that states that for all real numbers a, b, and c, the sum is always the same, regardless of their grouping. (p. 116)	**Propiedad asociativa de la suma** Propiedad que establece que para todos los números reales a, b y c, la suma siempre es la misma sin importar cómo se agrupen.	$a + b + c = (a + b) + c = a + (b + c)$
Associative Property of Multiplication The property that states that for all real numbers a, b, and c, their product is always the same, regardless of their grouping. (p. 116)	**Propiedad asociativa de la multiplicación** Propiedad que establece que para todos los números reales a, b y c, el producto siempre es el mismo, sin importar cómo se agrupen.	$a \cdot b \cdot c = (a \cdot b) \cdot c = a \cdot (b \cdot c)$
average The sum of a set of data divided by the number of items in the data set; also called *mean*. (p. 537)	**promedio** La suma de los elementos de un conjunto de datos dividida entre el número de elementos del conjunto. También se llama *media*.	Data set: 4, 6, 7, 8, 10 Average: $\frac{4 + 6 + 7 + 8 + 10}{5} = \frac{35}{5} = 7$

ENGLISH	SPANISH	EXAMPLES

B

back-to-back stem-and-leaf plot A stem-and-leaf plot that compares two sets of data by displaying one set of data to the left of the stem and the other to the right. (p. 533)

diagrama doble de tallo y hojas Diagrama de tallo y hojas que compara dos conjuntos de datos presentando uno de ellos a la izquierda del tallo y el otro a la derecha.

Data set A: 9, 12, 14, 16, 23, 27
Data set B: 6, 8, 10, 13, 15, 16, 21

Set A		Set B
9	0	6 8
6 4 2	1	0 3 5 6
7 3	2	1

Key: |2| 1 means 21
3 |2| means 23

bar graph A graph that uses vertical or horizontal bars to display data. (p. SB17)

gráfica de barras Gráfica en la que se usan barras verticales u horizontales para presentar datos.

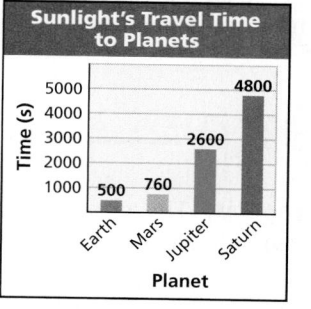

base (in numeration) When a number is raised to a power, the number that is used as a factor is the base. (p. 166)

base Cuando un número es elevado a una potencia, el número que se usa como factor es la base.

$3^5 = 3 \cdot 3 \cdot 3 \cdot 3 \cdot 3$; 3 is the base.

base (of a polygon) A side of a polygon, or the length of that side. (p. 435)

base (de un polígono) Lado de un polígono; cara de una figura tridimensional según la cual se mide o se clasifica la figura.

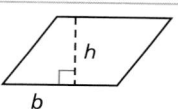

base (of a three-dimensional figure) A face of a three-dimensional figure by which the figure is measured or classified. (p. 480)

base (de una figura tridimensional) Cara de una figura tridimensional a partir de la cual se mide o se clasifica la figura.

 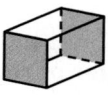
Bases of a cylinder   Bases of a prism

Base of a cone   Base of a pyramid

base (of a trapezoid) One of the two parallel sides of a trapezoid. (p. 440)

base (de un trapecio) Uno de los dos lados paralelos del trapecio.

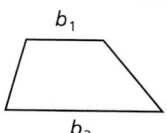

binomial A polynomial with two terms. (p. 590)

binomio Polinomio con dos términos.

$x + y$
$2a^2 - 3$
$4m^3n^2 + 6mn^4$

ENGLISH	SPANISH	EXAMPLES
bisect To divide into two congruent parts. (p. 382)	**trazar una bisectriz** Dividir en dos partes congruentes.	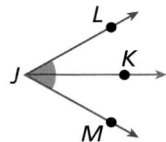 $\overrightarrow{JK}$ bisects $\angle LJM$
box-and-whisker plot A graph that displays the highest and lowest quarters of data as whiskers, the middle two quarters of the data as a box, and the median. (p. 543)	**gráfica de mediana y rango** Gráfica que muestra los valores máximo y mínimo, los cuartiles superior e inferior, así como la mediana de los datos.	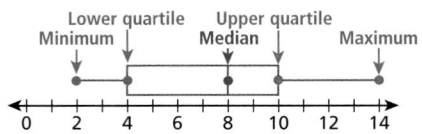

capacity The amount a container can hold when filled. (p. 512)	**capacidad** Cantidad que cabe en un recipiente cuando se llena.	A large milk container has a capacity of 1 gallon.
Celsius A metric scale for measuring temperature in which 0°C is the freezing point of water and 100°C is the boiling point of water; also called *centigrade*. (p. SB15)	**Celsius** Escala métrica para medir la temperatura, en la que 0 °C es el punto de congelación del agua y 100 °C es el punto de ebullición. También se llama *centígrado*.	
center (of a circle) The point inside a circle that is the same distance from all the points on the circle. (p. 446)	**centro (de un círculo)** Punto interior de un círculo que se encuentra a la misma distancia de todos los puntos de la circunferencia.	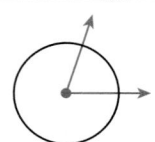
center of rotation The point about which a figure is rotated. (p. 410)	**centro de una rotación** Punto alrededor del cual se hace girar una figura.	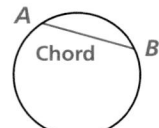
central angle An angle formed by two radii with its vertex at the center of a circle. (p. 447)	**ángulo central de un círculo** Ángulo formado por dos radios cuyo vértice se encuentra en el centro de un círculo.	
certain (probability) Sure to happen; an event that is certain has a probability of 1. (p. 556)	**seguro (probabilidad)** Que con seguridad sucederá. Representa una probabilidad de 1.	When rolling a number cube, it is certain that you will roll a number less than 7.
chord A segment with its endpoints on a circle. (p. 446)	**cuerda** Segmento de recta cuyos extremos forman parte de un círculo.	

Glossary/Glosario

circle The set of all points in a plane that are the same distance from a given point called the center. (p. 446)

círculo Conjunto de todos los puntos en un plano que se encuentran a la misma distancia de un punto dado llamado centro.

circle graph A graph that uses sectors of a circle to compare parts to the whole and parts to other parts. (p. SB21)

gráfica circular Gráfica que usa secciones de un círculo para comparar partes con el todo y con otras partes.

Residents of Mesa, AZ

65+ 13%
45–64
Under 18 27%
19%
11%
30%
18–24
25–44

circumference The distance around a circle. (p. 450)

circunferencia Distancia alrededor de un círculo.

Circumference

clockwise A circular movement to the right in the direction shown. (p. 412)

en el sentido de las manecillas del reloj Movimiento circular en la dirección que se indica.

coefficient The number that is multiplied by a variable in an algebraic expression. (p. 120)

coeficiente Número que se multiplica por una variable en una expresión algebraica.

5 is the coefficient in $5b$.

commission A fee paid to a person for making a sale. (p. 298)

comisión Pago que recibe una persona por realizar una venta.

commission rate The fee paid to a person who makes a sale expressed as a percent of the selling price. (p. 298)

tasa de comisión Pago que recibe una persona por hacer una venta, expresado como un porcentaje del precio de venta.

A commission rate of 5% and a sale of $10,000 results in a commission of $500.

common denominator A denominator that is the same in two or more fractions. (p. 70)

común denominador Denominador que es común a dos o más fracciones.

The common denominator of $\frac{5}{8}$ and $\frac{2}{8}$ is 8.

common factor A number that is a factor of two or more numbers. (p. SB6)

factor común Número que es factor de dos o más números.

8 is a common factor of 16 and 40.

common multiple A number that is a multiple of each of two or more numbers. (p. SB6)

común múltiplo Número que es múltiplo de dos o más números.

15 is a common multiple of 3 and 5.

Commutative Property of Addition The property that states that two or more numbers can be added in any order without changing the sum. (p. 116)

Propiedad conmutativa de la suma Propiedad que establece que sumar dos o más números en cualquier orden no altera la suma.

$8 + 20 = 20 + 8; a + b = b + a$

ENGLISH	SPANISH	EXAMPLES
Commutative Property of Multiplication The property that states that two or more numbers can be multiplied in any order without changing the product. (p. 116)	**Propiedad conmutativa de la multiplicación** Propiedad que establece que multiplicar dos o más números en cualquier orden no altera el producto.	$6 \cdot 12 = 12 \cdot 6; a \cdot b = b \cdot a$
compatible numbers Numbers that are close to the given numbers that make estimation or mental calculation easier. (p. 278)	**números compatibles** Números que están cerca de los números dados y hacen más fácil la estimación o el cálculo mental.	To estimate 7957 + 5009, use the compatible numbers 8000 and 5000: 8000 + 5000 = 13,000.
complementary angles Two angles whose measures add to 90°. (p. 379)	**ángulos complementarios** Dos ángulos cuyas medidas suman 90°.	The complement of a 53° angle is a 37° angle.
composite figure A figure made up of simple geometric shapes. (p. 436)	**figura compuesta** Figura formada por figuras geométricas simples.	
composite number A whole number greater than 1 that has more than two positive factors. (p. SB5)	**número compuesto** Número mayor que 1 que tiene más de dos factores que son números cabales.	4, 6, 8, and 9 are composite numbers.
compound event An event made up of two or more simple events. (p. 569)	**suceso compuesto** Suceso formado por dos o más sucesos simples.	Rolling a 3 on a number cube and spinning a 2 on a spinner is a compound event.
compound inequality A combination of more than one inequality. (p. 137)	**desigualdad compuesta** Combinación de dos o más desigualdades.	$x \geq -2$ or $x < 10; -2 \leq x < 10$
compound interest Interest earned or paid on principal and previously earned or paid interest. (p. 304)	**interés compuesto** Interés que se gana o se paga sobre el capital y los intereses previamente ganados o pagados.	If \$100 is put into an account with an interest rate of 5% compounded monthly, then after 2 years, the account will have $100 \left(1 + \frac{0.05}{12}\right)^{12 \cdot 2} = \$110.49$.
cone A three-dimensional figure with a circular base lying in one plane plus a vertex not lying on that plane. The remaining surface of the cone is formed by joining the vertex to points on the circle by line segments. (p. 481)	**cono** Figura tridimensional con una base circular que está en un plano más un vértice que no está en ese plano. El resto de la superficie del cono se forma uniendo el vértice con puntos del círculo por medio de segmentos de recta.	

ENGLISH	SPANISH	EXAMPLES

congruent Having the same size and shape. (p. 406)

congruentes Que tienen la misma forma y el mismo tamaño.

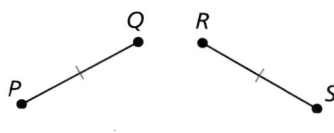

$$\overline{PQ} \cong \overline{RS}$$

---

congruent angles Angles that have the same measure. (p. 382)

ángulos congruentes Ángulos que tienen la misma medida.

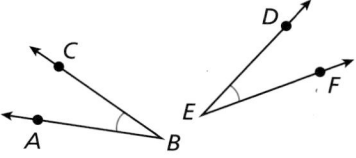

$$\angle ABC = \angle DEF$$

---

congruent segments Segments that have the same length. (p. 382)

segmentos congruentes Segmentos que tienen la misma longitud.

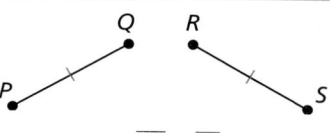

$$\overline{PQ} \cong \overline{SR}$$

---

constant A value that does not change. (p. 120)

constante Valor que no cambia.

$3, 0, \pi$

---

constant of variation The constant k in direct and inverse variation equations. (p. 357)

constante de variación La constante k en ecuaciones de variación directa e inversa.

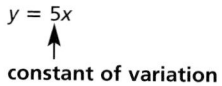

$y = 5x$

constant of variation

---

conversion factor A fraction whose numerator and denominator represent the same quantity but use different units; the fraction is equal to 1 because the numerator and denominator are equal. (p. 237)

factor de conversión Fracción cuyo numerador y denominador representan la misma cantidad pero con unidades distintas; la fracción es igual a 1 porque el numerador y el denominador son iguales.

$\dfrac{24\ \text{hours}}{1\ \text{day}}$ and $\dfrac{1\ \text{day}}{24\ \text{hours}}$

---

coordinate One of the numbers of an ordered pair that locate a point on a coordinate graph. (p. 322)

coordenada Uno de los números de un par ordenado que ubica un punto en una gráfica de coordenadas.

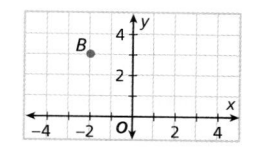

The coordinates of B are $(-2, 3)$

---

coordinate plane (coordinate grid) A plane formed by the intersection of a horizontal number line called the x-axis and a vertical number line called the y-axis. (p. 322)

plano cartesiano (cuadrícula de coordenadas) Plano formado por la intersección de una recta numérica horizontal llamada eje x y otra vertical llamada eje y.

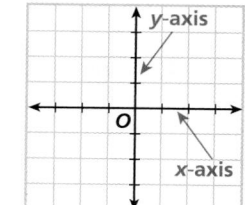

ENGLISH	SPANISH	EXAMPLES

correlation The description of the relationship between two data sets. (p. 548)

correlación Descripción de la relación entre dos conjuntos de datos.

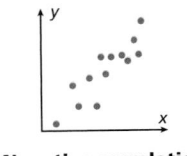

Positive correlation

No correlation

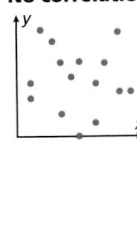

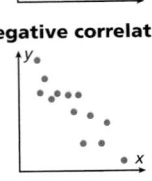

Negative correlation

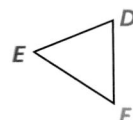

---

correspondence The relationship between two or more objects that are matched. (p. 406)

correspondencia La relación entre dos o más objetos que coinciden.

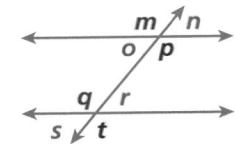

∠A and ∠D are corresponding angles.

$\overline{AB}$ and $\overline{DE}$ are corresponding sides.

---

corresponding angles (for lines) For two lines intersected by a transversal, a pair of angles that lie on the same side of the transversal and on the same sides of the other two lines. (p. 389)

ángulos correspondientes (en líneas) Dadas dos líneas cortadas por una transversal, el par de ángulos ubicados en el mismo lado de la transversal y en los mismos lados de las otras dos líneas.

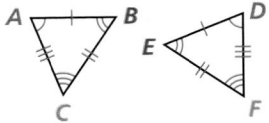

∠m and ∠q are corresponding angles.

---

corresponding angles (in polygons) Matching angles of two or more polygons. (p. 244)

ángulos correspondientes (en polígonos) Ángulos que están en la misma posición relativa en dos o más polígonos.

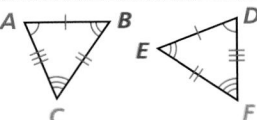

∠A and ∠D are corresponding angles.

---

corresponding sides Matching sides of two or more polygons. (p. 244)

lados correspondientes Lados que se ubican en la misma posición relativa en dos o más polígonos.

$\overline{AB}$ and $\overline{DE}$ are corresponding sides.

---

counterclockwise A circular movement to the left in the direction shown. (p. 412)

en sentido contrario a las manecillas del reloj Movimiento circular en la dirección que se indica.

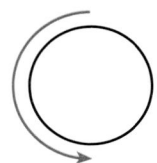

---

cross products In the statement $\frac{a}{b} = \frac{c}{d}$, bc and ad are the cross products. (p. 232)

productos cruzados En el enunciado $\frac{a}{b} = \frac{c}{d}$, bc y ad son productos cruzados.

For the proportion $\frac{2}{3} = \frac{4}{6}$, the cross products are $2 \cdot 6 = 12$ and $3 \cdot 4 = 12$.

Glossary/Glosario

ENGLISH	SPANISH	EXAMPLES
cube (geometric figure) A rectangular prism with six congruent square faces. (p. 477)	**cubo (figura geométrica)** Prisma rectangular con seis caras cuadradas congruentes.	
cube (in numeration) A number raised to the third power. (p. 168)	**cubo (en numeración)** Número elevado a la tercera potencia.	$2^3 = 2 \cdot 2 \cdot 2 = 8$ 8 is the cube of 2.
cubic function A polynomial function of degree 3. (p. 338)	**función cúbica** Función polinomial de grado 3.	$y = x^3$
customary system of measurement The measurement system often used in the United States. (p. SB15)	**sistema usual de medidas** El sistema de medidas que se usa comúnmente en Estados Unidos.	inches, feet, miles, ounces, pounds, tons, cups, quarts, gallons
cylinder A three-dimensional figure with two parallel congruent circular bases. The third surface of the cylinder consists of all parallel circles of the same radius whose centers lie on the segment joining the centers of the bases. (p. 481)	**cilindro** Figura tridimensional con dos bases circulares paralelas y congruentes. La tercera superficie del cilindro consiste en todos los círculos paralelos del mismo radio cuyo centro está en el segmento que une los centros de las bases.	

D

decagon A polygon with ten sides. (p. SB16)	**decágono** Polígono de diez lados.	
deductive reasoning The process of using logic to draw conclusions. (p. SB24)	**razonamiento deuctivo** Proceso en el que se utiliza la lógica para sacar conclusions.	
degree The unit of measure for angles or temperature. (p. 379)	**grado** Unidad de medida para ángulos y temperaturas.	
degree of a polynomial The highest power of the variable in a polynomial. (p. 591)	**grado de un polinomio** La potencia más alta de la variable en un polinomio.	The polynomial $4x^5 - 6x^2 + 7$ has degree 5.
denominator The bottom number of a fraction that tells how many equal parts are in the whole. (p. 66)	**denominador** Número que está abajo en una fracción y que indica en cuántas partes iguales se divide el entero.	In the fraction $\frac{2}{5}$, 5 is the denominator.
Density Property The property that states that between any two real numbers, there is always another real number. (p. 199)	**Propiedad de densidad** Propiedad según la cual entre dos números reales cualesquiera siempre hay otro número real.	

ENGLISH	SPANISH	EXAMPLES
dependent events Events for which the outcome of one event affects the probability of the other. (p. 569)	**sucesos dependientes** Dos sucesos son dependientes si el resultado de uno afecta la probabilidad del otro.	A bag contains 3 red marbles and 2 blue marbles. Drawing a red marble and then drawing a blue marble without replacing the first marble is an example of dependent events.
diagonal A line segment that connects two non-adjacent vertices of a polygon. (p. 403)	**diagonal** Segmento de recta que une dos vértices no adyacentes de un polígono.	
diameter A line segment that passes through the center of a circle and has endpoints on the circle, or the length of that segment. (p. 446)	**diámetro** Segmento de recta que pasa por el centro de un círculo y tiene sus extremos en la circunferencia, o bien la longitud de ese segmento.	
difference The result when one number is subtracted from another. (p. 10)	**diferencia** El resultado de restar un número de otro.	In $16 - 5 = 11$, 11 is the difference.
dimensions (geometry) The length, width, or height of a figure. (p. 480)	**dimensiones (geometría)** Longitud, ancho o altura de una figura.	
direct variation A relationship between two variables in which the data increase or decrease together at a constant rate. (p. 357)	**variación directa** Relación entre dos variables en la que los datos aumentan o disminuyen juntos a una tasa constante.	$y = 2x$
discount The amount by which the original price is reduced. (p. 295)	**descuento** Cantidad que se resta del precio original de un artículo.	
disjoint events Two events are disjoint if they cannot occur in the same trial of an experiment. (p. 566)	**sucesos desunidos** Dos sucesos son desunidos si no pueden ocurrir en la misma prueba de un experimento.	When rolling a number cube, rolling a 3 and rolling an even number are disjoint events.
Distributive Property The property that states if you multiply a sum by a number, you will get the same result if you multiply each addend by that number and then add the products. (p. 117)	**Propiedad distributiva** Propiedad que establece que, si multiplicas una suma por un número, obtienes el mismo resultado que si multiplicas cada sumando por ese número y luego sumas los productos.	$5 \cdot 21 = 5(20 + 1) =$ $(5 \cdot 20) + (5 \cdot 1)$
dividend The number to be divided in a division problem. (p. SB7)	**dividendo** Número que se divide en un problema de división.	In $8 \div 4 = 2$, 8 is the dividend.
divisible Can be divided by a number without leaving a remainder. (p. SB4)	**divisible** Que se puede dividir entre un número sin dejar residuo.	18 is divisible by 3.

ENGLISH	SPANISH	EXAMPLES
Division Property of Equality The property that states that if you divide both sides of an equation by the same nonzero number, the new equation will have the same solution. (p. 37)	**Propiedad de igualdad de la división** Propiedad que establece que puedes dividir ambos lados de una ecuación entre el mismo número distinto de cero, y la nueva ecuación tendrá la misma solución.	$4x = 12$ $\frac{4x}{4} = \frac{12}{4}$ $x = 3$
divisor The number you are dividing by in a division problem. (p. SB7)	**divisor** El número entre el que se divide en un problema de división.	In $8 \div 4 = 2$, 4 is the divisor.
domain The set of all possible input values of a function. (p. 326)	**dominio** Conjunto de todos los posibles valores de entrada de una función.	The domain of the function $y = x^2 + 1$ is all real numbers.
double-bar graph A bar graph that compares two related sets of data. (p. SB17)	**gráfica de doble barra** Gráfica de barras que compara dos conjuntos de datos relacionados.	

E

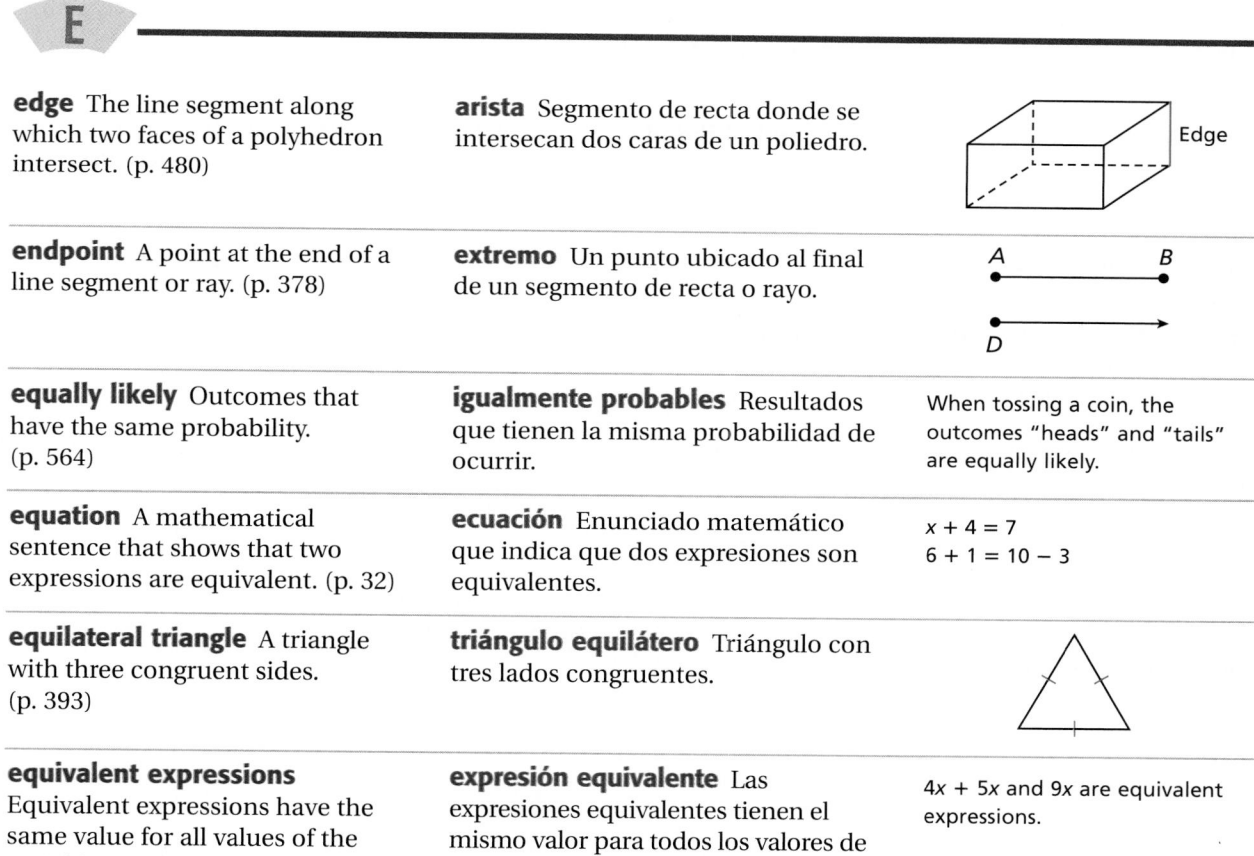

edge The line segment along which two faces of a polyhedron intersect. (p. 480)	**arista** Segmento de recta donde se intersecan dos caras de un poliedro.	Edge
endpoint A point at the end of a line segment or ray. (p. 378)	**extremo** Un punto ubicado al final de un segmento de recta o rayo.	A B D
equally likely Outcomes that have the same probability. (p. 564)	**igualmente probables** Resultados que tienen la misma probabilidad de ocurrir.	When tossing a coin, the outcomes "heads" and "tails" are equally likely.
equation A mathematical sentence that shows that two expressions are equivalent. (p. 32)	**ecuación** Enunciado matemático que indica que dos expresiones son equivalentes.	$x + 4 = 7$ $6 + 1 = 10 - 3$
equilateral triangle A triangle with three congruent sides. (p. 393)	**triángulo equilátero** Triángulo con tres lados congruentes.	
equivalent expressions Equivalent expressions have the same value for all values of the variables. (p. 120)	**expresión equivalente** Las expresiones equivalentes tienen el mismo valor para todos los valores de las variables.	$4x + 5x$ and $9x$ are equivalent expressions.

ENGLISH	SPANISH	EXAMPLES
equivalent ratios Ratios that name the same comparison. (p. 224)	**razones equivalentes** Razones que representan la misma comparación.	$\frac{1}{2}$ and $\frac{2}{4}$ are equivalent ratios.
estimate (n) An answer that is close to the exact answer and is found by rounding or other methods. **(v)** To find such an answer. (p. 278)	**estimación (s)** Una solución aproximada a la respuesta exacta que se halla mediante el redondeo u otros métodos. **estimar (v)** Hallar una solución aproximada a la respuesta exacta.	500 is an estimate for the sum 98 + 287 + 104.
evaluate To find the value of a numerical or algebraic expression. (p. 6)	**evaluar** Hallar el valor de una expresión numérica o algebraica.	Evaluate $2x + 7$ for $x = 3$. $2x + 7$ $2(3) + 7$ $6 + 7$ 13
even number A whole number that is divisible by two. (p. SB4)	**número par** Número cabal divisible entre 2.	2, 4, 6
event An outcome or set of outcomes of an experiment or situation. (p. 556)	**suceso** Un resultado o una serie de resultados de un experimento o una situación.	When rolling a number cube, the event "an odd number" consists of the outcomes 1, 3, and 5.
experiment (probability) In probability, any activity based on chance (such as tossing a coin). (p. 556)	**experimento (probabilidad)** En probabilidad, cualquier actividad basada en la posibilidad, como lanzar una moneda.	Tossing a coin 10 times and noting the number of "heads".
experimental probability The ratio of the number of times an event occurs to the total number of trials, or times that the activity is performed. (p. 560)	**probabilidad experimental** Razón del número de veces que ocurre un suceso al número total de pruebas o al número de veces que se realiza el experimento.	Kendra attempted 27 free throws and made 16 of them. Her experimental probability of making a free throw is $\frac{\text{number made}}{\text{number attempted}} = \frac{16}{27} \approx 0.59$.
exponent The number that indicates how many times the base is used as a factor. (p. 166)	**exponente** Número que indica cuántas veces se usa la base como factor.	$2^3 = 2 \times 2 \times 2 = 8$; 3 is the exponent.
exponential form A number is in exponential form when it is written with a base and an exponent. (p. 166)	**forma exponencial** Se dice que un número está en forma exponencial cuando se escribe con una base y un exponente.	4^2 is the exponential form for $4 \cdot 4$.
expression A mathematical phrase that contains operations, numbers, and/or variables. (p. 6)	**expresión** Enunciado matemático que contiene operaciones, números y/o variables.	$6x + 1$

F

face A flat surface of a polyhedron. (p. 480)	**cara** Superficie plana de un poliedro.	

ENGLISH	SPANISH	EXAMPLES
factor A number that is multiplied by another number to get a product. (p. SB4)	**factor** Número que se multiplica por otro para hallar un producto.	7 is a factor of 21 since $7 \cdot 3 = 21$.
Fahrenheit A temperature scale in which 32°F is the freezing point of water and 212°F is the boiling point of water. (p. SB15)	**Fahrenheit** Escala de temperatura en la que 32° F es el punto de congelación del agua y 212° F es el punto de ebullición.	
fair When all outcomes of an experiment are equally likely, the experiment is said to be fair. (p. 564)	**justo** Se dice de un experimento donde todos los resultados posibles son igualmente probables.	When tossing a coin, heads and tails are equally likely, so it is a fair experiment.
first quartile The median of the lower half of a set of data; also called *lower quartile*. (p. 542)	**primer cuartil** La mediana de la mitad inferior de un conjunto de datos. También se llama *cuartil inferior*.	
FOIL An acronym for the terms used when multiplying two binomials: the First, Inner, Outer, and Last terms. (p. 618)	**FOIL** Sigla en inglés de los términos que se usan al multiplicar dos binomios: los primeros, los externos, los internos y los últimos (First, Outer, Inner, Last).	$(x + 2)(x - 3) = x^2 - 3x + 2x - 6$ $= x^2 - x - 6$
formula A rule showing relationships among quantities. (p. 434)	**fórmula** Regla que muestra relaciones entre cantidades.	$A = \ell w$ is the formula for the area of a rectangle.
fraction A number in the form $\frac{a}{b}$, where $b \neq 0$. (p. 66)	**fracción** Número escrito en la forma $\frac{a}{b}$, donde $b \neq 0$.	$\frac{2}{3}$
frequency table A table that lists items together according to the number of times, or frequency, that the items occur. (p. SB19)	**tabla de frecuencia** Una tabla en la que se organizan los datos de acuerdo con el número de veces que aparece cada valor (o la frecuencia).	Data set: 1, 1, 2, 2, 3, 4, 5, 5, 5, 6, 6 Frequency table: Data / Frequency: 1 / 2, 2 / 2, 3 / 1, 4 / 1, 5 / 3, 6 / 2
function An input-output relationship that has exactly one output for each input. (p. 326)	**función** Relación de entrada-salida en la que a cada valor de entrada corresponde exactamente un valor de salida.	

ENGLISH	SPANISH	EXAMPLES

G

graph of an equation A graph of the set of ordered pairs that are solutions of the equation. (p. 123)

gráfica de una ecuación Gráfica del conjunto de pares ordenados que son soluciones de la ecuación.

$y = x - 1$

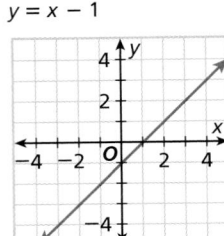

great circle A circle on a sphere such that the plane containing the circle passes through the center of the sphere. (p. 508)

círculo máximo Círculo de una esfera tal que el plano que contiene el círculo pasa por el centro de la esfera.

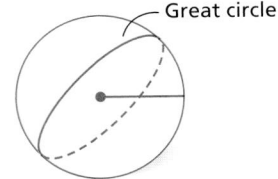
Great circle

greatest common divisor (GCD) The largest whole number that divides evenly into two or more given numbers. (p. SB6)

máximo común divisor (MCD) El mayor de los factores comunes compartidos por dos o más números dados.

The GCD of 27 and 45 is 9.

H

height In a triangle or quadrilateral, the perpendicular distance from the base to the opposite vertex or side. (p. 435)

altura En un triángulo o cuadrilátero, la distancia perpendicular desde la base de la figura al vértice o lado opuesto.

In a trapezoid, the perpendicular distance between the bases. (p. 440)

En un trapecio, la distancia perpendicular entre las bases.

In a prism or cylinder, the perpendicular distance between the bases. (p. 413)

En un prisma o cilindro, la distancia perpendicular entre las bases.

In a pyramid or cone, the perpendicular distance from the base to the opposite vertex. (p. 420)

En una pirámide o cono, la distancia perpendicular desde la base al vértice opuesto.

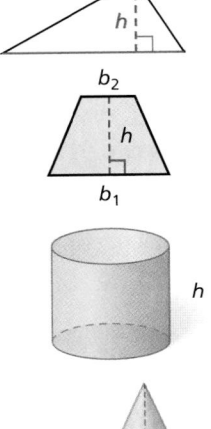

hemisphere A half of a sphere. (p. 508)

hemisferio La mitad de una esfera.

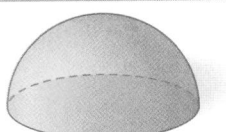

heptagon A seven-sided polygon. (p. SB16)

heptágono Polígono de siete lados.

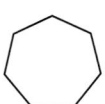

hexagon A six-sided polygon. (p. SB16)

hexágono Polígono de seis lados.

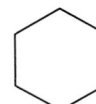

ENGLISH	SPANISH	EXAMPLES

histogram A bar graph that shows the frequency of data within equal intervals. (p. SB19)

histograma Gráfica de barras que muestra la frecuencia de los datos en intervalos iguales.

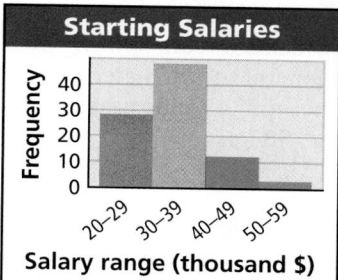

hypotenuse In a right triangle, the side opposite the right angle. (p. 203)

hipotenusa En un triángulo rectángulo, el lado opuesto al ángulo recto.

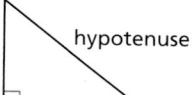

hypotenuse

 I

Identity Property of Multiplication The property that states that the product of 1 and any number is that number. (p. 37)

Propiedad de identidad del uno Propiedad que establece que el producto de 1 y cualquier número es ese número.

$4 \cdot 1 = 4$
$-3 \cdot 1 = -3$

Identity Property of Addition The property that states the sum of zero and any number is that number. (p. 32)

Propiedad de identidad del cero Propiedad que establece que la suma de cero y cualquier número es ese número.

$4 + 0 = 4$
$-3 + 0 = -3$

image A figure resulting from a transformation. (p. 410)

imagen Figura que resulta de una transformación.

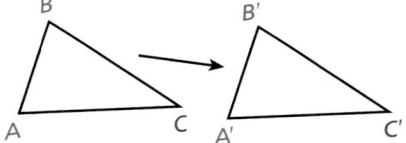

impossible (probability) Can never happen; an event that is impossible has a probability of 0. (p. 556)

imposible (en probabilidad) Que no puede ocurrir. Suceso cuya probabilidad de ocurrir es 0.

When rolling a standard number cube, rolling a 7 is an impossible event.

improper fraction A fraction in which the numerator is greater than or equal to the denominator. (p. SB9)

fracción impropia Fracción cuyo numerador es mayor que o igual al denominador.

$\frac{17}{5}, \frac{3}{3}$

independent events Events for which the outcome of one event does not affect the probability of the other. (p. 569)

sucesos independientes Dos sucesos son independientes si el resultado de uno no afecta la probabilidad del otro.

A bag contains 3 red marbles and 2 blue marbles. Drawing a red marble, replacing it, and then drawing a blue marble is an example of independent events.

indirect measurement The technique of using similar figures and proportions to find a measure. (p. 248)

medición indirecta La técnica de usar figuras semejantes y proporciones para hallar una medida.

Glossary/Glosario

ENGLISH	SPANISH	EXAMPLES
inductive reasoning The process of conjecturing that a general rule or statement is true because specific cases are true. (p. SB24)	**razonamiento inductivo** Proceso de razonamiento por el que se determina que una regal o enunciado son verdaderos porque ciertos casos específicos son verdaderos.	
inequality A mathematical statement that compares two expressions by using one of the following symbols: <, >, ≥, ≤, or ≠. (p. 136)	**desigualdad** Enunciado matemático que compara dos expresiones por medio de uno de los siguientes símbolos: <, >, ≥, ≤, o ≠.	$5 < 8$ $5x + 2 \geq 12$
input The value substituted into an expression or function. (p. 326)	**valor de entrada** Valor que se usa para sustituir una variable en una expresión o función.	For the function $y = 6x$, the input 4 produces an output of 24.
integers The set of whole numbers and their opposites. (p. 14)	**enteros** Conjunto de todos los números cabales y sus opuestos.	$\ldots -3, -2, -1, 0, 1, 2, 3, \ldots$
interest The amount of money charged for borrowing or using money. (p. 303)	**interés** Cantidad de dinero que se cobra por el préstamo o uso del dinero.	
interior angles Angles on the inner sides of two lines cut by a transversal. (p. 389)	**ángulos internos** Ángulos en los lados internos de dos líneas intersecadas por una transversal.	 $\angle r$, $\angle s$, $\angle t$, and $\angle v$ are interior angles.
intersecting lines Lines that cross at exactly one point. (p. 388)	**líneas secantes** Líneas que se cruzan en un solo punto.	
interval The space between marked values on a number line or the scale of a graph. (p. SB18)	**intervalo** El espacio entre los valores marcados en una recta numérica o en la escala de una gráfica.	
inverse operations Operations that undo each other: addition and subtraction, or multiplication and division. (p. 32)	**operaciones inversas** Operaciones que se cancelan mutuamente: suma y resta, o multiplicación y división.	Adding 3 and subtracting 3 are inverse operations: $5 + 3 = 8$; $8 - 3 = 5$ Multiplying by 3 and dividing by 3 are inverse operations: $2 \cdot 3 = 6$; $6 \div 3 = 2$
irrational number A real number that cannot be expressed as a ratio of two integers. (p. 198)	**número irracional** Número real que no se puede expresar como una razón de dos enteros.	$\sqrt{2}$, π
isolate the variable To get a variable alone on one side of an equation or inequality in order to solve the equation or inequality. (p. 32)	**despejar la variable** Dejar sola la variable en un lado de una ecuación o desigualdad para resolverla.	$\begin{array}{l} x + 7 = 22 \\ \underline{-7 \quad -7} \\ x \quad\;\; = 15 \end{array}$ $\qquad \begin{array}{l} \frac{12}{3} = \frac{3x}{3} \\ 4 = x \end{array}$

ENGLISH	SPANISH	EXAMPLES

isosceles triangle A triangle with at least two congruent sides. (p. 393)

triángulo isósceles Triángulo que tiene al menos dos lados congruentes.

L

lateral area The sum of the areas of the lateral faces of a prism or pyramid, or the area of the lateral surface of a cylinder or cone. (p. 498)

área lateral Suma de las áreas de las caras laterales de un prisma o pirámide, o área de la superficie lateral de un cilindro o cono.

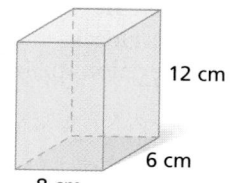

12 cm

6 cm

8 cm

Lateral area = 2(8)(12) + 2(6)(12)
= 336 cm²

lateral face In a prism or a pyramid, a face that is not a base. (p. 498)

cara lateral En un prisma o pirámide, una cara que no es la base.

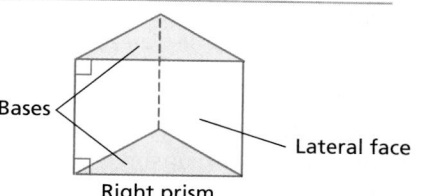

Bases

Lateral face

Right prism

lateral surface In a cylinder, the curved surface connecting the circular bases; in a cone, the curved surface that is not a base. (p. 499)

superficie lateral En un cilindro, superficie curva que une las bases circulares; en un cono, la superficie curva que no es la base.

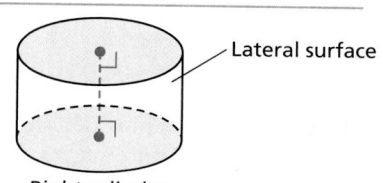

Lateral surface

Right cylinder

least common denominator (LCD) The least common multiple of two or more denominators. (p. 70)

mínimo común denominador (mcd) El mínimo común múltiplo de dos o más denominadores.

The LCD of $\frac{3}{4}$ and $\frac{5}{6}$ is 12.

least common multiple (LCM) The least number, other than zero, that is a multiple of two or more given numbers. (p. SB6)

mínimo común múltiplo (mcm) El menor de los números cabales, distinto de cero, que es múltiplo de dos o más números dados.

The LCM of 6 and 10 is 30.

legs In a right triangle, the sides that include the right angle; in an isosceles triangle, the pair of congruent sides. (p. 203)

catetos En un triángulo rectángulo, los lados adyacentes al ángulo recto. En un triángulo isósceles, el par de lados congruentes.

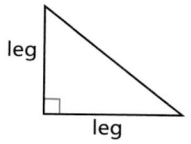

leg

leg

like terms Two or more terms that have the same variable raised to the same power. (p. 120)

términos semejantes Dos o más términos que contienen la misma variable elevada a la misma potencia.

In the expression 3a + 5b + 12a, 3a and 12a are like terms.

line A straight path that extends without end in opposite directions. (p. 378)

línea Trayectoria recta que se extiende de manera indefinida en direcciones opuestas.

←——————→

	ENGLISH	SPANISH	EXAMPLES

line graph A graph that uses line segments to show how data changes. (p. SB18)

gráfica lineal Gráfica que muestra cómo cambian los datos mediante segmentos de recta.

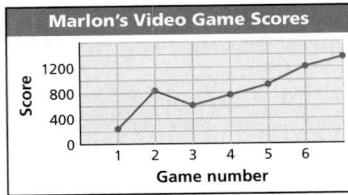

---

line of best fit A straight line that comes closest to the points on a scatter plot. (p. 549)

línea de mejor ajuste La línea recta que más se aproxima a los puntos de un diagrama de dispersión.

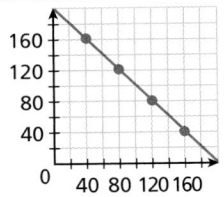

---

line of reflection A line that a figure is flipped across to create a mirror image of the original figure. (p. 410)

ínea de reflexión Línea sobre la cual se invierte una figura para crear una imagen reflejada de la figura original.

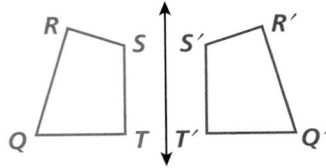

---

line plot A number line with marks or dots that show frequency. (p. 532)

diagrama de acumulación Recta numérica con marcas o puntos que indican la frecuencia.

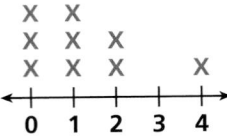

---

line segment A part of a line between two endpoints. (p. 378)

segmento de recta Parte de una línea con dos extremos.

---

linear equation An equation whose solutions form a straight line on a coordinate plane. (p. 330)

ecuación lineal Ecuación cuyas soluciones forman una línea recta en un plano cartesiano.

$y = 2x + 1$

---

linear function A function whose graph is a straight line. (p. 330)

función lineal Función cuya gráfica es una línea recta.

$y = x - 1$

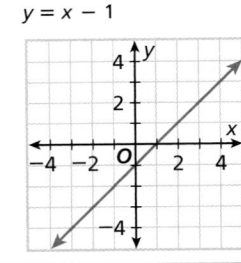

---

lower quartile The median of the lower half of a set of data; also called *first quartile*. (p. 542)

cuartil inferior La mediana de la mitad inferior de un conjunto de datos; también se llama *primer cuartil*.

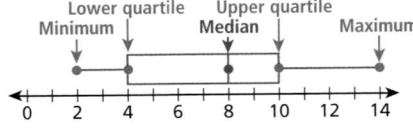

Glossary/Glosario

M

markup The amount by which a wholesale cost is increased. (p. 295)

margen de beneficio Cantidad que se agrega a un costo mayorista.

---

maximum The greatest value in a data set. (p. 543)

máximo El valor mayor de un conjunto de datos.

Data set: 4, 6, 7, 8, 10
Maximum: 10

---

mean The sum of a set of data divided by the number of items in the data set; also called *average*. (p. 537)

media La suma de todos los elementos de un conjunto de datos dividida entre el número de elementos del conjunto. También se llama *promedio*.

Data set: 4, 6, 7, 8, 10
Mean:
$$\frac{4 + 6 + 7 + 8 + 10}{5} = \frac{35}{5} = 7$$

---

measure of central tendency A measure used to describe the middle of a data set. (p. 538)

medida de tendencia dominante Medida que describe la parte media de un conjunto de datos.

mean or median

---

median The middle number, or the mean (average) of the two middle numbers, in an ordered set of data. (p. 537)

mediana El número intermedio o la media (el promedio) de los dos números intermedios en un conjunto ordenado de datos.

Data set: 4, 6, 7, 8, 10
Median: 7

---

metric system of measurement A decimal system of weights and measures that is used universally in science and commonly throughout the world. (p. SB15)

sistema métrico de medición Sistema decimal de pesos y medidas empleado universalmente en las ciencias y de uso común en todo el mundo.

centimeters, meters, kilometers, gram, kilograms, milliliters, liters

---

midpoint The point that divides a line segment into two congruent line segments. (p. 393)

punto medio El punto que divide un segmento de recta en dos segmentos de recta congruentes.

A B C
B is the midpoint of $\overline{AC}$.

---

minimum The least value in a data set. (p. 543)

mínimo El valor meno de un conjunto de datos.

Data set: 4, 6, 7, 8, 10
Minimum: 4

---

mixed number A number made up of a whole number that is not zero and a fraction. (p. SB9)

número mixto Número compuesto por un número cabal distinto de cero y una fracción.

$4\frac{1}{8}$

---

mode The number or numbers that occur most frequently in a set of data; when all numbers occur with the same frequency, we say there is no mode. (p. 537)

moda Número o números más frecuentes en un conjunto de datos; si todos los números aparecen con la misma frecuencia, no hay moda.

Data set: 3, 5, 8, 8, 10
Mode: 8

---

monomial A number or a product of numbers and variables with exponents that are whole numbers. (p. 178)

monomio Un número o un producto de números y variables con exponentes que son números cabales.

$3x^2y^4$

Glossary/Glosario

ENGLISH	SPANISH	EXAMPLES
multiple The product of any number and a non-zero whole number is a multiple of that number. (p. SB4)	**múltiplo** El producto de cualquier número y un número cabal distinto de cero es un múltiplo de ese número.	30, 40, and 90 are all multiples of 10.
Multiplication Property of Equality The property that states that if you multiply both sides of an equation by the same number, the new equation will have the same solution. (p. 38)	**Propiedad de igualdad de la multiplicación** Propiedad que establece que puedes multiplicar ambos lados de una ecuación por el mismo número y la nueva ecuación tendrá la misma solución.	$\frac{1}{3}x = 7$ $(3)\left(\frac{1}{3}x\right) = (3)(7)$ $x = 21$
multiplicative inverse One of two numbers whose product is 1; also called *reciprocal*. (p. 82)	**inverso multiplicativo** Uno de dos números cuyo producto es 1; también llamado *recíproco*.	The multiplicative inverse of $\frac{3}{4}$ is $\frac{4}{3}$.
mutually exclusive Two events are mutually exclusive if they cannot occur in the same trial of an experiment. (p. 566)	**mutuamente excluyentes** Dos sucesos son mutuamente excluyentes cuando no pueden ocurrir en la misma prueba de un experimento.	When rolling a number cube, rolling a 3 and rolling an even number are mutually exclusive events.

N

ENGLISH	SPANISH	EXAMPLES
negative correlation Two data sets have a negative correlation if one set of data values increases while the other decreases. (p. 549)	**correlación negativa** Dos conjuntos de datos tienen correlación negativa si los valores de un conjunto aumentan a medida que los valores del otro conjunto disminuyen.	
negative integer An integer less than zero. (p. 14)	**entero negativo** Entero menor que cero.	−2 is a negative integer.
net An arrangement of two-dimensional figures that can be folded to form a polyhedron. (p. 496)	**plantilla** Arreglo de figuras bidimensionales que se doblan para formar un poliedro.	
no correlation Two data sets have no correlation when there is no relationship between their data values. (p. 549)	**sin correlación** Caso en que los valores de dos conjuntos no muestran ninguna relación.	
numerator The top number of a fraction that tells how many parts of a whole are being considered. (p. 66)	**numerador** El número de arriba de una fracción; indica cuántas partes de un entero se consideran.	$\frac{4}{5}$ ← numerator
numerical expression An expression that contains only numbers and operations. (p. 6)	**expresión numérica** Expresión que incluye sólo números y operaciones.	$(2 \cdot 3) + 1$

O

obtuse angle An angle whose measure is greater than 90° but less than 180°. (p. 379)

ánlgulo obtuso Ángulo que mide más de 90° y menos de 180°.

obtuse triangle A triangle containing one obtuse angle. (p. 392)

triángulo obtusángulo Triángulo que tiene un ángulo obtuso.

octagon An eight-sided polygon. (p. SB16)

octágono Polígono de ocho lados.

odd number A whole number that is not divisible by two. (p. SB4)

número impar Número cabal que no es divisible entre 2.

1, 3, 5

opposites Two numbers that are an equal distance from zero on a number line; also called *additive inverse*. (p. 14)

opuestos Dos números que están a la misma distancia de cero en una recta numérica. También se llaman *inversos aditivos*.

5 and −5 are opposites.

order of operations A rule for evaluating expressions: First perform the operations in parentheses, then compute powers and roots, then perform all multiplication and division from left to right, and then perform all addition and subtraction from left to right. (p. SB14)

orden de las operaciones Regla para evaluar expresiones: primero se hacen las operaciones entre paréntesis, luego se hallan las potencias y raíces, después todas las multiplicaciones y divisiones de izquierda a derecha, y por último, todas las sumas y restas de izquierda a derecha.

$4^2 + 8 \div 2$ Simplify the power.
$16 + 8 \div 2$ Divide.
$16 + 4$ Add.
20

ordered pair A pair of numbers that can be used to locate a point on a coordinate plane. (p. 322)

par ordenado Par de números que sirven para ubicar un punto en un plano cartesiano.

The coordinates of B are $(-2, 3)$.

origin The point where the x-axis and y-axis intersect on the coordinate plane; (0, 0). (p. 322)

origen Punto de intersección entre el eje x y el eje y en un plano cartesiano: (0, 0).

outcome (probability) A possible result of a probability experiment. (p. 556)

resultado (en probabilidad) Posible resultado de un experimento de probabilidad.

When rolling a number cube, the possible outcomes are 1, 2, 3, 4, 5, and 6.

Glossary/Glosario **G21**

ENGLISH	SPANISH	EXAMPLES
outlier A value much greater or much less than the others in a data set. (p. 538)	**valor extremo** Un valor mucho mayor o menor que los demás valores de un conjunto de datos.	Most of data Mean ... Outlier
output The value that results from the substitution of a given input into an expression or function. (p. 326)	**valor de salida** Valor que resulta después de sustituir una variable por un valor de entrada determinado en una expresión o función.	For the function $y = 6x$, the input 4 produces an output of 24.

P

ENGLISH	SPANISH	EXAMPLES
parabola The graph of a quadratic function. (p. 334)	**parábola** Gráfica de una función cuadrática.	
parallel lines Lines in a plane that do not intersect. (p. 384)	**líneas paralelas** Líneas que se encuentran en el mismo plano pero que nunca se intersecan.	*r* *s*
parallel planes Planes that do not intersect. (p. 385)	**planos paralelos** Planos que no se cruzan.	Plane *AEF* and plane *CGH* are parallel planes.
parallelogram A quadrilateral with two pairs of parallel sides. (p. 399)	**paralelogramo** Cuadrilátero con dos pares de lados paralelos.	
pentagon A five-sided polygon. (p. SB16)	**pentágono** Polígono de cinco lados.	
percent A ratio comparing a number to 100. (p. 274)	**porcentaje** Razón que compara un número con el número 100.	$45\% = \frac{45}{100}$
percent of change The amount stated as a percent that a number increases or decreases. (p. 294)	**porcentaje de cambio** Cantidad en que un número aumenta o disminuye, expresada como un porcentaje.	
percent of decrease A percent change describing a decrease in a quantity. (p. 294)	**porcentaje de disminución** Porcentaje de cambio en que una cantidad disminuye.	An item that costs $8 is marked down to $6. The amount of the decrease is $2, and the percent of decrease is $\frac{2}{8} = 0.25 = 25\%$.

ENGLISH	SPANISH	EXAMPLES
percent of increase A percent change describing an increase in a quantity. (p. 294)	**porcentaje de incremento** Porcentaje de cambio en que una cantidad aumenta.	The price of an item increases from \$8 to \$12. The amount of the increase is \$4 and the percent of increase is $\frac{4}{8} = 0.5 = 50\%$
perfect square A square of a whole number. (p. 190)	**cuadrado perfecto** El cuadrado de un número cabal.	$5^2 = 25$, so 25 is a perfect square.
perimeter The sum of the lengths of the sides of a polygon. (p. 434)	**perímetro** La suma de las longitudes de los lados de un polígono.	18 ft 6ft perimeter = 18 + 6 + 18 + 6 = 48 ft
perpendicular bisector A line that intersects a segment at its midpoint and is perpendicular to the segment. (p. 382)	**mediatriz** Línea que cruza un segmento en su punto medio y es perpendicular al segmento.	ℓ A B
perpendicular lines Lines that intersect to form right angles. (p. 384)	**líneas perpendiculares** Líneas que al intersecarse forman ángulos rectos.	n m
perpendicular planes Planes that intersect at 90° angles. (p. 385)	**planos perpendiculares** Planos que se cruzan en ángulos de 90°.	
pi (π) The ratio of the circumference of a circle to the length of its diameter; $\pi \approx 3.14$ or $\frac{22}{7}$. (p. 450)	**pi (π)** Razón de la circunferencia de un círculo a la longitud de su diámetro; $\pi \approx 3.14$ ó $\frac{22}{7}$.	
plane A flat surface that extends forever. (p. 378)	**plano** Superficie plana que se extiende de manera indefinida en todas direcciones.	A C $\mathcal{R}$ B
point An exact location in space. (p. 378)	**punto** Ubicación exacta en el espacio.	P
polygon A closed plane figure formed by three or more line segments that intersect only at their endpoints (vertices). (p. 399)	**polígono** Figura plana cerrada, formada por tres o más segmentos de recta que se intersecan sólo en sus extremos (vértices).	
polyhedron A three-dimensional figure in which all the surfaces or faces are polygons. (p. 480)	**poliedro** Figura tridimensional cuyas superficies o caras tiene forma de polígonos.	
polynomial One monomial or the sum or difference of monomials. (p. 590)	**polinomio** Un monomio o la suma o la diferencia de monomios.	$2x^2 + 3xy - 7y^2$
population The entire group of objects or individuals considered for a survey. (p. SB22)	**población** Grupo completo de objetos o individuos que se desea estudiar.	In a survey about study habits of middle school students, the population is all middle school students.

ENGLISH	SPANISH	EXAMPLES
positive correlation Two data sets have a positive correlation when their data values increase or decrease together. (p. 549)	**correlación positiva** Dos conjuntos de datos tienen una correlación positiva cuando los valores de ambos conjuntos aumentan o disminuyen al mismo tiempo.	
positive integer An integer greater than zero. (p. 14)	**entero positivo** Entero mayor que cero.	$-4\ -3\ -2\ -1\ \ 0\ \ 1\ \ 2\ \ 3\ \ 4$ 2 is a positive integer.
power A number produced by raising a base to an exponent. (p. 166)	**potencia** Número que resulta al elevar una base a un exponente.	$2^3 = 8$, so 2 to the 3rd power is 8.
prime factorization A number written as the product of its prime factors. (p. SB5)	**factorización prima** Un número escrito como el producto de sus factores primos.	$10 = 2 \cdot 5$, $24 = 2^3 \cdot 3$
prime number A whole number greater than 1 that has exactly two factors, itself and 1. (p. SB5)	**número primo** Número cabal mayor que 1 que sólo es divisible entre 1 y él mismo.	5 is prime because its only factors are 5 and 1.
principal The initial amount of money borrowed or saved. (p. 302)	**capital** Cantidad inicial de dinero depositada o recibida en préstamo.	
principal square root The nonnegative square root of a number. (p. 190)	**raíz cuadrada principal** Raíz cuadrada no negativa de un número.	$\sqrt{25} = 5$; the principal square root of 25 is 5.
prism A three-dimensional figure with two congruent parallel polygonal bases. The remaining edges join corresponding vertices of the bases so that the remaining faces are rectangles. (p. 480)	**prisma** Figura tridimensional con dos bases poligonales congruentes y paralelas. El resto de las aristas se unen a los vértices correspondientes de las bases de manera que el resto de las caras sean rectángulos.	
probability A number from 0 to 1 (or 0% to 100%) that describes how likely an event is to occur. (p. 556)	**probabilidad** Un número entre 0 y 1 (ó 0% y 100%) que describe qué tan probable es un suceso.	A bag contains 3 red marbles and 4 blue marbles. The probability of randomly choosing a red marble is $\frac{3}{7}$.
product The result when two or more numbers are multiplied. (p. 26)	**producto** Resultado de multiplicar dos o más números.	The product of 4 and 8 is 32.
profit The difference between total income and total expenses. (p. 299)	**ganancia** Diferencia entre el total de ingresos y de gastos.	If total income is $2,400, and total expenses are $2,100, the profit is $2,400 − $2,100 = $300.
proportion An equation that states that two ratios are equivalent. (p. 232)	**proporción** Ecuación que establece que dos razones son equivalentes.	$\frac{2}{3} = \frac{4}{6}$
protractor A tool for measuring angles. (p. 478)	**transportador** Instrumento para medir ángulos.	

ENGLISH	SPANISH	EXAMPLES

pyramid A three-dimensional figure with a polygonal base lying in one plane plus one additional vertex not lying on that plane. The remaining edges of the pyramid join the additional vertex to the vertices of the base. (p. 480)

pirámide Figura tridimensional con una base poligonal en un plano más un vértice adicional que no está en ese plano. El resto de las aristas de la pirámide unen el vértice adicional con los vértices de la base.

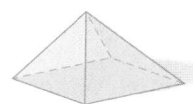

Pythagorean Theorem In a right triangle, the square of the length of the hypotenuse is equal to the sum of the squares of the lengths of the legs. (p. 203)

Teorema de Pitágoras En un triángulo rectángulo, la suma de los cuadrados de los catetos es igual al cuadrado de la hipotenusa.

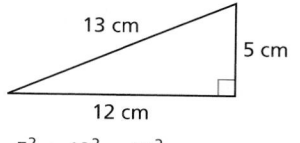

$5^2 + 12^2 = 13^2$
$25 + 144 = 169$

 Q

quadrant The x- and y-axes divide the coordinate plane into four regions. Each region is called a quadrant. (p. 322)

cuadrante El eje x y el eje y dividen el plano cartesiano en cuatro regiones. Cada región recibe el nombre de cuadrante.

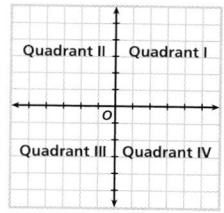

quadratic function A function of the form $y = ax^2 + bx + c$, where $a \neq 0$. (p. 334)

función cuadrática Función del tipo $y = ax^2 + bx + c$, donde $a \neq 0$.

$y = x^2 - 6x + 8$

quadrilateral A four-sided polygon. (p. 399)

cuadrilátero Polígono de cuatro lados.

quarterly Four times a year. (p. 305)

trimestral Cuatro veces al año.

quartile Three values, one of which is the median, that divide a data set into fourths. (p. 542)

cuartil Cada uno de tres valores, uno de los cuales es la mediana, que dividen en cuartos un conjunto de datos.

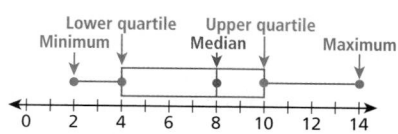

quotient The result when one number is divided by another. (p. SB7)

cociente Resultado de dividir un número entre otro.

In $8 \div 4 = 2$, 2 is the quotient.

 R

radical symbol The symbol $\sqrt{}$ used to represent the nonnegative square root of a number. (p. 192)

símbolo de radical El símbolo $\sqrt{}$ con que se representa la raíz cuadrada no negativa de un número.

$\sqrt{36} = 6$

ENGLISH	SPANISH	EXAMPLES
radius A line segment with one endpoint at the center of the circle and the other endpoint on the circle, or the length of that segment. (p. 446)	**radio** Segmento de recta con un extremo en el centro de un círculo y el otro en la circunferencia, o bien la longitud de ese segmento.	Radius
random sample A sample in which each individual or object in the entire population has an equal chance of being selected. (p. SB21)	**muestra aleatoria** Muestra en la que cada individuo u objeto de la población tiene la misma posibilidad de ser elegido.	Mr. Henson chose a random sample of the class by writing each student's name on a slip of paper, mixing up the slips, and drawing five slips without looking.
range (in statistics) The difference between the greatest and least values in a data set. (p. 537)	**rango (en estadística)** Diferencia entre los valores máximo y mínimo de un conjunto de datos.	Data set: 3, 5, 7, 7, 12 Range: $12 - 3 = 9$
range (of a function) The set of all possible output values of a function. (p. 326)	**rango (en una función)** El conjunto de todos los valores de salida posibles de una función.	The range of $y = |x|$ is $y \geq 0$.
rate A ratio that compares two quantities measured in different units. (p. 228)	**tasa** Una razón que compara dos cantidades medidas en diferentes unidades.	The speed limit is 55 miles per hour or 55 mi/h.
rate of change A ratio that compares the amount of change in a dependent variable to the amount of change in an independent variable. (p. 344)	**tasa de cambio** Razón que compara la cantidad de cambio de la variable dependiente con la cantidad de cambio de la variable independiente.	The cost of mailing a letter increased from 22 cents in 1985 to 25 cents in 1988. During this period, the rate of change was $\frac{\text{change in cost}}{\text{change in years}} = \frac{25 - 22}{1988 - 1985} = \frac{3}{3}$ = 1 cent per year.
rate of interest The percent charged or earned on an amount of money; see *simple interest.* (p. 302)	**tasa de interés** Porcentaje que se cobra por una cantidad de dinero prestada o que se gana por una cantidad de dinero ahorrada; ver *interés simple.*	
ratio A comparison of two numbers or quantities. (p. 224)	**razón** Comparación de dos números o cantidades.	12 to 25, 12:25, $\frac{12}{25}$
rational number A number that can be written in the form $\frac{a}{b}$, where a and b are integers and $b \neq 0$. (p. 66)	**número racional** Número que se puede expresar como $\frac{a}{b}$, donde a y b son números enteros y $b \neq 0$.	6 can be expressed as $\frac{6}{1}$. 0.5 can be expressed as $\frac{1}{2}$.
ray A part of a line that starts at one endpoint and extends forever. (p. 378)	**rayo** Parte de una línea que comienza en un extremo y se extiende de manera indefinida.	D
real number A rational or irrational number. (p. 198)	**número real** Número racional o irracional.	

ENGLISH	SPANISH	EXAMPLES
reciprocal One of two numbers whose product is 1; also called *multiplicative inverse.* (p. 82)	**recíproco** Uno de dos números cuyo producto es igual a 1. También se llama *inverso multiplicativo.*	The reciprocal of $\frac{2}{3}$ is $\frac{3}{2}$.
rectangle A parallelogram with four right angles. (p. 399)	**rectángulo** Paralelogramo con cuatro ángulos rectos.	
rectangular prism A three-dimensional figure that has three pairs of opposite parallel congruent faces that are rectangles. (p. 480)	**prisma rectangular** Figura tridimensional que tiene tres pares de caras opuestas, paralelas y congruentes que son rectángulos.	
reflection A transformation of a figure that flips the figure across a line. (p. 410)	**reflexión** Transformación que ocurre cuando se invierte una figura sobre una línea.	
regular polygon A polygon in which all angles are congruent and all sides are congruent. (p. SB16)	**polígono regular** Polígono en el que todos los ángulos y todos los lados son congruentes.	
regular pyramid A pyramid whose base is a regular polygon and whose lateral faces are all congruent. (p. 504)	**pirámide regular** Pirámide que tiene un polígono regular como base y caras laterales congruentes.	
regular tessellation A repeating pattern of congruent regular polygons that completely covers a plane with no gaps or overlaps. (p. 416)	**teselado regular** Patrón que se repite formado por polígonos regulares congruentes que cubren completamente un plano sin dejar espacios y sin superponerse.	
repeating decimal A rational number in decimal form in which a group of one or more digits (where all digits are not zero) repeat infinitely. (pp. 66, 191)	**decimal periódico** Número racional en forma decimal en el que un grupo de uno o más dígitos (donde todos los dígitos son distintos de cero) se repiten infinitamente.	$0.757575\ldots = 0.\overline{75}$
rhombus A parallelogram with all sides congruent. (p. 399)	**rombo** Paralelogramo en el que todos los lados son congruentes.	
right angle An angle that measures 90°. (p. 379)	**ángulo recto** Ángulo que mide exactamente 90°.	

right cone A cone in which a perpendicular line drawn from the base to the tip (vertex) passes through the center of the base. (p. 504)

cono recto Cono en el que una línea perpendicular trazada de la base a la punta (vértice) pasa por el centro de la base.

Axis

Right cone

---

right triangle A triangle containing a right angle. (p. 392)

triángulo rectángulo Triángulo que tiene un ángulo recto.

---

rise The vertical change when the slope of a line is expressed as the ratio $\frac{rise}{run}$, or "rise over run." (p. 345)

distancia vertical El cambio vertical cuando la pendiente de una línea se expresa como la razón $\frac{distancia\ vertical}{distancia\ horizontal}$, o "distancia vertical sobre distancia horizontal".

For the points $(3, -1)$ and $(6, 5)$, the rise is $5 - (-1) = 6$.

---

rotation A transformation in which a figure is turned around a point. (p. 410)

rotación Transformación que ocurre cuando una figura gira alrededor de un punto.

---

run The horizontal change when the slope of a line is expressed as the ratio $\frac{rise}{run}$, or "rise over run." (p. 345)

distancia horizontal El cambio horizontal cuando la pendiente de una línea se expresa como la razón $\frac{distancia\ vertical}{distancia\ horizontal}$, o "distancia vertical sobre distancia horizontal".

For the points $(3, -1)$ and $(6, 5)$, the run is $6 - 3 = 3$.

S

sales tax A percent of the cost of an item, which is charged by governments to raise money. (p. 298)

impuesto sobre la venta Porcentaje del costo de un artículo que los gobiernos cobran para recaudar fondos.

---

sample A part of the population. (p. SB21)

muestra Una parte de la población.

In a survey about the study habits of middle school students, a sample is a group of 100 randomly chosen middle school students.

---

sample space All possible outcomes of an experiment. (p. 556)

espacio muestral Conjunto de todos los resultados posibles de un experimento.

When rolling a number cube, the sample space is 1, 2, 3, 4, 5, 6.

---

scale The ratio between two sets of measurements. (p. 252)

escala La razón entre dos conjuntos de medidas.

1 cm : 5 mi

ENGLISH	SPANISH	EXAMPLES
scale drawing A drawing that uses a scale to make an object smaller than (a reduction) or larger than (an enlargement) the real object. (p. 252)	**dibujo a escala** Dibujo en el que se usa una escala para que un objeto se vea menor (reducción) o mayor (agrandamiento) que el objeto real al que representa.	A blueprint is an example of a scale drawing.
scale factor The ratio used to enlarge or reduce similar figures. (p. 253)	**factor de escala** Razón empleada para agrandar o reducir figuras semejantes.	
scale model A proportional model of a three-dimensional object. (p. 252)	**modelo a escala** Modelo proporcional de un objeto tridimensional.	
scalene triangle A triangle with no congruent sides. (p. 393)	**triángulo escaleno** Triángulo que no tiene lados congruentes.	
scatter plot A graph with points plotted to show a possible relationship between two sets of data. (p. 548)	**diagrama de dispersión** Gráfica de puntos que muestra una posible relación entre dos conjuntos de datos.	
scientific notation A method of writing very large or very small numbers by using powers of 10. (p. 182)	**notación científica** Método que se usa para escribir números muy grandes o muy pequeños mediante potencias de 10.	$12{,}560{,}000{,}000{,}000 = 1.256 \times 10^{13}$
second quartile The median of a set of data. (p. 476)	**segundo cuartil** Mediana de un conjunto de datos.	Data set: 4, 6, 7, 8, 10 Second quartile: 7
sector A region enclosed by two radii and the arc joining their endpoints. (p. 447)	**sector** Región encerrada por dos radios y el arco que une sus extremos.	
segment A part of a line between two endpoints. (p. 378)	**segmento** Parte de una línea entre dos extremos.	$\overline{GH}$
side One of the segments that form a polygon. (p. 399)	**lado** Uno de los segmentos que forman un polígono.	Side
similar Figures with the same shape but not necessarily the same size are similar. (p. 244)	**semejantes** Figuras que tienen la misma forma, pero no necesariamente el mismo tamaño.	

ENGLISH	SPANISH	EXAMPLES
simple interest A fixed percent of the principal. It is found using the formula $I = Prt$, where P represents the principal, r the rate of interest, and t the time. (p. 302)	**interés simple** Un porcentaje fijo del capital. Se calcula con la fórmula $I = Cit$, donde C representa el capital, i, la tasa de interés y t, el tiempo.	\$100 is put into an account with a simple interest rate of 5%. After 2 years, the account will have earned $I = 100 \cdot 0.05 \cdot 2 = \$10$.
simplest form A fraction is in simplest form when the numerator and denominator have no common factors other than 1. (p. SB8)	**mínima expresión** Una fracción está en su mínima expresión cuando el numerador y el denominador no tienen más factor común que 1.	Fraction: $\frac{8}{12}$ Simplest form: $\frac{2}{3}$
simplify To write a fraction or expression in simplest form. (p. SB8)	**simplificar** Escribir una fracción o expresión numérica en su mínima expresión.	
skew lines Lines that lie in different planes that are neither parallel nor intersecting. (p. 384)	**líneas oblicuas** Líneas que se encuentran en planos distintos, pore so no se intersecan ni son paralelas.	 $\overleftrightarrow{AE}$ and $\overleftrightarrow{CD}$ are skew lines.
slant height The distance from the base of a cone to its vertex, measured along the lateral surface. (p. 504)	**altura inclinada** Distancia de la base de un cono a su vértice, medida a lo largo de la superficie lateral.	 Slant height
slope A measure of the steepness of a line on a graph; the rise divided by the run. (p. 345)	**pendiente** Medida de la inclinación de una línea en una gráfica. Razón de la distancia vertical a la distancia horizontal.	Slope $= \frac{\text{rise}}{\text{run}} = \frac{3}{4}$
solution of an equation A value or values that make an equation true. (p. 32)	**solución de una ecuación** Valor o valores que hacen verdadera una ecuación.	Equation: $x + 2 = 6$ Solution: $x = 4$
solution of an inequality A value or values that make an inequality true. (p. 140)	**solución de una desigualdad** Valor o valores que hacen verdadera una desigualdad.	Inequality: $x + 3 \geq 10$ Solution: $x \geq 7$
solution set The set of values that make a statement true. (p. 136)	**conjunto solución** Conjunto de valores que hacen verdadero un enunciado.	Inequality: $x + 3 \geq 5$ Solution set: $x \geq 2$
solve To find an answer or a solution. (p. 32)	**resolver** Hallar una respuesta o solución.	

ENGLISH	SPANISH	EXAMPLES

sphere A three-dimensional figure with all points the same distance from the center. (p. 508)

esfera Figura tridimensional en la que todos los puntos están a la misma distancia del centro.

---

square A rectangle with four congruent sides. (p. 399)

cuadrado Rectángulo con cuatro lados congruentes.

---

square (numeration) A number raised to the second power. (p. 192)

cuadrado (en numeración) Número elevado a la segunda potencia.

In 5^2, the number 5 is squared.

---

square root One of the two equal factors of a number. (p. 190)

raíz cuadrada Uno de los dos factores iguales de un número.

$16 = 4 \cdot 4$, or $16 = -4 \cdot -4$, so 4 and -4 are square roots of 16.

---

stem-and-leaf plot A graph used to organize and display data so that the frequencies can be compared. (p. 533)

diagrama de tallo y hojas Gráfica que muestra y ordena los datos, y que sirve para comparar las frecuencias.

Stem	Leaves
3	2 3 4 4 7 9
4	0 1 5 7 7 7 8
5	1 2 2 3

Key: 3|2 means 3.2

---

straight angle An angle that measures 180°. (p. 379)

ángulo llano Ángulo que mide exactamente 180°.

---

substitute To replace a variable with a number or another expression in an algebraic expression. (p. 6)

sustituir Reemplazar una variable por un número u otra expresión en una expresión algebraica.

Substituting 3 for m in the expression $5m - 2$ gives $5(3) - 2 = 15 - 2 = 13$.

Subtraction Property of Equality The property that states that if you subtract the same number from both sides of an equation, the new equation will have the same solution. (p. 33)

Propiedad de igualdad de la resta Propiedad que establece que puedes restar el mismo número de ambos lados de una ecuación y la nueva ecuación tendrá la misma solución.

$$x + 6 = 8$$
$$\underline{-6 \quad -6}$$
$$x = 2$$

---

sum The result when two or more numbers are added. (p. 18)

suma Resultado de sumar dos o más números.

The sum of $6 + 7 + 1$ is 14.

---

supplementary angles Two angles whose measures have a sum of 180°. (p. 379)

ángulos suplementarios Dos ángulos cuyas medidas suman 180°.

30° 150°

---

surface area The sum of the areas of the faces, or surfaces, of a three-dimensional figure. (p. 498)

área total Suma de las áreas de las caras, o superficies, de una figura tridimensional.

12 cm
6 cm
8 cm

Surface area $= 2(8)(12) + 2(8)(6) + 2(12)(6) = 432 \text{ cm}^2$

Glossary/Glosario

ENGLISH	SPANISH	EXAMPLES
system of equations A set of two or more equations that contain two or more variables. (p. 131)	**sistema de ecuaciones** Conjunto de dos o más ecuaciones que contienen dos o más variables.	$\begin{cases} x + y = -1 \\ -x + y = -3 \end{cases}$

ENGLISH	SPANISH	EXAMPLES
term (in an expression) The parts of an expression that are added or subtracted. (p. 120)	**término (en una expresión)** Las partes de una expresión que se suman o se restan.	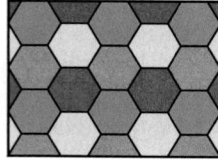
terminating decimal A decimal number that ends or terminates. (p. 66)	**decimal finito** Decimal con un número determinado de posiciones decimales.	6.75
tessellation A repeating pattern of plane figures that completely cover a plane with no gaps or overlaps. (p. 416)	**teselado** Patrón repetido de figuras planas que cubren totalmente un plano sin superponerse ni dejar huecos.	
theoretical probability The ratio of the number of equally likely outcomes in an event to the total number of possible outcomes. (p. 564)	**probabilidad teórica** Razón del número de resultados igualmente probables en un suceso al número total de resultados posibles.	When rolling a number cube, the theoretical probability of rolling a 4 is $\frac{1}{6}$.
third quartile The median of the upper half of a set of data; also called *upper quartile*. (p. 542)	**tercer cuartil** La mediana de la mitad superior de un conjunto de datos. También se llama *cuartil superior*.	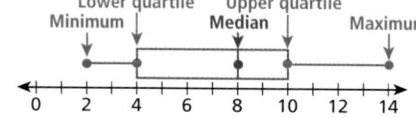
transformation A change in the size or position of a figure. (p. 410)	**transformación** Cambio en el tamaño o la posición de una figura.	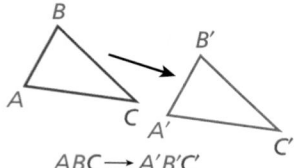
translation A movement (slide) of a figure along a straight line. (p. 410)	**traslación** Desplazamiento de una figura a lo largo de una línea recta.	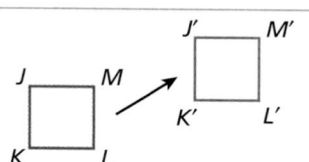
transversal A line that intersects two or more lines. (p. 389)	**transversal** Línea que cruza dos o más líneas.	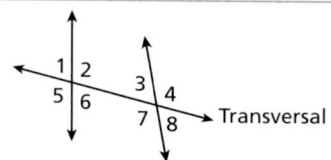
trapezoid A quadrilateral with exactly one pair of parallel sides. (p. 399)	**trapecio** Cuadrilátero con un par de lados paralelos.	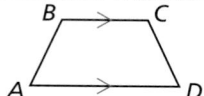

Glossary/Glosario

ENGLISH	SPANISH	EXAMPLES

tree diagram A branching diagram that shows all possible combinations or outcomes of an event. (p. SB23)

diagrama de árbol Diagrama ramificado que muestra todas las posibles combinaciones o resultados de un suceso.

H   T

1 2 3 4 5 6   1 2 3 4 5 6

---

trial In probability, a single repetition or observation of an experiment. (p. 556)

prueba En probabilidad, una sola repetición u observación de un experimento.

When rolling a number cube, each roll is one trial.

---

triangle A three-sided polygon (p. 392)

triángulo Polígono de tres lados.

Triangle Sum Theorem The theorem that states that the measures of the angles in a triangle add up to 180°. (p. 392)

Teorema de la suma del triángulo Teorema que establece que las medidas de los ángulos de un triángulo suman 180°.

---

triangular prism A three-dimensional figure with two congruent parallel triangular bases and whose other faces are rectangles. (p. 485)

prisma triangular Figura tridimensional con dos bases triangulares congruentes y paralelas cuyas otras caras son rectángulos.

---

trinomial A polynomial with three terms. (p. 590)

trinomio Polinomio con tres términos.

$4x^2 + 3xy - 5y^2$

U

unit analysis The process of changing one unit of measure to another. (p. 237)

conversión de unidades Proceso que consiste en cambiar una unidad de medida por otra.

---

unit conversion factor A fraction used in unit conversion in which the numerator and denominator represent the same amount but are in different units. (p. 237)

factor de conversión de unidades Fracción que se usa para la conversión de unidades, donde el numerador y el denominador representan la misma cantidad pero están en unidades distintas.

$\frac{60 \text{ min}}{1 \text{ h}}$ or $\frac{1 \text{ h}}{60 \text{ min}}$

---

unit price A unit rate used to compare prices. (p. 229)

precio unitario Tasa unitaria que sirve para comparar precios.

Cereal costs $0.23 per ounce.

---

unit rate A rate in which the second quantity in the comparison is one unit. (p. 228)

tasa unitaria Una tasa en la que la segunda cantidad de la comparación es la unidad.

10 cm per minute

---

upper quartile The median of the upper half of a set of data; also called *third quartile*. (p. 542)

cuartil superior La mediana de la mitad superior de un conjunto de datos; también se llama *tercer cuartil*.

Lower quartile   Upper quartile
Minimum   Median   Maximum

0 2 4 6 8 10 12 14

V

variable A symbol used to represent a quantity that can change. (p. 6)

variable Símbolo que representa una cantidad que puede cambiar.

In the expression 2x + 3, x is the variable.

---

vertex (of an angle) The common endpoint of the sides of the angle. (p. 379)

vértice de un ángulo Extremo común de los lados del ángulo.

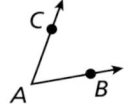

A is the vertex of ∠CAB.

---

vertex (of a polygon) The intersection of two sides of the polygon. (p. 399)

vértice (de un polígono) La intersección de dos lados del polígono.

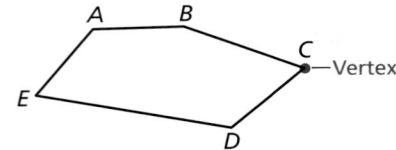

A, B, C, D, and E are vertices of the polygon.

---

vertex (of a polyhedron) A point at which three or more edges of a polyhedron intersect. (p. 480)

vértice (de un poliedro) Un punto en el que se intersecan tres o más aristas de un poliedro.

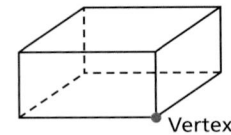

Vertex

---

vertical angles A pair of opposite congruent angles formed by intersecting lines. (p. 388)

ángulos opuestos por el vértice Par de ángulos opuestos congruentes formados por líneas secantes.

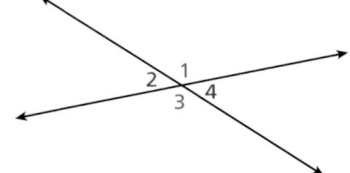

∠1 and ∠3 are vertical angles.

---

vertical line test A test used to determine whether a relation is a function. If any vertical line crosses the graph of a relation more than once, the relation is not a function. (p. 327)

prueba de linea vertical Prueba utilizada para determinar si una relación es una función. Si una línea vertical corta la gráfica de una relación más de una vez, la relación no es una función.

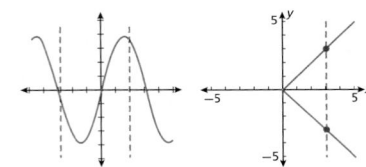

---

volume The number of cubic units needed to fill a given space. (p. 485)

volumen Número de unidades cúbicas que se necesitan para llenar un espacio.

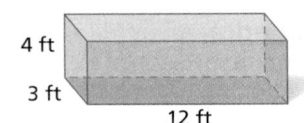

Volume = 3 · 4 · 12 = 144 ft³

X

x-axis The horizontal axis on a coordinate plane. (p. 322)

eje x El eje horizontal del plano cartesiano.

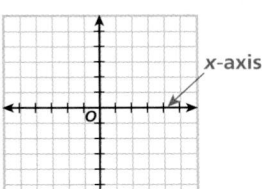

x-axis

Glossary/Glosario

ENGLISH	SPANISH	EXAMPLES
x-coordinate The first number in an ordered pair; it tells the distance to move right or left from the origin (0, 0). (p. 322)	**coordenada x** El primer número de un par ordenado; indica la distancia que debes moverte hacia la izquierda o la derecha desde el origen, (0, 0).	5 is the x-coordinate in (5, 3).

y-axis The vertical axis on a coordinate plane. (p. 322)	**eje y** El eje vertical del plano cartesiano.	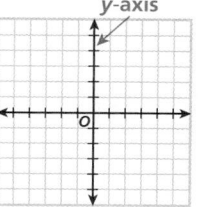
y-coordinate The second number in an ordered pair; it tells the distance to move up or down from the origin (0, 0). (p. 322)	**coordenada y** El segundo número de un par ordenado; indica la distancia que debes avanzar hacia arriba o hacia abajo desde el origen, (0, 0).	3 is the y-coordinate in (5, 3).

zero pair A number and its opposite, which add to 0. (p. 42)	**par nulo** Un número y su opuesto, cuya suma es 0.	18 and −18

Notes

Index

Index

Lower quartile, 542–543
Luxor Hotel, 352

Magic squares, 212
Magnitude, 6B
Making
  circle graphs, SB21
  conjectures, SB24
  scale models, 257–258
Mammoth Lakes, CA, 374
Manipulatives
  algebra tiles, 41–42, 124, 128, 129,
    594–595, 596, 602, 603, 604, 607,
    608, 609, 612, 616–617, 618
  analog clock, 447
  balance scale, 32
  calculators, 82, 168, 192, 196, 199, 200,
    278, 298, 302, 304, 450, 451
  centimeter cubes, 484, 486, 513
  coins, 560, 596
  compass, 382–383, 397
  cone nets, 505
  cubes, 513
  fraction bars, 66, 71, 88
  graphing calculator, 189, 547, 553, 603
  graph paper, 204, 256, 331, 399, 415,
    434, 439, 440, 459
  integer chips, 19
  number cubes, 304, 561
  pattern blocks, 415, 417
  protractors, 382–383, 407, 417, 478
  pyramid nets, 505
  rectangular prism, 496–497, 512
  ruler, 253, 256, 407, 478, 484, 491, 505
  sphere models, 509
  spreadsheet software, 530–531
  straightedges, 204, 379, 382–383, 397
  tangrams, 455
  tape measure, 253
  triangular prism, 496–497, 512
  two-color counters, 169, 570
Manufacturing, 280, 352
Map, concept, 433
Mars, 187
Mass, metric units of, SB16
Mastering the Standards, 58–59,
  110–111, 162–163, 218–219, 268–269,
  316–317, 372–373, 428–429, 472–473,
  524–525, 584–585, 630–631, *see also*
  Assessment
Math
  translating between words and, 63
  translating words into, 10–11
Math Background
  Teacher Note, 8, 12, 20, 24, 28, 35, 39,
    46, 68, 72, 76, 80, 85, 90, 96, 100,
    118, 122, 126, 132, 138, 142, 150,
    168B, 170, 174, 178, 181, 187, 194,
    198, 202, 208, 226, 230, 235, 240,
    246, 250, 254, 276, 281, 286, 290,
    296, 306, 324, 328, 332, 336, 340,
    347, 351, 380, 386, 390, 395, 401,

408, 413, 418, 437, 442, 448, 452,
    456, 460, 482, 488, 492, 501, 506,
    510, 514, 540, 545, 551, 558, 562, 567,
    572, 592, 598, 605, 610, 614, 620
  Teaching the Standards, 6B, 32B, 64B,
    94B, 116B, 136B, 168B, 192B, 224B,
    244B, 274B, 322B, 344B, 378B, 406B,
    434B, 496B, 530B, 590B, 602B
Math expressions
  translating, into word phrases, 11
  translating word phrases into, 10
Math Fact, 22, 37, 120, 168, 184, 237, 278,
  322, 378, 416, 508, 542, 590
Math Humor, 6, 10, 14, 18, 26, 32, 43, 66,
  70, 74, 78, 82, 87, 94, 98, 116, 124, 129,
  136, 140, 144, 148, 172, 176, 180, 192,
  196, 200, 205, 224, 228, 232, 244, 248,
  252, 274, 283, 288, 294, 298, 303, 326,
  330, 334, 338, 344, 349, 353, 357, 384,
  392, 398, 410, 434, 439, 446, 450, 454,
  458, 480, 485, 498, 504, 512, 532, 548,
  556, 564, 596, 603, 608, 612, 618
Math journals, keeping, 321
Matrushka dolls, 86
Maximum, 543
Mean, 537–538
Measurement, 69, 90
  conversion tables, SB15
  customary system of, 237–239
  indirect, 248–249
  metric system of, 237–239, SB15
**Measures of central tendency and
  range,** 537–538
Median, 530B, 537–538
Menkaure Pyramid, 209
Merced River, 112
Mercury (planet), 35, 186
Metamorphoses, 419
Meteorites, 535
Meteorology, 73
Meter, SB15
Methane, 333
Metric conversions, 237, SB15
Metric system of measurement, SB15
  converting between customary and,
    SB15
Midpoint, 393
Mile, SB15
Milligram, SB15
Milliliter, SB15
Millimeter, SB15
Minimum, 543
Mirror, liquid, 335
Mixed numbers,
  addition of, 87–88
  dividing fractions and, 82–84
  equivalent fractions and, SB9
  multiplying fractions and, 78–79
  subtraction of, 87
Mode, 537
Modeling
  equations with variables on both sides,
    128

polynomial addition, 602
polynomial subtraction, 607
polynomials, 594–595
two-step equations, 41–42
Models
  scale, 252–253, 259, *see also* Scale
    models
Mona Lisa, 247
Money, 38, 307
Monomials, 180
  division of, 180–181
  multiplication of, 180
  multiplication of polynomials by,
    612–613
  raising, to powers, 181
  square roots of, 193
Monterey Bay Aquarium, 240
Motivate
  *Motivate appears in every lesson.
  Some examples: 6, 10, 14, 18, 22*
Mountain bikes, 541
Multiple Choice
  *Multiple Choice test items are found
  in every lesson. Some examples: 9, 13,
  17, 21, 25*
  Answering Context-Based Test Items,
    582–583
  Eliminate Answer Choices, 56–57
  Teaching tip, 9, 17, 25, 36, 40, 47, 56,
    58, 69, 73, 77, 81, 86, 91, 97, 101, 110,
    119, 123, 127, 133, 139, 143, 162, 171,
    175, 183, 188, 203, 209, 218, 227, 231,
    236, 251, 255, 268, 277, 282, 287,
    291, 297, 307, 316, 325, 329, 333,
    337, 341, 348, 352, 356, 361, 372, 381,
    387, 391, 396, 402, 409, 414, 419,
    428, 438, 443, 449, 453, 457, 461,
    472, 483, 489, 493, 502, 506, 507,
    511, 515, 524, 536, 541, 546, 559, 573,
    593, 599, 606, 611, 615, 621, 630
Multiple, least common (LCM), 70, SB6
Multiple Representations, 234, 289, 323
Multiplication
  Associative Property of, 116B, 116–117
  of binomials, 616–617, 618–619
  Commutative Property, 116B
  of decimals, 79, 94
  Distributive Property, 116B
  of fractions
    and mixed numbers, 78–79
  of integers, 26–27
  of monomials, 180
  of numbers in scientific notation, 189
  of polynomials, by monomials, 602B,
    612–613
  of powers, 176
  by powers of ten, 184, SB7
  properties, 38
  of rational numbers, 78–79
  solving equations by, 37–39
  solving inequalities by, 144–145
Multiplication Property of Equality, 38
Multiplicative inverse, 82
Multi-Step, 39, 80, 90, 91, 97, 199, 209,
  231, 287, 296, 438, 440, 502

Multi-Step Application, 439, 619
Multi-step equations
    solving, 124–125, 128–131
Muscle contractions, 621
Music, 40, 449, 487
Mutually exclusive events, 566

Negative correlation, 549
Negative exponents, 172–173
Negative slope, 349
Neptune, 187
Nets, 496B
    of cones, 503
    of prisms and cylinders, 496–497
Newborns, 274
Newtons (N), 34
***n*-gons,** SB16
Niagara Falls, 91
Nickels, 275
Nielsen Television Ratings, 283
No correlation, 549
Nonagons, SB16
Notation
    scientific, *see* Scientific notation
    set-builder, 142
Note-Taking Strategies, *see* Reading and
    Writing Math
Notes, taking effective, 167
Number cubes, 304, 561
Number line, 18
Number Sense, 71, 79, 83
Numbers
    compatible, 278
    composite, SB5
    division of, in scientific notation,
      189
    finding, when percents are known,
      288–289
    irrational, 200
    mixed, SB9, *see also* Mixed numbers
    multiplication of, in scientific notation,
      189
    percents of, 283–284
    prime, SB5
    rational, 60–111, 200–201, *see also*
      Rational numbers
    real, 200–201
Numerator, 66
Numerical expressions, 6–7
Nutrition, 39, 96, 141, 356

Obtuse angles, 379
Obtuse triangles, 392, SB17
Ocean trenches, 29
Octagons, SB16
Of Mice and Men (Steinbeck), 143
One-Minute Section Planner, 6A, 32A,

64A, 94A, 116A, 136A, 168A, 192A,
224A, 244A, 274A, 294A, 322A, 344A,
378A, 406A, 434A, 446A, 478A, 496A,
530A, 556A, 590A, 602A
One-step equations
    solving, with decimals, 94
    solving, with fractions, 94–95
    solving, with integers, 32–34, 37–38
    solving, with rational numbers, 94–95
Online Resources
    Chapter Project Online, 2, 60, 112, 164,
      220, 270, 318, 374, 474, 526, 586
    Game Time Extra, 104, 154, 212, 260,
      310, 364, 422, 464, 518, 576, 624
    Homework Help Online
    Homework Help Online is available for
    every lesson. Refer to the go.hrw.com
    box at the beginning of each exercise
    set. Some examples: 8, 12, 16, 20, 24
    Lab Resources Online, 41, 64, 128, 189,
      204, 382, 478, 484, 496, 530, 547,
      553, 594, 602, 607, 616
    Parent Resources Online
    Parent Resources Online is available for
    every lesson. Refer to the go.hrw.com
    box at the beginning of each exercise
    set. Some examples: 8, 12, 16, 20, 24
    Project Teacher Support, 2, 60, 112, 164,
      220, 270, 318, 374, 430, 474, 526, 586
    Standards Practice Online, 58, 110, 162,
      218, 268, 316, 372, 428, 472, 524,
      584, 630
    Web Extra!, 25, 101, 195, 209, 236, 255,
      291, 419, 443, 483, 563, 599, 606
Open circle, 137
Operations
    binary, 116B
    inverse, 32
    order of, 6B, 6, 23–24, 27
    polynomials, 602B
Opposites, 14
Order of operations, 6B, 6, SB14
    using, 169, 173
Ordered pairs, 322B, 322
Ordering
    measurements, customary and metric,
      237
    rational numbers, 71
Organizing data, 532–534, SB18–SB21
Origami, 311
Origin, 322
Ounce, fluid, SB15
Outcomes, 556
    equally likely, 564
Outlier, 538–539
Output, 326

Pacing Guide
    A guide for pacing appears in every
    lesson and lab. Some examples: 6, 10,
    14, 18, 22
Pacific Wheel, 430, 453

Pairs, ordered, 322
Pandas, 6
Parabola, 334
Parallel lines, 388–389
    properties of transversals to, 389
    and skew lines, 384–385
Parallelograms, 399, SB17
    area of, 434B, 435–436
    perimeter of, 434–436
Parent Resources Online
    Parent Resources Online are available
    for every lesson. Refer to the
    go.hrw.com box at the beginning of
    each exercise set. Some examples: 8,
    12, 16, 20, 24
Parentheses, 6
Parthenon, 483
Pascal, Blaise, 556B
Pattern blocks, 415, 417
Patterns, 174, 286
    in integer exponents, looking for,
      172–173
Pediment, 445
Pei, I. M., 493
Peirsol, Aaron, 74
PEMDAS mnemonic, 6
Pentagons, 403, SB16
Percent problems, solving, 283–285,
    288–289
Percent(s), 274B
    applications of, 294B, 298–299
    of change, 294
    of decrease, 294–295
    defined, 274B, 274
    estimating with, 278–280
    finding, 283–285
      using an equation, 283, 284
      using a proportion, 283, 285
    fractions and decimals and,
      274B, 274–275
    of increase, 294–295
    known, finding numbers for,
      288–289
    of numbers, 283–284
Perfect squares, 192
Perimeter, 196, 434
    area and, 434B
    of parallelograms, 434–436
    of rectangles, 434–436
    of trapezoids, 439–441
    of triangles, 439–441
Periscopes, 391
Perpendicular bisectors, 382
Perpendicular lines, 384–385, 388–389
Pershing Square, CA, 474
Person-day, 39
Person-hour, 38
Physics, 591
Pi (π), 203, 446B, 450
Pint, SB15
Pixels, 193
Place value, SB2
Planes, 378

regular, 416
semiregular, 418
Test, cumulative, studying for a, 589
Test items, context-based, answering,
582–583
The Grapes of Wrath (Steinbeck), 143
Theorem, Pythagorean, *see* Pythagorean
Theorem
Theoretical probability, 556B, 564–566
Think and Discuss
*Think and Discuss is found in every
lesson. Some examples: 7, 11, 15, 19,
23*
Three-dimensional figures, 378B
classifying, 481
drawing, 477
exploring, 478–479
introduction to, 480–481
scaling, 512–513
surface area of, 496, 509
volume of, 484–487, 508
Tides, 28
Tiles, algebra, 41–42, 128, 594–595, 602,
607, 616–617
Time, investment, 303
Timeline, 25
Tips, 279
Tips from the Bag Ladies, 51, 105, 155, 213,
261, 311, 365, 423, 465, 519, 577, 625
To Kill a Mockingbird (Lee), 297
Ton, SB15
Torus, 518
Toys, 606
Transamerica Pyramid, 492
Transformations, 406B, 410
combining, 415
graphing, 410–412
Translating
math expressions into word phrases, 11
sentences into two-step equations, 43
word phrases into inequalities, 136
word phrases into math expressions, 10
between words and math, 63
Translations, 406B, 410
rotations and reflections and, 410–412
Transportation, 240, 241, 593
Transversals, 389
to parallel lines, properties of, 389
Trapezoids, 399, SB17
area of, 434B, 440–441
isosceles, SB17
perimeter of, 439
Travel, 125, 126
Tree diagrams, SB23
Trenches, ocean, 29
Trial, 556
Triangle Sum Theorem, 378B, 392
Triangles, 392–394, SB16–SB17
acute, 392, SB17
angles in, 392–394
area of, 440–441
classifying, 392–393
congruent, 406

equilateral, 393, SB17
isosceles, 393, SB17
obtuse, 392, SB17
perimeter of, 439
right, 392, SB17, *see also* Right triangles
scalene, 393, SB17
similar, 244–245
Triangular prism, 485, 496–497, 512
Triangular pyramid, 490
Trichotomy, Law of, 136B
Trinomials, 590
Trump Tower, 257
Tukey, John, 530B
Turns, *see* Rotation(s)
Twins, 406
Two-dimensional figures, 430–473
Two-step equations, 94B
modeling, 41–42
solving, 32B, 43–45
solving, with rational numbers, 98–99
Two-step inequalities, solving, 148–149

U

Umbra, 507
Undefined slope, 350
Understanding
reading lessons for, 115
reading problems for, 273
Unisphere, 483
Unit(s)
conversion factors, 237
customary, SB15
metric, SB15
Unit analysis, 237
Unit conversion factor, 237
Unit fractions, 104
Unit price, 229
Unit rates, 228–229
estimating, 229
rates and, 228–229
Unit square, 434B
United States census, 291
Universal Access
Advanced Learners/GATE, 23, 27, 75,
149, 177, 245, 289, 299, 327, 345,
393, 591
Through Auditory Cues, 141, 389
Through Cognitive Strategies, 83, 117,
499, 543, 557
Through Concrete Manipulatives, 11, 19,
38, 71, 88, 121, 130, 197, 275, 358,
407, 411, 447, 451, 455, 509, 513, 561,
597, 604, 609
Through Cooperative Learning, 7, 33,
95, 99, 125, 169, 193, 225, 304, 323,
339, 354, 399, 565, 613
Through Critical Thinking, 440, 570
Through Curriculum Integration, 238,
284, 331, 459, 538, 549
Through Diversity, 233, 295
Through Graphic Organizers, 15, 44,
137, 385, 481

Through Home Connection, 185, 229
Through Modeling, 201, 206, 249, 253,
379, 417, 486, 491, 505, 533, 619
Through Multiple Representations, 67,
79, 173, 350, 435
Through Number Sense, 279
Through Visual Cues, 145, 181, 335
Unlike denominators
addition of fractions with, 87–89
subtraction of fractions with, 87–89
Unpacking the Standards, 4, 62, 114,
166, 222, 272, 320, 376, 432, 476, 528,
588
Upper quartile, 542–543
Use your book for success, 5
Use your own words, 377
Using
formulas, 477
graphics, 470–471
nets to build prisms and cylinders,
496–497
similar figures, 248–249
slopes, 350
spreadsheets to construct graphs,
530–531
technology to make graphs,
530–531
your book for success, 5
your own words, 377

V

Value, absolute, 15
Variable(s), 6B
on both sides
modeling equations with, 128
solving equations with, 129–131
expressions and, 6–7
Variable rate of change, 344
Variation, direct, 357–359
Venn diagrams, 200
Venus, 187
Vertex
of an angle, 379
of a cone, 481
of a polygon, 399–400
of a polyhedron, 480
of a three-dimensional figure,
480
Vertical angles, 388
Vertical line test, 327
Visual, 15, 71, 72, 121, 137, 181, 245, 249,
275, 331, 339, 345, 385, 549
Volume, 478B, 485
Cavalieri's Principle, 478B
of cones, 490–491
of cylinders, 478B, 485–487
of prisms, 478B, 485–487
exploring, 484
of pyramids, 490–491
of similar three-dimensional figures,
512–513
of spheres, 508

Warm Up

Warm Up appears in every lesson. Some examples: 6, 10, 14, 18, 22

Weather, 119, 325

Web Extra!, 25, 101, 195, 209, 236, 255, 291, 419, 443, 483, 493, 563, 599, 606,

Weight, customary units of, SB15

Whales, 175

What's the Error?, 13, 21, 36, 69, 73, 81, 97, 119, 123, 127, 139, 147, 179, 183, 195, 203, 227, 231, 241, 277, 325, 352, 391, 453, 489, 493, 546, 559, 593

What's the Question?, 307, 329, 333, 402, 541, 615

Wheel, 446

Whole numbers
comparing and ordering, SB3
dividing, SB7
long division, SB7
rounding, SB2

Word phrases
translating, into inequalities, 136

translating, into math expressions, 10
translating math expressions into, 11

Words
into math, translating, 136
and math, translating between, 63
use your own, 377

Write a Problem, 40, 77, 143, 151, 188, 208, 247, 251, 282, 361, 409, 507, 573, 606

Write About It

Write About It exercises are found in every lesson. Some examples: 9, 13, 17, 21, 25

Writing
convincing arguments, 223
extended responses, 370–371
gridded responses, 160–161
inequalities, 136, 141
compound, 137
numbers in scientific notation, 184–185
numbers in standard form, 185
proportions, 232
short responses, 266–267

Writing Math, 66, 192, 388

Writing Strategies, *see also* Reading and Writing Math
Draw Three-Dimensional Figures, 477

Keep a Math Journal, 321
Translate Between Words and Math, 63
Use Your Own Words, 377
Write a Convincing Argument, 223

x-axis, 322
x-coordinate, 322

Yard, SB15
y-axis, 322
y-coordinate, 322
Yosemite National Park, 88, 112, 252

Zero power, 173
Zero slope, 349

Index

Notes

Notes

Notes

Notes

Credits

Staff Credits

Bruce Albrecht, Margaret Chalmers, Tica Chitrarachis, Lorraine Cooper, Marc Cooper, Jennifer Craycraft, Martize Cross, Nina Degollado, Julie Dervin, Michelle Dike, Lydia Doty, Sam Dudgeon, Kelli R. Flanagan, Stephanie Friedman, Jeff Galvez, Pam Garner, Diannia Green, Jennifer Gribble, Liz Huckestein, Jevara Jackson, Simon Key, Jane A. Kirschman, Kadonna Knape, Cathy Kuhles, Jill M. Lawson, Liann Lech, Virginia Messler, Susan Mussey, Kim Nguyen, Nathan O'Neal, Manda Reid, Michael Rinella, Annette Saunders, Kay Selke, Robyn Setzen, Patricia Sinnott, Victoria Smith, Dawn Marie Spinozza, Jeannie Taylor, Karen Vigil, Kira J. Watkins, Sherri Whitmarsh, David W. Wynn

Photo Credits

Frontmatter: viii © Gary Crabbe/Enlightened Images; ix © Ed Young/CORBIS; x © Dr. Eric Chalker/Index Stock Imagery, Inc.; xi © Peter Ginter/Bilderberg; xii Jenny Thomas/HRW; xiii © Ron Vesely/MLB Photos via Getty Images; xiv © John Kelly/Getty Images; xv © VEER/Christopher Talbot Frank/Getty Images; xvi © Richard Cummins/CORBIS; xvii © Robert Landau/CORBIS; xviii © Court Mast/Marling Mast/Getty Images; xix © Armando Arorizo/epa/Corbis

Chapter One: 2-3 (bkgd), © Gary Crabbe/Enlightened Images; 9 (l), The Granger Collection, New York; 9 (r), The Kobal Collection; 10 Robert Landau/CORBIS; 14 Don Couch/HRW; 17 © Layne Kennedy/CORBIS; 18 Victoria Smith/HRW; 21 Peter Van Steen; 25 (tc), Araldo de Luca/CORBIS; 25 (tl), Steve Vidler/SuperStock; 25 (br), The Art Archive/Napoleonic Museum Rome/Dagli Orti; 25 (tr), Bettmann/CORBIS; 26 Dennis MacDonald/PhotoEdit Inc.; 29 (l), Peter David/Getty Images; 34 Sam Dudgeon/HRW; 49 (t), iStockphoto; 49 (b), Sam Dudgeon/HRW; 50 Randall Hyman/HRW; 51 Sam Dudgeon/HRW

Chapter Two: 60-61 (bkgd), © Ed Young/CORBIS; 70 Getty Images; 73 NASA; 77 © Lester Lefkowitz/CORBIS; 78 Sam Dudgeon/HRW; 81 John Giustina/Bruce Coleman, Inc.; 86 Mark Tomalty/Masterfile; 88 Library of Congress; 91 (t), © Lester Lefkowitz/CORBIS; 91 (b), Sam Dudgeon/HRW; 93 (b), © Dean Conger/CORBIS; 98 Eric Gaillard/Reuters/CORBIS; 101 (t), © Torsten Blackwood/AFP/Getty Images; 101 (b), Karl H. Switak/Photo Researchers, Inc.; 103 AP Photo/Eau Claire Leader-Telegram/Steve Kinderman; 104 (b), Jenny Thomas/HRW; 105 (b), Sam Dudgeon/HRW

Chapter Three: 112-113 (bkgd), © Dr. Eric Chalker/Index Stock Imagery, Inc.; 127 Buddy Mays/CORBIS; 129 (l), © GK & Vikki Hart/Getty Images; 129 (r), © Artiga Photo/CORBIS; 133 Andrew Syred/Science Photo Library/Photo Researchers, Inc.; 135 (b), Sam Dudgeon/HRW; 143 (l), © Bettmann/CORBIS; 149 Sam Dudgeon/HRW; 152 (b), Jenny Thomas/HRW; 153 (t), © Comstock, Inc.; 153 (b), Dean Fox/SuperStock; 155 Sam Dudgeon/HRW

Chapter Four: 164-165 (bkgd), © Peter Ginter/Bilderberg; 172 S. Lowry/Univ. Ulster/Getty Images/Stone; 175 (t), Francois Gohier/Photo Researchers, Inc.; 175 (b), Flip Nicklin/Minden Pictures; 177 PEANUTS © Universal Press Syndicate; 183 © GK & Vikki Hart/Getty Images; 187 Joe McDonald/CORBIS; 193 © Roberto Rivera; 195 © David Young-Wolff/PhotoEdit, Inc.; 196 Sam Dudgeon/HRW; stained glass artist: Leanne Ohlenburg; 211 (t), Classic PIO Partners; 211 (bl), SciMAT/Photo Researchers, Inc.; 211 (br), SciMAT/Photo Researchers, Inc.; 212 (b), Randall Hyman/HRW; 213 Sam Dudgeon/HRW

Chapter Five: 220-221 (bkgd), Jenny Thomas/HRW; 224 (t), Dave Jacobs/Index Stock Imagery, Inc.; 227 (c), Sam Dudgeon/HRW; 236 (t), © 2004 EyeWire Collection; 236 (c), © Andrew Syred/Microscopix Photolibrary; 236 (b), Ed Reschke/Peter Arnold, Inc.; 240 (l), © Jonathan Sprague/Redux; 243 (b), Robb deWall/Crazy Horse Memorial; 244 (t), Sam Dudgeon/HRW; 247 Layne Kennedy/CORBIS; 248 Courtesy Troop 32, Arlington Heights, IL; 252 © National Geographic Image Collection; 253 Digital Art/CORBIS; 255 © David Young-Wolff/PhotoEdit Inc.; 257 Lee Snider/CORBIS; 259 (b), Richard Meier & Partners Architects LLP; 260 (t), © PhotoLink/Getty Images; 260 (b), Ken Karp/HRW; 261 Sam Dudgeon/HRW

Chapter Six: 270-271 © Ron Vesely/MLB Photos via Getty Images; 274 © Charles Gullung/Photonica/Getty Images; 281 Peter Van Steen/HRW; 284 Sam Dudgeon/HRW; 284 (green beans) © Royalty Free/CORBIS; 288 Jeff Rotman/Photo Researchers Inc.; 289 Hans Reinhard/Bruce Coleman, Inc.; 291 © Katy Winn/CORBIS; 293 (cricket) Digital Image © 2004 PhotoDisc; 293 (wasp) Digital Image © 2004 PhotoDisc; 293 (black & white beetle) Stockbyte; 293 (ladybug) Digital Image © 2004 PhotoDisc; 293 (mantis) Stockbyte; 293 (ant) Brand X Pictures; 293 (harlequin beetle) Digital Image ©2004 Artville; 293 (earwig) Brand X Pictures; 293 (green beetle) Brand X Pictures; 293 (mantis with extended wings) Brand X Pictures; 297 (r) Lyn Topinka/USGS/Cascades Volcano Observatory; 297 (l) © Katy Winn/CORBIS; 301 Sam Dudgeon/HRW; 307 Pornchai Kittiwongsakul/AFP/Getty Images; 309 (t) Stephanie Friedman/HRW; 309 (b) Sam Dudgeon/HRW; 310 (b) Victoria Smith/HRW; 311 Sam Dudgeon/HRW

Chapter Seven: 318-319 © John Kelly/Getty Images; 325 (l) © Stock Trek/PhotoDisc/Picture Quest; 329 Schenectady Museum/Hall of Electrical History Foundation/CORBIS; 333 © Ron Kimball Stock; 334 © Chip Simons Photography; 337 Sam Dudgeon/HRW; 341 © Andrew Sacks/Time Life Pictures/Getty Images; 357 © Sindre Ellingsen/Alamy; 361 E.R. Degginger/Bruce Coleman, Inc.; 363 (tr), Harry Engels/Photo Researchers, Inc.; 363 (b), Alan and Sandy Carey/Photo Researchers, Inc.; 363 (tl), Stephanie Friedman/HRW; 364 (b), Randall Hyman/HRW; 365 Sam Dudgeon/HRW

Chapter Eight: 374-375 (all), © VEER/Christopher Talbot Frank/Getty Images; 384 © 2008 Sol LeWitt/Artists Rights Society (ARS), New York; 387 Mark Schneider/Visuals Unlimited/Getty Images; 388 © Rodolfo Arpia/Alamy; 398 (all), Courtesy of Lucasfilm, Ltd. Star Wars: Episode I - The Phantom Menace © 1999 Lucasfilm Ltd. & TM. All rights reserved. Used under authorization. Unauthorized duplication is a violation of applicable law.; 406 (r), Seth Kushner/Getty Images/Stone; 406 (l), Science Photo Library/Photo Researchers, Inc.; 410 © Matthew Stockman/Getty Images; 416 Harry Lentz/Art Resource, NY; 421 Bob Burch/Index Stock Imagery, Inc.; 422 Jenny Thomas/HRW; 423 Sam Dudgeon/HRW

Chapter Nine: 430-431 (all), © Richard Cummins/CORBIS; 439 © Louie Psihoyos/CORBIS; 443 (t), © Royalty-Free/Corbis; 445 (b), Dave G. Houser/Houserstock; 446 (all), © Archivo Iconografico, S.A./CORBIS; 458 Larry Lefever/Grant Heilman Photography; 461 (t), William Hamilton/SuperStock; 463 (t), PhotoDisc/Getty Images; 463 (b), Grant Heilman /Grant Heilman Photography, Inc.; 464 Jenny Thomas/HRW; 465 Sam Dudgeon/HRW

Chapter Ten: 474-475 © Robert Landau/CORBIS; 483 (tr), © Charles & Josette Lenars/CORBIS; 483 (bl), © Kevin Fleming/CORBIS; 483 (tl), Steve Vidler/SuperStock; 483 (br), R.M. Arakaki/Imagestate; 485 Kenneth Hamm/Photo Japan; 489 (r), Dallas and John Heaton/CORBIS; 489 (l), G. Leavens/Photo Researchers, Inc.; 490 © Tor Eigeland/Alamy; 493 (l), Owen Franken/CORBIS; 493 (r), Steve Vidler/SuperStock; 495 (b), Sam Dudgeon/HRW; 498 © 2004 Kelly Houle; 505 (l), Robert & Linda Mitchell Photography; 506 Baldwin H. Ward & Kathryn C. Ward/CORBIS; 508 © NASA/Corbis; 511 (t), Darryl Torckler/Getty Images/Stone; 511 (tc), Dwight Kuhn Photography; 511 (bc), Sinclair Stammers/Science Photo Library/Photo Researchers, Inc.; 511 (b), Ron Austing; Frank Lane Picture Agency/CORBIS; 515 Chris Lisle/CORBIS; 515 © 2006 The LEGO Group; 517 Victoria Smith/HRW; 518 Sam Dudgeon/HRW; 519 Sam Dudgeon/HRW

Chapter Eleven: 526-527 © Court Mast/Marling Mast/Getty Images; 532 Digital Vision; 541 © Karl Weatherly/CORBIS; 542 Peter Van Steen/HRW/Kittens courtesy of Austin Humane Society/SPCA; 548 © Royalty Free/CORBIS; 560 AP Photo; 563 (l), Reuters/CORBIS; 563 (r), David Weintraub/Photo Researchers, Inc.; 564 Peter Van Steen/HRW; 568 Sam Dudgeon/HRW; 575 Design Pics; 576 Sam Dudgeon/HRW; 577 Sam Dudgeon/HRW

Chapter Twelve: 586-587 (all), © Armando Arorizo/epa/Corbis; 590 © Dave G. Houser/CORBIS; 599 (t), © Paul Eekhoff/Masterfile; 599 (b), Private Collection/Bridgeman Art Library/© 2002 Fletcher Benton/Artists Rights Society (ARS),, New York; 601 Steve Gottlieb/Stock Connection/PictureQuest; 603 Sam Dudgeon/HRW; 604 Sam Dudgeon/HRW; 606 Stephen Mallon/The Image Bank/Getty Images; 612 Sam Dudgeon/HRW; 613 Victoria Smith/HRW; 615 Victoria Smith/HRW; 618 © Mark Gibson Photography; 621 (b), Sam Dudgeon/HRW; 623 (t), iStock Photo; 623 (bl), © Jeff Greenberg/Photo Edit, Inc.; 623 (br), Photodisc/Getty Images; 624 (b), Sam Dudgeon/HRW; 625 (b), Sam Dudgeon/HRW; 586-587 (all), © Armando Arorizo/epa/Corbis

Student Handbook TOC: 632 John Langford/HRW; 633 Sam Dudgeon/HRW

All Teacher-to-Teacher photos courtesy of the teachers.

Formulas

Perimeter

Parallelogram	$P = 2w + 2\ell$
Polygon	$P =$ sum of the lengths of the sides

Circumference

Circle	$C = \pi d$ or $C = 2\pi r$

Volume

Prism	$V = Bh^*$
Rectangular prism	$V = \ell wh$
Cylinder	$V = Bh^*$ or $V = \pi r^2 h$
Pyramid	$V = \frac{1}{3}Bh^*$
Cone	$V = \frac{1}{3}Bh^*$ or $V = \frac{1}{3}\pi r^2 h$
Sphere	$V = \frac{4}{3}\pi r^3$

Area

Rectangle	$A = bh$ or $A = \ell w$
Parallelogram	$A = bh$
Triangle	$A = \frac{1}{2}bh$
Trapezoid	$A = \frac{1}{2}h(b_1 + b_2)$
Circle	$A = \pi r^2$

Surface Area

Prism	$S = 2B + Ph^*$
Cylinder	$S = 2\pi r^2 + 2\pi rh$
Regular Pyramid	$S = B + \frac{1}{2}P\ell^*$
Cone	$S = \pi r^2 + \pi r\ell$
Sphere	$S = 4\pi r^2$

*B represents the area of the base shape of a three-dimensional figure.

Probability

Experimental	probability $\approx \dfrac{\text{number of times the event occurs}}{\text{total number of trials}}$
Theoretical	probability $= \dfrac{\text{number of outcomes in the event}}{\text{number of outcomes in the sample space}}$
Dependent events	$P(A \text{ and } B) = P(A) \cdot P(B \text{ after } A)$
Independent events	$P(A \text{ and } B) = P(A) \cdot P(B)$